NORTH CAROLINA TEACHER'S EDITION

McDougal Littell
Science

GRADE  **6**

Space Science

Waves, Sound, and Light

Energy and the Changing Earth

Ecology

Earth's Surface

North Carolina Correlations

The material on pages 3–24, the North Carolina Correlations, will help you coordinate your teaching of *McDougal Littell Science* Grade 6 with the North Carolina Course of Study.

Quick Overview A quick overview of the objectives for Grade 6 and the units that cover them appears on pages 4–7 of the North Carolina Correlations.

Detailed Correlations The charts on pages 8–15 contain a detailed correlation of *McDougal Littell Science* Grade 6 to the **objectives for Grade 6. The first column of the charts lists the objectives. The second column identifies pages in the Student and Teacher's Edition that teach the material included in the objectives.**

Lesson-by-Lesson Correlations Pages 16–24 are organized by unit and chapter; those pages list the objectives covered by each lesson or feature in the textbook.

NORTH CAROLINA COURSE OF STUDY
Quick Overview of Correlations

Competency Goals and Objectives	Unit							
	IS	A	B	C	D	E	NC	R
COMPETENCY GOAL 1: The learner will design and conduct investigations to demonstrate an understanding of scientific inquiry.								
1.01 Identify and create questions and hypotheses that can be answered through scientific investigations.		●	●	●	●	●		●
1.02 Develop appropriate experimental procedures for given questions and student generated questions.		●	●	●	●			●
1.03 Apply safety procedures in the laboratory and in field studies.		●	●	●	●	●		●
1.04 Analyze variables in scientific investigations.		●	●	●	●			●
1.05 Analyze evidence to explain observations, make inferences and predictions, and develop the relationship between evidence and explanation.		●	●	●	●	●	●	●
1.06 Use mathematics to gather, organize, and present quantitative data resulting from scientific investigations.		●	●	●	●	●		●
1.07 Prepare models and/or computer simulations to test hypotheses and evaluate how data fit.		●			●	●		
1.08 Use oral and written language to communicate findings and defend conclusions of scientific investigations.		●	●	●	●	●	●	●
1.09 Use technologies and information systems to research, gather and analyze data, visualize data, disseminate findings to others.		●	●	●	●	●		●
1.10 Analyze and evaluate information from a scientifically literate viewpoint by reading, hearing, and/or viewing.		●	●	●	●	●		●
COMPETENCY GOAL 2: The learner will demonstrate an understanding of technological design.								
2.01 Explore evidence that "technology" has many definitions.	●	●	●	●	●	●		
2.02 Use information systems to identify scientific needs, human needs, or problems that are subject to technological solution; locate resources to obtain and test ideas.		●	●	●	●	●		
2.03 Evaluate technological designs for application of scientific principles, risks and benefits, constraints of design, and consistent testing protocols.	●	●	●	●	●	●		
2.04 Apply tenets of technological design to make informed consumer decisions about products, processes, and systems.	●		●	●				

Competency Goals and Objectives — Unit

Competency Goals and Objectives	IS	A	B	C	D	E	NC	R
COMPETENCY GOAL 3: The learner will build an understanding of the geological cycles, forces, processes, and agents, which shape the lithosphere.								
3.01 Evaluate the forces that shape the lithosphere.		•	•				•	
3.02 Examine earthquake and volcano patterns.		•	•					
3.03 Explain the model for the interior of the earth.		•	•					
3.04 Describe the processes which form and the uses of earth materials.		•	•				•	
3.05 Analyze soil properties that can be observed and measured to predict soil quality.		•			•		•	
3.06 Evaluate ways in which human activities have affected Earth's pedosphere and the measures taken to control the impact.		•			•		•	
3.07 Assess the use of technology and information systems in monitoring lithospheric phenomenon.		•	•					
3.08 Conclude that the good health of environments and organisms requires monitoring of the pedosphere, taking steps to maintain soil quality, and stewardship.		•					•	
COMPETENCY GOAL 4: The learner will investigate the cycling of matter.								
4.01 Describe the flow of energy and matter in natural systems.		•	•		•		•	
4.02 Evaluate the significant role of decomposers.					•			
4.03 Examine evidence that green plants make food.		•			•		•	
4.04 Evaluate the significance of photosynthesis to other organisms.		•			•		•	
4.05 Evaluate designed systems for ability to enable growth of certain plants and animals.					•	•	•	

Quick Overview of Correlations

Competency Goals and Objectives	Unit							
	IS	A	B	C	D	E	NC	R

COMPETENCY GOAL 5: The learner will build understanding of the Solar System.

5.01	Analyze the components and cycles of the solar system.		•				•		
5.02	Compare and contrast the Earth to other planets in terms of size, composition, relative distance from the sun, and ability to support life.						•		
5.03	Relate the influence of the sun and the moon's orbit to the gravitational effects produced on Earth.						•		
5.04	Describe space explorations and the understandings gained from them.						•		
5.05	Describe the setting of the solar system in the universe.						•		
5.06	Analyze the spin-off benefits generated by space exploration technology.						•		

COMPETENCY GOAL 6: The learner will conduct investigations and examine models and devices to build an understanding of the characteristics of energy transfer and/or transformation.

6.01	Determine how convection and radiation transfer energy.			•					
6.02	Analyze heat flow through materials or across space from warm objects to cooler objects until both objects are at equilibrium.			•					
6.03	Analyze sound as an example that vibrating materials generate waves that transfer energy.			•	•				
6.04	Evaluate data for qualitative and quantitative relationships associated with energy transfer and/or transformation.			•	•	•			
6.05	Analyze the physical interactions of light and matter.			•					
6.06	Analyze response to heat to determine the suitability of materials for use in technological design.		•						
6.07	Analyze the Law of Conservation of Energy.		•						

Competency Goals and Objectives	Unit							
	IS	A	B	C	D	E	NC	R
COMPETENCY GOAL 7: The learner will conduct investigations and use technologies and information systems to build an understanding of population dynamics.								
7.01 Describe ways in which organisms interact with each other and with non-living parts of the environment.					•		•	
7.02 Investigate factors that determine the growth and survival of organisms.					•			
7.03 Explain how changes in habitat may affect organisms.					•			
7.04 Evaluate data related to human population growth, along with problems and solutions.					•			
7.05 Examine evidence that overpopulation by any species impacts the environment.					•			
7.06 Investigate processes which operating over long periods of time have resulted in the diversity of plant and animal life present today.		•			•		•	

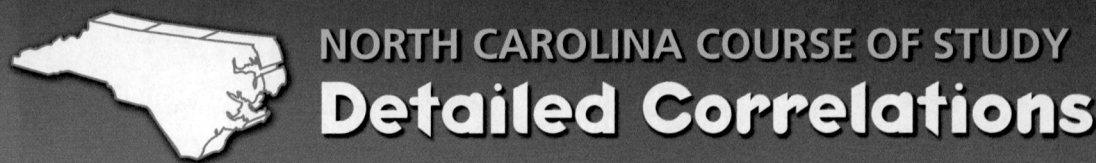
Competency Goals and Objectives	Student Edition/Teacher's Edition
COMPETENCY GOAL 1: The learner will design and conduct investigations to demonstrate an understanding of scientific inquiry.	
1.01 Identify and create questions and hypotheses that can be answered through scientific investigations.	A146, B13, B22, B80, B128, B154, C76, D14, D52, D106, E50, E93, E106, E120, R3, R29
1.02 Develop appropriate experimental procedures for: a. Given questions. b. Student generated questions.	A56, A146, A156, A169, B13, B56, B57, B81, C76, C90, C98, D15, D65, R28–R32
1.03 Apply safety procedures in the laboratory and in field studies: a. Recognize potential hazards. b. Manipulate materials and equipment. c. Conduct appropriate procedures.	A28, A43, A46, A56, A59, A98, A130, B9, B22, B27, B37, B41, B56, B80, B105, B113, B128, B154, C22, C48, C64, C90, C100, C115, C128, D19, D22, D25, D91, D106, E20, E44, E62, E88, E115, E120, R10–R19
1.04 Analyze variables in scientific investigations: a. Identify dependent and independent. b. Use of a control. c. Manipulate. d. Describe relationships between. e. Define operationally.	A46, A65, A130, A131, A146, A157, A160, B13, B27, B41, B49, B57, B81, B129, C20, C22, C23, C26, C101, D9, D65, E107, R5, R30, R31
1.05 Analyze evidence to: a. Explain observations. b. Make inferences and predictions. c. Develop the relationship between evidence and explanation.	A43, A46, A56, A57, A59, A60, A65, A67, A83, A85, A89, A94, A98, A102, A103, A115, A118, A122, A130, A131, A135, A146, A150, A157, A160, A165, A169, A175, B9, B13, B15, B23, B24, B27, B37, B41, B46, B49, B50, B57, B67, B69, B72, B81, B85, B90, B97, B103, B105, B107, B110, B111, B113, B120, B123, B129, B135, B137, B142, B146, B155, B159, C9, C13, C20, C23, C24, C26, C37, C40, C41, C45, C48, C53, C57, C58, C64, C65, C73, C76, C79, C87, C90, C93, C98, C100, C101, C113, C115, C119, C125, C126, C128, C131, C134, C139, D9, D15, D16, D19, D22, D25, D29, D45, D53, D57, D62, D63, D65, D81, D84, D91, D98, D107, E9, E13, E15, E21, E22, E23, E25, E33, E43, E44, E51, E52, E55, E62, E82, E85, E88, E97, E107, E115, E121, E122, E123, E130, E131, E135, E138, NC2–NC6, NC7–NC11, R2–R8, R34, R35, R44
1.06 Use mathematics to gather, organize, and present quantitative data resulting from scientific investigations: a. Measurement. b. Analysis of data. c. Graphing. d. Prediction models.	A23, A29, A32, A49, A67, A81, A88, A121, A131, A171, B23, B24, B27, B29, B32, B33, B89, B119, B145, B155, C15, C21, C32, C78, D9, D21, D35, D41, D45, D57, D69, D97, D111, E30, E43, E58, E82, E84, E129, R20, R21, R23–R27, R36–R44
1.07 Prepare models and/or computer simulations to: a. Test hypotheses. b. Evaluate how data fit.	A13, A20, A28, A32, A35, A135, A157, A169, D57, E44, E62
1.08 Use oral and written language to: a. Communicate findings. b. Defend conclusions of scientific investigations.	A29, A59, A81, A103, A111, A131, A157, B5, B15, B23, B32, B57, B65, B81, B129, B155, C5, C23, C65, C87, C101, C109, C125, C142, D5, D15, D40, D53, D62, D72, D77, D107, D110, E21, E51, E75, E121, NC2–NC6, NC7–NC11, R2–R9

Competency Goals and Objectives	Student Edition/Teacher's Edition
1.09 Use technologies and information systems to: a. Research. b. Gather and analyze data. c. Visualize data. d. Disseminate findings to others.	A4–A5, A7, A35, A41, A73, A113, A143, A164, B5, B7, B15, B35, B67, B103, B135, C5, C7, C29, C35, C71, C111, D7, D43, D53, D79, D88, E5, E7, E35, E41, E77, E113, E134, R8
1.10 Analyze and evaluate information from a scientifically literate viewpoint by reading, hearing, and/or viewing: a. Scientific text. b. Articles. c. Events in the popular press.	A2–A5, A30, A31, B2–B5, B15, C2–C5, D2–D5, E2–E5, E67, E134, R6, R7, R8

COMPETENCY GOAL 2: The learner will demonstrate an understanding of technological design.

2.01 Explore evidence that "technology" has many definitions. a. Artifact or hardware. b. Methodology or technique. c. System of production. d. Social-technical system.	xl–xli, A2–A5, A9–A11, A30–A34, B2–B5, B24–B28, B53–B55, B126–B127, C2–C5, C58–C63, C77–C86, C131–C138, D102–D105, E15–E19, E22–E29, E31–E34
2.02 Use information systems to: a. Identify scientific needs, human needs, or problems that are subject to technological solution. b. Locate resources to obtain and test ideas.	A2–A5, A7, A27, A30–A34, B2–B5, B15, B35, C2–C5, D43, D88, E5, E7, E22–E29, E35, E77, E134
2.03 Evaluate technological designs for: a. Application of scientific principles. b. Risks and benefits. c. Constraints of design. d. Consistent testing protocols.	xl–xli, A108–A111, A137, B15, B21, B24–B28, B56–B57, B62–B65, B126–B129, C64–C65, C87, C90–C92, C106–C109, C131–C138, D74–D77, D102–D103, E34, E72–E75
2.04 Apply tenets of technological design to make informed consumer decisions about: a. Products. b. Processes. c. Systems.	xl–xli, B15, B128–B129, C90–C92, C106–C109

Detailed Correlations

Competency Goals and Objectives	Student Edition/Teacher's Edition
COMPETENCY GOAL 3: The learner will build an understanding of the geological cycles, forces, processes, and agents, which shape the lithosphere.	
3.01 Evaluate the forces that shape the lithosphere including: a. Crustal plate movement. b. Folding and faulting. c. Deposition. d. Volcanic Activity. e. Earthquakes	A13, A37, A86, A87, A90, A99, A109, A110, A145–A149, A150, A152, A153, A155, A160–A163, A168, A169, A172, A173, A174, A175, B4–B5, B72, B73, B74, B76, B77–B79, B81, B82–B85, B87–B88, B90–B96, B97, B98, B99, B100, B101, B104, B105–B109, B110, B111–B115, B118, B122, B123, B125, B127, B130, B131, B132, B133, B136–B140, B142–B144, B146–B153, B156–B158, B162, B163, B164, B165, B166, B167, NC16
3.02 Examine earthquake and volcano patterns.	A86, A87, A99, B4, B86–B88, B96, B106, B108, B109, B110, B112, B113, B117, B118, B119, B121, B122–B124, B127, B130, B131, B132, B133, B149–B153, B155, B156–B162, B163, B164, B165, B166, B167
3.03 Explain the model for the interior of the earth.	A12, B68–B71, B73, B98, B99, B101
3.04 Describe the processes which form and the uses of earth materials. a. Rock cycle. b. Minerals. c. Characteristics of rocks. d. Economic use of rocks and minerals. e. Value of gems and precious metals. f. Common gems, minerals, precious metals and rocks found in North Carolina	A42–A48, A50–A57, A60–A66, A68, A69, A70, A71, A74–A80, A82–A85, A87, A89, A91–A95, A96, A98, A100, A101, A104, A105, A106, A107, A118–A120, A138, A139, A140, B139, NC16
3.05 Analyze soil properties that can be observed and measured to predict soil quality including: a. Color. b. Horizon profile. c. Infiltration. d. Soil temperature. e. Structure. f. Consistency. g. Texture. h. Particle size. i. pH. j. Fertility. k. Soil moisture.	A122–A129, A130–A131, A138, A139, A140, A141, A149, A154, D12–D13, D14–D15, NC7–NC11

Competency Goals and Objectives	Student Edition/Teacher's Edition
3.06 Evaluate ways in which human activities have affected Earth's pedosphere and the measures taken to control the impact: a. Vegetative cover. b. Agriculture. c. Land use. d. Nutrient balance. e. Soil as a vector.	A14, A39, A132–A136, A138, A139, D82–D85, D89–D96, D98–D105, D106–D107, NC7–NC11, NC14–NC15
3.07 Assess the use of technology and information systems in monitoring lithospheric phenomenon.	A2–A5, A30–A34, B116, B117, B118, B153
3.08 Conclude that the good health of environments and organisms requires: a. Monitoring of the pedosphere. b. Taking steps to maintain soil quality. c. Stewardship.	A132, A134–A136, NC7–NC11, NC12–NC13

COMPETENCY GOAL 4: The learner will investigate the cycling of matter.

4.01 Describe the flow of energy and matter in natural systems: a. Energy flows through ecosystems in one direction, from the sun through producers to consumers to decomposers. b. Matter is transferred from one organism to another and between organisms and their environment. c. Water, nitrogen, carbon dioxide, and oxygen are substances cycled between the living and non-living environment.	A10, A39, B9, B10, D10, D16, D17, D19, D22, D23–D28, D38, D39, D40, NC12–NC13
4.02 Evaluate the significant role of decomposers.	D25, D28, D39, D66–D68
4.03 Examine evidence that green plants make food. a. Photosynthesis is a process carried on by green plants and other organisms containing chlorophyll. b. During photosynthesis, light energy is converted into stored energy which the plant, in turn, uses to carry out its life processes.	A109, D12, D23, NC12–NC13

Competency Goals and Objectives	Student Edition/Teacher's Edition
4.04 Evaluate the significance of photosynthesis to other organisms: a. The major source atmospheric oxygen is photosynthesis. b. Carbon dioxide is removed from the atmosphere and oxygen is released during photosynthesis. c. Green plants are the producers of food that is used directly or indirectly by consumers.	A110, D17–D20, D22–D28, NC12–NC13
4.05 Evaluate designed systems for ability to enable growth of certain plants and animals.	D88, E24, NC14–NC15

COMPETENCY GOAL 5: The learner will build understanding of the Solar System.

Competency Goals and Objectives	Student Edition/Teacher's Edition
5.01 Analyze the components and cycles of the solar system including: a. Sun. b. Planets and moons. c. Asteroids and meteors. d. Comets. e. Phases. f. Seasons. g. Day/year. h. Eclipses.	A108, E10, E11, E13, E14, E43, E45–E49, E52–E56, E59–E66, E68, E69, E70, E71, E79, E80, E82, E83, E86, E87, E89–E92, E94–E96, E98, E99, E100–E105, E108, E109, E110, E111, E115–E119, E124, E126, E141
5.02 Compare and contrast the Earth to other planets in terms of: a. Size. b. Composition. c. Relative distance from the sun. d. Ability to support life.	E26, E32, E56, E80, E81, E85, E86, E88–E92, E94–E99, E101, E115
5.03 Relate the influence of the sun and the moon's orbit to the gravitational effects produced on Earth. a. Solar storms. b. Tides.	E65, E66, E68, E119

Competency Goals and Objectives / Student Edition/Teacher's Edition

Competency Goals and Objectives	Student Edition/Teacher's Edition
5.04 Describe space explorations and the understandings gained from them including: a. N.A.S.A. b. Technologies used to explore space. c. Historic timeline. d. Apollo mission to the moon. e. Space Shuttle. f. International Space Station. g. Future goals.	E18, E19, E22–E29, E31, E37, E38, E72–E75, E138, E139, E142
5.05 Describe the setting of the solar system in the universe including: a. Galaxy. b. Size. c. The uniqueness of Earth.	E10, E11, E27, E33, E39, E124, E128, E130–E132, E133, E135–E139, E140, E141
5.06 Analyze the spin-off benefits generated by space exploration technology including: a. Medical. b. Materials. c. Transportation. d. Processes. e. Future research.	E23–E25, E31–E34

COMPETENCY GOAL 6: The learner will conduct investigations and examine models and devices to build an understanding of the characteristics of energy transfer and/or transformation.

6.01	Determine how convection and radiation transfer energy.	B11, B50, B52, B55, B58, B59, B77, B81
6.02	Analyze heat flow through materials or across space from warm objects to cooler objects until both objects are at equilibrium.	B39, B44, B45, B50, B51, B52, B58, B59
6.03	Analyze sound as an example that vibrating materials generate waves that transfer energy. a. Frequency. b. Amplitude. c. Loudness. d. How sound travels through different material. e. Form and function of the human ear.	B11, C11, C14, C16–C21, C26, C30, C31, C33, C38–C44, C45–C51, C52–C56, C57, C66, C67, C68, C69
6.04	Evaluate data for qualitative and quantitative relationships associated with energy transfer and/or transformation.	B22–B23, B24, B27, B56–B57, B121, B128–B129, C9–C12, C15, C22–C23, C33, C42–C43, D22–D28

Detailed Correlations

Competency Goals and Objectives	Student Edition/Teacher's Edition
6.05 Analyze the physical interactions of light and matter: a. Absorption. b. Scattering. c. Color perception. d. Form and function of the human eye.	C93–C99, C102, C103, C104, C114, C126–C130, C142
6.06 Analyze response to heat to determine the suitability of materials for use in technological design: a. Conduction. b. Expansion. c. Contraction.	B42, B43, B50, B51, B54, B55, B58, B59
6.07 Analyze the Law of Conservation of Energy: a. Conclude that energy cannot be created or destroyed, but only changed from one form into another. b. Conclude that the amount of energy stays the same, although within the process some energy is always converted to heat. c. Some systems transform energy with less loss of heat than others.	B16–B21, B24–B28, B30, B31

COMPETENCY GOAL 7: The learner will conduct investigations and use technologies and information systems to build an understanding of population dynamics.

7.01 Describe ways in which organisms interact with each other and with non-living parts of the environment: a. Coexistence/Cooperation/Competition. b. Symbiosis. c. Mutual dependence.	D48, D54, D55–D61, D70, D71, D73, NC7–NC11, NC14–NC15
7.02 Investigate factors that determine the growth and survival of organisms including: a. Light. b. Temperature range. c. Mineral availability. d. Soil/rock type. e. Water. f. Energy.	D10–D13, D22–D28, D37, D51, D54–D61, D64, D65
7.03 Explain how changes in habitat may affect organisms.	D47, D48, D50, D55, D63, D67, D68, D94, D95, D108

Competency Goals and Objectives	Student Edition/Teacher's Edition
7.04 Evaluate data related to human population growth, along with problems and solutions: a. Waste disposal. b. Food supplies. c. Resource availability. d. Transportation. e. Socio-economic patterns.	D83, D87, D100, D101, D103, D104, D108
7.05 Examine evidence that overpopulation by any species impacts the environment.	D65, D83, D84, D87, D94, D109
7.06 Investigate processes which, operating over long periods of time, have resulted in the diversity of plant and animal life present today: a. Natural selection. b. Adaptation.	A164, D9, D11, NC2–NC6

NORTH CAROLINA COURSE OF STUDY
Lesson-by-Lesson Correlations

Section or Feature	Competency Goals and Objectives
Unit A Earth's Surface	
Frontiers of Science: Remote Sensing	1.09, 1.10, 2.01, 2.02, 3.07
Chapter 1 Views of Earth Today	
1.1 Technology is used to explore the Earth system.	1.07, 2.01, 3.01, 3.03, 3.06, 4.01
1.2 Maps and globes are models of Earth.	1.07
Math In Science: Using Proportions	1.06
1.3 Topographic maps show the shape of the land.	2.02
Chapter Investigation: Investigate Topographic Maps	1.03, 1.06, 1.07, 1.08
1.4 Technology is used to map Earth.	1.06, 1.07, 1.10, 2.01, 2.02, 3.07
Think Science: Interpreting Data	1.07, 1.09
Chapter 2 Minerals	
2.1 Minerals are all around us.	1.03, 1.04, 1.05, 3.04
Math in Science: Writing Fractions as Percents	1.06
2.2 A mineral is identified by its properties.	1.02, 1.03, 1.05, 3.04
Chapter Investigation: Mineral Identification	1.03, 1.05, 1.08
2.3 Minerals are valuable resources.	1.04, 1.05, 3.04
Science on the Job: Geometry for Gems	1.05, 1.06
Chapter 3 Rocks	
3.1 The rock cycle shows how rocks change.	3.04
Extreme Science: Rocks from Space	1.05, 1.06, 1.08
3.2 Igneous rocks form from molten rock.	1.05, 3.01, 3.02, 3.04
Math in Science: Estimating Area	1.06
3.3 Sedimentary rocks form from earlier rocks.	1.05, 3.01, 3.04

Section or Feature	Competency Goals and Objectives
3.4 Metamorphic rocks form as existing rocks change.	1.03, 1.05, 3.01, 3.02, 3.04
Chapter Investigation: Rock Classification	1.05, 1.08
Timelines in Science: History of the Earth System	1.08, 2.03, 3.01, 4.03, 4.04, 5.01
Chapter 4 Weathering and Soil Formation	
4.1 Mechanical and chemical forces break down rocks.	1.05, 3.04
Math in Science: Surface Area of a Prism	1.06
4.2 Weathering and organic processes form soil.	1.05, 3.05
Chapter Investigation: Testing Soil	1.03, 1.04, 1.05, 1.06, 1.08, 3.05
4.3 Human activities affect soil.	1.03, 1.05, 1.07, 3.06, 3.08
Science on the Job: Soil, Water, and Architecture	2.03
Chapter 5 Erosion and Deposition	
5.1 Forces wear down and build up Earth's surface.	1.01, 1.02, 1.04, 1.05, 3.01, 3.05
5.2 Moving water shapes land.	1.05, 3.01, 3.05
Chapter Investigation: Creating Stream Features	1.02, 1.04, 1.05, 1.07, 1.08
5.3 Waves and wind shape land.	1.05, 3.01
Connecting Sciences: Life on Dunes	1.09, 7.06
5.4 Glaciers carve land and move sediments.	1.02, 1.04, 1.05, 1.07, 3.01
Math in Science: Creating a Line Graph	1.06

Lesson-by-Lesson

Section or Feature	Competency Goals and Objectives
Unit B Energy and the Changing Earth	
Frontiers in Science: Studying Volcanoes	1.08, 1.09, 1.10, 2.01, 2.02, 3.01, 3.02
Chapter 1 Energy	
1.1 Energy exists in different forms.	1.01, 1.02, 1.03, 1.04, 1.05, 4.01, 6.01, 6.03
Think Science: Finding Solutions	1.05, 1.08, 1.09, 1.10, 2.02, 2.03, 2.04
1.2 Energy can change forms but is never lost.	2.03, 6.07
Chapter Investigation: Energy Conversions	1.01, 1.03, 1.05, 1.06, 1.08, 6.04
1.3 Technology improves the ways people use energy.	1.03, 1.04, 1.05, 1.06, 2.01, 2.03, 6.04, 6.07
Math in Science: Using Formulas	1.06
Chapter 2 Temperature and Heat	
2.1 Temperature depends on particle movement.	1.03, 1.04, 1.05, 6.02, 6.06
Math in Science: Metric Conversions	6.06
2.2 Energy flows from warmer to cooler objects.	1.05, 6.02
Science on the Job: Cooking with Heat	1.04, 1.05
2.3 The transfer of energy as heat can be controlled.	1.05, 2.01, 6.01, 6.02, 6.06
Chapter Investigation: Insulators	1.02, 1.03, 1.04, 1.05, 1.08, 2.03, 6.04
Timelines in Science: Temperature and Heat	1.08, 2.03
Chapter 3 Plate Tectonics	
3.1 Earth has several layers.	1.05, 3.01, 3.03
3.2 Continents change position over time.	3.01, 6.01
Chapter Investigation: Convection Currents and Plate Movement	1.01, 1.02, 1.03, 1.04, 1.05, 1.08, 3.01, 6.01
3.3 Plates move apart.	1.05, 3.01, 3.02
Math in Science: Calculating Equivalent Rates	1.06

Section or Feature	Competency Goals and Objectives
3.4 Plates converge or scrape past each other.	1.05, 3.01, 3.02
Think Science: Evaluating Conclusions	1.05, 3.01
Chapter 4 Earthquakes	
4.1 Earthquakes occur along faults.	1.03, 1.05, 3.01, 3.02
Extreme Science: When Earth Shakes	1.05, 3.01, 3.02
4.2 Earthquakes release energy.	1.03, 1.05, 3.01, 3.02, 3.07
Math in Science: Multiplication	1.06, 3.02
4.3 Earthquake damage can be reduced.	1.05, 2.01, 2.03, 3.01, 3.02, 6.04
Chapter Investigation: How Structures React in Earthquakes	1.01, 1.03, 1.04, 1.05, 1.08, 2.03, 2.04, 6.04
Chapter 5 Mountains and Volcanoes	
5.1 Movement of rock builds mountains.	1.05, 3.01, 3.04
Math in Science: Calculating the Mean of a Data Set	1.06
5.2 Volcanoes form as molten rock erupts.	1.05, 3.01, 3.02, 3.07
Chapter Investigation: Make Your Own Volcanoes	1.01, 1.03, 1.05, 1.06, 1.08, 3.01, 3.02
5.3 Volcanoes affect Earth's land, air, and water.	1.05, 3.01, 3.02
Science on the Job: Rangers at Yellowstone	3.01, 3.02

Lesson-by-Lesson

Section or Feature	Competency Goals and Objectives
Unit C Waves, Sound, and Light	
Frontiers in Science: Sound Medicine	1.08, 1.09, 1.10, 2.01, 2.02
Chapter 1 Waves	
1.1 Waves transfer energy.	1.05, 6.03, 6.04
Math in Science: Mean, Median, and Mode	1.06, 6.04
1.2 Waves have measurable properties.	1.04, 1.05, 1.06, 6.03, 6.04
Chapter Investigation: Wavelength	1.03, 1.04, 1.05, 1.08
1.3 Waves behave in predictable ways.	1.04, 1.05, 6.03
Connecting Sciences: Tsunamis!	1.09, 2.02
Chapter 2 Sound	
2.1 Sound is a wave.	1.05, 6.03, 6.04
Extreme Science: Sonic Booms	6.03
2.2 Frequency determines pitch.	1.03, 1.05, 6.03
2.3 Intensity determines loudness.	1.05, 6.03
Math in Science: Interpreting Graphs	1.05, 6.03
2.4 Sound has many uses.	1.05, 2.01
Chapter Investigation: Build a Stringed Instrument	1.03, 1.05, 1.08, 2.03
Chapter 3 Electromagnetic Waves	
3.1 Electromagnetic waves have unique traits.	1.01, 1.02, 1.05, 2.01
Math in Science: Using Exponents	1.06, 2.01
3.2 Electromagnetic waves have many uses.	1.05, 2.01
Think Science: Determining Relevance	1.05, 1.08, 2.03
3.3 The Sun is the source of most visible light.	1.02, 1.03, 1.05, 2.03, 2.04

Section or Feature	Competency Goals and Objectives
3.4 Light waves interact with materials.	1.02, 1.05, 6.05
Chapter Investigation: Wavelength and Color	1.03, 1.04, 1.05, 1.08
Timelines in Science: The Story of Light	1.08, 2.03
Chapter 4 Light and Optics	
4.1 Mirrors form images by reflecting light.	1.03, 1.05, 6.05
Math in Science: Measuring Angles	1.06
4.2 Lenses form images by refracting light.	1.05
Chapter Investigation: Looking at Lenses	1.05, 1.08
4.3 The eye is a natural optical tool.	1.03, 1.05, 6.05
4.4 Optical technology makes use of light waves.	1.05, 2.01, 2.03
Science on the Job: Optics in Photography	1.05

Unit D Ecology	
Frontiers in Science: Ecosystems on Fire	1.08, 1.10, 2.02
Chapter 1 Ecosystems and Biomes	
1.1 Ecosystems support life.	1.04, 1.05, 1.06, 3.05, 4.01, 4.03, 7.02, 7.06
Chapter Investigation: Soil Samples	1.01, 1.02, 1.05, 1.08, 3.05
1.2 Matter cycles through ecosystems.	1.03, 1.05, 4.01, 4.04
Math in Science: Adding Integers	1.06
1.3 Energy flows through ecosystems.	1.03, 1.05, 4.01, 4.02, 4.03, 4.04, 6.04, 7.02
Connecting Sciences: Biomagnification	1.05
1.4 Biomes contain many ecosystems.	1.06, 7.02

Lesson-by-Lesson

Section or Feature	Competency Goals and Objectives
Chapter 2 Interactions Within Ecosystems	
2.1 Groups of living things interact within ecosystems.	1.05, 1.06, 7.01, 7.02, 7.03
Chapter Investigation: Estimating Populations	1.01, 1.05, 1.08, 1.09
2.2 Organisms can interact in different ways.	1.05, 1.06, 1.07, 7.01, 7.02, 7.03
Think Science: Inferring	1.05, 1.08
2.3 Ecosystems are always changing.	1.02, 1.04, 1.05, 4.02, 7.02, 7.03, 7.05
Math in Science: Multiplying a Fraction by a Whole Number	1.06
Timelines in Science: Wilderness Conservation	1.08, 2.03
Chapter 3 Human Impact on Ecosystems	
3.1 Human population growth presents challenges.	1.05, 3.06, 7.04, 7.05
Science on the Job: Ecology in Urban Planning	1.09, 2.02, 4.05
3.2 Human activities affect the environment.	1.03, 1.05, 3.06, 7.03, 7.05
Math in Science: Finding Volumes	1.06
3.3 People are working to protect ecosystems.	1.05, 2.01, 2.05, 3.06, 7.04
Chapter Investigation: Cleaning Oil Spills	1.01, 1.03, 1.05, 1.08, 3.06

Unit E Space Science	
Frontiers in Science: Danger from the Sky	1.09, 1.10, 2.02
Chapter 1 Exploring Space	
1.1 Some space objects are visible to the human eye.	1.05, 5.01, 5.05
1.2 Telescopes allow us to study space from Earth.	1.05, 2.01, 5.04
Chapter Investigation: Observing Spectra	1.03, 1.05, 1.08

Section or Feature	Competency Goals and Objectives
1.3 Spacecraft help us explore beyond Earth.	1.05, 2.01, 2.02, 4.05, 5.02, 5.04, 5.06
Math in Science: Using Exponents	1.06
1.4 Space exploration benefits society.	1.05, 2.01, 2.03, 5.02, 5.04, 5.05, 5.06
Connecting Sciences: How Earth's Gravity Affects Plants	1.09, 2.02
Chapter 2 Earth, Moon, and Sun	
2.1 Earth rotates on a tilted axis and orbits the sun.	1.03, 1.05, 1.06, 1.07, 5.01
Chapter Investigation: Modeling Seasons	1.01, 1.05, 1.08
2.2 The Moon is Earth's natural satellite.	1.05, 5.01, 5.02
Math in Science: Making Line Graphs	1.06
2.3 Positions of the Sun and the Moon affect Earth.	1.03, 1.07, 1.05, 5.01, 5.03
Science on the Job: Astronomy in Archaeology	1.10
Timelines in Science: The Story of Astronomy	1.08, 2.03, 5.04
Chapter 3 Our Solar System	
3.1 Planets orbit the Sun at different distances.	1.05, 1.06, 5.01, 5.02
Math in Science: Using Percentages	1.06
3.2 The inner solar system has rocky planets.	1.03, 1.05, 5.01, 5.02
Think Science: Forming Hypotheses	1.01
3.3 The outer solar system has four giant planets.	1.05, 5.01, 5.02
3.4 Small objects are made of ice and rock.	5.01, 5.02
Chapter Investigation: Exploring Impact Craters	1.01, 1.04, 1.05
Chapter 4 Stars, Galaxies, and the Universe	
4.1 The Sun is our local star.	1.03, 1.05, 5.01, 5.02, 5.03
Chapter Investigation: Temperature, Brightness, and Color	1.01, 1.03, 1.05, 1.08

Lesson-by-Lesson

Section or Feature	Competency Goals and Objectives
4.2 Stars change over their life cycles.	1.05, 5.01, 5.05
Math in Science: Interpreting a Scatter Plot	1.06
4.3 Galaxies have different sizes and shapes.	1.05, 5.05
Extreme Science: When Galaxies Collide	1.09, 1.10, 2.01
4.4 The universe is expanding.	1.05, 5.04, 5.05

North Carolina Handbook	
Problem-Based Investigation: Natural Selection	1.05, 1.08, 7.06
Problem-Based Investigation: Soil Science	1.05, 1.08, 3.05, 3.06, 3.08, 7.01
Photosynthesis	3.08, 4.01, 4.03, 4.04
Designed Systems	3.06, 4.05, 7.01
Rocks and Minerals of North Carolina	3.01, 3.04

McDougal Littell

Science

GRADE

6

Space Science

Waves, Sound, and Light

Energy and the Changing Earth

Ecology

Earth's Surface

Unit A Credits
5C U.S. Geological Survey; **39B** Photographs by Sharon Hoogstraten; **71B** *left to right* Illustration by Gary Hincks; Illustrations by David A. Hardy; **111B** *top section, left to right* Illustrations by Mike Saunders; © Susan Rayfield/Photo Researchers; *bottom section, left to right* Illustrations by Rob Wood/Wood Ronsaville Harlin; Photograph courtesy of Sara Christopherson; **141B** *left to right* Illustrations by Gary Hincks; Mapquest; **141C** *left to right* Illustration by Raymond Turvey; Mapquest.

Unit B Credits
5B © Left Lane Productions/Corbis; **37C** © Joe Sohm/Visions of America, LLC/PictureQuest; **65C** Illustration by Stephen Durke; **101B** *left to right* Illustration by Precision Graphics; © Martin Miller/University of Oregon, Eugene, Oregon; **101C** Illustration by Stephen Durke; **133C** Illustration by Richard Bonson/Wildlife Art Ltd.

Unit C Credits
69C *left* Illustrations by Dan Stuckenschneider; *right* Illustration by Eric Chadwick; **109B** Photographs by Sharon Hoogstraten; **109C** © Kim Heacox/Getty Images; **109B** Illustration by Bart Vallecoccia.

Unit D Credits
5B © Grant Heilman Photography; Illustration by Martin Macrae/nbillustraion.co.uk; **5C** Illustration by Richard Bonson/Wildlife Art Ltd.; **41C** *both* Illustrations by Luigi Galante.

Unit E Credits
5B Illustration by Dan Stuckenschneider; **5C, 75B** Illustrations by David A. Hardy; **111B** Illustration by Julian Baum; **111C** *top* Illustration by Julian Baum; bottom David Malin Images/Anglo-Australian Observatory.

Acknowledgments
Excerpts and adaptations from *National Science Education Standards* by the National Academy of Sciences. Copyright © 1996 by the National Academy of Sciences. Reprinted with permission from the National Academies Press, Washington, D.C.

Excerpts and adaptations from *Benchmarks for Science Literacy: Project 2061.* Copyright © 1993 by the American Association for the Advancement of Science. Reprinted with permission.

ISBN: 0-618-46998-2   1 2 3 4 5 6 7 8 VJM 08 07 06 05 04

Internet Web Site: http://www.mcdougallittell.com

McDougal Littell Science

Effective Science Instruction Tailored for Middle School Learners

North Carolina Grade 6
Teacher's Edition Contents

Consultants and Reviewers

Science Consultants

Chief Science Consultant

James Trefil, Ph.D. is the Clarence J. Robinson Professor of Physics at George Mason University. He is the author or co-author of more than 25 books, including *Science Matters* and *The Nature of Science*. Dr. Trefil is a member of the American Association for the Advancement of Science's Committee on the Public Understanding of Science and Technology. He is also a fellow of the World Economic Forum and a frequent contributor to *Smithsonian* magazine.

Rita Ann Calvo, Ph.D. is Senior Lecturer in Molecular Biology and Genetics at Cornell University, where for 12 years she also directed the Cornell Institute for Biology Teachers. Dr. Calvo is the 1999 recipient of the College and University Teaching Award from the National Association of Biology Teachers.

Kenneth Cutler, M.S. is the Education Coordinator for the Julius L. Chambers Biomedical Biotechnology Research Institute at North Carolina Central University. A former middle school and high school science teacher, he received a 1999 Presidential Award for Excellence in Science Teaching.

Instructional Design Consultants

Douglas Carnine, Ph.D. is Professor of Education and Director of the National Center for Improving the Tools of Educators at the University of Oregon. He is the author of seven books and over 100 other scholarly publications, primarily in the areas of instructional design and effective instructional strategies and tools for diverse learners. Dr. Carnine also serves as a member of the National Institute for Literacy Advisory Board.

Linda Carnine, Ph.D. consults with school districts on curriculum development and effective instruction for students struggling academically. A former teacher and school administrator, Dr. Carnine also co-authored a popular remedial reading program.

Sam Miller, Ph.D. is a middle school science teacher and the Teacher Development Liaison for the Eugene, Oregon, Public Schools. He is the author of curricula for teaching science, mathematics, computer skills, and language arts.

Donald Steely, Ph.D. serves as principal investigator at the Oregon Center for Applied Science (ORCAS) on federal grants for science and language arts programs. His background also includes teaching and authoring of print and multimedia programs in science, mathematics, history, and spelling.

Vicky Vachon, Ph.D. consults with school districts throughout the United States and Canada on improving overall academic achievement with a focus on literacy. She is also co-author of a widely used program for remedial readers.

Content Reviewers

John Beaver, Ph.D.
Ecology
Professor, Director of Science Education Center
College of Education and Human Services
Western Illinois University
Macomb, IL

Donald J. DeCoste, Ph.D.
Matter and Energy, Chemical Interactions
Chemistry Instructor
University of Illinois
Urbana-Champaign, IL

Dorothy Ann Fallows, Ph.D., MSc
Diversity of Living Things, Microbiology
Partners in Health
Boston, MA

Michael Foote, Ph.D.
The Changing Earth, Life Over Time
Associate Professor
Department of the Geophysical Sciences
The University of Chicago
Chicago, IL

Lucy Fortson, Ph.D.
Space Science
Director of Astronomy
Adler Planetarium and Astronomy Museum
Chicago, IL

Elizabeth Godrick, Ph.D.
Human Biology
Professor, CAS Biology
Boston University
Boston, MA

Isabelle Sacramento Grilo, M.S.
The Changing Earth
Lecturer, Department of the Geological Sciences
Montana State University
Bozeman, MT

David Harbster, MSc
Diversity of Living Things
Professor of Biology
Paradise Valley Community College
Phoenix, AZ

Richard D. Norris, Ph.D.
Earth's Waters
Professor of Paleobiology
Scripps Institution of Oceanography
University of California, San Diego
La Jolla, CA

Donald B. Peck, M.S.
*Motion and Forces; Waves, Sound, and Light;
Electricity and Magnetism*
Director of the Center for Science Education (retired)
Fairleigh Dickinson University
Madison, NJ

Javier Penalosa, Ph.D.
Diversity of Living Things, Plants
Associate Professor, Biology Department
Buffalo State College
Buffalo, NY

Raymond T. Pierrehumbert, Ph.D.
Earth's Atmosphere
Professor in Geophysical Sciences (Atmospheric Science)
The University of Chicago
Chicago, IL

Brian J. Skinner, Ph.D.
Earth's Surface
Eugene Higgins Professor of Geology and Geophysics
Yale University
New Haven, CT

Nancy E. Spaulding, M.S.
Earth's Surface, The Changing Earth, Earth's Waters
Earth Science Teacher (retired)
Elmira Free Academy
Elmira, NY

Steven S. Zumdahl, Ph.D.
Matter and Energy, Chemical Interactions
Professor Emeritus of Chemistry
University of Illinois
Urbana-Champaign, IL

Susan L. Zumdahl, M.S.
Matter and Energy, Chemical Interactions
Chemistry Education Specialist
University of Illinois
Urbana-Champaign, IL

Safety Consultant

Juliana Texley, Ph.D.
Former K–12 Science Teacher and School Superintendent
Boca Raton, FL

English Language Advisor

Judy Lewis, M.A.
Director, State and Federal Programs for reading proficiency
and high risk populations
Rancho Cordova, CA

Research-Based Solutions for Your Classroom

The distinguished program consultant team and a thorough, research-based planning and development process assure that *McDougal Littell Science* supports all students in learning science concepts, acquiring inquiry skills, and thinking scientifically.

Standards-Based Instruction

Concepts and skills were selected based on careful analysis of national and state standards.

- National Science Education Standards
- North Carolina Competency Goals and Objectives
- Project 2061 Benchmarks for Science Literacy

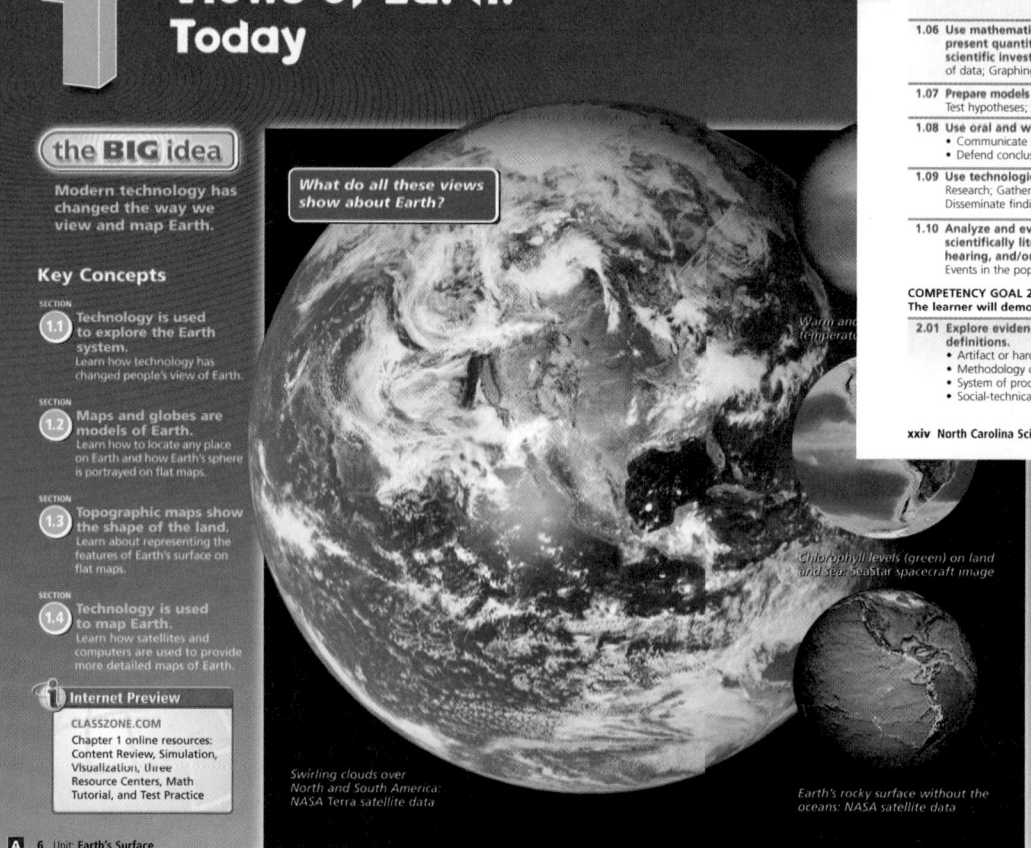

NORTH CAROLINA
Standard Course of Study

The chart below shows the goals and objectives of the North Carolina Standard Course of Study for your science course this year, and some of the places in *McDougal Littell Science* where you will find reading and practice to help you achieve those goals.

COMPETENCY GOAL 1
The learner will design and conduct investigations to demonstrate an understanding of scientific inquiry.

North Carolina Objectives	McDougal Littell Science
1.01 Identify and create questions and hypotheses that can be answered through scientific investigations.	Chapter Investigations and Think Science pages in each unit; Scientific Thinking Handbook, R3; Lab Handbook, R28–R35
1.02 Develop appropriate experimental procedures for: Given questions; Student-driven questions.	Design Your Own Investigations in each unit; Lab Handbook, R10–R35
1.03 Apply safety procedures in the laboratory and in field studies: Recognize potential hazards; Manipulate materials and equipment; Conduct appropriate procedures.	Explores, Investigates, and Chapter Investigations in each chapter; Lab Handbook, R10–R35
1.04 Analyze variables in scientific investigations: Identify dependent and independent; Use of a control; Manipulate; Describe relationships between; Define operationally.	Chapter Investigations and Think Science pages in each unit; Lab Handbook, R30–R35
1.05 Analyze evidence to: Explain observations; Make inferences and predictions; Develop the relationship between evidence and explanation.	Explores, Investigates, and Chapter Investigations in each chapter; Scientific Thinking Handbook, R2–R9; Lab Handbook, R10–R35; North Carolina Handbook: Natural Selection; Soil Science
1.06 Use mathematics to gather, organize, and present quantitative data resulting from scientific investigations: Measurement; Analysis of data; Graphing; Prediction models.	Chapter Investigations and Math in Science pages in each chapter; Lab Handbook, R10–R35; Math Handbook, R36–R44
1.07 Prepare models and/or computer simulations to: Test hypotheses; Evaluate how data fits.	Explores, Investigates, and Chapter Investigations in each unit; Unit A *Earth's Surface*, A13, A20, A32, A135
1.08 Use oral and written language to: • Communicate findings. • Defend conclusions of scientific investigations.	Unit Projects; Timelines in Science; Chapter Investigations; Chapter Reviews; North Carolina Handbook: Natural Selection; Soil Science
1.09 Use technologies and information systems to: Research; Gather and analyze data; Visualize data; Disseminate findings to others.	Explore the Big Idea in each chapter, Unit Projects; Connecting Sciences, Think Science in each unit
1.10 Analyze and evaluate information from a scientifically literate viewpoint by reading, hearing, and/or viewing: Scientific text; Articles; Events in the popular press.	Frontiers in Science features, *Scientific American* video segments, Internet resources at ClassZone.com and NSTA SciLinks; Scientific Thinking Handbook, R2–R9

COMPETENCY GOAL 2
The learner will demonstrate an understanding of technological design.

2.01 Explore evidence that "technology" has many definitions. • Artifact or hardware. • Methodology or technique. • System of production. • Social-technical system.	The Nature of Technology (pp. xl–xli) and Frontiers in Science and Timelines in Science features in each unit; Unit A *Earth's Surface*, 1.1, 1.4; Unit B *Energy and the Changing Earth*: 1.3, 2.3, 4.3; Unit C *Waves, Sound, and Light*: 2.4, 3.2, 4.4; Unit D *Ecology*, 3.3; Unit E *Space Science*, 1.2, 1.3, 1.4

xxiv North Carolina Science Grade 6

CHAPTER 1

Views of Earth Today

the BIG idea
Modern technology has changed the way we view and map Earth.

What do all these views show about Earth?

Key Concepts

SECTION 1.1
Technology is used to explore the Earth system.
Learn how technology has changed people's view of Earth.

SECTION 1.2
Maps and globes are models of Earth.
Learn how to locate any place on Earth and how Earth's sphere is portrayed on flat maps.

SECTION 1.3
Topographic maps show the shape of the land.
Learn about representing the features of Earth's surface on flat maps.

SECTION 1.4
Technology is used to map Earth.
Learn how satellites and computers are used to provide more detailed maps of Earth.

Internet Preview

CLASSZONE.COM
Chapter 1 online resources: Content Review, Simulation, Visualization, three Resource Centers, Math Tutorial, and Test Practice

Chlorophyll levels (green) on land and sea. SeaStar spacecraft image

Swirling clouds over North and South America: NASA Terra satellite data

Earth's rocky surface without the oceans: NASA satellite data

A 6 Unit: Earth's Surface

Internet Activity: Mapping
Go to ClassZone.com to learn more about mapping Earth from space. Find out about a NASA mission to develop the most accurate map of Earth ever made.

Observe and Think
Why do you think scientists need different maps produced from satellite data?

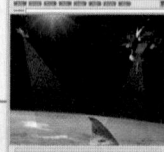

NSTA SciLINKS
scilinks.org
Earth's Spheres Code: MDL013

Chapter 1: Views of Earth Today 7 **A**

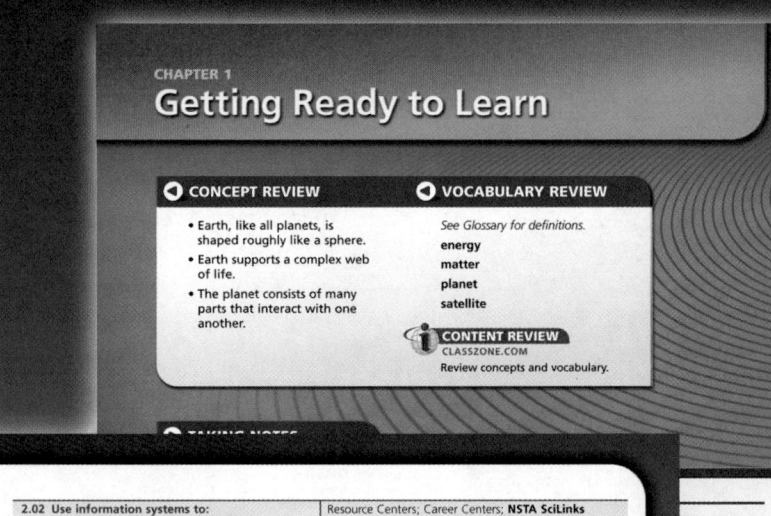

CHAPTER 1
Getting Ready to Learn

◁ CONCEPT REVIEW

- Earth, like all planets, is shaped roughly like a sphere.
- Earth supports a complex web of life.
- The planet consists of many parts that interact with one another.

◁ VOCABULARY REVIEW

See Glossary for definitions.

energy
matter
planet
satellite

ⓘ CONTENT REVIEW
CLASSZONE.COM
Review concepts and vocabulary.

2.02 Use information systems to: • Identify scientific needs, human needs, or problems that are subject to technological solution. • Locate resources to obtain and test ideas.	Resource Centers; Career Centers; **NSTA SciLinks**
2.03 Evaluate technological designs for: • Application of scientific principles. • Risks and benefits. • Constraints of design. • Consistent testing protocols.	Unit A *Earth's Surface,* Science on the Job Unit B *Energy and the Changing Earth,* 1.3, Chapter 2 Investigation; Think Science; 4.3; Chapter 4 Investigation Unit C *Waves, Sound, and Light,* 2.4, Chapter 2 Investigation; 3.2; Think Science; 4.4 Unit D *Ecology,* 3.3 Unit E *Space Science,* 1.4
2.04 Apply tenets of technological design to make informed consumer decisions about: Products; Systems; Processes.	Unit B *Energy and the Changing Earth,* Think Science; Chapter 4 Investigation Unit C *Waves, Sound, and Light,* 3.3 Investigate

COMPETENCY GOAL 3
The learner will build an understanding of the geological cycles, forces, processes, and agents which shape the lithosphere.

3.01 Evaluate the forces that shape the lithosphere including: Crustal plate movement; Folding and faulting; Deposition; Volcanic Activity; Earthquakes.	Unit A *Earth's Surface* Unit B *Energy and the Changing Earth* North Carolina Handbook: Rocks and Minerals
3.02 Examine earthquake and volcano patterns.	Unit B *Energy and the Changing Earth*
3.03 Explain the model for the interior of the earth.	Unit A *Earth's Surface* Unit B *Energy and the Changing Earth*
3.04 Describe the processes which form and the uses of earth materials. Rock cycle; Minerals; Characteristics of rocks; Economic use of rocks and minerals; Value of gems and precious metals; Common gems, minerals, precious metals and rocks found in N.C.	Unit A *Earth's Surface* North Carolina Handbook: Rocks and Minerals
3.05 Analyze soil properties that can be observed and measured to predict soil quality: Color; Horizon profile; Infiltration; Soil temperature; Structure; Consistency; Texture; Particle size; pH; Fertility; Soil moisture.	Unit A *Earth's Surface* North Carolina Handbook: Soil Science
3.06 Evaluate ways in which human activities have affected Earth's pedosphere and the measures taken to control the impact: Vegetative cover; Agriculture; Soil as a vector; Land use; Nutrient balance.	Unit A *Earth's Surface* Unit D *Ecology* North Carolina Handbook: Soil Science, Designed Systems
3.07 Assess use of technology and information systems in monitoring lithospheric phenomenon.	Unit A *Earth's Surface*
3.08 Conclude that the good health of environments and organisms requires: Monitoring of the pedosphere; Taking steps to maintain soil quality; Stewardship.	Unit A *Earth's Surface* Unit D *Ecology* North Carolina Handbook: Soil Science, Photosynthesis

xxv

VOCABULARY
Remember to draw a word triangle in your notebook for each vocabulary term.

The Earth system has four major parts.

A terrarium is a simple example of a **system**—an organized group of parts that work together to form a whole. To understand a system, you need to see how all its parts work together. This principle is true for a small terrarium, and it is true for planet Earth.

Both a terrarium and Earth are closed systems. They are closed because matter, such as soil or water, cannot enter or leave. However, energy can flow into or out of the system. Just as light and heat pass through the glass of the terrarium, sunlight and heat enter and leave the Earth system through the atmosphere.

Within the Earth system are four connected parts: the atmosphere (Earth's air), the hydrosphere (Earth's waters), the biosphere (Earth's living things), and the geosphere (Earth's interior and its rocks and soils). Each of these parts is an open system because both matter and energy move into and out of it. The four open systems work together to form one large, closed system called Earth.

Chapter 1: Views of Earth Today 9   **A**

Effective Instructional Strategies

McDougal Littell Science incorporates strategies that research shows are effective in improving student achievement. These strategies include

- Note taking and nonlinguistic representations (Marzano, Pickering, and Pollock)

- A focus on big ideas (Kame'enui and Carnine)

- Background knowledge and active involvement (Project CRISS)

Robert J. Marzano, Debra J. Pickering, and Jane E. Pollock, *Classroom Instruction That Works; Research-Based Strategies for Increasing Student Achievement* (ASCD, 2001)

Edward J. Kame'enui and Douglas Carnine, *Effective Teaching Strategies That Accommodate Diverse Learners* (Pearson, 2002)

Project CRISS (Creating Independence Through Student-Owned Strategies)

Comprehensive Research, Review, and Field Testing

An ongoing program of research and review guided the development of *McDougal Littell Science.*

- Program plans based on extensive data from classroom visits, research surveys, teacher panels, and focus groups

- All pupil edition activities and labs classroom-tested by middle school teachers and students

- All chapters reviewed for clarity and scientific accuracy by the Content Reviewers listed on page T5

- Selected chapters field-tested in the classroom to assess student learning, ease of use, and student interest

Content Organized Around Big Ideas

Each chapter develops a big idea of science, helping students to place key concepts in context.

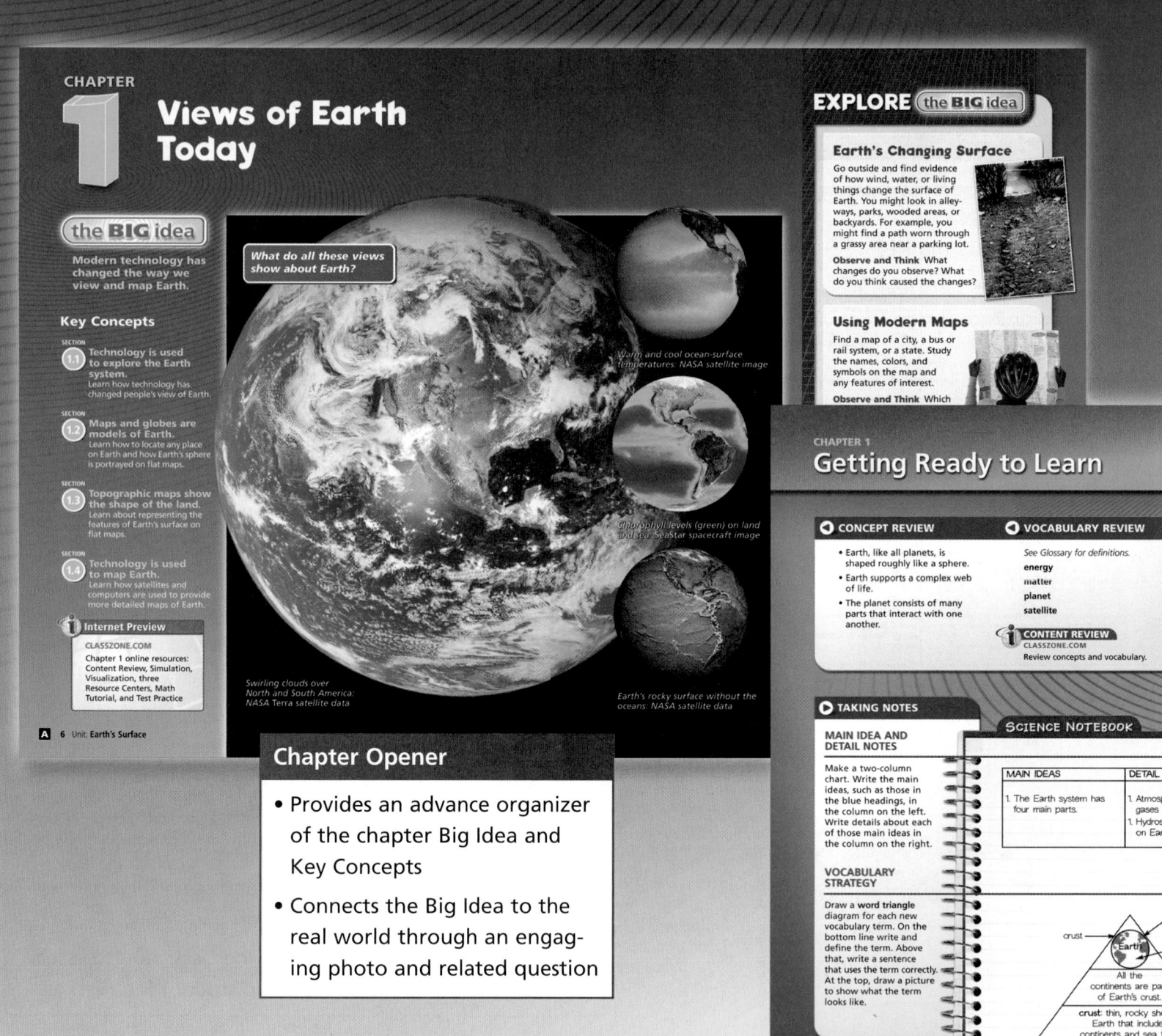

CHAPTER 1

Views of Earth Today

the BIG idea

Modern technology has changed the way we view and map Earth.

Key Concepts

SECTION 1.1 Technology is used to explore the Earth system.
Learn how technology has changed people's view of Earth.

SECTION 1.2 Maps and globes are models of Earth.
Learn how to locate any place on Earth and how Earth's sphere is portrayed on flat maps.

SECTION 1.3 Topographic maps show the shape of the land.
Learn about representing the features of Earth's surface on flat maps.

SECTION 1.4 Technology is used to map Earth.
Learn how satellites and computers are used to provide more detailed maps of Earth.

Internet Preview

CLASSZONE.COM
Chapter 1 online resources: Content Review, Simulation, Visualization, three Resource Centers, Math Tutorial, and Test Practice

A 6 Unit: Earth's Surface

What do all these views show about Earth?

Warm and cool ocean-surface temperatures: NASA satellite image

Chlorophyll levels (green) on land and sea: SeaStar spacecraft image

Swirling clouds over North and South America: NASA Terra satellite data

Earth's rocky surface without the oceans: NASA satellite data

EXPLORE the BIG idea

Earth's Changing Surface

Go outside and find evidence of how wind, water, or living things change the surface of Earth. You might look in alleyways, parks, wooded areas, or backyards. For example, you might find a path worn through a grassy area near a parking lot.

Observe and Think What changes do you observe? What do you think caused the changes?

Using Modern Maps

Find a map of a city, a bus or rail system, or a state. Study the names, colors, and symbols on the map and any features of interest.

Observe and Think Which

CHAPTER 1

Getting Ready to Learn

CONCEPT REVIEW

- Earth, like all planets, is shaped roughly like a sphere.
- Earth supports a complex web of life.
- The planet consists of many parts that interact with one another.

VOCABULARY REVIEW

See Glossary for definitions.

energy
matter
planet
satellite

CONTENT REVIEW
CLASSZONE.COM
Review concepts and vocabulary.

TAKING NOTES

MAIN IDEA AND DETAIL NOTES

Make a two-column chart. Write the main ideas, such as those in the blue headings, in the column on the left. Write details about each of those main ideas in the column on the right.

VOCABULARY STRATEGY

Draw a **word triangle** diagram for each new vocabulary term. On the bottom line write and define the term. Above that, write a sentence that uses the term correctly. At the top, draw a picture to show what the term looks like.

See the Note-Taking Handbook on pages R45–R51.

SCIENCE NOTEBOOK

MAIN IDEAS	DETAIL NC
1. The Earth system has four main parts.	1. Atmosphe gases sur
	1. Hydrosphe on Earth

crust

All the continents are part of Earth's crust.

crust: thin, rocky shell c Earth that includes continents and sea floo

A 8 Unit: Earth's Surface

Chapter Opener

- Provides an advance organizer of the chapter Big Idea and Key Concepts

- Connects the Big Idea to the real world through an engaging photo and related question

Visual Summary

- Summarizes Key Concepts using both text and visuals
- Reinforces the connection of Key Concepts to the Big Idea

Section Opener

- Highlights the Key Concept
- Connects new learning to prior knowledge
- Previews important vocabulary

The Big Idea Questions

- Help students connect their new learning back to the Big Idea
- Prompt students to synthesize and apply the Big Idea and Key Concepts

---

1 Chapter Review

the BIG idea

Modern technology has changed the way we view and map Earth.

CONTENT REVIEW
CLASSZONE.COM

KEY CONCEPTS SUMMARY

1.1 Technology is used to explore the Earth system.

The atmosphere, hydrosphere, biosphere, and geosphere work together to form one large system called Earth.

VOCABULARY
system p. 9
atmosphere p. 10
hydrosphere p. 10
biosphere p. 11
geosphere p. 12

1.2 Maps and globes are models of Earth.

Latitude and longitude are used to locate any point on Earth.

equator
prime meridian

All map projections distort Earth's surface.

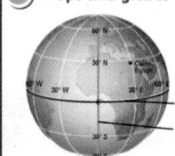

VOCABULARY
relief map p. 16
map scale p. 17
map legend p. 17
equator p. 18
latitude p. 18
prime meridian p. 19
longitude p. 19
projection p. 20

1.3 Topographic maps show the shape of the land.

Contour lines show elevation, slope, and relief.

Closed circles represent hilltops.

Contour lines show

Contour lines never cross.

VOCABULARY
topography p. 24
contour line p. 25
elevation p. 25
slope p. 25
relief p. 25

1.4 Technology is used to ma...

Remote-sensing technology gathers accurate data about Earth.

Reviewing Vocabulary

Copy and complete the chart below, using vocabulary terms from this chapter.

Term	Use	Appearance
map legend	to explain map symbols	chart of symbols
1. latitude	to show distance from the equator	
2. longitude		lines going from pole to pole
3.	to show land features	rippled and smooth areas
4. map scale	to represent distances	
5. equator		line at 0° latitude
6. prime meridian	to separate east and west hemispheres	
7.	to show height above sea level	line showing elevation
8. false-color image	to highlight information	

Reviewing Key Concepts

Multiple Choice *Choose the letter of the best answer.*

... correct

... ater

... part of

Thinking Critically

Use the topographic map below to answer the next seven questions.

marsh   road
buildings   unpaved road

22. APPLY Imagine you are hiking through this area. Which hill—C, D, or E—has the steepest slope? How do you know?

23. ANALYZE What is the topography of the land through which the curved road A goes?

24. IDENTIFY CAUSE The black and red squares at B represent buildings. Why do you think the buildings were placed here instead of somewhere else in the area?

25. APPLY The contour interval is 10 meters. What is the elevation of the highest point on the map?

26. SYNTHESIZE Sketch the two hills D and E. What would they look like to someone on the ground?

27. INFER Suppose someone wanted to build a road through the terrain on the far left side of the map. What are the advantages and disadvantages of such a route?

28. EVALUATE Do you think this area would be a good place to ride mountain bikes? Why or why not?

CHART INFORMATION *On a separate sheet of paper, write a word to fill each blank in the chart.*

Feature	Shown on Topographic Maps?	Belongs to Which Major System?
rivers	yes	hydrosphere
29. slope		
30. winds		
31. plants		
32. lakes		
33. relief		

the BIG idea

34. APPLY Look again at the photographs on pages 6–7. Now that you have finished the chapter, reread the question on the main photograph. What would you change in or add to your answer?

35. SYNTHESIZE Describe some of the types of information that new technology has provided about Earth.

36. DRAW CONCLUSIONS What type of technology do you think has done the most to change the way people view and map Earth? Explain your conclusion.

UNIT PROJECTS

If you are doing a unit project, make a folder for your project. Include in your folder a list of the resources you will need, the date on which the project is due, and a schedule to track your progress. Begin gathering data.

KEY CONCEPT

1.1 Technology is used to explore the Earth system.

BEFORE, you learned
- Earth has a spherical shape and supports a complex web of life
- Earth's environment is a system with many parts

NOW, you will learn
- About the Earth system and its four major parts
- How technology is used to explore the Earth system
- How the parts of the Earth system shape the surface

VOCABULARY
system p. 9
atmosphere p. 10
hydrosphere p. 10
biosphere p. 11
geosphere p. 12

THINK ABOUT

How do these parts work together?

Look closely at this terrarium. Notice that the bowl and its cover form a boundary between the terrarium and the outside world. What might happen to the entire terrarium if any part were taken away? What might happen if you placed the terrarium in a dark closet?

VOCABULARY
Remember to draw a word triangle in your notebook for each vocabulary term.

The Earth system has four major parts.

A terrarium is a simple example of a **system** —an organized group of parts that work together to form a whole. To understand a system, you need to see how all its parts work together. This principle is true for a small terrarium, and it is true for planet Earth.

Both a terrarium and Earth are closed systems. They are closed because matter, such as soil or water, cannot enter or leave. However, energy can flow into or out of the system. Just as light and heat pass through the glass of the terrarium, sunlight and heat enter and leave the Earth system through the atmosphere.

Within the Earth system are four connected parts: the atmosphere (Earth's air), the hydrosphere (Earth's waters), the biosphere (Earth's living things), and the geosphere (Earth's interior and its rocks and soils). Each of these parts is an open system because both matter and energy move into and out of it. The four open systems work together to form one large, closed system called Earth.

T9

Many Ways to Learn

Because students learn in so many ways, *McDougal Littell Science* gives them a variety of experiences with important concepts and skills. Text, visuals, activities, and technology all focus on Big Ideas and Key Concepts.

Hands-on Learning

- Activities that reinforce Key Concepts
- Skill Focus for important inquiry and process skills
- Multiple activities in every chapter, from quick Explores to full-period Chapter Investigations

Considerate Text

- Clear structure of meaningful headings
- Information clearly connected to main ideas
- Student-friendly writing style

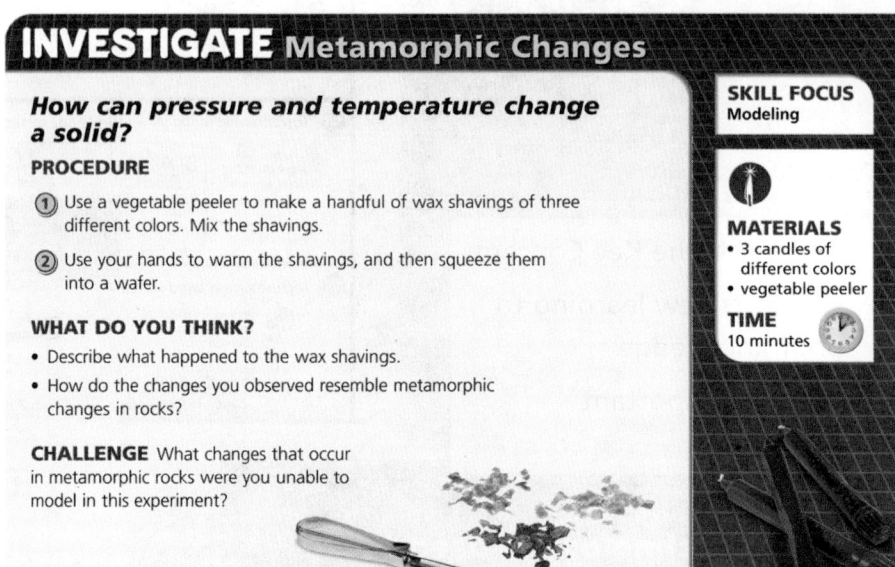

INVESTIGATE Metamorphic Changes

How can pressure and temperature change a solid?

PROCEDURE

1. Use a vegetable peeler to make a handful of wax shavings of three different colors. Mix the shavings.

2. Use your hands to warm the shavings, and then squeeze them into a wafer.

WHAT DO YOU THINK?

- Describe what happened to the wax shavings.
- How do the changes you observed resemble metamorphic changes in rocks?

CHALLENGE What changes that occur in metamorphic rocks were you unable to model in this experiment?

SKILL FOCUS
Modeling

MATERIALS
- 3 candles of different colors
- vegetable peeler

TIME
10 minutes

Metamorphic changes occur over large and small areas.

The types of metamorphic changes that occur depend on the types of parent rocks and the conditions of temperature and pressure. When both high temperature and high pressure are present, metamorphic changes can occur over very large areas. When only one of these conditions is present, changes tend to occur over smaller areas.

Change over Large Areas

Most metamorphic changes occur over large areas in which both temperature and pressure are high. An example is a region where large blocks of rock are pressing together and pushing up mountain ranges. This process can affect an area hundreds of kilometers wide and tens of kilometers deep. In such an area, rocks are buried, pressed together, bent, and heated. The pressure and heat cause the rocks to undergo metamorphism. Generally, the deeper below the surface the rocks are, the greater the metamorphic changes that occur in them. For example, a sedimentary rock may change to slate near the surface but become gneiss deep inside a mountain.

 **CHECK YOUR READING** Where can metamorphic changes occur over large areas?

Change over Small Areas

Some metamorphic changes occur over small areas. For example, magma can push into rocks underground, or surface rock can be covered by a lava flow. The magma or lava heats the rock it is in contact with, causing recrystallization. These changes are mainly due to high temperature, not pressure. The rocks get roasted but not squeezed. The thickness of rock changed by the heat can range from less than one meter to several hundred meters, depending on the amount and temperature of the molten rock.

Small areas of metamorphic rock can also be formed by high pressure alone. At or near Earth's surface, rocks move and grind past one another during earthquakes. Rocks that grind together in this way can be subjected to high pressures that cause metamorphic changes.

RESOURCE CENTER
CLASSZONE.COM

Find information on metamorphic rocks.

Metamorphic Changes

Changes can occur over hundreds of kilometers or over just a few centimeters.

Changes over Large Areas

Forces within Earth start to press rock layers together over hundreds of kilometers.

Heat and pressure change the rock layers that make up the mountains into metamorphic rocks.

Changes over Small Areas

Magma can push into rock layers and cause changes over areas ranging from a few centimeters to tens of meters.

The magma is hot enough to bake the surrounding rocks into metamorphic rocks.

READING VISUALS Compare how heat and pressure cause changes over the large and small areas shown above.

Integrated Technology

- Interaction with Key Concepts through Simulations and Visualizations

- Easy access to relevant Web resources through Resource Centers and SciLinks

- Opportunities for review through Content Reviews and Math Tutorials

Visuals That Teach

- Information-rich visuals directly connected to the text

- Thoughtful pairing of diagrams and real-world photos

- Reading Visuals questions to support student learning

Differentiated Instruction

A full spectrum of resources for differentiating instruction supports you in reaching the wide range of learners in your classroom.

1 INSTRUCT

Language Arts Connection

Have students think of related words that contain the same Greek prefixes as those used in each of the four parts of the Earth system. *Sample answer: hydrology, geology, biology* Tell students an atmometer is an instrument that measures rates of evaporation.

Develop Critical Thinking

CLASSIFY Have students classify each item below in its proper sphere.
- ocean floor *geosphere*
- hurricane *atmosphere*
- bird's nest *biosphere*
- mountain glacier *hydrosphere*

Teach from Visuals

Remind students that they can get a preview of chapter content by studying the visuals—photographs, maps, or diagrams—and reading captions.

To help students interpret the "Parts of the Earth System" visual on pp. 10–11, ask:
- What landforms do you recognize in this image of Earth? *Students should recognize the North American continent, and the northern part of South America. They may identify Florida, Cuba, the Gulf Coast, and Mexico; Greenland is also visible.*
- What does each of the four inset photographs show? *one of the Earth system's four major parts*
- What theme is shared by the photographs? *human exploration of the Earth system through the use of technology*

A 10 Unit: Earth's Surface

Atmosphere

READING TIP The names of the Earth system's four parts contain Greek prefixes. *Atmo-* refers to vapor or gas. *Hydro-* refers to water. *Bio-* refers to life, and *geo-* refers to earth.

The **atmosphere** (AT-muh-SFEER) is the mixture of gases that surrounds and protects Earth. The most abundant gases are nitrogen (about 78%) and oxygen (nearly 21%). The atmosphere also contains carbon dioxide, water vapor, and a few other gases.

Before the 1800s, all studies of the atmosphere had to be done from the ground. Today, scientists launch weather balloons, fly specially equipped planes, and view the atmosphere in satellite images. The data they collect show that the atmosphere interacts with the other parts of the Earth system to form complex weather patterns that circulate around Earth. The more scientists learn about these patterns, the more accurately they can predict local weather.

Hydrosphere

The **hydrosphere** (HY-druh-SFEER) is made up of all the water on Earth in oceans, lakes, glaciers, rivers, and streams and underground. Water covers nearly three-quarters of Earth's surface. Only about 3 percent of the hydrosphere is fresh water. Nearly 70 percent of Earth's fresh water is frozen in glaciers and polar ice caps.

Parts of the Earth System

Atmosphere
Over 400 cones make this weather balloon more stable as it gathers data about the atmosphere.

Hydrosphere
Scientists need special diving equipment to study Earth's oceans.

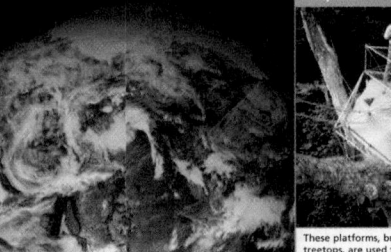

A 10 Unit: Earth's Surface

In the past 50 years, scientists have used deep-sea vehicles, special buoys, satellite images, and diving suits, such as the one shown on page 10, to study the world's oceans. They have discovered that the oceans contain several layers of cold and warm water. As these layers circulate, they form cold and warm ocean currents. The currents interact with wind patterns in the atmosphere and affect Earth's weather.

CHECK YOUR READING How does the hydrosphere affect the atmosphere?

Biosphere

The **biosphere** (BY-uh-SFEER) includes all life on Earth, in the air, on the land, and in the waters. The biosphere can be studied with a variety of technologies. For example, satellite photos are used to track yearly changes in Earth's plant and animal life. As the photograph below shows, special equipment allows scientists to study complex environments, such as rain forests, without damaging them.

Scientists have learned a lot about how the biosphere interacts with the other parts of the Earth system. For example, large forests act as Earth's "lungs," absorbing carbon dioxide and releasing oxygen into the atmosphere. When dead trees decay, they return nutrients to the soil.

CHECK YOUR READING Name one way the biosphere and the atmosphere interact.

MAIN IDEA AND DETAIL NOTES As you read this section, use this strategy to take notes.

Biosphere
These platforms, built in the treetops, are used to observe forest plants and animals.

Geosphere
In mines dug deep underground, scientists can explore Earth's minerals and rocks.

Chapter 1: **Views of Earth Today** 11

DIFFERENTIATE INSTRUCTION

More Reading Support

A What is a weather balloon used for? *studying the atmosphere*

B What percentage of Earth's fresh water is frozen? *nearly 70 percent*

English Learners Help English learners remember the differences between these similar-sounding terms: *atmosphere, hydrosphere, biosphere,* and *geosphere.* Suggest they separate each term into two parts by writing the prefix and *-sphere* on an index card. Under the Greek prefix, have them write the English meaning. *(Example: hydro- means water)* They can refer to these cards during lessons.

English Learners may not have prior knowledge of terrariums (p. 9), polar ice caps (p. 10), or computer modeling (p. 12).

DIFFERENTIATE INSTRUCTION

More Reading Support

C What is the biosphere? *all forms of life on Earth*

D Do plants absorb or release carbon dioxide? *absorb*

Advanced Have students hypothesize how oceans originated on our planet. Ask: How did Earth come to be a water planet? *Volcanic action released steam, which then condensed into liquid water. Some scientists also think that icy comets melted when they struck Earth, which added water to the planet.*

Teacher's Edition

- More Reading Support for below-level readers

- Strategies for below-level and advanced learners, English learners, and inclusion students

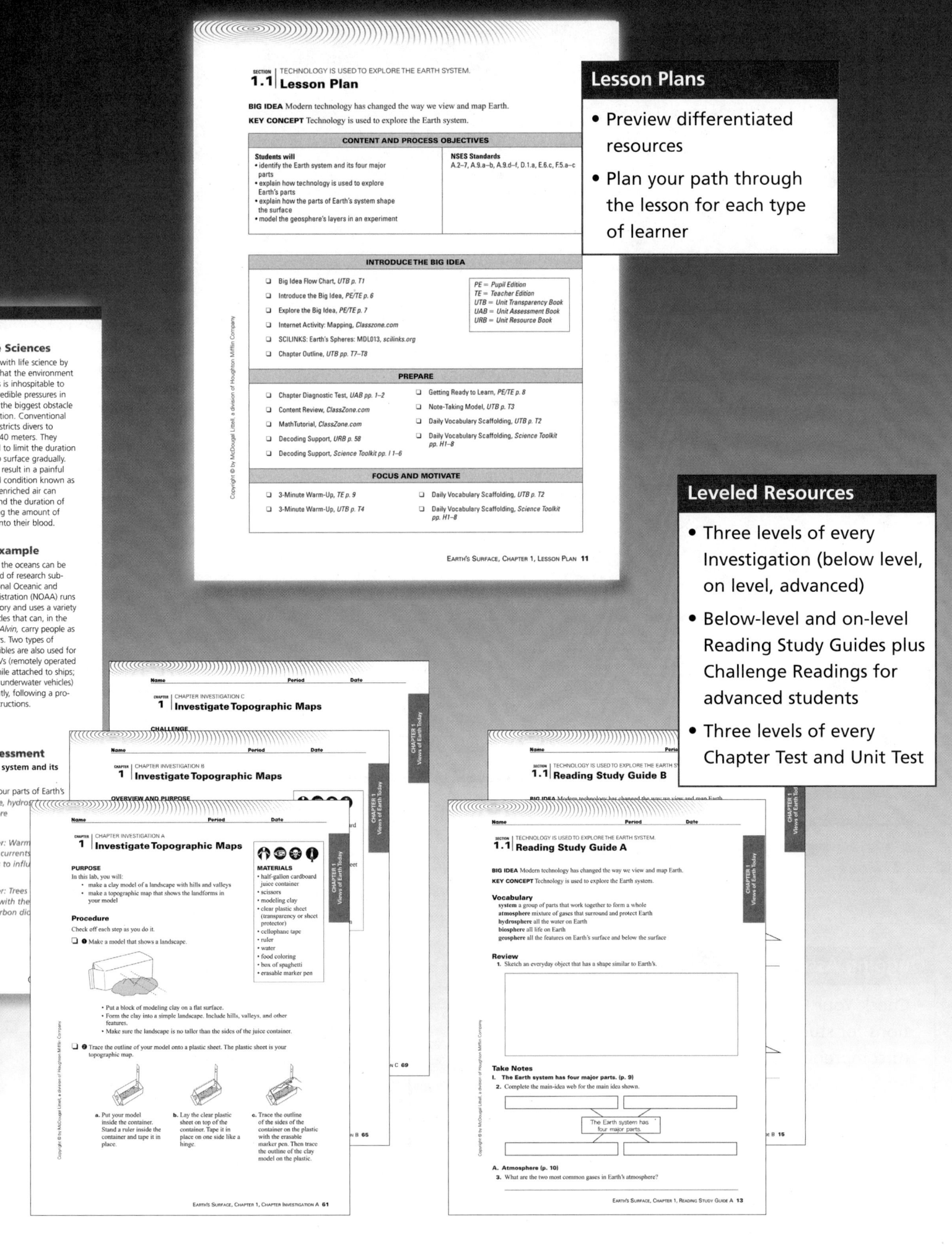

- Preview differentiated resources
- Plan your path through the lesson for each type of learner

SECTION | TECHNOLOGY IS USED TO EXPLORE THE EARTH SYSTEM.
1.1 | Lesson Plan

BIG IDEA Modern technology has changed the way we view and map Earth.

KEY CONCEPT Technology is used to explore the Earth system.

CONTENT AND PROCESS OBJECTIVES

Students will	NSES Standards
• identify the Earth system and its four major parts • explain how technology is used to explore Earth's parts • explain how the parts of Earth's system shape the surface • model the geosphere's layers in an experiment	A.2–7, A.9.a–b, A.9.d–f, D.1.a, E.6.c, F.5.a–c

INTRODUCE THE BIG IDEA

- ❏ Big Idea Flow Chart, *UTB p. T1*
- ❏ Introduce the Big Idea, *PE/TE p. 6*
- ❏ Explore the Big Idea, *PE/TE p. 7*
- ❏ Internet Activity: Mapping, *Classzone.com*
- ❏ SCILINKS: Earth's Spheres: MDL013, *scilinks.org*
- ❏ Chapter Outline, *UTB pp. T7–T8*

> PE = Pupil Edition
> TE = Teacher Edition
> UTB = Unit Transparency Book
> UAB = Unit Assessment Book
> URB = Unit Resource Book

PREPARE

- ❏ Chapter Diagnostic Test, *UAB pp. 1–2*
- ❏ Content Review, *ClassZone.com*
- ❏ MathTutorial, *ClassZone.com*
- ❏ Decoding Support, *URB p. 58*
- ❏ Decoding Support, *Science Toolkit pp. 1 1–6*
- ❏ Getting Ready to Learn, *PE/TE p. 8*
- ❏ Note-Taking Model, *UTB p. T3*
- ❏ Daily Vocabulary Scaffolding, *UTB p. T2*
- ❏ Daily Vocabulary Scaffolding, *Science Toolkit pp. H1–8*

FOCUS AND MOTIVATE

- ❏ 3-Minute Warm-Up, *TE p. 9*
- ❏ 3-Minute Warm-Up, *UTB p. T4*
- ❏ Daily Vocabulary Scaffolding, *UTB p. T2*
- ❏ Daily Vocabulary Scaffolding, *Science Toolkit pp. H1–8*

EARTH'S SURFACE, CHAPTER 1, LESSON PLAN **11**

Copyright © by McDougal Littell, a division of Houghton Mifflin Company

---

he Sciences

on with life science by
ct that the environment
ths is inhospitable to
ncredible pressures in
re the biggest obstacle
oration. Conventional
restricts divers to
n 40 meters. They
ful to limit the duration
to surface gradually.
an result in a painful
tal condition known as
n-enriched air can
tend the duration of
ting the amount of
d into their blood.

Example

of the oceans can be
aid of research sub-
tional Oceanic and
inistration (NOAA) runs
ratory and uses a variety
hicles that can, in the
s *Alvin*, carry people as
ters. Two types of
ersibles are also used for
OVs (remotely operated
while attached to ships;
us underwater vehicles)
ently, following a pro-
nstructions.

ssessment

h system and its
s

e four parts of Earth's
ere, hydros
here

wer: Warm
n currents
rns to influ

wer: Trees
es with the
carbon dio
n.

- Three levels of every Investigation (below level, on level, advanced)
- Below-level and on-level Reading Study Guides plus Challenge Readings for advanced students
- Three levels of every Chapter Test and Unit Test

| Name | Period | Date |

CHAPTER | CHAPTER INVESTIGATION C
1 | Investigate Topographic Maps

CHALLENGE

| Name | Period | Date |

CHAPTER | CHAPTER INVESTIGATION B
1 | Investigate Topographic Maps

OVERVIEW AND PURPOSE

| Name | Period | Date |

CHAPTER | CHAPTER INVESTIGATION A
1 | Investigate Topographic Maps

PURPOSE

In this lab, you will:
- make a clay model of a landscape with hills and valleys
- make a topographic map that shows the landforms in your model

MATERIALS
- half-gallon cardboard juice container
- scissors
- modeling clay
- clear plastic sheet (transparency or sheet protector)
- cellophane tape
- ruler
- water
- food coloring
- box of spaghetti
- erasable marker pen

Procedure

Check off each step as you do it.

❏ ❶ Make a model that shows a landscape.

- Put a block of modeling clay on a flat surface.
- Form the clay into a simple landscape. Include hills, valleys, and other features.
- Make sure the landscape is no taller than the sides of the juice container.

❏ ❷ Trace the outline of your model onto a plastic sheet. The plastic sheet is your topographic map.

a. Put your model inside the container. Stand a ruler inside the container and tape it in place.

b. Lay the clear plastic sheet on top of the container. Tape it in place on one side like a hinge.

c. Trace the outline of the sides of the container on the plastic with the erasable marker pen. Then trace the outline of the clay model on the plastic.

EARTH'S SURFACE, CHAPTER 1, CHAPTER INVESTIGATION A **61**

| Name | Period | Date |

SECTION | TECHNOLOGY IS USED TO EXPLORE THE EARTH SY
1.1 | Reading Study Guide B

BIG IDEA Modern technology has changed the way we view and map Earth.

| Name | Period | Date |

SECTION | TECHNOLOGY IS USED TO EXPLORE THE EARTH SYSTEM.
1.1 | Reading Study Guide A

BIG IDEA Modern technology has changed the way we view and map Earth.
KEY CONCEPT Technology is used to explore the Earth system.

Vocabulary
system a group of parts that work together to form a whole
atmosphere mixture of gases that surround and protect Earth
hydrosphere all the water on Earth
biosphere all life on Earth
geosphere all the features on Earth's surface and below the surface

Review
1. Sketch an everyday object that has a shape similar to Earth's.

Take Notes

I. The Earth system has four major parts. (p. 9)
2. Complete the main-idea web for the main idea shown.

> The Earth system has four major parts.

A. Atmosphere (p. 10)
3. What are the two most common gases in Earth's atmosphere?

EARTH'S SURFACE, CHAPTER 1, READING STUDY GUIDE A **13**

Effective Assessment

McDougal Littell Science incorporates a comprehensive set of resources for assessing student knowledge and performance before, during, and after instruction.

Diagnostic Tests

- Assessment of students' prior knowledge
- Readiness check for concepts and skills in the upcoming chapter

Ongoing Assessment

CHECK YOUR READING Answer: Wind and moving water wear away rocky surfaces; landmasses pushing together cause earthquakes and form volcanoes and other mountains; plants, animals, and people wear away or change Earth's surface.

EXPLORE (the BIG idea)

Revisit "Earth's Changing Surface" on p. 7. Have students explain the four parts of the Earth system worked together to account for their observations.

Reinforce (the BIG idea)

Have students relate the section to the Big Idea.

R Reinforcing Key Concepts, p. 21

1.1 ASSESS & RETEACH

Assess

A Section 1.1 Quiz, p. 3

Reteach

Draw a cutaway diagram on the board, similar to that on p. 12 but without indications of the boundaries between layers. Ask for volunteers to add the following information to the diagram:

- Locations of the atmosphere, hydrosphere, biosphere, and geosphere
- Compositions of the four spheres
- Boundaries and names of the geosphere's layers
- Composition or nature of each geosphere layer

Technology Resources

Have students visit ClassZone.com for reteaching of Key Concepts.

i CONTENT REVIEW

◉ CONTENT REVIEW CD-ROM

A 14 Unit: **Earth's Surface**

Mudslide in California

Atmosphere and Hydrosphere Heavy winter rains soak the ground until it cannot absorb any more water.

Biosphere People who build on fragile hillsides remove plants whose roots help hold the soil in place.

Geosphere With nothing to hold the water-soaked ground, it slides downhill, leaving a deep trench.

The photograph above shows a good example of how the four parts can suddenly change Earth's surface. A mudslide like this one can happen in a matter of minutes. Sometimes the side of a mountain may collapse, becoming a river of mud that can bury an entire town.

The four parts of the Earth system continue to shape the surface with every passing year. Scientists will continue to record these changes to update maps and other images of the planet's complex system.

CHECK YOUR READING Find three examples on pages 13 and 14 that show how the parts of the Earth system shape the planet's surface.

1.1 Review

KEY CONCEPTS

1. Define *system*. Compare an open and a closed system.
2. Name the four parts of the Earth system. List one fact about each part that scientists learned through modern technology.
3. Give two examples of how the Earth system's four parts can interact with each other.

CRITICAL THINKING

4. **Apply** One day you see that plants are dying in the class terrarium. What part might be missing from its system?
5. **Infer** You visit a state park and see a thin rock wall with a hole, like a window, worn through it. Which of the four parts of the Earth system might have made the hole? Explain.

◆ CHALLENGE

6. **Predict** Imagine that a meteorite 200 meters wide strikes Earth, landing in a wooded area. Describe one way that this event would affect the biosphere or the geosphere. **Hint:** A meteorite is traveling several thousand kilometers per hour when it strikes the ground.

A 14 Unit: **Earth's Surface**

ANSWERS

1. organized group of parts that work together to form a whole; closed system: energy but not matter can enter or leave; open system: matter and energy can enter or leave

2. atmosphere: complex weather patterns; hydrosphere: layers of cold and warm water; biosphere: yearly changes in plant and animal life; geosphere: features above and below Earth's surface

3. Storms in the atmosphere can change Earth's coastlines; animals can wear paths in Earth's surface.

4. water, air, or soil nutrients

5. hydrosphere (rain) or hydrosphere and atmosphere (rain and wind)

6. It would blast a huge crater in the geosphere. The heat would destroy nearby plants and animals in the biosphere.

Ongoing Assessment

- Check Your Reading questions for student self-check of comprehension
- Consistent Teacher's Edition prompts for assessing understanding of Key Concepts

Reviewing Vocabulary

Copy and complete the chart below, using vocabulary terms from this chapter.

Term	Use	Appearance
map legend	to explain map symbols	chart of symbols
1. latitude	to show distance from the equator	
2. longitude		lines going from pole to pole
3.	to show land features	rippled and smooth areas
4. map scale	to represent distances	
5. equator		line at 0° latitude
6. prime meridian	to separate east and west hemispheres	
7.	to show height above sea level	line showing elevation
8. false-color image	to highlight information	

Reviewing Key Concepts

Multiple Choice *Choose the letter of the best answer.*

9. Which Greek prefix is matched with its correct meaning?
   a. *hydro* = life
   b. *atmo* = gas
   c. *bio* = earth
   d. *geo* = water

10. What portion of Earth is covered by water?
    a. one-quarter
    b. one-half
    c. three-quarters
    d. seven-eights

11. The continents and ocean basins are part of Earth's
    a. crust
    b. mantle
    c. outer core
    d. inner core

12. Which Earth system includes humans?
    a. atmosphere
    b. biosphere
    c. hydrosphere
    d. geosphere

13. One way the atmosphere shapes Earth's surface is by
    a. winds
    b. floods
    c. earthquakes
    d. tunnels

14. How are the major parts of the Earth system related to each other?
    a. They rarely can be studied together.
    b. They often are in conflict.
    c. They usually work independently.
    d. They always affect each other.

15. A flat map shows Earth's curved surface by means of
    a. elevation
    b. topography
    c. relief
    d. projection

16. People use latitude and longitude lines mostly to identify
    a. map scales
    b. country names
    c. exact locations
    d. distances

17. The most accurate way to show Earth's surface is a
    a. globe
    b. conic projection
    c. cylindrical projection
    d. planar projection

18. One example of remote sensing is the use of
    a. contour lines
    b. projections
    c. GIS
    d. binoculars

Short Answer *Write a few sentences to answer each question.*

19. How does the Global Positioning System work? In your answer use each of the following terms. Underline each term in your answer.

24 satellites	computer	longitude
receiver	latitude	elevation

20. How do Mercator maps distort the view of Earth's surface?

21. How do people use sensors in making maps?

Section and Chapter Reviews

- Focus on Key Concepts and critical thinking skills
- A full range of question types and levels of thinking

Leveled Chapter and Unit Tests

- Three levels of test for every chapter and unit
- Same Big Ideas, Key Concepts, and essential skills assessed on all levels

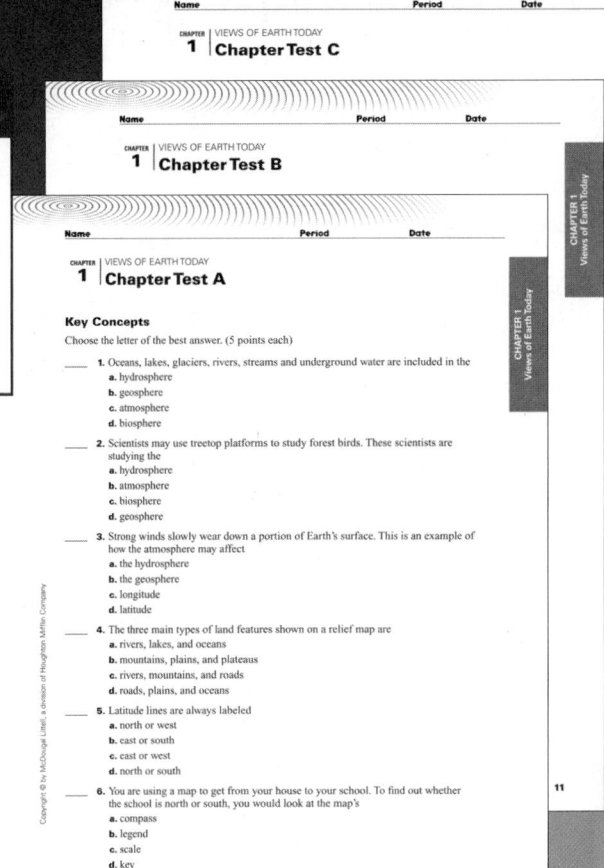

Key Concepts

Choose the letter of the best answer. (5 points each)

_____ 1. Oceans, lakes, glaciers, rivers, streams and underground water are included in the
   a. hydrosphere
   b. geosphere
   c. atmosphere
   d. biosphere

_____ 2. Scientists may use treetop platforms to study forest birds. These scientists are studying the
   a. hydrosphere
   b. atmosphere
   c. biosphere
   d. geosphere

_____ 3. Strong winds slowly wear down a portion of Earth's surface. This is an example of how the atmosphere may affect
   a. the hydrosphere
   b. the geosphere
   c. longitude
   d. latitude

_____ 4. The three main types of land features shown on a relief map are
   a. rivers, lakes, and oceans
   b. mountains, plains, and plateaus
   c. rivers, mountains, and roads
   d. roads, plains, and oceans

_____ 5. Latitude lines are always labeled
   a. north or west
   b. east or south
   c. east or west
   d. north or south

_____ 6. You are using a map to get from your house to your school. To find out whether the school is north or south, you would look at the map's
   a. compass
   b. legend
   c. scale
   d. key

EARTH'S SURFACE, CHAPTER 1, CHAPTER TEST A   7

Thinking Critically

Use the topographic map below to answer the next seven questions.

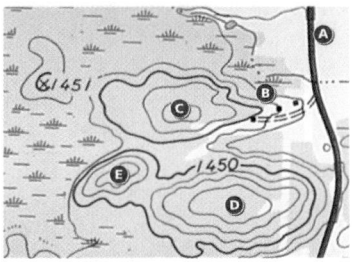

- ~~~ marsh   ▬ road
- ■ ■ buildings   ≈≈ unpaved road

22. APPLY Imagine you are hiking through this area. Which hill—C, D, or E—has the steepest slope? How do you know?

23. ANALYZE What is the topography of the land through which the curved road A goes?

24. IDENTIFY CAUSE The black and red squares at B represent buildings. Why do you think the buildings were placed here instead of somewhere else in the area?

25. APPLY The contour interval is 10 meters. What is the elevation of the highest point on the map?

26. SYNTHESIZE Sketch the two hills D and E. What would they look like to someone on the ground?

27. INFER Suppose someone wanted to build a road through the terrain on the far left side of the map. What are the advantages and disadvantages of such a route?

28. EVALUATE Do you think this area would be a good place to ride mountain bikes? Why or why not?

CHART INFORMATION *On a separate sheet of paper, write a word to fill each blank in the chart.*

Feature	Shown on Topographic Maps?	Belongs to Which Major System?
rivers	*yes*	*hydrosphere*
29. slope		
30. winds		
31. plants		
32. lakes		
33. relief		

the BIG idea

34. APPLY Look again at the photographs on pages 6–7. Now that you have finished the chapter, reread the question on the main photograph. What would you change in or add to your answer?

35. SYNTHESIZE Describe some of the types of information that new technology has provided about Earth.

36. DRAW CONCLUSIONS What type of technology do you think has done the most to change the way people view and map Earth? Explain your conclusion.

UNIT PROJECTS

If you are doing a unit project, make a folder for your project. Include in your folder a list of the resources you will need, the date on which the project is due, and a schedule to track your progress. Begin gathering data.

Rubrics

- Rubrics in Teacher's Edition for all extended-response questions
- Rubrics for all Unit Projects
- Alternative Assessment with rubric for each chapter
- A wide range of additional rubrics in the Science Toolkit

McDougal Littell Science

Science Toolkit

Transparencies, activity sheets, and teacher notes to support every aspect of science instruction
- Inquiry and experimental design
- Building science vocabulary
- Reading in the science content area
- Writing in the sciences
- Math in science
- Rubrics for investigations, projects, and presentations
- Test-taking strategies
- Daily vocabulary scaffolding
- Strategies for decoding
- Cooperative learning
- Planning for science fairs and competitions
- Lesson plans for substitute teachers

McDougal Littell Science: North Carolina Science Series

Each book in the three-book North Carolina Science series combines major concepts and topics from life, earth, and physical science.

- Carefully sequenced units and chapters that consistently connect new learning to prior knowledge

- Connections among the sciences and technology in each unit

- North Carolina Handbooks that give more instruction and problem-solving activities on specific topics

North Carolina Science Grade 6

A Earth's Surface
1. Views of Earth Today
2. Minerals
3. Rocks
4. Weathering and Soil Formation
5. Erosion and Deposition

B Energy and the Changing Earth
1. Energy
2. Temperature and Heat
3. Plate Tectonics
4. Earthquakes
5. Mountains and Volcanoes

C Waves, Sound, and Light
1. Waves
2. Sound
3. Electromagnetic Waves
4. Light and Optics

D Ecology
1. Ecosystems and Biomes
2. Interactions Within Ecosystems
3. Human Impact on Ecosystems

E Space Science
1. Exploring Space
2. Earth, Moon, and Sun
3. Our Solar System
4. Stars, Galaxies, and the Universe

North Carolina Science Grade 7

A Earth's Atmosphere
1. Earth's Changing Atmosphere
2. Weather Patterns
3. Weather Fronts and Storms
4. Climate and Climate Change

B Human Biology
1. Systems, Support, and Movement
2. Absorption, Digestion, and Exchange
3. Transport and Protection
4. Control and Reproduction
5. Growth, Development, and Health

C Cells and Heredity
1. The Cell
2. How Cells Function
3. Cell Division
4. Patterns of Heredity
5. DNA and Modern Genetics

D Motion and Forces
1. Motion
2. Forces
3. Gravity, Friction, and Pressure
4. Work and Energy
5. Machines

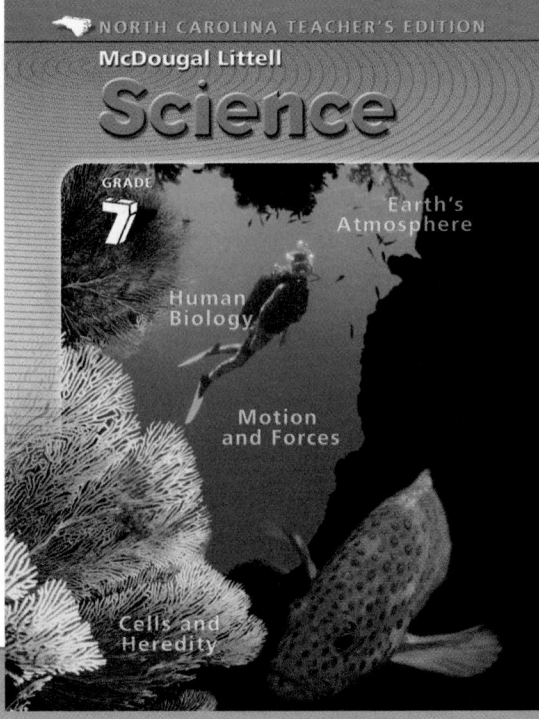

North Carolina Science Grade 8

A Earth's History and Resources
1. Plate Tectonics
2. Views of Earth's Past
3. Natural Resources

B Life Over Time
1. The History of Life on Earth
2. Classification of Living Things
3. Population Dynamics

C Earth's Waters
1. The Water Planet
2. Freshwater Resources
3. Ocean Systems
4. Ocean Environments

D Chemical Interactions
1. Atomic Structure and the Periodic Table
2. Chemical Bonds and Compounds
3. Chemical Reactions
4. Solutions
5. Carbon in Life and Materials

E Cells and Microbiology
1. The Cell
2. How Cells Function
3. Cell Division
4. Growth, Development, and Health
5. Single-Celled Organisms and Viruses

Teaching Resources

A wealth of print and technology resources help you adapt the program to your teaching style and to the specific needs of your students.

Book-Specific Print Resources

Unit Resource Book provides all of the teaching resources for the unit, organized by chapter and section.

- Family Letters
- *Scientific American Frontiers* Video Guide
- Unit Projects
- Lesson Plans
- Reading Study Guides (Levels A and B)
- Spanish Reading Study Guides
- Challenge Readings
- Challenge and Extension Activities
- Reinforcing Key Concepts
- Vocabulary Practice
- Math Support and Practice
- Investigation Datasheets
- Chapter Investigations (Levels A, B, and C)
- Additional Investigations (Levels A, B, and C)
- Summarizing the Chapter

Unit Assessment Book contains complete resources for assessing student knowledge and performance.

- Chapter Diagnostic Tests
- Section Quizzes
- Chapter Tests (Levels A, B, and C)
- Alternative Assessments
- Unit Tests (Levels A, B, and C)

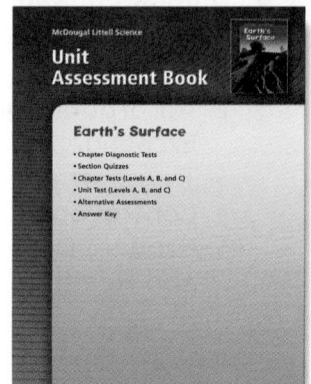

McDougal Littell Science

Unit Assessment Book

Earth's Surface

- Chapter Diagnostic Tests
- Section Quizzes
- Chapter Tests (Levels A, B, and C)
- Unit Test (Levels A, B, and C)
- Alternative Assessments
- Answer Key

Unit Transparency Book includes instructional visuals for each chapter.

- Three-Minute Warm-Ups
- Note-Taking Models
- Daily Vocabulary Scaffolding
- Chapter Outlines
- Big Idea Flow Charts
- Chapter Teaching Visuals

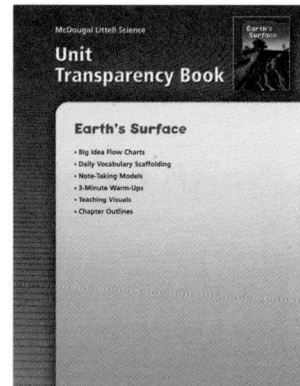

McDougal Littell Science

Unit Transparency Book

Earth's Surface

- Big Idea Flow Charts
- Daily Vocabulary Scaffolding
- Note-Taking Models
- 3-Minute Warm-Ups
- Teaching Visuals
- Chapter Outlines

Lab Manual

Note-Taking/ Reading Study Guide

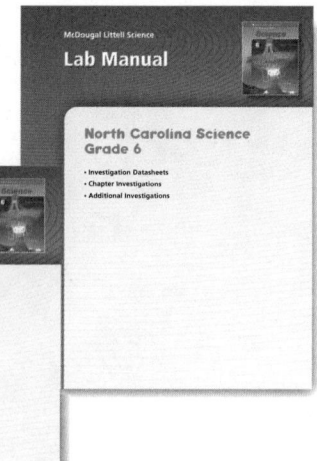

McDougal Littell Science

Lab Manual

North Carolina Science Grade 6

- Investigation Datasheets
- Chapter Investigations
- Additional Investigations

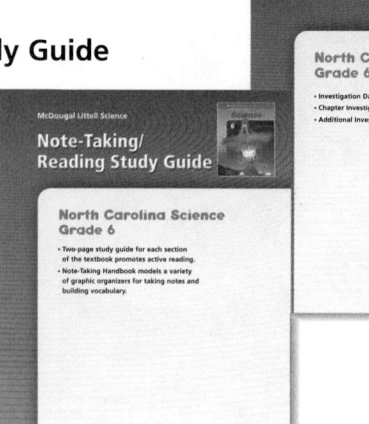

McDougal Littell Science

Note-Taking/ Reading Study Guide

North Carolina Science Grade 6

- Two-page study guide for each section of the textbook promotes active reading.
- Note-Taking Handbook models a variety of graphic organizers for taking notes and building vocabulary.

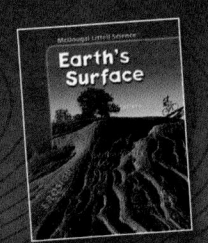

McDougal Littell Science

Unit Resource Book

Earth's Surface

Earth's Surface

- Family Letters (English and Spanish)
- *Scientific American Frontiers* Video Guides
- Unit Projects (with Rubrics)
- Lesson Plans
- Reading Study Guides (Levels A and B and Spanish)
- Challenge Activities and Readings
- Reinforcing Key Concepts
- Vocabulary Practice and Decoding Support
- Math Support and Practice
- Investigation Datasheets
- Chapter Investigations (Levels A, B, and C)
- Additional Investigations (Levels A, B, and C)
- Summarizing the Chapter

Program-Wide Print Resources

Process and Lab Skills

Problem Solving and Critical Thinking

Standardized Test Practice

Science Toolkit

City Science

Visual Glossary

Multi-Language Glossary

English Learners Package

Scientific American Frontiers Video Guide

How Stuff Works Express
This quarterly magazine offers opportunities to explore current science topics.

Technology Resources

Scientific American Frontiers **Video Program**
Each specially tailored segment from this award-winning PBS series correlates to a unit; available on VHS and DVD

Audio CDs Complete chapter texts read in both English and Spanish

Lab Generator CD-ROM
A searchable database of all activities from the program plus additional labs for each unit; edit and print your own version of labs

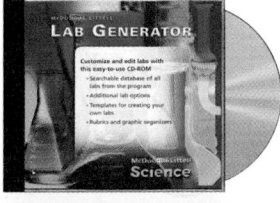

Test Generator CD-ROM

eEdition CD-ROM

EasyPlanner CD-ROM

Content Review CD-ROM

Power Presentations CD-ROM

Online Resources

  ClassZone.com

  Content Review Online

  eEdition Plus Online

  EasyPlanner Plus Online

  eTest Plus Online

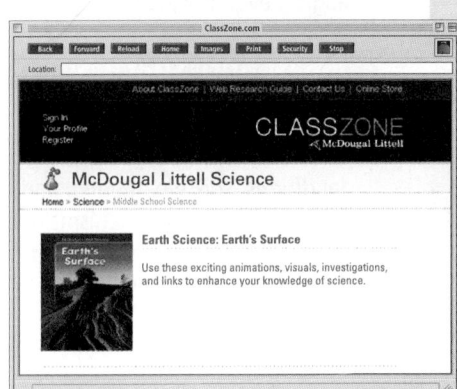

Correlation to National Science Education Standards

This chart provides an overview of how the five units of North Carolina Science Grade 6 address the *National Science Education Standards*.

A Earth's Surface
B Energy and the Changing Earth
C Waves, Sound, and Light
D Ecology
E Space Science

	Unit, Chapter, and Section
A. Science as Inquiry	
A.1– A.8 **Abilities necessary to do scientific inquiry** Identify questions for investigation; design and conduct investigations; use evidence; think critically and logically; analyze alternative explanations; communicate; use mathematics.	pp. R2–R44, all Chapter Investigations, all Think Science features
A.9 **Understandings about scientific inquiry** Different kinds of investigations for different questions; investigations guided by current scientific knowledge; importance of mathematics and technology for data gathering and analysis; importance of evidence, logical argument, principles, models, and theories; role of legitimate skepticism; scientific investigations lead to new investigations.	pp. xxxvi–xxxix, A1.4, B1.1, B3.4, C3.2, D2.2, E3.2
B. Physical Science	
B.1 **Properties and changes of properties in matter** Physical properties; substances, elements, and compounds; chemical reactions.	A2.2, B3.1
B.2 **Motions and forces** Position, speed, direction of motion; balanced and unbalanced forces.	E2.1, E2.2, E2.3
B.3 **Transfer of energy** Energy transfer; forms of energy; heat and light; electrical circuits; sun as source of Earth's energy.	B1.1, B1.2, B1.3, B2.1, B2.2, B2.3, C1.1, C3.3, C3.4, C4.1, C4.2, C4.3, D1.3, E1.2, E4.1, E4.2, E4.3, E4.4
C. Life Science	
C.3 **Regulation and behavior**	E1.4 (Connecting Sciences)
C.4 **Populations and ecosystems** Populations; ecosystems; producers, consumers, and decomposers; food webs; energy flow; population size and resource availability; population growth.	D1.1, D1.2, D1.3, D2.1, D2.2, D2.3, D3.1, D3.2, D3.3
C.5 **Diversity and adaptations of organisms** Unity and diversity; similarities in internal structures, chemical processes, and evidence of common ancestry; adaptation and biological evolution; extinction and fossil evidence.	A5.3 (Connecting Sciences)
D. Earth and Space Science	
D.1 **Structure of the earth system** Lithosphere, mantle, and core; plate movement and earthquakes, volcanoes, and mountain building; constructive and destructive forces on landforms; soil, weathering, and erosion; water and water cycle; atmosphere, weather, and climate; living organisms in earth system.	A1.1, A2.3, A3.1, A3.2, A3.3, A4.1, A4.2, A4.3, A5.1, A5.2, A5.3, B3.1, B3.2, B3.3, B3.4, B4.1, B4.2, B4.3, B5.1, B5.2, B5.3, D1.1, E3.2
D.2 **Earth's history** Continuity of earth processes; impact of occasional catastrophes; fossil evidence.	A4.3, A5.1, B3.2, B4.1, B5.1, E3.2, E3.4, E (Frontiers in Science)

		Unit, Chapter, and Section
D.3	**Earth in the solar system** Sun, planets, asteroids, comets; regular and predictable motion and day, year, phases of the moon, and eclipses; gravity and orbits; sun as source of energy for earth; cause of seasons.	A1.1, B1.2, B1.3, C3.3, D1.3, E1.1, E2.1, E2.2, E2.3, E3.1, E3.2, E3.3, E3.4

E. Science and Technology

E.1–E.5	**Abilities of technological design** Identify problems; design a solution or product; implement a proposed design; evaluate completed designs or products; communicate the process of technological design.	pp. xl–xli, A5.1, B1.1, B2.3, B3.4, B4.3, C2.4, C3.1, C3.3, C4.4
E.6	**Understandings about science and technology** Similarities and differences between scientific inquiry and technological design; contributions of people in different cultures; reciprocal nature of science and technology; nonexistence of perfectly designed solutions; constraints, benefits, and unintended consequences of technological designs.	pp. xl–xli, all Frontiers in Science and Timelines in Science features, A1.1, A1.2, A1.3, A1.4, B1.3, C4.4, D3.1, D3.2

F. Science in Personal and Social Perspectives

F.1	**Personal health** Exercise; fitness; hazards and safety; tobacco, alcohol, and other drugs; nutrition; STDs; environmental health.	D3.2
F.2	**Populations, resources, and environments** Overpopulation and resource depletion; environmental degradation.	B1.1, D3.1, D3.2, D3.3
F.3	**Natural hazards** Earthquakes, landslides, wildfires, volcanic eruptions, floods, storms; hazards from human activity; personal and societal challenges.	A1.1, A5.1, B4.3, B5.1, B5.2, B5.3, C3.2, D3.2, E3.4
F.4	**Risks and benefits** Risk analysis; natural, chemical, biological, social, and personal hazards; decisions based on risks and benefits.	B4.3, B5.3, D3.3, E (Frontiers in Science)
F.5	**Science and technology in society** Science's influence on knowledge and world view; societal challenges and scientific research; technological influences on society; contributions from people of different cultures and times; work of scientists and engineers; ethical codes; limitations of science and technology.	All Timelines in Science features, A1.1, A1.2, A1.4, B1.2, B1.3, C3.2, C3.3, C4.4, E1.2, E1.3, E1.4

G. History and Nature of Science

G.1	**Science as a human endeavor** Diversity of people working in science, technology, and related fields; abilities required by science.	pp. xxxvi–xxxix, all Frontiers in Sciences features
G.2	**Nature of science** Observations, experiments, and models; tentative nature of scientific ideas; differences in interpretation of evidence; evaluation of results of investigations, experiments, observations, theoretical models, and explanations; importance of questioning, response to criticism, and communication.	E1.2, E1.3, E4.4
G.3	**History of science** Historical examples of inquiry and relationships between science and society; scientists and engineers as valued contributors to culture; challenges of breaking through accepted ideas.	All Frontiers in Science and Timelines in Science features, B3.2, C2.4, E1.3

Correlation to Benchmarks

This chart provides an overview of how the five
units of North Carolina Science Grade 6 address the
Project 2061 *Benchmarks for Science Literacy.*

A Earth's Surface
B Energy and the Changing Earth
C Waves, Sound, and Light
D Ecology
E Space Science

	Unit, Chapter, and Section
1. The Nature of Science	
	The Nature of Science (pp. xxxvi–xxxix), Think Science features: A1.4, B1.1, B3.4, C3.2, D2.2, E3.2; Scientific Thinking Handbook (pp. R2-R9) Lab Handbook (pp. R10–R35)
3. The Nature of Technology	
	The Nature of Technology (pp. xl–xli); A1.1, A1.4, B3.3, C4.4, D3.3, E1.2, E1.3, E1.4; Timelines in Science features
4. The Physical Setting	
4.A THE UNIVERSE	
4.A.1 The Sun is a medium-sized star on the edge of a disk-shaped galaxy; galaxies contain billions of stars; the universe contains billions of galaxies.	E1.1, E4.1, E4.3, E4.4
4.A.2 Light from the Sun takes a few minutes to reach Earth; some galaxies are so far way that their light takes several billion years to reach Earth.	E1.2, E4.1, E4.2, E4.3, E4.4
4.A.3 Nine planets of very different size, composition, and surface features move around the Sun in nearly circular orbits.	E2.2, E3.2
4.A.4 Chunks of rock orbiting the Sun impact Earth's atmosphere and surface.	E (Frontiers in Science), E3.1, E3.4
4.B THE EARTH	
4.B.1 We live on a relatively small planet, the third from the Sun.	E3.1, E3.2
4.B.2 Three-fourths of Earth's surface is covered by a relatively thin layer of water; the entire planet is surrounded by a relatively thin blanket of air.	A1.1, A3.1, E3.2, E3.3
4.B.3 Everything near Earth pulled toward Earth's center by gravitation.	E2.1
4.B.4 Because Earth's axis is tilted, sunlight falls more intensely on different regions during the year, producing Earth's seasons and weather patterns.	E2.1, E3.2
4.B.5 The moon's orbit around Earth changes what part is lighted by the Sun and how much of that part can be seen from Earth—the phases of the Moon.	E2.3
4.B.6 Climates have sometimes changed abruptly; even small changes in atmospheric or ocean content can have widespread effects on climate.	A3.1, B3.2, B5.3, E3.4
4.B.10 Ability to recover minerals is as important as how abundant or rare they are; as they are used up, obtaining them becomes more difficult.	A (Frontiers in Science), A2.3
4.C PROCESSES THAT SHAPE THE EARTH	
4.C.1 Earth's interior is hot. Heat flow and movement of material within Earth cause earthquakes, volcanic eruptions, create mountains, and ocean basins.	A1.1, A3.1, A3.2, B3.1, B3.2, B3.3, B3.4, B4.1, B4.2, B4.3, B5.3
4.C.2 Some changes in Earth's surface are abrupt (earthquakes, volcanic eruptions) while other changes happen very slowly (motion of wind, water).	A5.1, A5.2, A5.3, B3.2, B4.1, B4.2, B5.1, B5.2
4.C.3 Sand, smaller particles, and dissolved minerals form solid rock.	A3.1, A3.3

	Unit, Chapter, and Section
4.C.4 Rock bears evidence of the minerals, temperatures, and forces that created it.	A3.1, A3.4
4.C.6 Soil composition, texture, fertility, and resistance to erosion are influenced by plant roots, debris, and organisms living in the soil.	A4.2
4.C.7 Human activities can change Earth's land, oceans, and atmosphere, sometimes rendering the environment unable to support some life forms.	A4.3, D3.1, D3.2, D3.3
4.D STRUCTURE OF MATTER	B2.1, B3.2
4.E ENERGY TRANSFORMATIONS	
4.E.1 Energy cannot be created or destroyed, but only changed from one form into another.	B1.2
4.E.2 Most of what goes on in the universe involves energy transformations.	B1.1, B1.2, B1.3, B2.2, B2.3, E1.1, E4.1
4.E.3 Heat can be transferred through materials by the collisions of atoms or across space by radiation; convection currents transfer heat in fluid materials.	B2.2, B2.3, E4.1
4.E.4 Energy appears in many different forms.	B1.1, B2.2, B2.3
4.F MOTION	
4.F.1 Light from the Sun is made up of many different colors of light; objects that give off or reflect light have a different mix of colors.	C3.2, C3.3, C3.4
4.F.2 Something can be "seen" when light waves emitted or reflected by it enter the eye.	C4.1, C4.3
4.F.4 Vibrations in materials set up wavelike disturbances (such as sound) that spread away from the source; waves move at different speeds in different materials.	C1.1, C1.2, C1.3, C2.1, C2.2, C3.1, C3.4
4.F.5 Human eyes respond to only a narrow range of wavelengths of electromagnetic radiation—visible light. Differences within that range are perceived as differences in color.	C3.2, C3.4, C4.3
4.G FORCES OF NATURE	E1.1, E1.2, E2.1, E3.1
5. The Living Environment	
5.A DIVERSITY OF LIFE	D2.1
5.D INTERDEPENDENCE OF LIFE	A4.2, D1.1, D1.3, D2.2
5.E FLOW OF MATTER AND ENERGY	
5.E.1 Food molecules as fuel and building material for all organisms; photosynthesis.	D1.3
5.E.2 Flow of energy through living systems; amount of matter remains constant.	A4.2, D1.2, D1.3
5.E.3 Energy changes in living thing; sunlight as source of almost all food energy.	D1.3
8. The Designed World	B1.3, D3.2, D3.3
9. The Mathematical World	All Math in Science features, A1.2
10. Historical Perspectives	B3.2, C4.4, E1.3, E2.3, E3.1, E4.1
12. Habits of Mind	
12.A VALUES AND ATTITUDES	Think Science features, A1.4, B1.1, B3.4, C3.2, D2.2, E3.2
12.B COMPUTATION AND ESTIMATION	All Math in Science features, pp. R10–R35
12.C MANIPULATION AND OBSERVATION	All Investigates and Chapter Investigations
12.D COMMUNICATION SKILLS	All Chapter Investigations, pp. R10–R35
12.E CRITICAL-RESPONSE SKILLS	Think Science features: A1.4, B1.1, B3.4, C3.2, D2.2, E3.2; Scientific Thinking Handbook (pp. R2–R9)

Planning the Unit

The Pacing Guide provides suggested pacing for all chapters in the unit as well as the two unit features shown below.

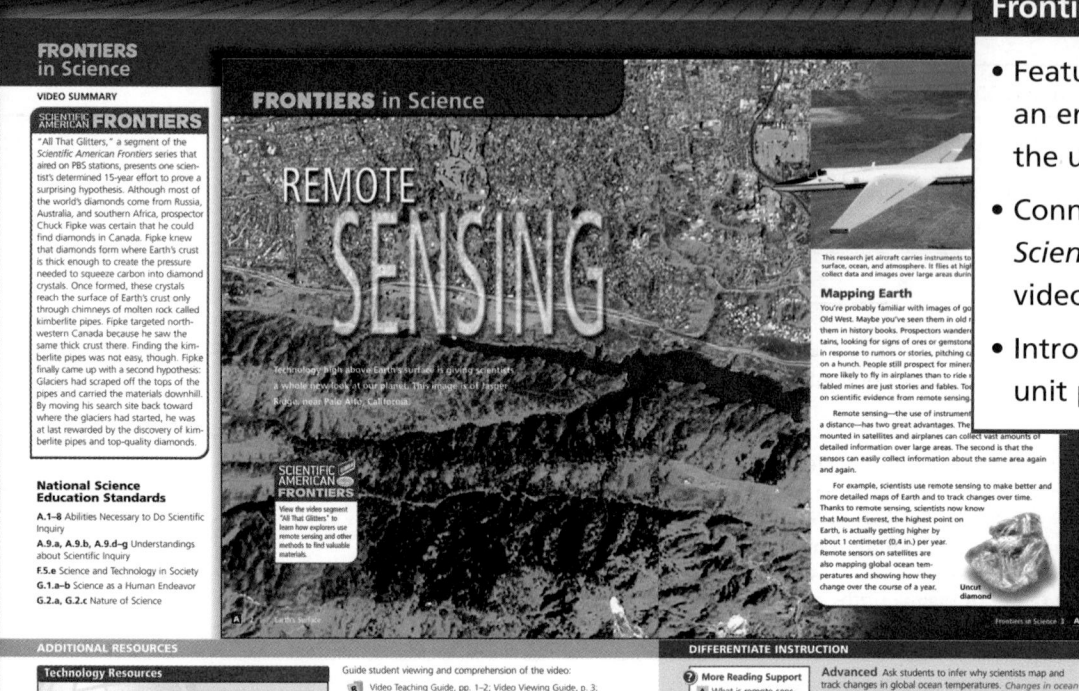

Frontiers in Science

- Features cutting-edge research as an engaging point of entry into the unit
- Connects to an accompanying *Scientific American Frontiers* video and viewing guide
- Introduces three options for unit projects

Timelines in Science

- Traces the history of key scientific discoveries
- Highlights interactions between science and technology

Earth's Surface Pacing Guide

The following pacing guide shows how the chapters in *Earth's Surface* can be adapted to fit your specific course needs.

	TRADITIONAL SCHEDULE (DAYS)	BLOCK SCHEDULE (DAYS)
Frontiers in Science: Remote Sensing	1	0.5
Chapter 1 Views of Earth Today		
1.1 Technology is used to explore the Earth system.	2	1
1.2 Maps and globes are models of Earth.	2	1
1.3 Topographic maps show the shape of the land.	2	1
1.4 Technology is used to map Earth.	2	1
Chapter Investigation	1	0.5
Chapter 2 Minerals		
2.1 Minerals are all around us.	2	1
2.2 A mineral is identified by its properties.	2	1
2.3 Minerals are valuable resources.	2	1
Chapter Investigation	1	0.5
Chapter 3 Rocks		
3.1 The rock cycle shows how rocks change.	2	1
3.2 Igneous rocks form from molten rock.	2	1
3.3 Sedimentary rocks form from earlier rocks.	2	1
3.4 Metamorphic rocks form as existing rocks change.	2	1
Chapter Investigation	1	0.5
Timelines in Science: History of the Earth System	1	0.5
North Carolina Handbook: Rocks and Minerals of North Carolina	1	0.5
Chapter 4 Weathering and Soil Formation		
4.1 Mechanical and chemical forces break down rocks.	2	
4.2 Weathering and organic processes form soil.	2	1
4.3 Human activities affect soil.	2	1
Chapter Investigation	1	0.5
North Carolina Handbook: Soil Science	1	0.5
Chapter 5 Erosion and Deposition		
5.1 Forces wear down and build up Earth's surface.	2	1
5.2 Moving water shapes land.	2	1
5.3 Waves and wind shape land.	2	1
5.4 Glaciers carve land and move sediments.	2	1
Chapter Investigation	1	0.5
Total Days for Unit	45	23

Energy and the Changing Earth Pacing Guide

The following pacing guide shows how the chapters in *Energy and the Changing Earth* can be adapted to fit your specific course needs.

	TRADITIONAL SCHEDULE (DAYS)	BLOCK SCHEDULE (DAYS)
Frontiers in Science: Studying Volcanoes	1	0.5
Chapter 1 Energy		
1.1 Energy exists in different forms.	2	1
1.2 Energy can change forms but is never lost.	2	1
1.3 Technology improves the way people use energy.	2	1
Chapter Investigation	1	0.5
Chapter 2 Temperature and Heat		
2.1 Temperature depends on particle movement.	2	1
2.2 Energy flows from warmer to cooler objects.	2	1
2.3 The transfer of energy as heat can be controlled.	2	1.5
Chapter Investigation	1	0.5
Chapter 3 Plate Tectonics		
3.1 Earth has several layers.	2	1
3.2 Continents change position over time.	2	1
3.3 Plates move apart.	2	1
3.4 Plates converge or scrape past each other.	2	1
Chapter Investigation	1	0.5
Timelines in Science: About Temperature and Heat	1	0.5
Chapter 4 Earthquakes		
4.1 Earthquakes occur along faults.	2	1
4.2 Earthquakes release energy.	2	1
4.3 Earthquake damage can be reduced.	2	1
Chapter Investigation	1	0.5
Chapter 5 Mountains and Volcanoes		
5.1 Movement of rock builds mountains.	2	1
5.2 Volcanoes form as molten rock erupts.	2	1
5.3 Volcanoes affect Earth's land, air, and water.	2	1
Chapter Investigation	1	0.5
Total Days for Unit	**39**	**20**

Waves, Sound, and Light Pacing Guide

The following pacing guide shows how the chapters in *Waves, Sound, and Light* can be adapted to fit your specific course needs.

	TRADITIONAL SCHEDULE (DAYS)	BLOCK SCHEDULE (DAYS)
Frontiers in Science: Sound Medicine	1	0.5
Chapter 1 Waves		
1.1 Waves transfer energy.	2	1
1.2 Waves have measurable properties.	2	1
1.3 Waves behave in predictable ways.	2	1
Chapter Investigation	1	0.5
Chapter 2 Sound		
2.1 Sound is a wave.	2	1
2.2 Frequency determines pitch.	2	1
2.3 Intensity determines loudness.	2	1
2.4 Sound has many uses.	2	1
Chapter Investigation	1	0.5
Chapter 3 Electromagnetic Waves		
3.1 Electromagnetic waves have unique traits.	2	1
3.2 Electromagnetic waves have many uses.	2	1
3.3 The Sun is the source of most visible light.	2	1
3.4 Light waves interact with materials.	2	1
Chapter Investigation	1	0.5
Timelines in Science: The Story of Light	1	0.5
Chapter 4 Light and Optics		
4.1 Mirrors form images by reflecting light.	2	1
4.2 Lenses form images by refracting light.	2	1
4.3 The eye is a natural optical tool.	2	1
4.4 Optical technology makes use of light waves.	2	1
Chapter Investigation	1	0.5
Total Days for Unit	**36**	**18**

Ecology Pacing Guide

The following pacing guide shows how the chapters in *Ecology* can be adapted to fit your specific course needs.

	TRADITIONAL SCHEDULE (DAYS)	BLOCK SCHEDULE (DAYS)
Frontiers in Science: Ecosystems on Fire	1	0.5
Chapter 1 Ecosystems and Biomes		
1.1 Ecosystems support life.	2	1
1.2 Matter cycles through ecosystems.	2	1
1.3 Energy flows through ecosystems.	2	1
1.4 Biomes contain many ecosystems.	2	1
Chapter Investigation	1	0.5
North Carolina Handbook: Photosynthesis	1	0.5
Chapter 2 Interactions Within Ecosystems		
2.1 Groups of living things interact within ecosystems.	2	1
2.2 Organisms can interact in different ways.	2	1
2.3 Ecosystems are always changing.	2	1
Chapter Investigation	1	0.5
North Carolina Handbook: Natural Selection	1	0.5
Timelines in Science: Wilderness Conservation	1	0.5
Chapter 3 Human Impact on Ecosystems		
3.1 Human population growth presents challenges.	2	1
3.2 Human activities affect the environment.	2	1
3.3 People are working to protect ecosystems.	2	1
Chapter Investigation	1	0.5
North Carolina Handbook: Designed Systems	1	0.5
Total Days for Unit	28	14

Space Science Pacing Guide

The following pacing guide shows how the chapters in *Space Science* can be adapted to fit your specific course needs.

	TRADITIONAL SCHEDULE (DAYS)	BLOCK SCHEDULE (DAYS)
Frontiers in Science: Danger from the Sky	1	0.5
Chapter 1 Exploring Space		
1.1 Some space objects are visible to the human eye.	2	1
1.2 Telescopes allow us to study space from Earth.	2	1
1.3 Spacecraft help us explore beyond Earth.	2	1
1.4 Space exploration benefits society.	2	1
Chapter Investigation	1	0.5
Chapter 2 Earth, Moon, and Sun		
2.1 Earth rotates on a tilted axis and orbits the Sun.	2	1
2.2 The Moon is Earth's natural satellite.	2	1
2.3 Positions of the Sun and Moon affect Earth.	2	1
Chapter Investigation	1	0.5
Timelines in Science: The Story of Astronomy	1	0.5
Chapter 3 Our Solar System		
3.1 Planets orbit the Sun at different distances.	2	1
3.2 The inner solar system has rocky planets.	2	1
3.3 The outer solar system has four giant planets.	2	1
3.4 Small objects are made of ice and rock.	2	1
Chapter Investigation	1	0.5
Chapter 4 Stars, Galaxies, and the Universe		
4.1 The Sun is our local star.	2	1
4.2 Stars change over their life cycles.	2	1
4.3 Galaxies have different sizes and shapes.	2	1
4.4 The universe is expanding.	2	1
Chapter Investigation	1	0.5
Total Days for Unit	36	18

Planning the Chapter

Complete planning support precedes each chapter.

CHAPTER

1 Views of Earth Today

Earth Science
UNIFYING PRINCIPLES

PRINCIPLE 1	PRINCIPLE 2	PRINCIPLE 3	PRINCIPLE 4
Heat energy inside Earth and radiation from the Sun provide energy for Earth's processes.	Physical forces, such as gravity, affect the movement of all matter on Earth and throughout the universe.	Matter and ene... among Earth's soil, atmospher... and living thing...	

Unit: Earth's Surface
BIG IDEAS

CHAPTER 1 Views of Earth Today
Modern technology has changed the way we view and map Earth.

CHAPTER 2 Minerals	CHAPTER 3 Rocks	C... W... F...
Minerals are basic building blocks of Earth.	Rocks change into other rocks over time.	N... ro... so...

CHAPTER 1 KEY CONCEPTS

SECTION 1.1	SECTION 1.2	SECTION 1...
Technology is used to explore the Earth system.	**Maps and globes are models of Earth.**	**Topographic... the shape of...**
1. The Earth system has four major parts.	1. Maps show natural and human-made features.	1. Topographic... tour lines to...
2. All four parts of the Earth system shape the planet's surface.	2. Latitude and longitude show locations on Earth.	2. Contour line... certain rules...
	3. Map projections distort the view of Earth's surface.	

The Big Idea Flow Chart is available on p. T1 in the **UNIT TRANSPARENCY BOOK.**

A 5A Unit: Earth's Surface

Previewing Content

SECTION
1.1 Technology is used to explore the Earth system. pp. 9–14

1. The Earth system has four major parts.
A **system** is a combination of parts that work together to form a whole. Earth is essentially a closed system in which energy enters and leaves but matter, with a few exceptions, does not. Earth has four interconnected parts that are open systems in which both matter and energy can leave and enter. Each part

SECTION
1.2 M... Ea...

1. Maps sh...
A map is... Earth as it...
• A reli... mounta...
• A map...

Previewing Content

SECTION
1.3 Topographic maps show the shape of the land. pp. 24–29

1. Topographic maps use contour lines to show features.
Topography is the shape of the land. Topographic maps show the surface features of particular areas, including natural features such as mountains, valleys, and bodies of water, as well as human-made features such as airports, bridges, and roads. They can be used to determine:
• **elevation:** how high a point is above sea level
• **slope:** the steepness of a landform
• **relief:** the difference in elevation between the high and low points of an area

Contour lines on a topographic map are lines that show the elevations of land above or below sea level; all points connected by a contour line have the same elevation.

2. Contour lines follow certain rules.
These rules can be used to interpret topographic maps:
• Contour lines never cross, because each line represents a specific elevation.
• Circles show the highest and lowest points.
• On a given map, the contour interval is always the same. The closer the contour lines, the steeper the slope; the more space between the lines, the more gradual the slope.
• Index contour lines are the darker, bolder, lines on a map, often marked with numbers that label elevations.

A **contour interval** is the difference in elevation between one contour line and the next.

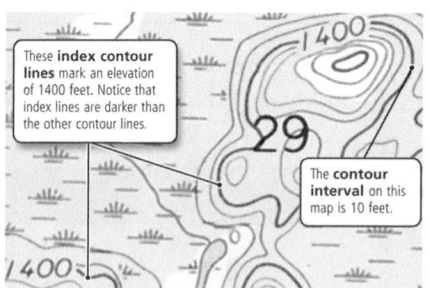

These **index contour lines** mark an elevation of 1400 feet. Notice that index lines are darker than the other contour lines.

The **contour interval** on this map is 10 feet.

SECTION
1.4 Technology is used to map Earth. pp. 30–35

1. Remote sensing provides detailed images of Earth.
Satellites use sensors to detect different types of energy from Earth's surface. They relay the data to computers on Earth, which process the data to create images.
• A **sensor** is any mechanical or electrical device that receives and responds to a signal, such as light.
• **False-color images** highlight particular information or features on a map or image.

Orbiting satellites used in mapmaking are equipped with sensors that constantly record data from Earth's surface. These instruments measure the invisible electromagnetic waves that every object emits. Because the waves are unique to particular types of objects, computers can identify objects through data analysis. The computers convert the data collected into a code, then to pixels, or electronic dots, which are are used to form images.

2. Geographic information systems display data in layers.
GIS combine data from satellite images, statistical surveys, and land surveys to make maps. A GIS map is a composite of several layers. Each layer is dedicated to a specific feature showing, for example, terrain, population, or roadways. The computer systems are used to assemble, store, manipulate, and display data about specific locations.

Common Misconceptions

MAP DISTORTION Many students viewing maps think that what they see are accurate images of Earth's landmasses and bodies of water. In fact, all map projections distort the shapes of Earth's landmasses and oceans.

TE This misconception is addressed on p. 20.

MISCONCEPTION DATABASE
CLASSZONE.COM Background on student misconceptions

A 5C Unit: Earth's Surface

Previewing Chapter Resources

Previewing Chapter Resources
- Section-by-section listing of all print and technology resources
- Suggested pacing
- Correlations to National Science Education Standards

TO ICONS   CD/CD-ROM   TE Teacher Edition
  INTERNET   PE Pupil Edition   R UNIT RESOURCE BOOK

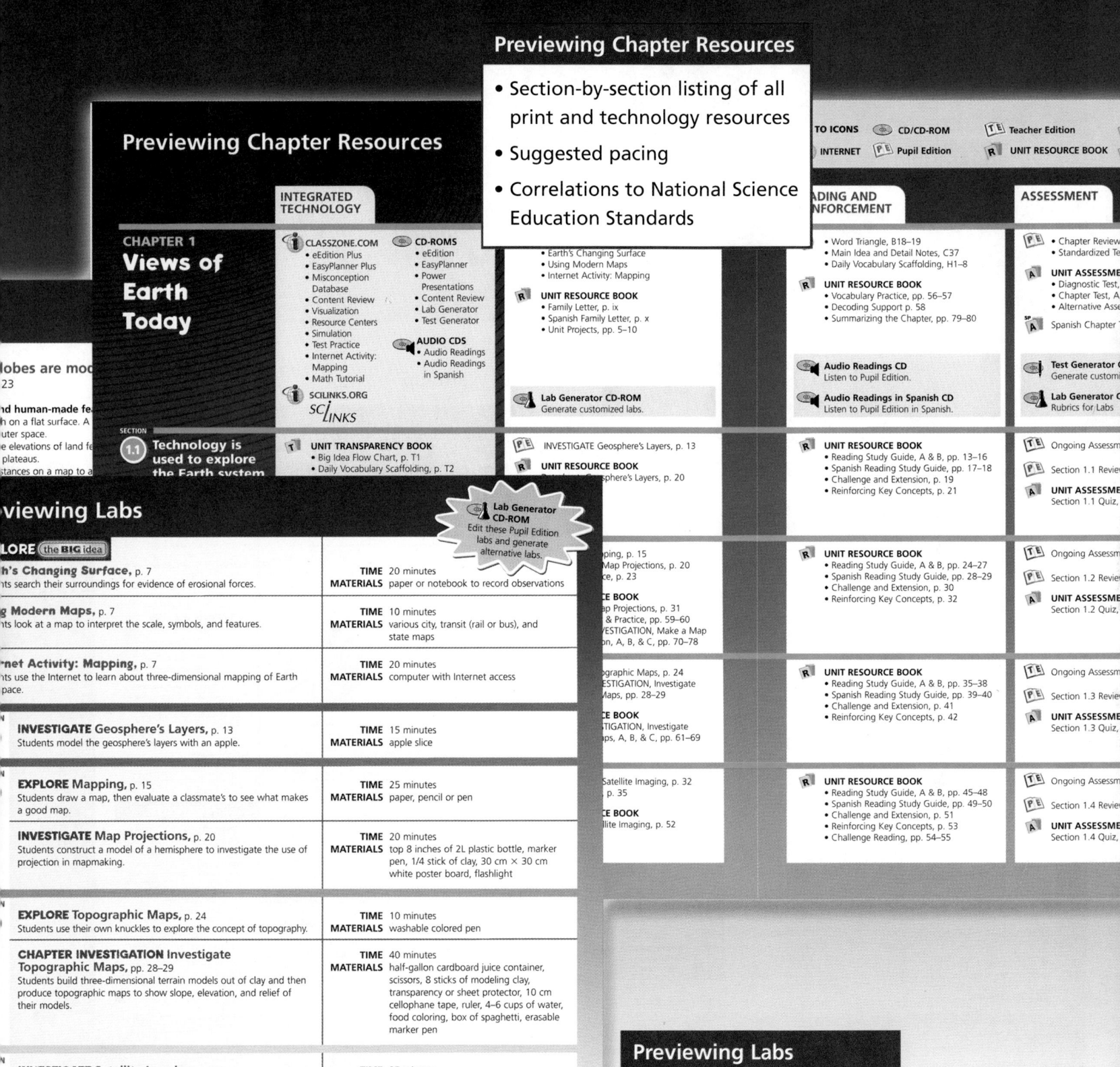

CHAPTER 1 **Views of Earth Today**	INTEGRATED TECHNOLOGY		READING AND ...NFORCEMENT	ASSESSMENT

CLASSZONE.COM
- eEdition Plus
- EasyPlanner Plus
- Misconception Database
- Content Review
- Visualization
- Resource Centers
- Simulation
- Test Practice
- Internet Activity: Mapping
- Math Tutorial

SCILINKS.ORG
SCI LINKS

CD-ROMS
- eEdition
- EasyPlanner
- Power Presentations
- Content Review
- Lab Generator
- Test Generator

AUDIO CDS
- Audio Readings
- Audio Readings in Spanish

- Earth's Changing Surface
- Using Modern Maps
- Internet Activity: Mapping

UNIT RESOURCE BOOK
- Family Letter, p. ix
- Spanish Family Letter, p. x
- Unit Projects, pp. 5–10

Lab Generator CD-ROM
Generate customized labs.

- Word Triangle, B18–19
- Main Idea and Detail Notes, C37
- Daily Vocabulary Scaffolding, H1–8

UNIT RESOURCE BOOK
- Vocabulary Practice, pp. 56–57
- Decoding Support p. 58
- Summarizing the Chapter, pp. 79–80

Audio Readings CD
Listen to Pupil Edition.

Audio Readings in Spanish CD
Listen to Pupil Edition in Spanish.

PE • Chapter Review, ...
  • Standardized Test ...

A **UNIT ASSESSMEN...**
- Diagnostic Test, p...
- Chapter Test, A, ...
- Alternative Asses...

SP A Spanish Chapter Te...

Test Generator CD
Generate customize...

Lab Generator CD
Rubrics for Labs

SECTION 1.1 Technology is used to explore the Earth system

UNIT TRANSPARENCY BOOK
- Big Idea Flow Chart, p. T1
- Daily Vocabulary Scaffolding, p. T2

PE INVESTIGATE Geosphere's Layers, p. 13

R **UNIT RESOURCE BOOK**
...osphere's Layers, p. 20

R **UNIT RESOURCE BOOK**
- Reading Study Guide, A & B, pp. 13–16
- Spanish Reading Study Guide, pp. 17–18
- Challenge and Extension, p. 19
- Reinforcing Key Concepts, p. 21

TE Ongoing Assessme...

PE Section 1.1 Review...

A **UNIT ASSESSMEN...**
Section 1.1 Quiz, p...

...ping, p. 15
...Map Projections, p. 20
...ce, p. 23

...CE BOOK
...ap Projections, p. 31
...& Practice, pp. 59–60
...VESTIGATION, Make a Map
...on, A, B, & C, pp. 70–78

R **UNIT RESOURCE BOOK**
- Reading Study Guide, A & B, pp. 24–27
- Spanish Reading Study Guide, pp. 28–29
- Challenge and Extension, p. 30
- Reinforcing Key Concepts, p. 32

TE Ongoing Assessme...

PE Section 1.2 Review...

A **UNIT ASSESSMEN...**
Section 1.2 Quiz, p...

...ographic Maps, p. 24
...ESTIGATION, Investigate
...Maps, pp. 28–29

...CE BOOK
...TIGATION, Investigate
...aps, A, B, & C, pp. 61–69

R **UNIT RESOURCE BOOK**
- Reading Study Guide, A & B, pp. 35–38
- Spanish Reading Study Guide, pp. 39–40
- Challenge and Extension, p. 41
- Reinforcing Key Concepts, p. 42

TE Ongoing Assessme...

PE Section 1.3 Review...

A **UNIT ASSESSMEN...**
Section 1.3 Quiz, p...

...Satellite Imaging, p. 32
..., p. 35

...CE BOOK
...llite Imaging, p. 52

R **UNIT RESOURCE BOOK**
- Reading Study Guide, A & B, pp. 45–48
- Spanish Reading Study Guide, pp. 49–50
- Challenge and Extension, p. 51
- Reinforcing Key Concepts, p. 53
- Challenge Reading, pp. 54–55

TE Ongoing Assessme...

PE Section 1.4 Review...

A **UNIT ASSESSMEN...**
Section 1.4 Quiz, p...

Previewing Labs

Lab Generator CD-ROM
Edit these Pupil Edition labs and generate alternative labs.

EXPLORE the BIG idea

...h's Changing Surface, p. 7
...nts search their surroundings for evidence of erosional forces.
TIME 20 minutes
MATERIALS paper or notebook to record observations

...g Modern Maps, p. 7
...nts look at a map to interpret the scale, symbols, and features.
TIME 10 minutes
MATERIALS various city, transit (rail or bus), and state maps

...rnet Activity: Mapping, p. 7
...nts use the Internet to learn about three-dimensional mapping of Earth
...pace.
TIME 20 minutes
MATERIALS computer with Internet access

INVESTIGATE Geosphere's Layers, p. 13
Students model the geosphere's layers with an apple.
TIME 15 minutes
MATERIALS apple slice

EXPLORE Mapping, p. 15
Students draw a map, then evaluate a classmate's to see what makes a good map.
TIME 25 minutes
MATERIALS paper, pencil or pen

INVESTIGATE Map Projections, p. 20
Students construct a model of a hemisphere to investigate the use of projection in mapmaking.
TIME 20 minutes
MATERIALS top 8 inches of 2L plastic bottle, marker pen, 1/4 stick of clay, 30 cm × 30 cm white poster board, flashlight

EXPLORE Topographic Maps, p. 24
Students use their own knuckles to explore the concept of topography.
TIME 10 minutes
MATERIALS washable colored pen

CHAPTER INVESTIGATION Investigate Topographic Maps, pp. 28–29
Students build three-dimensional terrain models out of clay and then produce topographic maps to show slope, elevation, and relief of their models.
TIME 40 minutes
MATERIALS half-gallon cardboard juice container, scissors, 8 sticks of modeling clay, transparency or sheet protector, 10 cm cellophane tape, ruler, 4–6 cups of water, food coloring, box of spaghetti, erasable marker pen

INVESTIGATE Satellite Imaging, p. 32
Students graph images to model how satellites send images to Earth.
TIME 25 minutes
MATERIALS graph paper, colored pen or pencil

Additional INVESTIGATION, Make a Map by Triangulation, A, B, & C, pp. 70–78; Teacher Instructions, pp. 348–349

Previewing Labs
- Brief descriptions of all chapter labs and activities
- Time and materials required for each activity

Planning the Lesson

Point-of-use support for each lesson provides a wealth of teaching options.

1. Prepare

- Concept and vocabulary review
- Note-taking and vocabulary strategies

2. Focus

- Set Learning Goals
- 3-Minute Warm-up

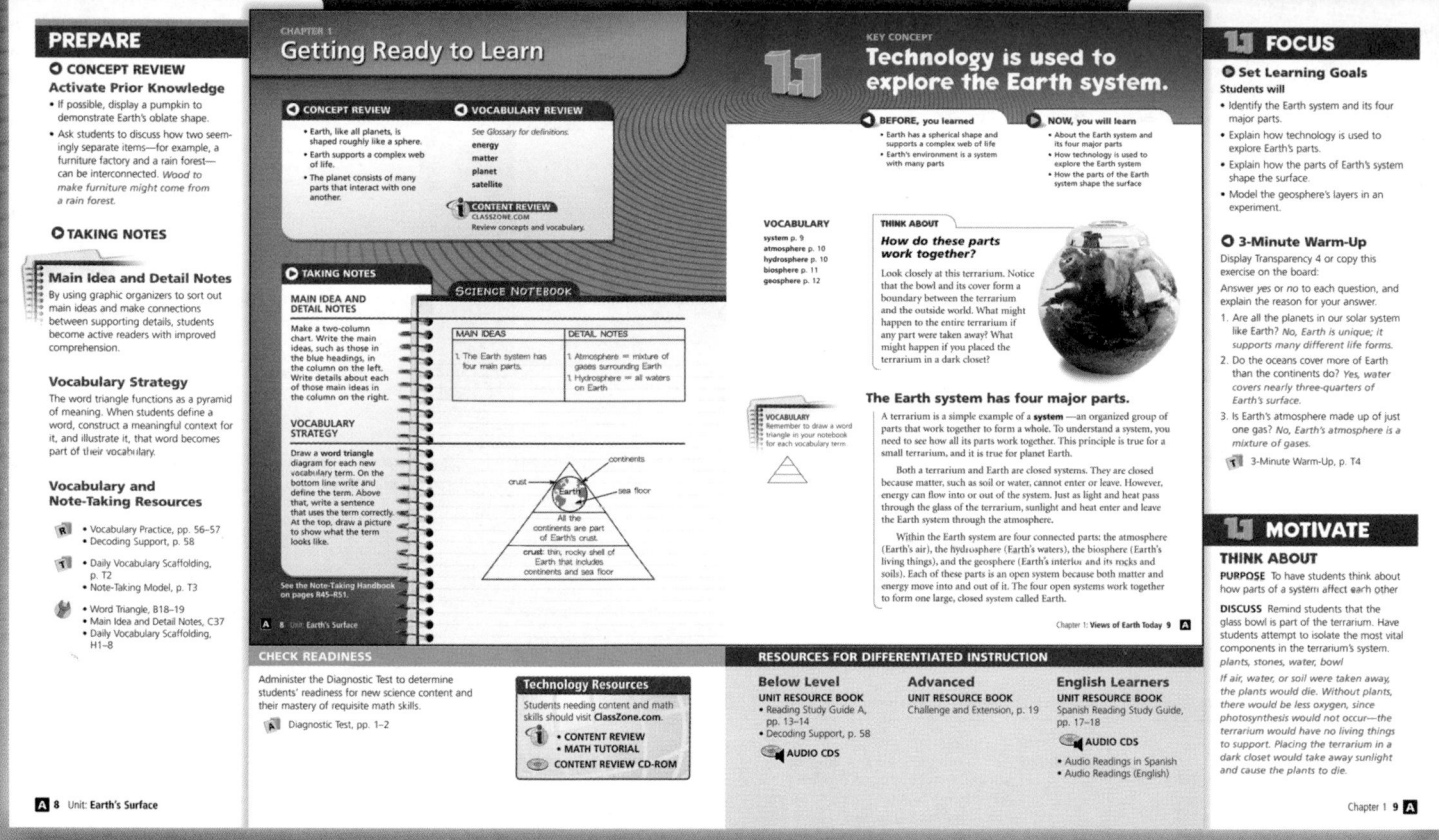

3. Motivate

- Engaging entry into the section
- Explore activity or Think About question

1.1 INSTRUCT

Language Arts Connection

Have students think of related words that contain the same Greek prefixes as those used in each of the four parts of the Earth system. *Sample answer: hydrology, geology, biology* Tell students an atmometer is an instrument that measures rates of evaporation.

Develop Critical Thinking

CLASSIFY Have students classify each item below in its proper sphere.
- ocean floor *geosphere*
- hurricane *atmosphere*
- bird's nest *biosphere*
- mountain glacier *hydrosphere*

Teach from Visuals

Remind students that they can get a preview of chapter content by studying the visuals—photographs, maps, or diagrams—and reading captions.

To help students interpret the "Parts of the Earth System" visual on pp. 10–11, ask:
- What landforms do you recognize in this image of Earth? *Students should recognize the North American continent, and the northern part of South America. They may identify Florida, Cuba, the Gulf Coast, and Mexico; Greenland is also visible.*
- What does each of the four inset photographs show? *one of the Earth system's four major parts*
- What theme is shared by the photographs? *human exploration of the Earth system through the use of technology*

Atmosphere

READING TIP The names of the Earth system's four parts contain Greek prefixes. *Atmo-* refers to vapor or gas, *Hydro-* refers to water, *Bio-* refers to life, and *geo-* refers to earth.

The **atmosphere** (AT-muh-SFEER) is the mixture of gases that surrounds and protects Earth. The most abundant gases are nitrogen (about 78%) and oxygen (nearly 21%). The atmosphere also contains carbon dioxide, water vapor, and a few other gases.

Before the 1800s, all studies of the atmosphere had to be done from the ground. Today, scientists launch weather balloons, fly specially equipped planes, and view the atmosphere in satellite images. The data they collect show that the atmosphere interacts with the other parts of the Earth system to form complex weather patterns that circulate around Earth. The more scientists learn about these patterns, the more accurately they can predict local weather.

Hydrosphere

The **hydrosphere** (HY-druh-SFEER) is made up of all the water on Earth, in oceans, lakes, glaciers, rivers, and streams and underground. Water covers nearly three-quarters of Earth's surface. Only about 3 percent of the hydrosphere is fresh water. Nearly 70 percent of Earth's fresh water is frozen in glaciers and polar ice caps.

Parts of the Earth System

Atmosphere — Over 400 cones make this weather balloon more stable as it gathers data about the atmosphere.

Hydrosphere — Scientists need special diving equipment to study Earth's oceans.

Biosphere — These platforms, built in the treetops, are used to observe forest plants and animals.

Geosphere — In mines dug deep underground, scientists can explore Earth's minerals and rocks.

10 Unit: Earth's Surface

In the past 50 years, scientists have used deep-sea vehicles, special buoys, satellite images, and diving suits, such as the one shown on page 10, to study the world's oceans. They have discovered that the oceans contain several layers of cold and warm water. As these layers circulate, they form cold and warm ocean currents. The currents interact with wind patterns in the atmosphere and affect Earth's weather.

CHECK YOUR READING How does the hydrosphere affect the atmosphere?

Biosphere

The **biosphere** (BY-uh-SFEER) includes all life on Earth, in the air, on the land, and in the waters. The biosphere can be studied with a variety of technologies. For example, satellite photos are used to track yearly changes in Earth's plant and animal life. As the photograph below shows, special equipment allows scientists to study complex environments, such as rain forests, without damaging them.

Scientists have learned a lot about how the biosphere interacts with the other parts of the Earth system. For example, large forests act as Earth's "lungs," absorbing carbon dioxide and releasing oxygen into the atmosphere. When dead trees decay, they return nutrients to the soil.

CHECK YOUR READING Name one way the biosphere and the atmosphere interact.

MAIN IDEA AND DETAIL NOTES As you read this section, use this strategy to take notes.

Chapter 1: Views of Earth Today 11

DIFFERENTIATE INSTRUCTION

More Reading Support
A What is a weather balloon used for? *studying the atmosphere*

English Learners Help English learners remember the differences between these similar-sounding terms: *atmosphere, hydrosphere, biosphere,* and *geosphere.* Suggest they separate each term into two parts by writing the prefix and *-sphere* on an index card. Under the Greek prefix, have them write the English [...]ing. (Example: *hydro-* means water.) They can refer to [...]rds during lessons.

[...] Learners may not have prior know[...] polar ice caps (p. 10), or computer [...]

DIFFERENTIATE INSTRUCTION

More Reading Support
C What is the biosphere? *all forms of life on Earth*
D Do plants absorb or release carbon dioxide? *absorb*

Advanced Have students hypothesize how oceans originated on our planet. Ask: How did Earth come to be a water planet? *Volcanic action released steam, which then condensed into liquid water. Some scientists also think that icy comets melted when they struck Earth, which added water to the planet.*

Chapter 1 11

Integrate the Sciences

Make a connection with life science by discussing the fact that the environment of the ocean depths is inhospitable to human life. The incredible pressures in the deep ocean are the biggest obstacle to undersea exploration. Conventional scuba equipment restricts divers to depths of less than 40 meters. They must also be careful to limit the duration of their dives and to surface gradually. Failure to do so can result in a painful and sometimes fatal condition known as the bends. Oxygen-enriched air can allow divers to extend the duration of their dives by limiting the amount of nitrogen absorbed into their blood.

Real World Example

The great depths of the oceans can be explored with the aid of research submersibles. The National Oceanic and Atmospheric Administration (NOAA) runs an undersea laboratory and uses a variety of submersible vehicles that can, in the case of the famous *Alvin,* carry people as deep as 4500 meters. Two types of unmanned submersibles are also used for sea exploration. ROVs (remotely operated vehicles) operate while attached to ships; AUVs (autonomous underwater vehicles) operate independently, following a programmed set of instructions.

Ongoing Assessment

Identify the Earth system and its four major parts
Ask: What are the four parts of Earth's system? *atmosphere, hydrosphere, biosphere, geosphere*

CHECK YOUR READING Answer: Warm and cold ocean currents interact with wind patterns to influence Earth's weather.

CHECK YOUR READING Answer: Trees exchange gases with the atmosphere, taking in carbon dioxide and giving off oxygen.

Ongoing Assessment

CHECK YOUR READING Answer: Wind and moving water wear away rocky surfaces; landmasses pushing together cause earthquakes and form volcanoes and other mountains; plants, animals, and people wear away or change Earth's surface.

EXPLORE (the BIG idea)

Revisit "Earth's Changing Surface" on p. 7. Have students explain the four parts of the Earth system worked together to account for their observations.

Reinforce (the BIG idea)

Have students relate the section to the Big Idea.

Reinforcing Key Concepts, p. 21

1.1 ASSESS & RETEACH

Assess

Section 1.1 Quiz, p. 3

Reteach

Draw a cutaway diagram on the board, similar to that on p. 12 but without indications of the boundaries between layers. Ask for volunteers to add the following information to the diagram:
- Locations of the atmosphere, hydrosphere, biosphere, and geosphere
- Compositions of the four spheres
- Boundaries and names of the geosphere's layers
- Composition or nature of each geosphere layer

Technology Resources

Have students visit **ClassZone.com** for reteaching of Key Concepts.

🔲 CONTENT REVIEW
💿 CONTENT REVIEW CD-ROM

14 Unit: Earth's Surface

Mudslide in California

Atmosphere and Hydrosphere Heavy winter rains soak the ground until it cannot absorb any more water.

Biosphere People who build on fragile hillsides remove plants whose roots help hold the soil in place.

Geosphere With nothing to hold the water-soaked ground, it slides downhill, leaving a deep trench.

The photograph above shows a good example of how the four parts can suddenly change Earth's surface. A mudslide like this one can happen in a matter of minutes. Sometimes the side of a mountain may collapse, becoming a river of mud that can bury an entire town.

The four parts of the Earth system continue to shape the surface with every passing year. Scientists will continue to record these changes to update maps and other images of the planet's complex system.

CHECK YOUR READING Find three examples on pages 13 and 14 that show how the parts of the Earth system shape the planet's surface.

1.1 Review

KEY CONCEPTS
1. Define *system.* Compare an open and a closed system.
2. Name the four parts of the Earth system. List one fact about each part that scientists learned through modern technology.
3. Give two examples of how the Earth system's four parts can interact with each other.

CRITICAL THINKING
4. **Apply** One day you see that plants are dying in the class terrarium. What part might be missing from its system?
5. **Infer** You visit a state park and see a thin rock with a hole, like a window, worn through it. Which of the four parts of the Earth system might have made the hole? Explain.

CHALLENGE
6. **Predict** Imagine that a meteorite 200 meters wide strikes Earth, landing in a wooded area. Describe one way that this event would affect the biosphere or the geosphere. **Hint:** A meteorite is traveling several thousand kilometers per hour when it strikes the ground.

14 Unit: Earth's Surface

ANSWERS

1. organized group of parts that work together to form a whole; closed system: energy but not matter can enter or leave; open system: matter and energy can enter or leave

2. atmosphere: complex weather patterns; hydrosphere: layers of cold and warm water; biosphere: yearly changes in plant and animal life; geosphere: features above and below Earth's surface

3. Storms in the atmosphere can change Earth's coastlines; animals can wear paths in Earth's surface.

4. water, air, or soil nutrients

5. hydrosphere (rain) or hydrosphere and atmosphere (rain and wind)

6. It would blast a huge crater in the geosphere. The heat would destroy nearby plants and animals in the biosphere.

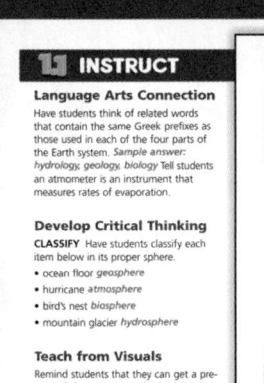

4. Instruct

- Teaching strategies
- Reading support
- Ongoing assessment
- Addressing misconceptions
- Differentiated instruction activities and tips

5. Assess & Reteach

- Answers to Section Review
- Reteaching activity
- Resources for review and assessment

Lab Materials List

The following charts list the consumables, nonconsumables, and equipment needed for all activities. Quantities are per group of four students. Lab aprons, goggles, water, books, paper, pens, pencils, and calculators are assumed to be available for all activities.

Materials kits are available. For more information, please call McDougal Littell at 1-800-323-5435.

Consumables

Description	Quantity per Group	Explore *page*	Investigate *page*	Chapter Investigation *page*
acetate, blue, 4" x 4"	1			C100
acetate, green, 4" x 4"	1			C100
acetate, red, 4" x 4"	1			C100
aluminum foil	9 ft	C113, E9	B27, B46	B22, B56, E120
antacid tablet, effervescent	1	B146		
apple	1 1/2		A13, A135, D25	
bag, paper lunch	2	D81		D52
bag, plastic sandwich	1	D16		
bag, zip-top sandwich	1	C26		
ball, Styrofoam 3"	1		E62	
balloon	1		C41	
banana	1/4		D25	
battery, AA	3			E120
battery, D cell	1	C79		
bean, white kidney, dry	1/2–1 cup			D52
bottle, plastic, 1-liter	1		B41	
bottle, plastic, 1-liter, with cap	1		D25	
bottle, plastic, 2-liter	2		A20	A130
bottle, plastic, pint	2			B56
can, aluminum soda	1			B22
candle, taper, various colors	3		A98	
candle, tea light	2			B80
cardboard, 5" x 5"	3			B154
cardboard, 10 cm x 10 cm	20		D57	
cardboard, 10 cm x 25 cm	1		C53	
cardboard, 12" x 12"	1		B93	
cardboard, 12" x 24"	1		B13	
cardboard, 15 cm x 15 cm	1			B128
cardboard tube, 12"	4	C58	C134	
carton, milk, half-gallon	2		C115	A28
cellophane, blue, 6" x 6"	1			E20
cellophane, red, 6" x 6"	1			E20
cellophane, yellow, 6" x 6"	1			E20
clay, modeling	13 sticks	A165, C131	A20, A169, B41, C128, E97	A28, B22, B56, B128, C124, E106
clay, modeling, blue	1		B93	
clay, modeling, green	1	B137		
clay, modeling, red	2	B137	B93	

Description	Quantity per Group	Explore page	Investigate page	Chapter Investigation page
clay, modeling, yellow	2	B137	B93	
coffee filter, basket	3		C98	
cornstarch	1/4 cup			D106
cotton ball	10–15			D106
craft stick	4	B105	B72, E97	B154
crouton	1			B22
cup, clear plastic	26	B69, C119, D63, E15	A46, A94, A118, B27, B46, B72, C98, E55, E88	
cup, paper	6–9		A94, D65	B154
Epsom salts	1 tbs		A46	
feather	1			D106
filter paper, fine, 4"	3			D14
flour	2–3 lb			E106
foam packing pellets	1 cup			B56
food coloring	1 bottle	B69, C24	A94, B41, C26	A28, B80, E106
gelatin, firm	1/4 cup		E88	
gelatin, liquid	1/4 cup		E55	
gravel	2 3/4 lb	A89, A165	A94, A169, B72, D25	B154
hydrochloric acid, dilute	25 mL			A58
ice	3–5 cups		A169, E55	
index card, white	10	B24, C131, E115	C128, D91	C124, E20
isopropyl alcohol	3/4 cup		B41	D106
knife, plastic	1		A135	
leaves, assorted	4–5		D25	
liquid dish detergent	1/4 cup			D106
marker, colored	6–8	B74, E9	A32, B93, B107	C124, E20
marker, erasable, black	1			A28
marker, felt-tip, black	1		E82	
marker, permanent, black	1	D22, D45, D63	A20, B85, C84, D25, D91	
marker, permanent, blue	1			D52
marker, permanent, red	1			D52
marker, water-soluble, black, various brands	3	A24	C98	
match, wood	10			B22, B80
milk	2 tsp	C93		
mineral oil	3–4 oz	C119		
napkin, square paper	6	B90		
newspaper, sheet	5	B120, B137		E106
oatmeal canister, small cardboard	1	B82		
paper clip	4–7	A150, E115		B22
paper fastener, brass	1		E13	
paper towel	5–7	A165, E85	E55	D106
paper, 3 cm x 3 cm	200		D57	
paper, 5" x 5"	3			D14
paper, construction, 8.5" x 11"	4	B74, D22		C22
paper, construction, black, 8.5" x 11"	6	A43, A115, E122, E130	A46	
paper, graph, 8.5" x 11"	4		A32, D35, D57	E50
paper, graph, large-grid, 8.5" x 11"	1	D45		

Description	Quantity per Group	Explore page	Investigate page	Chapter Investigation page
paper, striped or lined, 8" x 12"	1	B82		
paper, tracing 8.5" x 11"	1		D84	
paper, white, 8.5" x 11"	6	E15, E52	A122, C84	C22
paraffin wax block	2			E120
paraffin wax shavings	3 tsp	E79	E88	
pebble	1	B9		
pen, white gel	1	E130		
pencil, blue	1		D35, D57	
pencil, red	1		D35, D57	
petroleum jelly	2 tbs		D91	
pH test strip, universal	2			A130
pie plate, aluminum	3		A46	B22
plant, small houseplant	1	D16		
plaster of Paris	2 cups		A94	B154
plastic garbage bag, black, 4" x 4" piece	1		B27	
plastic garbage bag, white, 4" x 4" piece	1		B27	
plastic wrap	36"			B56
plate, paper	2		C128, E97	
poster board, white, 12" x 12"	2		A20	C124
pushpin	4			B80
rice	1/2 cup	D45		
rice cake, caramel	1/4			B22
roll of toilet paper, nontextured	1		E82	
rubber band, large	45	B37	B27, C41, C48 C53, E138	A130, B56, C64, E120
salt, rock	1 tbs	A43		
salt, table	2 1/4 cup	A43, B69, E15	A46, C41	E106
sand	9 3/4 lb	A89, A165, B9, B120 C26	A94, A169, E33, E88	B56, C22, D14, D106
sand, for stream table	5–10 lb			A156
seashell, whole or crushed	1–2		D19	
seaweed, stem	2			D106
seed, radish	25–50		D65	
shoebox, cardboard	1		C48	
shoebox, cardboard with lid	3			C64, C100, E20
shoebox lid, cardboard	2		E33	
soil, clay	50 mL			D14
soil, loam	50 mL			D14
soil, local	1/2 cup		A122	
soil, potting	8 lb	D98	A122, A146, D25, D65	A130, B56
spaghetti, uncooked	1/2 lb			A28
sponge	3			B80, D106
spoon, plastic	6	B69, E15, E79, E88		D14, D106
steel wool	1		A118	
sticky note	1			E50
stopper, cork	1			B22
straw, clear drinking	1		B41	

Description	Quantity per Group	Explore *page*	Investigate *page*	Chapter Investigation *page*
straw, stirring, small single-hole	15–20			B128
string, blue	60 cm		B113	
string, red	25 cm		B113	
string, white	600 cm	C37, E9	B85, B113, C20, D91	C22
sugar	1 1/4 tsp	D63		
tape, duct	1 roll		C134	
tape, electrical	1 roll	C79		
tape, masking	1 roll	C58, D16, D22	B85, B107, C20, C48, C115, D25, D57	C22, C100, C124, E120
tape, packing	8"		B13	
tape, transparent	1 roll	A150, B82, E130	B113	A28, E20
thread	15 cm	D22		
toothpick	1			D14
transparency, clear, 8.5" x 11"	1			A28
turmeric	1–2 mL			D106
vegetable oil	40 mL			D106
vinegar, white	1/4 cup		D19	
window screening, 6" x 6"	1			A130
wire, copper, uninsulated	110 cm	C79		E120
yarn	2–3 ft			D106
yeast	1 1/2 tsp	D63		

Nonconsumables

Description	Quantity per Group	Explore *page*	Investigate *page*	Chapter Investigation *page*
balance, triple-beam	1		B13, B46	B22, E106
bead, medium yellow	3		A65	
bead, small blue	8		A65	
bead, small green	4		A65	
bead, small red	2		A65	
bead, wood, 1/4", brightly colored	2–4 dozen		B72	
beaker, 100 mL	1		B46, D19	D106
beaker, 200 mL	2	B50		B56, D14
beaker, 500 mL	3	B50		D14, D106
bird food with sunflower seeds	1 lb		A65	
bowl, large plastic	1	B9, E79	B41, E55, E88	
bucket, large	1		E25	
bucket, small	1		E25	
can opener	1			B22
chair	1	C9		
coffee can, 1-pound with lid	1	A115		B56
coin, penny	6–10		B46	
coin, penny, copper (dated 1982 or earlier)	1		A56	A58
coin, quarter	1		A160	
compass	1	E52		
diffraction grating, mounted	1			E20
dishpan, plastic	1			A156

Description	Quantity per Group	Explore *page*	Investigate *page*	Chapter Investigation *page*
dowel rod, 1/4" diameter, 8"	8"		E62	B22
eyedropper	1			A58, D14
film canister with lid	1	B146		
flashlight with batteries	2	C93, E15, E122	A20	C124, E50
flowerpot with draining dish	2	D98		
fork, steel	1	C79		
funnel, small plastic	3			D14
globe	1			E50
golf ball	1		E33	
graduated cylinder, 100 mL	1		B46	B22, B56, C22
graduated cylinder, 250 mL	1			A130
hand lens	1	A43, A75	A122, D91	A58, A102, D14
jar, 1-quart with lid	1	A89		A130
jar, baby-food	1		C41	
jar, clear plastic, 2-liter with lid	1	C93		
lamp, gooseneck desk	1	D22, E115	C90, C128	C100, E20, E120
lamp, unshaded table	1		E44, E62	
lamp dimmer, plug-in or socket	1			E120
lens, convex	2	C131	C128, C134	C124
light bulb, compact fluorescent, 15-watt	1		C90	E20
light bulb, flashlight	2			E120
light bulb, incandescent, 45-watt	1	E115		
light bulb, incandescent, 60-watt	1	D22	C90, E44, E62	E20, E120
light bulb, incandescent, 75-watt	1		C128	C100
light bulb, incandescent, 100-watt	1		C90	
light bulb holder	2			E120
magnet, bar	1		B85	A58
map, local land use or zoning	1		D84	
marble, metal	3–5			E106
measuring cup, 1-cup	1	D98		
measuring cup, 2-cup/500 mL	1	A89, D63		
measuring spoon, 1/2-teaspoon	1	D63		
measuring spoon, tablespoon	1		A46	
measuring spoon, teaspoon	1	C93, D63		
meter stick	1	E122	B13, E123	C22, C124, E50, E106
mineral sample, calcite	1	A75	A56	A58
mineral sample, chalcopyrite	1		A56	
mineral sample, galena	1			A58
mineral sample, gypsum	1		A56	
mineral sample, hornblende	1		A56	
mineral sample, magnetite	1			A58
mineral sample, plagioclase	1			A58
mineral sample, pyrite	1			A58
mineral sample, quartz	1		A56	
mirror, 3 1/2" x 3 1/2"	2		C115	
mirror on a stand	1	C73		

Description	Quantity per Group	Explore _page_	Investigate _page_	Chapter Investigation _page_
mortar and pestle	1		D19	
object, small black	1			C100
object, small red	1			C100
object, small white	1			C100
object, small yellow	1			C100
pan, glass, 10" x 14"	1	C24	C26	B80
pan, metal, 4" x 8"	2			B80
pan, metal, 10" x 14"	2		A65, A146, A169	D106, E106
paper hole punch	1		D91	
pitcher	1		A146	A156
prism	1		C84	
protractor	1		C115	B154, E50
radio, portable	1	C79		
radiometer	1		C76	
ribbon	20 cm	C9		
ring stand with ring	1			B22
rock, flat	1	B120		
rock, medium	1	B9		
rock, small soft or chalk	4–6	A115		
rock sample, arkose sandstone	1			A102
rock sample, basalt	1		A77	
rock sample, conglomerate	1		A77	
rock sample, diorite	1			A102
rock sample, gabbro	1			A102
rock sample, gneiss	1		A77	A102
rock sample, granite	1		A77	
rock sample, phyllite	1		A77	
rock sample, pink granite	1	A75		
rock sample, pumice	1			A102
rock sample, quartz sandstone	1			A102
rock sample, sandstone	1		A77	
rock sample, schist	1			A102
rock sample, shale	1			A102
rope	2–3 m	C9		
ruler, metric	1	B24, B137, C26, C45, D63, E135	B113, C53, D65, D84, E138	A28, A156, B128, B154, C64, C100, E20, E106
scissors	1	B74, B82, D22	A46, B27, B113, C41, C53, C98, C115, D25, D91, E13, E97, E131	A28, A130, B80, B128, C22, C64, C100, E20
sea-floor model (1 file folder, 8–12 1" disc magnets, 24" masking tape, stapler, marker)	1		B85	
shake table (2 large box lids, 40 marbles, 4 rubber bands, stapler)	1			B128
sieve, fine	1			A156
solar calculator with no battery backup	1	B24		
spoon, large metal	1	C37		
spring toy	1	B111	C13	

Description	Quantity per Group	Explore page	Investigate page	Chapter Investigation page
steel file	1		A56	A58
stirring rod	3	D63	A46	
stopwatch	1	B50, D9, D98	B27, B46, C20	B56, D14
streak plate	1			A58
stream table with hose attachment or recirculating pump	1			A156
tennis ball	1	E9		
thermometer	3	B50, D9	B27, B46, C84	B56
thermometer, 12"	1			B22
tongs, test-tube	1			B56
toy car, large	1		B13	
TV with infrared remote control	1	C73		
tweezers	1		A122	
vegetable peeler	1		A98	
washer, metal, 1"	20	B120	B13, C20	
wood block, 3"	3	B137, C26	B142, E85	
wood block, rectangular, 6"	2–4			A156
wood block, triangular	3		B107, B142	

Unit Resource Book Datasheets

Description	Explore page	Investigate page	Chapter Investigation page
Apple Chart		A135	
Climate Graph		D35	
Distance Table		E82	
Earthquake Map		B113	
Galaxy Photo Sheet		E131	
Map of Mount Rainier Mudflows		B159	
Mineral Crystal Diagrams		A85	
Mineral Identification Key			A58
Mohs Scale			A58
Rock Classification Key			A102
Texture Flow Chart			A130
Time Zone Map	E43		

Safety Equipment

Description	Explore page	Investigate page	Chapter Investigation page
gloves	D98		B56, D14, D106

NORTH CAROLINA EDITION

McDougal Littell
Science

GRADE

6

Space Science

Waves, Sound,
and Light

Energy and
the Changing Earth

Ecology

Earth's
Surface

i

GRADE 6 CONTENTS

ISBN: 0-618-46434-4   X 2 3 4 5 6 7 8 VJM 08 07 06 05 04

Internet Web Site: http://www.mcdougallittell.com

Science Consultants

Chief Science Consultant

James Trefil, Ph.D. is the Clarence J. Robinson Professor of Physics at George Mason University. He is the author or co-author of more than 25 books, including *Science Matters* and *The Nature of Science*. Dr. Trefil is a member of the American Association for the Advancement of Science's Committee on the Public Understanding of Science and Technology. He is also a fellow of the World Economic Forum and a frequent contributor to *Smithsonian* magazine.

Rita Ann Calvo, Ph.D. is Senior Lecturer in Molecular Biology and Genetics at Cornell University, where for 12 years she also directed the Cornell Institute for Biology Teachers. Dr. Calvo is the 1999 recipient of the College and University Teaching Award from the National Association of Biology Teachers.

Kenneth Cutler, M.S. is the Education Coordinator for the Julius L. Chambers Biomedical Biotechnology Research Institute at North Carolina Central University. A former middle school and high school science teacher, he received a 1999 Presidential Award for Excellence in Science Teaching.

Instructional Design Consultants

Douglas Carnine, Ph.D. is Professor of Education and Director of the National Center for Improving the Tools of Educators at the University of Oregon. He is the author of seven books and over 100 other scholarly publications, primarily in the areas of instructional design and effective instructional strategies and tools for diverse learners. Dr. Carnine also serves as a member of the National Institute for Literacy Advisory Board.

Linda Carnine, Ph.D. consults with school districts on curriculum development and effective instruction for students struggling academically. A former teacher and school administrator, Dr. Carnine also co-authored a popular remedial reading program.

Donald Steely, Ph.D. serves as principal investigator at the Oregon Center for Applied Science (ORCAS) on federal grants for science and language arts programs. His background also includes teaching and authoring of print and multimedia programs in science, mathematics, history, and spelling.

Sam Miller, Ph.D. is a middle school science teacher and the Teacher Development Liaison for the Eugene, Oregon, Public Schools. He is the author of curricula for teaching science, mathematics, computer skills, and language arts.

Vicky Vachon, Ph.D. consults with school districts throughout the United States and Canada on improving overall academic achievement with a focus on literacy. She is also co-author of a widely used program for remedial readers.

Content Reviewers

John Beaver, Ph.D.
Ecology
Professor, Director of Science Education Center
College of Education and Human Services
Western Illinois University
Macomb, IL

Donald J. DeCoste, Ph.D.
Matter and Energy, Chemical Interactions
Chemistry Instructor
University of Illinois
Urbana-Champaign, IL

Dorothy Ann Fallows, Ph.D., MSc
Diversity of Living Things, Microbiology
Partners in Health
Boston, MA

Michael Foote, Ph.D.
The Changing Earth, Life Over Time
Associate Professor
Department of the Geophysical Sciences
The University of Chicago
Chicago, IL

Lucy Fortson, Ph.D.
Space Science
Director of Astronomy
Adler Planetarium and Astronomy Museum
Chicago, IL

Elizabeth Godrick, Ph.D.
Human Biology
Professor, CAS Biology
Boston University
Boston, MA

Isabelle Sacramento Grilo, M.S.
The Changing Earth
Lecturer, Department of the Geological Sciences
Montana State University
Bozeman, MT

David Harbster, MSc
Diversity of Living Things
Professor of Biology
Paradise Valley Community College
Phoenix, AZ

Richard D. Norris, Ph.D.
Earth's Waters
Professor of Paleobiology
Scripps Institution of Oceanography
University of California, San Diego
La Jolla, CA

Donald B. Peck, M.S.
Motion and Forces; Waves, Sound, and Light;
 Electricity and Magnetism
Director of the Center for Science Education (retired)
Fairleigh Dickinson University
Madison, NJ

Javier Penalosa, Ph.D.
Diversity of Living Things, Plants
Associate Professor, Biology Department
Buffalo State College
Buffalo, NY

Raymond T. Pierrehumbert, Ph.D.
Earth's Atmosphere
Professor in Geophysical Sciences (Atmospheric Science)
The University of Chicago
Chicago, IL

Brian J. Skinner, Ph.D.
Earth's Surface
Eugene Higgins Professor of Geology and Geophysics
Yale University
New Haven, CT

Nancy E. Spaulding, M.S.
Earth's Surface, The Changing Earth, Earth's Waters
Earth Science Teacher (retired)
Elmira Free Academy
Elmira, NY

Steven S. Zumdahl, Ph.D.
Matter and Energy, Chemical Interactions
Professor Emeritus of Chemistry
University of Illinois
Urbana-Champaign, IL

Susan L. Zumdahl, M.S.
Matter and Energy, Chemical Interactions
Chemistry Education Specialist
University of Illinois
Urbana-Champaign, IL

Safety Consultant

Juliana Texley, Ph.D.
Former K–12 Science Teacher and School Superintendent
Boca Raton, FL

English Language Advisor

Judy Lewis, M.A.
Director, State and Federal Programs for reading proficiency
and high risk populations
Rancho Cordova, CA

Teacher Panel Members

Carol Arbour
Tallmadge Middle School,
Tallmadge, OH

Patty Belcher
Goodrich Middle School,
Akron, OH

Gwen Broestl
Luis Munoz Marin Middle School,
Cleveland, OH

Al Brofman
Tehipite Middle School,
Fresno, CA

John Cockrell
Clinton Middle School,
Columbus, OH

Jenifer Cox
Sylvan Middle School,
Citrus Heights, CA

Linda Culpepper
Martin Middle School,
Charlotte, NC

Kathleen Ann DeMatteo
Margate Middle School,
Margate, FL

Melvin Figueroa
New River Middle School,
Ft. Lauderdale, FL

Doretha Grier
Kannapolis Middle School,
Kannapolis, NC

Robert Hood
Alexander Hamilton Middle School,
Cleveland, OH

Scott Hudson
Coverdale Elementary School,
Cincinnati, OH

Loretta Langdon
Princeton Middle School,
Princeton, NC

Carlyn Little
Glades Middle School,
Miami, FL

Ann Marie Lynn
Amelia Earhart Middle School,
Riverside, CA

James Minogue
Lowe's Grove Middle School,
Durham, NC

Joann Myers
Buchanan Middle School,
Tampa, FL

Barbara Newell
Charles Evans Hughes Middle School,
Long Beach, CA

Anita Parker
Kannapolis Middle School,
Kannapolis, NC

Greg Pirolo
Golden Valley Middle School,
San Bernardino, CA

Laura Pottmyer
Apex Middle School,
Apex, NC

Lynn Prichard
Booker T. Washington Middle Magnet
School, Tampa, FL

Jacque Quick
Walter Williams High School,
Burlington, NC

Robert Glenn Reynolds
Hillman Middle School,
Youngstown, OH

Stacy Rinehart
Lufkin Road Middle School,
Apex, NC

Theresa Short
Abbott Middle School,
Fayetteville, NC

Rita Slivka
Alexander Hamilton Middle School,
Cleveland, OH

Marie Sofsak
B F Stanton Middle School,
Alliance, OH

Nancy Stubbs
Sweetwater Union Unified School District,
Chula Vista, CA

Sharon Stull
Quail Hollow Middle School,
Charlotte, NC

Donna Taylor
Okeeheelee Middle School,
West Palm Beach, FL

Sandi Thompson
Harding Middle School,
Lakewood, OH

Lori Walker
Audubon Middle School & Magnet Center,
Los Angeles, CA

Teacher Lab Evaluators

Andrew Boy
W.E.B. DuBois Academy,
Cincinnati, OH

Jill Brimm-Byrne
Albany Park Academy,
Chicago, IL

Gwen Broestl
Luis Munoz Marin Middle School,
Cleveland, OH

Al Brofman
Tehipite Middle School,
Fresno, CA

Michael A. Burstein
The Rashi School,
Newton, MA

Trudi Coutts
Madison Middle School,
Naperville, IL

Jenifer Cox
Sylvan Middle School,
Citrus Heights, CA

Larry Cwik
Madison Middle School,
Naperville, IL

Melissa Dupree
Lakeside Middle School,
Evans, GA

Carl Fechko
Luis Munoz Marin Middle School,
Cleveland, OH

Jennifer Donatelli
Kennedy Junior High School,
Lisle, IL

Paige Fullhart
Highland Middle School,
Libertyville, IL

Sue Hood
Glen Crest Middle School,
Glen Ellyn, IL

William Luzader
Plymouth Community Intermediate School,
Plymouth, MA

Ann Min
Beardsley Middle School,
Crystal Lake, IL

Aileen Mueller
Kennedy Junior High School,
Lisle, IL

Nancy Nega
Churchville Middle School,
Elmhurst, IL

Oscar Newman
Sumner Math and Science Academy,
Chicago, IL

Lynn Prichard
Booker T. Washington Middle Magnet
School, Tampa, FL

Jacque Quick
Walter Williams High School,
Burlington, NC

Stacy Rinehart
Lufkin Road Middle School,
Apex, NC

Seth Robey
Gwendolyn Brooks Middle School,
Oak Park, IL

Kevin Steele
Grissom Middle School,
Tinley Park, IL

Teacher Panel Members

Carol Arbour
Tallmadge Middle School,
Tallmadge, OH

Patty Belcher
Goodrich Middle School,
Akron, OH

Gwen Broestl
Luis Munoz Marin Middle School,
Cleveland, OH

Al Brofman
Tehipite Middle School,
Fresno, CA

John Cockrell
Clinton Middle School,
Columbus, OH

Jenifer Cox
Sylvan Middle School,
Citrus Heights, CA

Linda Culpepper
Martin Middle School,
Charlotte, NC

Kathleen Ann DeMatteo
Margate Middle School,
Margate, FL

Melvin Figueroa
New River Middle School,
Ft. Lauderdale, FL

Doretha Grier
Kannapolis Middle School,
Kannapolis, NC

Robert Hood
Alexander Hamilton Middle School,
Cleveland, OH

Scott Hudson
Coverdale Elementary School,
Cincinnati, OH

Loretta Langdon
Princeton Middle School,
Princeton, NC

Carlyn Little
Glades Middle School,
Miami, FL

Ann Marie Lynn
Amelia Earhart Middle School,
Riverside, CA

James Minogue
Lowe's Grove Middle School,
Durham, NC

Joann Myers
Buchanan Middle School,
Tampa, FL

Barbara Newell
Charles Evans Hughes Middle School,
Long Beach, CA

Anita Parker
Kannapolis Middle School,
Kannapolis, NC

Greg Pirolo
Golden Valley Middle School,
San Bernardino, CA

Laura Pottmyer
Apex Middle School,
Apex, NC

Lynn Prichard
Booker T. Washington Middle Magnet
School, Tampa, FL

Jacque Quick
Walter Williams High School,
Burlington, NC

Robert Glenn Reynolds
Hillman Middle School,
Youngstown, OH

Stacy Rinehart
Lufkin Road Middle School,
Apex, NC

Theresa Short
Abbott Middle School,
Fayetteville, NC

Rita Slivka
Alexander Hamilton Middle School,
Cleveland, OH

Marie Sofsak
B F Stanton Middle School,
Alliance, OH

Nancy Stubbs
Sweetwater Union Unified School District,
Chula Vista, CA

Sharon Stull
Quail Hollow Middle School,
Charlotte, NC

Donna Taylor
Okeeheelee Middle School,
West Palm Beach, FL

Sandi Thompson
Harding Middle School,
Lakewood, OH

Lori Walker
Audubon Middle School & Magnet Center,
Los Angeles, CA

Teacher Lab Evaluators

Andrew Boy
W.E.B. DuBois Academy,
Cincinnati, OH

Jill Brimm-Byrne
Albany Park Academy,
Chicago, IL

Gwen Broestl
Luis Munoz Marin Middle School,
Cleveland, OH

Al Brofman
Tehipite Middle School,
Fresno, CA

Michael A. Burstein
The Rashi School,
Newton, MA

Trudi Coutts
Madison Middle School,
Naperville, IL

Jenifer Cox
Sylvan Middle School,
Citrus Heights, CA

Larry Cwik
Madison Middle School,
Naperville, IL

Melissa Dupree
Lakeside Middle School,
Evans, GA

Carl Fechko
Luis Munoz Marin Middle School,
Cleveland, OH

Jennifer Donatelli
Kennedy Junior High School,
Lisle, IL

Paige Fullhart
Highland Middle School,
Libertyville, IL

Sue Hood
Glen Crest Middle School,
Glen Ellyn, IL

William Luzader
Plymouth Community Intermediate School,
Plymouth, MA

Ann Min
Beardsley Middle School,
Crystal Lake, IL

Aileen Mueller
Kennedy Junior High School,
Lisle, IL

Nancy Nega
Churchville Middle School,
Elmhurst, IL

Oscar Newman
Sumner Math and Science Academy,
Chicago, IL

Lynn Prichard
Booker T. Washington Middle Magnet
School, Tampa, FL

Jacque Quick
Walter Williams High School,
Burlington, NC

Stacy Rinehart
Lufkin Road Middle School,
Apex, NC

Seth Robey
Gwendolyn Brooks Middle School,
Oak Park, IL

Kevin Steele
Grissom Middle School,
Tinley Park, IL

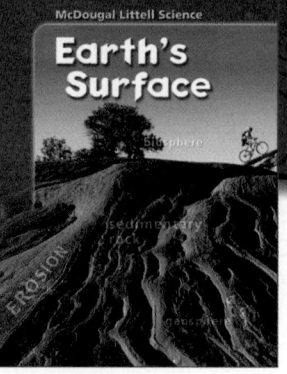

McDougal Littell Science

Earth's Surface

eEdition

UNIT A
Earth's Surface

Unit Features

1 Views of Earth Today — A6

the BIG idea

Modern technology has changed the way we view and map Earth.

2 Minerals — A40

the BIG idea

Minerals are basic building blocks of Earth.

Why can gold be separated from other minerals and rocks in a river? page A40

eEdition

UNIT B
Energy and the Changing Earth

How does heat from the Sun increase this giraffe's temperature?
page B34

eEdition

UNIT C
Waves, Sound, and Light

1 Waves   C6

the BIG idea

Waves transfer energy and interact in predictable ways.

2 Sound   C34

the BIG idea

Sound waves transfer energy through vibrations.

How is this guitar player producing sound? page C34

How does this
phone stay
connected?
page C70

3 Electromagnetic Waves

4 Light and Optics

Visual Highlights

eEdition

UNIT D
Ecology

Unit Features

*How many living and nonliving things can
you identify in this photograph? page D6*

How do living things interact? page D42

eEdition

UNIT E
Space Science

Unit Features

1 Exploring Space E6

the **BIG** idea

People develop and use technology to explore and study space.

2 Earth, Moon, and Sun E40

the **BIG** idea

Earth and the Moon move in predictable ways as they orbit the Sun.

What would you see if you looked at the Moon with a telescope? page E40

This image shows Jupiter with one of its large moons. How big are these objects compared with Earth? page E76

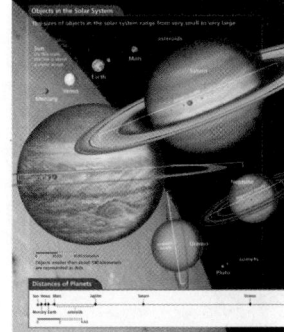

Features

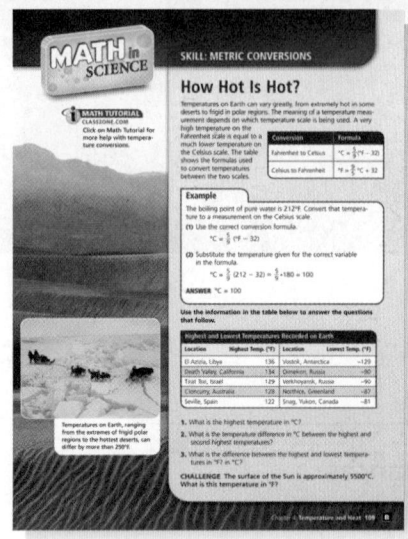

Math in Science

Think Science

Connecting Sciences

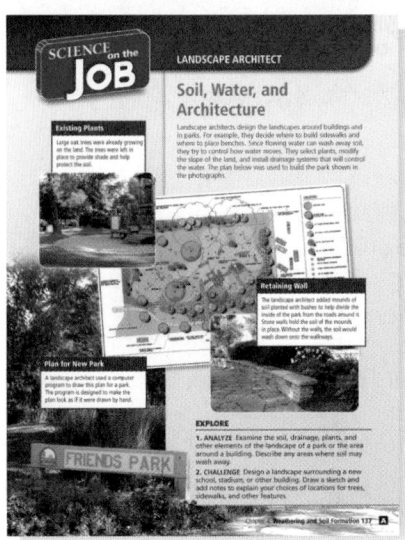

Science on the Job

Extreme Science

Frontiers in Science

Timelines in Science

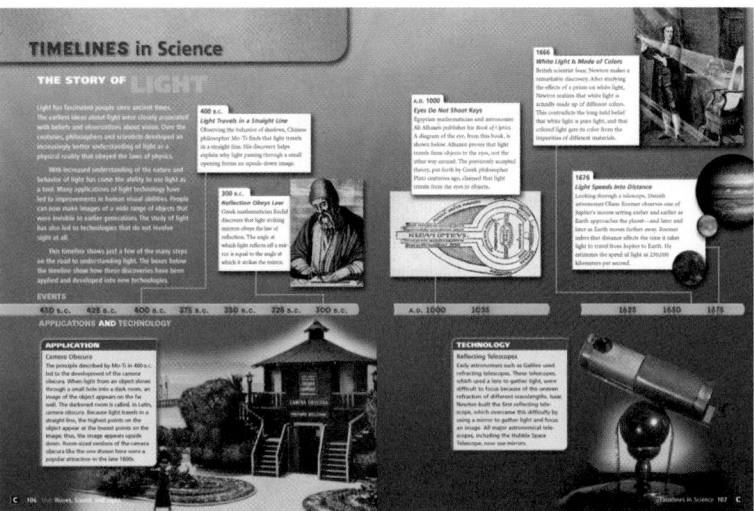

Internet Resources @ ClassZone.com

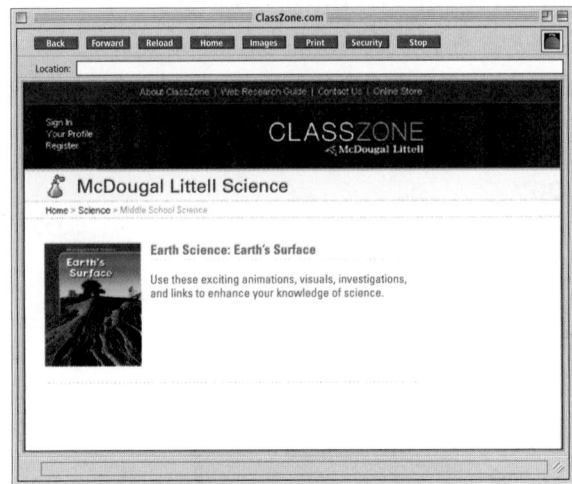

Simulations

Visualizations

Career Centers

Resource Centers

EARTH'S SURFACE
Resources for the following topics may be found at ClassZone.com: *Satellite Mapping, Map Projections, GIS, Precious Metals, Minerals, Gemstones, Meteorites and Impacts, Igneous Rocks, Sedimentary Rocks, Metamorphic Rocks, Earth System Research, Weathering, Soil, Mudflows, Rivers and Erosion, Glaciers.*

ENERGY AND THE CHANGING EARTH
Resources for the following topics may be found at ClassZone.com: *Kinetic Energy and Potential Energy, Electric Cars, Alternative Energy Sources, Temperature and Heat Research, Temperature and Temperature Scales, Thermal Energy, Earth's Interior, Effects of Plate Movement, Recent Earthquakes, Seismology, Tsunamis, Historic and Current Volcanic Eruptions, Effects of Volcanic Eruptions.*

WAVES, SOUND, AND LIGHT
Resources for the following topics may be found at ClassZone.com: *Waves, Wave Speed, Supersonic Aircraft, Sound Safety, Musical Instruments, The Electromagnetic Spectrum, Visible Light, Light Research, Optics, Microscopes and Telescopes, Lasers.*

ECOLOGY
Resources for the following topics may be found at ClassZone.com: *Prairie Ecosystems, Ecosystems, Cycles in Nature, Land and Aquatic Biomes, Symbiotic Relationships, Succession, Conservation Efforts, The Environment, Urban Expansion, Natural Resources, Ecosystem Recovery.*

SPACE SCIENCE
Resources for the following topics may be found at ClassZone.com: *Telescopes, Space Exploration, Seasons, Tides, Advances in Astronomy, Impact Craters, Moons of Giant Planets, Life Cycles of Stars, Galaxies, Galaxy Collisions.*

Math Tutorials

NSTA SciLinks

Codes for use with the NSTA SciLinks site may be found on every chapter opener.

Content Review

There is a content review for every chapter at ClassZone.com

Test Practice

There is a standardized test practice for every chapter at ClassZone.com

Explore the Big Idea

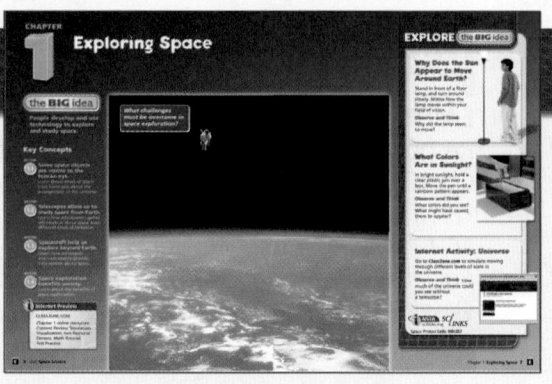

Chapter Opening Inquiry

Each chapter opens with hands-on explorations that introduce the chapter's Big Idea.

Chapter Investigations

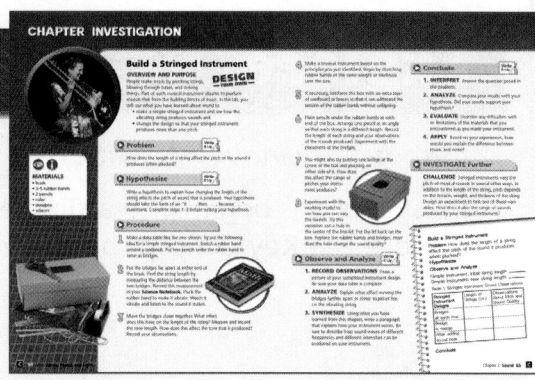

Full-Period Labs

The Chapter Investigations are in-depth labs that let you form and test a hypothesis, build a model, or sometimes design your own investigation.

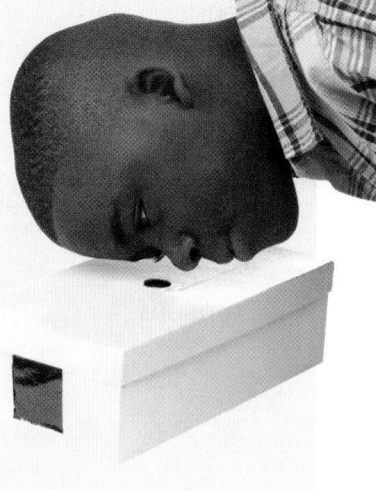

Explore

Introductory Inquiry Activities

Most sections begin with a simple activity that lets you
explore the Key Concept before you read the section.

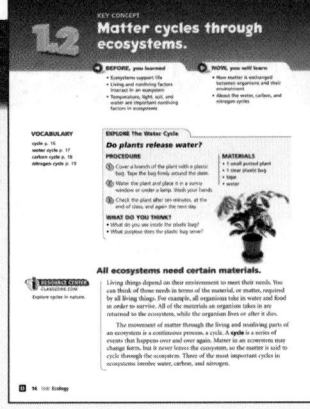

Investigate

Skill Labs

Each Investigate activity gives you a chance to practice a specific science skill related to the content that you're studying

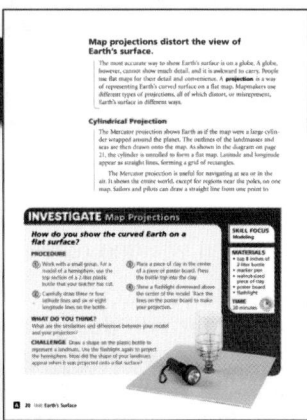

NORTH CAROLINA
Standard Course of Study

The chart below shows the goals and objectives of the North Carolina Standard Course of Study for your science course this year, and some of the places in *McDougal Littell Science* where you will find reading and practice to help you achieve those goals.

COMPETENCY GOAL 1
The learner will design and conduct investigations to demonstrate an understanding of scientific inquiry.

North Carolina Objectives	McDougal Littell Science
1.01 Identify and create questions and hypotheses that can be answered through scientific investigations.	**Chapter Investigations** and **Think Science** pages in each unit; Scientific Thinking Handbook, R3; Lab Handbook, R28–R35
1.02 Develop appropriate experimental procedures for: Given questions; Student-driven questions.	**Design Your Own Investigations** in each unit; Lab Handbook, R10–R35
1.03 Apply safety procedures in the laboratory and in field studies: Recognize potential hazards; Manipulate materials and equipment; Conduct appropriate procedures.	**Explores, Investigates,** and **Chapter Investigations** in each chapter; Lab Handbook, R10–R35
1.04 Analyze variables in scientific investigations: Identify dependent and independent; Use of a control; Manipulate; Describe relationships between; Define operationally.	**Chapter Investigations** and **Think Science** pages in each unit; Lab Handbook, R30–R35
1.05 Analyze evidence to: Explain observations; Make inferences and predictions; Develop the relationship between evidence and explanation.	**Explores, Investigates,** and **Chapter Investigations** in each chapter; Scientific Thinking Handbook, R2–R9; Lab Handbook, R10–R35; **North Carolina Handbook:** Natural Selection; Soil Science
1.06 Use mathematics to gather, organize, and present quantitative data resulting from scientific investigations: Measurement; Analysis of data; Graphing; Prediction models.	**Chapter Investigations** and **Math in Science** pages in each chapter; Lab Handbook, R10–R35; Math Handbook, R36–R44
1.07 Prepare models and/or computer simulations to: Test hypotheses; Evaluate how data fits.	**Explores, Investigates,** and **Chapter Investigations** in each unit; **Unit A *Earth's Surface*,** A13, A20, A32, A135
1.08 Use oral and written language to: • Communicate findings. • Defend conclusions of scientific investigations.	Unit Projects; **Timelines in Science; Chapter Investigations;** Chapter Reviews; **North Carolina Handbook:** Natural Selection; Soil Science
1.09 Use technologies and information systems to: Research; Gather and analyze data; Visualize data; Disseminate findings to others.	Explore the Big Idea in each chapter, Unit Projects, **Connecting Sciences, Think Science** in each unit
1.10 Analyze and evaluate information from a scientifically literate viewpoint by reading, hearing, and/or viewing: Scientific text; Articles; Events in the popular press.	**Frontiers in Science** features, *Scientific American* video segments, Internet resources at **ClassZone.com** and **NSTA SciLinks;** Scientific Thinking Handbook, R2–R9

COMPETENCY GOAL 2
The learner will demonstrate an understanding of technological design.

2.01 Explore evidence that "technology" has many definitions. • Artifact or hardware. • Methodology or technique. • System of production. • Social-technical system.	**The Nature of Technology** (pp. xl–xli) and **Frontiers in Science** and **Timelines in Science** features in each unit; **Unit A *Earth's Surface*,** 1.1, 1.4; **Unit B *Energy and the Changing Earth:*** 1.3, 2.3, 4.3; **Unit C *Waves, Sound, and Light:*** 2.4, 3.2, 4.4; **Unit D *Ecology,*** 3.3; **Unit E *Space Science*,** 1.2, 1.3, 1.4

2.02	Use information systems to: • Identify scientific needs, human needs, or problems that are subject to technological solution. • Locate resources to obtain and test ideas.	Resource Centers; Career Centers; **NSTA SciLinks**
2.03	**Evaluate technological designs for:** • Application of scientific principles. • Risks and benefits. • Constraints of design. • Consistent testing protocols.	**Unit A _Earth's Surface,_** Science on the Job **Unit B _Energy and the Changing Earth,_** 1.3, Chapter 2 Investigation; Think Science; 4.3; Chapter 4 Investigation **Unit C _Waves, Sound, and Light,_** 2.4, Chapter 2 Investigation; 3.2; Think Science; 4.4 **Unit D _Ecology,_** 3.3 **Unit E _Space Science,_** 1.4
2.04	**Apply tenets of technological design to make informed consumer decisions about:** Products; Systems; Processes.	**Unit B _Energy and the Changing Earth,_** Think Science; Chapter 4 Investigation **Unit C _Waves, Sound, and Light,_** 3.3 Investigate

COMPETENCY GOAL 3
The learner will build an understanding of the geological cycles, forces, processes, and agents which shape the lithosphere.

3.01	**Evaluate the forces that shape the lithosphere including:** Crustal plate movement; Folding and faulting; Deposition; Volcanic Activity; Earthquakes.	**Unit A _Earth's Surface_** **Unit B _Energy and the Changing Earth_** **North Carolina Handbook:** Rocks and Minerals
3.02	**Examine earthquake and volcano patterns.**	**Unit B _Energy and the Changing Earth_**
3.03	**Explain the model for the interior of the earth.**	**Unit A _Earth's Surface_** **Unit B _Energy and the Changing Earth_**
3.04	**Describe the processes which form and the uses of earth materials.** Rock cycle; Minerals; Characteristics of rocks; Economic use of rocks and minerals; Value of gems and precious metals; Common gems, minerals, precious metals and rocks found in N.C.	**Unit A _Earth's Surface_** **North Carolina Handbook:** Rocks and Minerals
3.05	**Analyze soil properties that can be observed and measured to predict soil quality:** Color; Horizon profile; Infiltration; Soil temperature; Structure; Consistency; Texture; Particle size; pH; Fertility; Soil moisture.	**Unit A _Earth's Surface_** **North Carolina Handbook:** Soil Science
3.06	**Evaluate ways in which human activities have affected Earth's pedosphere and the measures taken to control the impact:** Vegetative cover; Agriculture; Soil as a vector; Land use; Nutrient balance.	**Unit A _Earth's Surface_** **Unit D _Ecology_** **North Carolina Handbook:** Soil Science, Designed Systems
3.07	**Assess use of technology and information systems in monitoring lithospheric phenomenon.**	**Unit A _Earth's Surface_**
3.08	**Conclude that the good health of environments and organisms requires:** Monitoring of the pedosphere; Taking steps to maintain soil quality; Stewardship.	**Unit A _Earth's Surface_** **Unit D _Ecology_** **North Carolina Handbook:** Soil Science, Photosynthesis

COMPETENCY GOAL 4
The learner will investigate the cycling of matter.

4.01	**Describe the flow of energy and matter in natural systems:** • Energy flows through ecosystems in one direction, from the sun through producers to consumers to decomposers. • Matter is transferred from one organism to another and between organisms and their environments. • Water, nitrogen, carbon dioxide, and oxygen are substances cycled between the living and non-living environments.	**Unit A** *Earth's Surface* **Unit B** *Energy and the Changing Earth* **Unit D** *Ecology* **North Carolina Handbook:** Photosynthesis
4.02	**Evaluate the significant role of decomposers.**	**Unit D** *Ecology*
4.03	**Examine evidence that green plants make food.** • Photosynthesis is a process carried on by green plants and other organisms with chlorophyll. • During photosynthesis, light energy is converted into stored energy which the plant, in turn, uses to carry out its life processes.	**Unit D** *Ecology* **North Carolina Handbook:** Photosynthesis
4.04	**Evaluate the significance of photosynthesis to other organisms:** • The major source of atmospheric oxygen is photosynthesis. • Carbon dioxide is removed from the atmosphere and oxygen is released during photosynthesis. • Green plants are the producers of food that is used directly or indirectly by consumers.	**Unit D** *Ecology* **North Carolina Handbook:** Photosynthesis
4.05	**Evaluate designed systems for ability to enable growth of certain plants and animals.**	**Unit E** *Space Science* **North Carolina Handbook:** Designed Systems

COMPETENCY GOAL 5
The learner will build understanding of the Solar System.

5.01	**Analyze the components and cycles of the solar system including:** Sun; Planets and moons; Asteroids and meteors; Comets; Phases; Seasons; Day/year; Eclipses.	**Unit E** *Space Science*
5.02	**Compare and contrast the Earth to other planets in terms of:** Size; Relative distance from the sun; Composition; Ability to support life.	**Unit E** *Space Science*
5.03	**Relate the influence of the sun and the moon's orbit to the gravitational effects produced on Earth:** Solar storms; Tides.	**Unit E** *Space Science*
5.04	**Describe space explorations and the understandings gained from them including:** NASA; Technologies used to explore space; Historic timeline; Apollo mission to the moon; Space Shuttle; International Space Station; Future goals.	**Unit E** *Space Science*
5.05	**Describe the setting of the solar system in the universe including:** Galaxy; Size; The uniqueness of Earth.	**Unit E** *Space Science*
5.06	**Analyze the spin-off benefits generated by space exploration technology including:** Medical; Materials; Transportation; Processes; Future research.	**Unit E** *Space Science*

COMPETENCY GOAL 6

The learner will conduct investigations and examine models and devices to build an understanding of the characteristics of energy transfer and/or transformation.

6.01	Determine how convection and radiation transfer energy.	Unit B *Energy and the Changing Earth* Unit C *Waves, Sound, and Light* Unit E *Space Science*
6.02	Analyze heat flow through materials or across space from warm objects to cooler objects until both objects are at equilibrium.	Unit B *Energy and the Changing Earth*
6.03	Analyze sound as an example that vibrating materials generate waves that transfer energy. Frequency; Amplitude; Loudness; How sound travels through different material; Form and function of the human ear.	Unit C *Waves, Sound, and Light*
6.04	Evaluate data for qualitative and quantitative relationships associated with energy transfer and/or transformation.	Unit B *Energy and the Changing Earth* Unit C *Waves, Sound, and Light*
6.05	Analyze the physical interactions of light and matter: Absorption; Scattering; Color perception; Form and function of the human eye.	Unit C *Waves, Sound, and Light*
6.06	Analyze response to heat to determine the suitability of materials for use in technological design: Conduction; Contraction; Expansion.	Unit B *Energy and the Changing Earth*
6.07	Analyze the Law of Conservation of Energy: • Conclude that energy cannot be created or destroyed, but only changed from one form into another. • Conclude that the amount of energy stays the same, although within the process some energy is always converted to heat. • Some systems transform energy with less loss of heat than others.	Unit B *Energy and the Changing Earth*

COMPETENCY GOAL 7

The learner will conduct investigations and use technologies and information systems to build an understanding of population dynamics.

7.01	Describe ways in which organisms interact with each other and with non-living parts of the environment: Coexistence/Cooperation/Competition; Symbiosis; Mutual dependence.	Unit D *Ecology*
7.02	Investigate factors that determine the growth and survival of organisms including: Light; Temperature range; Mineral availability; Soil/rock type; Water; Energy.	Unit B *Earth's Surface* Unit D *Ecology* North Carolina Handbook: Designed Systems
7.03	Explain how changes in habitat may affect organisms.	Unit D *Ecology*
7.04	Evaluate data related to human population growth, along with problems and solutions: Waste disposal; Food supplies; Resource availability; Transportation; Socio-economic patterns.	Unit D *Ecology*
7.05	Examine evidence that overpopulation by any species impacts the environment.	Unit D *Ecology*
7.06	Investigate processes which over long periods of time have resulted in the diversity of plant and animal life today: Natural selection; Adaptation.	North Carolina Handbook: Natural Selection

Introducing Science

Scientists are curious. Since ancient times, they have been asking and answering questions about the world around them. Scientists are also very suspicious of the answers they get. They carefully collect evidence and test their answers many times before accepting an idea as correct.

In this book you will see how scientific knowledge keeps growing and changing as scientists ask new questions and rethink what was known before. The following sections will help get you started.

What Is Science?

Science is the systematic study of all of nature, from particles too small to see to the human body to the entire universe. However, no individual scientist can study all of nature. Therefore science is divided into many different fields. For example, some scientists are biologists, others are geologists, and still others are chemists or astronomers.

All the different scientific fields can be grouped into three broad categories: life science, earth science, and physical science.

- Life science focuses on the study of living things; it includes the fields of cell biology, botany, ecology, zoology, and human biology.
- Earth science focuses on the study of our planet and its place in the universe; it includes the fields of geology, oceanography, meteorology, and astronomy.
- Physical science focuses on the study of what things are made of and how they change; it includes the fields of chemistry and physics.

North Carolina Science Grade 6

This course pulls together units from the different categories of science to give you a broad picture of how scientists study Earth and space. For example, different kinds of scientists might study soil from different points of view. You will learn in Unit A that a geologist might study how soil forms. In Unit D, you will notice that an ecologist might focus on soil as part of an ecosystem—all the living and nonliving things that interact in the same habitat. Another example is the study of electromagnetic waves. In Unit C, you'll learn how physicists explain the way electromagnetic waves work. In Unit E, you'll read how astronomers use electromagnetic waves to study the universe.

Even though science has many different fields, all scientists have similar ways of thinking and approaching their work. For example, scientists use instruments as well as their minds to look for patterns in nature. Scientists also try to find explanations for the patterns they discover. As you study each unit, you will in part focus on the patterns that scientists have found within that particular specialized branch. At the same time, as you move from one unit to another, you will be blending knowledge from the different branches of science together to form a more general understanding of our universe.

Unifying Principles

As you learn, it helps to have a big picture of science as a framework for new information. McDougal Littell Science has identified unifying principles from each of the three broad categories of science: life science, earth science, and physical science. These unifying principles are described on the following pages. However, keep in mind that the broad categories of science do not have fixed borders. Earth science shades into life science, which shades into physical science, which shades back into earth science.

> ## the BIG idea
>
> Each chapter begins with a big idea. Keep in mind that each big idea relates to one or more of the unifying principles.

What Is Life Science?

Life science is the study of the great variety of living things that have lived or now live on Earth. Life science includes the study of the characteristics and needs that all living things have in common. It is also a study of changes—both daily changes and those that take place over millions of years. Probably most important, in studying life science you will explore the many ways that all living things—including you—depend on Earth and its resources.

A moose, like any other living thing, interacts with its environment. Eating is one obvious but important interaction. Food provides energy as well as most of the materials a moose needs to survive.

UNIFYING PRINCIPLES of Life Science

All living things share common characteristics.

Despite the variety of living things on Earth, there are certain characteristics common to all. The basic unit of life is the **cell.** Any living thing, whether it has one cell or many, is described as an **organism.** All organisms are characterized by

- organization—the way that an organism's body is arranged
- growth—the way that an organism grows and develops over its lifetime
- reproduction—the way that an organism produces offspring like itself
- response—the ways an organism interacts with its surroundings

All living things share common needs.

All living things have three basic needs: energy, materials, and living space. Energy enables an organism to carry out all the activities of life. The body of an organism needs water and other materials. Water is important because most of the chemical reactions in a cell take place in water. Organisms also require other materials. Plants, for example, need carbon dioxide to make energy-rich sugars, and most living things need oxygen. Living space is the environment in which an organism gets the energy and materials it needs.

Living things meet their needs through interactions with the environment.

The **environment** is everything that surrounds a living thing. This includes other organisms as well as nonliving factors, such as rainfall, sunlight, and soil. Any exchange of energy or materials between the living and nonliving parts of the environment is an **interaction.** Plants interact with the environment by capturing energy from the Sun and changing that energy into chemical energy that is stored in sugar. Animals can interact with plants by eating the plants and getting energy from the sugars that the plants have made.

The types and numbers of living things change over time.

A **species** is a group of living things so closely related that they can produce offspring together that can also reproduce. Scientists have named about 1.4 million different species. The great variety of species on Earth today is called **biodiversity.** Different species have different characteristics, or **adaptations,** that allow the members of that species to get their needs met in a particular environment. Over the millions of years that life has existed on Earth, new species have come into being and others have disappeared. The disappearance of a species is called **extinction.** Fossils of now extinct organisms is one way that scientists have of seeing how living things have changed over time.

What Is Earth Science?

Earth science is the study of Earth's interior, its rocks and soil, its oceans, its atmosphere, and outer space. For many years, scientists studied each of these topics separately. They learned many important things. More recently, however, scientists have looked more and more at the connections among the different parts of Earth—its oceans, atmosphere, living things, and rocks and soil. Scientists have also been learning more about other planets in our solar system, as well as stars and galaxies far away. Through these studies they have learned much about Earth and its place in the universe.

The universe is everything that exists, and everything in the universe is governed by the same physical laws. The same laws govern the stars shown in this picture and the page on which the picture is printed.

UNIFYING PRINCIPLES of Earth Science

Heat energy inside Earth and radiation from the Sun provide energy for Earth's processes.

Energy is the ability to cause change. All of Earth's processes need energy to occur. Earth's interior is very hot. This heat energy moves up to Earth's surface, where it provides the energy to build mountains, cause earthquakes, and make volcanoes erupt. Earth also receives energy from the Sun as **radiation**—energy that travels across distances in the form of certain types of waves. Energy from the Sun causes winds to blow, ocean currents to flow, and water to move from the ground to the atmosphere and back again.

Physical forces, such as gravity, affect the movement of all matter on Earth and throughout the universe.

What do the stars in a galaxy, the planet Earth, and your body have in common? For one thing, they are all made of matter. **Matter** is anything that has mass and takes up space. Rocks are matter. You are matter. Even the air around you is matter. Everything in the universe is also affected by the same physical forces. A **force** is a push or a pull. Forces affect how matter moves everywhere in the universe.

Matter and energy move among Earth's rocks and soil, atmosphere, waters, and living things.

Think of Earth as a huge system, or an organized group of parts that work together. Within this system, matter and energy move among the different parts. The four major parts of Earth's system are the

- **atmosphere,** which includes all the air surrounding the solid planet
- **geosphere,** which includes all of Earth's rocks and minerals, as well as Earth's interior
- **hydrosphere,** which includes oceans, rivers, lakes, and every drop of water on or under Earth's surface
- **biosphere,** which includes all the living things on Earth

Earth has changed over time and continues to change.

Events are always changing Earth's surface. Some events, such as the building or wearing away of mountains, occur over millions of years. Others, such as earthquakes, occur within seconds. A change can affect a small area or even the entire planet

What Is Physical Science?

Physical science is the study of what things are made of and how they change. It combines the study of both physics and chemistry. Physics is the study of matter, energy, and forces, and it includes such topics as motion, light, and electricity and magnetism. Chemistry is the study of the structure and properties of matter. It focuses especially on how substances change into different substances.

Like the tiles that make up this picture, the particles that make up all substances combine to make structures that we can see. Unlike these tiles, the individual particles themselves are too small to see.

UNIFYING PRINCIPLES of Physical Science

Matter is made of particles too small to see.

The tiny particles that make up all matter are called **atoms.** Just how tiny are atoms? They are far too small to see even through a powerful microscope. In fact, an atom is about a million times smaller than the period at the end of this sentence. There are more than 100 basic kinds of matter called **elements.** The atoms of any element are all alike but different from the atoms of any other element. Everything around you is made of atoms and combinations of atoms.

Matter changes form and moves from place to place.

You see objects moving and changing all around you. All changes in matter are the result of atoms moving and combining in different ways. Regardless of how much matter may change, however, under ordinary conditions it is never created or destroyed. Matter that seems to disappear merely changes into another form of matter.

Energy changes from one form to another, but it cannot be created or destroyed.

All the changes you see around you depend on energy. Energy, in fact, means the ability to cause change. Using energy means changing energy. But energy is never created or destroyed, no matter how often it changes form. This fact is known as the **law of conservation of energy.** The energy you may think you've lost when a match has burned out has only been changed into other forms of energy that are less useful to you.

Physical forces affect the movement of all matter on Earth and throughout the universe.

A **force** is a push or a pull. Every time you push or pull an object, you are applying a force to that object, whether or not the object moves. There are several forces—several pushes or pulls—acting on you right now. All these forces are necessary for you to do the things you do, even sitting and reading. **Gravity** keeps you on the ground. Gravity also keeps the Moon moving around Earth, and Earth moving around the Sun. **Friction** is the force that opposes motion. The friction between the bottoms of your shoes and the floor makes it possible for you to walk without slipping. Too much friction between a heavy box and the floor makes it hard to push the box across the floor.

The Nature of Science

You may think of science as a body of knowledge or a collection of facts. More important, however, science is an active process that involves certain ways of looking at the world.

Scientific Habits of Mind

Scientists are curious. They ask questions. A scientist who finds an unusual rock by the side of a river would ask questions such as, "Did this rock form in this area?" or "Did this rock form elsewhere and get moved here?" Questions like these make a scientist want to investigate.

Scientists are observant. They look closely at the world around them. A scientist who studies rocks can learn a lot about a rock just by picking it up, looking at its color, and feeling how heavy it is.

Scientists are creative. They draw on what they know to form possible explanations for a pattern, an event, or an interesting phenomenon that they have observed. Then scientists put together a plan for testing their ideas.

Scientists are skeptical. Scientists don't accept an explanation or answer unless it is based on evidence and logical reasoning. They continually question their own conclusions as well as the conclusions suggested by other scientists. Scientists only trust evidence that can be confirmed by other people or other methods.

Scientists use seismographs to observe and measure vibrations that move through the ground.

This scientist is collecting a sample of melted rock from a hot lava flow in Hawaii.

Science Processes at Work

You can think of science as a continuous cycle of asking and seeking answers to questions about the world. Although there are many processes that scientists use, all scientists typically do the following:

- Observe and ask a question
- Determine what is known
- Investigate
- Interpret results
- Share results

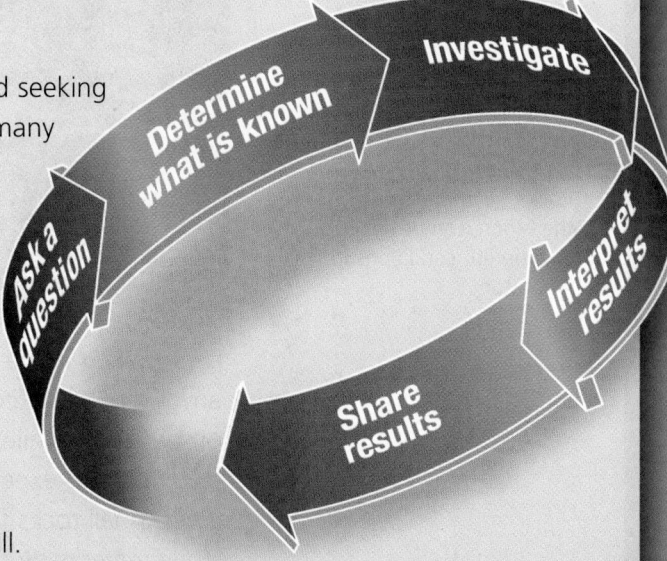

Observe and Ask a Question

It may surprise you that asking questions is an important skill. A scientific investigation may start when a scientist asks a question. Perhaps scientists observe an event or a process that they don't understand, or perhaps answering one question leads to another.

Determine What Is Known

When beginning an inquiry, scientists find out what is already known about a question. They study results from other scientific investigations, read journals, and talk with other scientists. The scientist who is trying to figure out where an unusual rock came from will study maps that show what types of rocks are already known to be in the area where the rock was found.

Investigate

Investigating is the process of collecting evidence. Two important ways of doing this are experimenting and observing.

An **experiment** is an organized procedure to study something under controlled conditions. For example, the scientist who found the rock by the river might notice that it is lighter in color where it is chipped. The scientist might design an experiment to determine why the rock is a different color on the inside. The scientist could break off a small piece of the inside of the rock and heat it up to see if it becomes the same color as the outside. The scientist would need to use a piece of the same rock that is being studied. A different rock might react differently to heat.

A scientist may use photography to study fast events, such as multiple flashes of lightning.

Rocks, such as this one from the Moon, can be subjected to different conditions in a laboratory.

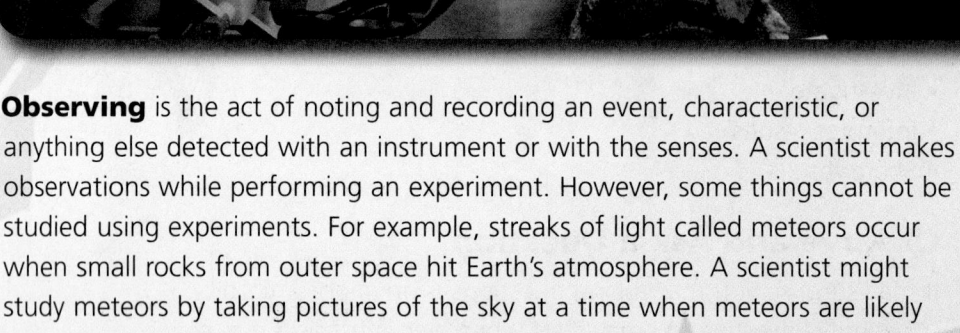

Observing is the act of noting and recording an event, characteristic, or anything else detected with an instrument or with the senses. A scientist makes observations while performing an experiment. However, some things cannot be studied using experiments. For example, streaks of light called meteors occur when small rocks from outer space hit Earth's atmosphere. A scientist might study meteors by taking pictures of the sky at a time when meteors are likely to occur.

Forming hypotheses and making predictions are two other skills involved in scientific investigations. A **hypothesis** is a tentative explanation for an observation or a scientific problem that can be tested by further investigation. For example, the scientist might make the following hypothesis about the rock from the beach:

The rock is a meteorite, which is a rock that fell to the ground from outer space. The outside of the rock changed color because it was heated up from passing through Earth's atmosphere.

A **prediction** is an expectation of what will be observed or what will happen. To test the hypothesis that the rock's outside is black because it is a meteorite, the scientist might predict that a close examination of the rock will show that it has many characteristics in common with rocks that are already known to be meteorites.

Interpret Results

As scientists investigate, they analyze their evidence, or data, and begin to draw conclusions. **Analyzing data** involves looking at the evidence gathered through observations or experiments and trying to identify any patterns that might exist in the data. Scientists often need to make additional observations or perform more experiments before they are sure of their conclusions. Many times scientists make new predictions or revise their hypotheses.

Scientists use computers to gather and interpret data.

Scientists make images such as this computer drawing of a landscape to help share their results with others.

Share Results

An important part of scientific investigation is sharing results of experiments. Scientists read and publish in journals and attend conferences to communicate with other scientists around the world. Sharing data and procedures gives scientists a way to test each others' results. They also share results with the public through newspapers, television, and other media.

The Nature of Technology

When you think of technology, you may think of cars, computers, and cell phones. Imagine having no refrigerator or radio. It's difficult to think of a world without the products of what we call technology. Technology, however, is more than just devices that make our daily activities easier. Technology is the process of using scientific knowledge to design solutions to real-world problems.

Science and Technology

Science and technology go hand in hand. Each depends upon the other. Even a device as simple as a thermometer is designed using knowledge of the ways different materials respond to changes in temperature. In turn, thermometers have allowed scientists to learn more about the world. Greater knowledge of how materials respond to changes in temperature helped engineers to build items such as refrigerators. They have also built thermometers that could be read automatically by computers. New technologies lead to new scientific knowledge and new scientific knowledge leads to even better technologies.

The Process of Technological Design

The process of technological design involves many choices. What, for example, should be done to protect the residents of an area prone to severe storms such as tornadoes and hurricanes? Build stronger homes that can withstand the winds? Try to develop a way to detect the storms long before they occur? Or learn more about hurricanes in order to find new ways to protect people from the dangers? The steps people take to solve the problem depend a great deal on what they already know about the problem as well as what can reasonably be done. As you learn about the steps in the process of technological design, think about the different choices that could be made at each step.

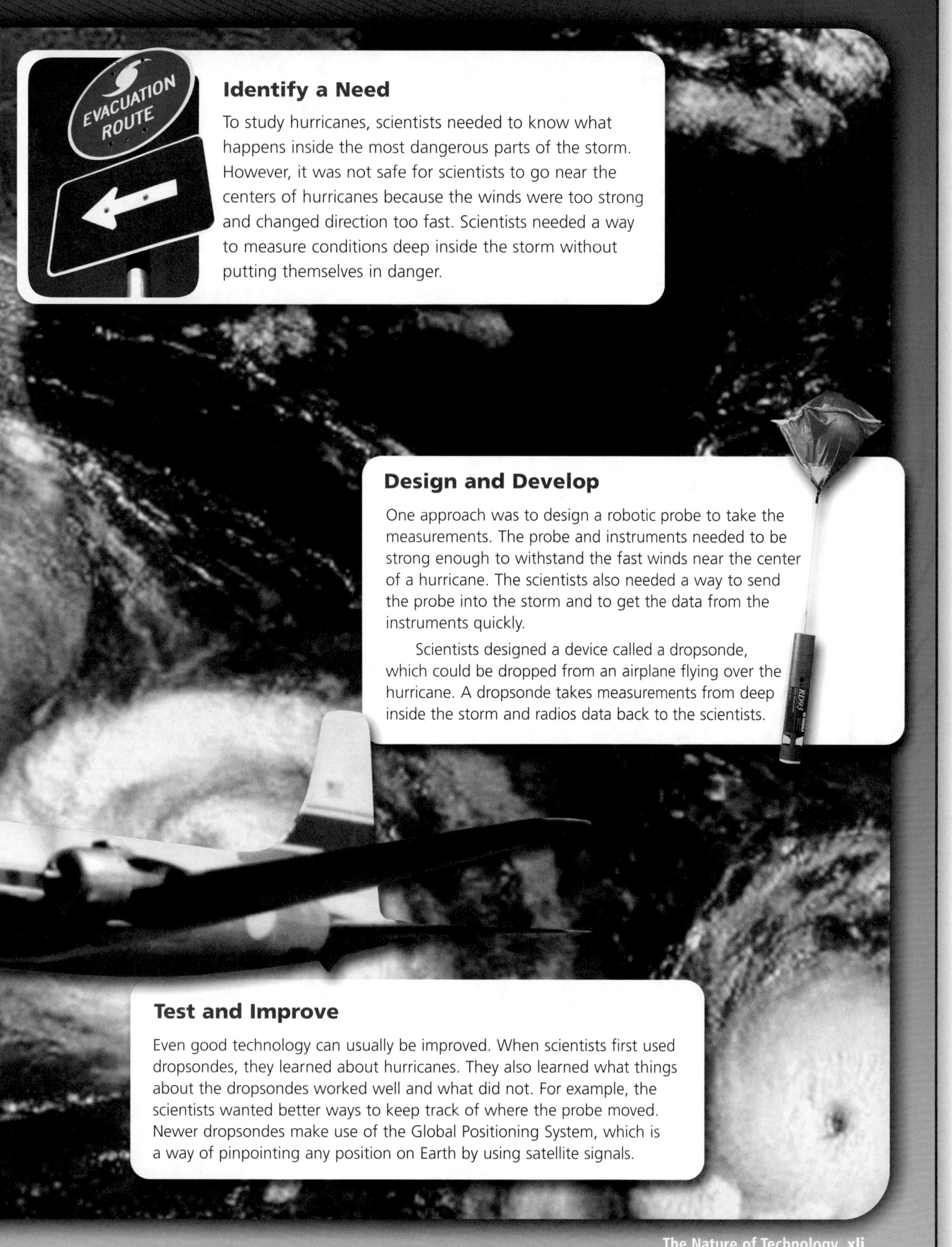

Identify a Need

To study hurricanes, scientists needed to know what happens inside the most dangerous parts of the storm. However, it was not safe for scientists to go near the centers of hurricanes because the winds were too strong and changed direction too fast. Scientists needed a way to measure conditions deep inside the storm without putting themselves in danger.

Design and Develop

One approach was to design a robotic probe to take the measurements. The probe and instruments needed to be strong enough to withstand the fast winds near the center of a hurricane. The scientists also needed a way to send the probe into the storm and to get the data from the instruments quickly.

Scientists designed a device called a dropsonde, which could be dropped from an airplane flying over the hurricane. A dropsonde takes measurements from deep inside the storm and radios data back to the scientists.

Test and Improve

Even good technology can usually be improved. When scientists first used dropsondes, they learned about hurricanes. They also learned what things about the dropsondes worked well and what did not. For example, the scientists wanted better ways to keep track of where the probe moved. Newer dropsondes make use of the Global Positioning System, which is a way of pinpointing any position on Earth by using satellite signals.

Using McDougal Littell Science

Reading Text and Visuals

This book is organized to help you learn. Use these boxed pointers as a path to help you learn and remember the **Big Ideas** and **Key Concepts**.

Take notes.

Use the strategies on the **Getting Ready to Learn** page.

Read the Big Idea.

As you read **Key Concepts** for the chapter, relate them to **the Big Idea**.

CHAPTER 2 Min

the **BIG** idea

Minerals are basic building blocks of Earth.

Key Concepts

SECTION 2.1
Minerals are all around us.
Learn about the characteristics all minerals share.

SECTION 2.2
A mineral is identified by its properties.
Learn how to identify minerals by observing and testing their properties.

SECTION 2.3
Minerals are valuable resources.
Learn how minerals form, how they are mined, and how they are used.

Internet Preview

CLASSZONE.COM
Chapter 2 online resources: Content Review, Visualization, three Resource Centers, Math Tutorial, Test Practice

A **40** Unit: Earth's Surface

CHAPTER 2
Getting Ready to Learn

CONCEPT REVIEW

- Earth has four main layers: crust, mantle, outer core, and inner core.
- Matter exists in the forms of gas, liquid, and solid.
- People use maps to show many different features of Earth.

VOCABULARY REVIEW

atom *See Glossary.*
geosphere p. 12

CONTENT REVIEW
CLASSZONE.COM
Review concepts and vocabulary.

TAKING NOTES

SUPPORTING MAIN IDEAS

Make a chart to show each main idea and the information that supports it. Copy each blue heading. Below each heading, add supporting information, such as reasons, explanations, and examples.

VOCABULARY STRATEGY

Place each vocabulary term at the center of a **description wheel**. On the spokes write some words explaining it.

See the Note-Taking Handbook on pages R45–R51.

SCIENCE NOTEBOOK

Minerals have four characteristics.

Minerals form naturally.

All minerals are solids.

Each mineral is always made of the sam element or elements.

All minerals have crystal structures.

atoms joined in a repeating 3-D pattern

formed by all minerals

CRYSTAL

A **42** Unit: Earth's Surface

Read each heading.

See how it fits into the outline of the chapter.

KEY CONCEPT

2.1 Minerals are all around us.

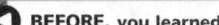

◀ **BEFORE,** you learned

- Earth is made of layers
- Earth's outermost rocky layer is the crust

▶ **NOW,** you will learn

- What the characteristics of minerals are
- How minerals are classified into groups
- Which mineral group is most common

Remember what you know.

Think about concepts you learned earlier and preview what you'll learn now.

VOCABULARY

mineral p. 43
element p. 45
crystal p. 46

EXPLORE Minerals

What are some characteristics of a mineral?

PROCEDURE

① Sprinkle some table salt on a sheet of colored paper. Look at a few grains of the salt through a magnifying glass. Then rub a few grains between your fingers.

② In your notebook, describe all the qualities of the salt that you observe.

③ Examine the rock salt in the same way and describe its qualities in your notebook. How do the two differ?

MATERIALS
- colored paper
- table salt
- rock salt
- magnifying glass

WHAT DO YOU THINK?
Salt is a mineral. From your observations of salt, what do you think are some characteristics of minerals?

Try the activities.

They will introduce you to science concepts.

Minerals have four characteristics.

You use minerals all the time. Every time you turn on a microwave oven or a TV, you depend on minerals. The copper in the wires that carry electricity to the device is a mineral. Table salt, or halite (HAYL-YT), is another mineral that you use in your everyday life.

Minerals have four characteristics. A **mineral** is a substance that

- forms in nature
- is a solid
- has a definite chemical makeup
- has a crystal structure

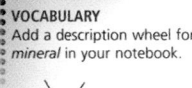

VOCABULARY
Add a description wheel for *mineral* in your notebook.

Learn the vocabulary.

Take notes on each term.

Chapter 2: **Minerals** 43 **A**

Reading Text and Visuals

Study the visuals.

- Read the title.
- Read all labels and captions.
- Figure out what the picture is showing. Notice colors, arrows, and lines.

Answer the questions.

Check Your Reading questions will help you remember what you read.

READING TiP

Proportions show relationships between amounts. For example, a quartz crystal always has two oxygen atoms for every silicon atom.

Read one paragraph at a time.

Look for a topic sentence that explains the main idea of the paragraph. Figure out how the details relate to that idea. One paragraph might have several important ideas; you may have to reread to understand.

READING TiP

Molten rock refers to rock that has become so hot that it has melted.

A 44 Unit: **Earth's Surface**

Minerals in Rocks

Most rocks are made up of minerals.

Quartz

Feldspar

Mica

granite

This piece of granite contains the minerals quartz, feldspar, and mica.

You might think that minerals and rocks are the same things. But a mineral must have the four characteristics listed on page 43. A rock has only two of these characteristics—it is a solid and it forms naturally. A rock usually contains two or more types of minerals.

Two samples of the same type of rock may vary greatly in the amounts of different minerals they contain. Minerals, however, are always made up of the same materials in the same proportions. A ruby is a mineral. Therefore, a ruby found in India has the same makeup as a ruby found in Australia.

CHECK YOUR READING How are minerals different from rocks?

Formed in Nature

Minerals are formed by natural processes. Every type of mineral can form in nature by processes that do not involve living organisms. As you will read, a few minerals can also be produced by organisms as part of their shells or bones.

Minerals form in many ways. The mineral halite, which is used as table salt, forms when water evaporates in a hot, shallow part of the ocean, leaving behind the salt it contained. Many types of minerals, including the ones in granite, develop when molten rock cools. Talc, a mineral that can be used to make baby powder, forms deep in Earth as high pressure and temperature cause changes in solid rock.

Doing Labs

To understand science, you have to see it in action. Doing labs helps you understand how things really work.

① Read the entire lab first.

② Follow the procedure.

③ Record the data.

CHAPTER INVESTIGATION

Mineral Identification

OVERVIEW AND PURPOSE In this activity, you will observe and perform tests on minerals. Then you will compare your observations to a mineral identification key.

▶ Procedure

1. Make a data table like the one shown in the notebook on the next page.

2. You will examine and identify five minerals. Get a numbered mineral sample from the mineral set. Record the number of your sample in your table.

3. First, observe the sample. Note the color and the luster of the sample. Write your observations in your table. In the row labeled "Luster," write *metallic* if the mineral appears shiny like metal. Write *nonmetallic* if the sample does not look like metal. For example, it may look glassy, pearly, or dull.

   step 3

4. Observe the sample through the hand lens. Look to see any signs of how the crystals in the mineral broke. If it appears that the crystals have broken along straight lines, put a check in the row labeled "Cleavage." If it appears that the sample has fractured, put a check in the appropriate row of your table.

   step 4

5. **CAUTION: Keep the streak plate on your desktop or table while you are doing the streak test. A broken streak plate can cause serious cuts.** Rub the mineral sample on the streak plate. If the sample does not leave a mark, the mineral is harder than the streak plate. Write *no* in the row labeled "Streak." If the sample does leave a mark on the streak plate, write the color of the streak in that row.

   step 5

MATERIALS
- numbered mineral samples
- hand lens
- streak plate
- copper penny
- steel file
- magnet
- dilute hydrochloric acid
- eyedropper
- Mohs scale
- Mineral Identification Key

6. Test each sample for its hardness on the Mohs scale. Try to scratch the sample with each of these items in order: a fingernail, a copper penny, and a steel file. In the Mohs scale, find the hardness number of the object that first scratches the sample. Write in the table that the mineral's hardness value is between that of the hardest item that did not scratch the sample and that of the item that did scratch it.

7. Test the sample with the magnet. If the magnet is attracted to the sample, put a check in the row labeled "Magnetic."

   step 7

8. Repeat steps 2 through 7 for each of the other numbered samples.

▶ Observe and Analyze   *Write It Up*

1. **INTERPRET DATA** Use the Mineral Identification Key and the information in your data table to identify your samples. Write the names of the minerals in your table.

2. **COLLECT DATA CAUTION: Before doing the acid test, put on your safety glasses, protective gloves, and lab apron. Acids can cause burns.** If you identified one of the samples as a carbonate mineral, such as calcite, you can check your identification with the acid test. Use the eyedropper to put a few drops of dilute hydrochloric acid on the mineral. If the acid bubbles, the sample is a carbonate.

▶ Conclude   *Write It Up*

1. **COMPARE AND CONTRAST** How are the minerals calcite and halite alike? Which property can you use to test whether a sample is calcite or halite?

2. **INTERPRET** Look at the data in your table. Name any minerals that you could identify on the basis of a single property.

3. **APPLY** Examine a piece of granite rock. On the basis of your examination of granite and your observations of the samples, try to determine what the light-colored, translucent mineral in the granite is and what the flaky, darker mineral is.

▶ INVESTIGATE Further

Specific gravity is another property used to identify minerals. The specific gravity of a mineral is determined by comparing the mineral's density with the density of water.

Find the specific gravity of an unknown mineral chosen from your teacher's samples. Attach your mineral with a string to a spring scale. Record its mass and label this value $M1$. Then suspend the mineral in a beaker of water. Record the measurement of the mineral's mass in water. Label this value $M2$. To determine the mineral's specific gravity, use the following equation:

$$\frac{M1}{M1 - M2} = \text{specific gravity}$$

Do all the other steps to identify the sample. Does the specific gravity you measured match the one listed for that mineral in the identification key?

Mineral Identification

Table 1 Mineral Properties

Property	Sample Number				
	1	2	3	4	5
Color					
Luster					
Cleavage					
Fracture					
Streak					
Hardness					
Magnetic					
Acid test					
Name of mineral					

A 58 Unit: Earth's Surface

Chapter 2: Minerals 59 A

④ Analyze your results.

⑤ Write your lab report.

Using Technology

The Internet is a great source of information about up-to-date science. The ClassZone Website and SciLinks have exciting sites for you to explore. Video clips and simulations can make science come alive.

Look for red banners.

Go to **ClassZone.com** to see simulations, visualizations, resources centers, and content review.

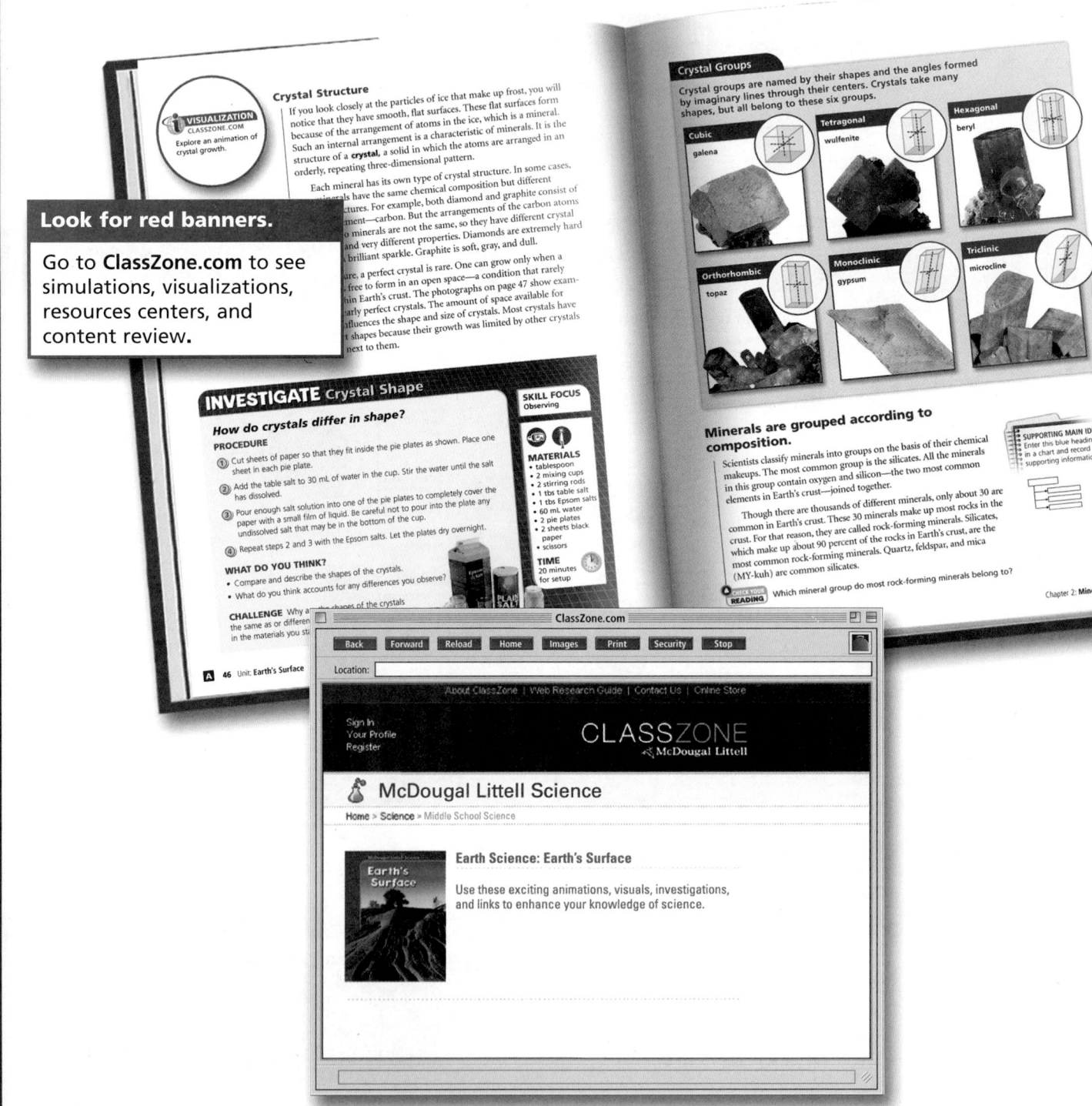

FRONTIERS in Science

REMOTE SENSING

...hnology high above Earth's surface is giving scientists ...hole new look at our planet. This image is of Jasper ...e, near Palo Alto, California.

SCIENTIFIC AMERICAN FRONTIERS

View the video segment "All That Glitters" to learn how explorers use remote sensing and other methods to find valuable materials.

A 2 ... Earth's Surface

Watch the videos.

See science at work in the **Scientific American Frontiers video.**

Look up SciLinks.

Go to **scilinks.org** to explore the topic.

NSTA
scilinks.org
SCiLINKS

The Sun **Code: MDL060**

Earth's Surface

biosphere

sedimentary rock

EROSION

geosphere

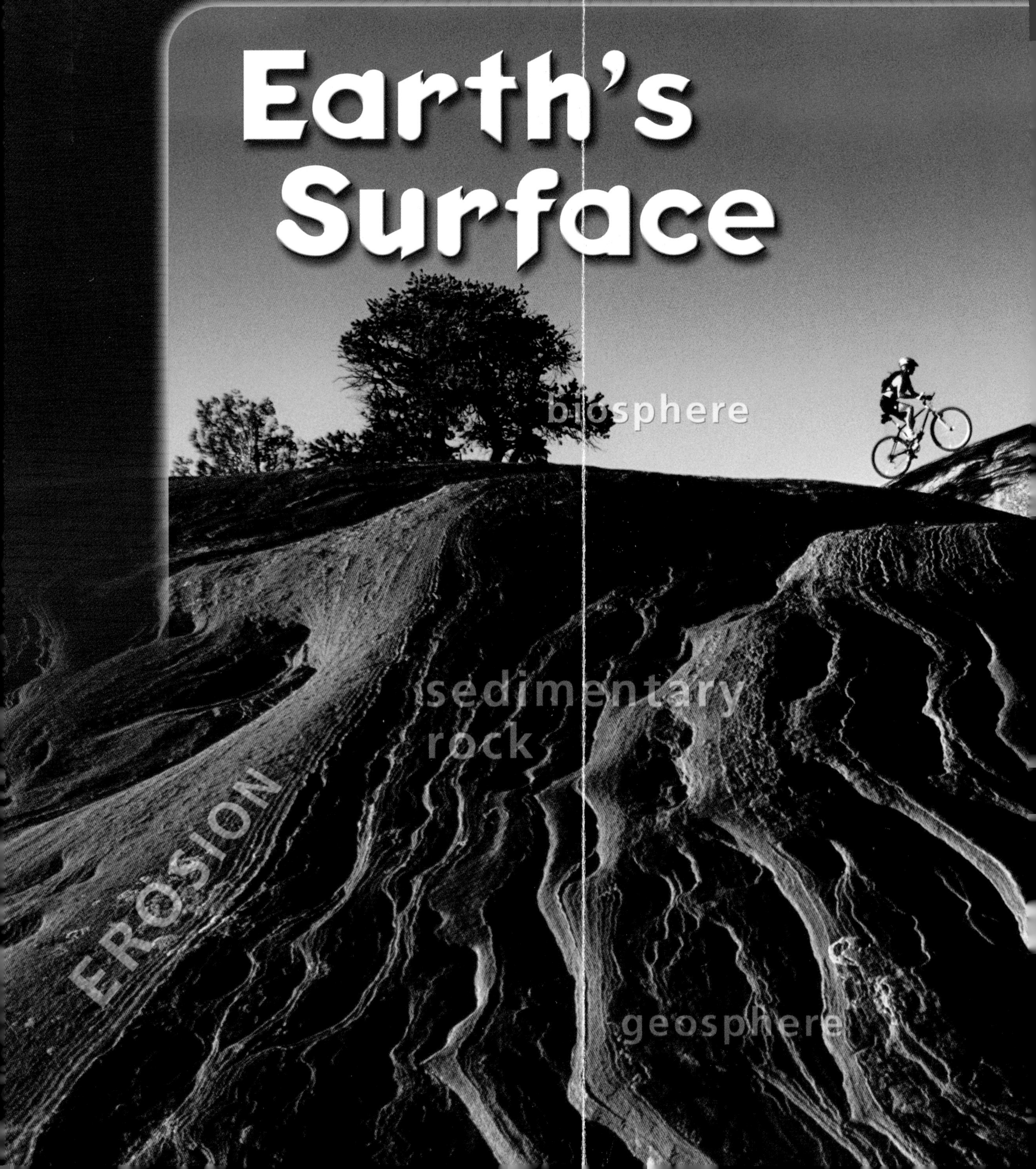

North Carolina Standards

In Unit A: Earth's Surface, students will learn and apply science concepts and skills related to the following goals from the North Carolina Standard Course of Study:

Competency Goal 1: The learner will design and conduct investigations to demonstrate an understanding of scientific inquiry. (Objectives 1.01–1.10)

Competency Goal 2: The learner will demonstrate an understanding of technological design. (Objectives 2.01–2.04)

Competency Goal 3: The learner will build an understanding of the geological cycles, forces, process, and agents which shape the lithosphere.

3.01   Evaluate the forces that shape the lithosphere.

3.03   Explain the model for the interior of the earth.

3.04   Describe the processes which form and the uses of earth materials.

3.05   Analyze properties that can be observed and measured to predict soil quality.

3.06   Evaluate ways in which human activities have affected Earth's pedosphere and the measures taken to control the impact.

3.07   Assess the use of technology and information systems in monitoring lithospheric phenomena.

3.08   Conclude that the good health of environments and organisms requires monitoring of the pedosphere, taking steps to maintain soil quality, and stewardship.

Competency Goal 4: The learner will investigate the cycling of matter.

4.01   Describe the flow of energy and matter in natural systems.

For a detailed lesson-by-lesson correlation of Unit A to the North Carolina Standard Course of Study, see Correlations pages 16–24 in the front of this Teacher's Edition.

North Carolina Handbook

The following sections of the North Carolina Handbook are also designed to be used in conjunction with this unit:

- Soil Science (pp. NC7–NC11)
- Rocks and Minerals of North Carolina (p. NC16)

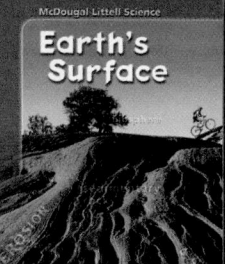

Earth's Surface
Contents Overview

Unit Features

1 Views of Earth Today   6

the **BIG** idea

Modern technology has changed the
way we view and map Earth.

2 Minerals   40

the **BIG** idea

Minerals are basic building
blocks of Earth.

3 Rocks   72

the **BIG** idea

Rocks change into other rocks
over time.

4 Weathering and Soil Formation   112

the **BIG** idea

Natural forces break rocks apart
and form soil, which supports life.

5 Erosion and Deposition   142

the **BIG** idea

Water, wind, and ice shape
Earth's surface.

FRONTIERS in Science

FRONTIERS in Science

VIDEO SUMMARY

SCIENTIFIC AMERICAN FRONTIERS

"All That Glitters," a segment of the *Scientific American Frontiers* series that aired on PBS stations, presents one scientist's determined 15-year effort to prove a surprising hypothesis. Although most of the world's diamonds come from Russia, Australia, and southern Africa, prospector Chuck Fipke was certain that he could find diamonds in Canada. Fipke knew that diamonds form where Earth's crust is thick enough to create the pressure needed to squeeze carbon into diamond crystals. Once formed, these crystals reach the surface of Earth's crust only through chimneys of molten rock called kimberlite pipes. Fipke targeted northwestern Canada because he saw the same thick crust there. Finding the kimberlite pipes was not easy, though. Fipke finally came up with a second hypothesis: Glaciers had scraped off the tops of the pipes and carried the materials downhill. By moving his search site back toward where the glaciers had started, he was at last rewarded by the discovery of kimberlite pipes and top-quality diamonds.

National Science Education Standards

A.1–8 Abilities Necessary to Do Scientific Inquiry

A.9.a, A.9.b, A.9.d–g Understandings about Scientific Inquiry

F.5.e Science and Technology in Society

G.1.a–b Science as a Human Endeavor

G.2.a, G.2.c Nature of Science

REMOTE SENSING

Technology high above Earth's surface is giving scientists a whole new look at our planet. This image is of Jasper Ridge, near Palo Alto, California.

SCIENTIFIC AMERICAN FRONTIERS

View the video segment "All That Glitters" to learn how explorers use remote sensing and other methods to find valuable materials.

ADDITIONAL RESOURCES

Technology Resources

 Scientific American Frontiers Video: *All That Glitters:* 11-minute video segment that introduces the unit.

 ClassZone.com
CAREER LINK, Mineralogist

Guide student viewing and comprehension of the video:

 Video Teaching Guide, pp. 1–2; Video Viewing Guide, p. 3; Video Wrap-Up, p. 4

Scientific American Frontiers Video Guide, pp. 19–22

Unit projects procedures and rubrics:

 Unit Projects, pp. 5–10

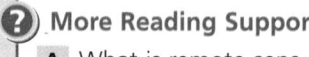

This research jet aircraft carries instruments to study Earth's land surface, ocean, and atmosphere. It flies at high altitudes, allowing it to collect data and images over large areas during a single flight.

Mapping Earth

You're probably familiar with images of gold prospectors in the Old West. Maybe you've seen them in old movies or read about them in history books. Prospectors wandered through the mountains, looking for signs of ores or gemstones, going here and there in response to rumors or stories, pitching camp in remote canyons on a hunch. People still prospect for minerals today, but they're more likely to fly in airplanes than to ride mules. And stories of fabled mines are just stories and fables. Today's prospectors rely on scientific evidence from remote sensing.

Remote sensing—the use of instruments to gather data from a distance—has two great advantages. The first is that sensors mounted in satellites and airplanes can collect vast amounts of detailed information over large areas. The second is that the sensors can easily collect information about the same area again and again.

For example, scientists use remote sensing to make better and more detailed maps of Earth and to track changes over time. Thanks to remote sensing, scientists now know that Mount Everest, the highest point on Earth, is actually getting higher by about 1 centimeter (0.4 in.) per year. Remote sensors on satellites are also mapping global ocean temperatures and showing how they change over the course of a year.

Uncut diamond

◗ Set Learning Goals
Students will

- Analyze how remote sensing is used to locate minerals.
- Discuss additional applications of remote sensing.
- Complete a unit project relating to map-reading, mineral formation, or glacial erosion.

Tell students that remote sensing is pushing the frontiers of science by giving scientists previously unattainable views of Earth. Ask them to predict how images of Earth taken high above its surface might be used to find minerals underground. Have them revise their predictions after viewing the "All That Glitters" video.

INSTRUCT

Technology Design

Ask students to identify the technological advantages of remote sensing over other types of data-gathering techniques. *Remote sensing takes much less time to cover large areas and to gather data repeatedly than does traveling on the ground to collect data, especially in rugged areas.*

Teach from Visuals

Have students identify features that are visible in the photograph. Ask: Could you see all these features if you were standing on the ground? Explain. *Features such as hills and trees might interfere with your view.*

Asking a Question

Because of remote sensing, scientists know that Mt. Everest is still growing. Have students develop questions related to this fact. *Sample answer: Why is Mt. Everest still growing? How big will it get?*

DIFFERENTIATE INSTRUCTION

? **More Reading Support**

A What is remote sensing? *using instruments to gather data from a distance*

Advanced Ask students to infer why scientists map and track changes in global ocean temperatures. *Changes in ocean temperatures may indicate climatic changes. Temperature changes could affect marine ecosystems, such as coral reefs.*

Integrate the Sciences

Remote-sensing instruments detect electromagnetic radiation, which includes radio waves, microwaves, infrared radiation, visible light, ultraviolet radiation, x-rays, and gamma rays. Electromagnetic waves are classified by wavelength—radio waves are the longest; gamma waves are the shortest.

Tell students that wavelength refers to the distance between similar points on successive waves. For example, wavelength is the distance between the crests, or highest points, of two waves.

Scientific Process

Ask students to identify the scientific processes described on this page. *collecting data, analyzing data*

Determining What Is Known

Ask: Why did some prospectors infer there might be diamonds in northern Canada? *The region is geologically similar to the world's major diamond-producing areas.*

Detecting Minerals from Above

One of the many uses of remote sensing is to find new sources of valuable minerals, such as diamonds. To detect minerals from airplanes or satellites, remote sensors make use of the energy in sunlight. Sunlight reaches Earth as radiation 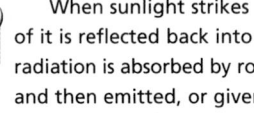 that travels in the form of waves. All objects absorb some types of radiation and reflect others. The particular wavelengths absorbed or reflected depend upon the materials that make up the objects. Each kind of material has a unique "fingerprint" of the wavelengths it absorbs and the wavelengths it reflects.

 When sunlight strikes Earth's surface, some of it is reflected back into the sky. Some of the radiation is absorbed by rocks and other objects and then emitted, or given off, in a different form. Remote sensors in airplanes and satellites collect the reflected and emitted radiation and analyze it to determine which types of rocks and minerals lie on the surface. The remote sensing

Energy from the Sun reflects at different wavelengths from materials at Earth's surface. Instruments on the jet analyze the reflected energy and map the surface.

systems collect so much data that computer processing and analysis are difficult and expensive. Still, the data are usually clear enough to show the types of minerals located in the regions scanned. However, minerals that are buried cannot be detected by remote sensing from aircraft or satellites. The sensors receive only energy reflected from the surface of the ground.

SCIENTIFIC AMERICAN FRONTIERS

View the "All that Glitters" segment of your *Scientific American Frontiers* video to see how finding certain common minerals can indicate the presence of a valuable mineral like diamond.

IN THIS SCENE FROM THE VIDEO ▶ a mineral prospector searches for diamonds in a cylinder of rock drilled from beneath Earth's surface.

SEARCHING FOR DIAMONDS People used to think that North America did not have many diamonds. However, northern Canada is geologically similar to the world's major diamond-producing areas:

southern Africa, Russia, and Australia. A few diamond prospectors kept searching, using remote sensing and other techniques. The prospectors looked for more common minerals that form under the same conditions as diamonds. They made maps showing where these minerals were most plentiful and used the maps to search for diamond-rich rock. Once the prospectors realized that the glaciers of the last ice age had moved the minerals, they looked for and found diamonds farther northward. Canada is now a big producer of diamonds.

DIFFERENTIATE INSTRUCTION

? More Reading Support

B Energy from the Sun travels in what form? *waves*

C How does light reach sensors? *It reflects from Earth's surface.*

Below Level Show students satellite images taken with remote-sensing instruments. Such images can be downloaded from government Web sites, including NASA and NOAA. Try to obtain images that include color-coded keys. The colors correspond to different wavelengths.

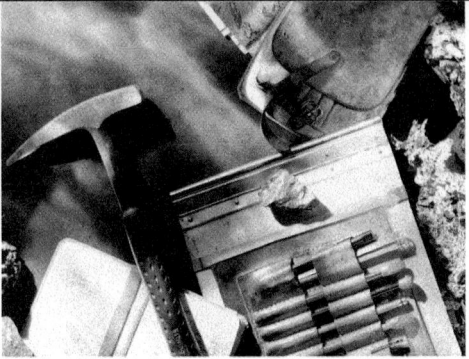

Remote sensing can show the presence of minerals that occur with diamonds, but people must still use older methods to collect samples for further analysis.

Prospecting for Diamonds

One of the major regions of mineral exploration in which remote sensing is used is in the Northwest Territories of Canada, where the first diamond mine began operating in 1998. The Canada Centre for Remote Sensing has helped develop sensing equipment that can fit easily onto light airplanes and computer equipment to analyze results quickly. The sensing equipment is used to detect certain types of minerals that are often found along with diamonds.

? **D** Using remote sensing to locate minerals associated with diamonds or valuable ores is only a beginning. The data cannot show how far the minerals or ores extend underground. Prospectors must still explore the area and take samples. However, remote sensing gives mineral prospectors an excellent idea of where to start looking.

? UNANSWERED Questions

As scientists use remote sensing to study Earth's land surface, ocean, and atmosphere, they work to answer new questions.

- Can remote sensing be used to locate sources of iron, platinum, or gold in areas that are difficult to explore on foot?
- How do changes in water temperature at the ocean surface affect long-range weather patterns and the health of ocean organisms?
- How do different types of clouds affect the amount of sunlight reaching Earth's surface and the average temperature of the surface?

UNIT PROJECTS

As you study this unit, work alone or with a group on one of the projects listed below.

Hiker's Guide Video

Like prospectors, wilderness hikers must be able to read maps that show the shape of the land. Prepare a video to teach hikers how to choose hiking and camping areas by reading maps.

- Obtain a topographic map of a wilderness area in a national or state park.
- Write a script outlining what you will teach and how you will videotape it.
- Present your video and display the maps you used.

Diamond Mine Model

Diamonds can be carried toward Earth's surface by kimberlite pipes. Show how diamonds are mined from kimberlite.

- Build a model of a diamond-mine tunnel that passes through kimberlite.
- Present your model to your class. Explain the relationship between kimberlite and diamonds.

Glacier Photo Essay

Make a photo essay showing how glaciers reshape Earth's surface as they move and melt.

- Find images of areas that are or have been affected by glaciers. Write captions for them.
- Present the images as a photo essay on a poster or in a portfolio.

 **CAREER CENTER**
CLASSZONE.COM

Learn more about careers in mineralogy.

? UNANSWERED Questions

Have students read the questions and think of some of their own. Remind them that scientists always end up with more questions—that inquiry is the driving force of science.

- With the class, generate on the board a list of new questions.
- Students can add to the list after they watch the Scientific American Frontiers Video.
- Students can use the list as a springboard for choosing their Unit Projects.

UNIT PROJECTS

Encourage students to pick the project that most appeals to them. Point out that each is long-term and will take several weeks to complete. You might group or pair students to work on projects and in some cases guide student choice. Some of the projects have student choice built into them. Each project has two worksheet pages, including a rubric. Use the pages to guide students through criteria, process, and schedule.

R Unit Projects, pp. 5–10

REVISIT concepts introduced in this article:

Chapter 1
- Technology is used to explore the Earth system, pp. 9–14
- Technology is used to map Earth, pp. 30–34

Chapter 2
- Mineral identification, pp. 50–57
- Minerals as resources, pp. 60–66

Chapter 5
- Glaciers carve land and move sediments, pp. 165–170

DIFFERENTIATE INSTRUCTION

 **More Reading Support**

D When searching for minerals, what can't the data from remote sensing show? *how far the minerals extend underground*

Differentiate Unit Projects Projects are appropriate for varying abilities. Allow students to choose the ones that interest them most and let them vary their product. Encourage below-level students to give visual or oral presentations or to record audio presentations about their topic. You might suggest that they try "Glacier Photo Essay." Encourage advanced students to complete "Hiker's Guide Video."

CHAPTER 1
Views of Earth Today

Earth Science
UNIFYING PRINCIPLES

PRINCIPLE 1

Heat energy inside Earth and radiation from the Sun provide energy for Earth's processes.

PRINCIPLE 2

Physical forces, such as gravity, affect the movement of all matter on Earth and throughout the universe.

PRINCIPLE 3

Matter and energy move among Earth's rocks and soil, atmosphere, waters, and living things.

PRINCIPLE 4

Earth has changed over time and continues to change.

Unit: Earth's Surface
BIG IDEAS

CHAPTER 1
Views of Earth Today

Modern technology has changed the way we view and map Earth.

CHAPTER 2
Minerals

Minerals are basic building blocks of Earth.

CHAPTER 3
Rocks

Rocks change into other rocks over time.

CHAPTER 4
Weathering and Soil Formation

Natural forces break rocks apart and form soil, which supports life.

CHAPTER 5
Erosion and Deposition

Water, wind, and ice shape Earth's surface.

CHAPTER 1
KEY CONCEPTS

SECTION	SECTION	SECTION 1.3	SECTION 1.4
Technology is used to explore the Earth system.	**Maps and globes are models of Earth.**	**Topographic maps show the shape of the land.**	**Technology is used to map Earth.**
1. The Earth system has four major parts.	1. Maps show natural and human-made features.	1. Topographic maps use contour lines to show features.	1. Remote sensing provides detailed images of Earth.
2. All four parts of the Earth system shape the planet's surface.	2. Latitude and longitude show locations on Earth.	2. Contour lines follow certain rules.	2. Geographic information systems display data in layers.
	3. Map projections distort the view of Earth's surface.		

The Big Idea Flow Chart is available on p. T1 in the **UNIT TRANSPARENCY BOOK.**

Previewing Content

SECTION

 1.1 Technology is used to explore the Earth system. pp. 9–14

1. The Earth system has four major parts.

A **system** is a combination of parts that work together to form a whole. Earth is essentially a closed system in which energy enters and leaves but matter, with a few exceptions, does not. Earth has four interconnected parts that are open systems in which both matter and energy can leave and enter. Each part affects the others.

- **atmosphere:** the gaseous envelope surrounding Earth and supporting life on the surface (78% nitrogen, 21% oxygen)
- **hydrosphere:** water in all its forms: gaseous (water vapor), solid (ice and snow), and liquid (rain, streams, oceans, etc.)
- **biosphere:** all living organisms in the Earth system and their environments
- **geosphere:** the rocks, soil, mountains, continents, ocean basins, and other physical features of Earth (except for water)

Note: Chapter 3 explains the rock cycle and helps to clarify the different layers of Earth's geosphere.

2. All four parts of the Earth system shape the planet's surface.

The atmosphere, hydrosphere, geosphere, and biosphere continuously reshape Earth's surface. Modern technology enables scientists to record, assess, and in some cases predict these changes. Plants, animals, and humans—all parts of the biosphere—can also dramatically change Earth's surface.

SECTION

 1.2 Maps and globes are models of Earth. pp. 15–23

1. Maps show natural and human-made features.

A map is a model of Earth on a flat surface. A globe represents Earth as if viewed from outer space.

- A **relief map** shows the elevations of land features, such as mountains, plains, and plateaus.
- A **map scale** relates distances on a map to actual distances on Earth's surface.
- A **map legend,** also called a key, explains the meaning of each symbol used on a map.

2. Latitude and longitude show locations on Earth.

A grid of imaginary lines over Earth helps pinpoint locations. **Latitude** lines circle the world parallel to the equator; they are also called parallels. **Longitude** lines, or meridians, run north-south between Earth's poles.

- The **equator** is the latitude line dividing Earth into northern and southern hemispheres.
- The **prime meridian** divides Earth into western and eastern hemispheres.

The Global Positioning System relies on satellite communications and electronic and computer technologies. By using a GPS receiver, a person can find not only the latitude and longitude of a place but its elevation as well.

3. Map projections distort the view of Earth's surface.

A globe is the most accurate way to represent Earth's surface. Mapmakers use different **projections** to make two-dimensional representations of the surface. Each kind of projection distorts the surface in some way.

- A cylindrical, or Mercator, projection distorts landmasses near the poles but shows true directions in straight lines (helpful for navigation).
- In a conic projection, shapes and distances are undistorted only along a particular parallel (useful for mapping large areas in the mid-latitudes).
- A planar projection can be used to plot the shortest distance between two points, but it distorts shapes away from the center point (useful for flight navigation).

Common Misconceptions

EARTH'S MANTLE Students may think that Earth's mantle is entirely liquid. The mantle, the thickest of Earth's layers, is primarily solid but has liquid properties due to the high pressures and temperatures in it.

 This misconception is addressed on p. 12.

MISCONCEPTION DATABASE

CLASSZONE.COM Background on student misconceptions

EARTH'S CRUST Many students may think that Earth's crust is very thick. In fact, this outermost layer of the geosphere is thin in comparison with the rest of Earth's rocky layers—only 5–70 kilometers thick.

 This misconception is addressed on p. 13.

Previewing Content

1.3 Topographic maps show the shape of the land. pp. 24–29

1. Topographic maps use contour lines to show features.
Topography is the shape of the land. Topographic maps show the surface features of particular areas, including natural features such as mountains, valleys, and bodies of water, as well as human-made features such as airports, bridges, and roads. They can be used to determine:

- **elevation:** how high a point is above sea level
- **slope:** the steepness of a landform
- **relief:** the difference in elevation between the high and low points of an area

Contour lines on a topographic map are lines that show the elevations of land above or below sea level; all points connected by a contour line have the same elevation.

2. Contour lines follow certain rules.
These rules can be used to interpret topographic maps:

- Contour lines never cross, because each line represents a specific elevation.
- Circles show the highest and lowest points.
- On a given map, the contour interval is always the same. The closer the contour lines, the steeper the slope; the more space between the lines, the more gradual the slope.
- Index contour lines are the darker, bolder, lines on a map, often marked with numbers that label elevations.

A **contour interval** is the difference in elevation between one contour line and the next.

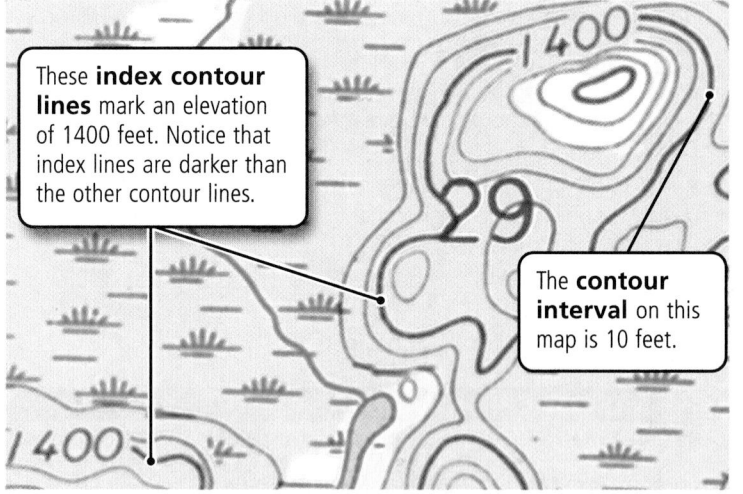

These **index contour lines** mark an elevation of 1400 feet. Notice that index lines are darker than the other contour lines.

The **contour interval** on this map is 10 feet.

1.4 Technology is used to map Earth. pp. 30–35

1. Remote sensing provides detailed images of Earth.
Satellites use sensors to detect different types of energy from Earth's surface. They relay the data to computers on Earth, which process the data to create images.

- A **sensor** is any mechanical or electrical device that receives and responds to a signal, such as light.
- **False-color images** highlight particular information or features on a map or image.

Orbiting satellites used in mapmaking are equipped with sensors that constantly record data from Earth's surface. These instruments measure the invisible electromagnetic waves that every object emits. Because the waves are unique to particular types of objects, computers can identify objects through data analysis. The computers convert the data collected into a code, then to pixels, or electronic dots, which are are used to form images.

2. Geographic information systems display data in layers.
GIS combine data from satellite images, statistical surveys, and land surveys to make maps. A GIS map is a composite of several layers. Each layer is dedicated to a specific feature showing, for example, terrain, population, or roadways. The computer systems are used to assemble, store, manipulate, and display data about specific locations.

Common Misconceptions

MAP DISTORTION Many students viewing maps think that what they see are accurate images of Earth's landmasses and bodies of water. In fact, all map projections distort the shapes of Earth's landmasses and oceans.

 MISCONCEPTION DATABASE
CLASSZONE.COM Background on student misconceptions

[T E] This misconception is addressed on p. 20.

Previsualing Labs

Lab Generator CD-ROM
Edit these Pupil Edition labs and generate alternative labs.

EXPLORE the BIG idea

Earth's Changing Surface, p. 7
Students search their surroundings for evidence of erosional forces.

TIME 20 minutes
MATERIALS paper or notebook to record observations

Using Modern Maps, p. 7
Students look at a map to interpret the scale, symbols, and features.

TIME 10 minutes
MATERIALS various city, transit (rail or bus), and state maps

Internet Activity: Mapping, p. 7
Students use the Internet to learn about three-dimensional mapping of Earth from space.

TIME 20 minutes
MATERIALS computer with Internet access

SECTION 1.1

INVESTIGATE Geosphere's Layers, p. 13
Students model the geosphere's layers with an apple.

TIME 15 minutes
MATERIALS apple slice

SECTION 1.2

EXPLORE Mapping, p. 15
Students draw a map, then evaluate a classmate's to see what makes a good map.

TIME 25 minutes
MATERIALS paper, pencil or pen

INVESTIGATE Map Projections, p. 20
Students construct a model of a hemisphere to investigate the use of projection in mapmaking.

TIME 20 minutes
MATERIALS top 8 inches of 2L plastic bottle, marker pen, 1/4 stick of clay, 30 cm × 30 cm white poster board, flashlight

SECTION 1.3

EXPLORE Topographic Maps, p. 24
Students use their own knuckles to explore the concept of topography.

TIME 10 minutes
MATERIALS washable colored pen

CHAPTER INVESTIGATION Investigate Topographic Maps, pp. 28–29
Students build three-dimensional terrain models out of clay and then produce topographic maps to show slope, elevation, and relief of their models.

TIME 40 minutes
MATERIALS half-gallon cardboard juice container, scissors, 8 sticks of modeling clay, transparency or sheet protector, 10 cm cellophane tape, ruler, 4–6 cups of water, food coloring, box of spaghetti, erasable marker pen

SECTION 1.4

INVESTIGATE Satellite Imaging, p. 32
Students graph images to model how satellites send images to Earth.

TIME 25 minutes
MATERIALS graph paper, colored pen or pencil

R **Additional INVESTIGATION,** Make a Map by Triangulation, A, B, & C, pp. 70–78; Teacher Instructions, pp. 348–349

Previewing Chapter Resources

| | INTEGRATED TECHNOLOGY | LABS AND ACTIVITIES |

CHAPTER 1
Views of Earth Today

 CLASSZONE.COM
- eEdition Plus
- EasyPlanner Plus
- Misconception Database
- Content Review
- Visualization
- Resource Centers
- Simulation
- Test Practice
- Internet Activity: Mapping
- Math Tutorial

 SCILINKS.ORG
SCILINKS

 CD-ROMS
- eEdition
- EasyPlanner
- Power Presentations
- Content Review
- Lab Generator
- Test Generator

 AUDIO CDS
- Audio Readings
- Audio Readings in Spanish

PE EXPLORE the Big Idea, p. 7
- Earth's Changing Surface
- Using Modern Maps
- Internet Activity: Mapping

R UNIT RESOURCE BOOK
- Family Letter, p. ix
- Spanish Family Letter, p. x
- Unit Projects, pp. 5–10

 Lab Generator CD-ROM
Generate customized labs.

SECTION 1.1
Technology is used to explore the Earth system.
pp. 9–14

Time: 2 periods (1 block)

R Lesson Plan, pp. 11–12

T UNIT TRANSPARENCY BOOK
- Big Idea Flow Chart, p. T1
- Daily Vocabulary Scaffolding, p. T2
- Note-Taking Model, p. T3
- 3-Minute Warm-Up, p. T4

PE INVESTIGATE Geosphere's Layers, p. 13

R UNIT RESOURCE BOOK
Datasheet, Geosphere's Layers, p. 20

SECTION 1.2
Maps and globes are models of Earth.
pp. 15–23

Time: 2 periods (1 block)

R Lesson Plan, pp. 22–23

- **VISUALIZATION,** Latitude and Longitude
- **RESOURCE CENTER,** Map Projections
- **MATH TUTORIAL**

T UNIT TRANSPARENCY BOOK
- Big Idea Flow Chart, p. T1
- Daily Vocabulary Scaffolding, p. T2
- 3-Minute Warm-Up, p. T4
- "Latitude and Longitude" Visual, p. T6

PE
- EXPLORE Mapping, p. 15
- INVESTIGATE Map Projections, p. 20
- Math in Science, p. 23

R UNIT RESOURCE BOOK
- Datasheet, Map Projections, p. 31
- Math Support & Practice, pp. 59–60
- Additional INVESTIGATION, Make a Map by Triangulation, A, B, & C, pp. 70–78

SECTION 1.3
Topographic maps show the shape of the land.
pp. 24–29

Time: 3 periods (1.5 blocks)

R Lesson Plan, pp. 33–34

 SIMULATION, Topographic Maps and Surface Features

T UNIT TRANSPARENCY BOOK
- Daily Vocabulary Scaffolding, p. T2
- 3-Minute Warm-Up, p. T5

PE
- EXPLORE Topographic Maps, p. 24
- CHAPTER INVESTIGATION, Investigate Topographic Maps, pp. 28–29

R UNIT RESOURCE BOOK
CHAPTER INVESTIGATION, Investigate Topographic Maps, A, B, & C, pp. 61–69

SECTION 1.4
Technology is used to map Earth.
pp. 30–35

Time: 3 periods (1.5 blocks)

R Lesson Plan, pp. 43–44

 RESOURCE CENTER, GIS

T UNIT TRANSPARENCY BOOK
- Big Idea Flow Chart, p. T1
- Daily Vocabulary Scaffolding, p. T2
- 3-Minute Warm-Up, p. T5
- Chapter Outline, pp. T7–8

PE
- INVESTIGATE Satellite Imaging, p. 32
- Think Science, p. 35

R UNIT RESOURCE BOOK
Datasheet, Satellite Imaging, p. 52

 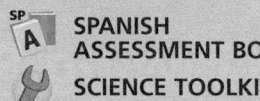

READING AND REINFORCEMENT

ASSESSMENT

STANDARDS

- Word Triangle, B18–19
- Main Idea and Detail Notes, C37
- Daily Vocabulary Scaffolding, H1–8

 UNIT RESOURCE BOOK
- Vocabulary Practice, pp. 56–57
- Decoding Support p. 58
- Summarizing the Chapter, pp. 79–80

 Audio Readings CD
Listen to Pupil Edition.

 Audio Readings in Spanish CD
Listen to Pupil Edition in Spanish.

- Chapter Review, pp. 36–38
- Standardized Test Practice, p. 39

 UNIT ASSESSMENT BOOK
- Diagnostic Test, pp. 1–2
- Chapter Test, A, B, & C, pp. 7–18
- Alternative Assessment, pp. 19–20

 Spanish Chapter Test, pp. 105–108

 Test Generator CD-ROM
Generate customized tests.

Lab Generator CD-ROM
Rubrics for Labs

National Standards
A.2–8, A.9.a–f, D.1.a, E.6.c, F.5.a–c

See p. 6 for the standards.

 UNIT RESOURCE BOOK
- Reading Study Guide, A & B, pp. 13–16
- Spanish Reading Study Guide, pp. 17–18
- Challenge and Extension, p. 19
- Reinforcing Key Concepts, p. 21

 Ongoing Assessment, pp. 11–12, 14

 Section 1.1 Review, p. 14

 UNIT ASSESSMENT BOOK
Section 1.1 Quiz, p. 3

National Standards
A.2–7, A.9.a–b, A.9.d–f, D.1.a, E.6.c, F.5.a–c

 UNIT RESOURCE BOOK
- Reading Study Guide, A & B, pp. 24–27
- Spanish Reading Study Guide, pp. 28–29
- Challenge and Extension, p. 30
- Reinforcing Key Concepts, p. 32

 Ongoing Assessment, pp. 15–19, 21–22

 Section 1.2 Review, p. 22

 UNIT ASSESSMENT BOOK
Section 1.2 Quiz, p. 4

National Standards
A.2–8, A.9.a–f, E.6.c, F.5.a–c

 UNIT RESOURCE BOOK
- Reading Study Guide, A & B, pp. 35–38
- Spanish Reading Study Guide, pp. 39–40
- Challenge and Extension, p. 41
- Reinforcing Key Concepts, p. 42

 Ongoing Assessment, pp. 25–27

 Section 1.3 Review, p. 27

 UNIT ASSESSMENT BOOK
Section 1.3 Quiz, p. 5

National Standards
A.2–7, A.9.a–b, A.9.e–f

 UNIT RESOURCE BOOK
- Reading Study Guide, A & B, pp. 45–48
- Spanish Reading Study Guide, pp. 49–50
- Challenge and Extension, p. 51
- Reinforcing Key Concepts, p. 53
- Challenge Reading, pp. 54–55

 Ongoing Assessment, pp. 31, 33–34

 Section 1.4 Review, p. 34

 UNIT ASSESSMENT BOOK
Section 1.4 Quiz, p. 6

National Standards
A.2–7, A.9.a–b, A.9.d–f, E.6.c, F.5.a–c

Previewing Resources for Differentiated Instruction

CHAPTER INVESTIGATION

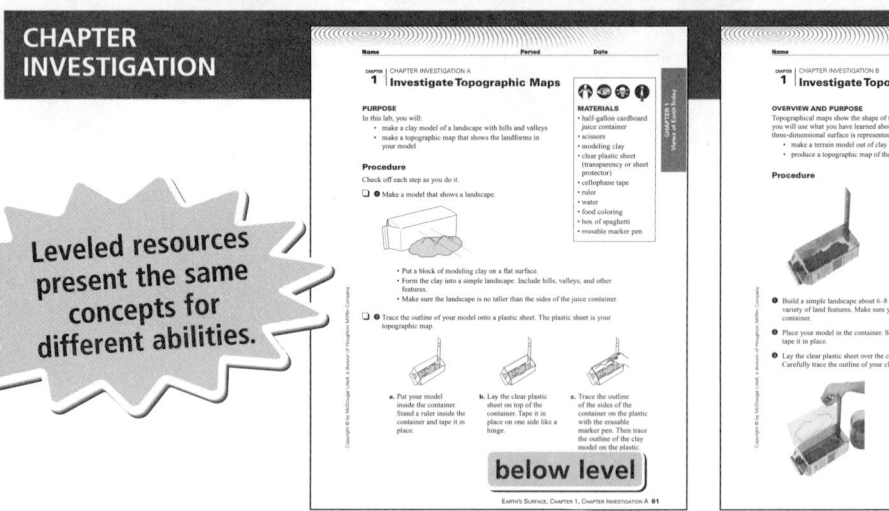

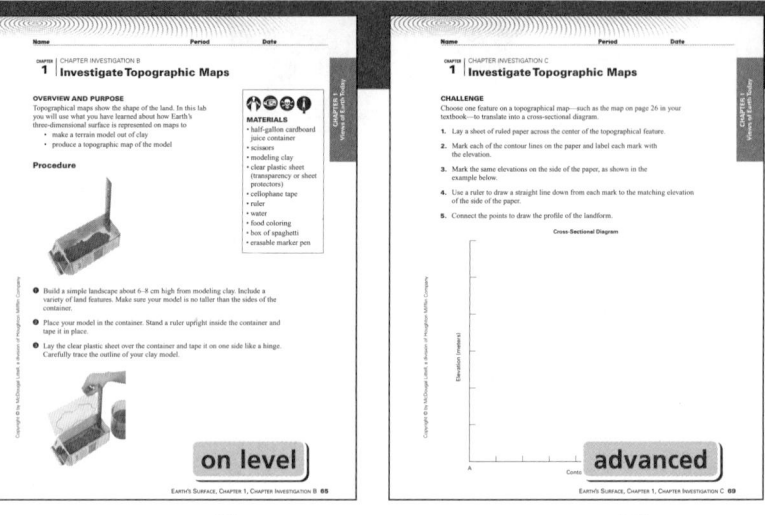

Leveled resources present the same concepts for different abilities.

below level

on level

advanced

R **UNIT RESOURCE BOOK,** pp. 61–64

R pp. 65–68

R pp. 65–69

READING STUDY GUIDE

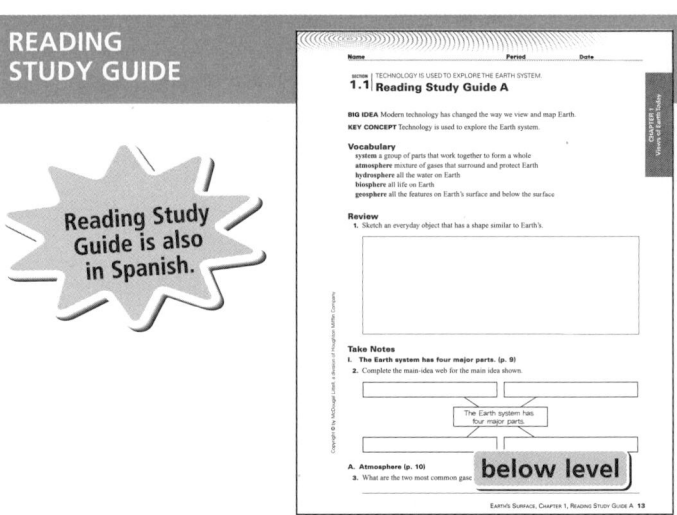

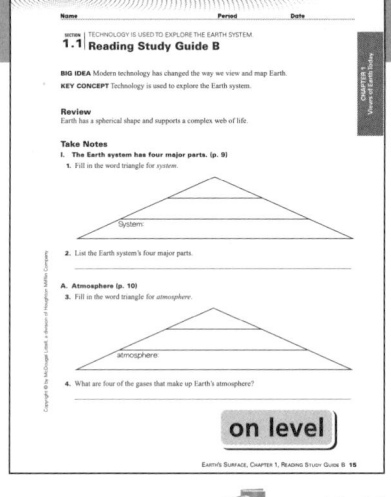

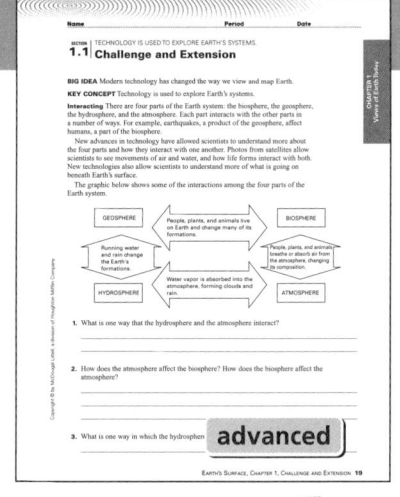

Reading Study Guide is also in Spanish.

below level

on level

advanced

R **UNIT RESOURCE BOOK,** pp. 13–14

R pp. 15–16

R p. 19

CHAPTER TEST

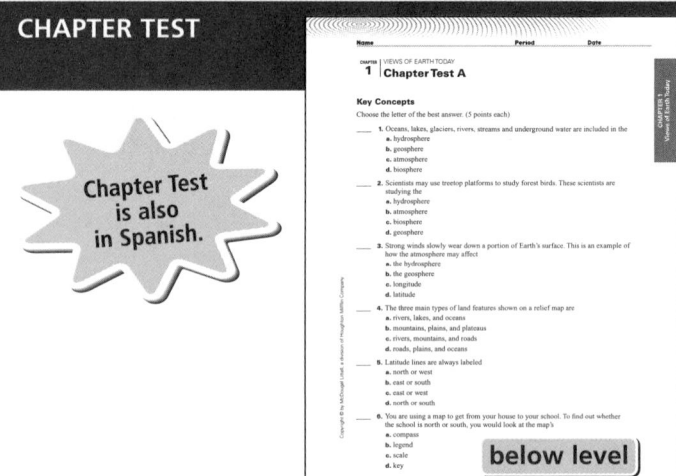

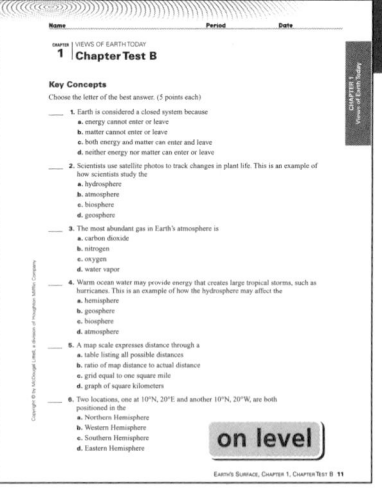

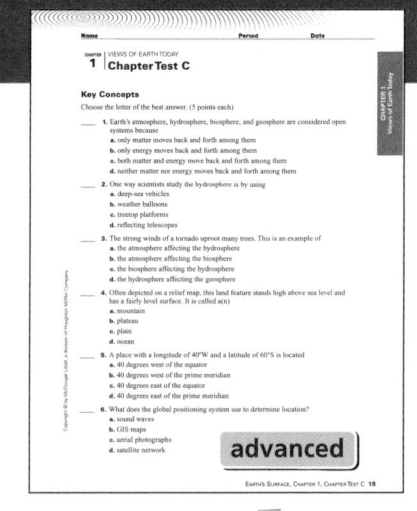

Chapter Test is also in Spanish.

below level

on level

advanced

A **UNIT ASSESSMENT BOOK,** pp. 7–10

A pp. 11–14

A pp. 15–18

TECHNOLOGY

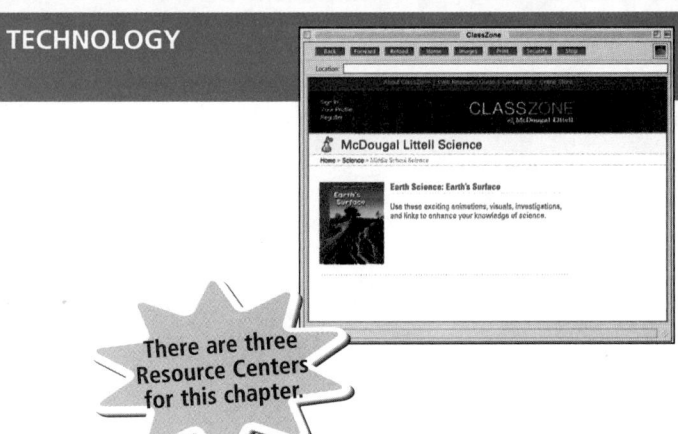

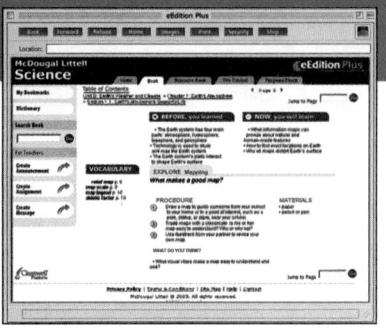

There are three Resource Centers for this chapter.

CLASSZONE.COM   CD/CD-ROMS   CLASSZONE.COM

VISUAL CONTENT

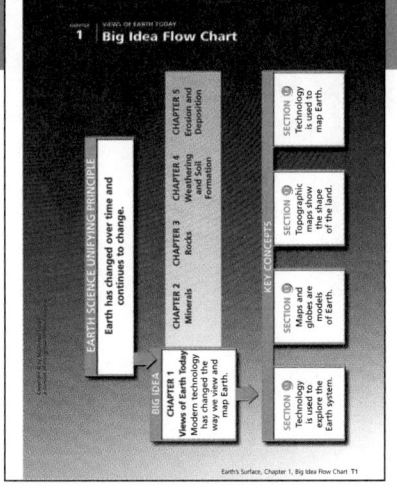

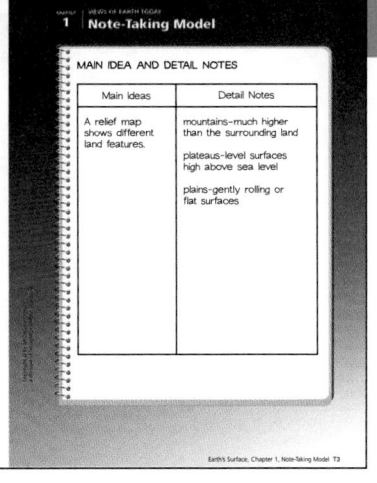

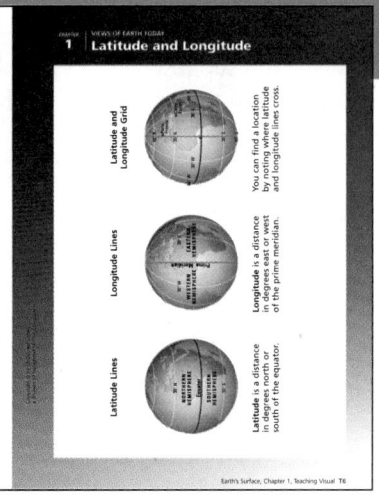

T UNIT TRANSPARENCY BOOK, p. T1   **T** p. T3   **T** p. T6

MORE SUPPORT

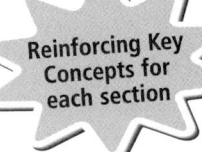

Reinforcing Key Concepts for each section

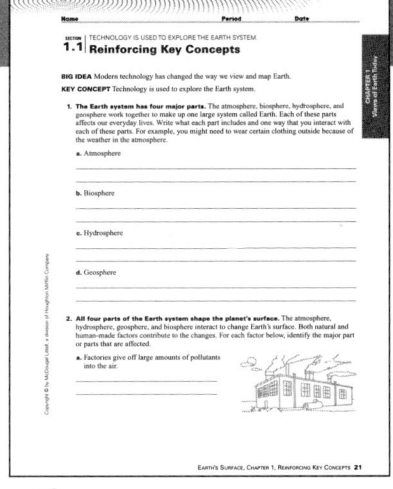

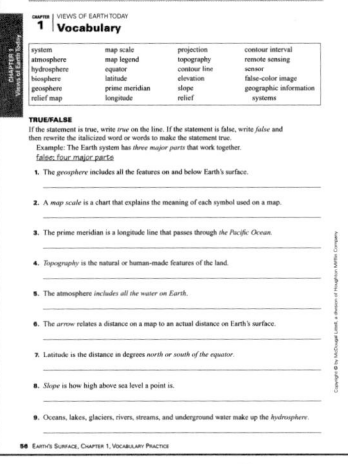

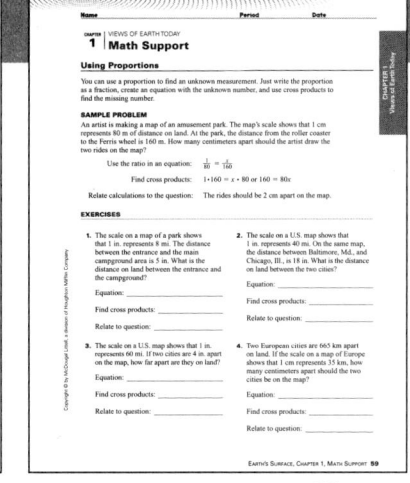

R UNIT RESOURCE BOOK, p. 21   **R** pp. 56–57   **R** p. 59

INTRODUCE

the BIG idea

Have students look at the satellite photographs and describe what they see. Have them discuss how the question in the box relates to the Big Idea. Ask:

- How is it possible to take such images of Earth?

- Do you remember the first time you saw a photograph of Earth taken from outer space? How did that particular view of our planet affect you?

- How do you suppose ancient people came up with their images of Earth?

National Science Education Standards

Content

D.1.a The solid earth is layered with a lithosphere; hot, convecting mantle; and dense metallic core.

E.6.c Science and technology are reciprocal. Science helps drive technology . . . technology is essential to science.

Process

A.2–8 Design and conduct an investigation; use tools to gather and interpret data; use evidence to describe, predict, explain, model; think critically to make relationships between evidence and explanation; recognize different explanations and predictions; communicate scientific procedures and explanations; use mathematics.

A.9.a–f Understand scientific inquiry by using different investigations, methods, mathematics, technology, explanations based on logic, evidence, and skepticism.

F.5.a–c Science and technology in society

CHAPTER

1 Views of Earth Today

the BIG idea

Modern technology has changed the way we view and map Earth.

> **What do all these views show about Earth?**

Key Concepts

SECTION
1.1 Technology is used to explore the Earth system. Learn how technology has changed people's view of Earth.

SECTION
1.2 Maps and globes are models of Earth. Learn how to locate any place on Earth and how Earth's sphere is portrayed on flat maps.

SECTION
1.3 Topographic maps show the shape of the land. Learn about representing the features of Earth's surface on flat maps.

SECTION
1.4 Technology is used to map Earth. Learn how satellites and computers are used to provide more detailed maps of Earth.

Internet Preview

CLASSZONE.COM
Chapter 1 online resources: Content Review, Simulation, Visualization, three Resource Centers, Math Tutorial, and Test Practice

A 6   Unit: **Earth's Surface**

Swirling clouds over North and South America: NASA Terra satellite data

INTERNET PREVIEW

CLASSZONE.COM   For student use with the following pages:

Review and Practice
- Content Review, pp. 8, 36
- Math Tutorial: Solving Proportions, p. 23
- Test Practice, p. 39

Activities and Resources
- Internet Activity: Mapping, p. 7
- Visualization: Latitude and Longitude, p. 18; Resource Centers: Map Projections, p. 22; GIS, p. 33; Simulation: Topographic Maps. . . p. 27

Earth's Spheres
Code: MDL013

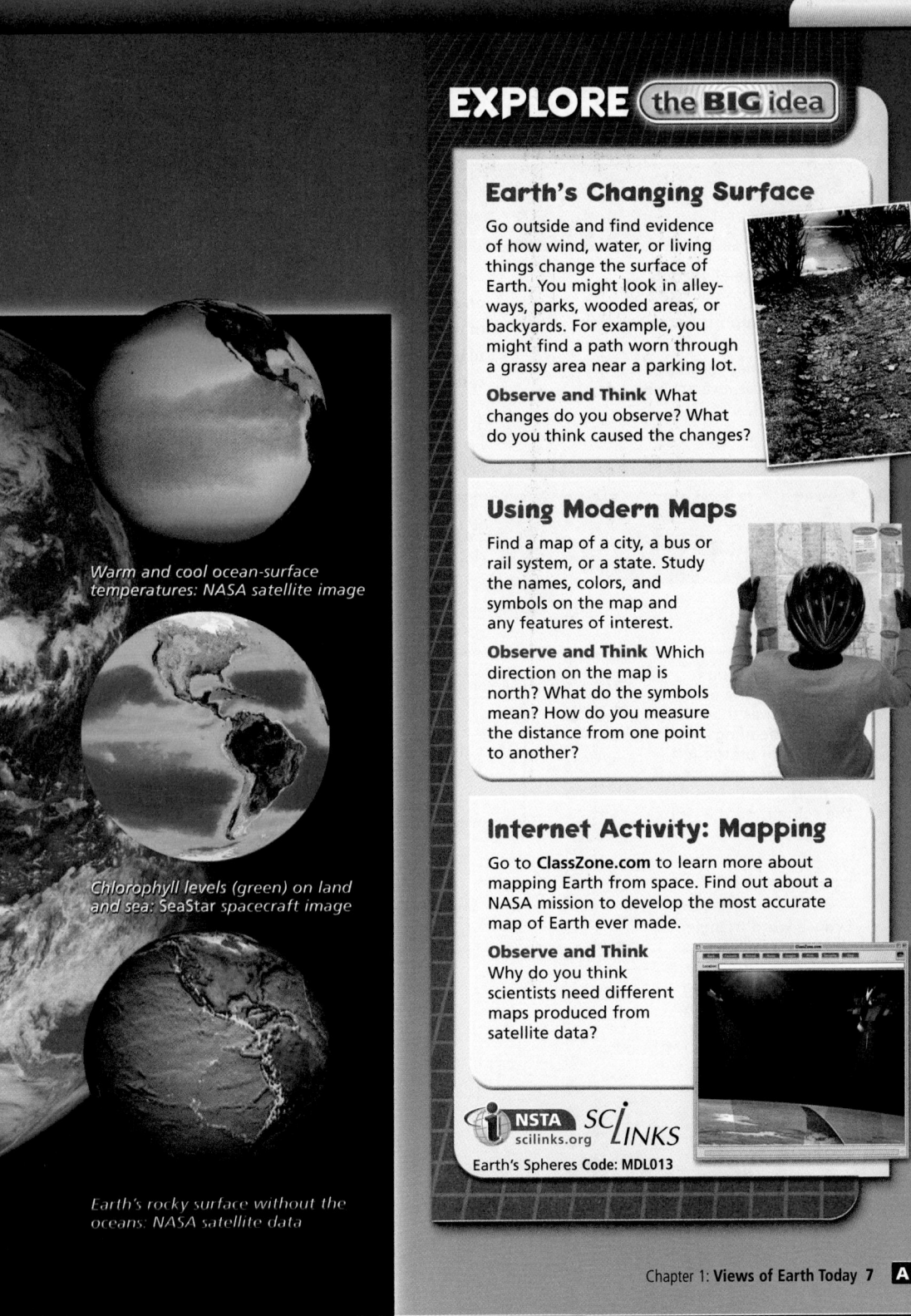

Warm and cool ocean-surface temperatures: NASA satellite image

Chlorophyll levels (green) on land and sea: SeaStar spacecraft image

Earth's rocky surface without the oceans: NASA satellite data

EXPLORE (the BIG idea)

Earth's Changing Surface

Go outside and find evidence of how wind, water, or living things change the surface of Earth. You might look in alleyways, parks, wooded areas, or backyards. For example, you might find a path worn through a grassy area near a parking lot.

Observe and Think What changes do you observe? What do you think caused the changes?

Using Modern Maps

Find a map of a city, a bus or rail system, or a state. Study the names, colors, and symbols on the map and any features of interest.

Observe and Think Which direction on the map is north? What do the symbols mean? How do you measure the distance from one point to another?

Internet Activity: Mapping

Go to **ClassZone.com** to learn more about mapping Earth from space. Find out about a NASA mission to develop the most accurate map of Earth ever made.

Observe and Think Why do you think scientists need different maps produced from satellite data?

NSTA scilinks.org **SCiLINKS**

Earth's Spheres Code: MDL013

Chapter 1: **Views of Earth Today** 7 **A**

EXPLORE (the BIG idea)

These inquiry-based activities are appropriate for use at home or as a supplement to classroom instruction.

Earth's Changing Surface

PURPOSE To introduce students to the erosional forces around them.

TIP *20 min.* If an outside activity is not feasible, students can conduct their investigations from a window.

Answer: Student observations may include evidence such as cracks in walls, ruts worn in alleys, and slope erosion. Students should reason that animal activity, including that of insects and people, and the forces of wind, water, and/or freezing caused such changes.

REVISIT after p. 14.

Using Modern Maps

PURPOSE To introduce students to map interpretation.

TIP *10 min.* Students can compare a local city map with a state or national road map.

Answer: Students should be able to show the arrow pointing north (or compass rose), use the map scale to figure actual distances, and use the legend to determine the meanings of symbols.

REVISIT after p. 17.

Internet Activity: Mapping

PURPOSE To introduce students to the latest technology used in the three-dimensional mapping of Earth.

TIP *20 min.* Ask students to predict the technologies required to map Earth.

Answer: Students may say scientists need to study different parts of Earth or to study how Earth is changing.

REVISIT after p. 34.

TEACHING WITH TECHNOLOGY

GPS If you have access to hand-held GPS units, you may wish to send students to opposite ends of the school and have them compare the readings. The Global Positioning System and related devices are introduced on p. 19.

Chapter 1 **7** **A**

◄ CONCEPT REVIEW

Activate Prior Knowledge

- If possible, display a pumpkin to demonstrate Earth's oblate shape.
- Ask students to discuss how two seemingly separate items—for example, a furniture factory and a rain forest—can be interconnected. *Wood to make furniture might come from a rain forest.*

► TAKING NOTES

Main Idea and Detail Notes

By using graphic organizers to sort out main ideas and make connections between supporting details, students become active readers with improved comprehension.

Vocabulary Strategy

The word triangle functions as a pyramid of meaning. When students define a word, construct a meaningful context for it, and illustrate it, that word becomes part of their vocabulary.

Vocabulary and Note-Taking Resources

R • Vocabulary Practice, pp. 56–57
- Decoding Support, p. 58

T • Daily Vocabulary Scaffolding, p. T2
- Note-Taking Model, p. T3

🔧 • Word Triangle, B18–19
- Main Idea and Detail Notes, C37
- Daily Vocabulary Scaffolding, H1–8

CHAPTER 1
Getting Ready to Learn

◄ CONCEPT REVIEW

- Earth, like all planets, is shaped roughly like a sphere.
- Earth supports a complex web of life.
- The planet consists of many parts that interact with one another.

◄ VOCABULARY REVIEW

See Glossary for definitions.

energy

matter

planet

satellite

ⓘ CONTENT REVIEW
CLASSZONE.COM
Review concepts and vocabulary.

► TAKING NOTES

MAIN IDEA AND DETAIL NOTES

Make a two-column chart. Write the main ideas, such as those in the blue headings, in the column on the left. Write details about each of those main ideas in the column on the right.

VOCABULARY STRATEGY

Draw a **word triangle** diagram for each new vocabulary term. On the bottom line write and define the term. Above that, write a sentence that uses the term correctly. At the top, draw a picture to show what the term looks like.

See the Note-Taking Handbook on pages R45–R51.

SCIENCE NOTEBOOK

MAIN IDEAS	DETAIL NOTES
1. The Earth system has four main parts.	1. Atmosphere = mixture of gases surrounding Earth
	1. Hydrosphere = all waters on Earth

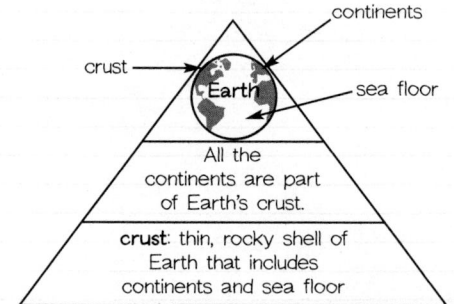

All the continents are part of Earth's crust.

crust: thin, rocky shell of Earth that includes continents and sea floor

---

CHECK READINESS

Administer the Diagnostic Test to determine students' readiness for new science content and their mastery of requisite math skills.

 Diagnostic Test, pp. 1–2

Technology Resources

Students needing content and math skills should visit **ClassZone.com**.

 • CONTENT REVIEW
• MATH TUTORIAL

 CONTENT REVIEW CD-ROM

KEY CONCEPT

1.1 Technology is used to explore the Earth system.

◀ **BEFORE, you learned**
- Earth has a spherical shape and supports a complex web of life
- Earth's environment is a system with many parts

▶ **NOW, you will learn**
- About the Earth system and its four major parts
- How technology is used to explore the Earth system
- How the parts of the Earth system shape the surface

VOCABULARY

system p. 9
atmosphere p. 10
hydrosphere p. 10
biosphere p. 11
geosphere p. 12

THINK ABOUT

How do these parts work together?

Look closely at this terrarium. Notice that the bowl and its cover form a boundary between the terrarium and the outside world. What might happen to the entire terrarium if any part were taken away? What might happen if you placed the terrarium in a dark closet?

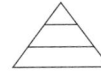

VOCABULARY
Remember to draw a word triangle in your notebook for each vocabulary term.

The Earth system has four major parts.

A terrarium is a simple example of a **system**—an organized group of parts that work together to form a whole. To understand a system, you need to see how all its parts work together. This principle is true for a small terrarium, and it is true for planet Earth.

Both a terrarium and Earth are closed systems. They are closed because matter, such as soil or water, cannot enter or leave. However, energy can flow into or out of the system. Just as light and heat pass through the glass of the terrarium, sunlight and heat enter and leave the Earth system through the atmosphere.

Within the Earth system are four connected parts: the atmosphere (Earth's air), the hydrosphere (Earth's waters), the biosphere (Earth's living things), and the geosphere (Earth's interior and its rocks and soils). Each of these parts is an open system because both matter and energy move into and out of it. The four open systems work together to form one large, closed system called Earth.

Chapter 1: **Views of Earth Today** 9 **A**

RESOURCES FOR DIFFERENTIATED INSTRUCTION

Below Level
UNIT RESOURCE BOOK
- Reading Study Guide A, pp. 13–14
- Decoding Support, p. 58

 **AUDIO CDS**

Advanced
UNIT RESOURCE BOOK
Challenge and Extension, p. 19

English Learners
UNIT RESOURCE BOOK
Spanish Reading Study Guide, pp. 17–18

 AUDIO CDS

- Audio Readings in Spanish
- Audio Readings (English)

1.1 FOCUS

▶ Set Learning Goals
Students will

- Identify the Earth system and its four major parts.
- Explain how technology is used to explore Earth's parts.
- Explain how the parts of Earth's system shape the surface.
- Model the geosphere's layers in an experiment.

◀ 3-Minute Warm-Up

Display Transparency 4 or copy this exercise on the board:

Answer *yes* or *no* to each question, and explain the reason for your answer.

1. Are all the planets in our solar system like Earth? *No, Earth is unique; it supports many different life forms.*

2. Do the oceans cover more of Earth than the continents do? *Yes, water covers nearly three-quarters of Earth's surface.*

3. Is Earth's atmosphere made up of just one gas? *No, Earth's atmosphere is a mixture of gases.*

T 3-Minute Warm-Up, p. T4

1.1 MOTIVATE

THINK ABOUT

PURPOSE To have students think about how parts of a system affect each other

DISCUSS Remind students that the glass bowl is part of the terrarium. Have students attempt to isolate the most vital components in the terrarium's system. *plants, stones, water, bowl*

If air, water, or soil were taken away, the plants would die. Without plants, there would be less oxygen, since photosynthesis would not occur—the terrarium would have no living things to support. Placing the terrarium in a dark closet would take away sunlight and cause the plants to die.

Language Arts Connection

Have students think of related words that contain the same Greek prefixes as those used in each of the four parts of the Earth system. *Sample answer: hydrology, geology, biology* Tell students an atmometer is an instrument that measures rates of evaporation.

Develop Critical Thinking

CLASSIFY Have students classify each item below in its proper sphere.

- ocean floor *geosphere*
- hurricane *atmosphere*
- bird's nest *biosphere*
- mountain glacier *hydrosphere*

Teach from Visuals

Remind students that they can get a preview of chapter content by studying the visuals—photographs, maps, or diagrams—and reading captions.

To help students interpret the "Parts of the Earth System" visual on pp. 10–11, ask:

- What landforms do you recognize in this image of Earth? *Students should recognize the North American continent, and the northern part of South America. They may identify Florida, Cuba, the Gulf Coast, and Mexico; Greenland is also visible.*
- What does each of the four inset photographs show? *one of the Earth system's four major parts*
- What theme is shared by the photographs? *human exploration of the Earth system through the use of technology*

READING TiP

The names of the Earth system's four parts contain Greek prefixes. *Atmo-* refers to vapor or gas. *Hydro-* refers to water. *Bio-* refers to life, and *geo-* refers to earth.

Atmosphere

The **atmosphere** (AT-muh-SFEER) is the mixture of gases that surrounds and protects Earth. The most abundant gases are nitrogen (about 78%) and oxygen (nearly 21%). The atmosphere also contains carbon dioxide, water vapor, and a few other gases.

Before the 1800s, all studies of the atmosphere had to be done from the ground. Today, scientists launch weather balloons, fly specially equipped planes, and view the atmosphere in satellite images. The data they collect show that the atmosphere interacts with the other parts of the Earth system to form complex weather patterns that circulate around Earth. The more scientists learn about these patterns, the more accurately they can predict local weather.

(?) A

Hydrosphere

The **hydrosphere** (HY-druh-SFEER) is made up of all the water on Earth in oceans, lakes, glaciers, rivers, and streams and underground. Water covers nearly three-quarters of Earth's surface. Only about 3 percent of the hydrosphere is fresh water. Nearly 70 percent of Earth's fresh water is frozen in glaciers and polar ice caps.

(?) B

Parts of the Earth System

Atmosphere

Over 400 cones make this weather balloon more stable as it gathers data about the atmosphere.

Hydrosphere

Scientists need special diving equipment to study Earth's oceans.

DIFFERENTIATE INSTRUCTION

(?) More Reading Support

A What is a weather balloon used for? *studying the atmosphere*

B What percentage of Earth's fresh water is frozen? *nearly 70 percent*

English Learners Help English learners remember the differences between these similar-sounding terms: *atmosphere, hydrosphere, biosphere,* and *geosphere.* Suggest they separate each term into two parts by writing the prefix and *-sphere* on an index card. Under the Greek prefix, have them write the English meaning. *(Example: hydro- means water)* They can refer to these cards during lessons.

English Learners may not have prior knowledge of terrariums (p. 9), polar ice caps (p. 10), or computer modeling (p. 12).

In the past 50 years, scientists have used deep-sea vehicles, special buoys, satellite images, and diving suits, such as the one shown on page 10, to study the world's oceans. They have discovered that the oceans contain several layers of cold and warm water. As these layers circulate, they form cold and warm ocean currents. The currents interact with wind patterns in the atmosphere and affect Earth's weather.

 **CHECK YOUR READING** How does the hydrosphere affect the atmosphere?

Biosphere

C The **biosphere** (BY-uh-SFEER) includes all life on Earth, in the air, on the land, and in the waters. The biosphere can be studied with a variety of technologies. For example, satellite photos are used to track yearly changes in Earth's plant and animal life. As the photograph below shows, special equipment allows scientists to study complex environments, such as rain forests, without damaging them.

D Scientists have learned a lot about how the biosphere interacts with the other parts of the Earth system. For example, large forests act as Earth's "lungs," absorbing carbon dioxide and releasing oxygen into the atmosphere. When dead trees decay, they return nutrients to the soil.

CHECK YOUR READING Name one way the biosphere and the atmosphere interact.

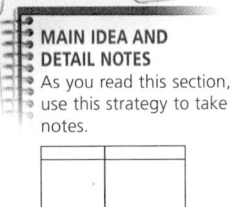

MAIN IDEA AND DETAIL NOTES
As you read this section, use this strategy to take notes.

Biosphere

These platforms, built in the treetops, are used to observe forest plants and animals.

Geosphere

In mines dug deep underground, scientists can explore Earth's minerals and rocks.

DIFFERENTIATE INSTRUCTION

 **More Reading Support**

C What is the biosphere? *all forms of life on Earth*

D Do plants absorb or release carbon dioxide? *absorb*

Advanced Have students hypothesize how oceans originated on our planet. Ask: How did Earth come to be a water planet? *Volcanic action released steam, which then condensed into liquid water. Some scientists also think that icy comets melted when they struck Earth, which added water to the planet.*

Integrate the Sciences

Make a connection with life science by discussing the fact that the environment of the ocean depths is inhospitable to human life. The incredible pressures in the deep ocean are the biggest obstacle to undersea exploration. Conventional scuba equipment restricts divers to depths of less than 40 meters. They must also be careful to limit the duration of their dives and to surface gradually. Failure to do so can result in a painful and sometimes fatal condition known as the bends. Oxygen-enriched air can allow divers to extend the duration of their dives by limiting the amount of nitrogen absorbed into their blood.

Real World Example

The great depths of the oceans can be explored with the aid of research submersibles. The National Oceanic and Atmospheric Administration (NOAA) runs an undersea laboratory and uses a variety of submersible vehicles that can, in the case of the famous *Alvin,* carry people as deep as 4500 meters. Two types of unmanned submersibles are also used for sea exploration. ROVs (remotely operated vehicles) operate while attached to ships; AUVs (autonomous underwater vehicles) operate independently, following a programmed set of instructions.

Ongoing Assessment

Identify the Earth system and its four major parts

Ask: What are the four parts of Earth's system? *atmosphere, hydrosphere, biosphere, geosphere*

CHECK YOUR READING *Answer: Warm and cold ocean currents interact with wind patterns to influence Earth's weather.*

CHECK YOUR READING *Answer: Trees exchange gases with the atmosphere, taking in carbon dioxide and giving off oxygen.*

Address Misconceptions

IDENTIFY Ask: Is Earth's mantle solid or liquid? If students say it is liquid, they may hold the misconception that Earth's mantle is entirely liquid because of the liquid-like properties of magma.

CORRECT Tell students that Earth's mantle, the thickest of Earth's layers, is primarily solid, but it does have liquid properties due to its high pressures and temperatures. Use an undercooked loaf of bread as an example. On the outside, the crust is solid, but as a person cuts into the loaf, there may be hot globs of unbaked dough.

REASSESS What represents Earth's mantle in the undercooked loaf of bread model? *the undercooked dough in the interior*

Ongoing Assessment

Explain how technology is used to explore Earth's parts.

Ask: What technology helps scientists to explore the geosphere? *Satellite images, instruments that measure sound waves, and computer modeling gather data about the geosphere.*

CHECK YOUR READING *Answer: Volcanoes throw gases and dust into the atmosphere.*

Geosphere

 E

The **geosphere** (JEE-uh-SFEER) includes all the features on Earth's surface—the continents, islands, and sea floor—and everything below the surface. As the diagram illustrates, the geosphere is made up of several layers: crust, mantle, and outer and inner core.

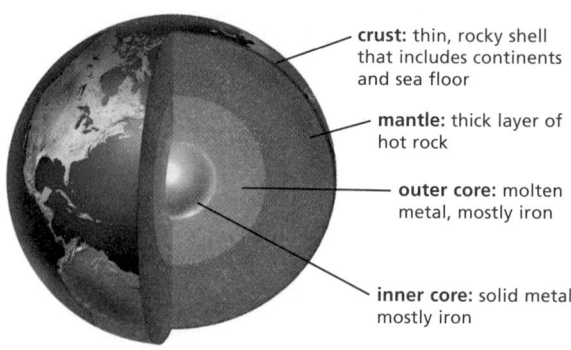

crust: thin, rocky shell that includes continents and sea floor

mantle: thick layer of hot rock

outer core: molten metal, mostly iron

inner core: solid metal, mostly iron

People have studied the surface of the geosphere for centuries. Not until the 1900s, however, were people able to study Earth from space or to explore deep within the planet. Today, scientists use satellite images, sound waves, and computer modeling to develop accurate pictures of features on and below Earth's surface. These images show that Earth constantly changes. Some changes are sudden—a volcano explodes, releasing harmful gases and dust into the air. Other changes, such as the birth of new islands, happen over millions of years.

CHECK YOUR READING Give an example of matter moving from the geosphere to the atmosphere.

Earth's continents have many unique landforms such as these rock towers in Cathedral Valley, Utah.

DIFFERENTIATE INSTRUCTION

? More Reading Support

E What is the geosphere? *all the features on Earth's surface—the continents, islands, and sea floor—and everything below the surface*

Below Level To help students remember the details of each "sphere," have them fill in this chart with important facts.

	Characteristics
Atmosphere	
Hydrosphere	
Biosphere	
Geosphere	

INVESTIGATE Geosphere's Layers

How can you model the geosphere's layers?
PROCEDURE

1. As a model of the layers in the geosphere, you will be using a quarter of an apple that your teacher has cut. Note: NEVER eat food in the science classroom.

2. Hold the apple slice and observe it carefully. Compare it with the diagram of the geosphere's layers on page 12.

3. Draw a diagram of the apple and label it with the names of the layers of the geosphere.

WHAT DO YOU THINK?

- What are the four parts of the apple slice?
- What major layer of the geosphere does each part of the apple resemble?

CHALLENGE What other object do you think would make a good model of the geosphere's layers? What model could you build or make yourself?

SKILL FOCUS
Modeling

MATERIALS
apple slice

TIME
15 minutes

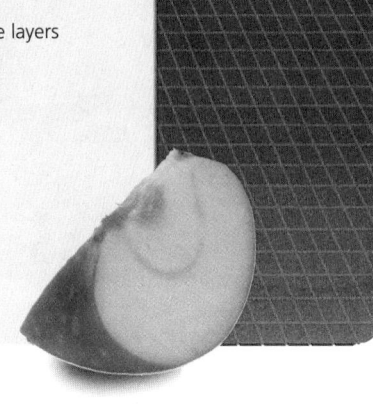

All four parts of the Earth system shape the planet's surface.

Earth's surface is worn away, built up, and reshaped every day by the atmosphere, the hydrosphere, the biosphere, and the geosphere. Here are some of the ways they affect the surface.

Atmosphere and Hydrosphere Not even the hardest stone can withstand wind and water. Over millions of years, rain, wind, and flowing water carve huge formations such as the Grand Canyon in Arizona or the rock towers of Utah, shown on page 12.

Geosphere Landmasses pushing together have set off earthquakes and formed volcanoes and mountain ranges around the world.

Biosphere Plants, animals, and human beings have also changed Earth's surface. For instance, earthworms help make soils more fertile. And throughout human history, people have dammed rivers and cleared forests for farmland.

You are part of this process, too. Every time you walk or ride a bike across open land, you are changing Earth's surface. Your feet or the bike's tires dig into the dirt, wearing away plants and exposing soil to sunlight, wind, and water. If you take the same route every day, over time you will wear a path in the land.

> **READING TiP**
> *Landmass* is a compound word made up of the words *land* and *mass*. Landmass means "a large area of land."

Chapter 1: **Views of Earth Today** 13 **A**

INVESTIGATE Geosphere's Layers

PURPOSE To model and identify the geosphere's layers

TIP *15 min.* Have students review Earth's layers before attempting to compare them with the layers of the apple.

WHAT DO YOU THINK? *outer skin = crust; layer next to skin = mantle; inner ring and layer = outer core; core and seed = inner cores*

CHALLENGE *a multicolored clay ball, a round pear, a hard-boiled egg; plastic-foam balls cut in half and painted*

 Datasheet, Geosphere's Layers, p. 20

Technology Resources

Customize this student lab as needed or look for an alternative. Print rubrics to assess student lab reports.

Lab Generator CD-ROM

Address Misconceptions

IDENTIFY Ask: Is Earth's crust thick or thin? If students say it is thick, they may not realize that Earth's crust is relatively thin.

CORRECT Explain that Earth's interior is active and hot but crustal rocks cool quickly at the lower surface temperatures. Crustal rocks form a thin layer around Earth that is only 5–70 kilometers deep.

REASSESS Ask: What makes Earth's crust thin? *Its closeness to the surface causes a thin layer of rock to cool quickly.*

Technology Resources

Visit **ClassZone.com** for background on common student misconceptions.

 MISCONCEPTION DATABASE

Chapter 1 **13** **A**

CHECK YOUR READING *Answer: Wind and moving water wear away rocky surfaces; landmasses pushing together cause earthquakes and form volcanoes and other mountains; plants, animals, and people wear away or change Earth's surface.*

EXPLORE (the **BIG** idea)

Revisit "Earth's Changing Surface" on p. 7. Have students explain the four parts of the Earth system worked together to account for their observations.

Reinforce (the **BIG** idea)

Have students relate the section to the Big Idea.

 Reinforcing Key Concepts, p. 21

1.1 ASSESS & RETEACH

Assess

A Section 1.1 Quiz, p. 3

Reteach

Draw a cutaway diagram on the board, similar to that on p. 12 but without indications of the boundaries between layers. Ask for volunteers to add the following information to the diagram:

- Locations of the atmosphere, hydrosphere, biosphere, and geosphere
- Compositions of the four spheres
- Boundaries and names of the geosphere's layers
- Composition or nature of each geosphere layer

Technology Resources

Have students visit **ClassZone.com** for reteaching of Key Concepts.

CONTENT REVIEW

CONTENT REVIEW CD-ROM

Mudslide in California

Atmosphere and Hydrosphere
Heavy winter rains soak the ground until it cannot absorb any more water.

Biosphere People who build on fragile hillsides remove plants whose roots help hold the soil in place.

Geosphere With nothing to hold the water-soaked ground, it slides downhill, leaving a deep trench.

The photograph above shows a good example of how the four parts can suddenly change Earth's surface. A mudslide like this one can happen in a matter of minutes. Sometimes the side of a mountain may collapse, becoming a river of mud that can bury an entire town.

The four parts of the Earth system continue to shape the surface with every passing year. Scientists will continue to record these changes to update maps and other images of the planet's complex system.

 **CHECK YOUR READING** Find three examples on pages 13 and 14 that show how the parts of the Earth system shape the planet's surface.

1.1 Review

KEY CONCEPTS

1. Define *system*. Compare an open and a closed system.
2. Name the four parts of the Earth system. List one fact about each part that scientists learned through modern technology.
3. Give two examples of how the Earth system's four parts can interact with each other.

CRITICAL THINKING

4. **Apply** One day you see that plants are dying in the class terrarium. What part might be missing from its system?
5. **Infer** You visit a state park and see a thin rock wall with a hole, like a window, worn through it. Which of the four parts of the Earth system might have made the hole? Explain.

◯ CHALLENGE

6. **Predict** Imagine that a meteorite 200 meters wide strikes Earth, landing in a wooded area. Describe one way that this event would affect the biosphere or the geosphere. **Hint:** A meteorite is traveling several thousand kilometers per hour when it strikes the ground.

A **14** Unit: **Earth's Surface**

ANSWERS

1. *organized group of parts that work together to form a whole; closed system: energy but not matter can enter or leave; open system: matter and energy can enter or leave*

2. *atmosphere: complex weather patterns; hydrosphere: layers of cold and* warm water; biosphere: yearly changes in plant and animal life; geosphere: features above and below Earth's surface

3. *Storms in the atmosphere can change Earth's coastlines; animals can wear paths in Earth's surface.*

4. *water, air, or soil nutrients*

5. *hydrosphere (rain) or hydrosphere and atmosphere (rain and wind)*

6. *It would blast a huge crater in the geosphere. The heat would destroy nearby plants and animals in the biosphere.*

1.2 Maps and globes are models of Earth.

◀ **BEFORE, you learned**

- The Earth system has four main parts: atmosphere, hydrosphere, biosphere, and geosphere
- Technology is used to study and map the Earth system
- The Earth system's parts interact to shape Earth's surface

▶ **NOW, you will learn**

- What information maps can provide about natural and human-made features
- How to find exact locations on Earth
- Why all maps distort Earth's surface

VOCABULARY

relief map p. 16
map scale p. 17
map legend p. 17
equator p. 18
latitude p. 18
prime meridian p. 19
longitude p. 19
projection p. 20

EXPLORE Mapping

What makes a good map?

PROCEDURE

① Draw a map to guide someone from your school to your home or to a point of interest, such as a park, statue, or store, near your school.

② Trade maps with a classmate. Is his or her map easy to understand? Why or why not?

③ Use feedback from your partner to revise your own map.

WHAT DO YOU THINK?
What visual clues make a map easy to understand and use?

MATERIALS
- paper
- pencil or pen

Maps show natural and human-made features.

Have you ever drawn a map to help someone get to your home? If so, your map is actually a rough model of your neighborhood, showing important streets and landmarks. Any map you use is a flat model of Earth's surface, showing Earth's features as seen from above.

On the other hand, a globe represents Earth as if you were looking at it from outer space. A globe is a sphere that shows the relative sizes and shapes of Earth's land features and waters.

In this section you will learn how maps and globes provide different types of information about Earth's surface. They can show everything from city streets to land features to the entire world.

CHECK YOUR READING How are maps and globes alike? How are they different?

▶ Set Learning Goals

Students will

- Describe the types of information that maps provide.
- Explain how to find exact locations.
- Explain why all maps distort Earth's surface.
- Experiment with models to project a curved surface onto a flat surface.

◀ 3-Minute Warm-Up

Display Transparency 4 or copy this exercise on the board:

Remember that the Earth system has four main parts that interact. Identify the parts involved in the following scenarios.

1. Wind blows a sailboat across a lake. *atmosphere/hydrosphere*

2. A bear digs under a log to search for food. *biosphere/geosphere*

3. People wear a path through a forest, and rain further erodes the path. *biosphere/hydrosphere/geosphere*

Ⓣ 3-Minute Warm-Up, p. T4

1.2 MOTIVATE

EXPLORE Mapping

PURPOSE To introduce students to the concept of maps as easy-to-use tools

TIP *25 min.* Encourage students to use well-known landmarks.

WHAT DO YOU THINK? *street names, landmarks, and compass directions*

Ongoing Assessment

CHECK YOUR READING *Answer: Both are models of Earth that show various features. Maps show Earth's features as if viewed from above. Globes show Earth as if seen from outer space.*

RESOURCES FOR DIFFERENTIATED INSTRUCTION

Below Level
UNIT RESOURCE BOOK
- Reading Study Guide A, pp. 24–25
- Decoding Support, p. 58

 **AUDIO CDS**

Ⓡ **Additional INVESTIGATION,** Make a Map by Triangulation, A, B, & C, pp. 70–78; Teacher Instructions, pp. 348–349

Advanced
UNIT RESOURCE BOOK
Challenge and Extension, p. 30

English Learners
UNIT RESOURCE BOOK
Spanish Reading Study Guide, pp. 28–29

 **AUDIO CDS**

- Audio Readings in Spanish
- Audio Readings (English)

1.2 INSTRUCT

Teach from Visuals

To help students interpret the relief map, ask:

- Where would you draw lines to divide the continent into thirds? *at the eastern edge of the Rockies and from the bottom of Lake Superior to the Mississippi Delta*

- How does the map show relief? *Different colors indicate different elevations, and shading gives a three-dimensional appearance to the landscape.*

- How can you tell which mountain ranges are highest? *High mountain ranges appear as large ripples, with the darkest shadows.*

Teach Difficult Concepts

Emphasize the term *three-dimensional* when describing the landscape view offered by relief maps.

Real World Example

Accurate relief maps are important for ensuring aviation safety, assessing risks of natural hazards, and creating sustainable urban development. A mission flown by the space shuttle *Endeavour* greatly advanced map accuracy for many parts of the world. The 2000 Shuttle Radar Topography Mission produced accurate three-dimensional measurements for more than 80 percent of Earth's land area. Every 15 minutes, the shuttle scanned an area the size of Alaska.

Ongoing Assessment

CHECK YOUR READING *Answer: Unlike a mountain, a plateau is fairly level; unlike a plain, a plateau is usually high above sea level.*

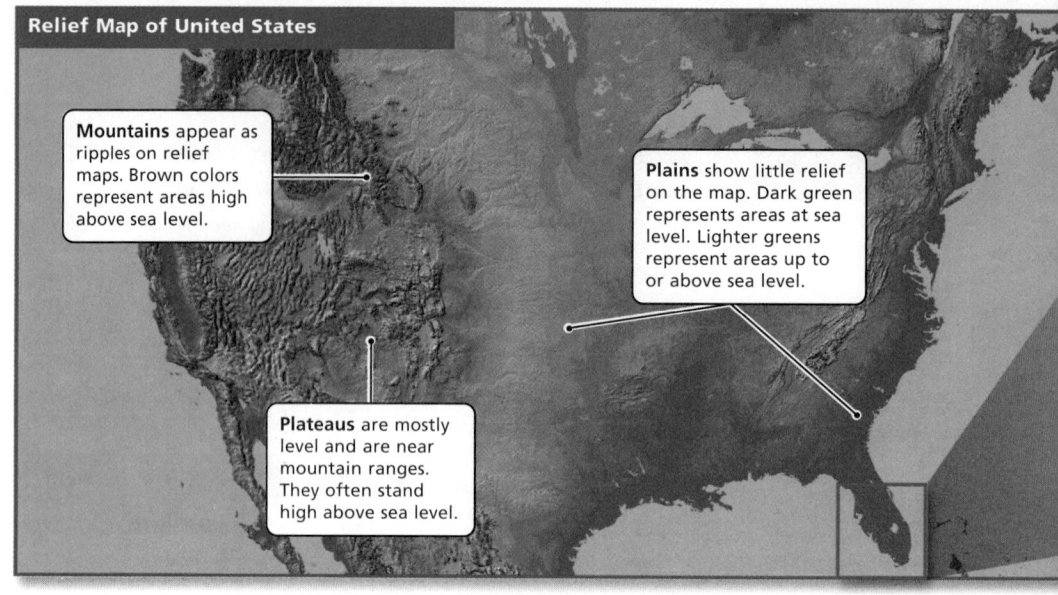

Relief Map of United States

Mountains appear as ripples on relief maps. Brown colors represent areas high above sea level.

Plains show little relief on the map. Dark green represents areas at sea level. Lighter greens represent areas up to or above sea level.

Plateaus are mostly level and are near mountain ranges. They often stand high above sea level.

VOCABULARY
Add a word triangle for *relief map* to your notebook.

Land Features on Maps

When scientists or travelers want to know what the landscape of an area actually looks like, they will often use a relief map. A **relief map,** such as the one above, shows how high or low each feature is on Earth. A mapmaker uses photographs or satellite images to build a three-dimensional view of Earth's surface. A relief map shows three main types of land features: mountains, plains, and plateaus.

Mountains stand higher than the land around them. A mountain's base may cover several square kilometers. A group of mountains is called a mountain range. Mountain ranges connected in a long chain form a mountain belt. The Rocky Mountains in the United States are part of a huge mountain belt that includes the Canadian Rockies and the Andes Mountains in South America.

Plateaus have fairly level surfaces but stand high above sea level. Plateaus are often found near large mountain ranges. In the United States, the Colorado Plateau is about 3350 meters (11,000 ft) above sea level. This plateau includes parts of Arizona, Colorado, New Mexico, and Utah.

Plains are gently rolling or flat features. The United States has two types of plains—coastal plains near the eastern and southeastern shores, and interior plains in the center of the nation. The interior Great Plains cover the middle third of the United States.

CHECK YOUR READING How is a plateau different from either a mountain or a plain?

A 16 Unit: Earth's Surface

DIFFERENTIATE INSTRUCTION

? More Reading Support

A What three main types of land features does a relief map show? *mountains, plains, and plateaus*

English Learners English learners may lack background knowledge of *sea level* on p. 16 and *cross products* on p. 23. Allow English learners to use their home countries as points of reference when learning to use maps. They might study street maps of major cities in their countries or use a globe to find their countries' latitude and longitude.

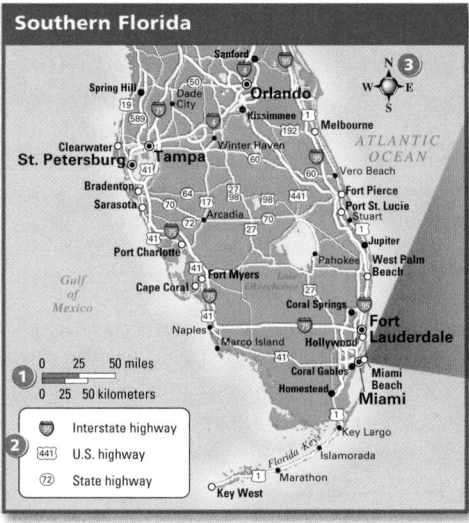

Southern Florida

Miami Beach, Detail

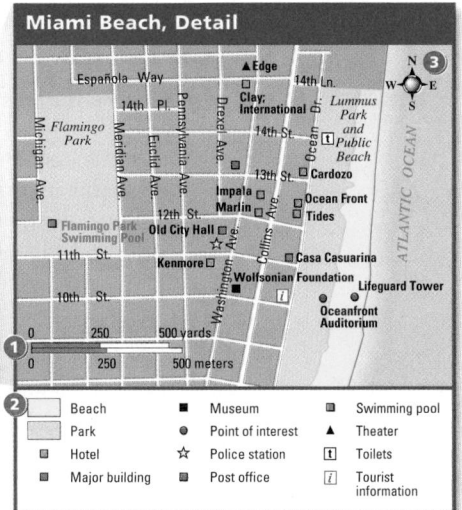

Scale and Symbols on Maps

The maps most people use are road and city maps like the ones above. These maps provide information about human-made features as well as some natural features. To use these maps, you need to know how to read a map scale and a map legend, or key.

1 A **map scale** relates distances on a map to actual distances on Earth's surface. Notice that on the map of southern Florida above, the scale is in kilometers and miles. On the Miami Beach map, the scale is in meters and yards. The smaller the area a map shows, the more detail it includes.

The scale can be expressed as a ratio, a bar, or equivalent units of distance. For example, a ratio of 1:25,000 means that 1 centimeter on the map represents 25,000 centimeters (0.25 kilometer) on Earth.

Three Types of Map Scale

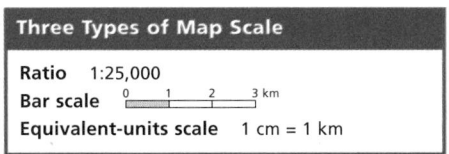

Ratio	1:25,000
Bar scale	
Equivalent-units scale	1 cm = 1 km

2 A **map legend,** also called a key, is a chart that explains the meaning of each symbol used on a map. Symbols can stand for highways, parks, and other features. The legend on the Miami Beach map shows major points of interest for tourists.

READING TiP

As used here, *legend* does not refer to a story. It is based on the Latin word *legenda*, which means "to be read."

3 A map usually includes a compass rose to show which directions are north, south, east, and west. In general, north on a map points to the top of the page.

CHECK YOUR READING What information do map scales and map legends provide?

DIFFERENTIATE INSTRUCTION

? More Reading Support

B Why do maps have scales? *to show how distances on the map are related to actual distances on Earth*

Advanced Briefly describe the characteristics of deltas, canyons, and valleys. Then have students search reference sources and the Internet to find relief maps that show these features. Ask them to identify as may deltas, valleys, and canyons as they can, and then describe how the three-dimensional quality of the relief maps allowed them to recognize the features.

R Challenge and Extension, p. 30

Teach from Visuals

To help students interpret the maps of southern Florida and Miami Beach, ask:

• How are the two maps related? *The first shows the southern part of Florida; the second enlarges one city in southern Florida—Miami Beach— to show more detail.*

• How are the two maps similar? *Both are oriented with north at the top, as indicated by the direction arrows.*

• How do you know where on the first map the second map is located? *A shaded region extends from the city's location on the first map to the second map.*

Develop Critical Thinking

APPLY Have students apply their knowledge of maps to plan a car trip from Orlando to Miami. Ask them to name the parts of the map where they would find the following information:

• types of roads they will follow *legend*
• direction(s) they will travel *compass rose*
• the distance they must drive *scale*
• cities and towns they will pass through *labels on the map*

EXPLORE (the BIG idea)

Revisit "Using Modern Maps" on p. 7. Have students share their answers.

Ongoing Assessment

Describe the types of information that maps provide about natural and human-made features.

Ask: What types of information do maps provide about natural and human-made features? *locations, elevations, shapes, and relief of natural features, as well as sizes and locations of cities and roads*

CHECK YOUR READING *Answer: A scale relates distances on a map to actual distances on Earth's surface. A legend explains the meaning of each symbol used on a map.*

History of Science

The latitude/longitude system of locating places on Earth was probably first developed around 150 A.D. by Claudius Ptolemy, a Greek astronomer and geographer. Ptolemy lived and worked in Alexandria, Egypt, which at that time was a crossroads for travelers. Ptolemy developed a grid of meridians (longitude lines) and parallels (latitude lines) to establish coordinates for as many as 8,000 places mentioned by the travelers he encountered.

Teach from Visuals

To help students interpret the "Latitude and Longitude" visual, ask:

- Is the equator a latitude line or a longitude line? *latitude line*
- What are the latitude and the longitude of the place where the equator and the prime meridian cross? *0°, 0°*
- Which set of lines divides Earth in a way similar to the division of an orange into segments? *longitude lines*

 This visual is also available as T6 in the Unit Transparency Book.

Teach Difficult Concepts

Students may become confused about the east-west latitude lines that indicate angular distances north and south on the globe and the north-south meridians that indicate angular distances east and west on the globe. Copy the diagram "Latitude and Longitude" on the board, using one color for latitude lines and a different color for longitude lines. Then write the coordinates of various locations, using the corresponding colors for the latitude and longitude measurements. Point out that latitude lines go to 90°, whereas longitude lines go to 180°.

Ongoing Assessment

READING VISUALS Answer: Cairo: 30° N, 30° E; Paris: 50° N; 2° E

VISUALIZATION
CLASSZONE.COM
Explore how latitude and longitude help you find locations on Earth's surface.

Latitude and longitude show locations on Earth.

Suppose you were lucky enough to find dinosaur bones in the desert. Would you know how to find that exact spot again? You would if you knew the longitude and latitude of the place. Latitude and longitude lines form an imaginary grid over the entire surface of Earth. This grid provides everyone with the same tools for navigation. Using latitude and longitude, you can locate any place on the planet.

Latitude

READING TiP
Hemi- is a Greek prefix meaning "half."

 C

 D

Latitude is based on an imaginary line that circles Earth halfway between the north and south poles. This line is called the **equator,** and it divides Earth into northern and southern hemispheres. A hemisphere is one half of a sphere.

Latitude is a distance in degrees north or south of the equator, which is 0°. A degree is 1/360 of the distance around a full circle. If you start at one point on the equator and travel all the way around the world back to that point, you have traveled 360 degrees.

The illustration below shows that latitude lines are parallel to the equator and are evenly spaced between the equator and the poles. Also, latitude lines are always labeled north or south of the equator to

Latitude and Longitude

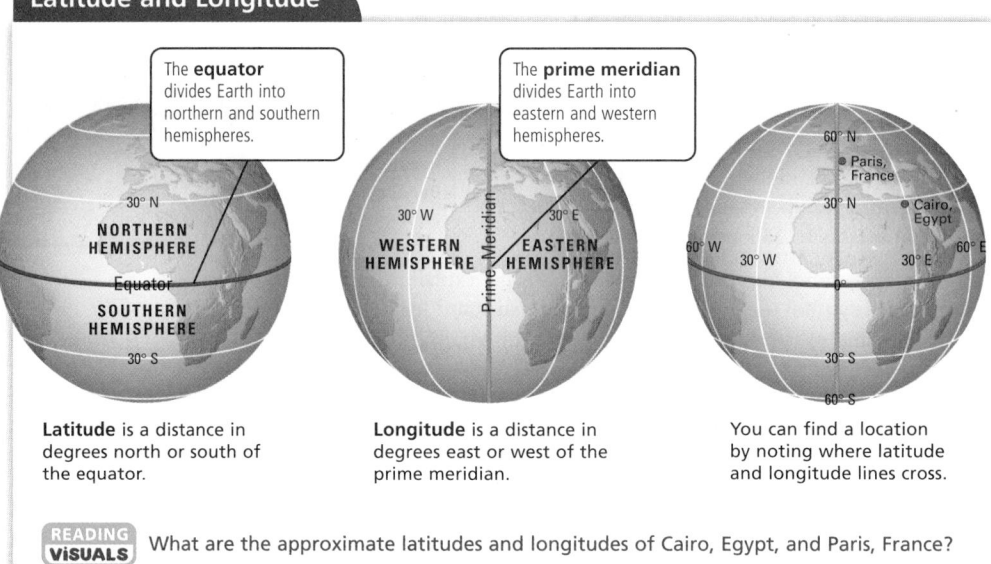

The **equator** divides Earth into northern and southern hemispheres.

The **prime meridian** divides Earth into eastern and western hemispheres.

Latitude is a distance in degrees north or south of the equator.

Longitude is a distance in degrees east or west of the prime meridian.

You can find a location by noting where latitude and longitude lines cross.

 **READING VISUALS** What are the approximate latitudes and longitudes of Cairo, Egypt, and Paris, France?

DIFFERENTIATE INSTRUCTION

More Reading Support

C What is the equator? *an imaginary line dividing Earth into two hemispheres*

D What is latitude? *distance in degrees north or south of the equator*

Below Level The game Battleship can help students gain a sense of latitude and longitude. One player calls out a coordinate set that consists of a letter from the vertical axis and a number from the horizontal axis. If one of the other player's ships is at those coordinates, then the ship is hit. The game is available at toy stores, or it can be reproduced by having students draw their "ships" on graphs with numbers on the *x*-axes and letters on the *y*-axes.

show whether a location is in the northern or southern hemisphere. For instance, the North Pole is 90° north, or 90°N, while the South Pole is 90° south, or 90°S. Latitude, however, is only half of what you need to locate any spot on Earth. You also need to know its longitude.

Longitude

Longitude is based on an imaginary line that stretches from the North Pole through Greenwich, England, to the South Pole. This line is called the **prime meridian.** Any place west of the prime meridian is in the Western Hemisphere. Any place east of the prime meridian is in the Eastern Hemisphere.

Longitude is a distance in degrees east or west of the prime meridian, which is 0°. Beginning at the prime meridian, longitude lines are numbered 0° to 180° west and 0° to 180° east.

Longitude lines are labeled east or west to indicate whether a location is in the eastern or western hemisphere. For example, the longitude of Washington, D.C., is about 78° west, or 78°W. The city of Hamburg, Germany, is about 10° east, or 10°E. If you understand latitude and longitude, you can find any spot on Earth's surface.

 **CHECK YOUR READING** Why do all cities in the United States have a north latitude and a west longitude?

READING TiP

There is an easy way to remember the difference between latitude and longitude. Think of longitude lines as the "long" lines that go from pole to pole.

Global Positioning System

 The Global Positioning System (GPS) is a network of satellites that are used to find the latitude, longitude, and elevation, or height above sea level, of any site. Twenty-four GPS satellites circle Earth and send signals that are picked up by receivers on the surface. At least three satellites need to be above the horizon for GPS to work. A computer inside a receiver uses the satellite signals to calculate the user's exact location—latitude, longitude, and elevation. GPS is an accurate, easy method for finding location.

GPS devices are used by many people, including pilots, sailors, hikers, and map makers. Some cars now have GPS receivers and digital road maps stored in their computers. A driver types in an address, and the car's computer finds the best way to get there.

 **CHECK YOUR READING** Explain how GPS can help someone find their exact location.

Never be lost again. This hiker turns on his GPS unit to find out his current latitude and longitude. He then locates the same degrees on his map to pinpoint his exact location.

Chapter 1: **Views of Earth Today 19** **A**

History of Science

Finding longitude at sea was a long-standing challenge for mariners. The determination of longitude requires a knowledge of time differences; measuring it by the positions of the Sun or stars, as was done for latitude, was impossible. Not until the 1700s, when reliable and precise clocks that could tolerate shipboard conditions were invented, was the problem solved. The clocks allowed mariners to compare local times with the time at Greenwich on the prime meridian, and thus enabled them to calculate exact longitudes.

Teaching with Technology

If you have access to hand-held GPS units, send students to opposite ends of the schoolyard or block and have them record degrees, minutes, and seconds of latitude and longitude. Compare students' data as part of a classroom discussion about GPS technology.

Real World Example

GPS measurements are accurate to within 10 to 20 meters for nonmilitary users, but this was not always the case. The U.S. government intentionally decreased the accuracy of non-military GPS signals for purposes of military security. Until 2000, these signals, altered under a program called "selective availability," were accurate only to within 100 meters.

Ongoing Assessment

Explain how to find exact locations.

Ask: How are latitude and longitude used to find exact locations on Earth? *Imaginary lines superimposed on the globe in a grid system allow people to plot locations as sets of coordinates.*

CHECK YOUR READING *Answer: because all U.S. cities are north of the equator and west of the prime meridian*

CHECK YOUR READING *Answer: A network of 24 satellites circling Earth send signals to ground receivers. A computer inside a GPS receiver uses the signals to calculate the user's exact latitude, longitude, and elevation.*

DIFFERENTIATE INSTRUCTION

? More Reading Support

E What is the GPS? *a network of satellites and ground receivers used to find exact position*

Additional Investigation To reinforce Section 1.2 learning goals, use the following full-period investigation:

 **Additional INVESTIGATION,** Make a Map by Triangulation, A, B, & C, pp. 70–78, 348–349 (Advanced students should complete Levels B and C.)

Below Level Have students create a chart to differentiate between characteristics of latitude and longitude.

Address Misconceptions

IDENTIFY Hold up a flat map of the world and ask: Does this accurately show the shapes and sizes of the continents and oceans? If students answer yes, they may hold the misconception that map projections are accurate images of Earth's landmasses and oceans.

CORRECT Hold a globe next to the map and ask students to point out differences in the shapes of extreme northern landmasses (such as Greenland). Ask them to consider why they look different.

REASSESS Ask: Is a globe or a map a better representation of the size and shape of Earth? Why? *A globe, because it is shaped like Earth and shows Earth's curved surface.*

INVESTIGATE Map Projections

PURPOSE To model map projections in order to understand how the curved Earth can be shown on a flat surface

TIPS *20 min.* Have students make the lines thick. Dim lights while students shine their flashlights into the plastic bottles.

WHAT DO YOU THINK? *Similarities: have longitude and latitude lines; represent one hemisphere. Differences: The projection is flat and its longitude lines radiate outward.*

CHALLENGE *The top of a landmass will show the greatest distortion; the bottom, the least.*

 Datasheet, Map Projections, p. 31

Map projections distort the view of Earth's surface.

The most accurate way to show Earth's surface is on a globe. A globe, however, cannot show much detail, and it is awkward to carry. People use flat maps for their detail and convenience. A **projection** is a way of representing Earth's curved surface on a flat map. Mapmakers use different types of projections, all of which distort, or misrepresent, Earth's surface in different ways.

Cylindrical Projection

The Mercator projection shows Earth as if the map were a large cylinder wrapped around the planet. The outlines of the landmasses and seas are then drawn onto the map. As shown in the diagram on page 21, the cylinder is unrolled to form a flat map. Latitude and longitude appear as straight lines, forming a grid of rectangles.

 The Mercator projection is useful for navigating at sea or in the air. It shows the entire world, except for regions near the poles, on one map. Sailors and pilots can draw a straight line from one point to

INVESTIGATE Map Projections

How do you show the curved Earth on a flat surface?

PROCEDURE

1. Work with a small group. For a model of a hemisphere, use the top section of a 2-liter plastic bottle that your teacher has cut.

2. Carefully draw three or four latitude lines and six or eight longitude lines on the bottle.

3. Place a piece of clay in the center of a piece of poster board. Press the bottle top into the clay.

4. Shine a flashlight downward above the center of the model. Trace the lines on the poster board to make your projection.

WHAT DO YOU THINK?
What are the similarities and differences between your model and your projection?

CHALLENGE Draw a shape on the plastic bottle to represent a landmass. Use the flashlight again to project the hemisphere. How did the shape of your landmass appear when it was projected onto a flat surface?

SKILL FOCUS
Modeling

MATERIALS
- top 8 inches of 2-liter bottle
- marker pen
- walnut-sized piece of clay
- poster board
- flashlight

TIME
20 minutes

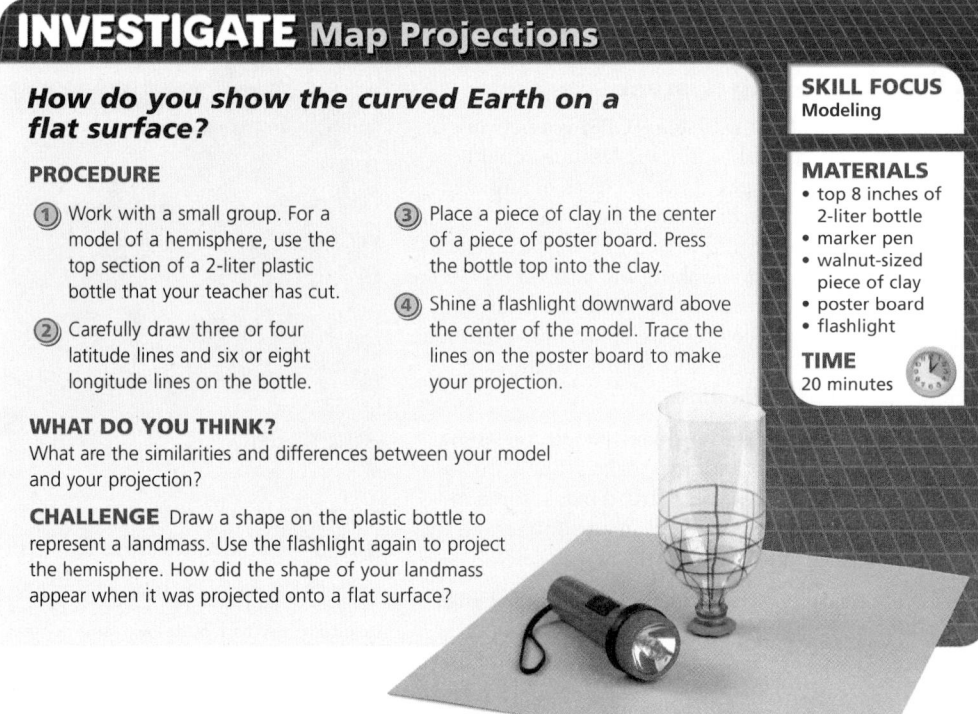

DIFFERENTIATE INSTRUCTION

More Reading Support

F How is the Mercator projection useful? *It shows almost the entire world on one map and allows navigators to plot courses by drawing straight lines between points.*

Alternative Assessment If students have difficulty writing answers to questions for "Investigate Map Projections," have them talk about the similarities and differences between their models and their projections.

Inclusion Tape or glue pipe cleaners or yarn on top of the lines of an exemplary projection so students with vision impairments can get a sense of the distortion.

another to plot a course. The problem with Mercator maps is that areas far away from the equator appear much larger than they really are. On the map below, Greenland looks bigger than South America. In reality, South America is about eight times larger than Greenland.

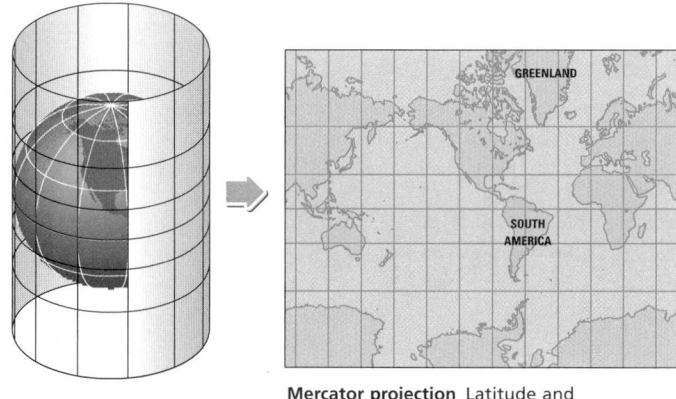

Mercator projection Latitude and longitude lines form a grid of rectangles. Areas away from the equator are distorted.

Conic Projections

Conic projections are based on the shape of a cone. The diagram below shows how a cone of paper might be wrapped around the globe. The paper touches the surface only at the middle latitudes, halfway between the equator and the North Pole.

When the cone is flattened out, the latitude lines are curved slightly. The curved lines represent the curved surface of Earth. This allows the map to show the true sizes and shapes of some landmasses.

Conic projections are most useful for mapping large areas in the middle latitudes, such as the United States. However, landmasses near the equator or near the north or south pole will be distorted.

 What are the main uses of Mercator and conic projections?

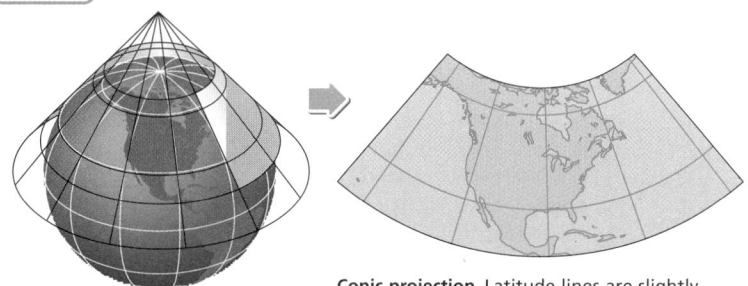

Conic projection Latitude lines are slightly curved. Only mid-latitude areas are the correct size and shape.

Chapter 1: **Views of Earth Today 21** **A**

DIFFERENTIATE INSTRUCTION

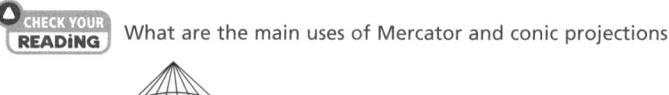 **More Reading Support**

G What regions are conic projections most useful for mapping? *regions in the middle latitudes, roughly halfway between the equator and the poles*

Advanced Encourage students to draw pictures of the continental United States as they imagine it might look in a conic projection, a Mercator projection, and a planar projection. Later, show them maps of each type. Discuss with students any differences between their conceptions and the appearance of the United States on each of the actual maps.

Teach Difficult Concepts

Some students will have difficulty understanding map projections and the differences among various types. Emphasize that each projection is most accurate for a different region of the globe. To help students understand, you might try the following demonstration.

Teacher Demo

Use construction paper to model a Mercator projection. Wrap a globe in the paper so that it touches the globe at the equator and forms a cylinder. Show the view looking down on the North Pole. Explain that where the paper touches, the distortion is least, and where the paper is most distant from the globe—near the poles—the most distortion occurs. On the globe, longitude lines meet at the poles. In the projection, the longitude lines are spread out until they are parallel, so that the land becomes "stretched out of shape."

Develop Critical Thinking

EVALUATE Ask students which type of map projection each of the following people would be likely to use:

• an airline pilot calculating the fastest route from Los Angeles to Sydney, Australia *planar or Mercator*

• a ship captain plotting a course from New York to London *planar or Mercator*

• a mapmaker drawing the state of Iowa *conic*

Ongoing Assessment

Explain why all maps distort Earth's surface.

Ask: Why does a map always distort features of Earth's surface? *because Earth is a sphere and representing it on a flat map involves stretching one area or another out of shape*

CHECK YOUR READING *Answer: Mercator: navigation; conic: mapping areas in the middle latitudes accurately*

 **CHECK YOUR READING** *Answer: north and south polar regions*

Metacognitive Strategy

Ask students to write a sentence or two describing how this lesson changed the way they think about maps.

Reinforce (the **BIG** idea)

Have students relate the section to the Big Idea.

 Reinforcing Key Concepts, p. 32

1.2 ASSESS & RETEACH

Assess

 Section 1.2 Quiz, p. 4

Reteach

Display a map of a state; region, or community and ask students to identify the features that make it useful. List their answers on the board. Ask:

• Does the map show land features? If so, what features?

• What type of scale does it have?

• Where can you find the meanings of the symbols used on the map?

• Does the map indicate latitudes and longitudes? If so, what units are used?

• What type of projection may have been used to produce this map? Why?

Ask students to pull out the maps they made in the activity on page 15. Discuss any improvements they might make to their maps.

Technology Resources

Have students visit **ClassZone.com** for reteaching of Key Concepts.

 CONTENT REVIEW

 CONTENT REVIEW CD-ROM

Planar Projections

 **RESOURCE CENTER** CLASSZONE.COM
Find out more about map projections and how they are used.

Planar projections were developed to help people find the shortest distance between two points. They are drawn as if a circle of paper were laid on a point on Earth's surface. As you look at the diagram below, notice how the shape of the sphere is transferred to the flat map. When a planar map represents the polar region, the longitude lines meet at the center like the spokes of a wheel.

A planar map is good for plotting ocean or air voyages and for showing the north and south polar regions. However, landmasses farther away from the center point are greatly distorted.

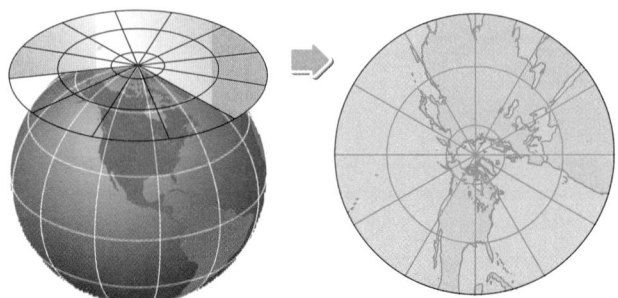

Planar projection Only areas near the center point are the correct size and shape.

The Mercator, conic, and planar projections are all attempts to solve the problem of representing a curved surface on a flat map. Each projection can show certain areas of the world accurately but distorts other areas.

 **CHECK YOUR READING** What areas does the planar projection show accurately?

1.2 Review

KEY CONCEPTS

1. What natural and human-made features can maps show? Give two examples of each.

2. Explain how latitude and longitude can help you locate any place on Earth.

3. Why do all flat maps distort Earth's surface?

CRITICAL THINKING

4. **Provide Examples** Imagine that your family is on a long car trip. What symbols on a road map would you pay the most attention to? Explain.

5. **Apply** Use a world map to find the approximate latitudes and longitudes of Moscow, Russia; Tokyo, Japan; Denver, Colorado; and La Paz, Bolivia.

⚫ CHALLENGE

6. **Apply** Working with a partner or with a small group, select the shortest airline route from Chicago to London, using a globe and a Mercator map. **Hint:** Notice that as you go farther north on the globe, the longitude lines become closer together.

A 22 Unit: **Earth's Surface**

ANSWERS

1. natural: mountains, rivers; human-made: bridges, roads

2. The exact location of any place can be expressed as a number of degrees north or south of the equator (latitude) and a number of degrees east or west of the prime meridian (longitude).

3. Earth is a sphere. It is impossible to portray a curved surface as flat without some distortion.

4. Students should mention direction arrows and symbols for highways, food, fuel, and lodging.

5. Moscow: 56° N, 38° E
Tokyo: 36° N, 140° E
Denver: 40° N, 105° W
La Paz: 17° S, 68° W

6. The shortest airline route will be an arctic route across the Atlantic Ocean.

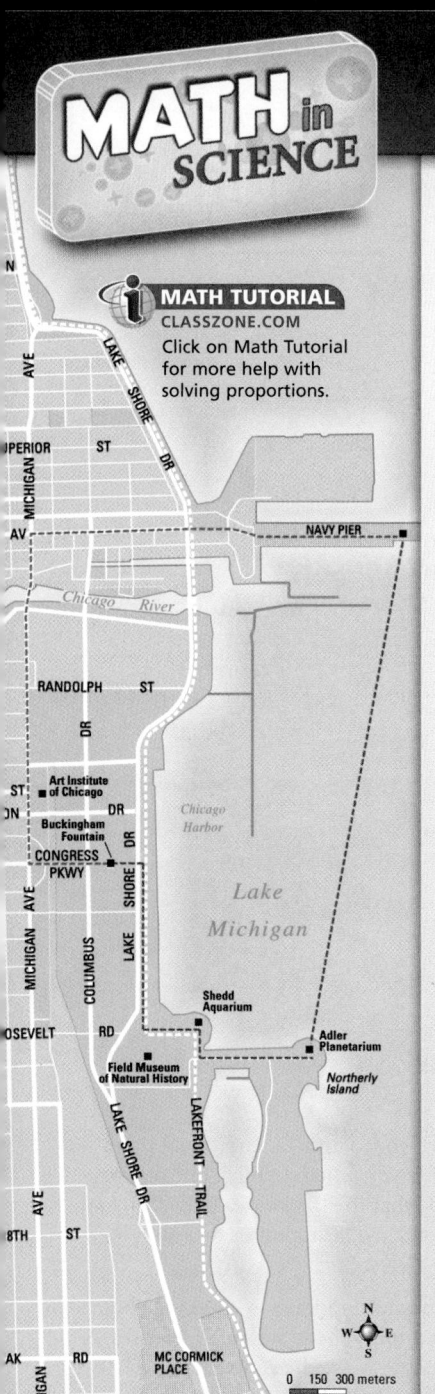

MATH in SCIENCE

SKILL: USING PROPORTIONS

MATH TUTORIAL
CLASSZONE.COM
Click on Math Tutorial for more help with solving proportions.

How Far Is It?

A science class is visiting Chicago and is using the map on the left to walk to the lakefront museums. Remember, a map scale shows how distances on the map compare to actual distances on the ground.

Buckingham Fountain

Example

In this case, the map scale indicates that 1 centimeter on the map represents 300 meters on the ground. The map scale shows this as equivalent units. By using these units to write a proportion, you can use cross products to determine actual distances.

What distance does 3 cm on the map represent? Set up the problem like this:

$$\frac{1\ cm}{300\ m} = \frac{3\ cm}{x}$$

(1) $1 \cdot x = 3 \cdot 300$

(2) $x = 3 \cdot 300$

(3) $x = 900$

ANSWER 3 centimeters on the map represents 900 meters on the ground.

Use cross products and a metric ruler to answer the following questions.

1. The science class divides into two groups. Each group starts at Buckingham Fountain. How far, in meters, will one group walk to get to the Adler Planetarium if they follow the red dotted line?

2. How far, in meters, will the other group walk to get to the end of Navy Pier if they follow the blue dotted line?

3. The group that walked to Adler decides to take a boat to join the other group at Navy Pier. How far, in meters, is their boat ride along the red dotted line?

CHALLENGE What is the total distance, in kilometers, that the two groups traveled? Set up the problem as a proportion. **Hint:** There are 1000 meters in a kilometer.

Chapter 1: **Views of Earth Today** 23 **A**

MATH IN SCIENCE
Math Skills Practice for Science

Set Learning Goal

To use a map scale to determine the actual distance on Earth represented by a distance on a map

Present the Science

Point out to students that this map represents a relatively small area and that many maps will show larger areas. Ask them to predict how the scales of these other maps will differ from the one shown here.

Develop Algebra Skills

Remind students that the goal of using cross products is to isolate the variable on one side of the equation. Review the applicable algebra rules, and show several examples of the use of cross products.

Close

Ask students to imagine situations in which it would be appropriate to use large-scale and small-scale maps. *Large-scale maps: navigating city streets or hiking in a small nature reserve; Small-scale maps: on an interstate driving trip or a cross-country flight* Ask which type they are most familiar with using. *Answers will vary. Many students have probably used road maps, the scales of which depend on the size of their states.*

• Math Support, p. 59
• Math Practice, p. 60

Technology Resources

Students can visit **ClassZone.com** for practice using properties.

MATH TUTORIAL

ANSWERS

1. 2100 m   2. 4200 m   3. 2700 m

CHALLENGE 2100 m + 2700 m + 4200 m = 9000 m

$$\frac{1\ km}{1000\ m} = \frac{X}{9000\ m}$$

$$X \cdot 1000\ m = 1\ km \cdot 9000\ m$$

$$X = \frac{1\ km \cdot 9000\ m}{1000\ m}$$

$$X = 9\ km$$

Chapter 1 **23** **A**

◉ Set Learning Goals

Students will

- Explain how contour lines show elevation, relief, and slope.
- Explain the rules for contour lines.
- Describe the common symbols used on topographic maps.

◎ 3-Minute Warm-Up

Display Transparency 5 or copy this exercise on the board:

Match each definition with the correct term.

Definitions

1. distance in degrees from equator *b*
2. relates distance on a map to actual distance on Earth's surface *a*
3. distance in degrees from prime meridian *d*

Terms

a. map scale   c. longitude
b. latitude   d. projection

 3-Minute Warm-Up, p. T5

EXPLORE Topographic Maps

PURPOSE To introduce the concept that contour lines connect points of equal elevation

TIP *10 min.* Students should look at their knuckles from the side and from the top to see how the circles change.

WHAT DO YOU THINK? *Knuckles rise like a mountain range when fist is clenched; flatten out like a plain when hand is open flat; circles represent a way to draw the shape of knuckles.*

Language Arts Connection

Topography comes from the ancient Greek word *topographia,* "description of a place."

KEY CONCEPT

1.3 Topographic maps show the shape of the land.

◀ **BEFORE, you learned**

- Different maps provide information about natural and human-made features
- Latitude and longitude are used to find places on Earth
- All flat maps distort Earth's surface

▶ **NOW, you will learn**

- How contour lines show elevation, slope, and relief
- What rules contour lines follow
- What common symbols are used on topographic maps

VOCABULARY

topography p. 24
contour line p. 25
elevation p. 25
slope p. 25
relief p. 25
contour interval p. 26

VOCABULARY
Add a word triangle for *topography* to your notebook.

EXPLORE Topographic Maps

How can you map your knuckles?

PROCEDURE

MATERIAL
washable colored pen

① Hold your fist closed, knuckles up, as shown in the photo.

② Draw circles around the first knuckle. Make sure the circles are the same distance from each other.

③ Flatten out your hand. Observe what happens. Write down your observations.

WHAT DO YOU THINK?
- How does the height of your knuckles change when you clench your fist, then flatten out your hand?
- What do you think the circles represent?

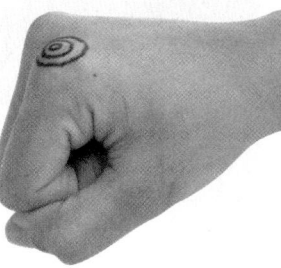

Topographic maps use contour lines to show features.

Imagine you are on vacation with your family in a national park. You have a simple trail map that shows you where to hike. But the map does not tell you anything about what the land looks like. Will you have to cross any rivers or valleys? How far uphill or downhill will you have to hike?

To answer these questions, you need to know something about the topography of the area. **Topography** is the shape, or features, of the land. These features can be natural—such as mountains, plateaus, and plains—or human-made—such as dams and roads. To show the topography of an area, mapmakers draw a topographic map.

RESOURCES FOR DIFFERENTIATED INSTRUCTION

Below Level

UNIT RESOURCE BOOK
- Reading Study Guide A, pp. 35–36
- Decoding Support, p. 58

 **AUDIO CDS**

Advanced

UNIT RESOURCE BOOK
Challenge and Extension, p. 41

English Learners

UNIT RESOURCE BOOK
Spanish Reading Study Guide, pp. 39–40

 **AUDIO CDS**

- Audio Readings in Spanish
- Audio Readings (English)

A

B

A topographic map is a flat map that uses lines to show Earth's surface features. Distance and elevation can be given in feet or meters. Take a look at the topographic map of Mount Hood on this page. The wiggly lines on the map are called **contour lines,** and they show an area's elevation, slope, and relief.

❶ The **elevation** of a place is how high above sea level it is. An area can range from a few meters to several thousand meters above sea level. The numbers on the contour lines show the elevations of different points in the Mount Hood area.

❷ The **slope** of a landform or area is how steep it is. The more gradual the slope, the farther apart the contour lines on the map. The steeper the slope, the closer together the contour lines.

❸ The **relief** of an area is the difference between its high and low points. For example, subtracting the lowest elevation on the map from the highest gives you a measure of the area's relief.

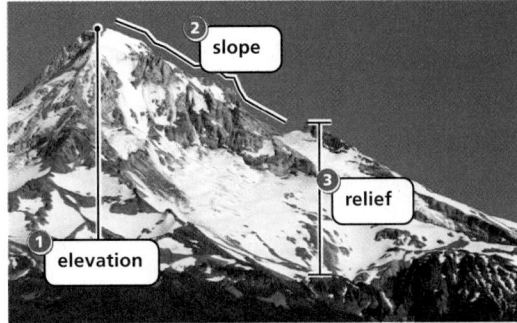

CHECK YOUR READING What is the difference between elevation and slope?

Mount Hood Topographic Map

A topographic map shows the land as if you were above the land looking down on it.

❶ Contour lines show the mountain's peak as seen from above. The **elevation** here is given in meters.

❷ Contour lines close together show a steep **slope.** Lines farther apart show a more gentle slope.

❸ The different elevations on a map indicate an area's **relief.**

WILDERNESS
MOUNT HOOD
3426
1500
Fork
Lamberson Butte
1750
South Fork
36

READING VISUALS What is the elevation of the top of Mount Hood?

Chapter 1: **Views of Earth Today** 25 **A**

DIFFERENTIATE INSTRUCTION

English Learners Have English learners verbally explain the differences between *elevation, slope,* and *relief.* Point out that on p. 25, the words *gradual* and *gentle* are used in different places to describe slope. Help English learners understand what these words mean in this context, and that they are synonyms.

Teach Difficult Concepts

Some students have a hard time visualizing the shape of landscapes from looking at topographic maps. Ask them to picture a rock protruding from a puddle's surface. Ask: What shape would you make if you drew around the rock where it contacted the water surface? *roughly circular* To help students understand, you might try the demonstration below.

Teacher Demo

Use a spring toy to show how contour lines indicate steepness. Set it vertically to show its "contour lines" stacked on top of one another. While holding the bottom firmly in place, push the top to one side and have students view it from above. They should see the "contour lines" spread out as the slope becomes gentler. Stretch one end of the spring into a gradual slope and stack the other end into a steeper slope. This will show both close and spread-apart contour lines.

Teach from Visuals

To help students interpret the topographic map of Mount Hood, ask:

- How do the contour lines indicate the location of Mount Hood's peak? *The peak is within the smallest circle in the series of closed circles.*

- Where on the map are the slopes most gradual? *The contour lines are farthest apart near the map's right edge, indicating gentler slopes.*

Ongoing Assessment

Explain how contour lines show elevation, relief, and slope.

Ask: How do contour lines tell you the elevation of a mountain? *Numbers on the contour lines indicate specific heights.*

 *Answer: Elevation is height above sea level, whereas slope is the steepness of the land.*

 *Answer: 3426 meters*

History of Science

In 1879, Congress assigned the task of mapping the country to the U.S. Geological Survey. The USGS published its first topographic map that same year. In the 1940s, the USGS began producing maps from aerial photographs, using a technique known as photogrammetry. Today a series of more than 54,000 connected maps cover the lower 48 states and Hawaii. Each map shows an area, or quadrangle, measuring 7.5 minutes of latitude by 7.5 minutes of longitude. The 2700 maps of Alaska each cover a quadrangle of 15 minutes of latitude and longitude.

Teach from Visuals

To help students interpret the topographic map of Ely, ask:

• What is the highest elevation labeled on the map? *A peak in the middle of the map is labeled at 1427 ft.*

• What is the elevation between the index contour lines on this map? *50 ft.*

Develop Critical Thinking

INFER Discuss contour intervals with students. They have read that contour intervals can vary from map to map. Ask students the following:

How would the contour interval of a topographic map of the Mount Everest region differ from that of a topographic map of Kansas? *The Mount Everest area has greater relief; therefore, the map would have a larger contour interval than would the Kansas map.*

Ongoing Assessment

Explain the rules for contour lines.

Ask: What rules apply to contour lines? *Contour lines never cross, form closed circles around high and low points, and are spaced at equal intervals of elevation. Some are darkened and may have labels indicating elevations.*

READING VISUALS *Answer: Highest point is within the fifth contour line above the index contour line labeled 1400 ft.*
5 × 10 = 50 ft, 1400 + 50 = 1450 ft

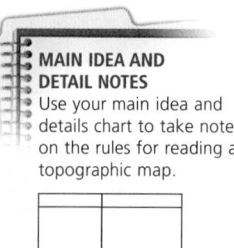

MAIN IDEA AND DETAIL NOTES
Use your main idea and details chart to take notes on the rules for reading a topographic map.

?
C

Contour lines follow certain rules.

Contour lines on topographic maps can help you visualize landforms. Think of the following statements as rules for reading such maps:

• **Lines never cross.** Contour lines never cross, because each line represents an exact elevation.

• **Circles show highest and lowest points.** Contour lines form closed circles around mountaintops, hilltops, and the centers of depressions, which are sunken areas in the ground. Sometimes, the elevation of a mountain or hill is written in meters or feet in the middle of the circle.

• **Contour interval is always the same on a map.** The **contour interval** is the difference in elevation from one contour line to the next. For example, the contour interval on the map below is 10 feet. This means that the change in elevation between contour lines is always 10 feet. The contour interval can differ from map to map, but it is always the same on a particular map.

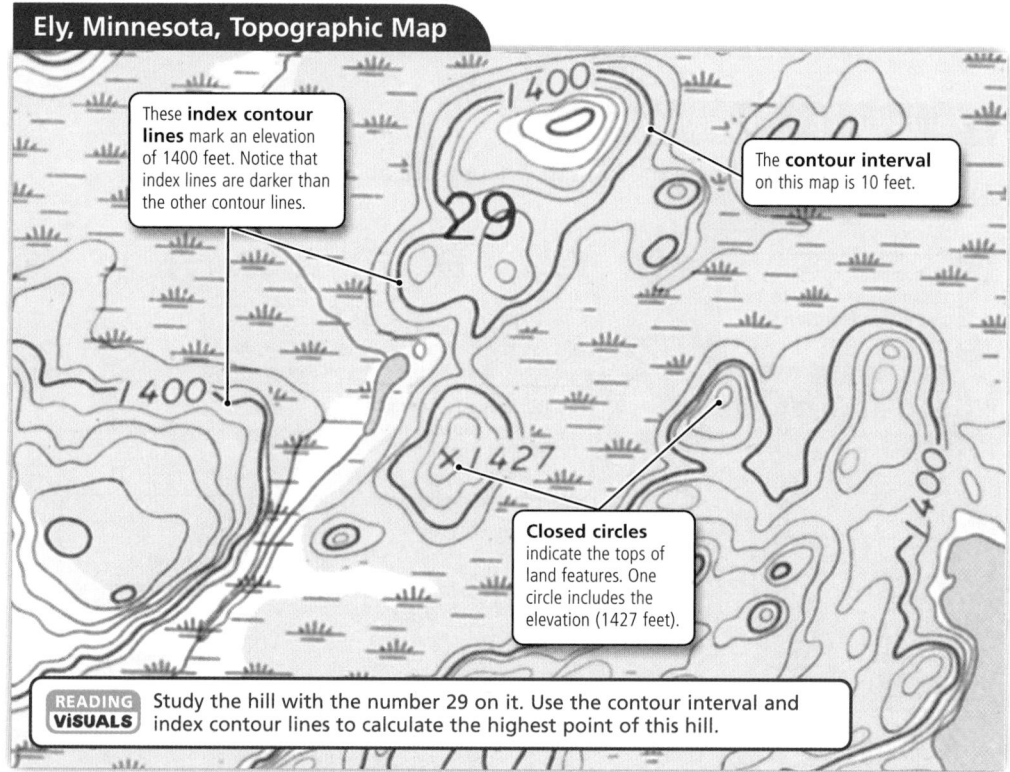

Ely, Minnesota, Topographic Map

These **index contour lines** mark an elevation of 1400 feet. Notice that index lines are darker than the other contour lines.

The **contour interval** on this map is 10 feet.

Closed circles indicate the tops of land features. One circle includes the elevation (1427 feet).

READING VISUALS Study the hill with the number 29 on it. Use the contour interval and index contour lines to calculate the highest point of this hill.

DIFFERENTIATE INSTRUCTION

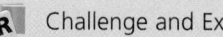

? More Reading Support

C What is a contour interval? *It is the change in elevation from one contour line to the next.*

Advanced To challenge students, ask: How might each of these people use a topographic map in their work: an air rescue pilot, a river captain, a professional mountain climber, a cross-country ski guide. *Pilot: to search terrain and know where to land; river captain: to pilot his boat safely along a river channel; climber: to plan a route up a mountain; guide: to choose a route that matches the abilities of the people he or she leads.*

R Challenge and Extension, p. 41

- **Index contour lines mark elevations.** The darker contour lines on a map are called index contour lines. Numbers that indicate elevations are often written on these lines. To calculate higher or lower elevations, simply count the number of lines above or below an index line. Then multiply that number by the contour interval. For instance, on the Ely map, one index line marks 1400 feet. To find the elevation of a point three lines up from this index line, you would multiply 10 feet (the contour interval) by 3. Add the result, 30, to 1400. The point's elevation is 1430 feet.

SIMULATION
CLASSZONE.COM

Discover the relationship between topographic maps and surface features.

 **CHECK YOUR READING** What information do index contour lines provide?

Besides contour lines, topographic maps also contain symbols for natural and human-made features. Below are some common map symbols that the United States Geological Survey (USGS) uses on its topographic maps.

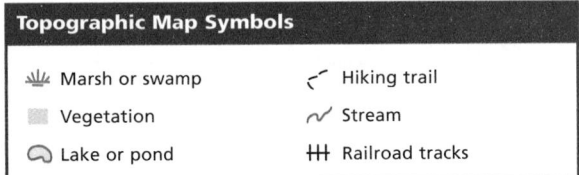

Topographic Map Symbols

Marsh or swamp	Hiking trail
Vegetation	Stream
Lake or pond	Railroad tracks

The USGS provides topographic maps for nearly every part of the United States. These maps cover urban, rural, and wilderness areas. Hikers and campers are not the only ones who use topographic maps. Engineers, archaeologists, forest rangers, biologists, and others rely on them as well.

1.3 Review

KEY CONCEPTS
1. How do contour lines show elevation, slope, and relief?
2. Why do contour lines never cross on a topographic map?
3. How would you show the top of a hill, an area of vegetation, or a hiking trail on a topographic map?

CRITICAL THINKING
4. **Apply** For an area with gently sloping hills and little relief, would you draw contour lines close together or far apart? Explain why.
5. **Compare and Contrast** How would a road map and a topographic map of the same area differ? What information would each provide?

CHALLENGE
6. **Synthesize** Work with a group to make a topographic map of the area around your school. First decide how big an area you will include. Then choose a contour interval, a map scale, and symbols for buildings, sports fields, and other features. Let other students test the map's accuracy.

ANSWERS

1. The numbers on the contour lines show elevation. The distance between contour lines shows slope. The differences between high and low places show relief.

2. Each one represents a specific elevation. Closed circles represent high and low

points; contour intervals are always the same for any given map.

3. with a closed circle; green shading

4. far apart; the changes in elevation are gradual.

5. road: would show the highway network, bodies of

water, and cities; topographic: would show how the landscape looks and how high or low the land is

6. Students should include contour interval, index contour lines, elevation figures, compass rose, legend, and scale.

Ongoing Assessment

Describe the common symbols used on topographic maps.

Describe some symbols used on topographic maps. *railroad track: a line crossed by short perpendicular lines; marsh: a stylized tuft of marsh grass; lake or pond: an area outlined in blue; stream: a blue line; hiking trail: a broken black line.*

 **CHECK YOUR READING** *Answer: Many are labeled with specific elevations.*

Reinforce the BIG idea

Have students relate the section to the Big Idea.

 Reinforcing Key Concepts, p. 42

1.3 ASSESS & RETEACH

Assess
 Section 1.3 Quiz, p. 5

Reteach

Provide students with a topographic map of a wilderness area in a mountain region. Ask them to plan a cross-country hike from one significant feature shown on the map to another some distance away. Each student can trace a route in pencil on the printout, then describe the route and the reason it was chosen. Ask for volunteers to present their routes to the class.

Technology Resources

Have students visit **ClassZone.com** for reteaching of Key Concepts.

 CONTENT REVIEW

 CONTENT REVIEW CD-ROM

Focus

PURPOSE To recognize the features of a landscape by looking at contour lines on a topographic map

OVERVIEW Students will create a topographic map by tracing onto a plastic sheet the waterlines around a clay landscape model at various water levels. Student maps will show

- slopes
- changes in elevation
- relief of landforms
- tops of hills

Lab Preparation

- Have beakers or empty cans on hand so that students can use them to fill and partially empty their containers.
- Have students read through the investigation for homework the night before doing the experiment in class. Copy and distribute datasheets and rubrics as you see fit.

 UNIT RESOURCE BOOK, pp. 61–69

 SCIENCE TOOLKIT, F15

Lab Management

- Suggest that different groups form different types of landscapes so they can compare their maps at the end.
- Caution students to avoid dripping water on their clear plastic sheets, as this will wash away their inked lines.
- Tracing the contour lines onto paper is easier if students hold the sheets against a window so that light can shine through.

SAFETY Remind students to avoid spilling water on the floor and to immediately wipe up any spills that occur.

INCLUSION Students can prepare containers the day before to have more time to spend on the investigation.

Teaching with Technology

Use an overhead projector to display students' maps.

CHAPTER INVESTIGATION

Investigate Topographic Maps

OVERVIEW AND PURPOSE Topographical maps show the shape of the land. In this lab you will use what you have learned about how Earth's three-dimensional surface is represented on maps to
- make a terrain model out of clay
- produce a topographical map of the model

▶ Procedure

1 Build a simple landscape about 6–8 cm high from modeling clay. Include a variety of land features. Make sure your model is no taller than the sides of the container.

2 Place your model into the container. Stand a ruler upright inside the container and tape it in place.

3 Lay the clear plastic sheet over the container and tape it on one side like a hinge. Carefully trace the outline of your clay model.

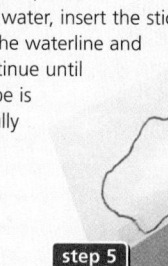
step 3

4 Add 2 cm of colored water to the container.

5 Insert spaghetti sticks into the model all around the waterline. Place the sticks about 3 cm apart. Make sure the sticks are vertical and are no taller than the sides of the container.

6 Lower the plastic sheet back over the container. Looking straight down on the container, make a dot on the sheet wherever you see a spaghetti stick. Connect the dots to trace the contour line accurately onto your map.

7 Continue adding water, 2 cm at a time. Each time you add water, insert the sticks into the model at the waterline and repeat step 6. Continue until the model landscape is underwater. Carefully drain the water when finished.

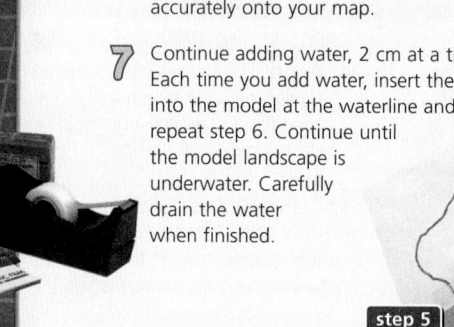
step 5

MATERIALS
- half-gallon cardboard juice container
- scissors
- modeling clay
- clear plastic sheet (transparency or sheet protector)
- cellophane tape
- ruler
- water
- food coloring
- box of spaghetti
- erasable marker pen

INVESTIGATION RESOURCES

 CHAPTER INVESTIGATION, Investigate Topographic Maps
- Level A, pp. 61–64
- Level B, pp. 65–68
- Level C, p. 69

Advanced students should complete Levels B & C.

 Writing a Lab Report, D12–13

Technology Resources

Customize this student lab as needed or look for an alternative. Print rubrics to assess student lab reports.

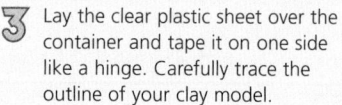 **Lab Generator CD-ROM**

▶ Observe and Analyze
Write It Up

1. Compare your topographical map with the three-dimensional model. Remember that contour lines connect points of equal elevation. What do widely spaced or tightly spaced contour lines mean? What does a closed circle mean?

2. Make a permanent record of your map to keep in your **Science Notebook** by carefully tracing the contour lines onto a sheet of white paper. To make reading the map easier, use a different color for an index contour line.

3. What is the contour interval of your model landscape? For example, each 2 centimeters might represent 20 meters in an actual landscape. Record the elevation of the index contour line on your map.

▶ Conclude
Write It Up

1. INFER How would you determine the elevation of a point located halfway between two contour lines?

2. EVALUATE Describe any errors that you may have made in your procedure or any places where errors might have occurred.

3. APPLY Explain how you would use a topographic map if you were planning a hiking trip or a cross-country bike race.

▶ INVESTIGATE Further

CHALLENGE Choose one feature on a topographical map—such as the map on page 26—to translate into a cross-sectional diagram.

1. Lay a piece of ruled paper across the center of the topographical feature.

2. Mark each of the contour lines on the ruled paper and label each mark with the elevation.

3. Mark the same elevations on the side of the paper, as shown in the example.

4. Use a ruler to draw a straight line down from each mark to the matching elevation on the side of the paper.

5. Connect the points to draw a profile of the landform.

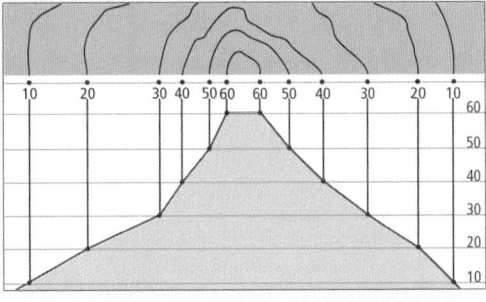

INVESTIGATE TOPOGRAPHIC MAPS
Observe and Analyze
Figure 1. Topographic Map of Model

Conclude

▶ Observe and Analyze
Write It Up

1. Contour lines are widely spaced where slopes are gentle; closely spaced contour lines represent places where slopes are steep. Closed circles indicate a hilltop, mountaintop, or a depression center.

2. Student maps should correspond to the landscapes they made in their cartons.

3. The contour interval is 2 cm. Elevation answers will vary but should match students' hypothetical contour intervals.

▶ Conclude
Write It Up

1. Find the average (mean) of the elevations represented by the two lines.

2. Students should recognize that their lines are accurate only if they looked at the waterlines from straight above. Even the slightest angle in viewing will throw off the location of a line. Also, their maps are accurate only if they carefully filled the cartons to the specified levels.

3. For hiking or backpacking, a topographic map can help one avoid steep climbs and find the least strenuous route between points. In planning a cross-country race, one might want to choose more challenging slopes, easily identified by consulting the map.

▶ INVESTIGATE Further

CHALLENGE The profiles produced by this method will vary. Have students mark the elevation of each contour line beneath the point where it touches the sheet of ruled paper. This will make it easier for them to graph the topography. Be sure students use the vertical axis for elevation.

Post-Lab Discussion

• Place the drained cartons, still containing the landscapes, on a lab bench. Use an overhead projector to display the plastic-sheet map produced by each group. Ask students to find the landscape that matches each map.

• Sketch your own map onto a plastic sheet and display to the class. Ask students to describe the landscape it portrays.

• Discuss which rules of topographic maps students came to understand better while constructing their own maps.

◉ Set Learning Goals

Students will

- Explain how remote-sensing images can provide detailed and accurate information about Earth.
- Explain how geographic data can be displayed in layers to build maps.
- Experiment to graph an image that models how satellites send images to Earth.

◐ 3-Minute Warm-Up

Display Transparency 5 or copy this exercise on the board:

Decide if these statements are true. If not, correct them.

1. Topographic maps show elevation but not relief. *Topographic maps show elevation, relief, and slope.*

2. Closely spaced contour lines indicate gradual slopes. *Closely spaced contour lines indicate steep slopes.*

3. Mountaintops are enclosed by circles on topographic maps. *true*

 3-Minute Warm-Up, p. T5

1.4 MOTIVATE

THINK ABOUT

PURPOSE To have students think about the wide range of information technology can provide

DISCUSS This image shows the Washington Monument, the Mall, and the Jefferson Memorial (the round building at bottom left). *Sample answers: buildings, roadways, bridges, Jefferson Memorial, Washington Mall, and trees. Scientists could use such images to study the environment, mapmakers would have accurate images to base maps on, and engineers could study traffic patterns, urban growth, water use, and other factors.*

KEY CONCEPT

1.4 Technology is used to map Earth.

◁ BEFORE, you learned	▷ NOW, you will learn
• Contour lines are used on topographic maps to show elevation, slope, and relief • Contour lines follow certain rules • Map symbols show many natural and human-made features	• How remote-sensing images can provide detailed and accurate information about Earth • How geographic data can be displayed in layers to build maps

VOCABULARY

remote sensing p. 30
sensor p. 31
false-color image p. 32
geographic information systems p. 33

THINK ABOUT

What can you see in this image?

Satellites can record all types of information about Earth's surface. This image shows a section of Washington, D.C. The satellite that collected the data is 680 kilometers (420 mi) above Earth. What familiar items can you see in the picture? How might images like this be useful to scientists, mapmakers, and engineers?

Remote sensing provides detailed images of Earth.

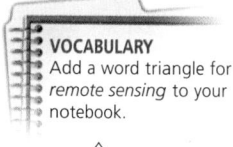

VOCABULARY
Add a word triangle for *remote sensing* to your notebook.

If you have ever looked at an object through a pair of binoculars, you have used remote sensing. **Remote sensing** is the use of scientific equipment to gather information about something from a distance. Remote-sensing technology can be as simple as a camera mounted on an airplane or as complex as a satellite orbiting Earth.

To get an idea of how important remote sensing is, imagine you are a mapmaker in the 1840s. You have been asked to draw a map of a state, but you have no cameras, no photographs from airplanes, and no satellites to help you. To get a good view of the land, you have to climb to the highest points and carefully draw every hill, valley, river, and landform below you. It will take you months to map the state.

A **30** Unit: Earth's Surface

RESOURCES FOR DIFFERENTIATED INSTRUCTION

Below Level
UNIT RESOURCE BOOK
- Reading Study Guide A, pp. 45–46
- Decoding Support, p. 58

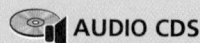 **AUDIO CDS**

Advanced
UNIT RESOURCE BOOK
- Challenge and Extension, p. 51
- Challenge Reading, pp. 54–55

English Learners
UNIT RESOURCE BOOK
Spanish Reading Study Guide, pp. 49–50

 **AUDIO CDS**

- Audio Readings in Spanish
- Audio Readings (English)

Today, that same map would take far less time to make. Modern mapmakers use remote-sensing images from airplanes and satellites to develop highly detailed and accurate maps of Earth's surface.

Airplane cameras use film to record data, but satellites use sensors to build images of Earth. A **sensor** is a mechanical or electrical device that receives and responds to a signal, such as light. Satellite sensors detect far more than your eyes can see. They collect information about the different types of energy coming from Earth's surface. The satellites then send that information to computers on Earth.

The computers turn the information into images, as shown in the illustration below. Satellite data can be used to build an image of the entire planet, a single continent, or a detail of your area. For example, the image on the right shows a closeup of the Jefferson Memorial in Washington, D.C.

This satellite image includes the Jefferson Memorial, walkways, and roads. See if you can find the memorial in the image on page 30.

CHECK YOUR READING Explain how remote sensing is used to gather information about Earth.

Satellite Imaging

Objects on Earth reflect or emit different types of energy. Satellite sensors can detect and record these energies.

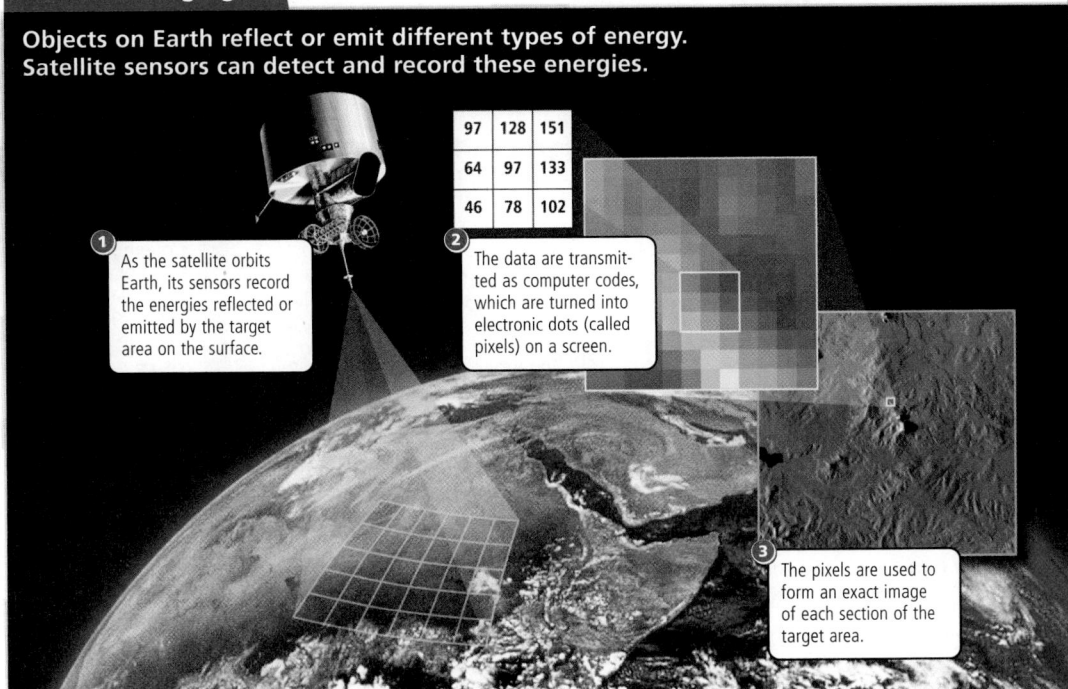

97	128	151
64	97	133
46	78	102

1. As the satellite orbits Earth, its sensors record the energies reflected or emitted by the target area on the surface.

2. The data are transmitted as computer codes, which are turned into electronic dots (called pixels) on a screen.

3. The pixels are used to form an exact image of each section of the target area.

Chapter 1: **Views of Earth Today** 31 **A**

DIFFERENTIATE INSTRUCTION

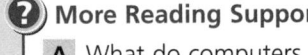 **More Reading Support**

A What do computers do with the information from sensors? *They change the information into images.*

English Learners To help English learners, revisit the three steps shown in the visual "Satellite Imaging." Use less technical, more familiar language to explain how an image is produced—for example, "The satellite looks at one spot on Earth. Then it records what levels of energy it sees. It sends the record to a computer, which changes the energy readings to dots on a screen. The dots combine to make a picture." Also, students may not have prior knowledge of memorial buildings (p. 31) and the use of the term *games* with reference to the Olympics (p. 35).

INSTRUCT

Integrate the Sciences

Satellite imaging plays an important role in the monitoring of global climate change. One ongoing research project at Glacier National Park in Montana seeks to determine how a mountain wilderness responds to changes in climate. The latest in remote-sensing technologies, as well as GIS, have helped to produce 3-D maps and computer animations of the dynamics of the ecosystem—including data on snowpack density, stream discharge, and evapotranspiration. One clear pattern revealed by the satellite imaging is the retreat of the park's glaciers. Of the glaciers documented there in 1850, only a third remain. The remaining ones are far smaller than before and continue to shrink each year.

Teach from Visuals

To help students interpret the visual "Satellite Imaging," ask:

- What does the grid that is superimposed on Earth represent? *the target area for the satellite's sensors*

- What sort of data is the satellite collecting? *energies reflected by different objects on Earth*

- What is the relationship between the three inset images in the diagram? *The first shows data as computer codes; the second shows the data converted to pixels, the third shows an image formed from the pixels.*

Ongoing Assessment

CHECK YOUR READING *Answer: Remote sensing includes photographing Earth from airplanes and gathering images with satellites. Satellites record data about Earth and change the data into computer codes. Software converts the codes to pixels that are used to build images of areas on Earth targeted by the satellites.*

Chapter 1 **31** **A**

Teach from Visuals

To help students interpret the visual of vegetation affected by forest fires, ask:

- How did the appearance of the area change over three weeks? *A much greater area is burning; a smaller area of vegetation remains.*

- What caused these changes? *the two forest fires spread over a wide area*

INVESTIGATE Satellite Imaging

PURPOSE Graph an image in order to understand how satellites send images to Earth

TIP *25 min.* Suggest that students label each column and row on their paper with numbers and letters.

WHAT DO YOU THINK? *The image would be shorter if you skipped a row and longer if you added a row; this could distort the image. Increasing the number and size of the squares would make the image larger, and it would take longer to send; decreasing the number and size would make the image smaller, and it could be sent in less time.*

CHALLENGE *See students' work. Pairs might need more time to complete the challenge.*

 Datasheet, Satellite Imaging, p. 52

Metacognitive Strategy

Discuss with students any problems they encountered in "receiving" the codes.

 One of the ways scientists study changes is by using false-color images. In one type of **false-color image**, Earth's natural colors are replaced with artificial ones to highlight special features. For example, fire officials used false-color images like the ones below to track the spread of a dangerous wildfire in southern Oregon.

July 21, 2002

Small fires break out.

In this false-color image, vegetation is bright green, burned areas are red, fire is bright pink, and smoke is blue.

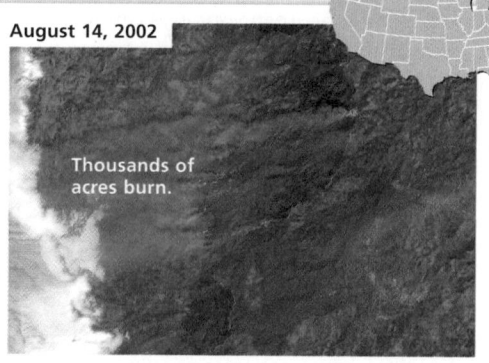

August 14, 2002

Thousands of acres burn.

Three weeks later, as this false-color image clearly shows, the fires had spread over a large area.

INVESTIGATE Satellite Imaging

How do satellites send images to Earth?

PROCEDURE

1. Work with a partner. One of you will be the "sensor," and the other will be the "receiving station."

2. The sensor draws the initials of a famous person on a piece of graph paper. The receiving station does NOT see the drawing.

3. The sensor sends the picture to the receiving station. For blank squares, the sensor says "Zero." For filled-in squares, the sensor says "One." Be sure to start at the top row and read left to right, telling the receiving station when a new row begins.

4. The receiving station transfers the code to the graph paper. At the end, the receiver has three tries to guess whose initials were sent.

SKILL FOCUS
Modeling

MATERIALS
- graph paper
- pen or pencil
- *for Challenge:* colored pens or pencils

TIME

25 minutes

WHAT DO YOU THINK?

- What would happen if you accidentally skipped or repeated a row?

- If you increased or decreased the number and size of the squares, how would this affect the picture?

CHALLENGE Use a variety of colors to send other initials or an image. Your code must tell the receiver which color to use for each square.

DIFFERENTIATE INSTRUCTION

More Reading Support

B What are false color images? *pictures in which Earth's natural colors are changed to artificial ones that better highlight Earth's features*

Inclusion Students with vision impairments may have trouble using the standard-sized grid on graph paper. Use the enlargement capability of a copy machine to increase the grid size, then outline the grid with a bold marker. Have students use the bold marker for filling in the squares as other students read off the zeros and ones.

 Challenge and Extension, p. 51

Geographic information systems display data in layers.

Any good city map will show you what is on the surface—buildings, streets, parks, and other features. But suppose you need to know about tunnels under the city. Or maybe you want to know where the most students live. An ordinary map, even one based on remote-sensing images, will not tell you what you want to know.

Instead, you would turn to geographic information systems. **Geographic information systems** (GIS) are computer systems that can store and arrange geographic data and display the data in many different types of maps. Scientists, city planners, and engineers all use GIS maps to help them make decisions. For example, suppose your city wants to build a new airport. It must be away from populated areas and near major highways. The illustration below shows how city officials might use GIS to pick the best site.

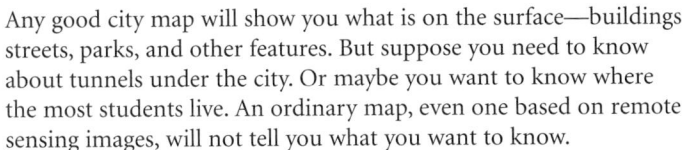
RESOURCE CENTER
CLASSZONE.COM
Find out more about how GIS is used.

Geographic Information Systems

GIS can be used to produce maps that help people make decisions.

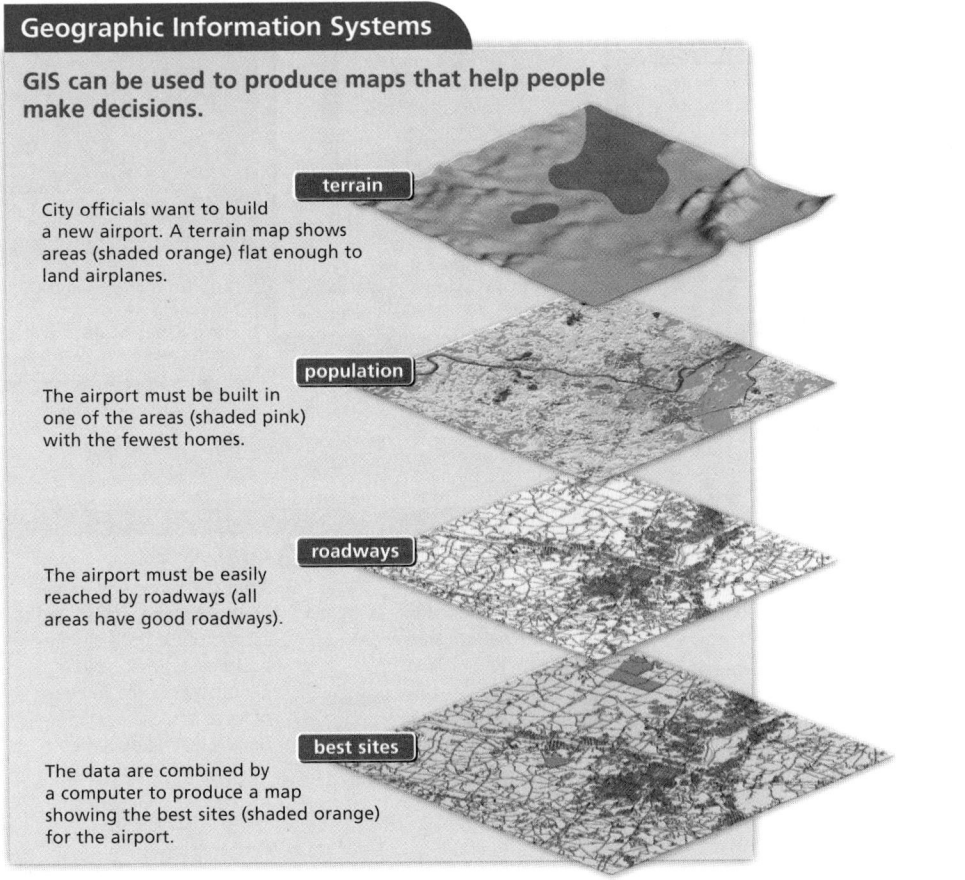

City officials want to build a new airport. A terrain map shows areas (shaded orange) flat enough to land airplanes.

terrain

The airport must be built in one of the areas (shaded pink) with the fewest homes.

population

The airport must be easily reached by roadways (all areas have good roadways).

roadways

The data are combined by a computer to produce a map showing the best sites (shaded orange) for the airport.

best sites

Chapter 1: **Views of Earth Today** 33 **A**

 More Reading Support

C What does *GIS* stand for? *geographic information systems*

Below Level The acronyms *GPS* and *GIS* might be confusing for some students. Write each acronym on the board and have volunteers provide information to add under it. You might also have students make up their own memory aids to help them remember the difference between GIS and GPS. For instance, they might write "GIS" vertically to remind them it refers to data layers.

Advanced Have students who are interested in GIS and other mapping technologies read the following article:

 Challenge Reading, pp. 54–55

Teach Difficult Concepts

Students may have a hard time visualizing, on the basis of the description of data layers, how GIS works. Explain that GIS maps contain "made-to-order" information. To help students understand, try the following demonstration.

Teacher Demo

Display transparencies with an overhead projector to simulate GIS map layers. Tell students they are developers seeking to place a teen clothing store in the best possible location. On the first transparency, draw a simple map with the boundaries of a hypothetical community outlined in black. On a second transparency, draw roads and highways in blue and set it on top of the first transparency on the projector. Next, cluster some pink-outlined patches at one corner of the map near a highway. Tell students that these represent areas with more than 10 teens per 100 population. Note how arranging the data in layers makes it easy to decide where to locate the store. Have students agree on a suitable location.

Teach from Visuals

To help students interpret the visual about GIS, ask:

• Why is a terrain map included in this composite? *Airplanes need flat runways for landings.*

• How are the individual maps combined? *A computer stores the data in the individual maps and uses the data to build a composite map.*

Ongoing Assessment

Explain how geographic data can be displayed in layers to build maps.

Ask: How can combining the data in various map layers be useful? *It can help scientists, city planners, and engineers make decisions.*

Ongoing Assessment

 CHECK YOUR READING *Answer: GIS maps can help engineers, city planners, and scientists by combining different geographic information in one map that can be easily read, showing what is above and below the surface, presenting all the different types of information needed to make a decision, and indicating changes in the environment.*

EXPLORE (the **BIG** idea)

Revisit "Internet Activity: Mapping" on p. 7. Have students summarize the technologies used to map Earth.

Reinforce (the **BIG** idea)

Have students relate the section to the Big Idea.

 R Reinforcing Key Concepts, p. 53

1.4 ASSESS & RETEACH

Assess

A Section 1.4 Quiz, p. 6

Reteach

Ask students to come to the board to fill in frame game or four square note-taking organizers for each of the technological terms defined in this section. Include a definition, examples, nonexamples, and characteristics. *(Remote sensing: use of scientific equipment to gather information from a distance; camera or satellite; microscope; uses technology to gain a grander perspective)*

Technology Resources

Have students visit **ClassZone.com** for reteaching of Key Concepts.

 CONTENT REVIEW

 CONTENT REVIEW CD-ROM

Any geographic information can be entered into GIS and converted into a map. These systems are especially useful in displaying information about changes in the environment.

For example, near Long Valley in California, the volcano known as Mammoth Mountain began giving off carbon dioxide, or CO_2. As the gas rose through the soil, it began killing the roots of trees nearby. Scientists measured the flow of CO_2 around Horseshoe Lake and other areas. They used computer software to build the maps shown below.

 **CHECK YOUR READING** Summarize the ways GIS maps can be helpful to engineers, city planners, and scientists.

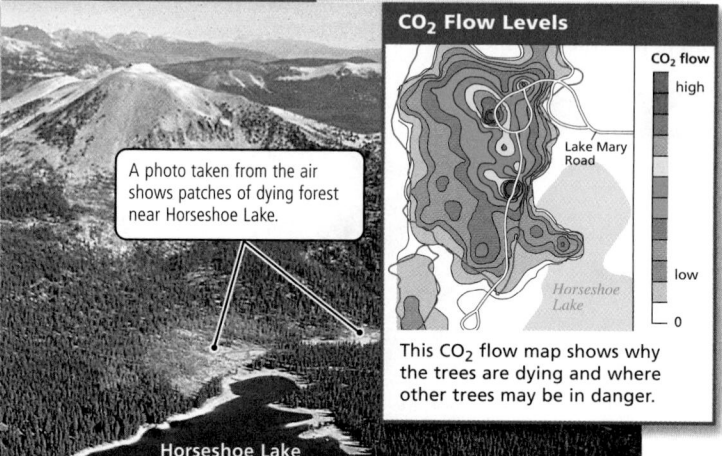

Mammoth Mountain

A photo taken from the air shows patches of dying forest near Horseshoe Lake.

Horseshoe Lake

CO_2 Flow Levels

CO_2 flow
high
low
0

Lake Mary Road

Horseshoe Lake

This CO_2 flow map shows why the trees are dying and where other trees may be in danger.

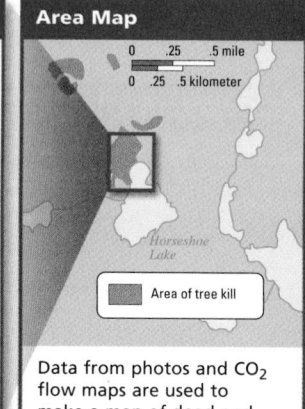

Area Map

0 .25 .5 mile
0 .25 .5 kilometer

Horseshoe Lake

Area of tree kill

Data from photos and CO_2 flow maps are used to make a map of dead and dying trees.

1.4 Review

KEY CONCEPTS

1. How are satellites used to make images of Earth from outer space?
2. What are some of the types of information obtained by remote sensing?
3. Explain in your own words what is a GIS map?

CRITICAL THINKING

4. **Infer** Explain how satellite images might be used to predict what a natural area might look like in 50 or 100 years.
5. **Evaluate** If you wanted to compare a region before and during a flood, how could false-color images help you?

CHALLENGE

6. **Analyze** Work with a small group. Suppose you wanted to ask the city to build a skateboard park. What types of information would you need in order to propose a good site? Draw a map to display each type of information.

ANSWERS

1. Satellites collect information about different types of energy.

2. surface features of Earth, changes in the environment, images for making maps

3. layers of data depicting different information, stacked on top of each other

4. They could reveal rates of change that would help in predicting what the same area might look like in the future.

5. They could highlight the wet areas before and during the flood.

6. Information needed might include which sites (1) have enough space for the park, (2) are near public transportation routes, and (3) are near schools.

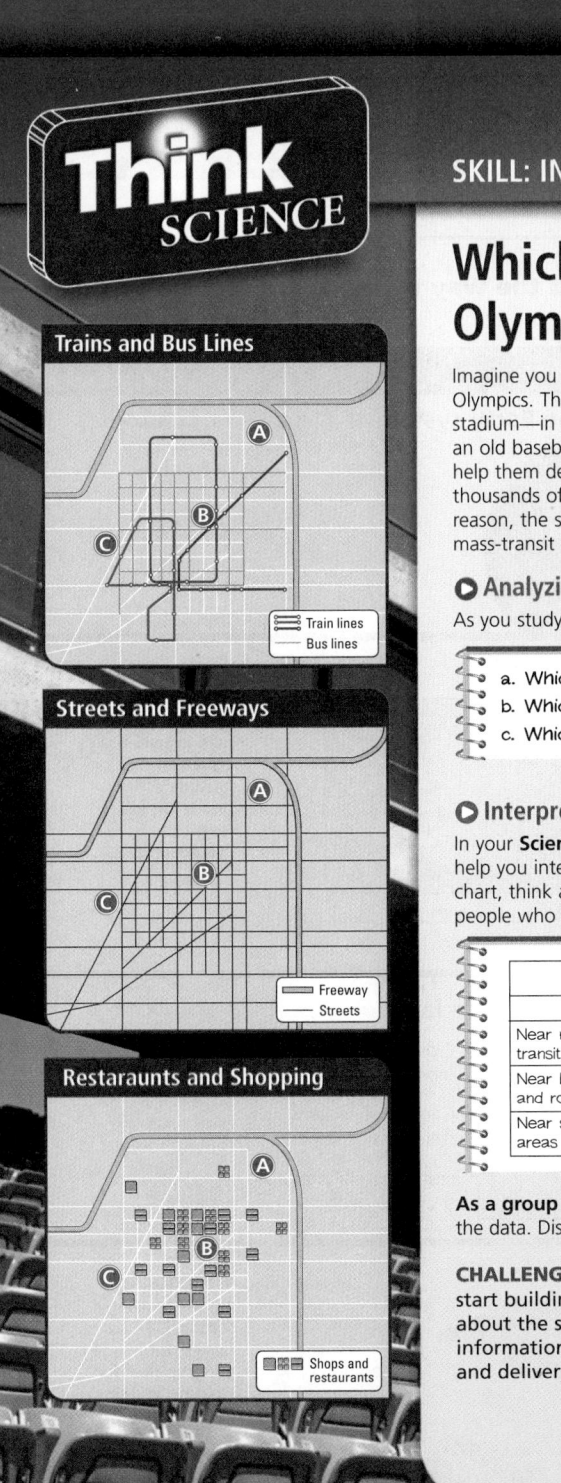

Trains and Bus Lines

Train lines
Bus lines

Streets and Freeways

Freeway
Streets

Restaraunts and Shopping

Shops and restaurants

Think SCIENCE

SKILL: INTERPRETING DATA

Which Site Is Best for an Olympic Stadium?

Imagine you live in a city that has been chosen to host the Summer Olympics. The only question is where to build the Olympic stadium—in the center of town, in the suburbs, or on the site of an old baseball park. The city government has developed maps to help them decide which is the best site. The planners know that thousands of people will come to see the games. Therefore, they reason, the stadium should be (1) easy to reach by car, (2) close to mass-transit stops, and (3) near restaurants and shops.

▶ Analyzing Map Data

As you study the maps, keep these requirements in mind.

> a. Which site(s) is/are closest to bus and train lines?
> b. Which site(s) is/are easiest to reach by car?
> c. Which site(s) is/are close to shopping areas?

▶ Interpreting Data

In your **Science Notebook,** create a chart like the one below to help you interpret the data displayed on the maps. As you fill in the chart, think about which site offers the greatest benefits to all the people who will attend the Olympic Games.

	Site Ⓐ		Site Ⓑ		Site Ⓒ	
	Yes	No	Yes	No	Yes	No
Near mass transit						
Near highways and roads						
Near shopping areas						

As a group Choose the best site based on your interpretation of the data. Discuss your choice with other groups to see if they agree.

CHALLENGE Once the site is chosen, the planners will start building the stadium. What types of information about the site will they need? Sketch maps displaying the information. **Hint:** The stadium will need electricity, water, and delivery of supplies.

Set Learning Goal

To choose among event sites by analyzing data in GIS map layers

Present the Science

GIS maps are in broad use today, across a variety of applications. Ask students how this activity demonstrates why the technology has proved to be a time-saver. *Without GIS technology, vast amounts of research are necessary to supply what can be achieved in a few keystrokes using GIS technology.*

Guide the Activity

• Point out to students that the three requirements will help them choose the best site.

• The chart allows for objective interpretation of the data. Have students discuss whether they find it useful to organize the information in this way.

• Ask students for any other information they would want to know if they were actually making such a decision. Would additional GIS layers help?

Close

Ask: How does the chart help? *The chart provides a way to compare the places.*

ANSWERS

As a Group Site B; it is close to train and bus lines, reachable by car, and has the most nearby shops and restaurants of the three sites.

CHALLENGE Student maps will vary but should include the geology of the site; existing gas, water, sewer systems; power and telephone lines; access roads; and so on.

BACK TO

the BIG idea

Have students summarize the technologies used in mapping and viewing Earth and the benefits they provide. *Viewing technologies include satellites and deep-sea vehicles. Mapping technologies include satellites and airplanes, remote-sensing equipment, the Global Positioning System (GPS), and geographic information systems (GIS). They provide information about Earth's interior and its oceans, as well as views from above the atmosphere. Computer systems aid in the interpretation of what we see.*

◖ KEY CONCEPTS SUMMARY

SECTION 1.1
Give two examples that illustrate the statement to the left of the globe. *water evaporates from a lake (hydrosphere and atmosphere); an animal decomposes and the ground absorbs nutrients (biosphere and geosphere)*

SECTION 1.2
Explain the difference in accuracy between the globe and the map. *The shapes and sizes of landmasses and oceans are relatively accurate on the globe; shapes, sizes, or both are distorted on the map because it is flat.*

SECTION 1.3
How does the map shown here provide useful information? *The contour lines and symbols show the shape and features of the land.*

SECTION 1.4
What types of information might the satellite on the left gather for inclusion in the map layers on the right? *Sample answers: vegetation, waterways, forest fires, population, roadways, temperatures*

Review Concepts

- Big Idea Flow Chart, p. T1
- Chapter Outline, pp. T7–T8

---

1 Chapter Review

the BIG idea

Modern technology has changed the way we view and map Earth.

 CONTENT REVIEW
CLASSZONE.COM

◖ KEY CONCEPTS SUMMARY

1.1 Technology is used to explore the Earth system.

The atmosphere, hydrosphere, biosphere, and geosphere work together to form one large system called Earth.

VOCABULARY
system p. 9
atmosphere p. 10
hydrosphere p. 10
biosphere p. 11
geosphere p. 12

1.2 Maps and globes are models of Earth.

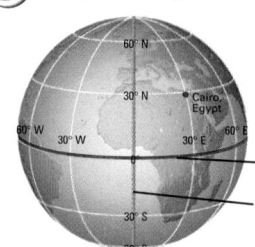

Latitude and longitude are used to locate any point on Earth.

— equator

— prime meridian

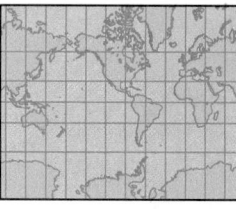

All map projections distort Earth's surface.

VOCABULARY
relief map p. 16
map scale p. 17
map legend p. 17
equator p. 18
latitude p. 18
prime meridian p. 19
longitude p. 19
projection p. 20

1.3 Topographic maps show the shape of the land.

Contour lines show elevation, slope, and relief.

Contour lines never cross.

Closed circles represent hilltops.

Contour lines show steepness of slope.

Index contour lines show elevation.

VOCABULARY
topography p. 24
contour line p. 25
elevation p. 25
slope p. 25
relief p. 25
contour interval p. 26

1.4 Technology is used to map Earth.

Remote-sensing technology gathers accurate data about Earth.

Geographic information systems are computer programs used to merge layers of information.

VOCABULARY
remote sensing p. 30
sensor p. 31
false-color image p. 32
geographic information systems p. 33

Technology Resources

Have students visit **ClassZone.com** or use the CD-ROM for a cumulative review of concepts.

 CONTENT REVIEW

CONTENT REVIEW CD-ROM

Engage students in a whole-class interactive review of Key Concepts. Edit content as you wish.

 POWER PRESENTATIONS

Reviewing Vocabulary

Copy and complete the chart below, using vocabulary terms from this chapter.

Term	Use	Appearance
map legend	to explain map symbols	chart of symbols
1. latitude	to show distance from the equator	
2. longitude		lines going from pole to pole
3.	to show land features	rippled and smooth areas
4. map scale	to represent distances	
5. equator		line at 0° latitude
6. prime meridian	to separate east and west hemispheres	
7.	to show height above sea level	line showing elevation
8. false-color image	to highlight information	

Reviewing Key Concepts

Multiple Choice *Choose the letter of the best answer.*

9. Which Greek prefix is matched with its correct meaning?
- **a.** *hydro* = life
- **b.** *atmo* = gas
- **c.** *bio* = earth
- **d.** *geo* = water

10. What portion of Earth is covered by water?
- **a.** one-quarter
- **b.** one-half
- **c.** three-quarters
- **d.** seven-eights

11. The continents and ocean basins are part of Earth's
- **a.** crust
- **b.** mantle
- **c.** outer core
- **d.** inner core

12. Which Earth system includes humans?
- **a.** atmosphere
- **b.** biosphere
- **c.** hydrosphere
- **d.** geosphere

13. One way the atmosphere shapes Earth's surface is by
- **a.** winds
- **b.** floods
- **c.** earthquakes
- **d.** tunnels

14. How are the major parts of the Earth system related to each other?
- **a.** They rarely can be studied together.
- **b.** They often are in conflict.
- **c.** They usually work independently.
- **d.** They always affect each other.

15. A flat map shows Earth's curved surface by means of
- **a.** elevation
- **b.** topography
- **c.** relief
- **d.** projection

16. People use latitude and longitude lines mostly to identify
- **a.** map scales
- **b.** country names
- **c.** exact locations
- **d.** distances

17. The most accurate way to show Earth's surface is a
- **a.** globe
- **b.** conic projection
- **c.** cylindrical projection
- **d.** planar projection

18. One example of remote sensing is the use of
- **a.** contour lines
- **b.** projections
- **c.** GIS
- **d.** binoculars

Short Answer *Write a few sentences to answer each question.*

19. How does the Global Positioning System work? In your answer use each of the following terms. Underline each term in your answer.

24 satellites	computer	longitude
receiver	latitude	elevation

20. How do Mercator maps distort the view of Earth's surface?

21. How do people use sensors in making maps?

Reviewing Vocabulary

1. lines parallel to the equator
2. to show distance from the prime meridian
3. relief map
4. a ratio or a bar
5. to separate north and south hemispheres
6. a line at 0° longitude
7. contour lines
8. artificial colors replacing Earth's natural colors

Reviewing Key Concepts

9. b
10. c
11. a
12. b
13. a
14. d
15. d
16. c
17. a
18. d

19. A network of <u>24 satellites</u> send signals that can be picked up by a <u>receiver</u> on Earth. Using these signals, a <u>computer</u> inside the receiver calculates the <u>latitude</u>, <u>longitude</u>, and <u>elevation</u> of its location.

20. Mercator maps make areas far away from the equator look much larger than they really are. Greenland is only one-eighth the size of South America, but it appears larger.

21. Sensors are mechanical or electrical devices that receive and respond to different types of energy. Since they can detect far more than human eyes can see, they provide more-detailed information to use in making maps.

ASSESSMENT RESOURCES

UNIT ASSESSMENT BOOK
- Chapter Test A, pp. 7–10
- Chapter Test B, pp. 11–14
- Chapter Test C, pp. 15–18
- Alternative Assessment, pp. 19–20

SPANISH ASSESSMENT BOOK
Spanish Chapter Test, pp. 105–108

Technology Resources

Edit test items and answer choices.

 Test Generator CD-ROM

Visit **ClassZone.com** to extend test practice.

 Test Practice

Thinking Critically

22. E, because the contour lines are closest together near this hill

23. It is nearly flat.

24. They are near an unpaved road that leads to a paved road.

25. more than 1480 meters (in the loop that contains D)

26. E should look steep with a valley separating it from D; D should be slightly higher, with a gentler slope.

27. The main advantage is that the land is mostly flat; the main disadvantage is that it is a marsh.

28. Since there are several hills, mountain biking would be appropriate.

29. yes, geosphere

30. no, atmosphere

31. yes, biosphere

32. yes, hydrosphere

33. yes, geosphere

the BIG idea

34. Students' responses should indicate what they have learned in this chapter.

35. Maps of the ocean floor and some other types of information might be considered new. Most of what people have learned from new technologies is more detailed and precise versions of older information.

36. Sample answer: Satellites have provided new information about each part of the Earth system and is probably the technology that has changed the way people view and map Earth the most.

UNIT PROJECTS

Give students the appropriate Unit Project worksheets from the URB for their projects. Both directions and rubrics can be used as a guide.

 Unit Projects, pp. 5–10

Thinking Critically

Use the topographic map below to answer the next seven questions.

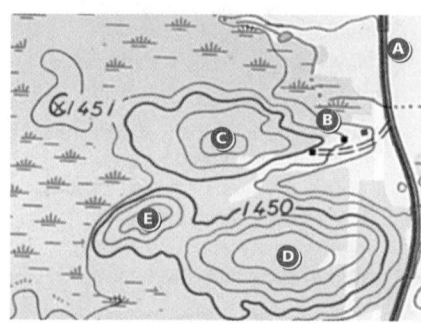

marsh | road
buildings | unpaved road

22. **APPLY** Imagine you are hiking through this area. Which hill—C, D, or E—has the steepest slope? How do you know?

23. **ANALYZE** What is the topography of the land through which the curved road A goes?

24. **IDENTIFY CAUSE** The black and red squares at B represent buildings. Why do you think the buildings were placed here instead of somewhere else in the area?

25. **APPLY** The contour interval is 10 meters. What is the elevation of the highest point on the map?

26. **SYNTHESIZE** Sketch the two hills D and E. What would they look like to someone on the ground?

27. **INFER** Suppose someone wanted to build a road through the terrain on the far left side of the map. What are the advantages and disadvantages of such a route?

28. **EVALUATE** Do you think this area would be a good place to ride mountain bikes? Why or why not?

CHART INFORMATION *On a separate sheet of paper, write a word to fill each blank in the chart.*

Feature	Shown on Topographic Maps?	Belongs to Which Major System?
rivers	*yes*	*hydrosphere*
29. slope		
30. winds		
31. plants		
32. lakes		
33. relief		

the BIG idea

34. **APPLY** Look again at the photographs on pages 6–7. Now that you have finished the chapter, reread the question on the main photograph. What would you change in or add to your answer?

35. **SYNTHESIZE** Describe some of the types of information that new technology has provided about Earth.

36. **DRAW CONCLUSIONS** What type of technology do you think has done the most to change the way people view and map Earth? Explain your conclusion.

UNIT PROJECTS

If you are doing a unit project, make a folder for your project. Include in your folder a list of the resources you will need, the date on which the project is due, and a schedule to track your progress. Begin gathering data.

MONITOR AND RETEACH

If students have trouble answering items 22–28, review the Mount Hood topographic map on p. 25 and the definitions of these words: *contour lines, elevation, slope, relief.*

Students may benefit from summarizing one or more sections of the chapter.

 Summarizing the Chapter, pp. 79–80

Standardized Test Practice

For practice on your state test, go to . . . 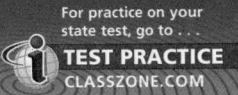 **TEST PRACTICE** CLASSZONE.COM

Analyzing a Diagram

This diagram shows the four major parts of the Earth system. Use it to answer the questions below.

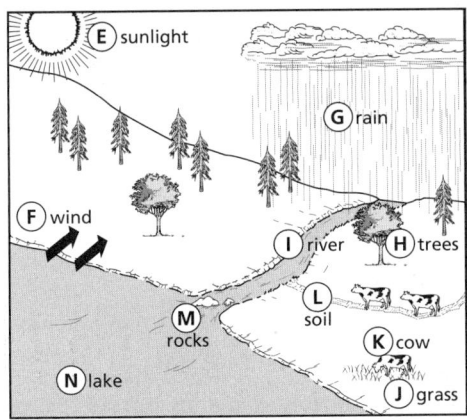

1. Where is the main source of energy for the Earth system?

a. E   **c.** G
b. F   **d.** L

2. Where is the biosphere shaping the geosphere?

a. E   **c.** L
b. F   **d.** M

3. Where is matter moving from one part of the hydrosphere to another?

a. I to N   **c.** J to H
b. G to H   **d.** N to M

4. Which items belong to the geosphere?

a. F and G   **c.** I and N
b. H and J   **d.** M and L

5. Which process is occurring at M where water is running over the rocks?

a. The geosphere is shaping the atmosphere.
b. The atmosphere is shaping the biosphere.
c. The hydrosphere is shaping the geosphere.
d. The biosphere is shaping the geosphere.

6. Where is matter moving from the atmosphere to the biosphere?

a. E and F   **c.** G and H
b. F and M   **d.** I and G

7. At K, the cow is eating grass. What kind of movement in the Earth system does this represent?

a. from the atmosphere to the hydrosphere
b. from the hydrosphere to the biosphere
c. between two parts of the geosphere
d. between two parts of the biosphere

8. Which is an example of how the hydrosphere is supported by the geosphere?

a. I, because the river receives the rain
b. H, because the trees are rooted in the ground
c. M, because the river drains into the lake
d. N, because the lake is contained by a basin

Extended Response

Answer the two questions below in detail. Include some of the terms shown in the word box. In your answers, underline each term you use.

geosphere	surface	system
atmosphere	hydrosphere	biosphere

9. Rain falls and soaks into the soil. Plants and animals use some of the water. More of the water drains into a river, then enters the ocean. Describe this process as movements among the major parts of the Earth system.

10. Describe an example of how people can shape the surface of the geosphere.

Analyzing a Diagram

1. a	5. c
2. c	6. c
3. a	7. d
4. d	8. d

Extended Response

9. RUBRIC

4 points for a response that correctly answers the question and uses the following terms accurately:

- geosphere
- atmosphere
- hydrosphere
- biosphere

Sample: Rain falls through the <u>atmosphere</u> (air) and soaks into the surface of the <u>geosphere</u> (soil). Some of the water is used by the <u>biosphere</u> (plants and animals). Some of the water drains into other parts of the <u>hydrosphere</u> (bodies of water).

3 points for a response that uses three terms accurately

2 points for a response that correctly answers the question and uses one term accurately

1 point for a response that correctly answers the question but doesn't use the terms

10. RUBRIC

4 points for a response that correctly answers the question and uses the following terms accurately:

- geosphere
- surface

Sample: People can shape the <u>surface</u> of the <u>geosphere</u> by using a steam shovel to dig a hole on a lot to flatten the soil. After the hole is dug, a construction crew can build a house on that spot.

3 points for a response that correctly answers the question and uses the term *geosphere* accurately

2 points for a response that correctly answers the question but doesn't use either of the terms

1 point for a response that uses the term *geosphere* accurately but doesn't answer the question satisfactorily

---

METACOGNITIVE ACTIVITY

Have students answer the following questions in their **Science Notebook:**

1. Which fact or facts in this chapter surprised you the most?

2. How do the concepts in this chapter relate to your life?

3. As you begin thinking about your Unit Project, what concept or concepts in this chapter have influenced your thinking?

Earth Science
UNIFYING PRINCIPLES

PRINCIPLE 1

Heat energy inside Earth and radiation from the Sun provide energy for Earth's processes.

PRINCIPLE 2

Physical forces, such as gravity, affect the movement of all matter on Earth and throughout the universe.

PRINCIPLE 3

Matter and energy move among Earth's rocks and soil, atmosphere, waters, and living things.

PRINCIPLE 4

Earth has changed over time and continues to change.

Unit: Earth's Surface
BIG IDEAS

CHAPTER 1
Views of Earth Today
Modern technology has changed the way we view and map Earth.

CHAPTER 2
Minerals

Minerals are basic building blocks of Earth.

CHAPTER 3
Rocks
Rocks change into other rocks over time.

CHAPTER 4
Weathering and Soil Formation
Natural forces break rocks apart and form soil, which supports life.

CHAPTER 5
Erosion and Deposition
Water, wind, and ice shape Earth's surface.

CHAPTER 2
KEY CONCEPTS

SECTION 2.1

Minerals are all around us.

1. Minerals have four characteristics.
2. Minerals are grouped according to composition.

SECTION 2.2

A mineral is identified by its properties.

1. A mineral's appearance helps identify it.
2. The way a mineral breaks helps identify it.
3. A mineral's density and hardness help identify it.
4. Some minerals have special properties.

SECTION 2.3

Minerals are valuable resources.

1. Minerals have many uses in industry.
2. Minerals have many uses in the arts.
3. Minerals form in several ways.
4. Many minerals are mined.

T The Big Idea Flow Chart is available on p. T9 in the **UNIT TRANSPARENCY BOOK.**

Previewing Content

2.1 Minerals are all around us. pp. 43–49

1. Minerals have four characteristics.

Minerals are the building blocks of most rocks. Minerals differ from rocks by having uniform compositions and orderly internal structures. The four characteristics of minerals are explained in the following chart:

Four Characteristics of Minerals	
Characteristic	**Example or Explanation**
Forms in nature	Many minerals form when molten rock cools.
Is a solid	Ice is a mineral, but liquid water and water vapor are not minerals.
Has a definite chemical makeup	The mineral halite has one atom of the **element** sodium for every atom of the element chlorine.
Has a **crystal** structure	In all minerals, the atoms are arranged in an orderly, repeating, three-dimensional pattern.

2. Minerals are grouped according to composition.

Minerals are classified into groups on the basis of their chemical composition. The most common group is the silicates, which contain the elements oxygen and silicon joined together. These two elements are the most common ones in Earth's crust.

2.2 A mineral is identified by its properties. pp. 50–59

1. A mineral's appearance helps identify it.

- The samples of hematite below differ in surface color but have the same streak. All samples of a mineral have the same streak. **Streak** is the color of a thin line of powder left behind when a mineral is scraped across a surface. The photograph on the right shows that a mineral's streak can be quite different from its surface color.

- A mineral's **luster** is the way light reflects from its surface. The two major types of luster are metallic and nonmetallic. The hematite specimen on the left has a nonmetallic luster; the one on the right has a metallic luster.

2. The way a mineral breaks helps identify it.

- The crystals of a mineral may display **cleavage,** a tendency to break along flat surfaces, or **fracture,** a tendency to break into pieces of irregular shapes.
- The way a mineral breaks depends on how its atoms are bonded. In minerals with cleavage, the bonds are weaker in the direction that the crystal breaks. In minerals that fracture, the bonds are about equally strong in all directions.

3. A mineral's density and hardness help identify it.

- **Density** is the amount of mass in a given volume. A dense mineral feels heavier than a less dense mineral of the same size.
- **Hardness** is a mineral's resistance to being scratched. This characteristic is measured according to the Mohs scale, which is based on the fact that a harder mineral will scratch a softer one.

4. Some minerals have special properties.

- Some minerals react with acid.
- Some minerals fluoresce: they glow in ultraviolet light.
- A few minerals respond to magnets.
- A few minerals are radioactive.

Previewing Content

2.3 Minerals are valuable resources.
pp. 60–67

1. Minerals have many uses in industry.
Modern society depends on minerals in making machines and everyday products. This chart gives a few examples.

Mineral Uses in Industry	
Mineral	**Product**
Chromite (source of chromium)	car
Gibbsite (source of aluminum)	soda can
Hematite (source of iron)	iron cooking pot

2. Minerals have many uses in the arts.
Gems and such metals as gold and silver are used in jewelry making and other decorative arts. Minerals are also used as pigments in dyes and paints.

3. Minerals form in several ways.
Minerals form when the atoms of one or more elements join together and crystals begin to grow. This can occur when

- water at Earth's surface evaporates
- hot water within Earth's crust cools
- **magma** or **lava** cools and becomes solid
- heat or pressure deep within Earth causes minerals to change
- organisms produce minerals to form shells or bones

4. Many minerals are mined.
A rock that contains enough of a mineral to be mined for a profit is called an **ore.** When minerals lie at or near Earth's surface, they may be recovered by surface-mining methods, including

- separation from other materials in a stream, either by hand or by machine
- strip mining, which involves stripping away the surface vegetation, soil, and rock to dig out an ore
- open-pit mining, which involves digging a deep pit to mine an ore

Deep-mining methods are used when ores lie far below Earth's surface.

Common Misconceptions

FORMATION IN NATURE Students may have difficulty identifying materials that is formed by natural processes. For example, they might consider a brick to be natural because it contains minerals, or they might consider a mineral sample to have been manufactured once it has been cut or polished.

 This misconception is addressed on p. 62.

 MISCONCEPTION DATABASE
CLASSZONE.COM Background on student misconceptions

Previewing Labs

Lab Generator
CD-ROM
Edit these Pupil Edition labs and generate alternative labs.

EXPLORE the BIG idea

How Do You Turn Water into a Mineral? p. 41
Students are introduced to one of the properties of a mineral.

TIME 5 minutes
MATERIALS water, ice cube, penny

What Makes Up Rocks? p. 41
Students look for minerals in rocks.

TIME 10 minutes
MATERIALS 3 different rocks

Internet Activity: Minerals, p. 41
Students find out about minerals that are also precious metals.

TIME 20 minutes
MATERIALS computer with Internet access

SECTION 2.1

EXPLORE Minerals, p. 43
Students examine salt to infer some of the characteristics of a mineral.

TIME 10 minutes
MATERIALS colored paper, table salt, rock salt, magnifying glass

INVESTIGATE Crystal Shape, p. 46
Students observe different shapes that crystals have.

TIME 20 minutes for setup
MATERIALS 1 tablespoon, 2 mixing cups, 2 stirring rods, 1 Tbs table salt, 1 Tbs Epsom salts, 60 mL water, 2 pie plates, 2 sheets black paper, scissors

---

SECTION 2.2

INVESTIGATE Hardness of Minerals, p. 56
Students classify minerals by testing hardness.

TIME 20 minutes
MATERIALS samples of 5 minerals, copper penny (1982 or earlier), steel file

CHAPTER INVESTIGATION Mineral Identification, pp. 58–59
Students test unknown minerals to identify them.

R • Mineral Identification Key, pp. 121–122
• Mohs Scale, p. 123

TIME 40 minutes
MATERIALS numbered mineral samples, hand lens, streak plate, copper penny, steel file, magnet, dilute hydrochloric acid, eyedropper, Mohs Scale, Mineral Identification Key

---

SECTION 2.3

EXPLORE Minerals at Your Fingertips, p. 60
Students examine a pencil to identify how minerals in the pencil are useful.

TIME 10 minutes
MATERIALS No. 2 and No. 4 wooden pencils, paper

INVESTIGATE Mining, p. 65
Students sort seeds and beads to draw conclusions about the benefits and costs of mining ores.

TIME 25 minutes
MATERIALS 1 pound wild-birdseed mix with sunflower seeds, shallow pan, 2 small red beads, 4 small green beads, 8 small blue beads, 3 medium yellow beads

---

R **Additional INVESTIGATION,** Stalagmites and Stalactites, A, B, & C, pp. 133–141; Teacher Instructions, pp. 348–349

Previewing Chapter Resources

	INTEGRATED TECHNOLOGY	LABS AND ACTIVITIES

CHAPTER 2
Minerals

 CLASSZONE.COM
- eEdition Plus
- EasyPlanner Plus
- Misconception Database
- Content Review
- Test Practice
- Visualizations
- Resource Centers
- Internet Activity: Minerals
- Math Tutorial

 CD-ROMS
- eEdition
- EasyPlanner
- Power Presentations
- Content Review
- Lab Generator
- Test Generator

 AUDIO CDS
- Audio Readings
- Audio Readings in Spanish

SCILINKS.ORG
SCiLINKS

 EXPLORE the Big Idea, p. 41
- How Do You Turn Water into a Mineral?
- What Makes Up Rocks?
- Internet Activity: Minerals

UNIT RESOURCE BOOK
Unit Projects, pp. 5–10

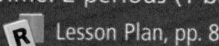 **Lab Generator CD-ROM**
Generate customized labs.

SECTION
2.1 Minerals are all around us.
pp. 43–49

Time: 2 periods (1 block)
 Lesson Plan, pp. 81–82

- **RESOURCE CENTER,** Minerals
- **VISUALIZATION,** Crystal Growth
- **MATH TUTORIAL**

 UNIT TRANSPARENCY BOOK
- Big Idea Flow Chart, p. T9
- Daily Vocabulary Scaffolding, p. T10
- Note-Taking Model, p. T11
- 3-Minute Warm-Up, p. T12

- EXPLORE Minerals, p. 43
- INVESTIGATE Crystal Shape, p. 46
- Math in Science, p. 49

 UNIT RESOURCE BOOK
- Datasheet, Crystal Shape, p. 90
- Math Support, p. 119
- Math Practice, p. 120

SECTION
2.2 A mineral is identified by its properties.
pp. 50–59

Time: 3 periods (1.5 blocks)
 Lesson Plan, pp. 92–93

 UNIT TRANSPARENCY BOOK
- Daily Vocabulary Scaffolding, p. T10
- 3-Minute Warm-Up, p. T12

- INVESTIGATE Hardness of Minerals, p. 56
- CHAPTER INVESTIGATION, Mineral Identification, pp. 58–59

 UNIT RESOURCE BOOK
- Datasheet, Hardness of Minerals, p. 101
- Mineral Identification Key, pp. 121–122
- Mohs Scale, p. 123
- CHAPTER INVESTIGATION, Mineral Identification, A, B, & C, pp. 124–132

SECTION
2.3 Minerals are valuable resources.
pp. 60–67

Time: 3 periods (1.5 blocks)
 Lesson Plan, pp. 103–104

 RESOURCE CENTER, Gemstones

 UNIT TRANSPARENCY BOOK
- Big Idea Flow Chart, p. T9
- Daily Vocabulary Scaffolding, p. T10
- 3-Minute Warm-Up, p. T13
- "Mineral Formation" Visual, p. T14
- Chapter Outline, pp. T15–T16

- EXPLORE Minerals at Your Fingertips, p. 60
- INVESTIGATE Mining, p. 65
- Science on the Job, p. 67

 UNIT RESOURCE BOOK
- Datasheet, Mining, p. 112
- Additional INVESTIGATION, Stalagmites and Stalactites, A, B, & C, pp. 133–141

READING AND REINFORCEMENT

ASSESSMENT

STANDARDS

 • Description Wheel, B20–21
• Supporting Main Ideas, C42
• Daily Vocabulary Scaffolding, H1–8

R **UNIT RESOURCE BOOK**
• Vocabulary Practice, pp. 116–117
• Decoding Support, p. 118
• Summarizing the Chapter, pp. 142–143

 Audio Readings CD
Listen to Pupil Edition.

 Audio Readings in Spanish CD
Listen to Pupil Edition in Spanish.

PE • Chapter Review, pp. 69–70
• Standardized Test Practice, p. 71

A **UNIT ASSESSMENT BOOK**
• Diagnostic Test, pp. 21–22
• Chapter Test, A, B, & C, pp. 26–37
• Alternative Assessment, pp. 38–39

SP A Spanish Chapter Test, pp. 109–112

 Test Generator CD-ROM
Generate customized tests.

 Lab Generator CD-ROM
Rubrics for Labs

National Standards
A.2–8, A.9.a–c, A.9.e–f

See p. 40 for the standards.

R **UNIT RESOURCE BOOK**
• Reading Study Guide, A & B, pp. 83–86
• Spanish Reading Study Guide, pp. 87–88
• Challenge and Extension, p. 89
• Reinforcing Key Concepts, p. 91

 Ongoing Assessment, pp. 44–48

PE Section 2.1 Review, p. 48

A **UNIT ASSESSMENT BOOK**
Section 2.1 Quiz, p. 23

National Standards
A.2–8, A.9.a–c, A.9.e–f

R **UNIT RESOURCE BOOK**
• Reading Study Guide, A & B, pp. 94–97
• Spanish Reading Study Guide, pp. 98–99
• Challenge and Extension, p. 100
• Reinforcing Key Concepts, p. 102

 Ongoing Assessment, pp. 50–51, 53–57

PE Section 2.2 Review, p. 57

A **UNIT ASSESSMENT BOOK**
Section 2.2 Quiz, p. 24

National Standards
A.2–7, A.9.a–b, A.9.e–f

R **UNIT RESOURCE BOOK**
• Reading Study Guide, A & B, pp. 105–108
• Spanish Reading Study Guide, pp. 109–110
• Challenge and Extension, p. 111
• Reinforcing Key Concepts, p. 113
• Challenge Reading, pp. 114–115

 Ongoing Assessment, pp. 60–66

PE Section 2.3 Review, p. 66

A **UNIT ASSESSMENT BOOK**
Section 2.3 Quiz, p. 25

National Standards
A.2–8, A.9.a–c, A.9.e–f

Previewing Resources for Differentiated Instruction

CHAPTER INVESTIGATION

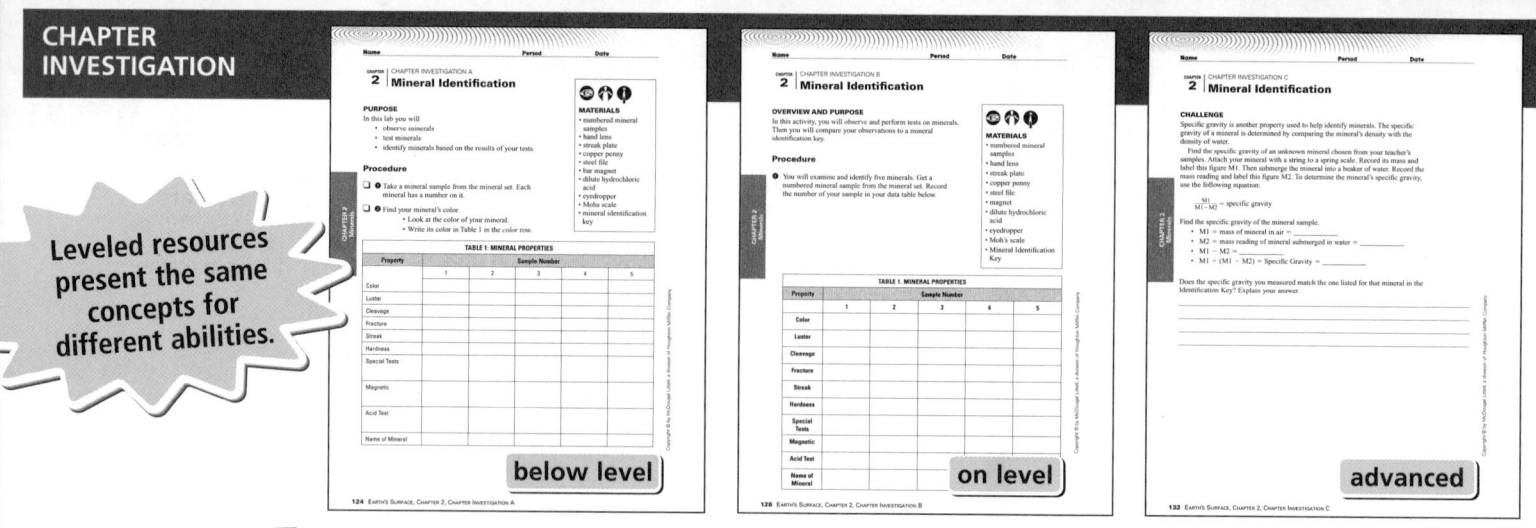

Leveled resources present the same concepts for different abilities.

below level

on level

advanced

R UNIT RESOURCE BOOK, pp. 124–127   **R** pp. 128–131   **R** pp. 128–132

READING STUDY GUIDE

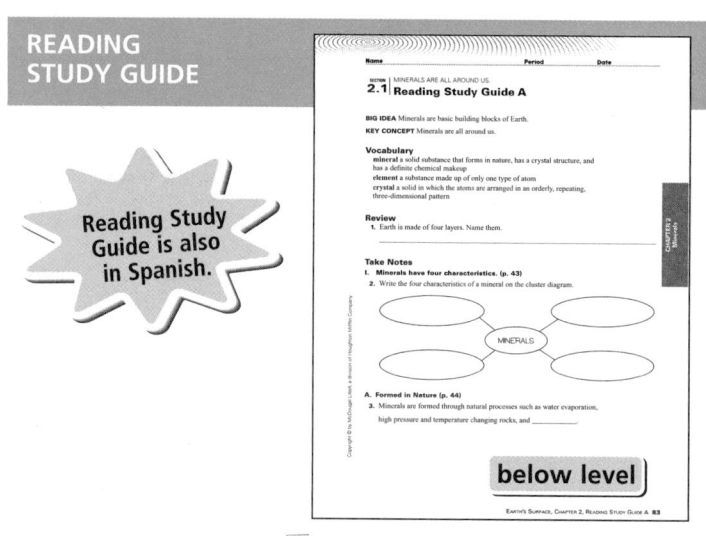

Reading Study Guide is also in Spanish.

below level

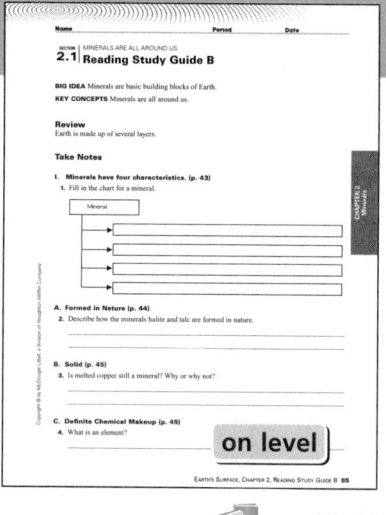

on level

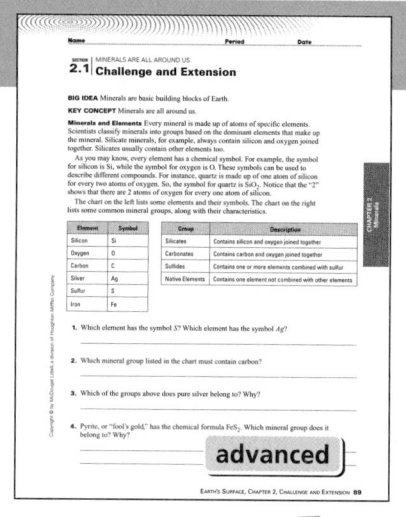

advanced

R UNIT RESOURCE BOOK, pp. 83–84   **R** pp. 85–86   **R** p. 89

CHAPTER TEST

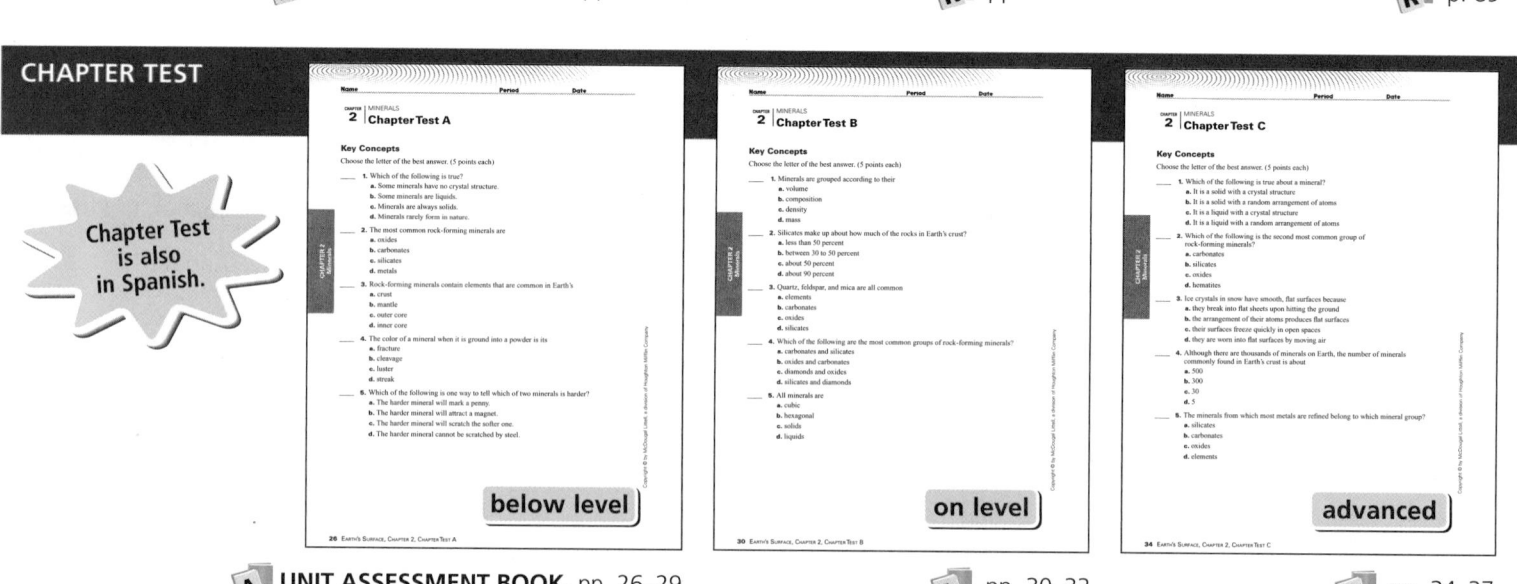

Chapter Test is also in Spanish.

below level

on level

advanced

A UNIT ASSESSMENT BOOK, pp. 26–29   **A** pp. 30–33   **A** pp. 34–37

TECHNOLOGY

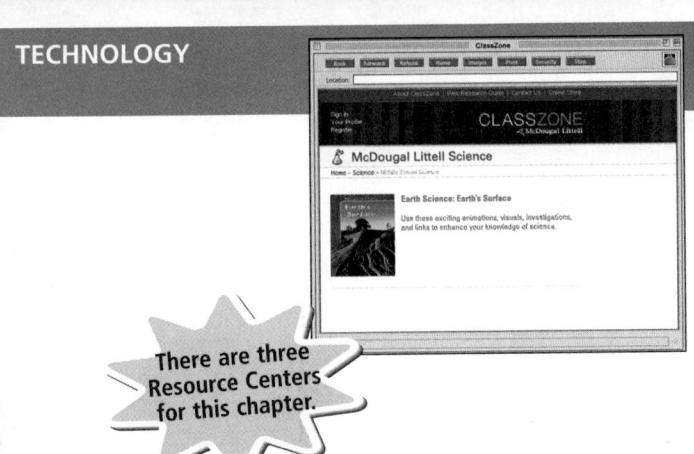

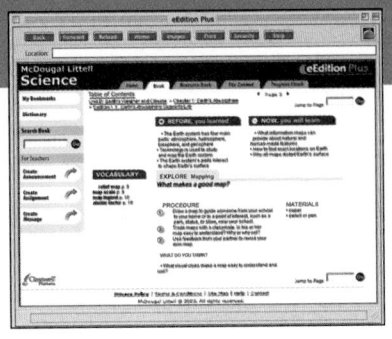

There are three Resource Centers for this chapter.

CLASSZONE.COM

CD/CD-ROMS

CLASSZONE.COM

VISUAL CONTENT

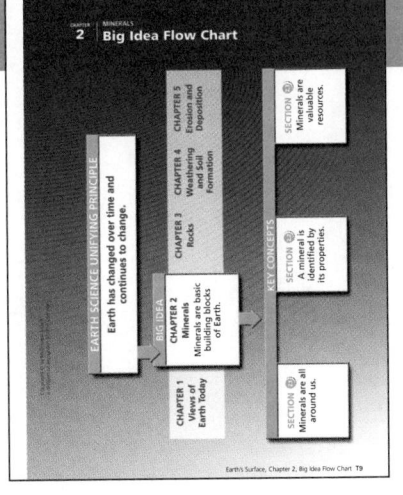

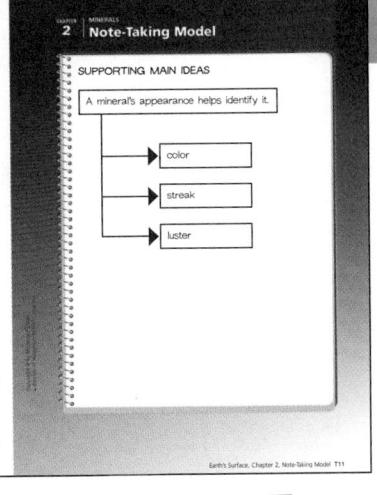

T **UNIT TRANSPARENCY BOOK,** p. T9

T p. T11

T p. T14

MORE SUPPORT

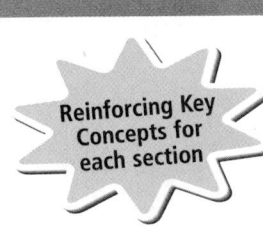

Reinforcing Key Concepts for each section

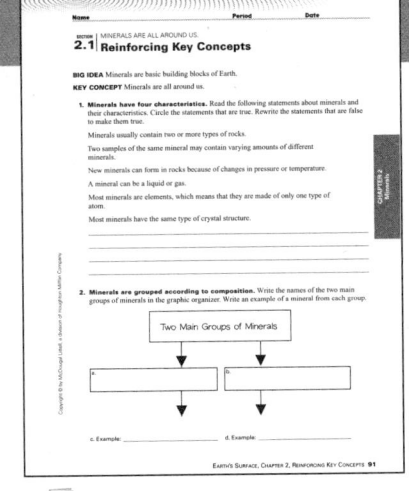

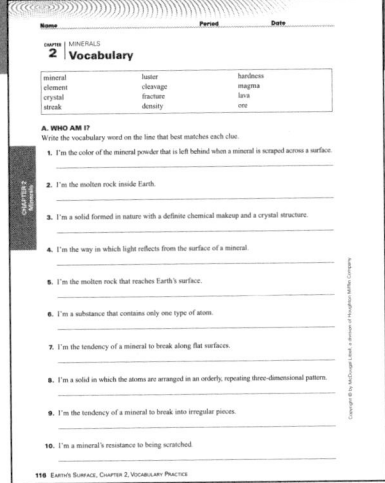

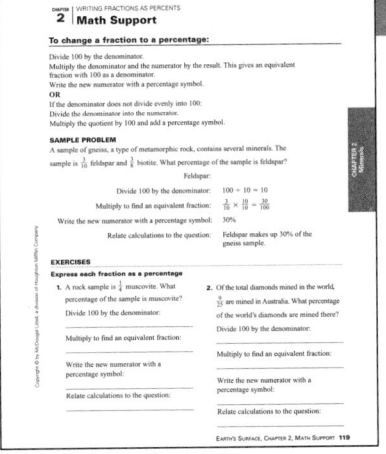

R **UNIT RESOURCE BOOK,** p. 91

R pp. 116–117

R p. 119

INTRODUCE

the BIG idea

Have students look at the photograph of the boy panning for gold and discuss how the question in the box links to the Big Idea. Ask:

- What do you think happens to gold as the water is swirled in the pan?
- Why would the gold settle to the bottom?

National Science Education Standards

Process

A.2–8 Design and conduct an investigation; use tools to gather and interpret data; use evidence to describe, predict, explain, model; think critically to make relationships between evidence and explanation; recognize different explanations and predictions; communicate scientific procedures and explanations; use mathematics.

A.9.a–c, A.9.e–f Understand scientific inquiry by using different investigations, methods, mathematics, and explanations based on logic, evidence, and skepticism.

CHAPTER

2 Minerals

the BIG idea

Minerals are basic building blocks of Earth.

Key Concepts

SECTION
2.1 Minerals are all around us.
Learn about the characteristics all minerals share.

SECTION
2.2 A mineral is identified by its properties.
Learn how to identify minerals by observing and testing their properties.

SECTION
2.3 Minerals are valuable resources.
Learn how minerals form, how they are mined, and how they are used.

Internet Preview

CLASSZONE.COM

Chapter 2 online resources: Content Review, Visualization, three Resource Centers, Math Tutorial, Test Practice

A 40 Unit: Earth's Surface

Why can gold be separated from other minerals and rocks in a river?

INTERNET PREVIEW

CLASSZONE.COM For student use with the following pages:

Review and Practice
- Content Review: pp. 42, 68
- Math Tutorial: Percents and Fractions, p. 49
- Test Practice, p. 71

Activities and Resources
- Internet Activity: Minerals, p. 41
- Resource Center: Minerals, p. 48; Gemstones, p. 61
- Visualization: Crystal Growth, p. 46

Identifying Minerals
Code: MDL014

EXPLORE (the BIG idea)

How Do You Turn Water into a Mineral?

Freeze some water into ice cubes. Then compare water, an ice cube, and a penny. Liquid water is not a mineral, but ice is. The surface of the penny is made of the mineral copper.

Observe and Think
How are the water, ice cube, and penny similar? How are they different? What do you think one of the properties of a mineral is?

What Makes Up Rocks?

Find three different rocks near your home or school. Examine them closely with a magnifying glass.

Observe and Think
Describe the rocks. How many materials can you see in each rock? How do you think they got there?

Internet Activity: Minerals

Go to **ClassZone.com** to find out more about minerals that are also precious metals.

Observe and Think
In addition to jewelry, how many different uses can you find for gold?

NSTA
scilinks.org
SCI**LINKS**

Identifying Minerals **Code: MDL014**

TEACHING WITH TECHNOLOGY

PC Microscope If you have a PC microscope with appropriate software, use this technology to examine grains of salt while performing the activity on p. 43.

EXPLORE (the BIG idea)

These inquiry-based activities are appropriate for use at home or as a supplement to classroom instruction.

How Do You Turn Water into a Mineral?

PURPOSE To introduce students to characteristics of minerals. Students describe ice, copper, and water to infer that a mineral is a solid.

TIP *5 min.* Tell students that sometimes the obvious answer is the correct one.

Answer: The water and the ice cube are made of the same substance. The ice cube and the penny are solid. Water is liquid. One of the properties of a mineral is that it is solid.

REVISIT after p. 45.

What Makes Up Rocks?

PURPOSE To introduce students to materials that make up rocks. Students examine three rocks with a magnifying glass.

TIP *10 min.* Have students find three rock samples that look different.

Answer: Some rocks may look as though they are made up of only one material. Others may be made up of two or more materials that differ in color and texture. The materials formed by natural processes within Earth or on Earth's surface.

REVISIT after p. 63.

Internet Activity: Minerals

PURPOSE To introduce students to different uses of gold.

TIP *20 min.* Ask students to list uses of gold before they visit the Web site.

Sample answers: money, decoration, tooth fillings

REVISIT after p. 61.

◐ CONCEPT REVIEW

Activate Prior Knowledge

- Draw a diagram of Earth's four main layers on the board and ask students to identify them.

- Ask students to identify examples of the three states of matter within the classroom, such as air (gas), a bottle of water (liquid), and a desk (solid).

- Have students list some features of Earth that maps show, such as rivers, lakes, and mountains.

▷ TAKING NOTES

Supporting Main Ideas

Identifying supporting information for main ideas is a basic reading and study skill that not only helps students understand the concepts presented in the text but also prepares them for taking standardized tests. Encourage students to look for topic sentences and examples when filling in supporting information.

Vocabulary Strategy

A description wheel helps students develop many associations with a word. These personal associations help with both recall and understanding. Be sure each phrase on the "spokes" helps to describe what the center word denotes.

Vocabulary and Note-Taking Resources

- Vocabulary Practice, pp. 116–117
- Decoding Support, p. 118

- Daily Vocabulary Scaffolding, p. T10
- Note-Taking Model, p. T11

- Description Wheel, B20–21
- Supporting Main Ideas, C42
- Daily Vocabulary Scaffolding, H1–8

CHAPTER 2

Getting Ready to Learn

◐ CONCEPT REVIEW

- Earth has four main layers: crust, mantle, outer core, and inner core.
- Matter exists in the forms of gas, liquid, and solid.
- People use maps to show many different features of Earth.

◐ VOCABULARY REVIEW

atom *See Glossary.*
geosphere p. 12

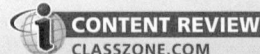
CONTENT REVIEW
CLASSZONE.COM
Review concepts and vocabulary.

▷ TAKING NOTES

SUPPORTING MAIN IDEAS

Make a chart to show each main idea and the information that supports it. Copy each blue heading. Below each heading, add supporting information, such as reasons, explanations, and examples.

VOCABULARY STRATEGY

Place each vocabulary term at the center of a **description wheel**. On the spokes write some words explaining it.

See the Note-Taking Handbook on pages R45–R51.

SCIENCE NOTEBOOK

> Minerals have four characteristics.
> > Minerals form naturally.
> > All minerals are solids.
> > Each mineral is always made of the same element or elements.
> > All minerals have crystal structures.

atoms joined in a repeating 3-D pattern

formed by all minerals

CRYSTAL

A 42 Unit: **Earth's Surface**

CHECK READINESS

Administer the Diagnostic Test to determine students' readiness for new science content and their mastery of requisite math skills.

 Diagnostic Test, pp. 21–22

Technology Resources

Students needing content and math skills should visit **ClassZone.com**.

- **CONTENT REVIEW**
- **MATH TUTORIAL**

- **CONTENT REVIEW CD-ROM**

KEY CONCEPT

Minerals are all around us.

 BEFORE, you learned
- Earth is made of layers
- Earth's outermost rocky layer is the crust

 NOW, you will learn
- What the characteristics of minerals are
- How minerals are classified into groups
- Which mineral group is most common

VOCABULARY
mineral p. 43
element p. 45
crystal p. 46

EXPLORE Minerals

What are some characteristics of a mineral?

PROCEDURE

① Sprinkle some table salt on a sheet of colored paper. Look at a few grains of the salt through a magnifying glass. Then rub a few grains between your fingers.

② In your notebook, describe all the qualities of the salt that you observe.

③ Examine the rock salt in the same way and describe its qualities in your notebook. How do the two differ?

MATERIALS
- colored paper
- table salt
- rock salt
- magnifying glass

WHAT DO YOU THINK?
Salt is a mineral. From your observations of salt, what do you think are some characteristics of minerals?

Minerals have four characteristics.

You use minerals all the time. Every time you turn on a microwave oven or a TV, you depend on minerals. The copper in the wires that carry electricity to the device is a mineral. Table salt, or halite (HAYL-YT), is another mineral that you use in your everyday life.

Minerals have four characteristics. A **mineral** is a substance that

VOCABULARY
Add a description wheel for *mineral* in your notebook.

- forms in nature
- is a solid
- has a definite chemical makeup
- has a crystal structure

Chapter 2: **Minerals 43** **A**

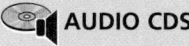

2.1 FOCUS

O Set Learning Goals
Students will
- Identify the characteristics of minerals.
- Explain how minerals are classified into groups.
- Identify which mineral group is most common.
- Observe different crystal shapes in an experiment.

O 3-Minute Warm-Up

Display Transparency 12 or copy this exercise on the board:

Decide if these statements are true. If not, correct them.

1. Water and ice are minerals. *Ice is a mineral, but water is not.*

2. Minerals can be found in rocks. *true*

3. Minerals exist as gas, liquid, and solid. *Matter exists as gas, liquid, and solid. Minerals are solids.*

🔲 3-Minute Warm-Up, p. T12

2.1 MOTIVATE

EXPLORE Minerals
PURPOSE To promote inquiry into the characteristics of minerals

TIP *10 min.* Divide the class into small groups to share observations.

WHAT DO YOU THINK? *Answers will vary but may include that minerals are solid and sparkly.*

Teaching with Technology

Students might use a PC microscope to examine the grains of salt.

Teach from Visuals

To help students interpret the diagram of minerals in rocks, ask:

- How can you tell that the rock has different minerals in it? *It contains materials of different colors.*

- How do the minerals differ in appearance? *They differ in color and texture.*

Teach Difficult Concepts

Many texts give as one of the characteristics of minerals that they are inorganic, not derived from living organisms. This is not strictly accurate because many living organisms produce minerals to form their shells, bones, and other hard parts. However, a substance that forms *only* by an organic process cannot be considered a mineral. For example, sugar forms organically; it never forms inorganically (without a process involving a living organism). Therefore, sugar is not a mineral, even though it has all the other required characteristics. A substance must form from an inorganic process as well to be considered a mineral. Calcite is an example of a mineral that forms both inorganically (when it precipitates from water) and organically (when marine organisms form their shells). To help students understand, you might try the demonstration.

Teacher Demo

Place a handful of sugar on a piece of colored paper and a handful of salt next to it. Ask if both materials are minerals. Explain that the sugar is not a mineral but the salt is. All sugar comes from plants, which are living organisms. Thus, sugar is an organic product. Salt does not come from a living organism. It precipitates out of water.

Ongoing Assessment

CHECK YOUR READING *Answer: A mineral always has the same composition, but rocks do not.*

Minerals in Rocks

Most rocks are made up of minerals.

Quartz

Feldspar

Mica

granite

This piece of granite contains the minerals quartz, feldspar, and mica.

You might think that minerals and rocks are the same things. But a mineral must have the four characteristics listed on page 43. A rock has only two of these characteristics—it is a solid and it forms naturally. A rock usually contains two or more types of minerals.

Two samples of the same type of rock may vary greatly in the amounts of different minerals they contain. Minerals, however, are always made up of the same materials in the same proportions. A ruby is a mineral. Therefore, a ruby found in India has the same makeup as a ruby found in Australia.

CHECK YOUR READING How are minerals different from rocks?

Formed in Nature

B Minerals are formed by natural processes. Every type of mineral can form in nature by processes that do not involve living organisms. As you will read, a few minerals can also be produced by organisms as part of their shells or bones.

Minerals form in many ways. The mineral halite, which is used as table salt, forms when water evaporates in a hot, shallow part of the ocean, leaving behind the salt it contained. Many types of minerals, including the ones in granite, develop when molten rock cools. Talc, a mineral that can be used to make baby powder, forms deep in Earth as high pressure and temperature cause changes in solid rock.

READING TiP
Proportions show relationships between amounts. For example, a quartz crystal always has two oxygen atoms for every silicon atom.

READING TiP
Molten rock refers to rock that has become so hot that it has melted.

A 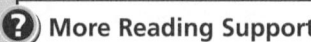 44 Unit: **Earth's Surface**

DIFFERENTIATE INSTRUCTION

? **More Reading Support**

A How are minerals related to rocks? *Rocks contain minerals.*

B How do minerals form? *by natural processes*

English Learners This section has a number of phrasal verbs, such as *made up* (p. 44) and *takes up* (p. 45). English learners may read these phrases incorrectly by combining the meanings of the two words. Provide some synonyms for these phrasal verbs. If necessary, have students draw a sketch that helps them remember the meanings.

Solid

A mineral is a solid—that is, it has a definite volume and a rigid shape. Volume refers to the amount of space an object takes up. For example, a golf ball has a smaller volume than a baseball, and a baseball has a smaller volume than a basketball.

A substance that is a liquid or a gas is not a mineral. However, in some cases its solid form is a mineral. For instance, liquid water is not a mineral, but ice is.

Definite Chemical Makeup

Each mineral has a definite chemical makeup: it consists of a specific combination of atoms of certain elements. An **element** is a substance that contains only one type of atom. In turn, an atom is the smallest particle an element can be divided into.

Everything you can see or touch is made up of atoms. Some substances, including the minerals gold and copper, consist of just one element. All the atoms in gold or copper are of the same type. However, most substances contain atoms of more than one element. Most minerals are compounds, substances consisting of several elements in specific proportions. Halite, for example, has one atom of sodium for every atom of chlorine.

The types of atoms that make up a mineral are part of what makes the mineral unique. The way in which the atoms are bonded, or joined together, is also important. As you will read, many properties of minerals are related to how strong or weak the bonds are.

> **READING TiP**
> You may remember *compound* from compound words—words formed by joining together smaller words: *note + book = notebook*. Likewise, a chemical compound has two or more elements joined together.

Atoms in Minerals

copper

The mineral copper is made up only of copper atoms.

Atoms in Copper

copper

halite

The mineral halite is made up of equal numbers of sodium and chlorine atoms.

Atoms in Halite

chlorine

sodium

READING ViSUALS How do the diagrams show that copper consists of only one element and halite is a compound?

Integrate the Sciences

There are more than 100 chemical elements. Their atoms are made up of protons, neutrons, and electrons. It is the electron structure of an atom that determines the kind of bonds it forms. Atoms form bonds either by sharing electrons or by transferring electrons.

EXPLORE (the BIG idea)

Revisit "How Do You Turn Water into a Mineral?" on p. 41. Have students explain the reasons for their observations.

Teach from Visuals

To help students interpret the diagrams of atoms in minerals, ask:

- What do the circles in each diagram represent? *atoms*
- Which atoms in halite are smaller? *sodium*

Ongoing Assessment

 *Answer: All the atoms in the copper diagram are the same color. The atoms in the halite diagram are two different colors.*

DIFFERENTIATE INSTRUCTION

 More Reading Support

C Why is a mineral a solid? *It has a definite volume and a rigid shape.*

D Define *definite chemical makeup.* *specific combination of atoms*

Advanced Explain chemical formulas to students. The chemical formula of copper is Cu, and that of halite is NaCl. The proportion of an element in a compound is indicated by a number following the element symbol, such as H_2O for water. Have students use a mineral identification book to explain the chemical formulas of minerals mentioned in this chapter.

R Challenge and Extension, p. 89

INVESTIGATE Crystal Shape

PURPOSE To observe how crystal shapes can differ

TIPS *20 min.* Students will be able to see the desired results within one day.

- At the beginning of the experiment, have students record hypotheses and describe the results they expect to obtain.

- Have students revise their hypotheses as necessary after completing the experiment.

WHAT DO YOU THINK? *Crystals of table salt are cube-shaped; crystals of Epsom salts are long and thin. The crystals are different shapes because the substances have different crystal structures.*

CHALLENGE *The crystal structure does not change. The table salt looks about the same, although the sizes of its crystals might be different. The Epsom salts crystals look different because they were broken and ground up at the start; then they were able to form larger, more perfect crystals.*

 Datasheet, Crystal Shape, p. 90

Ongoing Assessment

Identify the characteristics of minerals.

Ask: What characteristics does ice have that make it a mineral? *It forms in nature, is a solid, has a definite chemical makeup, and has a crystal structure.*

 **VISUALIZATION**
CLASSZONE.COM
Explore an animation of crystal growth.

Crystal Structure

If you look closely at the particles of ice that make up frost, you will notice that they have smooth, flat surfaces. These flat surfaces form because of the arrangement of atoms in the ice, which is a mineral. Such an internal arrangement is a characteristic of minerals. It is the structure of a **crystal,** a solid in which the atoms are arranged in an orderly, repeating three-dimensional pattern.

Each mineral has its own type of crystal structure. In some cases, two minerals have the same chemical composition but different crystal structures. For example, both diamond and graphite consist of just one element—carbon. But the arrangements of the carbon atoms in these two minerals are not the same, so they have different crystal structures and very different properties. Diamonds are extremely hard and have a brilliant sparkle. Graphite is soft, gray, and dull.

In nature, a perfect crystal is rare. One can grow only when a mineral is free to form in an open space—a condition that rarely exists within Earth's crust. The photographs on page 47 show examples of nearly perfect crystals. The amount of space available for growth influences the shape and size of crystals. Most crystals have imperfect shapes because their growth was limited by other crystals forming next to them.

INVESTIGATE Crystal Shape

How do crystals differ in shape?

PROCEDURE

1. Cut sheets of paper so that they fit inside the pie plates as shown. Place one sheet in each pie plate.

2. Add the table salt to 30 mL of water in the cup. Stir the water until the salt has dissolved.

3. Pour enough salt solution into one of the pie plates to completely cover the paper with a small film of liquid. Be careful not to pour into the plate any undissolved salt that may be in the bottom of the cup.

4. Repeat steps 2 and 3 with the Epsom salts. Let the plates dry overnight.

WHAT DO YOU THINK?

- Compare and describe the shapes of the crystals.
- What do you think accounts for any differences you observe?

CHALLENGE Why are the shapes of the crystals the same as or different from the shapes in the materials you started with?

SKILL FOCUS
Observing

MATERIALS
- tablespoon
- 2 mixing cups
- 2 stirring rods
- 1 tbs table salt
- 1 tbs Epsom salts
- 60 mL water
- 2 pie plates
- 2 sheets black paper
- scissors

TIME
20 minutes for setup

DIFFERENTIATE INSTRUCTION

 More Reading Support

E How can two minerals have the same chemical composition and still be different minerals? *They can have different crystal structures.*

Alternative Assessment As an alternative to having students write answers the questions for "Investigate Crystal Shape," you might have groups orally report and discuss their results, and their responses to the questions.

Crystal Groups

Crystal groups are named by their shapes and the angles formed by imaginary lines through their centers. Crystals take many shapes, but all belong to these six groups.

Cubic

galena

Tetragonal

wulfenite

Hexagonal

beryl

Orthorhombic

topaz

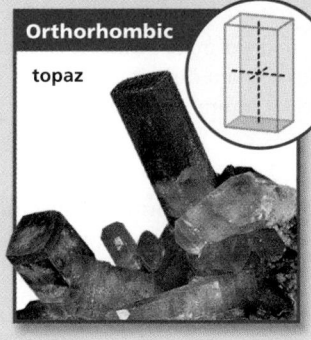

Monoclinic

gypsum

Triclinic

microcline

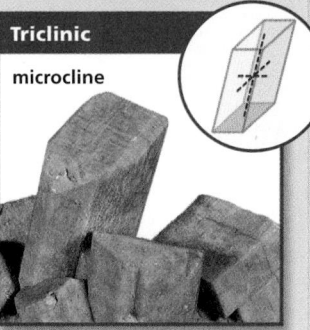

Minerals are grouped according to composition.

Scientists classify minerals into groups on the basis of their chemical makeups. The most common group is the silicates. All the minerals in this group contain oxygen and silicon—the two most common elements in Earth's crust—joined together.

Though there are thousands of different minerals, only about 30 are common in Earth's crust. These 30 minerals make up most rocks in the crust. For that reason, they are called rock-forming minerals. Silicates, which make up about 90 percent of the rocks in Earth's crust, are the most common rock-forming minerals. Quartz, feldspar, and mica (MY-kuh) are common silicates.

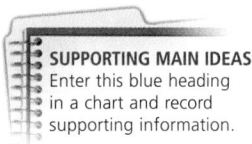

SUPPORTING MAIN IDEAS
Enter this blue heading in a chart and record supporting information.

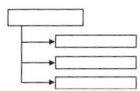

 Which mineral group do most rock-forming minerals belong to?

DIFFERENTIATE INSTRUCTION

? More Reading Support

F What is the most common group of minerals? *silicates*

G What do all silicates contain? *oxygen and silicon joined together*

Below Level Help students make the connection between the most common elements and the most common mineral group.

Most Common in Earth's Crust	
Elements	**Mineral Group**
oxygen, silicon	silicates (contain oxygen + silicon)

Teach from Visuals

To help students interpret the diagram of crystal groups, ask:

- What differences do you notice in the crystal shapes? *numbers of sides, lengths and widths of sides, types of angles*
- Which crystal group has a different number of sides from the others? *hexagonal*

Teach Difficult Concepts

Some students might think that minerals, crystals, and rocks are different terms for the same things. Hold up a well-formed mineral crystal and a rock sample like granite in which different minerals are visible. Point out features such as regular, repeating shapes and symmetry in the crystal. Point out individual minerals and irregular mineral shapes in the rock.

Develop Critical Thinking

SYNTHESIZE Help students synthesize information by asking: Why aren't all mineral samples made up of visible, well-formed crystals? *All minerals have a crystal structure, but individual crystals in a mineral sample might be too small to see, or they might be poorly formed because they were crowded together.*

Ongoing Assessment

Explain how minerals are classified into groups.

Ask: How do scientists classify minerals into groups? *on the basis of their chemical makeups*

 *Answer: silicates*

Teach from Visuals

To help students interpret the graph of common elements of Earth's crust, ask:

• What kind of graph is this? *a pie or circle graph*

• What main idea does the graph show? *that oxygen and silicon are the most abundant elements in Earth's crust*

Reinforce (the **BIG** idea)

Have students relate the section to the Big Idea.

 Reinforcing Key Concepts, p. 91

2.1 ASSESS & RETEACH

Assess

 Section 2.1 Quiz, p. 23

Reteach

• Hold up a sample of a mineral, such as a piece of chalk. Ask students what four characteristics it has that make it a mineral. List the four characteristics on the board and ask volunteers to explain each one.

• Hold up a common rock (make sure the rock is not limestone or another carbonate). Ask students what group the minerals in the rock most likely belong to. Have students explain what silicates contain and why they are the most common mineral group in Earth's crust.

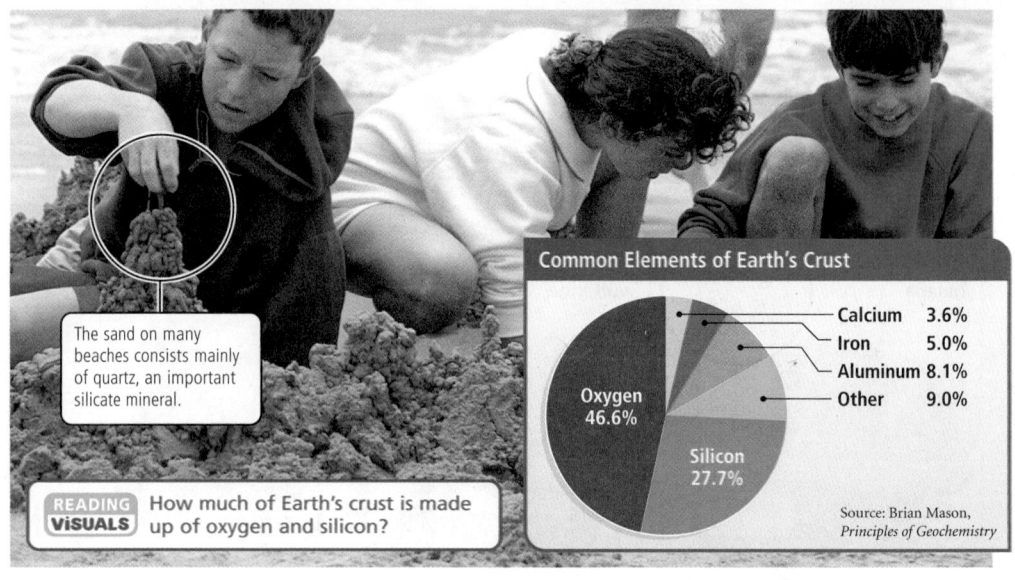

The sand on many beaches consists mainly of quartz, an important silicate mineral.

Common Elements of Earth's Crust

- Oxygen 46.6%
- Silicon 27.7%
- Calcium 3.6%
- Iron 5.0%
- Aluminum 8.1%
- Other 9.0%

Source: Brian Mason, Principles of Geochemistry

READING VISUALS How much of Earth's crust is made up of oxygen and silicon?

RESOURCE CENTER
CLASSZONE.COM
Find information on minerals.

The second most common group of rock-forming minerals is the carbonates. All the minerals in this group contain carbon and oxygen joined together. Calcite (KAL-SYT), which is common in seashells, is a carbonate mineral.

There are many other mineral groups. All are important, even though their minerals may not be as common as rock-forming minerals. For instance, the mineral group known as oxides contains the minerals from which most metals, such as tin and copper, are refined. An oxide consists of an element, usually a metal, joined to oxygen. This group includes hematite (HEE-muh-TYT), a source of iron.

CHECK YOUR READING Why is the oxide mineral group important?

2.1 Review

KEY CONCEPTS

1. What are the four characteristics of a mineral?

2. On what basis do scientists classify minerals?

3. What is the most common group of minerals? What percentage of the crust do they make up?

CRITICAL THINKING

4. **Classify** Can oil and natural gas be classified as minerals? Why or why not?

5. **Apply** When a piece of quartz is heated to a very high temperature, it melts into a liquid. Is it still a mineral? Why or why not?

● CHALLENGE

6. **Interpret** You can see perfect crystals lining the inside of certain rocks when they are broken open. How do you think the crystals were able to form?

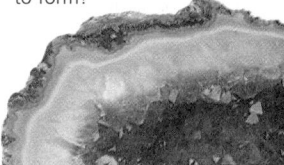

ANSWERS

1. A mineral forms in nature, is a solid, has a definite chemical makeup, and has a crystal structure.

2. Scientists classify minerals into groups on the basis of their chemical makeups.

3. The silicate group is the most common, and these minerals make up about 90% of the crust.

4. Oil and natural gas cannot be classified as minerals, because they are not solids, do not form crystals, and do not have a definite chemical makeup.

5. Melted quartz is not a mineral, because it is not a solid.

6. The minerals had room to grow into perfect crystals because the rocks are hollow.

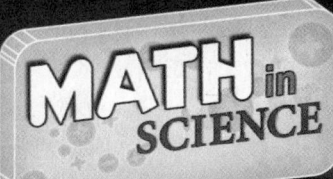

MATH in SCIENCE

MATH TUTORIAL
CLASSZONE.COM
Click on Math Tutorial for more help with percents and fractions.

SKILL: WRITING FRACTIONS AS PERCENTS

Minerals in Rocks

Like most rocks, granite is a mixture of several minerals. Each mineral makes up a certain proportion, or fraction, of the granite. You can compare mineral amounts by expressing each mineral's fraction as a percentage.

Granite

Example

To change a fraction to a percentage, you must find an equivalent fraction with 100 as the denominator. Suppose, for example, you want to change the fraction $\frac{1}{5}$ to a percentage. First, divide 100 by the denominator 5, which gives you 20. Then, multiply both the numerator and denominator by 20 to find the percentage.

$$\frac{1}{5} \cdot \frac{20}{20} = \frac{20}{100} \text{ or } 20\% \qquad \frac{1}{5} \text{ is } 20\%$$

The table below shows the fraction of each mineral in a granite sample.

Minerals in Granite Sample

Mineral	Fraction of Granite Sample	Percentage of Granite
Quartz	$\frac{1}{4}$	?
Feldspar	$\frac{13}{20}$	?
Mica	$\frac{3}{50}$	?
Dark minerals	$\frac{1}{25}$	?

Answer the following questions.

1. On your paper, copy the table and fill in the percentage of each mineral in the granite sample above.

2. Which minerals make up the greatest and smallest percentages of the granite?

3. In another granite sample, feldspar makes up $\frac{3}{5}$ and mica makes up $\frac{2}{25}$. What is the percentage of each mineral in the rock?

CHALLENGE The mineral hornblende is often one of the dark minerals in granite. If hornblende makes up $\frac{1}{32}$ of a granite sample, what percentage of the rock is hornblende?

MATH IN SCIENCE
Math Skills Practice for Science   A

Set Learning Goal

To find and compare the percentages of various minerals in a rock

Present the Science

The percentages of component minerals is one of the factors used in classifying rocks. The percentage of each component mineral typically varies within a certain range from sample to sample of the same type of rock. Granite is a common rock in Earth's crust.

Develop Algebra Skills

- Use the fraction $\frac{3}{10}$ to demonstrate on the board this method of changing a fraction to a percentage. First, divide 100 by the denominator, 10, which gives you 10. Then multiply the numerator and the denominator by 10 to find the percentage.

$$\frac{3}{10} \cdot \frac{10}{10} = \frac{30}{100} \text{ or } 30\%$$

- Students may have other methods of changing fractions to percentages. If so, have them share their methods.

Close

Ask: What does the percentage of a mineral in a rock tell you? *It tells you what portion of the rock is made up of that mineral.*

 • Math Support, p. 119
   • Math Practice, p. 120

Technology Resources

Students can visit **ClassZone.com** for practice in writing fractions as percentages.

 MATH TUTORIAL

ANSWERS

1. 25%, 65%, 6%, 4%

2. greatest percentage: feldspar; smallest percentage: dark minerals

3. feldspar, 3/5 · 20/20 = 60/100 or 60%
   mica, 2/25 · 4/4 = 8/100 or 8%

CHALLENGE 1/32 · 3.125/3.125 = 3.125/100 or 3.125%

Set Learning Goals

Students will

- Explain which mineral properties are most important in identification.
- Explain how to identify minerals by their properties.
- Classify some common minerals according to their hardness by doing an experiment.

3-Minute Warm-Up

Display Transparency 12 or copy this exercise on the board:

Answer *yes* or *no* to each question, and then explain the reason for your answer.

1. A spelunker finds a crystal of a white substance inside a cave. Could the substance be a mineral? *Yes, it could be. The substance is a solid, may have formed in nature, and may have a definite chemical makeup.*

2. Are metals the most common minerals in Earth's crust? *No, minerals of the silicate group are the most common minerals in Earth's crust.*

 3-Minute Warm-Up, p. T12

THINK ABOUT

PURPOSE To introduce the concept that the same mineral can vary in appearance

DISCUSS Explain that some minerals cannot be identified on the basis of their appearance alone because many minerals look alike. Ask students to think about other characteristics that might help them identify minerals.

Ongoing Assessment

CHECK YOUR READING *Answer: A mineral can occur in more than one color.*

KEY CONCEPT

2.2 A mineral is identified by its properties.

◀ **BEFORE, you learned**

- All minerals have four characteristics
- Most minerals in Earth's crust are silicates

▶ **NOW, you will learn**

- Which mineral properties are most important in identification
- How minerals are identified by their properties

VOCABULARY

streak p. 51
luster p. 52
cleavage p. 53
fracture p. 53
density p. 54
hardness p. 55

THINK ABOUT

What can you tell by looking at a mineral?

The photographs at the right show five pieces of the mineral fluorite (FLUR-YT). As you can see, the pieces are very different in color and size. Fluorite occurs in many colors, even in colorless forms. Its crystals can be well formed or poorly formed. Also, the sides of the crystals may be smooth or rough.

If you came across fluorite while hiking, would you know what it was by just looking at it? Probably not. Read on to find out how you could identify it.

READING TiP

The word *characteristic* is used for a feature that is typical of a person or thing. It can be used as a noun or an adjective.

A mineral's appearance helps identify it.

To identify a mineral, you need to observe its properties—characteristic features that identify it. You might begin by looking at the mineral's color. However, many minerals occur in more than one color, so you would need to examine other properties as well. You might also notice how the mineral reflects light, which determines how shiny or dull it is. Most minerals reflect light in characteristic ways. In this section you will read about how the properties of a mineral—including its appearance—are used to identify it.

 **CHECK YOUR READING** Why do you need to look at properties other than color to identify a mineral?

A 50 Unit: **Earth's Surface**

RESOURCES FOR DIFFERENTIATED INSTRUCTION

Below Level
UNIT RESOURCE BOOK
- Reading Study Guide A, pp. 94–95
- Decoding Support, p. 118

 **AUDIO CDS**

Advanced
UNIT RESOURCE BOOK
Challenge and Extension, p. 100

English Learners
UNIT RESOURCE BOOK
Spanish Reading Study Guide, pp. 98–99

 **AUDIO CDS**

- Audio Readings in Spanish
- Audio Readings (English)

Color and Streak

Some minerals can be almost any color, but most minerals have a more limited color range. For example, a particular mineral may almost always be brown to black.

Three main factors cause minerals to vary in color. First, a mineral may get its color from tiny amounts of an element that is not part of its normal chemical makeup. For example, a sample of pure quartz is clear and colorless, but tiny amounts of iron can give quartz a violet color. This violet variety of quartz is called amethyst. Second, a mineral's color can change when it is at or near Earth's surface and is in contact with the atmosphere or water. Third, mineral crystals can have defects in their crystal structures that change their color.

Some minerals have a different color when they are ground into a fine powder than when they are left whole. A mineral's **streak** is the color of the powder left behind when the mineral is scraped across a surface. Geologists use a tile of unglazed porcelain, called a streak plate, as a tool to identify minerals by their streaks. Streak is a better clue to a mineral's identity than surface color is. Look at the photographs of hematite below. Even though the mineral samples are different colors, both leave a reddish brown streak when scraped across a streak plate. All samples of the same mineral have the same streak.

CHECK YOUR READING What is the difference between color and streak?

READING TiP
A geologist is a scientist who studies Earth.

Streak

These samples are of the mineral hematite. They are different colors, but they have the same streak.

This hematite looks dull because it has tiny crystals that reflect light in all directions.

This hematite looks shiny because it has larger crystals.

READING VISUALS What is a clue that both samples are of the same mineral?

Chapter 2: **Minerals** 51 **A**

2.2 INSTRUCT

Teach from Visuals

To help students interpret the illustration of streaks, ask:

- What causes the difference in the shininess of the two mineral samples? *the sizes of the crystals*

- What fact about mineral properties do these two photos illustrate? *A mineral can vary in color, but it always has the same streak.*

Ongoing Assessment

CHECK YOUR READING *Answer: Color is a property of a whole mineral; streak is the color of the powdered mineral.*

READING VISUALS *Answer: They have the same streak.*

DIFFERENTIATE INSTRUCTION

More Reading Support

A What is streak? *the color of the mineral powder left behind when a mineral is scraped across a surface*

English Learners Have students write definitions for this section's vocabulary terms in their Science Word Dictionaries. Encourage English learners to explain orally the difference between the concepts of density and hardness. Make sure English learners understand the cause-and-effect relationship of sentences containing an *If* clause. On p. 52, for example, ask students: "What can happen if a mineral is broken to reveal a fresh surface?" *Its characteristic luster can be seen.*

Real World Example

The way a mineral breaks not only helps in identifying it but also may affect the way it is used. Flint, a type of quartz, breaks into smooth, curved flakes. People once used flint to make knives, spearheads, arrowheads, and scrapers.

Teacher Demo

Break samples of such soft minerals as fluorite and mica to demonstrate other types of cleavage. Have students describe the shapes that each mineral breaks into. **Safety Note:** Avoid touching or rubbing your eyes after handling mica.

Luster

READING TiP

Luster comes from the Latin *lūstrāre*, "to make bright." But luster isn't always bright or shiny. Some minerals have lusters that are waxlike or dull.

A mineral's **luster** is the way in which light reflects from its surface. The two major types of luster are metallic and nonmetallic. The mineral pyrite has a metallic luster. It looks as if it were made of metal. A mineral with a nonmetallic luster can be shiny, but it does not appear to be made of metal. An example of a nonmetallic luster is the glassy luster of garnet. Compare the lusters of pyrite and garnet in the photographs below.

Pyrite has a metallic luster.

Garnet crystals in this rock have a nonmetallic luster.

Like a mineral's color, its luster may vary from sample to sample. If a mineral has been exposed to the atmosphere or to water, its surface luster can become dull. However, if the mineral is broken to reveal a fresh surface, its characteristic luster can be seen.

The way a mineral breaks helps identify it.

SUPPORTING MAIN IDEAS
Enter this blue heading in a chart and record supporting information.

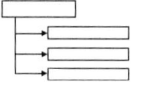

If you hit a piece of calcite with a hammer, the calcite will break into tilted blocks. You can peel off layers of mica because it splits into thin, flat sheets. Each kind of mineral always breaks in the same way, and this property can help identify a mineral. In fact, the way a mineral breaks is a better clue to its identity than are its color and luster.

Cleavage

Cleavage is a tendency to break along flat surfaces.

Calcite has cleavage.

It breaks along flat surfaces because the bonds between its atoms are less strong in some directions than in others.

DIFFERENTIATE INSTRUCTION

More Reading Support

B What are the two main types of luster? *metallic and nonmetallic*

C Which better identifies a mineral, its luster or the way it breaks? *the way it breaks*

Below Level Some students may benefit from seeing a number of examples of minerals with various forms of cleavage and fracture. Show and discuss other examples. A field guide to minerals or a picture book on minerals may help.

Cleavage

Cleavage is the tendency of a mineral to break along flat surfaces. The way in which a mineral breaks depends on how its atoms are bonded, or joined together. In a mineral that displays cleavage, the bonds of the crystal structure are weaker in the directions in which the mineral breaks.

When geologists describe the cleavage of a mineral, they consider both the directions in which the mineral breaks and the smoothness of the broken surfaces. Mica has cleavage in one direction and breaks into sheets. The photographs on page 52 show that calcite has cleavage in three directions and breaks into tilted blocks. Because the broken surfaces of both mica and calcite are smooth, these minerals are said to have perfect cleavage.

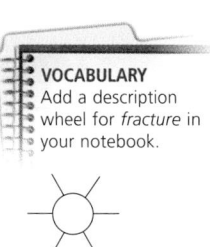

Carbon Bonds in Graphite

strong bonds within layers

weak bonds between layers

carbon atoms

In graphite, carbon atoms are arranged in layers. Graphite has cleavage because the weak bonds between the layers break easily.

Fracture

Fracture is the tendency of a mineral to break into irregular pieces. Some minerals such as quartz break into pieces with curved surfaces, as shown below. Other minerals may break differently—perhaps into splinters or into rough or jagged pieces.

In a mineral that displays fracture, the bonds that join the atoms are fairly equal in strength in all directions. The mineral does not break along flat surfaces because there are no particular directions of weakness in its crystal structure.

VOCABULARY
Add a description wheel for *fracture* in your notebook.

 How does the strength of the bonds between atoms determine whether a mineral displays cleavage or fracture?

Fracture

Fracture is a tendency to break into irregular pieces.

Quartz does not have cleavage. It breaks by fracturing.

It breaks along irregular surfaces because the bonds between its atoms are about the same strength in every direction.

DIFFERENTIATE INSTRUCTION

 More Reading Support

D What determines how a mineral breaks? *how its atoms are bonded*

Advanced Students may notice that mineral identification books describe both cleavages and fractures for some minerals. Challenge students to offer an explanation. Then explain that a mineral may exhibit cleavage in certain directions and fracture in other directions.

 Challenge and Extension, p. 100

Teach from Visuals

To help students interpret the illustrations of cleavage and fracture at the bottom of pp. 52 and 53, ask:

• How do the broken pieces of calcite differ from the broken pieces of quartz? *The calcite breaks into blocks with flat surfaces, whereas the quartz breaks into chunks with curved surfaces.*

• What is the way calcite breaks called? *cleavage*

• What is the way quartz breaks called? *fracture*

Mathematics Connection

Geometry is essential in identifying a mineral's crystal structure. The angles between a mineral's atoms determine the mineral's crystal shape and where cleavage planes occur within the crystal. For example, the arrangements of atoms in quartz cause its crystals to form as hexagonal prisms, which you can see in the photograph on this page. The illustration of carbon bonds in graphite shows why this mineral displays perfect cleavage in one direction. The weak bonds between layers of carbon atoms break easily, allowing parallel sheets of carbon atoms to slide past one another.

The angle of cleavage can also be useful in identifying a mineral. Feldspar, for example, has cleavage in two directions at right angles, while calcite has cleavage in three directions not at right angles.

Develop Critical Thinking

APPLY Ask students to apply the principles of cleavage and fracture by giving examples of other things that break where "bonds" are weak. For example, jeans might tear in the knees where the fabric is worn, and a rope might break where it is frayed.

Ongoing Assessment

CHECK YOUR READING *Answer: A mineral that has cleavage has weaker bonds in one or more directions. A mineral that fractures has bonds that are fairly equal in strength in all directions.*

Integrate the Sciences

Mass is described in one of two ways: as the amount of matter in an object or as an object's resistance to change in its motion. Mass and weight are not the same thing. Weight is the force of attraction between an object and Earth. An object's weight depends on its distance from Earth, while its mass does not change. For the purposes of this lesson, it is simpler for students to think of mass as the amount of matter in an object. Density, then, is the amount of matter that a specific volume of a mineral has— or how much matter is packed into a given space.

Teach from Visuals

To help students interpret the visual, ask:

- How is the baseball like the zincite sample? *The baseball is denser than the tennis ball, just as the zincite is denser than the quartz.*

- If you held the zincite and the quartz in your hands, which would feel heavier? *the zincite*

Ongoing Assessment

READING VISUALS *Answer: The quartz sample would need to be about twice the size of the zincite sample.*

A mineral's density and hardness help identify it.

A tennis ball is not as heavy or as hard as a baseball. You would be able to tell the two apart even with your eyes closed by how heavy and hard they feel. You can identify minerals in a similar way.

Density

READING TiP
The unit of density is grams per cubic centimeter and is abbreviated as g/cm³.

Even though a baseball and a tennis ball are about the same size, the baseball has more mass and so is more dense. A substance's **density** is the amount of mass in a given volume of the substance. For example, 1 cubic centimeter of the mineral pyrite has a mass of 5.1 grams, so pyrite's density is 5.1 grams per cubic centimeter.

Density is very helpful in identifying minerals. For example, gold and pyrite look very similar. Pyrite is often called fool's gold. However, you can tell the two minerals apart by comparing their densities. Gold is much denser than pyrite. The mass of a piece of gold is almost four times the mass of a piece of pyrite of the same size. A small amount of a very dense mineral, such as gold, can have more mass and be heavier than a larger amount of a less dense mineral, such as pyrite. A mineral's density is determined by the kinds of atoms that make up

? E

Comparing Densities

Differences in density can be used to tell minerals apart.

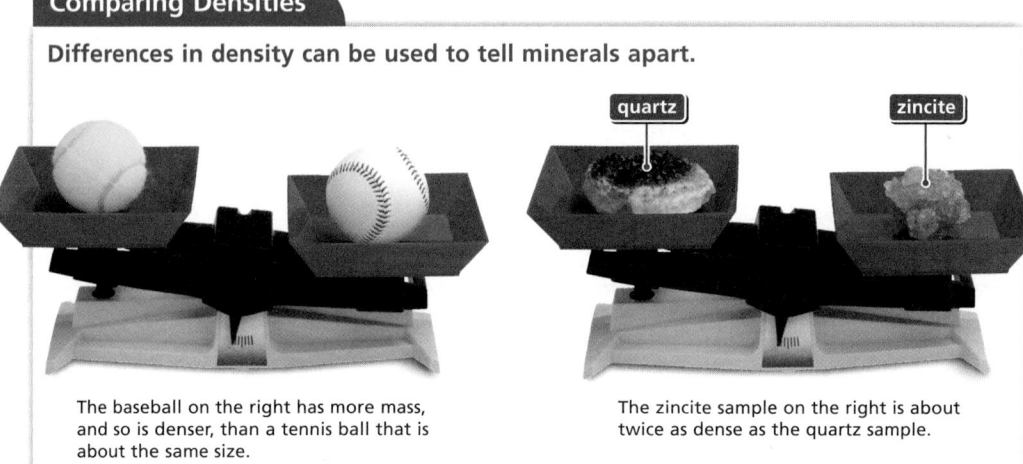

quartz | zincite

The baseball on the right has more mass, and so is denser, than a tennis ball that is about the same size.

The zincite sample on the right is about twice as dense as the quartz sample.

READING VISUALS Estimate the size a piece of quartz would have to be to balance the zincite sample.

DIFFERENTIATE INSTRUCTION

?) More Reading Support

E How is density used in identifying minerals? *Differences in density are used to tell similar-looking minerals apart.*

Inclusion To reinforce the concept that minerals differ in density, allow students with visual impairments and learning disabilities to hold samples of different minerals with the same volume to compare how heavy they feel. Tell students the samples all have the same volume, but that they vary in terms of how much material they contain. Then ask students to rank the minerals from least to most dense.

the mineral, as well as how closely the atoms are joined together. An experienced geologist can estimate the density of a mineral by lifting it. But to get an exact measurement, geologists use special scales.

 **CHECK YOUR READING** Why does a piece of gold weigh much more than a piece of pyrite that is the same size?

Hardness

One way to tell a tennis ball from a baseball without looking at them is to compare their densities. Another way is to test which one is harder. Hardness is another dependable clue to a mineral's identity.

A mineral's **hardness** is its resistance to being scratched. Like a mineral's cleavage, a mineral's hardness is determined by its crystal structure and the strength of the bonds between its atoms. Harder minerals have stronger bonds.

A scale known as the Mohs scale is often used to describe a mineral's hardness. This scale is based on the fact that a harder mineral will scratch a softer one. As you can see in the chart at the right, ten minerals are numbered in the scale, from softest to hardest. Talc is the softest mineral and has a value of 1. Diamond, the hardest of all minerals, has a value of 10.

A mineral can be scratched only by other minerals that have the same hardness or are harder. To determine the hardness of an unknown mineral, you test whether it scratches or is scratched by the minerals in the scale. For example, if you can scratch an unknown mineral with apatite but not with fluorite, the mineral's hardness is between 4 and 5 in the Mohs scale.

In place of minerals, you can use your fingernail, a copper penny, and a steel file to test an unknown mineral. To avoid damage to the minerals, you can test whether the mineral scratches these items. When using a penny to test hardness, make sure its date is 1982 or earlier. Only older pennies are made mainly of copper, which has a hardness of about 3.

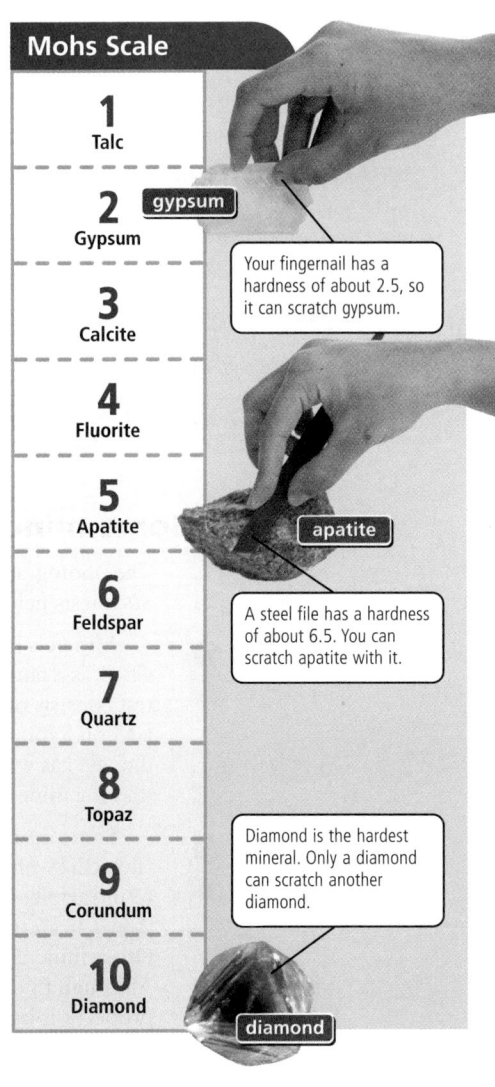

Mohs Scale

1 Talc
2 Gypsum
3 Calcite
4 Fluorite
5 Apatite
6 Feldspar
7 Quartz
8 Topaz
9 Corundum
10 Diamond

Your fingernail has a hardness of about 2.5, so it can scratch gypsum.

A steel file has a hardness of about 6.5. You can scratch apatite with it.

Diamond is the hardest mineral. Only a diamond can scratch another diamond.

gypsum
apatite
diamond

Teach from Visuals

To help students interpret the illustration of the Mohs scale, ask:

• Which is the hardest, 1 or 10? *10*

• Which minerals in the scale can scratch apatite? *feldspar, quartz, topaz, corundum, and diamond*

• If a mineral can be scratched by quartz but not by feldspar, what is its hardness? *between 6 and 7*

History of Science

The Mohs scale is named for Friedrich Mohs, an Austrian mineralogist who invented it in 1822. Before the Mohs scale came into common use, miners and mineralogists customarily scratched minerals to identify them, but the Mohs scale made the method more systematic. Mohs devoted much of his career to developing a classification system for minerals.

Real World Example

Talcum powder, which is made up largely of talc, is the same as baby powder. Talc is a mineral so soft it can be applied to a baby's skin.

Ongoing Assessment

Explain how to identify minerals by their properties.

Ask: What common properties of minerals are used to identify an unknown mineral? *color, streak, luster, cleavage, fracture, density, and hardness*

CHECK YOUR READING *Answer: Gold is much more dense than pyrite.*

DIFFERENTIATE INSTRUCTION

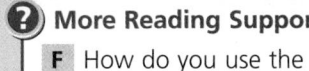

? More Reading Support

F How do you use the Mohs scale to rank the hardness of an unknown mineral? *You see which minerals on the scale can scratch it.*

Below Level Ask students whether the graphite in pencils is hard or soft compared with other minerals. After students have guessed, ask them to think about what is involved when they write with a pencil. Point out that the output can be thought of as a streak of graphite particles. Little force is exerted in making this streak, so the mineral must be soft. Then tell students that graphite in pencil lead has a hardness of between 1 and 2 on the Mohs scale.

Chapter 2 55 **A**

INVESTIGATE Hardness of Minerals

PURPOSE To classify minerals according to their hardness

TIP *20 min.* Advise students that they should be certain they actually made a scratch on a mineral, not just a mark that will rub off.

WHAT DO YOU THINK? *Answers will vary; check to see that answers are consistent with what you know the minerals' hardness to be. You could determine which mineral is harder by testing which can scratch the other.*

CHALLENGE *Any mineral harder than 6.5 on the Mohs scale could be used to test the hardness of a mineral that is not scratched by a steel file.*

 Datasheet, Hardness of Minerals, p. 101

Technology Resources

Customize this student lab as needed or look for an alternative. Print rubrics to assess student lab reports.

 Lab Generator CD-ROM

Metacognitive Strategy

Ask students if any of their results surprised them. For example, was any mineral actually softer than it looked or felt?

Ongoing Assessment

CHECK YOUR READING *Answer: Calcite will always react with hydrochloric acid, but some specimens may not fluoresce.*

INVESTIGATE Hardness of Minerals

How hard are some common minerals?

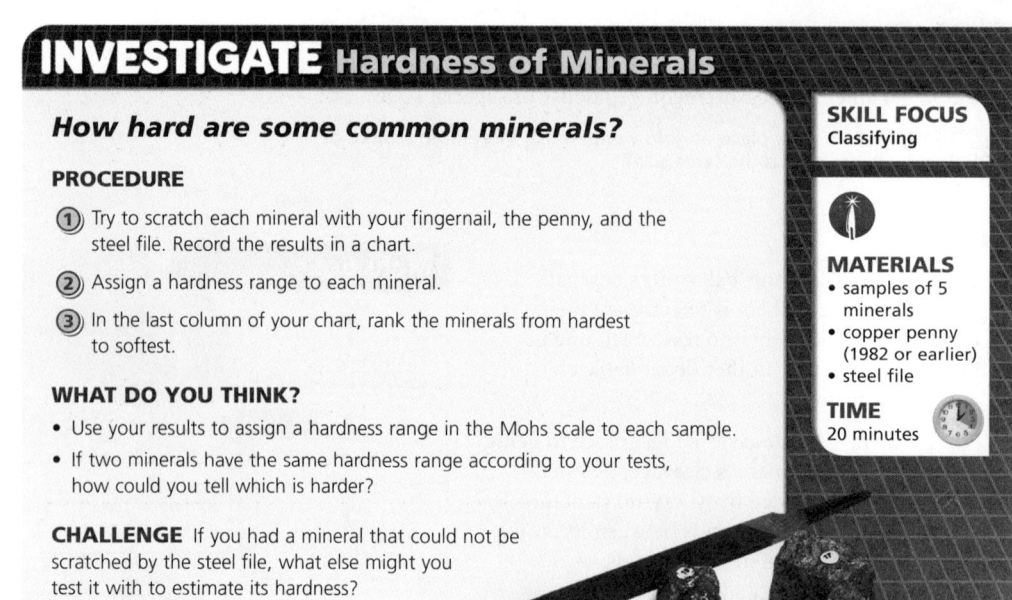

SKILL FOCUS
Classifying

MATERIALS
• samples of 5 minerals
• copper penny (1982 or earlier)
• steel file

TIME
20 minutes

PROCEDURE

1. Try to scratch each mineral with your fingernail, the penny, and the steel file. Record the results in a chart.

2. Assign a hardness range to each mineral.

3. In the last column of your chart, rank the minerals from hardest to softest.

WHAT DO YOU THINK?

• Use your results to assign a hardness range in the Mohs scale to each sample.

• If two minerals have the same hardness range according to your tests, how could you tell which is harder?

CHALLENGE If you had a mineral that could not be scratched by the steel file, what else might you test it with to estimate its hardness?

Some minerals have special properties.

The photographs on page 57 show how geologists test some minerals. Such tests help them identify minerals that have unusual properties.

 Minerals in the carbonate group, such as calcite, react with acid. Chalk is a familiar item that is made up of carbonate minerals. The test consists of putting a drop of a weak solution of hydrochloric acid on a mineral sample. If the acid reacts with the mineral, carbon dioxide gas will form and bubble out of the acid. The bubbles show that the mineral is a carbonate.

 Some minerals have a property known as fluorescence (flu-REHS-uhns). Fluorescent minerals glow when they are exposed to ultraviolet (UHL-truh-VY-uh-liht) light. The word *fluorescence* comes from the name of the mineral fluorite, which has this property. Other minerals that display fluorescence include calcite and willemite. Although fluorescence is an interesting and sometimes dramatic property, it has limited value in mineral identification. Different samples of the same mineral may or may not display fluorescence, and they may glow in different colors.

 **CHECK YOUR READING** To identify calcite, why would it be more useful to test with dilute hydrochloric acid than to check for fluorescence?

DIFFERENTIATE INSTRUCTION

? More Reading Support

G What group of minerals react with hydrochloric acid? *carbonates*

H How do minerals display fluorescence? *They glow when exposed to ultraviolet light.*

Advanced Have interested students locate and review a field guide to minerals. Have them write a paragraph summarizing how to use a field guide to identify minerals. Give students four common mineral samples to identify.

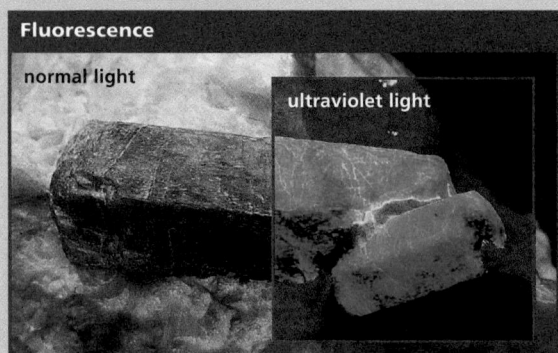
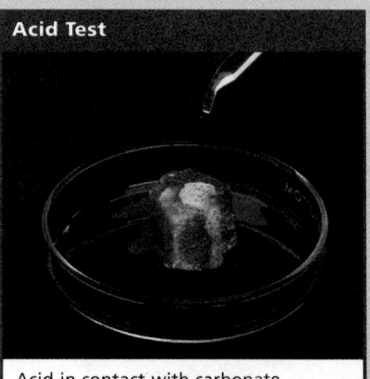
A few minerals respond to magnets. A magnet is pulled toward these minerals. The mineral magnetite strongly attracts magnets, and some other minerals weakly attract magnets. To test a mineral, hold a magnet loosely and bring it close to the mineral. You will be able to notice if there is even a small pull of the magnet toward the mineral. Magnets are commonly used in laboratories and industries to separate magnetic minerals from other minerals.

Some rare minerals have a property known as radioactivity. They contain unstable elements that change into other elements over time. As this happens, they release energy. Geologists can measure this energy and use it to identify minerals that contain unstable elements.

2.2 Review

KEY CONCEPTS

1. Why is color not a reliable clue to the identity of a mineral?

2. What is the difference between cleavage and fracture?

3. Describe what would happen if you rubbed a mineral with a Mohs hardness value of 7 against a mineral with a value of 5.

CRITICAL THINKING

4. **Analyze** Which mineral-identification tests would be easy for a person to perform at home? Which would be difficult?

5. **Draw Conclusions** Diamond and graphite contain only carbon atoms. How can you tell which mineral's atoms are bonded more closely?

⬤ CHALLENGE

6. **Apply** The mineral topaz has perfect cleavage in one direction. It also displays fracture. Explain why a mineral such as topaz can display both cleavage and fracture.

ANSWERS

1. Some minerals can occur in different colors.

2. Cleavage produces smooth, flat surfaces. Fracture produces irregular surfaces.

3. The one with a hardness of 5 would be scratched, because the mineral with a hardness of 7 is harder.

4. Tests for color, luster, cleavage, fracture, and hardness would be easy. Density, reaction with acid, fluorescence, and radioactivity would be more difficult to test for.

5. by comparing their hardnesses

6. A mineral can display both cleavage and fracture if its bonds are weaker in certain directions and of fairly equal strength in others.

Focus

PURPOSE Students will identify minerals by performing tests and referring to a Mineral Identification Key

OVERVIEW Students will observe and test five minerals, recording the color, luster, cleavage or fracture, streak, hardness, magnetism, and reaction with acid of each. Students will find that

- calcite and halite are similar in color, density, and luster but can be distinguished by an acid test
- a mineral such as magnetite can be identified by a single property
- the light-colored, translucent material in granite is quartz, and the flaky, darker mineral is mica

Lab Preparation

- If possible, choose samples of the minerals calcite, halite, magnetite, quartz, and mica for students to identify.
- Prior to the investigation, have students read through the investigation and prepare their data tables. Or you may wish to copy and distribute datasheets and rubrics.

 UNIT RESOURCE BOOK, pp. 121–132

SCIENCE TOOLKIT, F15

Lab Management

Students may have difficulty distinguishing crystal faces from cleavage surfaces. Advise them that crystal faces tend to be duller than recently broken cleavage surfaces. If many flat surfaces are lined up in the same direction, they are probably cleavage surfaces.

SAFETY Students should not handle broken streak plates. They should wear safety glasses, protective gloves, and lab aprons for the acid test. Students should not rub or touch their eyes after handling mica.

CHAPTER INVESTIGATION

Mineral Identification

OVERVIEW AND PURPOSE In this activity, you will observe and perform tests on minerals. Then you will compare your observations to a mineral identification key.

▶ Procedure

1. Make a data table like the one shown in the notebook on the next page.

2. You will examine and identify five minerals. Get a numbered mineral sample from the mineral set. Record the number of your sample in your table.

step 3

3. First, observe the sample. Note the color and the luster of the sample. Write your observations in your table. In the row labeled "Luster," write *metallic* if the mineral appears shiny like metal. Write *nonmetallic* if the sample does not look like metal. For example, it may look glassy, pearly, or dull.

4. Observe the sample through the hand lens. Look to see any signs of how the crystals in the mineral broke. If it appears that the crystals have broken along straight lines, put a check in the row labeled "Cleavage." If it appears that the sample has fractured, put a check in the appropriate row of your table.

step 4

5. **CAUTION: Keep the streak plate on your desktop or table while you are doing the streak test. A broken streak plate can cause serious cuts.** Rub the mineral sample on the streak plate. If the sample does not leave a mark, the mineral is harder than the streak plate. Write *no* in the row labeled "Streak." If the sample does leave a mark on the streak plate, write the color of the streak in that row.

step 5

MATERIALS

- numbered mineral samples
- hand lens
- streak plate
- copper penny
- steel file
- magnet
- dilute hydrochloric acid
- eyedropper
- Mohs scale
- Mineral Identification Key

INVESTIGATION RESOURCES

 CHAPTER INVESTIGATION, Mineral Identification,
- Mineral Identification Key, pp. 121–122
- Mohs Scale, p. 123
- Level A, pp. 124–127
- Level B, pp. 128–131
- Level C, p. 132
Advanced students: Levels B & C

 • Writing a Lab Report, D12–13

Technology Resources

Customize this student lab as needed or look for an alternative. Print rubrics to assess student lab reports.

Lab Generator CD-ROM

6. Test each sample for its hardness on the Mohs scale. Try to scratch the sample with each of these items in order: a fingernail, a copper penny, and a steel file. In the Mohs scale, find the hardness number of the object that first scratches the sample. Write in the table that the mineral's hardness value is between that of the hardest item that did not scratch the sample and that of the item that did scratch it.

7. Test the sample with the magnet. If the magnet is attracted to the sample, put a check in the row labeled "Magnetic."

step 7

8. Repeat steps 2 through 7 for each of the other numbered samples.

Observe and Analyze [Write It Up]

1. **INTERPRET DATA** Use the Mineral Identification Key and the information in your data table to identify your samples. Write the names of the minerals in your table.

2. **COLLECT DATA** CAUTION: Before doing the acid test, put on your safety glasses, protective gloves, and lab apron. Acids can cause burns. If you identified one of the samples as a carbonate mineral, such as calcite, you can check your identification with the acid test. Use the eyedropper to put a few drops of dilute hydrochloric acid on the mineral. If the acid bubbles, the sample is a carbonate.

Conclude [Write It Up]

1. **COMPARE AND CONTRAST** How are the minerals calcite and halite alike? Which property can you use to test whether a sample is calcite or halite?

2. **INTERPRET** Look at the data in your table. Name any minerals that you could identify on the basis of a single property.

3. **APPLY** Examine a piece of granite rock. On the basis of your examination of granite and your observations of the samples, try to determine what the light-colored, translucent mineral in the granite is and what the flaky, darker mineral is.

▶ INVESTIGATE Further

Specific gravity is another property used to identify minerals. The specific gravity of a mineral is determined by comparing the mineral's density with the density of water.

Find the specific gravity of an unknown mineral chosen from your teacher's samples. Attach your mineral with a string to a spring scale. Record its mass and label this value M1. Then suspend the mineral in a beaker of water. Record the measurement of the mineral's mass in water. Label this value M2. To determine the mineral's specific gravity, use the following equation:

$$\frac{M1}{M1 - M2} = \text{specific gravity}$$

Do all the other steps to identify the sample. Does the specific gravity you measured match the one listed for that mineral in the identification key?

Mineral Identification

Table 1. Mineral Properties

Property	Sample Number				
	1	2	3	4	5
Color					
Luster					
Cleavage					
Fracture					
Streak					
Hardness					
Magnetic					
Acid test					
Name of mineral					

Chapter 2: **Minerals 59** **A**

▶ Observe and Analyze [Write It Up]

SAMPLE DATA Refer to the Mineral Identification Key.

1. See students' data tables.

2. If one of the minerals was calcite, students' acid tests should verify its identification.

▶ Conclude [Write It Up]

1. Calcite and halite can be similar in color, and both have a nonmetallic luster. They feel not very different in density. The acid test will show which is calcite. Also, calcite can scratch halite.

2. Answers will vary, depending on the mineral samples available to the students. Magnetite is an example of a mineral that can be identified by a single property (attraction to a magnet).

3. The light-colored, translucent mineral is quartz, and the flaky, darker mineral is mica.

▶ INVESTIGATE Further

Measured specific gravity might not match the value listed for many reasons, including a lack of precise instruments to make measurements with.

Post-Lab Discussion

• Have students look at the results in their data tables and identify examples of minerals for which they needed to look at a combination of properties in order to identify them.

• Ask students which minerals they found most difficult to identify and why.

▶ Set Learning Goals

Students will

- Identify ways minerals are used in industry and art.
- Explain how minerals form.
- Explain how minerals are mined.
- Draw conclusions, from an experiment, about the benefits and costs of mining.

◀ 3-Minute Warm-Up

Display Transparency 13 or copy this exercise on the board:

Match each definition with its term.

Definitions

1. the mass of a substance in a given volume *c*

2. the tendency to break along flat surfaces *a*

3. the color of a thin line of mineral powder left behind when a mineral is scraped across a surface *d*

Terms

a. cleavage   d. streak

b. fracture   e. luster

c. density

 3-Minute Warm-Up, p. T13

EXPLORE Minerals at Your Fingertips

PURPOSE To introduce the concept that minerals have many everyday uses

TIP *10 min.* To expand, you might discuss other items containing minerals.

WHAT DO YOU THINK? *Graphite rubs off on the paper, leaving a mark that is similar to the mark a mineral may leave on a streak plate. A No. 4 pencil is more useful than a No. 2 pencil when a goal is to reduce smearing or smudging.*

Ongoing Assessment

CHECK YOUR READING *Sample answer: quartz in glass, fluorite in toothpaste, mica in paint*

KEY CONCEPT

2.3 Minerals are valuable resources.

◀ **BEFORE, you learned**

- Minerals are classified according to their compositions and crystal structures
- A mineral can be identified by its properties

▶ **NOW, you will learn**

- How minerals are used in industry and art
- How minerals form
- How minerals are mined

VOCABULARY

magma p. 62
lava p. 62
ore p. 64

EXPLORE Minerals at Your Fingertips

What is an everyday use of minerals?

PROCEDURE

① Observe the core of a wooden pencil. Even though it is called lead, it is made of a mixture of minerals—clay and graphite. A No. 4 pencil has more clay in its lead.

② Use each pencil to draw something, noticing how each marks the page.

WHAT DO YOU THINK?

- How is using a pencil similar to a streak test?
- When would a No. 4 pencil be more useful than a No. 2 pencil?

MATERIALS

- No. 2 wooden pencil
- No. 4 wooden pencil
- paper

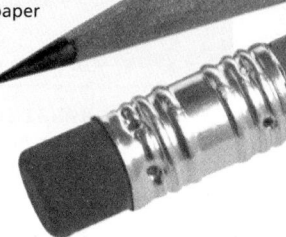

Minerals have many uses in industry.

Minerals are necessary to our modern way of life. Mineral deposits are sources of

- metals for cars and airplanes
- quartz and feldspar for glass
- fluorite and calcite for toothpaste
- silver compounds for photographic film
- mica and talc for paint

These examples illustrate just a few of the many ways we depend on minerals.

 **CHECK YOUR READING** Give three examples of the use of minerals in familiar products.

RESOURCES FOR DIFFERENTIATED INSTRUCTION

Below Level

UNIT RESOURCE BOOK

- Reading Study Guide A, pp. 105–106
- Decoding Support, p. 118

 **AUDIO CDS**

R Additional **INVESTIGATION,**
Stalagmites and Stalactites, A, B, & C, pp. 133–141; Teacher Instructions, pp. 348–349

Advanced

UNIT RESOURCE BOOK

- Challenge and Extension, p. 111
- Challenge Reading, pp. 114–115

English Learners

UNIT RESOURCE BOOK

Spanish Reading Study Guide, pp. 109–110

 **AUDIO CDS**

- Audio Readings in Spanish
- Audio Readings (English)

Minerals have many uses in the arts.

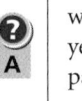

No matter what month you were born in, there is a mineral associated with it—your birthstone. The tradition of birthstones is hundreds of years old. It is one example of the value that people place on the particularly beautiful minerals known as gemstones. In fact, the ancient Egyptians used gems in necklaces and other jewelry at least 4000 years ago.

When gemstones are found, they are usually rough and irregularly shaped. Before a gemstone is used in jewelry, a gem cutter grinds it into the desired shape and polishes it. This process increases the gemstone's beauty and sparkle. The material used to shape and polish a gemstone must be at least as hard as the gemstone itself. Metals, such as gold and silver, also are used in jewelry making and other decorative arts. Both gold and silver are usually combined with copper to increase their hardness.

RESOURCE CENTER
CLASSZONE.COM

Learn more about gemstones.

READING TiP
Corundum and diamond are the two hardest minerals in the Mohs scale. They are often used to grind and polish gemstones.

CHECK YOUR READING How are minerals prepared for use in jewelry? What other questions do you have about how minerals are used?

Uses of Minerals

Common Uses of Minerals	
Mineral	**Products**
Quartz (source of silicon)	Optics, glass, abrasives, gems
Hematite (source of iron)	Machines, nails, cooking utensils
Gibbsite (source of aluminum)	Soda cans, shopping carts
Dolomite (source of magnesium)	Insulators, medicines
Chromite (source of chromium)	Automobile parts, stainless steel
Galena (source of lead)	Batteries, fiber optics, weights
Kaolinite (found in clay)	Ceramics, paper, cosmetics
Beryl (source of beryllium)	Aircraft frames, gems (green form is emerald)

Technology

A clear quartz crystal was sliced to make this computer chip. Minerals such as copper, silver, and gold are commonly used in electronics.

Industry

Diamonds are used as abrasives, as in this drill tip. Minerals are also used in such products as insulators and water filters.

Arts

Cinnabar is ground up to make the pigment known as vermilion. Other minerals are also used as pigments in dyes and paints. Gemstones are used in jewelry, as are platinum and gold.

Chapter 2: **Minerals** 61 **A**

Teach from Visuals

Explain that some minerals are combined with other minerals to make products, while others are refined to extract useful elements from them.

To help students interpret the chart of mineral uses, ask:

• What mineral does the aluminum for soda cans come from? *gibbsite*

• Where does the lead used in batteries and weights come from? *galena*

• What is a mineral used to make abrasives? *quartz*

Real World Example

Diamonds are used both in jewelry making and in industry. Diamonds that are not gem quality are used in industry because of their hardness. Manufacturers of automobiles, airplanes, and other machinery use diamonds to cut, grind, bore, and shape hard metal. The demand for industrial diamonds is so great that synthetic diamonds are often used.

EXPLORE (the **BIG** idea)

Revisit "Internet Activity: Minerals" on p. 41. Have students discuss what they found.

Ongoing Assessment

Identify ways minerals are used in industry and art.

Ask: How are minerals used in industry and art? *Students might list any of the examples given in the visual on this page.*

CHECK YOUR READING *Answer: Gemstones are shaped and polished for use in jewelry. Gold and silver are usually combined with copper to make them harder. Students' questions about how minerals are used will vary.*

DIFFERENTIATE INSTRUCTION

? More Reading Support

A What are gemstones? *beautiful minerals used in jewelry*

B What are gemstones like when they are found? *rough and irregularly shaped*

English Learners English learners may be unfamiliar with the tradition of birthstones mentioned on this page. Because *magma* and *lava* have similar definitions, make sure that students understand what distinguishes magma from lava. Magma is molten rock inside Earth. Lava is molten rock that has reached Earth's surface.

Address Misconceptions

IDENTIFY Hold up a sample of a polished mineral, an unaltered mineral, and a brick. Ask: Which of these is a material that formed by natural processes? Students who do not select the polished mineral may hold the misconception that after people cut or polish a mineral, it is no longer a natural material. Students who select the brick may think that it is natural because it contains some minerals.

CORRECT Tell students that people make bricks by shaping a mixture of minerals and other substances into rectangular blocks that are then baked. Unlike minerals, bricks do not form in nature.

REASSESS Ask: Why is the polished mineral considered to be a natural material and the brick is not? *The mineral, despite being polished, formed in nature, but the brick was manufactured by people.*

Technology Resources

Visit **ClassZone.com** for background on common student misconceptions.

 MISCONCEPTION DATABASE

Teach Difficult Concepts

To help students grasp how a material can be formed or changed by changes in temperature, mention some examples that students are familiar with, such as

- flour and other ingredients' changing into bread when they are baked in an oven
- water vapor in the air's condensing and falling as rain when the temperature drops

Ask students to think of other examples.

Ongoing Assessment

 *Answer: These two processes of mineral formation are similar because both involve atoms' joining together to form mineral crystals.*

Minerals form in several ways.

> **REMINDER**
> An element is a substance that contains only one type of atom. For instance, oxygen is an element. Pure oxygen contains only oxygen atoms.

? C

Minerals form within Earth or on Earth's surface by natural processes. Minerals develop when atoms of one or more elements join together and crystals begin to grow. Recall that each type of mineral has its own chemical makeup. Therefore, what types of minerals form in an area depends in part on which elements are present there. Temperature and pressure also affect which minerals form.

Water evaporates. Water usually has many substances dissolved in it. Minerals can form when the water evaporates. For example, when salt water evaporates, the atoms that make up halite, which is used as table salt, join to form crystals. Other minerals form from evaporation too, depending on the substances dissolved in the water. The mineral gypsum often forms as water evaporates.

Hot water cools. As hot water within Earth's crust moves through rocks, it can dissolve minerals. When the water cools, the dissolved minerals separate from the water and become solid again. In some cases, minerals are moved from one place to another. Gold can dissolve in hot water that moves through the crust. As the water cools and the gold becomes solid again, it can fill cracks in rocks. In other cases, the minerals that form are different from the ones that dissolved. Lead from the mineral galena can later become part of the mineral wulfenite as atoms join together into new minerals.

? D

Molten rock cools. Many minerals grow from magma. **Magma**—molten rock inside Earth—contains all the types of atoms that are found in minerals. As magma cools, the atoms join together to form different minerals. Minerals also form as lava cools. **Lava** is molten rock that has reached Earth's surface. Quartz is one of the many minerals that crystallize from magma and lava.

Heat and pressure cause changes. Heat and pressure within Earth cause new minerals to form as bonds between atoms break and join again. The mineral garnet can grow and replace the minerals chlorite and quartz as their atoms combine in new ways. The element carbon is present in some rocks. At high temperatures carbon forms the mineral graphite, which is used in pencils.

Organisms produce minerals. A few minerals are produced by living things. For example, ocean animals such as oysters and clams produce calcite and other carbonate minerals to form their shells. Even you produce minerals. Your body produces one of the main minerals in your bones and teeth—apatite.

 CHECK YOUR READING How is the formation of minerals as molten rock cools similar to the formation of minerals as water evaporates?

DIFFERENTIATE INSTRUCTION

? More Reading Support

C Where do minerals form? *within Earth or on Earth's surface*

D What substance contains all the types of atoms that are found in minerals? *magma*

Additional Investigation To reinforce Section 2.3 learning goals, use the following full-period investigation:

R **Additional INVESTIGATION,** Stalagmites and Stalactites, A, B, & C, pp. 133–141, 348–349 (Advanced students should complete Levels B and C.)

Advanced Have students interested in learning about how the presence of hematite may indicate that Mars once had hot springs read the following article:

R Challenge Reading, pp. 114–115

Mineral Formation

Minerals form at Earth's surface and within Earth.

Water evaporates.

As water evaporates along a shoreline, it leaves behind substances that were dissolved in it. Here, gypsum is forming.

Hot water cools.

Gold dissolved in hot water can fill cracks in rocks as the water cools.

Molten rock cools.

Minerals such as quartz grow as molten rock cools.

Heat and pressure cause changes.

Graphite forms inside Earth when carbon is subjected to great heat.

READING VISUALS Each of the four processes shown involves heat. What is the heat source for rapid evaporation of water at Earth's surface?

Teach from Visuals

To help students interpret the illustration of mineral formation, ask:

• In this visual, how do the locations of the examples of mineral formation change from the top of the picture to the bottom? *They go from the surface of Earth to deeper and deeper within Earth.*

• Where does the evaporation of water to form gypsum take place? *on Earth's surface, along a shoreline*

• Where and how can gold crystallize? *underground, in cracks in rocks, as hot water cools*

• What might be a source of heat for underground water? *magma*

• Where does magma cool and form minerals first? *around the edges of the body of magma*

• How does graphite form? *by the exposure of carbon to high heat within Earth*

 The visual "Mineral Formation" is available as T14 in the Unit Transparency Book.

EXPLORE (the BIG idea)

Revisit "What Makes Up Rocks?" on p. 41. Have students explain the reasons for what they observed.

Ongoing Assessment

Explain how minerals form.

Ask: In general, what causes minerals to form? *changes in the temperature or state of a liquid, or high heat or pressure*

 *Answer: the Sun*

DIFFERENTIATE INSTRUCTION

Below Level Have students copy the headings in this visual and draw their own pictures of each process. Advise students to keep in mind the main idea—that minerals form through natural processes. You can also ask students to create a two-column chart. In one column, labeled "Mineral Formation," have them write the different types of mineral formation listed on p. 62. Students should label the other column "Minerals" and list examples that go along with each type of formation.

Teach from Visuals

To help students interpret the map of minerals and ores around the world, ask:

• Which mineral resources might the United States need to import? *aluminum, diamond, gold*

• From what continents could the United States import aluminum? *South America, Africa, Asia, Australia*

• What symbol is used to identify copper? *a circle*

Social Studies Connection

The sorting action of currents often results in the settling of heavy minerals at certain locations in rivers. Mineral deposits that develop in this way are called placers. The California gold rush of 1848 occurred as a result of the discovery of such placers. By following the deposits upstream, people located the source rocks of the deposits in the Sierra Nevada.

Ongoing Assessment

 **READING VISUALS** *Answer: Copper is most common.*

Minerals and Ores Around the World

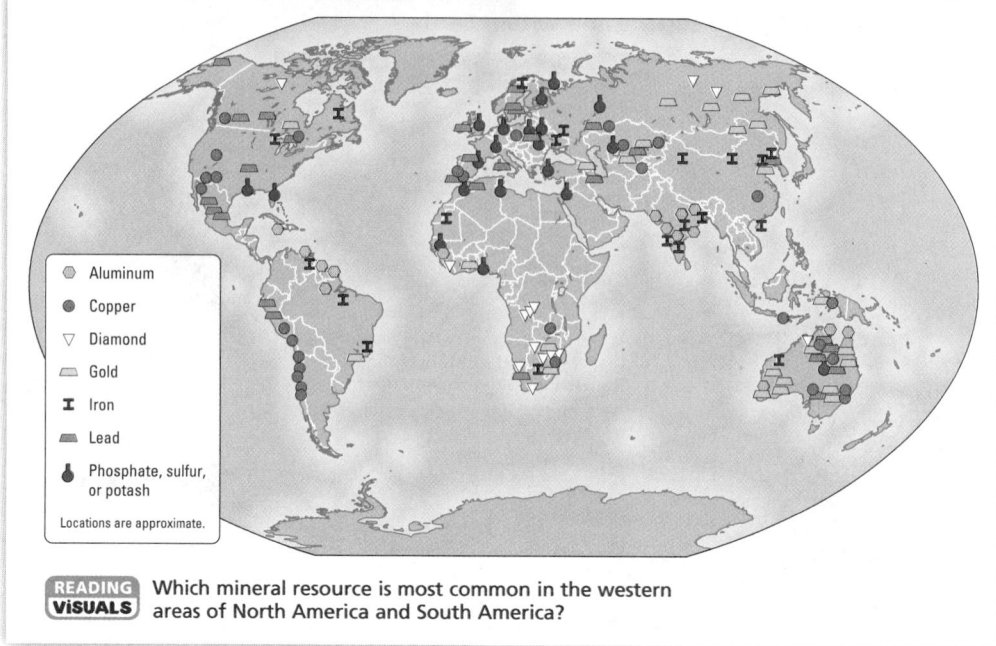

Legend:
- ⬭ Aluminum
- ⬤ Copper
- ▽ Diamond
- ⬭ Gold
- ✚ Iron
- ▬ Lead
- 🔨 Phosphate, sulfur, or potash

Locations are approximate.

READING VISUALS Which mineral resource is most common in the western areas of North America and South America?

Many minerals are mined.

Before minerals can be used to make products, they must be removed from the ground. Some minerals are found near Earth's surface, while others lie deep underground. Some minerals are found at a wide range of depths, from the surface to deep within Earth.

Most minerals are combined with other minerals in rocks. For any mineral to be worth mining, there must be a fairly large amount of the mineral present in a rock. Rocks that contain enough of a mineral to be mined for a profit are called **ores.**

READING TiP
To make a profit, mine owners must be able to sell ores for more than it cost them to dig the ores out.

 E

Surface Mining

Minerals at or near Earth's surface are recovered by surface mining. Some minerals, such as gold, are very dense. These minerals can build up in riverbeds as less dense minerals are carried away by the water. In a method called panning, a miner uses a pan to wash away unwanted minerals that are less dense. The gold and other dense minerals stay in the bottom of the pan and can then be further separated. In bigger riverbed mining operations, miners use machines to dig out and separate the valuable minerals.

 F

DIFFERENTIATE INSTRUCTION

? More Reading Support

E What is an ore? *a rock that contains enough of a mineral to be mined for a profit*

F What is panning? *using a pan to sort out heavier minerals*

Advanced Students will need to look closely to match the minerals on the map key to the minerals' sources on the chart. Have students consult reference sources to find the uses for any minerals or ores on the map key that don't appear in the chart.

 Challenge and Extension, p. 111

Another method of surface mining is strip mining. Miners strip away plants, soil, and unwanted rocks from Earth's surface. Then they use special machines to dig out an ore.

Like strip mining, open-pit mining involves removing the surface layer of soil. Miners then use explosives to break up the underlying rock and recover the ore. As they dig a deep hole, or pit, to mine the ore, they build roads up the sides of the pit. Trucks carry the ore to the surface. Ores of copper and of iron are obtained by open-pit mining.

If an Olympic-sized swimming pool were filled with rock from this mine, it might contain enough copper to make a solid "beach ball" 146 cm (60 in.) in diameter.

 **CHECK YOUR READING** How are strip mining and open-pit mining similar? How are they different?

INVESTIGATE Mining

What are the benefits and costs of mining ores?

PROCEDURE

1. Put the wild-birdseed into a pan. Add the beads to the birdseed and mix well.

2. Search through the seeds and separate out the beads and sunflower seeds, placing each kind in a different pile. Take no more than 3 minutes.

3. Assign a value to each of the beads and seeds: red bead, $5; green bead, $4; blue bead, $3; sunflower seed, $2. Count up the value of your beads and seeds. For every yellow bead, subtract $100, which represents the cost of restoring the land after mining.

WHAT DO YOU THINK?

- How does the difficulty of finding the red beads relate to the difficulty of finding the most valuable ores?

- How does the total value of the blue beads and the sunflower seeds compare to the total value of the red and green beads? What can you conclude about deciding which materials to mine?

CHALLENGE The sunflower seeds and the red, green, and blue beads could represent minerals that contain copper, gold, iron, and silver. Which bead or seed is most likely to represent each mineral? Explain your choices.

SKILL FOCUS
Drawing conclusions

MATERIALS
- 1 pound wild-birdseed mix with sunflower seeds
- shallow pan
- 2 small red beads
- 4 small green beads
- 8 small blue beads
- 3 medium yellow beads

TIME
25 minutes

 Chapter 2: **Minerals 65** **A**

Ongoing Assessment

Explain how minerals are mined.

Ask: What do strip mining, open-pit mining, and deep mining have in common? *They all involve digging into the Earth to recover ores.*

Reinforce (the **BIG** idea)

Have students relate the section to the Big Idea.

 Reinforcing Key Concepts, p. 113

2.3 ASSESS & RETEACH

Assess

 Section 2.3 Quiz, p. 25

Reteach

Help students review this section's concepts by writing the heading "Uses of Minerals" on the board, with these three headings under it: "Technology," "Industry," and "Arts." Have students list examples of mineral uses and products under each heading. *Sample answers: Technology: computer chips, electronics, photographic film, fiber optics; Industry: machines (including cars and aircraft), batteries, abrasives, drill tips, insulators, water filters; Arts: gemstones and metals for jewelry, paints, dyes, glass, ceramics*

Technology Resources

Have students visit **ClassZone.com** for reteaching of Key Concepts.

 CONTENT REVIEW

 CONTENT REVIEW CD-ROM

Deep Mining

Deep-mining methods are needed when an ore lies far below Earth's surface. These methods are used to obtain many minerals. Miners dig an opening to reach a deep ore. When the ore is inside a mountain or hill, miners can cut a level passage to reach the mineral they want. Miners dig a vertical passage to reach an ore that lies underground in a flat area or under a mountain.

From the main passage, miners blast, drill, cut, or dig the ore. If the passage is horizontal, they keep digging farther and farther into the hill or mountain. If it is vertical, they remove the ore in layers.

These gold miners are working underground near Carlin, Nevada. The world's deepest gold mine is in South Africa and extends almost 3 km (2 mi) underground.

2.3 Review

KEY CONCEPTS

1. Give two examples of the use of minerals in industry and two examples of the use of minerals in the arts.
2. What are the five ways in which minerals form?
3. What is required for rocks to be considered ores?

CRITICAL THINKING

4. **Infer** Would an ore at Earth's surface or an ore deep underground be more expensive to mine? Explain.
5. **Apply** The mineral quartz has been used as a gemstone for thousands of years. What minerals could jewelry makers use to grind and polish quartz?

◆ CHALLENGE

6. **Analyze** Both strip mining and open-pit mining are types of surface mining. When might miners choose to use open-pit mining rather than strip mining to obtain an ore?

ANSWERS

1. Answers will vary but may include examples from the chart on p. 61.

2. as water evaporates, as hot water cools, as molten rock cools, as heat and pressure change existing minerals, and as organisms produce minerals for shells or bones

3. The rocks must be rich in minerals that people want. The minerals must be worth more than it costs to mine the ores.

4. the ore deep underground, since it is harder to reach

5. quartz, topaz, corundum, or diamond

6. Open-pit mining would be used when the ore extends too deep within Earth to be recovered by strip mining.

SCIENCE on the JOB

GEM CUTTER

Geometry for Gems

If you found a gemstone in nature, it would probably look dull and rough. You might want to take it to a gem cutter, who would use a grinding wheel to shape and polish your rough stone into a beautiful gem. You would also discover that a lot of the rough gemstone is ground away into powder.

Gem cutters use geometry to help them choose the best final shapes of gems. Geometry also helps them to shape gems with many small, flat surfaces at specific angles. These surfaces are called facets, and they make the gems sparkle.

Starred Gems

Some gems—such as certain rubies, sapphires, and forms of quartz—show a six-pointed star when cut in a rounded shape instead of facets. These gems contain tiny flaws aligned at 120-degree angles. When light hits the flaws, it scatters in a star-shaped pattern. The star ruby shown here is a good example of these beautiful gems.

Deeply Colored Gems

Some gems are shaped to show off their rich colors rather than their sparkle. These gems have fewer and larger facets. Also, many brightly colored gems contain lighter and darker areas of color. The gems are shaped so that the richest color is toward the bottom. Light entering one of these gems strikes the bottom and reflects the rich color to the viewer's eye.

Sparkling Gems

How much a gem sparkles depends on the geometric angles at which it is cut. If the overall angle of the bottom part of a gem is too shallow (A) or too steep (C), light will go through the gem.

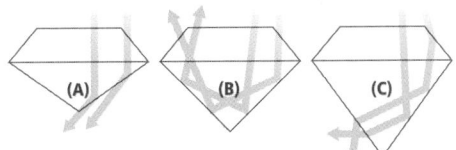

However, if the angles are correct (B), light will bounce around inside the gem as it is reflected to the viewer's eye. The more facets a gem has, the more the light will bounce, and the more the gem will sparkle.

EXPLORE

1. **COMPARE** Table salt, which is the mineral halite, sparkles as light is reflected from its crystal faces. Snow, which is the mineral ice, also sparkles in sunlight. How are the crystal faces of salt and snow similar to facets? How are they different?

2. **CHALLENGE** When would it be best for a gem cutter to split an irregularly shaped crystal into two or more smaller stones before grinding them into finished gems? Remember, one larger stone is usually more valuable than two smaller ones.

Chapter 2: Minerals **67** **A**

BACK TO

the BIG idea

Ask students to give examples of minerals that they see in nature, wear on their bodies, and use in their homes. *Sample answers: quartz in a granite rock, gold in a necklace, and iron in a steel fork*

◗ KEY CONCEPTS SUMMARY

SECTION 2.1

Ask: What does it mean to say that a mineral has a definite chemical makeup? *The mineral consists of a specific combination of atoms of certain elements.*

Ask: What is a crystal? *a solid in which atoms are arranged in an orderly, repeating three-dimensional pattern*

SECTION 2.2

Ask: What is a property? *a characteristic feature that identifies something*

Ask: Which of the properties listed in the table are more useful in identifying a mineral? less useful? *more useful: cleavage, density, hardness; less useful: color, luster*

SECTION 2.3

Ask: What three uses of copper are illustrated? *electric wiring, piping, sculpture*

Ask: When can minerals form in nature? *Minerals can form when water evaporates, organisms form shells and bones, hot water cools, molten rock cools, and heat and pressure cause changes.*

Review Concepts

- Big Idea Flow Chart, p. T9
- Chapter Outline, pp. T15–T16

Chapter Review

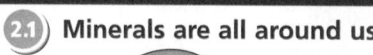

the BIG idea

Minerals are basic building blocks of Earth.

CONTENT REVIEW
CLASSZONE.COM

◗ KEY CONCEPTS SUMMARY

2.1 Minerals are all around us.

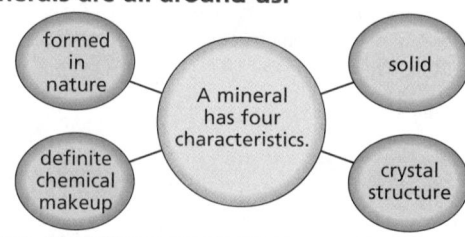

formed in nature

A mineral has four characteristics.

solid

definite chemical makeup

crystal structure

VOCABULARY
mineral p. 43
element p. 45
crystal p. 46

2.2 A mineral is identified by its properties.

Mineral Properties	wulfenite
color	orange
streak	white
luster	nonmetallic
cleavage	yes
density	6.9
hardness	3

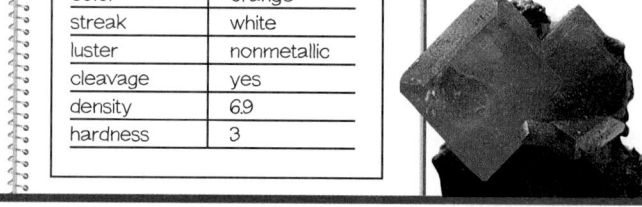

VOCABULARY
streak p. 51
luster p. 52
cleavage p. 53
fracture p. 53
density p. 54
hardness p. 55

2.3 Minerals are valuable resources.

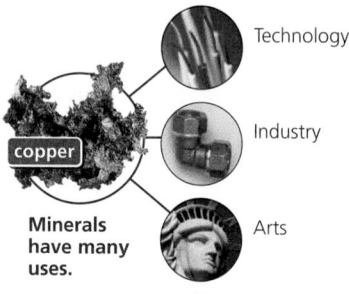

Technology

Industry

copper

Arts

Minerals have many uses.

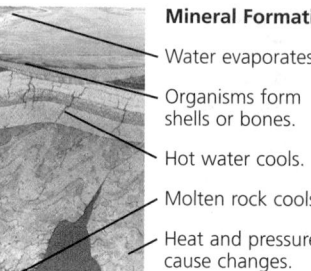

Mineral Formation

Water evaporates.

Organisms form shells or bones.

Hot water cools.

Molten rock cools.

Heat and pressure cause changes.

VOCABULARY
magma p. 62
lava p. 62
ore p. 64

Technology Resources

Have students visit **ClassZone.com** or use the CD-ROM for a cumulative review of concepts.

Engage students in a whole-class interactive review of Key Concepts. Edit content as you wish.

 CONTENT REVIEW

 CONTENT REVIEW CD-ROM

 POWER PRESENTATIONS

Reviewing Vocabulary

On a separate sheet of paper, write a sentence describing the relationship between the two vocabulary terms.

1. mineral, crystal

2. cleavage, fracture

3. magma, lava

4. element, density

5. mineral, ore

6. element, magma

Reviewing Key Concepts

Multiple Choice *Choose the letter of the best answer.*

7. A mineral is a substance that forms
   a. from rocks   c. from one element
   b. in nature   d. in liquid

8. A crystal structure is characteristic of
   a. an element   c. magma
   b. a rock   d. a mineral

9. A mineral is made up of one or more
   a. ores   c. compounds
   b. rocks   d. elements

10. How is it possible for two different minerals to have the same chemical composition?
    a. They have different crystal structures.
    b. One is formed only by organisms.
    c. Only one is a rock-forming mineral.
    d. They have different appearances.

11. Most minerals in Earth's crust belong to the silicate mineral group because this group contains the
    a. rarest elements on Earth
    b. most common elements on Earth
    c. most valuable metals on Earth
    d. largest crystals on Earth

12. Which of the following is the least reliable clue to a mineral's identity?
    a. color   c. hardness
    b. density   d. luster

13. Many properties of a mineral are related to the
    a. number of elements of which it is made
    b. other types of minerals present as it formed
    c. strength of bonds between its atoms
    d. speed at which it formed

14. What types of minerals form in an area depends in part on
    a. which elements are present
    b. the types of rock present
    c. the density of rocks present
    d. whether crystals can form

15. Open-pit mining is used to obtain ores that lie
    a. under flat land
    b. deep in Earth's crust
    c. near the surface of Earth
    d. in riverbeds

16. Gemstones are used in
    a. building materials
    b. paper products
    c. automobile parts
    d. jewelry making

Short Answer *Write a short answer for each question.*

17. Why aren't all solids minerals? Include the term *crystal structure* in your answer.

18. Why is a mineral's streak more useful in identifying it than its color?

19. If you drop dilute hydrochloric acid on the mineral aragonite, it bubbles. What mineral group do you think aragonite belongs to? Why?

20. Describe how the strength of the bonds between atoms in a mineral determines whether the mineral displays cleavage or fracture.

Reviewing Vocabulary

Sample answers:

1. *All minerals form crystals.*

2. *Mineral crystals show cleavage when they break along flat surfaces and fracture when they break along irregular surfaces.*

3. *Magma is molten rock inside Earth, and lava is molten rock at Earth's surface.*

4. *The types of elements that make up a mineral help determine the density of the mineral.*

5. *A rock that contains enough of a mineral to be mined for profit is an ore.*

6. *As magma cools, different elements join together to form minerals.*

Reviewing Key Concepts

7. *b*

8. *d*

9. *d*

10. *a*

11. *b*

12. *a*

13. *c*

14. *a*

15. *c*

16. *d*

17. *Not all solids have atoms arranged in crystal structures—that is, in orderly, repeating three-dimensional patterns.*

18. *A mineral can occur in different colors but always has the same streak.*

19. *Aragonite belongs to the carbonate group, because carbonates react with acid.*

20. *If the bond strength is nearly equal in all directions, the mineral will fracture. If the bond strength is weaker in a direction, the mineral will break along a cleavage surface in that direction.*

ASSESSMENT RESOURCES

UNIT ASSESSMENT BOOK
- Chapter Test A, pp. 26–29
- Chapter Test B, pp. 30–33
- Chapter Test C, pp. 34–37
- Alternative Assessment, pp. 38–39

SPANISH ASSESSMENT BOOK
Spanish Chapter Test, pp. 109–112

Technology Resources

Edit test items and answer choices.

🔘| **Test Generator CD-ROM**

Visit **ClassZone.com** to extend test practice.

ⓘ **Test Practice**

Thinking Critically

21. The density of sperrylite might fall somewhere between those of arsenic and platinum (between 5.7 g/cm³ and 19.0 g/cm³).

22. Topaz is harder and more dense than quartz, so testing these properties would allow one to tell them apart.

23. to find platinum, because it is more dense and will settle to the bottom

24. Aragonite is not hard, so it would be easily scratched in jewelry.

25. A piece of platinum would be about seven times heavier than a piece of quartz that is the same size.

26. The layers of salt were left after the ancient ocean dried up.

27. A different mineral would be mined for chromium, and the price of chromium would go up because its main source was gone.

28. The bones would become weak.

29. Metal ores are not that common in Earth's crust. If they were more common, the average density of the crust would be higher.

the **BIG** idea

30. Minerals are not basic components of gas-giant planets. One of the characteristics of minerals is that they are solids.

31. Now there are lots of products made from metals, such as cars, electronic equipment for music and television, and furnaces and air conditioners. These products would be much harder to find and much more expensive if minerals with metals were rare. Many of those products would never have been invented if metals were rare.

UNIT PROJECTS

Collect schedules, materials lists, and questions. Be sure dates and materials are obtainable, and questions are focused.

 Unit Projects, pp. 5–10

 70 Unit: **Earth's Surface**

Thinking Critically

Properties such as hardness and density are used to identify minerals. Use the information from the chart to answer the next five questions.

Mineral	Hardness	Density (g/cm³)
platinum	4.5	19.0
aragonite	4	3
topaz	8	3.5
quartz	7	2.7
arsenic	3.5	5.7

21. **COMPARE** Platinum can combine with arsenic to form the mineral sperrylite. How do you think the density of sperrylite compares with the densities of platinum and arsenic?

22. **APPLY** Gems made of topaz are much more valuable than those made of quartz, even though the two minerals can look similar. Describe two methods you could use to identify quartz.

23. **APPLY** Would a miner be more likely to use the method of panning to find platinum or to find topaz? Why?

24. **INFER** Aragonite forms very attractive crystals, yet this common mineral is rarely used in jewelry. Why do you think this is?

25. **DEDUCE** About how many times heavier than a piece of quartz would you expect a piece of platinum of the same size to be? Show your work.

26. **HYPOTHESIZE** *Halite* is the mineral name for table salt. Thick layers of halite are mined near Detroit, Michigan. At one time, an ocean covered the area. Write a hypothesis that explains how the halite formed there.

27. **PREDICT** The mineral chromite is the main ore of the metal chromium. What might happen after all the chromite on Earth is mined?

28. **PREDICT** The mineral apatite is a compound in your bones and teeth. Apatite contains the elements phosphorus and calcium. How might your bones be affected if you do not have enough of these elements in your diet?

29. **DRAW CONCLUSIONS** You live on the surface of Earth's crust. The average density of the crust is about 2.8 grams per cubic centimeter. Most metal ores have densities greater than 5 grams per cubic centimeter. How common do you think metal ores are in the crust? Why?

the **BIG** idea

30. **ANALYZE** Minerals are basic components of planets such as Earth and Mars. Other planets in our solar system, such as Jupiter and Saturn, are called gas giants because they are composed mainly of the gases hydrogen and helium. They do not have solid surfaces. Do you think that minerals are basic components of gas giants? Why or why not?

 Mars

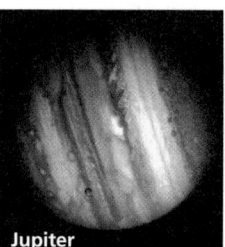 Jupiter

31. **INFER** Minerals make up much of Earth. People use minerals as sources of many materials, such as metals. Some metals are used to make machine parts or build houses. How would your life be different if minerals that contain metals were rare in Earth's crust?

UNIT PROJECTS

If you need to do an experiment for your unit project, gather the materials. Be sure to allow enough time to observe results before the project is due.

MONITOR AND RETEACH

If students have trouble applying the concepts in items 21–25, have them create a poster that explains the properties of hardness and density in minerals. They should review pp. 54–55 in Section 2.2 to help them create the poster.

Students may benefit from summarizing one or more sections of the chapter.

 Summarizing the Chapter, pp. 142–143

Standardized Test Practice

For practice on your state test, go to . . .

i TEST PRACTICE
CLASSZONE.COM

Analyzing a Table

This table shows characteristics of four minerals. Use it to answer the questions below.

Sample	Cleavage or Fracture	Density (g/cm³)	Hardness (in Mohs scale)	Magnetic
E	cleavage	3.7	8.5	no
F	fracture	5.2	5.5	yes
G	fracture	2.7	7.0	no
H	cleavage	2.7	3.0	no

1. Which sample is most dense?
  a. E   **c.** G
  b. F   **d.** H

2. Which sample is hardest?
  a. E   **c.** G
  b. F   **d.** H

3. What will happen if G is rubbed against each of the other samples?
  a. It will scratch only E.
  b. It will scratch only F.
  c. It will scratch only H.
  d. It will scratch F and H.

4. Which statement accurately describes how one of the samples will affect a magnet?
  a. E will attract the magnet.
  b. F will attract the magnet.
  c. G will be pushed away from the magnet.
  d. H will be pushed away from the magnet.

5. Which sample or samples have a crystal structure?
  a. E, F, G, and H   **c.** E and H
  b. only F   **d.** F and G

6. Which samples are likely to break along flat surfaces?
  a. E and G   **c.** G and H
  b. F and G   **d.** E and H

7. An unidentified mineral sample has a density of 2.9 grams per cubic centimeter and a hardness of 6.7. Which mineral is it most like?
  a. E   **c.** G
  b. F   **d.** H

8. Which is true about one-cubic-centimeter pieces of these samples?
  a. Each would have the same weight.
  b. E would be heaviest.
  c. F would be heaviest.
  d. H would be heaviest.

Extended Response

Answer the two questions below in detail. Include some of the terms shown in the word box. In your answers underline each term you use.

chemical makeup	element	compound
crystal structure	Mohs scale	hardness

9. Describe the characteristics of minerals that make them different from rocks.

10. Describe the type of mineral that would work best on the tip of a drill designed to make holes in hard materials.

Chapter 2: **Minerals 71** **A**

Analyzing a Table

1. b   3. d   5. a   7. c
2. a   4. b   6. d   8. c

Extended Response

9. RUBRIC
4 points for a response that correctly answers the question and uses the following terms accurately:
  • chemical makeup
  • crystal structure
  • element

Sample: A substance must have four characteristics in order to be a mineral: it must have formed in nature; it must be a solid; it must have a definite <u>chemical makeup</u>, or combination of <u>elements</u>; and it must have a <u>crystal structure</u>. To be a rock, a substance need only have formed in nature and be a solid.

3 points correctly uses two terms
2 points correctly answers the question and uses one term accurately
1 point correctly answers the question but does not use the terms

10. RUBRIC
4 points for a response that correctly answers the question and uses the following terms accurately:
  • Mohs scale
  • hardness

Sample: Diamond would be the best mineral to use for a drill tip because it is the hardest mineral on the <u>Mohs scale</u>. The Mohs scale ranks minerals by <u>hardness</u>. Diamond is at the top of the scale, with a value of 10. A diamond is a good drill tip because it can drill through softer materials without wearing away.

3 points correctly answers the question and uses one term accurately
2 point correctly answers the question but does not use the terms

METACOGNITIVE ACTIVITY

Have students answer the following questions in their **Science Notebook:**

1. Look around the outside of your home or school. Can you find any minerals that you did not notice before reading this chapter? Make a list of any minerals you see and briefly describe why you believe each is a mineral.

2. Did anything you learned about minerals in this chapter surprise you? If so, what surprised you and why?

3. How do the concepts in this chapter relate to your Unit Project?

CHAPTER 3 Rocks

Earth Science
UNIFYING PRINCIPLES

PRINCIPLE 1	PRINCIPLE 2	PRINCIPLE 3	PRINCIPLE 4
Heat energy inside Earth and radiation from the Sun provide energy for Earth's processes.	Physical forces, such as gravity, affect the movement of all matter on Earth and throughout the universe.	Matter and energy move among Earth's rocks and soil, atmosphere, waters, and living things.	Earth has changed over time and continues to change.

Unit: Earth's Resources
BIG IDEAS

CHAPTER 1 **Views of Earth Today**	CHAPTER 2 **Minerals**	CHAPTER 3 Rocks	CHAPTER 4 **Weathering and Soil Formation**	CHAPTER 5 **Erosion and Deposition**
Modern technology has changed the way we view and map Earth.	Minerals are basic building blocks of Earth.	Rocks change into other rocks over time.	Natural forces break rocks apart and form soil, which supports life.	Water, wind, and ice shape Earth's surface.

CHAPTER 3
KEY CONCEPTS

SECTION **3.1**	SECTION **3.2**	SECTION **3.3**	SECTION **3.4**
The rock cycle shows how rocks change.	**Igneous rocks form from molten rock.**	**Sedimentary rocks form from earlier rocks.**	**Metamorphic rocks form as existing rocks change.**
1. Most rocks are made of minerals.	1. Magma and lava form different types of igneous rocks.	1. Some rocks form from rock particles.	1. Heat and pressure change rocks.
2. Our world is built of rocks.	2. Igneous rocks make long-lasting landforms.	2. Some rocks form from plants or shells.	2. Metamorphic changes occur over large and small areas.
3. Rocks change as they move through the rock cycle.		3. Some rocks form when dissolved minerals re-form from water.	3. Most metamorphic rocks develop bands of minerals.
		4. Sedimentary rocks show the action of wind and water.	

The Big Idea Flow Chart is available on p. T17 in the **UNIT TRANSPARENCY BOOK**.

Previewing Content

 3.1 **The rock cycle shows how rocks change.** pp. 75–81

1. Most rocks are made of minerals.

A **rock** is a naturally formed solid that is usually made up of one or more types of minerals. However, a few types of rocks contain mostly one mineral, and a few have no minerals. Coal, for example, is a rock that may have no minerals. It is made up of the remains of ancient plants that have been compressed.

2. Our world is built of rocks.

Earth consists mostly of rock. Because rocks are common, long-lasting, and can be beautiful, they're used for many purposes, such as for constructing buildings, carving sculptures and monuments, and building roads. Rocks may contain minerals that are sources of metals or other valuable resources.

3. Rocks change as they move through the rock cycle.

The **rock cycle** describes the natural processes that form, change, break down, and re-form rocks. The following diagram shows the three types of rocks and the rock cycle.

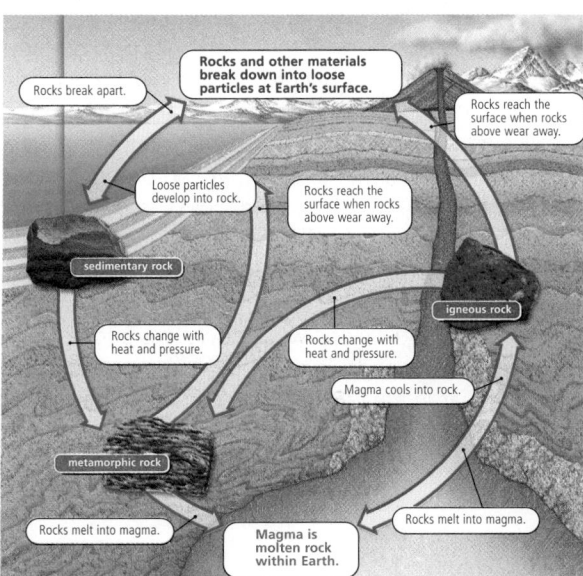

Rocks break apart.

Rocks and other materials break down into loose particles at Earth's surface.

Rocks reach the surface when rocks above wear away.

Loose particles develop into rock.

Rocks reach the surface when rocks above wear away.

sedimentary rock

Rocks change with heat and pressure.

Rocks change with heat and pressure.

igneous rock

Magma cools into rock.

metamorphic rock

Rocks melt into magma.

Rocks melt into magma.

Magma is molten rock within Earth.

 3.2 **Igneous rocks form from molten rock.** pp. 82–88

1. Magma and lava form different types of igneous rocks.

An igneous rock is classified on the basis of its mineral composition and the size of its mineral crystals. Rocks formed from magma can have the same composition as rocks formed from lava, but the sizes of their crystals differ. The sizes of the mineral crystals depend on how quickly the magma or lava cooled.

- An **intrusive igneous rock** forms when magma cools within Earth. High temperatures within Earth allow the magma to cool slowly, and large crystals form.
- An **extrusive igneous rock** forms when lava cools on Earth's surface. The cooler temperatures at the surface cause lava to harden quickly, and tiny crystals form.

Most igneous rocks contain silicate minerals. After identifying the texture of a rock, geologists classify the rock based on how silica-rich its minerals are. In general, the higher the silica content, the lighter the color of the rock.

2. Igneous rocks make long-lasting landforms.

Both intrusive and extrusive igneous rocks form natural land features. An intrusive igneous rock that formed under the surface can become exposed over time when the rock it surrounds wears away. The following illustrations show an example of this process.

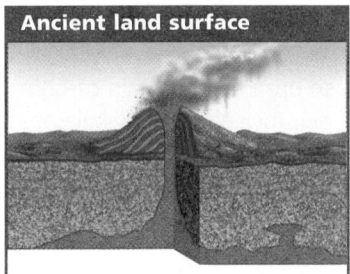

Ancient land surface

When the volcano stopped erupting, the magma inside the volcano cooled.

Present-day land surface

Rock that formed under the volcano is now at the surface.

Common Misconceptions

CHANGES IN ROCKS Students may think that Earth has always been the way it is now, which means that rocks do not change. This misconception might come from observation of mountains, landforms, and rocks that appear to be permanent. In fact, rocks change as they move through the rock cycle.

 This misconception is addressed on p. 78.

MISCONCEPTION DATABASE

CLASSZONE.COM Background on student misconceptions

EARTH'S AGE Students may think the changes described in this chapter happen quickly. Some, however, occur over millions of years. This misconception may be the result of a poor understanding of large numbers.

 This misconception is addressed on p. 86.

Previewing Content

3.3 Sedimentary rocks form from earlier rocks. pp. 89–95

1. Some rocks form from rock particles.

Sedimentary rock is named after **sediment.** Sediments are materials that settle out of water or air. Most sedimentary rocks develop from layers of sediments that are deposited on land or underwater. Loose material can be deposited and then pressed or cemented into rock as shown in this diagram.

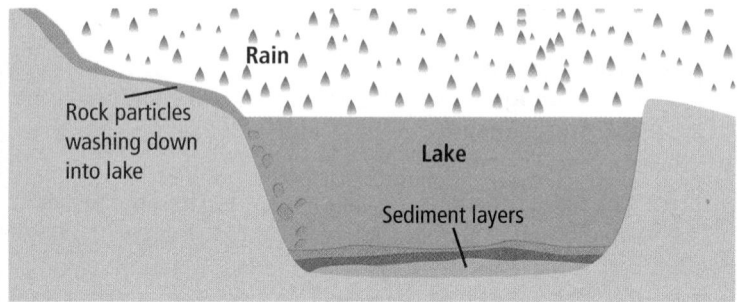

Rain

Rock particles washing down into lake

Lake

Sediment layers

2. Some rocks form from plants or shells.

A process similar to the one that produces sedimentary rocks from rock particles also produces rocks from plant remains or shells.

- Coal forms in swamps as plants die and layers of dead and decaying plants build up. The weight of sediments above presses plant material into coal. Often a fossil is preserved in coal. A **fossil** is the trace or remains of an organism of a past time, preserved in rock.
- The shells and skeletons of ocean organisms contain carbonate minerals. As the organisms die, their shells and skeletons settle on the ocean floor, building up layers of sediment. Over time, the layers become buried, pressed together, and cemented to form limestone.

3. Some rocks form when dissolved minerals re-form from water.

As rainwater washes over rock, it picks up minerals and rock particles. Some of the minerals dissolve in the water. When the water evaporates, it leaves behind the minerals, which can form thick layers of rock.

4. Sedimentary rocks show the action of wind and water.

Geologists examine layers of sedimentary rock to find out how conditions in an area have changed over time. Sedimentary rocks can contain clues such as the following:

- Fossils of fish indicate an area was once covered by water.
- Particle size can indicate how fast water was moving in a river, current, or flood.
- Crossbeds and ripples can show the direction of wind or water currents.
- Mud cracks show that an area had wet periods followed by dry periods.

3.4 Metamorphic rocks form as existing rocks change. pp. 96–103

1. Heat and pressure change rocks.

Metamorphism is the process that changes an existing rock by heat or pressure or both. The parent rock may be a sedimentary rock, an igneous rock, or even another metamorphic rock. During metamorphism, the structure of a rock changes and new minerals may grow, but the rock remains solid and does not melt.

Heat and pressure can break the bonds that join atoms in minerals. Then the atoms can join together differently as new bonds form in a process called **recrystallization.** This process has two main results: individual mineral crystals can grow larger, and atoms can combine in different ways to form new minerals.

2. Metamorphic changes occur over large and small areas.

When both high temperature and high pressure are present, metamorphic changes can occur over large areas. This occurs when large blocks of rock press together and push up mountain ranges. Rocks become buried, compressed, bent, and heated, causing large zones to form metamorphic rock. When only one condition—either high heat or high pressure—is present, metamorphic changes tend to occur over small areas. Magma and lava can heat rocks they touch and cause recrystallization. In repeated earthquakes along a fault, the pressure from rocks grinding together can produce metamorphic changes.

3. Most metamorphic rocks develop bands of minerals.

Foliation is a an arrangement of minerals in flat or wavy parallel bands. Foliation develops when rocks are under pressure and minerals line up in bands. It is common in metamorphism that occurs over a large area. Foliation does not develop if rocks consist mainly of one type of mineral, however, or if rocks are not subjected to pressure that is higher in a particular direction.

Previewing Labs

Lab Generator CD-ROM
Edit these Pupil Edition labs and generate alternative labs.

EXPLORE (the BIG idea)

How Can Rocks Disappear? p. 73
Students are introduced to the idea that rocks can dissolve.

TIME 10 minutes
MATERIALS chalk, vinegar, clear plastic cup

What Causes Rocks to Change? p. 73
Students are introduced to changes in a solid caused by temperature changes and pressure.

TIME 20 minutes
MATERIALS modeling clay, plastic wrap, heavy books

Internet Activity: Rocks, p. 73
Students are introduced to how rocks form and change.

TIME 20 minutes
MATERIALS computer with Internet access

SECTION 3.1

EXPLORE Rocks and Minerals, p. 75
Students observe the differences between a rock and a mineral.

TIME 10 minutes
MATERIALS mineral sample, rock sample, magnifying glass

INVESTIGATE Classification of Rocks, p. 77
Students design a system for classifying rocks.

TIME 20 minutes
MATERIALS 6 rock samples

SECTION 3.2

INVESTIGATE Crystal Size, p. 85
Students analyze how cooling time affects crystal size.

R Mineral Crystal Diagrams, p. 164

TIME 20 minutes
MATERIALS Mineral Crystal Diagrams

SECTION 3.3

EXPLORE Particle Layers, p. 89
Students observe how particle size determines the way rock particles settle from water.

TIME 10 minutes
MATERIALS jar, measuring cup, water, 1/3 cup gravel, 1/3 cup sand

INVESTIGATE Rock Layers, p. 94
Students create a model to show how sedimentary rocks form in layers.

TIME 20 minutes
MATERIALS 1 paper cup, 3 mixing cups, 6 Tbs plaster of Paris, 3 Tbs water, 4 Tbs gravel, 2 Tbs sand, 3 drops food coloring

---

SECTION 3.4

INVESTIGATE Metamorphic Changes, p. 98
Students model how pressure and temperature can change a solid.

TIME 10 minutes
MATERIALS 3 candles of different colors, vegetable peeler

CHAPTER INVESTIGATION Rock Classification,
pp. 102–103
Students classify rock samples as igneous, sedimentary, or metamorphic.

R Rock Classification Key, p. 196

TIME 40 minutes
MATERIALS 6–8 rock samples, Rock Classification Key, magnifying glass

---

R **Additional INVESTIGATION,** Modeling Rock Formation, A, B, & C, pp. 206–214; Teacher Instructions, pp. 348–349

Previewing Chapter Resources

	INTEGRATED TECHNOLOGY	LABS AND ACTIVITIES

CHAPTER 3
Rocks

 CLASSZONE.COM
- eEdition Plus
- EasyPlanner Plus
- Content Review
- Test Practice
- Simulation
- Visualization
- Resource Centers
- Internet Activity: Rocks
- Math Tutorial

 CD-ROMS
- eEdition Plus
- EasyPlanner
- Power Presentations
- Content Review
- Lab Generator
- Test Generator

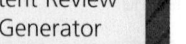 **AUDIO CDS**
- Audio Readings
- Audio Readings in Spanish

SCILINKS.ORG
SCI LINKS

 EXPLORE the Big Idea, p. 73
- How Can Rocks Disappear?
- What Causes Rocks to Change?
- Internet Activity: Rocks

UNIT RESOURCE BOOK
Unit Projects, pp. 5–10

Lab Generator CD-ROM
Generate customized labs.

 SECTION 3.1

The rock cycle shows how rocks change.
pp. 75–81

Time: 2 periods (1 block)

 Lesson Plan, pp. 144–145

 RESOURCE CENTER, Meteorites and Impacts

 UNIT TRANSPARENCY BOOK
- Big Idea Flow Chart, p. T17
- Daily Vocabulary Scaffolding, p. T18
- Note-Taking Model, p. T19
- 3-Minute Warm-Up, p. T20
- "The Rock Cycle" Visual, p. T22

 • EXPLORE Rocks and Minerals, p. 75
- INVESTIGATE Classification of Rocks, p. 77
- Extreme Science, p. 81

 UNIT RESOURCE BOOK
- Datasheet, Classification of Rocks, p. 153
- Additional INVESTIGATION, Modeling Rock Formation, A, B, & C, pp. 206–214

 SECTION 3.2

Igneous rocks form from molten rock.
pp. 82–88

Time: 2 periods (1 block)

 Lesson Plan, pp. 155–156

 • **VISUALIZATION,** Igneous Crystal Formation
- **RESOURCE CENTER,** Igneous Rocks
- **MATH TUTORIAL**

UNIT TRANSPARENCY BOOK
- Daily Vocabulary Scaffolding, p. T18
- 3-Minute Warm-Up, p. T20

 • INVESTIGATE Crystal Size, p. 85
- Math in Science, p. 88

 UNIT RESOURCE BOOK
- Mineral Crystal Diagrams, p. 164
- Datasheet, Crystal Size, p. 165
- Math Support, p. 194
- Math Practice, p. 195

 SECTION 3.3

Sedimentary rocks form from earlier rocks.
pp. 89–95

Time: 2 periods (1 block)

 Lesson Plan, pp. 167–168

 RESOURCE CENTER, Sedimentary Rocks

 UNIT TRANSPARENCY BOOK
- Daily Vocabulary Scaffolding, p. T18
- 3-Minute Warm-Up, p. T21

 • EXPLORE Particle Layers, p. 89
- INVESTIGATE Rock Layers, p. 94

 UNIT RESOURCE BOOK
Datasheet, Rock Layers, p. 176

SECTION 3.4

Metamorphic rocks form as existing rocks change.
pp. 96–103

Time: 4 periods (2 blocks)

 Lesson Plan, pp. 178–179

 RESOURCE CENTER, Metamorphic Rocks

UNIT TRANSPARENCY BOOK
- Big Idea Flow Chart, p. T17
- Daily Vocabulary Scaffolding, p. T18
- 3-Minute Warm-Up, p. T21
- Chapter Outline, pp. T23–T24

 • INVESTIGATE Metamorphic Changes, p. 98
- CHAPTER INVESTIGATION, Rock Classification, pp. 102–103

 UNIT RESOURCE BOOK
- Datasheet, Metamorphic Changes, p. 187
- Rock Classification Key, p. 196
- CHAPTER INVESTIGATION, Rock Classification, A, B, & C, pp. 197–205

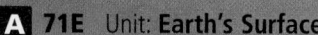

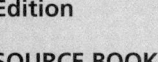

READING AND REINFORCEMENT

ASSESSMENT

STANDARDS

- Magnet Words, B24–25
- Main Idea Web, C38–39
- Daily Vocabulary Scaffolding, H1–8

 UNIT RESOURCE BOOK
- Vocabulary Practice, pp. 191–192
- Decoding Support, p. 193
- Summarizing the Chapter, pp. 215–216

Audio Readings CD
Listen to Pupil Edition.

Audio Readings in Spanish CD
Listen to Pupil Edition in Spanish.

 • Chapter Review, pp. 105–106
- Standardized Test Practice, p. 107

 UNIT ASSESSMENT BOOK
- Diagnostic Test, pp. 40–41
- Chapter Test, A, B, & C, pp. 46–57
- Alternative Assessment, pp. 58–59

 Spanish Chapter Test, pp. 113–116

 Test Generator CD-ROM
Generate customized tests.

Lab Generator CD-ROM
Rubrics for Labs

National Standards
A.1–8, A.9.a–c, A.9.e–g, D.1.d, D.1.k

See p. 72 for the standards.

 UNIT RESOURCE BOOK
- Reading Study Guide, A & B, pp. 146–149
- Spanish Reading Study Guide, pp. 150–151
- Challenge and Extension, p. 152
- Reinforcing Key Concepts, p. 154

 Ongoing Assessment, pp. 77–80

 Section 3.1 Review, p. 80

UNIT ASSESSMENT BOOK
Section 3.1 Quiz, p. 42

National Standards
A.1–8, A.9.a–b, A.9.e–g, D.1.d, D.1.k

 **UNIT RESOURCE BOOK**
- Reading Study Guide, A & B, pp. 157–160
- Spanish Reading Study Guide, pp. 161–162
- Challenge and Extension, p. 163
- Reinforcing Key Concepts, p. 166
- Challenge Reading, pp. 189–190

 Ongoing Assessment, pp. 83–87

 Section 3.2 Review, p. 87

UNIT ASSESSMENT BOOK
Section 3.2 Quiz, p. 43

National Standards
A.2–8, A.9.a–c, A.9.e–f, D.1.d

 **UNIT RESOURCE BOOK**
- Reading Study Guide, A & B, pp. 169–172
- Spanish Reading Study Guide, pp. 173–174
- Challenge and Extension, p. 175
- Reinforcing Key Concepts, p. 177

 Ongoing Assessment, pp. 89–91, 93, 95

 Section 3.3 Review, p. 95

UNIT ASSESSMENT BOOK
Section 3.3 Quiz, p. 44

National Standards
A.2–7, A.9.a–b, A.9.e–f, D.1.d, D.1.k

 UNIT RESOURCE BOOK
- Reading Study Guide, A & B, pp. 180–183
- Spanish Reading Study Guide, pp. 184–185
- Challenge and Extension, p. 186
- Reinforcing Key Concepts, p. 188

 Ongoing Assessment, pp. 96–101

Section 3.4 Review, p. 101

UNIT ASSESSMENT BOOK
Section 3.4 Quiz, p. 45

National Standards
A.2–7, A.9.a–b, A.9.e–f, D.1.d

Previewing Resources for Differentiated Instruction

CHAPTER INVESTIGATION

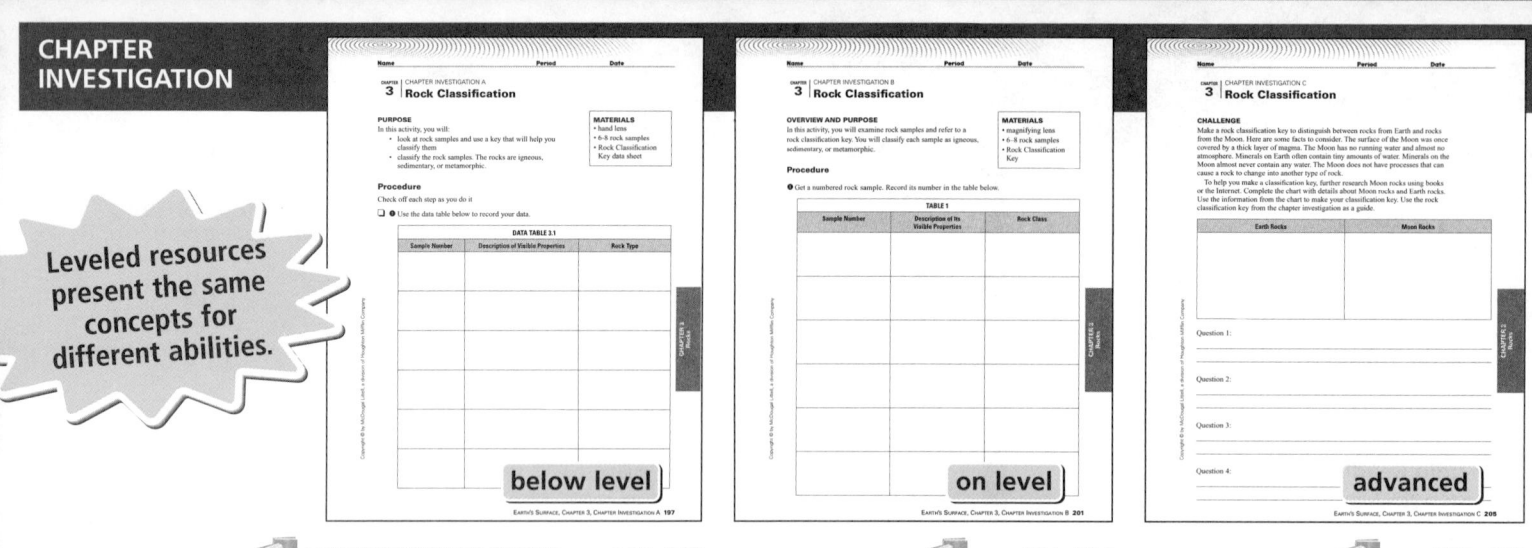

Leveled resources present the same concepts for different abilities.

below level

R UNIT RESOURCE BOOK, pp. 197–200

on level

R pp. 201–204

advanced

R pp. 201–205

READING STUDY GUIDE

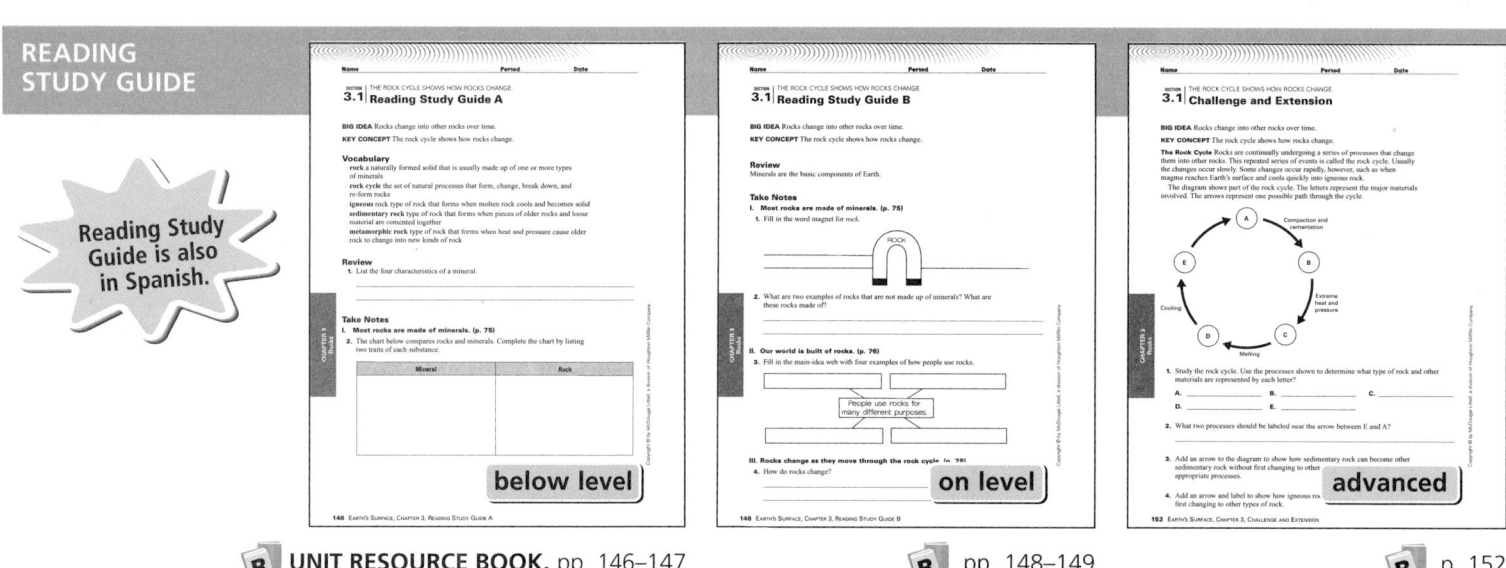

Reading Study Guide is also in Spanish.

below level

R UNIT RESOURCE BOOK, pp. 146–147

on level

R pp. 148–149

advanced

R p. 152

CHAPTER TEST

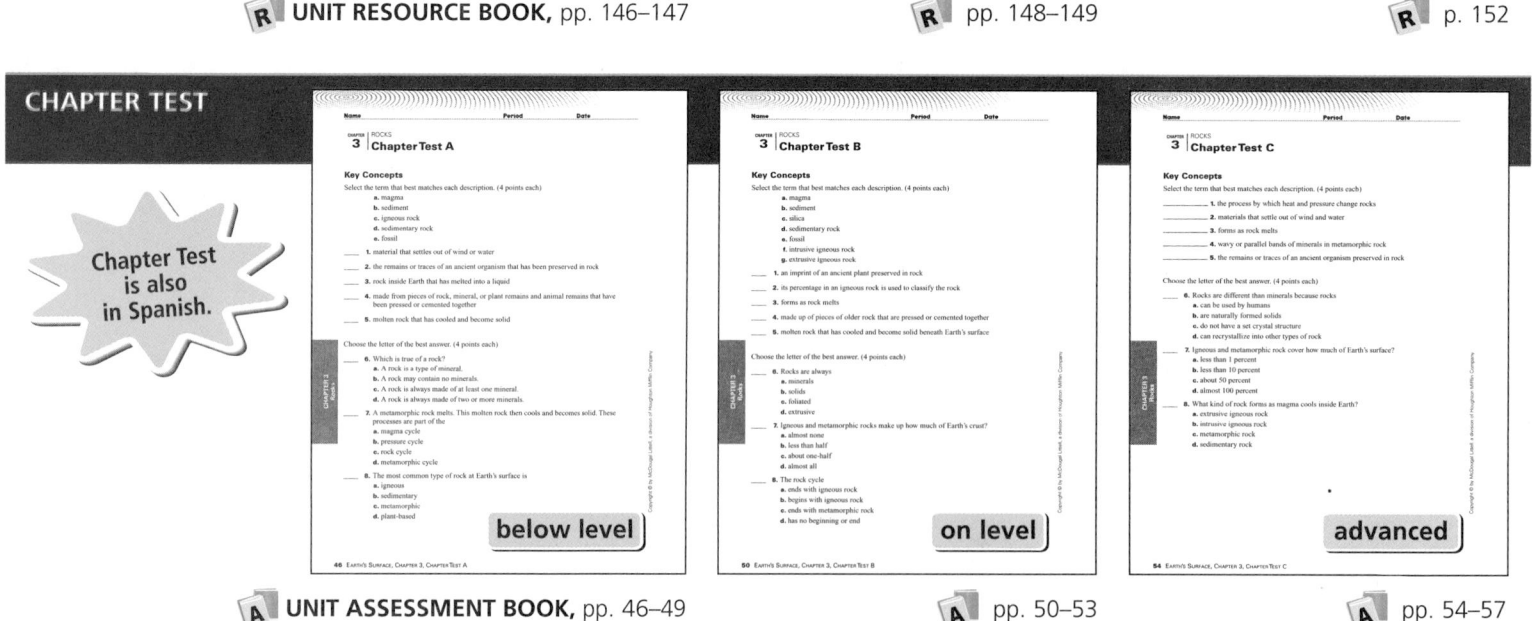

Chapter Test is also in Spanish.

below level

A UNIT ASSESSMENT BOOK, pp. 46–49

on level

A pp. 50–53

advanced

A pp. 54–57

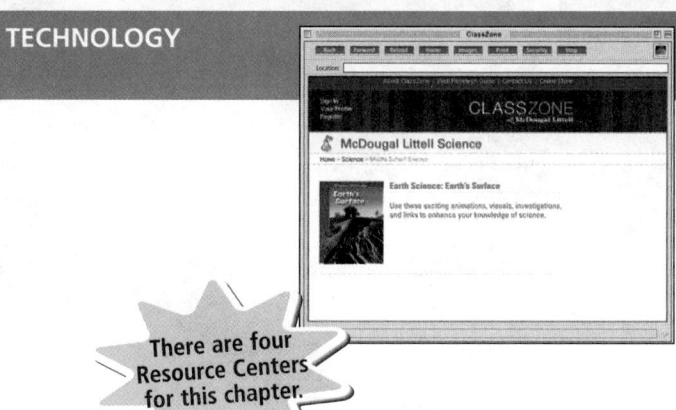

There are four Resource Centers for this chapter.

CLASSZONE.COM

CD/CD-ROMS

CLASSZONE.COM

VISUAL CONTENT

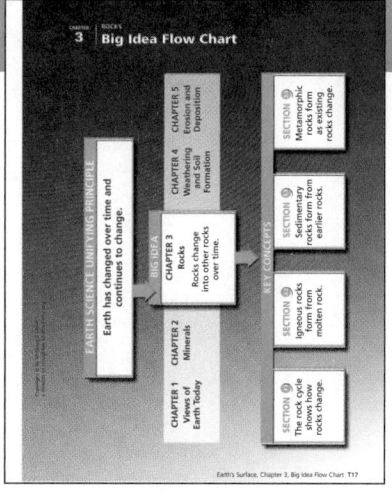

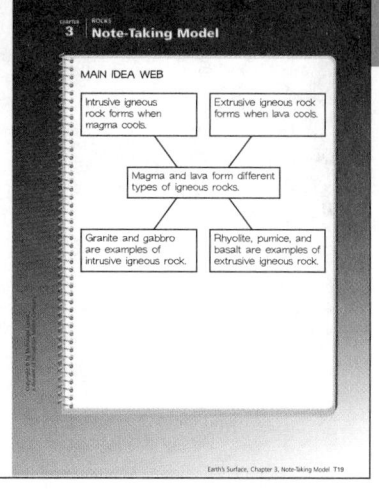

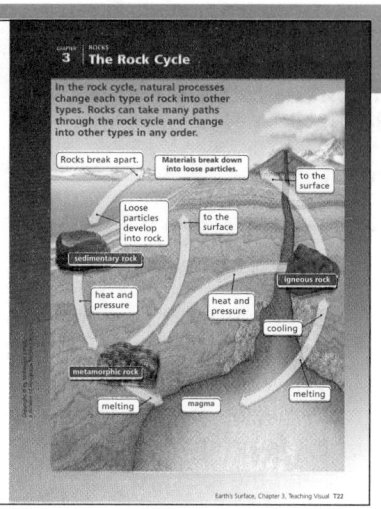

UNIT TRANSPARENCY BOOK, p. T17

p. T19

p. T22

MORE SUPPORT

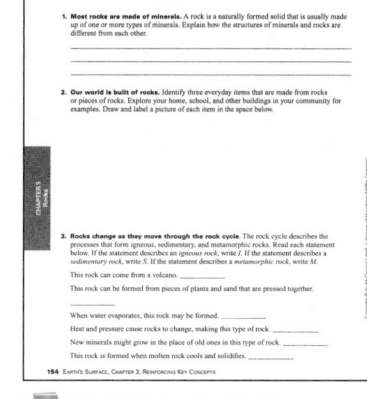

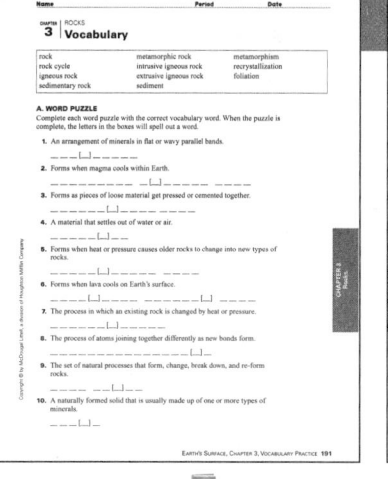

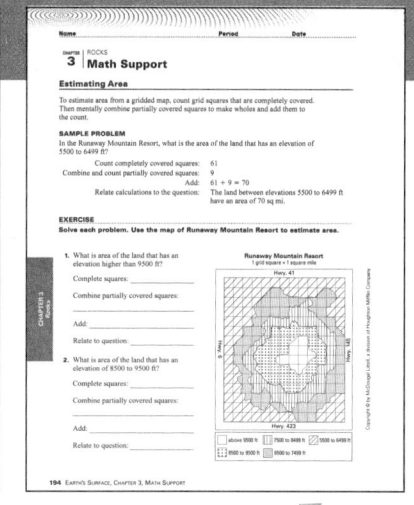

Reinforcing Key Concepts for each section

UNIT RESOURCE BOOK, p. 154

pp. 191–192

p. 194

INTRODUCE

the **BIG** idea

Have students look at the photograph of the rock climbers and discuss how the question in the box links to the Big Idea:

- Ask: What could happen to these rocks to make them change?
- Ask: Would the changes be gradual or rapid?
- Ask: What do you already know about the different ways that rocks form?

National Science Education Standards

Content

D.1.d Some changes in the solid earth can be described as the "rock cycle." Old rocks at Earth's surface weather, forming sediments that are buried, then compacted, heated, and often recrystallized into new rock. Eventually, those new rocks may be brought to the surface by the forces that drive plate motions, and the rock cycle continues.

D.1.k Living organisms have played many roles in the Earth system, producing some types of rocks, and contributing to the weathering of rocks.

Process

A.1–8 Identify questions that can be answered through scientific investigations; design and conduct an investigation; use tools; use evidence; think critically to make relationships between evidence and explanation; recognize different explanations and predictions; communicate scientific procedures and explanations; use mathematics.

A.9.a–c, A.9.e–g Understand scientific inquiry by using different investigations, methods, mathematics, and explanations based on logic, evidence, and skepticism. Data often results in new investigations.

CHAPTER

3 Rocks

the **BIG** idea

Rocks change into other rocks over time.

> **How long will these rocks remain as they are?**

Key Concepts

SECTION 3.1
The rock cycle shows how rocks change. Learn the types of rock and how they change over time.

SECTION 3.2
Igneous rocks form from molten rock. Learn how igneous rocks form within Earth and at Earth's surface.

SECTION 3.3
Sedimentary rocks form from earlier rocks. Learn how layers of loose materials develop into sedimentary rocks.

SECTION 3.4
Metamorphic rocks form as existing rocks change. Learn how one type of rock can change into another.

Internet Preview

CLASSZONE.COM

Chapter 3 online resources: Content Review, Simulation, Visualization, four Resource Centers, Math Tutorial, Test Practice

INTERNET PREVIEW

CLASSZONE.COM For student use with the following pages:

Review and Practice
- Content Review: pp. 74, 104
- Math Tutorial: Estimating Area, p. 88
- Test Practice, p. 107

Activities and Resources
- Internet Activity: Rocks, p. 73
- Resource Centers: Meteorites and Impacts, p. 81; Igneous Rocks, p. 86; Sedimentary Rocks, p. 90; Metamorphic Rocks, p. 99
- Visualization: Igneous Crystal Formation, p. 84

NSTA scilinks.org **SCILINKS**

The Rock Cycle
Code: MDL015

How Can Rocks Disappear?

Chalk is made of carbonate minerals, as is a type of rock called limestone. Put a piece of chalk in a cup. Pour vinegar over the chalk.

Observe and Think Describe what happens to the chalk. How do you think this change could happen to limestone in nature? **Hint:** Think about the amount of time it might take.

What Causes Rocks to Change?

Make two balls out of modeling clay and freeze them. Take the clay balls out of the freezer and put them on paper. Cover one ball with plastic wrap and stack books on top of it.

Observe and Think Observe how the clay balls change over time. How might rocks respond to changes in temperature, pressure, or both?

Internet Activity: Rocks

Go to **ClassZone.com** to explore how rocks form and change.

Observe and Think Give three examples of the ways in which rocks are continually changing.

NSTA scilinks.org
SCILINKS

The Rock Cycle **Code: MDL015**

TEACHING WITH TECHNOLOGY

Video Camera You might want to tape groups of students showing and explaining the models they created for "Investigate Rock Layers," p. 94. Play the videotape during an open house or during the wait time at parent conferences.

These inquiry-based activities are appropriate for use at home or as a supplement to classroom instruction.

How Can Rocks Disappear?

PURPOSE To introduce students to the concept that rocks can dissolve.

TIP *10 min.* Advise students to use a small piece of chalk and cover it with the vinegar. Standard classroom chalk works best. Some forms or colors of washable chalk will not react with vinegar.

Answer: The chalk bubbles and dissolves in the vinegar. Rainwater, which is naturally acidic, can dissolve limestone in nature, although it takes a much longer time.

REVISIT after p. 92.

What Causes Rocks to Change?

PURPOSE To model the effects of temperature and pressure changes on rocks. Students use books to apply pressure to one of the balls.

TIP *20 min.* Have students wait and observe the clay balls near the end of the class period.

Answer: The clay ball with the books on top of it will flatten out much more than the other clay ball will. A rock subjected to higher temperature and pressure will change more than a similar rock under more moderate conditions.

REVISIT after p. 97.

Internet Activity: Rocks

PURPOSE To introduce students to ways that different rocks form and change.

TIP *20 min.* Have students take notes on what they learn from this site.

Answer: being worn down and broken apart, forming within Earth and then being exposed at the surface, and becoming another type of rock

REVISIT after p. 79.

Getting Ready to Learn

PREPARE

◑ CONCEPT REVIEW

Activate Prior Knowledge

- Call on volunteers to give examples of the chemical composition of a few minerals that were mentioned in the chapter on minerals. For example, students might recall that gold consists only of gold atoms, quartz consists of one atom of silicon for every two atoms of oxygen, and halite is made up of equal numbers of sodium and chlorine atoms.

- Hold up a cube and remind students that this is one of the shapes that mineral crystals might have. In a crystal, atoms are arranged in an orderly, repeating, three-dimensional pattern.

- Have students turn to the visual on p. 64 to summarize the ways minerals form.

◑ TAKING NOTES

Main Idea Web

Writing down main ideas and connecting them with important details that support each main idea will help students process and remember the chapter content.

Vocabulary Strategy

The word magnet strategy will help students visualize the fact that a single word can have several meanings.

Vocabulary and Note-Taking Resources

- Vocabulary Practice, pp. 191–192
- Decoding Support, p. 193

- Daily Vocabulary Scaffolding, p. T18
- Note-Taking Model, p. T19

- Magnet Words, B24–25
- Main Idea Web, C38–39
- Daily Vocabulary Scaffolding, H1–8

◑ CONCEPT REVIEW

- Every mineral has a specific chemical composition.
- A mineral's atoms are arranged in a crystal structure.
- Minerals form under a variety of conditions.

◑ VOCABULARY REVIEW

mineral p. 43

crystal p. 46

magma p. 62

lava p. 62

CONTENT REVIEW
CLASSZONE.COM
Review concepts and vocabulary.

▶ TAKING NOTES

MAIN IDEA WEB

Write each new blue heading in the center box. In the boxes around it, take notes about important terms and details that relate to the main idea.

VOCABULARY STRATEGY

Draw a **magnet word** diagram for each new vocabulary term. Around the "magnet" write words and ideas related to the term.

See the Note-Taking Handbook on pages R45–R51.

SCIENCE NOTEBOOK

| Rocks are not the same as minerals. | Different types of rocks contain different minerals. |

Most rocks are made of minerals.

| A rock may be made up of only one mineral. | A few kinds of rocks contain no minerals at all. |

Solid — ROCK

Formed naturally — Usually made up of minerals

A 74 Unit: Earth's Surface

CHECK READINESS

Administer the Diagnostic Test to determine students' readiness for new science content and their mastery of requisite math skills.

 Diagnostic Test, pp. 40–41

Technology Resources

Students needing content and math skills should visit **ClassZone.com**.

- **CONTENT REVIEW**
- **MATH TUTORIAL**

 CONTENT REVIEW CD-ROM

The rock cycle shows how rocks change.

◄ **BEFORE, you learned**

- Minerals are basic components of Earth
- Minerals form in many different ways

▶ **NOW, you will learn**

- What the three types of rocks are
- How one type of rock can change into another
- How common each rock type is in Earth's crust

VOCABULARY

rock p. 75
rock cycle p. 78
igneous rock p. 78
sedimentary rock p. 78
metamorphic rock p. 78

EXPLORE Rocks and Minerals

How do rocks differ from minerals?

PROCEDURE

① Closely examine the rock and mineral samples. What do you notice about the forms, shapes, colors, and textures of the rock and the mineral?

② In your notebook, make lists of the characteristics of the rock and of the mineral.

MATERIALS
- mineral sample
- rock sample
- magnifying glass

WHAT DO YOU THINK?
- What are the similarities and differences between the rock and the mineral?
- What additional observations or tests might help you determine other differences between rocks and minerals?

Most rocks are made of minerals.

If you have ever put together a jigsaw puzzle, you know that each piece is an important part of the final picture. Just as the pieces combine to form the picture, minerals combine to form most rocks. Another way to consider the relationship between minerals and rocks is to compare rocks to words. Just as letters combine to make up words, minerals combine to make up rocks. A **rock** is a naturally formed solid that is usually made up of one or more types of minerals.

The structure of rocks is different from that of minerals. A mineral is always made of the same elements in the same proportions. All minerals have an orderly crystal structure. In contrast, the proportion of different minerals in a particular kind of rock may vary. In addition, the minerals in a rock can be all jumbled together.

Chapter 3: **Rocks** 75 **A**

Below Level

UNIT RESOURCE BOOK
- Reading Study Guide A, pp. 146–147
- Decoding Support, p. 193

AUDIO CDS

R Additional INVESTIGATION,
Modeling Rock Formation, A, B, & C, pp. 206–214;
Teacher Instructions, pp. 348–349

Advanced

UNIT RESOURCE BOOK
Challenge and Extension, p. 152

English Learners

UNIT RESOURCE BOOK
Spanish Reading Study Guide, pp. 150–151

AUDIO CDS

- Audio Readings in Spanish
- Audio Readings (English)

◉ Set Learning Goals
Students will
- Identify the three types of rocks.
- Explain how one type of rock can change into another.
- Tell how common each rock type is in Earth's crust.
- Design a system for classifying rocks in an experiment.

◐ 3-Minute Warm-Up

Display Transparency 20 or copy this exercise on the board:

Draw and label two diagrams:

1. Show the relationship between minerals and rocks. *Students might draw a rock with specks of different sizes and shades, and label the specks as minerals and the entire object as a rock.*

2. Show Earth's solid and molten layers. *Students should draw a cutaway diagram of Earth's interior like the one shown on p. 12. Diagrams should be labeled as follows: crust and mantle—solid rock; outer core—molten metal; inner core—solid metal.*

T 3-Minute Warm-Up, p. T20

EXPLORE Rocks and Minerals

PURPOSE To spark students' thinking about the differences between rocks and minerals

TIP *10 min.* If possible, choose a rock and a mineral that clearly differ in shape, color, and texture.

WHAT DO YOU THINK? *Sample answers: similarities: rocks and minerals are both solid and can have similar appearances. Differences: a mineral has a more uniform appearance than a rock; a mineral has visible crystals and rocks do not.*

Teach from Visuals

Note that the two rocks pictured are examples of a common type of rock and an unusual type of rock. To help students interpret the visual, ask:

- How does the obsidian differ in appearance from the gabbro? *The obsidian appears more uniform in color and texture than the gabbro. The obsidian looks glassy, and the gabbro looks grainy.*

- How does this difference in appearance reflect their compositions? *The obsidian is a natural glass and contains no minerals. Gabbro is made up of several types of minerals, which results in grains of different colors.*

Teach Difficult Concepts

Students may not understand what natural glass is. While most glass is manufactured, natural glass forms in nature. Obsidian forms from hot lava that cools so quickly that crystals do not have time to develop. The chemical composition of obsidian is the same as that of granite, but obsidian's structure is different.

A few types of rocks are made up of one kind of mineral, and a few contain no minerals at all. Limestone, for example, can be composed entirely of the mineral calcite. Obsidian (ahb-SIHD-ee-uhn) is a rock that contains no minerals. It consists of natural glass, which is not a mineral because it does not have a crystal structure. Coal is another rock that is not composed of minerals. It is made up of the remains of ancient plants that have been buried and pressed into rock.

Gabbro, like most rocks, is made up of several types of minerals.

Obsidian is an unusual rock because it contains no minerals.

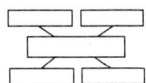

MAIN IDEA WEB
As you read, write each blue heading in a central box and record important details in boxes around it.

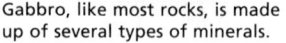

These huge cliffs on the coast of the Hawaiian island of Kauai show only a tiny part of the rock that makes up Earth.

Our world is built of rocks.

Earth is built almost entirely of rock. When you look at Earth's surface, you can see soil, plants, rivers, and oceans. These surface features, however, form only a very thin covering on the planet. Between this thin layer and Earth's metallic core, Earth is made of solid and molten rock.

Because rocks are so common, it is not surprising that people use them for many different purposes, including

- the building of houses and skyscrapers
- the sources of metals, such as iron, aluminum, and copper
- the carving of statues and other works of art
- as a base for pavement for roads and highways

A   76   Unit: Earth's Surface

DIFFERENTIATE INSTRUCTION

? More Reading Support

A How does coal differ from most rocks? *It is not composed of minerals.*

B What does Earth consist mostly of? *rock*

English Learners English learners may have difficulty reading sentences that have introductory clauses and phrases. When this happens, have them find the comma that separates a clause from the rest of the sentence. Then have them locate the subject of the sentence. They might benefit from some examples on this page, such as *When you look at Earth's surface . . .* and *Because rocks are so common. . . .*

People value rocks because rocks last a long time and because some are beautiful. Ancient rock structures and carvings give us a link to our distant past. Many famous monuments and sculptures are made from rocks. Granite blocks form part of the Great Wall of China. Limestone blocks make up the Great Pyramid in Egypt. The faces of four U.S. presidents are carved in the granite of Mount Rushmore.

This sculptor in Indonesia, like artists throughout the world, shapes rocks into lasting works of art.

CHECK YOUR READING Why do people use rocks for many different purposes?

People study rocks to learn how areas have changed through time. For example, rocks show that North America, as well as most of the rest of the world, has been buried under thick layers of ice many times. You could learn about the types of rocks in your area by collecting and identifying them. You could also examine a map that shows types of rocks and where they are located. This type of map is called a geologic map. The map may be of a large area, such as your state, or a smaller area, such as your county.

INVESTIGATE Classification of Rocks

How can rocks be classified?

Geologists classify rocks by their physical characteristics. Design your own system for classifying rocks, as a scientist might.

SKILL FOCUS
Classifying

MATERIALS
6 rock samples

TIME
20 minutes

PROCEDURE

1. Examine the rock samples. Look at their physical characteristics.
2. Make a list of the differences in the physical characteristics of the rocks.
3. Use your list to decide which characteristics are most important in classifying the rocks into different types. Make a chart in which these characteristics are listed and used to classify the rocks into types.

WHAT DO YOU THINK?

- Which physical characteristic is most helpful in classifying the rocks?
- Which physical characteristic is least helpful in classifying the rocks?

CHALLENGE Is it possible to classify rocks only by the characteristics you can see?

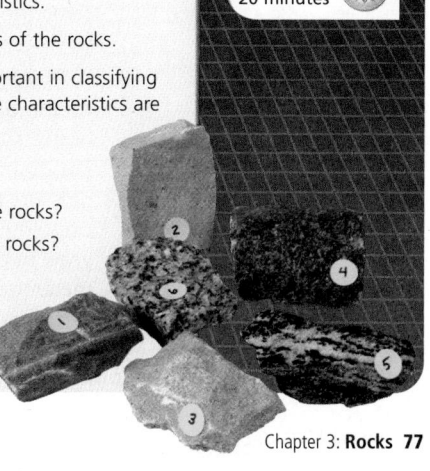

Chapter 3: **Rocks** 77 **A**

Address Misconceptions

IDENTIFY Ask: How does a rock change over time? If students answer, "Rocks don't change" or "I can't think of any ways," they may hold the misconception that rocks are permanent and unchanging.

CORRECT As a class, review the definition of *rock cycle* at the top of p. 78. Have students study the diagram of the rock cycle on p. 79 and discuss each step. Explain that the arrows show the different ways rocks can move through the cycle.

REASSESS Ask: What kinds of changes does a rock go through over many years? *A rock changes into a different rock type or re-forms into the same rock type.* Why do rocks seem to be unchanging? *The rock cycle usually moves slowly. It is often hard to notice the changes.*

Technology Resources

Visit **ClassZone.com** for background on common student misconceptions.

 MISCONCEPTION DATABASE

Real World Example

Samples of all three types of rocks might be found along a road cut or in an area in which the bedrock is exposed. In nature, rock types can be found mixed together. In one road cut you might find basalt, an igneous rock; shale, a sedimentary rock; and schist, a metamorphic rock.

Ongoing Assessment

Identify the three types of rocks.

Ask: How do the three types of rocks differ? *They differ in the way they form. Igneous rock forms when molten rock cools and becomes solid. Most sedimentary rock forms as pieces of older rocks, plants, and other loose material get pressed and cemented into rock. Metamorphic rock forms as heat or pressure or both cause older rocks to change into new types of rock.*

CHECK YOUR READING *Answer: Igneous, sedimentary, and metamorphic. Sample question: What forces cause rocks to move within Earth?*

 VOCABULARY
Add a magnet word diagram for *rock cycle* to your notebook. Then add diagrams for the names of the rock types.

D

Rocks change as they move through the rock cycle.

When you want to describe a person you can depend on, you may say that he or she is "like a rock." That's the way people think of rocks—as solid and unchanging. Nevertheless, rocks do change. But the changes usually occur over a huge span of time—thousands to millions of years. The **rock cycle** is the set of natural processes that form, change, break down, and re-form rocks.

A cycle is made up of repeating events that happen one after another. This does not mean that rocks move through the rock cycle in a particular order. As the illustration shows on page 79, a rock at any point in the cycle can change in two or three different ways. Like all cycles, the rock cycle has no beginning or ending but goes on continually.

Rock Types

E

The three types of rocks are classified by how they form.

- **Igneous rock** (IHG-nee-uhs) forms when molten rock cools and becomes solid. Igneous rock can form within Earth, or it can form on Earth's surface. Igneous rocks that originally formed at great depths can reach Earth's surface over time. Deep rocks may be raised closer to the surface when mountains are pushed up. At the same time, other processes can wear away the rocks that cover the deeper rocks.

- Most **sedimentary rock** (SEHD-uh-MEHN-tuh-ree) forms when pieces of older rocks, plants, and other loose material get pressed or cemented together. Loose material is carried by water or wind and then settles out, forming layers. The lower layers of material can get pressed into rock by the weight of the upper layers. Also, new minerals can grow in the spaces within the material, cementing it together. Some sedimentary rocks form in other ways, as when water evaporates, leaving behind minerals that were dissolved in it.

- **Metamorphic rock** (MEHT-uh-MAWR-fihk) forms when heat or pressure cause older rocks to change into new types of rocks. For example, a rock can get buried deeper in the crust, where pressure and temperature are much greater. The new conditions cause the structure of the rock to change and new minerals to grow in place of the original minerals. The rock becomes a metamorphic rock. Like igneous rocks, metamorphic rocks can be raised to Earth's surface over time.

 **CHECK YOUR READING** What are the three rock types? What questions do you have about how rocks move through the rock cycle?

READING TiP
When material dissolves in water, it breaks into many tiny parts. When the water evaporates, the parts join together and the material becomes solid again.

DIFFERENTIATE INSTRUCTION

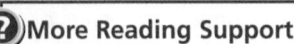 **More Reading Support**

D What is the rock cycle? *a set of natural processes that form, change, break down, and re-form rocks*

E How are the types of rocks classified? *by how they form*

Below Level Use graphic organizers like this chart to help students organize information.

Type of Rock	How It Forms
Igneous	Molten rock cools
Sedimentary	Pieces of rock and other materials get pressed together
Metamorphic	Heat or pressure changes rock

The Rock Cycle

In the rock cycle, natural processes change each type of rock into other types. Rocks can take many paths through the rock cycle and change into other types in any order.

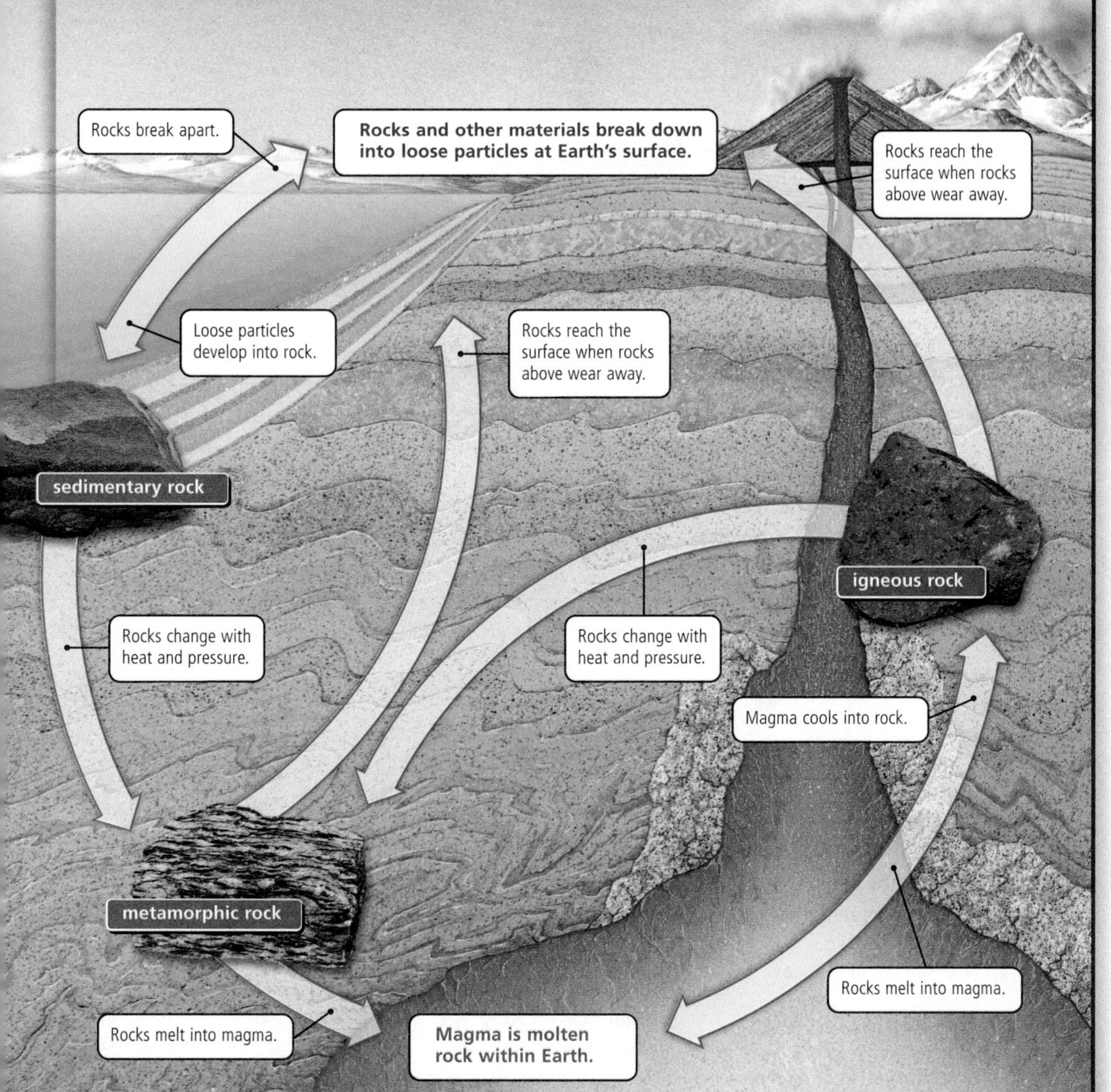

Rocks break apart.

Rocks and other materials break down into loose particles at Earth's surface.

Rocks reach the surface when rocks above wear away.

Loose particles develop into rock.

Rocks reach the surface when rocks above wear away.

sedimentary rock

igneous rock

Rocks change with heat and pressure.

Rocks change with heat and pressure.

Magma cools into rock.

metamorphic rock

Rocks melt into magma.

Rocks melt into magma.

Magma is molten rock within Earth.

READING VISUALS What are three different ways an igneous rock can change as it moves to another stage of the rock cycle?

Chapter 3: Rocks **79** **A**

DIFFERENTIATE INSTRUCTION

Additional Investigation To reinforce Section 3.1 learning goals, use the following full-period investigation:

R **Additional INVESTIGATION,** Modeling Rock Formation, A, B, & C, pp. 206–214, 348–349
(Advanced students should complete Levels B and C.)

Advanced Challenge students to create flow charts or PowerPoint presentations depicting the ways that rocks can move through the rock cycle.

R Challenge and Extension, p. 152

Teach from Visuals

To help students interpret the visual of the rock cycle, ask: What do the arrows pointing in two directions mean? *The process could go either way.*

 This visual is also available as T22 in the Unit Transparency Book.

EXPLORE (the BIG idea)

Revisit "Internet Activity: Rocks" on p. 73. Have students relate their examples to the rock cycle diagram.

Develop Critical Thinking

COMPARE AND CONTRAST In discussing the rock cycle, have students compare and contrast it with the water cycle.

Sample answer: Both cycles are natural processes that are continual and involve changes in matter, but the water cycle involves just one compound, water, while the rock cycle involves many types of rocks.

History of Science

James Hutton, a Scottish physician and farmer, is often called the father of modern geology. In the late 1700s he proposed a theory of the rock cycle based on his observations of rocks in Scotland.

Ongoing Assessment

Explain how one type of rock can change into another.

Ask: How can metamorphic rock change into sedimentary rock? *At Earth's surface, metamorphic rock breaks into loose pieces. These loose pieces get pressed and cemented together to form sedimentary rock.*

READING VISUALS *Answer: An igneous rock can reach the surface as overlying rocks are worn away. Inside Earth an igneous rock can be changed by heat and pressure into a metamorphic rock, or it can melt again and then cool into another igneous rock.*

Ongoing Assessment

 CHECK YOUR READING *Answer: Sedimentary rock would not be found deep in Earth's crust because it forms at the surface. When it gets buried deep enough, it changes into igneous or metamorphic rock.*

Reinforce (the **BIG** idea)

Have students relate the section to the Big Idea.

 R Reinforcing Key Concepts, p. 154

3.1 ASSESS & RETEACH

Assess

A Section 3.1 Quiz, p. 42

Reteach

- Hold up a sedimentary rock and tell students that it is the most common type of rock on Earth's surface but the least common in Earth's crust as a whole. Explain that sedimentary rock forms as rock at Earth's surface gets broken into pieces. These rock particles are carried away by water or wind, settle in layers, and get pressed and cemented together.

- Next hold up an igneous rock and a metamorphic rock and tell students that these are the most common types of rock that make up Earth's crust. Explain that igneous rock forms when molten rock cools, and metamorphic rock forms when heat and pressure change another type of rock.

Technology Resources

Have students visit **ClassZone.com** for reteaching of Key Concepts.

 CONTENT REVIEW

 CONTENT REVIEW CD-ROM

A 80 Unit: Earth's Surface

Rocks in the Crust

Even though sedimentary rock is common at Earth's surface, as a whole the crust consists mainly of igneous and metamorphic rock.

Surface of Crust

Igneous and metamorphic rock 25%

Sedimentary rock 75%

Entire Crust

Sedimentary rock 5%

Igneous and metamorphic rock 95%

Rocks in the Crust

Igneous, sedimentary, and metamorphic rocks are all found in Earth's crust. But these rock types are not evenly distributed. Most of Earth's crust—95 percent of it—consists of igneous rock and metamorphic rock. Sedimentary rock, which forms a thin covering on Earth's surface, makes up only 5 percent of the crust.

The distribution of rock types is a reflection of the rock cycle. Sedimentary rocks are most common at the surface because they are formed by processes that occur at the surface. Most igneous rocks and metamorphic rocks are formed by processes that occur deeper within Earth.

CHECK YOUR READING Would you expect to find sedimentary rock deep in Earth's crust? Why or why not?

3.1 Review

KEY CONCEPTS

1. How are rocks and minerals different?

2. What are the three types of rock?

3. Which rock types are most common within Earth's crust? Which type is most common at Earth's surface?

CRITICAL THINKING

4. **Analyze** Why is the set of natural processes by which rocks change into other types of rocks called a cycle?

5. **Infer** Which type of rock would you expect to be common on the floor of a large, deep lake? Why?

CHALLENGE

6. **Synthesize** Draw a diagram showing how an igneous rock could change into a metamorphic rock and how the metamorphic rock could change into a sedimentary rock.

A 80 Unit: Earth's Surface

ANSWERS

1. Minerals have an orderly crystal structure and a definite composition, but rocks do not.

2. igneous, sedimentary, metamorphic

3. igneous and metamorphic; sedimentary

4. because the steps occur over and over and have no beginning or end

5. sedimentary; because layers of sediment can build up in the center of a large lake

6. The diagram should show the following: heat and/or

pressure change the igneous rock into a metamorphic rock; the metamorphic rock reaches the surface as overlying rocks are worn away; at the surface, the metamorphic rock breaks down into sediments, which are then cemented together to form sedimentary rock.

EXTREME SCIENCE

Rocks from Space

Earth makes its own rocks. But some rocks come from space and land on Earth's surface. About 30,000 rocks with masses greater than 100 grams (3.5 oz) fall to Earth's surface every year. That's a rate of more than 80 rocks per day!

- A rock from space that reaches Earth's surface after passing through its atmosphere is called a meteorite.
- Most meteorites go unnoticed when they strike Earth. Either they fall in areas where there are few people, or they fall into the ocean.
- The largest rock from space ever found on Earth is called the Hoba meteorite. It weighs 60 tons! It landed in what is now Namibia, Africa, about 80,000 years ago.

A meteorite impact formed Barringer Crater, which is located in the Arizona desert.

This rock is a piece of the meteorite that formed Barringer Crater.

Meteorite Hunters Search Ice

Meteorite hunters search the icy wastes of Antarctica for these rocks. Do more meteorites fall there? No. But they are easy to see against the ice. The cold also helps preserve them in their original condition. In addition, the movements of the ice gather meteorites together in certain locations.

Meteorites Blast Earth

Large meteorites are very rare. This is fortunate, because they hit with great power. About 50,000 years ago, a meteorite that was about 45 meters (150 ft) in diameter slammed into what is now Arizona and blasted a crater 1.2 kilometers (0.75 mi) wide. Craters from ancient impacts may be hard to recognize because the land has been reshaped by geological processes. Evidence can still be found, though. The energy of an impact is so high that some minerals, such as quartz, are permanently altered.

A streak of light marks the path of a rock from space through Earth's atmosphere. The rock probably burned up completely before it could land.

EXPLORE

1. **PREDICT** Oceans cover about 71 percent of Earth's surface. Calculate how many meteorites with masses greater than 100 grams are likely to fall into the ocean each year. How many are likely to fall on land?

2. **CHALLENGE** Use information from the Resource Center to describe how a meteorite impact could have helped cause the dinosaurs to become extinct.

 RESOURCE CENTER
CLASSZONE.COM
Learn more about meteorites and meteorite impacts.

EXTREME SCIENCE
Fun and Motivating Science

Set Learning Goal

To understand that meteorites are rocks from space and thousands land on Earth each year

Present the Science

Students may not realize that rocks are a basic component not only of Earth but also of many other objects within the solar system. Many meteorites are fragments from the breakup of comets or from collisions between asteroids. Some are lunar fragments produced when an asteroid hits the Moon.

Discussion Questions

Ask: Are meteorites common or rare on Earth? *They are fairly common. An average of about 80 meteorites with a mass of at least 100 grams hit Earth's surface each day.*

Ask: Why are people rarely bothered by meteorites? *Most fall into the ocean or in areas where few people live.*

Ask: What evidence of meteorites has been found? *the meteorites themselves, craters left by their impacts, changes in minerals caused by their impacts*

Close

Ask: What would happen if a large meteorite hit a city? *All or a large part of the city would be completely destroyed and many people would be killed.*

Technology Resources

Students can visit **ClassZone.com** to find out more about the meteorite theory of dinosaur extinction.

RESOURCE CENTER

EXPLORE

1. *PREDICT meteorites falling into the ocean each year: 30,000 × 0.71 = 21,300; meteorites falling on land each year: 30,000 × 0.29 = 8700*

2. *CHALLENGE A meteorite could have helped cause dinosaurs to become extinct by throwing large amounts of dust into the atmosphere, temporarily changing Earth's climate.*

Students will

- Explain why igneous rocks formed at Earth's surface are different from those formed within Earth.
- Recognize why silica content is important in classifying igneous rocks.
- Explain why igneous rocks can make long-lasting landforms.
- Analyze how cooling time affects crystal size in an experiment.

● 3-Minute Warm-Up

Display Transparency 20 or copy this exercise on the board:

Complete each statement.

1. Most rocks are made up of _____. *minerals*

2. The most common types of rock in Earth's crust are _____. *igneous rock and metamorphic rock*

3. Igneous rock can form deep within Earth or on _____. *Earth's surface*

[T] 3-Minute Warm-Up, p. T20

3.2 MOTIVATE

THINK ABOUT

PURPOSE To understand how two rocks made of the same minerals can look very different

DISCUSS Tell students that they are not expected to know the "right" answer, but should feel free to speculate. *Students may answer that even though the rocks contain the same minerals, they look different because the sizes of their mineral crystals are very different.*

KEY CONCEPT

3.2 Igneous rocks form from molten rock.

◀ **BEFORE, you learned**

- Earth's interior is very hot
- Most minerals in Earth's crust are silicates

▶ **NOW, you will learn**

- Why igneous rocks formed at Earth's surface are different from those formed within Earth
- Why silica content is important in classifying igneous rocks
- Why igneous rocks can make long-lasting landforms

VOCABULARY

intrusive igneous rock p. 83
extrusive igneous rock p. 83

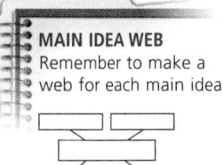

MAIN IDEA WEB
Remember to make a web for each main idea.

THINK ABOUT

Why do two rocks made of the same minerals look very different?

Look at a sample of granite and a sample of rhyolite (RY-uh-LYT). These two igneous rocks contain the same minerals, so their chemical compositions are very similar. Yet granite and rhyolite look very different. What do you think might cause this difference?

granite

rhyolite

Magma and lava form different types of igneous rocks.

Igneous rocks form from molten rock, but where does molten rock come from? The temperature inside Earth increases with depth. That is, the farther down you go, the hotter it gets. Deep within Earth, temperatures are hot enough—750°C to 1250°C (about 1400°F to 2300°F)—to melt rock. This molten rock is called magma. Molten rock that reaches Earth's surface is called lava.

An igneous rock is classified on the basis of its mineral composition and the size of its mineral crystals. A rock formed from magma can have the same composition as a rock formed from lava. The rocks, though, will have different names, because the sizes of their crystals will be very different. You will read why later in this section.

People's decisions about how to use igneous rocks are based in part on the rocks' crystal sizes. For example, rocks with large mineral crystals are often used as building stones because they are attractive.

RESOURCES FOR DIFFERENTIATED INSTRUCTION

Below Level

UNIT RESOURCE BOOK
- Reading Study Guide A, pp. 157–158
- Decoding Support, p. 193

 **AUDIO CDS**

Advanced

UNIT RESOURCE BOOK
- Challenge and Extension, p. 163
- Challenge Reading, pp. 189–190

English Learners

UNIT RESOURCE BOOK
Spanish Reading Study Guide, pp. 161–162

AUDIO CDS

- Audio Readings in Spanish
- Audio Readings (English)

Origin of Igneous Rocks

Depending on where they form, igneous rocks are classified as intrusive (ihn-TROO-sihv) or extrusive (ihk-STROO-sihv). An **intrusive igneous rock** is one that forms when magma cools within Earth. An **extrusive igneous rock** is one that forms when lava cools on Earth's surface.

Granite is a common intrusive rock in continents. If magma with the same composition reaches the surface, it forms extrusive rocks such as rhyolite and pumice (PUHM-ihs). Basalt (buh-SAWLT) is an extrusive igneous rock that forms the ocean floor. Gabbro is an intrusive rock that has the same composition as basalt.

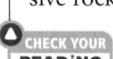 How are gabbro and basalt similar? How are they different?

You can see extrusive igneous rocks at Earth's surface. But intrusive igneous rocks form within Earth. How do they reach the surface? Forces inside Earth can push rocks up, as when mountains form. Also, water and wind break apart and carry away surface rocks. Then deeper rocks are uncovered at the surface.

Types of Igneous Rocks

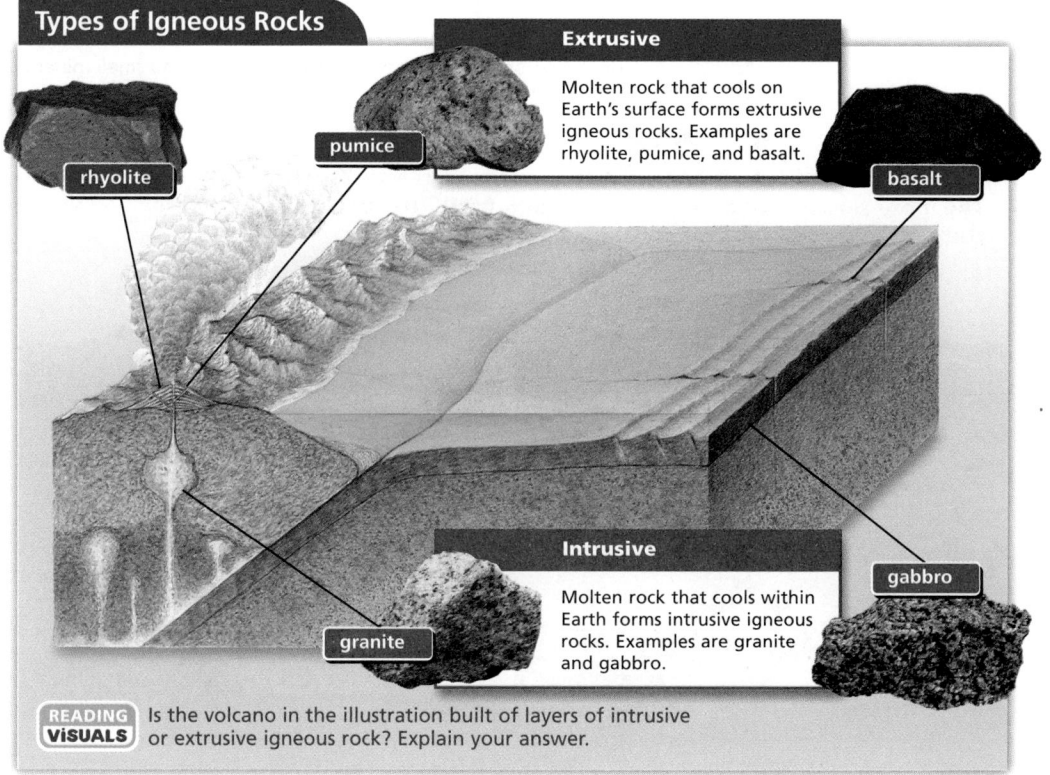

Extrusive

Molten rock that cools on Earth's surface forms extrusive igneous rocks. Examples are rhyolite, pumice, and basalt.

rhyolite

pumice

basalt

Intrusive

Molten rock that cools within Earth forms intrusive igneous rocks. Examples are granite and gabbro.

granite

gabbro

READING VISUALS Is the volcano in the illustration built of layers of intrusive or extrusive igneous rock? Explain your answer.

History of Science

James Hutton, the Scottish physician and farmer regarded as the father of modern geology, was the scientist who deduced that granite formed from the cooling of molten rock deep within Earth. He observed intrusions of granite within sedimentary rock as he worked in his fields. He noticed that the granite seemed to have invaded fractures in the sedimentary rock while the granite was molten. He also noted the coarse texture of the granite, which would be expected from slow cooling and slow crystallization.

Teach from Visuals

To help students interpret the visual of cooling molten rock, ask:

• Because diorite forms deep within Earth, would you expect it to have large or small mineral crystals? Why? *large, because minerals grow larger with longer cooling times*

• Since basalt forms on Earth's surface, would you expect it to have large or small mineral crystals? Why? *small, because it cools quickly*

Ongoing Assessment

Explain why igneous rocks formed at Earth's surface are different from those formed within Earth.

Ask: Why do igneous rocks that form at Earth's surface have small mineral crystals, while those that form deep within Earth have large mineral crystals? *At Earth's surface, molten rock cools quickly and small crystals form. Deep within Earth, molten rock takes longer to cool and large crystals form.*

CHECK YOUR READING *Answer: An igneous rock can have both small and large mineral crystals if it started cooling slowly within Earth and then erupted at the surface, where it finished cooling quickly.*

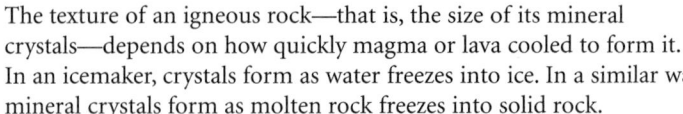 **VISUALIZATION** CLASSZONE.COM

Explore an animation showing how crystals form as molten rock cools.

B

Textures of Igneous Rocks

The texture of an igneous rock—that is, the size of its mineral crystals—depends on how quickly magma or lava cooled to form it. In an icemaker, crystals form as water freezes into ice. In a similar way, mineral crystals form as molten rock freezes into solid rock.

The magma that forms intrusive igneous rocks stays below the surface of Earth. Large crystals can form in intrusive rocks because

• the interior of Earth is very hot
• the high temperatures allow magma to cool slowly
• slow cooling allows time for large mineral crystals to form

The lava that forms extrusive igneous rocks reaches Earth's surface. Very small crystals form in extrusive rocks because

• the surface of Earth is cooler than Earth's interior
• the lower temperatures cause the lava to cool quickly
• there is no time for large mineral crystals to form

Some igneous rocks contain crystals of very different sizes. These rocks formed from magma that started cooling within Earth and then erupted onto the surface. The large crystals grew as the magma cooled slowly. The small crystals grew as the lava cooled quickly.

 **CHECK YOUR READING** How does an igneous rock that has both large and small mineral crystals form?

Crystal Size and Cooling Time

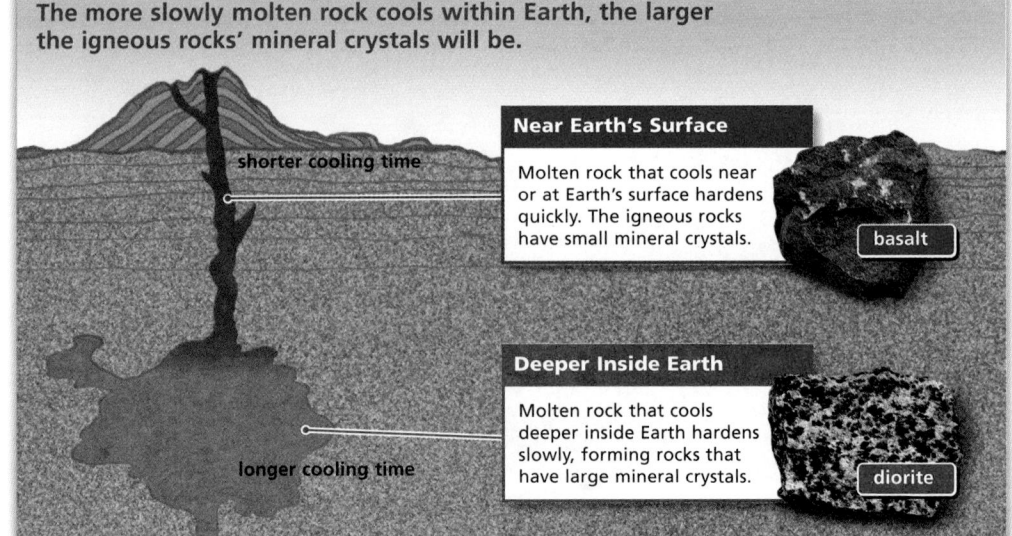

The more slowly molten rock cools within Earth, the larger the igneous rocks' mineral crystals will be.

shorter cooling time

Near Earth's Surface
Molten rock that cools near or at Earth's surface hardens quickly. The igneous rocks have small mineral crystals.

basalt

longer cooling time

Deeper Inside Earth
Molten rock that cools deeper inside Earth hardens slowly, forming rocks that have large mineral crystals.

diorite

 **A** 84 Unit: Earth's Surface

DIFFERENTIATE INSTRUCTION

 **More Reading Support**

B How do the high temperatures within Earth affect the cooling of magma? *The high temperatures allow magma to cool slowly.*

Advanced Tell students that most mineral crystals have imperfect shapes. Ask them to infer why. *Sample answer: Most crystals do not grow in open spaces where their shapes can form perfectly. Instead, most crystals grow in small, crowded places, where they are pushed against one another.*

R Challenge and Extension, p. 163

INVESTIGATE Crystal Size

How does cooling time affect crystal size?

PROCEDURE

1. Look at the Mineral Crystal Diagrams datasheet.

2. Describe your observations of the crystals in each of the igneous-rock diagrams A–C on the lines provided.

3. Describe what is shown in each of graphs 1–3 on the lines provided.

4. Match each igneous-rock diagram with its corresponding graph.

5. On the back of the paper, explain why you matched each crystal diagram with a particular graph.

WHAT DO YOU THINK?

- Which diagram shows an intrusive igneous rock, such as gabbro?
- Where do you think the rock shown in diagram B formed? Explain your answer.

CHALLENGE Write a hypothesis to explain why the rock shown in diagram C might be found at a shallow depth in Earth's crust.

SKILL FOCUS
Analyzing

MATERIALS
Mineral Crystal Diagrams datasheet

TIME
20 Minutes

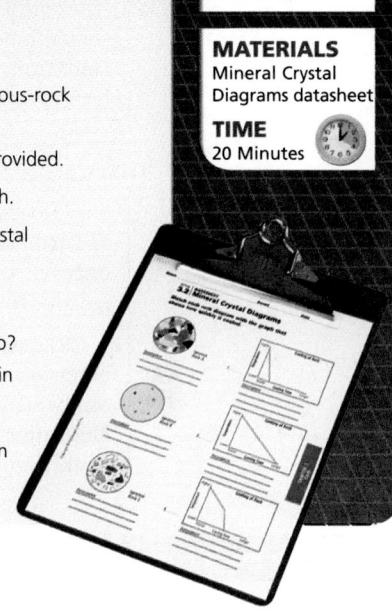

Composition of Igneous Rocks

Texture is not enough to identify an igneous rock. Think about substances that have similar textures, such as sugar and salt. A spoonful of sugar and a spoonful of salt both consist of small white grains. However, sugar and salt are different materials—that is, they have different compositions. Likewise, different igneous rocks might have similar textures. To identify them, you must also consider their compositions.

Most igneous rocks are mainly made up of silicate minerals, which you read about in the last chapter. The silicate mineral group is the most common group in Earth's crust. Silicate minerals contain varying amounts of silica, a compound of silicon and oxygen. After identifying the texture of an igneous rock, geologists classify the rock on the basis of how rich it is in silica.

Special equipment must be used to determine a rock's exact composition, but you can estimate the level of silica in an igneous rock by looking at its color. Igneous rocks with high levels of silica, such as granite and rhyolite, are typically light in color. Those with low levels of silica, such as gabbro and basalt, are dark in color.

 **CHECK YOUR READING** Would you expect a light gray igneous rock to be rich or poor in silica? Why?

Chapter 3: **Rocks** 85 **A**

DIFFERENTIATE INSTRUCTION

? More Reading Support

C What is silica? *a compound made up of silicon and oxygen*

Below Level Draw the following chart on the board to summarize what students have learned about common igneous rocks. Ask students to copy the chart in their Science Notebooks.

Crystal Size	Silica Content	
	High	**Low**
Large	Granite	Gabbro
Small	Rhyolite	Basalt

INVESTIGATE Crystal Size

PURPOSE To analyze how cooling time affects crystal size

TIP *20 min.* Demonstrate for students how the crystals shown in one of the crystal diagrams are similar to crystals in a classroom sample of igneous rock.

INCLUSION For students with vision impairments, make tactile versions of the crystal diagrams. Use pebbles for the diagram of large crystals, sand for the diagram of tiny crystals, and a few pebbles embedded in sand for the diagram of mixed-size crystals.

WHAT DO YOU THINK? *The diagram of large crystals represents an intrusive rock (diagram A). Diagram B represents a rock that formed at Earth's surface because its tiny crystals show that it cooled very quickly.*

CHALLENGE *Diagram C represents a rock that cooled at different depths. Large crystals formed as magma started cooling slowly at a deeper depth; then tiny crystals formed when the magma rose close to the surface and finished cooling quickly.*

R
- Mineral Crystals Diagrams, p. 164
- Datasheet, Crystal Size, p. 165

Technology Resources

Customize this student lab as needed or look for an alternative. Print rubrics to assess student lab reports.

 Lab Generator CD-ROM

Ongoing Assessment

Recognize why silica content is important in classifying igneous rocks.

Ask: How does silica content affect an igneous rock? *The lower the level of silica in an igneous rock, the darker in color the rock will tend to be.*

CHECK YOUR READING *Answer: A light gray igneous rock would most likely be rich in silica because such rocks tend to be lighter in color.*

Chapter 3 **85** **A**

Address Misconceptions

IDENTIFY Ask: About how old is the oldest rock on Earth? If students give an answer in the hundreds or thousands, they may hold the misconception that Earth is much younger than it really is.

CORRECT Tell students "Ship Rock actually formed . . . below the surface of Earth about 30 million years ago," (p. 86). Write the following numbers on the board, lining up the zeroes, and read each one aloud.

3,000
30,000
300,000
3,000,000
30,000,000

Compare the numbers by reading each number aloud.

REASSESS Ask: How can you tell that 30 million is a much larger number than 3000? *30 million has many more zeroes than 3000 does.* Would you say that rocks such as Ship Rock are many thousands of years old or many millions of years old? *many millions*

Technology Resources

Visit **ClassZone.com** for background on common student misconceptions.

 MISCONCEPTION DATABASE

Teach from Visuals

To help students interpret the visual of an intrusive rock formation and the way it formed, ask: Why did this intrusive rock formation remain while the surrounding rock was worn away? *The intrusive rock was harder than the rock that once surrounded it.*

Develop Critical Thinking

APPLY Help students apply what they have learned by asking what happens to the surrounding weaker rock that wears away from an igneous rock formation. *Answer: It forms sediment.*

Ongoing Assessment

READING ViSUALS *Answer: the mushroom-shaped intrusive rock formation near the surface on the right*

 RESOURCE CENTER CLASSZONE.COM
Find out more about igneous rocks.

Igneous rocks make long-lasting landforms.

In northwestern New Mexico, a great peak rises out of a flat, barren desert. The Navajo call the peak Tsé Bit'a'í (tseh biht-ah-ih), meaning "rock with wings." In English, it's called Ship Rock, because it looks something like a sailing ship. Ship Rock is an example of the kinds of landforms that are made of igneous rocks. A landform is a natural feature on Earth's land surface.

Intrusive Rock Formations

Ship Rock actually formed about one kilometer below the surface of Earth 30 million years ago. It is all that remains of magma that once fed a volcano. The magma cooled slowly and formed intrusive igneous rock.

? D As magma pushes up toward Earth's surface, it makes channels and other formations underground. Formations of intrusive igneous rock can be harder and more lasting than other types of rock. Notice in the illustration below how igneous rock has been left at the surface as other, weaker types of rock have been worn away.

Intrusive Rock Formation

Wind and water wear away surrounding, weaker rock to reveal intrusive rock formations, such as Ship Rock.

READING ViSUALS Where in the bottom illustration is more intrusive rock likely to be uncovered next?

Ancient Land Surface

Magma that remains below the surface will later become intrusive igneous rock.

Present-Day Land Surface

Surface rock has worn away to reveal some of the intrusive rock.

DIFFERENTIATE INSTRUCTION

? More Reading Support

D How are formations of intrusive igneous rock different from other types of rock? *They can be harder and more lasting than other types of rock.*

Advanced Tell students that there are many other impressive igneous landforms in the western United States besides Ship Rock. Have interested students research the carving of Crazy Horse Mountain in the Black Hills of South Dakota and write a short report on their findings. Reports should include the fact that the mountain started millions of years ago as magma, cooled into granite, and then slowly pushed above Earth's crust. Have students infer why the Crazy Horse carving, begun in 1948, still has decades of work to go before it is finished.

R Challenge Reading, pp. 189–190

Extrusive Rock Formations

When magma makes its way to Earth's surface through a volcano or crack, the lava may erupt in different ways. Some lava can build huge plateaus when it erupts from long cracks in Earth's surface. Lava that is low in silica, such as basalt lava, flows easily and spreads out in thin sheets over great distances. The Columbia Plateau in Oregon and Washington is made of basalt. When lava that is low in silica erupts at a single point, it can build up a huge volcano with gently sloping sides. The Hawaiian Islands are a chain of volcanoes that are built of basalt lava. The volcanoes started erupting on the sea floor and over a very long time grew tall enough to rise above the surface of the ocean as islands.

 READING TiP
Notice what properties of basalt lava allow it to build large plateaus.

Lava that contains a greater amount of silica does not flow easily. Silica-rich lava tends to build cone-shaped volcanoes with steep sides. Volcanoes fed by silica-rich magma tend to erupt explosively. Because the magma is thick and sticky, pressure can build up in volcanoes until they explode. An example is Mount St. Helens in the state of Washington. Its 1980 eruption reduced the volcano's height by 400 meters (about 1300 ft). Lava flows are adding new extrusive igneous rock. At the current rate it will take more than 200 years for the volcano to reach its pre-1980 height.

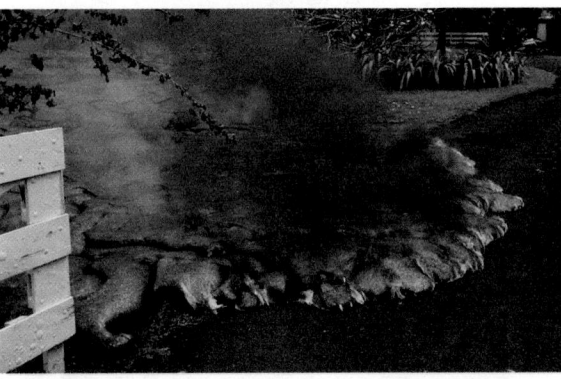

Basalt lava can flow long distances. Here it is spreading over a road in Hawaii.

 **CHECK YOUR READING** Why does silica-rich lava tend to build steep volcanoes instead of spreading out?

3.2 Review

KEY CONCEPTS

1. What is the main difference between intrusive and extrusive igneous rocks?
2. What are the two major properties used to classify igneous rocks?
3. Why can intrusive igneous rocks be left behind when surrounding rocks are worn away?

CRITICAL THINKING

4. **Draw Conclusions** If granite within Earth melts and then erupts at the surface, what type of extrusive rock is likely to form?
5. **Analyze** Would you expect extrusive rocks produced by an explosive volcano to be light or dark in color? Why?

▲ CHALLENGE

6. **Synthesize** Why are the names *intrusive* and *extrusive* appropriate for the two types of igneous rocks?

ANSWERS

1. *Intrusive rocks cool slowly below Earth's surface, while extrusive rocks cool quickly on Earth's surface.*

2. *crystal size and silica content*

3. *Igneous rocks can be harder than other rock types and may not wear away as quickly.*

4. *rhyolite (also pumice and obsidian)*

5. *light in color because an explosive volcano is likely to have silica-rich lava*

6. *Intrusive means "to push in." Magma pushes into earlier rocks and cools to form intrusive igneous rocks.*

Extrusive means "to push out." Lava is pushed out onto Earth's surface, where it cools to form extrusive igneous rocks.

Ongoing Assessment

CHECK YOUR READING *Answer: Steep volcanoes are built by silica-rich lava because it does not flow easily.*

Reinforce (the **BIG** idea)

Have students relate the section to the Big Idea.

Ⓡ Reinforcing Key Concepts, p. 166

3.2 ASSESS & RETEACH

Assess

Ⓐ Section 3.2 Quiz, p. 43

Reteach

Write the following headings and subheadings on the board. Have students use their textbooks to fill in the key ideas for each subheading. Call on student volunteers to write the information on the board.

Intrusive Igneous Rock

What it forms from:

Where it forms:

Size of its mineral crystals:

Kinds of rock formations:

Extrusive Igneous Rock

What it forms from:

Where it forms:

Size of its mineral crystals:

Kinds of rock formations:

Technology Resources

Have students visit **ClassZone.com** for reteaching of Key Concepts.

 CONTENT REVIEW

 CONTENT REVIEW CD-ROM

Set Learning Goal

To estimate the area covered by a lava flow by using a grid

Present the Science

Explain that lava flows can cover large areas, but these areas have very irregular boundaries. Using a grid is a practical way to estimate area when boundaries are irregular.

Develop Estimation Skills

Advise students to count and write down the number of completely covered grid squares first. To make it easier to add the fractions, advise students to estimate all partially filled-in grids in fourths or another common denominator. Remind students that when they add fractions with the same denominator, they only need to add the numerators.

DIFFERENTIATION TIP Students with visual impairments may have difficulty seeing and counting the grid squares. Pair such students with a partner for this activity. If students have trouble keeping count, photocopy and distribute the grid so students can check off squares as they are counted.

Close

Ask: In what other types of situations might earth scientists use a grid to estimate the area affected? *floods, avalanches, earthquakes, fires, other natural disasters*

- Math Support, p. 194
- Math Practice, p. 195

Technology Resources

Students can visit **ClassZone.com** for practice estimating area.

 MATH TUTORIAL

MATH in SCIENCE

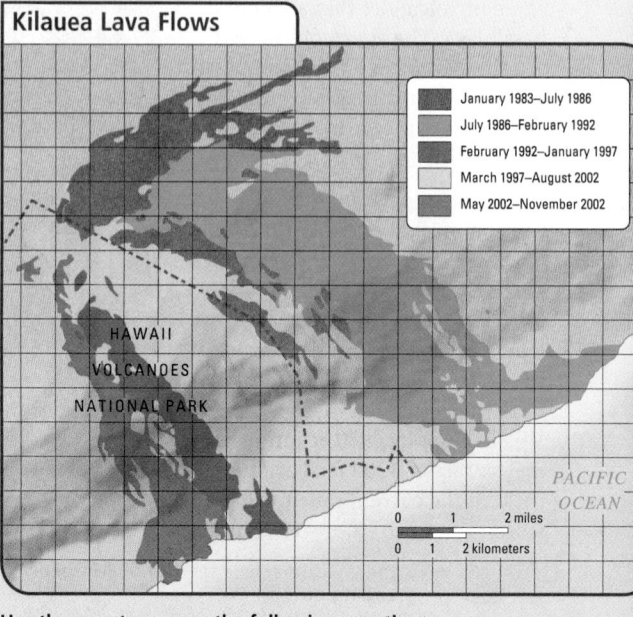

MATH TUTORIAL
CLASSZONE.COM
Click on Math Tutorial for more help with estimating areas.

Resurfacing Earth

Lava flows from volcanoes are common on the island of Hawaii. The map below shows lava flows from the Kilauea volcano. The flow shown in blue destroyed more than 180 homes and covered the region in a layer of lava up to 25 meters thick.

Kilauea Lava Flows

■	January 1983–July 1986
■	July 1986–February 1992
■	February 1992–January 1997
■	March 1997–August 2002
■	May 2002–November 2002

HAWAII
VOLCANOES
NATIONAL PARK

PACIFIC OCEAN

0   1   2 miles
0   1   2 kilometers

Use the map to answer the following questions.

1. How many squares does the lava flow shown in yellow cover? First, count the complete grid squares covered by the lava flow shown in yellow. Next, think of partially covered grid squares as fractions, and add them together to get whole squares. Finally, add the number of these squares to the number of complete squares.

2. What is the area of the flow in square kilometers?

3. Use the same method to estimate the areas of the flows shown in purple and blue.

CHALLENGE To estimate the area covered by all the lava flows shown on the map, would it be better to estimate the area of each flow separately and then add the results together? Or would it be better to estimate the total area of the flows in one step? Explain your reasoning.

A 88 Unit: Earth's Surface

ANSWERS

1. about 39

2. 39 km²

3. purple: 8 squares, 8 km²; blue: 37 squares, 37 km²

CHALLENGE *It would be better to estimate all flows together. More grid squares could be counted as completely full, and fewer partially filled squares would need to be added together.*

KEY CONCEPT

3.3 Sedimentary rocks form from earlier rocks.

◀ **BEFORE, you learned**

- Most rocks are made of minerals
- Some ocean organisms build their shells from minerals
- Dissolved minerals re-form as water evaporates

▶ **NOW, you will learn**

- What kinds of materials make up sedimentary rocks
- What the processes that form sedimentary rocks are
- How sedimentary rocks record past conditions

VOCABULARY

sediment p. 89

EXPLORE Particle Layers

What happens as rock particles settle in water?

PROCEDURE

① Pour 2 cups of water into the jar.

② Add the gravel and sand to the water.

③ Shake the jar for a few seconds and then set it down on a counter. Observe and record what happens to the materials in the water.

MATERIALS
- jar
- measuring cup
- water
- 1/3 cup gravel
- 1/3 cup sand

WHAT DO YOU THINK?
- What determines how the materials settle to the bottom of the jar?
- In a lake, how would a mixture of different-sized rock particles settle to the bottom?

Some rocks form from rock particles.

If the sand grains on a beach become naturally cemented together, they form a sedimentary rock called sandstone. Most sedimentary rock forms as sandstone does—from loose material that gets pressed together or cemented into rock. Sedimentary rock forms in other ways, too.

Sedimentary rock takes its name from the word *sediment*, which means "something that settles." **Sediments** are materials that settle out of water or air. In addition to loose pieces of rocks and minerals, pieces of plant and animal remains can also make up sediments. Sedimentary rocks develop from layers of sediments that build up on land or underwater.

VOCABULARY
Add a magnet word diagram for *sediment* to your notebook.

 **CHECK YOUR READING** What types of material can make up sediments?

Chapter 3: Rocks **89** **A**

RESOURCES FOR DIFFERENTIATED INSTRUCTION

Below Level
UNIT RESOURCE BOOK
- Reading Study Guide A, pp. 169–170
- Decoding Support, p. 193

 **AUDIO CDS**

Advanced
UNIT RESOURCE BOOK
Challenge and Extension, p. 175

English Learners
UNIT RESOURCE BOOK
Spanish Reading Study Guide, pp. 173–174

 **AUDIO CDS**

- Audio Readings in Spanish
- Audio Readings (English)

Teach from Visuals

To help students interpret the visual showing sediment particles, ask:

- As water currents slow down, what size of particles settles first? *the largest, gravel*

- What size of particles settles next? *the next smallest, sand, and then silt and clay*

- What does the type of sedimentary rock that forms depend on? *the size of rock particles from which it forms*

Integrate the Sciences

The faster a current flows, the larger the particles it can carry. Gravity works against the ability of water to carry particles. A basic law of physics states that all particles, no matter what their size, fall to Earth at the same speed in a vacuum. But in a fluid such as water, larger particles settle faster than smaller ones. Density is also a factor; however, the most common minerals in sediments have similar densities.

Ongoing Assessment

Identify the types of materials that make up sedimentary rocks.

Ask: How does most sedimentary rock develop? *Sedimentary rock develops as layers of sediments (rock particles, minerals, and plant and animal remains) build up on land or underwater.*

READING VISUALS *Answer: in the middle, because silt and clay particles can settle only from very slow-moving water*

Forming and Transporting Rock Particles

A sandy ocean beach, a gravel bar in a river, and a muddy lake bottom all consist mainly of rock particles. These particles were broken away from rocks by the action of water or wind or a combination of both. Such particles may vary in size from boulders to sand to tiny bits of clay.

 Just as water washes mud off your hands as it runs over them, rainwater washes away rock particles as it flows downhill. The water carries these rock particles to streams and rivers, which eventually empty into lakes or oceans. Strong winds also pick up sand and rock dust and carry them to distant places.

As winds or water currents slow down, rock particles settle on the land or at the bottom of rivers, lakes, and oceans. The sediments form layers as larger particles settle first, followed by smaller ones.

RESOURCE CENTER
CLASSZONE.COM
Find information on sedimentary rocks.

Forming Loose Sediments into Rocks

If you have ever watched workers building a road, you know that they first put down layers of gravel and other materials. Then they press the layers together, using a huge roller. In a similar way, layers of sediments

Sorting Sediments by Size

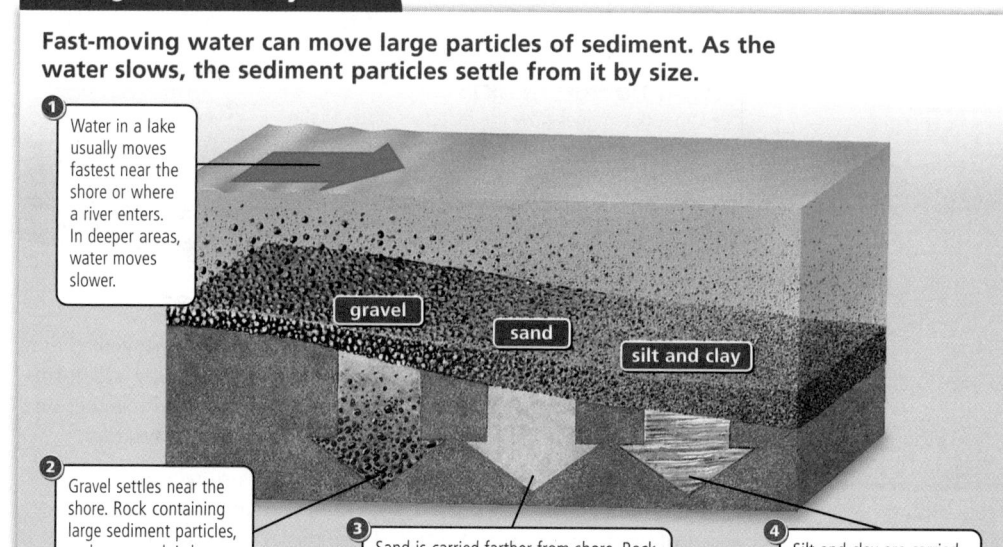

Fast-moving water can move large particles of sediment. As the water slows, the sediment particles settle from it by size.

1. Water in a lake usually moves fastest near the shore or where a river enters. In deeper areas, water moves slower.

2. Gravel settles near the shore. Rock containing large sediment particles, such as gravel, is known as conglomerate.

3. Sand is carried farther from shore. Rock that forms from sand-sized particles is known as sandstone.

4. Silt and clay are carried into deep water. Rock that forms from silt- and clay-sized particles is known as shale.

gravel — sand — silt and clay

READING VISUALS Is shale more likely to form near the shore or near the middle of a big lake or ocean?

DIFFERENTIATE INSTRUCTION

? More Reading Support

A How do rock particles get into streams and rivers? *Rainwater washes away rock particles as it flows downhill, and it carries these particles into streams and rivers.*

English Learners Point out the introductory clauses beginning with *If* on pp. 90–91 and p. 93. Tell English learners that these clauses require them to recall something or imagine a hypothetical situation. Point out that while the clauses beginning with *If* are fragments, the main clauses that follow contain the subject and are complete sentences. English learners might also lack prior knowledge about the white cliffs of Dover, mentioned on p. 92.

composed of rock particles may get pressed together to form rock. One layer gets buried by another, and then another. The overlying layers apply pressure to, or press down on, the sediments underneath.

Small particles of sediment, such as silt and clay, may be formed into rock by pressure alone. In other sedimentary rocks the particles are held together by minerals that have crystallized between them, acting as cement. Over a long time, these processes transform loose sediments into sedimentary rocks.

CHECK YOUR READING What are two processes that can change sediments into rocks?

Some rocks form from plants or shells.

Processes similar to the ones that produce sedimentary rocks from rock particles also produce rocks from shells or plant remains. These remains are fossils. A fossil is the remains or trace of an organism from long ago.

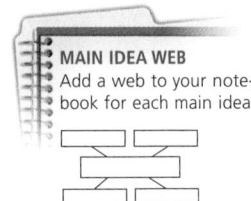

MAIN IDEA WEB
Add a web to your notebook for each main idea.

Coal

If you look at a piece of coal through a magnifying glass, you may be able to make out the shapes of bits of wood or leaves. That is because coal is made up of remains of plants—dead wood, bark, leaves, stems, and roots. Coal is an unusual sedimentary rock because it forms from plants instead of earlier rocks.

The coal people use today started forming millions of years ago in swamps. As plants died, their remains fell upon the remains of earlier plants. Then layers of other sediments buried the layers of plant remains. The weight of the sediments above pressed the plant material into coal.

?
B

The dark layer in these rocks is coal.

Here, you can see fossils of ancient plants preserved in coal.

Integrate the Sciences

Both geologists and biologists have used fossils to learn about Earth's history. The British naturalist Charles Darwin based his theory of evolution partly on his study of fossil organisms and his understanding of Earth's geologic history. He also observed animals and plants in their native environments.

Teach from Visuals

To help students interpret the photographs of coal:

- Ask: What kind of plant appears to be preserved in the sample of coal? *fern*

- Tell students this coal formed in an ancient swamp. Ask: Does the land in the photograph appear to be a swamp? *no*

- Ask: What does this tell you about the area? *The environment has changed over time.*

Ongoing Assessment

CHECK YOUR READING *Answer: Sediments can be put under pressure or cemented together by new minerals to form rock.*

DIFFERENTIATE INSTRUCTION

? **More Reading Support**

B How is a rock like coal formed? *Plant remains are buried under layers of sediment. The weight of the sediments above presses the plant material into coal.*

Below Level Have students draw a diagram of the process by which coal forms. The diagram should show layers of plant remains, with the layers becoming more and more compacted as the depth increases.

Teach from Visuals

To help students interpret the photographs showing limestone formation, ask:

• In the three photographs, what overall change do you see in the rock? *The shells become harder to see.*

• What caused this change? *The minerals in the shells dissolved and re-formed to produce limestone.*

• How does the limestone in the coral reef pictured at the bottom of the page differ from the limestone in the top photographs? *The limestone in the coral reefs is added directly to the reef. It is not loose sediment first.*

Integrate the Sciences

Limestone is a biochemical sedimentary rock. Many marine organisms take in dissolved calcium carbonate from seawater and then secrete it to form their shells. Coral organisms, called polyps, do the same thing. Most coral polyps live in colonies, and the ones that form coral reefs attach themselves to one another. Coral reefs contain the skeletons of millions of coral polyps.

EXPLORE (the **BIG** idea)

Revisit "How Can Rocks Disappear?" on p. 73. Have students relate their results to the formation of limestone.

Limestone

Limestone is made up of carbonate minerals, such as calcite. The shells and skeletons of ocean organisms are formed of these minerals. When the organisms die, the shells and skeletons settle on the ocean floor as layers of sediment. Over time, the layers become buried, pressed together, and cemented to form limestone. The photographs below show how loose shells can become limestone.

These shells were made by ocean organisms.

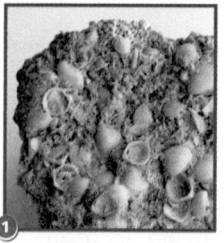

① The shells get cemented together into limestone as some of their minerals dissolve and re-form.

② Individual shells become harder to see as minerals in the limestone continue to dissolve and re-form.

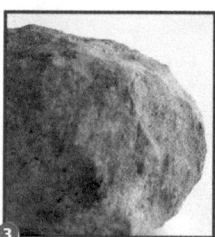

③ Over time, what was once loose sediment becomes limestone with no recognizable shells.

READING TiP

Notice that limestone made up of cemented shells and the limestone in coral reefs were both formed by ocean organisms.

?
C

The famous white cliffs of Dover, England, consist of a type of limestone called chalk. The limestone began to form millions of years ago, when the land was under the ocean. The rock developed from shells of tiny organisms that float in the ocean. Most limestone comes from shells and skeletons of ocean organisms. The materials the organisms use to build their shells and skeletons are present in ocean water because they were dissolved from earlier rocks. Like almost all sedimentary rock, limestone forms from material that came from older rocks.

Coral reefs also consist of limestone that comes from organisms. However, in the case of reefs, the limestone is produced directly as coral organisms build their skeletons one on top of another. In the formation of coral, the rock does not go through a loose-sediment stage.

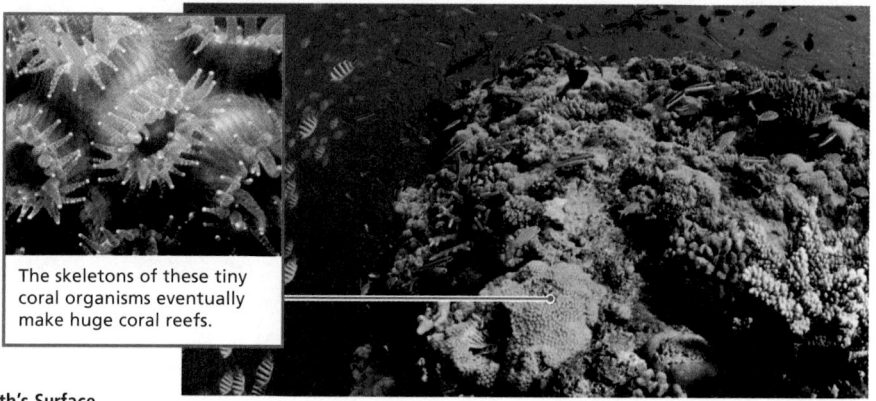

The skeletons of these tiny coral organisms eventually make huge coral reefs.

A 92 Unit: **Earth's Surface**

DIFFERENTIATE INSTRUCTION

 More Reading Support

C Where does most limestone come from? *the shells and skeletons of ocean organisms*

Advanced Have students explain how the formation of limestone demonstrates the rock cycle. *Minerals from existing rocks dissolve in rainwater and are carried by rivers to the oceans. Ocean organisms use dissolved carbonate minerals to form their shells. When the organisms die, their shells build up on the ocean floor and form layers of sediment. The layers get buried and then pressed and cemented together to form limestone.*

R Challenge and Extension, p. 175

Some rocks form when dissolved minerals re-form from water.

If you have grown crystals in a container, you know that some substances can dissolve in water and then re-form as the water evaporates. The same process happens in nature. Some sedimentary rocks are made up of minerals that crystallized as water dried up.

The water in oceans, lakes, rivers, and streams contains minerals that came from rocks. Some of these minerals are in solid form. As rainwater washes over rocks, it picks up pieces of minerals and rock particles and carries them into streams and rivers, where many of them settle to the bottom. However, some of the minerals dissolve in the water and are carried along with it.

Water often flows through cracks in rock that is near Earth's surface. As water moves through limestone, some of the rock dissolves. A large open space, or cave, can be left in the rock. As the water flows and drips through the cave, some of it evaporates. The new limestone that forms can take many odd and beautiful shapes.

Sometimes minerals crystallize along the edges of lakes and oceans where the climate is dry and a lot of water evaporates quickly. Over time, the minerals build up and form layers of sedimentary rock. Rock salt and gypsum form in this way. Under the city of Detroit, for example, is a large bed of rock salt that developed when part of an ancient ocean dried up.

Water is shaping this limestone cavern. Water dissolves and transports minerals, then leaves the minerals behind as it evaporates.

CHECK YOUR READING How are the origins of rock salt and some limestone similar?

These limestone towers in Mono Lake, California, formed underwater. They are now above the surface because the lake level has dropped.

Chapter 3: Rocks 93 **A**

DIFFERENTIATE INSTRUCTION

? More Reading Support

D Where do the minerals dissolved in water come from? *from rainwater washing over rocks*

Alternative Assessment Have students draw and label diagrams showing the three ways sedimentary rock is formed: rock particles that build up and get pressed together, shells or plant remains that build up and get pressed together, dissolved minerals that re-form from water.

Teach from Visuals

To help students interpret the photographs of limestone formations, ask:

- How do the stalactites pictured in the top right photograph form? *Water that drips from the roof of a cave leaves behind minerals to form stalactites.*

- What do the towers in the photograph at the bottom of the page have in common with these stalactites? *They both consist of limestone that had been dissolved in water.*

Teach Difficult Concepts

Students may not understand how the limestone towers in Mono Lake formed. Streams from the Eastern Sierras flow into Mono Lake, carrying salts and dissolved minerals. As a result, the lake water contains large amounts of carbonates. The lake is also fed by underground springs that carry calcium. In the lake, the calcium combines with carbonate, and the compound precipitates out as limestone. Over a long period of time, the limestone builds up into underwater towers around the mouths of the springs.

Real World Example

The deposits that form on a water faucet are an everyday example of minerals precipitating out of water.

Ongoing Assessment

Describe the three groups of sedimentary rocks.

Ask: How do the three groups of sedimentary rocks form? *from rock particles that build up in layers and get pressed together; from shells or plant remains that build up in layers and get pressed together; from dissolved minerals that re-form from water*

CHECK YOUR READING *Answer: Both can dissolve in water, be carried to a new location, and re-form as the water evaporates.*

Chapter 3 **93** **A**

INVESTIGATE Rock Layers

PURPOSE Make a model to show how sedimentary rocks form in layers

TIP *20 min.* Divide the class into small groups for this activity.

WHAT DO YOU THINK? *Layers of sediment are deposited at different times and contain sediments of different sizes. Layers of sediment made up mainly of pebbles or gravel would be deposited when water is moving very quickly, such as during a flood or where a mountain river spreads out and water slows down. The middle layer of sand-size sediment would be deposited when water has slowed down but is still moving fairly quickly. The plaster of Paris is similar to minerals that grow between the particles of sediment and cement them together.*

CHALLENGE *A model of how limestone forms could be made in a similar way, using shells in place of sand or pebbles.*

 Datasheet, Rock Layers, p. 176

Technology Resources

Customize this student lab as needed or look for an alternative. Print rubrics to assess student lab reports.

 Lab Generator CD-ROM

Metacognitive Strategy

Ask students to write a few sentences at the end of their lab reports describing how making this model helped them understand the process of sedimentary rock formation.

Teaching with Technology

If you have access to a video camera, you might tape groups of students showing the models they created and explaining the answers to the Investigate questions. You could show the videotape at an open house or play it during the wait time at parent conferences.

INVESTIGATE Rock Layers

How do sedimentary rocks form in layers?

PROCEDURE

1. Prepare the plaster of Paris by mixing it with the water.

2. Mix 2 tablespoons of the gravel with 2 tablespoons of the plaster of Paris and pour the mixture into the paper cup.

3. Mix the sand with 2 tablespoons of the plaster of Paris and the food coloring. Add the mixture to the paper cup, on top of the gravel mixture.

4. Mix the rest of the gravel with the rest of the plaster of Paris. Add the mixture to the paper cup, on top of the sand mixture.

5. After the mixtures harden for about 5 minutes, tear apart the paper cup and observe the layers.

MATERIALS
- 1 paper cup
- 3 mixing cups
- 6 tbs plaster of Paris
- 3 tbs water
- 4 tbs gravel
- 2 tbs sand
- 3 drops food coloring

TIME
20 minutes

WHAT DO YOU THINK?

- How is the procedure you used to make your model similar to the way sedimentary rock forms?

- Describe how similar layers of real rock could form.

CHALLENGE How would you create a model to show the formation of fossil-rich limestone?

Sedimentary rocks show the action of wind and water.

READING TiP

Notice that sedimentary rocks are laid down in layers. As conditions in an area change, so do the characteristics of the layers.

Sedimentary rocks are laid down in layers, with the oldest layers on the bottom. A geologist studying layers of sedimentary rocks can tell something about what conditions were like in the past. For instance, fossils of fish or shells in a layer of rock show that the area was covered by a lake or an ocean long ago.

Fossils are not the only way to tell something about what past conditions were like. The sediments themselves contain a great deal of information. For example, a layer of sedimentary rock may contain sediment particles of different sizes. The largest particles are at the very bottom of the layer. Particles higher in the layer become increasingly smaller. A layer like this shows that the water carrying the sediment was slowing down. The largest particles dropped out when the water was moving quickly. Then smaller and smaller particles dropped out.

DIFFERENTIATE INSTRUCTION

 More Reading Support

E What do fossils of fish in a layer of rock indicate? *that the area was covered by a lake or ocean long ago*

Below Level After completing the Investigate in roughly 20 minutes, some students may think that actual sedimentary rock layers are also formed over short time periods. Stress that the layers of rock are formed over thousands to millions of years and continue to change.

Crossbeds

The tilted layers in these sandstone rocks are called crossbeds. The layers were once moving sand dunes.

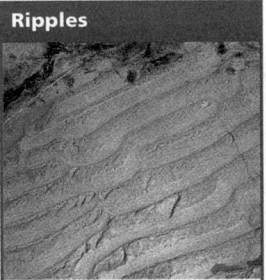

Ripples

The surface of this sandstone preserves ancient sand ripples.

Mud Cracks

As wet silt and clay dry out, cracks develop on the surface of the sediment.

as the water slowed. This type of layer is often created by a flood, when a large amount of water is at first moving quickly.

Sedimentary rocks can give information about the directions in which long-ago wind or water currents were traveling when sediments settled from them. Sand can be laid down in tilted layers on the slopes of sand dunes or sandbars. Sand can also form ripples as water or wind moves over its surface. If the sand has been buried and cemented into sandstone, a geologist can examine it and tell the direction in which the water or wind was moving.

Some rocks made of clay or silt have cracks that developed when the mud from which they formed dried out. Mud cracks show that the rocks formed in areas where wet periods were followed by dry periods.

 **CHECK YOUR READING** What could a geologist learn by finding rocks that have ripples or mud cracks?

 **Review**

KEY CONCEPTS

1. What types of material can make up sediments?
2. Describe the three processes by which sedimentary rocks form.
3. Describe how a sedimentary rock can show how fast water was flowing when its sediments were laid down.

CRITICAL THINKING

4. **Infer** Why is coal called a fossil fuel?
5. **Analyze** How could the speed of flowing water change to lay down alternating layers of sand and mud?

⚠ CHALLENGE

6. **Synthesize** How is it possible for a single sedimentary rock to contain rock particles, animal shells, and minerals that crystallized from water?

Chapter 3: **Rocks 95** **A**

ANSWERS

1. *pieces of minerals, rocks, plant and animal remains*

2. *pieces of minerals and rocks are cemented together; shells and skeletons of ocean animals are cemented together; dissolved minerals are left behind as water evaporates*

3. *A rock made of large pieces shows that water was moving quickly.*

4. *It is made of the remains of ancient plants.*

5. *Weather patterns cause flow rates of rivers to vary. Sand settles from faster-moving water; smaller pieces of*

silt and clay that make up mud settle from slower-moving water.

6. *A rock that forms from sediment on a beach could have pieces of shells and rocky sand cemented together by minerals that crystallized from water.*

Ongoing Assessment

Explain how sedimentary rocks record past conditions.

Ask: What can geologists learn about past conditions by examining dunes, bars, and ripples? *the direction that wind or water currents were traveling and carrying sediments*

 CHECK YOUR READING *Answer: Ripples preserved in rocks show that sand was once moving along that surface. Mud cracks show that an area was once wet and then became very dry.*

Reinforce [the **BIG** idea]

Have students relate the section to the Big Idea.

R Reinforcing Key Concepts, p. 177

3.3 ASSESS & RETEACH

Assess

A Section 3.3 Quiz, p. 44

Reteach

Copy the following information on the board and use it for review.

How sedimentary rock forms

- From layers of rock particles that are pressed and cemented together
- From layers of shells or plants that pressed and cemented together
- From dissolved minerals that are left behind as water evaporates

What sedimentary rocks can tell us about past conditions

- Fossils of fish indicate an area was once covered with water.
- Layering with the largest particles first might indicate that a flood occurred.

Technology Resources

Have students visit **ClassZone.com** for reteaching of Key Concepts.

 CONTENT REVIEW

 CONTENT REVIEW CD-ROM

Chapter 3 **95** **A**

Set Learning Goals

Students will

- Explain how a rock can change into another type of rock.
- Explain how new minerals can grow in existing rocks.
- Experiment to model how pressure and temperature can change a solid.

3-Minute Warm-Up

Display Transparency 21 or copy this exercise on the board:

Match each definition to the correct term.

Definitions

1. the set of natural processes that form, change, break down, and re-form rocks **e**
2. rock that forms as heat or pressure cause older rocks to change into new types of rocks **c**
3. rock that forms when magma cools within Earth **b**

Terms

a. extrusive igneous   d. sedimentary

b. intrusive igneous   e. rock cycle

c. metamorphic

 3-Minute Warm-Up, p. T21

THINK ABOUT

PURPOSE To have students explore how a rock changes into another type of rock

DISCUSS Talk about conditions that occur under Earth's surface. *Sample answer: Students might predict that shale that is put under great pressure and high heat changes into schist while remaining solid.*

Ongoing Assessment

CHECK YOUR READING *Answer: for gemstones, in pencils, as a material for builders and artists*

3.4 Metamorphic rocks form as existing rocks change.

◀ **BEFORE, you learned**

- Igneous rocks form as molten rock cools
- Sedimentary rocks form from earlier rocks

▶ **NOW, you will learn**

- How a rock can change into another type of rock
- How new minerals can grow in existing rocks

VOCABULARY

metamorphism p. 96
recrystallization p. 97
foliation p. 100

THINK ABOUT

How does a rock change into another kind of rock?

Examine a sample of shale and a sample of schist (shihst). Shale, a sedimentary rock, can change into schist. Think about how this change could occur without the shale's melting or breaking apart. Make a prediction about what process changes shale into schist.

shale

schist

Heat and pressure change rocks.

When you cook popcorn, you use heat to increase the pressure within small, hard kernels until they explode into a fluffy snack. Cooking popcorn is just one example of the many ways in which heat and pressure can change the form of things—even things like rocks.

The process in which an existing rock is changed by heat or pressure—or both—is called **metamorphism** (MEHT-uh-MAWR-FIHZ-uhm). The original sedimentary or igneous rock is called the parent rock. The resulting rock is a metamorphic rock. Even a metamorphic rock can be a parent rock for another type of metamorphic rock.

Many of the metamorphic rocks people use were once sedimentary rocks. Limestone is the parent rock of marble, which is used by builders and artists. Shale can be the parent rock of schist, which can be a source of the gemstone garnet. Some schists are a source of the mineral graphite, which is used in pencils.

READING TiP

Rocks change into other rocks by the process of metamorphism. A similar word, *metamorphosis*, refers to what happens when a caterpillar changes into a butterfly.

 **CHECK YOUR READING**   Give an example of a way people use metamorphic rocks.

RESOURCES FOR DIFFERENTIATED INSTRUCTION

Below Level

UNIT RESOURCE BOOK

- Reading Study Guide A, pp. 180–181
- Decoding Support, p. 193

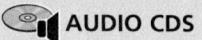 **AUDIO CDS**

Advanced

UNIT RESOURCE BOOK

Challenge and Extension, p. 186

English Learners

UNIT RESOURCE BOOK

Spanish Reading Study Guide, pp. 184–185

AUDIO CDS

- Audio Readings in Spanish
- Audio Readings (English)

During metamorphism, rocks undergo many changes. One type of change occurs when pressure causes a rock's minerals to flatten out in one direction. Other changes can occur in a rock's minerals, but the rock remains solid. Rocks do not melt when they undergo metamorphism. If the temperature gets high enough to melt the rock, the end result is an igneous rock, not a metamorphic rock.

Heat and pressure can break the bonds that join atoms in minerals. Then the atoms can join together differently as new bonds form. This process is called **recrystallization.** It has two main results. First, individual mineral crystals can grow larger as more atoms join their crystal structures. Second, atoms can combine in different ways, and new minerals can form in place of older ones. For example, shale is a sedimentary rock that is formed from silt and clay. During recrystallization, garnet can form from these materials.

How Rocks Change

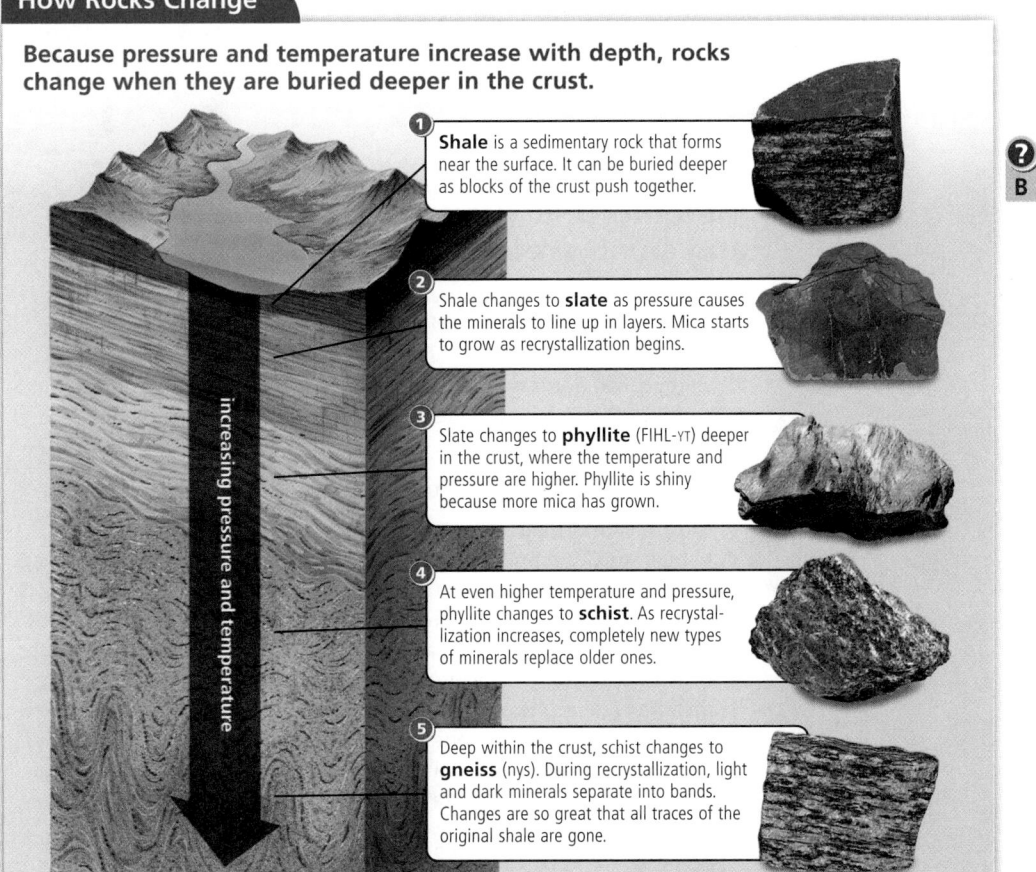

Because pressure and temperature increase with depth, rocks change when they are buried deeper in the crust.

increasing pressure and temperature

1 **Shale** is a sedimentary rock that forms near the surface. It can be buried deeper as blocks of the crust push together.

2 Shale changes to **slate** as pressure causes the minerals to line up in layers. Mica starts to grow as recrystallization begins.

3 Slate changes to **phyllite** (FIHL-YT) deeper in the crust, where the temperature and pressure are higher. Phyllite is shiny because more mica has grown.

4 At even higher temperature and pressure, phyllite changes to **schist**. As recrystallization increases, completely new types of minerals replace older ones.

5 Deep within the crust, schist changes to **gneiss** (nys). During recrystallization, light and dark minerals separate into bands. Changes are so great that all traces of the original shale are gone.

Chapter 3: Rocks 97 **A**

DIFFERENTIATE INSTRUCTION

 **More Reading Support**

A Do rocks melt during metamorphism? *No, rocks remain solid during metamorphism.*

B What is a common parent rock for slate and gneiss? *shale*

English Learners Have English learners write the words *metamorphism, recrystallization,* and *foliation* in their Science Word Dictionaries. They might also want to write abbreviated definitions for these and other terms in the chapter on index cards. Students can use these cards for quick reference.

3.4 INSTRUCT

Teach from Visuals

To help students interpret the visual about how rocks change, ask:

• What does the arrow on this illustration indicate? *that in Earth's crust, pressure and temperature increase with depth*

• How does the level of metamorphism change as the depth, temperature, and pressure increase? *The amount of metamorphism increases as depth, temperature, and pressure increase.*

Teacher Demo

As you discuss the illustration, show actual samples of shale, slate, phyllite, schist, and gneiss, if available. You might place the samples on each row of a bookshelf in the order shown to emphasize the fact that they form at different depths. Pass each rock around the room, and have students describe the differences they see among the five metamorphic rocks.

EXPLORE (the **BIG** idea)

Revisit "What Causes Rocks to Change?" on p. 73. Have students relate their results to the concepts introduced in this section.

Ongoing Assessment

Explain how a rock can change into another type of rock.

Ask: What is one type of change that can occur during metamorphism? *Pressure can cause a rock's minerals to flatten out in one direction.*

Explain how new minerals can grow in existing rocks.

Ask: How do new minerals grow in existing rocks? *Heat and pressure break the bonds that join atoms in minerals. The atoms can then join together differently as new bonds form in a process called recrystallization.*

Chapter 3 **97** **A**

PURPOSE To model how pressure and temperature can change a solid

TIP *10 min.* Demonstrate for students the correct way to use a vegetable peeler.

WHAT DO YOU THINK? *They pressed together into one mass. The shavings were pressed into less space and tended to line up in a particular direction. Warmth from students' hands made the wax easier to work with—that is, more flexible and less likely to break. These changes also happen in rocks that are put under pressure and higher temperature.*

CHALLENGE *This activity does not model recrystallization or metamorphism due only to higher temperature.*

 Datasheet, Metamorphic Changes, p. 187

Technology Resources

Customize this student lab as needed or look for an alternative. Print rubrics to assess student lab reports.

Lab Generator CD-ROM

Ongoing Assessment

Observe how pressure and temperature can change a solid.

Ask: What effect can an increase in temperature have on a solid? What effect can increased pressure have? *Increased temperature can make a solid more pliable. Increased pressure can compact a solid.*

CHECK YOUR READING *Answer: where large blocks of rock press together and push up mountains*

INVESTIGATE Metamorphic Changes

How can pressure and temperature change a solid?

PROCEDURE

1. Use a vegetable peeler to make a handful of wax shavings of three different colors. Mix the shavings.

2. Use your hands to warm the shavings, and then squeeze them into a wafer.

WHAT DO YOU THINK?

• Describe what happened to the wax shavings.

• How do the changes you observed resemble metamorphic changes in rocks?

CHALLENGE What changes that occur in metamorphic rocks were you unable to model in this experiment?

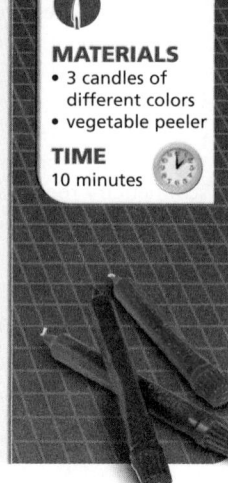

SKILL FOCUS
Modeling

MATERIALS
• 3 candles of different colors
• vegetable peeler

TIME
10 minutes

Metamorphic changes occur over large and small areas.

The types of metamorphic changes that occur depend on the types of parent rocks and the conditions of temperature and pressure. When both high temperature and high pressure are present, metamorphic changes can occur over very large areas. When only one of these conditions is present, changes tend to occur over smaller areas.

Change over Large Areas

 Most metamorphic changes occur over large areas in which both temperature and pressure are high. An example is a region where large blocks of rock are pressing together and pushing up mountain ranges. This process can affect an area hundreds of kilometers wide and tens of kilometers deep. In such an area, rocks are buried, pressed together, bent, and heated. The pressure and heat cause the rocks to undergo metamorphism. Generally, the deeper below the surface the rocks are, the greater the metamorphic changes that occur in them. For example, a sedimentary rock may change to slate near the surface but become gneiss deep inside a mountain.

CHECK YOUR READING Where can metamorphic changes occur over large areas?

DIFFERENTIATE INSTRUCTION

**More Reading Support**

C When do most metamorphic changes occur over very large areas? *when high temperature and high pressure are both present*

Below Level To help students visualize the way that rocks get pushed up into mountains, take a small stack of papers and push their ends so that they compress and billow up.

Change over Small Areas

Some metamorphic changes occur over small areas. For example, magma can push into rocks underground, or surface rock can be covered by a lava flow. The magma or lava heats the rock it is in contact with, causing recrystallization. These changes are mainly due to high temperature, not pressure. The rocks get roasted but not squeezed. The thickness of rock changed by the heat can range from less than one meter to several hundred meters, depending on the amount and temperature of the molten rock.

Small areas of metamorphic rock can also be formed by high pressure alone. At or near Earth's surface, rocks move and grind past one another during earthquakes. Rocks that grind together in this way can be subjected to high pressures that cause metamorphic changes.

RESOURCE CENTER
CLASSZONE.COM
Find information on metamorphic rocks.

Metamorphic Changes

Changes can occur over hundreds of kilometers or over just a few centimeters.

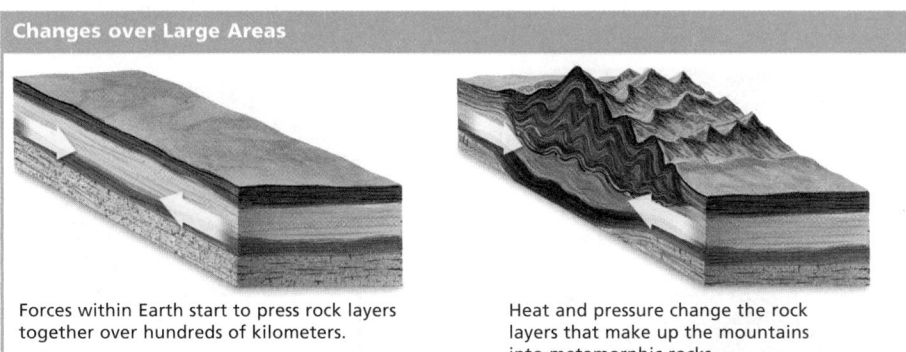

Changes over Large Areas

Forces within Earth start to press rock layers together over hundreds of kilometers.

Heat and pressure change the rock layers that make up the mountains into metamorphic rocks.

Changes over Small Areas

Magma can push into rock layers and cause changes over areas ranging from a few centimeters to tens of meters.

The magma is hot enough to bake the surrounding rocks into metamorphic rocks.

 **READING VISUALS** Compare how heat and pressure cause changes over the large and small areas shown above.

Real World Example

If students have never seen the deformation of rock that occurs in an earthquake, they may have a hard time imagining it. Tell them to think about how a car crumples up in a collision.

Teach from Visuals

To help students interpret the illustrations of metamorphic changes, ask:

- In each pair of diagrams, how does the first diagram differ from the second? *The first diagram shows an area of rock before it undergoes metamorphism. The second diagram shows the same area of rock after it has been changed.*

- What causes the metamorphic changes in rock over the large area shown in the top diagrams? *heat and pressure*

- In the bottom diagrams, how does the invading magma affect the rock around it? *It bakes the surrounding rock and causes metamorphic changes.*

Ongoing Assessment

READING VISUALS *Answer: Both heat and pressure are important in causing changes over large areas. In the example shown for changes over small areas, only heat is important.*

DIFFERENTIATE INSTRUCTION

 **More Reading Support**

D What is needed to cause metamorphic changes in rock over a small area? *either high temperature or high pressure*

Advanced The two major types of metamorphism discussed here are called regional metamorphism and contact metamorphism. Have students infer which type applies to small areas *(contact metamorphism)* and which type applies to large areas *(regional metamorphism)*, and explain their reasoning.

R Challenge and Extension, p. 186

Teach from Visuals

To help students interpret the visual about foliation, ask:

- In which type of rock are the minerals lined up like a stack of papers? *the foliated rock*

- In which type of rock are the minerals arranged like pieces of a puzzle? *the nonfoliated rock*

Teacher Demo

To demonstrate the idea of foliated and nonfoliated rocks visually, hold up a fistful of pencils in one hand and a jar of mixed nuts in the other. Ask students to identify the kind of rock represented in each of your hands. Tell students that foliation can be observed both microscopically and with the unaided eye. If available, show a few clear examples of foliation in rocks.

Ongoing Assessment

READING VISUALS *Answer: In the foliated rock the minerals are lined up in seemingly parallel bands or layers. In the nonfoliated rock there is no apparent banding or parallelism.*

Most metamorphic rocks develop bands of minerals.

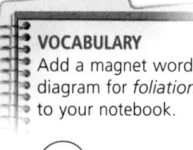

VOCABULARY
Add a magnet word diagram for *foliation* to your notebook.

Some buildings have floors covered with tiles of the metamorphic rock slate. This rock is especially useful for tiles because it displays foliation, a common property of metamorphic rocks. **Foliation** is an arrangement of minerals in flat or wavy parallel bands. Slate can be split into thin sheets along the boundaries between its flat bands of minerals.

You may be familiar with the word *foliage*. Both *foliage* and *foliation* come from the Latin word *folium*, meaning "leaf." Foliated rocks either split easily into leaflike sheets or have bands of minerals that are lined up and easy to see.

Foliated Rocks

Foliation develops when rocks are under pressure. Foliation is common in rocks produced by metamorphic changes that affect large areas. However, as you will see, a metamorphic rock that consists almost entirely of one type of mineral does not show foliation.

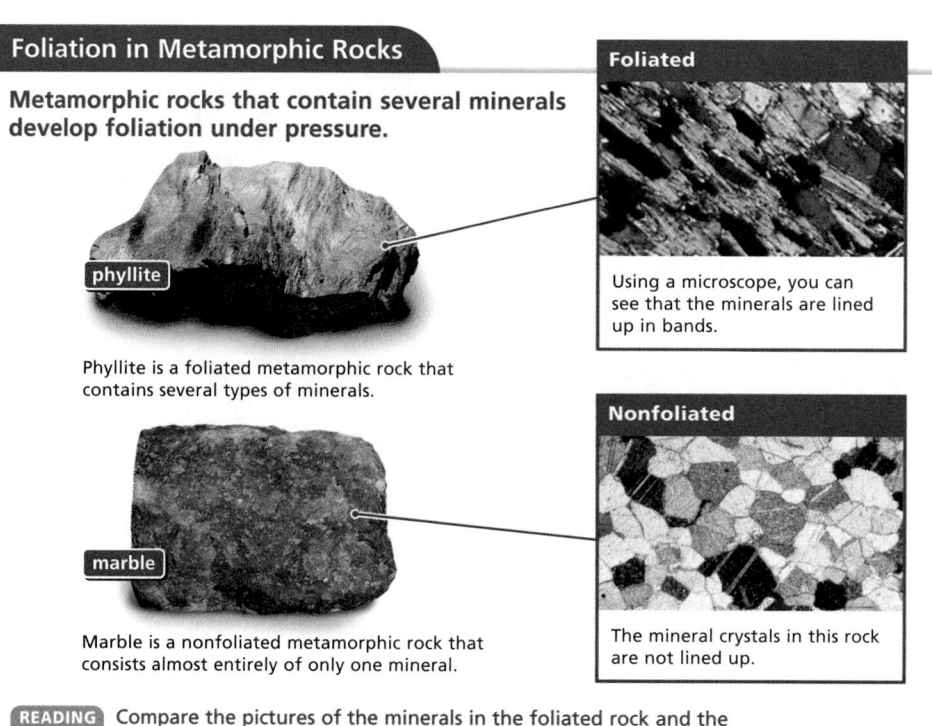

Foliation in Metamorphic Rocks

Metamorphic rocks that contain several minerals develop foliation under pressure.

phyllite

Phyllite is a foliated metamorphic rock that contains several types of minerals.

marble

Marble is a nonfoliated metamorphic rock that consists almost entirely of only one mineral.

Foliated

Using a microscope, you can see that the minerals are lined up in bands.

Nonfoliated

The mineral crystals in this rock are not lined up.

READING VISUALS Compare the pictures of the minerals in the foliated rock and the nonfoliated rock. What is different about their arrangements?

DIFFERENTIATE INSTRUCTION

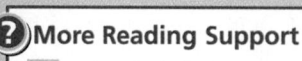 **More Reading Support**

E What is foliation? *an arrangement of minerals in flat or wavy parallel bands*

Below Level You might suggest that students remember the meaning of the terms *foliated* and *nonfoliated* by thinking:

foliated = banded

nonfoliated = nonbanded

Foliation develops when minerals flatten out or line up in bands. At low levels of metamorphism, the bands are extremely thin, as in slate. With higher pressure and temperature, the mineral mica can grow and make the rock look shiny, as is common in phyllite and schist. At even higher levels of metamorphism, the minerals in the rock tend to separate into light and dark bands, like those in gneiss.

 **CHECK YOUR READING** How do rocks change as foliation develops?

Nonfoliated Rocks

Metamorphic rocks that do not show foliation are called nonfoliated rocks. One reason a metamorphic rock may not display foliation is that it is made up mainly of one type of mineral, so that different minerals cannot separate and line up in layers. One common nonfoliated metamorphic rock is marble, which develops from limestone. Marble is used as a decorative stone. It is good for carving and sculpting. Because marble is nonfoliated, it does not split into layers as an artist is working with it. Another example of a nonfoliated rock is quartzite. It forms from sandstone that is made up almost entirely of pieces of quartz.

Another reason that a metamorphic rock may lack foliation is that it has not been subjected to high pressure. Hornfels is a metamorphic rock that can form when a rock is subjected to high temperatures. Hornfels, which often forms when magma or lava touches other rock, is nonfoliated.

 **CHECK YOUR READING** What are two reasons a metamorphic rock might not show foliation?

 **Review**

KEY CONCEPTS

1. What conditions can cause a sedimentary or igneous rock to change into a metamorphic rock?

2. How do new minerals grow within existing rocks?

3. Why do bands of minerals develop in most metamorphic rocks?

CRITICAL THINKING

4. **Draw Conclusions** Would gneiss be more likely to form at shallow depths or at great depths where mountains are being pushed up? Why?

5. **Infer** Would you expect to find foliated or nonfoliated metamorphic rocks next to a lava flow? Why?

◔ CHALLENGE

6. **Synthesize** What features of sedimentary rocks are unlikely to be found in metamorphic rocks? What features of metamorphic rocks do not occur in sedimentary rocks?

Chapter 3: Rocks **101** **A**

ANSWERS

1. increasing temperature or pressure or both

2. Heat and pressure can break bonds in minerals, and the atoms can then join in new ways to make new minerals.

3. because most rocks contain several types of minerals

4. deep below the surface; because it takes high temperature and pressure to form this rock

5. nonfoliated; because it would have been changed by

the heat of lava flows and not by high pressure

6. pieces of sediment, fossils, ripple marks, and mud cracks; flat or wavy bands of minerals, a shiny surface due to mica, and growth of new minerals from old ones

Focus

PURPOSE Students will learn how to classify rocks as igneous, sedimentary, or metamorphic.

OVERVIEW Students will use a classification key to identify six to eight rock samples as igneous, sedimentary, or metamorphic. Students will find that a key makes rock classification fairly easy.

Lab Preparation

- Copy and distribute the Rock Classification Key to each group of students. Review how to use it.

- You might increase the number of rock samples to ten, if possible. Do not use slate (too similar to shale) or limestone (can be difficult to identify without testing with hydrochloric acid).

- Prior to the investigation, have students read through the investigation and prepare their data tables. Or you may wish to copy and distribute datasheets and rubrics.

 UNIT RESOURCE BOOK, pp. 196–205

SCIENCE TOOLKIT, F15

Lab Management

- Remind students that visual properties include size of particles or mineral crystals, layering, and banding.

- If students do not understand how to use the classification key, demonstrate the process with one rock sample.

INCLUSION Encourage students with vision impairments to handle the rock samples to feel their textures.

CHAPTER INVESTIGATION

Rock Classification

OVERVIEW AND PURPOSE In this activity you will examine rock samples and refer to a rock classification key. You will classify each sample as igneous, sedimentary, or metamorphic.

▷ Procedure

1. Make a data table like the one shown on the **Science Notebook** page.

2. Get a numbered rock sample. Record its number in your data table.

3. Observe the sample as a whole. Then closely examine it with the hand lens. Record in your table all visible properties of the sample. For example, include properties such as mineral or sediment size, layering, or banding.

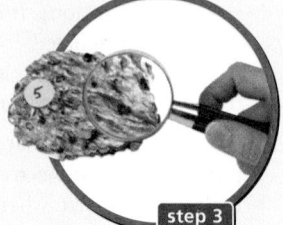

step 3

4. Look at the Rock Classification Key. Each item in the key consists of paired statements. Start with item 1 of the key. Choose the statement that best describes the rock you are examining. Look at the end of the statement and then go to the item number indicated.

MATERIALS
- magnifying glass
- 6–8 rock samples
- Rock Classification Key

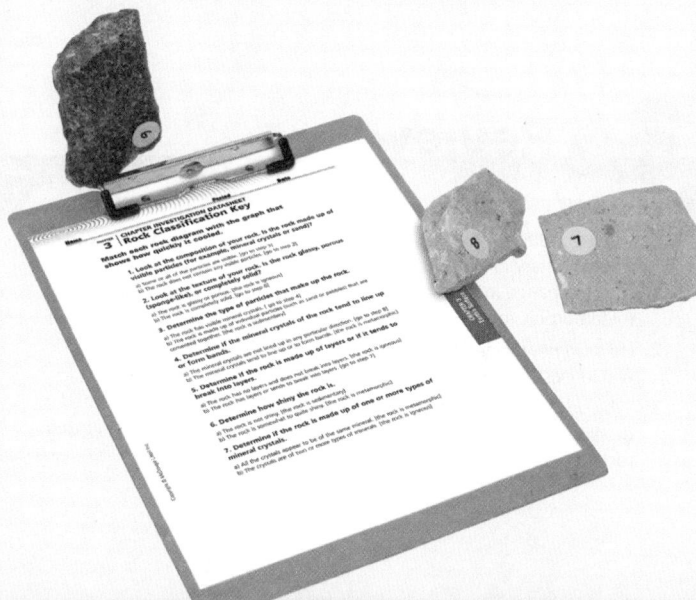

INVESTIGATION RESOURCES

 CHAPTER INVESTIGATION, Rock Classification
- Rock Classification Key, p. 196
- Level A, pp. 197–200
- Level B, pp. 201–204
- Level C, p. 205

Advanced students should complete Levels B & C.

 Writing a Lab Report, D12–13

Technology Resources

Customize this student lab as needed or look for an alternative. Print rubrics to assess student lab reports.

💿 **Lab Generator CD-ROM**

⑤ Examine the rock sample again and choose the statement that best describes the rock.

⑥ Continue to work through the key until your choices lead you to a classification that fits your rock. Repeat steps 2–5 for each of the numbered samples.

▶ Observe and Analyze

Write It Up

1. **INTERPRET** Referring to the Rock Classification Key and the observations you recorded, write the type of each rock in your data table.

2. **IDENTIFY LIMITS** What problems, if any, did you experience in applying the key? Which samples did not seem to fit easily into a category? How could you improve the key?

▶ Conclude
Write It Up

1. **COMPARE AND CONTRAST** How are igneous and metamorphic rocks similar? How can you tell them apart?

2. **ANALYZE** Examine a sample of sedimentary rock in which visible particles are cemented together. In addition to sight, what other sense could help you classify this sample?

3. **APPLY** What have you learned from this investigation that would help you make a classification key that someone else could follow? How might you make a key to classify the recordings in a music collection? Write two pairs of numbered statements that would start the classification process.

▶ INVESTIGATE Further

CHALLENGE Make a rock classification key to distinguish between rocks from Earth and rocks from the Moon. Here are some facts to consider. The surface of the Moon was once covered by a thick layer of magma. The Moon has no running water and almost no atmosphere. Minerals on Earth often contain tiny amounts of water. Minerals on the Moon almost never contain any water. The Moon does not have processes that can cause a rock to change into another type of rock.

An astronaut photographed this rock on the Moon. The rock sits in a valley that formed 4 billion years ago. The rock may not have changed or moved since that time.

Rock Classification
Observe and Analyze
Table 1. Rock Sample Properties

Sample Number	Description of Visible Properties	Rock Type

Conclude

Chapter 3: **Rocks 103** **A**

▶ Observe and Analyze

Write It Up

SAMPLE DATA 1, mineral crystals and speckled, igneous; 2, sea fossils, sedimentary; 3, wavy bands and shiny, metamorphic

1. *Answers will vary depending on which samples you supply.*

2. *Students' answers will vary.*

▶ Conclude
Write It Up

1. *Igneous and metamorphic rocks are similar in that they are both made of mineral crystals that fit tightly together and may be large enough to see without magnification. They are different in that the minerals in metamorphic rocks tend to be lined up in bands or layers.*

2. *Touch could help identify a sedimentary rock made up of relatively large particles.*

3. *Answers will vary. A key for a music collection might start with questions such as what type of music it is, when it was recorded, or who the recording artist is.*

▶ INVESTIGATE Further

CHALLENGE Review students' keys distinguishing rocks from Earth and rocks from Earth's moon. See the Unit Resource Book, p. 205, for more guidance.

Post-Lab Discussion

• Write the names of the three types of rocks on the board. Call on student volunteers to use their results and the classification key to list identifying characteristics of each type of rock.

• Refer students back to the classification systems they designed for the Investigate on p. 77. Compare and contrast the characteristics with those of the Rock Classification Key.

• Discuss other possible uses of classification keys. For example, a classification key could be used in identifying plants, birds, and so on.

BACK TO

the BIG idea

Have students look at the photograph on pp. 72–73. Ask them to use the photograph to summarize what they've learned about rocks and the changes rocks go through. *Answer: The rocks won't remain the way they are because rocks are continually changing as they move through the rock cycle. All types of rocks (igneous, sedimentary, and metamorphic) change into other types of rocks over time.*

◀ KEY CONCEPTS SUMMARY

SECTION 3.1

Ask: True or false: Rocks move in only one direction through the rock cycle. *False; rocks can move in any direction because any type of rock can change into any other type of rock over time.*

SECTION 3.2

Ask: What is the difference between extrusive and intrusive igneous rocks? *Extrusive rocks cool quickly at Earth's surface; intrusive rocks cool slowly within Earth.*

SECTION 3.3

Ask: Where are the small particles on the diagram? *on top of the large particles which are at the bottom*

SECTION 3.4

Ask: Where do metamorphic rocks form? Why? *in areas of high heat or pressure, or both*

Review Concepts

- Big Idea Flow Chart, p. T17
- Chapter Outline, pp. T23–T24

 Chapter Review

the BIG idea

Rocks change into other rocks over time.

CONTENT REVIEW
CLASSZONE.COM

◀ KEY CONCEPTS SUMMARY

3.1 The rock cycle shows how rocks change.

Processes at Earth's surface and heat within Earth cause rocks to change into other types of rocks.

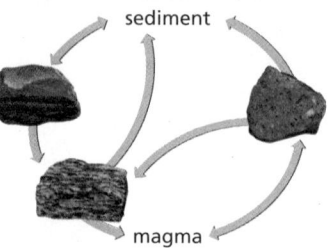
sediment

magma

VOCABULARY
rock p. 75
rock cycle p. 78
igneous rock p. 78
sedimentary rock p. 78
metamorphic rock p. 78

3.2 Igneous rocks form from molten rock.

As molten rock cools, minerals crystallize and form igneous rocks.

igneous

Extrusive igneous rocks cool quickly at Earth's surface.

Intrusive igneous rocks cool slowly within Earth.

VOCABULARY
intrusive igneous rock p. 83
extrusive igneous rock p. 83

3.3 Sedimentary rocks form from earlier rocks.

Layers of sedimentary rocks form as
- sediments are pressed or cemented together
- dissolved minerals re-form as water evaporates

sedimentary

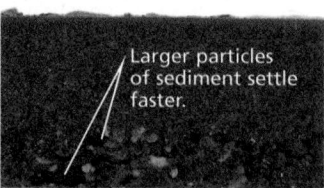
Larger particles of sediment settle faster.

VOCABULARY
sediment p. 89

3.4 Metamorphic rocks form as existing rocks change.

Metamorphic rocks form as the structure of the parent rocks change and as their minerals recrystallize.

metamorphic

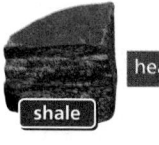
shale → heat and pressure → schist

VOCABULARY
metamorphism p. 96
recrystallization p. 97
foliation p. 100

A 104 Unit: Earth's Surface

Technology Resources

Have students visit **ClassZone.com** or use the CD-ROM for a cumulative review of concepts.

 CONTENT REVIEW

 CONTENT REVIEW CD-ROM

Engage students in a whole-class interactive review of Key Concepts. Edit content as you wish.

 POWER PRESENTATIONS

Reviewing Vocabulary

Copy and complete the chart below. There may be more than one correct response.

Rock Type	Forms From	Example / Identifying characteristic
intrusive igneous rock	magma	1. / large mineral crystals
extrusive igneous rock	2.	basalt / 3.
sedimentary rock	4.	conglomerate / contains large pieces of earlier rocks
sedimentary rock	ancient plant remains	5. / may contain plant fossils
sedimentary rock	6.	limestone / 7.
foliated metamorphic rock	parent rock that has several types of minerals	8. / minerals are lined up
nonfoliated metamorphic rock	9.	10. / 11.

Reviewing Key Concepts

Multiple Choice *Choose the letter of the best answer.*

12. The three groups of rock are sedimentary, metamorphic, and
    a. limestone
    c. igneous
    b. granite
    d. coal

13. The rock cycle shows how rocks continually
    a. increase in size
    b. increase in number
    c. become more complex
    d. change over time

14. Which kind of rock forms when molten rock cools?
    a. metamorphic
    c. igneous
    b. sedimentary
    d. extrusive

15. An existing rock can change into another type of rock when it is subjected to great
    a. pressure
    c. flooding
    b. winds
    d. foliation

16. Which kind of rock forms by recrystallization?
    a. intrusive igneous
    b. extrusive igneous
    c. sedimentary
    d. metamorphic

17. Geologists classify an igneous rock on the basis of its crystal size and the amount of _____ its minerals contain.
    a. carbon
    c. sediment
    b. silica
    d. foliation

18. Pieces of rock can settle from water and get cemented into
    a. metamorphic rock
    b. sedimentary rock
    c. igneous rock
    d. extrusive rock

19. Rock salt is an example of a sedimentary rock that develops from dissolved minerals as
    a. water evaporates
    b. magma cools
    c. sediments break down
    d. sand settles in water

Short Answer *Write a short answer to each question.*

20. What is the difference between a rock and a mineral?

21. Compare the distribution of rock types at Earth's surface to their distribution in the entire crust. How are any differences related to processes occurring in the rock cycle?

22. How is the texture of an igneous rock related to the rate at which it cooled?

Reviewing Vocabulary

Sample answers:
1. granite or gabbro
2. lava
3. tiny mineral crystals
4. pieces of earlier rocks
5. coal
6. shells or dissolved minerals
7. contains shells or is made of carbonate minerals that bubble in contact with hydrochloric acid
8. slate, phyllite, schist, or gneiss
9. parent rock that has one main type of mineral
10. marble, quartzite, or hornfels
11. made of carbonate minerals or found next to an igneous intrusion

Reviewing Key Concepts

12. c
13. d
14. c
15. a
16. d
17. b
18. b
19. a
20. Unlike a mineral, a rock does not necessarily have a particular composition or internal structure.
21. Most of the rocks at Earth's surface are sedimentary, but the crust as a whole is made up almost entirely of igneous and metamorphic rocks. The processes that produce sedimentary rocks occur only at the surface; when these rocks are buried, they are subjected to metamorphism.
22. The more slowly an igneous rock cools from molten rock, the larger its crystals can grow.

ASSESSMENT RESOURCES

 UNIT ASSESSMENT BOOK
- Chapter Test A, pp. 46–49
- Chapter Test B, 50–53
- Chapter Test C, pp. 54–57
- Alternative Assessment, pp. 58–59

 SPANISH ASSESSMENT BOOK
Spanish Chapter Test, pp. 113–116

Technology Resources

Edit test items and answer choices.

 Test Generator CD-ROM

Visit **ClassZone.com** to extend test practice.

 Test Practice

Thinking Critically

23. fossils of plants

24. sedimentary; because of the fossils

25. Earlier rocks broke apart. Tiny
    pieces of the rocks were carried
    until they settled from still water or
    water that was moving very slowly.
    The layer of sediment was buried
    and pressed together. Over time it
    became sedimentary rock.

26. Its minerals would flatten out in
    one direction and the rock would
    become foliated. New minerals
    would grow in it.

27. mud cracks; moving layers of sand;
    was covered by water

28. sedimentary

29. metamorphic

30. igneous

31. metamorphic

32. sedimentary

the BIG idea

33. The diagram might show any type of
    rock breaking down into sediments,
    which become sedimentary rock over
    time. As some of the rock is worn
    away, cliffs form. Finally, the diagram
    should show that rocks of the cliff
    will wear away into sediment, which
    can become sedimentary rock again.

34. The material in the mountain rock
    dissolves in rainwater and is carried
    into an ocean. The ocean organism
    uses the dissolved material to form
    its shell.

UNIT PROJECTS

Check to make sure students are working on their projects. Check schedules
and work in progress.

 Unit Projects, pp. 5–10

Thinking Critically

Use the photograph below to answer the next four questions.

23. **INFER** What are the dark markings on
    the rock?

24. **OBSERVE** Which of the three groups of rocks
    does this rock belong to? How do you know?

25. **SUMMARIZE** Describe the process by which
    this rock most likely formed.

26. **PREDICT** If this rock were subjected to
    metamorphism, how might it change?

27. **APPLY** Copy and complete the concept
    map below.

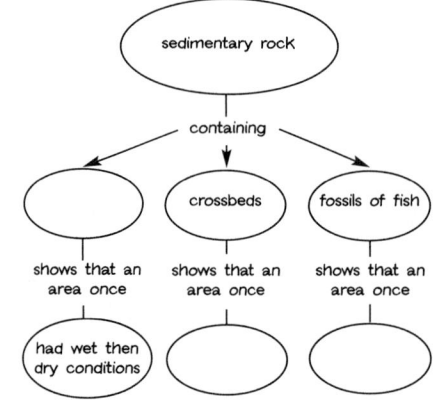

sedimentary rock

containing

crossbeds   fossils of fish

shows that an
area once

shows that an
area once

shows that an
area once

had wet then
dry conditions

PREDICT Which of the three rock types—
igneous, sedimentary, or metamorphic—
would you be most likely to find in each area?

Area	Rock Type
28. the bottom of a large lake	
29. older rock surrounding an igneous intrusion	
30. a lava flow from a volcano	
31. a part of the surface that was once deep within a mountain range	
32. the sides of a cave	

the BIG idea

33. Look again at the photograph on pages 72–73.
    Using your knowledge of the rock cycle, draw
    a diagram showing how sedimentary rocks can
    form cliffs at Earth's surface. Then add to the
    diagram by showing how the rocks are likely
    to change over time.

34. Describe how material in a rock near the top
    of a mountain can later be used by an ocean
    organism in forming its shell.

UNIT PROJECTS

Check your schedule for your unit project. How
are you doing? Be sure that you've placed data or
notes from your research in your project folder.

MONITOR AND RETEACH

If students have trouble applying the concepts in item 33, group those
students and have them work together to draw a diagram of the
process by which sedimentary rock forms from eroded rock particles.

Students may benefit from summarizing one or more sections of
the chapter.

 Summarizing the Chapter, pp. 215–216

Standardized Test Practice

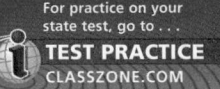 For practice on your state test, go to . . .
TEST PRACTICE
CLASSZONE.COM

Analyzing a Diagram

This diagram shows a simple version of the rock cycle. Use it to answer the questions below.

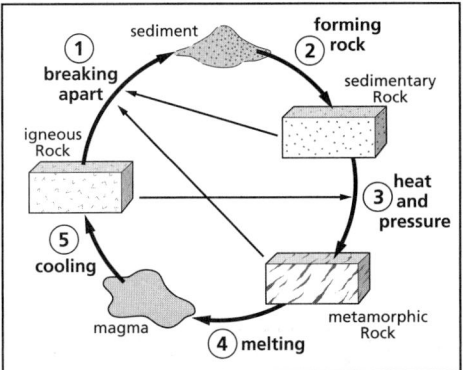

1. Where are loose materials developing into rock?
a. 1   c. 4
b. 2   d. 5

2. Where are sand and other small particles forming from rock?
a. 1   c. 4
b. 2   d. 5

3. Where is magma developing into rock?
a. 1   c. 4
b. 3   d. 5

4. Where is molten rock forming?
a. 1   c. 4
b. 3   d. 5

5. Where are heat and pressure changing solid rock into another type of rock without melting it?
a. 1   c. 4
b. 3   d. 5

6. According to the diagram, what can happen to sedimentary rock?
a. It can become sediment or magma.
b. It can become igneous rock or magma.
c. It can become sediment or metamorphic rock.
d. It can become sediment, metamorphic rock, or magma.

7. How could you change the diagram to show that igneous rock can become magma again?
a. Add an arrow from igneous rock to metamorphic rock.
b. Add an arrow from heat and pressure to igneous rock.
c. Add an arrow from igneous rock to melting.
d. Add an arrow from melting to igneous rock.

8. What must happen to rock that formed inside Earth before it can become sediment?
a. It must reach the surface as rock above it wears away.
b. It must become magma and erupt from a volcano.
c. Heat and pressure must change it into sediment.
d. It must become sedimentary rock while inside Earth.

Extended Response

Answer the two questions below in detail. Include some of the terms shown in the word box. In your answers underline each term you use.

pressed together   buried   mineral crystals cooling time

9. Most sedimentary rock forms from pieces of existing rocks. Explain why coal is an unusual sedimentary rock and how coal forms.

10. Melba is trying to decide whether an igneous rock formed deep inside Earth or at the surface. What should she look for? Why?

Analyzing a Diagram

1. b   3. d   5. b   7. c
2. a   4. c   6. c   8. a

Extended Response

9. RUBRIC

4 points for a response that correctly answers the question and uses the following terms accurately:
- pressed together
- buried

Sample: Coal is an unusual sedimentary rock because it forms from plant remains instead of from rocks. Millions of years ago, plants died and were <u>pressed together</u> to form layers. Other layers of sediment <u>buried</u> the plant remains and pressed them into coal.

3 points for a response that correctly answers the question and uses one term accurately
2 points for a response that correctly answers the question, but does not use the terms

10. RUBRIC

4 points for a response that correctly answers the question and uses the following terms accurately:
- mineral crystals
- cooling time

Sample: Melba should look at the igneous rock's texture. If it has small <u>mineral crystals</u>, it is a surface rock that had a quick <u>cooling time</u>. If it has large mineral crystals, it was formed deep within Earth and had a slow cooling time.

3 points for a response that correctly answers the question and uses one term accurately
2 points for a response that correctly answers the question, but does not use the terms

---

METACOGNITIVE ACTIVITY

Have students answer the following questions in their **Science Notebook:**

1. What types of rocks do you think surround your school? What about your environment influenced your answer?

2. How do the concepts in this chapter relate to your life? What would you like to learn more about?

3. How might you change your Unit Project now that you have learned more about rocks?

TIMELINES in Science

FOCUS

● Set Learning Goals

Students will

- Examine the history of the Earth system.
- Compare technologies used to study the Earth system.
- Model the principle of superposition.

National Science Education Standards

A.9.a–g Understandings about Scientific Inquiry

E.6.a–c Understandings about Science and Technology

F.5.a–e, F.5.g Science and Technology in Society

G.1.a–b Science as a Human Endeavor

G.2.a Nature of Science

G.3.a–c History of Science

INSTRUCT

The top half of the timeline shows major events in the history of the Earth system. The bottom half discusses advances in the technology used to study Earth and its applications. Note that the technology used to study a particular event in Earth's history was often developed billions of years after the event itself took place.

Technology

MEASURING AGE To determine the age of extremely ancient rocks using radioactive dating, scientists use radioactive elements with extremely long half-lives, such as uranium-238. Uranium-238 has a half-life of 4.5 billion years. Point out that this element changes too slowly to measure recent events. Ask: What would you use to measure more recent rock ages? *a radioactive element with a shorter half-life*

HISTORY OF THE EARTH SYSTEM

Systems of air, water, rocks, and living organisms have developed on Earth during the planet's 4.6 billion years of history. More and more scientists have become curious about how these parts of Earth work together. Today, scientists think of these individual systems as part of one large Earth system.

The timeline shows a few events in the history of the Earth system. Scientists have developed special tools and procedures to study this history. The boxes below the timeline show how technology has led to new knowledge about the Earth system and how that knowledge has been applied.

4.6 BYA

Earth Forms in New Solar System
The Sun and nine planets, one of which is Earth, form out of a cloud of gas and dust. Earth forms and grows larger as particles collide with it. While Earth is still young, a slightly smaller object smashes into it and sends huge amounts of material flying into space. Some of this material forms a new object—the Moon.

EVENTS

5 BYA
Billion Years Ago

APPLICATIONS AND TECHNOLOGY

TECHNOLOGY

Measuring Age of Solar System
In 1956, Clair C. Patterson published his estimate that the solar system was 4.55 billion years old. Previously, scientists had learned how to use radioactive elements present in rocks to measure their ages. Patterson used this technology to determine the ages of meteorites that were formed along with the solar system and later fell to Earth. Since 1956, scientists have studied more samples and used new technologies. These studies have generally confirmed Patterson's estimate.

This iron meteorite fell in Siberia in 1947. Data from such meteorites are clues to how and when the solar system formed.

A 108 Unit: Earth's Surface

DIFFERENTIATE INSTRUCTION

Below Level To help students grasp the broad scope of this timeline, draw it as one continuous line on the chalkboard. Explain that *BYA* and *MYA* mean "billions of years ago" and "millions of years ago." Point out that the first half of the timeline is separated by intervals of one billion years. Ask: How many years separate intervals in the second half of the timeline? *two hundred million years*

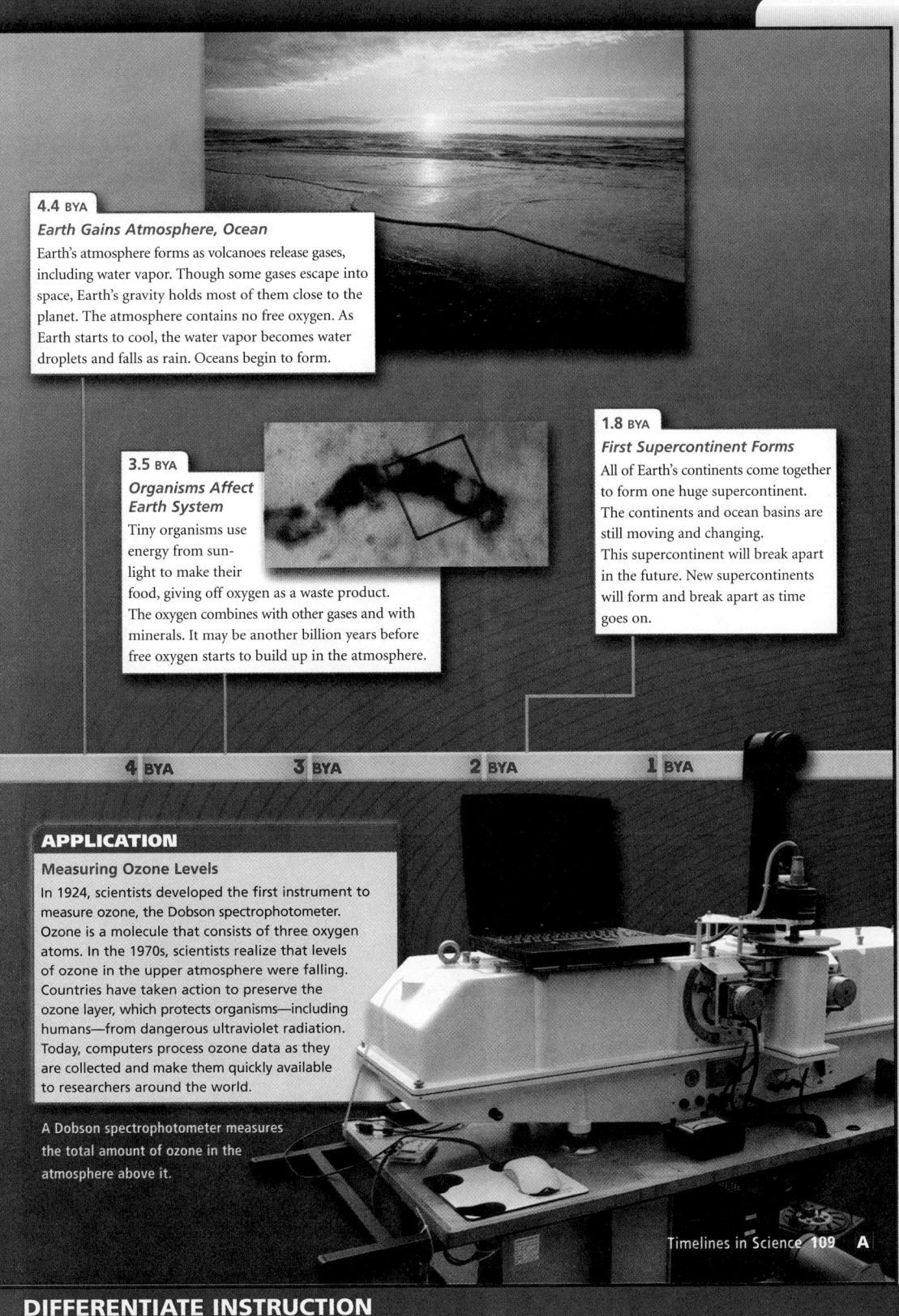

4.4 BYA

Earth Gains Atmosphere, Ocean

Earth's atmosphere forms as volcanoes release gases, including water vapor. Though some gases escape into space, Earth's gravity holds most of them close to the planet. The atmosphere contains no free oxygen. As Earth starts to cool, the water vapor becomes water droplets and falls as rain. Oceans begin to form.

3.5 BYA

Organisms Affect Earth System

Tiny organisms use energy from sunlight to make their food, giving off oxygen as a waste product. The oxygen combines with other gases and with minerals. It may be another billion years before free oxygen starts to build up in the atmosphere.

1.8 BYA

First Supercontinent Forms

All of Earth's continents come together to form one huge supercontinent. The continents and ocean basins are still moving and changing. This supercontinent will break apart in the future. New supercontinents will form and break apart as time goes on.

4 BYA   **3 BYA**   **2 BYA**   **1 BYA**

APPLICATION

Measuring Ozone Levels

In 1924, scientists developed the first instrument to measure ozone, the Dobson spectrophotometer. Ozone is a molecule that consists of three oxygen atoms. In the 1970s, scientists realize that levels of ozone in the upper atmosphere were falling. Countries have taken action to preserve the ozone layer, which protects organisms—including humans—from dangerous ultraviolet radiation. Today, computers process ozone data as they are collected and make them quickly available to researchers around the world.

A Dobson spectrophotometer measures the total amount of ozone in the atmosphere above it.

Timelines in Science **109** **A**

Integrate the Sciences

The tiny organisms that first began to photosynthesize are called cyano-bacteria. Fossils of these blue-green microorganisms (*cyan* stems from the Greek word *kuanos*, meaning "dark blue") have been found in rocks in western Australia. The cells of certain species of modern algae are nearly identical to their ancient counterparts.

Scientific Process

Help students understand that many environmental problems that affect the Earth system require ongoing data collection and analysis. Ask: Why do scientists continue to monitor ozone levels? *The levels can change quickly. A long record of change can aid scientists in identifying patterns and trends.*

DIFFERENTIATE INSTRUCTION

English Learners Encourage students to develop their own science dictionary that lists unfamiliar terms, such as *meteorite*, *ozone*, and *supercontinent*. Students can write definitions next to each new term. They can also draw diagrams to help them remember the terms.

Scientific Process

As students read about when animals first appeared in the fossil record, ask them how scientists might go about testing the hypothesis that some of the animals were attached to the sea floor. *Sample answer: Continue to search for additional, complete fossils; compare the fossils with present-day animals.*

Technology

CORE SAMPLES Ask: How do scientists who are studying Earth's current climate and geology use data gathered from cores? *Sample answer: The data could help scientists identify long-term patterns that explain current climate or geologic events.*

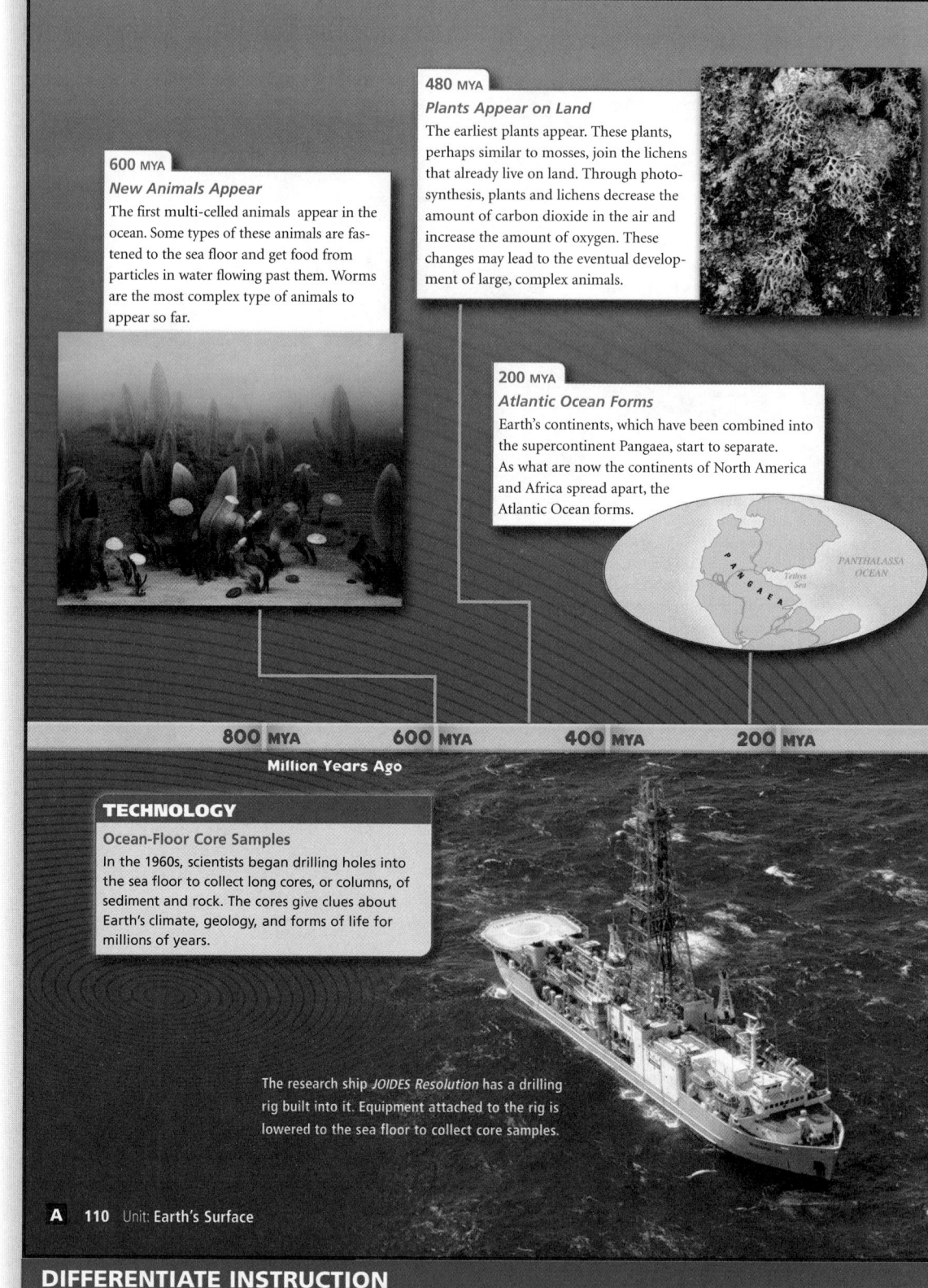

480 MYA

Plants Appear on Land

The earliest plants appear. These plants, perhaps similar to mosses, join the lichens that already live on land. Through photosynthesis, plants and lichens decrease the amount of carbon dioxide in the air and increase the amount of oxygen. These changes may lead to the eventual development of large, complex animals.

600 MYA

New Animals Appear

The first multi-celled animals appear in the ocean. Some types of these animals are fastened to the sea floor and get food from particles in water flowing past them. Worms are the most complex type of animals to appear so far.

200 MYA

Atlantic Ocean Forms

Earth's continents, which have been combined into the supercontinent Pangaea, start to separate. As what are now the continents of North America and Africa spread apart, the Atlantic Ocean forms.

| 800 MYA | 600 MYA | 400 MYA | 200 MYA |

Million Years Ago

TECHNOLOGY

Ocean-Floor Core Samples

In the 1960s, scientists began drilling holes into the sea floor to collect long cores, or columns, of sediment and rock. The cores give clues about Earth's climate, geology, and forms of life for millions of years.

The research ship *JOIDES Resolution* has a drilling rig built into it. Equipment attached to the rig is lowered to the sea floor to collect core samples.

A **110** Unit: Earth's Surface

DIFFERENTIATE INSTRUCTION

Advanced In terms of geologic time, life has been part of the history of the Earth system for a short time. Ask students to solve the following problem: Plants have existed for what percentage of Earth's total history? *about 10 percent*

$$\left(\frac{4.8 \times 10^8}{4.6 \times 10^9} = \frac{4.8}{46} = 0.104, \text{ or about } 10\% \right)$$

12,000 years ago

Earth Emerges from Ice—Again

Earth's temperature warms slightly. Kilometers-thick ice sheets that formed during the latest of Earth's many ice ages start to melt. Forests and grasslands expand. Sea level rises about 100 meters (330 ft), and the ocean floods the edges of the continents.

1972

New View of Earth

Harrison "Jack" Schmitt, an astronaut traveling 24,000 kilometers (15,000 mi) above Earth, takes a photograph. It is the first to show Earth fully lit by the Sun, and the image is sometimes called the Blue Marble. It helps people see the planet as one system.

i RESOURCE CENTER
CLASSZONE.COM

Learn more about the Earth system.

100 MYA   Today

APPLICATION

International Space Station

The International Space Station has laboratories in which scientists study Earth, the solar system, and the universe. Also, scientists are doing research to better understand the effects of very low gravity on people. This work is part of an effort to develop the life-support systems needed for people to remain in space a long time. Eventually it might aid in the further exploration of space by humans.

INTO THE FUTURE

In almost every area of life, from music to food to sports, the world has become more connected. Science is no exception. In the past century, scientists have begun to monitor the ozone layer. They have realized that the processes that cause continents to change positions also cause earthquakes and volcanic eruptions to occur.

Changes in technology are likely to help scientists increase their understanding of the Earth system. For example, instruments on artificial satellites measure changes in clouds, ocean life, and land temperatures. These types of data help scientists understand how changes in one part of Earth affect other parts.

ACTIVITIES

Taking a Core Sample

Add layers of damp sand of different colors to a paper cup. Switch cups with a partner. Press a clear straw through the sand, put your finger over the top of the straw, and pull the straw out. Determine the order in which your partner added the sand layers. How would you know if there was a layer of sand that did not go across the entire cup?

Writing About Science

Imagine you are living in microgravity like the astronauts on the International Space Station. Write a detailed description of two hours of your day.

Timelines in Science **111** **A**

INTO THE FUTURE

Point out that the International Space Station is a prime example of how the world has become more connected. Scientists from more than a dozen nations, including the United States, are working together to study Earth and other parts of the universe. Discuss how increased global cooperation may be the key to solving many problems that affect the Earth system, such as global climate change, acid rain, deforestation, and depletion of world fisheries.

ACTIVITIES

Taking a Core Sample

Tell students that the sand represents different layers of rock and soil under Earth's surface. Stress that they should keep their finger over the top of the straw as they examine the sand within—otherwise, the sand will spill out. *If a particular color of sand was not in the straw, than that layer did not go across the entire cup.*

Writing About Science

Have students first discuss how the minute amount of gravity physically affects astronauts in space. Remind them about or show them scenes of astronauts floating inside spacecraft. Suggest that students do some research before writing their descriptions, which might take the form of daily journals.

Technology Resources

Students can visit **ClassZone.com** for information on the Earth system.

DIFFERENTIATE INSTRUCTION

Advanced Have students extend the "Taking a Core Sample" activity by modeling how erosion removes soil and rock from the geologic record. For example, they could blow across the sand-filled cup to model wind erosion or sprinkle water into the cup to model water erosion.

Alternative Writing Projects Have students imagine that they are astronauts and that the photograph of Earth taken by Harrison Schmitt is a postcard that they are sending home to Earth. Have them write a short note to a friend, describing Earth from the point of view of an observer in space.

Weathering and Soil Formation

Earth Science
UNIFYING PRINCIPLES

PRINCIPLE 1

Heat energy inside Earth and radiation from the Sun provide energy for Earth's processes.

PRINCIPLE 2

Physical forces, such as gravity, affect the movement of all matter on Earth and throughout the universe.

PRINCIPLE 3

Matter and energy move among Earth's rocks and soil, atmosphere, waters, and living things.

PRINCIPLE 4

Earth has changed over time and continues to change.

Unit: Earth's Surface
BIG IDEAS

CHAPTER 1
Views of Earth Today

Modern technology has changed the way we view and map Earth.

CHAPTER 2
Minerals

Minerals are basic building blocks of Earth.

CHAPTER 3
Rocks

Rocks change into other rocks over time.

CHAPTER 4
Weathering and Soil Formation
Natural forces break rocks apart and form soil, which supports life.

CHAPTER 5
Erosion and Deposition

Water, wind, and ice shape Earth's surface.

CHAPTER 4
KEY CONCEPTS

SECTION **4.1**	SECTION **4.2**	SECTION **4.3**
Mechanical and chemical forces break down rocks.	**Weathering and organic processes form soil.**	**Human activities affect soil.**
1. Weathering breaks rocks into smaller pieces.	1. Soil is a mixture of weathered rock particles and other materials.	1. Soil is a necessary resource.
2. Mechanical weathering produces physical changes in rocks.	2. Climate and landforms affect soil.	2. Land-use practices can harm soil.
3. Chemical weathering changes the mineral composition of rocks.	3. The activities of organisms affect soil.	3. Soil can be protected and conserved.
4. Weathering occurs at different rates.	4. Properties of soil can be observed and measured.	

The Big Idea Flow Chart is available on p. T25 in the **UNIT TRANSPARENCY BOOK.**

Previewing Content

4.1 Mechanical and chemical forces break down rocks. pp. 115–121

1. Weathering breaks rocks into smaller pieces.
Weathering is the process by which natural forces break down rock into particles called sediments. The two main types of weathering are mechanical and chemical. **Mechanical weathering** involves a physical change in rock. **Chemical weathering** changes the composition of rock.

2. Mechanical weathering produces physical changes in rocks.
The agents of mechanical weathering include
- ice wedging
- pressure release
- plant root growth
- abrasion

When water freezes in the cracks and pores of rocks, it expands and ice breaks apart the rocks. Pressure release occurs when intrusive rocks are pushed to the surface; pressure on the rock is released and the rock expands. **Exfoliation** is a process in which layers or sheets of rock gradually break off. The diagrams below show how ice and pressure release cause mechanical weathering.

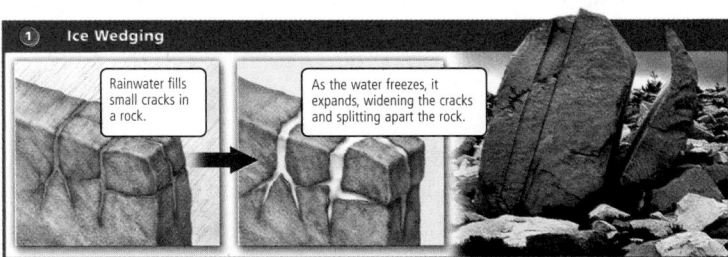

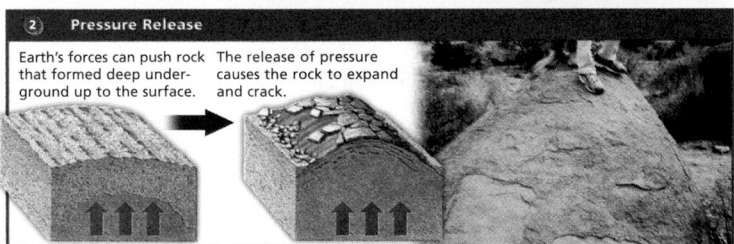

Plants can take root in cracks of rocks and wedge the cracks open. Moving water can break up rocks by **abrasion,** which is the process of wearing down an object by friction.

3. Chemical weathering changes the mineral composition of rocks.
When certain minerals in rock react with air and water, they dissolve or are changed into different minerals. For example, small amounts of atmospheric carbon dioxide can react with precipitation to form a weak acid. This acidic rainwater can move through soil and break down minerals in rocks. Chemical weathering also occurs when water and oxygen react with iron to form rust. This process, known as oxidation, gives rocks a reddish color.

4. Weathering occurs at different rates.
Weathering generally occurs over the course of hundreds, thousands, or even millions of years. The factors that influence rates of weathering include
- surface area
- rock composition
- climate

When a rock is broken down, more of its surface area is exposed to air and water. As surface area increases, rates of weathering increase. Rates of weathering vary for different types of rocks—the igneous rock granite, for example, weathers more slowly than a softer rock, such as limestone. Because water is needed for chemical weathering to occur, and heat increases the rate of chemical weathering, chemical weathering occurs faster in wet, hot regions than it does in cold, dry regions.

Common Misconceptions

DENSITY OF WATER Students may think that the density of water does not change when it freezes. In fact, when water freezes, it becomes less dense as it expands. This is why ice is a powerful agent of mechanical weathering—water in the pores of rocks can freeze, expand, and split rocks apart.

 This misconception is addressed on p. 116.

MISCONCEPTION DATABASE
CLASSZONE.COM Background on student misconceptions

CHANGES IN ROCKS Some students might think that rocks do not change or break down over time by natural processes. They may not understand that smaller stones are the result of larger rocks breaking apart or that something so seemingly strong and unchanging as a boulder can be dissolved or broken apart by something so seemingly "weak" as water.

 This misconception is addressed on p. 117.

Previewing Content

SECTION

4.2 Weathering and organic processes form soil. pp. 122–131

1. Soil is a mixture of weathered rock particles and other materials.

Soil is a mixture of sediment, organic matter, water, and air. The type of soil that forms in an area depends on the following factors:

- rock type
- climate
- landforms
- plant cover
- organisms
- time

Soil develops in horizontal layers called soil horizons. A **soil horizon** is a layer of soil with properties that differ from those of the soil layer above or below it. The A horizon is the upper layer of soil, or topsoil. The B horizon lies below the A horizon; it has little organic matter. The C horizon is the deepest layer of soil; it consists mainly of weathered parent rock. A **soil profile** refers to the soil horizons found in a particular location.

2. Climate and landforms affect soil.

Climate influences the characteristics and thickness of the soil that develops from weathered rock. Four types of soil that form in different regions include

- tropical (thin surface layer of humus)
- desert (shallow with little organic matter)
- temperate (dark and rich in organic matter and minerals)
- arctic (less-developed horizons)

3. The activities of organisms affect soil.

Plants provide most of the organic matter that eventually forms humus. Bacteria and fungi are microorganisms that decompose dead plants and animals and produce nutrients that plants need to grow. Animals such as earthworms and ants loosen and mix soil as they burrow through it. They also bring partly weathered rock particles to the surface and return nutrients to the soil when their bodies decompose.

4. Properties of soil can be observed and measured.

Soil scientists study numerous soil properties, including texture, color, pore space, and chemistry. The texture of a soil is determined by the size of the weathered rock particles it contains. Soil scientists classify sediments into three categories: sand, silt, and clay. The color of a soil reflects other properties, such as chemical composition and humus content. *Pore space* refers to the spaces between soil particles. *Chemistry* refers to the pH of water in soil, which, in turn, determines how easily nutrients will be made available to plant roots.

SECTION

4.3 Human activities affect soil. pp. 132–137

1. Soil is a necessary resource.

Soil supports the growth of plants, which, in turn, provide humans with food, clothes, medicines, lumber, and oxygen. Soil also helps filter water and recycle nutrients. In addition, soil provides a habitat for many organisms.

2. Land-use practices can harm soil.

Farming, construction and development, and mining are among the main activities that impact soil resources. Improvements in farming methods have helped to reduce soil loss. However, farming methods still lead to substantial soil loss. Fertilizers added to soil can make it difficult for soil organisms to produce nutrients naturally. These fertilizers can also cause pollution when runoff carries the excess nutrients into rivers, lakes, and oceans. Overgrazing by large animals destroys plant cover. This problem can result in **desertification,** or the expansion of desert conditions into areas where the natural plant cover has been removed. Construction and development also involve the removal of protective plant cover. Soil can be transported by rain and wind into rivers and lakes and can negatively impact the aquatic environments. Similar problems exist with mining. Mining can also expose sulfide minerals to air and water. The resulting chemical reaction produces sulfuric acid. The acidic water can drain from the mine and pollute nearby soils.

3. Soil can be protected and conserved.

Most soil conservation methods are designed to hold soil in place and keep it fertile. Conservation methods include the following:

- crop rotation, or planting different crops on the same field at different times
- conservation tillage, which reduces the number of times fields are plowed in a year
- terraces, or flat, steplike areas built on a hillside to reduce runoff and soil erosion
- contour plowing, or plowing along the contours of a slope to reduce runoff and soil erosion
- windbreaks, or rows of trees planted between fields to reduce wind erosion

---

Common Misconceptions

SOIL TEXTURE Students may be confused about the scientific meaning of the word *clay.* Here, *clay* refers to small, flat sediment

MISCONCEPTION DATABASE

CLASSZONE.COM Background on student misconceptions

particles in soil. Like modeling clay, soils that contain a lot of clay particles are sticky when wet and hard when dry.

  This misconception is addressed on p. 128.

Previewing Labs

Lab Generator CD-ROM
Edit these Pupil Edition labs and generate alternative labs.

EXPLORE (the BIG idea)

Ice Power, p. 113
Students observe how water expands when it freezes to learn about one of the natural forces that break up rock.

TIME 10 minutes
MATERIALS plastic container, water, freezer

Getting the Dirt on Soil, p. 113
Students are introduced to the properties of soil by investigating how quickly water moves through different soil samples.

TIME 10 minutes
MATERIALS tin can, metric ruler, marker, water, clock or stopwatch

Internet Activity: Soil Formation, p. 113
Students use the Internet to learn about soil formation.

TIME 20 minutes
MATERIALS computer with Internet access

SECTION 4.1

EXPLORE Mechanical Weathering, p. 115
Students observe rock particles to investigate the forces that break down rocks.

TIME 15 minutes
MATERIALS coffee can with lid, several rocks, a piece of dark-colored construction paper

INVESTIGATE Chemical Weathering, p. 118
Students identify variables in an experiment about rust formation.

TIME 15 minutes
MATERIALS steel wool, 3 plastic cups, water

SECTION 4.2

EXPLORE Soil Composition, p. 122
Students compare and contrast different soil samples to learn about soil composition.

TIME 15 minutes
MATERIALS 1/2 cup potting soil, 1/2 cup local soil sample, 2 pieces of white paper, hand lens, tweezers

CHAPTER INVESTIGATION Testing Soil, pp. 130–131
Students test a soil sample to measure and identify soil properties.
  ® Texture Flow Chart, p. 257

TIME 40 minutes
MATERIALS 900 mL dried soil sample, 250 mL graduated cylinder, 1 qt jar with lid, water, 2 L plastic bottle, scissors, 15 × 15 cm piece of window screening, rubber band, pH test strips, clock with second hand or stopwatch, Texture Flow Chart

---

SECTION 4.3

INVESTIGATE Soil Conservation, p. 135
Students cut up an apple to model the amount of fertile soil on Earth.
  ® Apple Chart, p. 247

TIME 20 minutes
MATERIALS Apple Chart, apple, plastic knife

® **Additional INVESTIGATION,** Soil Formation, A, B, & C, pp. 267–275; Teacher Instructions, pp. 348–349

Previewing Chapter Resources

	INTEGRATED TECHNOLOGY	**LABS AND ACTIVITIES**

CHAPTER 4

Weathering and Soil Formation

 CLASSZONE.COM
- eEdition Plus
- EasyPlanner Plus
- Misconception Database
- Content Review
- Test Practice
- Visualizations
- Resource Centers
- Internet Activity: Soil Formation
- Math Tutorial

 SCILINKS.ORG

SCLINKS

 CD-ROMS
- eEdition
- EasyPlanner
- Power Presentations
- Content Review
- Lab Generator
- Test Generator

 AUDIO CDS
- Audio Readings
- Audio Readings in Spanish

 EXPLORE the Big Idea, p. 113
- Ice Power
- Getting the Dirt on Soil
- Internet Activity: Soil Formation

UNIT RESOURCE BOOK
Unit Projects, pp. 5–10

 Lab Generator CD-ROM
Generate customized labs.

SECTION
4.1

Mechanical and chemical forces break down rocks.
pp. 115–121

Time: 2 periods (1 block)

 Lesson Plan, pp. 217–218

- **RESOURCE CENTER,** Weathering
- **VISUALIZATION,** Chemical Weathering
- **MATH TUTORIAL**

 UNIT TRANSPARENCY BOOK
- Big Idea Flow Chart, p. T25
- Daily Vocabulary Scaffolding, p. T26
- Note-Taking Model, p. T27
- 3-Minute Warm-Up, p. T28
- "Mechanical Weathering" Visual, p. T30

- EXPLORE Mechanical Weathering, p. 115
- INVESTIGATE Chemical Weathering, p. 118
- Math in Science, p. 121

 UNIT RESOURCE BOOK
- Datasheet, Chemical Weathering, p. 226
- Math Support, p. 255
- Math Practice, p. 256

SECTION
4.2

Weathering and organic processes form soil.
pp. 122–131

Time: 3 periods (1.5 blocks)

 Lesson Plan, pp. 228–229

 RESOURCE CENTER, Soil

 UNIT TRANSPARENCY BOOK
- Daily Vocabulary Scaffolding, p. T26
- 3-Minute Warm-Up, p. T28

- EXPLORE Soil Composition, p. 122
- CHAPTER INVESTIGATION, Testing Soil, pp. 130–131

 UNIT RESOURCE BOOK
- Texture Flow Chart, p. 257
- CHAPTER INVESTIGATION, Testing Soil, A, B, & C, pp. 258–266
- Additional INVESTIGATION, Soil Formation, A, B, & C, pp. 267–275

SECTION
4.3

Human activities affect soil.
pp. 132–137

Time: 3 periods (1.5 blocks)

 Lesson Plan, pp. 238–239

 UNIT TRANSPARENCY BOOK
- Big Idea Flow Chart, p. T25
- Daily Vocabulary Scaffolding, p. T26
- 3-Minute Warm-Up, p. T29
- Chapter Outline, pp. T31–T32

- INVESTIGATE Soil Conservation, p. 135
- Science on the Job, p. 137

 UNIT RESOURCE BOOK
- Apple Chart, p. 247
- Datasheet, Soil Conservation, p. 248

KEY TO ICONS

 CD/CD-ROM

 Teacher Edition

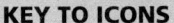 INTERNET

 Pupil Edition

 UNIT RESOURCE BOOK

T UNIT TRANSPARENCY BOOK

A UNIT ASSESSMENT BOOK

SP A SPANISH ASSESSMENT BOOK

 SCIENCE TOOLKIT

READING AND REINFORCEMENT

ASSESSMENT

STANDARDS

- Choose Your Own Strategy, B18–27
- Combination Notes, C36
- Daily Vocabulary Scaffolding, H1–8

 UNIT RESOURCE BOOK
- Vocabulary Practice, pp. 252–253
- Decoding Support, p. 254
- Summarizing the Chapter, pp. 276–277

 Audio Readings CD
Listen to Pupil Edition.

 Audio Readings in Spanish CD
Listen to Pupil Edition in Spanish.

 PE
- Chapter Review, pp. 138–140
- Standardized Test Practice, p. 141

 A **UNIT ASSESSMENT BOOK**
- Diagnostic Test, pp. 60–61
- Chapter Test, A, B, & C, pp. 65–76
- Alternative Assessment, pp. 77–78

 SP A Spanish Chapter Test, pp. 117–120

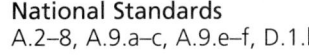 **Test Generator CD-ROM**
Generate customized tests.

Lab Generator CD-ROM
Rubrics for Labs

National Standards
A.2–8, A.9.a–c, A.9.e–f, D.1.e, D.1.k

See p. 112 for the standards

 UNIT RESOURCE BOOK
- Reading Study Guide, A & B. pp. 219–222
- Spanish Reading Study Guide, pp. 223–224
- Challenge and Extension, p. 225
- Reinforcing Key Concepts, p. 227
- Challenge Reading, pp. 250–251

 TE Ongoing Assessment, pp. 116–120

 PE Section 4.1 Review, p. 120

 A **UNIT ASSESSMENT BOOK**
Section 4.1 Quiz, p. 62

National Standards
A.2–8, A.9.a–c, A.9.e–f, D.1.k

R **UNIT RESOURCE BOOK**
- Reading Study Guide, A & B. pp. 230–233
- Spanish Reading Study Guide, pp. 234–235
- Challenge and Extension, p. 236
- Reinforcing Key Concepts, p. 237

 TE Ongoing Assessment, pp. 122–129,

 PE Section 4.2 Review, p. 129

 A **UNIT ASSESSMENT BOOK**
Section 4.2 Quiz, p. 63

National Standards
A.2–8, A.9.a–c, A.9.e–f, D.1.e, D.1.k

 UNIT RESOURCE BOOK
- Reading Study Guide, A & B, pp. 240–243
- Spanish Reading Study Guide, pp. 244–245
- Challenge and Extension, p. 246
- Reinforcing Key Concepts, p. 249

TE Ongoing Assessment, pp. 132–134, 136

PE Section 4.3 Review, p. 136

A **UNIT ASSESSMENT BOOK**
Section 4.3 Quiz, p. 64

National Standards
A.2–7, A.9.a–b, A.9.e–f, D.1.k

Previewing Resources for Differentiated Instruction

CHAPTER INVESTIGATION

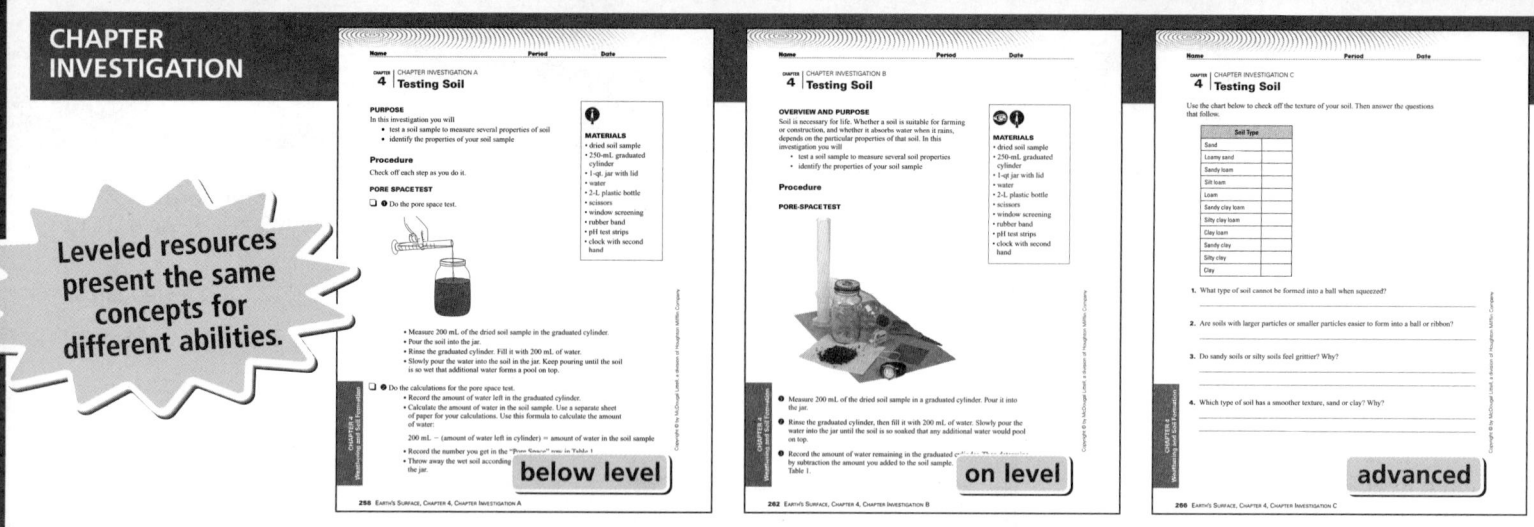

below level

UNIT RESOURCE BOOK, pp. 258–261

on level

pp. 262–265

advanced

pp. 262–266

Leveled resources present the same concepts for different abilities.

READING STUDY GUIDE

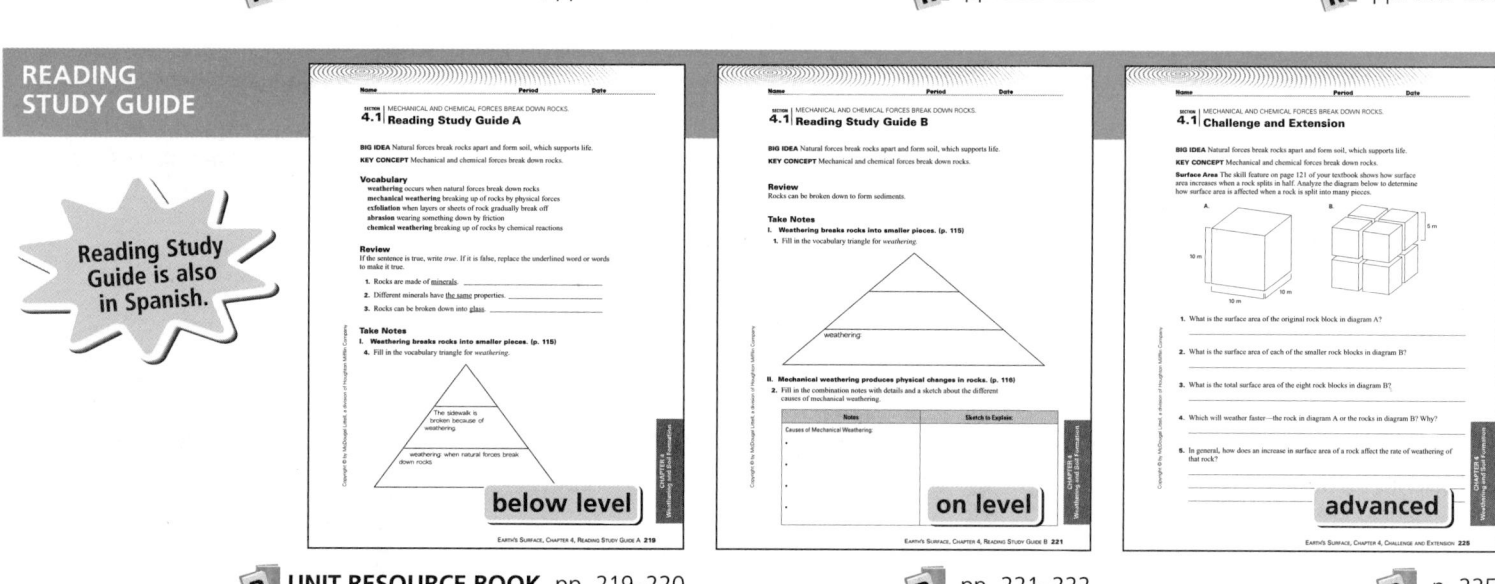

below level

UNIT RESOURCE BOOK, pp. 219–220

on level

pp. 221–222

advanced

p. 225

Reading Study Guide is also in Spanish.

CHAPTER TEST

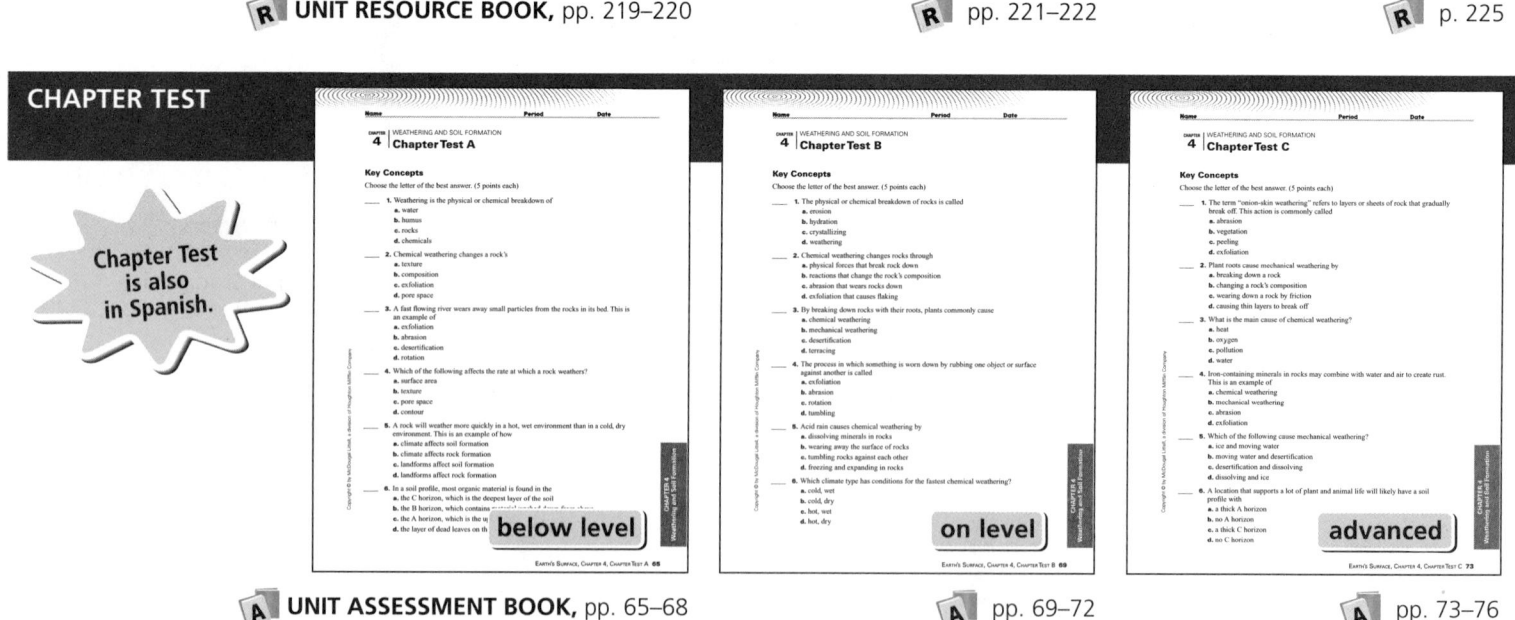

below level

UNIT ASSESSMENT BOOK, pp. 65–68

on level

pp. 69–72

advanced

pp. 73–76

Chapter Test is also in Spanish.

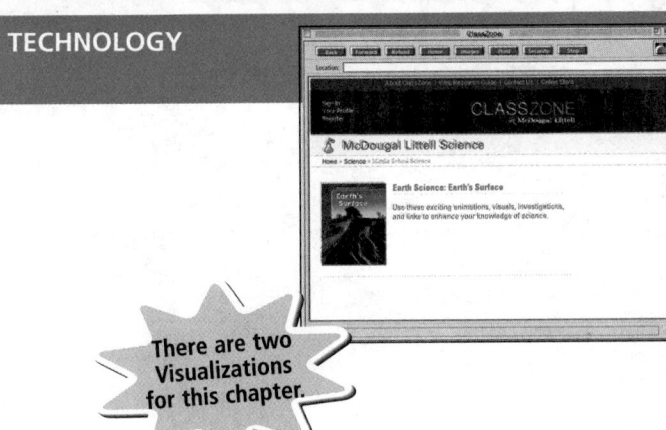

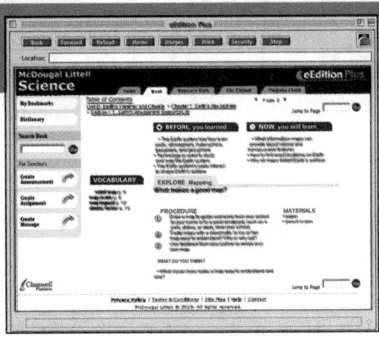

There are two Visualizations for this chapter.

CLASSZONE.COM　　　**CD/CD-ROMS**　　　**CLASSZONE.COM**

VISUAL CONTENT

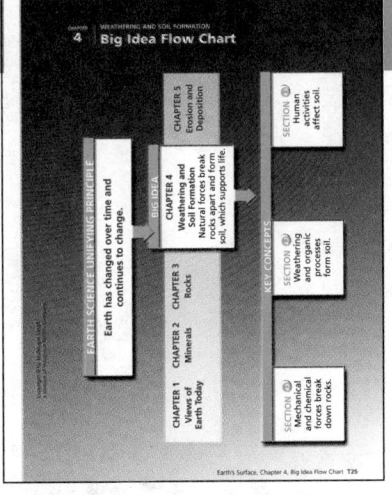

UNIT TRANSPARENCY BOOK, p. T25

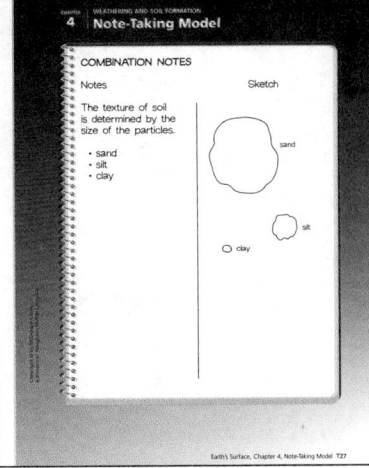

T p. T27

T p. T30

MORE SUPPORT

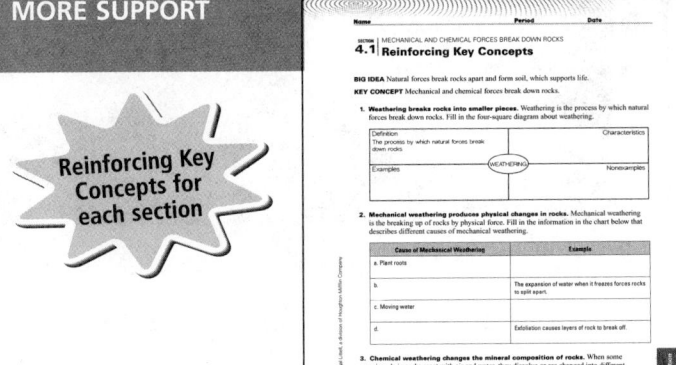

Reinforcing Key Concepts for each section

UNIT RESOURCE BOOK, p. 227

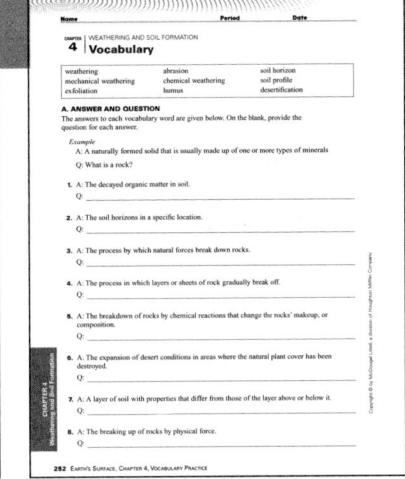

R pp. 252–253

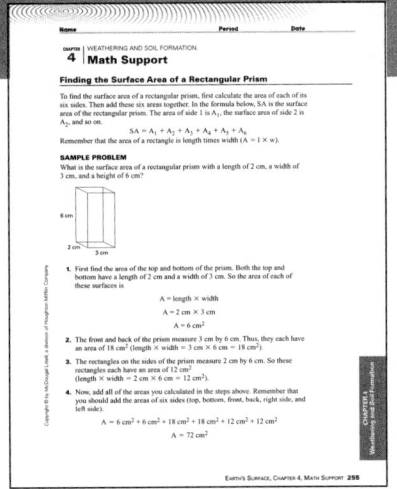

R p. 255

INTRODUCE

the BIG idea

Have students look at the photograph of the rocky landscape and discuss how the question in the box links to the Big Idea. For further discussion:

- What are some examples of natural forces?
- Which natural forces might break apart rocks?
- What might happen to rocks after they break apart?

National Science Education Standards

Content

D.1.e Soil consists of weathered rocks and decomposed organic material from dead plants, animals, and bacteria. Soils are often found in layers, with each having a different chemical composition and texture.

D.1.k Living organisms have played many roles in the earth system, including affecting the composition of the atmosphere, producing some types of rocks, and contributing to the weathering of rocks.

Process

A.2–8 Design and conduct an investigation; use tools to gather and interpret data; use evidence to describe, predict, explain, model; think critically to make relationships between evidence and explanation; recognize different explanations and predictions; communicate scientific procedures and explanations; use mathematics.

A.9.a–c, A.9.e–f Understand scientific inquiry by using different investigations, methods, mathematics, and explanations based on logic, evidence, and skepticism.

CHAPTER

Weathering and Soil Formation

the BIG idea

Natural forces break rocks apart and form soil, which supports life.

How is rock related to soil?

Key Concepts

SECTION 4.1 Mechanical and chemical forces break down rocks.
Learn about the natural forces that break down rocks.

SECTION 4.2 Weathering and organic processes form soil.
Learn about the formation and properties of soil.

SECTION 4.3 Human activities affect soil.
Learn how land use affects soil and how soil can be protected and conserved.

Internet Preview

CLASSZONE.COM

Chapter 4 online resources: Content Review, two Visualizations, two Resource Centers, Math Tutorial, Test Practice

A 112   Unit: Earth's Surface

INTERNET PREVIEW

CLASSZONE.COM For student use with the following pages:

Review and Practice
- Content Review, pp. 114, 138
- Math Tutorial: Surface Area of Rectangular Prisms, p. 121
- Test Practice, p. 141

Activities and Resources
- Internet Activity: Soil Formation, p. 113
- Resource Centers: Weathering, p. 116; Soil, p. 129
- Visualization: Chemical Weathering, p. 118

NSTA scilinks.org *SCiLINKS*

Soil Conservation
Code: MDL016

EXPLORE (the BIG idea)

Ice Power

Fill a plastic container to the top with water and seal the lid tightly. Place it in the freezer overnight. Check on your container the next morning.

Observe and Think
What happened to the container? Why?

Getting the Dirt on Soil

Remove the top and bottom of a tin can. Be careful of sharp edges. Measure and mark 2 cm from one end of the can. Insert the can 2 cm into the ground, up to the mark. Fill the can with water and time how long it takes for the can to drain. Repeat the procedure in a different location.

Observe and Think
What do you think affects how long it takes for soil to absorb water?

Internet Activity: Soil Formation

Go to **ClassZone.com** to watch how soil forms. Learn how materials break down and contribute to soil buildup over time.

Observe and Think
What do rocks and soil have in common? What do organic matter and soil have in common?

NSTA
scilinks.org
SCI LINKS
Soil Conservation Code: MDL016

Chapter 4: Weathering and Soil Formation 113 **A**

EXPLORE (the BIG idea)

These inquiry-based activities are appropriate for use at home or as a supplement to classroom instruction.

Ice Power

PURPOSE To introduce students to one of the natural forces that can break up rocks. By observing how water expands when it freezes, students will understand how ice can split rocks apart.

TIP *10 min.* Suggest that students check the containers and lids for cracks before beginning the activity.

Answer: The lid popped off. The water froze and expanded.

REVISIT after p. 116.

Getting the Dirt on Soil

PURPOSE To introduce students to the properties of soil, such as pore space. Pore space affects how easily water moves through soil.

TIP *10 min.* Tell students to choose two sites that have markedly different soils. If soils are uniform in your area, conduct this activity using other soil samples.

Answer: How tightly it is packed. Water moves most easily through loose soil and soil with large particles, such as sand. It moves less easily through heavily packed soils and soil with small particles, such as clay.

REVISIT after p. 129.

Internet Activity: Soil Formation

PURPOSE To introduce students to the process of soil formation.

TIP *20 min.* As students conduct their research, encourage them to use graphic organizers and draw pictures to better understand the connection between weathered rock and soil.

Answer: Rocks break down through weathering to form sediment, which becomes part of soil. Organic matter is also a part of soil.

REVISIT after p. 127.

TEACHING WITH TECHNOLOGY

PC Microscope If you have the software for a PC microscope, allow students to view bacteria and fungi after teaching about the micro-organisms that affect soil on p. 126. A PC microscope can also be used to analyze soil samples during the activity on p. 122.

CBL and Probeware Use a pH sensor in the Chapter Investigation on pp. 130–131 if probeware is available.

CONCEPT REVIEW
Activate Prior Knowledge

- Cover your desk with newspaper. Then place a rock, a small pile of coarse sediments, and a sample of soil on the newspaper.

- Have students examine the rock, sediments, and soil. Ask them to compare and contrast the items.

- Refer to the "Rock Cycle" visual on p. T22 of the Unit Transparency Book. Have students recall the natural forces that form and change rocks. Ask them to infer which of these forces might play a role in forming soil.

TAKING NOTES

Combination Notes

Encourage students to closely examine the visuals in each section. These visuals can serve as guides for students' sketches of new concepts and can prompt students to ask questions as they draw their diagrams.

Choose Your Own Strategy

Allow students to choose their own strategies to suit their needs. This will help to build confidence in their ability to take notes that are meaningful for them. Remind students that different strategies may be appropriate for different topics or sections in the chapter.

Vocabulary and Note-Taking Resources

- Vocabulary Practice, pp. 252–253
- Decoding Support, p. 254

- Daily Vocabulary Scaffolding, p. T26
- Note-Taking Model, p. T27

- Choose Your Own Strategy, B18–27
- Combination Notes, C36
- Daily Vocabulary Scaffolding, H1–8

CONCEPT REVIEW

- The atmosphere, hydrosphere, biosphere, and geosphere interact to shape Earth's surface.
- Natural processes form, change, break down, and re-form rocks.

VOCABULARY REVIEW

cleavage p. 53
fracture p. 53
rock p. 75
rock cycle p. 78
sediment p. 89

CONTENT REVIEW
CLASSZONE.COM
Review concepts and vocabulary.

TAKING NOTES

COMBINATION NOTES

To take notes about a new concept, first make an informal outline of the information. Then make a sketch of the concept and label it so that you can study it later.

CHOOSE YOUR OWN STRATEGY

Take notes about new vocabulary terms, using one or more of the strategies from earlier chapters—**magnet word, word triangle,** or **description wheel.** Feel free to mix and match the strategies, or use an entirely different vocabulary strategy.

See the Note-Taking Handbook on pages R45–R51.

SCIENCE NOTEBOOK

NOTES

Causes of Mechanical Weathering
- Ice
- Pressure Release
- Plant Roots
- Moving Water

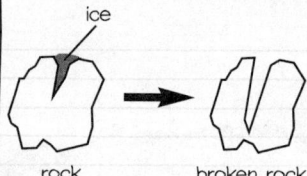

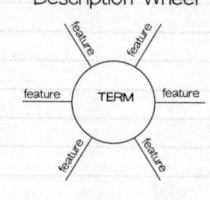

 114 Unit: Earth's Surface

CHECK READINESS

Administer the Diagnostic Test to determine students' readiness for new science content and their mastery of requisite math skills.

 Diagnostic Test, pp. 60–61

Technology Resources

Students needing content and math skills should visit **ClassZone.com.**

- **CONTENT REVIEW**
- **MATH TUTORIAL**
- **CONTENT REVIEW CD-ROM**

4.1 Mechanical and chemical forces break down rocks.

◀ **BEFORE, you learned**

- Minerals make up most rocks
- Different minerals have different properties
- Rocks are broken down to form sediments

▶ **NOW, you will learn**

- How mechanical weathering breaks down rocks
- How chemical weathering changes rocks
- What factors affect the rate at which weathering occurs

VOCABULARY

weathering p. 115
mechanical weathering p. 116
exfoliation p. 116
abrasion p. 116
chemical weathering p. 118

EXPLORE Mechanical Weathering

What causes rocks to break down?

PROCEDURE

1. Place a handful of rocks on a piece of dark-colored construction paper. Observe the rocks and take notes on their appearance.
2. Place the rocks in a coffee can. Put the lid on the can and shake the can forcefully for 2 minutes, holding the lid tightly shut.
3. Pour the rocks onto the construction paper. Observe them and take notes on any changes in their appearance.

WHAT DO YOU THINK?

- What happened to the rocks and why?
- What forces in nature might affect rocks in similar ways?

MATERIALS

- coffee can with lid
- rocks
- dark-colored construction paper

Weathering breaks rocks into smaller pieces.

Think about the tiniest rock you have ever found. How did it get so small? It didn't start out that way! Over time, natural forces break rocks into smaller and smaller pieces. If you have ever seen a concrete sidewalk or driveway that has been cracked by tree roots, you have seen this process. The same thing can happen to rocks.

Weathering is the process by which natural forces break down rocks. In this section you will read about two kinds of weathering. One kind occurs when a rock is physically broken apart—like the cracked sidewalk. Another kind occurs when a chemical reaction changes the makeup of a rock.

VOCABULARY
Remember to add *weathering* to your notebook, using the vocabulary strategy of your choice.

Chapter 4: **Weathering and Soil Formation** 115 **A**

RESOURCES FOR DIFFERENTIATED INSTRUCTION

Below Level

UNIT RESOURCE BOOK
- Reading Study Guide A, pp. 219–220
- Decoding Support, p. 254

 **AUDIO CDS**

Advanced

UNIT RESOURCE BOOK
- Challenge and Extension, p. 225
- Challenge Reading, pp. 250–251

English Learners

UNIT RESOURCE BOOK
Spanish Reading Study Guide, pp. 223–224

AUDIO CDS

- Audio Readings in Spanish
- Audio Readings (English)

4.1 FOCUS

▶ Set Learning Goals

Students will

- Describe how mechanical weathering breaks down rocks.
- Explain how chemical weathering breaks down rocks.
- Identify the factors that affect the rate at which weathering occurs.
- Identify variables in an experiment about rust formation.

◀ 3-Minute Warm-Up

Display Transparency 28 or copy this exercise on the board:

Decide if these statements are true. If not, correct them.

1. The set of natural processes that form, change, and re-form rocks is called the rock cycle. *true*

2. A rock is usually made up of only one type of mineral. *A rock is usually made of more than one type of mineral.*

3. Igneous rock develops from layers of sediment. *Sedimentary rock develops from layers of sediment.*

T 3-Minute Warm-Up, p. T28

4.1 MOTIVATE

EXPLORE Mechanical Weathering

PURPOSE To introduce students to the forces that break down rocks

TIP *15 min.* This activity works best with relatively soft rocks, such as shale, limestone, sandstone, and pumice. If no rocks are available, use pieces of chalk—chalk is made up of the same compounds as limestone.

WHAT DO YOU THINK? *When they were shaken in the can, the rocks struck one another. Little pieces of the rocks broke off. In nature, moving water could affect rocks in a similar way.*

EXPLORE (the BIG idea)

Revisit "Ice Power" on p. 113. Have students discuss how their results relate to mechanical weathering.

Address Misconceptions

IDENTIFY Ask: What happens to the density of water when it freezes? If students say that the density remains the same, they may have difficulty understanding that ice can be an agent of mechanical weathering.

CORRECT As a class, review the results of "Ice Power" on p. 113. Point out that the water's density actually decreased as the ice expanded and the water molecules became less compact. As the ice expanded, it pushed against the walls of the container and forced the top to pop off.

REASSESS Reinforce the connection between the activity and mechanical weathering. Ask: How are the results of the activity similar to what might happen to a rock if water entered its cracks and pores and then froze? *The water would expand as it freezes, which could cause the rock to break apart.*

Technology Resources

Visit **ClassZone.com** for background on common student misconceptions.

 MISCONCEPTION DATABASE

Develop Critical Thinking

CONNECT Invite students to think of examples of physical weathering in their daily lives. If they need help when brainstorming, ask if they can think of any sidewalks that are cracked and uneven as a result of tree roots growing under or into them.

Ongoing Assessment

CHECK YOUR READING *Answer: Moving water can cause rocks to grind against one another. Water itself also causes abrasion.*

 **RESOURCE CENTER**
CLASSZONE.COM

Learn more about weathering.

 A

READING TiP

The word *expand* means "to increase in size or volume."

Mechanical weathering produces physical changes in rocks.

If you smash a walnut with a hammer, you will break it into a lot of small pieces, but you will not change what it is. Even though the pieces of the walnut are no longer connected together, they are still composed of the same materials. **Mechanical weathering**—the breaking up of rocks by physical forces—works in much the same way. In this natural process, physical forces split rocks apart but do not change their composition—what they are made of. Ice wedging, pressure release, plant root growth, and abrasion can all cause mechanical weathering.

1 Ice Wedging When water freezes, it expands. When water freezes in the cracks and pores of rocks, the force of its expansion is strong enough to split the rocks apart. This process, which is called ice wedging, can break up huge boulders. Ice wedging is common in places where temperatures rise above and fall below the freezing point for water, which is 0°C (32°F).

2 Pressure Release Rock deep within Earth is under great pressure from surrounding rocks. Over time, Earth's forces can push the rock up to the surface, or the overlying rocks and sediment can wear away. In either case, the pressure inside the rock is still high, but the pressure on the surface of the rock is released. This release of pressure causes the rock to expand. As the rock expands, cracks form in it, leading to exfoliation. **Exfoliation** (ehks-FOH-lee-AY-shuhn) is a process in which layers or sheets of rock gradually break off. This process is sometimes called onion-skin weathering, because the rock surface breaks off in thin layers similar to the layers of an onion.

3 Plant Root Growth Trees, bushes, and other plants may take root in cracks in rocks. As the roots of these plants grow, they wedge open the cracks. The rock—even if it is large—can be split completely apart.

4 Abrasion Water can wear down rocks on riverbeds and along shorelines by abrasion. **Abrasion** (uh-BRAY-zhuhn) is the process of wearing down by friction, the rubbing of one object or surface against another. The force of moving water alone can wear away particles of rock. Water also causes rocks to tumble downstream. The tumbling rocks wear down as they grind against the riverbed and against each other. Ocean waves beating against a rocky shore also wear down rocks by abrasion.

 **CHECK YOUR READING** How does moving water weather rocks?

 **DIFFERENTIATE INSTRUCTION**

More Reading Support

A Which type of weathering occurs when physical forces break apart rocks? *mechanical*

B Which physical force causes exfoliation? *pressure release*

English Learners This section has a number of phrasal verbs, such as *make up* and *break down*. While these terms might initially serve to simplify an idea for a student, they could in fact confuse an English learner. Instruct students not to read *up* and *down* as literal directions, and offer synonyms to clarify the meaning of these and other phrasal verbs.

Mechanical Weathering

Ice wedging, pressure release, plant root growth, and abrasion can all break apart rocks.

① Ice Wedging

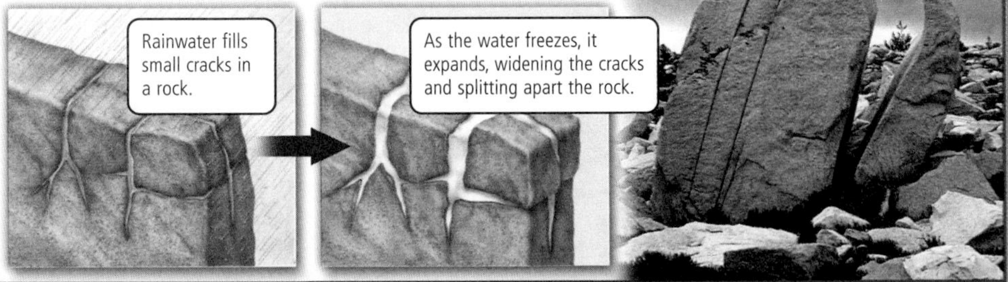

Rainwater fills small cracks in a rock.

As the water freezes, it expands, widening the cracks and splitting apart the rock.

② Pressure Release

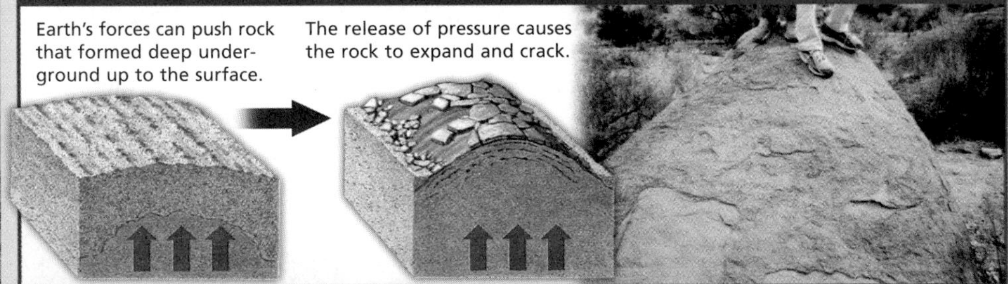

Earth's forces can push rock that formed deep underground up to the surface.

The release of pressure causes the rock to expand and crack.

③ Plant Roots

When plants grow in cracks in a rock, their roots can widen the cracks and force the rock apart.

④ Abrasion

Flowing water can move rocks, causing them to rub together and wear down into rounded shapes.

READING VISUALS What evidence of mechanical weathering can you see in each photograph above?

DIFFERENTIATE INSTRUCTION

Alternative Assessment Show students several samples of "beach glass" (or "sea glass"), but do not tell them what the samples are. Instead, explain that the smooth pieces once had sharp edges. Have students study the photographs in the visual "Mechanical Weathering." Then ask: Which physical force likely caused the mechanical weathering? Explain your answer. *Moving water likely weathered the pieces because water wears down rocks and other hard objects into smooth, rounded shapes.*

Teach from Visuals

To help students interpret the visual on mechanical weathering, ask:

• What do all these processes have in common? *They are physical forces.*

• Which two processes seem most alike? Why? *Mechanical weathering by ice and plant roots seem most similar. Both involve a force that fills a crack in a rock and then splits the rock apart.*

 This visual is also available as T30 in the Unit Transparency Book.

Address Misconceptions

IDENTIFY Ask: Where do pebbles and small particles of rock come from? If students do not say "larger rocks," they may hold the misconception that rocks do not change or break down naturally.

CORRECT Pass around a piece of sandstone. Ask students to describe it. *hard, solid, strong* Then hold another piece of sandstone and rub the rocks together over a sheet of black paper. Show students the grains that have fallen on the paper.

REASSESS Ask: What made the rocks break? *abrasion, or the friction from rubbing the rocks together* What makes rocks rub together in nature? *moving water, wind, glacial ice*

Technology Resources

Visit **ClassZone.com** for background on common student misconceptions.

 MISCONCEPTION DATABASE

Ongoing Assessment

Describe how mechanical weathering breaks down rocks.

Ask: What happens to the composition of a rock during mechanical weathering? *It stays the same; mechanical weathering breaks down rocks physically, not chemically.*

READING VISUALS *Answer: Ice wedging: fine crack; no plant roots. Pressure release: "peeling" of rock in layers. Plant roots: tree growing in a crack. Abrasion: moving water.*

INVESTIGATE Chemical Weathering

PURPOSE To identify variables in an experiment about rust formation

TIP *15 min.* For best results, use inexpensive steel wool with thin fibers for this activity.

WHAT DO YOU THINK? *The steel wool that was exposed to both air and water rusted. The steel wool that was exposed to air alone did not rust. The steel wool that was exposed to water alone did not rust. Both water and air are necessary for rusting to occur.*

CHALLENGE *The inside of the steel wool did not have enough exposure to both air and water to rust.*

 Datasheet, Chemical Weathering, p. 226

Technology Resources

Customize this student lab as needed or look for an alternative. Print rubrics to assess student lab reports.

 Lab Generator CD-ROM

Develop Critical Thinking

APPLY Refer students to R30 of the Lab Handbook or write the definitions for *independent variable* and *dependent variable* on the board. Ask students to identify the independent and dependent variables in the "Chemical Weathering" activity. *The independent variable is the amount of air and water that is coming into contact with the steel wool. The dependent variable is the amount of rust that forms on each piece of steel wool.*

Ongoing Assessment

Explain how chemical weathering breaks down rocks.

Ask: What happens to some minerals in rocks when they react with air and water? *They dissolve or are changed into different minerals.*

Chemical weathering changes the mineral composition of rocks.

 **VISUALIZATION**
CLASSZONE.COM
Watch chemical weathering in action.

If you have seen an old rusty nail, you have witnessed the result of a chemical reaction and a chemical change. The steel in the nail contains iron. Oxygen in air and water react with the iron to form rust.

 Minerals in rocks also undergo chemical changes when they react with water and air. **Chemical weathering** is the breakdown of rocks by chemical reactions that change the rocks' makeup, or composition. When minerals in rocks come into contact with air and water, some dissolve and others react and are changed into different minerals.

Dissolving

 Water is the main cause of chemical weathering. Some minerals completely dissolve in ordinary water. The mineral halite, which is the same compound as table salt, dissolves in ordinary water. Many more minerals dissolve in water that is slightly acidic—like lemonade. In the atmosphere, small amounts of carbon dioxide dissolve in rainwater. The water and carbon dioxide react to form a weak acid. After falling to Earth, the rainwater moves through the soil, picking up additional

INVESTIGATE Chemical Weathering

What is necessary for rust to form?

PROCEDURE

(1) Place a piece of steel wool in a cup filled to the top with water. Place a second piece of steel wool in a cup with a small amount of water. The water should touch but not cover the steel wool. Place a third piece in a cup with no water.

(2) Allow the three cups to sit overnight. Observe the appearance of the steel wool in each container the next day.

WHAT DO YOU THINK?

• What happened to the steel wool in each cup?

• Judging by the appearance of the pieces of steel wool, what do you think is necessary for rusting to occur?

CHALLENGE Tear the steel wool that rusted most apart and compare the appearances of the inside and the outside. Why might the inside and the outside look different?

SKILL FOCUS
Identifying variables

MATERIALS
• steel wool
• 3 cups
• water

TIME
15 minutes

 **DIFFERENTIATE INSTRUCTION**

? **More Reading Support**

C Which type of weathering changes the makeup of a rock? *chemical weathering*

D What is the main cause of chemical weathering? *water*

Advanced Ask students to find out which weak acid is formed as a result of chemical weathering. *carbonic acid* Where else is carbonic acid found? *soft drinks* How does the weathering of minerals by carbonic acid in rocks connect to students' lives? *It chemically weathers tooth enamel and leads to decay.*

 Challenge and Extension, p. 225

Have students who are interested in the effects of weathering on the Great Sphinx read the following article:

Challenge Reading, pp. 250–251

About 100 Years Ago

Today

READING VISUALS **INFER** This ancient stone monument was moved from a desert in Egypt to New York City in 1881. How and why has it changed?

carbon dioxide from decaying plants. The slightly acidic water breaks down minerals in rocks. In the process, the rocks may also break apart into smaller pieces.

Air pollution can make rainwater even more acidic than it is naturally. Power plants and automobiles produce gases such as sulfur dioxide and nitric oxide, which react with water vapor in the atmosphere to form acid rain. Acid rain causes rocks to weather much faster than they would naturally. The photographs above show how acid rain can damage a granite column in just a hundred years.

?
E

Rusting

?
F

The oxygen in the air is also involved in chemical weathering. Many common minerals contain iron. When these minerals dissolve in water, oxygen in the air and the water combines with the iron to produce iron oxides, or rust. The iron oxides form a coating that colors the weathered rocks like those you see in the photograph of Oak Creek Canyon in Arizona.

The rocks in Oak Creek Canyon are reddish because iron in the rocks reacted with water and air to produce iron oxides.

 CHECK YOUR READING How is air involved in chemical weathering?

Chapter 4: **Weathering and Soil Formation** 119 **A**

Mechanical and chemical weathering are presented as two separate processes in this section. However, in nature, the two processes work together. To help students grasp this concept, remind them that mechanical weathering breaks rocks apart. As a result, more surface area is exposed to air and water. Ask: How would this affect rates of chemical weathering? *Rates of chemical weathering would increase.*

Teacher Demo

To demonstrate how some minerals dissolve in slightly acidic water, place two pieces of chalk in a large pan. Tell students that chalk is made up of the same compounds as limestone. Then sprinkle drops of vinegar on one piece of chalk while a volunteer sprinkles drops of water on the other piece. Ask students to describe their observations. *The chalk sprinkled with vinegar fizzed. The chalk sprinkled with tap water did not react.* Have them predict what might happen to limestone that is placed in slightly acidic water. *The limestone would react with the water and eventually dissolve.*

Ongoing Assessment

READING VISUALS *Answer: Now, the images are harder to see; some of the stone has worn away. It was probably dissolved by acid rain.*

CHECK YOUR READING *Answer: Pollutants in the air can react with water to form acid rain. Air and water can also react with iron to form rust.*

DIFFERENTIATE INSTRUCTION

? **More Reading Support**

E Does acid rain increase or decrease rates of weathering? *increase*

F Which gas in the air helps produce rust? *oxygen*

Below Level Students might have difficulty realizing that rocks rust. They might associate rusting only with metals. Remind students that ores are rocks that are mined for minerals, such as iron. Ask: Which elements are involved in rusting? *iron and oxygen*

Ongoing Assessment

Identify which factors affect the rate at which weathering occurs.

Ask: What are three factors that influence the rate of weathering? *surface area, rock composition, and climate*

Reinforce (the BIG idea)

Have students relate the section to the Big Idea.

 Reinforcing Key Concepts, p. 227

4.1 ASSESS & RETEACH

Assess

 Section 4.1 Quiz, p. 62

Reteach

Make two separate description wheels—one for mechanical weathering and one for chemical weathering. On the spokes for the mechanical weathering wheel, include the terms *ice wedging, pressure release, plant root growth,* and *abrasion.* For chemical weathering, include *dissolving, rusting, chemical reactions,* and *weak acids.* Use the wheels to discuss the characteristics of the two types of weathering and the differences between the two. Then have students write one or two sentences that compare and contrast the two types of weathering. *Sample sentences: Both kinds of weathering break down rocks naturally. Mechanical weathering breaks rocks apart without changing their composition, but chemical weathering changes their composition.*

Technology Resources

Have students visit **ClassZone.com** for reteaching of Key Concepts.

 CONTENT REVIEW

 CONTENT REVIEW CD-ROM

A 120 Unit: **Earth's Surface**

COMBINATION NOTES
Record in your notes three factors that affect the rate at which rock weathers.

Weathering occurs at different rates.

Most weathering occurs over long periods of time—hundreds, thousands, or even millions of years. It can take hundreds or thousands of years for a very hard rock to wear down only a few millimeters—a few times the thickness of your fingernail. But the rate of weathering is not the same for all rocks. Factors such as surface area, rock composition, and location influence the rate of weathering.

Surface Area The more of a rock's surface that is exposed to air and water, the faster the rock will break down. A greater surface area allows chemical weathering to affect more of a rock.

① Over time, mechanical weathering breaks a rock into smaller pieces.

② As a result, more of the rock's surface is exposed to chemical weathering.

Rock Composition Different kinds of rock break down at different rates. Granite, for example, breaks down much more slowly than limestone. Both of these rocks are often used for tombstones and statues.

Climate Water is needed for chemical weathering to occur, and heat speeds up chemical weathering. As a result, chemical weathering occurs faster in hot, wet regions than it does in cold, dry regions. However, mechanical weathering caused by freezing and thawing occurs more in cold regions than in hot regions.

4.1 Review

KEY CONCEPTS

1. What is weathering?
2. What are four causes of mechanical weathering?
3. How do water and air help cause chemical weathering?
4. Describe three factors that affect the rate at which weathering occurs.

CRITICAL THINKING

5. **Infer** How does mechanical weathering affect the rate of chemical weathering?
6. **Predict** Would weathering affect a marble sculpture inside a museum? Explain your answer.

⚠ CHALLENGE

7. **Infer** The word *weather* is most commonly used to refer to the state of the atmosphere at a certain time. Why do you think the same word is used to refer to the breakdown of rocks?

A 120 Unit: **Earth's Surface**

ANSWERS

1. the process by which natural forces break down rock
2. ice wedging, pressure release, plant roots, moving water
3. They can cause rusting.
4. surface area: the more of a rock's surface that is exposed, the faster the rock will weather; rock composition: certain types of rock break down more quickly than others; climate: temperature and moisture in a location affect the rate of weathering
5. It breaks up rocks and increases the surface area of the rock. More rock is exposed to air and water, so the rate of chemical weathering increases.
6. No; the sculpture would be protected from rain, heat, and wind.
7. Characteristics of weather, such as rain and temperature, help to break down rock.

MATH TUTORIAL
CLASSZONE.COM

Click on Math Tutorial for
more help with finding
the surface areas of
rectangular prisms.

Weathering has broken apart these
rocks in the Isles of Scilly, England.

Rock Weathering

How quickly a rock weathers depends, in part, on its surface area.
The greater the surface area, the more quickly the rock weathers.
Do you think a rock will weather more quickly if you break it in half?
You can find out by using a rectangular prism to represent the rock.

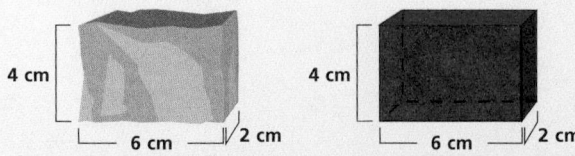

Example

To find the surface area of the prism, add the areas of its faces.

(1) Find the area of each face.

Area of **top** (or **bottom**) face: 6 cm × 2 cm = **12 cm²**
Area of **front** (or **back**) face: 6 cm × 4 cm = **24 cm²**
Area of **right** (or **left**) face: 4 cm × 2 cm = **8 cm²**

(2) Add the areas of all six faces to find the surface area.

Surface area = 12 cm² + 12 cm² + 24 cm² + 24 cm²
     + 8 cm² + 8 cm²
   = 88 cm²

ANSWER The surface area of the prism is 88 cm².

For the rock broken in half, you can use two smaller rectangular
prisms to represent the two halves.

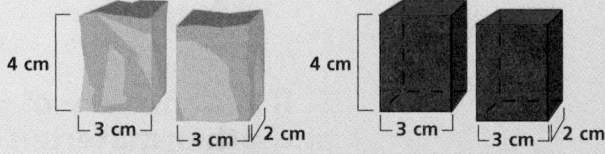

Answer the following questions.

1. What is the surface area of each of the smaller
   rectangular prisms?

2. How does the total surface area of the two smaller prisms
   compare with the surface area of the larger prism?

3. Will the rock weather more quickly in one piece or broken in half?

CHALLENGE If the two smaller prisms both broke in half, what
would be the total surface area of the resulting four prisms?

121 **A**

ANSWERS

1. top & bottom: 3 cm × 2 cm = 6 cm²; front & back: 4 cm × 3 cm =
   12 cm²; sides: 4 cm × 2 cm = 8 cm²; 6 cm² + 6 cm² + 12 cm² +
   12 cm² + 8 cm² + 8 cm² = 52 cm²

2. 104 cm² > 88 cm²; total SA of smaller prisms is greater

3. broken in half; because its surface area would be larger

CHALLENGE If all four prisms were to break horizontally, or parallel
to their bases, their total surface area would be 128 cm². If they
were to break vertically, or perpendicular to their bases, their total
surface area would be 136 cm².

Set Learning Goal

To find the surface area of a rectangular
prism

Present the Science

More than 200 low-lying islands make
up the Isles of Scilly, located in the British
Isles. Only five of the islands are inhabited.
The islands are made up mostly of hard
granitic rocks that intruded, or were thrust
by natural forces, into older rocks.
Influenced by the Gulf Stream, the climate
of the isles is relatively warm and wet,
which accelerates rates of weathering.

Develop Measurement Skills

Remind students that surface area refers
to the area of the sides, or faces, of an
object. For rectangles, area is found by
multiplying length times width.

DIFFERENTIATION TIP For students
with learning disabilities, use the dimensions given in the feature to construct a
rectangular prism out of cardboard.
Allow students to label the faces (front:
6 cm × 4 cm, top: 6 cm × 2 cm, right
face: 4 cm × 2 cm, and so on) before
adding the areas of the faces.

Close

Ask: What could eventually happen to a
rock that is weathered into smaller and
smaller pieces? *It could break down
into tiny rock particles, or sediment,
that could eventually form other rocks.*

• Math Support, p. 255
• Math Practice, p. 256

Technology Resources

Students can visit **ClassZone.com** for
more help in finding the surface areas
of rectangular prisms.

 MATH TUTORIAL

Students will

- Explain what soil consists of.
- Describe how climate and landforms affect a soil's characteristics.
- Recognize how the activities of organisms affect a soil's characteristics.
- Observe how the properties of soil differ.

◔ 3-Minute Warm-Up

Display Transparency 28 or copy this exercise on the board:

Imagine you are hiking in a forest and pass a young oak tree growing in the crack of a large rock. Describe what will happen to the rock as the tree grows into a full-grown oak. *The rock will break up.* Is this an example of mechanical or chemical weathering? *mechanical weathering* What is likely to happen as a result? *More rock will be exposed and the rock will weather even more quickly.*

 3-Minute Warm-Up, p. T28

4.2 MOTIVATE

EXPLORE Soil Composition

PURPOSE To help students recognize similarities and differences among soils

TIP *15 min.* Have each student bring in a small bag of soil from his or her neighborhood to use as local soil samples.

WHAT DO YOU THINK? *Potting soil is darker and contains small, white balls; the local soil sample is slightly lighter in color and may contain rock fragments. Both are loose and similar in texture. Materials may have been added to the potting soil.*

Ongoing Assessment

CHECK YOUR READING *Answer: Food grows in soil and we build on it.*

KEY CONCEPT

4.2 Weathering and organic processes form soil.

◁ **BEFORE, you learned**

- Weathering processes break down rocks
- Climate influences the rate of weathering

▷ **NOW, you will learn**

- What soil consists of
- How climate and landforms affect a soil's characteristics
- How the activities of organisms affect a soil's characteristics
- How the properties of soil differ

VOCABULARY

humus p. 123
soil horizon p. 124
soil profile p. 124

EXPLORE Soil Composition

What makes soils different?

PROCEDURE

① Spread some potting soil on a piece of white paper. Spread another type of soil on another piece of white paper.

② Examine the two soil samples with a hand lens. Use the tweezers to look for small pieces of rock or sand, humus, and clay. Humus is brown or black, and clay is lighter in color. Record your observations.

MATERIALS

- potting soil
- local soil sample
- white paper (2 pieces)
- hand lens
- tweezers

WHAT DO YOU THINK?

- How do the two soil samples differ? How are they alike?
- What might account for the differences between the two soils?

Soil is a mixture of weathered rock particles and other materials.

Soil may not be the first thing you think of when you wake up in the morning, but it is a very important part of your everyday life. You have spent your whole life eating food grown in soil, standing on soil, and living in buildings built on soil. Soil is under your feet right now—or at least there used to be soil there before the building you are in was constructed. In this section you will learn more about the world of soil beneath your feet.

 CHECK YOUR READING Why is soil important?

RESOURCES FOR DIFFERENTIATED INSTRUCTION

Below Level

UNIT RESOURCE BOOK
- Reading Study Guide A, pp. 230–231
- Decoding Support, p. 254

 **AUDIO CDS**

R **Additional INVESTIGATION,** Soil Formation, A, B, & C, pp. 267–275; Teacher Instructions, pp. 348–349

Advanced

UNIT RESOURCE BOOK
Challenge and Extension, p. 236

English Learners

UNIT RESOURCE BOOK
Spanish Reading Study Guide, pp. 234–235

 **AUDIO CDS**

- Audio Readings in Spanish
- Audio Readings (English)

Soil Composition

Soil is a mixture of four materials: weathered rock particles, organic matter, water, and air. Weathered rock particles are the main ingredient of soil. Soils differ, depending on what types of rock the rock particles came from—for example, granite or limestone.

Water and air each make up about 20 to 30 percent of a soil's volume. Organic matter makes up about 5 percent. The word *organic* (awr-GAN-ihk) means "coming from living organisms." Organic matter in soil comes from the remains and waste products of plants, animals, and other living organisms. For example, leaves that fall to a forest floor decay and become part of the soil. The decayed organic matter in soil is called **humus** (HYOO-muhs).

All soils are not the same. Different soils are made up of different ingredients and different amounts of each ingredient. In the photographs below, the black soil contains much more decayed plant material than the red soil. The black soil also contains more water. The kind of soil that forms in an area depends on a number of factors, including

- the kind of rock in the area
- the area's climate, or overall weather pattern over time
- the landforms in the area, such as mountains and valleys
- the plant cover in the area
- the animals and other organisms in the area
- time

The composition of a soil determines what you can grow in it, what you can build on it, and what happens to the rainwater that falls on it.

VOCABULARY
A description wheel would be a good choice for taking notes about the term *humus*.

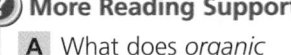 **COMPARE AND CONTRAST** These two soils look different because they contain different ingredients. How would you describe their differences?

Chapter 4: **Weathering and Soil Formation** 123 **A**

4.2 INSTRUCT

Develop Critical Thinking

INFER Have students use what they have learned thus far about soil composition to make inferences about the types of soils best suited for growing crops. Tell them to study the photographs of the two soils on this page. Ask: Which soil might be better for growing crops? Explain your answer. *The darker soil might be better because it contains more humus and more water.*

Ongoing Assessment

Explain what soil consists of.

Ask: Which four materials make up soil? *weathered rock particles, organic matter, water, and air*

READING VISUALS *Answer: The soil in the photograph on the left is darker. The soil in the photograph on the right is more reddish.*

DIFFERENTIATE INSTRUCTION

? More Reading Support

A What does *organic* mean? *coming from living organisms*

B What is humus? *decayed organic matter in soil*

English Learners The factors that affect soil composition include rocks, climate, landforms, plants, animals, and time. Use the first letter of each factor to make a mnemonic statement, such as this, Really clever little people always teach. Encourage students to develop their own memory devices to help them remember key concepts throughout the chapter. Students may also have trouble when presented with hypothetical questions, such as the last question of this section's review: "What kinds of roots might you expect to find...?"

Chapter 4 **123** **A**

To help students interpret the visual of a soil profile, ask:

• Why is a ruler included in the visual? *to show the depth of each soil horizon*

• Why does the black arrow point downward? *to show that the C horizon extends downward*

• Where would you expect to find the most organic matter? the least? *most: A horizon; least: C horizon*

Real World Example

Gardeners often use compost to add organic matter to soils with thin top layers. Compost consists of leaves, grass clippings, and other organic materials that decompose into a rich fertilizer for plants. One recent scientific study combined compost with recycling to achieve crops with higher yields. The study involved spreading shredded telephone books directly on crops; shredded newspaper was also added to more traditional compost materials, such as yard waste. Yields of corn, soybeans, and cotton all increased as a result of using the recycled materials.

Ongoing Assessment

CHECK YOUR READING *Answer: horizontal layers of soil with properties that differ from those of the layer above or below it*

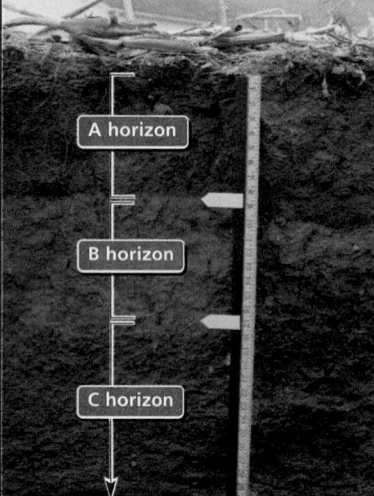

This soil profile in Hagerstown, Maryland, shows distinct A, B, and C horizons.

A horizon

B horizon

C horizon

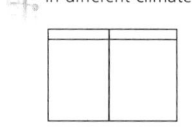

COMBINATION NOTES Record in your notes four categories of soil that form in different climate regions.

Soil Horizons

If you dig a deep hole in the ground, you might notice that the deeper soil looks different. As you dig down, you will find larger rock particles that are less weathered. There is also less organic matter in deeper soil.

Soil develops in a series of horizontal layers called soil horizons. A **soil horizon** is a layer of soil with properties that differ from those of the layer above or below it. Geologists label the main horizons A, B, and C. In some places there may also be a layer of dead leaves and other organic matter at the surface of the ground.

• **The A horizon** is the upper layer of soil and is commonly called topsoil. It contains the most organic matter of the three horizons. Because of the humus the A horizon contains, it is often dark in color.

• **The B horizon** lies just below the A horizon. It has little organic matter and is usually brownish or reddish in color. It contains clay and minerals that have washed down from the A horizon.

• **The C horizon** is the deepest layer of soil. It consists of the largest and least-weathered rock particles. Its color is typically light yellowish brown.

The soil horizons in a specific location make up what geologists call a **soil profile.** Different locations can have very different soil profiles. The A horizon, for example, may be very thick in some places and very thin in others. In some areas, one or more horizons may even be missing from the profile. For example, a soil that has had only a short time to develop might be missing the B horizon.

CHECK YOUR READING What are soil horizons?

Climate and landforms affect soil.

Different kinds of soils form in different climates. The soil that forms in a hot, wet climate is different from the soil of a cold, dry climate. Climate also influences the characteristics and thickness of the soil that develops from weathered rock. Tropical, desert, temperate, and arctic soils are four types of soil that form in different climate regions.

The shape of the land also affects the development of soil. For example, mountain soils may be very different from the soils in nearby valleys. The cold climate on a mountain results in slow soil formation, and the top layer of soil continually washes down off the slopes. As a result, mountain slopes have soils with thin A horizons that cannot support large plants. The soil that washes down the slopes builds up in the surrounding valleys, so the valleys may have soils with thick A horizons that can support many plants.

A 124 Unit: Earth's Surface

? C

DIFFERENTIATE INSTRUCTION

? **More Reading Support**

C What are four kinds of soil that form in different climate regions? *tropical, desert, temperate, and arctic*

Alternative Assessment Bring potting soil, clay, and gravel to class. Give students plastic cups and ask them to arrange the three materials into a soil profile with A, B, and C horizons. Afterward have students explain their models. Have kinesthetic learners and students with visual impairments describe the texture of the horizons. *Potting soil is rich in organic matter and would represent the A horizon. The clay would represent the B horizon. The gravel is rock and would represent the C horizon.*

World Soil Types

Different types of soils form in different climates.

Tropical Soils

Tropical soils form in warm, rainy regions. Heavy rains wash away minerals, leaving only a thin surface layer of humus. Tropical soils are not suitable for growing most crops.

Desert Soils

Desert soils form in dry regions. These soils are shallow and contain little organic matter. Because of the low rainfall, chemical weathering and soil formation occur very slowly in desert regions.

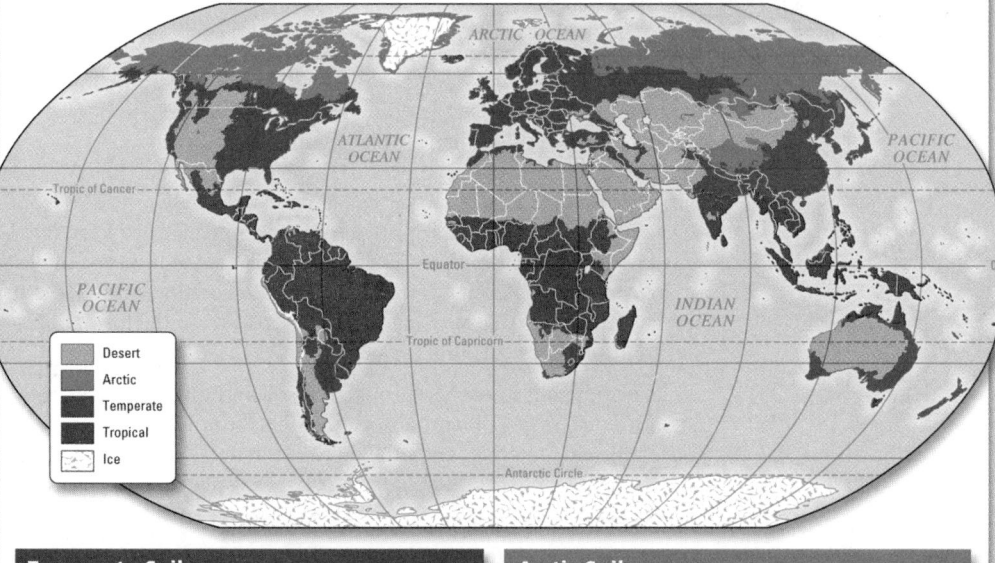

Legend:
- Desert
- Arctic
- Temperate
- Tropical
- Ice

Temperate Soils

Temperate soils form in regions with moderate rainfall and temperatures. Some temperate soils are dark-colored, rich in organic matter and minerals, and good for growing crops.

Arctic Soils

Arctic soils form in cold, dry regions where chemical weathering is slow. They typically do not have well-developed horizons. Arctic soils contain a lot of rock fragments.

Chapter 4: **Weathering and Soil Formation 125** **A**

DIFFERENTIATE INSTRUCTION

Inclusion Have students who are color blind describe other qualities of the soil horizons pictured on p. 124. For example, the A horizon contains roots, the B horizon looks somewhat smooth like clay, whereas the C horizon appears grainy like sand or crushed rock. For the "World Soil Types" visual, ask students to describe what shades they see and infer, based on the descriptions of each soil type, where each soil type is found.

Teach from Visuals

As students examine the visual on world soil types, have them refer to a world map that identifies countries and continents. To help students interpret the visual:

• Have students name a country on the map with tropical soils. Do the same for the other types of soils. *Sample answers: tropical, Brazil; desert, Saudi Arabia; temperate, eastern United States; arctic, northern Canada*

• Ask: Which visual clue helped you to locate these areas? *the color key*

• Ask: Which type of soil does your area have? *Make sure the answer is correct for your region.*

History of Science

For thousands of years, people have looked for ways to improve the soils in their area. Desert soils, for example, are not naturally suited for growing crops. As early as 2000 B.C., Egyptian farmers overcame this problem by building canals to transport water from the Nile River to their crops. Irrigation is still used today to change dry landscapes into fertile fields. One method, drip irrigation, involves laying pipes along rows of plants. The pipes are punctured with holes. Water flows out of these holes and onto the roots of plants. Unlike some irrigation techniques that spray water over a wide area, drip irrigation delivers water directly to the plants and thus helps to conserve water.

Develop Critical Thinking

COMPARE To reinforce the concept of the effect of climate on soils, have students compare and contrast the "World Soil Types" visual with a climate map from a reference source.

Ongoing Assessment

Describe how climate and landforms affect a soil's characteristics.

Ask: Why don't arctic soils have well-developed horizons? *Chemical weathering occurs slowly there because the climate is cold and dry, so the soil is full of rocks.*

Integrate the Sciences

Organisms that live in soil have to survive changes such as variations in temperature and water level. Earthworms, for example, are well adapted to life underground. They respond to changes in their environment by estivation, a state similar to hibernation. Some earthworm species secrete a mucus that protects their tightly curled bodies during estivation.

Teaching with Technology

If you have the available software, allow students to examine microorganisms through a PC microscope. Students should make sketches of their observations.

Ongoing Assessment

CHECK YOUR READING *Answer: Plants break down and become a part of the organic matter that forms humus.*

CHECK YOUR READING *Answer: Animals loosen and mix the soil, bring partly weathered rock particles to the surface, and return nutrients to the soil when they decompose.*

COMBINATION NOTES
Record in your notes three types of organisms that affect soil characteristics.

READING TiP
A decomposer is an organism that decomposes, or breaks down, dead plants and animals.

E

The activities of organisms affect soil.

Under the ground beneath your feet is a whole world of life forms that are going about their daily activities. The living organisms in a soil have a huge impact on the soil's characteristics. In fact, without them, the soil would not be able to support the wide variety of plants that people depend on to live. The organisms that affect the characteristics of soils include plants, microorganisms (MY-kroh-AWR-guh-NIHZ-uhmz), and animals.

Plants, such as trees and grasses, provide most of the organic matter that gets broken down to form humus. Trees add to the organic matter in soil as they lose their branches and leaves. Trees and other plants also contribute to humus when they die and decompose, or break down.

CHECK YOUR READING How are plants and humus related?

Microorganisms include decomposers such as bacteria and fungi (FUHN-jy). The prefix *micro-* means "very small." Microorganisms are so small that they can be seen only with a microscope. A spoonful of soil may contain more than a million microorganisms!

These microorganisms decompose dead plants and animals and produce nutrients that plants need to grow. Plants absorb these nutrients from the soil through their roots. Nitrogen, for example, is one of the nutrients plants need to grow. Microorganisms change the nitrogen in dead organic matter—and nitrogen in the air—into compounds that plants can absorb and use. Some bacteria also contribute to the formation of soil by producing acids that break down rocks.

The cycling of nutrients through the soil and through plants is a continuous process. Plants absorb nutrients from the soil and use those nutrients to grow. Then they return the nutrients to the soil when they die or lose branches and leaves. New plants then absorb the nutrients from the soil and start the cycle over again.

Animals such as earthworms, ants, termites, mice, gophers, moles, and prairie dogs all make their homes in the soil. All of these animals loosen and mix the soil as they tunnel through it. They create spaces in the soil, thereby adding to its air content and improving its ability to absorb and drain water. Burrowing animals also bring partly weathered rock particles to the surface of the ground, where they become exposed to more weathering. Just like plants, animals return nutrients to the soil when their bodies decompose after death.

CHECK YOUR READING How do animals affect soil? Name at least three ways.

DIFFERENTIATE INSTRUCTION

 **More Reading Support**

D Where does most humus come from? *plants*

E Which type of organisms are bacteria and fungi? *microorganism or decomposer*

Alternative Assessment Have students make cycle concept maps showing how nutrients continually cycle through the soil and living organisms. Concept maps should show several ovals containing statements linked by arrows. The statements within the ovals might read: Plants absorb nutrients from soil and use them to grow. Plants die or lose branches and leaves. Nutrients return to soil as they decay.

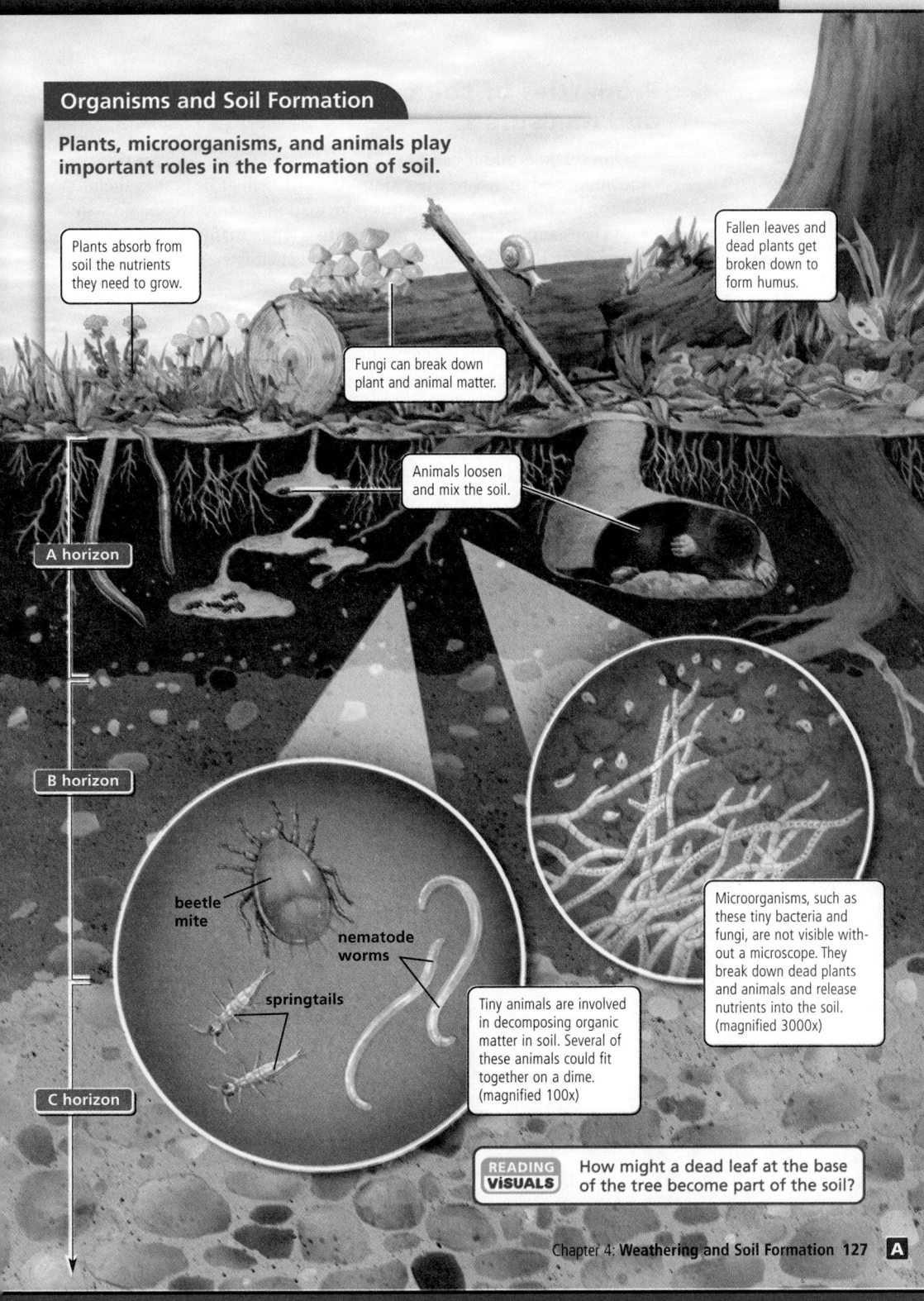

Organisms and Soil Formation

Plants, microorganisms, and animals play important roles in the formation of soil.

Plants absorb from soil the nutrients they need to grow.

Fungi can break down plant and animal matter.

Fallen leaves and dead plants get broken down to form humus.

Animals loosen and mix the soil.

A horizon

B horizon

C horizon

beetle mite

nematode worms

springtails

Tiny animals are involved in decomposing organic matter in soil. Several of these animals could fit together on a dime. (magnified 100x)

Microorganisms, such as these tiny bacteria and fungi, are not visible without a microscope. They break down dead plants and animals and release nutrients into the soil. (magnified 3000x)

READING VISUALS How might a dead leaf at the base of the tree become part of the soil?

Chapter 4: **Weathering and Soil Formation** 127 **A**

Teach from Visuals

To help students interpret the visual illustrating organisms and soil formation, ask:

- Name five decomposers in the visual. *beetle mite, springtails, nematode worms, bacteria, and fungi*

- How does the visual show the decomposers? *The organisms are shown in enlarged circles.* Why were they shown this way? *because they are so small*

- In which soil horizon are most organisms found? *the A horizon* Why do you think this is so? *The A horizon contains the most organic matter. Organisms need the nutrients in organic matter to survive. Also, air and water are more plentiful in the A horizon.*

EXPLORE (the **BIG** idea)

Revisit "Internet Activity: Soil Formation" on p. 113. Have students discuss how the visual of organisms and soil formation relates to the activity.

Ongoing Assessment

Recognize how the activities of organisms affect a soil's characteristics.

Ask: What might happen to the process of soil formation if all microorganisms disappeared? *These organisms decompose organic matter. Some also produce acids that help to break down rocks. Without microorganisms, the rate of soil formation would slow down drastically, and soils would consist mainly of weathered rock.*

READING VISUALS *Answer: It might be decomposed by animals and microorganisms and form humus.*

DIFFERENTIATE INSTRUCTION

Additional Investigation To reinforce Section 4.2 learning goals, use the following full-period investigation:

R **Additional INVESTIGATION,** Soil Formation, A, B, & C, pp. 267–275, pp. 348–349 (Advanced students should complete Levels B and C.)

Below Level Invite students to give oral summaries of the "Organisms and Soil Foundation" visual. Encourage them not to use the captions for reference.

Address Misconceptions

Address Misconceptions

IDENTIFY Ask: What is clay? If students' responses refer to modeling clay, they may not realize that *clay* occurs naturally.

CORRECT Discuss all experiences that students have had with clay, such as digging it up in a garden or backyard, seeing it in a soil profile at a construction site, and working with modeling clay. Explain that natural clay is composed of one or more minerals formed as a result of the weathering of other minerals. For example, the mineral feldspar weathers into a variety of clays. Clay particles are very small but almost always are stuck together to form clumps of different sizes. Some modeling clays that artists use are natural. Others, such as children's modeling clay, are made from waxes and other materials. All clays, though, become soft when wet and hard when dry.

REASSESS Ask: How is clay in soil different from children's modeling clay? *Clay in soil is made from weathered minerals; children's modeling clay is made of waxes and other materials.*

Technology Resources

Visit **ClassZone.com** for background on common student misconceptions.

 MISCONCEPTION DATABASE

Develop Critical Thinking

APPLY Place a bowl of sugar, a bowl of flour, and a bowl of modeling clay on your desk. Allow students to feel the different textures of the materials. Ask: Which soil texture does each material represent? *Sugar represents sand. Flour represents silt. Modeling clay represents clay.*

Ongoing Assessment

Observe how the properties of soil differ.

Ask: What determines the texture of a soil? *the size of the weathered rock particles that make up the soil*

Properties of soil can be observed and measured.

 F

Observations and tests of soil samples reveal what nutrients the soils contain and therefore what kinds of plants will grow best in them. Farmers and gardeners use this information to improve the growth of crops and other plants. Soil scientists study many soil properties, including texture, color, pore space, and chemistry.

Texture

 G

The texture of a soil is determined by the size of the weathered rock particles it contains. Soil scientists classify the rock particles in soils into three categories, on the basis of size: sand, silt, and clay. Sand particles are the largest and can be seen without a microscope. Silt particles are smaller than sand particles—too small to be seen without a microscope. Clay particles are the smallest. Most soils contain a mixture of sand, silt, and clay. The texture of a soil influences how easily air and water move through the soil.

Soil Texture

The texture of a soil is determined by the amounts of sand, silt, and clay it contains.

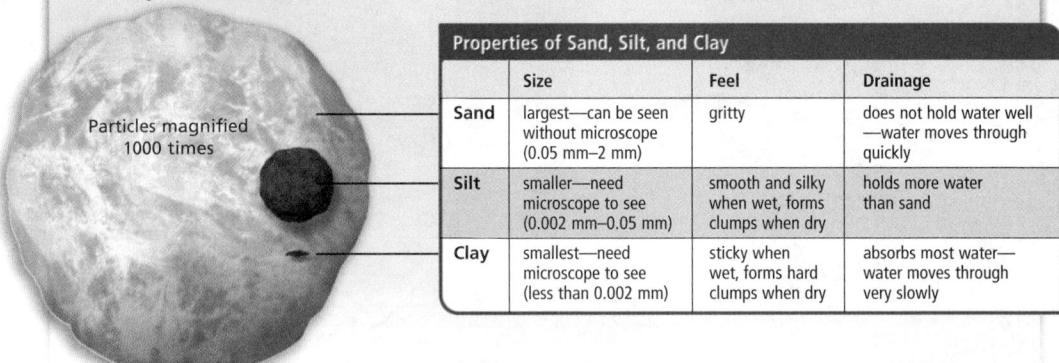

Particles magnified 1000 times

Properties of Sand, Silt, and Clay			
	Size	**Feel**	**Drainage**
Sand	largest—can be seen without microscope (0.05 mm–2 mm)	gritty	does not hold water well—water moves through quickly
Silt	smaller—need microscope to see (0.002 mm–0.05 mm)	smooth and silky when wet, forms clumps when dry	holds more water than sand
Clay	smallest—need microscope to see (less than 0.002 mm)	sticky when wet, forms hard clumps when dry	absorbs most water—water moves through very slowly

sand   silt   clay

A **128** Unit: **Earth's Surface**

More Reading Support

F Which soil properties do scientists study? *texture, color, pore space, and chemistry*

G What are the three categories of soil texture? *sand, silt, and clay*

Advanced Soil-quality indicators are used by the USDA Natural Resources Conservation Service to monitor changes in soil. The indicators include physical, chemical, and biological characteristics of soil. Have interested students obtain samples of soil-quality indicators and explain how they are used. *The indicators provide information that helps guide land-use decisions. They allow scientists to evaluate conservation techniques, monitor trends, assess soil health, and improve soil quality.*

R Challenge and Extension, p. 236

Color

The color of a soil is a clue to its other properties. Soil colors include red, brown, yellow, green, black, and even white. Most soil colors come from iron compounds and humus. Iron gives soil a reddish color. Soils with a high humus content are usually black or brown. Besides indicating the content of a soil, color may also be a clue to how well water moves through the soil—that is, how well the soil drains. Bright-colored soils, for instance, drain well.

RESOURCE CENTER
CLASSZONE.COM
Investigate soil.

Pore Space

Pore space refers to the spaces between soil particles. Water and air move through the pore spaces in a soil. Plant roots need both water and air to grow. Soils range from about 25 to 60 percent pore space. An ideal soil for growing plants has 50 percent of its volume as pore space, with half of the pore space occupied by air and half by water.

This gardener is adding lime to the soil to make it less acidic.

Chemistry

Plants absorb the nutrients they need from the water in soil. These nutrients may come from the minerals or the organic matter in the soil. To be available to plant roots, the nutrients must be dissolved in water. How well nutrients dissolve in the water in soil depends on the water's pH, which is a measure of acidity. Farmers may apply lime to make soil less acidic. To make soil more acidic, an acid may be applied.

 CHECK YOUR READING How does soil acidity affect whether the nutrients in soil are available to plants?

4.2 Review

KEY CONCEPTS

1. What are the main ingredients of soil?
2. How do climate and landforms affect soils' characteristics?
3. How do the activities of organisms affect the characteristics of soil?
4. Describe four properties of soil.

CRITICAL THINKING

5. **Compare and Contrast** How would a soil containing a lot of sand differ from a soil with a lot of clay?
6. **Infer** Which would you expect to be more fertile, the soil on hilly land or the soil on a plain? Why?

CHALLENGE

7. **Synthesize** What kinds of roots might you expect to find on plants that grow in arctic soils? Why?

Chapter 4: **Weathering and Soil Formation** 129 **A**

CHAPTER INVESTIGATION

Focus

PURPOSE To measure and identify soil properties

OVERVIEW Students will use appropriate technology to test a soil sample for pore space, pH, and particle size. Students will find the following:

- Pore space affects soil's ability to absorb water.
- Different soils have different pH levels.
- Different soils contain different amounts of sand, silt, and clay.

Lab Preparation

On the day before conducting this experiment, have students bring in samples of soil. To ensure a variety of soil samples, suggest that each group obtain soil from a different area, such as topsoil from a garden, compacted soil from a park, and subsoil with gravel from a playground.

Prior to the investigation have students read through the investigation and prepare their data tables. Or you may wish to copy and distribute datasheets and rubrics.

 UNIT RESOURCE BOOK, pp. 257–266

 SCIENCE TOOLKIT, F15

Lab Management

- If the screen over the bottle clogs, have students add about 2 cm of sand above the screen before adding the soil.
- Draw bar graphs on the chalkboard so groups can compare their data. Graphs should show the porosity, permeability, pH, and particle size of the samples.

SAFETY Tell students to be careful when using scissors.

Teaching with Technology

If you have probeware, have students use a pH sensor to obtain pH measurements.

Testing Soil

OVERVIEW AND PURPOSE Soil is necessary for life. Whether a soil is suitable for farming or construction, and whether it absorbs water when it rains, depends on the particular properties of that soil. In this investigation you will

- test a soil sample to measure several soil properties
- identify the properties of your soil sample

▶ Procedure

PORE-SPACE TEST

1. Measure 200 mL of the dried soil sample in a graduated cylinder. Pour it into the jar.

2. Rinse the graduated cylinder, then fill it with 200 mL of water. Slowly pour the water into the jar until the soil is so soaked that any additional water would pool on top.

3. Record the amount of water remaining in the graduated cylinder. Then determine by subtraction the amount you added to the soil sample. Make a soil properties chart in your **Science Notebook** and record this number in it.

4. Discard the wet soil according to your teacher's instructions, and rinse the jar.

MATERIALS
- dried soil sample
- 250 mL graduated cylinder
- 1 qt jar, with lid
- water
- 2 L plastic bottle
- scissors
- window screening
- rubber band
- pH test strips
- clock with second hand
- *for Challenge:* Texture Flow Chart

pH TEST AND DRAINAGE TEST

5. Cut off the top of a plastic bottle and use a rubber band to attach a piece of window screening over its mouth. Place the bottle top, mouth down, into the jar.

6. Use the graduated cylinder to measure 200 mL of soil, and pour the soil into the inverted bottle top.

7. Rinse the graduated cylinder, and fill it with 100 mL of water. Test the water's pH, using a pH test strip. Record the result in the "before" space in your soil properties chart.

8. Pour the water into the soil. Measure the amount of time it takes for the first drips to fall into the jar. Record the result in your soil properties chart.

top of plastic bottle

jar

step 5

window screening

INVESTIGATION RESOURCES

 CHAPTER INVESTIGATION, Testing Soil
- Texture Flow Chart, p. 257
- Level A, pp. 258–261
- Level B, pp. 262–265
- Level C, p. 266

Advanced students should complete Levels B & C.

 Writing a Lab Report, D12–13

Technology Resources

Customize this student lab as needed or look for an alternative. Print rubrics to assess student lab reports.

 Lab Generator CD-ROM

Once the water stops dripping, remove the bottle top. Use a new pH strip to measure the pH of the water in the jar. Record this measurement in the "after" space in your soil properties chart and note any differences in the appearance of the water before and after its filtering through the soil.

Discard the wet soil according to your teacher's instructions, and rinse the jar.

PARTICLE-TYPE TEST

Add water to the jar until it is two-thirds full. Pour in soil until the water level rises to the top of the jar, then replace the lid. Shake the jar, and set it to rest undisturbed on a countertop overnight.

The next day, observe the different soil layers. The sample should have separated into sand (on the bottom), silt (in the middle), and clay (on the top). Measure the height of each layer, as well as the overall height of the three layers. Record your measurements in your soil properties chart.

Use the following formula to calculate the percentage of each kind of particle in the sample:

$$\frac{\text{height of layer}}{\text{total height of all layers}} \times 100$$

Record your results and all calculations in your soil properties chart.

▶ Observe and Analyze

1. **RECORD** Complete your soil properties chart.

2. **IDENTIFY** How did steps 1–3 test your soil sample's pore space?

3. **IDENTIFY** How did steps 5–9 test your soil sample's drainage rate?

▶ Conclude

1. **EVALUATE** In step 3 you measured the amount of space between the soil particles in your sample. In step 8 you measured how quickly water passed through your sample. Are these two properties related? Explain your answer.

2. **EVALUATE** Would packing down or loosening up your soil sample change any of the properties you tested? Explain your answer.

3. **INTERPRET** What happened to the pH of the water that passed through the soil? Why do you think that happened?

4. **ANALYZE** Look at the percentages of sand, silt, and clay in your sample. How do the percentages help to explain the properties you observed and measured?

▶ INVESTIGATE Further

CHALLENGE Soil texture depends on the size of the weathered rock particles the soil contains. Use the Texture Flow Chart to determine the texture of your soil sample.

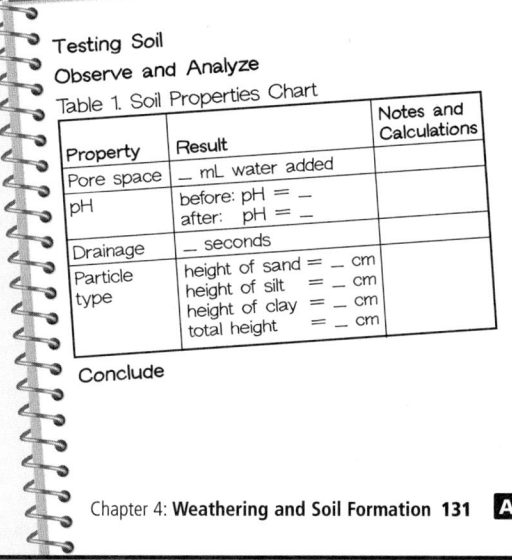

Testing Soil

Observe and Analyze

Table 1. Soil Properties Chart

Property	Result	Notes and Calculations
Pore space	__ mL water added	
pH	before: pH = __ after: pH = __	
Drainage	__ seconds	
Particle type	height of sand = __ cm height of silt = __ cm height of clay = __ cm total height = __ cm	

Conclude

Chapter 4: **Weathering and Soil Formation** 131 **A**

▶ Observe and Analyze

SAMPLE DATA Sample 1: pore space, 17%; pH before: 6, pH after: 6; drainage, 3.6 seconds; composition: sand 75%, silt 9.1%, clay 15.2%. Sample 2: pore space, 13%, pH before: 6, pH after: 5; drainage, 9.8 seconds; composition: sand 71.4%, silt 21%, clay 7.1%

1. Make sure students' charts are complete.

2. by measuring the amount of water the soil absorbed

3. by measuring the time that passed before the first drop of water fell

▶ Conclude

1. Yes, the two properties are related. When there is more space between the soil particles, the water drains more quickly.

2. Packing down the soil would decrease pore space and the rate of drainage. Loosening the soil would increase the rate of drainage.

3. It became more acidic. The water dissolved chemicals as it passed through the soil.

4. Sample answer: The soil was mostly sandy so water moved through it quickly.

▶ INVESTIGATE Further

CHALLENGE Answers will vary depending on the samples that were used.

Post-Lab Discussion

• To reinforce the idea that soil is an essential resource, have students provide examples of ways to recycle the soil samples used in this experiment. *The soil could be used to pot plants for the classroom or placed in a garden.*

• Discuss possible sources of error for this investigation, such as inaccurately measuring the water in the pore space test or miscalculating particle size. Ask: How could these errors have been avoided? *by repeating trials, rechecking calculations*

Students will

• Explain why soil is a necessary resource.

• Describe how the way in which people use land affects the soil.

• Demonstrate how to conserve soil.

• Model Earth's soil in an experiment.

◗ 3-Minute Warm-Up

Display Transparency 29 or copy this exercise on the board:

Draw a diagram of a soil profile. Include and label the following: A horizon, B horizon, C horizon, humus, decomposers. Include arrows showing nutrients cycling between organisms and soil. *Diagrams should resemble the visual "Organisms and Soil Formation" on p. 127, and should show nutrients flowing down from decaying plants into the soil and back up into plant roots.*

T 3-Minute Warm-Up, p. T29

4.3 MOTIVATE

THINK ABOUT

PURPOSE To understand how land use affects soil

DISCUSS Give students a few minutes to look out the windows before they make their tables. Encourage students to exchange ideas as they make lists of effects and to add to their tables as they read this section.

Sample answer: In schoolyards, plant cover is worn down to expose soil. Soil used in a garden may be washed away by rain.

Ongoing Assessment

CHECK YOUR READING *Answer: Soil sustains life by supporting the growth of plants, purifying water, recycling nutrients.*

4.3 Human activities affect soil.

◀ **BEFORE,** you learned

• Soils consist mainly of weathered rock and organic matter

• Soils vary, depending on climate

• Organisms affect the characteristics of soil

• Soil properties can be measured

▶ **NOW,** you will learn

• Why soil is a necessary resource

• How people's use of land affects soil

• How people can conserve soil

VOCABULARY

desertification p. 133

THINK ABOUT

How does land use affect soil?

Look outside for evidence of ways that people have affected the soil. Make a list of all the things that you can see or think of. Use your list to make a two-column table with the headings "Activity" and "Effects."

Soil is a necessary resource.

Soil helps sustain life on Earth—including your life. You already know that soil supports the growth of plants, which in turn supply food for animals. Therefore, soil provides you with nearly all the food you eat. But that's not all. Many other items you use, such as cotton clothing and medicines, come from plants. Lumber in your home comes from trees. Even the oxygen you breathe comes from plants.

Besides supporting the growth of plants, soil plays other life-sustaining roles. Soil helps purify, or clean, water as it drains through the ground and into rivers, lakes, and oceans. Decomposers in soil also help recycle nutrients by breaking down the remains of plants and animals, releasing nutrients that living plants use to grow. In addition, soil provides a home for a variety of living things, from tiny one-celled organisms to small mammals.

CHECK YOUR READING Why is soil a necessary resource?

RESOURCES FOR DIFFERENTIATED INSTRUCTION

Below Level

UNIT RESOURCE BOOK
• Reading Study Guide A, pp. 240–241
• Decoding Support, p. 254

 **AUDIO CDS**

Advanced

UNIT RESOURCE BOOK
Challenge and Extension, p. 246

English Learners

UNIT RESOURCE BOOK
Spanish Reading Study Guide, pp. 244–245

 **AUDIO CDS**

• Audio Readings in Spanish
• Audio Readings (English)

Land-use practices can harm soil.

The way people use land can affect the levels of nutrients and pollution in soil. Any activity that exposes soil to wind and rain can lead to soil loss. Farming, construction and development, and mining are among the main activities that impact soil resources.

Farming

Farming is very important to society because almost all of the world's food is grown on farms. Over the 10,000 years humans have been farming, people have continually improved their farming methods. However, farming has some harmful effects and can lead to soil loss.

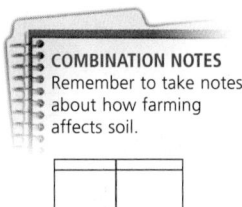

COMBINATION NOTES
Remember to take notes about how farming affects soil.

Farmers often add nutrients to soil in the form of organic or artificial fertilizers to make their crops grow better. However, some fertilizers can make it difficult for microorganisms in the soil to produce nutrients naturally. Fertilizers also add to water pollution when rainwater draining from fields carries the excess nutrients to rivers, lakes, and oceans.

Over time, many farming practices lead to the loss of soil. All over the world, farmers clear trees and other plants and plow up the soil to plant crops. Without its natural plant cover, the soil is more exposed to rain and wind and is therefore more likely to get washed or blown away. American farmers lose about five metric tons of soil for each metric ton of grain they produce. In many other parts of the world, the losses are even higher.

Another problem is overgrazing. Overgrazing occurs when farm animals eat large amounts of the land cover. Overgrazing destroys natural vegetation and causes the soil to wash or blow away more easily. In many dry regions of the world, overgrazing and the clearing of land for farming have led to desertification. **Desertification** (dih-ZUR-tuh-fih-KAY-shuhn) is the expansion of desert conditions in areas where the natural plant cover has been destroyed.

Exposed soil can be blown away by wind or washed away by rain.

DIFFERENTIATE INSTRUCTION

 More Reading Support

A What are some land-use practices that impact soil resources? *farming, construction and development, and mining*

English Learners English learners may be confused by the use of the imperative mood in "Investigate Soil Conservation" on p. 135. Make sure English learners understand that "you" is absent from the directions but still implied: "Cut the apple into quarters" means "You cut the apple into quarters."

Use the *Chapter Review* on p. 138 to help students focus on key concepts and vocabulary.

Real World Example

The Dust Bowl is a large area in the southern Great Plains that serves as a dramatic example of how farming techniques can impact soil resources. Much of this area's natural grassland was plowed up for wheat farms in the early 1900s. More grassland was destroyed by overgrazing. An extended drought, beginning in 1931, dried the soil. Wind erosion then carried away millions of tons of topsoil. The dust traveled for hundreds of kilometers, darkened the skies at midday over New England, and left once-fertile lands barren and depleted of soil.

Teach Difficult Concepts

Students may have a difficult time understanding how plant cover helps to decrease soil erosion. Explain that the roots of plants help to hold soil together. Do the following demonstration to reinforce the concept.

Teacher Demo

Place a sample of loose soil in a large rectangular pan. Place a piece of grassy sod in a similar pan. Put both pans on the floor. Blow a fan on the pans and have students observe what happens. As an alternative (if blowing soil is a concern), try putting pans on an angle and pouring equal amounts of water on each to see how much soil washes away. Ask: Which pan had less soil erosion? Why? *The pan with the sod had less soil erosion because the grass helped to hold the soil together.*

Ongoing Assessment

Explain why soil is a necessary resource.

Ask: Name three things that you use that could not exist without soil. *food, clothes, houses*

The top of this hill in San Bernardino County, California, was cleared for a housing development. A house will be built on each flat plot of land.

Construction and Development

To make roads, houses, shopping malls, and other buildings, people need to dig up the soil. Some of the soil at construction sites washes or blows away because its protective plant cover has been removed. The soil that is washed or blown away ends up in nearby low-lying areas, in rivers and streams, or in downstream lakes or reservoirs. This soil can cause problems by making rivers and lakes muddy and harming the organisms that live in them. The buildup of soil on riverbeds raises the level of the rivers and may cause flooding. The soil can also fill up lakes and reservoirs.

Mining

Some methods of mining cause soil loss. For example, the digging of strip mines and open-pit mines involves the removal of plants and soil from the surface of the ground.

By exposing rocks and minerals to the air and to rainwater, these forms of mining speed up the rate of chemical weathering. In mining operations that expose sulfide minerals, the increased chemical weathering causes a type of pollution known as acid drainage. Abandoned mines can fill with rainwater. Sulfide minerals react with the air and the water to produce sulfuric acid. Then the acid water drains from the mines, polluting the soil in surrounding areas.

CHECK YOUR READING How do some methods of mining affect the soil?

To make this open-pit mine in Cananea, Mexico, plants and soil were removed from the surface of the ground.

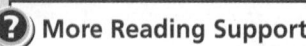 **134** Unit: Earth's Surface

---

Soil can be protected and conserved.

Soil conservation is very important, because soil can be difficult or impossible to replace once it has been lost. Soil takes a very long time to form. A soil with well-developed horizons may take hundreds of thousands of years to form! Most soil conservation methods are designed to hold soil in place and keep it fertile. Below are descriptions of a few of the many soil conservation methods that are used by farmers around the world.

Crop rotation is the practice of planting different crops on the same field in different years or growing seasons. Grain crops, such as wheat, use up a lot of the nitrogen—a necessary plant nutrient—in the soil. The roots of bean crops, such as soybeans, contain bacteria that restore nitrogen to the soil. By rotating these crops, farmers can help maintain soil fertility.

Conservation tillage includes several methods of reducing the number of times fields are tilled, or plowed, in a year. The less soil is disturbed by plowing, the less likely it is to be washed or blown away. In one method of conservation tillage, fields are not plowed at all. The remains of harvested crops are simply left on the fields to cover and protect the soil. New seeds are planted in narrow bands of soil.

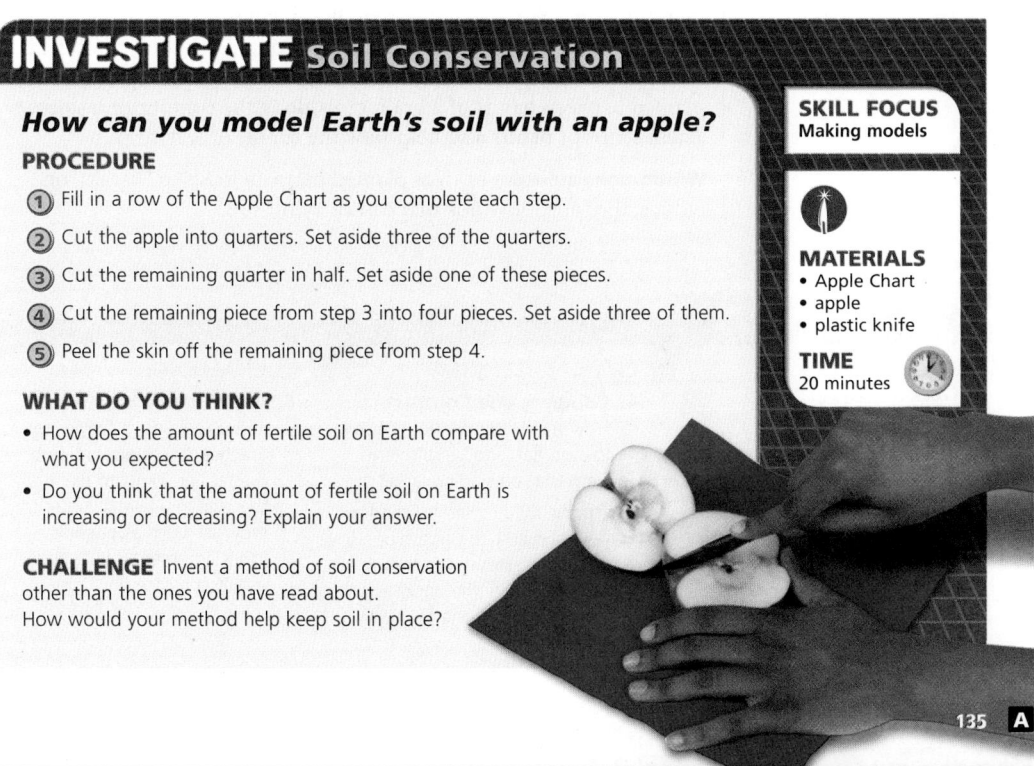

INVESTIGATE Soil Conservation

How can you model Earth's soil with an apple?

PROCEDURE

1. Fill in a row of the Apple Chart as you complete each step.
2. Cut the apple into quarters. Set aside three of the quarters.
3. Cut the remaining quarter in half. Set aside one of these pieces.
4. Cut the remaining piece from step 3 into four pieces. Set aside three of them.
5. Peel the skin off the remaining piece from step 4.

WHAT DO YOU THINK?
- How does the amount of fertile soil on Earth compare with what you expected?
- Do you think that the amount of fertile soil on Earth is increasing or decreasing? Explain your answer.

CHALLENGE
Invent a method of soil conservation other than the ones you have read about. How would your method help keep soil in place?

SKILL FOCUS
Making models

MATERIALS
- Apple Chart
- apple
- plastic knife

TIME
20 minutes

135 A

DIFFERENTIATE INSTRUCTION

 **More Reading Support**

C Why do farmers rotate crops? *to maintain soil fertility*

Advanced Have students conduct research to assess the viability of the method of soil conservation that they thought of in "Investigate Soil Conservation." For example, if a student suggested that animals be moved more often to prevent overgrazing, he or she may find that many farmers have limited acreage. Have students make charts listing the advantages and disadvantages of their methods.

 Challenge and Extension, p. 246

PURPOSE To make a model to understand the amount of fertile soil on Earth

TIPS *20 min.*

- Students should place the apple on the table before cutting it—they should not cut the apple while holding it in their hands. If you have any concerns about students using plastic knives, try this activity as a teacher demonstration.

- Students with physical disabilities can be paired with students who will not have difficulty using a knife. Make sure all students participate in the activity. Those who cannot cut the apples can record results.

WHAT DO YOU THINK? *It was less than expected. The amount of fertile soil on Earth is probably decreasing because the human population is growing. More people are now using the land.*

CHALLENGE *Sample answer: You could move animals around more often so they don't overgraze an area.*

 • Apple Chart, p. 247
- Datasheet, Soil Conservation, p. 248

Technology Resources

Customize this student lab as needed or look for an alternative. Print rubrics to assess student lab reports.

 Lab Generator CD-ROM

Develop Critical Thinking

APPLY Tell students that renewable resources are those that can be easily replaced, at the same rate that they are used, by natural processes. Nonrenewable resources take more than 100 years to replace. Point out that soil is replaced by natural processes. Have students apply this information to what they know about soil. Ask: Would you consider soil a renewable or nonrenewable resource? *Soil is a nonrenewable resource because well-developed soils may take hundreds of thousands of years to form.*

Reinforce (the **BIG** idea)

Have students relate the section to the Big Idea.

 Reinforcing Key Concepts, p. 249

ASSESS & RETEACH

Assess

[A] Section 4.3 Quiz, p. 64

Reteach

Make a table on the chalkboard that uses the following headings: Soil Cover, Average Yearly Soil Loss (tons/hectare), and Runoff Rate (percentage). Fill in the table by using the following data: bare soil has an annual soil loss of 41 tons/ha and a runoff rate of 30%; corn has an annual soil loss of 19.7 tons/ha and a runoff rate of 29%; a crop rotation of corn, wheat, and clover has an annual soil loss of 2.7 ton/ha and a runoff rate of 14%; blue- grass has an annual soil loss of 0.3 tons/ha and a runoff rate of 12%. Ask: Which soil cover would be best for a farmer? *crop rotation of corn, wheat, and clover* Why? *The farmer would be able to har- vest several crops while conserving soil.*

Technology Resources

Have students visit **ClassZone.com** for reteaching of Key Concepts.

 CONTENT REVIEW

 CONTENT REVIEW CD-ROM

Terracing

Contour Plowing

READING VISUALS **COMPARE** Both terracing and contour plowing are soil conservation methods used on sloping land. How does each method help conserve soil?

Terraces are flat, steplike areas built on a hillside to hold rainwater and prevent it from running downhill. Crops are planted on the flat tops of the terraces.

Contour plowing is the practice of plowing along the curves, or contours, of a slope. Contour plowing helps channel rainwater so that it does not run straight downhill, carrying away soil with it. A soil conservation method called strip-cropping is often combined with contour plowing. Strips of grasses, shrubs, or other plants are planted between bands of a grain crop along the contour of a slope. These strips of plants also help slow the runoff of water.

Windbreaks are rows of trees planted between fields to "break," or reduce, the force of winds that can carry off soil.

Review

KEY CONCEPTS

1. Why is soil a necessary resource?
2. How do land-use practices in farming, construction and development, and mining affect soil?
3. Describe at least three methods of soil conservation.

CRITICAL THINKING

4. **Compare and Contrast** How might the problem of soil loss on flat land be different from that on sloping land?
5. **Apply** If you were building a new home in an undeveloped area, what steps would you take to reduce the impact of construction on the soil?

CHALLENGE

6. **Apply** You have advised an inexperienced farmer to practice strip-cropping, but the farmer wants to plant all the land in wheat in order to grow as much as possible. What argument would you use to convince the farmer?

ANSWERS

1. It sustains life by supporting plant growth, purifying water, recycling nutrients.

2. These practices can result in the removal of plants and soil.

3. crop rotation: planting dif- ferent crops in the same field at different times; terraces and contour plowing: prevent

rainwater from running downhill; windbreaks: trees planted to block wind

4. flat land: likely caused by wind or by human activities; sloping land: more influ- enced by natural processes

5. avoid building on slopes, reuse plants and soil that are

removed during construction to recover slopes, and use vegetation to reduce runoff

6. Strip-cropping can help to prevent soil loss by slowing runoff. The long-term consequences of soil loss are very severe because soil is a life-sustaining resource.

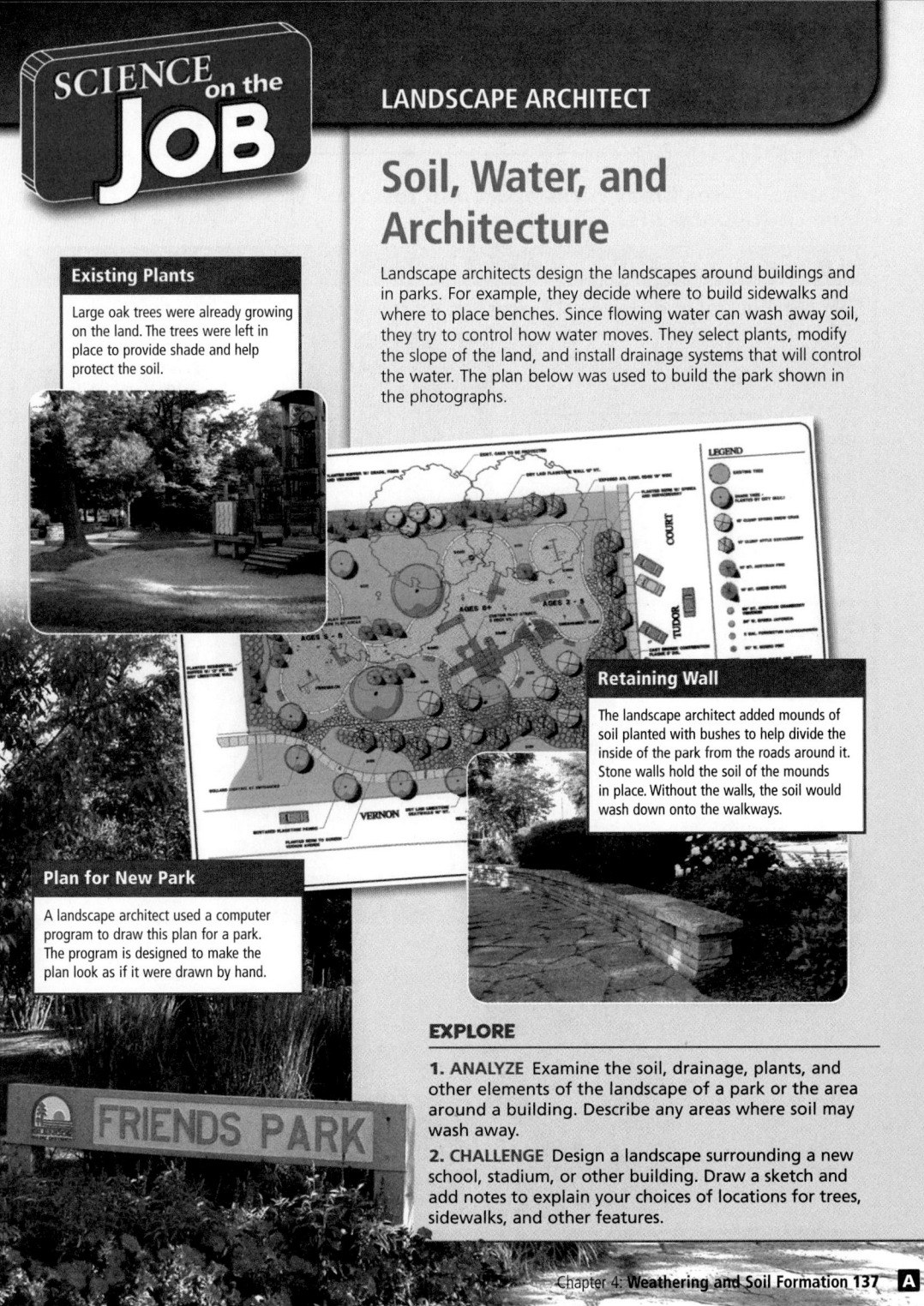

SCIENCE on the JOB

LANDSCAPE ARCHITECT

Soil, Water, and Architecture

Landscape architects design the landscapes around buildings and in parks. For example, they decide where to build sidewalks and where to place benches. Since flowing water can wash away soil, they try to control how water moves. They select plants, modify the slope of the land, and install drainage systems that will control the water. The plan below was used to build the park shown in the photographs.

Existing Plants

Large oak trees were already growing on the land. The trees were left in place to provide shade and help protect the soil.

Retaining Wall

The landscape architect added mounds of soil planted with bushes to help divide the inside of the park from the roads around it. Stone walls hold the soil of the mounds in place. Without the walls, the soil would wash down onto the walkways.

Plan for New Park

A landscape architect used a computer program to draw this plan for a park. The program is designed to make the plan look as if it were drawn by hand.

EXPLORE

1. ANALYZE Examine the soil, drainage, plants, and other elements of the landscape of a park or the area around a building. Describe any areas where soil may wash away.

2. CHALLENGE Design a landscape surrounding a new school, stadium, or other building. Draw a sketch and add notes to explain your choices of locations for trees, sidewalks, and other features.

Chapter 4: **Weathering and Soil Formation 137** Ⓐ

EXPLORE

1. *ANALYZE* Soil will wash away from areas where there is little or no plant cover.

2. *CHALLENGE* Students' sketches should reflect concepts learned in this chapter, such as conservation techniques to help reduce soil loss.

SCIENCE ON THE JOB
Relevance of Science to Non-science Jobs

Set Learning Goal

To understand why landscape architects have to know about soil and climate characteristics

Present the Science

The U.S. Environmental Protection Agency (EPA) recommends using native plants for both commercial and residential landscaping. According to the EPA, native plants are ideally suited to their local environments; once they have become established, they require little maintenance. Barring a drought, they do not need watering, and the need for potentially harmful herbicides and pesticides is greatly reduced.

Discussion Questions

- Ask: Why do landscape architects try to control how water moves? *Moving water can wash away soil—landscape architects want to reduce soil loss.*

- Ask: Why must landscape architects know about the climate and soil of an area in order to control how water moves? *The climate data would tell landscape architects how much precipitation an area receives, which, in turn, is related to how much water is carried into in rivers, lakes, and streams. The soil data would indicate how easily water moves through the ground.*

DIFFERENTIATION TIP Enlarge the plan for the park so that students with visual impairments can see its details more clearly.

Close

Ask: How does a retaining wall help to reduce soil loss? *A wall keeps soil from being washed away by rain or blown away by wind.*

BACK TO

the **BIG** idea

Refer students back to the photograph on pp. 112–113. Ask them to explain how such a large rock can eventually become part of the soil. *Over a long period of time, mechanical and chemical weathering can break down the rock into small particles called sediment. Sediment mixes with organic matter, water, and air to form soil.*

◉ KEY CONCEPTS SUMMARY

SECTION 4.1

Ask: Which type of weathering involves a physical change in rocks? *mechanical*

Ask: What might be causing the chemical weathering on the monument in the photograph? *acidic rainwater*

SECTION 4.2

Ask: In addition to living organisms, which factors affect the type of soil that forms in an area? *rock type, climate, landforms, and time*

Ask: How do plants affect soil? *They provide most of the organic matter that gets broken down to form humus.*

SECTION 4.3

Ask: How might farming affect soil? *Farming practices can cause soil loss or deplete nutrients in soil.*

Ask: How do windbreaks reduce soil loss? *The rows of trees reduce the force of winds that carry off soil.*

Review Concepts

• Big Idea Flow Chart, p. T25
• Chapter Outline, pp. T31–T32

 Chapter Review

the **BIG** idea

Natural forces break rocks apart and form soil, which supports life.

 **CONTENT REVIEW**
CLASSZONE.COM

◉ **KEY CONCEPTS SUMMARY**

4.1 Mechanical and chemical forces break down rocks.

Over time, **mechanical weathering** breaks a rock into smaller pieces.

Chemical weathering affects exposed rock surfaces.

VOCABULARY
weathering p. 115
mechanical
 weathering p. 116
exfoliation p. 116
abrasion p. 116
chemical weathering
 p. 118

4.2 Weathering and organic processes form soil.

Soil has measurable properties, such as color, texture, pore space, and chemistry.

Soil is a mixture of weathered rock, organic matter, water, and air.

Plants, microorganisms, and animals affect soil characteristics.

VOCABULARY
humus p. 123
soil horizon p. 124
soil profile p. 124

4.3 Human activities affect soil.

Soil is essential to life and takes a long time to form. It is difficult or impossible to replace soil that has been lost.

Soil Loss
Farming, construction and development, and mining are three human activities that affect soil.

Soil Conservation
Soil conservation practices help keep soil from blowing or washing away.

VOCABULARY
desertification p. 133

Technology Resources

Have students visit **ClassZone.com** or use the CD-ROM for a cumulative review of concepts.

Engage students in a whole-class interactive review of Key Concepts. Edit content as you wish.

 CONTENT REVIEW

 CONTENT REVIEW CD-ROM

 POWER PRESENTATIONS

Reviewing Vocabulary

Copy the three-column chart below. Complete the chart for each term. The first one has been done for you.

Term	Definition	Example
EXAMPLE chemical weathering	the breakdown of rocks by chemical reactions that change the rocks' mineral composition	Iron reacts with air and water to form iron oxides or rust.
1. mechanical weathering		
2. abrasion		
3. exfoliation		
4. desertification		

Reviewing Key Concepts

Multiple Choice *Choose the letter of the best answer.*

5. The force of expanding water in the cracks and pores of a rock is an example of
   a. chemical weathering
   b. mechanical weathering
   c. oxidation
   d. desertification

6. The breakdown of a rock by acidic water is an example of
   a. chemical weathering
   b. mechanical weathering
   c. oxidation
   d. desertification

7. Soil is a mixture of what four materials?
   a. granite, limestone, nitrogen, and air
   b. plant roots, iron oxides, water, and air
   c. rock particles, plant roots, humus, and nitrogen
   d. rock particles, humus, water, and air

8. What is the main component of soil?
   a. humus
   b. water
   c. air
   d. rock particles

9. What is humus?
   a. the decomposed rock particles in soil
   b. the decomposed organic matter in soil
   c. the material that makes up the B horizon
   d. the material that makes up the C horizon

10. Three factors that affect the rate of weathering are
    a. microorganisms, plants, and animals
    b. weather, landforms, and rainfall
    c. surface area, rock composition, and climate
    d. texture, color, and pore space

11. Microorganisms affect the quality of soil by
    a. decomposing organic matter
    b. creating tunnels
    c. absorbing water
    d. increasing mechanical weathering

12. The movement of air and water through a soil is influenced most by the soil's
    a. color and chemistry
    b. texture and pore space
    c. pH and nitrogen content
    d. microorganisms

13. Contour plowing, strip-cropping, and terracing are conservation methods designed to reduce the
    a. runoff of water
    b. activity of microorganisms
    c. acidity of soil
    d. pore space of soil

Short Answer *Write a few sentences to answer each question.*

14. How do farming, construction and development, and mining affect soil?

15. How do ice wedging, pressure release, plant root growth, and abrasion cause mechanical weathering?

16. How do air and water cause chemical weathering?

Reviewing Vocabulary

1. the breaking up of rocks by physical forces; plant roots growing in cracks of rocks

2. the process of wearing something down by friction; moving water

3. the process in which layers or sheets of rock gradually break off; pressure that causes rock to expand, form cracks, and break off

4. the expansion of desert conditions in areas where the natural plant cover has been destroyed; overgrazing that can lead to desertification.

Reviewing Key Concepts

5. b

6. a

7. d

8. d

9. b

10. c

11. a

12. b

13. a

14. They can cause plant and soil removal. Loss of soil can have other negative effects, such as flooding.

15. They break up rock by physical forces. Water in cracks and pores of rocks freezes, then expands. Pressure release causes rocks to expand and crack. Plant roots that grow in cracks cause rocks to wedge open and enlarge cracks. Moving water results in abrasion of rocks by friction.

16. Air and water cause chemical weathering by reacting with minerals and elements, such as oxygen.

ASSESSMENT RESOURCES

 UNIT ASSESSMENT BOOK
- Chapter Test A, pp. 65–68
- Chapter Test B, pp. 69–72
- Chapter Test C, pp. 73–76
- Alternative Assessment, pp. 77–78

 SPANISH ASSESSMENT BOOK
Spanish Chapter Test, pp. 117–120

Technology Resources

Edit test items and answer choices.

 Test Generator CD-ROM

Visit **ClassZone.com** to extend test practice.

 Test Practice

Thinking Critically

17. Student profiles should be similar to the soil profile on p. 124.

18. The dark color indicates that the soil is rich in organic matter.

19. The A horizon is most affected because it is most exposed to plant roots, animals, air, water, and other agents of weathering.

20. Use terraces or contour plowing to reduce soil loss. Rotate crops so soil remains fertile.

21. A good soil for growing crops would be dark and composed of silt with lots of organic matter and a 50 percent porosity.

22. Mechanical weathering involves a physical change in rocks. Chemical weathering involves a chemical change. Both break up rocks.

23. increased demand on soil resources and further soil loss

24. in deltas, lakes, and oceans

25. Perhaps, but soil can take hundreds of thousands of years to replace by natural processes.

26. Sample answer: from left to right, top to bottom: mechanical weathering; chemical weathering; rounded rocks; exfoliation; damaged statue; rust; moving water; pressure release; acidic water; oxygen and water

27. Students should add the following to their concept maps: surface area, rock composition, and climate.

the BIG idea

28. Student diagrams will vary.

29. Sample answer: A rabbit eats a plant, then dies and decays to form humus. Humus provides the nutrients needed for new plant growth.

UNIT PROJECTS

Students should have begun designing their models or presentations by this time. Remind them to continue researching as needed. Encourage them to try different solutions to any problems.

 Unit Projects, pp. 5–10

Thinking Critically

Use the photograph to answer the next three questions.

17. **APPLY** Make a sketch of the soil profile above, labeling the A, B, and C horizons.

18. **OBSERVE** What does the color of the top layer indicate about this soil?

19. **APPLY** Which part of the profile is most affected by chemical and mechanical weathering? Why?

20. **APPLY** Suppose that you own gently sloping farmland. Describe the methods that you would use to hold the soil in place and maintain its fertility.

21. **SYNTHESIZE** Describe the composition, color, texture, and amount of pore space of a soil that would be good for growing crops.

22. **COMPARE AND CONTRAST** How does mechanical weathering differ from chemical weathering? How are the two processes similar?

23. **PREDICT** What effect will the continued growth of the world's population likely have on soil resources?

24. **ANALYZE** Soil loss is a problem all over the world. Where might lost soil end up?

25. **ANALYZE** Can lost soil be replaced? Explain.

26. **ANALYZE** Copy the concept map below and fill it in with the following terms and phrases.

acidic water	chemical weathering
damaged statue	exfoliation
mechanical weathering	moving water
oxygen and water	pressure release
rounded rocks	rust

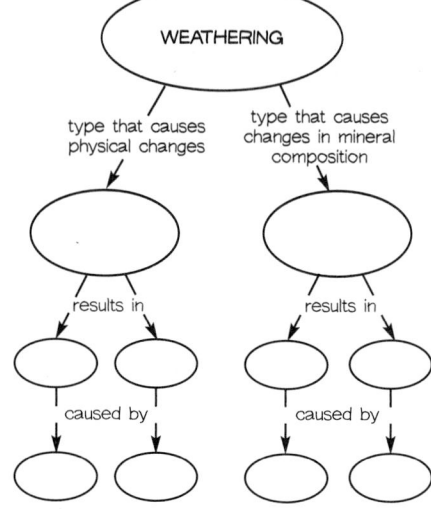

27. **ANALYZE** Add to the concept map to show the three factors that affect the rate of weathering.

the BIG idea

28. **MODEL** Draw a diagram that shows an example of a natural force breaking rocks apart to form soil that supports life.

29. **SYNTHESIZE** A cycle is a series of events or actions that repeats regularly. Describe a cycle that involves soil and living things.

UNIT PROJECTS

If you need to create graphs or other visuals for your project, be sure you have grid paper, poster board, markers, or other supplies.

MONITOR AND RETEACH

If students have trouble applying the concepts in items 17–19, refer them back to the visual on p. 124. Then use different-colored chalk to make a sketch of a soil profile. **Part 1** should be labeled the A horizon. It is usually dark in color. **Part 2** should be labeled the B horizon. It is usually brownish or reddish in color. **Part 3** should be labeled the C horizon. It consists of light yellowish brown rock.

Students may benefit from summarizing one or more sections of the chapter.

R Summarizing the Chapter, pp. 276–277

Standardized Test Practice

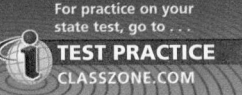

For practice on your state test, go to . . .
TEST PRACTICE
CLASSZONE.COM

Analyzing a Table

The table indicates some of the characteristics of four soil samples. Use the table to answer the questions below.

Sample	Color	Ability to Hold Water	Percentage of Pore Space	Percentage of Humus
1	black	average	50%	9%
2	yellowish brown	low	70%	3%
3	reddish brown	average	60%	3%
4	very red	average to low	65%	2%

1. Soils that contain a lot of sand do not hold water very well. Which sample probably contains the most sand?

  a. 1   **c.** 3
  b. 2   **d.** 4

2. Iron gives soil a reddish color. Which sample probably contains the most iron?

  a. 1   **c.** 3
  b. 2   **d.** 4

3. Crops grow best in soils with about half of their volume consisting of pore space. Which soil has an ideal amount of pore space for growing crops?

  a. 1   **c.** 3
  b. 2   **d.** 4

4. What soil color might indicate a high level of organic matter?

  a. black   **c.** red-brown
  b. yellow   **d.** red

5. How is pore space related to a soil's ability to hold water?

  a. The more pore space, the more water the soil can hold.
  b. The more pore space, the less water the soil can hold.
  c. The less pore space, the more humus the soil can hold.
  d. The less pore space, the less humus the soil can hold.

Extended Response

Answer the two questions below in detail. Include some of the terms shown in the word box. In your answers, underline each term you use.

abrasion	moving water
chemical weathering	plant roots
ice	rusting
mechanical weathering	

6. Jolene is comparing a rock from a riverbed and a rock from deep underground. One is very smooth. The other has very sharp edges. Explain which rock was probably found in each location.

7. In a museum, Hank sees two iron knives that were made in the early 1800s. One has spent 200 years on the top of a fortress wall. The other one has been stored in the museum for 200 years. Why might the two knives look different?

Analyzing a Table

1. b   3. a   5. d
2. d   4. a

Extended Response

6. RUBRIC

4 points for a response that answers the question and uses the following terms accurately:

- moving water
- abrasion
- mechanical weathering

Sample: The smooth rock was probably found in the river. <u>*Moving water*</u> *tumbled the rock against other rocks and against the riverbed. This type of* <u>*mechanical weathering*</u>, *in which an object is worn down by friction, is called* <u>*abrasion.*</u> *The sharp-edged rock was underground, so it was not as affected by mechanical weathering.*

3 points for a response that correctly answers the question and uses two terms accurately

2 points for a response that correctly answers the question and uses one term accurately

1 point for a response that correctly answers the question but doesn't use any of the terms

7. RUBRIC

4 points for a response that correctly answers the question and uses the following terms accurately:

- rusting
- chemical weathering

Sample: The knife that was found on the fortress wall might have been affected by <u>*rusting*</u> *because it was exposed to air and water. The knife that was stored in the museum would not have changed as much because it was indoors in a more controlled climate, so it was less affected by* <u>*chemical weathering*</u>.

3 points for a response that correctly answers the question and uses the term *chemical weathering* accurately

2 points for a response that correctly answers the question but doesn't use either term

---

METACOGNITIVE ACTIVITY

Have students answer the following questions in their **Science Notebook:**

1. How is soil important to you?

2. How has this chapter changed the way you look at rocks?

3. What about this chapter applies to your Unit Project? Should you make any alterations to your project because of what you have learned?

CHAPTER 5
Erosion and Deposition

Earth Science
UNIFYING PRINCIPLES

PRINCIPLE 1	PRINCIPLE 2	PRINCIPLE 3
Heat energy inside Earth and radiation from the Sun provide energy for Earth's processes.	Physical forces, such as gravity, affect the movement of all matter on Earth and throughout the universe.	Matter and energy move among Earth's rocks and soil, atmosphere, waters, and living things.

PRINCIPLE 4

Earth has changed over time and continues to change.

Unit: Earth's Surface
BIG IDEAS

CHAPTER 1 **Views of Earth Today**	CHAPTER 2 **Minerals**	CHAPTER 3 **Rocks**	CHAPTER 4 **Weathering and Soil Formation**
Modern technology has changed the way we view and map Earth.	Minerals are basic building blocks of Earth.	Rocks change into other rocks over time.	Natural forces break rocks apart and form soil, which supports life.

CHAPTER 5 Erosion and Deposition

Water, wind, and ice shape Earth's surface.

CHAPTER 5
KEY CONCEPTS

SECTION 5.1   SECTION 5.2   SECTION 5.3   SECTION 5.4

Forces wear down and build up Earth's surface.	**Moving water shapes land.**	**Waves and wind shape land.**	**Glaciers carve land and move sediments.**
1. Natural forces move and deposit sediments.	1. Streams shape Earth's surface.	1. Waves and currents shape shorelines.	1. Glaciers are moving bodies of ice.
2. Gravity can move large amounts of rock and soil.	2. Water moving underground forms caverns.	2. Wind shapes land.	2. Glaciers deposit large amounts of sediment.

The Big Idea Flow Chart is available on p. T33 in the **UNIT TRANSPARENCY BOOK.**

Previewing Content

Forces wear down and build up Earth's surface. pp. 145–149

1. Natural forces move and deposit sediments.
Weathered rock and soil is constantly moving from place to place in the process of **erosion.**
- Erosion is carried out by the action of water, wind, and ice.
- Water, wind, and ice move and deposit eroded material.
- Gravity plays a role in all types of erosion and **deposition.**

2. Gravity can move large amounts of rock and soil.
Gravity can pull rock and soil downhill by several types of **mass wasting.**
- Rockfalls and rockslides occur on steep slopes and involve small or large masses of rock.
- Mudflows occur when rocks, soil, and plants flow downhill with enough water to form a muddy mixture. Mudflows move quickly down steep slopes and can have devastating effects on towns in their path.
- Creep is the slow movement of soil down a gentle hillside. Its effects are slow but noticeable, as in these tilted fence posts.

Originally, the fence posts stand vertically in the ground.

Over many years, the soil holding the posts slowly shifts downhill, and the posts lean.

Moving water shapes land. pp. 150–157

1. Streams shape Earth's surface.
Running water shapes the landscape over most of Earth. Systems of streams drain water and move sediment from a **drainage basin.**
- As streams flow and carry sediment, they form valleys and **floodplains.**
- As a stream continues on its course, it usually slows down, picking up less sediment and depositing more. The slope becomes flatter, the stream and valley become wider, and the stream forms meanders, or looping curves.
- Where the stream enters the ocean, it builds up sediment in a **delta.**
- At the base of mountains, streams can flatten out and form **alluvial fans.**

Drainage basins come in all sizes, depending on what part of the stream you look at. In the continental view below, one **divide** creates two basins in North America. But each river and small stream also has its own basin, divided by higher land.

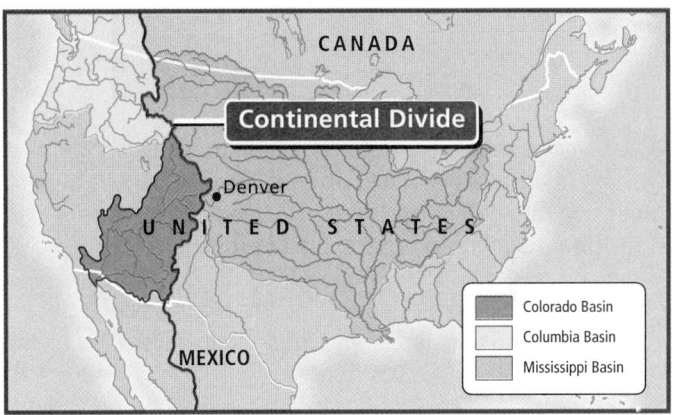

2. Water moving underground forms caverns.
Not all rainwater flows into streams. Some of it evaporates, some is absorbed by plants, and some becomes groundwater. Groundwater that is slightly acidic can dissolve some rocks. This process hollows out rock, creating caves and caverns. In limestone areas, caverns are not uncommon. **Sinkholes** may form when the roof of a cavern near the surface collapses.

Common Misconceptions

THE ROLE OF GRAVITY Many students think about gravity's role only in obvious cases, such as a free-falling object. They often don't consider the role gravity plays in more subtle downward movements, such as flowing rivers or settling sediments.

 This misconception is addressed on p. 148.

MISCONCEPTION DATABASE
CLASSZONE.COM Background on student misconceptions

GROUNDWATER Students commonly visualize groundwater as an underground lake or stream. While such features do exist in some caverns, most groundwater fills cracks and pores in rock and the spaces between rock and soil particles.

 This misconception is addressed on p. 154.

Previewing Content

1. Waves and currents shape shorelines.

The energy of waves, powered by wind, shapes shorelines through erosion and deposition. Pounding waves break cliffs into small rocks and grains of sand. Waves and currents carry away this sediment and deposit it along the shore, building up beaches. **Longshore drift** is the movement of sand along the shore in a zigzag pattern, as shown below. **Longshore current** is the movement of water along a shore as waves strike the shore at an angle.

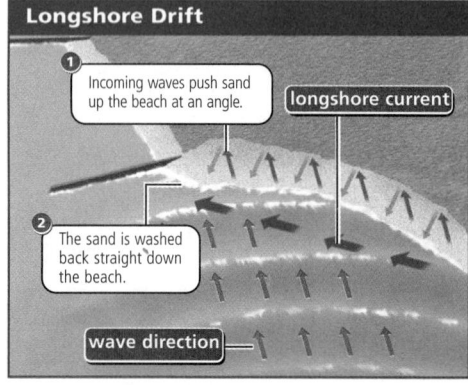

Longshore Drift

1. Incoming waves push sand up the beach at an angle.

longshore current

2. The sand is washed back straight down the beach.

wave direction

Ocean waves and currents shape sand into many landforms. Typically, these features build up over many years, but hurricanes and other storms can quickly change their shape.

- **Sandbars** are ridges of sand built up by the action of waves and currents.
- Spits are above-water ridges joined to land at one end.
- **Barrier islands** are large, emerged sandbars, parallel to the shore.

2. Wind shapes land.

Wind erosion and deposition are greatest in dry areas with few plants to hold the soil in place. High-energy wind scoops up sand and dust and deposits them as the wind energy wanes.

- **Dunes** are mounds of sand. They form on ocean and lake shores and in deserts.
- Layers of dust, called **loess,** can become fertile soil.
- Desert pavement is a layer of gravel and larger stones, left behind when dry winds blow away fine-grained sediments.

1. Glaciers are moving bodies of ice.

Glaciers build up in cold regions where more snow falls each year than melts. Today glaciers cover about 10 percent of Earth, in mountain ranges and near the poles. During the last ice age, however, glaciers covered almost 30 percent of the land surface.

- Alpine glaciers flow down mountain valleys, widening narrow V-shaped valleys into deeper U-shaped valleys.
- Continental glaciers spread out into broad sheets. They cover most of Greenland and Antarctica.

2. Glaciers deposit large amounts of sediment.

A melting glacier leaves behind different kinds of **moraines,** landforms made of sediment. These moraines form a variety of hills, ridges, and blankets of **till.** Retreating glaciers also leave behind lakes of many sizes.

- Small **kettle lakes** form from blocks of ice that melt, leaving bowl-like depressions.
- Large lakes form when glaciers gouge river valleys into huge depressions and fill them with water. The Great Lakes are one example, shown in this series of drawings.

  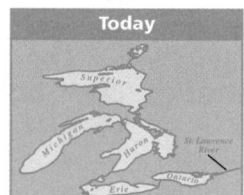

14,000 Years Ago	7000 Years Ago	Today
The ice sheet covering a land of river valleys began to retreat.	Water filled the bowls carved out by the ice.	The Great Lakes contain 20 percent of the world's fresh lake water.

Common Misconceptions

WAVES Many students think waves are a major means by which water moves. However, waves are a movement of energy through water, not a movement of the water itself.

 This misconception is addressed on p. 159.

 MISCONCEPTION DATABASE
CLASSZONE.COM Background on student misconceptions

RETREATING GLACIERS Some students think that when a glacier retreats, it actually moves backward. In fact, a glacier retreats by melting at its leading edge—the glacier does not "back up."

 This misconception is addressed on p. 168.

Previewing Labs

Lab Generator CD-ROM
Edit these Pupil Edition labs and generate alternative labs.

EXPLORE the BIG idea

Where Has Water Been? p. 143
Students observe the effects of water flowing on the ground.

TIME 10 minutes
MATERIALS none

How Do Waves Shape Land? p. 143
Students make a model beach and observe how waves affect shorelines.

TIME 10 minutes
MATERIALS sand and gravel, pie tin, water, cup

Internet Activity: Wind Erosion, p. 143
Students are introduced to the effects of wind erosion.

TIME 20 minutes
MATERIALS computer with Internet access

SECTION 5.1

INVESTIGATE Erosion, p. 146
Students design an experiment to find out how the slope of the land is affected by the action of rainwater.

TIME 25 minutes
MATERIALS soil, 2 large trays, pitcher of water

SECTION 5.2

EXPLORE Divides, p. 150
Students make a model divide and observe how a divide works.

TIME 10 minutes
MATERIALS sheet of paper, tape, several paper clips

CHAPTER INVESTIGATION
Creating Stream Features, pp. 156–157
Students set up a stream table and observe the formation of different features in a model stream.

TIME 40 minutes
MATERIALS stream table with hose attachment or recirculating pump, sieve (optional), wood blocks, sand (at least 2 lbs), ruler, water, sink with drain, pitcher (optional), bucket (optional)

SECTION 5.3

INVESTIGATE Longshore Drift, p. 160
Students push a coin up a slope to model how sand moves along a beach.

TIME 15 minutes
MATERIALS 2 or 3 books, coin

SECTION 5.4

EXPLORE Glaciers, p. 165
Students observe how a model glacier changes landscapes as it erodes and deposits material.

TIME 5 minutes
MATERIALS modeling clay, paper towel, ice cube containing sand and gravel

---

INVESTIGATE Kettle Lake Formation, p. 169
Students design an experiment to show how kettle lakes form.

TIME 30 minutes
MATERIALS shallow tray, ice cubes, modeling clay, sand, gravel, flexible lamp or hair dryer (optional), water

---

 Additional INVESTIGATION, Rivers Change the Land, A, B, & C, pp. 337–345; Teacher Instructions, pp. 348–349

Previewing Chapter Resources

	INTEGRATED TECHNOLOGY	LABS AND ACTIVITIES

CHAPTER 5
Erosion and Deposition

 CLASSZONE.COM
- eEdition Plus
- EasyPlanner Plus
- Misconception Database
- Content Review
- Test Practice
- Visualizations
- Resource Centers
- Internet Activity: Wind Erosion
- Math Tutorial

 SCILINKS.ORG
SCILINKS

 CD-ROMS
- eEdition
- EasyPlanner
- Power Presentations
- Content Review
- Lab Generator
- Test Generator

 AUDIO CDS
- Audio Readings
- Audio Readings in Spanish

 EXPLORE the Big Idea, p. 143
- Where Has Water Been?
- How Do Waves Shape Land?
- Internet Activity: Wind Erosion

 UNIT RESOURCE BOOK
Unit Projects, pp. 5–10

 Lab Generator CD-ROM
Generate customized labs.

SECTION 5.1
Forces wear down and build up Earth's surface.
pp. 145–149

Time: 2 periods (1 block)
 Lesson Plan, pp. 278–279

 RESOURCE CENTER, Mudflows

 UNIT TRANSPARENCY BOOK
- Big Idea Flow Chart, p. T33
- Daily Vocabulary Scaffolding, p. T34
- Note-Taking Model, p. T35
- 3-Minute Warm-Up, p. T36

INVESTIGATE Erosion, p. 146

UNIT RESOURCE BOOK
Datasheet, Erosion, p. 287

SECTION 5.2
Moving water shapes land.
pp. 150–157

Time: 3 periods (1.5 blocks)
 Lesson Plan, pp. 289–290

- **RESOURCE CENTER,** Rivers and Erosion
- **VISUALIZATION,** Cave Formation

 UNIT TRANSPARENCY BOOK
- Daily Vocabulary Scaffolding, p. T34
- 3-Minute Warm-Up, p. T36

- EXPLORE Divides, p. 150
- CHAPTER INVESTIGATION, Creating Stream Features, pp. 156–157

UNIT RESOURCE BOOK
- CHAPTER INVESTIGATION, Creating Stream Features, A, B, & C, pp. 328–336
- Additional INVESTIGATION, Rivers Change the Land, A, B, & C, pp. 337–345

SECTION 5.3
Waves and wind shape land.
pp. 158–164

Time: 2 periods (1 block)
 Lesson Plan, pp. 299–300

 UNIT TRANSPARENCY BOOK
- Daily Vocabulary Scaffolding, p. T34
- 3-Minute Warm-Up, p. T37

- INVESTIGATE Longshore Drift, p. 160
- Connecting Sciences, p. 164

UNIT RESOURCE BOOK
Datasheet, Longshore Drift, p. 308

SECTION 5.4
Glaciers carve land and move sediments.
pp. 165–171

Time: 2 periods (1 block)
 Lesson Plan, pp. 310–311

- **RESOURCE CENTER,** Glaciers
- **MATH TUTORIAL**

 UNIT TRANSPARENCY BOOK
- Big Idea Flow Chart, p. T33
- 3-Minute Warm-Up, p. T37
- "Types of Glaciers and Movement" Visual, p. T38
- Chapter Outline, pp. T39–T40

- EXPLORE Glaciers, p. 165
- INVESTIGATE Kettle Lake Formation, p. 169
- Math in Science, p. 171

UNIT RESOURCE BOOK
- Datasheet, Kettle Lake Formation, p. 319
- Math Support & Practice, pp. 326–327

READING AND REINFORCEMENT

ASSESSMENT

STANDARDS

- Four Square, B22–23
- Choose Your Own Strategy, C36–C42
- Daily Vocabulary Scaffolding, H1–8

UNIT RESOURCE BOOK
- Vocabulary Practice, pp. 323–324
- Decoding Support, p. 325
- Summarizing the Chapter, pp. 346–347

Audio Readings CD
Listen to Pupil Edition.

Audio Readings in Spanish CD
Listen to Pupil Edition in Spanish.

- Chapter Review, pp. 172–174
- Standardized Test Practice, p. 175

UNIT ASSESSMENT BOOK
- Diagnostic Test, pp. 79–80
- Chapter Test, A, B, & C, pp. 85–96
- Alternative Assessment, pp. 97–98
- Unit Test, A, B, & C, pp. 99–110
- Spanish Chapter Test, pp. 121–124
- Spanish Unit Test, pp. 125–128

Test Generator CD-ROM
Generate customized tests.

Lab Generator CD-ROM
Rubrics for Labs

National Standards
A.2–8, A.9.a–c, A.9.e–f, D.1.c, E.2–5, F.3.c

See p. 142 for the standards.

UNIT RESOURCE BOOK
- Reading Study Guide, A & B, pp. 280–283
- Spanish Reading Study Guide, pp. 284–285
- Challenge and Extension, p. 286
- Reinforcing Key Concepts, p. 288

Ongoing Assessment, pp. 146–149

Section 5.1 Review, p. 149

UNIT ASSESSMENT BOOK
Section 5.1 Quiz, p. 81

National Standards
A.2–7, A.9.a–b, A.9.e–f, D.1.c, E.2–5, F.3.c

UNIT RESOURCE BOOK
- Reading Study Guide, A & B, pp. 291–294
- Spanish Reading Study Guide, pp. 295–296
- Challenge and Extension, p. 297
- Reinforcing Key Concepts, p. 298

Ongoing Assessment, pp. 152–153, 155

Section 5.2 Review, p. 155

UNIT ASSESSMENT BOOK
Section 5.2 Quiz, p. 82

National Standards
A.2–7, A.9.a–b, A.9.e–f, D.1.c

UNIT RESOURCE BOOK
- Reading Study Guide, A & B, pp. 301–304
- Spanish Reading Study Guide, pp. 305–306
- Challenge and Extension, p. 307
- Reinforcing Key Concepts, p. 309

Ongoing Assessment, pp. 161, 163

Section 5.3 Review, p. 163

UNIT ASSESSMENT BOOK
Section 5.3 Quiz, p. 83

National Standards
A.2–7, A.9.a–b, A.9.e–f, D.1.c

UNIT RESOURCE BOOK
- Reading Study Guide, A & B, pp. 312–315
- Spanish Reading Study Guide, pp. 316–317
- Challenge and Extension, p. 318
- Reinforcing Key Concepts, p. 320
- Challenge Reading, pp. 321–322

Ongoing Assessment, pp. 166–168, 170

Section 5.4 Review, p. 170

UNIT ASSESSMENT BOOK
Section 5.4 Quiz, p. 84

National Standards
A.2–8, A.9.a–c, A.9.e–f, D.1.c

Previewing Resources for Differentiated Instruction

CHAPTER INVESTIGATION

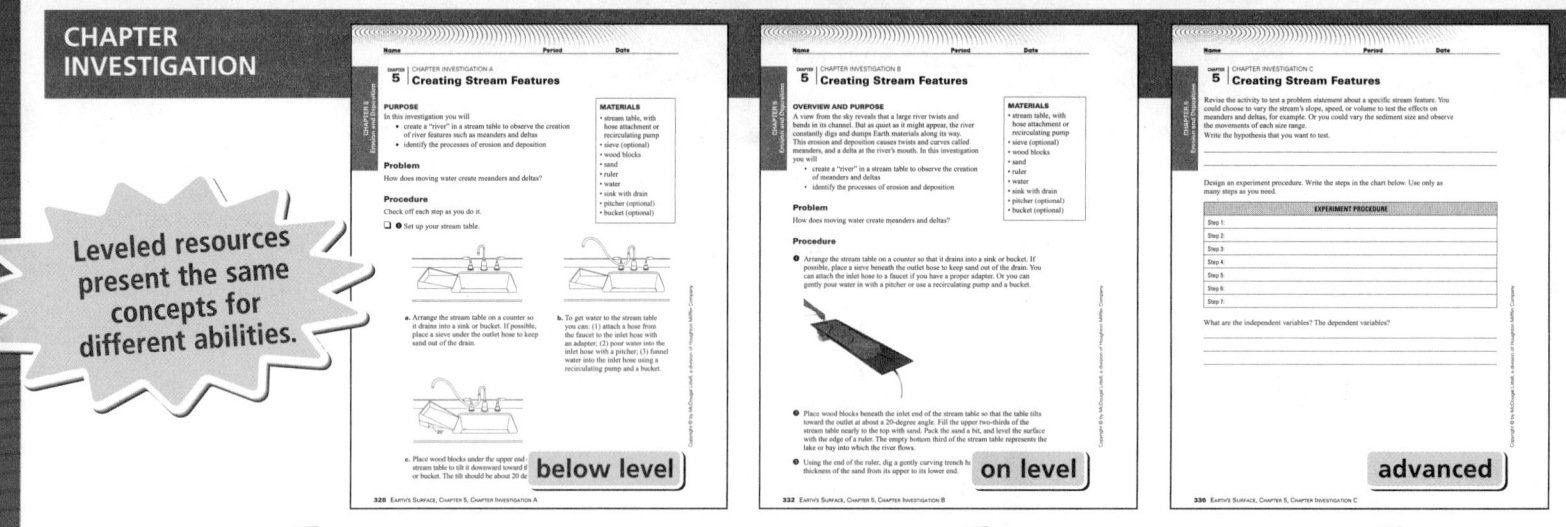

Leveled resources present the same concepts for different abilities.

below level

on level

advanced

R **UNIT RESOURCE BOOK,** pp. 328–331   **R** pp. 332–335   **R** pp. 332–336

READING STUDY GUIDE

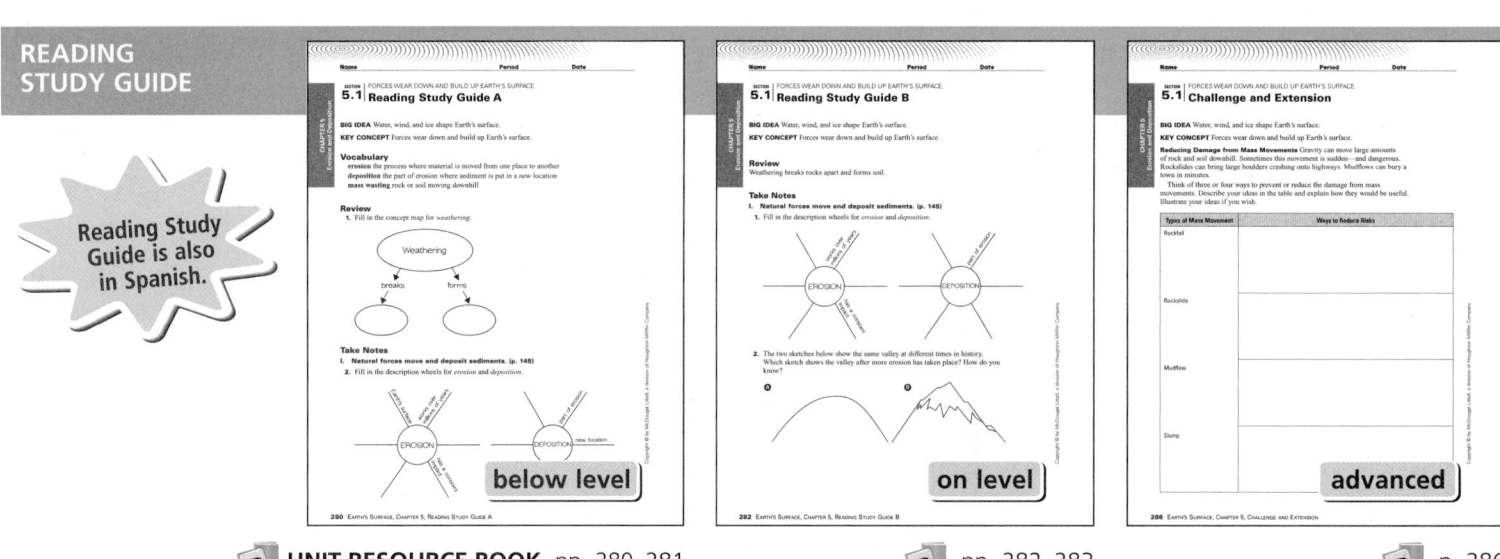

Reading Study Guide is also in Spanish.

below level

on level

advanced

R **UNIT RESOURCE BOOK,** pp. 280–281   **R** pp. 282–283   **R** p. 286

CHAPTER TEST

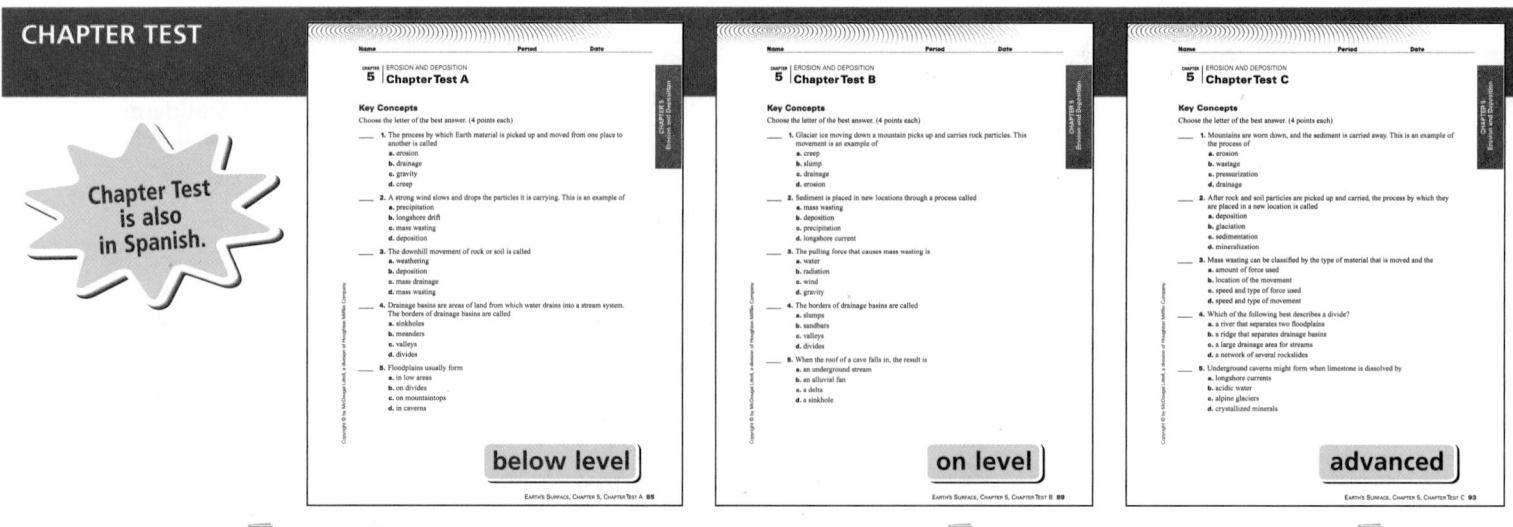

Chapter Test is also in Spanish.

below level

on level

advanced

A **UNIT ASSESSMENT BOOK,** pp. 85–88   **A** pp. 89–92   **A** pp. 93–96

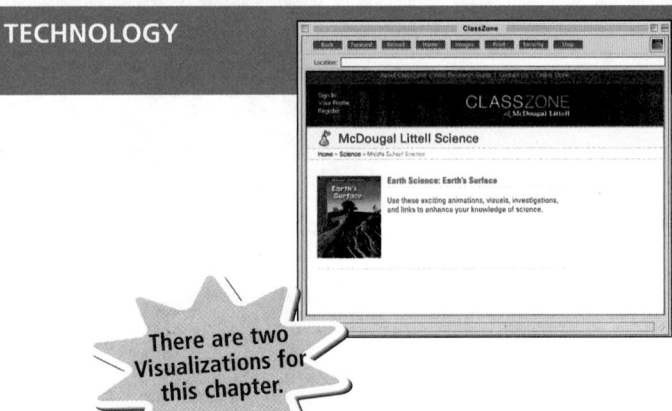

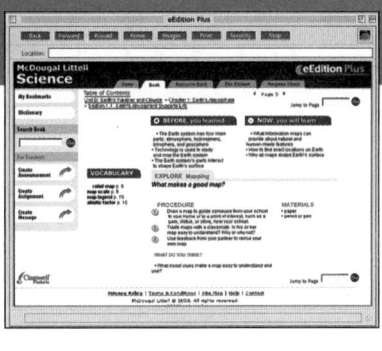

There are two Visualizations for this chapter.

CLASSZONE.COM

CD/CD-ROMS

CLASSZONE.COM

VISUAL CONTENT

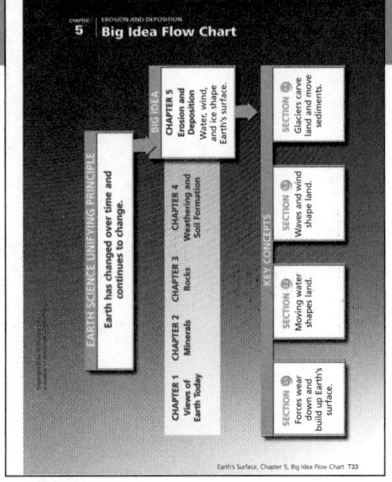

UNIT TRANSPARENCY BOOK, p. T33

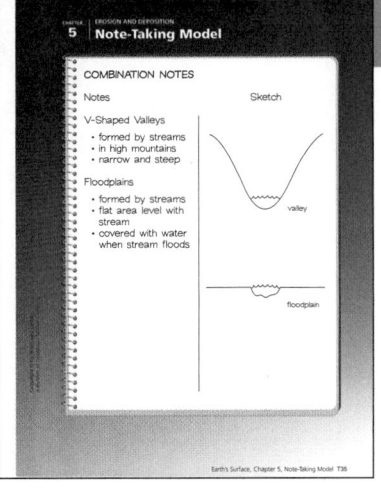

p. T35

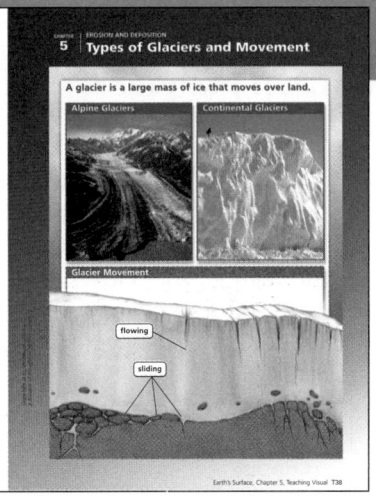

p. T38

MORE SUPPORT

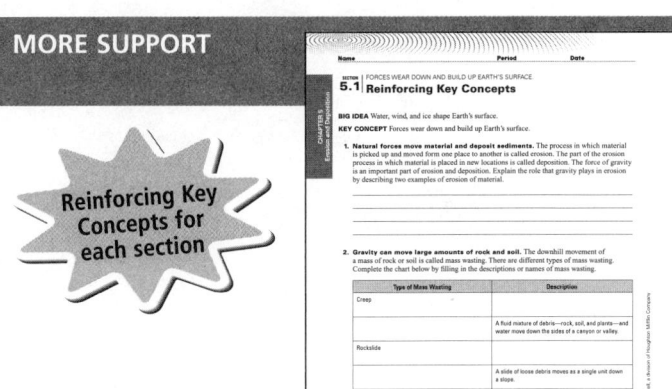

Reinforcing Key Concepts for each section

UNIT RESOURCE BOOK, p. 288

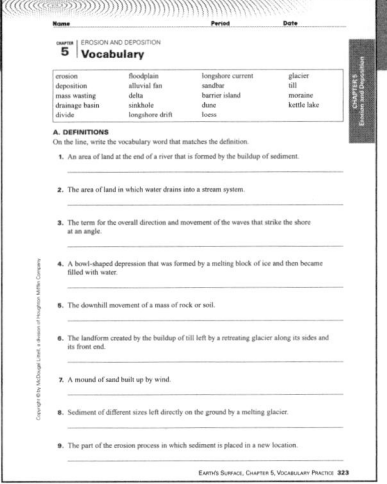

pp. 323–324

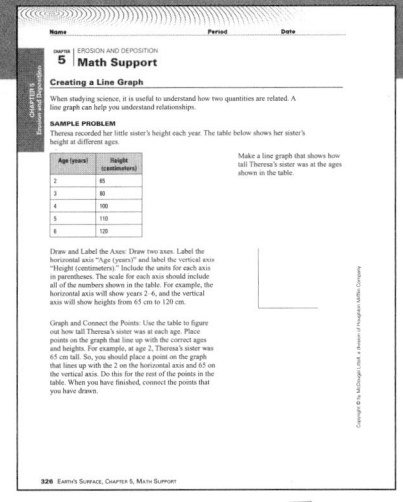

p. 326

Erosion and Deposition

CHAPTER

Erosion and Deposition

INTRODUCE

the BIG idea

Have students look at the photograph of the glacier and discuss how the question in the box links to the Big Idea:

- How thick do you think the ice is?
- How long do you think the ice has been here?
- Do you think the ice moves quickly or slowly?

National Science Education Standards

Content

D.1.c Landforms are the result of a combination of constructive and destructive forces. Constructive forces include crustal deformation, volcanic eruption, and deposition of sediment, while destructive forces include weathering and erosion.

Process

A.2–8 Design and conduct an investigation; use tools to gather and interpret data; use evidence to describe, predict, explain, model; think critically to make relationships between evidence and explanation; recognize different explanations and predictions; communicate scientific procedures and explanations; use mathematics.

A.9.a–c, A.9.e–f Understand scientific inquiry by using different investigations, models, mathematics, and explanations based on logic, evidence, and skepticism.

E.2–5 Design, implement, and evaluate a solution or product; communicate technological design.

F.3.c Natural hazards can present personal and societal challenges; may result in significant costs.

the BIG idea

Water, wind, and ice shape Earth's surface.

How can ice carve a valley?

Key Concepts

SECTION 5.1 Forces wear down and build up Earth's surface. Learn how natural forces shape and change the land.

SECTION 5.2 Moving water shapes land. Learn about the effects of water moving over land and underground.

SECTION 5.3 Waves and wind shape land. Discover how waves and wind affect land.

SECTION 5.4 Glaciers carve land and move sediments. Learn about the effect of ice moving over land.

Internet Preview

CLASSZONE.COM
Chapter 5 online resources: Content Review, two Visualizations, three Resource Centers, Math Tutorial, Test Practice

A 142 Unit: Earth's Surface

INTERNET PREVIEW

CLASSZONE.COM For student use with the following pages:

Review and Practice
- Content Review, pp. 144, 172
- Math Tutorial: Making a Line Graph, p. 171
- Test Practice, p. 175

Activities and Resources
- Internet Activity: p. 143
- Resource Centers: Mudflows, p. 148; Rivers and Erosion, p. 152; Glaciers, p. 166
- Visualization: Cave Formation, p. 154

NSTA scilinks.org **SCiLINKS**

Wind Erosion
Code: MDL017

EXPLORE (the BIG idea)

Where Has Water Been?

Think about what water does when it falls and flows on the ground. Go outside your school or home and look at the ground and pavement carefully. Look in dry places for evidence of where water has been.

Observe and Think What evidence did you find? How does it show that water was in a place that is now dry?

How Do Waves Shape Land?

Pile a mixture of sand and gravel on one side of a pie tin to make a "beach." Slowly add water away from the beach until the tin is about one-third full. Use your hand to make waves in the tin and observe what happens.

Observe and Think What happened to the beach? How did the waves affect the sand and gravel?

Internet Activity: Wind Erosion

Go to **ClassZone.com** to learn about one type of wind erosion. See how wind can form an arch in rock.

Observe and Think How long do you think it would take for wind to form an arch?

NSTA scilinks.org SCiLINKS

Wind Erosion Code: MDL017

TEACHING WITH TECHNOLOGY

Digital Camera Photograph students' stream tables in the Chapter Investigation on pp. 156–157.

CBL and Probeware If you have a CBL and a turbidity probe, measure the lack of clarity in a stream after teaching p. 152.

EXPLORE (the BIG idea)

These inquiry-based activities are appropriate for use at home or as a supplement to classroom instruction.

Where Has Water Been?

PURPOSE To introduce students to the concept that moving water shapes the land. Students observe the effects of water flowing on the ground.

TIP *10 min.* Suggest students make drawings of the evidence they find.

Sample answer: Water moved soil and other materials and deposited them. The evidence was grooves in the dirt along a curb and leaves gathered around a storm-drain cover.

REVISIT after p. 153.

How Do Waves Shape Land?

PURPOSE To demonstrate how the action of waves shape the landscape. Students make a model beach and observe how waves affect shorelines.

TIP *10 min.* Suggest students make waves in different directions so that the waves hit the beach at different angles.

Answer: Materials on the beach shifted position. The waves pulled some of the sand away from the beach or moved it from one area of the beach to another. The gravel moved a little, but less than the sand.

REVISIT after p. 159.

Internet Activity: Wind Erosion

PURPOSE To model how wind can erode weathered material from rock.

TIP *20 min.* Have students compare wind erosion to sandblasting.

Answer: millions of years

REVISIT after p. 163.

PREPARE

◐ CONCEPT REVIEW

Activate Prior Knowledge

- Set out two cookies, one whole and one that has been crumbled into tiny pieces.

- Tell students that the intact cookie represents a rock. Ask what the crumbled cookie might represent. *smaller rocks and rock particles*

- Discuss what processes changed the crumbled cookie and relate these processes to weathering of rock.

▶ TAKING NOTES

Choose Your Own Strategy

Allowing students to choose their own note-taking strategy will help build confidence in their ability to take notes that are meaningful for them. Encourage students to experiment with their own strategies based on those they have encountered in earlier chapters. Remind them that different strategies may be appropriate for different topics or sections in the chapter.

Vocabulary Strategy

Having students use four square diagrams will help them see more than simple definitions of words. Students will get a more complete view of vocabulary terms in the context of the section.

Vocabulary and Note-Taking Resources

- Vocabulary Practice, pp. 323–324
- Decoding Support, p. 325

- Daily Vocabulary Scaffolding, p. T34
- Note-Taking Model, p. T35

- Four Square, B22–23
- Choose Your Own Strategy, C36–C42
- Daily Vocabulary Scaffolding, H1–8

Getting Ready to Learn

◐ CONCEPT REVIEW

- Weathering breaks down rocks.
- Water and ice are agents of weathering.
- Soil contains weathered rock and organic material.

◐ VOCABULARY REVIEW

sediment p. 89
weathering p. 115
abrasion p. 116

ⓘ CONTENT REVIEW
CLASSZONE.COM
Review concepts and vocabulary.

▶ TAKING NOTES

CHOOSE YOUR OWN STRATEGY

Take notes using one or more of the strategies from earlier chapters—**main idea and detail notes, supporting main ideas, main idea web,** or **combination notes.** Feel free to mix and match the strategies, or use an entirely different note-taking strategy.

VOCABULARY STRATEGY

Write each new vocabulary term in the center of a **four square** diagram. Write notes in the squares around each term. Include a definition, some characteristics, and some examples of the term. If possible, write some things that are not examples of the term.

See the Note-Taking Handbook on pages R45–R51.

SCIENCE NOTEBOOK

Supporting Main Ideas

Main Idea Web

Main Idea and Detail Notes

Definition	Characteristics
process in which weathered particles are picked up and moved	gravity is important part; wind and ice are agents

EROSION

Examples	Nonexamples
mass wasting, mudflow, slump, creep	longshore current, humus

CHECK READINESS

Administer the Diagnostic Test to determine students' readiness for new science content and their mastery of requisite math skills.

 Diagnostic Test, pp. 79–80

Technology Resources

Students needing content and math skills should visit **ClassZone.com**.

- CONTENT REVIEW
- MATH TUTORIAL

 CONTENT REVIEW CD-ROM

KEY CONCEPT

5.1 Forces wear down and build up Earth's surface.

◀ **BEFORE, you learned**

- Weathering breaks rocks apart
- Weathering forms soil

▶ **NOW, you will learn**

- How erosion moves and deposits rock and soil
- How gravity causes movement of large amounts of rock and soil

VOCABULARY

erosion p. 145
deposition p. 145
mass wasting p. 147

THINK ABOUT

How did natural forces shape this landform?

This valley in Iceland was formed by the action of water. How long might it have taken to form? Where did the material that once filled the valley go?

VOCABULARY
Use four square diagrams to take notes about the terms *erosion* and *deposition*.

Natural forces move and deposit sediments.

The valley in the photograph was formed by the movement of water. The water flowed over the land and carried away weathered rock and soil, shaping a valley where the water flows. In this section you will learn about the processes that shape landscapes.

The process in which weathered particles are picked up and moved from one place to another is called **erosion** (ih-ROH-zhuhn). Erosion has a constant impact on Earth's surface. Over millions of years, it wears down mountains by removing by products of weathering and depositing them elsewhere. The part of the erosion process in which sediment is placed in a new location, or deposited, is called **deposition** (DEHP-uh-ZIHSH-uhn).

The force of gravity is an important part of erosion and deposition. Gravity causes water to move downward, carrying and depositing sediment as it flows. Gravity can pull huge masses of ice slowly down mountain valleys. And gravity causes dust carried by the wind to fall to Earth.

Chapter 5: Erosion and Deposition 145 **A**

RESOURCES FOR DIFFERENTIATED INSTRUCTION

Below Level
UNIT RESOURCE BOOK
- Reading Study Guide A, pp. 280–281
- Decoding Support, p. 325

 **AUDIO CDS**

Advanced
UNIT RESOURCE BOOK
Challenge and Extension, p. 286

English Learners
UNIT RESOURCE BOOK
Spanish Reading Study Guide, pp. 284–285

AUDIO CDS

- Audio Readings in Spanish
- Audio Readings (English)

5.1 FOCUS

▶ Set Learning Goals
Students will

- Describe how erosion and deposition move rock and soil.
- Explain how gravity causes the mass movement of rock and soil.
- Design an experiment that shows how rainwater affects sloping land.

◀ 3-Minute Warm-Up

Display Transparency 36 or copy this exercise on the board:

Decide if the statements are true. If not true, correct them.

1. Weathering can be caused by mechanical and chemical processes. *true*
2. Soil builds up entirely from weathered rocks. *from weathered rocks and organic material*
3. Weathering proceeds most quickly in warm, dry areas. *most slowly*

T 3-Minute Warm-Up, p. T36

5.1 MOTIVATE

THINK ABOUT

PURPOSE To introduce the idea that natural forces shape the landscape

DISCUSS Ask students to describe situations that show the ability of moving water to transport materials. Discuss where the material ends up. *Examples might include a canoe traveling downstream, sediment traveling downstream, ocean waves moving beach sand, raindrops pitting a sandy beach, a hose washing dirt off a car. Water flows over the surface, carries away rock and soil, and deposits it downhill.*

Answer: The valley probably took a very long time to form. Material was carried away by the stream.

INVESTIGATE Erosion

PURPOSE To design an experiment that shows the effects of rainwater on various slopes

TIPS *25 min.*

- You may want to have students measure the height or angle of their slope. Students could also measure the volume of soil eroded from the flat and sloped soil.

- Encourage students to pour the water slowly, so that they can examine what the water does to the soil particles and how it flows through the soil.

WHAT DO YOU THINK? *More soil eroded on the sloping land than on the flat land. Variables included the slope of the soil, the amount of water poured on the soil, where it was poured, and the force of the water. The erosion caused by water is greater on slopes than on flat land.*

CHALLENGE *Sample answer: Use soil in tray to build model river channels, riverbanks, and land. Add water to the river until it overflows its banks slightly. Observe how the sediment settles around the river. Repeat in another tray with more water.*

 Datasheet, Erosion, p. 287

Technology Resources

Customize this student lab as needed or look for an alternative. Print rubrics to assess student lab reports.

 Lab Generator CD-ROM

Ongoing Assessment

CHECK YOUR READING *Answer: Erosion moves sediment in water, wind, and ice.*

Erosion of weathered rock by the movement of water, wind, and ice occurs in three major ways:

- **Water** Rainwater and water from melting snow flow down sloping land, carrying rock and soil particles. The water makes its way to a river, which then carries the sediment along. The sediment gets deposited on the river's bottom, banks, or floodplain, or near its mouth. Waves in oceans and lakes also carry sediment and deposit it to form beaches and other features.

- **Wind** Strong winds lift tiny particles of dust and carry them long distances. When the wind dies down, the particles drop to the ground. Wind can also push larger particles of sand along the ground.

- **Ice** As ice moves slowly downhill, it transports rock and soil particles that are embedded in it.

CHECK YOUR READING What are the three major ways in which erosion moves sediment?

INVESTIGATE Erosion

How does the effect of rainwater on sloping land differ from its effect on flat land?

DESIGN —YOUR OWN— EXPERIMENT

Streams are one of the main agents of erosion on Earth. Design an experiment to show the effect that rainwater has on sloping land.

PROCEDURE

1. Figure out how to use the soil, water, and trays to test the effects of rainwater on sloping land and on flat land.

2. Write up your procedure.

3. Carry out your experiment.

WHAT DO YOU THINK?

- What were the results of your experiment? Did it work? Why or why not?

- What were the variables in your experiment?

- What does your experiment demonstrate about erosion and running water?

CHALLENGE How would you design an experiment to demonstrate the relationship between floods and erosion?

SKILL FOCUS
Designing experiments

MATERIALS
- soil
- 2 large trays
- pitcher of water

TIME
25 minutes

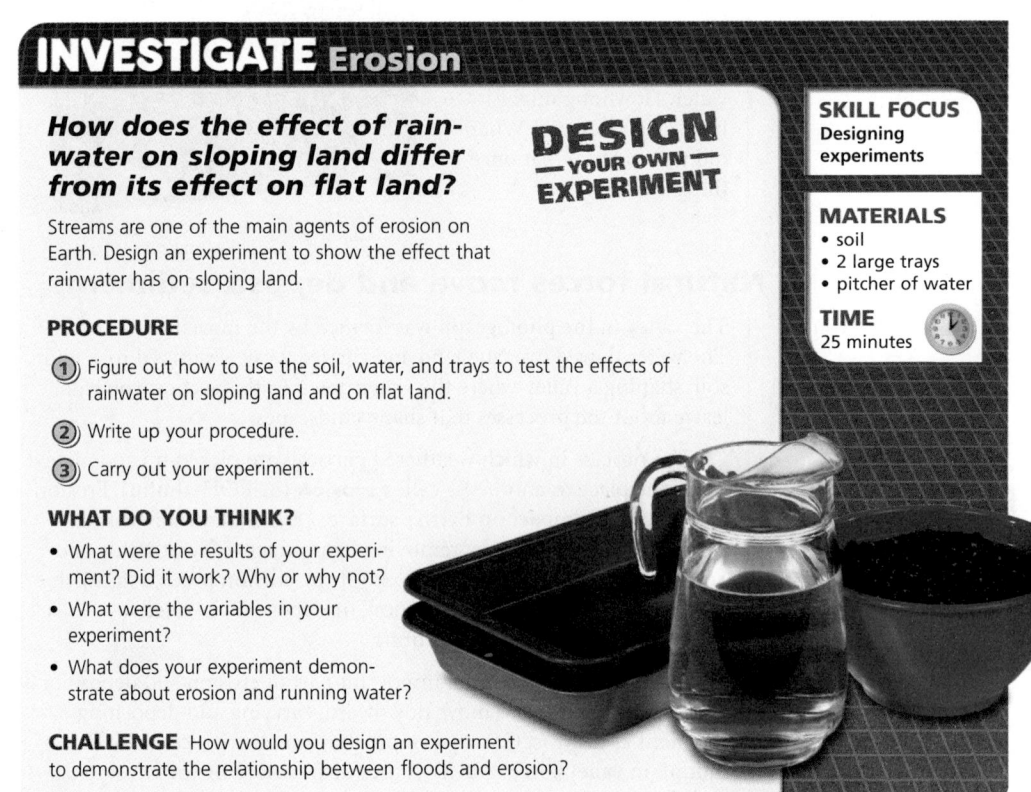

DIFFERENTIATE INSTRUCTION

 More Reading Support

A What carries rock and soil particles? *rainwater and water from melting snow, wind, ice*

English Learners To be sure that English learners understand the difference between erosion and deposition, place the terms on the classroom's Science Word Wall with brief definitions for each. English learners may be unfamiliar with certain idioms used in the English language. The phrase "wind dies down" on p. 146 may be confusing to someone reading it literally. Help English learners recognize idioms and understand their meanings.

Gravity can move large amounts of rock and soil.

Along the California coast many homes are built atop beautiful cliffs, backed by mountains and looking out to the sea. These homes may seem like great places to live. They are, however, in a risky location.

The California coast region and other mountainous areas have many landslides. A landslide is one type of **mass wasting**—the downhill movements of masses of rock and soil.

In mass wasting, gravity pulls material downward. A triggering event, such as heavy rain or an earthquake, might loosen the rock and soil. As the material becomes looser, it gives way to the pull of gravity and moves downward.

Mass wasting can occur suddenly or gradually. It can involve tons of rock sliding down a steep mountain slope or moving little by little down a gentle hillside. One way to classify an occurrence of mass wasting is by the type of material that is moved and the speed of the movement. A sudden, fast movement of rock and soil is called a landslide. Movements of rock are described as slides or falls. Movement of mud or soil is described as a mudflow.

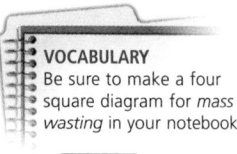

VOCABULARY
Be sure to make a four square diagram for *mass wasting* in your notebook.

Mass Wasting of Rock

Mass wasting of rock includes rockfalls and rockslides:

- In a rockfall, individual blocks of rock drop suddenly and fall freely down a cliff or steep mountainside. Weathering can break a block of rock from a cliff or mountainside. The expansion of water that freezes in a crack, for example, can loosen a block of rock.

- In a rockslide, a large mass of rock slides as a unit down a slope. A rockslide can reach a speed of a hundred kilometers per hour. Rockslides can be triggered by earthquakes.

Mass wasting of rock often takes place in high mountains. In some places, rocks can fall or slide onto roads. You might also see evidence of rockfalls and rockslides at the base of steep cliffs, where piles of rock slope outward.

Rockslides, such as this one in California, can drop huge amounts of rock onto highways.

Chapter 5: Erosion and Deposition **147** **A**

DIFFERENTIATE INSTRUCTION

More Reading Support

B What force causes mass wasting? *gravity*

C What are two forms of mass wasting? *rockfall, rockslide*

Below Level The term *mass wasting* may be difficult for students to understand. Discuss the meaning of each word in the term. *Mass* refers to a large amount of material. *Wasting* refers to destruction. Together, the words refer to the destruction of a large amount of material, or the destruction of a hillside.

Teach from Visuals

To help students interpret the photograph of a rockslide, ask:

- How would you describe the area? *steep slopes, loose rock*
- What type of mass wasting is shown? *rockslide*
- Why is this movement not called a rockfall? *The mass of rock is too great.*

Teacher Demo

Demonstrate how water acts as a lubricant to trigger mass wasting. Place a layer of soil and gravel mixture on a board. Pack the mixture tightly. Tilt the surface slightly, so that the mixture does not move. Ask students to predict what will happen when you pour a small amount of water near the top of the surface. Test their predictions. The water should lubricate the mixture enough to start it sliding down the surface.

Teach Difficult Concepts

The various forms of mass wasting are not always distinctly different. The difference between a rockfall and a rockslide, for example, is that the former involves small blocks of rock while the latter involves a large mass of rock. Ask: What do rockfalls and rockslides have in common? *They both involve rocks pulled down steep slopes by gravity.*

Ongoing Assessment

Describe how erosion and deposition move rock and soil.

Ask: How does erosion and deposition occur in a creek? *The flowing water picks up and moves sediment. Some sediment gets deposited along the creek bottom or along its banks.*

Real World Example

The mudflow in the town on Armero, Colombia, was one of the greatest natural disasters in South American history. About 23,000 people died—20,000 in Armero and 3,000 in other valleys. Armero lay directly in the path of the 40-meter-high wall of mud traveling 40 kilometers per hour. It struck just after 11 P.M., when most people were asleep. The mud buried all but the highest parts of the town in 15 minutes.

Develop Critical Thinking

APPLY Ask students what might be done to limit the damage done by mudflows. Answers may include limiting the amount of development in valleys prone to mudflows, developing a warning system, and constructing barriers along the path that dangerous mudflows are likely to take. Point out that such barriers are common in Japan.

Address Misconceptions

IDENTIFY Ask: What force causes creep? If students do not say gravity, they may hold the misconception that gravity causes downward motion only in obvious cases, such as a free-falling object.

CORRECT Hold out a ball and drop it. Ask students what caused the ball to drop. Then let the ball roll down a surface that is barely tilted. Ask what caused the ball to roll. Point out that gravity acts on the ball regardless of the angle at which it is allowed to fall.

REASSESS Ask: Why does a slow-moving river flow? *Gravity pulls it downhill.*

Ongoing Assessment

CHECK YOUR READING *Answer: Mudflows can occur as a flow of water moves down a mountainside or valley and picks up debris from soaked land or ash from a volcano.*

Mudflows in 1999 in Venezuela happened very quickly and took as many as 30,000 lives.

? D

 **RESOURCE CENTER**
CLASSZONE.COM
Learn more about mudflows.

? E

In this example of slump, at Mesa Verde National Park in Colorado, a huge mass of rock and soil moved downward.

A 148

Mudflow

Sometimes a mountain slope collapses. Then a mixture of rock, soil, and plants—called debris (duh-BREE)—falls or slides down. Like mass wasting of rock, mass movements of debris are common in high mountains with steep slopes.

A major type of mass wasting of debris is a mudflow. A mudflow consists of debris with a large amount of water. Mudflows often happen in mountain canyons and valleys after heavy rains. The soil becomes so heavy with water that the slope can no longer hold it in place. The mixture of soil, water, and debris flows downward, picking up sediment as it rushes down. When it reaches a valley, it spreads in a thin sheet over the land.

Mudflows also occur on active volcanoes. In 1985, a huge mudflow destroyed the town of Armero, Colombia, and killed more than 20,000 people. When a volcano erupted there, the heat caused ice and snow near the top of the volcano to melt, releasing a large amount of water that mixed with ash from the volcano. The mixture of ash and water rushed down the volcano and picked up debris. It formed gigantic mudflows that poured into all the surrounding valleys.

Mount St. Helens, a volcanic mountain in the state of Washington, is a place where large mudflows have occurred. During an eruption in 1980, some mudflows from the volcano traveled more than 90 kilometers (56 mi) from the mountain.

CHECK YOUR READING What causes a mudflow to occur?

Slumps and Creep

Slumps and creep are two other main types of mass wasting on hilly land. These forms of mass wasting can be much less dramatic than rockslides or mudflows. But they are the types of mass movement that you are most likely to see evidence of.

DIFFERENTIATE INSTRUCTION

? **More Reading Support**

D What is debris made of? *rock, soil, and plants*

E What is a mudflow made of? *water and debris*

Advanced Have students find on a map the places mentioned in the text (Armero, Colombia, and Mount St. Helens in Washington). Then have them find on the map other places they think would be prone to mudflows. They should look not only in mountainous areas but in areas with active volcanoes.

R Challenge and Extension, p. 286

A slump is a slide of loose debris that moves as a single unit. Slumps can occur along roads and highways where construction has made slopes unstable. They can cover sections of highway with debris. Like other types of mass movement, slumps can be triggered by heavy rain.

The slowest form of mass movement of soil or debris is creep. The soil or debris moves at a rate of about 1 to 10 millimeters a year—a rate too slow to actually be seen. But evidence of creep can be seen on hillsides that have old fences or telephone poles. The fences or poles may lean downward, or some may be out of line. They have been moved by the creeping soil. The soil closer to the surface moves faster than the soil farther down, which causes the fences or poles to lean.

Even the slight slope of this land in Alberta, Canada, caused these posts to tilt because of creep.

Originally, the fence posts stand vertically in the ground.

Over many years, the soil holding the posts slowly shifts downhill, and the posts lean.

Creep can affect buildings as well. The weight of a heavy mass of soil moving slowly downhill can be great enough to crack a building's walls. Creep affects all hillsides covered with soil, but its rate varies. The wetter the soil, the faster it will creep downhill.

5.1 Review

KEY CONCEPTS

1. How does erosion change landscapes?
2. Describe why weathering is important in erosion.
3. How can gravity move large amounts of rock and soil?

CRITICAL THINKING

4. **Compare and Contrast** What is the main difference between erosion and mass wasting?
5. **Infer** What force and what cause can contribute to both erosion and mass wasting?

⬨ CHALLENGE

5. **Rank** Which of the four locations would be the best and worst places to build a house? Rank the four locations and explain your reasoning.

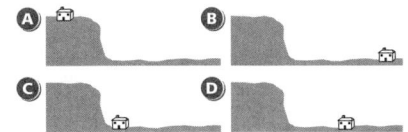

Chapter 5: **Erosion and Deposition** 149 **A**

ANSWERS

1. *Forces of erosion move soil, sediment, and rock from one place to another.*

2. *Weathering breaks down rock into pieces, which may be carried away and deposited.*

3. *Gravity moves large amounts of rock and soil downhill as the rock and soil loosen for various reasons.*

4. *Mass wasting involves only the force of gravity whereas erosion occurs with movement of another material such as water, air, or ice.*

5. *the force of gravity and the downhill movement of water*

6. *ABDC or BADC; if land is very stable, A is a good location*

Ongoing Assessment

Explain how gravity causes the mass movement of rock and soil.

Ask: Where would you expect to see a road sign saying, "Caution: Falling Rock"? *in rocky areas with steep slopes*

Reinforce (the BIG idea)

Have students relate the section to the Big Idea.

R Reinforcing Key Concepts, p. 288

5.1 ASSESS & RETEACH

Assess

A Section 5.1 Quiz, p. 81

Reteach

Create a chart that compares the different kinds of mass wasting: rockfall, rockslide, mudflow, slump, creep. Include columns headed Type of Mass Wasting, Type of Material, Speed, and Evidence. Have students fill in individual charts, or make the chart on the board.

Technology Resources

Have students visit **ClassZone.com** for reteaching of Key Concepts.

i CONTENT REVIEW

◉ CONTENT REVIEW CD-ROM

◉ Set Learning Goals

Students will

- Explain how moving water shapes Earth's surface.
- Explain how water moving underground forms natural features.
- Discover through experimentation how streams shape the landscape.

◉ 3-Minute Warm-Up

Display Transparency 36 or copy this exercise on the board:

1. What four things cause erosion of small rock particles? *rain, snow, winds, ice*

2. What force causes mass wasting, mudflows, slump, creep? *gravity*

 3-Minute Warm-Up, p. T36

5.2 MOTIVATE

EXPLORE Divides

PURPOSE To introduce the concept of a divide

TIP *10 min.* The height from which students drop the paper clips is not important as long as the clips land close to the paper ridge.

WHAT DO YOU THINK? *Water falling on a natural ridge must also flow to one side or the other.*

◀ **BEFORE, you learned**

- Erosion is the movement of rock and soil
- Gravity causes mass movements of rock and soil

▶ **NOW, you will learn**

- How moving water shapes Earth's surface
- How water moving underground forms caves and other features

VOCABULARY

drainage basin p. 151
divide p. 151
floodplain p. 152
alluvial fan p. 153
delta p. 153
sinkhole p. 155

EXPLORE Divides

How do divides work?

PROCEDURE

① Fold the sheet of paper in thirds and tape it as shown to make a "ridge."

② Drop the paper clips one at a time directly on top of the ridge from a height of about 30 cm. Observe what happens and record your observations.

WHAT DO YOU THINK?
How might the paper clips be similar to water falling on a ridge?

MATERIALS
- sheet of paper
- paper clips

Streams shape Earth's surface.

If you look at a river or stream, you may be able to notice something about the land around it. The land is higher than the river. If a river is running through a steep valley, you can easily see that the river is the low point. But even in very flat places, the land is sloping down to the river, which is itself running downhill in a low path through the land.

Running water is the major force shaping the landscape over most of Earth. From the broad, flat land around the lower Mississippi River to the steep mountain valleys of the Himalayas, water running downhill changes the land. Running water shapes a variety of landforms by moving sediment in the processes of erosion and deposition. In this section, you will learn how water flows on land in systems of streams and rivers and how water shapes and changes landscapes. You also will learn that water can even carve out new features underground.

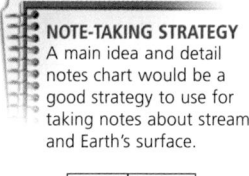

NOTE-TAKING STRATEGY
A main idea and detail notes chart would be a good strategy to use for taking notes about streams and Earth's surface.

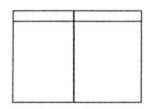

RESOURCES FOR DIFFERENTIATED INSTRUCTION

Below Level

UNIT RESOURCE BOOK
- Reading Study Guide A, pp. 291–292
- Decoding Support, p. 325

 **AUDIO CDS**

R **Additional INVESTIGATION,**
Rivers Change the Land, A, B, & C, pp. 337–345;
Teacher Instructions, pp. 348–349

Advanced

UNIT RESOURCE BOOK
Challenge and Extension, p. 297

English Learners

UNIT RESOURCE BOOK
Spanish Reading Study Guide, pp. 295–296

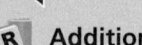 **AUDIO CDS**

- Audio Readings in Spanish
- Audio Readings (English)

Drainage Basins and Divides

When water falls or ice melts on a slope, some of the water soaks into the ground and some of it flows down the slope in thin sheets. But within a short distance this water becomes part of a channel that forms a stream. A stream is any body of water—large or small—that flows down a slope along a channel.

Streams flow into one another to form complex drainage systems, with small streams flowing into larger ones. The area of land in which water drains into a stream system is called a **drainage basin.** In most drainage basins, the water eventually drains into a lake or an ocean. For example, in the Mississippi River drainage basin, water flows into the Mississippi, and then drains into the Gulf of Mexico, which is part of the ocean.

Drainage basins are separated by ridges called divides, which are like continuous lines of high land. A **divide** is a ridge from which water drains to one side or the other. Divides can run along high mountains. On flatter ground, a divide can simply be the the highest line of land and can be hard to see.

Divides are the borders of drainage basins. A basin can be just a few kilometers wide or can drain water from a large portion of a continent. The Continental Divide runs from Alaska to Mexico. Most water that falls west of the Continental Divide ends up draining into the Pacific Ocean. Most water that falls east of it drains into the Gulf of Mexico and Atlantic Ocean.

Divides and Drainage Basins

Divides are ridges that form the borders of drainage basins.

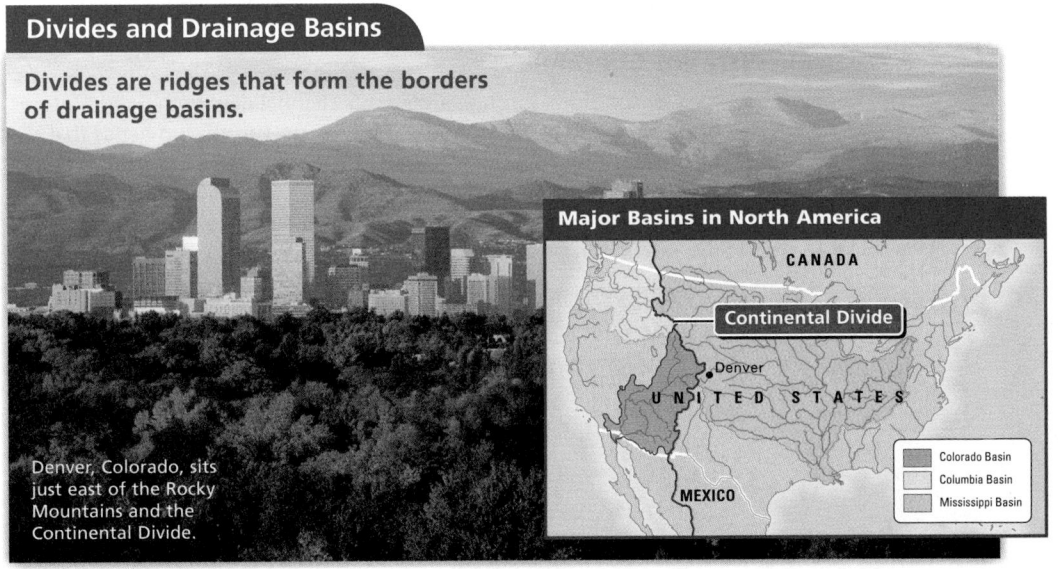

Denver, Colorado, sits just east of the Rocky Mountains and the Continental Divide.

Major Basins in North America

CANADA

Continental Divide

Denver

UNITED STATES

MEXICO

Colorado Basin
Columbia Basin
Mississippi Basin

Chapter 5: **Erosion and Deposition** 151 A

Real World Example

The formation of stream channels can be seen on a small scale on a barren hill at a construction site. After several rainfalls, a pattern of channels usually develops down the hillsides. Many of the smaller channels join the larger ones at an angle, forming a system of gullies.

Teach from Visuals

To help students interpret the map of the United States, ask:

- Where does water drain from the Columbia Basin? (First, show the students where the Pacific and Atlantic oceans and Gulf of Mexico are.) *the Pacific Ocean*

- Is our community included in one of the drainage basins shown here? If so, which one? If not, why not? *If not, it is because water in that area drains into a different river system.*

- Can two rivers be part of the same drainage basin? Explain your answer. *Yes, because divides cause water to flow in one direction. Water flows into various streams that are all part of one system.*

Teach Difficult Concepts

A divide is easy to visualize along a mountain ridge, but students may have a harder time visualizing a divide on relatively flat land. Explain that even on flat or gently rolling land, there will be a continuous line that is higher than the surrounding land and that functions as a divide.

DIFFERENTIATE INSTRUCTION

? More Reading Support

A What makes up a stream system? *all the streams that drain water from one area of land*

B What do you call the area drained by a stream system? *a drainage basin*

Additional Investigation To reinforce Section 5.2 learning goals, use the following full-period investigation:

R **Additional INVESTIGATION,** Rivers Change the Land, A, B, & C, pp. 337–345, 348–349
(Advanced students should complete Levels B and C.)

English Learners Many sentences in this section begin with introductory clauses of phrases that tell when or where, such as *When water falls or ice melts on a slope.* Help students separate these phrases and understand their relation as modifiers to the math clause of the sentence, which contains the subject.

Teach Difficult Concepts

Distinguish a V-shaped valley from other kinds of valleys. Explain that the V shape refers to a cross section of the valley, that is, a "slice" across the valley. Show students a picture of a typical V-shaped valley, such as the Yellowstone River valley.

Teach from Visuals

To help students interpret the photograph of the meanders and oxbow lakes, ask:

- How might the river have looked thousands of years ago? *Its course was different, and the oxbow lakes were part of the river.*

- How might the river look thousands of years from now? *Its course will be different, and some of the meanders will probably be cut off as oxbow lakes.*

Teaching with Technology

To measure the lack of clarity in a stream with sediments, use a CBL and a turbidity probe.

Ongoing Assessment

CHECK YOUR READING *Answer: Floods deposit a lot of sediment onto the floodplain, which makes that land good for growing crops.*

Downtown Davenport, Iowa, sits in the floodplain of the Mississippi River and was covered with water when the river flooded in 1993.

RESOURCE CENTER
CLASSZONE.COM
Find out more about rivers and erosion.

The meanders of this river and oxbow lakes formed as the river deposited sediment and changed course.

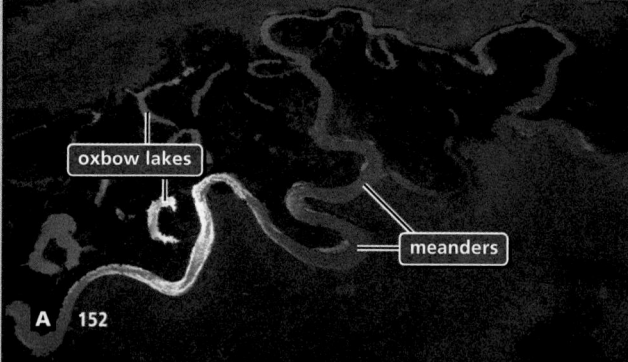

oxbow lakes

meanders

A 152

Valleys and Floodplains

C

As streams flow and carry sediment from the surface of the land, they form valleys. In high mountains, streams often cut V-shaped valleys that are narrow and steepwalled. In lower areas, streams may form broad valleys that include floodplains. A **floodplain** is an area of land on either side of a stream that is underwater when the stream floods. The floodplain of a large river may be many kilometers wide.

When a stream floods, it deposits much of the sediment that it carries onto its floodplain. This sediment can make the floodplain very fertile—or able to support a lot of plant growth. In the United States, the floodplains of the Mississippi River are some of the best places for growing crops.

 **CHECK YOUR READING** Why is fertile land often found on flat land around rivers?

Stream Channels

As a stream flows through a valley, its channel may run straight in some parts and curve around in other parts. Curves and bends that form a twisting, looping pattern in a stream channel are called meanders (mee-AN-duhrz). The moving water erodes the outside banks and deposits sediment along the inside banks. Over many years, meanders shift position.

D

During a flood, the stream may cut a new channel that bypasses a meander. The cut-off meander forms a crescent-shaped lake, which is called an oxbow lake. This term comes from the name of a U-shaped piece of wood that fits under the neck of an ox and is attached to its yoke.

DIFFERENTIATE INSTRUCTION

 More Reading Support

C What area of land floods when a stream overflows its banks? *floodplain*

D What do you call curves and bends in a stream channel? *meanders*

Advanced Have students draw a sequence of three to five diagrams showing how an oxbow lake can form. The drawings should show how erosion of the outside banks of two meanders can form a loop so that the meanders meet, allowing the water to take a shorter course and cutting off the loop to form an oxbow lake.

R Challenge and Extension, p. 297

Alluvial Fans and Deltas

Besides shaping valleys and forming oxbow lakes, streams also create landforms called alluvial fans and deltas. Both of these landforms are formed by the deposition of sediment.

An **alluvial fan** (uh-LOO-vee-uhl) is a fan-shaped deposit of sediment at the base of a mountain. It forms where a stream leaves a steep valley and enters a flatter plain. The stream slows down and spreads out on the flatter ground. As it slows down, it can carry less sediment. The slower-moving water drops some of its sediment, leaving it at the base of the slope.

A **delta** is an area of land formed by the buildup of sediment at the end, or mouth, of a river. When a river enters the ocean, the river's water slows down, and the river drops much of its sediment. This sediment gradually builds up to form a plain. Like alluvial fans, deltas tend to be fan-shaped. Over a very long time, a river may build up its delta far out into the sea. A large river, such as the Mississippi, can build up a huge delta. Like many other large rivers on Earth, the Mississippi has been building up its delta out into the sea for many thousands of years.

This alluvial fan is formed by a stream flowing into the Jago River in Alaska.

From Divide to Delta

On their path to the ocean, streams and rivers slow down and flatten out.

1 Rainwater falls, or snow and ice melt. Streams form.

2 In high areas, streams flow through V-shaped valleys and are narrow and somewhat straight.

3 As land flattens, streams and rivers widen and take curvier paths.

4 Rivers form deltas as they empty into the ocean and deposit sediment.

READING VISUALS Where does the illustration show meanders?

153 **A**

? More Reading Support

E Why does an alluvial fan form where a stream enters a much flatter area? *The stream slows down and deposits much of its sediment.*

Alternative Assessment Have students draw pictures to answer these questions.
- What does an oxbow lake look like?
- How does a meandering river look compared to a nonmeandering river?
- What shape do an alluvial fan and a delta have?
- How does a river valley in the fast-moving part of the river look compared to the slow-moving part of the river?

Teach from Visuals

To help students interpret the diagram of the divide and delta, ask:
- Why are there no waterfalls in area 3? *The land is too flat.*
- Why are streams fast-flowing in area 2? *The land is steep.*
- Which areas would be good for white-water rafting? *1 and 2*
- Why does the river get wider farther downstream? *Other streams join it, bringing more water and sediment.*
- Do you think every river looks like this one? Explain. *No; every major river has these characteristics to some degree, but each river is different depending on the shape of the land, the climate, human interference, and so on.*

EXPLORE (the BIG idea)

Revisit "Where Has Water Been?" on p. 143. Have students use the terms they have learned to explain where water has been.

Ongoing Assessment

Explain how moving water shapes Earth's surface.

Ask: How is a river like a sculptor? *A river carves out valleys and shapes Earth's surface like a sculptor carves out rock or clay and shapes that material into different forms.*

READING VISUALS *Answer: at area 3, where the land flattens*

Address Misconceptions

IDENTIFY Have students draw a picture of what water usually looks like underground. If they show water as a large pool, lake, or free-flowing stream, they may hold the misconception that groundwater usually forms large open-air reservoirs.

CORRECT Show students a jar half-filled with potting soil on top of some pebbles. Ask what the jar will look like after you pour a cup of water into it. Pour the water. It will soak into the soil and reach the spaces between the pebbles. Explain that this is the usual condition of groundwater. Mention that water fills the pores of some kinds of solid rock.

REASSESS Ask: What model best shows water underground: a bathtub filled with water or a bathtub filled with rocks and a bucket of water poured over the rocks? *the tub of rocks and water*

Technology Resources

Visit **ClassZone.com** for background on common student misconceptions.

 MISCONCEPTION DATABASE

Teach from Visuals

To help students interpret the visual of cavern formation, ask:

- How can rainwater soak into the ground? *It trickles through the spaces between soil and rock particles.*

- Where is the water table in this diagram? *in the caves at the bottom of the diagram, at the level of the stream*

- What might happen as the caves near the surface get larger? *The ground above might collapse.*

Teacher Demo

Place a few drops of vinegar on a piece of limestone. The limestone will fizz, showing that it is dissolving. Ask why the vinegar is so effective at dissolving the limestone. *Vinegar contains acid.*

Water moving underground forms caverns.

Not all rainwater runs off the land and flows into surface streams. Some of it evaporates, some is absorbed by plants, and some soaks into the ground and becomes groundwater. At a certain depth below the surface, the spaces in soil and rock become completely filled with water. The top of this water-filled region is called the water table. The water below the water table is called groundwater.

The water table is at different distances below the surface in different places. Its level also can change over time in the same location, depending on changes in rainfall. Below the water table, groundwater flows slowly through underground beds of rock and soil, where it causes erosion to take place.

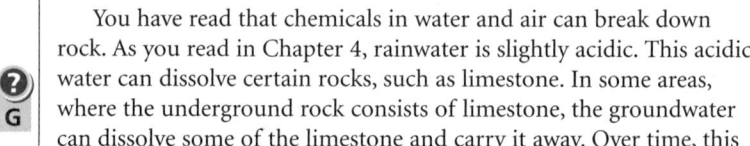

VISUALIZATION
CLASSZONE.COM

Observe the process of cave formation.

You have read that chemicals in water and air can break down rock. As you read in Chapter 4, rainwater is slightly acidic. This acidic water can dissolve certain rocks, such as limestone. In some areas, where the underground rock consists of limestone, the groundwater can dissolve some of the limestone and carry it away. Over time, this

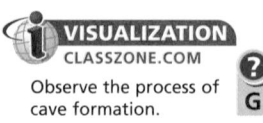
Cavern Formation

Caves form as water underground dissolves limestone, leaving open spaces.

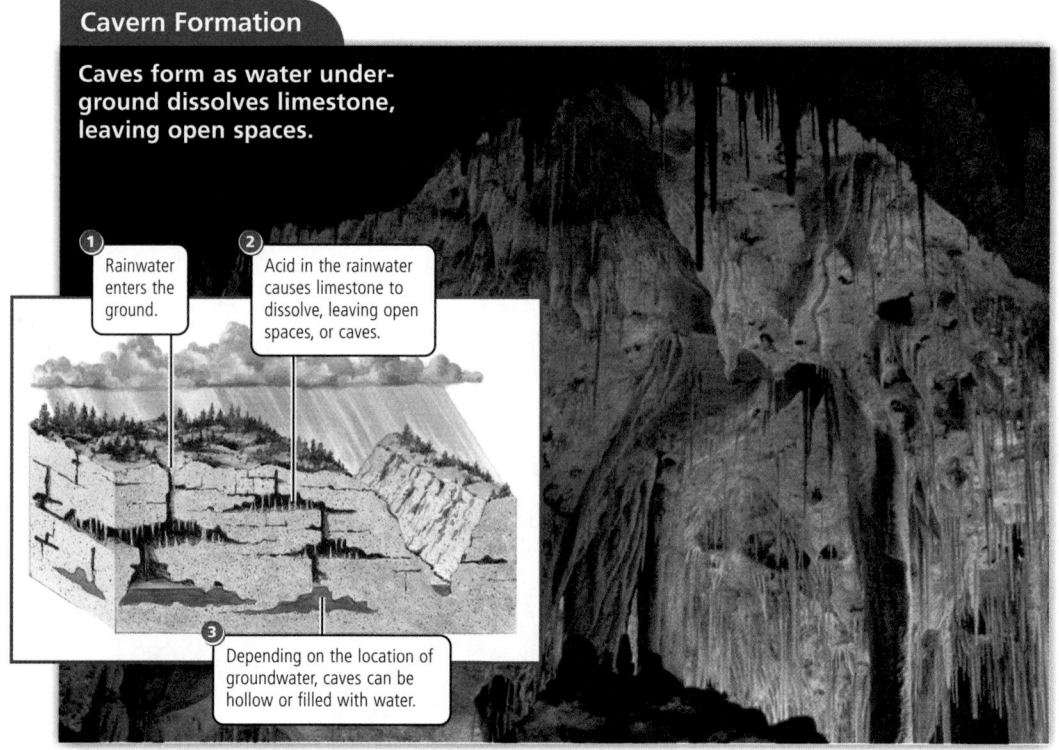

1. Rainwater enters the ground.

2. Acid in the rainwater causes limestone to dissolve, leaving open spaces, or caves.

3. Depending on the location of groundwater, caves can be hollow or filled with water.

DIFFERENTIATE INSTRUCTION

More Reading Support

F What is the name of the highest level of water underground? *water table*

G Why can groundwater dissolve limestone? *Rainwater is acidic.*

Advanced Have students investigate and explain the formation of the slender deposits that form on the ceiling and floor of caves (stalactites and stalagmites).

This sinkhole took down a large part of a parking lot in Atlanta, Georgia.

process produces open spaces, or caves. Large caves are called caverns. If the water table drops, a cavern may fill with air.

Some caverns have huge networks of rooms and passageways. Mammoth Cave in Kentucky, for example, is part of a cavern system that has more than 560 kilometers (about 350 mi) of explored passageways. Within the cavern are lakes and streams.

A surface feature that often occurs in areas with caverns is a sinkhole. A **sinkhole** is a basin that forms when the roof of a cave becomes so thin that it suddenly falls in. Sometimes it falls in because water that supported the roof has drained away. Landscapes with many sinkholes can be found in southern Indiana, south central Kentucky, and central Tennessee. In Florida, the collapse of shallow underground caverns has produced large sinkholes that have destroyed whole city blocks.

 **CHECK YOUR READING** Why do caverns form in areas with limestone?

5.2 Review

KEY CONCEPTS

1. What is the difference between a drainage basin and a divide?

2. How do streams change as they flow from mountains down to plains?

3. How do caverns form?

CRITICAL THINKING

4. **Sequence** Draw a cartoon with three panels showing how a sinkhole forms.

5. **Compare and Contrast** Make a Venn diagram to compare and contrast alluvial fans and deltas.

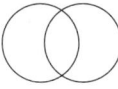

CHALLENGE

6. **Apply** During a flood, a river drops the largest pieces of its sediment on the floodplain close to its normal channel. Explain why. (**Hint:** Think about the speed of the water.)

Chapter 5: Erosion and Deposition **155** **A**

ANSWERS

1. A drainage basin is an area into which water flows from a divide. A divide forms a border of drainage basins.

2. As streams flow toward flat plains, they are in valleys that are V-shaped. Streams then become less steep and then wider and curvier.

3. Rainwater that is slightly acidic dissolves limestone underground, creating caverns.

4. A cavern fills with water. The water drains. The "ceiling" falls in.

5. alluvial fan: base of mountain; delta: mouth of river; both: formed by deposition when water slows, fan-shaped

6. Faster water has more power to carry large pieces. Water is faster in its channel than it is on the floodplain.

CHAPTER INVESTIGATION

Focus

PURPOSE To observe the formation of meanders, deltas, and alluvial fans in a model stream

OVERVIEW Students will construct a model stream in a stream table. They will observe the processes of erosion and deposition over the life of the stream. Students will find the following:

- The river channel and valley widen with time.
- Meanders widen with time.
- Alluvial fans and deltas form.

Lab Preparation

- The ideal source of water is from a narrow hose attached to a tap or pump. The flow from a pitcher is harder to control, but students could slowly pour water into a funnel attached to a hose.
- If draining the stream table into a sink, be sure to use a fine sieve or nylon stocking to prevent sand from going into the drain.

Prior to the investigation, have students read through the investigation. You may wish to copy and distribute datasheets and rubrics.

 UNIT RESOURCE BOOK, pp. 328–336

 SCIENCE TOOLKIT, F15

Lab Management

- The channel students dig should be fairly deep.
- Encourage students to conduct this experiment slowly, starting with a stream of water poured slowly at as shallow an angle as possible.

SAFETY Water is bound to get on the floor during this experiment. Students should wipe up spills immediately.

INCLUSION Students with visual impairments could gently feel the various features being formed in the stream table.

CHAPTER INVESTIGATION

Creating Stream Features

OVERVIEW AND PURPOSE A view from the sky reveals that a large river twists and bends in its channel. But as quiet as it might appear, the river constantly digs and dumps Earth materials along its way. This erosion and deposition causes twists and curves called meanders, and a delta at the river's mouth. In this investigation you will

- create a "river" in a stream table to observe the creation of meanders and deltas
- identify the processes of erosion and deposition

▶ Problem

How does moving water create meanders and deltas?

▶ Procedure

MATERIALS
- stream table, with hose attachment or recirculating pump
- sieve (optional)
- wood blocks
- sand
- ruler
- water
- sink with drain
- pitcher (optional)
- bucket (optional)

1 Arrange the stream table on a counter so that it drains into a sink or bucket. If possible, place a sieve beneath the outlet hose to keep sand out of the drain. You can attach the inlet hose to a faucet if you have a proper adapter. Or you can gently pour water in with a pitcher or use a recirculating pump and a bucket.

2 Place wood blocks beneath the inlet end of the stream table so that the table tilts toward the outlet at about a 20 degree angle. Fill the upper two-thirds of the stream table nearly to the top with sand. Pack the sand a bit, and level the surface with the edge of a ruler. The empty bottom third of the stream table represents the lake or bay into which the river flows.

3 Using the end of the ruler, dig a gently curving trench halfway through the thickness of the sand from its upper to its lower end.

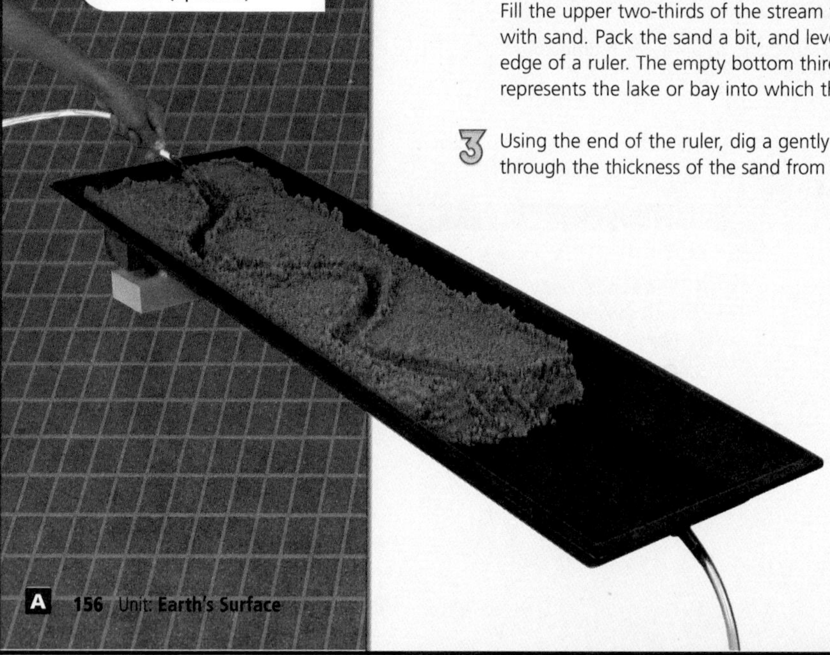

INVESTIGATION RESOURCES

 CHAPTER INVESTIGATION, Creating Stream Features
- Level A, pp. 328–331
- Level B, pp. 332–335
- Level C, p. 336

Advanced students should complete Levels B & C.

 Writing a Lab Report, D12–13

Technology Resources

Customize this student lab as needed or look for an alternative. Print rubrics to assess student lab reports.

 Lab Generator CD-ROM

4. Direct a gentle flow of tap water into the upper end of the trench. Increase the flow slightly when the water begins to move through the trench. You may have to try this several times before you find the proper rate of flow to soak the sand and fill the stream channel. Avoid adding so much water that it pools at the top before moving into the channel. You can also change the stream table's tilt.

5. Once you are successful in creating a river, observe its shape and any movement of the sand. Continue until the top part of the sand is completely washed away and your river falls apart. Scrape the sand back into place with the ruler and repeat the procedure until you thoroughly understand the stream and sand movements.

▶ Observe and Analyze | Write It Up

1. **RECORD** Diagram your stream-table setup, and make a series of drawings showing changes in your river over time. Be sure to label the river's features, as well as areas of erosion and deposition. Be sure to diagram the behavior of the sand at the river's mouth.

2. **RECORD** Write a record of the development of your river from start to finish. Include details such as the degree of tilt you used, your method of introducing water into the stream table, and features you observed forming.

▶ Conclude | Write It Up

1. **EVALUATE** How do you explain the buildup of sand at the mouth of your river? Use the words *speed, erosion,* and *deposition* in your answer. Did the slope of the stream change over time?

2. **INTERPRET** Where in your stream table did you observe erosion occurring? Deposition? What features did each process form?

3. **INFER** What might have occurred if you had increased the amount or speed of the water flowing into your river?

4. **IDENTIFY LIMITS** In what ways was your setup a simplified version of what would actually occur on Earth? Describe the ways in which an actual stream would be more complex.

5. **APPLY** Drawing on what you observed in this investigation, make two statements that relate the age of a stream to (1) the extent of its meanders and (2) to the size of its delta or alluvial fan.

▶ INVESTIGATE Further

CHALLENGE Revise this activity to test a problem statement about a specific stream feature. You could choose to vary the stream's slope, speed, or volume to test the changes' effects on meanders and deltas, for example. Or you could vary the sediment size and observe the movements of each size. Write a hypothesis and design an experimental procedure. Identify the independent and dependent variables.

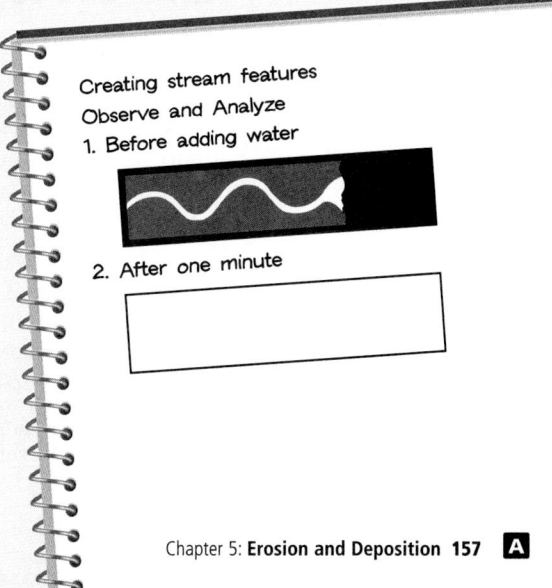

Creating stream features
Observe and Analyze
1. Before adding water

2. After one minute

Chapter 5: **Erosion and Deposition** 157 **A**

Post-Lab Discussion

Ask: How might scientists use stream tables to gather information or to solve a problem? *Stream tables can be used to study the effects of sediment of different sizes or the slope of a stream on how the stream changes over time. Stream tables can be useful for modeling how a dam or pollution might affect a river.*

▶ Observe and Analyze | Write It Up

1. *Observe students' diagrams. They will likely show a widening of the stream channel and meanders over time. Students might use two colors to show the original stream channel and the new stream after water flows. They should show where material has been picked up by erosion and where it has been put down by deposition.*

2. *Students should identify where erosion and deposition occur, and where meanders might have formed or changed and where a delta might have formed.*

▶ Conclude | Write It Up

1. *As the <u>speed</u> of the stream slows, the sand that is carried by the river in the process of <u>erosion</u> settles out by the process of <u>deposition</u> at the river's mouth. The slope may have flattened and been reduced by buildup of sand, although unlike real river valleys, the tray has a constant slope.*

2. *Erosion occurred along most of the stream banks, especially at the outside of the curves, which may have formed into new meanders. Deposition occurred at the inside of the meanders and especially at the mouth (end) of the river, where a delta would form.*

3. *more erosion, a deepening of the channel, possibly a flood*

4. *The setup had only one stream, the surface was only sand and spread evenly; the stream was very short, and the amount of time was brief. An actual stream would have water flowing into it from other streams and down its banks, the structure of the land would be different and variable, the stream and land would be exposed to weather, and changes would occur over a long time.*

5. *The older the stream, the more extreme its meanders will be and the larger its delta or alluvial fan will be.*

▶ INVESTIGATE Further

CHALLENGE Experimental design should vary one aspect of the stream, keeping other conditions constant.

5.3 FOCUS

● Set Learning Goals

Students will

- Describe how waves and currents shape shorelines.
- Explain how wind shapes landscapes.
- Model in an experiment how sand moves along a beach.

● 3-Minute Warm-Up

Display Transparency 37 or copy this exercise on the board:

Draw a map of a river. Label the river with an arrow to show its direction of flow. Add three small streams that join the river. Label each stream with an arrow to show its direction of flow. *Maps should show each stream meeting the river at an angle, producing a tree-like pattern. The flow of the streams should be the same as that of the main river.*

[T] 3-Minute Warm-Up, p. T37

5.3 MOTIVATE

THINK ABOUT

PURPOSE To introduce waves as a force of erosion

DISCUSS Ask students what probably surrounded the stone pillars millions of years ago. Ask: Why do you think these are left over from large areas of rock? *The pillars are made of hard rock that was among softer or fractured rock that was easier to weather and disintegrate.*

KEY CONCEPT

5.3 Waves and wind shape land.

◀ **BEFORE,** you learned

- Stream systems shape Earth's surface
- Groundwater creates caverns and sinkholes

▶ **NOW,** you will learn

- How waves and currents shape shorelines
- How wind shapes land

VOCABULARY

longshore drift p. 159
longshore current p. 159
sandbar p. 160
barrier island p. 160
dune p. 161
loess p. 162

THINK ABOUT

How did these pillars of rock form?

The rock formations in this photograph stand along the shoreline near the small town of Port Campbell, Australia. What natural force created these isolated stone pillars? What evidence of this force can you see in the photograph?

NOTE-TAKING STRATEGY
Remember to organize your notes in a chart or web as you read.

Waves and currents shape shorelines.

The stone pillars, or sea stacks, in the photograph above are a major tourist attraction in Port Campbell National Park. They were formed by the movement of water. The constant action of waves breaking against the cliffs slowly wore them away, leaving behind pillarlike formations. Waves continue to wear down the pillars and cliffs at the rate of about two centimeters (one inch) a year. In the years to come, the waves will likely wear away the stone pillars completely.

The force of waves, powered by wind, can wear away rock and move thousands of tons of sand on beaches. The force of wind itself can change the look of the land. Moving air can pick up sand particles and move them around to build up dunes. Wind can also carry huge amounts of fine sediment thousands of kilometers.

In this section, you'll read more about how waves and wind shape shorelines and a variety of other landforms.

RESOURCES FOR DIFFERENTIATED INSTRUCTION

Below Level
UNIT RESOURCE BOOK
- Reading Study Guide A, pp. 301–302
- Decoding Support, p. 325

 **AUDIO CDS**

Advanced
UNIT RESOURCE BOOK
Challenge and Extension, p. 307

English Learners
UNIT RESOURCE BOOK
Spanish Reading Study Guide, pp. 305–306

 AUDIO CDS

- Audio Readings in Spanish
- Audio Readings (English)

Shorelines

Some shorelines, like the one near Port Campbell, Australia, are made up of steep, rock cliffs. As waves crash against the rock, they wear away the bottom of the cliffs. Eventually, parts of the cliffs above break away and fall into the water, where they are worn down and carried away by the water.

While high, rocky coasts get worn away, low coastlines often get built up. As you read earlier, when a stream flows into an ocean or a lake, it deposits its sediment near its mouth. This sediment mixes with the sediment formed by waves beating against the coast. Waves and currents move this sediment along the shore, building up beaches. Two terms are used to describe the movement of sediment and water along a shore: *longshore drift* and *longshore current.*

- **Longshore drift** is the zigzag movement of sand along a beach. Waves formed by wind blowing across the water far from shore may hit a shoreline at an angle. These angled waves carry sand up onto the shore, and then gravity pulls the water and sand directly back into the water. The sand gradually moves down the beach. The illustration below shows longshore drift.

- A **longshore current** is movement of water along a shore as waves strike the shore at an angle. The direction of the longshore current can change from day to day as the direction of the waves striking the shore changes.

Longshore drift moves large amounts of sand along beaches. It can cause a beach to shrink at one location and grow at another.

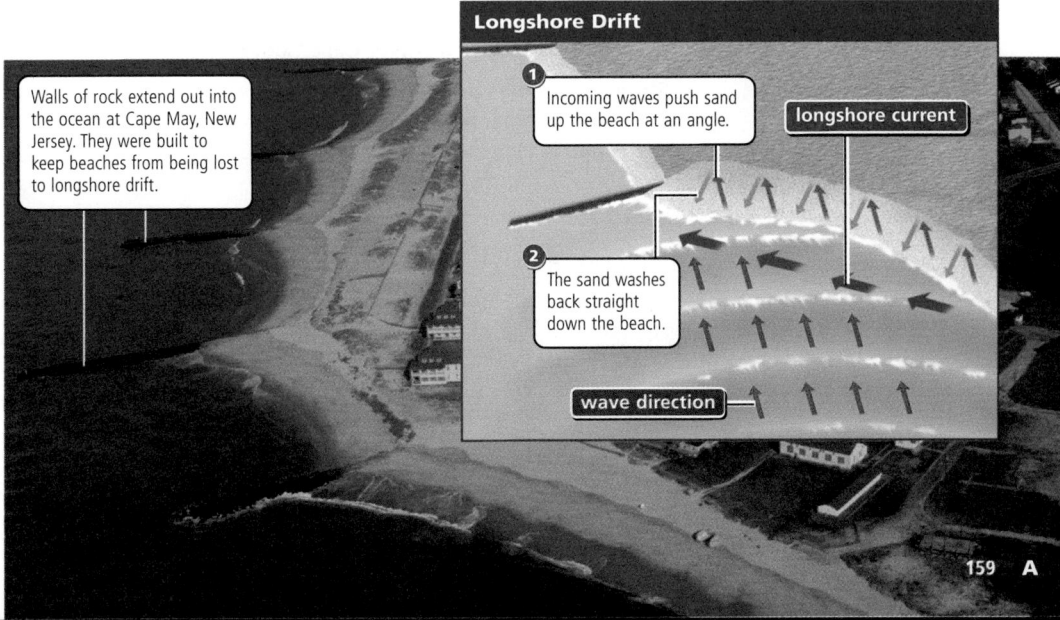

Walls of rock extend out into the ocean at Cape May, New Jersey. They were built to keep beaches from being lost to longshore drift.

Longshore Drift

1. Incoming waves push sand up the beach at an angle.

longshore current

2. The sand washes back straight down the beach.

wave direction

159 A

Address Misconceptions

IDENTIFY Ask: Are ocean waves a movement of energy or water? If students do not say energy, they may hold the misconception that waves move masses of water forward.

CORRECT Set up a long trough of water. A plastic trough used for moistening wallpaper works well. Place a cork or other float in the middle of the water. Use your hand to create a gentle wave to demonstrate that the float rises and falls on the wave but does not move forward.

REASSESS Remind students that water waves move energy, not material. Ask: How might a message in a bottle thrown into the sea near Europe end up on the shores of the United States? *Currents, rather than waves, could take it there.*

Teach from Visuals

To help students interpret the diagram and photograph of longshore drift, ask:

- What evidence of longshore drift can you see in the photograph? *sand accumulated at the base of each rock wall; curve of shoreline between each wall*

- How would the beaches at Cape May be different if the jetties weren't there? *They would be smaller.*

Technology Resources

Visit **ClassZone.com** for background on common student misconceptions.

 MISCONCEPTION DATABASE

Metacognitive Strategy

Ask students to find clues in the terms *longshore drift* and *longshore current* that help them remember what the terms mean.

EXPLORE the BIG idea

Revisit "How Do Waves Shape Land?" on p. 143. Have students explain their results.

DIFFERENTIATE INSTRUCTION

 **More Reading Support**

A Where does beach sand come from? *from sediment brought to the shore by rivers and from rocks eroded along the shoreline*

Below Level Have students model longshore drift by moving their finger diagonally across their desk, straight back, diagonally across, and so on until they reach the edge of the desk. Ask them how many kinds of movements they made. *three: diagonal, straight back, and the general movement across the desk* Compare these movements to those of longshore drift.

INVESTIGATE Longshore Drift

PURPOSE To model the concept of longshore drift

TIP *15 min.* Tell students to place the books far up on their desk, so that the coin falls onto the desk instead of the floor.

WHAT DO YOU THINK? *The coin moved at an angle on its way up and generally straight back, perpendicular to the edge of the book, on its way down. The book surface is the beach, the coin is the sand, and the movement of the finger is the wave.*

CHALLENGE *From right to left; flick from the lower left corner to change the current's direction.*

 Datasheet, Longshore Drift, p. 308

Technology Resources

Customize this student lab as needed or look for an alternative. Print rubrics to assess student lab reports.

 Lab Generator CD-ROM

Teach from Visuals

To help students interpret the diagram of sand deposition, ask: How are sandbars and barrier islands related? *Barrier islands build up as sandbars parallel to a coastline accumulate enough deposition to rise above the surface. Sandbars are buildups of sand and may be underwater. They are not always parallel to the coast and do not always become barrier islands.*

INVESTIGATE Longshore Drift

How does sand move along a beach?

PROCEDURE

1. Prop up a book as shown.
2. Hold a coin with your finger against the bottom right corner of the book.
3. Gently flick the coin up the slope of the book at an angle. The coin should slide back down the book and fall off the bottom. If necessary, readjust the angle of the book and the strength with which you are flicking the coin.
4. Repeat step 3 several times. Observe the path the coin takes. Record your observations. Include a diagram that shows the general path the coin takes as it slides up and down the book.

WHAT DO YOU THINK?

- What path did the coin take on its way up? On its way down?
- In this model of longshore drift, what represents the beach, what represents the sand, and what represents a wave?

CHALLENGE In this model, in which direction will the longshore current move? How could you change the model to change the direction of the current?

Sandbars and Barrier Islands

As they transport sand, ocean waves and currents shape a variety of coastal landforms. Longshore currents, for example, often deposit sand along shorelines. The sand builds up to form sandbars. A **sandbar** is a ridge of sand built up by the action of waves and currents. A sandbar that has built up above the water's surface and is joined to the land at one end is called a spit. The tip of Cape Cod, Massachusetts, is a spit.

B

Strong longshore currents that mostly move in one direction may produce sandbars that build up over time into barrier islands. A **barrier island** is a long, narrow island that develops parallel to a coast.

C

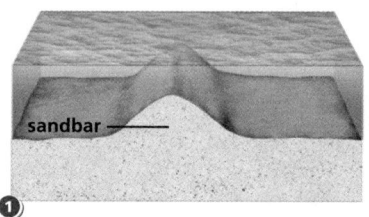
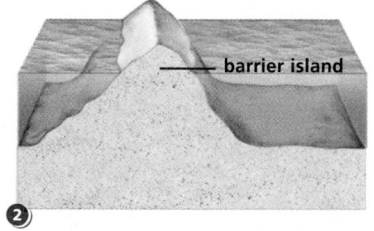

① Waves and currents move and build up sand deposits to form a sandbar under the water surface.

② As more sand is deposited, the sandbar rises above the surface to become a barrier island.

DIFFERENTIATE INSTRUCTION

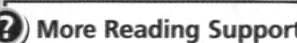

? More Reading Support

B Where might you see a spit? *extending from a beach*

C From what structure do both spits and barrier islands form? *sandbars*

Below Level
Show students a large-scale map of Massachusetts and point out Cape Cod. Have students find and point out the spit at the cape's tip. Use maps of other places along the East Coast to point out spits and barrier islands.

Advanced
Have students develop a PowerPoint presentation, using scanned photographs of a variety of spits and barrier islands. They should include photographs of jetties, the shape of beaches that result, and maps that show the locations.

 Challenge and Extension, p. 307

This lighthouse on a barrier island in North Carolina had to be moved because of beach erosion. The photograph shows the lighthouse before it was moved.

D

A barrier island gets its name from the fact that it forms a barrier between the ocean waves and the shore of the mainland. As a barrier island builds up, grasses, bushes, and trees begin to grow on it.

Barrier islands are common along gently sloping coasts around the world. They occur along the coasts of New Jersey and North Carolina and along the coastline of the Gulf of Mexico. Padre Island in Texas is a barrier island about 180 kilometers (110 mi) in length.

Barrier islands constantly change shape. Hurricanes or other storms can speed up the change. During large storms, waves can surge across the land, carrying away huge amounts of sediment and depositing it elsewhere. Houses on beaches can be destroyed in storms.

CHECK YOUR READING How and where do barrier islands form?

Wind shapes land.

At Indiana Dunes National Lakeshore, not far from the skyscrapers of Chicago, you can tumble or slide down huge sand dunes. First-time visitors to the Indiana dunes find it hard to believe that sand formations like these can be found so far from a desert or an ocean. What created this long stretch of dune land along the southern shore of Lake Michigan? The answer: wind. A **dune** is a mound of sand built up by wind.

E

Like water, wind has the power to transport and deposit sediment. Although wind is a less powerful force of erosion than moving water, it can still shape landforms, especially in dry regions and in areas that have few or no plants to hold soil in place. Wind can build up dunes, deposit layers of dust, or make a land surface as hard as pavement.

Chapter 5: **Erosion and Deposition** 161 **A**

Teach from Visuals

To help students interpret the dune diagram and photograph, ask:

- Which side of the dune in the diagram has the most gentle slope? *the side that the wind blows into*

- On the steep side of the dune, why doesn't the wind blow the sand away, making a gentle slope? *because the dune blocks the wind*

- From which side do you think the wind blows in the area shown in the photograph? Why do you think so? *from left to right because the gentler slopes are on the left*

Teacher Demo

Use a hair dryer and a tray of dry sand to demonstrate how a dune forms around an obstacle. Place a stone in the tray and blow sand against it (starting from a distance to avoid causing a mess). A dune will form. Ask: Once the stone is covered, why does sand continue to collect? *The small dune itself acts as an obstacle.*

SAFETY Make sure the hair dryer and windblown sand are directed away from students.

These hills of sand are at the Great Sand Dunes National Monument in Colorado.

Dune Formation

Even a light breeze can carry dust. A moderate wind can roll and slide grains of sand along a beach or desert, creating ripples. Only a strong wind, however, can actually pick up and carry sand particles. When the wind dies down or hits something—such as a cliff or a hill—it drops the sand. Over time, the deposits of sand build up to create dunes.

Some dunes start out as ripples that grow larger. Others form as wind-carried sand settles around a rock, log, or other obstacle. In climates with enough rainfall, plants begin to grow on dunes a short distance from beaches.

Dunes form only where there are strong winds and a constant supply of loose sand. They can be found on the inland side of beaches of oceans and large lakes, on the sandy floodplains of large rivers, and in sandy deserts.

Dunes can form in a variety of sizes and shapes. They can reach heights of up to 300 meters (about 1000 ft). Some dunes are curved; others are long straight ridges; still others are mound-shaped hills. A dune usually has a gentle slope on the side that faces the wind and a steeper slope on the side sheltered from the wind.

Loess

Besides forming dunes, wind also changes the soil over large regions of Earth by depositing dust. A strong wind storm can move millions of tons of dust. As the wind dies down, the dust drops to the ground. Deposits of fine wind-blown sediment are called **loess** (LOH-uhs).

In some regions, deposits of loess have built up over thousands and even millions of years. Loess is a valuable resource because it forms good soil for growing crops.

DIFFERENTIATE INSTRUCTION

? **More Reading Support**

F What two conditions are needed for dunes to form? *strong winds and loose sand*

G What are deposits of wind-blown sediment? *loess*

Below Level Students may have a hard time appreciating the size that sand dunes can reach. Compare the size of the tallest dunes (300 meters, or 1000 feet) to something familiar, such as a skyscraper or a local hill.

English Learners Remind students that these words are generalizations that mean nearly the same thing: *mostly, mainly, typically, usually, often, commonly.*

This loess deposit in Iowa built up over many thousands of years.

Loess covers about 10 percent of the land surface of Earth. China has especially large deposits of loess, covering hundreds of thousands of square kilometers. Some of the deposits are more than 300 meters (about 1000 ft) thick. Such thick deposits take a long time to develop. Some of the loess deposits in China are 2 million years old. Winds blowing over the deserts and dry regions of central Asia carried the dust that formed these deposits.

Parts of east central Europe and the Mississippi Valley in the United States also contain significant loess deposits. In the central United States, loess deposits are between 8 and 30 meters (25 and 100 ft) thick.

Desert Pavement

Not only does wind shape land surfaces by depositing dust; it also shapes land surfaces by removing dust. When wind blows away all the smallest particles from a mixture of sand, silt, and gravel, it leaves behind just a layer of stones and gravel. This stony surface is called desert pavement because it looks like a cobblestone pavement. The coarse gravel and rocks are too large to be picked up by wind.

Desert pavement is made up of particles too large to be picked up by wind.

 CHECK YOUR READING How are both loess and desert pavement formed by wind?

5.3 Review

KEY CONCEPTS
1. What kinds of landforms do longshore drift and longshore currents produce?
2. How do dunes form?
3. How does loess form, and why is it important?

CRITICAL THINKING
4. **Identify Cause and Effect** Is longshore drift the cause or effect of a longshore current? Explain.
5. **Predict** What effect would a barrier island have on the shoreline of the mainland?

⚠ CHALLENGE
6. **Hypothesize** The south and east shores of Lake Michigan have large areas of sand dunes, but the north and west shores do not. Write a hypothesis that explains why. You might want to use a map and draw the shape of Lake Michigan to explain.

Chapter 5: **Erosion and Deposition** 163 **A**

ANSWERS

1. beaches, sandbars, barrier islands, and spits

2. Strong winds pile up sand in mounds.

3. Loess forms as winds deposit fine sediments from elsewhere. It can form thick deposits of fertile soil.

4. It is the effect. Longshore drift is the movement of sand, which is caused by longshore current, which is the force of the water moving in a direction.

5. It might lessen the force of the waves on the mainland

shore, especially during storms.

6. North and west: wind is blowing sand toward the water, so areas of dunes don't form. South and east: wind is blowing inland, where there is room for sand to pile up into dunes.

Set Learning Goal

To make generalizations about organisms adapted to life on a sand dune

Present the Science

Sand food grows in the dunes of southeastern California and nearby southwestern Arizona. The only part of the plant that is above ground is the flower head, which pushes above the sand during early spring. It is pollinated by flies, beetles, and butterflies and produces seeds. Sand food has no chlorophyll and cannot produce its own food. It absorbs carbohydrates and amino acids produced by the host plant.

Discussion Questions

- How do the roots of American beach grass help hold sand in place? *The roots act like a mesh or net that prevents sand from moving.*

- How might the sand food harm other plants? *It takes food from them.*

- Why is Fowler's toad most active at night? *It is cooler then, so the toad is in less danger of drying out.*

DIFFERENTIATION TIP Have students discuss in small groups the questions in the captions. List each group's ideas on the board and have a class discussion.

Close

Ask: What general statement can you make about organisms and harsh environments? *Organisms that live in harsh environments have adapted to the conditions in those environments.*

Life on Dunes

The leaves of American beach grass contain silica, the main component of sand. The leaves are therefore very tough. Why is this important on a dune?

Fowler's toads have a brownish or greenish color that makes them hard to see against a sandy background. How would this help protect them from animals that want to eat them?

Sand dunes are a difficult environment for most organisms. For example, few plants can gather enough nutrition from sand to grow quickly. However, any plant that grows slowly is likely to be buried by the shifting sand. Plants and animals that thrive on dunes generally have unusual traits that help them survive in dune conditions.

American Beach Grass

Among the first plants to grow on new coastal dunes is American beach grass. It grows faster as sand begins to bury it, and it can grow up to 1 meter (more than 3 ft) per year. Its large root system—reaching down as much as 3 meters (about 10 ft)—helps it gather food and water. The roots also help hold sand in place. As the grass's roots make the dunes stable, other plants can begin to grow there.

Sand Food

One of the most unusual plants in desert dunes is called sand food. It is one of the few plants that cannot convert sunlight into energy it can use. Instead, its long underground stem grabs onto the root of another plant and sucks food from it. Most of the plant is the stem. Sand food plants may be more than 2 meters (almost 7 ft) long.

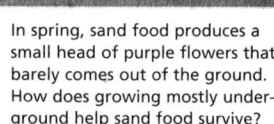

Fowler's Toad

Fowler's toad is one of the animals that can live in coastal dunes. During the day, sunlight can make the top layer of the sand very hot and dry. These toads dig down into the sand, where they are safe, cool, and moist. They are most active at night.

In spring, sand food produces a small head of purple flowers that barely comes out of the ground. How does growing mostly underground help sand food survive?

EXPLORE

1. **GENERALIZE** Dune plants often have long roots. Propose an explanation for this.
2. **CHALLENGE** Use library or Internet resources to learn about another plant or animal that lives on dunes. Describe how it has adapted to the conditions in which it lives.

EXPLORE

1. GENERALIZE *Water and nutrients are scarce on dunes. The long roots allow plants to reach water and nutrients deep in the sand.*

2. CHALLENGE *Answers should address the environment's effect on the organism as well as its adaptation to the environment.*

Answers to caption questions: Tough leaves can withstand abrasion and deter plant eaters. Toad camouflage makes it hard for predators to find the toad. Underground growth is less subject to drying and sand scour.

KEY CONCEPT

5.4 Glaciers carve land and move sediments.

 BEFORE, you learned
- Running water shapes landscapes
- Wind changes landforms

 NOW, you will learn
- How moving ice erodes land
- How moving ice deposits sediment and changes landforms

VOCABULARY

glacier p. 165
till p. 168
moraine p. 168
kettle lake p. 169

EXPLORE Glaciers

How do glaciers affect land?

PROCEDURE

① Flatten the clay on top of a paper towel.

② Drag the ice cube across the clay as shown. Record your observations.

③ Leave the ice cube to melt on top of the clay.

WHAT DO YOU THINK?
- What happened when you dragged the ice cube across the clay?
- What happened to the sand and gravel in the ice cube as it melted?

MATERIALS
- modeling clay
- paper towel
- ice cube containing sand and gravel

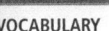

 VOCABULARY
Remember to add a four square diagram for *glacier* to your notebook.

Glaciers are moving bodies of ice.

You might not think of ice as something that moves. But think about what happens to an ice cube on a table. The cube begins to melt, makes a small puddle, and may slide a little. The water under the cube makes the table surface slippery, which allows the ice cube to slide.

A similar process happens on a much larger scale with glaciers. A **glacier** is a large mass of ice that moves over land. A glacier forms in a cold region when more snow falls than melts each year. As the snow builds up, its weight presses the snow on the bottom into ice. On a mountain, the weight of a heavy mass of ice causes it to flow downward, usually slowly. On flatter land, the ice spreads out as a sheet. As glaciers form, move, and melt away, they shape landscapes.

Chapter 5: **Erosion and Deposition** 165 **A**

Chapter 5 **165** **A**

Teach from Visuals

To help students interpret the visual "Ice Age in North America," display a political map of your area. Ask:

• Was our area covered with ice during the last ice age? *Answers will vary.*

• If an area was not covered by ice, can you assume that the landscape was unaffected by the glaciers? Explain. *No; areas free of ice might have been affected by water flow from melted ice or by wind-blown sediment.*

Real World Example

Evidence of glaciers during the last ice age are seen throughout North America. Grooves gouged into rocks can be seen in New York City's Central Park. Mounds of glacial sediment formed teardrop-shaped hills called drumlins, which are scattered in the Midwest and New England. The fertile soils of the Great Plains are largely a result of thick deposits of loess, sediment that was pulverized by glaciers and then blown far away.

Teacher Demo

Show students a handful of snow, crushed ice, or the frost from inside a freezer. Squeeze the material into a ball. Ask:

• What does squeezing do to the particles? *It presses them together, so they form ice. They melt a little next to your hands.*

• How is this like what happens in a glacier? *A glacier forms when snow compacts to form ice. The ice partially melts on the bottom, which helps the glacier flow.*

Ongoing Assessment

CHECK YOUR READING *The two major types are alpine glaciers, which form in mountain valleys, and continental glaciers, which form on large landmasses near the poles.*

Extent of Glaciers

Glaciers can exist only in places where it is cold enough for water to stay frozen year round. Glaciers are found in mountain ranges all over the world and in land regions near the north and south poles.

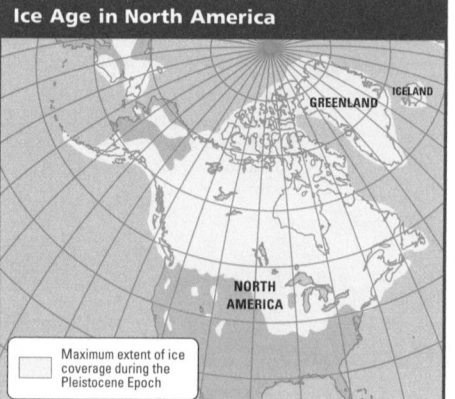

Ice Age in North America

GREENLAND ICELAND

NORTH AMERICA

Maximum extent of ice coverage during the Pleistocene Epoch

Today, glaciers cover about 10 percent of Earth's land surface. However, the amount of land surface covered by glaciers has varied greatly over Earth's history. Glaciers have expanded during long cold periods called ice ages and have disappeared during long warm periods. About 30,000 years ago—during the last major ice age—glaciers extended across the northern parts of North America and Eurasia. They covered nearly 30 percent of the present land surface of Earth.

There are two major types of glaciers: alpine glaciers and continental glaciers.

 **RESOURCE CENTER** CLASSZONE.COM

Learn more about the movement and effects of glaciers.

 **A**

Alpine Glaciers

Alpine glaciers, also called valley glaciers, form in mountains and flow down through valleys. As these glaciers move, they cause erosion, breaking up rock and carrying and pushing away the resulting sediment. Over time, an alpine glacier can change a V-shaped mountain valley into a U-shaped valley with a wider, flatter bottom.

Some glaciers extend all the way down into the lower land at the bases of mountains. At an alpine glacier's lower end, where temperatures are warmer, melting can occur. The melting glacier drops sediment, and streams flowing from the glacier carry some of the sediment away. If an alpine glacier flows into the ocean, big blocks may break off and become icebergs.

Continental Glaciers

Continental glaciers, also called ice sheets, are much larger than alpine glaciers. They can cover entire continents, including all but the highest mountain peaks. An ice sheet covered most of Canada and the northern United States during the last ice age. This ice sheet melted and shrank about 10,000 years ago.

Today, ice sheets cover most of Greenland and Antarctica. Each of these glaciers is shaped like a wide dome over the land. The ice on Antarctica is as much as 4500 meters (15,000 ft) thick.

 B

 **CHECK YOUR READING** What are the two major types of glaciers and where do they form?

DIFFERENTIATE INSTRUCTION

? More Reading Support

A Where do alpine glaciers form? *in mountain valleys*

B What areas do continental glaciers cover today? *most of Greenland and Antarctica*

English Learners Note that English learners may be confused by words that function as both nouns and verbs. For example, in "Investigate Kettle Lake Formation" on p. 169, the word *model* can be found as a noun and a verb. The phrase "design a model of the process" uses the word as a noun. But the phrase "model how sediment builds up around ice blocks" uses the word as a verb.

Types of Glaciers and Movement

A glacier is a large mass of ice that moves over land.

Alpine Glaciers

A glacier, such as this one in Alaska, changes the landscape as it moves down a mountain valley.

Continental Glaciers

Huge sheets of ice cover the continent of Antarctica and other land regions.

Glacier Movement

Gravity causes the ice in a glacier to move downhill. Two different processes cause glaciers to move: flowing and sliding.

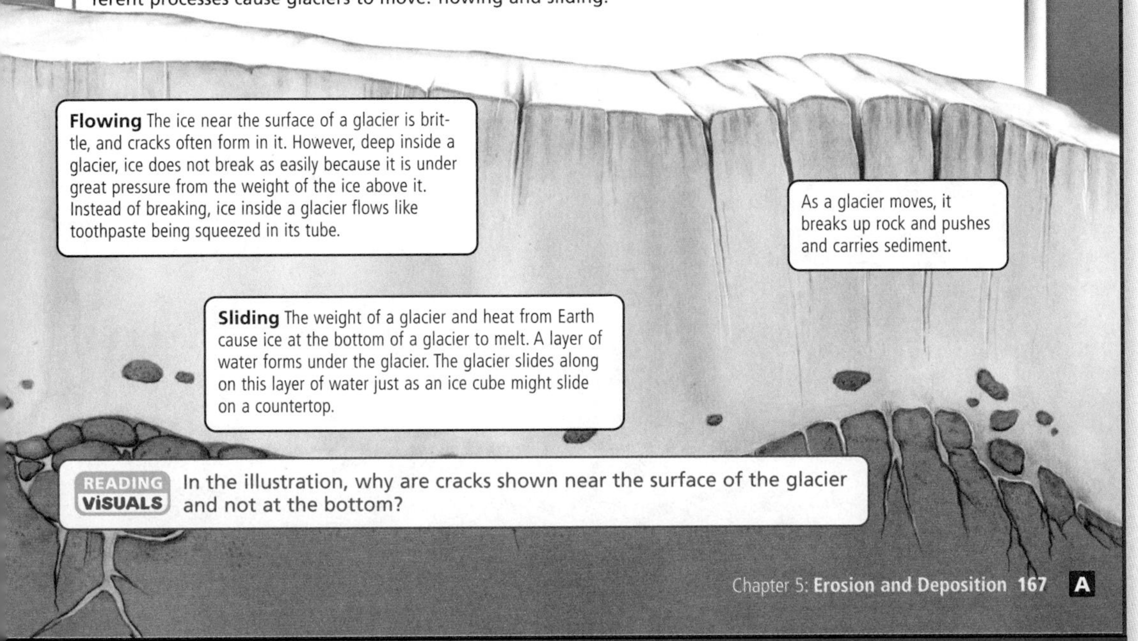

Flowing The ice near the surface of a glacier is brittle, and cracks often form in it. However, deep inside a glacier, ice does not break as easily because it is under great pressure from the weight of the ice above it. Instead of breaking, ice inside a glacier flows like toothpaste being squeezed in its tube.

As a glacier moves, it breaks up rock and pushes and carries sediment.

Sliding The weight of a glacier and heat from Earth cause ice at the bottom of a glacier to melt. A layer of water forms under the glacier. The glacier slides along on this layer of water just as an ice cube might slide on a countertop.

READING VISUALS In the illustration, why are cracks shown near the surface of the glacier and not at the bottom?

Chapter 5: **Erosion and Deposition** 167 **A**

DIFFERENTIATE INSTRUCTION

Below Level Some students may not grasp what 10 percent and 30 percent land coverage means. Draw two circle graphs showing each of these quantities. Then transfer these concepts to maps of the world's landmasses.

Teach from Visuals

To help students interpret the diagram of glacier movement, ask:

- What causes the dark lines on the alpine glacier? *rocks picked up by the glacier along its route*
- When do cracks form in the top of the glacier? *when the glacier flows over a large bump in the rocky bed*
- Where would you find water in a glacier? *under the ice*

T This visual is also available as T38 in the Unit Transparency Book.

Integrate the Sciences

During the ice ages, large mammals such as woolly mammoths and saber-toothed cats roamed the plains and open woodlands that existed in North America just south of the glaciers. When the glaciers melted at the end of the last ice age, about 10,000 years ago, these large mammals became extinct. Some scientists think the change to a warmer climate led to extinctions, perhaps by changing the habitat and food sources. Some researchers think the mammals were hunted to extinction by humans. Others suggest that humans may have introduced deadly diseases into mammal populations. Perhaps a combination of factors is to blame.

Ongoing Assessment

READING VISUALS *Near the bottom of the glacier, the ice is under so much pressure that it flows instead of cracking. Near the surface, the ice is brittle and cracks.*

Address Misconceptions

IDENTIFY Ask students how a glacier moves as it retreats. If they describe the glacier as backing up, they may hold the misconception that glaciers move backward.

CORRECT Tell students that in order for a glacier to move backward, it would have to move against gravity. It can't do that. Remind students that a glacier retreats by melting at its leading edge, where it is warmer. A retreating glacier is melting at the bottom at a faster rate than it can accumulate ice at the top.

REASSESS Give students a mass of modeling clay and a plastic knife. The clay represents an alpine glacier. Have students demonstrate how a glacier retreats. *Students should use the knife to cut off slices of the glacier at its leading edge.*

Technology Resources

Visit **ClassZone.com** for background on common student misconceptions.

 MISCONCEPTION DATABASE

Ongoing Assessment

Explain how moving ice erodes land.

Ask: How is an alpine glacier like a plow? *The glacier scoops up rock and soil and plucks rocks from the sides of valleys. The sediment moves with the glacier.*

CHECK YOUR READING *Sketches should show lateral moraines on the sides of the glacier, end moraine at the farthest advance, and ground moraines underneath.*

A moving glacier left visible abrasion lines on this rock.

A glacier scooped out this valley in California and left behind lateral moraines.

Glaciers deposit large amounts of sediment.

As glaciers have melted and retreated, they have shaped the landscapes of many places on Earth. As a glacier moves or expands, it transports a vast amount of sediment—a mix of boulders, small rocks, sand, and clay. It acts like a plow, pushing rock and soil and plucking out big blocks of rock. As a glacier moves over rock, it scratches and scrapes the rock in a process called abrasion. Abrasion leaves visible grooves on rock surfaces.

Moraines

When glaciers expand and advance and then melt and retreat, they affect both the land underneath them and the land around them. A glacier pushes huge amounts of sediment to its sides and front. When the glacier retreats, the deposits of sediment remain as visible evidence that ice once moved through. The sediment left directly on the ground surface by a retreating glacier is called **till.**

A deposit of till left behind by a retreating glacier is called a **moraine** (muh-RAYN). The ridges of till deposited at the sides of a glacier are called lateral moraines. The till that marks the farthest advance of a glacier forms a deposit called an end moraine. Moraines formed by continental glaciers, such as those in North America during the ice age, can be huge—many kilometers long.

The blanket of till that a glacier deposits along its bottom is called a ground moraine. Rock deposits from glaciers can often be identified as till because the till rocks are different, in type or age, from the rock that was present before the glacier formed.

CHECK YOUR READING Draw a sketch of a glacier and label where lateral, end, and ground moraines would form.

Lateral moraines

A 168 Unit: Earth's Surface

DIFFERENTIATE INSTRUCTION

? More Reading Support

C What is till made of? *sediment of different sizes left by a glacier*

D What do you call a buildup of till left by a glacier? *a moraine*

Below Level Help students understand the difference between the moraines discussed in the text. Make a table that lists *lateral moraine, end moraine,* and *ground moraine* and their definitions. Ask students to think of analogies to help them distinguish between the different types, such as relating *lateral* to a lateral pass in football, which is a short pass to the side.

Lakes

Besides ridges, hills, and blankets of till, melting glaciers also leave behind depressions of various sizes that can become lakes. Landscapes shaped by glaciers are often dotted with small kettle lakes as well as larger lakes. A **kettle lake** is a bowl-shaped depression that was formed by a block of ice from a glacier and then became filled with water.

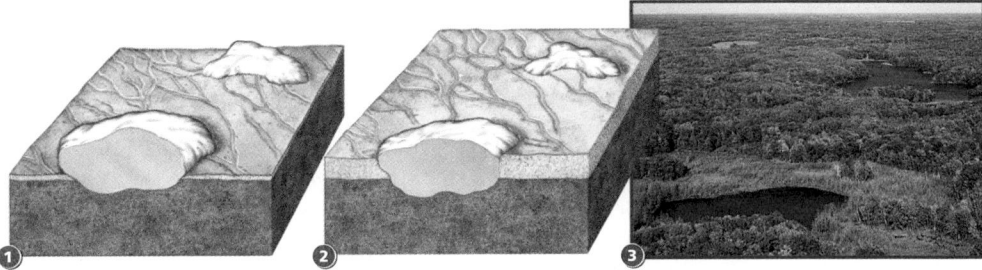

1. As a glacier moves away, it leaves huge blocks of ice.

2. Over time, sediment builds up around the ice.

3. The ice melts, leaving behind bowls that become kettle lakes. These lakes are in Wisconsin.

The last ice sheet in North America formed many kettle lakes in some regions. Kettle lakes are common in Michigan, Wisconsin, and Minnesota.

INVESTIGATE Kettle Lake Formation

How do kettle lakes form?

Kettle lakes form when sediment builds up around blocks of ice left behind by a retreating glacier. Use what you know about kettle lake formation to design a model of the process.

DESIGN —YOUR OWN— EXPERIMENT

PROCEDURE

1. Use the tray, the ice cubes, and the other materials to model how sediment builds up around ice blocks.

2. Write a description of the process you used to make your model.

WHAT DO YOU THINK?

- Describe how your model worked. What did you do first? What happened next?
- Did your model accurately represent the formation of kettle lakes? Did it work? Why or why not?
- What were the limitations of your model? Are there any aspects of kettle lake formation that are not represented? If so, what are they?

SKILL FOCUS
Designing experiments

MATERIALS
- shallow tray
- ice cubes
- modeling clay
- sand
- gravel
- water

TIME
30 minutes

169 **A**

Teach from Visuals

To help students interpret the diagram of kettle lake formation, ask:

- What does the huge block of ice left behind a retreating glacier do to the ground? *leaves a depression*
- What makes the depression that the ice is in even deeper? *Sediments build up around the ice.*

History of Science

In the 1830s, Louis Agassiz, a biologist, began studying glaciers in Switzerland. He hypothesized that glaciers in the upper valleys at one time extended down the valleys, gouging them out and pushing rocks forward like a huge plow. After studying glaciated areas throughout Europe and North America, he also hypothesized the existence of an ice age.

INVESTIGATE Kettle Lake Formation

PURPOSE To design an experiment to show how kettle lakes form

TIPS *30 min.*

- Suggest to students that they use the clay to represent the land in which the ice becomes embedded.
- To speed up the experiment, use a hair dryer or lamp to melt the ice. Exercise caution using electrical devices around the melting ice.

WHAT DO YOU THINK? *An experiment might be to place ice cube in pan, build up clay and materials around it, and use a lamp to melt the cube. The model's limitations might include that materials collapsed where the ice was. Groundwater and rain to fill the lake were not represented.*

R Datasheet, Kettle Lake Formation, p. 319

Ongoing Assessment

Explore ways that moving ice deposits sediments and changes landforms.

Ask: How would an alpine glacier change a V-shaped river valley? *The glacier would widen and deepen the valley and leave moraines.*

 *Answer: It gouged out great depressions of land and dammed them with rock. The weight of ice made the land sink.*

Reinforce

Have students relate the section to the Big Idea.

 Reinforcing Key Concepts, p. 320

5.4 ASSESS & RETEACH

Assess

 Section 5.4 Quiz, p. 84

Reteach

Draw a Venn diagram on the board. Label one side Alpine Glaciers and the other Continental Glaciers. List these terms: till, moraine, kettle lake, erosion, deposition, valley, ice sheet, icebergs, Greenland, abrasion, Finger Lakes, Lake Superior, and Lake Michigan. Have students place each term in the diagram in its appropriate place under Alpine Glaciers, Continental Glaciers, or in the middle overlapping portion to show the term applies to both glacier types.

Technology Resources

Have students visit **ClassZone.com** for reteaching of Key Concepts.

 CONTENT REVIEW

 CONTENT REVIEW CD-ROM

Great Lakes Formation

① **14,000 Years Ago**

The ice sheet covering a land of river valleys began to retreat.

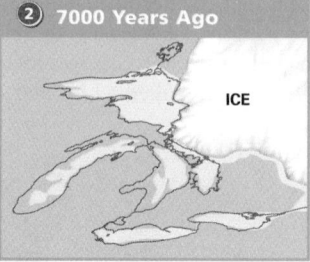

② **7000 Years Ago**

Water filled the bowls carved out by the ice.

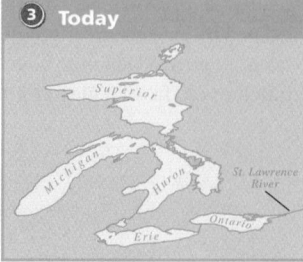

③ **Today**

The Great Lakes contain 20 percent of the world's fresh lake water.

Many large lakes are the result of ice ages. In some places, lakes formed after glaciers in valleys melted and left behind moraines that dammed the valleys. Many of these lakes are long and narrow, like the Finger Lakes in New York, which are named for their slender shape.

The Great Lakes were formed thousands of years ago as an ice sheet moved over the land and then melted. A million years ago, the region of the Great Lakes had many river valleys. The ice sheet gouged out large depressions in the land and left piles of rock and debris that blocked water from draining out. In some areas, where the deepest Great Lakes are now, the enormous weight of the glacier actually caused the land to sink as much as one kilometer.

The ice sheet started to melt about 14,000 years ago. By about 7000 years ago, it had melted past what would become Lake Erie and Lake Ontario, the lakes farthest to the east.

 What are two ways the ice sheet formed the Great Lakes?

5.4 Review

KEY CONCEPTS

1. Describe the two processes that cause glaciers to move.

2. What are the two major types of glaciers, and where are they found?

3. Describe the land features left behind by glaciers that have melted and shrunk.

CRITICAL THINKING

4. **Compare and Contrast** Identify two ways in which the erosion effects of glaciers differ from those of rivers.

5. **Predict** How would glaciers be affected by changes in climate, such as global warming and global cooling?

○ CHALLENGE

6. **Infer** Regions near the equator are generally the warmest on Earth. However, in one small area of Africa, there are glaciers close to the equator. Form a hypothesis to explain why these glaciers exist.

ANSWERS

1. gravity and water making the bottom slippery cause flowing and sliding

2. Alpine glaciers: mountain valleys. Continental glaciers: most of Antarctica and Greenland.

3. Glaciers leave behind U-shaped valleys, moraines, abrasions, till, kettle lakes.

4. Glaciers crush rock and move large rocks. Rivers move smaller sediments. Glaciers pile up distinctive features called moraines; rivers create sandbars, meanders, and deltas.

5. Warming melts glaciers and shrinks ice sheets; cooling causes glaciers to expand and form in new places.

6. Temperatures cool at high altitudes. High mountains could be cold enough year-round for glaciers near the equator.

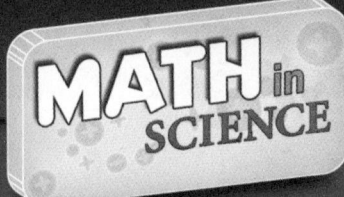

MATH in SCIENCE

MATH TUTORIAL

Click on Math Tutorial for more help making line graphs.

SKILL: CREATING A LINE GRAPH

Snow Line Elevation and Latitude

Glaciers form above the snow line, the lowest elevation at which there is permanent snow in the summer. The snow line elevation depends on temperature and precipitation. In the hot tropics the snow line is high in the mountains, while at the poles it is near sea level. The table shows the snow line elevations at different locations on Earth. The latitude of each location indicates how far the location is from the equator; the latitude of the equator is 0 degrees and the latitude of the North Pole is 90 degrees.

Location	Latitude (degrees north)	Snow Line Elevation (meters)
North Pole	90	0
Juneau, Alaska	58	1050
Glacier National Park	49	2600
Sierra Nevada	37	3725
Himalayas (East Nepal)	28	5103
Ecuador	0	4788

Follow the steps below to make a line graph of the data.

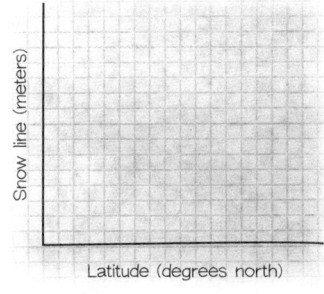

(1) On a sheet of graph paper, draw and label axes. Put latitude on the horizontal axis and snow line elevation on the vertical axis.

(2) Choose and mark a scale for each axis.

(3) Graph each point.

(4) Draw line segments to connect the points.

Use your graph to answer the following questions.

1. Mount Kenya is very close to the equator. Estimate the snow line elevation on Mount Kenya.

2. Mount Rainier is at 47 degrees north latitude and is 4389 meters tall. Can there be glaciers on Mount Rainier? If so, estimate the elevation above which the glaciers form.

3. Mount Washington in New Hampshire is at 45 degrees north latitude and is 1917 meters tall. Can there be glaciers on Mount Washington? If so, estimate their lowest elevation.

CHALLENGE Temperatures are hotter at the equator than at 28 degrees north latitude. Why is the snow line lower at the equator in Ecuador? (**Hint:** The answer involves precipitation.)

Chapter 5: **Erosion and Deposition** 171 **A**

MATH IN SCIENCE
Math Skills Practice for Science

Set Learning Goal

To create and interpret a line graph showing how snow-line elevation relates to latitude

Present the Science

Glaciers need not only cold temperatures to form but sufficient precipitation. Moist, cold air tends to drop most of its snow on the windward side of coastal mountain ranges. The leeward side has a much drier climate. Therefore, in regions where wind generally blows from west to east, glaciers are likely to be more abundant on western slopes of a mountain range.

Develop Graphing Skills

Guide students to set up a scale that makes sense. For example, each scale has to include at least the lowest and highest values they are graphing. It is usually a good idea to mark a scale that goes a little beyond the highest value. Degrees of latitude, however, only go up to 90.

DIFFERENTIATION TIP Students may need to review how to plot coordinate points. Demonstrate how the grid of graph paper makes it easy to follow lines up and across to plot points.

Close

Have students look at the line that connects all the points. Ask: If you plotted the snow line elevation of 20 more mountains, how would you expect the line on the graph to change? *The general shape of the line would be the same.*

 • Math Support, p. 326
• Math Practice, p. 327

Technology Resources

Students can visit **ClassZone.com** to practice creating a line graph.

 MATH TUTORIAL

BACK TO

the BIG idea

Have students look at the photograph at the bottom of p. 168. Ask them to describe the different kinds of erosion that have occurred in this area in the past and that are going on today. Students should cite evidence where possible. *Lateral moraines and U-shaped valley are evidence of glacier erosion. Streams continue to erode the valley floor. Mass wasting probably happens along the valley walls. Wind erodes exposed rock somewhat.*

◖ KEY CONCEPTS SUMMARY

SECTION 5.1
Ask: What forces created the landscape shown in the photograph? *erosion caused by moving water, wind, and ice*

SECTION 5.2
Ask: How did the features on the left side of the diagram form? *Rainwater, slightly acidic, trickled through ground, dissolved limestone to form caves.*

Ask: How did the feature on the right side of the diagram form? *Flowing water of a stream eroded land and formed a steep-walled V-shaped valley.*

SECTION 5.3
Ask: Why are these stone formations separated from the cliff to the left? *Waves breaking against rock wore some away, leaving stone pillars.*

Ask: What happens to the rocks that the waves erode? *They may eventually become sand and form beaches.*

SECTION 5.4
Ask: How do glaciers change landscapes through erosion and deposition? *Glaciers widen/deepen valleys, create lakes, deposit sediment as ridges.*

Review Concepts
🗂 • Big Idea Flow Chart, p. T33
 • Chapter Outline, pp. T39–T40

---

5 Chapter Review

the BIG idea
Water, wind, and ice shape Earth's surface.

◖ **KEY CONCEPTS SUMMARY**

5.1 Forces wear down and build up Earth's surface.

Water, wind, and ice move sediment in the process called **erosion**. The placement of sediment in a new location is **deposition**, part of the erosion process.

VOCABULARY
erosion p. 145
deposition p. 145
mass wasting p. 147

5.2 Moving water shapes land.

Water drains from land in **drainage basins**, which are separated by **divides**. As water flows over land and underground, it moves sediment and changes land features.

VOCABULARY
drainage basin p. 151
divide p. 151
floodplain p. 152
alluvial fan p. 153
delta p. 153
sinkhole p. 155

5.3 Waves and wind shape land.

The action of water moves sand and builds up new landforms, such as sandbars and barrier islands. Wind forms dunes.

VOCABULARY
longshore drift p. 159
longshore current p. 159
sandbar p. 160
barrier island p. 160
dune p. 161
loess p. 162

5.4 Glaciers carve land and move sediments.

Glaciers are large bodies of ice that change landscapes as they move.

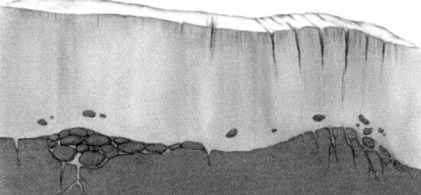

VOCABULARY
glacier p. 165
till p. 168
moraine p. 168
kettle lake p. 169

A 172 Unit: Earth's Surface

Technology Resources

Have students visit **ClassZone.com** or use the CD-ROM for a cumulative review of concepts.

 CONTENT REVIEW

 CONTENT REVIEW CD-ROM

Engage students in a whole-class interactive review of Key Concepts. Edit content as you wish.

 POWER PRESENTATIONS

Reviewing Vocabulary

Copy and complete the chart below. Explain how each landscape feature is formed.

Feature	How It Forms
EXAMPLE delta	A river deposits sediment as it enters the ocean.
1. alluvial fan	
2. sinkhole	
3. sandbar	
4. barrier island	
5. dune	
6. loess	
7. moraine	
8. kettle lake	

Reviewing Key Concepts

Multiple Choice *Choose the letter of the best answer.*

9. The first stage in the erosion process is
   a. deposition
   b. mass wasting
   c. drainage
   d. weathering

10. The main natural force responsible for mass movements of rocks and debris is
    a. rainwater   **c.** gravity
    b. wind   **d.** fire

11. A sinkhole is formed by the collapse of
    a. an alluvial fan
    b. a cavern
    c. a moraine
    d. a kettle lake

12. Rivers transport sediment to
    a. drainage basins
    b. oceans and lakes
    c. the water table
    d. moraines

13. Drainage basins are separated by
    a. a moraine   **c.** a tributary
    b. a divide   **d.** a barrier island

14. In high mountains, a valley carved by a stream has the shape of
    a. a U   **c.** a plate
    b. a crescent   **d.** a V

15. An oxbow lake is formed by the cutting off of
    a. a meander   **c.** a sinkhole
    b. a drainage basin **d.** a glacier

16. Sandbars, spits, and barrier islands can all be built up by
    a. glaciers   **c.** wind
    b. ocean waves   **d.** mass wasting

17. A dune is a sand mound built up primarily by
    a. gravity   **c.** glaciers
    b. running water **d.** wind

18. Strong winds can transport large quantities of
    a. gravel   **c.** dry sand
    b. wet sand   **d.** clay

19. A mountain valley carved by a glacier has the shape of
    a. a U   **c.** a bowl
    b. a crescent   **d.** a V

Short Answer *Answer each of the following questions in a sentence or two.*

20. How is deposition part of the erosion process?

21. How can rainwater in the Rocky Mountains end up in the ocean?

22. What is the effect of a longshore current on a beach?

23. Why is a mass movement of mud called a flow?

24. What visual evidence is a sign of creep?

25. What is the connection between icebergs and glaciers?

Reviewing Vocabulary

1. Water flows from a steep slope onto flat ground and deposits sediment in a fan shape.

2. The ceiling above a cavern falls in, often because the water that supported the ceiling drops.

3. Sand builds up from the action of waves and currents.

4. Longshore current builds up a sandbar above the water's surface parallel to shore.

5. Strong winds pile up sand in a mound.

6. Wind transports and deposits fine-grained sediment.

7. A glacier piles up sediment along its sides and end and underneath on the ground.

8. Sediment builds up around a block of ice left behind by a glacier.

Reviewing Key Concepts

9. d

10. c

11. b

12. b

13. b

14. d

15. a

16. b

17. d

18. c

19. a

20. Deposition is the stage of erosion in which material is dropped at a new place.

21. Rain falls to the ground, flows into a stream or streams in the drainage basin, and flows from stream to stream until it reaches the ocean.

22. It can shift sand along the shore.

23. It contains water, which makes it flow downhill.

24. fence posts and telephone poles standing at an angle or cracks in buildings

25. Icebergs occur as ice breaks off glaciers at the ocean shoreline.

ASSESSMENT RESOURCES

 UNIT ASSESSMENT BOOK
- Chapter Test A, pp. 85–88
- Chapter Test B, pp. 89–92
- Chapter Test C, pp. 93–96
- Alternative Assessment, pp. 97–98
- Unit Test, A, B, & C, pp. 99–110

 SPANISH ASSESSMENT BOOK
- Spanish Chapter Test, pp. 121–124
- Spanish Unit Test, pp. 125–128

Technology Resources

Edit test items and answer choices.

 Test Generator CD-ROM

Visit **ClassZone.com** to extend test practice.

 Test Practice

Thinking Critically

26. Arrow should point toward the ocean bay at the bottom of the picture.

27. along the sides of the glaciers, the dark bands inside of them

28. on either side of the main glacier

29. because it ends in the bay

30. B is narrower, more V-shaped. A is in a U-shaped valley. B might not be glaciated.

31. U-shaped valley, abrasion marks, till, rocks different from underlying rocks, moraines, kettle or large lakes

32. Both are deposits of material moved in erosion. Till is carried by glacial ice; deltas are near rivers.

33. Advantage: river deposited sediment for good soil. Disadvantage: river might flood and ruin crops.

34. Similar: movement of large amounts of material, powered by gravity. Mudflows mix water, sediment. Mass wasting of rock can be dry rocks sliding downhill.

35. In eastern part; wind slows down, drops sediment, forms loess.

36. Is ground loose or wet? Is slope steep, causing creep?

37. Erosion: sediment carried to site of ice block. Deposition: sediment is deposited around the ice.

the **BIG** idea

38. The snow falls onto either side of the divide. Meltwater, including glacier water, flows downhill, moves sediment (erosion). Water flows into streams, which lead to ocean. Streams deposit material.

39. Sample answer: (1) A stream moves sediment down a hill and spreads it. Gravity pulls the water down. (2) Wind carries sediment. When the wind loses strength, gravity pulls sediment to the ground. (3) Gravity pulls alpine glaciers down valley.

UNIT PROJECTS

Use the appropriate rubrics from the URB to evaluate their presentations.

 Unit Projects, pp. 5–10

Thinking Critically

This photograph shows two glaciers joining to form one (A). Make a sketch of the glaciers to answer the next three questions.

26. **APPLY** Place an arrow to show which direction the main glacier (A) is moving.

27. **ANALYZE** Mark the places where you think till would be found.

28. **APPLY** Mark the location of a lateral moraine.

29. **ANALYZE** Why does the main glacier not have an end moraine?

30. **COMPARE AND CONTRAST** Compare the main glacier valley in the photograph with the valley at the far right (B). How are the valleys different? Explain why they might be different.

31. **APPLY** In exploring an area of land, what clues would you look for to determine whether glaciers were once there?

32. **COMPARE AND CONTRAST** How is a deposit of till from a glacier similar to a river delta? How is it different?

33. **EVALUATE** If you were growing crops on a field near a slow-moving, curvy river, what would an advantage of the field's location be? What might be a disadvantage?

34. **COMPARE AND CONTRAST** How are mudflows and mass wasting of rock similar? How are they different? Include references to speed and types of material in your answer.

35. **INFER** If the wind usually blows from west to east over a large area of land, and the wind usually slows down over the eastern half of the area, where would you be likely to find loess in the area? Explain your answer.

36. **APPLY** If you were considering a location for a house and were concerned about creep, what two factors about the land would you consider?

37. **SYNTHESIZE** Describe how the process of erosion and deposition are involved in the formation of kettle lakes.

the **BIG** idea

38. **SYNTHESIZE** Describe how snow falling onto the Continental Divide in the Rocky Mountains can be part of the process of erosion and deposition. Include the words *divide, glacier, stream,* and *ocean* in your answer.

39. **PROVIDE EXAMPLES** Choose three examples of erosion processes—one each from Sections 5.2, 5.3, and 5.4. Explain how gravity is involved in each of these processes.

UNIT PROJECTS

Evaluate all the data, results, and information in your project folder. Prepare to present your project. Be ready to answer questions posed by your classmates about your results.

MONITOR AND RETEACH

If students are having trouble applying the concepts in items 26–30, refer them to the photograph of an alpine glacier on p. 167 and review the discussion about moraines on p. 168. Have them compare the lateral moraines in the photograph on p. 168 with those on the glacier on p. 167.

Students may benefit from summarizing one or more sections of the chapter.

R Summarizing the Chapter, pp. 346–347

Standardized Test Practice

For practice on your state test, go to . . .
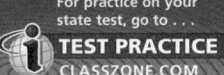
TEST PRACTICE
CLASSZONE.COM

Analyzing a Diagram

Use the diagram to answer the questions below.

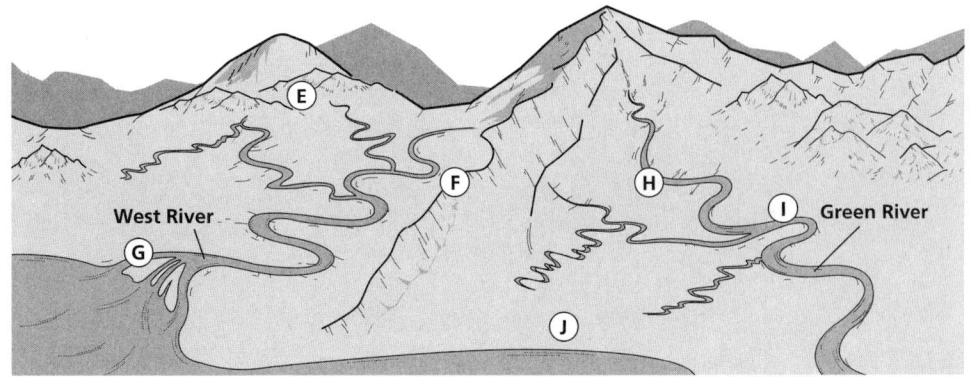

West River

Green River

E F G H I J

1. Where would a glacier be most likely to form?

  a. E   **c.** G

  b. F   **d.** H

2. Where is a divide?

  a. E   **c.** H

  b. F   **d.** I

3. Where is a delta?

  a. E   **c.** G

  b. F   **d.** J

4. Which process could move sediment from point E to point G?

  a. weathering   **c.** deposition

  b. erosion   **d.** drifting

5. Which word best describes the building up of sediment at point G?

  a. weathering   **c.** deposition

  b. erosion   **d.** drifting

6. Why might the water in the Green River move faster at point H than at point I?

  a. The river at point H is warmer.

  b. The river at point H is smaller.

  c. The slope at point H is steeper.

  d. More rain falls at point H.

Extended Response

Answer the two questions below in detail. Include some of the terms shown in the word box. In your answers, underline each term you use.

ocean waves	currents	barrier island
grass	glaciers	kettle lakes

7. Each year, Clark and his family visit the ocean. Clark notices that a sandbar near the coast is slightly larger each year. Predict what will happen if this trend continues.

8. Annika often goes fishing at one of several small, round lakes that are within 20 miles of her house in Minnesota. How might these lakes have formed?

Analyzing a Diagram

1. a	3. c	5. c
2. b	4. b	6. c

Extended Response

7. RUBRIC

4 points for a response that correctly describes the development of a barrier island and uses all of the following terms accurately:

- ocean waves   • grass   • currents

Sample answer: <u>Currents</u> *will continue to move sand along the shore and deposit it on the sandbar. Eventually, enough sediment will be deposited so that the sandbar builds up above the water surface and becomes a barrier island.* <u>Ocean waves</u> *breaking on the barrier island will deposit more sediment, mostly sand, and the island will grow. As the island builds up,* <u>grass</u> *and other plants will start growing.*

3 points describes the development adequately and uses two terms accurately

2 points describes the development partially and uses one term accurately

1 point describes the development partially but uses no terms

8. RUBRIC

4 points for a response that correctly identifies three processes (melting of ice sheet, deposition of sediment around ice block, melting of ice to form lake) and uses the following terms:

- glaciers   • kettle lakes

Sample answer: During the last ice age, huge continental <u>glaciers</u>, *or ice sheets, advanced into the area of Minnesota and other parts of North America. As the ice sheet in Minnesota melted, it left huge blocks of ice that created depressions in the ground. Sediment from the ice sheet was deposited around the ice blocks. When the ice melted, these depressions became bowl-shaped lakes called* <u>kettle lakes</u>. *Annika's fishing lake is one of them.*

3 points describes two processes correctly and uses both terms accurately

2 points describes one process correctly and uses both terms accurately

1 point describes one process partially and uses one term accurately

---

METACOGNITIVE ACTIVITY

Have students answer the following questions in their **Science Notebook:**

1. How did the activities in this chapter help you learn about erosion and deposition?

2. What information about erosion and deposition could help you the most in the future?

3. How are the concepts of erosion and deposition part of your Unit Project?

Energy and the Changing Earth

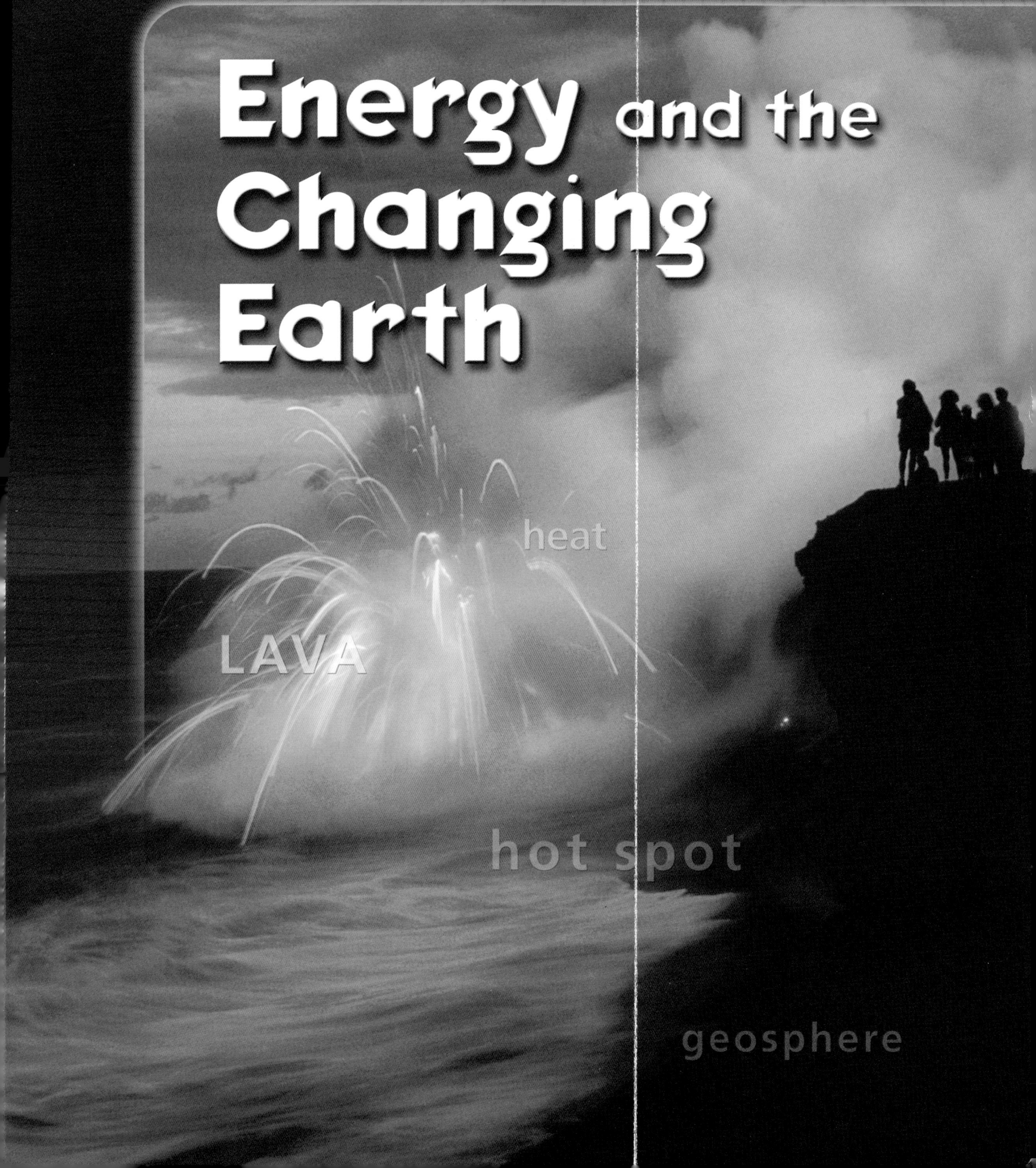

heat

LAVA

hot spot

geosphere

North Carolina Standards

In Unit B: Energy and the Changing Earth, students will learn and apply science concepts and skills related to the following goals from the North Carolina Standard Course of Study:

Competency Goal 1: The learner will design and conduct investigations to demonstrate an understanding of scientific inquiry. (Objectives 1.01–1.10)

Competency Goal 2: The learner will demonstrate an understanding of technological design. (Objectives 2.01–2.04)

Competency Goal 3: The learner will build an understanding of the geological cycles, forces, process, and agents which shape the lithosphere.

3.01   Evaluate the forces that shape the lithosphere.

3.02   Examine earthquake and volcano patterns.

3.03   Explain the model for the interior of the earth.

Competency Goal 4: The learner will investigate the cycling of matter.

4.01   Describe the flow of energy and matter in natural systems.

Competency Goal 6: The learner will conduct investigations and examine models and devices to build an understanding of the characteristics of energy transfer and/or transformation.

6.01   Determine how convection and radiation transfer energy.

6.02   Analyze heat flow through materials.

6.04   Evaluate data for qualitative and quantitative relationships associated with energy transfer and/or transformation.

6.06   Analyze response to heat to determine the suitability of materials for use in technological design.

6.07   Analyze the Law of Conservation of Energy.

For a detailed lesson-by-lesson correlation of Unit B to the North Carolina Standard Course of Study, see Correlations pages 16–24 in the front of this Teacher's Edition.

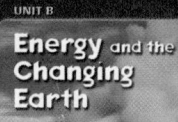

UNIT B
Energy and the Changing Earth

Energy and the Changing Earth
Contents Overview

Unit Features

1 Energy   6

the **BIG** idea

Energy has different forms, but it is
always conserved.

2 Temperature and Heat   34

the **BIG** idea

Heat is a flow of energy due to
temperature differences.

3 Plate Tectonics   66

the **BIG** idea

The movement of tectonic plates
causes geologic changes on Earth.

4 Earthquakes   102

the **BIG** idea

Earthquakes release stress that has
built up in rocks.

5 Mountains and Volcanoes   134

the **BIG** idea

Mountains and volcanoes form as
tectonic plates move.

VIDEO SUMMARY

SCIENTIFIC AMERICAN FRONTIERS

"Paradise Postponed" is a segment of the *Scientific American Frontiers* series that aired on PBS stations. The "paradise" of the title is the Caribbean island of Montserrat. Like the Hawaiian Islands, Montserrat was formed by volcanic activity millions of years ago. Montserrat's volcano had not erupted for 400 years. Then a series of massive eruptions beginning in 1995 produced hot steam and ash that melted buildings and destroyed towns. Two-thirds of the residents have moved away from the island for safety reasons. Around 3000 people live in the northern third of the island, as far away from the volcano as possible. They are not allowed into the evacuated area around the volcano, known as the "exclusion zone." Scientists from the Montserrat Volcano Observatory risk their lives to collect data and predict the likelihood of future eruptions.

National Science Education Standards

A.1–8 Abilities Necessary to Do Scientific Inquiry

A.9.a–b, A.9.d–g Understandings about Scientific Inquiry

F.5.e Science and Technology in Society

G.1.a–b Science as a Human Endeavor

G.2.a, G.2.c Nature of Science

FRONTIERS in Science

Studying VOLCANOES with Satellites

New ways of viewing Earth are giving scientists powerful tools for learning about and predicting volcanic eruptions.

SCIENTIFIC AMERICAN FRONTIERS

View the video segment "Paradise Postponed" to learn how scientists study volcanoes and predict eruptions.

During a 1997 eruption of the Soufrière Hills volcano on Montserrat, volcanic material flowed all the way to the ocean.

ADDITIONAL RESOURCES

Technology Resources

 Scientific American Frontiers Video: *Paradise Postponed:* 20-minute video segment that introduces the unit.

 ClassZone.com
CAREER LINK, Volcanologist

Guide student viewing and comprehension of the video:

 Video Teaching Guide, pp. 1–2; Video Viewing Guide, p. 3; Video Wrap-Up, p. 4

Scientific American Frontiers Video Guide, pp. 23–26

Unit projects procedures and rubrics:

 Unit Projects, pp. 5–10

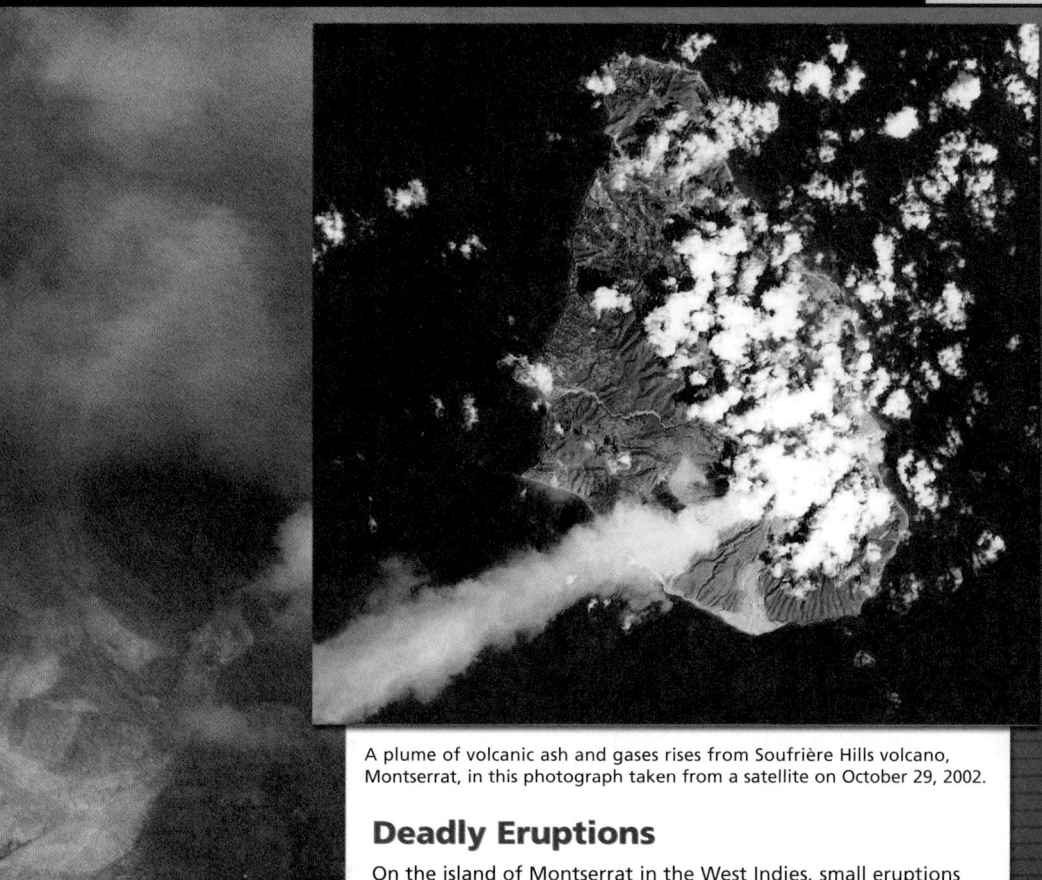

A plume of volcanic ash and gases rises from Soufrière Hills volcano, Montserrat, in this photograph taken from a satellite on October 29, 2002.

Deadly Eruptions

On the island of Montserrat in the West Indies, small eruptions of the Soufrière Hills volcano began in 1995. These early warnings gave people time to move away several months before the first of the large explosions. **A**

People living in the towns near Nevado del Ruiz volcano in Colombia were not so fortunate. On a night in November 1985, a storm hid the snow-covered volcano. No one could see the start of an eruption. Huge amounts of snow and ice melted and mixed with volcanic ash to form mudflows that killed 25,000 people. The flow that buried much of the town of Armero traveled 74 kilometers in just two and one-half hours.

Throughout history volcanic eruptions have caused some of the world's worst disasters. Warnings might have saved hundreds of thousands of lives. But in most cases people had no idea that a rain of rock, a cloud of toxic gases, or other deadly effects of an erupting volcano would soon engulf their area. By the time people realized that a volcano was erupting, it was too late to get away. Today, scientists monitor volcanoes around the world to help avoid such tragedies. **B**

DIFFERENTIATE INSTRUCTION

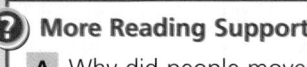 **More Reading Support**

A Why did people move away from the Soufrière Hills volcano? *They realized its danger.*

B Why do scientists monitor volcanoes? *to save human lives*

Advanced Have students locate Montserrat and Nevado del Ruiz on a world map. Give them a second map showing Earth's plate boundaries. Ask students to describe any relationships they see. *Montserrat and Nevado del Ruiz are on or near plate boundaries.*

FOCUS

▶ Set Learning Goals
Students will

• Determine how satellite data are used to predict and monitor volcanic eruptions.

• Discuss effects of volcanic eruptions.

• Complete a unit project relating to evaluating information about volcanic eruptions, mapmaking, or fossil preservation.

Tell students that scientific frontiers often involve areas of study that directly benefit society. Point out that the eruption of the Nevado del Ruiz volcano killed as many as 25,000 people. After students have viewed the video "Paradise Postponed," discuss why there is a need to predict volcanic eruptions.

INSTRUCT

Scientific Process

Ask: Why do scientists want to predict volcanic eruptions? *to save lives*

Technology Design

Have students compare the eruptions of Soufrière Hills and the Nevado del Ruiz volcano. Ask:

• What factor made the Nevado del Ruiz eruption so deadly? *The start of the eruption was not visible.*

• How do scientists hope to avert great loss of human life from volcanoes? *They monitor activity that may warn of a large eruption.*

Teach from Visuals

Have students study the photograph and related captions on pp. 2–3. Ask: Is Soufrière Hills Volcano still active? How do you know? *The volcano is probably still active. It has had several large, recent eruptions.*

Integrate the Sciences

Major volcanic eruptions release clouds of dust that can block sunlight for years, affecting global climate. Volcanic gases can react with atmospheric moisture to produce acid rain. Scientists hypothesize that these combined effects may have caused major extinctions in the past. In fact, some scientists hypothesize that the largest extinction on Earth, which occurred about 250 million years ago, was related to a series of huge volcanic eruptions.

Scientific Process

Volcanologists use observation and analysis to find signals to predict volcanic eruptions. Ask:

- Why did scientists predict that the Pavlof Volcano would soon erupt? *A weather satellite detected an area of increased heat on the volcano.*

- What system is now in place to alert scientists in this situation? *Computers check satellite data and send e-mails when they detect any unusually hot areas.*

Sharing Results

Ask students to give an example of how scientists in different fields share information. *Sample answer: Meteorologists use satellites to measure cloud temperatures. When a satellite detected increased heat on Pavlof Volcano, meteorologists shared the information with volcanologists.*

A 1996 eruption of Alaska's Pavlof volcano was the first to be predicted with the use of data from space. The satellite image recorded during the eruption shows an area of hot ground on the volcano in red.

Predicting Volcanic Eruptions

Scientists who study volcanoes paid close attention when an instrument on a weather satellite unexpectedly "saw" hot ground in 1996. The instrument's usual function is to measure cloud temperatures, but it detected an area of increased heat on Alaska's Pavlof volcano. The scientists predicted that the volcano would soon erupt. Three days later, it did. This eruption was the first to be predicted with information from space. Now computers check satellite data as they receive the data. Any unusually hot areas trigger an automatic e-mail alert to scientists.

In 1999, NASA launched the *Terra* satellite as part of a program to study Earth's surface and atmosphere. Among *Terra's* instruments is one that detects heat given off by the planet's surface. When scientists observe an unusual increase in surface temperature, they determine whether magma is rising underground. In some cases unusual heat has been the first sign that a volcano is building toward an eruption.

After an Eruption

Satellites are also used to monitor eruptions as they happen. Lava flows show up clearly, as you can see in the *Terra* image on page 5. In addition, satellites are used to track the locations of volcanic ash and gas clouds. Airplanes flying into this material can be severely damaged, so pilots need to know where it is. Volcanic material in

SCIENTIFIC AMERICAN FRONTIERS

View the "Paradise Postponed" segment of your *Scientific American Frontiers* video to learn how scientists monitor volcanic eruptions.

IN THIS SCENE FROM THE VIDEO ▶ Scientist Barry Voigt examines the effects of a powerful eruption that occurred a few days earlier.

STUDYING VOLCANOES Until 1995, the Caribbean island of Montserrat was a peaceful tourist destination. Then, the island's volcano began to erupt. Over the next two years, the volcano erupted dozens of times, spewing out hot ash, rocks, and gases. These eruptions destroyed most of the island's towns and drove away many residents.

Scientists from around the world have come to Montserrat to find out how well they can predict eruptions. Seismic stations buried near the volcano detect earthquakes, which can be a sign that the volcano is about to erupt. Scientists can also predict an eruption by studying changes in the lava dome that has built up on the volcano. When an eruption does occur, scientists visit the site to collect rocks and measure the volcanic ash flow.

DIFFERENTIATE INSTRUCTION

? More Reading Support

C Which eruption was the first to be predicted from information from space? *Pavlof volcano in 1996*

English Learners Have students identify scientific process words found in the text, such as *detect, predict, determine, observe,* and *monitor.* Review the meanings of these terms. Have students use each word in a different context.

Data collected by the *Terra* satellite show the progress of a Hawaiian lava flow as it enters the ocean on May 13, 2000 (left), and on August 1, 2000 (right).

the air can be difficult to see or to distinguish from normal clouds, especially at night. Satellites are particularly helpful in identifying and tracking eruptions in remote areas where there are few or no observers.

Explosive Neighbors

Satellites such as *Terra* are among the tools scientists use to monitor restless volcanoes near urban areas. Mount Rainier, a volcano in Washington, looms near the large cities of Seattle and Tacoma. In the past, heat from eruptions has melted large amounts of the ice and snow at the top of the volcano, creating mudflows that destroyed everything in their path. Another extremely dangerous volcano is Mount Vesuvius, near Naples, Italy. Timely warnings before eruptions of such volcanoes can allow authorities to safely evacuate the millions of people who live near them.

UNANSWERED Questions

Even when scientists predict that a volcano will erupt soon, many questions still cannot be answered.

- How powerful will the next eruption be?
- On what day (or even during what week) will the volcano erupt?
- How much magma is rising under the volcano, and how fast is it rising? Will it stop?

UNIT PROJECTS

As you study this unit, work alone or with a group on one of the projects listed below.

Review Movie Science

Review a movie that features a volcanic eruption to evaluate how accurate the movie's depiction of a volcano is.

- Visit the U.S. Geological Survey Web site for a list of movies about volcanoes, such as *Dante's Peak*.
- Evaluate one movie and prepare a report on it for a radio or TV spot.

Earthquake Report

Make a map of the volcanic eruptions and earthquakes that occur around the world while you are studying this unit.

- Write a news script and create a graphic to show the events' locations and intensities.
- Present your findings as a special TV report for an evening news program.

Ash-Fall Fossil Exhibit

Prepare an exhibit showing how volcanic ash can preserve fossils of the organisms it buries. You could begin by researching Ashfall Fossil Beds State Historical Park in Nebraska.

- Create a poster that shows the major steps in the formation of fossils of creatures in volcanic ash.
- Make models or tracings of some ash-fall fossils.
- Display the poster and models as a classroom or Web-site exhibit.

 **CAREER CENTER**
CLASSZONE.COM

Learn more about careers in volcanology.

UNANSWERED Questions

Have students read the questions and think of some of their own. Remind them that scientists always end up with more questions—that inquiry is the driving force of science.

- With the class, generate on the board a list of new questions.
- Students can add to the list after they watch the Scientific American Frontiers Video.
- Students can use the list as a springboard for choosing their Unit Projects.

UNIT PROJECTS

Encourage students to pick the project that most appeals to them. Point out that each will take several weeks to complete. You might group or pair students to work on projects. Each project has two worksheet pages, including a rubric. Use the pages to guide students through criteria, process, and schedule.

R Unit Projects, pp. 5–10

REVISIT concepts introduced in this article:

Chapter 3
- Movement of tectonic plates, pp. 78–88

Chapter 5
- Volcano formation, pp. 146–155
- Effects of volcanoes, pp. 156–163

DIFFERENTIATE INSTRUCTION

? More Reading Support

D Where could satellite monitoring of volcanoes save the most lives? *near cities*

Differentiate Unit Projects Projects are appropriate for varying abilities. Allow students to choose the ones that interest them most and let them vary their product. Encourage below level students to give visual or oral presentations or to record audio presentations about their topic.

Below Level Encourage students to try "Review Movie Science."

Advanced Challenge students to complete "Earthquake Report."

Energy

Earth Science
UNIFYING PRINCIPLES

PRINCIPLE 1

Heat energy inside Earth and radiation from the Sun provide energy for Earth's processes.

PRINCIPLE 2

Physical forces, such as gravity, affect the movement of all matter on Earth and throughout the universe.

PRINCIPLE 3

Matter and energy move among Earth's rocks and soil, atmosphere, waters, and living things.

PRINCIPLE 4

Earth has changed over time and continues to change.

Unit: Energy and the Changing Earth
BIG IDEAS

CHAPTER 1
Energy

Energy has different forms, but it is always conserved.

CHAPTER 2
Temperature and Heat

Heat is a flow of energy due to temperature differences.

CHAPTER 3
Plate Tectonics

The movement of tectonic plates causes geologic changes on Earth.

CHAPTER 4
Earthquakes

Earthquakes release stress that has built up in rocks.

CHAPTER 5
Mountains and Volcanoes

Mountains and volcanoes form as tectonic plates move.

CHAPTER 1
KEY CONCEPTS

SECTION 1.1

Energy exists in different forms.

1. Different forms of energy have different uses.

2. Kinetic energy and potential energy are the two general types of energy.

SECTION 1.2

Energy can change forms but is never lost.

1. Energy changes forms.

2. Energy is always conserved.

3. Energy conversions may produce unwanted forms of energy.

SECTION 1.3

Technology improves the ways people use energy.

1. Technology improves energy conversions.

2. Technology improves the use of energy resources.

The Big Idea Flow Chart is available on p. T1 in the **UNIT TRANSPARENCY BOOK.**

Previewing Content

1.1 Energy exists in different forms.
pp. 9–15

1. Different forms of energy have different uses.
Energy is the ability to cause a change. Different forms of energy cause different changes to occur.

- Mechanical energy involves the position and motion of objects. Mechanical energy is a combination of potential energy and kinetic energy; it may be either or both.
- Sound energy is energy associated with a transfer of vibrations through a solid, liquid, or gas.
- Chemical energy is energy that is stored in the chemical composition of matter due to the atoms, bonds, and arrangement of atoms in substances.
- Thermal energy is the total amount of energy within an object due to the motion of all of the object's particles.
- Electromagnetic energy is energy in electromagnetic waves, including visible light, ultraviolet light, *x*-rays, and microwaves. Electromagnetic energy can travel through a vacuum.
- Nuclear energy holds atomic nuclei together.

2. Kinetic energy and potential energy are the two general types of energy.
Kinetic energy (KE) is the energy of motion. The amount of kinetic energy that any object has depends on its mass and speed. An increase in speed causes a much larger increase in kinetic energy than does an increase in mass.

Potential energy (PE) is energy that is stored in an object as a result of its position, shape, or chemical composition.

- Gravitational potential energy is due to an object's position above Earth's surface. Gravitational potential energy is related to an object's mass and its height above the ground.
- Elastic potential energy is due to position and shape in an object being compressed or flexed. Examples include a compressed spring or a stretched rubber band. Not every object that is compressed will contain elastic potential energy, for example, aluminum foil crumpled into a ball.
- Chemical potential energy is due to a substance's chemical composition—the atoms and bonds contained within the substance. Different substances contain different amounts of chemical potential energy. Examples include energy stored in fossil fuels and in molecules of foods.

1.2 Energy can change forms but is never lost. pp. 16–23

1. Energy changes forms.
Energy can be converted from one form to another. Often, energy must change forms in order for it to be useful. Many energy transformations occur between potential and kinetic energy. A ski jumper at the top of a slope has gravitational potential energy, which is converted into kinetic energy as the ski jumper moves down the slope. The ski jumper can regain potential energy through the kinetic energy of a chairlift that carries the jumper back up the hill. When gasoline is burned in a car's engine, the chemical potential energy of the fuel is converted into the car's motion, and energy released as heat from the car's engine is the kinetic energy of particle motion.

2. Energy is always conserved.
The **law of conservation of energy** states that energy is neither created nor destroyed. When it appears that energy has been lost, it has simply changed form or been transferred to another object. In the soccer ball photograph below, the soccer ball's kinetic energy decreases, but the energy is converted into sound and heat. As a result, the total amount of energy never changes.

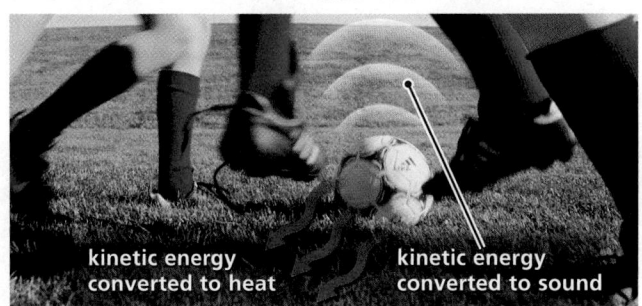

kinetic energy converted to heat   kinetic energy converted to sound

3. Energy conversions may produce unwanted forms of energy.
When energy changes forms, the total amount of energy does not change, but some of the energy may convert to unusable or unwanted forms. **Energy efficiency** is a measure of usable energy after an energy conversion. The more energy-efficient the energy conversion, the more energy is changed into the desired form.

Common Misconceptions

ENERGY AND MATTER Students may think that everything that exists is matter, including heat, light, and electricity. Matter has mass and takes up space, whereas energy does not.

 This misconception is addressed on p. 10.

 MISCONCEPTION DATABASE
CLASSZONE.COM Background on student misconceptions

ENERGY AT REST Many students might think that objects at rest do not have any energy. Objects that are not moving do possess different forms of energy, such as gravitational potential energy and chemical potential energy.

 This misconception is addressed on p. 13.

Previewing Content

SECTION

1.3 Technology improves the ways people use energy. pp. 24–29

1. Technology improves energy conversions.

Because most energy conversions are very inefficient, an important goal of technology is to improve energy efficiency.

- LEDs convert almost all the electricity they use into light.
- Hybrid cars, which use both a gasoline engine and electrical energy from batteries, are more efficient than conventional gasoline-powered cars.

2. Technology improves the use of energy resources.

Fossil fuels, the most commonly used energy source, are a non-renewable resource. A major goal of technology research is a more efficient usage of other energy sources.

- Solar cells convert sunlight to electrical energy. Solar energy is available in unlimited amounts, is quiet and clean, and is nonpolluting. It is inefficient, however, and the materials used to make solar cells are expensive.
- Windmills are used to convert the kinetic energy of wind into electrical energy. Like solar energy, wind energy is an inexhaustible source of energy that is nonpolluting, but there are limitations to the usefulness of wind power. It takes a large number of windmills to produce enough electrical energy to make a windfarm economically viable. Also, wind power is limited to regions of the country where wind is relatively constant.

Common Misconceptions

 MISCONCEPTION DATABASE
CLASSZONE.COM Background on student misconceptions

CONSERVATION OF ENERGY Students may think that "conservation of energy" means that energy should be conserved; this misconception arises due to different uses of the word *conservation*. In terms of the law of conservation of energy, conservation means that the total amount of energy in the universe does not change.

TE This misconception is addressed on p. 20.

Previewing Labs

EXPLORE the BIG idea

A Penny for Your Energy, p. 7
Students explore the transfer of energy from a warm object to a cold object.

TIME 10 minutes
MATERIALS cold glass bottle, cooking oil, coin

Hot Dog! p. 7
Students use a solar-energy collector to cook a hot dog.

TIME 40 minutes
MATERIALS cardboard, aluminum foil, wooden skewer, hot dog, 2 corks

---

Internet Activity: Energy, p. 7
Students investigate the relationship between potential and kinetic energy.

TIME 20 minutes
MATERIALS computer with Internet access

SECTION 1.1

EXPLORE Energy, p. 9
Students observe that all objects, even when stationary, have energy.

TIME 10 minutes
MATERIALS large plastic bowl, sand, pebble, rock

INVESTIGATE Potential Energy, p. 13
Students design an experiment to change the amount of potential energy an object has.

TIME 30 minutes
MATERIALS model car, meter stick, weights, balance, tape, cardboard, books

---

SECTION 1.2

CHAPTER INVESTIGATION
Energy Conversions, pp. 22–23
Students investigate the amount of energy stored in different kinds of food by constructing a simple calorimeter and burning food samples.

TIME 40 minutes
MATERIALS can opener, empty aluminum can, dowel rod, tap water, graduated cylinder, ring stand with ring, thermometer, aluminum pie plate, aluminum foil, large paper clip, cork, modeling clay, croutons, caramel rice cakes, balance, wooden matches

---

SECTION 1.3

EXPLORE Solar Cells, p. 24
Students investigate the size of a solar cell needed to provide electrical energy for a solar calculator.

TIME 10 minutes
MATERIALS solar calculator without backup battery, ruler, index card

---

INVESTIGATE Solar Energy, p. 27
Students observe how the color of a solar-energy collector affects the amount of energy collected.

TIME 20 minutes
MATERIALS 2 plastic cups, white and black plastic to cover cups, 2 rubber bands, scissors, 2 thermometers, stopwatch, aluminum foil

---

R **Additional INVESTIGATION,** Build a Roller Coaster, A, B, & C, pp. 59–67; Teacher Instructions, pp. 320–321

Previewing Chapter Resources

| | **INTEGRATED TECHNOLOGY** | **LABS AND ACTIVITIES** |

CHAPTER 1
Energy

CLASSZONE.COM
- eEdition Plus
- EasyPlanner Plus
- Misconception Database
- Content Review
- Test Practice
- Simulation
- Visualization
- Resource Centers
- Internet Activity: Energy
- Math Tutorial

SCILINKS.ORG
SCILINKS

CD-ROMS
- eEdition
- EasyPlanner
- Power Presentations
- Content Review
- Lab Generator
- Test Generator

AUDIO CDS
- Audio Readings
- Audio Readings in Spanish

P E EXPLORE the Big Idea, p. 7
- A Penny for Your Energy
- Hot Dog!
- Internet Activity: Energy

R **UNIT RESOURCE BOOK**
- Unit Projects, pp. 5–10
- Family Letter, p. ix
- Spanish Family Letter, p. x

 Lab Generator CD-ROM
Generate customized labs.

SECTION

Energy exists in different forms.
pp. 9–15

Time: 2 periods (1 block)
 Lesson Plan, pp. 11–12

 RESOURCE CENTERS, Kinetic Energy and Potential Energy; Electric Cars

 UNIT TRANSPARENCY BOOK
- Big Idea Flow Chart, p. T1
- Daily Vocabulary Scaffolding, p. T2
- Note-Taking Model, p. T3
- 3-Minute Warm-Up, p. T4

P E
- EXPLORE Energy, p. 9
- INVESTIGATE Potential Energy, p. 13
- Think Science, p. 15

 UNIT RESOURCE BOOK
Datasheet, Potential Energy, p. 20

SECTION

Energy can change forms but is never lost.
pp. 16–23

Time: 3 periods (1.5 blocks)
 Lesson Plan, pp. 22–23

 UNIT TRANSPARENCY BOOK
- Daily Vocabulary Scaffolding, p. T2
- 3-Minute Warm-Up, p. T4
- "Converting Energy" Visual, p. T6

P E CHAPTER INVESTIGATION, Energy Conversions, pp. 22–23

 UNIT RESOURCE BOOK
- Additional INVESTIGATION, Build a Roller Coaster, A, B, & C, pp. 59–67
- CHAPTER INVESTIGATION, Energy Conversions, A, B, & C, pp. 50–58

SECTION

Technology improves the ways people use energy.
pp. 24–29

Time: 3 periods (1.5 blocks)
 Lesson Plan, pp. 32–33

- **VISUALIZATION,** Solar Cells
- **RESOURCE CENTER,** Alternative Energy Sources
- **MATH TUTORIAL**

 UNIT TRANSPARENCY BOOK
- Big Idea Flow Chart, p. T1
- Daily Vocabulary Scaffolding, p. T2
- 3-Minute Warm-Up, p. T5
- Chapter Outline, pp. T7–T8

P E
- EXPLORE Solar Cells, p. 24
- INVESTIGATE Solar Energy, p. 27
- Math in Science, p. 29

 UNIT RESOURCE BOOK
- Datasheet, Solar Energy, p. 41
- Math Support, p. 48
- Math Practice, p. 49

KEY TO ICONS

 CD/CD-ROM

 Teacher Edition

 UNIT TRANSPARENCY BOOK

 SPANISH ASSESSMENT BOOK

 INTERNET

 Pupil Edition

 UNIT RESOURCE BOOK

 UNIT ASSESSMENT BOOK

SCIENCE TOOLKIT

READING AND REINFORCEMENT

ASSESSMENT

STANDARDS

- Frame Game, B26–27
- Mind Map, C40–41
- Daily Vocabulary Scaffolding, H1–8

 UNIT RESOURCE BOOK
- Vocabulary Practice, pp. 45–46
- Decoding Support, p. 47
- Summarizing the Chapter, pp. 68–69

 **Audio Readings CD**
Listen to Pupil Edition.

Audio Readings in Spanish CD
Listen to Pupil Edition in Spanish.

- Chapter Review, pp. 31–32
- Standardized Test Practice, p. 33

 UNIT ASSESSMENT BOOK
- Diagnostic Test, pp. 1–2
- Chapter Test, A, B, & C, pp. 6–17
- Alternative Assessment, pp. 18–19

  Spanish Chapter Test, pp. 221–224

Test Generator CD-ROM
Generate customized tests.

Lab Generator CD-ROM
Rubrics for Labs

National Standards
A.2–8, A.9.a–f, B.3.a, E.2–5, E.6.c–e, F.5.a–c

See p. 6 for the standards.

 UNIT RESOURCE BOOK
- Reading Study Guide, A & B, pp. 13–16
- Spanish Reading Study Guide, pp. 17–18
- Challenge and Extension, p. 19
- Reinforcing Key Concepts, p. 21

 Ongoing Assessment, pp. 10–14

 Section 1.1 Review, p. 14

 UNIT ASSESSMENT BOOK
Section 1.1 Quiz, p. 3

National Standards
A.2–7, A.9.a–b, A.9.e–f, B.3.a, E.2–5, E.6.d–e

 UNIT RESOURCE BOOK
- Reading Study Guide, A & B, pp. 24–27
- Spanish Reading Study Guide, pp. 28–29
- Challenge and Extension, p. 30
- Reinforcing Key Concepts, p. 31

 Ongoing Assessment, pp. 16–21

 Section 1.2 Review, p. 21

 UNIT ASSESSMENT BOOK
Section 1.2 Quiz, p. 4

National Standards
A.2–8, A.9.a–f, B.3.a, E.6.c–e, F.5.a–c

 UNIT RESOURCE BOOK
- Reading Study Guide, A & B, pp. 34–37
- Spanish Reading Study Guide, pp. 38–39
- Challenge and Extension, p. 40
- Reinforcing Key Concepts, p. 42
- Challenge Reading, pp. 43–44

 Ongoing Assessment, pp. 25, 27–28

 Section 1.3 Review, p. 28

 UNIT ASSESSMENT BOOK
Section 1.3 Quiz, p. 5

National Standards
A.2–8, A.9.a–f, B.3.a, E.6.c–e, F.5.a–c

Previewing Resources for Differentiated Instruction

CHAPTER INVESTIGATION

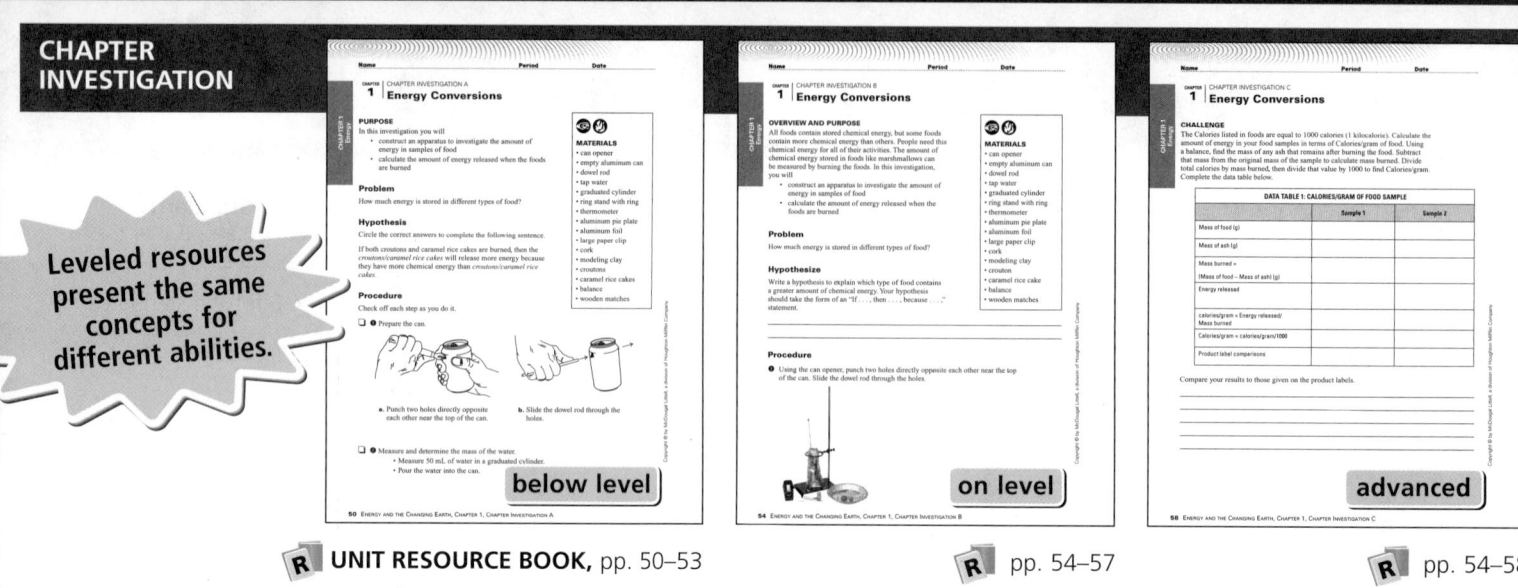

below level

on level

advanced

R **UNIT RESOURCE BOOK,** pp. 50–53   R pp. 54–57   R pp. 54–58

> Leveled resources present the same concepts for different abilities.

READING STUDY GUIDE

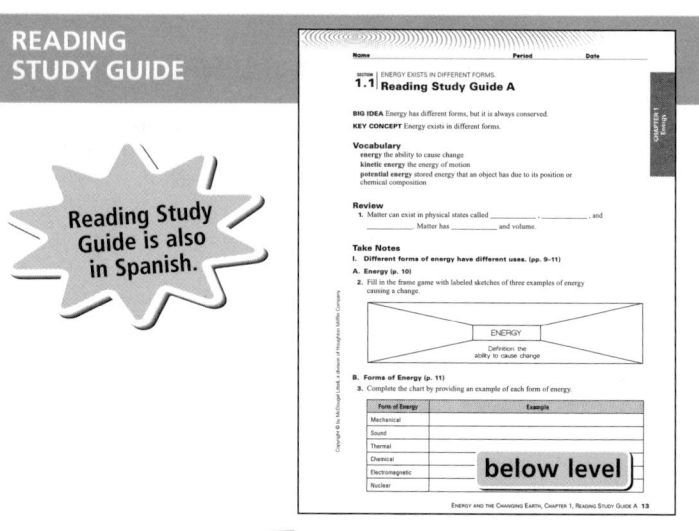
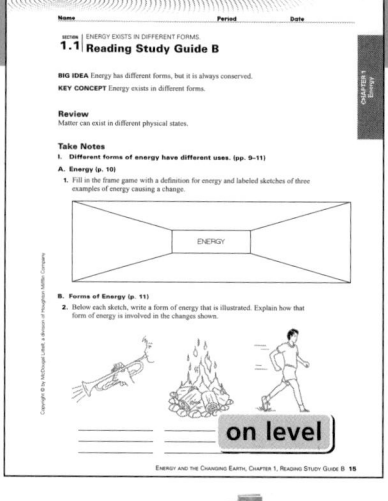
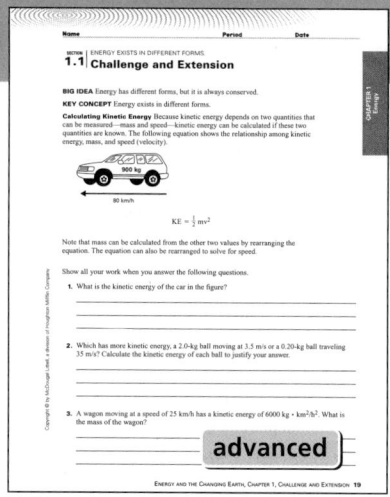

below level

on level

advanced

R **UNIT RESOURCE BOOK,** pp. 13–14   R pp. 15–16   R p. 19

> Reading Study Guide is also in Spanish.

CHAPTER TEST

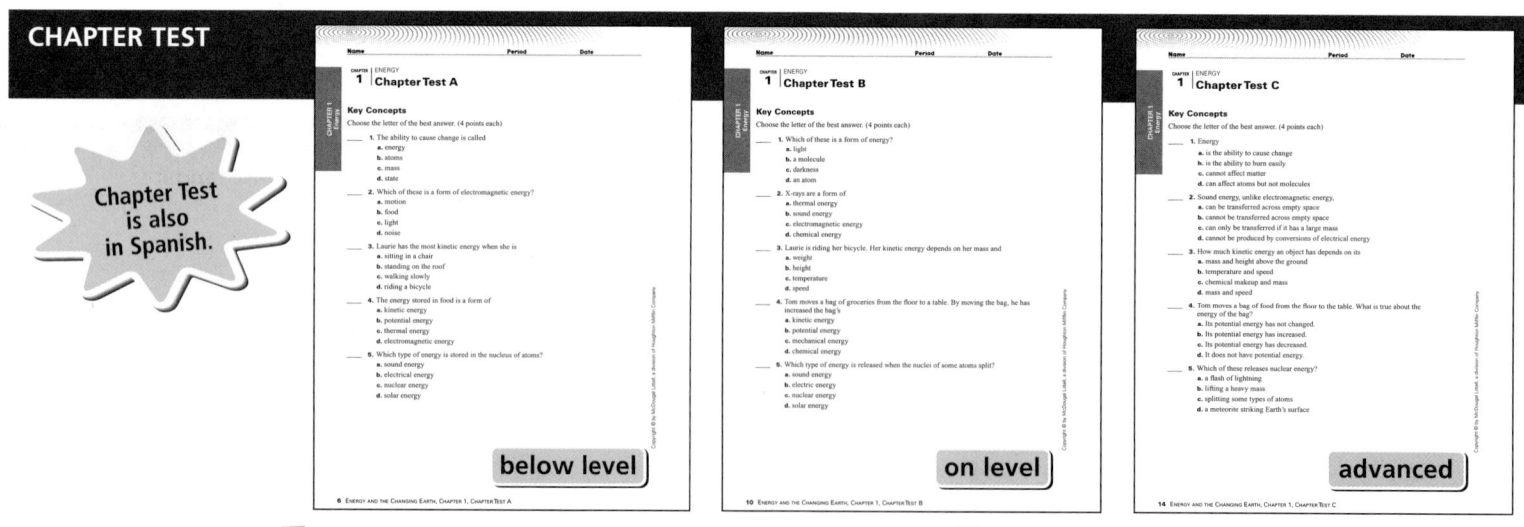

below level

on level

advanced

A **UNIT ASSESSMENT BOOK,** pp. 6–9   A pp. 10–13   A pp. 14–17

> Chapter Test is also in Spanish.

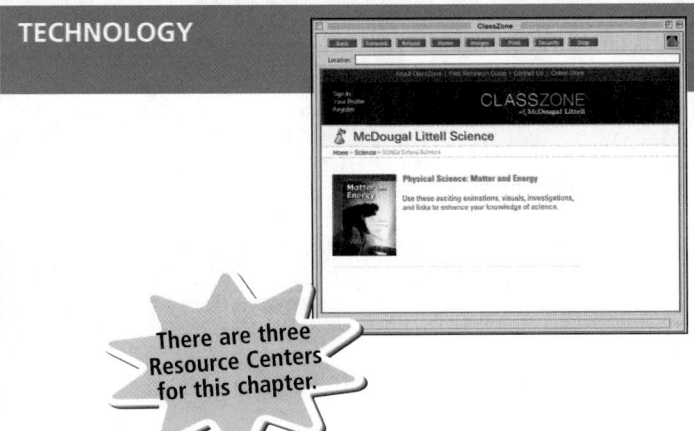

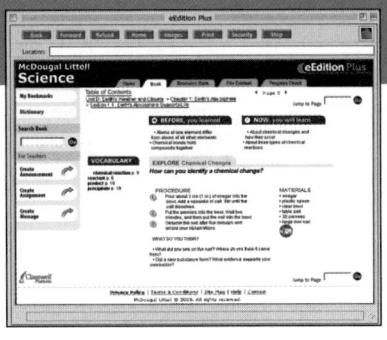

There are three Resource Centers for this chapter.

CLASSZONE.COM

CD/CD-ROMS

CLASSZONE.COM

VISUAL CONTENT

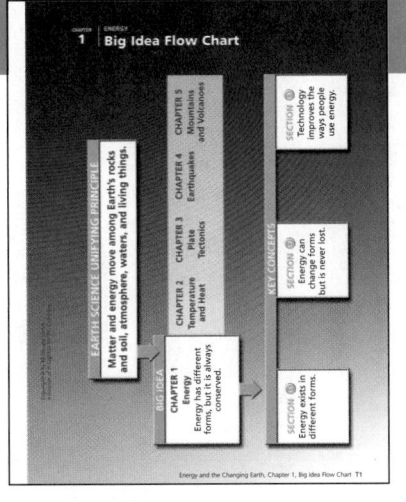

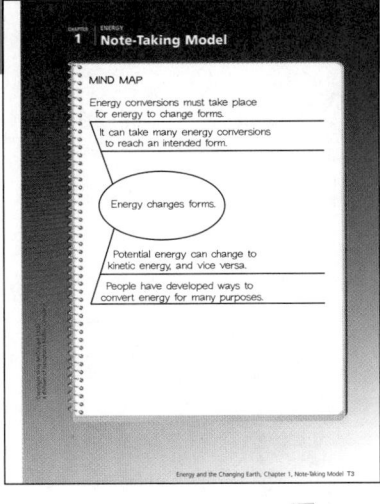

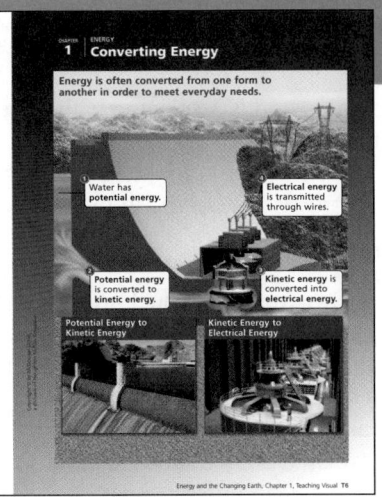

 **UNIT TRANSPARENCY BOOK,** p. T1

 p. T3

 p. T6

MORE SUPPORT

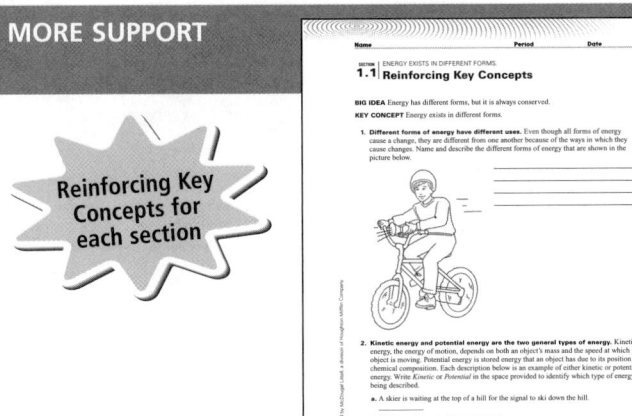

Reinforcing Key Concepts for each section

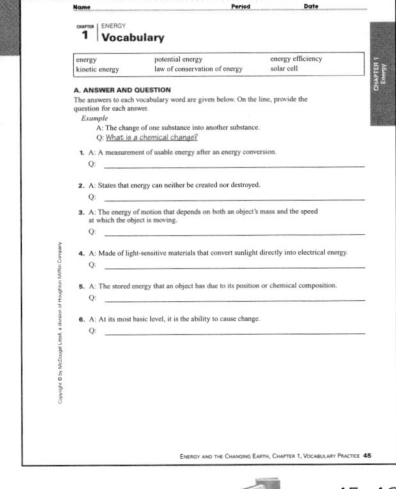

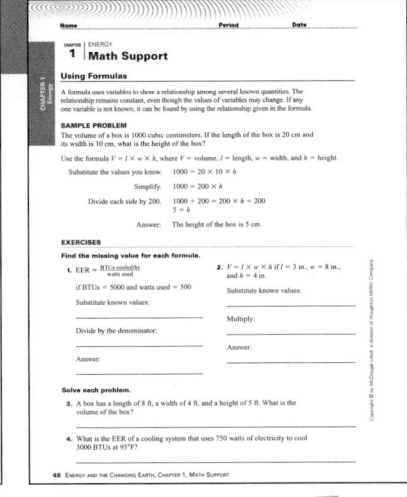

UNIT RESOURCE BOOK, p. 21

pp. 45–46

p. 48

CHAPTER

1 Energy

INTRODUCE

the **BIG** idea

Have students look at the photograph of cyclists and discuss how the question in the box links to the Big Idea:

- Where in the photograph can energy be observed?
- Where in the photograph can energy be inferred?

National Science Education Standards

Content

B.3.a Energy is a property of many substances and is associated with heat, light, electricity, mechanical motion, sound, nuclei, and the nature of a chemical. Energy is transferred in many ways.

Process

A.2–8 Design and conduct an investigation; use tools to gather and interpret data; use evidence to describe, predict, explain, model; think critically to make relationships between evidence and explanation; recognize different explanations and predictions; communicate scientific procedures and explanations; use mathematics.

A.9.a–f Understand scientific inquiry by using different investigations, methods, mathematics, technology, explanations based on logic, evidence, and skeptisicm.

E.2–5 Design, implement, and evaluate a solution or product; communicate technological design.

E.6.c–e Science and technology are reciprocal; technological designs have constraints.

F.5.a–c Science and technology in society.

G.1.b Science requires different abilities.

the **BIG** idea

Energy has different forms, but it is always conserved.

What different forms of energy are shown in this photograph?

Key Concepts

SECTION
1.1 **Energy exists in different forms.**
Learn about several different forms of energy.

SECTION
1.2 **Energy can change forms but is never lost.**
Learn about the law of conservation of energy.

SECTION
1.3 **Technology improves the ways people use energy.**
Learn how technology can be used to make energy conversions more efficient.

Internet Preview

CLASSZONE.COM
Chapter 1 online resources: Content Review, Simulation, Visualization, three Resource Centers, Math Tutorial, Test Practice

INTERNET PREVIEW

CLASSZONE.COM For student use with the following pages:

Review and Practice
- Content Review, pp. 8, 30
- Math Tutorial: Rates, p. 29
- Test Practice, p. 33

Activities and Resources
- Internet Activity: p. 7
- Resource Centers: Kinetic and Potential Energy, p. 12; Electric Cars, p. 15; Alternative Energy Sources, p. 28. Visualization: Solar Cells, p. 26

NSTA scilinks.org *SCiLINKS*

Forms of Energy
Code: MDL063

A Penny for Your Energy

Chill an empty glass bottle. Immediately complete the following steps: Rub a drop of cooking oil around the rim of the bottle. Place a coin on the rim so the oil forms a seal between the coin and the bottle. Wrap your hands around the bottle.

Observe and Think What happened to the coin? What do you think caused this to happen?

Hot Dog!

Cover a piece of cardboard with aluminum foil, and bend it into the shape of a U. Poke a wooden skewer through a hot dog, and through each side of the cardboard. Push corks over both ends of the skewer so the cardboard does not flatten out. Place your setup in direct sunlight for 30 minutes.

Observe and Think What happened to the hot dog? Were there any changes you had to make while the hot dog was in sunlight?

Internet Activity: Energy

Go to **ClassZone.com** to investigate the relationship between potential energy and kinetic energy.

Observe and Think How did you change potential energy? How do these changes affect kinetic energy?

NSTA
scilinks.org
SCiLINKS

Forms of Energy **Code: MDL063**

Chapter 1: **Energy 7** B

TEACHING WITH TECHNOLOGY

Video Camera You may wish to film students as they design their experiments for "Investigate Potential Energy" on p. 13. As they watch the video, encourage them to write down ideas for how to improve the design of their experiments.

CBL and Probeware If CBL equipment and probeware are available, have students substitute a temperature probe for the thermometer in the Chapter Investigation on pp. 22–23 and "Investigate Solar Energy" on p. 27.

These inquiry-based activities are appropriate for use at home or as a supplement to classroom instruction.

A Penny for Your Energy

PURPOSE To explore the transfer of energy from a warm object to a cold object. Students make a coin vibrate by causing air to warm and expand.

TIP *10 min.* Make sure the coin will completely cover the opening of the bottle but not extend too far over the rim.

Answer: The coin vibrated and jumped on the top of the bottle. The air sealed inside the bottle warmed and expanded as a result of energy transferred from the student's hands to the trapped air.

REVISIT after p. 18.

Hot Dog!

PURPOSE To observe and use a solar-energy collector. Students cook a hot dog with solar energy.

TIPS *40 min.* Students should not eat the hot dog. Students should try this at home with an adult. The experiment should be done in direct sunlight during the middle of the day.

Answer: The hot dog cooked. The solar collector needed adjustment to keep sunlight reflected on the hot dog.

REVISIT after p. 27.

Internet Activity: Energy

PURPOSE To investigate the relationship between potential and kinetic energy.

TIP *20 min.* Students should understand that potential energy is related to position.

Answer: As the mass and height of an object was increased, the potential energy increased. The object will thus have more kinetic energy.

REVISIT after p. 14.

Chapter 1 **7** B

○ CONCEPT REVIEW

Activate Prior Knowledge

If students have not been previously exposed to the concepts of matter, atoms, and energy, have them read the Unifying Principles of Physical Science (pp. xxxiv-xxxv) for background information.

• To demonstrate that matter has mass and volume, have students measure a small object such as a domino and calculate its volume. Have them find the mass of the object on a balance.

• Ask: Does all matter, even a gas that cannot be seen, have mass and volume? *Yes; molecules of the gas have mass and take up space.*

○ TAKING NOTES

Mind Map

A mind map allows students to include as much information and detail about a concept as they choose. Encourage students to use the mind map to take notes in a way that will help them to remember relationships between concepts, definitions, and examples.

Vocabulary Strategy

A frame game diagram organizes characteristics of a vocabulary term into a coherent pattern. By filling in their own words, examples, and descriptions, students personalize their understanding of the term and can connect personal experience to the term's meaning.

Vocabulary and Note-Taking Resources

 • Vocabulary Practice, pp. 45–46
• Decoding Support, p. 47

 • Daily Vocabulary Scaffolding, p. T2
• Note-Taking Model, p. T3

 • Frame Game, B26–27
• Mind Map, C40–41
• Daily Vocabulary Scaffolding, H1–8

◀ CONCEPT REVIEW

• Matter has mass and is made of tiny particles.
• Gravity is the force that objects exert on each other because of their mass.
• Matter can be changed physically or chemically.

◀ VOCABULARY REVIEW

See Glossary for definitions.

atom

chemical change

mass

matter

physical change

 CONTENT REVIEW
CLASSZONE.COM
Review concepts and vocabulary.

▶ TAKING NOTES

MIND MAP

Write each main idea, or blue heading, in an oval; then write details that relate to each other and to the main idea. Organize the details so that each spoke of the web has notes about one part of the main idea.

VOCABULARY STRATEGY

Write each new vocabulary term in the center of a **frame game** diagram. Decide what information to frame it with. Use examples, descriptions, parts, sentences that use the term in context, or pictures. You can change the frame to fit each term.

See the Note-Taking Handbook on pages R45–R51.

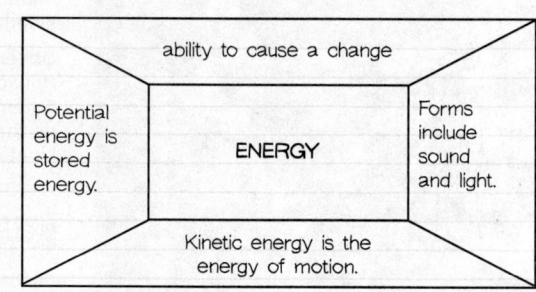

SCIENCE NOTEBOOK

ability to cause a change

different changes from different forms

DIFFERENT FORMS OF ENERGY HAVE DIFFERENT USES.

sunlight — electromagnetic energy

motion — mechanical energy

food — chemical energy

ability to cause a change

Potential energy is stored energy.

ENERGY

Forms include sound and light.

Kinetic energy is the energy of motion.

CHECK READINESS

Administer the Diagnostic Test to determine students' readiness for new science content and their mastery of requisite math skills.

 Diagnostic Test, pp. 1–2

Technology Resources

Students needing content and math skills should visit **ClassZone.com**.

 • **CONTENT REVIEW**
• **MATH TUTORIAL**

 CONTENT REVIEW CD-ROM

1.1 Energy exists in different forms.

◀ **BEFORE,** you learned

- All substances are made of matter
- Matter has both physical and chemical properties
- Matter can exist in different physical states

▶ **NOW,** you will learn

- How energy causes change
- About common forms of energy
- About kinetic energy and potential energy

VOCABULARY

energy p. 10
kinetic energy p. 12
potential energy p. 13

EXPLORE Energy

How can you demonstrate energy?

PROCEDURE

1. Fill the bowl halfway with sand. Place the bowl on the floor as shown. Make sure the sand is level.

2. Place a pebble and a rock near the edge of a table above the bowl of sand.

3. Gently push the pebble off the table into the sand. Record your observations.

4. Remove the pebble, and make sure the sand is level. Gently push the rock off the table into the sand. Record your observations.

MATERIALS
- large plastic bowl
- sand
- pebble
- rock

WHAT DO YOU THINK?
- What happened to the sand when you dropped the pebble? when you dropped the rock?
- How can you explain any differences you observed?

Different forms of energy have different uses.

Energy takes many different forms and has many different effects. Just about everything you see happening around you involves energy. Lamps and other appliances in your home operate on electrical energy. Plants use energy from the Sun to grow. You use energy provided by the food you eat to carry out all of your everyday activities—eating, exercising, reading, and even sitting and thinking. In this chapter, you will learn what these and other forms of energy have in common.

Chapter 1: Energy **9** **B**

1.1 FOCUS

▶ Set Learning Goals
Students will
- Recognize how energy causes change.
- Describe common forms of energy.
- Illustrate that the two general types of energy are kinetic energy and potential energy.
- Design an experiment to investigate and change potential energy.

◀ 3-Minute Warm-Up

Display Transparency 4 or copy this exercise on the board:

Draw a two-column chart. In the left column, write a list of things you already know about energy. In the right column, write some questions that you have about energy. *Discuss students' charts; answers should not indicate that energy is matter or a thing.*

 3-Minute Warm-Up, p. T4

1.1 MOTIVATE

EXPLORE Energy

PURPOSE To observe that all objects have energy, even when they are stationary

TIPS *10 min.*
- Bowls with wide openings work best.
- Packing peanuts may be used instead of sand.

WHAT DO YOU THINK? *The pebble made a small dent in the sand; the rock made a much larger dent in the sand. The rock contains more (potential) energy due to the force of gravity.*

Address Misconceptions

IDENTIFY Ask: Is light a substance? If students say yes, they may hold the misconception that energy is a form of matter, that is, an object.

CORRECT Have students list the properties that matter must have. Discuss whether light and other forms of energy have mass and volume.

REASSESS Ask students to write a short paragraph differentiating between an object and a property of an object. Ask: Which is energy? *a property of an object*

Technology Resources

Visit **ClassZone.com** for background on common student misconceptions.

 MISCONCEPTION DATABASE

Teach Difficult Concepts

Students may think that energy is associated only with living things. In fact, all things, both living and nonliving, have energy.

Place a domino at the base of a ramp. Have students roll a marble down the ramp so that it knocks over the domino. Ask: What knocked the domino over? *the marble's energy* Ask students to design another way to demonstrate that inanimate objects have energy that can cause a change.

Teach from Visuals

To help students identify energy and its effects, ask: What other changes might be occurring in the picture? *people moving in cars; trees moving; sounds*

Ongoing Assessment

Recognize how energy causes change.

Ask: What is the most fundamental quality of energy? *Its ability to cause change.*

CHECK YOUR READING *Sample answer: Hitting a baseball changes its direction and speed.*

Energy

 A All forms of energy have one important point in common—they cause changes to occur. The flow of electrical energy through a wire causes a cool, dark bulb to get hot and glow. The energy of the wind causes a flag to flutter.

You are a source of energy that makes changes in your environment. For example, when you pick up a tennis racquet or a paintbrush, you change the position of that object. When you hit a tennis ball or smooth paint on a canvas, you cause further changes. Energy is involved in every one of these actions. At its most basic level, **energy** is the ability to cause change.

CHECK YOUR READING Provide your own example of energy and how it causes a change.

The photograph below shows a city street. All of the activities that take place on every street in any city require energy, so there are many changes taking place in the picture. Consider one of the cars. A person's energy is used to turn the key that starts the car. The key's movement starts the car's engine and gasoline begins burning. Gasoline provides the energy for the car to move. The person's hand, the turning key, and the burning gasoline all contain energy that causes change.

 **VOCABULARY** Remember to use a frame game diagram for *energy* and other vocabulary terms.

The motion of the cars and the glow of the streetlights are changes produced by energy.

DIFFERENTIATE INSTRUCTION

 More Reading Support

A What do all forms of energy have in common? *They cause changes.*

English Learners Help English learners understand complex sentences. Give students several difficult sentences and ask them to circle the subject and verb. Be sure students circle the entire subject—often it is more than one word. For example, in the sentence "Just about everything you see happening around you involves energy" (p. 9), students should circle "Just about everything you see happening around you" as the subject and "involves" as the verb.

Forms of Energy

Scientists classify energy into many forms, each of which causes change in a different way. Some of these forms are described below.

Mechanical Energy The energy that moves objects is mechanical energy. The energy that you use to put a book on a shelf is mechanical energy, as is energy that a person uses to turn a car key.

Sound Energy Sound results from the vibration of particles in a solid, liquid, or gas. People and other animals are able to detect these tiny vibrations with structures in their ears that vibrate due to the sound. So, when you hear a car drive past, you are detecting vibrations in the air produced by sound energy. Sound cannot travel through empty space. If there were no air or other substance between you and the car, you would not hear sounds from the car.

Chemical Energy Energy that is stored in the chemical composition of matter is chemical energy. The amount of chemical energy in a substance depends on the types and arrangement of atoms in the substance. When wood or gasoline burns, chemical energy produces heat. The energy used by the cells in your body comes from chemical energy stored in the foods you eat.

Thermal Energy The total amount of energy from the movement of particles in matter is thermal energy. Recall that matter is made of atoms, and atoms combined in molecules. The atoms and molecules in matter are always moving. The energy of this motion in an object is the object's thermal energy. You will learn more about thermal energy in the next chapter.

Electromagnetic Energy Electromagnetic (ih-LEHK-troh-mag-NEHT-ihk) energy is transmitted through space in the form of electromagnetic waves. Unlike sound, electromagnetic waves can travel through empty space. These waves include visible light, x-rays, and microwaves. X-rays are high energy waves used by doctors and dentists to look at your bones and teeth. Microwaves can be used to cook food or to transmit cellular telephone calls but contain far less energy than x-rays. The Sun releases a large amount of electromagnetic energy, some of which is absorbed by Earth.

Nuclear Energy The center of an atom—its nucleus—is the source of nuclear energy. A large amount of energy in the nucleus holds the nuclear particles together. When a heavy atom's nucleus breaks apart, or when the nuclei (NOO-klee-EYE) of two small atoms join together, energy is released. Nuclear energy released from the fusing of small nuclei to form larger nuclei keeps the Sun burning.

CHECK YOUR READING How does chemical energy cause a change? What about electromagnetic energy?

APPLY Where in this photograph can you find chemical, sound, and mechanical energy?

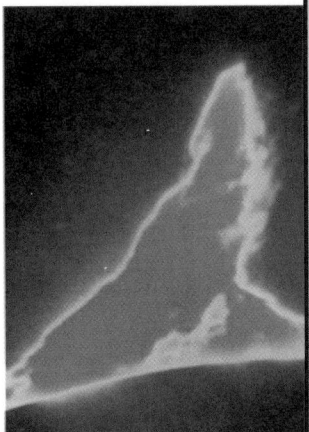

This solar flare releases electromagnetic energy and thermal energy produced by nuclear energy in the Sun.

Integrate the Sciences

The chemical energy stored in food is not used directly for energy by cells. A complex series of reactions known as cellular respiration changes the molecules in food into a usable source of energy.

Teach Difficult Concepts

Thermal energy is not heat, but the two are related. Heat is a process that transfers energy from warmer objects to cooler objects. The result of this transfer of energy is an increase in the cooler object's thermal energy and a decrease in the warmer object's thermal energy.

Ongoing Assessment

Describe common forms of energy.

Ask: What are three forms of electromagnetic energy. *Sample answer: visible light, x-rays, microwaves*

PHOTO CAPTION Answer: Sample answer: chemical energy in the drummers' bodies, sound energy from the drums, mechanical energy in the moving drumsticks

CHECK YOUR READING *Sample answers: Chemical energy can cause a change through its release when a substance is burned. Electromagnetic energy can cause a change when food is cooked in a microwave oven.*

DIFFERENTIATE INSTRUCTION

 **More Reading Support**

B What is the energy that moves objects?
mechanical energy

C What is the energy stored in the chemical composition of matter?
chemical energy

Inclusion If you demonstrate sound energy to your class, students with hearing impairments will be able to feel the energy through its conversion to mechanical waves, that is, vibrations in the floor, the desk, and other objects.

Teacher Demo

To help students understand that decreasing an object's speed decreases its kinetic energy, do the following demonstration. Set up a ramp. Position a small object at the end of the ramp. Roll a small ball down the ramp so that it knocks over the object. Decrease the angle of the ramp to decrease the speed of the ball, then roll the ball down again. Continue to decrease the speed in this way until the ball has insufficient kinetic energy to knock over the object. To demonstrate the relationship between mass and kinetic energy, repeat the above procedure, keeping the ramp at the same angle but using balls with different mass. Find a ball with so little mass that the ball cannot knock over the object. Use a balance (or kitchen scale to measure objects in increments of 10 grams) to measure the mass of the balls to confirm that they have different masses.

Teach Difficult Concepts

Mechanical energy is a combination of potential energy and kinetic energy. Mechanical energy results from the position of objects (potential energy), the movement of objects (kinetic energy), or both.

Teach from Visuals

To help students interpret the photos of the speed skater, ask: Where did the skater's kinetic energy come from? *from chemical energy stored in the skater's muscles*

Ongoing Assessment

Answer: If the skater with less mass is moving faster, he or she could have more kinetic energy.

 **RESOURCE CENTER**
CLASSZONE.COM

Learn more about kinetic energy and potential energy.

Kinetic energy and potential energy are the two general types of energy.

All of the forms of energy can be described in terms of two general types of energy—kinetic energy and potential energy. Anything that is moving, such as a car that is being driven or an atom in the air, has kinetic energy. All matter also has potential energy, or energy that is stored and can be released at a later time.

Kinetic Energy

READING TIP

Kinetic means "related to motion."

 D

The energy of motion is called **kinetic energy.** It depends on both an object's mass and the speed at which the object is moving.

All objects are made of matter, and matter has mass. The more matter an object contains, the greater its mass. If you held a bowling ball in one hand and a soccer ball in the other, you could feel that the bowling ball has more mass than the soccer ball.

- **Kinetic energy increases as mass increases.** If the bowling ball and the soccer ball were moving at the same speed, the bowling ball would have more kinetic energy because of its greater mass.

E

- **Kinetic energy increases as speed increases.** If two identical bowling balls were rolling along at different speeds, the faster one would have more kinetic energy because of its greater speed. The speed skater in the photographs below has more kinetic energy when he is racing than he does when he is moving slowly.

High Speed

This skater has a large amount of kinetic energy when moving at a high speed.

Low Speed

When the same skater is moving more slowly, he has less kinetic energy.

READING VISUALS   **APPLY** How could a skater with less mass than another skater have more kinetic energy?

DIFFERENTIATE INSTRUCTION

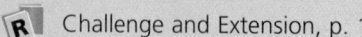

? **More Reading Support**

D What is kinetic energy? *the energy of motion*

E What is the relationship between speed and kinetic energy? *As speed increases, kinetic energy increases.*

Advanced Introduce students to the formula for kinetic energy, $KE = 1/2\ mv^2$. Use examples to show that the kinetic energy of an object varies directly with its mass and with the square of the velocity (speed). Ask students to explain why changing the velocity of an object has a much greater impact on its kinetic energy than changing its mass.

R Challenge and Extension, p. 19

Potential Energy

Suppose you are holding a soccer ball in your hands. Even if the ball is not moving, it has energy because it has the potential to fall. **Potential energy** is the stored energy that an object has due to its position or chemical composition. The ball's position above the ground gives it potential energy.

The most obvious form of potential energy is potential energy that results from gravity. Gravity is the force that pulls objects toward Earth's surface. The giant boulder on the right has potential energy because of its position above the ground. The mass of the boulder and its height above the ground determine how much potential energy it has due to gravity.

It is easy to know whether an object has kinetic energy because the object is moving. It is not so easy to know how much and what form of potential energy an object has, because objects can have potential energy from several sources. For example, in addition to potential energy from gravity, substances contain potential energy due to their chemical composition—the atoms they contain.

Because the boulder could fall, it has potential energy from gravity.

CHECK YOUR READING How can you tell kinetic energy and potential energy apart?

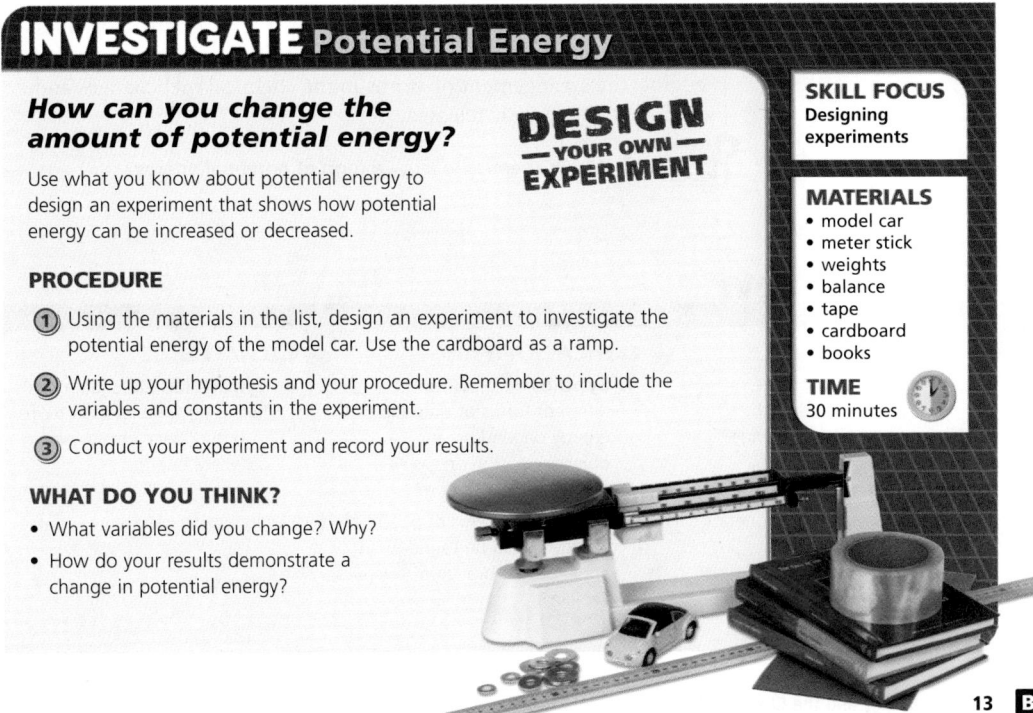

INVESTIGATE Potential Energy

How can you change the amount of potential energy?

Use what you know about potential energy to design an experiment that shows how potential energy can be increased or decreased.

DESIGN — YOUR OWN — EXPERIMENT

PROCEDURE

1. Using the materials in the list, design an experiment to investigate the potential energy of the model car. Use the cardboard as a ramp.

2. Write up your hypothesis and your procedure. Remember to include the variables and constants in the experiment.

3. Conduct your experiment and record your results.

WHAT DO YOU THINK?

- What variables did you change? Why?
- How do your results demonstrate a change in potential energy?

SKILL FOCUS
Designing experiments

MATERIALS
- model car
- meter stick
- weights
- balance
- tape
- cardboard
- books

TIME
30 minutes

13 B

DIFFERENTIATE INSTRUCTION

Ongoing Assessment

Illustrate that the two general types of energy are kinetic energy and potential energy.

Ask: How might riding down a waterslide involve both potential and kinetic energy? *At the top of the slide, you have potential energy and no kinetic energy. As you move down the slide, potential energy changes to kinetic energy.*

 *Answer: It is energy that is stored in molecules.*

EXPLORE (the BIG idea)

Revisit "Internet Activity: Energy" on p. 7. Have students explain the relationship between potential and kinetic energy.

Reinforce (the BIG idea)

Have students relate the section to the Big Idea.

 Reinforcing Key Concepts, p. 21

1.1 ASSESS & RETEACH

Assess

A Section 1.1 Quiz, p. 3

Reteach

Ask students how water flowing over a waterfall involves kinetic and potential energy. *Flowing water has kinetic energy; the water has potential energy due to gravity.* Ask: What forms of energy can be observed? *mechanical in the motion of the water; sound from the water*

Technology Resources

Have students visit **ClassZone.com** for reteaching of Key Concepts.

 CONTENT REVIEW

 CONTENT REVIEW CD-ROM

Pulling the string, which bends the bow, gives the bow potential energy.

Chemical energy in the fuel of a model rocket engine is potential energy.

Another form of potential energy related to an object's position comes from stretching or compressing an object. Think about the spring that is pushed down in a jack-in-the-box. The spring's potential energy increases when the spring is compressed and decreases when it is released. Look at the bow that is being bent in the photograph on the left. When the bowstring is pulled, the bow bends and stores energy. When the string is released, both the string and the bow return to their normal shape. Stored energy is released as the bow and the string straighten out and the arrow is pushed forward.

When a rock falls or a bow straightens, potential energy is released. In fact, in these examples, the potential energy produced either by gravity or by bending is changed into kinetic energy.

Chemical energy, such as the energy stored in food, is less visible, but it is also a form of potential energy. This form of potential energy depends on chemical composition rather than position. It is the result of the atoms, and the bonds between atoms, that make up the molecules in food. When these molecules are broken apart, and their atoms rearranged through a series of chemical changes, energy is released.

The fuel in a model rocket engine also contains chemical energy. Like the molecules that provide energy in your body, the molecules in the fuel store potential energy. When the fuel ignites in the rocket engine, the arrangement of atoms in the chemical fuel changes and its potential energy is released.

 Why is chemical energy a form of potential energy?

1.1 Review

KEY CONCEPTS	CRITICAL THINKING	⬤ CHALLENGE
1. List three ways you use energy. How does each example involve a change?	**4. Synthesize** How do the different forms of potential energy depend on an object's position or chemical composition?	**6. Synthesize** Describe a stone falling off a tabletop in terms of both kinetic energy and potential energy.
2. What are some changes that can be caused by sound energy? by electromagnetic energy?	**5. Infer** What forms of potential energy would be found in an apple on the branch of a tree? Explain.	
3. What two factors determine an object's kinetic energy?		

ANSWERS

1. Answers could include any activity, but should indicate what change results.

2. sound—vibrations in a solid, liquid, or gas; electromagnetic—lighting a dark room

3. mass and speed

4. an object's position above the ground; an object's compressed or stretched position; chemical potential depends on the atoms and bonds in an object.

5. gravitational, because of the apple's position; chemical, *because the apple can be eaten for chemical energy*

6. The stone has potential energy due to gravity. The amount of energy depends on its mass and height. The greater its potential energy, the greater its kinetic energy when it falls.

Gasoline or Electric?

Cars use a significant amount of the world's energy. Most cars get their energy from the chemical energy of gasoline, a fossil fuel. Cars can also get their energy from sources other than gasoline. For many years, engineers have been working to design cars that run only on electricity. The goals of developing these new cars include reducing air pollution and decreasing the use of fossil fuels. So why have electric cars not replaced gasoline-powered cars?

▶ Advantages of Electric Cars

- Electric motors are more simple than gasoline engines.
- Electric cars use energy more efficiently than gasoline-powered cars, so they are cheaper to operate.
- Controlling pollution at power plants that produce electricity is easier than controlling pollution from cars.
- Electric motors are quieter than gasoline engines.
- Electric cars do not produce smog, which is a major health concern in large cities.

▶ Disadvantages of Electric Cars

- At this time, electric cars can travel only about 100 miles on a single battery charge.
- It takes several hours to recharge the batteries of an electric car using today's charging systems.
- The batteries of an electric car need to be replaced after being recharged about 600 times.
- An electric car's range is decreased by heating or cooling the inside of the car because, unlike batteries in gasoline-powered cars, its batteries are not recharged during driving.

▶ Finding Solutions

As a Group

What technology would need to be improved for electric cars to replace gasoline-powered cars? What facilities that do not exist today would be needed to serve electric cars?

As a Class

Compare your group's solutions to those of other groups. Use the Internet to research hybrid vehicles. How would these vehicles solve some of the problems that you identified?

 **RESOURCE CENTER** Find out more
CLASSZONE.COM about electric cars.

ANSWERS

AS A GROUP Battery technology needs to improve and facilities for recharging car batteries have to be built.

AS A CLASS Hybrid electric vehicles solve some of the problems of electric cars because they combine electric power with the power of the internal combustion engine. They are more efficient and less polluting.

THINK SCIENCE
Scientific Methods of Thinking

Set Learning Goal

To learn about electric cars and weigh their advantages and disadvantages

Present the Science

Batteries are the weak link in the development of economical and practical electric cars. The batteries are heavy, bulky, and expensive. They must be recharged (a slow process) and have to be replaced regularly. For this reason, research has centered on hybrid electric vehicles (HEVs) and on fuel cells. HEVs are an intermediate step between purely electric cars and gasoline-powered cars, and were meant to be a temporary solution until better batteries were developed.

Guide the Activity

DIFFERENTIATION TIP Have slower learners discuss the general characteristics of the advantages and disadvantages of electric cars and organize them into a chart. Be sure students identify health and the environment as advantages, and convenience as a disadvantage.

Point out that most energy sources have advantages and disadvantages. Discuss a major energy source for your area and how it benefits people and what problems it causes.

COOPERATIVE LEARNING STRATEGY Divide the class into groups of four. Have each group discuss what would have to be done to make electric cars convenient and practical.

Close

Ask: What might be the advantages if all future cars were electric powered? *Smog and pollution would be decreased.*

Technology Resources

Have students visit **ClassZone.com** to find out more about electric cars

 RESOURCE CENTER

Set Learning Goals

 **Students will**

- Explain how energy can be converted from one form to another.
- Restate the law of conservation of energy.
- Understand that energy conversions may be inefficient.

 **3-Minute Warm-Up**

Display Transparency 4 or copy this exercise on the board:

Decide if these statements are true. If not true, correct them.

1. Chemical energy is based on the movement of particles within matter. *thermal energy*

2. Nuclear energy holds an atom's nucleus together. *true*

3. Electromagnetic energy is the energy used to move objects. *mechanical energy*

4. Kinetic energy is energy of motion, and potential energy is stored energy. *true*

 3-Minute Warm-Up, p. T4

1.2 MOTIVATE

THINK ABOUT

PURPOSE To identify how energy changes forms several times when a match is lit

DISCUSS Have students suggest energy changes in other everyday events. *Using a stove, turning on a light, and using an electric appliance all involve energy changing forms.*

Answer: The energy to strike the match initially comes from the person who uses the match.

Ongoing Assessment

 *Answer: Chemical energy becomes mechanical energy in the match. The match's mechanical energy changes into heat and light released by the burning match.*

KEY CONCEPT

1.2 Energy can change forms but is never lost.

◁ BEFORE, you learned

- Energy causes change
- Energy has different forms
- Kinetic energy and potential energy are the two general types of energy

▷ NOW, you will learn

- How energy can be converted from one form to another
- About the law of conservation of energy
- How energy conversions may be inefficient

VOCABULARY

law of conservation of energy p. 20
energy efficiency p. 21

THINK ABOUT

How does energy change form?

Potential energy is stored in the chemicals on the head of a match. The flame of a burning match releases that energy as light and heat. Where does the energy to strike the match come from in the first place?

MIND MAP
Use a mind map to take notes about how energy changes forms.

Energy changes forms.

A match may not appear to have any energy by itself, but it does contain potential energy that can be released. The chemical energy stored in a match can be changed into light and heat. Before the chemical energy in the match changes forms, however, other energy conversions must take place.

Plants convert energy from the Sun into chemical energy, which is stored in the form of sugars in their cells. When a person eats food that comes from plants—or from animals that have eaten plants—the person's cells can release this chemical energy. Some of this chemical energy is converted into the kinetic energy that a person uses to rub the match over a rough surface to strike it. The friction between the match and the striking surface produces heat. The heat provides the energy needed to start the chemical changes that produce the flame. From the Sun to the flame, at least five energy conversions have taken place.

 **CHECK YOUR READING** How is a person's chemical energy changed into another form of energy in the lighting of a match?

RESOURCES FOR DIFFERENTIATED INSTRUCTION

Below Level

UNIT RESOURCE BOOK
- Reading Study Guide A, pp. 24–25
- Decoding Support, p. 47

 **AUDIO CDS**

 Additional INVESTIGATION,
Build a Roller Coaster, A, B, & C, pp. 59–67; Teacher Instructions, pp. 320–321

Advanced

UNIT RESOURCE BOOK
Challenge and Extension, p. 30

English Learners

UNIT RESOURCE BOOK
Spanish Reading Study Guide, pp. 28–29

 **AUDIO CDS**

- Audio Readings in Spanish
- Audio Readings (English)

Conversions Between Potential Energy and Kinetic Energy

The results of some energy conversions are obvious, such as when electrical energy in a light bulb is changed into light and heat. Other energy conversions are not so obvious. The examples below and on page 18 explore, step by step, some ways in which energy conversions occur in the world around you.

Potential energy can be changed into kinetic energy and back into potential energy. Look at the illustrations and photograph of the ski jumper shown below.

① At first, the ski jumper is at the top of the hill. This position gives him potential energy (PE) due to gravity.

② As the ski jumper starts moving downhill, some of his potential energy changes into kinetic energy (KE). Kinetic energy moves him down the slope to the ramp.

③ When the ski jumper takes off from the ramp, some of his kinetic energy is changed back into potential energy as he rises in the air.

When the ski jumper descends to the ground, his potential energy once again changes into kinetic energy. After the ski jumper lands and stops moving, how might he regain the potential energy that he had at the top of the hill? The kinetic energy of a ski lift can move the ski jumper back up the mountain and give him potential energy again.

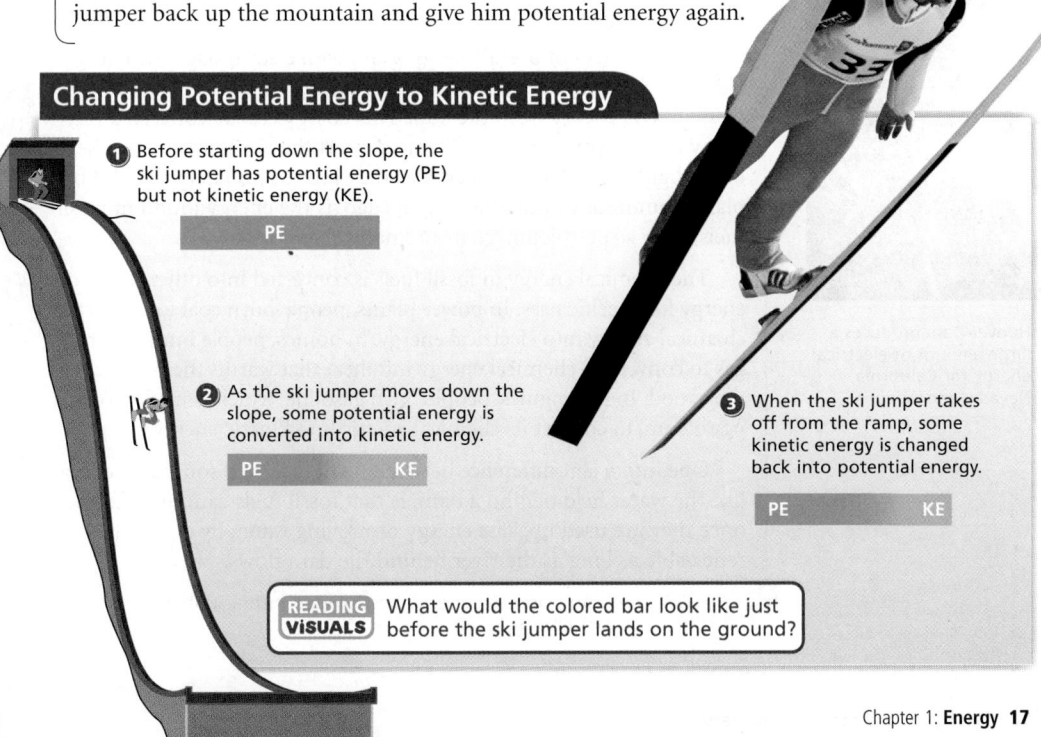

Changing Potential Energy to Kinetic Energy

① Before starting down the slope, the ski jumper has potential energy (PE) but not kinetic energy (KE).

PE

② As the ski jumper moves down the slope, some potential energy is converted into kinetic energy.

PE   KE

③ When the ski jumper takes off from the ramp, some kinetic energy is changed back into potential energy.

PE   KE

READING VISUALS What would the colored bar look like just before the ski jumper lands on the ground?

Chapter 1: **Energy** 17   **B**

Teach from Visuals

To help students interpret the graphic of energy changes in ski jumping, ask:

- Why does the ski jumper have potential energy? *At the top, he has potential energy due to gravity.*

- Why is some potential energy converted to kinetic energy in step 2? *The skier has descended and moves faster as a result. Kinetic energy is the energy of motion.*

- When does the ski jumper have the most potential energy after he takes off from the jump? *at the skier's point of greatest height*

- Why does the ski jumper's potential energy increase for a short time after taking off from the jump? *because his height above the ground increases*

Develop Critical Thinking

INFER Have students infer what energy changes are involved if a different ski jumper slides down the slope. Ask:

- How could another ski jumper have a greater amount of potential energy than the one shown in the illustration? *start from a greater height, have a greater mass*

- How would the energies involved change if the ski jumper was much heavier? *His mass would be larger, and therefore his potential and kinetic energy would also be larger; he would exert a greater force on the ground when he landed.*

- When the ski jumper has landed and stopped moving, does he still possess a form of potential energy? Explain. *yes; chemical potential energy from molecules obtained from food*

Ongoing Assessment

READING VISUALS   *Answer: It would be all yellow.*

DIFFERENTIATE INSTRUCTION

 **More Reading Support**

A What type of energy moves a skier down a hill? *kinetic energy*

Additional Investigation To reinforce Section 1.2 learning goals, use the following full-period investigation:

 **Additional INVESTIGATION,** Build a Roller Coaster, A, B, & C, pp. 59–67, 320–321 (Advanced students should complete Levels B and C.)

English Learners Students may need background knowledge of a ski jumper and ski lifts (p. 17). For the section review (p. 21), tell students what a trampoline is and make sure English learners understand the direction *Suppose*.

Chapter 1 **17** **B**

EXPLORE (the BIG idea)

Revisit "A Penny for Your Energy" on p. 7. Have students describe the energy transfer that took place.

Teach Difficult Concepts

Students may confuse the transfer of energy with transformation of energy. In a transfer of energy, energy moves from one object to another. This occurs in the activity "A Penny for Your Energy," where thermal energy is transferred from warm hands to the cold bottle. Transformation of energy is the conversion of one energy form to another, such as when generators convert the mechanical energy of moving water to electrical energy. Ask students to describe examples of energy transfer and transformation. Make a table listing student responses on the board.

Teacher Demo

To demonstrate the conversion of sound energy to mechanical energy, position a fully inflated balloon in front of a stereo speaker. Students will be able to feel the vibrations from a loud sound by placing their hands lightly on the balloon.

Ongoing Assessment

Explain how energy can be converted from one form to another.

Ask: What energy conversions take place when fireworks explode? *Chemical energy in the firework chemicals is converted into light, heat, and sound energy.*

CHECK YOUR READING *Sample answer: The potential energy of water behind a dam can be changed into electrical energy.*

Using Energy Conversions

READING TIP
As you read about the process for producing electrical energy, follow the steps on page 81.

People have developed ways to convert energy from one form to another for many purposes. Read about the energy conversion process below, and follow that process in the illustrations on page 19 to see how energy in water that is stored behind a dam is changed into electrical energy.

1. The water held behind the dam has potential energy because of its position.
2. Some of the water is allowed to flow through a tunnel within the dam. The potential energy in the stored water changes into kinetic energy when the water moves through the tunnel.
3. The kinetic energy of the moving water turns turbines within the dam. The water's kinetic energy becomes kinetic energy in the turbines. The kinetic energy of the turning turbines is converted into electrical energy by electrical generators.
4. Electrical energy is transported away from the dam through wires. The electrical energy is converted into many different forms of energy and is used in many different ways. For example, at a concert or a play, electrical energy is converted into light and heat by lighting systems and into sound energy by sound systems.

As you can see, several energy conversions occur in order to produce a usable form of energy—potential energy becomes kinetic energy, and kinetic energy becomes electrical energy.

Hoover Dam produces a large amount of electrical energy for California, Nevada, and Arizona.

Other sources of useful energy begin with electromagnetic energy from the Sun. In fact, almost all of the energy on Earth began as electromagnetic energy from the Sun. This energy can be converted into many other forms of energy. Plants convert the electromagnetic energy of sunlight into chemical energy as they grow. This energy, stored by plants hundreds of millions of years ago, is the energy found in fossil fuels, such as petroleum, coal, and natural gas. **B**

The chemical energy in fossil fuels is converted into other forms of energy for specific uses. In power plants, people burn coal to convert its chemical energy into electrical energy. In homes, people burn natural gas to convert its chemical energy into heat that warms them and cooks their food. In car engines, people burn gasoline, which is made from petroleum, to convert its chemical energy into kinetic energy. **C**

One important difference between fossil fuels and sources of energy like the water held behind a dam, is that fossil fuels cannot be replaced once they are used up. The energy of moving water, by contrast, is renewable as long as the river behind the dam flows.

CHECK YOUR READING How can potential energy be changed into a usable form of energy?

DIFFERENTIATE INSTRUCTION

More Reading Support

B How did almost all of Earth's energy begin? *as electromagnetic energy from the Sun*

C What kind of energy do fossil fuels contain? *chemical energy*

Below Level Have students make a flow chart that follows the path of energy from the Sun to plants to fossil fuels to a coal-burning power plant to students' homes. Students should label each stage of energy conversion with the forms of energy.

Converting Energy

Energy is often converted from one form to another in order to meet everyday needs.

① Water held behind the dam has **potential energy.**

② **Potential energy** is converted to **kinetic energy** when the water moves through the tunnel.

③ **Kinetic energy** is used to turn turbines. This **mechanical energy** is converted into **electrical energy** by generators.

④ **Electrical energy** is transmitted through wires, and then converted into many other forms of energy.

Potential Energy to Kinetic Energy

The potential energy of water behind the dam becomes the kinetic energy of moving water.

Kinetic Energy to Electrical Energy

The kinetic energy of turning turbines becomes electrical energy in these generators.

READING VISUALS How many different energy conversions are described in this diagram?

DIFFERENTIATE INSTRUCTION

Advanced Students could extend their knowledge of a hydroelectric dam by thinking about why a dam is needed. Ask: Why can't water simply be removed from a river and made to turn turbines? Ask them to design experiments using water and a pin wheel to observe that there must be a difference in elevation because the energy to turn the turbines comes from falling water.

R Challenge and Extension, p. 30

Teach from Visuals

To help students interpret the diagrams of energy conversions in a hydroelectric power plant, ask:

• Why does the water behind the dam have potential energy? *Because of its position, it has potential energy due to gravity.*

• What is the function of the moving water? *It turns the blades of turbines, which power the generators.*

 The visual "Converting Energy" is available as T6 in the Unit Transparency Book.

Metacognitive Strategy

Ask students to discuss whether or not they find it easier to understand the conversion of energy from one form to another if they study a large diagram. What changes would they make in the diagram on this page to make it more useful?

Real World Example

The Hoover Dam does more than provide electric power to a large portion of the southwestern United States. It also prevents annual spring flooding by the lower Colorado River, provides water for irrigation, and helps form an artificial lake (Lake Mead). During dam construction, the Colorado River was diverted through four concrete tunnels. At one time, Hoover Dam, which was completed in 1935, was the largest hydroelectric plant in the world.

Ongoing Assessment

READING VISUALS *Answer: three; potential to kinetic, kinetic (mechanical) to electrical, electrical to many other forms*

Energy is always conserved.

When you observe energy conversions in your daily life, it may seem that energy constantly disappears. After all, if you give a soccer ball kinetic energy by kicking it along the ground, it will roll for a while but eventually stop. Consider what might have happened to the ball's kinetic energy.

As the ball rolls, it rubs against the ground. Some kinetic energy changes into heat as a result of friction. Some of the ball's energy also changes into sound energy that you can hear as the ball moves. Although the ball loses kinetic energy, the overall amount of energy in the universe does not decrease. The photograph below shows how the soccer ball's kinetic energy decreases.

The soccer ball's kinetic energy decreases as that energy is changed into sound energy and heat.

kinetic energy converted to heat

kinetic energy converted to sound

In the soccer ball example, the ball loses energy, but this energy is transferred to other parts of the universe. Energy is conserved. The **law of conservation of energy** states that energy can neither be created nor destroyed. Conservation of energy is called a law because this rule is true in all known cases. Although in many instances it may appear that energy is gained or lost, it is really only changed in form.

? **D**

READING TIP
Conservation refers to a total that does not change.

CHECK YOUR READING Explain what is meant by the law of conservation of energy.

Conservation of energy is a balance of energy in the universe. When a soccer ball is kicked, a certain amount of energy is transferred by the kick. The ball gains an equal amount of energy, mostly in the form of kinetic energy. However, the ball's kinetic energy decreases as some of that energy is converted into sound energy and heat from the friction between the ball and the ground.

? **E**

According to the law of conservation of energy, the amount of energy that a soccer player gives to the ball by kicking it is equal to the energy the ball gains. The energy the ball loses, in turn, is equal to the amount of energy that is transferred to the universe as sound energy and heat as the ball slows down.

DIFFERENTIATE INSTRUCTION

? **More Reading Support**

D Why is conservation of energy a law? *It is true in all known cases.*

E How does a ball's kinetic energy decrease? *It changes to heat and sound.*

Alternative Assessment Have students think of examples to explain the law of conservation of energy. For example, when food is warmed in a microwave oven, the thermal energy of the food increases through energy conversions. Electrical energy enters the microwave oven, in which it is converted into other forms of energy including electromagnetic energy (microwaves). The microwaves transfer energy to the food, but the total amount of energy is not changed.

Energy conversions may produce unwanted forms of energy.

When energy changes forms, the total amount of energy is conserved. However, the amount of useful energy is almost always less than the total amount of energy. For example, consider the energy used by an electric fan. The amount of electrical energy used is greater than the kinetic energy of the moving fan blades. Because energy is always conserved, some of the electrical energy flowing into the fan's motor is obviously changed into unusable or unwanted forms.

The fan converts a significant portion of the electrical energy into the kinetic energy of the fan blades. At the same time, some electrical energy changes into heat in the fan's motor. If the fan shakes, some of the electrical energy is being turned into unwanted kinetic energy. The more efficiently the fan uses electrical energy, though, the more energy will be transformed into kinetic energy that moves the air.

Energy efficiency is a measurement of usable energy after an energy conversion. You may be familiar with energy-efficient household appliances. These appliances convert a greater percentage of energy into the desired form than inefficient ones. The more energy-efficient a fan is, the more electrical energy it turns into kinetic energy in the moving blades. Less electrical energy is needed to operate appliances that are energy efficient.

Some electrical energy is converted into unwanted sound energy.

Some electrical energy is converted into kinetic energy of the fan blades.

Some electrical energy is converted into unwanted heat.

 **CHECK YOUR READING** What does it mean when an energy conversion is efficient?

1.2 Review

KEY CONCEPTS
1. Describe an energy conversion you have observed in your own life.
2. Explain the law of conservation of energy in your own words.
3. Give an example of an energy conversion that produces unwanted forms of energy.

CRITICAL THINKING
4. **Synthesize** Suppose you are jumping on a trampoline. Describe the conversions that occur between kinetic energy and potential energy.
5. **Infer** Look at the ski jumper on page 17. Has all of his potential energy likely been changed into kinetic energy at the moment he lands? Explain.

CHALLENGE
6. **Communicate** Draw and label a diagram that shows at least three different energy conversions that might occur when a light bulb is turned on.

ANSWERS

1. Sample answer: a flashlight, chemical energy becomes electrical energy, which becomes visible light.

2. Energy can change forms, but the overall amount of energy is constant.

3. Sample answer: Incandescent bulbs release heat in addition to light.

4. Potential energy is greatest at the highest point. Potential energy converts into kinetic energy until hitting the trampoline. Kinetic energy converts to potential energy in the trampoline to the lowest point, and is converted to kinetic energy back into the air.

5. No; some energy changed into heat and sound.

6. chemical energy to mechanical energy when turning a switch; mechanical energy to electrical energy; electrical energy to light and heat in the bulb

---

Ongoing Assessment
Understand that energy conversions may be inefficient.

Ask: Which energy conversion is more efficient—a soccer ball kicked along a smooth sidewalk or a soccer ball kicked in a field of tall weeds? Why? *the sidewalk, because less energy will be changed into heat by friction*

CHECK YOUR READING Answer: *Most of the energy that enters an energy conversion changes into the desired form of energy.*

Reinforce (the **BIG** idea)
Have students relate the section to the Big Idea.

R Reinforcing Key Concepts, p. 31

1.2 ASSESS & RETEACH

Assess
A Section 1.2 Quiz, p. 4

Reteach
Remind students about the law of conservation of energy and the concept of conversions between potential and kinetic energy. A roller coaster is a good example of these concepts. Draw a simple roller coaster on the board. Make sure each hill is lower than the previous hill. Ask students to identify points of substantial potential energy (at the top of hills) and kinetic energy (at the bottom of hills). Ask: Why must each hill be lower than the previous hill? *Kinetic energy decreases due to friction. If two adjacent hills were the same height, the coaster would not be able to make it to the top of the second hill because it would not have enough kinetic energy.*

Technology Resources
Have students visit **ClassZone.com** for reteaching of Key Concepts.

 CONTENT REVIEW

 CONTENT REVIEW CD-ROM

CHAPTER INVESTIGATION

Focus

PURPOSE To investigate the amount of energy stored in different types of food

OVERVIEW Students will construct an apparatus to trap the energy released from different food samples when they burn. Students will collect data and calculate the amount of energy each food contained. They will find the following:

- The water in the can traps the energy that is released by the burning food.
- The temperature increase in the water is greater when burning foods high in fats than when burning foods high in carbohydrates.
- Fats contain more energy than carbohydrates.

Lab Preparation

- Students can bring many of the materials, such as aluminum cans, from home.
- Punch holes in the cans before class to save time.
- Prior to the investigation, have students read through the investigation and prepare their data tables. You may wish to copy and distribute datasheets and rubrics.

 UNIT RESOURCE BOOK, pp. 50–58

 SCIENCE TOOLKIT, F14

Lab Management

- Warn students not to eat the food samples.

SAFETY Advise students with long hair to tie it back. Students wearing long, loose sleeves should roll them up. Desks should be cleared of all non-essential and flammable materials.

Teaching with Technology

Have students use a temperature probe to record temperature changes.

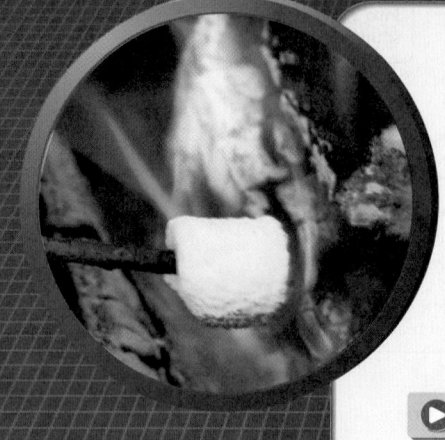

Energy Conversions

OVERVIEW AND PURPOSE All foods contain stored chemical energy, but some foods contain more chemical energy than others. People need this chemical energy for all of their activities. The amount of chemical energy stored in foods like marshmallows can be measured by burning the foods. In this investigation, you will

- construct an apparatus to investigate the amount of energy in samples of food
- calculate the amount of energy released when the foods are burned

 Problem ▸ *Write It Up*

How much energy is stored in different types of food?

 Hypothesize ▸ *Write It Up*

Write a hypothesis to explain which type of food contains a greater amount of chemical energy. Your hypothesis should take the form of an "If . . . , then . . . , because . . ." statement.

▸ **Procedure**

 MATERIALS
- can opener
- empty aluminum can
- dowel rod
- water
- graduated cylinder
- ring stand with ring
- thermometer
- aluminum pie plate
- aluminum foil
- tape
- large paper clip
- cork
- modeling clay
- crouton
- caramel rice cake
- balance
- wooden matches

1. Create a data table similar to the one shown on the sample notebook page.

2. Using the can opener, punch two holes directly opposite each other near the top of the can. Slide the dowel rod through the holes as shown in the photograph to the left.

3. Measure 50 mL of water with a graduated cylinder, and pour the water into the can. Record the mass of the water. (**Hint:** 1 mL of water = 1 gram)

4. Rest the ends of the dowel rod on the ring in the ring stand to hold the can in the air. Carefully place the thermometer in the can. Measure and record the initial temperature ($T1$) of the water in the can.

5. Make a collar of aluminum foil and tape it around the can as shown. Leave enough room to insert the burner platform and food sample.

INVESTIGATION RESOURCES

 CHAPTER INVESTIGATION, Energy Conversions
- Level A, pp. 50–53
- Level B, pp. 54–57
- Level C, p. 58

Advanced students should complete Levels B & C.

 Writing a Lab Report, D12–13

Technology Resources

Customize this student lab as needed or look for an alternative. Print rubrics to assess student lab reports.

▸ **Lab Generator CD-ROM**

6. Construct the burner platform as follows: Open up the paper clip. Push the straightened end into a cork, and push the bottom of the cork into the clay. Push the burner onto the pie plate so it will not move. Put the pie plate under the ring.

step 6

7. Find and record the mass of the crouton. Place the crouton on the flattened end of the burner platform. Adjust the height of the ring so the bottom of the can is about 4 cm above the crouton.

8. Use a match to ignite the crouton. Allow the crouton to burn completely. Measure and record the final temperature (T2) of the water.

9. Empty the water from the can and repeat steps 3–8 with a caramel rice cake. The mass of the rice cake should equal the mass of the crouton.

▶ Observe and Analyze Write It Up

1. **RECORD OBSERVATIONS** Make sure to record all measurements in the data table.

2. **CALCULATE** Find the energy released from the food samples by following the next two steps.

   Calculate and record the change in temperature.
   change in temperature = T2 – T1

   Calculate and record the energy released in calories. One calorie is the energy needed to raise the temperature of 1 g of water by 1°C.
   energy released = (mass of water · change in temperature · 1 cal/g°C)

3. **GRAPH** Make a bar graph showing the number of calories in each food sample. Which type of food contains a greater amount of chemical energy?

▶ Conclude Write It Up

1. **INTERPRET** Answer the question posed in the problem.

2. **INFER** Did your results support your hypothesis? Explain.

3. **EVALUATE** What happens to any energy released by the burning food that is not captured by the water? How could you change the setup for a more accurate measurement?

4. **APPLY** Find out how much fat and carbohydrate the different foods contain. Explain the relationship between this information and the number of calories in the foods.

▶ INVESTIGATE Further

CHALLENGE The Calories listed in foods are equal to 1000 calories (1 kilocalorie). Calculate the amount of energy in your food samples in terms of Calories per gram of food (Calories/g). Using a balance, find the mass of any ash that remains after burning the food. Subtract that mass from the original mass of the sample to calculate mass burned. Divide total calories by mass burned, then divide that value by 1000 to find Calories/g. Compare your results to those given on the product labels.

Energy Conversions
Problem How much energy is stored in different types of food?

Hypothesize

Observe and Analyze
Table 1. Energy in Food

	Sample 1	Sample 2
Mass of water (g)		
Initial water temp. (T1) (°C)		
Final water temp. (T2) (°C)		
Mass of food (g)		
Change in temp. (T2 – T1) (°C)		
Energy released (mass · change in temp. · cal/g°C)		

Conclude

▶ Observe and Analyze Write It Up

1. Sample data: Rice snack (Sample 1): mass of water 50 g; T1 20°C; T2 24°C; Crouton (Sample 2): mass of water 50 g; T1 20°C; T2 32°C. Mass of food will depend on the size of the sample.

2. For the sample data, the rice snack produced 200 calories and the crouton 600 calories.

3. See students' graphs; croutons

▶ Conclude Write It Up

1. The amount of energy stored in food depends on the nutrients in it. Fats store more energy than carbohydrates.

2. Answers will vary depending on the initial hypothesis.

3. It went into the air. A container that is completely closed and insulated to prevent the loss of heat would improve accuracy.

4. Fats contain more calories than carbohydrates, so the food that contains more fat should release more energy when it is burned.

▶ INVESTIGATE Further

CHALLENGE Students will need to keep the ashes from their food samples to find how much the mass changed. Students' results will probably vary from the values given on product labels because the equipment used is crude, contributing to a high percent of error.

Post-Lab Discussion

• Ask: Why was it important that the same amount of water be used in each trial? *A greater mass of water would heat up more slowly with a given amount of energy.*

• Ask: What energy conversions occurred in this lab? Where was energy transferred to? *Chemical energy from the food molecules changed to thermal energy (heat), electromagnetic energy (light), and sound energy when the food was burned. Some of the thermal energy was captured by the water. Additional thermal energy was lost to the air and to the equipment.*

1.3 FOCUS

▶ Set Learning Goals

Students will

- Summarize how technology can improve energy conversions.
- Evaluate advantages and disadvantages of different types of energy conversions.
- Recognize how technology can improve the use of natural resources.
- Experiment to observe how the collection of solar energy is affected by the color of a solar collector.

◀ 3-Minute Warm-Up

Display Transparency 5 or copy this exercise on the board:

Match each definition with the correct term.

Definitions

1. energy you have when you are running *b*
2. energy you have while standing still on a diving board *d*
3. measure of useable energy after an energy conversion *e*

Terms

a. conservation of energy
b. kinetic energy
c. sound energy
d. potential energy
e. energy efficiency

T 3-Minute Warm-Up, p. T5

1.3 MOTIVATE

EXPLORE Solar Cells

PURPOSE To explore the size of a solar cell needed to provide electrical energy for a solar calculator

TIP *10 min.* The calculator must not have a battery backup.

WHAT DO YOU THINK? *Answers will depend on the calculator and light conditions. A large solar cell would keep the calculator working under relatively poor lighting conditions.*

KEY CONCEPT

1.3 Technology improves the ways people use energy.

◀ BEFORE, you learned	▶ NOW, you will learn
• Energy can change forms • When energy changes forms, the overall amount of energy remains the same • Energy conversions usually produce unwanted forms of energy	• How technology can improve energy conversions • About advantages and disadvantages of different types of energy conversions • How technology can improve the use of natural resources

VOCABULARY

solar cell p. 26

EXPLORE Solar Cells

Why does a solar calculator need a large solar cell?

PROCEDURE

1. Measure the area of the calculator's solar cell. (**Hint:** area = length • width)
2. Turn the calculator on. Make sure that there is enough light for the calculator to work.
3. Gradually cover the solar cell with the index card. Observe the calculator's display as you cover more of the cell.
4. Measure the uncovered area of the solar cell when the calculator no longer works.

MATERIALS

- solar calculator without backup battery
- ruler
- index card

WHAT DO YOU THINK?

- How much of the solar cell is needed to keep the calculator working?
- Why might a solar calculator have a solar cell that is larger than necessary?

MIND MAP
Use a mind map to take notes about technology that improves energy conversions.

Technology improves energy conversions.

In many common energy conversions, most of the wasted energy is released as heat. One example is the common incandescent light bulb. Amazingly, only about 5 percent of the electrical energy that enters an incandescent light bulb is converted into light. That means that 95 percent of the electrical energy turns into unwanted forms of energy. Most is released as heat and ends up in the form of thermal energy in the surrounding air. To decrease this amount of wasted energy, scientists have investigated several more efficient types of lights.

RESOURCES FOR DIFFERENTIATED INSTRUCTION

Below Level

UNIT RESOURCE BOOK
- Reading Study Guide A, pp. 34–35
- Decoding Support, p. 47

 **AUDIO CDS**

Advanced

UNIT RESOURCE BOOK
- Challenge and Extension, p. 40
- Challenge Reading, pp. 43–44

English Learners

UNIT RESOURCE BOOK
Spanish Reading Study Guide, pp. 38–39

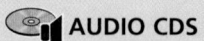 **AUDIO CDS**

- Audio Readings in Spanish
- Audio Readings (English)

Efficient Lights

Research to replace light bulbs with a more energy-efficient source of light has resulted in the light-emitting diode, or LED. LEDs have the advantage of converting almost all of the electrical energy they use into light.

The first LEDs were not nearly as bright as typical light bulbs, but over time scientists and engineers have been able to produce brighter LEDs. LEDs have many uses, including television remote controls, computer displays, outdoor signs, giant video boards in stadiums, and traffic signals. LEDs are also used to transmit information through fiber optic cables that connect home audio and visual systems.

CHECK YOUR READING How are LEDs more efficient than incandescent lights?

LEDs that produce infrared light are used in remote controls.

Efficient Cars

Another common but inefficient energy conversion is the burning of gasoline in cars. A large percentage of gasoline's chemical energy is not converted into the car's kinetic energy. Some of the kinetic energy is then wasted as heat from the car's engine, tires, and brakes. Here, too, efficiency can be improved through advances in technology.

Fuel injectors, common in cars since the 1980s, have improved the efficiency of engines. These devices carefully monitor and control the amount of gasoline that is fed into a car's engine. This precise control of fuel provides a significant increase in the distance a car can travel on a tank of gasoline. More recently, hybrid cars have been developed. These cars use both gasoline and electrical energy from batteries. These cars are very fuel efficient. Even better, some of the kinetic energy lost during braking in hybrid cars is used to generate electrical energy to recharge the car's batteries.

Hybrid cars may look very similar to typical gasoline-powered cars, but their engines are different.

Teach Difficult Concepts

Students may think that some energy conversions are 100% efficient. Have students hammer a nail into a board. They should immediately feel the nail head, which should be warm. Ask students to write a short description of the energy conversions that took place and an explanation of why the nail head became warm. *Chemical energy in muscles converted to mechanical energy. Some mechanical energy was converted into heat due to friction.*

History of Science

The first visible LED, a red light, was developed in the late 1960s. LEDs that produce yellow, orange, green, blue, and white light were later developed. LED technology is known as electroluminescence and uses semiconductors such as gallium arsenide. Different semiconductors have different properties, so they can be used to produce LEDs with different characteristics.

Ongoing Assessment

Summarize how technology can improve energy conversions.

Ask: What is one aspect of an energy conversion that technology tries to improve? *efficiency*

CHECK YOUR READING *Answer: They convert almost all of the electrical energy that enters them into light.*

DIFFERENTIATE INSTRUCTION

 More Reading Support

A Why replace light bulbs with LEDs? *LEDs are more efficient*

B How is a large amount of gasoline's energy wasted? *as heat*

English Learners The English language uses many words and phrases in ways that make little sense when taken literally. Examples from this section include "ends up" (p. 24) and "over time" (p. 28 in the Check Your Reading question). Help students by pointing out such phrases and tell them not to read such prepositions literally. Encourage them to use the context of the sentence to decipher the phrases' meanings.

Real World Example

In July 2003, teams of university students from the United States and Canada raced the solar-powered cars they had spent months designing and building. The race, called the American Solar Challenge, is sponsored by the U.S. Department of Energy. The route follows Route 66 across the Great Plains, the Rocky Mountains, and the southwestern desert, from Chicago to southern California. In the 2003 race, speeds of 75 miles per hour were recorded.

Teacher Demo

Connect a set of solar cells to a small electric motor that drives a propeller. Have students predict what will happen when the apparatus is placed under a light source. This will work outdoors on a bright, sunny day or in the classroom with a bright lamp. Ask: where does the energy come from and where does it go? *Electromagnetic energy is converted into mechanical energy in the propeller.*

Teach from Visuals

To help students interpret the visual of the solar car, ask:

- Where would the solar cells have to be on the car? *on the top exterior*

- Why might such a large area of the car be covered with solar cells? *to capture as much light as possible because solar cells are inefficient*

- What would happen to the car on a rainy day? *The car would not run unless it had a backup energy supply.*

Develop Critical Thinking

COMPARE Have students compare the conversion of solar energy in a solar car and in the leaves of a plant. *In a solar car, solar energy is converted to electrical energy. In a plant, solar energy is converted to chemical energy during photosynthesis.*

Ongoing Assessment

 *unlimited supplies, no harmful waste products*

Technology improves the use of energy resources.

Much of the energy used on Earth comes from fossil fuels such as coal, petroleum, and natural gas. However, the supply of fossil fuels is limited. So, scientists and engineers are exploring the use of several alternative energy sources. Today, for example, both solar energy and wind energy are used on a small scale to generate electrical energy.

Solar energy and wind energy have several advantages compared to fossil fuels. Their supply is not limited, and they do not produce the same harmful waste products that fossil fuels do. However, there are also many obstacles that must be overcome before solar energy and wind energy, among other alternative energy sources, are as widely used as fossil fuels.

 **CHECK YOUR READING** What are the advantages of solar energy and wind energy as compared to fossil fuels?

Solar Energy

 **VISUALIZATION** CLASSZONE.COM
Observe how solar cells produce electricity.

C

Solar cells are important in today's solar energy technology. Modern **solar cells** are made of several layers of light-sensitive materials, which convert sunlight directly into electrical energy. Solar cells provide the electrical energy for such things as satellites in orbit around Earth, hand-held calculators, and, as shown below, experimental cars.

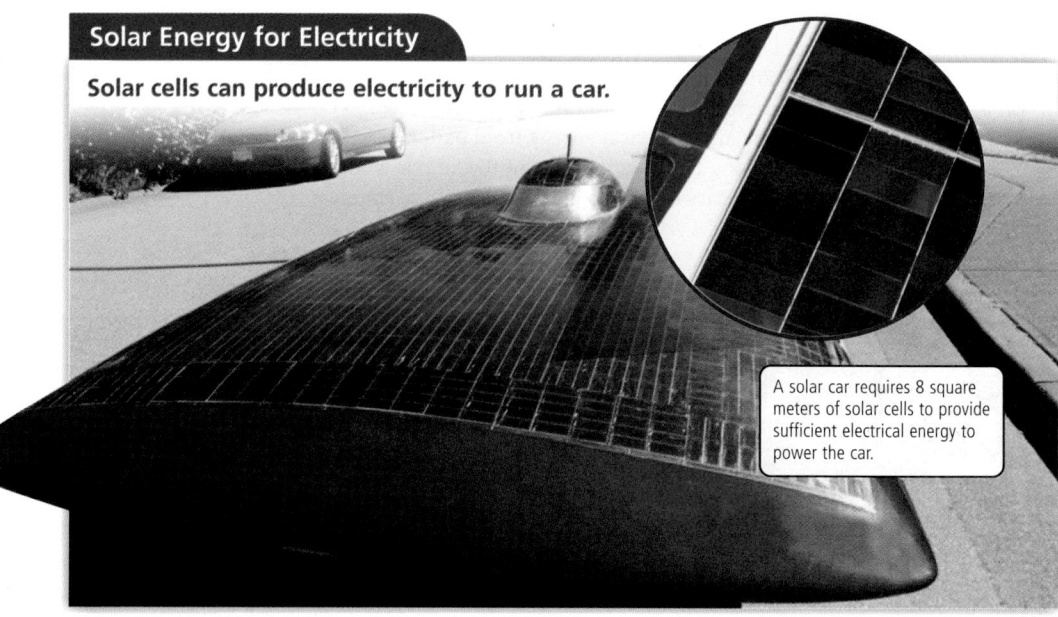

Solar Energy for Electricity

Solar cells can produce electricity to run a car.

A solar car requires 8 square meters of solar cells to provide sufficient electrical energy to power the car.

B 26 Unit: Energy and the Changing Earth

DIFFERENTIATE INSTRUCTION

 **More Reading Support**

C What energy conversion occurs in solar cells? *Sunlight is converted to electrical energy.*

Below Level Have students compare solar and wind energy to fossil fuel energy. Students should make a table that lists each type of energy source and some of the characteristics of each type. Have students mark an "X" in the box on the table to indicate that the energy has that characteristic. Discuss with students how the energy sources are alike and how they are different.

Solar cells produce electrical energy quietly and cleanly. However, they are not yet commonly used because the materials used to make them are very expensive. What's more, solar cells are not very efficient in producing electrical energy. Large numbers of solar cells produce only a relatively small amount of electrical energy. Typical solar cells convert only about 12 to 15 percent of the sunlight that reaches them into electrical energy. However, solar cells currently being developed could have efficiencies close to 40 percent.

In addition to converting the Sun's light directly into electrical energy, people have used the Sun's radiation for heating. In ancient Rome, glass was used to trap solar energy indoors so that plants could be grown in the winter. Today radiation from the Sun is still used to grow plants in greenhouses and to warm buildings. The photograph above shows a house that uses solar energy in both ways. The solar cells on the roof provide electrical energy, and the large windows help to trap the warmth. In fact, some solar power systems also use that warmth to produce additional electrical energy.

Solar energy can be used in homes to provide heat and electrical energy.

CHECK YOUR READING How can energy from the Sun be used by people?

INVESTIGATE Solar Energy

What improves the collection of solar energy?

PROCEDURE

1. Cover the top of one cup with white plastic, and cover the top of the other cup with black plastic. Secure the plastic with a rubber band.

2. Use the scissors to make a small hole in the center of each cup's plastic lid. Insert a thermometer through each opening.

3. Place the cups in direct sunlight, and record their temperatures every minute for 10 minutes.

WHAT DO YOU THINK?

- Which cup showed a greater temperature change? Why do you think this happened?

- Make a line graph of your results to show the change in temperature in each cup.

CHALLENGE
Try the experiment again, using aluminum foil instead of white plastic. How do the results differ with the aluminum foil? Why might this be the case?

SKILL FOCUS
Observing

MATERIALS
- 2 plastic cups
- white plastic
- black plastic
- 2 rubber bands
- scissors
- 2 thermometers
- stopwatch
for Challenge:
- aluminum foil

TIME
20 minutes

DIFFERENTIATE INSTRUCTION

? More Reading Support

D Why is solar power not commonly used? *It is inefficient and expensive.*

E How can the Sun's heat be used? *It can be trapped to provide heat.*

Alternative Assessment Have small groups orally present their data and graphs for peer review. Then lead a discussion to reach a consensus for each question.

Advanced Have interested students conduct research and make a poster presenting limitations and real sites or locations of one of the alternative energy sources discussed on pp. 26–28.

R • Challenge and Extension, p. 40
• Challenge Reading, pp. 43–44

PURPOSE To observe how the collection of solar energy is affected by the color of the collector

TIPS *20 min.*

- The plastics should be the same thickness; garbage bags can be used.
- Be careful not to rip the plastic and aluminum; a faulty seal may lead to inaccurate data.

WHAT DO YOU THINK? *The cup with black plastic; the black plastic absorbs more sunlight. Check students' graphs.*

CHALLENGE *Aluminum foil will reflect sunlight but absorb more energy than the white plastic; a cup covered with aluminum foil should show a temperature increase between black plastic and white plastic.*

R Datasheet, Solar Energy, p. 41

Technology Resources

Customize this student lab as needed or look for an alternative. Print rubrics to assess student lab reports.

Lab Generator CD-ROM

Teaching with Technology

If probeware is available, students can use a temperature probe in place of a thermometer. Graphing calculators can be used to graph students' data.

EXPLORE (the BIG idea)

Revisit "Hot Dog!" on p. 7. Have students explain why the hot dog cooked.

Ongoing Assessment

Evaluate advantages and disadvantages in energy conversions.

Ask: What is an advantage to heating a home with solar power? What is a disadvantage? *advantage: nonpolluting; disadvantage: materials are expensive*

CHECK YOUR READING *Sample answer: to produce electrical energy; to warm buildings*

Ongoing Assessment

Recognize how technology can improve the use of natural resources.

Ask: How can technology help conserve natural resources? *by making energy conversion more efficient*

 Answer: Wind has been used to propel ships, pump water, and grind grains. Now it is also used to produce electricity at windfarms.

PHOTO CAPTION Answer: to capture as much energy from the wind as possible

Integrate the Sciences

A new branch of meteorology involves offshore wind power. Wind and wave characteristics are studied at sea for the purpose of developing offshore wind farms for electric power. Denmark is a global leader in this field because of strong political support and the mandatory purchase of wind power output by utilities.

Reinforce (the **BIG** idea)

Have students relate the section to the Big Idea.

 Reinforcing Key Concepts, p. 42

1.3 ASSESS & RETEACH

Assess

A Section 1.3 Quiz, p. 5

Reteach

Have students brainstorm the best locations (in terms of weather conditions) for using solar and wind energy. Use a weather map for reference. Then ask students to list the limitations of these alternative energy sources and brainstorm how technology might help.

Technology Resources

Have students visit **ClassZone.com** for reteaching of Key Concepts.

 CONTENT REVIEW

 CONTENT REVIEW CD-ROM

INFER Why might so many windmills be needed at a windfarm?

Wind Energy

For many centuries, people have used the kinetic energy of wind to sail ships, and, by using windmills, to grind grain and pump water. More recently, windmills have been used to generate electrical energy. In the early 1900s, for example, windmills were already being used to produce electrical energy in rural areas of the United States.

Like the technological advances in the use of solar energy, advances in capturing and using wind energy have helped to improve its efficiency and usefulness. One way to better capture the wind's energy has been to build huge windmill farms in areas that receive a consistent amount of wind. Windmill farms are found in several states, including Kansas, California, and New York. Other methods of more efficiently capturing wind energy include the use of specially shaped windmill blades that are made of new, more flexible materials.

 **RESOURCE CENTER** CLASSZONE.COM

Find out more about alternative energy sources.

 How has the use of wind energy changed over time?

1.3 Review

KEY CONCEPTS

1. Provide an example of a common technology that does not efficiently convert energy. Explain.

2. Describe two ways in which hybrid cars are more energy-efficient than gasoline-powered cars.

3. List two advantages and two disadvantages of solar power.

CRITICAL THINKING

4. **Compare and Contrast** How are LEDs similar to incandescent light bulbs? How are they different?

5. **Synthesize** What are two ways in which the Sun's energy can be captured and used? How can both be used in a home?

○CHALLENGE

6. **Draw Conclusions** Satellites orbiting Earth use solar cells as their source of electrical energy. Why are solar cells ideal energy sources for satellites?

ANSWERS

1. Sample answer: incandescent lights—heat instead of light

2. They use less fuel and convert heat from brakes into electrical energy.

3. advantages: clean, unlimited supplies; disadvantages:

inefficient, expensive materials

4. Both produce light. LEDs are more efficient and have several applications. Incandescent lights are brighter than most LEDs.

5. solar cells for electricity; trapping heat to warm the building

6. They receive more constant sunlight.

Indoor ice rinks require cooling
systems that can keep ice
frozen even when the outdoor
temperature is 95°F.

SKILL: USING FORMULAS

Cool Efficiency

Energy efficiency is important because energy supplies are limited. The energy used by appliances such as air conditioners is measured in British thermal units, or BTUs. One BTU warms one pound of water by 1°F. The cooling ability of an air conditioner is measured by the number of BTUs it can move. Consider the number of BTUs that an air conditioning system must move in an ice rink.

An air conditioner typically has an energy efficiency ratio (EER) rating. The EER measures how efficiently a cooling system operates when the outdoor temperature is 95°F. The EER is the ratio of cooling per hour to the amount of electricity used, which is measured in watts. The higher the EER, the more energy efficient the air conditioner is.

$$EER = \frac{BTUs/hr}{watts\ used}$$

Example

Suppose an air conditioner uses 750 watts of electricity to cool 6000 BTUs per hour at 95°F. Calculate the air conditioner's EER.

(1) Use the formula above to calculate the EER.

$$EER = \frac{BTUs/hr}{watts\ used}$$

(2) Enter the known values into the formula.

$$EER = \frac{6000\ BTUs/hr}{750\ watts\ used}$$

(3) Solve the formula for the unknown value.

$$EER = \frac{6000\ BTUs/hr}{750\ watts\ used} = 8$$

ANSWER EER = 8 BTUs/hr per watt used

Answer the following questions.

1. What is the EER of a cooling system that uses 500 watts of electricity to move 6000 BTUs per hour at 95°F?

2. What is the EER of a cooling system that uses 1500 watts of electricity to move 12,000 BTUs per hour at 95°F?

3. Which air conditioner in the two questions above is more efficient?

CHALLENGE How many BTUs per hour would an air conditioner move at 95°F if it had an EER of 10 and used 1200 watts of electricity?

MATH IN SCIENCE
Math Skills Practice for Science

Set Learning Goal

To use a mathematical formula to calculate the energy efficiency of cooling systems

Present the Science

A cooling system with a high EER rating is more efficient in that it uses less electricity to deliver a given amount of cooling power. Similarly, heating systems with high EER ratings more efficiently use energy to produce a given amount of warming power. An EER of 14 is close to the upper limit of current technology. Efficient window air conditioners have EER ratings of about 10. Central air conditioning systems have EER ratings of around 12.

Develop Algebra Skills

- Remind students that the numerator of a fraction is above the line and the denominator is below.

- To help students use the formula for calculating EER, remind them that the line in the formula means "divided by." Thus, the numerator, BTUs, per hour, should be divided by the denominator, watts.

- The units of an EER rating are BTUs per hour per watt. The rating measures output of the air conditioner divided by input.

Close

Ask: What other types of appliances could have an EER rating? *refrigerators, freezers, furnaces, hot water heaters*

- Math Support, p. 48
- Math Practice, p. 49

Technology Resources

Students can visit **ClassZone.com** for practice with rates.

 MATH TUTORIAL

ANSWERS

1. 6000 BTUs/500 watts = 12 BTUs cooled/hr per watt used

2. 12,000 BTUs/1500 watts = 8 BTUs cooled/hr per watt used

3. the one in item 1

CHALLENGE EER = 10 = × BTUs/1200 watts
× = 10 (1200) = 12,000

BACK TO

the BIG idea

Make two sets of index cards with each card naming a form of energy. One set should be labeled "Original energy form" and the other "Converted to." Call on students to choose one card from each set and give an example of that energy conversion.

◖ KEY CONCEPTS SUMMARY

SECTION 1.1
Ask: What do all forms of energy have in common? *They all have the ability to produce a change.*

Ask: How does changing a skater's mass and speed affect his or her kinetic energy? *Increasing mass or speed increases kinetic energy. Decreasing either decreases kinetic energy.*

SECTION 1.2
Ask: When will kinetic energy decrease and potential energy increase? *after taking off from the jump as the skier is rising in the air*

Ask: Is kinetic energy destroyed when that occurs? *No, energy is never created nor destroyed*

SECTION 1.3
Ask: Why is it important to use technology to better use natural resources? *Many sources of energy are limited in supply, and those that aren't limited are used inefficiently.*

Review Concepts

- Big Idea Flow Chart, p. T1
- Chapter Outline, pp. T7–T8

---

1 Chapter Review

the BIG idea

Energy has different forms, but it is always conserved.

CONTENT REVIEW
CLASSZONE.COM

◖ KEY CONCEPTS SUMMARY

 Energy exists in different forms.
- Energy is the ability to cause a change.
- Different forms of energy produce changes in different ways.
- Kinetic energy depends on mass and speed.

Potential energy depends on position and chemical composition.

VOCABULARY
energy p. 10
kinetic energy p. 12
potential energy p. 13

 Energy can change forms but is never lost.
- Energy often needs to be transformed in order to produce a useful form of energy.
- The law of conservation of energy states that energy is never created or destroyed.

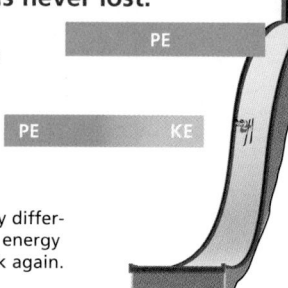

Energy can be transformed in many different ways, including from potential energy (PE) to kinetic energy (KE) and back again.

VOCABULARY
law of conservation of
  energy p. 20
energy efficiency p. 21

 Technology improves the ways people use energy.
- Different forms of technology are being developed and used to improve the efficiency of energy conversions.
- Solar cells convert sunlight into electrical energy.

VOCABULARY
solar cell p. 26

New solar cells convert light into electrical energy more efficiently than those in the past.

Technology Resources

Have students visit **ClassZone.com** or use the CD-ROM for a cumulative review of concepts.

Engage students in a whole-class interactive review of Key Concepts. Edit content as you wish.

 CONTENT REVIEW

 CONTENT REVIEW CD-ROM

 POWER PRESENTATIONS

Reviewing Vocabulary

Review vocabulary terms by making a four square diagram for each term as shown in the example below. Include a definition, characteristics, examples from real life, and, if possible, nonexamples of the term.

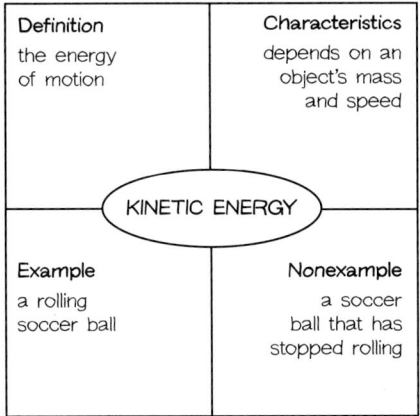

Definition	Characteristics
the energy of motion	depends on an object's mass and speed

KINETIC ENERGY

Example	Nonexample
a rolling soccer ball	a soccer ball that has stopped rolling

1. energy

2. potential energy

3. conservation of energy

4. energy efficiency

Reviewing Key Concepts

Multiple Choice *Choose the letter of the best answer.*

5. All forms of energy are a combination of
   a. mechanical energy and chemical energy
   b. chemical energy and kinetic energy
   c. potential energy and thermal energy
   d. potential energy and kinetic energy

6. Which type of energy is transmitted by vibrations of air?
   a. electromagnetic
   c. nuclear
   b. sound
   d. chemical

7. When energy is converted from one form to another, what is usually produced?
   a. chemical energy
   c. heat
   b. gravity
   d. nuclear energy

8. An object's kinetic energy is determined by its
   a. position and composition
   b. speed and position
   c. mass and speed
   d. height and width

9. Which of the following is a conversion from chemical energy to mechanical energy?
   a. a dark light bulb starting to glow
   b. food being heated in an oven
   c. a ball rolling down a hill
   d. a person lifting a weight

10. An energy-efficient electric fan converts a large portion of the electrical energy that enters it into
    a. an unwanted form of energy
    b. kinetic energy of the fan blades
    c. thermal energy in the fan's motor
    d. sound energy in the fan's motor

11. The energy in wind used to generate electricity is
    a. chemical energy
    b. sound energy
    c. potential energy
    d. kinetic energy

12. A skier on a hill has potential energy due to
    a. speed
    c. compression
    b. energy efficiency
    d. position

Short Answer *Write a short answer to each question.*

13. Explain how the law of conservation of energy might apply to an energy conversion that you observe in your daily life.

14. Describe a situation in which chemical energy is converted into mechanical energy. Explain each step of the energy conversion process.

Reviewing Vocabulary

1. Sample answer—Definition: the ability to cause a change; Characteristics: is conserved; Examples: sound, chemical, mechanical; Nonexample: matter

2. Sample answer—Definition: stored energy; Characteristics: depends on position or chemical composition; Example: skier at top of ramp; Nonexample: skier at bottom of hill due to position

3. Sample answer—Definition: energy cannot be created or destroyed; Characteristics: energy may seem to disappear when it changes form, but it is transferred or changed; Example: air gains thermal energy (heat) transferred during a conversion

4. Sample answer—Definition: useful energy after an energy conversion; Characteristics: high efficiency—less energy is needed to run the appliance; Example: Inefficient light bulbs convert electrical energy to light and a large amount of heat.

Reviewing Key Concepts

5. d

6. b

7. c

8. c

9. d

10. b

11. d

12. d

13. Answers should suggest that the amount of energy entering a process may appear to decrease during an energy conversion but actually changes into a different energy form.

14. Answers could involve a process that uses chemical energy in a person's muscles to move or lift an object.

ASSESSMENT RESOURCES

 UNIT ASSESSMENT BOOK
- Chapter Test A, pp. 6–9
- Chapter Test B, pp. 10–13
- Chapter Test C, pp. 14–17
- Alternative Assessment, pp. 18–19

 SPANISH ASSESSMENT BOOK
Spanish Chapter Test, pp. 221–224

Technology Resources

Edit test items and answer choices.

 Test Generator CD-ROM

Visit **ClassZone.com** to extend test practice.

 Test Practice

Thinking Critically

15. *potential energy: 5 (or 1) because height is greatest; kinetic energy: 4 (or 2), because speed is greatest*

16. *2; the skater's height above the ground begins to increase.*

17. *No, because the conversions between potential and kinetic energy are not 100% efficient, so some energy is being converted into unwanted forms.*

18. *Energy will be converted into heat and sound due to the friction of the skates against the ramp.*

19. *5—all potential; 4—mostly kinetic, some potential; 3—all kinetic; 2—mostly kinetic, some potential; 1—all potential*

20. *Both convert sunlight into another energy form. Plants turn light into chemical energy; solar cells convert light into electrical energy.*

21. *Both are relatively inefficient and require a steady input of light or wind. New materials are being developed, and large groups of solar cells or windmills are used to capture as much energy as possible.*

22. *the machine that does not get hot, because less energy is being transformed through unwanted heat and more is being turned into the desired form of energy*

23. *40; Energy must be conserved.*

24. *Answers might include striking a match; check students' diagrams.*

the BIG idea

25. *Answers will vary; check students' answers.*

26. *Answers will vary; check students' answers.*

Thinking Critically

The illustrations below show an in-line skater on a ramp. Use the illustrations to answer the next five questions.

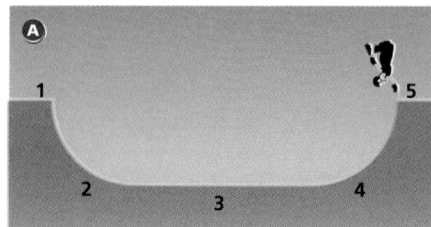

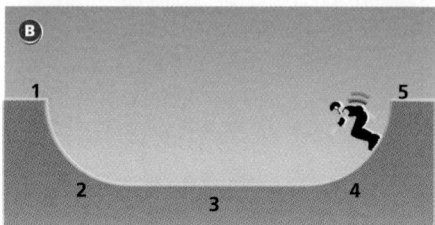

15. **OBSERVE** At what point in the illustrations would the skater have the most potential energy? the most kinetic energy? Explain.

16. **SYNTHESIZE** At what point in illustration B will the skater's kinetic energy begin to be changed back into potential energy? Explain.

17. **INFER** When the skater's kinetic energy is changed back into potential energy, will this amount of potential energy likely be equal to the skater's potential energy in illustration A? Why or why not?

18. **PREDICT** Describe how energy may appear to decrease in the example shown above. What energy conversions that produce unwanted forms of energy are occurring? Explain.

19. **SYNTHESIZE** Draw colored bars that might represent the potential energy and kinetic energy of the skater at each of the five labeled points on illustration A. Explain why you drew the bars the way you did. (**Hint:** See the illustration on p. 17.)

20. **SYNTHESIZE** How are plants and solar cells similar? How are the ways in which they capture sunlight and convert it into other forms of energy different? Explain.

21. **COMPARE** Explain how energy sources such as solar energy and wind energy have similar problems that must be overcome. How have scientists tried to address these problems?

22. **INFER** Suppose that one air conditioner becomes very hot when it is working but another air conditioner does not. Which air conditioner is more energy efficient? How can you tell?

23. **DRAW CONCLUSIONS** Suppose a vacuum cleaner uses 100 units of electrical energy. All of this energy is converted into thermal and sound energy (from the motor), and into the kinetic energy of air being pulled into the vacuum cleaner. If 60 units of electrical energy are converted into thermal energy and sound energy, how much electrical energy is converted into the desired form of energy? How do you know?

24. **COMMUNICATE** Describe a process in which energy changes forms at least twice. Draw and label a diagram that shows these energy conversions.

the BIG idea

25. **APPLY** Look again at the photograph on pages 6 and 7 and consider the opening question. How might your answer have changed after reading the chapter?

26. **COMMUNICATE** How have your ideas about energy and its different forms changed after reading the chapter? Provide an example from your life to describe how you would have thought of energy compared to how you might think about it now.

UNIT PROJECTS

If you are doing a unit project, make a folder for your project. Include in your folder a list of the resources you will need, the date on which the project is due, and a schedule to keep track of your progress. Begin gathering data.

MONITOR AND RETEACH

If students have trouble applying the concept of conservation of energy in items 13, 17, 18, and 23, explain that when one object gains energy, another object must have lost the same amount of energy. Divide a group of 25 paper clips into several smaller groups that represent different forms of energy. Explain that the paper clips can be moved from group to group, but that the total number will still equal 25.

Students may benefit from summarizing one or more sections of the chapter.

  Summarizing the Chapter, pp. 68–69

Standardized Test Practice

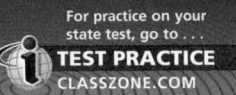

For practice on your state test, go to . . .
TEST PRACTICE
CLASSZONE.COM

Interpreting Graphs

Study the graph below. Then answer the first five questions.

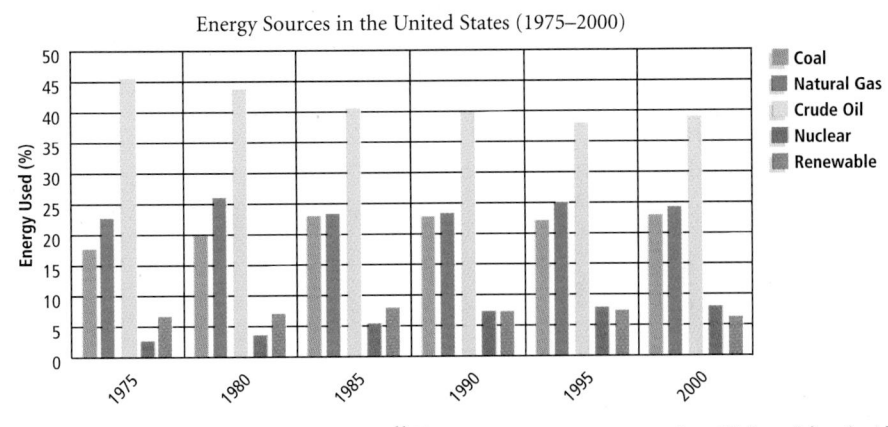

Energy Sources in the United States (1975–2000)

Source: U.S. Energy Information Administration, Monthly Energy Review (June 2003)

1. In which year did the greatest percentage of energy used in the United States come from crude oil?
   a. 1975   **c.** 1995
   b. 1980   **d.** 2000

2. What three sources of energy account for about 80 percent of all energy used in each year shown?
   a. coal, crude oil, nuclear
   b. natural gas, crude oil, renewable
   c. coal, natural gas, crude oil
   d. crude oil, nuclear, renewable

3. Which sources of energy show a greater percentage in 2000 as compared to 1980?
   a. crude oil, renewable   **c.** coal, nuclear
   b. natural gas, crude oil   **d.** coal, crude oil

4. The use of which energy source tended to decrease between 1975 and 2000?
   a. coal   **c.** crude oil
   b. natural gas   **d.** nuclear

5. The use of which source of energy steadily increased between 1975 and 1995?
   a. coal   **c.** nuclear
   b. crude oil   **d.** renewable

Extended Response

Answer the questions in detail. Include some of the terms from the word box on the right. Underline each term you use in your answers.

chemical energy	potential energy
electrical energy	sound energy
mechanical energy	thermal energy

6. When gasoline is burned in a moving car's engine, which forms of energy are being used? Which forms of energy are produced? Explain.

7. Name two appliances in your home that you believe are inefficient. What about them indicates that they may be inefficient?

Chapter 1: Energy **33** **B**

Interpreting Graphs

1. *a*   2. *c*   3. *c*   4. *c*   5. *c*

Extended Response

6. RUBRIC
4 points for a response that correctly answers both questions, gives an accurate explanation, and uses the following terms correctly:
   • chemical energy
   • mechanical energy
   • sound energy
   • thermal energy
   • potential energy

Sample: The <u>chemical energy</u> of gasoline is <u>potential energy</u> that is converted into several other forms of energy listed when a car is driven. For example, <u>sound energy</u> and <u>thermal energy</u> are produced in the car's engine and <u>mechanical energy</u> moves the car.

3 points correctly answers one of the questions, gives an accurate explanation, and uses the terms correctly
2 points correctly answers at least one question but fails to give an accurate explanation, and uses at least three terms correctly
1 point does not correctly answer either question and fails to give an accurate explanation, but uses at least three terms correctly

7. RUBRIC
4 points for a response that correctly answers both questions and gives two correct examples.

Sample: The refrigerator and air conditioner are inefficient. They produce unwanted heat and <u>sound energy</u> from <u>electrical energy</u>.

3 points correctly answers both questions and gives one correct example
2 points correctly answers both questions but does not give any correct examples
1 point correctly answers one question and gives one correct example

---

METACOGNITIVE ACTIVITY

Have students answer the following questions in their **Science Notebook:**

1. What misconceptions about energy did you have? Have these misconceptions been corrected?

2. Which topics in this chapter would you like to learn more about?

3. What goals have you set for your Unit Project? What is the next step you will complete?

 # Temperature and Heat

Earth Science
UNIFYING PRINCIPLES

PRINCIPLE 1	**PRINCIPLE 2**	**PRINCIPLE 3**	**PRINCIPLE 4**
Heat energy inside Earth and radiation from the Sun provide energy for Earth's processes.	Physical forces, such as gravity, affect the movement of all matter on Earth and throughout the universe.	Matter and energy move among Earth's rocks and soil, atmosphere, waters, and living things.	Earth has changed over time and continues to change.

Unit: Energy and the Changing Earth
BIG IDEAS

CHAPTER 1 **Energy**	**CHAPTER 2** **Temperature and Heat**	**CHAPTER 3** **Plate Tectonics**	**CHAPTER 4** **Earthquakes**	**CHAPTER 5** **Mountains and Volcanoes**
Energy has different forms, but it is always conserved.	Heat is a flow of energy due to temperature differences.	The movement of tectonic plates causes geologic changes on Earth.	Earthquakes release stress that has built up in rocks.	Mountains and volcanoes form as tectonic plates move.

CHAPTER 2
KEY CONCEPTS

SECTION (2.1)	SECTION (2.2)	SECTION (2.3)
Temperature depends on particle movement.	**Energy flows from warmer to cooler objects.**	**The transfer of energy as heat can be controlled.**
1. All matter is made of moving particles.	**1.** Heat is different from temperature.	**1.** Energy moves as heat in three ways.
2. Temperature can be measured.	**2.** Some substances change temperature more easily than others.	**2.** Different materials are used to control the transfer of energy.

T The Big Idea Flow Chart is available on p. T9 in the **UNIT TRANSPARENCY BOOK.**

Previewing Content

 2.1 **Temperature depends on particle movement.** pp. 37–43

1. All matter is made of moving particles.

The **kinetic theory of matter** states that all the particles in matter are constantly in motion. As a result, all particles have kinetic energy. Particles in solids, liquids, and gases move differently.

- Particles in a solid vibrate in fixed positions but do not move past each other. Particles in a liquid are not tightly bound to each other, as in a solid, and slide past each other. Particles in a gas are separated by greater distances than those in a solid or liquid.
- All the particles in a substance are not moving at the same speed and can change speeds.
- **Temperature** is a measurement of the average kinetic energy of all particles in an object or location.

2. Temperature can be measured.

The two common temperature scales (Fahrenheit and Celsius) are based on the physical properties of pure water and are expressed in terms of degrees. A third temperature scale is the Kelvin scale, which is an absolute temperature scale. The zero point of the Kelvin scale is absolute zero, which is the complete absence of particle movement. Absolute zero is 0 K, which is equal to −273.15°C.

Thermometers measure temperature. Often, the physical property used to measure temperature is expansion or contraction. All gases, many liquids, and most solids expand when temperature increases.

- Thermometers filled with a liquid (alcohol or mercury) measure temperature through the uniform expansion or contraction of the liquid over a wide range of temperatures.
- Thermometers can also measure temperature through electrical resistance, infrared radiation, and the differential expansion of materials.

 2.2 **Energy flows from warmer to cooler objects.** pp. 44–49

1. Heat is different from temperature.

Heat, temperature, and thermal energy are closely related but not the same.

- Temperature is the average kinetic energy of particles in a substance or location.
- **Heat** is a flow of energy from an object or location at a higher temperature to an object or location at a lower temperature. The transfer of energy through heat continues as long as the temperature difference exists. When energy is transferred in this way, the thermal energy of both objects or locations changes.
- **Thermal energy** is the total kinetic energy of particles in a substance or location.

The most common units of heat measurement are the calorie and the joule.

- A **calorie** is the amount of energy needed to raise the temperature of 1 gram of water by 1° C.
- A Calorie with a capital C—the measure used with food and nutrition—is a kilocalorie, or 1000 calories.
- A **joule** is the standard scientific unit for measuring energy. One calorie is equal to 4.18 joules, so 4.18 joules of energy raises the temperature of 1 gram of water by 1°C.

2. Some substances change temperature more easily than others.

Each substance needs to absorb a different amount of energy in order for its temperature to increase. A substance's **specific heat** is the amount of energy that is required for 1 gram of that substance to increase in temperature by 1°C.

Any amount of a particular substance has the same specific heat. However, the more mass an object has, the more energy is required to produce an increase in its temperature and, conversely, the more energy must be released to produce a decrease in temperature.

Common Misconceptions

 MISCONCEPTION DATABASE
CLASSZONE.COM Background on student misconceptions

CONSTANT MOTION OF PARTICLES Students may have difficulty understanding that all particles in matter are in constant motion. Particles in solids vibrate in place, particles in liquids slide past one another, and particles in gases move freely in all directions.

 This misconception is addressed on p. 38.

DEFINITION OF TEMPERATURE Students may think that temperature is a measure of an object's heat. Temperature measures the average kinetic energy of the particles in an object.

 This misconception is addressed in Teach Difficult Concepts on p. 39.

Previewing Content

 The transfer of energy as heat can be controlled. pp. 50–57

1. Energy moves as heat in three ways.

Energy is transferred between objects or locations when there are temperature differences between them. Depending on both the medium and the objects themselves, energy can be transferred by conduction, convection, or radiation.

- **Conduction** is the process through which energy is transferred through physical contact. Particles of a warmer object collide with particles of a cooler object and transfer some of their energy to the cooler object. Materials that easily transfer energy are **conductors;** those that are poor conductors are called **insulators.**

- **Convection** is the process that transfers energy in gases and liquids. Differences in density between substances are produced by differences in temperature. A warmer region of gas or liquid is less dense than a cooler region, due to thermal expansion. The warmer, less dense gas or liquid is pushed up by cooler, denser gas or liquid that sinks in underneath. The cycle of convection accounts for currents in bodies of water and winds in the atmosphere.

- **Radiation** is energy that travels as electromagnetic waves, such as visible light, infrared light, and x-rays. All objects radiate at least a small amount of energy. Often, when radiation is absorbed by an object, the transfer of energy as heat occurs. Radiation differs from conduction and convection in that it can transfer energy through a vacuum.

2. Different materials are used to control the transfer of energy.

Materials are used for different purposes depending on whether they are good or poor conductors of energy. Many insulators contain or trap a layer of air, which is a poor conductor. Human-made insulators are similar to, and often based upon, insulators found in nature.

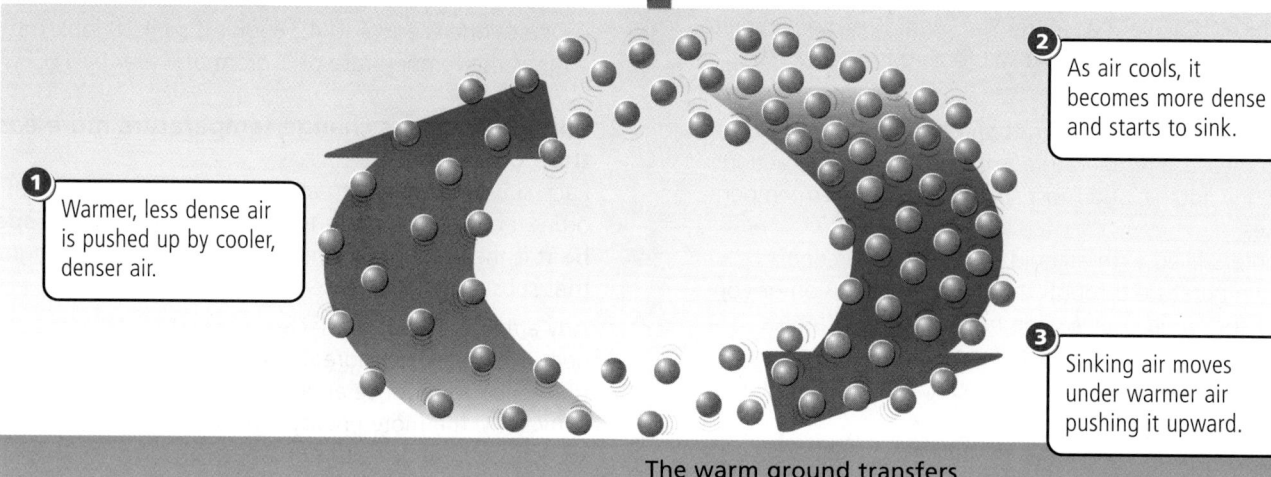

① Warmer, less dense air is pushed up by cooler, denser air.

② As air cools, it becomes more dense and starts to sink.

③ Sinking air moves under warmer air pushing it upward.

The warm ground transfers energy to the air by conduction.

Common Misconceptions

HEAT Some students may think that heat is a fluid that literally flows from one object to another and that heat and cold are different, rather than being at opposite ends of an energy flow. Heat is the flow of energy from a warm substance to a cooler substance.

 This misconception is addressed on p. 45.

 MISCONCEPTION DATABASE
CLASSZONE.COM Background on student misconceptions

DIRECTION OF HEAT FLOW Because students have often heard that heat rises, they may think that heat only travels upward. Heat can transfer energy in all directions, depending upon the process that is involved.

 This misconception is addressed on p. 52.

Previewing Labs

Lab Generator CD-ROM
Edit these Pupil Edition labs and generate alternative labs.

EXPLORE the BIG idea

Moving Colors, p. 35
Students observe food coloring in hot and cold water to investigate motion and temperature.

TIME 10 minutes
MATERIALS 2 plastic cups, hot and cold water, eyedropper, food coloring

Does It Chill? p. 35
Students investigate how soil acts as an insulator.

TIME 30 minutes
MATERIALS outdoor thermometer, paper cup, freezer, soil, stopwatch

Internet Activity: Kinetic Theory, p. 35
Students observe the relationship between the kinetic energy of particles and temperature.

TIME 20 minutes
MATERIALS computer with Internet access

SECTION 2.1

EXPLORE Temperature, p. 37
Students discover how a transfer of energy and increased motion produce an increase in temperature.

TIME 10 minutes
MATERIALS large rubber band

INVESTIGATE Temperature Measurements, p. 41
Students make thermometers and observe how thermal expansion can be used to measure temperature.

TIME 30 minutes
MATERIALS small plastic bottle, alcohol solution, food coloring, clear plastic straw, clay, bowl, ice water, hot tap water

---

SECTION 2.2

INVESTIGATE Heat Transfer, p. 46
Students investigate the specific heat of different materials by measuring a change in temperature.

TIME 30 minutes
MATERIALS graduated cylinder, balance, room-temperature water, pennies, aluminum foil, 100 mL beaker, 3 plastic cups, hot tap water, thermometer, stopwatch

---

SECTION 2.3

EXPLORE Conduction, p. 50
Students observe the direction in which energy is transferred through direct contact between objects at different temperatures.

TIME 10 minutes
MATERIALS 500 mL beaker, hot tap water, cold water, 2 thermometers, stopwatch, 200 mL beaker

CHAPTER INVESTIGATION
Insulators, pp. 56–57
Students design and test an insulated bottle to slow a change in the temperature of water as compared to a noninsulated control bottle.

TIME 40 minutes
MATERIALS 2 small plastic bottles, 2 thermometers, modeling clay, graduated cylinder, hot or cold tap water, foam packing peanuts, plastic wrap, aluminum foil, soil, sand, rubber bands, coffee can, beaker, stopwatch, graph paper

---

 Additional INVESTIGATION, Observing Convection, A, B, & C, pp. 118–126; Teacher Instructions, pp. 320–321

Previewing Chapter Resources

	INTEGRATED TECHNOLOGY		**LABS AND ACTIVITIES**

CHAPTER 2
Temperature and Heat

 CLASSZONE.COM
- eEdition Plus
- EasyPlanner Plus
- Misconception Database
- Content Review
- Test Practice
- Simulations
- Resource Centers
- Internet Activity: Kinetic Theory
- Math Tutorial

 SCILINKS.ORG
SCILINKS

 **CD-ROMS**
- eEdition
- EasyPlanner
- Power Presentations
- Content Review
- Lab Generator
- Test Generator

 AUDIO CDS
- Audio Readings
- Audio Readings in Spanish

 EXPLORE the Big Idea, p. 35
- Moving Colors
- Does It Chill?
- Internet Activity: Kinetic Theory

UNIT RESOURCE BOOK
Unit Projects, pp. 5–10

 Lab Generator CD-ROM
Generate customized labs.

SECTION
 (2.1) **Temperature depends on particle movement.**
pp. 37–43

Time: 2 periods (1 block)
 Lesson Plan, pp. 70–71

 • **RESOURCE CENTER,** Temperature and Temperature Scales
- **MATH TUTORIAL**

 UNIT TRANSPARENCY BOOK
- Big Idea Flow Chart, p. T9
- Daily Vocabulary Scaffolding, p. T10
- Note-Taking Model, p. T11
- 3-Minute Warm-Up, p. T12

 • EXPLORE Temperature, p. 37
- INVESTIGATE Temperature Measurements, p. 41
- Math in Science, p. 43

UNIT RESOURCE BOOK
- Datasheet, Temperature Measurements, p. 79
- Math Support, p. 107
- Math Practice, p. 108

SECTION
 (2.2) **Energy flows from warmer to cooler objects.**
pp. 44–49

Time: 2 periods (1 block)
 Lesson Plan, pp. 81–82

 RESOURCE CENTER, Thermal Energy

UNIT TRANSPARENCY BOOK
- Daily Vocabulary Scaffolding, p. T10
- 3-Minute Warm-Up, p. T12

 • INVESTIGATE Heat Transfer, p. 46
- Science on the Job, p. 49

UNIT RESOURCE BOOK
Datasheet, Heat Transfer, p. 90

SECTION
 (2.3) **The transfer of energy as heat can be controlled.**
pp. 50–57

Time: 4 periods (2 blocks)
 Lesson Plan, pp. 92–93

 SIMULATION, Conduction, Convection, or Radiation

UNIT TRANSPARENCY BOOK
- Big Idea Flow Chart, p. T9
- Daily Vocabulary Scaffolding, p. T10
- 3-Minute Warm-Up, p. T13
- "Insulation" Visual, p. T14
- Chapter Outline, pp. T15–T16

 • EXPLORE Conduction, p. 50
- CHAPTER INVESTIGATION, Insulators, pp. 56–57

UNIT RESOURCE BOOK
- CHAPTER INVESTIGATION, Insulators, A, B, & C, pp. 109–117
- Additional INVESTIGATION, Observing Convection, A, B, & C, pp. 118–126

KEY TO ICONS

 CD/CD-ROM

 INTERNET

 Pupil Edition

 Teacher Edition

UNIT RESOURCE BOOK

UNIT TRANSPARENCY BOOK

UNIT ASSESSMENT BOOK

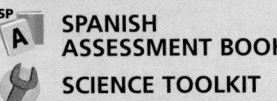 SPANISH ASSESSMENT BOOK

SCIENCE TOOLKIT

READING AND REINFORCEMENT

- Description Wheel, B20–21
- Choose Your Own Strategy, C35–44
- Daily Vocabulary Scaffolding, H1–8

UNIT RESOURCE BOOK
- Vocabulary Practice, pp. 104–105
- Decoding Support, p. 106
- Summarizing the Chapter, pp. 127–128

 Audio Readings CD
Listen to Pupil Edition.

Audio Readings in Spanish CD
Listen to Pupil Edition in Spanish.

UNIT RESOURCE BOOK
- Reading Study Guide, A & B, pp. 72–75
- Spanish Reading Study Guide, pp. 76–77
- Challenge and Extension, p. 78
- Reinforcing Key Concepts, p. 80

UNIT RESOURCE BOOK
- Reading Study Guide, A & B, pp. 83–86
- Spanish Reading Study Guide, pp. 87–88
- Challenge and Extension, p. 89
- Reinforcing Key Concepts, p. 91

UNIT RESOURCE BOOK
- Reading Study Guide, A & B, pp. 94–97
- Spanish Reading Study Guide, pp. 98–99
- Challenge and Extension, p. 100
- Reinforcing Key Concepts, p. 101
- Challenge Reading, pp. 102–103

ASSESSMENT

- Chapter Review, pp. 59–60
- Standardized Test Practice, p. 61

UNIT ASSESSMENT BOOK
- Diagnostic Test, pp. 20–21
- Chapter Test, A, B, & C, pp. 25–36
- Alternative Assessment, pp. 37–38
Spanish Chapter Test, pp. 225–228

 Test Generator CD-ROM
Generate customized tests.

 Lab Generator CD-ROM
Rubrics for Labs

 Ongoing Assessment, pp. 39–42

 Section 2.1 Review, p. 42

 UNIT ASSESSMENT BOOK
Section 2.1 Quiz, p. 22

 Ongoing Assessment, pp. 44–48

 Section 2.2 Review, p. 48

 UNIT ASSESSMENT BOOK
Section 2.2 Quiz, p. 23

Ongoing Assessment, pp. 51, 53–55

Section 2.3 Review, p. 55

UNIT ASSESSMENT BOOK
Section 2.3 Quiz, p. 24

STANDARDS

National Standards
A.1–8, A.9.a–g, B.3.a–b, E.2–5

See p. 34 for the standards.

National Standards
A.2–8, A.9.a–c, A.9.e–f, B.3.a

National Standards
A.2–7, A.9.a–b, A.9.d–f, B.3.a–b

National Standards
A.1–8, A.9.a–g, B.3.a, E.2–5

Previewing Resources for Differentiated Instruction

CHAPTER INVESTIGATION

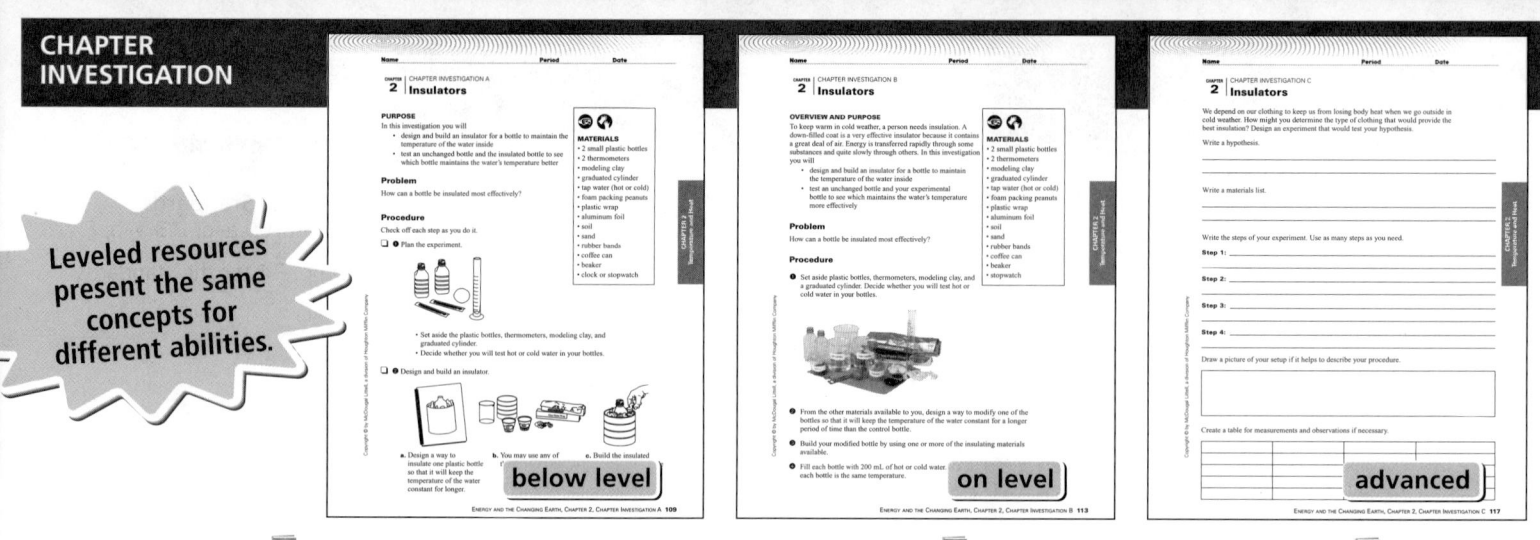

Leveled resources present the same concepts for different abilities.

UNIT RESOURCE BOOK, pp. 109–112   pp. 113–116   pp. 113–117

READING STUDY GUIDE

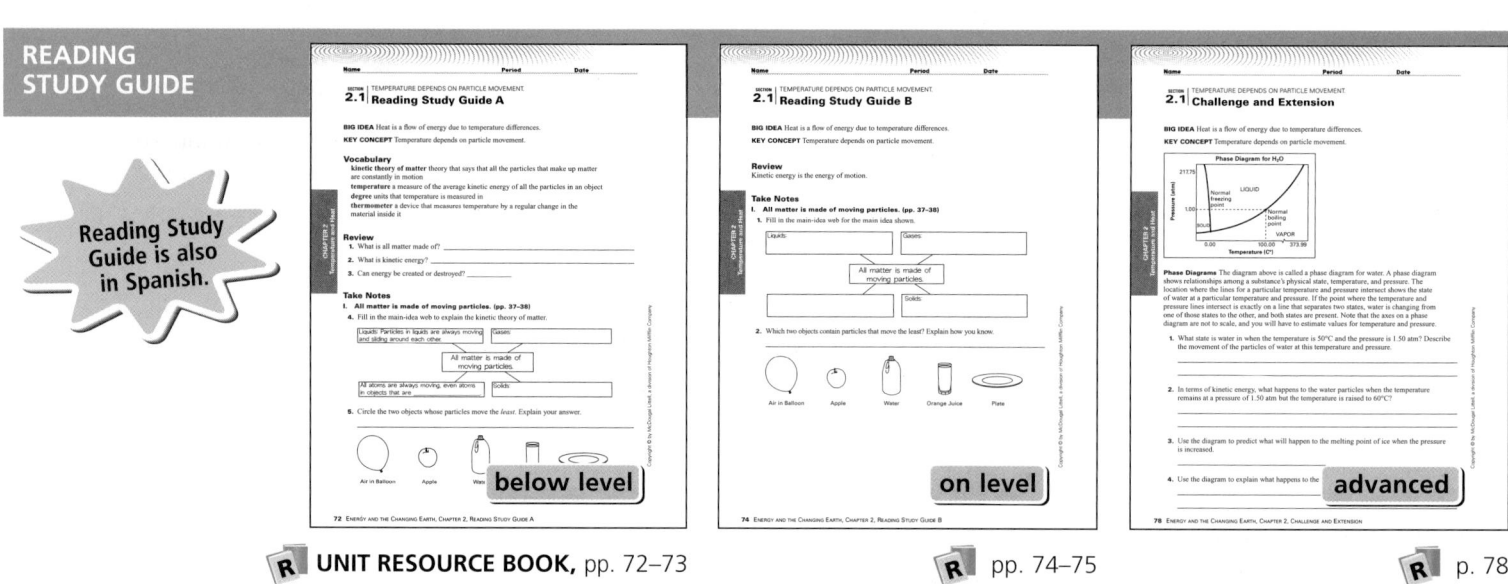

Reading Study Guide is also in Spanish.

UNIT RESOURCE BOOK, pp. 72–73   pp. 74–75   p. 78

CHAPTER TEST

Chapter Test is also in Spanish.

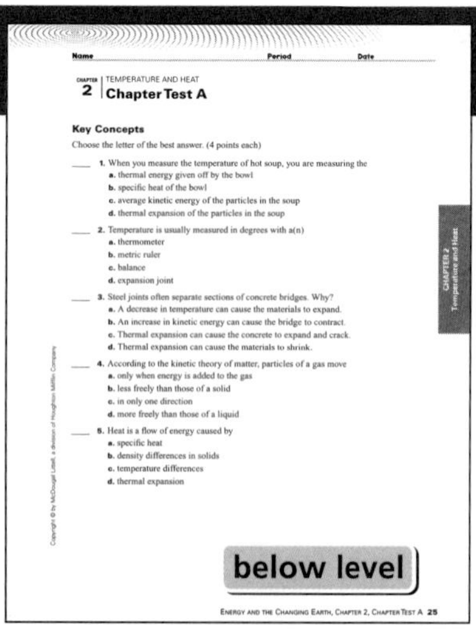

UNIT ASSESSMENT BOOK, pp. 25–28 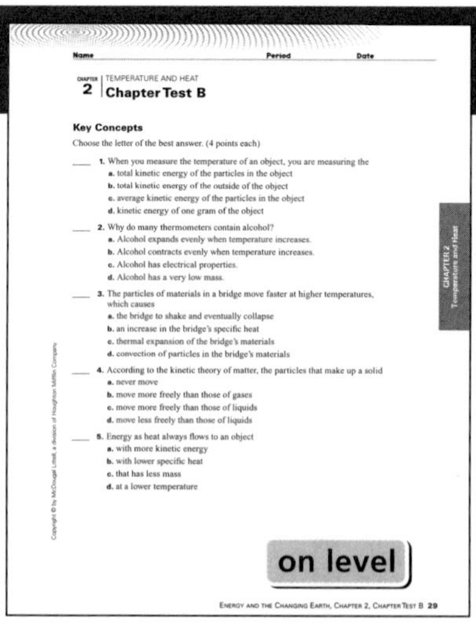   pp. 29–32 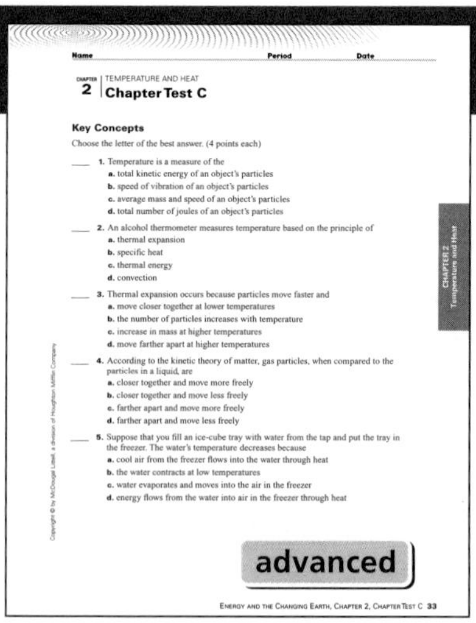   pp. 33–36

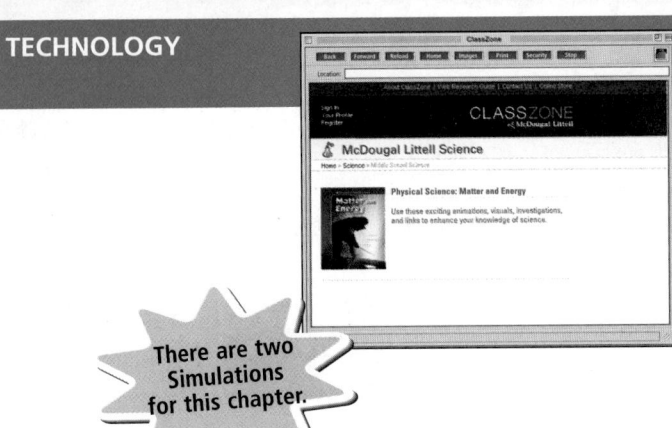

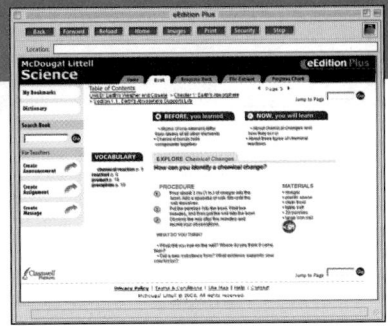

There are two Simulations for this chapter.

CLASSZONE.COM   **CD/CD-ROMS**   **CLASSZONE.COM**

VISUAL CONTENT

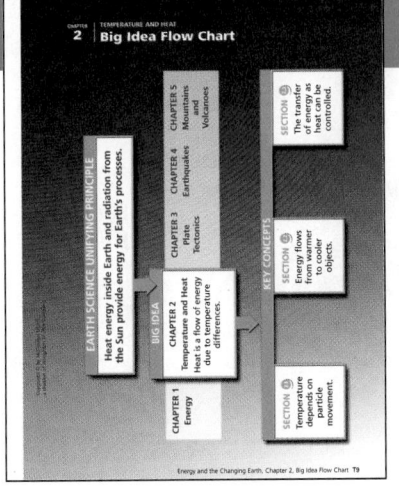

UNIT TRANSPARENCY BOOK, p. T9

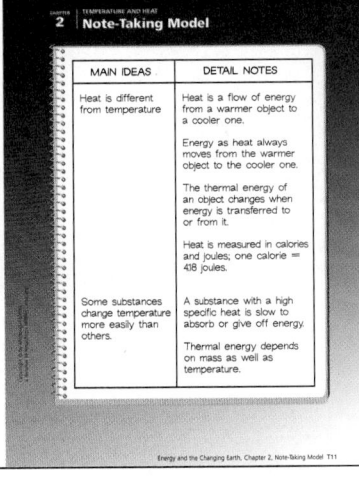

p. T11

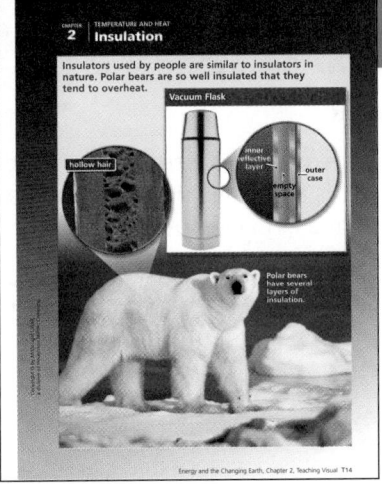

p. T14

MORE SUPPORT

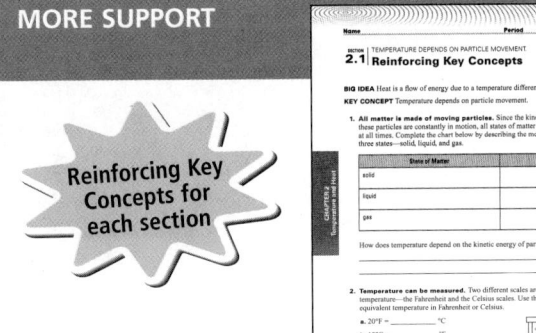

Reinforcing Key Concepts for each section

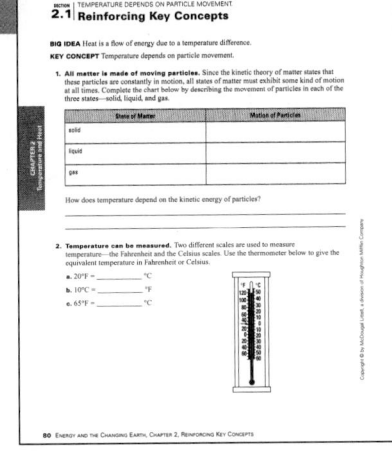

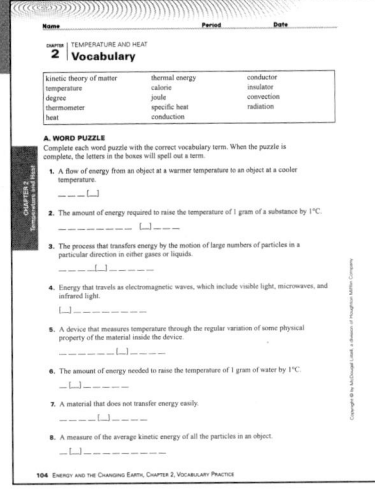

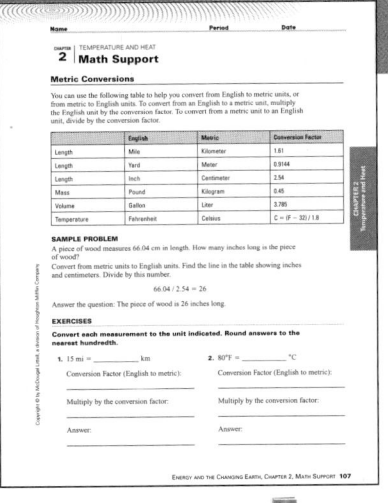

UNIT RESOURCE BOOK, p. 80

pp. 104–105

p. 107

INTRODUCE

the BIG idea

Have students look at the photograph of a giraffe in a sunny environment and discuss how the question in the box links to the Big Idea. Ask:

- How can you tell that energy travels from the Sun to Earth?
- What sources of energy are there after the Sun has set?

National Science Education Standards

Content

B.3.a Energy is a property of many substances, is associated with heat, and is transferred in many ways.

B.3.b Heat moves in predictable ways, flowing from warmer objects to cooler ones, until both reach the same temperature.

Process

A.1–8 Identify questions that can be answered through scientific investigations; design and conduct an investigation; use tools to gather and interpret data; use evidence to describe, predict, explain, model; think critically to make relationships between evidence and explanation; recognize different explanations and predictions; communicate scientific procedures and explanations; use mathematics.

A.9.a–g Understand scientific inquiry by using different investigations, methods, mathematics, technology, and explanations based on logic, evidence, and skepticism. Data often results in new investigations.

E.2–5 Design, implement, and evaluate a solution or product; communicate technological design.

CHAPTER

2 Temperature and Heat

the BIG idea

Heat is a flow of energy due to temperature differences.

> **How does heat from the Sun increase this giraffe's temperature?**

Key Concepts

SECTION 2.1 Temperature depends on particle movement. Learn how kinetic energy is the basis of temperature.

SECTION 2.2 Energy flows from warmer to cooler objects. Learn about differences between temperature and heat, and how temperature changes in different substances.

SECTION 2.3 The transfer of energy as heat can be controlled. Learn how energy is transferred through heat, and how that transfer can be controlled.

Internet Preview

CLASSZONE.COM

Chapter 2 online resources: Content Review, two Simulations, two Resource Centers, Math Tutorial, Test Practice

B 34   Unit: **Energy and the Changing Earth**

INTERNET PREVIEW

CLASSZONE.COM   For student use with the following pages:

Review and Practice
- Content Review, pp. 36, 58
- Math Tutorial: Temperature Conversions, p. 43
- Test Practice, p. 61

Activities and Resources
- Internet Activity, p. 35
- Resource Centers: Temperature & Temperature Scales, p. 40; Thermal Energy, p. 45
- Simulation: Conduction, Convection, or Radiation, p. 53

NSTA scilinks.org *SCiLINKS*

Kinetic Theory
Code: MDL064

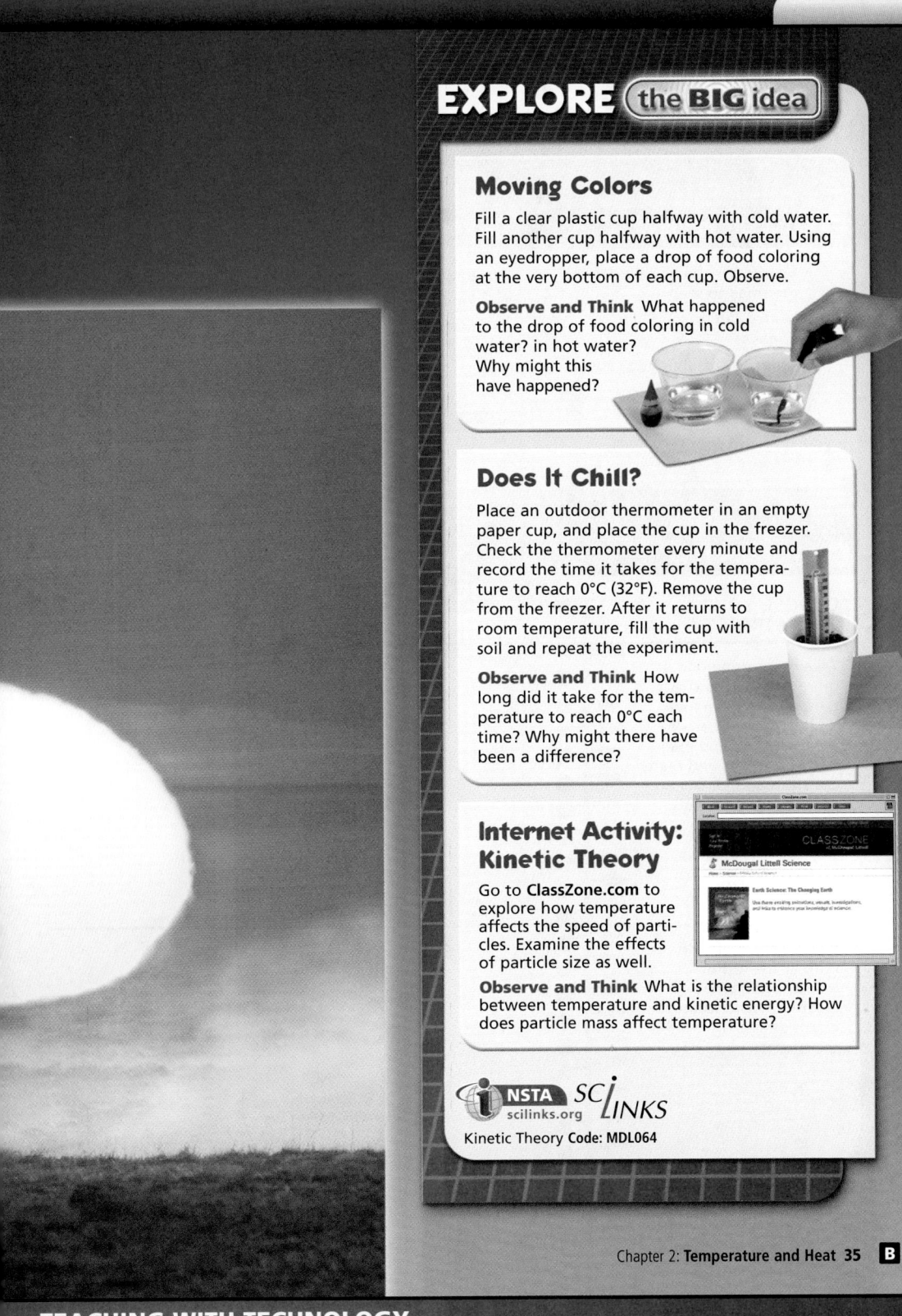

EXPLORE (the BIG idea)

Moving Colors

Fill a clear plastic cup halfway with cold water. Fill another cup halfway with hot water. Using an eyedropper, place a drop of food coloring at the very bottom of each cup. Observe.

Observe and Think What happened to the drop of food coloring in cold water? in hot water? Why might this have happened?

Does It Chill?

Place an outdoor thermometer in an empty paper cup, and place the cup in the freezer. Check the thermometer every minute and record the time it takes for the temperature to reach 0°C (32°F). Remove the cup from the freezer. After it returns to room temperature, fill the cup with soil and repeat the experiment.

Observe and Think How long did it take for the temperature to reach 0°C each time? Why might there have been a difference?

Internet Activity: Kinetic Theory

Go to **ClassZone.com** to explore how temperature affects the speed of particles. Examine the effects of particle size as well.

Observe and Think What is the relationship between temperature and kinetic energy? How does particle mass affect temperature?

NSTA
scilinks.org
SCI LINKS

Kinetic Theory Code: MDL064

Chapter 2: **Temperature and Heat** 35 **B**

TEACHING WITH TECHNOLOGY

CBL and Probeware If a probeware system is available, students can use a temperature probe to measure temperature changes for "Investigate Heat Transfer" on p. 46, "Explore Conduction" on p. 50, and to record and graph temperature changes in the Chapter Investigation, pp. 56–57.

EXPLORE (the BIG idea)

These inquiry-based activities are appropriate for use at home or as a supplement to classroom instruction.

Moving Colors

PURPOSE To observe that particles in matter move faster at higher temperatures than at lower temperatures. Students observe a drop of food coloring in cold water and in hot water.

TIP *10 min.* Have students use clear cups. Caution students not to get food coloring on their hands or clothing.

Answer: The food coloring spreads out faster in hot water than in cold water because the molecules in the hot water are moving faster.

REVISIT after p. 39.

Does It Chill?

PURPOSE To investigate how soil, as an insulator, slows changes in temperature. Students observe and record the temperature in a freezer.

TIP *30 min.* Have students read the thermometer and return it to the freezer as quickly as possible each time. Remind students to keep track of the time.

Answer: The thermometer in the soil should take longer to reach 0°C because soil acts as an insulator.

REVISIT after p. 51.

Internet Activity: Kinetic Theory

PURPOSE To observe that particle size and speed are related to temperature.

TIP *20 min.* Students should observe the kinetic energy of particles.

Answer: Temperature is the average kinetic energy of particles in an object; the greater the kinetic energy, the higher the temperature. The size of a particle affects its average kinetic energy.

REVISIT after p. 38.

Chapter 2 **35** **B**

PREPARE

CONCEPT REVIEW

Activate Prior Knowledge

Place an ice cube in a beaker, and place the beaker on a hot plate. Ask:

- How will the ice cube change? *It will melt into water, then evaporate and boil into water vapor.*

- What causes the ice cube to change into liquid water, then into water vapor? *energy.*

- How is energy related to these changes? *The addition of energy raises the temperature and produces the changes in physical state.*

TAKING NOTES

Choose Your Own Strategy

Choosing different strategies for taking notes can help students learn which strategies work best for them. Students can choose their own strategy or use the strategy suggested on the first page of each section. Encourage students to use their notes to test themselves.

Vocabulary Strategy

Description wheels can include as much information as students want to add. They are handy study devices when students look back through their notes.

Vocabulary and Note-Taking Resources

- Vocabulary Practice, pp. 104–105
- Decoding Support, p. 106

- Daily Vocabulary Scaffolding, p. T10
- Note-Taking Model, p. T11

- Description Wheel, B20–21
- Choose Your Own Strategy, C35–44
- Daily Vocabulary Scaffolding, H1–8

CONCEPT REVIEW

- Matter is made of particles too small to see.
- Matter can be solid, liquid, or gas.
- Energy is the ability to cause a change.
- There are different forms of energy.

VOCABULARY REVIEW

energy p. 10

kinetic energy p. 12

matter *See Glossary.*

CONTENT REVIEW
CLASSZONE.COM

Review concepts and vocabulary.

TAKING NOTES

CHOOSE YOUR OWN STRATEGY

Take notes using one or more note-taking strategies, such as **main idea and detail notes, main idea web,** or **mind map.** Feel free to mix and match the strategies, or use an entirely different note-taking strategy.

VOCABULARY STRATEGY

Place each vocabulary term at the center of a **description wheel** diagram. Write some words describing it on the spokes.

See the Note-Taking Handbook on pages R45–R51.

SCIENCE NOTEBOOK

Main Idea and Detail Notes

Mind Map

Main Idea Web

solids, liquids, gases   temperature

KINETIC THEORY OF MATTER

kinetic energy   particle movement

CHECK READINESS

Administer the Diagnostic Test to determine students' readiness for new science content and their mastery of requisite math skills.

 Diagnostic Test, pp. 20–21

Technology Resources

Students needing content and math skills should visit **ClassZone.com**.

- CONTENT REVIEW
- MATH TUTORIAL

 CONTENT REVIEW CD-ROM

2.1 Temperature depends on particle movement.

◀ **BEFORE, you learned**
- All matter is made of particles
- Kinetic energy is the energy of motion
- Energy can be transferred or changed but is never created or destroyed

▶ **NOW, you will learn**
- How temperature depends on kinetic energy
- How temperature is measured
- How changes in temperature can affect matter

VOCABULARY

kinetic theory of matter p. 38
temperature p. 39
degree p. 40
thermometer p. 41

EXPLORE Temperature

What can cause a change in temperature?

PROCEDURE

1. Work with a partner. Hold the rubber band with both hands. Without stretching it, hold it to the underside of your partner's wrist.

2. Move the rubber band away, then quickly stretch it once and keep it stretched. Hold it to the underside of your partner's wrist.

3. Move the rubber band away and quickly let it return to its normal size. Hold it to the underside of your partner's wrist.

MATERIALS
large rubber band

WHAT DO YOU THINK?
- What effect did stretching the rubber band have on the temperature of the rubber band?
- What may have caused this change to occur?

NOTE-TAKING STRATEGY
You could take notes on the movement of particles in matter by using a main idea web.

All matter is made of moving particles.

You have read that any object in motion has kinetic energy. All the moving objects you see around you—from cars to planes to butterflies—have kinetic energy. Even objects so small that you cannot see them, such as atoms, are in motion and have kinetic energy.

You might think that a large unmoving object, such as a house or a wooden chair, does not have any kinetic energy. However, all matter is made of atoms, and atoms are always in motion, even if the objects themselves do not change their position. The motion of these tiny particles gives the object energy. The chair you are sitting on has some amount of energy. You also have energy, even when you are not moving.

Chapter 2: **Temperature and Heat 37** B

RESOURCES FOR DIFFERENTIATED INSTRUCTION

Below Level

UNIT RESOURCE BOOK
- Reading Study Guide A, pp. 72–73
- Decoding Support, p. 106

 **AUDIO CDS**

Advanced

UNIT RESOURCE BOOK
Challenge and Extension, p. 78

English Learners

UNIT RESOURCE BOOK
Spanish Reading Study Guide, pp. 76–77

AUDIO CDS
- Audio Readings in Spanish
- Audio Readings (English)

2.1 FOCUS

▶ Set Learning Goals

Students will
- Explain how temperature depends on kinetic energy.
- Describe how temperature is measured.
- Describe how changes in temperature can affect matter.
- Observe experimentally how thermal expansion can be used to measure temperature.

◀ 3-Minute Warm-Up

Display Transparency 12 or copy this exercise on the board:

Decide if these statements are true. If not, correct them.

1. Solids and liquids are made of particles, but gases are made of air, which is not made of particles. *Gases are also made of particles.*

2. Kinetic energy is the energy of motion. *true*

3. Kinetic energy depends on position and chemical composition. *Kinetic energy depends on mass and speed. (Potential energy depends on position and chemical composition.)*

▭ 3-Minute Warm-Up, p. T12

2.1 MOTIVATE

EXPLORE Temperature

PURPOSE To discover how a transfer of energy and increased motion produce an increase in temperature

TIP *10 min.* Use thick rubber bands that will not break easily. Students should wear safety goggles. Caution students to avoid stretching the rubber bands to their breaking point.

WHAT DO YOU THINK? *The temperature increased because stretching the rubber band added energy to it.*

Address Misconceptions

IDENTIFY Ask: What states of matter have particles always in motion? If students do not mention all states of matter, they may think that some particles in matter are not in constant motion.

CORRECT Demonstrate the kinetic theory of matter in relation to solids, liquids, and gases using a clear plastic container holding beads or other small objects. Fill the container. Shake it to demonstrate a solid. If the container is completely full, the "particles" will move around slightly and will be in constant contact. Remove a portion of the objects, then shake the container to demonstrate a liquid. The "particles" will still collide but will move past each other and move more freely. Finally, remove all but a few objects, then shake the container to demonstrate a gas. The "particles" will move most freely and barely interact.

REASSESS Ask students to describe the motion of particles in their desks and chairs. *Particles are vibrating in place.* Reiterate that particles in all matter are always in motion.

Technology Resources

Visit **ClassZone.com** for background on common student misconceptions.

 MISCONCEPTION DATABASE

Teach from Visuals

To help students interpret the diagrams of particles in solid, liquid, and gas, ask:

- What do the particles in the solid, liquid, and gas have in common? *They are all in constant motion.*

- How are the solid, liquid, and gas different? *The freedom with which the particles can move varies.*

EXPLORE (the BIG idea)

Revisit "Internet Activity: Kinetic Theory" on p. 35. Have students explain their observations.

Ongoing Assessment

CHECK YOUR READING *that particles in matter are in constant motion and have kinetic energy*

▼ **REMINDER**
Kinetic energy is the energy of motion.

READING TiP
In illustrations of particle movement, more motion lines mean a greater speed.

The Kinetic Theory of Matter

Physical properties and physical changes are the result of how particles of matter behave. The **kinetic theory of matter** states that all of the particles that make up matter are constantly in motion. As a result, all particles in matter have kinetic energy. The kinetic theory of matter helps explain the different states of matter—solid, liquid, and gas.

❶ The particles in a solid, such as concrete, are not free to move around very much. They vibrate back and forth in the same position and are held tightly together by forces of attraction.

❷ The particles in a liquid, such as water in a pool, move much more freely than particles in a solid. They are constantly sliding around and tumbling over each other as they move.

❸ In a gas, such as the air around you or in a bubble in water, particles are far apart and move around at high speeds. Particles might collide with one another, but otherwise they do not interact much.

Particles do not always move at the same speed. Within any group of particles, some are moving faster than others. A fast-moving particle might collide with another particle and lose some of its speed. A slow-moving particle might be struck by a faster one and start moving faster. Particles have a wide range of speeds and often change speeds.

CHECK YOUR READING What is the kinetic theory of matter?

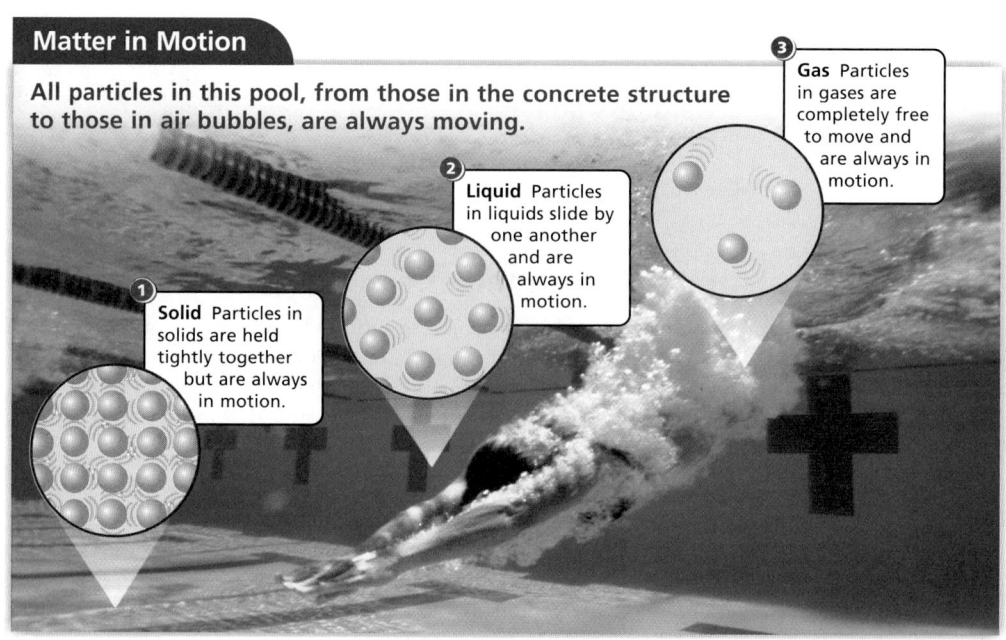

Matter in Motion

All particles in this pool, from those in the concrete structure to those in air bubbles, are always moving.

❸ Gas Particles in gases are completely free to move and are always in motion.

❷ Liquid Particles in liquids slide by one another and are always in motion.

❶ Solid Particles in solids are held tightly together but are always in motion.

DIFFERENTIATE INSTRUCTION

❓ More Reading Support

A What does the kinetic theory of matter say? *All the particles in matter are constantly in motion.*

English Learners Have students write the definitions of *temperature, degree,* and *thermometer* in their Science Word Dictionaries. English learners may require background knowledge of "smoothie" (p. 39), and the phrase "into account" (p. 42). Tell students to take something into account means to consider it.

Temperature and Kinetic Energy

Particles of matter moving at different speeds have different kinetic energies because kinetic energy depends on speed. It is not possible to know the kinetic energy of each particle in an object. However, the average kinetic energy of all the particles in an object can be determined.

Temperature is a measure of the average kinetic energy of all the particles in an object. If a liquid, such as hot cocoa, has a high temperature, the particles in the liquid are moving very fast and have a high average kinetic energy. The cocoa feels hot. If a drink, such as a fruit smoothie, has a low temperature, the particles in the liquid are moving more slowly and have a lower average kinetic energy. The smoothie feels cold.

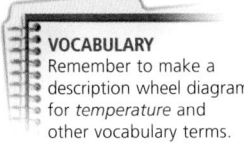

VOCABULARY
Remember to make a description wheel diagram for *temperature* and other vocabulary terms.

hot liquid   cold liquid

You experience the connection between temperature and the kinetic energy of particles every day. For example, to raise the temperature of your hands on a cold day—to warm your hands—you have to add energy, perhaps by putting your hands near a fire or a hot stove. The added energy makes the particles in your hands move faster. If you let a hot bowl sit on a table for a while, the particles in the bowl slow down due to collisions with particles in the air and in the table. The temperature of the bowl decreases, and it becomes cooler.

Temperature is the measurement of the average kinetic energy of particles, not just their speed. Recall that kinetic energy depends on mass as well as speed. Particles in a metal doorknob do not move as fast as particles in air. However, the particles in a doorknob have more mass and they can have the same amount of kinetic energy as particles in air. As a result, the doorknob and the air can have equal temperatures.

CHECK YOUR READING How does temperature change when kinetic energy increases?

DIFFERENTIATE INSTRUCTION

More Reading Support

B What measures the average kinetic energy of particles in an object? *temperature*

C What does kinetic energy depend on in addition to speed? *mass*

Below Level Students may have trouble with the idea that a large object with slow-moving particles can have a higher temperature than air with fast-moving particles. Have students feel a metal object and the air around it to compare their temperatures. Place the metal object under a lamp. After the metal is warm, have students compare how the metal and the air around it feel. Point out that even though particles of a gas move faster than particles of a solid, the particles in metal have more mass, and the average kinetic energy of its particles has increased more than that of the air particles.

Teach from Visuals

To help students interpret the diagrams of particles in hot and cold liquids, ask: How are the particles in the two liquids different? *The particles in the hot liquid are moving faster and have a higher average kinetic energy.*

Teach Difficult Concepts

Students might think that temperature is a measure of an object's heat. To help students understand what temperature actually measures, put out three large containers of water. One should have cold tap water, one should have hot tap water, and one should have room-temperature water. Have students put one hand in the cold and hot water for a few seconds, then have them put both hands in the room-temperature water. Ask students what temperature measures. *average kinetic energy of all the particles in an object* Point out that room-temperature water feels different to each hand because of temperature differences, not temperature measure itself.

Technology Resources

Visit **ClassZone.com** for background on common student misconceptions.

MISCONCEPTION DATABASE

EXPLORE (the **BIG** idea)

Revisit "Moving Colors" on p. 35. Have students explain their results.

Ongoing Assessment

Explain how temperature depends on kinetic energy.

Ask: If the average kinetic energy of an object's particles decreases, what happens to its temperature? *It decreases.*

CHECK YOUR READING *Answer: It increases.*

History of Science

In the 1800s, scientist William Thomson, Lord Kelvin, developed an absolute temperature scale with 0 representing absolute zero. At this theoretical temperature the particles in matter stop moving and have no kinetic energy. The Celsius scale uses the same magnitude of units as the Kelvin scale, and 0 K is equal to −273.15° Celsius. Therefore, to convert Celsius to Kelvin, add 273.15° to the Celsius temperature. This conversion is only necessary in the case of particular temperature values, but not for a change in temperature. That is, an increase of 10 K is equal to an increase of 10°C.

Note that the Kelvin scale employs no degree symbol, unlike the Fahrenheit and Celsius scales.

Teach from Visuals

To help students interpret the photograph of the temperature scales, ask:

- What is the temperature of Death Valley in the photograph? *49°C or 120°F*

- Why is it important to include the scale when giving a temperature? *The number is meaningless if the scale is unknown.*

Ongoing Assessment

CHECK YOUR READING *Answer: They both measure temperature in terms of degrees. They have different numbers of degrees between the freezing point and boiling point of water, and the zero point of the Celsius scale is fixed at the freezing point of water, whereas the zero point of the Fahrenheit scale is not.*

RESOURCE CENTER
CLASSZONE.COM
Find out more about temperature and temperature scales.

During a summer day in Death Valley, California, the temperature can reach 49°C (120°F).

Temperature can be measured.

You have read that a warmer temperature means a greater average kinetic energy. How is temperature measured and what does that measurement mean? Suppose you hear on the radio that the temperature outside is 30 degrees. Do you need to wear a warm coat to spend the day outside? The answer depends on the temperature scale being used. There are two common temperature scales, both of which measure the average kinetic energy of particles. However, 30 degrees on one scale is quite different from 30 degrees on the other scale.

Temperature Scales

To establish a temperature scale, two known values and the number of units between the values are needed. The freezing and boiling points of pure water are often used as the standard values. These points are always the same under the same conditions and they are easy to reproduce. In the two common scales, temperature is measured in units called **degrees** (°), which are equally spaced units between two points.

The scale used most commonly in the United States for measuring temperature—in uses ranging from cooking directions to weather reports—is the Fahrenheit (FAR-uhn-HYT) scale (°F). It was developed in the early 1700s by Gabriel Fahrenheit. On the Fahrenheit scale, pure water freezes at 32°F and boils at 212°F. Thus, there are 180 degrees—180 equal units—between the freezing point and the boiling point of water.

The temperature scale most commonly used in the rest of the world, and also used more often in science, is the Celsius (SEHL-see-uhs) scale (°C). This scale was developed in the 1740s by Anders Celsius. On the Celsius scale, pure water freezes at 0°C and boils at 100°C, so there are 100 degrees—100 equal units—between these two temperatures.

Recall the question asked in the first paragraph of this page. If the outside temperature is 30 degrees, do you need to wear a warm coat? If the temperature is 30°F, the answer is yes, because that temperature is colder than the freezing point of water. If the temperature is 30°C, the answer is no—it is a nice warm day (86°F).

CHECK YOUR READING How are the Fahrenheit and Celsius temperature scales different? How are they similar?

DIFFERENTIATE INSTRUCTION

? More Reading Support

D What are the equally spaced units between two points? *degrees*

E What temperature scale is often used by scientists? *Celsius*

Advanced Have students calibrate the thermometers they make in the investigation on p. 41. Students should make a mark on the straw to indicate the alcohol level at a low temperature, and another mark for the level at a high temperature. The actual temperature should be measured with a real thermometer at the same time. Have students test a temperature midway between their calibration points.

 Challenge and Extension, p. 78

Thermometers

Temperature is measured by using a device called a thermometer. A **thermometer** measures temperature through the regular variation of some physical property of the material inside the thermometer. A mercury or alcohol thermometer, for example, can measure temperature because the liquid inside the thermometer always expands or contracts by a certain amount in response to a change in temperature.

Liquid-filled thermometers measure how much the liquid expands in a narrow tube as the temperature increases. The distances along the tube are marked so that the temperature can be read. At one time, thermometers were filled with liquid mercury because it expands or contracts evenly at both high and low temperatures. This means that mercury expands or contracts by the same amount in response to a given change in temperature. However, mercury is dangerous to handle, so many thermometers today are filled with alcohol instead.

Some thermometers work in a different way—they use a material whose electrical properties change when the temperature changes. These thermometers can be read by computers. Some show the temperature on a display panel and are often used in cars and in homes.

CHECK YOUR READING How do liquid-filled thermometers work?

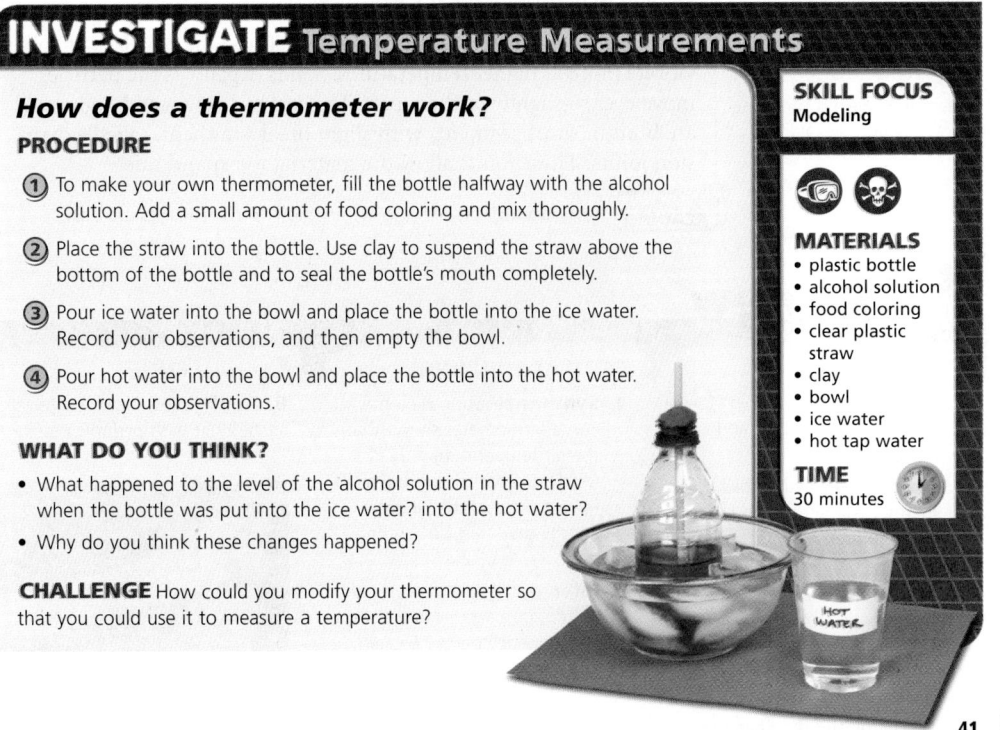

INVESTIGATE Temperature Measurements

How does a thermometer work?

PROCEDURE

1. To make your own thermometer, fill the bottle halfway with the alcohol solution. Add a small amount of food coloring and mix thoroughly.

2. Place the straw into the bottle. Use clay to suspend the straw above the bottom of the bottle and to seal the bottle's mouth completely.

3. Pour ice water into the bowl and place the bottle into the ice water. Record your observations, and then empty the bowl.

4. Pour hot water into the bowl and place the bottle into the hot water. Record your observations.

WHAT DO YOU THINK?

• What happened to the level of the alcohol solution in the straw when the bottle was put into the ice water? into the hot water?

• Why do you think these changes happened?

CHALLENGE How could you modify your thermometer so that you could use it to measure a temperature?

SKILL FOCUS
Modeling

MATERIALS
• plastic bottle
• alcohol solution
• food coloring
• clear plastic straw
• clay
• bowl
• ice water
• hot tap water

TIME
30 minutes

41 **B**

Ongoing Assessment

Describe how changes in temperature can affect matter.

Ask: What happens to all gases, many liquids, and most solids when their temperature increases? *They expand.*

 *Answer: The particles move faster and move apart from each other very slightly.*

Real World Example

Thermal expansion can be used to solve problems. For example, a metal lid stuck on a jar will expand if held under hot tap water, and the jar will open more easily. Also, home thermostats contain a coil made of two metals with different rates of expansion. When the temperature drops, the coil bends one way, and when the temperature rises, it bends the other way.

Reinforce (the **BIG** idea)

Have students relate the section to the Big Idea.

 Reinforcing Key Concepts, p. 80

2.1 ASSESS & RETEACH

Assess

 Section 2.1 Quiz, p. 22

Reteach

Ask volunteers to explain each concept and give examples.

• how temperature depends on kinetic energy
• what is needed for a temperature scale
• how a thermometer works
• what thermal expansion is

Technology Resources

Have students visit **ClassZone.com** for reteaching of Key Concepts.

 CONTENT REVIEW

 CONTENT REVIEW CD-ROM

During construction of the Gateway Arch in St. Louis, engineers had to account for thermal expansion.

Thermal Expansion

The property that makes liquid-filled thermometers work is called thermal expansion. Thermal expansion affects many substances, not just alcohol and liquid mercury. All gases, many liquids, and most solids expand when their temperature increases.

Construction engineers often have to take thermal expansion into account because steel and concrete both expand with increasing temperature. An interesting example involves the construction of the Gateway Arch in St. Louis, which is built mostly of steel.

The final piece of the Arch to be put into place was the top segment joining the two legs. The Arch was scheduled to be completed in the middle of the day for its opening ceremony. However, engineers knew that the side of the Arch facing the Sun would get hot and expand due to thermal expansion.

This expansion would narrow the gap between the legs and prevent the last piece from fitting into place. In order to complete the Arch, workers sprayed water on the side facing the Sun. The water helped cool the Arch and decreased the amount of thermal expansion. Once the final segment was in place, engineers made the connection strong enough to withstand the force of the expanding material.

Thermal expansion occurs in solids because the particles of solids vibrate more at higher temperatures. Solids expand as the particles move ever so slightly farther apart. This is why bridges and highways are built in short segments with slight breaks in them, called expansion joints. These joints allow the material to expand safely.

 **CHECK YOUR READING** Why do objects expand when their temperatures increase?

2.1 Review

KEY CONCEPTS

1. Describe the relationship between temperature and kinetic energy.

2. Describe the way in which thermometers measure temperature.

3. How can you explain thermal expansion in terms of kinetic energy?

CRITICAL THINKING

4. **Synthesize** Suppose a mercury thermometer shows that the air temperature is 22°C (72°F). Do particles in the air have more average kinetic energy than particles in the mercury? Explain.

5. **Infer** If a puddle of water is frozen, do particles in the ice have kinetic energy? Explain.

CHALLENGE

6. **Apply** Why might a sidewalk be built with periodic breaks in it?

ANSWERS

1. *Temperature is a measurement of average kinetic energy of particles in a substance. As the average kinetic energy increases, so does temperature.*

2. *through the regular variation of a physical property in response to a change in temperature*

3. *When the kinetic energy of particles in an object increases, they move faster and move farther apart from one another.*

4. *No; the temperatures are the same, so the particles of both have the same average kinetic energy.*

5. *Yes; particles in solids are always in motion.*

6. *As concrete expands and contracts with changes in temperature, it needs room to move.*

MATH in SCIENCE

MATH TUTORIAL
CLASSZONE.COM

Click on Math Tutorial for more help with temperature conversions.

Temperatures on Earth, ranging from the extremes of frigid polar regions to the hottest deserts, can differ by more than 250°F.

SKILL: METRIC CONVERSIONS

How Hot Is Hot?

Temperatures on Earth can vary greatly, from extremely hot in some deserts to frigid in polar regions. The meaning of a temperature measurement depends on which temperature scale is being used. A very high temperature on the Fahrenheit scale is equal to a much lower temperature on the Celsius scale. The table shows the formulas used to convert temperatures between the two scales.

Conversion	Formula
Fahrenheit to Celsius	$°C = \frac{5}{9}(°F - 32)$
Celsius to Fahrenheit	$°F = \frac{9}{5}°C + 32$

Example

The boiling point of pure water is 212°F. Convert that temperature to a measurement on the Celsius scale.

(1) Use the correct conversion formula.

$$°C = \frac{5}{9}(°F - 32)$$

(2) Substitute the temperature given for the correct variable in the formula.

$$°C = \frac{5}{9}(212 - 32) = \frac{5}{9} \cdot 180 = 100$$

ANSWER °C = 100

Use the information in the table below to answer the questions that follow.

Highest and Lowest Temperatures Recorded on Earth			
Location	Highest Temp. (°F)	Location	Lowest Temp. (°F)
El Azizia, Libya	136	Vostok, Antarctica	−129
Death Valley, California	134	Oimekon, Russia	−90
Tirat Tsvi, Israel	129	Verkhoyansk, Russia	−90
Cloncurry, Australia	128	Northice, Greenland	−87
Seville, Spain	122	Snag, Yukon, Canada	−81

1. What is the highest temperature in °C?

2. What is the temperature difference in °C between the highest and second highest temperatures?

3. What is the difference between the highest and lowest temperatures in °F? in °C?

CHALLENGE The surface of the Sun is approximately 5500°C. What is this temperature in °F?

ANSWERS

1. °C = 5/9 (136−32) = 5/9 (104) = 57.8

2. °C = 5/9 (134−32) = 5/9 (104) = 56.7; 57.8 − 56.7 = 1.1

3. 136 − (−129) = 265°F; 57.8 − (−89.4) = 147.2°C

CHALLENGE °F = 9/5 (5500) + 32 = 9900 + 32 = 9932

MATH IN SCIENCE
Math Skills Practice for Science

Set Learning Goal

To convert temperatures from Fahrenheit to Celsius and Celsius to Fahrenheit

Present the Science

Both common temperature scales have advantages. The Fahrenheit scale uses smaller degrees, so it is more accurate for weather reports. The Celsius scale is more closely tied to a physical constant (water's freezing point) and is more commonly used in science.

Develop Algebra Skills

- Remind students that the numerator of the fraction is above the line, and the denominator is below. To help them remember which part of the fraction to multiply, emphasize that they divide by the denominator.

- Point out that when converting from Fahrenheit to Celsius, the parentheses mean that the 32 is subtracted before multiplying by 5/9. When converting Celsius to Fahrenheit, the 32 is added after multiplying by 9/5.

DIFFERENTIATION TIP Use graph paper to model multiplying the fractions 1/5 and 1/9 by a number such as 45. Shade squares that show the fraction as a portion of a larger number.

Close

Ask: Why is knowing how to convert from one temperature scale to another useful? *Sample answer: Most people are more familiar with one scale than the other. Without conversion, temperatures given in an unfamiliar scale are meaningless.*

- Math Support, p. 107
- Math Practice, p. 108

Technology Resources

Students can visit **ClassZone.com** for practice with temperature conversions.

 MATH TUTORIAL

Students will

• Compare heat and temperature.

• Describe how heat is measured.

• Understand why some substances change temperature more easily than others.

• Measure heat transfer in an experiment.

◐ 3-Minute Warm-Up

Display Transparency 12 or copy this exercise on the board:

Match the correct temperature scale to the descriptions.

Temperature Scale

1. Fahrenheit *b*

2. Celsius *a, c, d*

Description

a. freezing point of water is 0°

b. freezing point of water is 32°

c. used by scientists and most countries

d. 100 units between freezing and boiling points of water

 T 3-Minute Warm-Up, p. T12

2.2 MOTIVATE

THINK ABOUT

PURPOSE To introduce that different substances warm up at different rates

DISCUSS Have students brainstorm answers to the question in the text. *More energy is needed to warm water.*

Ongoing Assessment

Explain how heat is different from temperature.

Ask: How does heat differ from temperature? *Heat is the flow of energy; temperature is a measure of it.*

CHECK YOUR READING *Answer: the flow of energy from warmer to cooler objects*

2.2 Energy flows from warmer to cooler objects.

◀ BEFORE, you learned

• All matter is made of moving particles

• Temperature is the measurement of average kinetic energy of particles in an object

• Temperature can be measured

▶ NOW, you will learn

• How heat is different from temperature

• How heat is measured

• Why some substances change temperature more easily than others

VOCABULARY

heat p. 44
thermal energy p. 45
calorie p. 46
joule p. 46
specific heat p. 47

THINK ABOUT

Why does water warm up so slowly?

If you have ever seen food being fried in oil or butter, you know that the metal frying pan heats up very quickly, as does the oil or butter used to coat the pan's surface.

However, if you put the same amount of water as you put oil in the same pan, the water warms up more slowly. Why does water behave so differently from the metal, oil, or butter?

NOTE-TAKING STRATEGY
The mind map organizer would be a good choice for taking notes on heat.

Heat is different from temperature.

Heat and temperature are very closely related. As a result, people often confuse the concepts of heat and temperature. However, they are not the same. Temperature is a measurement of the average kinetic energy of particles in an object. **Heat** is a flow of energy from an object at a higher temperature to an object at a lower temperature.

If you add energy as heat to a pot of water, the water's temperature starts to increase. The added energy increases the average kinetic energy of the water molecules. Once the water starts to boil, however, adding energy no longer changes the temperature of the water. Instead, the heat goes into changing the physical state of the water from liquid to gas rather than increasing the kinetic energy of the water molecules. This fact is one demonstration that heat and temperature are not the same thing.

 **CHECK YOUR READING** What is heat?

RESOURCES FOR DIFFERENTIATED INSTRUCTION

Below Level

UNIT RESOURCE BOOK

• Reading Study Guide A, pp. 83–84

• Decoding Support, p. 106

 **AUDIO CDS**

Advanced

UNIT RESOURCE BOOK

Challenge and Extension, p. 89

English Learners

UNIT RESOURCE BOOK

Spanish Reading Study Guide, pp. 87–88

AUDIO CDS

• Audio Readings in Spanish

• Audio Readings (English)

Heat and Thermal Energy

Suppose you place an ice cube in a bowl on a table. At first, the bowl and the ice cube have different temperatures. However, the ice cube melts, and the water that comes from the ice will eventually have the same temperature as the bowl. This temperature will be lower than the original temperature of the bowl but higher than the original temperature of the ice cube. The water and the bowl end up at the same temperature because the particles in the ice cube and the particles in the bowl continually bump into each other and energy is transferred from the bowl to the ice.

RESOURCE CENTER
CLASSZONE.COM

Learn more about thermal energy.

Heat is always the transfer of energy from an object at a higher temperature to an object at a lower temperature. So energy flows from the particles in the warmer bowl to the particles in the cold ice and, later, the cooler water. If energy flowed in the opposite direction— from cooler to warmer—the ice would get colder and the bowl would get hotter, and you know that never happens.

CHECK YOUR READING In which direction does heat always transfer energy?

When energy flows from a warmer object to a cooler object, the thermal energy of both of the objects changes. **Thermal energy** is the total random kinetic energy of particles in an object. Note that temperature and thermal energy are different from each other. Temperature is an average and thermal energy is a total. A glass of water can have the same temperature as Lake Superior, but the lake has far more thermal energy because the lake contains many more water molecules.

Another example of how energy is transferred through heat is shown on the right. Soon after you put ice cubes into a pitcher of lemonade, energy is transferred from the warmer lemonade to the colder ice. The lemonade's thermal energy decreases and the ice's thermal energy increases. Because the particles in the lemonade have transferred some of their energy to the particles in the ice, the average kinetic energy of the particles in the lemonade decreases. As a result, the temperature of the lemonade decreases.

Energy is transferred from the warmer lemonade to the cold ice through heat until their temperatures are equal.

CHECK YOUR READING How are heat and thermal energy related to each other?

DIFFERENTIATE INSTRUCTION

 **More Reading Support**

A What does heat do? *transfers energy*

B What is the total random kinetic energy of all particles in an object? *thermal energy*

English Learners English learners rely on patterns and conventions in the English language, and may not recognize cause-and-effect relationships in sentences that do not follow *if/then* format. Point out the cause-and-effect relationship in the following sentence from this page: "Because the particles in the lemonade have transferred . . ., the average kinetic energy of the particles in the lemonade decreases." Encourage students to look for introductory clauses and phrases rather than a particular word, such as *if.*

Address Misconceptions

IDENTIFY Ask students how a flow of energy through heat differs from the flow of a fluid such as water. If students fail to recognize that heat is not a physical form of matter like water, they may hold the misconception that heat is a form of matter that literally flows from one object to another.

CORRECT Hold an ice cube in the palm of your hand. Ask students to describe the flow of heat. Point out that energy, not particles of matter, flows from your hand to the ice cube.

REASSESS Ask: What flows from one place to another when an object is heated? *energy*

Technology Resources

Visit **ClassZone.com** for background on common student misconceptions.

MISCONCEPTION DATABASE

Teach from Visuals

To help students interpret the diagram of heat transfer from lemonade to ice, ask:

- In what direction does heat transfer energy in the diagram? *from the warm lemonade to the cold ice*
- What happens to the ice's thermal energy? *It increases.*
- What happens to the lemonade's thermal energy? *It decreases.*

Teach Difficult Concepts

Heat is often thought of as both a form of energy and a way in which energy can be transferred. Point out that in this chapter, heat is not a form of energy but rather the flow of energy.

Ongoing Assessment

 *Answer: from warmer to cooler*

 *Answer: As heat transfers energy, the thermal energy of the warmer object decreases, and the thermal energy of the cooler object increases.*

INVESTIGATE Heat Transfer

PURPOSE To investigate the specific heat of different materials by measuring a change in temperature

TIPS *30 min.*

- You might want to have students bring pennies from home.
- The hot water should be at least 60ºC for the best results.

WHAT DO YOU THINK? *The cup to which water is added will show the greatest change in temperature; the cup to which the pennies are added will show the smallest change in temperature. Different substances absorb different amounts of energy to show changes in temperature.*

CHALLENGE *Little energy is required to increase their temperatures.*

 Datasheet, Heat Transfer, p. 90

Technology Resources

Customize this student lab as needed or look for an alternative. Print rubrics to assess student lab reports.

 Lab Generator CD-ROM

Teaching with Technology

A probeware system with a temperature probe can be used to measure temperatures.

Metacognitive Strategy

Ask students what they could do to improve the accuracy of their results.

Ongoing Assessment

Describe how heat is measured.

Ask: What is a calorie? *energy to raise the temperature of 1 g of water 1ºC*

CHECK YOUR READING *Answer: in calories or joules; the amount of energy transferred between substances*

VOCABULARY Remember to make description wheel diagrams for *calorie, joule,* and other vocabulary terms.

Measuring Heat

The most common units of heat measurement are the calorie and the joule (jool). One **calorie** is the amount of energy needed to raise the temperature of 1 gram of water by 1°C. The **joule** (J) is the standard scientific unit in which energy is measured. One calorie is equal to 4.18 joules.

You probably think of calories in terms of food. However, in nutrition, one Calorie—written with a capital C—is actually one kilocalorie, or 1000 calories. This means that one Calorie in food contains enough energy to raise the temperature of 1 kilogram of water by 1°C. So, each Calorie in food contains 1000 calories of energy.

How do we know how many Calories are in a food, such as a piece of chocolate cake? The cake is burned inside an instrument called a calorimeter. The amount of energy released from the cake through heat is the number of Calories transferred from the cake to the calorimeter. The energy transferred to the calorimeter is equal to the amount of energy originally in the cake. A thermometer inside the calorimeter measures the increase in temperature from the burning cake, which is used to calculate how much energy is released.

CHECK YOUR READING How is heat measured?

INVESTIGATE Heat Transfer

Which substances change temperature faster?

PROCEDURE

1. Using the graduated cylinder and the balance, separately measure 20 g of room-temperature water, 20 g of pennies, and 20 g of aluminum foil. Pour the water into a beaker until it is needed.

2. Using the graduated cylinder, pour 50 mL of hot water into each of the cups. Record the water temperature in each cup.

3. Pour the room-temperature water into one cup. Place the pennies in the second cup and the foil in the third. After 5 minutes, record the temperature of the water in each of the cups.

WHAT DO YOU THINK?

- How did the temperature changes in the three cups compare?
- What might account for the differences you observed?

CHALLENGE Why might items such as pots and pans be made of materials like copper, stainless steel, or iron?

SKILL FOCUS Measuring

MATERIALS
- graduated cylinder
- balance
- room-temperature water
- pennies
- aluminum foil
- hot tap water
- 100 mL beaker
- 3 plastic cups
- thermometer
- stopwatch

TIME 30 minutes

DIFFERENTIATE INSTRUCTION

More Reading Support

C What are two common units for measuring heat? *calorie and joule*

D How many calories are in a Calorie, with a capital C? *1000*

Advanced Have students investigate and compare the number of Calories in fats, carbohydrates, and proteins; the number of Calories in foods they like; or the number of Calories that different people need. Have students make a table of their results to share with the class. What happens when too many Calories are consumed?

 Challenge and Extension, p. 89

Some substances change temperature more easily than others.

Have you ever seen an apple pie taken right out of the oven? If you put a piece of pie on a plate to cool, you can touch the pie crust in a few minutes and it will feel only slightly warm. But if you try to take a bite, the hot pie filling will burn your mouth. The pie crust cools much more quickly than the filling, which is mostly water.

Specific Heat

The amount of energy required to raise the temperature of 1 gram of a substance by 1°C is the **specific heat** of that substance. Every substance has its own specific heat value. So, each substance absorbs a different amount of energy in order to show the same increase in temperature.

If you look back at the definition of a calorie, you will see that it is defined in terms of water—one calorie raises the temperature of 1 gram of water by 1°C. So, water has a specific heat of exactly 1.00 calorie per gram per °C. Because one calorie is equal to 4.18 J, it takes 4.18 J to raise the temperature of one gram of water by 1°C. In joules, water's specific heat is 4.18 J per gram per °C. If you look at the specific heat graph shown below, you will see that 4.18 is an unusually large value. For example, one gram of iron has to absorb only 0.45 joules for its temperature to increase by 1°C.

A substance with a high specific heat value, like water, not only has to absorb a large quantity of energy for its temperature to increase, but it also must release a large quantity of energy for its temperature to decrease. This is why the apple pie filling can still be hot while the pie crust is cool. The liquid filling takes longer to cool. The high specific heat of water is also one reason it is used as a coolant in car radiators. The water can absorb a great deal of energy and protect the engine from getting too hot.

> **READING TIP**
> Joules per gram per °C is shown as $\frac{J}{g°C}$.

CHECK YOUR READING How is specific heat related to a change in temperature?

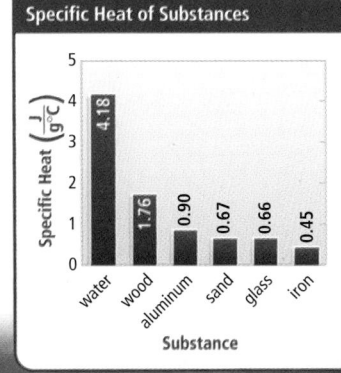

Specific Heat of Substances

(bar graph: Specific Heat (J/g°C) vs. Substance)
- water: 4.18
- wood: 1.76
- aluminum: 0.90
- sand: 0.67
- glass: 0.66
- iron: 0.45

> **APPLY** More energy is needed to warm water than many other substances. What materials in this photograph might be warmer than the water?

Chapter 2: **Temperature and Heat** 47 **B**

To help students interpret the graph of specific heat, ask: What is the specific heat of wood? *1.76 J/g°C* What does this mean? *One gram of wood absorbs 1.76 J for its temperature to rise 1°C.*

Teach Difficult Concepts

As the atoms of elements become larger, less energy is required to produce an increase in temperature. Hydrogen has the greatest specific heat value (14.3 J/g°C) and is the smallest atom. The general relationship between atomic mass and specific heat was expressed by the Dulong-Petit law in 1819, about 50 years before Mendeleyev's modern periodic table.

Teacher Demo

To help students understand how substances absorb varying amounts of energy, do the following demonstration. Light a candle and ask students what will happen if you hold an index card over the flame. Hold the card over the flame; it will catch fire. (Keep a bucket of water nearby to put out the fire.) Gather some crayon shavings and place them on top of a second index card. Ask students what they think will happen this time. Hold the card and shavings over the flame. The shavings will melt, but the card will not burn. Remove the card after the wax is melted. Ask students why this second index card did not burn.

Ongoing Assessment

Understand why some substances change temperature more easily than others.

Ask: What determines the amount of energy a substance needs to absorb to increase its temperature? *specific heat*

PHOTO CAPTION Answer: metals, sand, wood, glass

CHECK YOUR READING *Answer: The greater a substance's specific heat, the more energy is required to raise that substance's temperature.*

DIFFERENTIATE INSTRUCTION

 More Reading Support

E What is the amount of energy needed to raise the temperature of 1 gram of a specific substance by 1°C? *the substance's specific heat*

Below Level If students have trouble understanding the concept of specific heat, ask them for examples of substances that get hot faster and stay hot longer than other substances. Possible examples include fruit or other fillings with a high water content inside muffins or pies. Explain that substances that stay hot longer have a higher specific heat value.

Chapter 2 **47** **B**

Ongoing Assessment

 Answer: The more mass an object has, the more thermal energy it has.

Teach Difficult Concepts

To help students understand that a substance with a low temperature can have more thermal energy than a substance with a higher temperature, place a gallon jug of hot water and a cup of hotter water on a table. Record the temperature of the water in both containers and have students carefully feel the outside of the containers. Wait 20 minutes and repeat the observations. The gallon of hot water should be warmer. Point out that the mass of a substance, in addition to its temperature, determines how much thermal energy it has.

Reinforce (the BIG idea)

Have students relate the section to the Big Idea.

 Reinforcing Key Concepts, p. 91

2.2 ASSESS & RETEACH

Assess

A Section 2.2 Quiz, p. 23

Reteach

Divide the class into groups. Make a three-column chart on the board to compare and contrast heat, thermal energy, and specific heat. Ask volunteers to fill in the chart with examples, characteristics, and misconceptions for each term.

Technology Resources

Have students visit **ClassZone.com** for reteaching of Key Concepts.

 CONTENT REVIEW

 CONTENT REVIEW CD-ROM

Specific Heat and Mass

Recall that thermal energy is the total kinetic energy of all particles in an object. So, thermal energy depends on the object's mass. Suppose you have a cup of water at a temperature of 90°C (194°F) and a bathtub full of water at a temperature of 40°C (104°F). Which mass of water has more thermal energy? There are many more water molecules in the bathtub, so the water in the tub has more thermal energy.

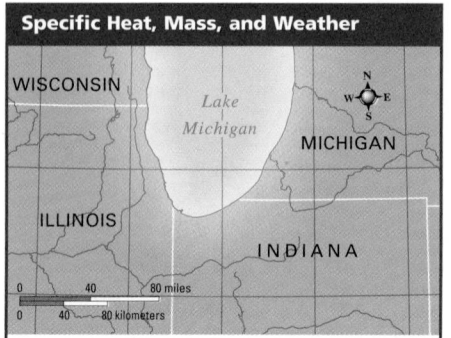

Specific Heat, Mass, and Weather

The temperature of a large body of water influences the temperature of nearby land. The green shading shows how far this effect extends.

The water in the cup has the same specific heat as the water in the tub. However, the cup of water will cool more quickly than the water in the bathtub. The tub of water has to release more thermal energy to its surroundings, through heat, to show a decrease in temperature because it has so much more mass.

This idea is particularly relevant to very large masses. For example, Lake Michigan holds 4.92 quadrillion liters (1.30 quadrillion gallons) of water. Because of the high specific heat of water and the mass of water in the lake, the temperature of Lake Michigan changes very slowly.

The temperature of the lake affects the temperatures on its shores. During spring and early summer, the lake warms slowly, which helps keep the nearby land cooler. During the winter, the lake cools slowly, which helps keep the nearby land warmer. Temperatures within about 15 miles of the lake can differ by as much as 6°C (about 10°F) from areas farther away from the lake.

As you will read in the next section, the way in which a large body of water can influence temperatures on land depends on how energy is transferred through heat.

CHECK YOUR READING How does an object's thermal energy depend on its mass?

2.2 Review

KEY CONCEPTS
1. How is temperature related to heat?
2. How do the units that are used to measure heat differ from the units that are used to measure temperature?
3. Describe specific heat in your own words.

CRITICAL THINKING
4. **Compare and Contrast** How are a calorie and a joule similar? How are they different?
5. **Synthesize** Describe the relationships among kinetic energy, temperature, heat, and thermal energy.

CHALLENGE
6. **Infer** Suppose you are spending a hot summer day by a pool. Why might the water in the pool cool the air near the pool?

ANSWERS

1. Heat transfers energy because a temperature difference exists.

2. Heat is measured in terms of temperature change.

3. the amount of energy that 1 gram of a substance needs to absorb to increase in temperature by 1°C

4. Both are used to measure heat. The joule is the standard unit for energy. One calorie equals 4.18 joules.

5. Temperature is the average kinetic energy of particles in an object; thermal energy is the total kinetic energy of particles in an object. Heat transfers thermal energy between objects due to temperature differences.

6. Water has a high specific heat, and heat transfers energy from the air to the cooler water.

Cooking with Heat

A chef makes many decisions about cooking a meal based on heat and temperature. The appropriate temperature and cooking method must be used. A chef must calculate the cooking time of each part of the meal so that everything is finished at the same time. A chef also needs to understand how heat moves through food. For example, if an oven temperature is too hot, meat can be overcooked on the outside and undercooked on the inside.

Bread vs. Meat

Chefs have to understand how energy as heat is transferred to different foods. For example, the fluffy texture of bread comes from pockets of gas that separate its fibers. The gas is a poor conductor of energy. Therefore, more energy and a longer cooking time are needed to cook bread than to cook an equal amount of meat.

What Temperature?

Eggs cook very differently under different temperatures. For example, temperature is important when baking meringue, which is made of egg whites and sugar. A Key lime pie topped with meringue is baked at 400°F to make a meringue that is soft. However, meringue baked at 275°F makes light and crisp dessert shells.

Roasting and Heat

The shape of the food being roasted is just as important as what is being roasted. Heat moves more quickly through food with a thin shape than it will through food with a thicker shape.

EXPLORE

1. **COMPARE** Using a cookbook, find the oven temperatures for baking biscuits, potatoes, and beef. Could you successfully cook a roast and biscuits in the oven at the same time?

2. **CHALLENGE** Crack open three eggs. Lightly beat one egg in each of three separate bowls. Follow the steps below.
   1. Heat about two cups of water to 75°C in a small pan.
   2. Pour one of the eggs into the water in the pan.
   3. Observe the egg and record your observations.
   4. Repeat steps 1–3 twice, once with boiling water and then with room-temperature water.

   Describe the differences that you observed among the three eggs. What may account for these differences?

Set Learning Goal

To understand why chefs need knowledge of heat and temperature

Present the Science

Many foods, such as beef, chicken, pork, and eggs, can contain microorganisms such as bacteria that cause food poisoning. Cooking foods until they reach a certain temperature kills these bacteria. Meat thermometers and other thermometers help ensure that foods reach the correct temperature. In addition, refrigerating leftovers and keeping foods cold help slow the growth of bacteria. Heat and temperature are also important to a chef because part of the job involves the presentation and appeal of food. The structure of protein changes when exposed to high temperatures, so a chef has to know how the texture of foods containing a large amount of protein will change during and after cooking.

Discussion Questions

- Ask: What can cause meat to be overcooked on the outside and undercooked on the inside? *an oven temperature that is too hot*

- Ask: How does the shape of a roast affect how fast it cooks? *Heat moves more quickly through a thin roast than a thick roast.*

Close

Ask: How do chefs use their knowledge of heat and temperature? *to choose the right temperature and cooking method; to finish cooking every part of the meal at the right time; to understand how heat moves through food*

EXPLORE

1. *COMPARE By changing the length of time they are in the oven, or by putting them in the oven at different times.*

2. *CHALLENGE The egg in room-temperature water doesn't visibly change. In boiling water it stays in one piece and turns white right away. In 75°C water it spreads out and slowly turns slightly white. The water temperature determines what happens to the eggs.*

● Set Learning Goals

Students will

• Explain how energy is transferred through heat.

• Describe how materials are used to control the transfer of energy through heat.

◐ 3-Minute Warm-Up

Display Transparency 13 or copy this exercise on the board:

Match each definition with the correct term.

Definitions

1. the flow of energy from warmer objects to cooler objects *c*

2. the average kinetic energy of particles in an object *a*

3. the total kinetic energy of particles in an object *d*

Terms

a. temperature

b. specific heat

c. heat

d. thermal energy

e. kinetic energy

 T 3-Minute Warm-Up, p. T13

EXPLORE Conduction

PURPOSE To observe the transfer of energy between objects in direct contact

TIP *10 min.* Make sure the hot water in the large beaker does not overflow into the smaller beaker.

WHAT DO YOU THINK? *The temperature of the cold water increased, and the temperature of the hot water decreased. Energy flowed from warm to cooler; the changes in temperature are indicated by the two thermometers.*

KEY CONCEPT

2.3 The transfer of energy as heat can be controlled.

◁ **BEFORE, you learned**

• Temperature is the average amount of kinetic energy of particles in an object

• Heat is the flow of energy from warmer objects to cooler objects

▷ **NOW, you will learn**

• How energy is transferred through heat

• How materials are used to control the transfer of energy through heat

VOCABULARY

conduction p. 51
conductor p. 51
insulator p. 51
convection p. 52
radiation p. 53

EXPLORE Conduction

How can you observe a flow of energy?

PROCEDURE

① Fill the large beaker halfway with hot tap water. Fill the small beaker halfway with cold water. Place a thermometer in each beaker. Record the temperature of the water in each beaker.

② Without removing the water in either beaker, place the small beaker inside the large beaker. Record the temperature in each beaker every 30 seconds for 2 minutes.

MATERIALS

• 500 mL beaker
• hot tap water
• 200 mL beaker
• cold water
• 2 thermometers
• stopwatch

WHAT DO YOU THINK?

• How did the water temperature in each beaker change?

• In which direction did energy flow? How do you know?

NOTE-TAKING STRATEGY
Main idea and detail notes would be a useful strategy for taking notes on how heat transfers energy.

Energy moves as heat in three ways.

Think about what you do to keep warm on a cold day. You may wear several layers of clothing, sit next to a heater, or avoid drafty windows. On a hot day, you may wear light clothing and sit in the shade of a tree. In all of these situations, you are trying to control the transfer of energy between yourself and your surroundings.

Recall that heat is always a transfer of energy from objects at a higher temperature to objects at a lower temperature. How does energy get transferred from a warmer object to a cooler one? There are three different ways in which this transfer of energy can occur—by conduction, convection, and radiation. So, in trying to control heat, it is necessary to control conduction, convection, and radiation.

RESOURCES FOR DIFFERENTIATED INSTRUCTION

Below Level

UNIT RESOURCE BOOK
• Reading Study Guide A, pp. 94–95
• Decoding Support, p. 106

 AUDIO CDS

R Additional INVESTIGATION, Observing Convection, A, B, & C, pp. 118–126; Teacher Instructions, pp. 320–321

Advanced

UNIT RESOURCE BOOK
• Challenge and Extension, p. 100
• Challenge Reading, pp. 102–103

English Learners

UNIT RESOURCE BOOK
Spanish Reading Study Guide, pp. 98–99

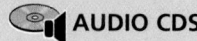 **AUDIO CDS**

• Audio Readings in Spanish
• Audio Readings (English)

Conduction

One way in which energy is transferred as heat is through direct contact between objects. **Conduction** is the process that moves energy from one object to another when they are touching physically. If you have ever picked up a bowl of hot soup, you have experienced conduction.

Conduction occurs any time that objects at different temperatures come into contact with each other. The average kinetic energy of particles in the warmer object is greater than that of the particles in the cooler object. When particles of the objects collide, some of the kinetic energy of the particles in the warmer object is transferred to the cooler object. As long as the objects are in contact, conduction continues until the temperatures of the objects are equal.

Conduction can also occur within a single object. In this case, energy is transferred from the warmer part of the object to the cooler part of the object by heat. Suppose you put a metal spoon into a cup of hot cocoa. Energy will be conducted from the warm end of the spoon to the cool end until the temperature of the entire spoon is the same.

Some materials transfer the kinetic energy of particles better than others. **Conductors** are materials that transfer energy easily. Often, conductors also have a low specific heat. For example, metals are typically good conductors. You know that when one end of a metal object gets hot, the other end quickly becomes hot as well. Consider pots or pans that have metal handles. A metal handle becomes too hot to touch soon after the pan is placed on a stove that has been turned on.

Other materials, called **insulators,** are poor conductors. Insulators often have high specific heats. Some examples of insulators are wood, paper, and plastic foam. In fact, plastic foam is a good insulator because it contains many small spaces that are filled with air. A plastic foam cup will not easily transfer energy by conduction. As a result, plastic foam is often used to keep cold drinks cold or hot drinks hot. Think about the pan handle mentioned above. Often, the handle is made of a material that is an insulator, such as wood or plastic. Although a wood or plastic handle will get hot when the pan is on a stove, it takes a much longer time for wood or plastic to get hot as compared to a metal handle.

VOCABULARY
Remember to make a description wheel diagram for *conduction* and other vocabulary terms.

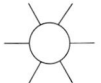

Conduction transfers energy from the cocoa to the mug to the person's hands.

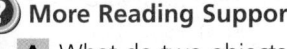 **CHECK YOUR READING** How are conductors and insulators different?

DIFFERENTIATE INSTRUCTION

? More Reading Support

A What do two objects need for conduction to occur? *touch and a temperature difference*

B What are poor conductors of energy? *insulators*

English Learners Point out different word forms to English learners as they appear in the text.

| conductor | insulator | radiate |
| conduction | insulation | radiation |

Have students look up one of the pairs of words and compare their definitions. Ask students what they might conclude about the word ending *-tion.*

Teacher Demo

To help students understand heat conduction, place a small amount of wax at various spots on a copper rod and ask students to predict what will happen to the wax if the rod is heated on one end. Have students share their predictions about what will happen and their reasons for those predictions. Then use a candle to heat one end of the copper rod so students can test their predictions. The wax closest to the heat source will melt first, and the wax farthest away will melt last. Based on their observations, have them discuss the behavior of heat when a copper rod is heated.

Teach from Visuals

To help students interpret the photograph of conduction from the mug of cocoa, ask: What is happening in the photograph? *The hot cocoa transfers energy through the wall of the mug to the hand holding the mug and to the air.*

Develop Critical Thinking

PREDICT Have students predict what will happen in terms of particle movement when energy is conducted from the hot cocoa through the mug to a person's hands. *Particles that are moving faster will bump into slower particles and transfer energy.*

EXPLORE (the **BIG** idea)

Revisit "Does It Chill?" on p. 35. Have students explain their results.

Ongoing Assessment

CHECK YOUR READING *Answer: Conductors easily transfer energy, but insulators do not. Conductors often have low specific heats, and insulators often have high specific heats.*

Address Misconceptions

IDENTIFY Ask: In what direction, such as upward, downward, or sideways, is energy transferred through heat? If students say only upward, they may hold the misconception that heat only rises.

CORRECT Point out that the common phrase "Heat rises" is misleading. Have students look at the diagram again. Point out that warm air is pushed up by cooler, denser air. To show that heat can travel in any direction, use a radiant heat source. Have students put their hand close to the heat source, but not above it, to observe that heat travels in all directions. The demonstration on p. 51 also shows how heat travels in different directions.

REASSESS Ask students to describe what causes warm air to rise. *It is pushed up by cooler, denser air.*

Technology Resources

Visit **ClassZone.com** for background on common student misconceptions.

 MISCONCEPTION DATABASE

Teach from Visuals

To help students interpret the diagram of convection in air, ask:

- What happens to air as it cools? *It becomes more dense and sinks.*

- What happens to cooler, denser air when it moves under warm air? *It is warmed by conduction from the ground.*

Integrate the Sciences

Convection is the process thought to be responsible for the movement of Earth's internal energy. As hot mantle near Earth's core rises toward the crust, it cools and is pushed aside by hot mantle rising beneath it. It continues to cool, becomes more dense, and sinks back toward Earth's core, creating convection currents.

Ongoing Assessment

 READING VISUALS *more dense at 2 where air is cool; less dense at 1 where air is warmer*

Convection

 C

▼ REMINDER
Density = $\frac{mass}{Volume}$

READING TiP
As you read about the cycle that occurs during convection, follow the steps in the illustration below.

Energy can also be transferred through the movement of gases or liquids. **Convection** is the process that transfers energy by the movement of large numbers of particles in the same direction within a liquid or gas. In most substances, as the kinetic energy of particles increases, the particles spread out over a larger area. An increased distance between particles causes a decrease in the density of the substance. Convection occurs when a cooler, denser mass of the gas or liquid replaces a warmer, less dense mass of the gas or liquid by pushing it upward.

Convection is a cycle in nature responsible for most winds and ocean currents. When the temperature of a region of air increases, the particles in the air spread out and the air becomes less dense.

① Cooler, denser air flows in underneath the warmer, less dense air, and pushes the warmer air upward.

② When this air cools, it becomes more dense than the warmer air beneath it.

③ The cooled air sinks and moves under the warmer air.

Convection in liquids is similar. Warm water is less dense than cold water, so the warm water is pushed upward as cooler, denser water moves underneath. When the warm water that has been pushed up cools, its density increases. The cycle continues when this more dense water sinks, pushing warmer water up again.

Recall that a large body of water, such as Lake Michigan, influences the temperature of the land nearby. This effect is due to convection. During the spring and early summer, the lake is cool and warms more slowly than the land. The air above the land gets warmer than the air over the water. The warmer air above the land is less dense than the cooler air above the water. The cooler, denser air moves onshore and pushes the warmer air up. The result is a cooling breeze from the lake.

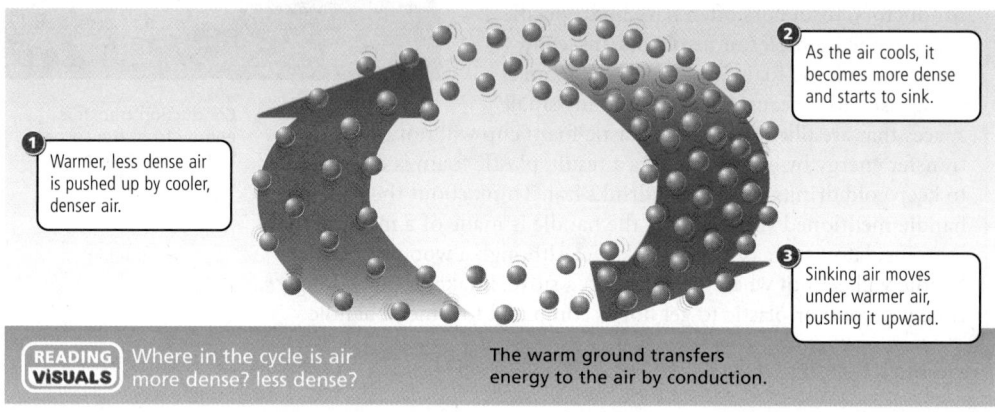

① Warmer, less dense air is pushed up by cooler, denser air.

② As the air cools, it becomes more dense and starts to sink.

③ Sinking air moves under warmer air, pushing it upward.

The warm ground transfers energy to the air by conduction.

READING VISUALS Where in the cycle is air more dense? less dense?

DIFFERENTIATE INSTRUCTION

? More Reading Support

C What is the process that transfers energy by the motion of many particles in liquids or gases? *convection*

Additional Investigation To reinforce Section 2.3 learning goals, use the following full-period investigation:

R **Additional INVESTIGATION**, Observing Convection, A, B, & C, pp. 118–126, 320–321

Below Level Remind students that density is the amount of mass of a substance in a certain volume. Because the particles in warm air are farther apart than the particles in cold air, a certain volume of warm air has fewer particles than the same volume of cold air. Warm air therefore is less dense than cold air.

Radiation

Radiation is another way in which energy can be transferred from one place to another. **Radiation** is energy that travels as electromagnetic waves, which include visible light, microwaves, and infrared (IHN-fruh-REHD) light. The Sun is the most significant source of radiation that you experience on a daily basis. However, all objects—even you—emit radiation and release energy to their surroundings.

Consider radiation from the Sun. You can feel radiation as heat when radiation from the Sun warms your skin. The radiation emitted from the Sun strikes the particles in your body and transfers energy. This transfer of energy increases the movement of particles in your skin, which you detect as an increase in temperature. Of course, you are not the only object on Earth that absorbs the Sun's radiation. Everything—from air to concrete sidewalks—absorbs radiation that increases particle motion and produces an increase in temperature.

When radiation is emitted from one object and then is absorbed by another, the result is often a transfer of energy through heat. Like both conduction and convection, radiation can transfer energy from warmer to cooler objects. However, radiation differs from conduction and convection in a very significant way. Radiation can travel through empty space, as it does when it moves from the Sun to Earth. If this were not the case, radiation from the Sun would have no effect on Earth.

When radiation from the Sun is absorbed, energy is transferred through heat.

SIMULATION
CLASSZONE.COM

Identify examples of conduction, convection, or radiation.

CHECK YOUR READING How does radiation transfer energy?

Different materials are used to control the transfer of energy.

Energy is always being transferred between objects at different temperatures. It is often important to slow this movement of energy. For example, if energy were always transferred quickly and efficiently through heat, it would not be possible to keep a building warm during a cold day or to keep cocoa hot in a thermos.

Chapter 2: **Temperature and Heat** 53 **B**

Teach from Visuals

To help students interpret the diagrams and photographs of the polar bear and the vacuum flask, ask:

• Why is the polar bear's hollow hair an effective insulator? *Air inside the hair does not easily conduct energy from the warm bear to the cold air.*

• What is the insulator in the vacuum flask? *empty space*

 This visual is also available as T14 in the Unit Transparency Book.

Integrate the Sciences

In some homes, much of the energy used for heating is wasted because energy flows through leaks around windows and doors and in floors, walls, and ceilings. Using more fuel and electricity adds to the pollution of the environment and to the depletion of nonrenewable resources. Properly insulating a home makes it more energy efficient and saves money.

Develop Critical Thinking

EVALUATE In addition to hollow guard hairs and a thick layer of fat, polar bears have other characteristics that help keep them warm in their environment. Their fur is oily, and their skin is black. How might these characteristics help? *Radiation that penetrates a polar bear's fur is absorbed more readily by the black pigment of the skin; the oily fur repels water so a polar bear can easily shake off water before the water freezes into ice.*

Ongoing Assessment

READING VISUALS *Sample answer: It provides insulation and slows the transfer of energy through conduction. In the hair, air is the insulator; in the vacuum flask, empty space is the insulator.*

Insulation

Insulators used by people are similar to insulators in nature. Polar bears are so well insulated that they tend to overheat.

The polar bear's hollow guard hair is an effective insulator because air inside the hair does not easily conduct energy.

hollow hair

Vacuum Flask

hot liquid (inside flask)

air (outside flask)

inner reflective layer

outer case

empty space

The empty space between layers in a vacuum flask prevents the conduction of energy through heat.

Polar bears have several layers of insulation. They have a layer of fat up to 11 cm thick, a 2.5–5.0 cm thick layer of fur, and an outer layer of hollow guard hairs.

READING VISUALS How is the polar bear's hollow hair similar to the empty space in a vacuum flask? How is it different?

B 54 Unit: Energy and the Changing Earth

DIFFERENTIATE INSTRUCTION

Alternative Assessment Have students write a paragraph describing the insulators in the photograph and how they work.

Insulators are used to control and slow the transfer of energy from warmer objects to cooler objects because they are poor conductors of energy. You can think of an insulator as a material that keeps cold things cold or hot things hot.

Sometimes people say that insulation "keeps out the cold." An insulator actually works by trapping energy. During the winter, you use insulators such as wool to slow the loss of your body heat to cold air. The wool traps air against your body, and because both air and wool are poor conductors, you lose body heat at a slower rate. Fiberglass insulation in the outer walls of a building works in the same way. The fiberglass slows the movement of energy from a building to the outside during cold weather, and it slows the movement of energy into the building during hot weather.

A vacuum flask, or thermos, works in a slightly different way to keep liquids either hot or cold. Between two layers of the flask is an empty space. This space prevents conduction between the inside and outside walls of the flask. Also, the inside of the flask is covered with a shiny material that reflects much of the radiation that strikes it. This prevents radiation from either entering or leaving the flask.

Insulators that people use are often very similar to insulators in nature. Look at the photograph of the polar bear on page 120. Because of the arctic environment in which the polar bear lives, it needs several different types of insulation. The polar bear's fur helps to trap a layer of air against its body to keep warmth inside. Polar bears also have guard hairs that extend beyond the fur. These guard hairs are hollow and contain air. Because air is a poor conductor, the bear's body heat is not easily released into the air.

 **CHECK YOUR READING** How does insulation keep a building warm?

 **Review**

KEY CONCEPTS

1. What are three ways in which energy can be transferred through heat? Provide an example of each.
2. Explain how convection is a cycle in nature.
3. Describe how an insulator can slow a transfer of energy.

CRITICAL THINKING

4. **Compare and Contrast** Describe the similarities and differences among conduction, convection, and radiation.
5. **Synthesize** Do you think solids can undergo convection? Why or why not? Explain.

○ CHALLENGE

6. **Infer** During the day, wind often blows from a body of water to the land. What do you think would happen at night? Explain.

Ongoing Assessment

Describe how different materials are used to control the transfer of energy through heat.

Ask: What property do materials that are used to control the transfer of energy as heat have in common? *They trap energy.*

  *Answer: by slowing the transfer of energy from the building to the cooler outside air*

Reinforce （the **BIG** idea）

Have students relate the section to the Big Idea.

 Reinforcing Key Concepts, p. 101

2.3 ASSESS & RETEACH

Assess

Section 2.3 Quiz, p. 24

Reteach

Ask students to help you make a Venn diagram on the board that compares conduction, convection, and radiation. Ask volunteers to come forward and contribute examples of each.

Technology Resources

Have students visit **ClassZone.com** for reteaching of Key Concepts.

 CONTENT REVIEW

 CONTENT REVIEW CD-ROM

ANSWERS

1. Sample answer: conduction, metal spoon in hot cocoa; convection, air moving in a cycle; radiation, sunlight transferring energy to skin

2. Warm air is pushed up by cooler, denser air. As air cools, it becomes more dense, sinks, and moves under warmer air.

3. It is a poor conductor, so energy is only slowly transferred.

4. All are ways that heat transfers energy. Conduction occurs only with direct contact. Convection occurs in a cycle in gases or liquids. Radiation travels as EM waves through empty space.

5. No; particles in a solid cannot move freely.

6. The land cools more quickly than the water, and wind blows from the land to the water.

Focus

PURPOSE To design and test an insulated bottle that slows a change in the temperature of water as compared to a noninsulated control bottle

OVERVIEW Students will design and build an insulated bottle. They will measure the temperature change of water in the insulated bottle and a control bottle. Students will find the following:

- The temperature of the water in the control bottle should change more than that of the water in the insulated bottle.

- Insulation slows the transfer of energy through heat.

Lab Preparation

- Have students bring in small plastic bottles that hold over 200 mL. Each group should use two identical bottles.

- Prior to the investigation, have students read through the investigation and prepare their data tables. Or you may wish to copy and distribute datasheets and rubrics.

 R UNIT RESOURCE BOOK, pp. 109–117

SCIENCE TOOLKIT, F13

Lab Management

- Review with students how to put the thermometers in the bottles and hold them in place with clay so that they do not touch the bottom or sides of the bottle.

- Students should be ready to insert the thermometers and clay before getting the hot or cold water.

Teaching with Technology

A probeware system with a temperature probe can be used to measure and record temperatures. A CBL system can graph the data.

CHAPTER INVESTIGATION

MATERIALS
- 2 small plastic bottles
- 2 thermometers
- modeling clay
- graduated cylinder
- tap water (hot or cold)
- foam packing peanuts
- plastic wrap
- aluminum foil
- soil
- sand
- rubber bands
- coffee can
- beaker
- stopwatch

Insulators

OVERVIEW AND PURPOSE

To keep warm in cold weather, a person needs insulation. A down-filled coat, such as the one worn by the girl in the photograph, is a very effective insulator because it contains a great deal of air. Energy is transferred rapidly through some substances and quite slowly through others. In this investigation, you will

- design and build an insulator for a bottle to maintain the temperature of the water inside
- test an unchanged bottle and your experimental bottle to see which maintains the water's temperature more effectively

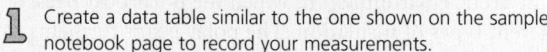 **Problem**

How can a bottle be insulated most effectively?

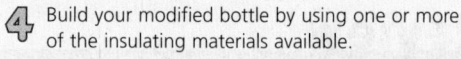 **Procedure**

1. Create a data table similar to the one shown on the sample notebook page to record your measurements.

2. Set aside plastic bottles, thermometers, modeling clay, and a graduated cylinder. Decide whether you will test hot or cold water in your bottles.

3. From the other materials available to you, design a way to modify one of the bottles so that it will keep the temperature of the water constant for a longer period of time than the control bottle.

4. Build your modified bottle by using one or more of the insulating materials available.

B 56 Unit: Energy and the Changing Earth

INVESTIGATION RESOURCES

 R CHAPTER INVESTIGATION, Insulators
- Level A, pp. 109–112
- Level B, pp. 113–116
- Level C, p. 117

Advanced students should complete Levels B & C.

 Writing a Lab Report, D12–13

Technology Resources

Customize this student lab as needed or look for an alternative. Print rubrics to assess student lab reports.

 Lab Generator CD-ROM

5. Fill each bottle with 200 mL of hot or cold water. Make sure that the water in each bottle is the same temperature.

6. Place a thermometer into each bottle. The thermometers should touch only the water, not the bottom or sides of the bottles. Use modeling clay to hold the thermometers in place in the bottles.

7. Record the starting temperature of the water in both bottles. Continue to observe and record the temperature of the water in both bottles every 2 minutes for 30 minutes. Record these temperatures in your data table.

step 6

▶ Observe and Analyze

Write It Up

1. **COMMUNICATE** Draw the setup of your experimental bottle in your notebook. Be sure to label the materials that you used to insulate your experimental bottle.

2. **RECORD OBSERVATIONS** Make sure you record all of your measurements and observations in the data table.

3. **GRAPH** Make a double line graph of the temperature data. Graph temperature versus time. Plot the temperature on the vertical axis, or y-axis, and the time on the horizontal axis, or x-axis. Use different colors to show the data from the different bottles.

4. **IDENTIFY VARIABLES, CONTROLS, AND CONSTANTS** Which bottle was the control? What was the variable? What were the constants in both setups?

5. **ANALYZE** Obtain the experimental results from two other groups that used a different insulator. Compare your results with the results from the other groups. Which bottle changed temperature most quickly?

▶ Conclude
Write It Up

1. **EVALUATE** Explain why the materials used by different groups might have been more or less effective as insulators. How might you change your design to improve its insulating properties?

2. **IDENTIFY LIMITS** Describe possible sources of error in the procedure or any points at which errors might have occurred. Why is it important to use the same amount of water in both bottles?

3. **APPLY** Energy can be transferred as heat by radiation, conduction, and convection. Which of these processes might be slowed by the insulation around your bottle? Explain.

▶ INVESTIGATE Further

CHALLENGE We depend on our clothing to keep us from losing body heat when we go outside in cold weather. How might you determine the type of clothing that would provide the best insulation? Design an experiment that would test your hypothesis.

Insulators
Problem How can a bottle be insulated most effectively?

Observe and Analyze
Table 1. Water Temperature Measurements

Time (min)	Control Bottle Temperature (°C)	Experimental Bottle Temperature (°C)
0		
2		
4		
6		
8		
10		

Conclude

Chapter 2: **Temperature and Heat** 57 **B**

▶ Observe and Analyze

Write It Up

1. See students' drawings.

2. See students' tables.

3. The graph should indicate that the water in the insulated bottle has a more stable temperature than the water in the control bottle.

4. The control was the unmodified bottle. The variable was the insulating material used. The amount and the starting temperature of the water were the same for both setups.

5. Answers will vary depending on the different insulators being compared.

▶ Conclude
Write It Up

1. Sample answer: The most effective designs used materials that have the highest specific heats and contain a large amount of air. Materials that are tightly packed are less effective. A design may be improved by using a material with more effective insulating properties.

2. Possible sources of error include different starting temperatures, inaccurate volume measurements, thermometers touching the bottom or sides of the bottles, inaccurate temperature measurements, different-sized bottles, and one bottle being disturbed more than the other. The same amount of water is important because both bottles need to start with the same thermal energy.

3. Conduction is the form of energy transfer that will be most affected by the materials available, although transfer by radiation will also be affected.

▶ INVESTIGATE Further

CHALLENGE Answer: Students' experiments should have a control and test different types of clothing materials.

Post-Lab Discussion

Ask: Why didn't it matter if you used hot or cold water? *Heat is the transfer of energy from a warmer substance to a colder substance. The insulating material slows down the transfer of energy either from the hot water to the cooler bottle and air or from the warm air and bottle to the colder water.*

BACK TO

the **BIG** idea

Have students look at the photograph on pp. 34–35. Ask them to summarize how heat affects temperatures in the photograph. *Radiation from the Sun is transferring energy to particles in the ground and the giraffe's skin. This increases the kinetic energy of the particles in the ground and skin, which increases their temperatures.*

◀ KEY CONCEPTS SUMMARY

SECTION 2.1

Ask: Which liquid has particles with a higher average kinetic energy, and how do you know? *The particles in the hot liquid have a higher average kinetic energy and are moving faster, as shown by the motion lines.*

SECTION 2.2

Ask: What is happening to energy in the lemonade and ice? *Energy is transferred through heat from the lemonade to the cooler ice.*

Ask: When will the transfer of energy stop? *when there is no temperature difference*

SECTION 2.3

Ask: How does energy transferred differently by conduction, convection, and radiation? *Conduction requires direct contact, convection requires movement of gases or liquids, and radiation travels via electromagnetic waves.*

Review Concepts

- Big Idea Flow Chart, p. T9
- Chapter Outline, pp. T15–T16

 # Chapter Review

the **BIG** idea

Heat is a flow of energy due to temperature differences.

CONTENT REVIEW
CLASSZONE.COM

◀ KEY CONCEPTS SUMMARY

2.1 Temperature depends on particle movement.
- All particles in matter have kinetic energy.
- Temperature is the measurement of the average kinetic energy of particles in an object.
- Temperature is commonly measured on the Fahrenheit or Celsius scales.

hot liquid

cold liquid

Particles in a warmer substance have a greater average kinetic energy than particles in a cooler substance.

VOCABULARY
kinetic theory of matter p. 38
temperature p. 39
degree p. 40
thermometer p. 41

2.2 Energy flows from warmer to cooler objects.
- Heat is a transfer of energy from an object at a higher temperature to an object at a lower temperature.
- Different materials require different amounts of energy to change temperature.

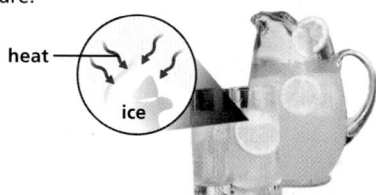
heat

Energy is transferred from the warmer lemonade to the cold ice through heat.

ice

VOCABULARY
heat p. 44
thermal energy p. 45
calorie p. 46
joule p. 46
specific heat p. 47

2.3 The transfer of energy as heat can be controlled.
- Energy can be transferred by conduction, convection, and radiation.
- Different materials are used to control the transfer of energy.

VOCABULARY
conduction p. 51
conductor p. 51
insulator p. 51
convection p. 52
radiation p. 53

Types of Energy Transfer		
Conduction	**Convection**	**Radiation**
• Energy transferred by direct contact • Energy flows directly from warmer object to cooler object • Can occur within one object • Continues until object temperatures are equal	• Occurs in gases and liquids • Movement of large number of particles in same direction • Occurs due to difference in density • Cycle occurs while temperature differences exist	• Energy transferred by electromagnetic waves such as light, microwaves, and infrared radiation • All objects radiate energy • Can transfer energy through empty space

B **58** Unit: **Energy and the Changing Earth**

Technology Resources

Have students visit **ClassZone.com** or use the CD-ROM for a cumulative review of concepts.

 CONTENT REVIEW

 CONTENT REVIEW CD-ROM

Engage students in a whole-class interactive review of Key Concepts. Edit content as you wish.

 POWER PRESENTATIONS

Reviewing Vocabulary

Make a frame for each of the vocabulary terms listed below. Write the term in the center. Decide what information to frame it with. Use definitions, examples, descriptions, parts, or pictures.

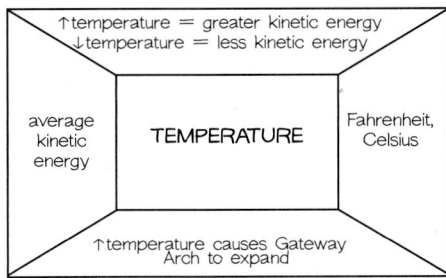

↑temperature = greater kinetic energy
↓temperature = less kinetic energy

average kinetic energy

TEMPERATURE

Fahrenheit, Celsius

↑temperature causes Gateway Arch to expand

1. kinetic theory of matter
2. heat
3. thermal energy
4. conduction
5. convection
6. radiation

In two or three sentences, describe how the terms in the following pairs are related to each other. Underline each term in your answers.

7. calorie, joule

8. conductor, insulator

Reviewing Key Concepts

Multiple Choice *Choose the letter of the best answer.*

9. What is the zero point in the Celsius scale?
   a. the freezing point of pure water
   b. the boiling point of pure water
   c. the freezing point of mercury
   d. the boiling point of alcohol

10. Energy is always transferred through heat from?
    a. an object with a lower specific heat to one with a higher specific heat
    b. a cooler object to a warmer object
    c. an object with a higher specific heat to one with a lower specific heat
    d. a warmer object to a cooler object

11. The average kinetic energy of particles in an object can be measured by its
    a. heat
    b. thermal energy
    c. calories
    d. temperature

12. How is energy transferred by convection?
    a. by direct contact between objects
    b. by electromagnetic waves
    c. by movement of groups of particles in gases or liquids
    d. by movement of groups of particles in solid objects

13. The total kinetic energy of particles in an object is
    a. heat
    b. thermal energy
    c. calories
    d. temperature

14. Water requires more energy than an equal mass of iron for its temperature to increase by a given amount because water has a greater
    a. thermal energy
    b. specific heat
    c. temperature
    d. kinetic energy

15. Energy from the Sun travels to Earth through which process?
    a. temperature
    b. conduction
    c. radiation
    d. convection

16. An insulator keeps a home warm by
    a. slowing the transfer of cold particles from outside to inside
    b. increasing the specific heat of the air inside
    c. slowing the transfer of energy from inside to outside
    d. increasing the thermal energy of the walls

17. Conduction is the transfer of energy from a warmer object to a cooler object through
    a. a vacuum
    b. a gas
    c. direct contact
    d. empty space

Short Answer *Write a short answer to each question.*

18. How are kinetic energy and temperature related to each other?

19. What is the difference between heat and temperature?

Reviewing Vocabulary

1. Frames should include that the kinetic theory of matter states that all particles in matter are in constant motion.

2. Frames should include that heat is the transfer of energy from an object at a higher temperature to one at a lower temperature.

3. Frames should include that thermal energy is the total amount of kinetic energy of the particles in an object.

4. Frames should include that conduction transfers energy through direct contact between objects.

5. Frames should include that convection transfers energy through the movement of many particles of a gas or liquid.

6. Frames should include that radiation transfers energy through electromagnetic waves.

7. Sample answer: The calorie and the joule are measures of heat. One calorie is the amount of energy needed to raise the temperature of 1 g of water by 1°C. One calorie is equal to 4.18 joules.

8. Sample answer: Conductors easily transfer energy, and insulators slow the transfer of energy. Conductors typically have a low specific heat, and insulators typically have a high specific heat.

Reviewing Key Concepts

9. a
10. d
11. d
12. c
13. b
14. b
15. c
16. c
17. c

18. Temperature measures the average kinetic energy of particles in a substance.

19. Heat is the transfer of energy between objects that differ in temperature. Temperature is a measurement of the average kinetic energy of particles in an object.

ASSESSMENT RESOURCES

 UNIT ASSESSMENT BOOK
- Chapter Test A, pp. 25–28
- Chapter Test B, pp. 29–32
- Chapter Test C, pp. 33–36
- Alternative Assessment, pp. 37–38

 SPANISH ASSESSMENT BOOK
Spanish Chapter Test, pp. 225–228

Technology Resources

Edit test items and answer choices.

 Test Generator CD-ROM

Visit **ClassZone.com** to extend test practice.

 Test Practice

Thinking Critically

20. B has the higher temperature because its particles are moving faster.

21. If A were chilled, its particles would slow down and become more tightly packed. If B were warmed, its particles would speed up and have more space between them.

22. Energy would flow from B to A because B is warmer and heat always transfers energy from warm substances to cooler substances.

23. The illustrations would be identical because heat will transfer energy until the substances are the same temperature.

24. Both processes transfer energy. Convection occurs in large regions of gases and liquids, but not in solids. Conduction occurs by direct contact between substances.

25. Radiation directly from the Sun is being avoided. Conduction to any part of the body in contact with the ground is still felt. Convection might be felt if air is moving.

26. Check students' diagrams; answers should be similar in concept to the convection diagram on p. 52

Using Math Skills in Science

27. about 20°F

28. 100 calories

29. 418 joules

30. 45 joules

the BIG idea

31. Answers will vary.

32. Answers should indicate that the kinetic theory of matter states that all particles of matter are in constant motion.

UNIT PROJECTS

Collect schedules, materials lists, and questions. Be sure dates and materials are obtainable, and questions are focused.

 Unit Projects, pp. 5–10

Thinking Critically

The illustrations below show particle movement in a substance at two different temperatures. Use the illustrations to answer the next four questions.

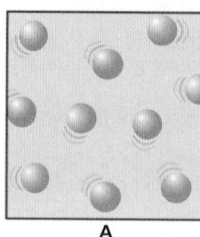 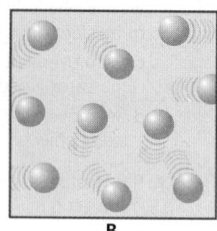

A   B

20. **OBSERVE** Which illustration represents the substance when it is at a higher temperature? Explain.

21. **PREDICT** What would happen to the particles in illustration A if the substance were chilled? What would happen if the particles in illustration B were warmed?

22. **PREDICT** If energy is transferred from one of the substances to the other through heat, in which direction would the energy flow (from A to B, or from B to A)? Why?

23. **COMMUNICATE** Suppose energy is transferred from one of the substances to the other through heat. Draw a sketch that shows what the particles of both substances would look like when the transfer of energy is complete. Explain.

24. **COMPARE AND CONTRAST** How are conduction and convection similar? How are they different?

25. **DRAW CONCLUSIONS** Suppose you are outdoors on a hot day and you move into the shade of a tree. Which form of energy transfer are you avoiding? Which type of energy transfer are you still feeling? Explain.

26. **COMMUNICATE** Draw a sketch that shows how convection occurs in a liquid. Label the sketch to indicate how the process occurs in a cycle.

Using Math Skills in Science

Use the illustrations of the two thermometers below to answer the next four questions.

A   B

27. How much of a change in temperature occurred between A and B in the Fahrenheit scale?

28. Suppose the temperatures were measured in 10 g of water. How much energy, in calories, would have been added to cause that increase in temperature? (Hint: 1 calorie raises the temperature of 1 g of water by 1°C.)

29. Again, suppose the temperatures shown above were measured in 10 g of water. How much energy, in joules, would have been added? (Hint: 1 calorie = 4.18 joules.)

30. Suppose that the temperatures were measured for 10 g of iron. How much energy, in joules, would have been added to cause the increase in temperature? (Hint: see graph on p. 47.)

the BIG idea

31. **ANALYZE** Look back at the photograph and the question on pages 34 and 35. How has your understanding of temperature and heat changed after reading the chapter?

32. **COMMUNICATE** Explain the kinetic theory of matter in your own words. What, if anything, about the kinetic theory of matter surprised you?

UNIT PROJECTS

If you need to do an experiment for your unit project, gather the materials. Be sure to allow enough time to observe results before the project is due.

MONITOR AND RETEACH

If students have trouble applying the concepts of heat transfer in items 24–26, suggest that they review the illustrations on pp. 51–53. Have them draw and label a diagram that includes all three processes (conduction, convection, and radiation) in a natural setting.

Students may benefit from summarizing one or more sections of the chapter.

 Summarizing the Chapter, pp. 127–128

Standardized Test Practice

For practice on your state test, go to . . .
TEST PRACTICE
CLASSZONE.COM

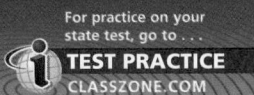

Interpreting Diagrams

The diagrams below illustrate the process that occurs in sea and land breezes.

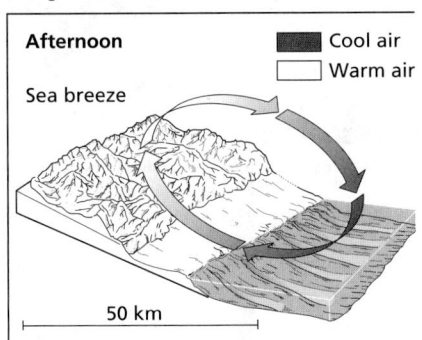

Afternoon

Sea breeze

■ Cool air
□ Warm air

50 km

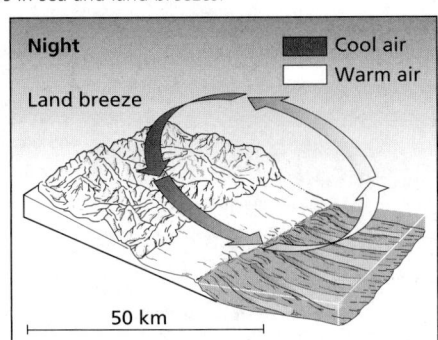

Night

Land breeze

■ Cool air
□ Warm air

50 km

Use the diagrams above to answer the next five questions.

1. What happens during the day?
   a. Cool air from the land flows out to sea.
   b. Warm air from the land flows out to sea close to sea level.
   c. Cool air from the sea flows to the land.
   d. Warm air from the sea flows to the land.

2. What characteristic of large bodies of water explains why the seawater is cooler than the land in the hot afternoon sun?
   a. Water is liquid while the land is solid.
   b. Water has a higher specific heat than land.
   c. Land is a better insulator than water.
   d. Land has a higher specific heat than water.

3. What process causes the warm air to move upward over the land during the day?
   a. convection   **c.** evaporation
   b. condensation   **d.** radiation

4. Warm air is pushed upwards by cooler air during convection because the warm air
   a. is more dense   **c.** is less dense
   b. has more mass   **d.** has less mass

5. About how far over water does this land breeze extend?
   a. 1 kilometer   **c.** 25 kilometers
   b. 10 kilometers   **d.** 50 kilometers

Extended Response

Answer the two questions below in detail. Include some of the terms from the word box on the right. Underline each term that you use in your answer.

| boiling point | heat | specific heat |
| conduction | freezing point | zero point |

6. What are the differences between the Fahrenheit and Celsius temperature scales? Which one is used in science? Why might this be the case?

7. Suppose you place three spoons—one metal, one plastic, and one wood—into a cup filled with hot water. The bowl end of the spoon is inside the cup and the handle is sticking up into the air. On each handle, you place a bead, held to the spoon by a dab of margarine. From which spoon will the bead fall first, and why?

Interpreting Diagrams

1. c   2. b   3. a   4. c   5. c

Extended Response

6. RUBRIC

4 points for a response that correctly answers the three questions and uses the following terms accurately:
   • freezing point
   • boiling point
   • zero point

Sample: The Fahrenheit and Celsius scales have a different number of degrees between the <u>freezing point</u> and <u>boiling point</u> of water. On the Fahrenheit scale, the freezing point of water is 32° and the boiling point is 212°. On the Celsius scale, the freezing point of water is 0° and the boiling point is 100°. Scientists use the Celsius scale because it has a well-defined <u>zero point</u>.

3 points correctly answers two questions and uses two terms correctly
2 points correctly answers two questions and uses one term correctly
1 point correctly answers one of the questions

7. RUBRIC

4 points for a response that answers the question correctly and uses the following terms accurately:
   • conduction
   • specific heat
   • heat

Sample: The bead will fall first from the metal spoon because metal has a higher conductivity and a lower <u>specific heat</u> than wood and plastic, so it warms up faster. <u>Heat</u> transfers energy from the hot water to the metal spoon by <u>conduction</u>. Heat transfers energy through the spoon and melts the margarine.

3 points correctly answers the question and uses one term accurately
2 points correctly answers the question
1 point does not correctly answer the question but uses the terms accurately

METACOGNITIVE ACTIVITY

Have students answer the following questions in their **Science Notebook:**

1. What did you find the most challenging to understand about temperature and heat?

2. Which topics in this chapter would you like to learn more about?

3. How have you solved a problem while working on your Unit Project?

▶ Set Learning Goals

Students will

- Observe how scientists created new theories of temperature and heat by building on earlier observations.
- Learn the characteristics of temperature and heat and how they are measured.
- Write a procedure for an experiment to test a specific method of calculating temperature.

National Science Education Standards

A.9.a–b, A.9.d–g, Understandings About Scientific Inquiry

E.6.a–c Understandings About Science and Technology

F.5.a–e, F.5.g Science and Technology in Society

G.1.a–b Science as a Human Endeavor

G.2.a Nature of Science

G.3.a–c History of Science

Point out to students that the top half of the timeline shows major events in the scientific study of temperature and heat and the years in which they occurred. The bottom half addresses the developments in technology based on the scientific discoveries in the top half. The gap between 320 B.C. and A.D. 1600 represents a block of time that has been omitted.

Teach from Visuals

350 B.C. To help students better understand the ancient Greek theory of matter, have them review the diagram of the basic qualities of matter. Ask students to create a table of the four basic substances and their characteristics to illustrate which substances were thought to have which two qualities.

TIMELINES in Science

ABOUT TEMPERATURE AND HEAT

Most likely, the first fires early people saw were caused by lightning. Eventually, people realized that fire provided warmth and light, and they learned how to make it themselves. During the Stone Age 25,000 years ago, people used firewood to cook food as well as to warm and light their shelters. Wood was the first fuel.

This timeline shows a few of the many steps on the path toward understanding temperature and heat. Notice how the observations and ideas of previous thinkers sparked new theories by later scientists. The boxes below the timeline show how technology has led to new insights and to applications related to temperature and heat.

445 B.C.

Four Basic Substances Named

Greek philosopher Empedocles says that everything on Earth is made of some combination of four basic substances: earth, air, fire, and water. Different types of matter have different qualities depending on how they combine these substances.

350 B.C.

Aristotle Expands Theory of Matter

Greek philosopher Aristotle names four basic qualities of matter: dryness, wetness, hotness, and coldness. Each of the four basic substances has two of these qualities.

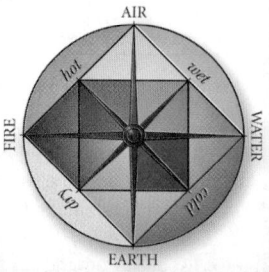

EVENTS

| 480 B.C. | 440 B.C. | 400 B.C. | 360 B.C. | 320 B.C. |

APPLICATIONS AND TECHNOLOGY

People have been trying to understand and control heat since early times.

DIFFERENTIATE INSTRUCTION

Below Level For students who may have difficulty understanding how information is organized on a timeline, point out the dates on the center line. Explain how the dates become more recent when read from left to right. Show them the lines connecting the event boxes to the specific dates on the timeline. Discuss how timelines are a good way to show the order in which events happened.

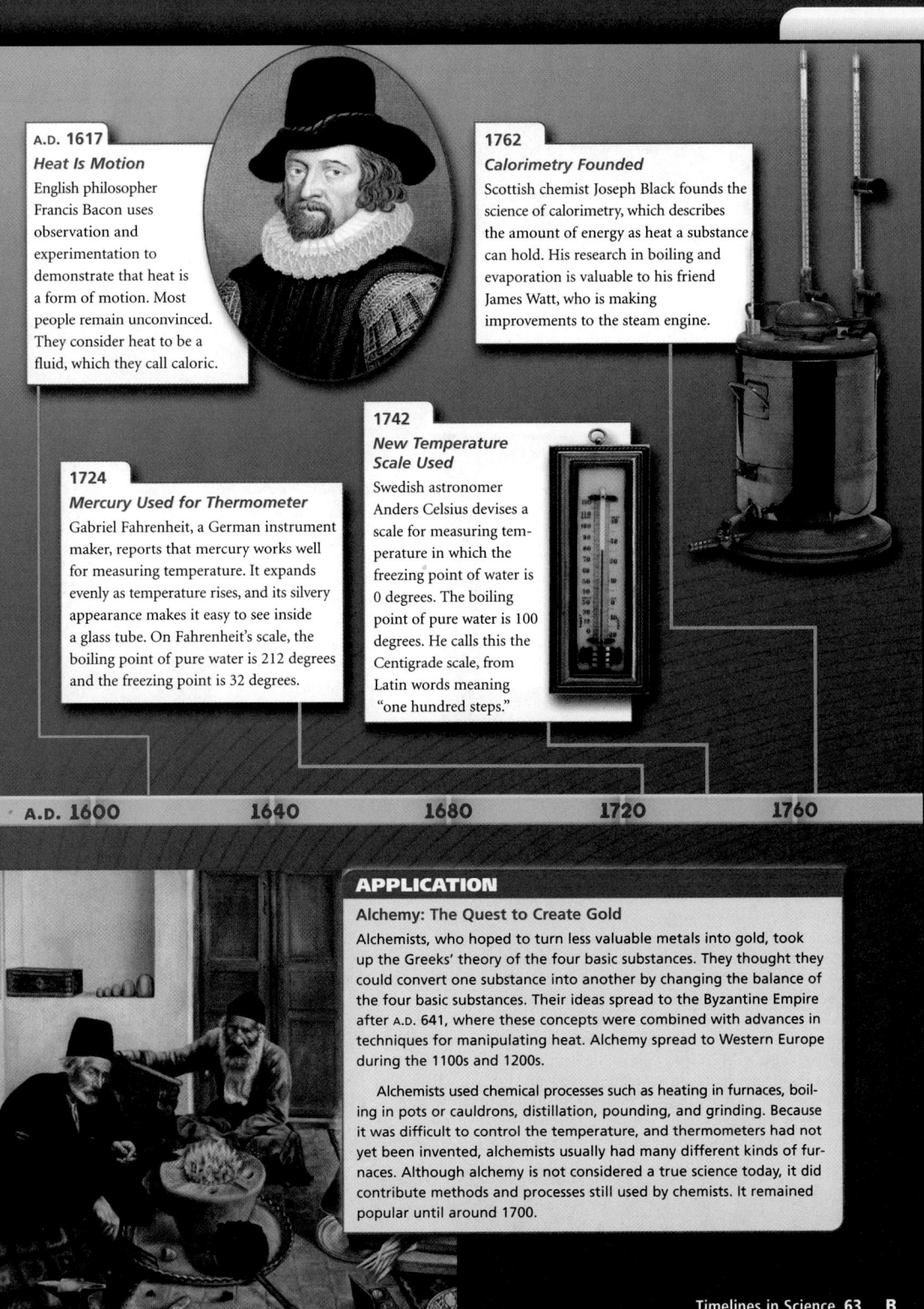

A.D. 1617
Heat Is Motion
English philosopher Francis Bacon uses observation and experimentation to demonstrate that heat is a form of motion. Most people remain unconvinced. They consider heat to be a fluid, which they call caloric.

1762
Calorimetry Founded
Scottish chemist Joseph Black founds the science of calorimetry, which describes the amount of energy as heat a substance can hold. His research in boiling and evaporation is valuable to his friend James Watt, who is making improvements to the steam engine.

1724
Mercury Used for Thermometer
Gabriel Fahrenheit, a German instrument maker, reports that mercury works well for measuring temperature. It expands evenly as temperature rises, and its silvery appearance makes it easy to see inside a glass tube. On Fahrenheit's scale, the boiling point of pure water is 212 degrees and the freezing point is 32 degrees.

1742
New Temperature Scale Used
Swedish astronomer Anders Celsius devises a scale for measuring temperature in which the freezing point of water is 0 degrees. The boiling point of pure water is 100 degrees. He calls this the Centigrade scale, from Latin words meaning "one hundred steps."

A.D. 1600   1640   1680   1720   1760

APPLICATION

Alchemy: The Quest to Create Gold
Alchemists, who hoped to turn less valuable metals into gold, took up the Greeks' theory of the four basic substances. They thought they could convert one substance into another by changing the balance of the four basic substances. Their ideas spread to the Byzantine Empire after A.D. 641, where these concepts were combined with advances in techniques for manipulating heat. Alchemy spread to Western Europe during the 1100s and 1200s.

Alchemists used chemical processes such as heating in furnaces, boiling in pots or cauldrons, distillation, pounding, and grinding. Because it was difficult to control the temperature, and thermometers had not yet been invented, alchemists usually had many different kinds of furnaces. Although alchemy is not considered a true science today, it did contribute methods and processes still used by chemists. It remained popular until around 1700.

Timelines in Science **63** **B**

Scientific Process
1724 Gabriel Fahrenheit improved on existing technology to measure temperature through his observations and investigations. He found that mercury was more accurate in measuring temperature than the alcohol thermometers of the time. Fahrenheit then developed the mercury thermometer, which we still use today.

Sharing Results
1762 Chemist Joseph Black experimented with the amount of heat a substance can hold. His results helped James Watt, who was working on improvements to the steam engine. Ask students what research Black was conducting that was critical to Watt's work. *boiling and evaporation*

Mathematics Connection
1742 The Celsius scale is the metric scale for measuring temperature. Most countries use the Celsius scale for everyday temperature measurement. Scientists also use this scale for their experiments. In the United States, the Fahrenheit scale is used to measure temperature. To convert a Celsius temperature to a Fahrenheit temperature, multiply the Celsius temperature by 9/5 and then add 32 to the result. Write the formula $°F = 9/5(°C) + 32$ on the board. Ask students to convert 35°C to Fahrenheit. *95°F*

Application
ALCHEMY While alchemy is no longer considered a true science, for some time it was a major source of chemical knowledge. Because alchemists experimented with turning metals such as lead into gold, they gained wide knowledge about chemical substances. The alchemist's workshop became the forerunner of the modern chemistry laboratory. Alchemists used tools such as funnels, beakers, and balances. Although alchemists failed to produce gold from other materials, their experimentation was successful in other ways. Ask students what impact alchemy had on science and technology. *Alchemy created many chemical processes and tools that are still used by chemists today.*

DIFFERENTIATE INSTRUCTION

Advanced Have students use the temperature conversion formula shown in the Mathematics Connection on this page to convert Fahrenheit to Celsius. Ask students what the formula for the conversion is. $°C = 5/9 (°F − 32)$ Then ask students to convert 98.6°F to Celsius. *37°C*

Scientific Process

Refer students to Francis Bacon's observations on page 63. Despite his experiments, people still believed that heat is fluid rather than a form of motion. Thompson's observations about friction and heat provided evidence that contradicted the leading hypothesis of the time. With evidence against the fluid theory of heat mounting, scientists began to consider seriously other ideas about the nature of heat.

Technology

VACUUM FLASK The reflective silver coating that a vacuum flask, or thermos, uses to keep fluids hot is the same type of technology that NASA used on the Mars rover. To keep heat from escaping out of the rover body and cold air from entering during landing, the outside of the rover's body was painted gold. This coating helps reduce energy that is spread outward from the rover's body. It also prevents the body from emitting heat energy into its cold surroundings.

Integrate the Sciences

One way in which clouds are formed is by convection, that is, when warm air rises. The Sun's heat causes Earth's water (from lakes, oceans, and rivers) to evaporate into the air. When that air is heated, it becomes less dense than the surrounding air. As a result, it rises. As the moist air continues to rise, it expands and becomes cooler. The water vapor in the air condenses and forms clouds.

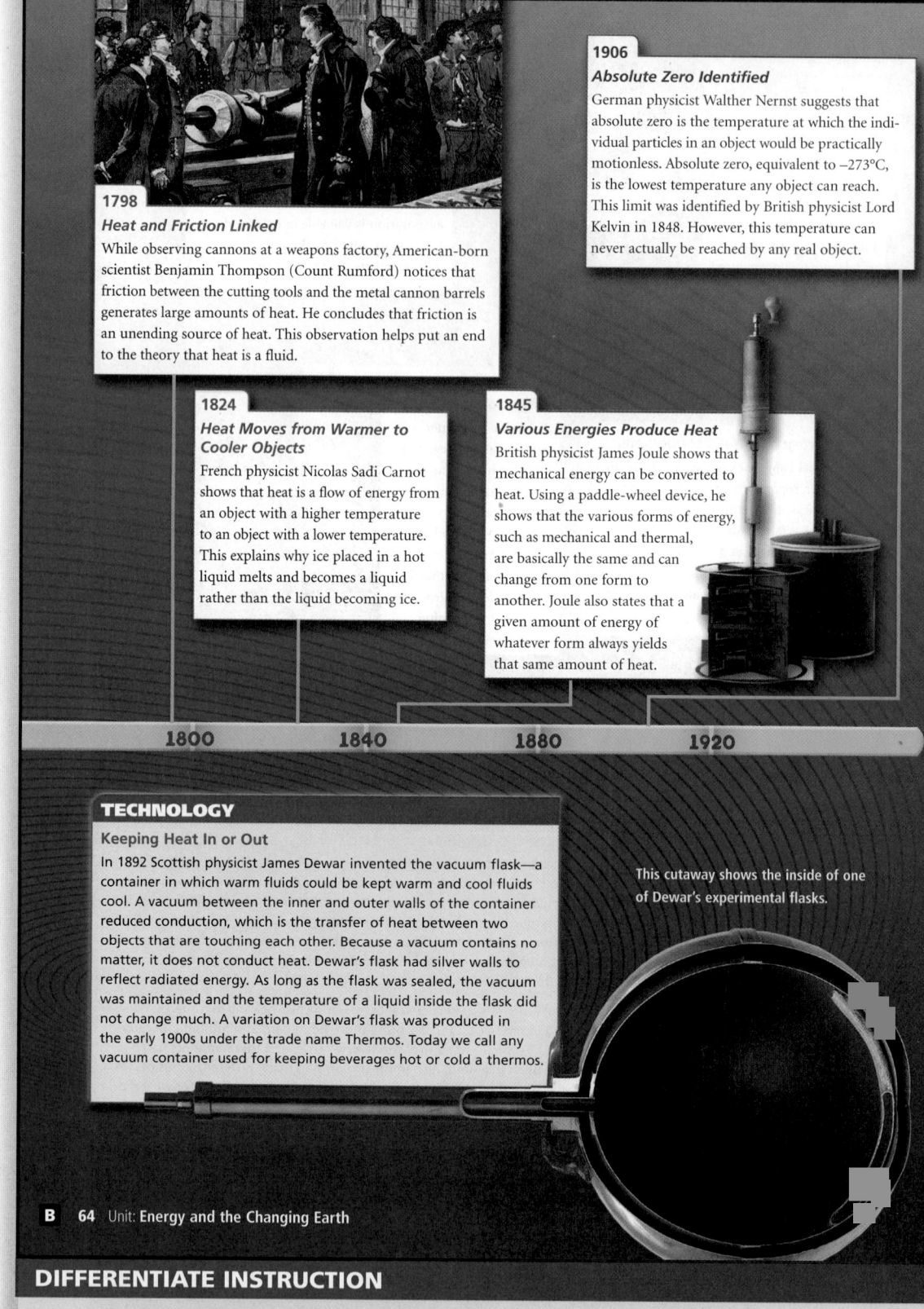

1798

Heat and Friction Linked

While observing cannons at a weapons factory, American-born scientist Benjamin Thompson (Count Rumford) notices that friction between the cutting tools and the metal cannon barrels generates large amounts of heat. He concludes that friction is an unending source of heat. This observation helps put an end to the theory that heat is a fluid.

1906

Absolute Zero Identified

German physicist Walther Nernst suggests that absolute zero is the temperature at which the individual particles in an object would be practically motionless. Absolute zero, equivalent to −273°C, is the lowest temperature any object can reach. This limit was identified by British physicist Lord Kelvin in 1848. However, this temperature can never actually be reached by any real object.

1824

Heat Moves from Warmer to Cooler Objects

French physicist Nicolas Sadi Carnot shows that heat is a flow of energy from an object with a higher temperature to an object with a lower temperature. This explains why ice placed in a hot liquid melts and becomes a liquid rather than the liquid becoming ice.

1845

Various Energies Produce Heat

British physicist James Joule shows that mechanical energy can be converted to heat. Using a paddle-wheel device, he shows that the various forms of energy, such as mechanical and thermal, are basically the same and can change from one form to another. Joule also states that a given amount of energy of whatever form always yields that same amount of heat.

1800   1840   1880   1920

TECHNOLOGY

Keeping Heat In or Out

In 1892 Scottish physicist James Dewar invented the vacuum flask—a container in which warm fluids could be kept warm and cool fluids cool. A vacuum between the inner and outer walls of the container reduced conduction, which is the transfer of heat between two objects that are touching each other. Because a vacuum contains no matter, it does not conduct heat. Dewar's flask had silver walls to reflect radiated energy. As long as the flask was sealed, the vacuum was maintained and the temperature of a liquid inside the flask did not change much. A variation on Dewar's flask was produced in the early 1900s under the trade name Thermos. Today we call any vacuum container used for keeping beverages hot or cold a thermos.

This cutaway shows the inside of one of Dewar's experimental flasks.

DIFFERENTIATE INSTRUCTION

Below Level 1798 Have students rub their hands together to demonstrate how friction produces heat.

2003

Wasps Stay Cool

Scientists in Israel have found evidence that some wasps have an internal air-conditioning system. Like a refrigerator, the wasp uses energy to stay cooler than the air around it. The energy may come from several sources, such as the energy generated by an electric current produced when the wasp's shell is exposed to sunlight. This ability to stay cool allows wasps to hunt for food even on very hot days.

 RESOURCE CENTER
CLASSZONE.COM

Learn about current temperature and heat research.

1960　　2000

INTO THE FUTURE

As scientists are able to create colder and colder temperatures in the laboratory, they gain new insight into the scientific theories that explain temperature and heat. Advances in our knowledge of temperature and heat will lead to future applications.

- Scientists have developed a car that can run on hydrogen cooled into its liquid state. Before cars that run on this supercooled fuel become common, a system of refueling stations must be established.

- Understanding how some materials, such as silicon, conduct energy as heat may result in medical advances through better scanning and imaging technology.

- At temperatures approaching absolute zero (−273°C), a unique state of matter can be formed that is different from a solid, liquid, or gas. This rare state of matter could possibly be used to help produce extremely small circuits for use in miniature computers or other electronics.

ACTIVITIES

Design a Procedure

Many people claim that it is possible to determine the temperature by listening to the chirping of crickets. Crickets are sensitive to changes in air temperature and chirp more quickly when the temperature rises. To calculate the temperature in degrees Celsius, count the number of chirps in 7 seconds and add 5.

Write a procedure for an experiment that would test this claim. What factors would you consider testing? What range of temperatures would you test?

Writing About Science

Alchemy has fascinated people for centuries. Research its influence on both the technology and procedures of modern chemistry. Write a short report.

Application

USING THERMAL ENERGY FROM PONDS The idea of using ponds with a salt gradient to collect and store thermal energy was developed after natural examples of such ponds were discovered. The energy from these ponds can be used for applications such as purifying water and producing electricity. Ask students what some of the benefits of using solar-energy ponds might be. *provides clean, cost-effective electricity*

INTO THE FUTURE

Have students divide into small groups. Have each group come up with a list of possible inventions or ideas based on what they read about temperature and heat. An example might be a portable solar-powered DVD player. Then have each group prepare a presentation about their invention, describing what it is and how it works. Presentations might consist of bulletin-board displays, videos done as news segments, or oral reports with visual aids.

ACTIVITIES

Design a Procedure

Refer students to the steps of the scientific process as they write their procedure for the experiment. Remind them to include in their procedure ways to record findings clearly.

Writing About Science

Suggest that students look up the history of alchemy on the Internet or in the library. Some might focus on contributions of a specific culture, such as Egyptian, Chinese, Indian, or Islamic alchemists.

Technology Resources

Students can visit **ClassZone.com** for information about temperature and heat.

DIFFERENTIATE INSTRUCTION

Advanced Encourage students to trace the development of ideas from the ancient Greeks to the present. Students might create a visual or model that represents each new idea as building on the previous idea.

CHAPTER

3 Plate Tectonics

Earth Science
UNIFYING PRINCIPLES

PRINCIPLE 1

Heat energy inside Earth and radiation from the Sun provide energy for Earth's processes.

PRINCIPLE 2

Physical forces, such as gravity, affect the movement of all matter on Earth and throughout the universe.

PRINCIPLE 3

Matter and energy move among Earth's rocks and soil, atmosphere, waters, and living things.

PRINCIPLE 4

Earth has changed over time and continues to change.

Unit: Energy and the Changing Earth
BIG IDEAS

CHAPTER 1
Energy

Energy has different forms, but it is always conserved.

CHAPTER 2
Temperature and Heat

Heat is a flow of energy due to temperature differences.

CHAPTER 3
Plate Tectonics

The movement of tectonic plates causes geologic changes on Earth.

CHAPTER 4
Earthquakes

Earthquakes release stress that has built up in rocks.

CHAPTER 5
Mountains and Volcanoes

Mountains and volcanoes form as tectonic plates move.

CHAPTER 3
KEY
CONCEPTS

SECTION 3.1

Earth has several layers.

1. Earth is made up of materials with different densities.
2. Earth's layers have different properties.
3. The lithosphere is made up of many plates.

SECTION 3.2

Continents change position over time.

1. Continents join together and split apart.
2. The theory of plate tectonics explains how plates and their continents move.

SECTION 3.3

Plates move apart.

1. Tectonic plates have different boundaries.
2. The sea floor spreads apart at divergent boundaries.
3. Continents split apart at divergent boundaries.
4. Hot spots can be used to track plate movements.

SECTION 3.4

Plates converge or scrape past each other.

Tectonic plates:

1. push together at convergent boundaries.
2. scrape past each other at transform boundaries.
3. The theory of plate tectonics helps geologists today.

The Big Idea Flow Chart is available on p. T17 in the **UNIT TRANSPARENCY BOOK.**

Previewing Content

SECTION

3.1 Earth has several layers. pp. 69–73

1. Earth is made up of materials with different densities.
Scientists theorize that Earth began as a spinning mass of rocks and dust about 5 billion years ago. Explosions from comets and asteroids crashing into its surface, along with the pressure of Earth's gravity, produced enough heat to melt materials inside Earth. Over time, dense material sank to the center of Earth and less dense material moved toward the surface, forming Earth's layers.

2. Earth's layers have different properties.
The table below shows how Earth's layers differ in composition, temperature, and thickness. Earth's crust and the top of the mantle form the **lithosphere,** which sits on a layer of hotter, softer rock in the upper mantle called the **asthenosphere.**

Earth's Layers		
Layer of Earth	Composition	Temp/Thickness
inner core	solid metals	7000°–8000° C 2400 km diameter
outer core	liquid metals	4400°–6100° C 2300 km thick
mantle	heated rock	870°–4400° C 2900 km thick
crust	cooler rock	0°–700° C 6–70 km thick

3. The lithosphere is made up of many plates.
The lithosphere is split into large and small slabs of rocks called **tectonic plates,** which fit together like a jigsaw puzzle. Most of the large tectonic plates contain both continental and oceanic crust. The discovery of Earth's layers and tectonic plates helped scientists answer the mystery of how the continents moved to their present positions.

SECTION

3.2 Continents change position over time. pp. 74–81

1. Continents join together and split apart.
A German scientist named Alfred Wegener proposed the hypothesis of **continental drift** in the early 1900s, stating that Earth's continents were once joined in a single landmass and gradually moved apart. Fossils, studies of ancient climates, and rock formations provided evidence for continental drift. For example, rock formations in Brazil matched rock formations in western Africa, showing that the two continents had once been joined and moved apart.

2. The theory of plate tectonics explains how plates and their continents move.
Scientists combined Wegener's continental drift hypothesis with information they gained from mapping the sea floor to develop the **theory of plate tectonics.** Along spreading centers in the sea floor, melted rock rises through cracks, cools, and forms new crust that builds up **mid-ocean ridges.** Old crust gets pushed aside, and the sea floor slowly spreads apart. Earth doesn't get larger, however, because oceanic crust is destroyed along deep-ocean trenches, where the oceanic plates sink into the asthenosphere. The diagram shows how the motions of convection currents, ridge push, and slab pull move Earth's huge tectonic plates.

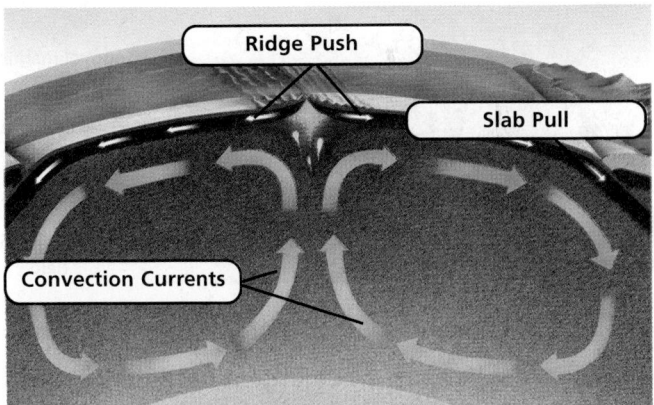

Ridge Push

Slab Pull

Convection Currents

Common Misconceptions

CHANGES IN SCIENCE Students may think that scientific changes mainly involve facts and occur mostly through the invention of new technology for observation and measurement. In reality, entire theories sometimes change because of new observations or reinterpretations of previous evidence.

 This misconception is addressed on p. 76.

 MISCONCEPTION DATABASE
CLASSZONE.COM Background on student misconceptions

Previewing Content

3.3 Plates move apart. pp. 82–89

1. Tectonic plates have different boundaries.
A plate boundary is where the edges of two plates meet. A **divergent boundary** occurs where plates move apart. Most divergent boundaries are found in the ocean. A **convergent boundary** occurs where plates push together. A **transform boundary** occurs where two plates scrape past each other.

2. The sea floor spreads apart at divergent boundaries.
Mid-ocean ridges and **rift valleys** occur at divergent boundaries in the ocean. Mid-ocean ridges form the longest mountain chains on Earth. Most contain a rift valley along their center. From studying sea-floor rock, scientists discovered that Earth's magnetic north and south poles have switched places a number of times over the planet's long history. These switches are called **magnetic reversals** and are caused by changes in Earth's magnetic field. As the diagram below shows, bands of rock on either side of a mid-ocean ridge record periods of magnetic reversals. As molten material at a divergent boundary cools, some magnetic minerals line up with the Earth's magnetic field. When the material hardens, these minerals are permanently fixed like tiny compass needles pointing north and south.

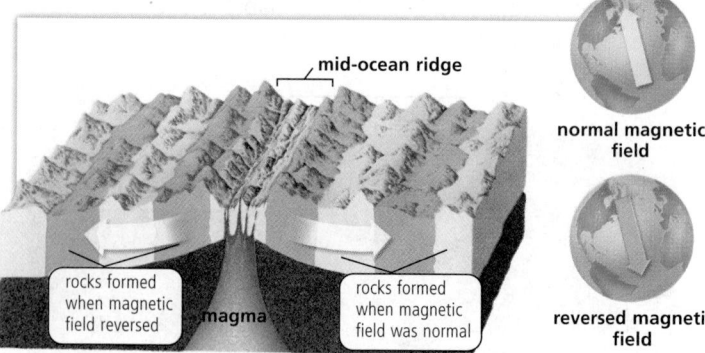

mid-ocean ridge

rocks formed when magnetic field reversed

magma

rocks formed when magnetic field was normal

normal magnetic field

reversed magnetic field

3. Continents split apart at divergent boundaries.
Divergent boundaries on continents also produce rift valleys. Magma rising through cracked, thinned crust forms volcanoes. As rift valleys grow wider, the continent begins to split apart. If a rift valley continues to widen, the thinned valley floor sinks below sea level and water from a nearby ocean or river may fill the valley and form a sea or lake.

4. Hot spots can be used to track plate movements.
A **hot spot** is an area of volcanic activity that develops above where magma rises in a plume from the mantle. A hot spot can be used to measure plate movement because it generally stays in one place while the tectonic plate above it keeps moving. Hot spots can provide a fixed point for measuring the speed and direction of plate movements.

3.4 Plates converge or scrape past each other. pp. 90–97

1. Tectonic plates push together at convergent boundaries.
There are three types of convergent boundaries.
- **Continental-continental collisions** occur where two continental plates collide, crumpling and folding the rock between them. If the rocks push high enough, they form mountains.
- **Oceanic-oceanic subductions** occur where two oceanic plates collide and the older, denser plate sinks beneath the top plate, forming deep-ocean trenches and island arcs.
- **Oceanic-continental subductions** occur where an oceanic plate sinks beneath a continental plate, forming a deep-ocean trench and volcanic coastal mountains.

2. Tectonic plates scrape past each other at transform boundaries.
At a **transform boundary,** two plates move past each other in opposite directions, and their edges scrape and grind against each other. No crust is formed or destroyed at a transform boundary. This type of boundary occurs on the sea floor and on land. The following chart compares the different types of plate boundaries.

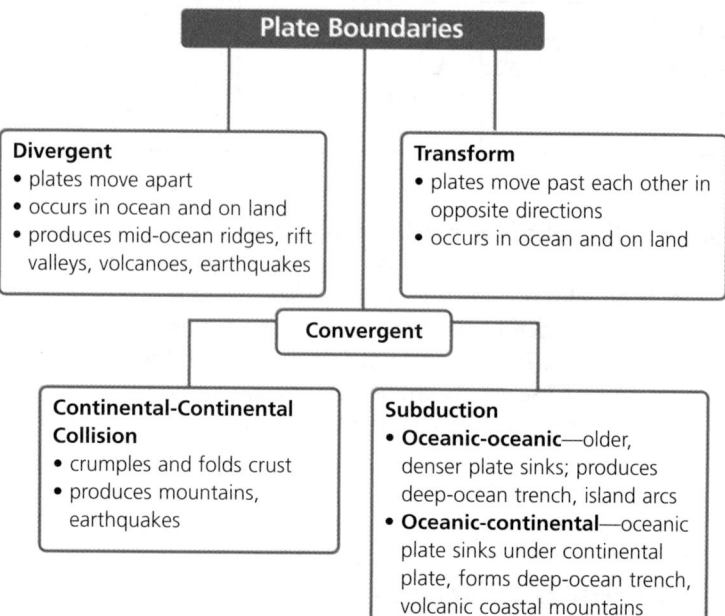

Plate Boundaries

Divergent
- plates move apart
- occurs in ocean and on land
- produces mid-ocean ridges, rift valleys, volcanoes, earthquakes

Transform
- plates move past each other in opposite directions
- occurs in ocean and on land

Convergent

Continental-Continental Collision
- crumples and folds crust
- produces mountains, earthquakes

Subduction
- **Oceanic-oceanic**—older, denser plate sinks; produces deep-ocean trench, island arcs
- **Oceanic-continental**—oceanic plate sinks under continental plate, forms deep-ocean trench, volcanic coastal mountains

3. The theory of plate tectonics helps geologists today.
The plate tectonics theory enables geologists to understand how Earth's continents and ocean basins formed. It also helps them to predict earthquakes and volcanic activity.

Previewing Labs

EXPLORE the BIG idea

Watching a Pot Boil, p. 67
Students observe convection currents.

TIME 10 minutes
MATERIALS medium-size pot, water, sponge, hot plate

Earth's Moving Surface, p. 67
Students are introduced to the concept of plate motions and their effects.

TIME 10 minutes
MATERIALS peanut butter, jelly, two slices of bread, plastic knife

---

Internet Activity: Earth's Interior, p. 67
Students are introduced to the latest ideas about how Earth formed and the properties of Earth's layers.

TIME 20 minutes
MATERIALS computer with Internet access

SECTION 3.1

EXPLORE Density, p. 69
Students pour salt water into fresh water to observe that a denser material sinks.

TIME 15 minutes
MATERIALS 2 clear plastic cups for water, 1 tsp table salt, measuring spoons, food coloring

---

INVESTIGATE Earth's Different Layers, p. 72
Students model how the varying density of materials helped to form Earth's layers.

TIME 15 minutes
MATERIALS clear plastic cup, 1/4 cup small colored wooden beads, 2/3 cup fine gravel, stirring stick

---

SECTION 3.2

EXPLORE Movements of Continents, p. 74
Students model how the outlines of land masses can be a clue to the movement of continents.

TIME 20 minutes
MATERIALS 1 sheet of paper per group, 3–4 colored marking pens, scissors

---

CHAPTER INVESTIGATION
Convection Currents and Plate Movement, pp. 80–81
Students observe how convection currents can move floating objects above.

TIME 40 minutes
MATERIALS oven-glass lasagna pan, 2 bread pans or 2 bricks, 2 small candles, matches, liquid food coloring, 2 sponges, 3–4 pushpins, scissors, water

---

SECTION 3.3

EXPLORE Divergent Boundaries, p. 82
Students model how plates move apart at a divergent boundary.

TIME 15 minutes
MATERIALS small oatmeal box with a slit cut in the side, piece of striped paper, scissors, tape

---

INVESTIGATE Magnetic Reversals, p. 85
Students explore mapping the sequences of magnetic reversals.
 Sea-floor Model Instructions, p. 159

TIME 20 minutes
MATERIALS 10 cm of string, masking tape, bar magnet, marking pen, sea-floor model

---

SECTION 3.4

EXPLORE Tectonic Plates, p. 90
Students model the collision of tectonic plates and observe the effects.

TIME 10 minutes
MATERIALS 6 square napkins

INVESTIGATE Convergent Boundaries, p. 93
Students design models to show how plates interact along collision and subduction convergent boundaries.

TIME 30 minutes
MATERIALS box of clay in 3 or more colors, poster board, marker pens

---

 Additional INVESTIGATION, Magnetic Patterns on the Ocean Floor, A, B, & C, pp. 189–197; Teacher Instructions, pp. 320–321

Previewing Chapter Resources

| | **INTEGRATED TECHNOLOGY** | **LABS AND ACTIVITIES** |

CHAPTER 3
Plate Tectonics

 CLASSZONE.COM
- eEdition Plus
- EasyPlanner Plus
- Misconception Database
- Content Review
- Test Practice
- Visualizations
- Resource Centers
- Internet Activity: Earth's Interior
- Math Tutorial

 SCILINKS.ORG
SCILINKS

 CD-ROMS
- eEdition
- EasyPlanner
- Power Presentations
- Content Review
- Lab Generator
- Test Generator

AUDIO CDS
- Audio Readings
- Audio Readings in Spanish

P E EXPLORE the Big Idea, p. 67
- Watching a Pot Boil
- Earth's Moving Surface
- Internet Activity: Earth's Interior

R **UNIT RESOURCE BOOK**
Unit Projects, pp. 5–10

Lab Generator CD-ROM
Generate customized labs.

SECTION 3.1
Earth has several layers. pp. 69–73

Time: 2 periods (1 block)
R Lesson Plan, pp. 129–130

T **UNIT TRANSPARENCY BOOK**
- Big Idea Flow Chart, p. T17
- Daily Vocabulary Scaffolding, p. T18
- Note-Taking Model, p. T19
- 3-Minute Warm-Up, p. T20

P E • EXPLORE Density, p. 69
- INVESTIGATE Earth's Different Layers, p. 72

R **UNIT RESOURCE BOOK**
Datasheet, Earth's Different Layers, p. 141

SECTION 3.2
Continents change position over time. pp. 74–81

Time: 3 periods (1.5 blocks)
R Lesson Plan, pp. 140–141

 VISUALIZATION, Continental Movement Over Time

T **UNIT TRANSPARENCY BOOK**
- Daily Vocabulary Scaffolding, p. T18
- 3-Minute Warm-Up, p. T20

P E • EXPLORE Movements of Continents, p. 74
- CHAPTER INVESTIGATION, Convection Currents and Plate Movement, pp. 80-81

R **UNIT RESOURCE BOOK**
CHAPTER INVESTIGATION, Convection Currents and Plate Movement, A, B, & C, pp. 180–188

SECTION 3.3
Plates move apart. pp. 82–89

Time: 2 periods (1 block)
R Lesson Plan, pp. 150–151

 MATH TUTORIAL

T **UNIT TRANSPARENCY BOOK**
- Daily Vocabulary Scaffolding, p. T18
- 3-Minute Warm-Up, p. T21

P E • EXPLORE Divergent Boundaries, p. 82
- INVESTIGATE Magnetic Reversals, p. 85
- Math in Science, p. 89

R **UNIT RESOURCE BOOK**
- Sea-Floor Model Instructions, p. 159
- Datasheet, Magnetic Reversals, p. 160
- Math Support & Practice, pp. 178–179
- Additional INVESTIGATION, Magnetic Patterns on the Ocean Floor, A, B, & C, pp. 189–197

SECTION 3.4
Plates converge or scrape past each other. pp. 90–97

Time: 3 periods (1.5 blocks)
R Lesson Plan, pp. 162–163

 • **VISUALIZATION,** Plate Boundaries
- **RESOURCE CENTER,** Effects of Plate Movement

T **UNIT TRANSPARENCY BOOK**
- Big Idea Flow Chart, p. T17
- Daily Vocabulary Scaffolding, p. T18
- 3-Minute Warm-Up, p. T21
- "Tectonic Plate Boundaries" Visual, p. T22
- Chapter Outline, pp. T23–T24

P E • EXPLORE Tectonic Plates, p. 90
- INVESTIGATE Convergent Boundaries, p. 93
- Think Science, p. 97

R **UNIT RESOURCE BOOK**
Datasheet, Convergent Boundaries, p. 171

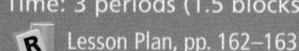

B **65E** Unit: **Energy and the Changing Earth**

 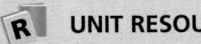
READING AND REINFORCEMENT

- Description Wheel, B20–21
- Supporting Main Ideas, C42
- Daily Vocabulary Scaffolding, H1–8

 UNIT RESOURCE BOOK
- Vocabulary Practice, pp. 175–176
- Decoding Support, p. 177
- Summarizing the Chapter, pp. 198–199

 Audio Readings CD
Listen to Pupil Edition.

Audio Readings in Spanish CD
Listen to Pupil Edition in Spanish.

 UNIT RESOURCE BOOK
- Reading Study Guide, A & B, pp. 131–134
- Spanish Reading Study Guide, pp. 135–136
- Challenge and Extension, p. 137
- Reinforcing Key Concepts, p. 139

 UNIT RESOURCE BOOK
- Reading Study Guide, A & B, pp. 142–145
- Spanish Reading Study Guide, pp. 146–147
- Challenge and Extension, p. 148
- Reinforcing Key Concepts, p. 149

 UNIT RESOURCE BOOK
- Reading Study Guide, A & B, pp. 152–155
- Spanish Reading Study Guide, pp. 156–157
- Challenge and Extension, p. 158
- Reinforcing Key Concepts, p. 161
- Challenge Reading, pp. 173–174

 UNIT RESOURCE BOOK
- Reading Study Guide, A & B, pp. 164–167
- Spanish Reading Study Guide, pp. 168–169
- Challenge and Extension, p. 170
- Reinforcing Key Concepts, p. 172

ASSESSMENT

- Chapter Review, pp. 99–100
- Standardized Test Practice, p. 101

 UNIT ASSESSMENT BOOK
- Diagnostic Test, pp. 39–40
- Chapter Test, A, B, & C, pp. 45–56
- Alternative Assessment, pp. 57–58

 Spanish Chapter Test, pp. 129–132

 Test Generator CD-ROM
Generate customized tests.

 Lab Generator CD-ROM
Rubrics for Labs

 Ongoing Assessment, pp. 70–72

 Section 3.1 Review, p. 73

 UNIT ASSESSMENT BOOK
Section 3.1 Quiz, p. 41

 Ongoing Assessment, pp. 75–79

 Section 3.2 Review, p. 79

 UNIT ASSESSMENT BOOK
Section 3.2 Quiz, p. 42

 Ongoing Assessment, pp. 83, 85–86, 88

 Section 3.3 Review, p. 88

UNIT ASSESSMENT BOOK
Section 3.3 Quiz, p. 43

 Ongoing Assessment, pp. 91–96

 Section 3.4 Review, p. 96

 UNIT ASSESSMENT BOOK
Section 3.4 Quiz, p. 44

STANDARDS

National Standards
A.2–8, A.9.a–c, A.9.e–f, D.1.a–c, E.2–5

See p. 66 for the standards

National Standards
A.2–7, A.9.a–b, A.9.e–f

National Standards
A.2–7, A.9.a–b, A.9.e–f, D.1.b–c

National Standards
A.2–8, A.9.a–c, A.9.e–f, D.1.b–c

National Standards
A.2–7, A.9.a–b, A.9.e–f, D.1.b–c, E.2–5

Previewing Resources for Differentiated Instruction

CHAPTER INVESTIGATION

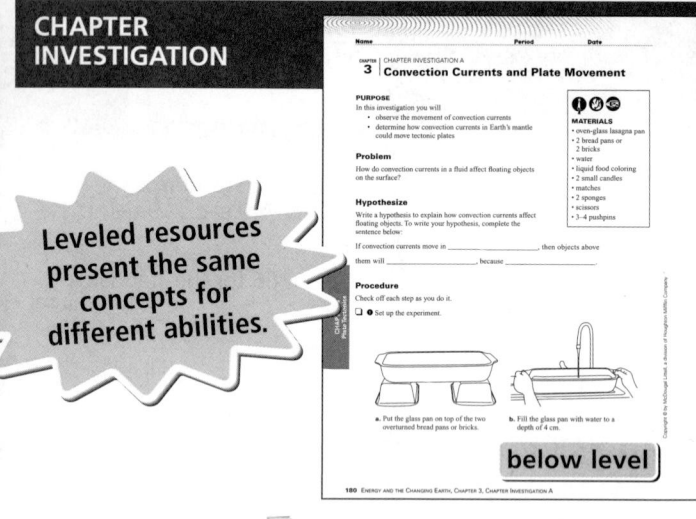

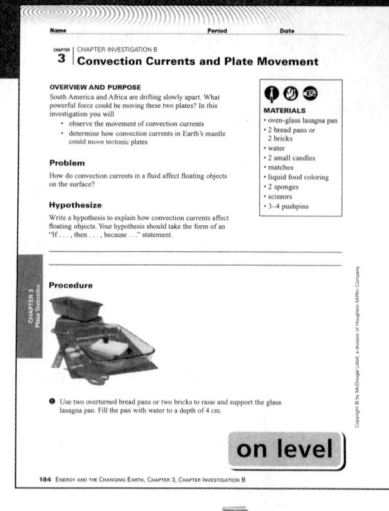

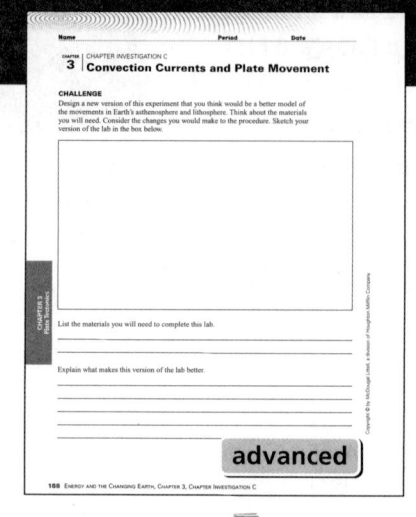

Leveled resources present the same concepts for different abilities.

R UNIT RESOURCE BOOK, pp. 180–183

R pp. 184–187

R pp. 184–188

READING STUDY GUIDE

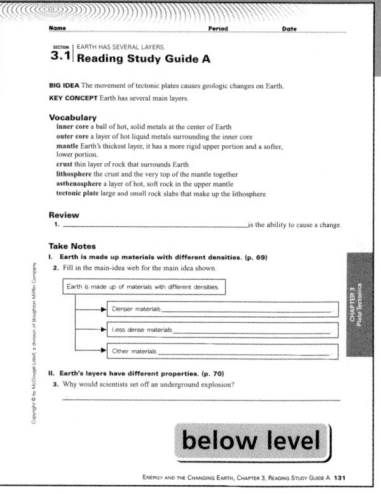

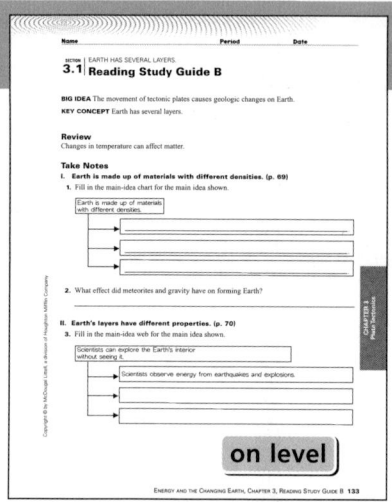

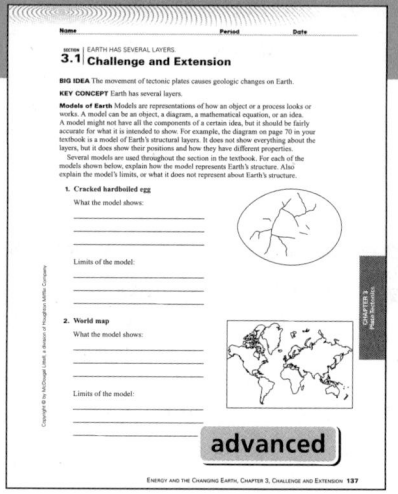

Reading Study Guide is also in Spanish.

R UNIT RESOURCE BOOK, pp. 131–132

R pp. 133–134

R p. 137

CHAPTER TEST

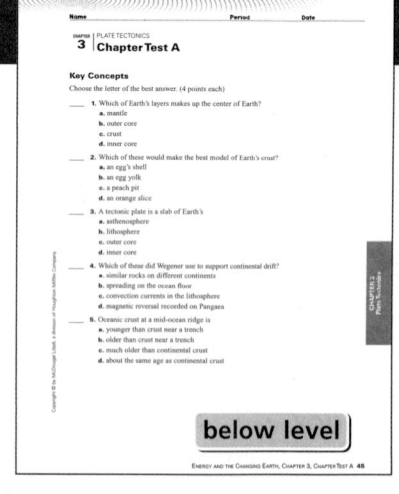

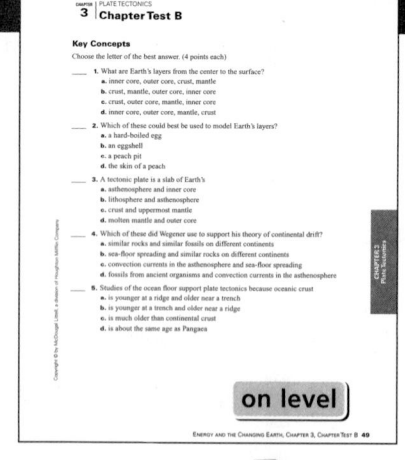

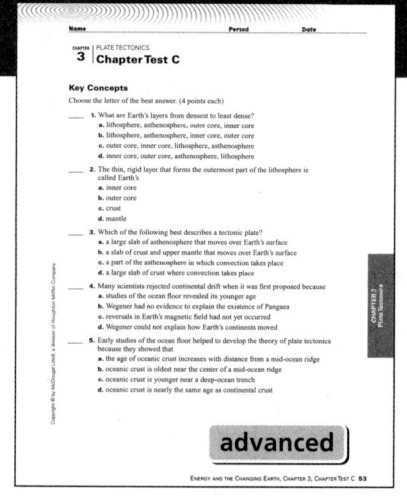

Chapter Test is also in Spanish.

A UNIT ASSESSMENT BOOK, pp. 45–48

A pp. 49–52

A pp. 53–56

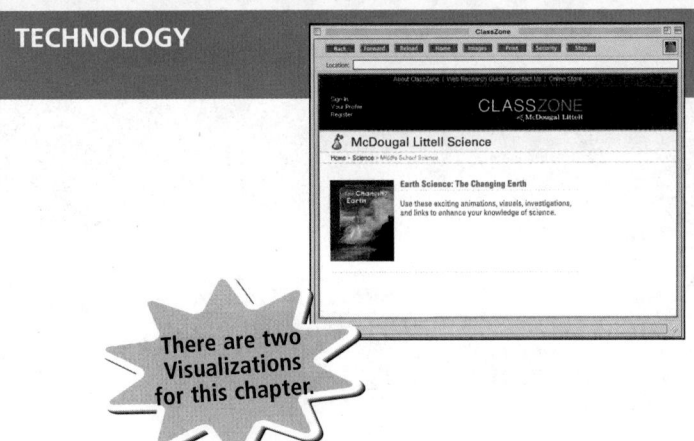

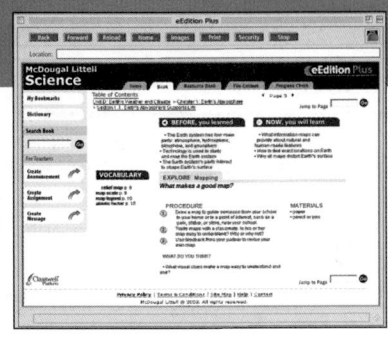

CLASSZONE.COM   CD/CD-ROMS   CLASSZONE.COM

VISUAL CONTENT

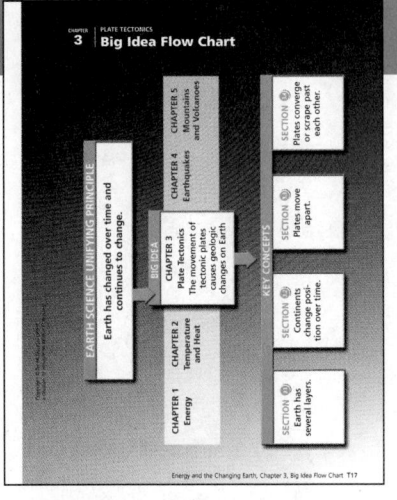

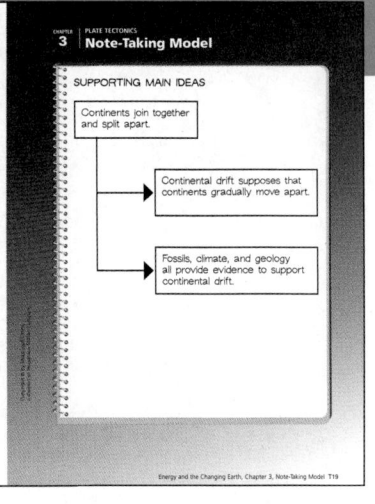

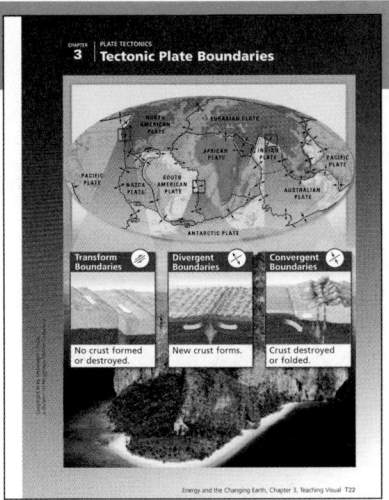

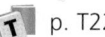

UNIT TRANSPARENCY BOOK, p. T17   p. T19   p. T22

MORE SUPPORT

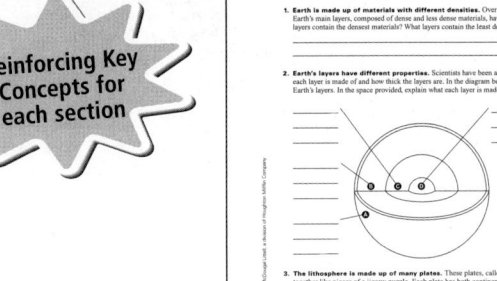

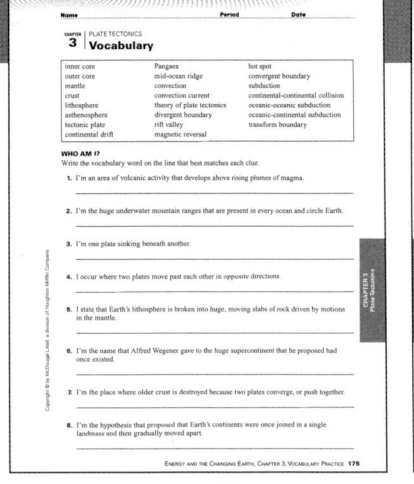

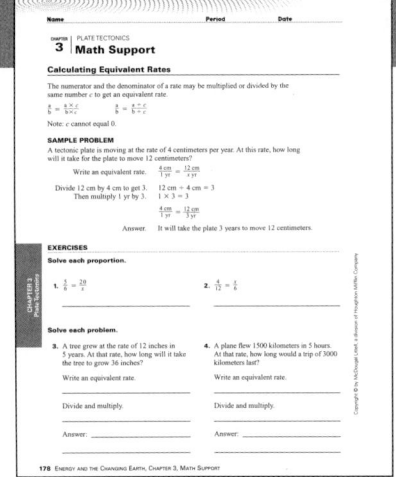

R **UNIT RESOURCE BOOK,** p. 139   **R** pp. 175–176   **R** p. 178

INTRODUCE

the BIG idea

Have students look at the photograph of a huge crack in the Earth and discuss how the question in the box links to the Big Idea:

- Where have you seen similar cracks? What caused them?
- What clues would you look for to determine the cause of the crack in the photograph?

National Science Education Standards

Content

D.1.a The solid Earth is layered with a lithosphere, hot, convecting mantle, and dense metallic core.

D.1.b Lithospheric plates constantly move at rates of centimeters per year in response to movements in the mantle. Major geological events result from these plate motions.

D.1.c Land forms are the result of a combination of constructive and destructive forces. Constructive forces include crustal deformation and volcanic eruption.

Process

A.2–8 Design and conduct an investigation; use tools to gather and interpret data; use evidence to describe, predict, explain, model; think critically to make relationships between evidence and explanation; recognize different explanations and predictions; communicate scientific procedures and explanations; use mathematics.

A.9.a–c, A.9.e–f Understand scientific inquiry by using different investigations, models, mathematics, and explanations based on logic, evidence, and skepticism.

E.2–5 Design, implement, and evaluate a solution or product; communicate technological design.

CHAPTER
3 Plate Tectonics

the BIG idea

The movement of tectonic plates causes geologic changes on Earth.

What might have made this huge crack in the Earth?

Key Concepts

SECTION 3.1 Earth has several layers. Learn about Earth's interior and its rigid surface plates.

SECTION 3.2 Continents change position over time. Learn how continental drift and plate tectonics changed the way people view Earth.

SECTION 3.3 Plates move apart. Learn about the three types of plate boundaries and what happens when plates move apart.

SECTION 3.4 Plates converge or scrape past each other. Learn what geologic events occur at these plate boundaries.

Internet Preview

CLASSZONE.COM
Chapter 3 online resources: Content Review, two Visualizations, one Resource Center, Math Tutorial, and Test Practice

INTERNET PREVIEW

CLASSZONE.COM For student use with the following pages:

Review and Practice
- Content Review, pp. 68, 98
- Math Tutorial: Rates, p. 89
- Test Practice, p. 101

Activities and Resources
- Internet Activity: Earth's Interior, p. 67
- Visualizations: Continental Movement, p. 76; Plate Boundaries, p. 93
- Resource Center: Effects of Plate Movement, p. 97

NSTA *SCiLINKS*
scilinks.org
Plates **Code: MDL052**

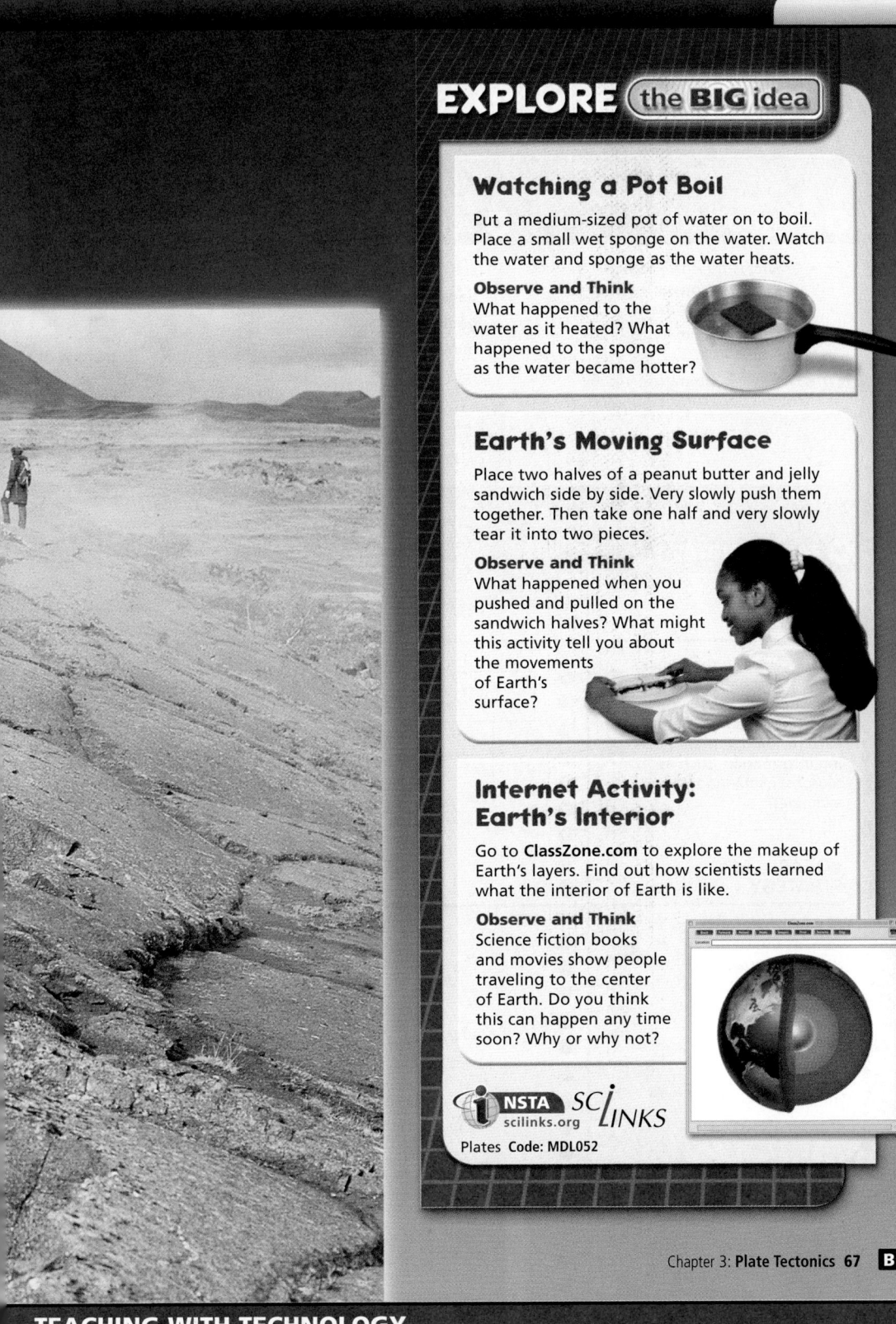

EXPLORE (the BIG idea)

Watching a Pot Boil

Put a medium-sized pot of water on to boil. Place a small wet sponge on the water. Watch the water and sponge as the water heats.

Observe and Think
What happened to the water as it heated? What happened to the sponge as the water became hotter?

Earth's Moving Surface

Place two halves of a peanut butter and jelly sandwich side by side. Very slowly push them together. Then take one half and very slowly tear it into two pieces.

Observe and Think
What happened when you pushed and pulled on the sandwich halves? What might this activity tell you about the movements of Earth's surface?

Internet Activity: Earth's Interior

Go to **ClassZone.com** to explore the makeup of Earth's layers. Find out how scientists learned what the interior of Earth is like.

Observe and Think
Science fiction books and movies show people traveling to the center of Earth. Do you think this can happen any time soon? Why or why not?

NSTA
scilinks.org
SCiLINKS

Plates **Code: MDL052**

TEACHING WITH TECHNOLOGY

CD-ROM While teaching p. 83, use a computer to display a map of the ocean floor on CD-ROM for students to study the Mid-Atlantic Ridge and its rift valley.

Video Camera You might film groups of students showing and describing the models they develop for the investigation on p. 93.

EXPLORE (the BIG idea)

These inquiry-based activities are appropriate for use at home or as a supplement to classroom instruction.

Watching a Pot Boil

PURPOSE To give students experience watching convection currents in a fluid.

TIP *10 min.* Ask students to observe what happens as the water begins to heat up. Do this as a demonstration, or tell students to be very careful.

Answer: Students should notice that water begins to form bubbles, then streams of bubbles, then begins to roll faster and faster as it boils. The sponge will move to the side of the pan and keep moving.

REVISIT after p. 78.

Earth's Moving Surface

PURPOSE To give students a model of how Earth's tectonic plates move and what happens at the plate edges.

TIP *10 min.* Advise students to apply slow, even pressure. Have students watch what happens not only to each sandwich half, but also to the individual layers.

Answer: Pushing the sandwich halves together will bend and fold the layers. Students can infer that Earth's surface will act in the same way.

REVISIT after p. 95.

Internet Activity: Earth's Interior

PURPOSE To introduce students to the latest ideas about the formation and properties of Earth's layers.

TIP *20 min.* Students should appreciate the complexity of Earth's layers and the fact that scientists still have many unanswered questions.

Answer: No. Earth's interior is far too hot for any living thing to survive.

REVISIT after p. 73.

⦾ CONCEPT REVIEW
Activate Prior Knowledge

- Place on your desk two glasses, one of them half filled with hot water and the other half filled with cold water.

- Drop an ice cube into each glass of water.

- Ask students to explain the changes they see in each ice cube in terms of heat energy and conduction.

⦿ TAKING NOTES

Supporting Main Ideas

Identifying main ideas and supporting details is a basic reading comprehension skill students will need to master if they are to perform well on standardized tests. If students have a hard time remembering the information they put in their charts, they may be including too much information with the supporting details they identify.

Vocabulary Strategy

Description wheels can include definitions, uses, examples, and other kinds of details. Students can include as many spokes as they want, and each spoke should be a different detail. Description wheels can be useful study aids when students review their notes.

Vocabulary and Note-Taking Resources

- Vocabulary Practice, pp. 175–176
- Decoding Support, p. 177

- Daily Vocabulary Scaffolding, p. T18
- Note-Taking Model, p. T19

🔧
- Description Wheel, B20–21
- Supporting Main Ideas, C42
- Daily Vocabulary Scaffolding, H1–8

◀ CONCEPT REVIEW

- Gravity is the force that objects exert on each other because of their mass.
- Energy is the ability to cause a change.
- Energy can be transferred by conduction, convection, and radiation.

◀ VOCABULARY REVIEW

See Glossary for definitions.

density

geology

mineral

rock

ⓘ CONTENT REVIEW
CLASSZONE.COM
Review concepts and vocabulary.

▶ TAKING NOTES

SUPPORTING MAIN IDEAS

Make a chart to show main ideas and the information that supports them. Copy each blue heading. Below each heading, add supporting information, such as reasons, explanations, and examples.

VOCABULARY STRATEGY

Place each vocabulary term at the center of a **description wheel** diagram. Write some words describing it on the spokes.

See the Note-Taking Handbook on pages R45–R51.

SCIENCE NOTEBOOK

Earth is made up of materials with different densities.

→ Dense materials—such as iron and nickel—sink toward center

→ Less dense materials rise toward surface

at center of Earth

2400 km diameter

INNER CORE

hot, solid ball

under great pressure

dense iron and nickel

CHECK READINESS

Administer the Diagnostic Test to determine students' readiness for new science content and their mastery of requisite math skills.

 Diagnostic Test, pp. 39–40

Technology Resources

Students needing content and math skills should visit **ClassZone.com**.

- **CONTENT REVIEW**
- **MATH TUTORIAL**

 CONTENT REVIEW CD-ROM

KEY CONCEPT
3.1 Earth has several layers.

◀ **BEFORE, you learned**

- Heat is the flow of energy from warmer objects to cooler objects
- Energy causes change
- Changes in temperature can affect matter

▶ **NOW, you will learn**

- About the different properties of Earth's layers
- About the plates that make up Earth's outermost layers

VOCABULARY

inner core p. 70
outer core p. 70
mantle p. 71
crust p. 71
lithosphere p. 71
asthenosphere p. 71
tectonic plate p. 72

EXPLORE Density

Will a denser material sink or float?

PROCEDURE

①　Add equal amounts of water to 2 cups. Add 3 spoonfuls of salt to one of the cups and stir until the salt is dissolved.

②　Add 10 drops of food coloring to the same cup in which you dissolved the salt.

③　Gently pour about a third of the colored salt water into the cup of fresh water. Observe what happens.

WHAT DO YOU THINK?

- What did you observe when the two types of water were mixed?
- What does this activity tell you about materials of different density?

MATERIALS

- 2 clear plastic cups
- tap water
- table salt
- plastic spoon
- food coloring

SUPPORTING MAIN IDEAS
Support the main ideas about Earth's layers with details and examples.

Earth is made up of materials with different densities.

Scientists think that about 4.6 billion years ago, Earth formed as bits of material collided and stuck together. The planet grew larger as more and more material was added. These impacts, along with radioactive decay and Earth's gravity, produced intense heat. The young planet became a glowing ball of melted rock.

In time, denser materials, such as iron and nickel, sank toward the center of Earth. Less dense materials moved toward the surface. Other materials settled between the planet's center and its surface. Slowly, Earth's main layers formed—the core, the mantle, and the crust.

Chapter 3: **Plate Tectonics** 69　**B**

RESOURCES FOR DIFFERENTIATED INSTRUCTION

Below Level
UNIT RESOURCE BOOK
- Reading Study Guide A, pp. 131–132
- Decoding Support, p. 177

 **AUDIO CDS**

Advanced
UNIT RESOURCE BOOK
Challenge and Extension, p. 137

English Learners
UNIT RESOURCE BOOK
Spanish Reading Study Guide, pp. 135–136

 **AUDIO CDS**

- Audio Readings in Spanish
- Audio Readings (English)

3.1 FOCUS

● Set Learning Goals
Students will

- Describe the different properties of Earth's layers.
- Describe the plates that make up Earth's outermost layers.
- Model Earth's layers in an experiment.

◐ 3-Minute Warm-Up

Display Transparency 20 or copy this exercise on the board:

Decide if each statement is true. If not, correct it.

1. Particles within any group always move at the same speed. *Within any group of particles, some are moving faster or slower than others.*

2. Heat is the flow of energy from a warmer object to a cooler object. *True*

3. A pond has more thermal energy than a lake. *A lake has more thermal energy because it has more water molecules.*

4. Radiation differs from convection and conduction because it can travel through space. *True*

 3-Minute Warm-Up, p. T20

3.1 MOTIVATE

EXPLORE Density

PURPOSE To observe how a dense material will sink when combined with a less dense material

TIP *15 min.* To avoid disturbing the layers of water, students should pour the water gently and not shake or stir the water.

WHAT DO YOU THINK? *The salt water sank to the bottom because it contains more matter in the form of salt, making it denser than the fresh water. The fresh water rose to the surface because it contains less matter than the salt water.*

Integrate the Sciences

The difference in pressure between the inner core and outer core accounts for the different states of matter in the two layers. The more pressure there is, the less atoms can move. The less atoms move, the more solid the material remains despite intense heat. Scientists do not know for sure what causes the intense heat in Earth's core. It may be due partly to the radioactive decay of some materials in the core.

Teach from Visuals

To help students interpret the diagram of Earth's layers, ask:

• How does the density of material differ from the inner core to the crust? *It becomes less dense.*

• How does the temperature of the material change from the inner core to the crust? *It decreases.*

• Which layer of Earth is the thinnest? *the crust*

Ongoing Assessment

READING VISUALS *Answer: Greater pressure in the inner core squeezes atoms together so closely that the core remains solid. Less pressure in the outer core allows the metals to remain liquid.*

VOCABULARY
Draw a description wheel in your notebook for each term. You might want to include the pronunciation of some terms.

Earth's layers have different properties.

How do scientists know what Earth's deep interior is like? After all, no one has seen it. To explore the interior, scientists study the energy from earthquakes or underground explosions they set off. The energy travels through Earth somewhat like ripples move through a pond. The energy moves slower through less dense materials or liquids and faster through denser materials or solids. In this way, scientists infer what each layer is made of and how thick the layers are, as shown in the diagram below.

Core, Mantle, Crust

? **A** The core is Earth's densest region and is made up of two parts. The **inner core** is a ball of hot, solid metals. There is enormous pressure at the center of Earth. This squeezes the atoms of the metals so closely together that the core remains solid despite the intense heat.

The **outer core** is a layer of liquid metals that surrounds the inner core. The temperature and pressure in the outer core are lower than in the inner core. The lower pressure allows the metals to remain liquid.

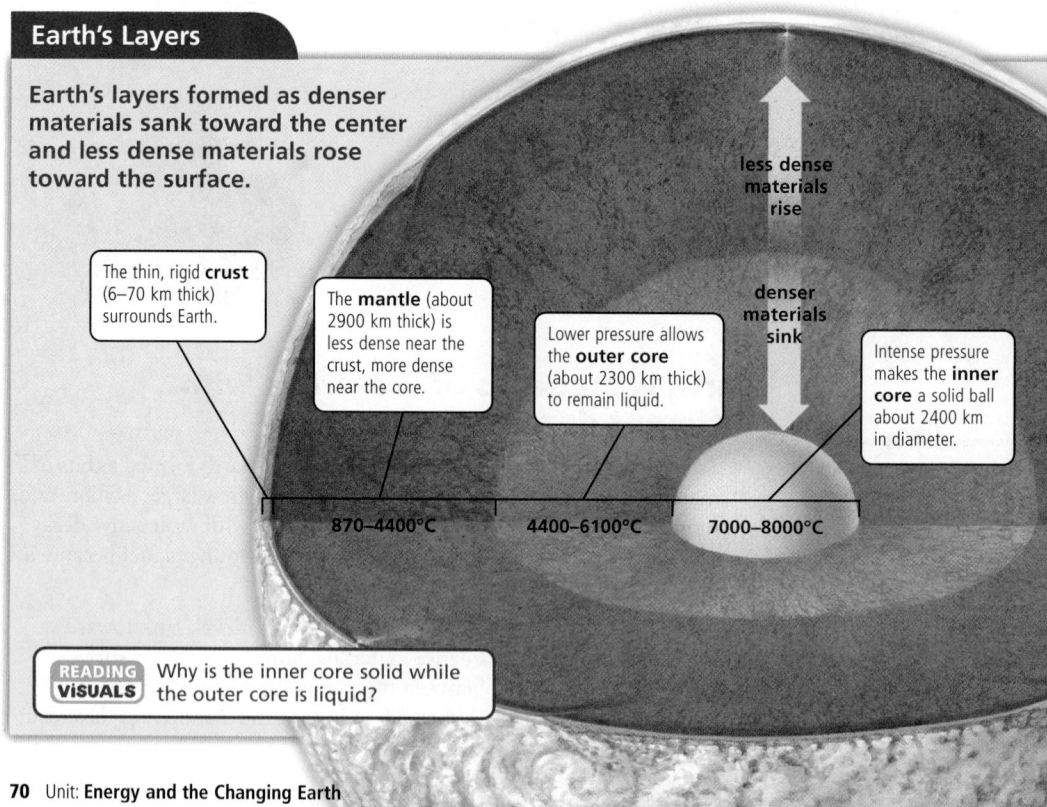

Earth's Layers

Earth's layers formed as denser materials sank toward the center and less dense materials rose toward the surface.

less dense materials rise

denser materials sink

The thin, rigid **crust** (6–70 km thick) surrounds Earth.

The **mantle** (about 2900 km thick) is less dense near the crust, more dense near the core.

Lower pressure allows the **outer core** (about 2300 km thick) to remain liquid.

Intense pressure makes the **inner core** a solid ball about 2400 km in diameter.

870–4400°C   4400–6100°C   7000–8000°C

READING VISUALS Why is the inner core solid while the outer core is liquid?

DIFFERENTIATE INSTRUCTION

? **More Reading Support**

A Which is Earth's densest region? *the core*

English Learners Make sure English learners understand how to read and follow activity directions. Some students may be unfamiliar with the imperative mood of a verb used in most activities when the subject "you" is understood but not stated. For example, students are directed to "Stir the beads and gravel . . ." (p. 72). Tell students this means the reader, or "you," should stir the beads and gravel.

The **mantle** is Earth's thickest layer, measuring nearly 2900 kilometers (1700 mi). It is made of hot rock that is less dense than the metallic core. The very top part of the mantle is cool and rigid. Just below that, the rock is hot and soft enough to move like a thick paste.

The **crust** is a thin layer of cool rock. It surrounds Earth somewhat like a shell surrounds an egg. There are two basic types of crust. Continental crust includes all continents and some major islands. Oceanic crust includes all the ocean floors. As the diagram below shows, Earth's crust is thinnest under the oceans and thickest under continental mountain ranges. The crust is home to all life on Earth.

Lithosphere and Asthenosphere

Earth's crust and the very top of the mantle together form the **lithosphere** (LIHTH-uh-SFEER). The Greek prefix *litho-* means "stone" or "rock." This layer is the most rigid of all the layers. The lithosphere sits on top of the **asthenosphere** (as-THEHN-uh-SFEER), a layer of hotter, softer rock in the upper mantle. The Greek word *asthenés* means "weak." This layer is not actually weak, but it is soft enough to flow slowly like hot tar. You can imagine the lithosphere as solid pieces of pavement resting on hot tar.

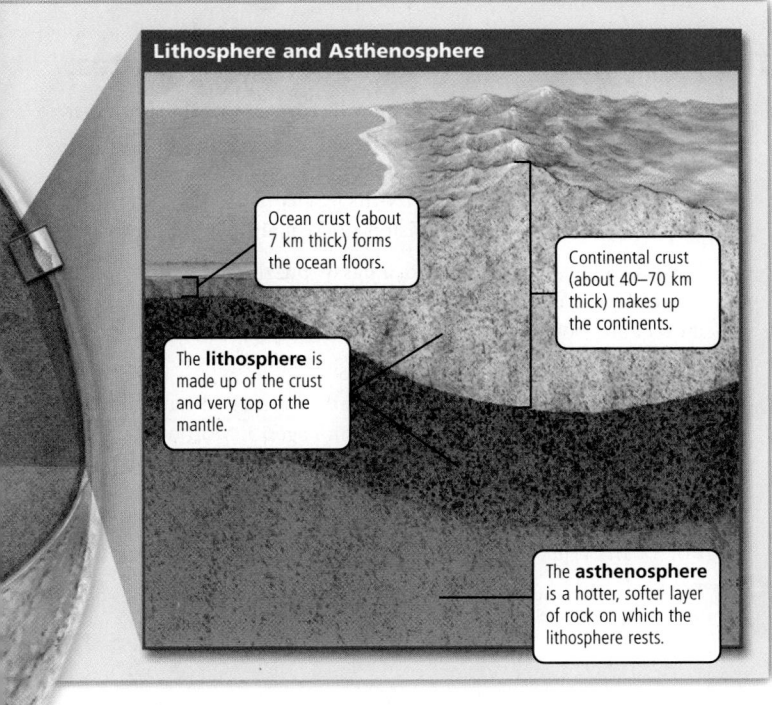

Lithosphere and Asthenosphere

Ocean crust (about 7 km thick) forms the ocean floors.

Continental crust (about 40–70 km thick) makes up the continents.

The **lithosphere** is made up of the crust and very top of the mantle.

The **asthenosphere** is a hotter, softer layer of rock on which the lithosphere rests.

Teach Difficult Concepts

Some students may have difficulty understanding the composition of the asthenosphere. Explain that the mantle gets cooler and less fluid as it nears the crust. The asthenosphere is not a liquid or a solid. It is like a hot, thick paste, such as tar. Some other materials that are neither liquid nor solid are toothpaste and rubber cement.

Teach from Visuals

To help students interpret the diagram of Earth's top layers, ask:

• Where is Earth's crust thinnest? *under the oceans*

• Where is it thickest? *under mountains*

Ongoing Assessment

Describe the different properties of Earth's layers.

Ask: What are Earth's four layers like? *The inner core is a ball of hot, solid metals; the outer core is liquid metals; the mantle has a layer of cool, rigid rock at the top and a layer of hotter, softer rock below it; and the crust is a thin layer of cool rock that surrounds Earth. The layers become less dense and less hot from the center to the outermost layer.*

Ask: What layer is home to all life on Earth? *the crust*

DIFFERENTIATE INSTRUCTION

 **More Reading Support**

B What is Earth's thickest layer? *the mantle*

C What does the lithosphere consist of? *the crust and the very top of the mantle*

Inclusion To visually model the nature of the asthenosphere and lithosphere, spread a layer of toothpaste on top of a rubber ball. Then place a small piece of paper on top of the toothpaste. Explain that the toothpaste represents the asthenosphere, and the paper represents the lithosphere. The ball represents the lower mantle and the inner and outer cores.

Advanced

R Challenge and Extension, p. 137

INVESTIGATE Earth's Different Layers

PURPOSE To create a model of how Earth's layers formed

TIP *15 min.* Advise students to pour the water slowly down the inside of the cup to avoid disturbing the layers.

WHAT DO YOU THINK? *The wooden beads separated from the gravel and rose to the surface. The model shows that denser materials sink to the bottom (or center) and less dense materials rise to the top.*

CHALLENGE *Students might place a solid layer of clay in the bottom of the cup to represent the solid core.*

 Datasheet, Earth's Different Layers, p. 138

Technology Resources

Customize this student lab as needed or look for an alternative. Print rubrics to assess student lab reports.

 Lab Generator CD-ROM

Real World Example

The lithospheric plates that make up Earth's crust could also be compared to a sheet of ice on a river or lake. When the ice first starts to break up, it forms many moving pieces. The pieces still form a surface that covers the water.

Ongoing Assessment

Describe the plates that make up Earth's outermost layers.

Ask: What is the lithosphere like? *It is split into many large and small slabs of rock.*

 *Answer: The oceanic crust of the plates is underwater.*

INVESTIGATE Earth's Different Layers

How can you model Earth's layers?

PROCEDURE

① Put a layer of wooden beads about 1 centimeter thick at the bottom of a clear plastic cup or small jar.

② Put a layer of gravel about 2 centimeters thick on top of the wooden beads. Stir the beads and gravel until they are well mixed.

③ Put another layer of gravel about 1 centimeter thick on top of the mix. Do NOT mix this layer of gravel.

④ SLOWLY fill the cup about two-thirds full of water. Be sure not to disturb the layers in the cup.

⑤ Stir the beads and gravel with the stick. Observe what happens.

WHAT DO YOU THINK?

• What happened to the materials when you stirred them?
• How do you think this model represents the layers of Earth?

CHALLENGE What could you add to the model to represent Earth's solid core?

SKILL FOCUS
Modeling

MATERIALS
• clear plastic cup
• small colored wooden beads
• gravel
• stirring stick
• tap water

TIME
15 minutes

The lithosphere is made up of many plates.

READING TiP

The word *tectonic* comes from the Greek *tecktōn*, which means "builder." Tectonic plates are constantly building and changing landforms and oceans around Earth.

As scientists studied Earth's surface, they discovered that the lithosphere does not form a continuous shell around Earth. Instead, they found that the lithosphere is broken into many large and small slabs of rock called **tectonic plates** (tehk-TAHN-ihk). Scientists do not know exactly how or when in Earth's history these giant plates formed.

Tectonic plates fit together like a jigsaw puzzle that makes up the surface of Earth. You could compare the lithosphere to the cracked shell of a hard-boiled egg. The shell may be broken into many pieces, but it still forms a "crust" around the egg itself.

Most large tectonic plates include both continental crust and oceanic crust, as shown in the diagram on page 13. Most of the thicker continental crust rises above the ocean. The rest of the plate is thin oceanic crust, or sea floor, and is underwater. The next time you look at the continents on a world map, remember you are seeing only the part of Earth's crust that rises above the ocean.

CHECK YOUR READING Why do you see only the dry land areas of tectonic plates on a typical world map?

DIFFERENTIATE INSTRUCTION

 **More Reading Support**

D What two types of crust do most large tectonic plates contain? *oceanic and continental*

Below Level To help students understand the discussion of continental and oceanic crust, use a world map with ocean basins to show how much of Earth's crust lies underwater. Point out where the African Plate's oceanic crust forms part of the sea floor of the Atlantic and Indian Oceans and the Mediterranean Sea (discussed on p. 73).

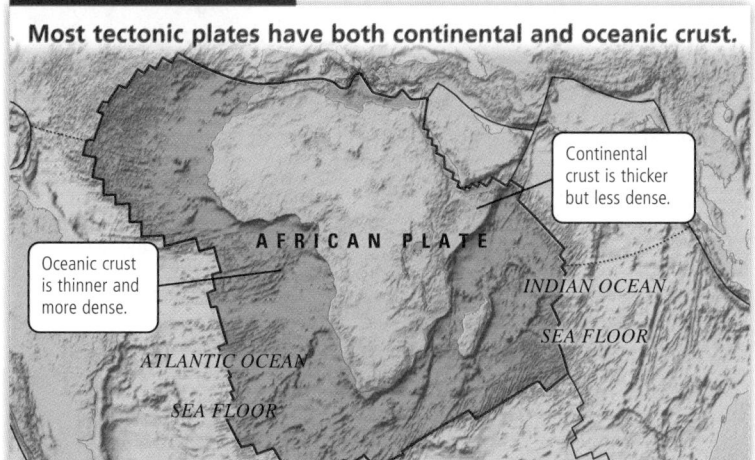

African Plate

Most tectonic plates have both continental and oceanic crust.

AFRICAN PLATE

Continental crust is thicker but less dense.

Oceanic crust is thinner and more dense.

INDIAN OCEAN

SEA FLOOR

ATLANTIC OCEAN

SEA FLOOR

In the diagram above, notice how much of the African Plate, shaded darker blue, lies underwater. The continent of Africa, which looks large on a world map, is actually about half the size of the entire plate. The plate's oceanic crust forms part of the sea floor of the Atlantic and Indian oceans and of the Mediterranean Sea. The ocean crusts of other plates make up the rest of the sea floors.

Earth's layers and tectonic plates are two of the most important discoveries in geology. They helped solve a mystery that had puzzled people for nearly 400 years. The mystery involved two questions. Have the continents always been where they are today? If not, how did they move to their present positions? In Section 3.2, you will find out how scientists are answering these questions.

3.1 Review

KEY CONCEPTS

1. Briefly describe the inner and outer cores, the mantle, and the crust.
2. In what ways is the lithosphere different from the asthenosphere?
3. Describe the structure of most tectonic plates.

CRITICAL THINKING

4. **Draw Conclusions** Suppose you are looking at a scene that has mountains near an ocean. Where do you think the crust would be the thickest? Why?
5. **Hypothesize** What would Earth look like if most of its crust was above sea level?

○ CHALLENGE

6. **Predict** You have learned that Earth's lithosphere is made up of many plates. How do you think this fact might help scientists solve the mystery of the moving continents?

ANSWERS

1. hot, dense, solid inner core; hot liquid outer core; thick mantle of heated rock; thin, rigid crust

2. lithosphere: made up of the rigid crust and very top part of the mantle; asthenosphere: weaker, softer rock just below the lithosphere

3. They have both thinner oceanic crust and thicker continental crust.

4. thickest under the mountains because the crust is thickest on the continents

5. There would be low plains and valleys surrounding all continents because that part of the crust uncovered by

oceans is thinner and lower than the continental crust.

6. If Earth's crust was all in one piece, the continents could not move. But since the crust is made up of many plates, the plates might be able to move separately.

Teach from Visuals

To help students interpret the map of tectonic plates, ask:

- Does the African Plate include all of Africa? *yes*
- Does the African Plate include only Africa? *No, it also includes much of the Atlantic and Indian Oceans.*

EXPLORE (the **BIG** idea)

Revisit "Internet Activity: Earth's Interior" on p. 67. Have students describe what they would experience on an imaginary trip to the center of Earth.

Reinforce (the **BIG** idea)

Have students relate the section to the Big Idea.

 Reinforcing Key Concepts, p. 139

3.1 ASSESS & RETEACH

Assess

 Section 3.1 Quiz, p. 41

Reteach

Help students review this section's concepts by showing them a hardboiled egg that has been cut in half. Keep the shell on and make sure it is cracked. Ask students how this egg can be seen as a useful model of Earth's structure. *Parts of the egg can be used to represent layers of Earth.* Ask what each part of the egg represents. *yolk: core; egg white: mantle; shell: crust; sections of cracked shell: tectonic plates*

Technology Resources

Have students visit **ClassZone.com** for reteaching of Key Concepts.

 CONTENT REVIEW

 CONTENT REVIEW CD-ROM

Students will

- Explain how the continental drift hypothesis was developed.
- Explain evidence for plate movement scientists have gathered from observations of the sea floor.
- Describe how scientists developed the theory of plate tectonics.

◄ 3-Minute Warm-Up

Display Transparency 20 or copy this exercise on the board:

Draw a diagram showing and labeling Earth's four layers. Identify the lithosphere and the asthenosphere on your diagram. *Diagram should show the inner core, outer core, mantle, and crust. The crust and the top part of the mantle should be labeled lithosphere. The adjacent part of the mantle should be labeled asthenosphere.*

 3-Minute Warm-Up, p. T20

3.2 MOTIVATE

EXPLORE Movements of Continents

PURPOSE To model how the shape of coastlines and land features could be a clue to the movement of continents

TIP *20 min.* Make sure students draw some of their land features, such as mountain ranges, large enough to cross from one side of the landmass to the other. Their drawings should be complex enough to be a challenge to put together.

WHAT DO YOU THINK? *Clues would include outlines of the pieces and landforms drawn on the pieces. Students should notice that Africa and South America seem to fit together.*

KEY CONCEPT

3.2 Continents change position over time.

◄ BEFORE, you learned

- Earth's main layers are the core, the mantle, and the crust
- The lithosphere and asthenosphere are the topmost layers of Earth
- The lithosphere is made up of tectonic plates

► NOW, you will learn

- How the continental drift hypothesis was developed
- About evidence for plate movement from the sea floor
- How scientists developed the theory of plate tectonics

VOCABULARY

continental drift p. 74
Pangaea p. 76
mid-ocean ridge p. 76
convection p. 77
convection current p. 77
theory of plate tectonics p. 78

VOCABULARY
Draw a description wheel in your notebook for *continental drift*.

EXPLORE Movements of Continents

How do you put together a giant continent?

PROCEDURE

1. Work with a small group. Draw the outline of a large landmass. Fill in mountains, rivers, lakes, and any other features you like.

2. Cut out your landmass, then tear the drawing into several pieces and mix the pieces up. Ask another group to put the puzzle together.

WHAT DO YOU THINK?
- What clues helped you fit the pieces together?
- Do any lands on a world map seem to fit together?

MATERIALS
- sheet of paper
- colored marking pens
- scissors

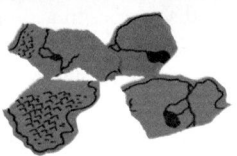

Continents join together and split apart.

The idea that Earth's surface might be moving is not new. As far back as the 1500s, when mapmakers started including North and South America in their world maps, they noticed something curious. The western coast of Africa and the eastern coast of South America seemed to fit together like pieces in a puzzle. Were these continents joined at one time?

In the late 1800s, German scientist Alfred Wegener (VAY-guh-nuhr) began studying this question. In 1912, he proposed a hypothesis known as **continental drift.** According to Wegener's hypothesis, Earth's continents were once joined in a single landmass and gradually moved, or drifted, apart. For many years, people did not accept Wegener's ideas. Not until the mid-1900s did scientists find new evidence that made them consider continental drift more seriously.

RESOURCES FOR DIFFERENTIATED INSTRUCTION

Below Level
UNIT RESOURCE BOOK
- Reading Study Guide A, pp. 142–143
- Decoding Support, p. 177

 **AUDIO CDS**

Advanced
UNIT RESOURCE BOOK
Challenge and Extension, p. 148

English Learners
UNIT RESOURCE BOOK
Spanish Reading Study Guide, pp. 146–147

 **AUDIO CDS**

- Audio Readings in Spanish
- Audio Readings (English)

Evidence for Continental Drift

Wegener gathered evidence for his hypothesis from fossils, from studies of ancient climate, and from the geology of continents.

Fossils Wegener learned that the fossils of an ancient reptile, *Mesosaurus* (MEHZ-uh-SAWR-uhs), had been discovered in South America and western Africa. This small reptile lived about 270 million years ago. Its fossils were not found anywhere else in the world. Wegener said this fact could easily be explained if South America and Africa were once joined, as shown in the map below.

Climate Evidence of climate change also supported Wegener's hypothesis. For example, Greenland today lies near the Arctic Circle and is mostly covered in ice. Yet fossils of tropical plants can be found on its shores. In contrast, South Africa today has a warm climate. Yet its rocks were deeply scratched by ice sheets that once covered the area.

Wegener suggested that these continents had moved, carrying their fossils and rocks with them. Greenland, for example, had once been near the equator and had slowly moved to the Arctic Circle. South Africa, once closer to the South Pole, had moved slowly north to a warmer region.

Geology Wegener's best evidence for continental drift came from the kinds of rocks that make up the continents. He showed that the type of rock found in Brazil matched the rock found in western Africa. Also, limestone layers in the Appalachian Mountains of North America were exactly like the limestone in Scotland's Highlands.

> **READING TiP**
>
> *Climate* refers to a pattern of wind, temperature, and rain or snow that occurs in a region over time. Earth's climates have changed many times in the planet's long history.

CHECK YOUR READING Which evidence for continental drift do you think is the most convincing? Explain your answer.

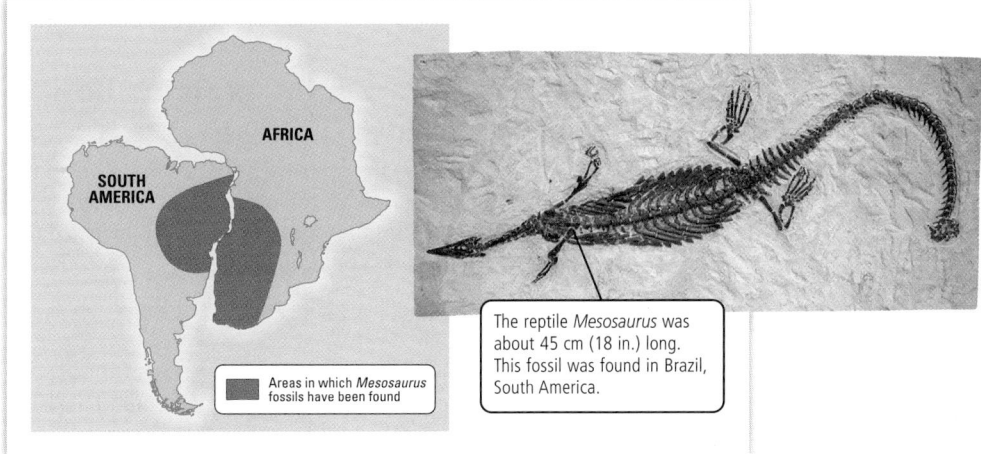

AFRICA
SOUTH AMERICA

Areas in which *Mesosaurus* fossils have been found

The reptile *Mesosaurus* was about 45 cm (18 in.) long. This fossil was found in Brazil, South America.

DIFFERENTIATE INSTRUCTION

English Learners Help English learners with words such as *still, yet, instead, in contrast, but,* or *however,* which signal a clause or a sentence with a contrasting meaning to the clause or sentence that precedes these words. For example, ". . . South Africa has a warm climate, *yet* its rocks are deeply scratched by sheets of ice. . . ." "Yet" signals a contrast between "warm climate" and "sheets of ice."

3.2 INSTRUCT

Teach from Visuals

To help students interpret the outline map of South America and Africa, ask:

- What do the shaded areas on the outline maps of South America and Africa represent? *where Mesosaurus fossils have been found*

- What do you notice about the location of the shaded areas and the coastlines of the two continents? *The shaded areas are located where the coastlines fit together.*

- What does this evidence suggest? *The two continents were once joined.*

Develop Critical Thinking

HYPOTHESIZE Have students reread the evidence that Wegener found. Then ask them to develop alternative hypotheses that might explain the same evidence. For instance, the continents might have been connected by land bridges. Ask students to discuss why they think their hypotheses explain the evidence.

History of Science

During Wegener's time, many scientists were aware that fossils of identical plants and animals from the same time period had been found in South America and in Africa. Wegener's critics came up with their own hypotheses, such as the following: land bridges once connected the continents; plants and animals reached distant lands by floating on rafts of driftwood; animals swam across thousands of miles of ocean. There was no evidence for any of these hypotheses, yet Wegener's critics continued to reject his ideas until the 1960s.

Ongoing Assessment

 *Answer: Answers will vary, but students should be able to give reasons for their choices.*

Teach from Visuals

To help students interpret the four maps of Pangaea and continental drift, ask:

- What was Earth like 200 million years ago? *It had one large continent and one huge ocean.*
- By 180 million years ago, how had Earth changed? *It had split into two continents.*
- How long ago did most of the major continents become separate? *65 million years ago*

Address Misconceptions

IDENTIFY Ask students to give examples of scientific changes that they have noticed in the past few years. If they cite examples that focus solely on inventions of new technology, they may hold the misconception that technology or new discoveries are necessary for scientific change.

CORRECT Point out that scientific changes also involve developing new theories to explain observations or to reinterpret previous evidence. The facts may not change, but the explanation of those facts changes and can alter how we see the world.

REASSESS Ask: How is Wegener's work an example of how science changes? *Wegener made new observations and reinterpreted existing evidence to develop his hypothesis of continental drift.*

Ongoing Assessment

Explain how the continental drift hypothesis was developed.

Ask: How did Wegener develop the continental drift hypothesis? *To explain the fact that the western coast of Africa and the eastern coast of South America seemed to fit together, Wegener gathered evidence from fossils, from studies of ancient climate, and from the rock formations on both continents.*

Pangaea and Continental Drift

For Wegener, all the evidence pointed to a single conclusion. The continents had once been joined in a huge supercontinent he called **Pangaea** (pan-JEE-uh). *Pangaea* comes from the Greek word meaning "all lands." This giant continent reached from pole to pole and was centered over the area where Africa lies today.

Pangaea began to split apart some 200 million years ago. In time, the continents moved to where they are today. Yet Wegener could not explain *how* the continents moved. Because of this, his critics called continental drift "a fairy tale" and rejected his hypothesis.

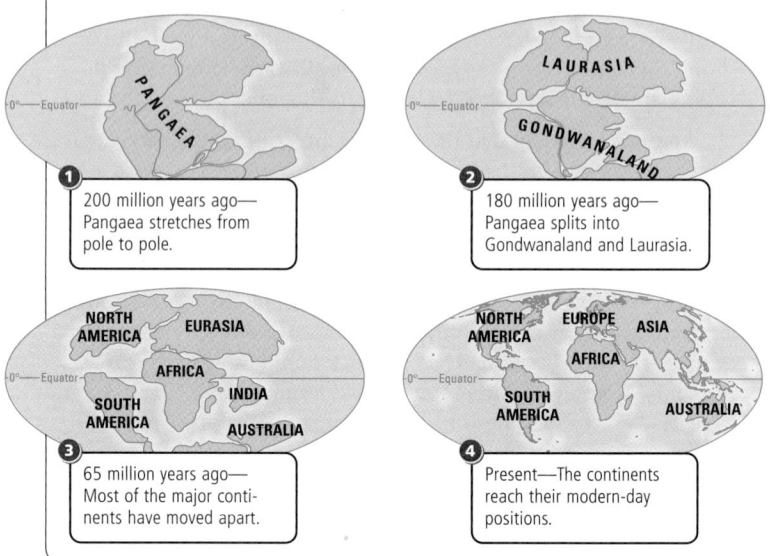

1 200 million years ago—Pangaea stretches from pole to pole.

2 180 million years ago—Pangaea splits into Gondwanaland and Laurasia.

3 65 million years ago—Most of the major continents have moved apart.

4 Present—The continents reach their modern-day positions.

The theory of plate tectonics explains how plates and their continents move.

For many years, Wegener's ideas were pushed aside. Then in the mid-1900s, scientists proved that tectonic plates move. They also offered explanations about how the plates move. Their work eventually led to the theory of plate tectonics, which built on some of Wegener's ideas.

Evidence from the Sea Floor

Scientists began mapping the sea floor in detail in the 1950s. They expected the floor to be smooth and level. Instead, they found huge underwater mountain ranges, called **mid-ocean ridges.** These ridges appeared in every ocean, circling Earth like seams in a baseball.

DIFFERENTIATE INSTRUCTION

 More Reading Support

B What is Pangaea? *Wegener's name for the supercontinent that once reached from pole to pole.*

Advanced Challenge students to add to the visual presentation on p. 76 by drawing a fifth map showing how the continents might look 100 million years from now. Refer students to the map on p. 79 to see the directions in which the major plates are moving. You might also refer them to pp. 86–87 for a discussion of rift valleys. *Maps should show a wider Atlantic Ocean. They might also show that the Red Sea has widened, the Mediterranean has narrowed, and a long narrow sea has formed in the Great Rift Valley as eastern Africa begins to split from the continent.*

Sea-Floor Spreading Scientists learned that the ridges form along cracks in the crust. Molten rock rises through these cracks, cools, and forms new oceanic crust. The old crust is pulled away to make room for new material. In this way, the sea floor slowly spreads apart. Scientists call these areas spreading centers. You will read more about spreading centers in Section 1.3.

Age of the Sea Floor Further evidence that the sea floor is spreading apart came from the age of the rocks in the crust. Scientists drilled into the sea floor from a specially equipped vessel called the *Glomar Challenger*. The rock samples revealed that the youngest rock is closest to the ridge, while the oldest rock is farthest away.

The samples also showed that even the oldest ocean floor is young—only 160 to 180 million years old. Continental crust is much older—up to 4 billion years old. These data confirmed that the ocean floor is constantly forming and moving away from the mid-ocean ridges like a conveyor belt. As the sea floor moves, so do the tectonic plates and their continents.

Ocean Trenches Yet, if the sea floor has been spreading for millions of years, why is Earth not getting larger? Scientists discovered the answer when they found huge trenches, like deep canyons, in the sea floor. At these sites, dense oceanic crust is sinking into the asthenosphere. Old crust is being destroyed at the same rate that new crust is forming. Thus, Earth remains the same size.

Scientists now had proof that tectonic plates move. But the same question remained. *How* could the plates move thousands of kilometers around the planet? The asthenosphere provided a possible answer.

 How does the age of the sea floor show that plates move?

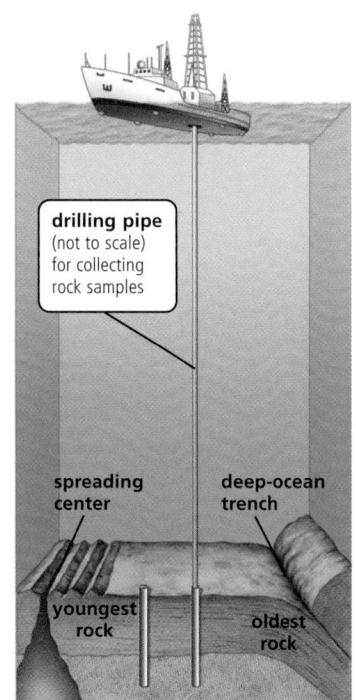

drilling pipe
(not to scale)
for collecting
rock samples

spreading center | **deep-ocean trench**

youngest rock | **oldest rock**

Scientists drill into the sea floor to obtain rock samples. The different ages of the rocks prove that plates move.

Causes of Plate Movement

Tectonic plates rest on the asthenosphere, a layer of soft, hot rock. Rock in this layer and in the mantle just below it moves by convection. **Convection** is energy transfer by the movement of a material. You have seen convection if you have ever boiled a pot of water. The water at the bottom of the pot heats up, becomes less dense, and rises. At the surface, it cools, becomes denser, and sinks, only to be heated and rise again.

The rock in the asthenosphere acts in a similar way. The hot, soft rock rises, cools, and sinks, then is heated and rises again. If this sinking and rising motion continues, it is called a **convection current**—a motion that transfers heat energy in a material.

Chapter 3: Plate Tectonics **77** **B**

Teach from Visuals

To help students interpret the drilling diagram, ask:

- What kind of rock samples did scientists find closest to a spreading center? *youngest rock*
- What kind of rock samples did scientists find farther from the spreading center? *old rock*
- What did this evidence indicate? *that new rock was being created at the spreading center and older rock was being pushed away from the spreading center*

History of Science

Scientific knowledge of the ocean floor increased greatly during World War I (1914–1918). Ships with echo-sounding devices measured the depth of the ocean at various locations. They recorded the time it took for sound to reach the ocean floor and bounce back. The recordings showed that a mountain chain existed in the central Atlantic Ocean. As exploration of the sea floor expanded in the 1950s, scientists discovered that this mountain chain nearly circled the Earth.

Ongoing Assessment

CHECK YOUR READING *Answer: Rock is youngest near the ridge, and older as you get farther away, showing that the older rock was carried away from the ridge some time ago.*

DIFFERENTIATE INSTRUCTION

 **More Reading Support**

C What happens at a spreading center? *sea floor slowly spreads apart*

D How does rock in the asthenosphere move? *by convection*

Below Level To help students see how Wegener's ideas moved from a hypothesis to a theory, outline on the board the mounting evidence that supported his idea. Emphasize that a hypothesis is an unproved explanation of observations and evidence. A theory is a well-tested and widely accepted explanation that is consistent with all available evidence. It can explain all or most of the data and can be used to predict future events.

EXPLORE the BIG idea

Revisit "Watching a Pot Boil" on p. 67. Have students explain their results.

Teach from Visuals

To help students interpret the plate movement diagram, ask:

- In what direction do convection currents move on each side of a spreading center? *outward from the center*

- In what direction would the plates move as a result? *in opposite directions away from the spreading center*

Ongoing Assessment

Describe how scientists developed the theory of plate tectonics.

Ask: What did geologists in the late 1960s combine to develop the theory of plate tectonics? *information about tectonic plates, about the sea floor, and about movements in the mantle*

READING VISUALS *Answer: Higher temperatures near the bottom heat up the material and cause it to rise. Lower temperatures near the surface cool the material and cause it to sink.*

Convection currents in the mantle are much slower than those in boiling water. The rock creeps only a few centimeters a year. The diagram below shows convection currents circulating. The tectonic plates in the lithosphere are carried on the asthenosphere like long, heavy boxes moved on huge rollers. Over millions of years, convection currents carry the plates thousands of kilometers.

Scientists suspect that two other motions—slab pull and ridge push—help move these huge plates. Slab pull occurs where gravity pulls the edge of a cool, dense plate into the asthenosphere, as shown in the diagram below. Because plates are rigid, the entire plate is dragged along. Ridge push occurs when material from a mid-ocean ridge slides downhill from the ridge. The material pushes the rest of the plate.

Putting the Theory Together

▼ REMINDER
A scientific theory is a well-tested explanation that is consistent with all available evidence.

E

Geologists combined their knowledge of Earth's plates, the sea floor, and the asthenosphere to develop the **theory of plate tectonics.** The theory states that Earth's lithosphere is made up of huge plates that move over the surface of the Earth.

The map on page 19 shows Earth's major tectonic plates and the directions in which they move. They are the African, the Antarctic, the Australian, the Indian, the Eurasian, the Nazca, the North and South American, and the Pacific plates.

Causes of Plate Movement

Convection currents, slab pull, and ridge push move Earth's huge tectonic plates.

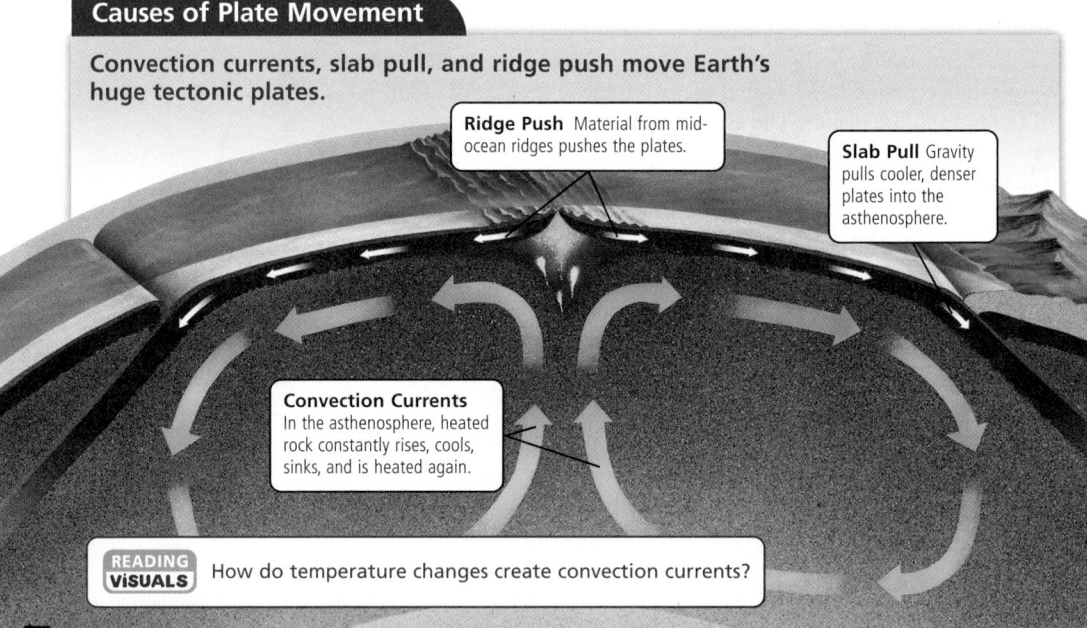

Ridge Push Material from mid-ocean ridges pushes the plates.

Slab Pull Gravity pulls cooler, denser plates into the asthenosphere.

Convection Currents In the asthenosphere, heated rock constantly rises, cools, sinks, and is heated again.

READING VISUALS How do temperature changes create convection currents?

DIFFERENTIATE INSTRUCTION

? More Reading Support

E What does the theory of plate tectonics state? *Earth's lithosphere is made up of huge, moving plates that are carried over Earth's surface.*

Advanced Have students who excel in mathematics calculate how far a plate would move in 200 million years if it moved at the rate of 3 cm per year. *Answer: 200,000,000 × 3 cm = 600,000,000 cm. 600,000,000 ÷ 100,000 = 6000 km* Ask students to consult reference sources to find out the width of the Atlantic Ocean. Then have them discuss how their calculations and findings relate to the theory of plate tectonics. *(The width of the Atlantic Ocean varies from about 2900 to 8800 km.)*

 Challenge and Extension, p. 148

Tectonic Plates

Earth's lithosphere is made up of moving plates.

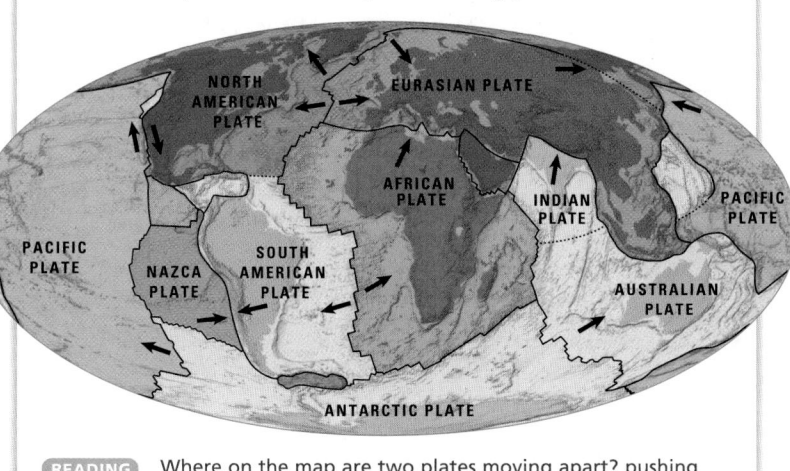

NORTH AMERICAN PLATE

EURASIAN PLATE

AFRICAN PLATE

INDIAN PLATE

PACIFIC PLATE

PACIFIC PLATE

NAZCA PLATE

SOUTH AMERICAN PLATE

AUSTRALIAN PLATE

ANTARCTIC PLATE

READING ViSUALS Where on the map are two plates moving apart? pushing together? scraping past each other?

As scientists studied the plates, they realized that one plate could not shift without affecting the others nearby. They found that plates can move apart, push together, or scrape past each other. The arrows on the map above show each type of plate motion.

Plate movements cause great changes in Earth's crust. Most major earthquakes, volcanoes, and mountain ranges appear where tectonic plates meet. You will learn why as you read more about plate movements.

3.2 Review

KEY CONCEPTS

1. What evidence did Wegener gather to support his continental drift hypothesis?

2. Give three types of evidence from the sea floor that prove Earth's tectonic plates move.

3. Explain how motions in the asthenosphere can move tectonic plates around Earth.

CRITICAL THINKING

4. **Apply** A friend tells you he read on a Web site that Earth is getting smaller. What can you tell him that shows Earth's size is not changing?

5. **Evaluate** What other types of scientists, besides geologists, would find the theory of plate tectonics useful in their work?

⚠ CHALLENGE

6. **Infer** Use the arrows on the map above and your knowledge of sea-floor spreading and ocean trenches to answer these questions: What is happening to the size of the Atlantic Ocean? What can you infer is happening to the size of the Pacific Ocean? Explain your answers.

ANSWERS

1. ancient climate clues that showed continents had once been in different locations; the same rock layers and fossils appeared on two widely separated continents

2. sea-floor spreading, different ages of sea-floor rock, mid-ocean trenches

3. Circulation of heated and cooling material forms convection currents that can carry tectonic plates.

4. The oceanic crust is sinking into trenches, but at the same time, the sea floor is spreading. Both happen at the same rate, so Earth stays the same size.

5. biologists and oceanographers

6. Because of sea-floor spreading the Atlantic Ocean is getting wider; the Pacific Ocean must be getting narrower because the size of Earth stays roughly the same.

Ongoing Assessment

READING ViSUALS *Sample answer: the North and South American plates are moving apart from the Eurasian and African plates; the Nazca Plate and the South American Plate are pushing together; the Pacific Plate and the North American Plate are scraping past each other.*

Teach from Visuals

To help students interpret the map of Earth's tectonic plates, ask:

• How many major plates are shown on the map? *9*

• Are most of the plates shown moving apart or pushing into each other? *pushing into each other*

Reinforce (the **BIG** idea)

Have students relate the section to the Big Idea.

R Reinforcing Key Concepts, p. 149

3.2 ASSESS & RETEACH

Assess

A Section 3.2 Quiz, p. 42

Reteach

Help students review this section's concepts by writing these heads on the board: "Evidence for Continental Drift" and "Evidence for Plate Tectonics." Call on students to identify the main ideas for each. *Evidence for Continental Drift: fossils, climate, rock formations. Evidence for Plate Tectonics: sea-floor spreading, sea-floor rock of different ages, mid-ocean trenches.*

Technology Resources

Have students visit **ClassZone.com** for reteaching of Key Concepts.

 CONTENT REVIEW

 CONTENT REVIEW CD-ROM

Focus

PURPOSE To observe the movement of convection currents in order to determine how they move tectonic plates

OVERVIEW Students will use candles to heat water in a pan and create convection currents to move drops of food coloring and sponges. Students will find the following:

- Heat creates convection currents in water.
- These currents move objects on the surface of the water.

Lab Preparation

- Work with the class as a group to write the hypothesis for the experiment.
- Have students create their own lab datasheets. They should make a full-page, two-column chart with the column headings *Cold Water* and *Hot Water* and the row headings *Food Coloring* and *Sponges.*
- Create two stations, each with a set of the materials listed.
- Prior to the investigation, have students read through the investigation and prepare their data tables. Or you may wish to copy and distribute datasheets and rubrics.

 UNIT RESOURCE BOOK, pp. 180–181

SCIENCE TOOLKIT, F14

Lab Management

- If possible, students should work in small groups. Each student should have the chance to do something in the experiment—for example, light the candles, hold the sponges, write the observations, and so on.
- Tell students to line up the matching "coastlines" so they are centered lengthwise over the candles.

SAFETY Advise students to be careful with the matches and to return them to you as soon as they finish.

CHAPTER INVESTIGATION

Convection Currents and Plate Movement

OVERVIEW AND PURPOSE South America and Africa are drifting slowly apart. What powerful force could be moving these two plates? In this investigation you will

- observe the movement of convection currents
- determine how convection currents in Earth's mantle could move tectonic plates

▶ Problem

Write It Up

How do convection currents in a fluid affect floating objects on the surface?

▶ Hypothesize

Write It Up

Write a hypothesis to explain how convection currents affect floating objects. Your hypothesis should take the form of an "If . . . , then . . . , because . . ." statement.

MATERIALS
- oven-glass lasagna pan
- 2 bread pans or 2 bricks
- water
- liquid food coloring
- 2 small candles
- matches
- 2 sponges
- scissors
- 3–4 pushpins

▶ Procedure

1. Use two overturned bread pans or two bricks to raise and support the glass lasagna pan. Fill the pan with water to a depth of 4 cm.

2. Hold the food coloring over the middle of the pan. Squeeze several drops into the water. Be careful not to touch or disturb the water with the plastic tip or your hands. Write down your observations.

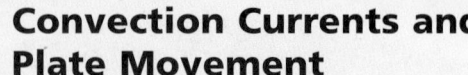

step 3

3. Light the two candles and place them beneath the center of the pan. Then squeeze several more drops of food coloring into the middle of the pan.

4. Observe what happens for a few minutes, then write down your observations. After you have finished, blow out the candles and wait until the water cools.

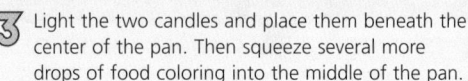
step 5

5. Moisten the two sponges. Cut one into the shape of South America and the other into the shape of Africa. Insert the pushpins as shown in the photo.

INVESTIGATION RESOURCES

CHAPTER INVESTIGATION, Convection Currents and Plate Movement
- Level A, pp. 180–183
- Level B, pp. 184–187
- Level C, p. 188

Advanced students should complete Levels B & C.

Writing a Lab Report, D12–13

Technology Resources

Customize this student lab as needed or look for an alternative. Print rubrics to assess student lab reports.

 Lab Generator CD-ROM

6. Place the sponges on top of the water in the center of the pan. Fit the two sponges together along their coastlines.

7. Gently hold the sponges together until the water is still, then let go. Observe them for a few minutes and record what you saw.

8. Light the candles again. Place them under the pan and directly beneath the two sponges.

9. Gently hold the sponges together again until the water heats up. Then carefully let go of the sponges, trying not to disturb the water.

10. Observe the sponges for a few minutes, and then record your observations.

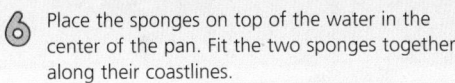 **Observe and Analyze** Write It Up

1. **RECORD** Draw diagrams to show how the food coloring and the sponges moved in cold water and in heated water. Use arrows to indicate any motion.

2. **ANALYZE** Did the food coloring and the sponges move more with or without the candles? Use what you have learned about convection to explain the role of the candles.

▶ **Conclude** Write It Up

1. **EVALUATE** Water is a fluid, but the asthenosphere is not. What properties of the asthenosphere allow it to move like a fluid and form convection currents?

2. **COMPARE AND CONTRAST** In what ways is your setup like Earth's asthenosphere and lithosphere? In what ways is your setup different?

3. **ANALYZE** Compare your results with your hypothesis. Do your observations support your hypothesis? Why or why not?

4. **INTERPRET** Write an answer to your problem statement.

5. **IDENTIFY CONTROLS** Did your experiment include controls? If so, what purpose did they serve here?

6. **APPLY** In your own words, explain how the African continent and the South American continent are drifting apart.

7. **APPLY** Suppose you own an aquarium. You want to make sure your fish are warm whether they swim near the top or near the bottom of the aquarium. The pet store sells two types of heaters. One heater extends 5 cm below the water's surface. The other heater rests on the bottom of the aquarium. Based on what you learned in this activity, which heater would you choose, and why?

▶ **INVESTIGATE Further**

CHALLENGE Design a new version of this experiment that you think would be a better model of the movements in Earth's asthenosphere and lithosphere. What materials will you need? What changes would you make to the procedure? Sketch your version of the lab, and explain what makes it better.

Convection Currents and Plate Movement
Problem How do convection currents in a fluid affect floating objects on the surface?
Hypothesize
Observe and Analyze
Diagram 1. Sponges on Unheated Water

Conclude

▶ **Observe and Analyze** Write It Up

SAMPLE DATA Drops of food coloring and sponges do not move in cold water. They move apart in heated water.

1. *Diagrams will show no motion in cold water, and will show objects moving apart in heated water.*

2. *More with the candles. Candles heated the water at the bottom; hot water rose to the surface where it cooled; the cool water sank, only to be heated once again. Candles keep convection currents going.*

▶ **Conclude** Write It Up

1. *The heated rock is soft and able to move, so it can circulate slowly.*

2. *Similar: heat source, layers, objects on the surface. Different: water is more fluid, the candles are concentrated in one spot, the sponges are much smaller and don't cover the surface area.*

3. *Students should explain why their hypothesis was supported or not.*

4. *Student answers should mention the fact that convection currents move objects on the surface.*

5. *Yes, the controls were the food coloring and the sponges in cold water. The controls served to show there was not another cause of movement.*

6. *At the mid-ocean ridge, the new crust is pushing the old crust aside. The spreading center moves the oceanic crust like a conveyor belt. As the crust moves, the continents are carried farther and farther apart.*

7. *Heater that rests on bottom—it will create convection currents that circulate warm water throughout the entire aquarium.*

▶ **INVESTIGATE Further**

CHALLENGE Students can work in small groups to design new versions of the experiment. Ask them to present their versions to the class. If possible, have them conduct their experiments and report on the results.

Post-Lab Discussion

Ask students the following questions:

• What difficulties or errors did you encounter when doing this lab? *Students may say holding the continents together or getting them centered over the candles.*

• How did this experiment affect your understanding of convection currents? *Answers will vary, but students should mention how watching the action of the food coloring or sponges moving made convection currents more clear.*

▶ Set Learning Goals

Students will

- Identify different plate boundaries.
- Explain what happens when plates move apart.
- Determine how to measure the direction and speed of plates.
- Model the magnetic reversal of Earth's poles in an experiment.

● 3-Minute Warm-Up

Display Transparency 21 or copy this exercise on the board:

Match each definition with the correct term.

Definitions

1. huge landmass in which all continents were once joined *a*

2. hypothesis that Earth's continents were once joined in a single landmass and gradually moved apart *d*

3. theory that Earth's lithosphere is made up of huge, moving plates that are carried around the planet by motions in the mantle *b*

Terms

a. Pangaea   c. sea-floor spreading

b. plate tectonics   d. continental drift

 3-Minute Warm-Up, p. T21

3.3 MOTIVATE

EXPLORE Divergent Boundaries

PURPOSE To model how plates move apart at a divergent boundary

TIP *15 min.* Make sure students pull the pieces out slowly enough to see how the two sides match.

WHAT DO YOU THINK? *The two pieces of paper move away from the crack in the center at the same rate. There might be a similar formation of new crust pushing the old crust back.*

KEY CONCEPT

3.3 Plates move apart.

◀ **BEFORE, you learned**

- The continents join and break apart
- The sea floor provides evidence that tectonic plates move
- The theory of plate tectonics helps explain how the plates move

▶ **NOW, you will learn**

- About different plate boundaries
- What happens when plates move apart
- How the direction and speed of plates can be measured

VOCABULARY

divergent boundary p. 82
convergent boundary p. 82
transform boundary p. 82
rift valley p. 83
magnetic reversal p. 84
hot spot p. 87

EXPLORE Divergent Boundaries

What happens when plates move apart?

PROCEDURE

① Cut the piece of striped paper into two symmetrical pieces slightly less wide than the slit in the oatmeal box.

② Match up the lines of the two pieces and tape the pieces together at one edge. Push the taped edge into the box until only a few centimeters of the free edges show at the top.

③ Grasp each piece of paper, one in each hand. Slowly pull the two pieces horizontally out of the cylinder, pulling them in opposite directions.

WHAT DO YOU THINK?

How is your model similar to the process of sea-floor spreading?

MATERIALS

- scissors
- piece of striped paper
- tape
- small oatmeal box with slit cut in side

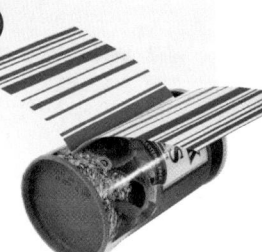

Tectonic plates have different boundaries.

READING TiP

Use word meanings to help remember science terms.

diverge = to go in different directions

converge = to come together from different directions

transform = to change

A plate boundary is where the edges of two plates meet. After studying the way plates move, geologists identified three types of boundaries.

- A **divergent boundary** (dih-VUR-juhnt) occurs where plates move apart. Most divergent boundaries are found in the ocean.

- A **convergent boundary** (kuhn-VUR-juhnt) occurs where plates push together.

- A **transform boundary** occurs where plates scrape past each other.

In this section, you will discover what happens at divergent boundaries in the ocean and on land. You will read more about convergent and transform boundaries in Section 3.4.

RESOURCES FOR DIFFERENTIATED INSTRUCTION

Below Level

UNIT RESOURCE BOOK

- Reading Study Guide A, pp. 152–153
- Decoding Support, p. 177

 **AUDIO CDS**

 Additional INVESTIGATION,
Magnetic Patterns on the Ocean Floor, A, B, & C, pp. 189–197; Teacher Instructions, pp. 320–321

Advanced

UNIT RESOURCE BOOK

- Challenge and Extension, p. 158
- Challenge Reading, pp. 173–174

English Learners

UNIT RESOURCE BOOK

Spanish Reading Study Guide, pp. 156–157

AUDIO CDS

- Audio Readings in Spanish
- Audio Readings (English)

The sea floor spreads apart at divergent boundaries.

In the ocean, divergent boundaries are also called spreading centers. Mid-ocean ridges mark these sites where the ocean floor is spreading apart. As the ridges continue to widen, a gap called a **rift valley** forms. Here molten material rises to build new crust.

Mid-Ocean Ridges and Rift Valleys

Mid-ocean ridges are the longest chain of mountains on Earth. Most of these ridges contain a rift valley along their center, as shown in the diagram below. When molten material rises from the asthenosphere, cold ocean water cools the rock until it becomes solid. As the plates move apart, new cracks open in the solid rock. More molten material rises and hardens. The growing ridge stands high above the sea floor.

The world's longest ridge, the Mid-Atlantic Ridge, runs the length of the Atlantic Ocean. Here the North and South American plates are moving away from the Eurasian and African plates. The ridge extends nearly 11,000 kilometers (6214 mi) from Iceland to near Antarctica. The rift valley is 24 kilometers (15 mi) wide and 9 kilometers (6 mi) deep—about 7 kilometers (4 mi) deeper than the Grand Canyon!

Divergent Boundary in the Ocean

Mid-ocean ridges, rift valleys, and new crust mark where the sea floor spreads apart.

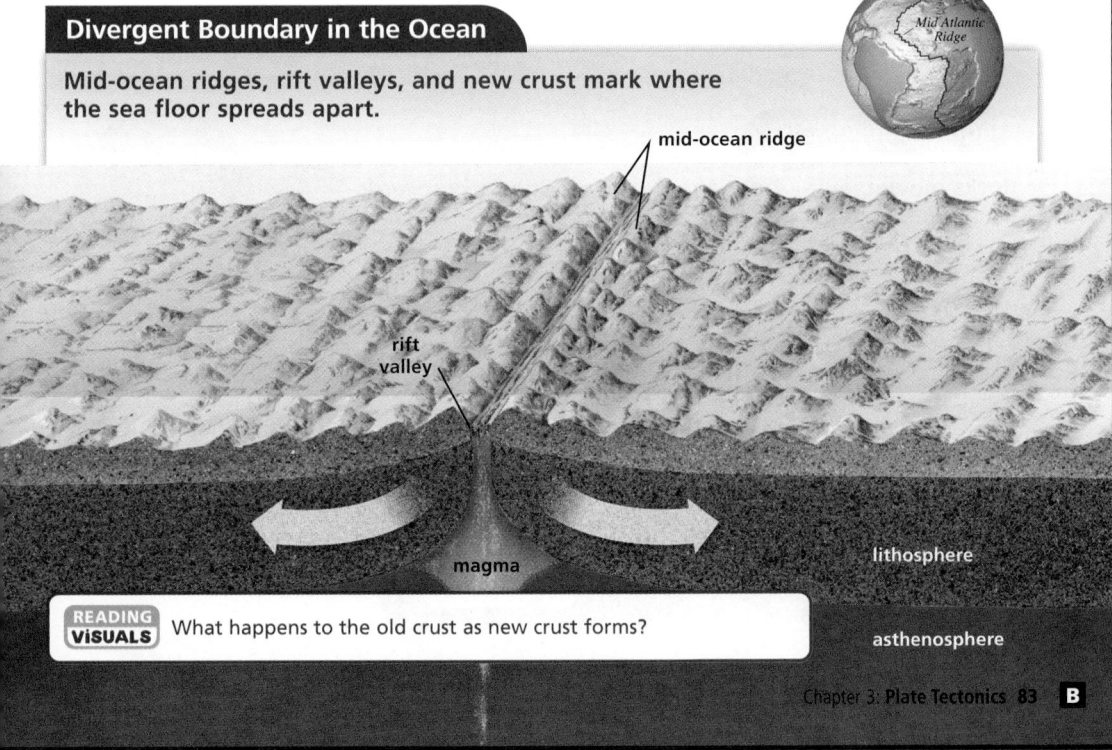

mid-ocean ridge

rift valley

magma

lithosphere

asthenosphere

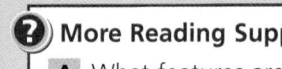 What happens to the old crust as new crust forms?

Chapter 3: Plate Tectonics **83** B

DIFFERENTIATE INSTRUCTION

? More Reading Support

A What features are found at divergent boundaries in the ocean? *mid-ocean ridges and rift valleys*

English Learners The paragraphs on this page have a variety of introductory clauses and phrases. For example, "As the ridges continue to widen, a gap called a rift valley forms." Have English learners find the comma that separates the introductory clause or phrase from the rest of the sentence. Then help them locate the subject of the sentence. Photocopy and distribute this and other pages and have students practice identifying introductory clauses and phrases.

3.3 INSTRUCT

Real World Example

A divergent boundary might be compared to a crack in a sidewalk where a tree has pushed through. The tree will eventually spread the sidewalk and stretch the crack wider and wider. As the tree keeps growing, it will carry the broken edges of the sidewalk upward with it, creating a type of "ridge."

Teaching with Technology

Provide students with a map of the ocean floor on CD-ROM so that they can study the Mid-Atlantic Ridge and its rift valley. Have students zoom in on the ridge to examine it more closely.

Teach from Visuals

To help students interpret the divergent boundary diagram, ask:

- What creates a rift valley? *as the sea floor spreads, it creates a gap between the ridges*

- What does the globe show? *the location of the Mid-Atlantic Ridge*

Ongoing Assessment

Explain what happens when oceanic plates move apart.

Ask: How do rift valleys and mid-ocean ridges form at spreading centers? *Rift valleys form as plates move apart. Rising magma fills the crack, and the rock cools. As more magma flows into the crack, the rock splits, is pushed aside, and produces ridges on either side of the rift valley.*

READING VISUALS *Answer: The old crust is split and pushed aside, forming horizontal cracks. The old crust forms part of the ridge.*

Teach Difficult Concepts

Students may have difficulty understanding magnetic reversals and the difference between the Earth's magnetic poles and geographic poles. Use a globe to explain that the Earth's geographic poles mark the ends of an imaginary "pole" around which the Earth spins. The magnetic poles mark the "top" and "bottom" of Earth's magnetic field. They are located *near* the geographic poles but not at the same points. This is because Earth's magnetic field is constantly shifting and moving, causing the poles to change location as well.

Integrate the Sciences

Physical scientists believe that the circulating flow of molten rock in the outer core produces Earth's magnetism. The outer core, being liquid, rotates at a different speed than the more solid layers. Scientists theorize that these differences in rotation produce the fluctuation in Earth's magnetic field. But as yet no one knows exactly why or how the changes occur.

Teach from Visuals

To help students interpret the magnetic reversals diagram, ask:

- What do the arrows in the two globes represent? *the direction of magnetic north on Earth*

- What pattern can you see on each side of the mid-ocean ridge? *The magnetic reversals have been recorded in identical patterns on both sides of the ridge.*

Sea-Floor Rock and Magnetic Reversals

You read earlier that the sea floor is younger near a mid-ocean ridge and older farther away. As scientists continued to study the sea-floor rock, they made a surprising discovery about Earth's magnetic field.

To understand Earth's magnetic field, you can compare the planet to a bar magnet, which has a north and a south pole. Earth's magnetic field affects the entire planet, as shown in the diagram below. Notice that Earth's geographic and magnetic poles are not in the same place.

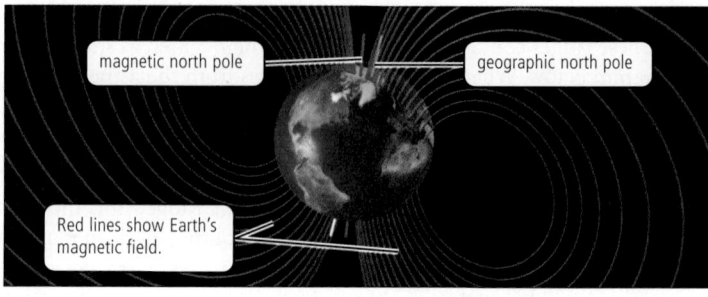

magnetic north pole

geographic north pole

Red lines show Earth's magnetic field.

B

Unlike a bar magnet, however, Earth's magnetic poles switch places every so often. The north pole becomes the south pole and the south pole becomes the north pole. This switch in direction is called a **magnetic reversal.** Such reversals are caused by changes in Earth's magnetic field. As yet, no one knows why these changes happen. In contrast, Earth's geographic poles never change places.

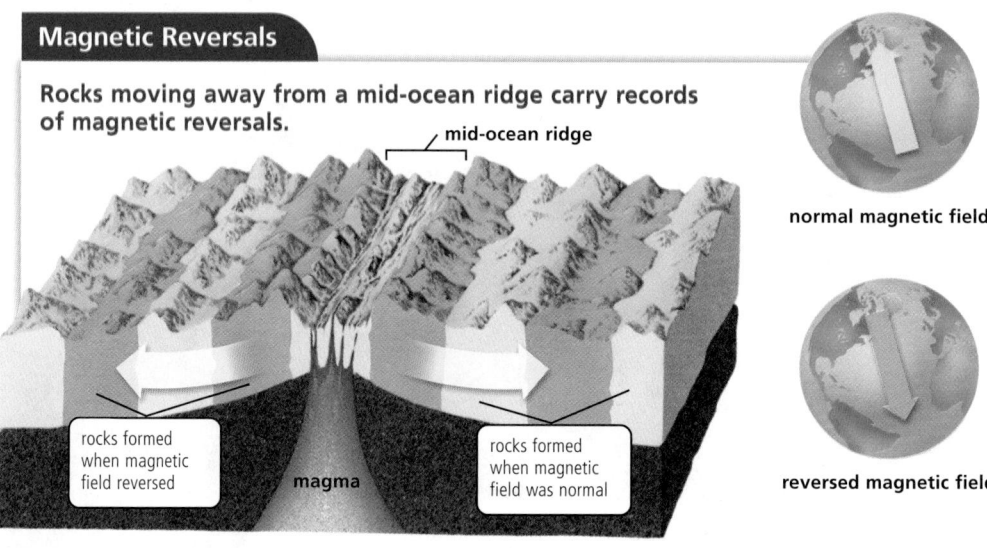

Magnetic Reversals

Rocks moving away from a mid-ocean ridge carry records of magnetic reversals.

mid-ocean ridge

rocks formed when magnetic field reversed

magma

rocks formed when magnetic field was normal

normal magnetic field

reversed magnetic field

DIFFERENTIATE INSTRUCTION

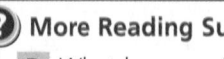 **More Reading Support**

B What happens in a magnetic reversal? *Earth's magnetic north and south poles switch places.*

Below Level Provide a bar magnet and iron filings so students can see how a magnetic field works. Have students use a compass to mark the north end of the magnet. Then have them reverse the bar magnet and observe how the compass needle switches direction to follow the new north.

Advanced Have students who are interested in magnetic reversals read the following article.

R Challenge Reading, pp. 173–174

Scientists found that each magnetic reversal is recorded in the sea-floor rock. These records are especially clear at some mid-ocean ridges. As the molten material rises and cools, some magnetic minerals line up with the Earth's magnetic field. When the material hardens, these minerals are permanently fixed like tiny compass needles pointing north and south. Whenever the magnetic field reverses, the cooling minerals record the change.

As shown in the diagram on page 84, the records of magnetic reversals line up like stripes in the rock. As the two plates move away from a mid-ocean ridge, each plate carries a record of magnetic reversals with it. The records are the same on either side of the ridge.

As scientists continued to map the ocean floor, they found more records of these reversals. By dating the rock, scientists had further evidence of plate movement. The youngest rock records the most recent reversal, which happened only about 760,000 years ago. The oldest rock, farthest from the mid-ocean ridge, records reversals that happened more than 150 million years ago.

CHECK YOUR READING Explain how records of magnetic reversals show that plates move apart.

INVESTIGATE Magnetic Reversals

How can you map magnetic reversals?
PROCEDURE

1. Wrap one end of the string around the middle of the bar magnet. Tape the string in place as shown.

2. Place a small piece of tape on one end of the magnet. Label the tape "N" to represent north.

3. Hold the bar magnet over one end of the sea-floor model as shown. Move the magnet SLOWLY toward the other end of the sea-floor model. Record your observations.

WHAT DO YOU THINK?

- What did the magnet reveal about the sea-floor model? Draw a diagram showing any pattern that you might have observed.

- Which part of the model represents the youngest sea floor? Which part represents the oldest sea floor?

CHALLENGE If Earth's magnetic field had never reversed in the past, how would the sea-floor model be different?

SKILL FOCUS
Modeling

MATERIALS
- string
- bar magnet
- masking tape
- marking pen
- sea-floor model

TIME
20 minutes

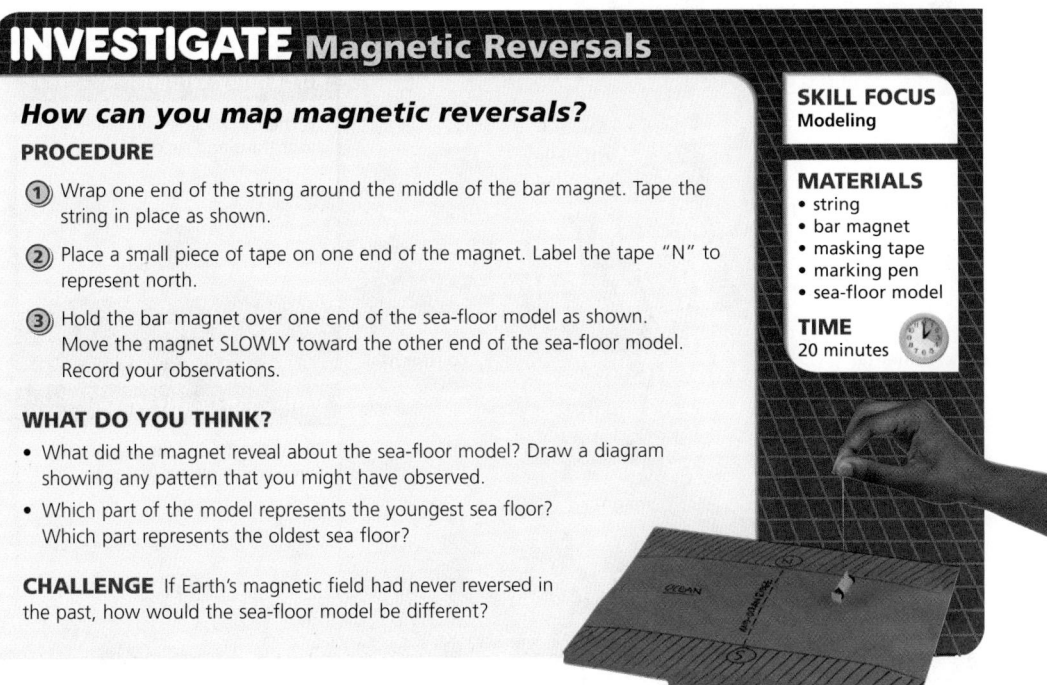

Chapter 3: **Plate Tectonics** 85 **B**

History of Science

In the 1950s, scientists mapping the ocean floor began using magnetometers that were adapted from submarine-detecting devices developed during World War II. Their discovery of the magnetic striping of the ocean floor surprised and puzzled scientists. Then in 1963, two English and two Canadian scientists independently proposed the idea that the pattern of magnetic striping corresponded to episodes of magnetic reversals in Earth's history.

INVESTIGATE Magnetic Reversals

PURPOSE To explore the effects of magnetic reversals

TIPS *20 min.* Make the sea-floor model before class using the instructions on p. 159 of the Unit Resource Book. Have students hold the magnet in the center of the model and move it *slowly* from one end to the other. If students move it too quickly, they will not see the magnet flip directions.

WHAT DO YOU THINK? *magnetic reversals; diagrams should show striped pattern that is the same on both sides. youngest: near the mid-ocean ridge; oldest: closest to the outside edges of the model*

CHALLENGE *The model would show one uniform direction for magnetic north and south.*

- Sea-floor Model Instructions, p. 159
- Datasheet, Magnetic Reversals, p. 160

DIFFERENTIATE INSTRUCTION

More Reading Support

C Where is each magnetic reversal recorded? *in the sea-floor rock*

Additional Investigation To reinforce Section 3.3 learning goals, use the following full-period investigation:

Additional INVESTIGATION, Magnetic Patterns on the Ocean Floor, A, B, & C, pp. 189–197, 320–321 (Advanced students should complete Levels B and C.)

Advanced Challenge students to explain how the sea-floor model for the investigation on this page was made.

Challenge and Extension, p. 158

Ongoing Assessment

CHECK YOUR READING *Answer: The farther away from the ridge, the older the record of reversals on both sides of the ridge. This shows that the plates move away from the center.*

Real World Example

You might compare the bulging and sinking of the crust at a continental divergent boundary to an asphalt road in winter. As water under the road freezes and expands, it causes the land and the asphalt to rise. When the water melts, it creates a small crater into which the road sinks. A pothole results.

Integrate the Sciences

The Great Rift Valley is not only a remarkable geological feature, it also supports a rich diversity of vegetation and wildlife. Mountain gorillas live in the rain forests on volcanic mountains. The grasslands of the Serengeti are home to herds of antelope, wildebeest, zebras, gazelles, and elephant as well as lions, leopards, and cheetahs.

Teach from Visuals

To help students interpret the divergent boundary diagrams, ask:

- In what direction are the plates moving in the large diagram? *away from each other*
- Do rift valleys grow wider or narrower as magma rises? *wider*
- What happens to the valley floor as the rift widens? *thins and sinks*

Ongoing Assessment

Describe what happens when continental plates move apart.

Ask: What happens to the crust when a continental plate begins to split? *The crust bulges and then splits and falls inward, creating a rift valley.*

CHECK YOUR READING *The valley can be flooded by waters from nearby oceans or rivers, eventually forming a lake or sea.*

Continents split apart at divergent boundaries.

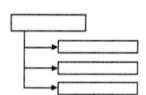

SUPPORTING MAIN IDEAS
Use this diagram to help you take notes on how continents split apart.

Like the sea floor, continents also spread apart at a divergent boundary. The boundary begins to form when hot material rises from deep in the mantle. This heat causes the crust to bulge upward. The crust cracks as it is stretched, and a rift valley forms, as shown in the diagram below. Magma rises through the cracked, thinned crust, forming volcanoes. As the rift valley grows wider, the continent begins to split apart.

If the rift valley continues to widen, the thinned valley floor sinks lower and lower until it is below sea level. Water from nearby oceans or rivers may fill the valley and form a sea or a lake. In the Middle East, for example, the Arabian Plate and African Plate have been moving apart for several million years. Over time, the waters of the Indian Ocean gradually filled the rift valley, forming the Red Sea. This sea is slowly getting wider as the plates continue to move apart.

? D

CHECK YOUR READING What happens when the floor of a rift valley sinks below sea level?

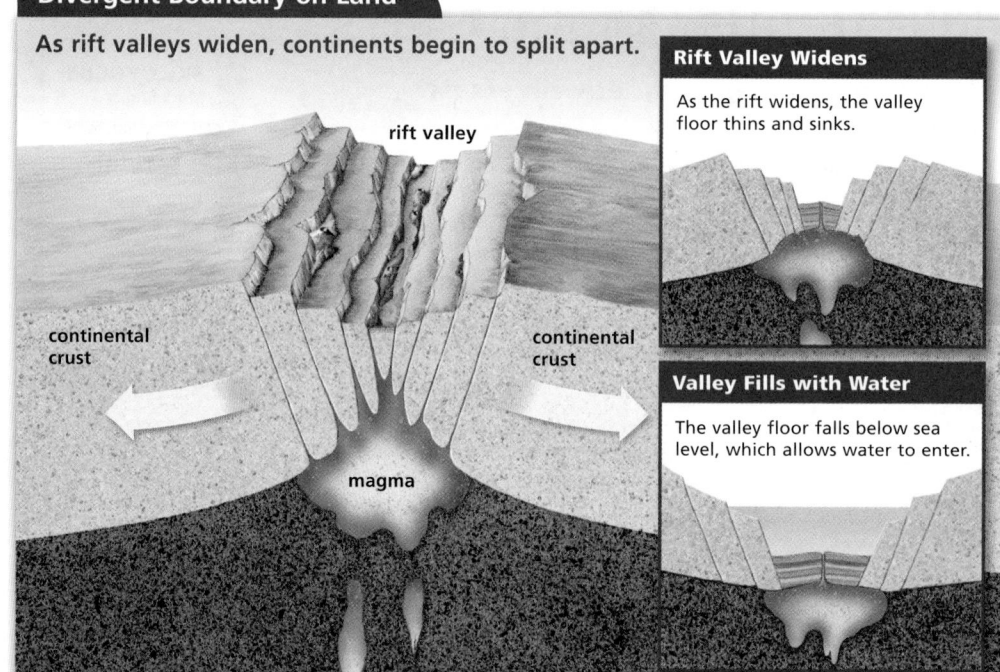

Divergent Boundary on Land

As rift valleys widen, continents begin to split apart.

rift valley

continental crust

continental crust

magma

Rift Valley Widens
As the rift widens, the valley floor thins and sinks.

Valley Fills with Water
The valley floor falls below sea level, which allows water to enter.

DIFFERENTIATE INSTRUCTION

 More Reading Support

D What is slowly happening to the Red Sea? *It is getting wider.*

Below Level On a physical map, point out the location of the Red Sea and note that it is part of the Great Rift Valley system that extends from Syria to Mozambique. Students should be able to visualize from the map how Saudi Arabia split away from Africa and water from the Indian Ocean formed the Red Sea.

The Great Rift Valley in eastern Africa, shown in the photograph above, is a good example of a continental rift valley. It is getting wider as the African Plate splits apart. This huge valley is thousands of kilometers long and as much as 1800 meters (5900 ft) deep.

PREDICT Rift valleys, like the Great Rift Valley in Africa, occur where plates are moving apart. What will happen to the Rift Valley when it gets low enough?

Hot spots can be used to track plate movements.

In some places, called **hot spots,** heated rock rises in plumes, or thin columns, from the mantle. Volcanoes often develop above the plume. Although most hot spots occur far from plate boundaries, they offer a way to measure plate movement. This is because a hot spot generally stays in one place while the tectonic plate above it keeps moving.

At a hot spot, the heat from the plume partly melts some of the rock in the tectonic plate above it. It is like holding a candle under a wax tablet. Eventually, the wax above the flame will melt. Likewise, if the plate stays over the hot spot long enough, the rock above it will melt.

In time, a volcano will form at the surface of the plate. The volcano may become high enough to rise above the sea as an island. For example, the Hawaiian Islands are being built as the Pacific Plate moves slowly over a hot spot.

The Hawaiian islands are located in the middle of the Pacific Plate. The largest island, Hawaii, is still over the hot spot.

The idea of hot spot volcanoes may be difficult for students to understand. You might have students view an animation of the process on the Internet or you might try the following demonstration.

Teacher Demo
Demonstrate the concept of a hot spot using a candle and wax tablet. As you hold a lit candle under a tablet of wax, tell students that the wax tablet is like a tectonic plate, and the candle is a like plume of magma rising from the mantle. The tablet melts under the hot candle just as the rock of a tectonic plate would melt under a hot spot. When you move the tablet, another spot starts to melt.

Ongoing Assessment
PHOTO CAPTION Answer: If the Rift Valley sinks low enough, water from the Red Sea will flood the valley.

DIFFERENTIATE INSTRUCTION

More Reading Support

E What is a hot spot? *volcanic activity that develops above a plume, which is a stream of magma rising from the mantle*

Alternative Assessment Have students draw diagrams that show how a hot spot can be used to track plate movements. Ask them to mark which landforms (volcanic islands or volcanic mountains) were created first, second, and so on. More advanced students might want to assign a direction and speed to their tectonic plate and calculate the ages of the landforms, starting from a specific point in time, say, 100,000,000 years ago.

Ongoing Assessment

Teach from Visuals

To help students interpret the diagram of hot spots, ask: How might the Hawaiian Islands be different a million years from now? Why? *Volcanic eruptions on the Big Island likely will have stopped as plate movement carries it away from the hot spot. Another island or two might form over the hot spot.*

Reinforce (the BIG idea)

Have students relate the section to the Big Idea.

 Reinforcing Key Concepts, p. 161

3.3 ASSESS & RETEACH

Assess

 Section 3.3 Quiz, p. 43

Reteach

Help students review this section's concepts by encouraging them to draw diagrams of the following features: a divergent boundary in the ocean, magnetic reversals on either side of a mid-ocean ridge, a continental divergent boundary, and a hot spot. Refer them to the diagrams on pp. 83–86, and 88.

Technology Resources

Have students visit **ClassZone.com** for reteaching of Key Concepts.

 CONTENT REVIEW

 CONTENT REVIEW CD-ROM

Hot Spots

Tectonic plates move over hot spots in the mantle.

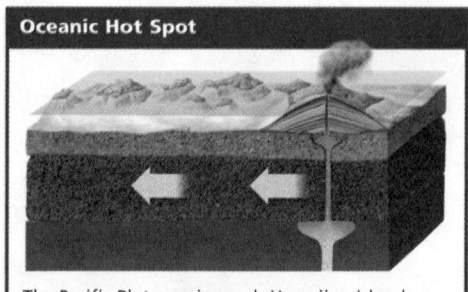

Oceanic Hot Spot

The Pacific Plate carries each Hawaiian island away from the hot spot. Eventually, a new volcano forms over the plume.

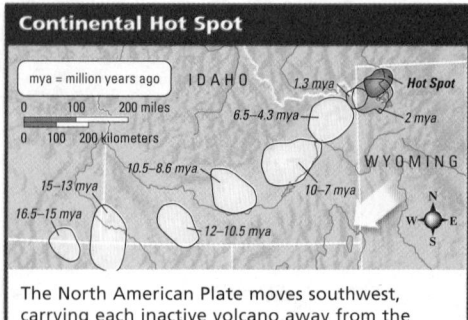

Continental Hot Spot

mya = million years ago
0   100   200 miles
0   100   200 kilometers

IDAHO   1.3 mya   Hot Spot
6.5–4.3 mya   2 mya
WYOMING
10.5–8.6 mya   10–7 mya
15–13 mya
16.5–15 mya   12–10.5 mya

The North American Plate moves southwest, carrying each inactive volcano away from the Yellowstone hot spot.

 **READING VISUALS** Which island or landform in each diagram was formed first? How do you know?

When the plate moves on, it carries the first volcano away from the hot spot. Heat from the mantle plume will then melt the rock at a new site, forming a new volcano. The diagram on the left shows this process.

Many hot spots provide a fixed point that scientists can use to measure the speed and direction of plate movements. For example, the Yellowstone hot spot under the North American Plate has formed a chain of inactive volcanoes, as shown in the diagram on the right. Scientists estimate that the North American Plate is moving southwest at about 2.3 cm (1 in.) per year.

CHECK YOUR READING How does a hot-spot volcano form?

3.3 Review

KEY CONCEPTS

1. Name and describe the three types of plate movements.
2. Create a two-column chart with the headings: Divergent boundary; Features. Fill in the chart for divergent boundaries at sea and on land.
3. How are hot spots used to track plate motion?

CRITICAL THINKING

4. **Predict** Suppose a magnetic reversal occurred today. How would new rocks at mid-ocean ridges differ from rocks that formed last year?
5. **Infer** A huge crack runs through Iceland, an island that lies above the Mid-Ocean Ridge. What do you think is happening to this country?

● CHALLENGE

6. **Hypothesize** Look carefully at the diagram above and the Hawaiian Islands picture on page 87. Notice that some hot spot islands or landforms are larger than other islands or landforms in the same chain. Develop a hypothesis, based on plate movement, that might explain this fact.

B 88 Unit: **Energy and the Changing Earth**

ANSWERS

1. *divergent, moving apart; convergent, pushing together; transform, scraping past*

2. *Oceanic: mid-ocean ridges, rift valleys, new crust; Continental: rift valleys, volcanoes, new crust*

3. *provide a fixed point to measure speed and motion*

of plate above

4. *The magnetic minerals in the new rocks would be aligned in the opposite direction.*

5. *The Mid-Atlantic Ridge is a divergent boundary, so the island would be pulling apart into two sections.*

6. *Sample:* **If** *melted rock rising through the crust builds islands or landforms,* **then** *a larger island or landform would have to be over the hot spot longer* **because** *it would need more time to acquire material before being carried away.*

SKILL: CALCULATING EQUIVALENT RATES

MATH TUTORIAL
CLASSZONE.COM
Click on Math Tutorial
for more help with
rates.

Arabian Plate

Red Sea

African Plate

This satellite photograph shows
where the Arabian Plate and
the African Plate are moving
apart. As a result, the Red Sea
is slowly growing wider.

Tracking Tectonic Plates

Scientists use lasers to track the movements of
tectonic plates. They bounce laser light off
satellites and measure the distance from each
satellite to the ground. As the plates move, the
distance changes. With this tracking system,
scientists know exactly how much tectonic
plates move each year.

You can use equivalent rates to predict
how far two divergent plates will move over a
given time. A rate is a ratio of two measures
expressed in different units, such as

$$\frac{10 \text{ cm}}{4 \text{ yr}}$$

This 0.61-meter-
wide satellite is
covered with mir-
rors to reflect laser
light back to Earth.

Example

If Boston, Massachusetts, and Lisbon, Portugal, are moving apart
at an average rate of 10 cm every 4 years, how much farther
apart will they move in 20 years?

Solution

Write an equivalent rate.

$$\frac{10 \text{ cm}}{4 \text{ yr}} = \frac{?}{20 \text{ yr}}$$

Divide 20 yr by
4 yr to get 5,
then multiply
10 cm by 5.

$$20 \div 4 = 5$$

$$10 \times 5 = 50$$

$$\frac{10 \text{ cm}}{4 \text{ yr}} = \frac{50 \text{ cm}}{20 \text{ yr}}$$

ANSWER Boston and Lisbon will move 50 centimeters farther
apart in 10 years.

Answer the following questions.

1. If New York, New York, and London, England, are moving apart
at an average rate of 5 cm every 2 years, how much farther
apart will they move in 8 years?

2. If Miami, Florida, and Casablanca, Morocco, are moving apart at
an average rate of 25 cm every 10 years, how much farther
apart will they move in 30 years?

3. If Portland, Maine, and Dublin, Ireland, are moving apart at an
average rate of 50 cm every 20 years, how much farther apart
will they move in 10 years?

CHALLENGE If Halifax, Nova Scotia, and Birmingham, England,
are moving apart at an average rate of 5 cm every 2 years,
how long will it take them to move 35 cm farther apart?

Chapter 3: **Plate Tectonics** 89 **B**

MATH IN SCIENCE
Math Skills Practice for Science

Set Learning Goal

To use ratios to predict how much farther apart two tectonic plates will move

Present the Science

The field of *space geodesy*—space-based
techniques of precisely measuring widely
separated points on Earth—grew rapidly
in the late 1970s. The techniques are
based on military and aerospace technology. Besides satellite laser ranging, the
Global Positioning System (GPS) is also
used to measure plate movement.

Develop Algebra Skills

• Remind students that equivalent rates
are like equivalent fractions. In the
example problem, you are finding an
equivalent fraction by multiplying the
numerator by the same factor as the
denominator.

• Ask: How many centimeters are in an
inch? *2.54* About how many inches is
10 centimeters? *about 4*

DIFFERENTIATION TIP For AD/HD students, provide both verbal and visual
instruction on how to find equivalent
rates by working the example problem
on the board.

Close

Ask students how scientists might use
long-range predictions of plate movements. *to predict sites of earthquakes or
volcanic activity or where new hot-spot
volcanoes or mountains might form*

• Math Support, p. 178
• Math Practice, p. 179

Technology Resources

Students can visit **ClassZone.com** for
practice in writing equivalent rates.

  MATH TUTORIAL

ANSWERS

1. 20 cm   *2. 75 cm*   *3. 25 cm*

CHALLENGE 14 years

$$\frac{5 \text{ cm}}{2 \text{ yr}} = \frac{35 \text{ cm}}{?}$$

$$\frac{35}{5} = 7$$

$$7 \cdot 2 = 14$$

$$\frac{5 \text{ cm}}{2 \text{ yr}} = \frac{35 \text{ cm}}{14 \text{ yr}}$$

Set Learning Goals

Students will

- Describe what happens when two continental plates converge.
- Identify what happens when an oceanic plate converges with another plate.
- Explain what happens when one plate scrapes past another plate.
- Design an experiment to model colliding plates.

3-Minute Warm-Up

Display Transparency 21 or copy this exercise on the board:

Decide if these statements are true. If not, correct them.

1. At a divergent boundary, tectonic plates collide. *At a divergent boundary, tectonic plates move apart.*

2. Rift valleys appear at divergent boundaries in the ocean and on land. *true*

3. Divergent boundaries in the ocean are also called spreading centers. *true*

 3-Minute Warm-Up, p. T21

34 **MOTIVATE**

EXPLORE Tectonic plates

PURPOSE To model the collision of tectonic plates and observe the effects

TIPS *10 min.* Advise students not to hold the napkins too close to the edges. They should push the napkins together slowly so they can watch what happens when the edges meet. If they get only one kind of action, such as one set of napkins going under the other set, have them do the activity more slowly or more quickly to get a variety of actions.

WHAT DO YOU THINK? *Napkins should slide under, over, or bunch up together. Students should be able to infer that tectonic plates will move in similar ways.*

KEY CONCEPT

3.4 Plates converge or scrape past each other.

◀ **BEFORE, you learned**

- Plates move apart at divergent boundaries
- In the oceans, divergent boundaries mark where the sea floor spreads apart
- On land, continents split apart at divergent boundaries

▶ **NOW, you will learn**

- What happens when two continental plates converge
- What happens when an oceanic plate converges with another plate
- What happens when one plate scrapes past another plate

VOCABULARY

subduction p. 90
continental-continental collision p. 91
oceanic-oceanic subduction p. 92
oceanic-continental subduction p. 93

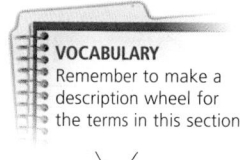

VOCABULARY
Remember to make a description wheel for the terms in this section.

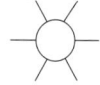

EXPLORE Tectonic Plates

What happens when tectonic plates collide?

PROCEDURE

① Arrange six square napkins in two rows.

② Slowly push the two rows of napkins together. Observe what happens.

WHAT DO YOU THINK?
- In what ways did the napkin edges move?
- How might your observations relate to the movement of tectonic plates?

MATERIALS
6 square napkins

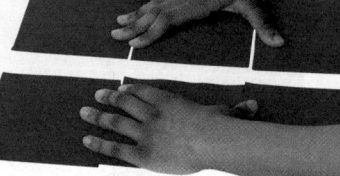

Tectonic plates push together at convergent boundaries.

You read earlier that new crust forms at divergent boundaries where plates move apart. At convergent boundaries, where plates push together, crust is either folded or destroyed.

When two plates with continental crust collide, they will crumple and fold the rock between them. A plate with older, denser oceanic crust will sink beneath another plate. The crust melts in the asthenosphere and is destroyed. When one plate sinks beneath another, it is called **subduction.** The word is based on the Latin prefix *sub-*, meaning "under," and the Latin *ducere*, meaning "to lead." Therefore, subduction is a process in which one plate is "led under" another.

There are three types of convergent boundaries: where two continental plates meet, where two oceanic plates meet, or where an oceanic plate and a continental plate meet. Major geologic events occur at all three types of boundaries.

RESOURCES FOR DIFFERENTIATED INSTRUCTION

Below Level
UNIT RESOURCE BOOK
- Reading Study Guide A, pp. 164–165
- Decoding Support, p. 177

 **AUDIO CDS**

Advanced
UNIT RESOURCE BOOK
Challenge and Extension, p. 170

English Learners
UNIT RESOURCE BOOK
Spanish Reading Study Guide, pp. 168–169

 **AUDIO CDS**

- Audio Readings in Spanish
- Audio Readings (English)

Continental-Continental Collision

A

A **continental-continental collision** occurs where two plates carrying continental crust push together. Because both crusts are the same density, neither plate can sink beneath the other. If the plates keep moving, their edges crumple and fold, as in the diagram below.

You can see the same effect if you put two blocks of clay on a table and push them together. If you push hard enough, one or both of the blocks will buckle. One cannot sink under the other, so the clay folds under the pressure.

The European Alps began rising nearly 40 million years ago as a section of the African Plate collided with the European Plate.

B

In some cases, the folded crust can be pushed up high enough to form mountains. Some of the world's largest mountains appear along continent-continent boundaries. For instance, the European Alps, shown in the photograph at right, are found where the African and European plates are colliding. The tallest mountains in the world, the Himalayas, first formed when the Indian Plate began colliding with the European Plate.

The Himalayas and the Alps are still forming today. As long as the plates keep moving, these mountains will keep rising higher.

 Explain how colliding plates form mountain ranges.

Convergent Boundary—Collision

Rocks crumple and fold to form mountains.

 READING VISUALS Why can neither plate sink under the other?

Chapter 3: **Plate Tectonics** 91 **B**

3.4 INSTRUCT

History of Science

The Burgess Shale is an important site where thousands of fossils of sea animals have been found in a mountain range. Located in Yoho National Park in the Rocky Mountains in British Columbia, the site contains fossils that are more than 500 million years old. The fossils formed in an underwater mudslide that preserved not just the hard skeletons but also the soft body parts of the animals. When the animals were buried, the area formed a reef near the coast of North America, which at that time was located near the equator. Similar fossil deposits, not nearly as well preserved, have been found in mountains around the world.

Teach from Visuals

To help students interpret the continental collision diagram, ask:

- What does the diagram show is happening to the rocks in the crust? *The wavy lines show how the rocks are bent and folded as the two plates push together.*

- What kind of landform occurs at a collision zone? *mountain range*

Ongoing Assessment

Describe what happens when two continental plates converge.

Ask: What happens to the plate edges when two continental plates collide? *Because neither plate can sink under the other, the edges crumple and fold.*

 *Answer: Plates push together until rocks crumple and fold, rising higher and eventually forming mountain ranges.*

READING VISUALS *Answer: Both plates are the same density so neither one can sink under the other.*

DIFFERENTIATE INSTRUCTION

? **More Reading Support**

A What is an area where two continental plates push together? *a continental-continental collision*

B When does folded crust form mountains? *when it is pushed up high*

English Learners Point out to English learners the different word forms found in this section. For example, *collide* and *collision, subduct* and *subduction, converge* and *convergent,* and *ocean* and *oceanic.* Help students understand how the different word forms relate to parts of speech and to understanding a sentence.

Chapter 3 **91** **B**

Teach Difficult Concepts

Students may have difficulty understanding the formation of volcanoes at subduction zones. Emphasize that volcanoes can appear fairly far from where the plates originally meet because the leading edge of the subducted plate is melting some distance from the initial point of subduction. Wherever two plates meet, the pressure can create crustal cracks over a wide area. Melted rock can rise through the cracks to form volcanoes at the surface.

Teach from Visuals

To help students interpret the diagram of oceanic subduction, ask:

- What kinds of plates are involved in subduction? *either two oceanic plates or an oceanic plate and a continental plate*

- What features occur when an oceanic plate sinks beneath another oceanic plate? *a trench and volcanic islands*

- What features occur when an oceanic plate sinks beneath a continental plate? *a trench and coastal mountains and volcanoes*

Ongoing Assessment

READING VISUALS *Answer: Crust is being formed at the mid-ocean ridge and where magma reaches the surface to slowly form islands and coastal volcanoes. Crust is being destroyed where plates subduct and melt.*

Oceanic-Oceanic Subduction

 C

An **oceanic-oceanic subduction** occurs where one plate with oceanic crust sinks, or subducts, under another plate with oceanic crust. The older plate sinks because it is colder and denser than the younger plate. When the older crust reaches the asthenosphere, it melts in the intense heat. Two main features form at oceanic-oceanic subductions: deep-ocean trenches and island arcs.

Deep-Ocean Trenches These trenches are like deep canyons that form in the ocean floor as a plate sinks. Most deep-ocean trenches are found in the Pacific Ocean. For example, at the Mariana Trench, the Pacific Plate is sinking under the Philippine Plate. This trench is the deepest place in the world's oceans, extending nearly 11,000 meters (36,000 ft) into the sea floor.

 D

Island Arcs There are chains of volcanic islands that form on the top plate, parallel to a deep-ocean trench. As oceanic crust of the sinking plate melts, magma rises through the top plate. Over time, the flows build up a series of islands. Island arcs include the Philippine Islands, the Aleutian Islands of Alaska, and the islands of Japan.

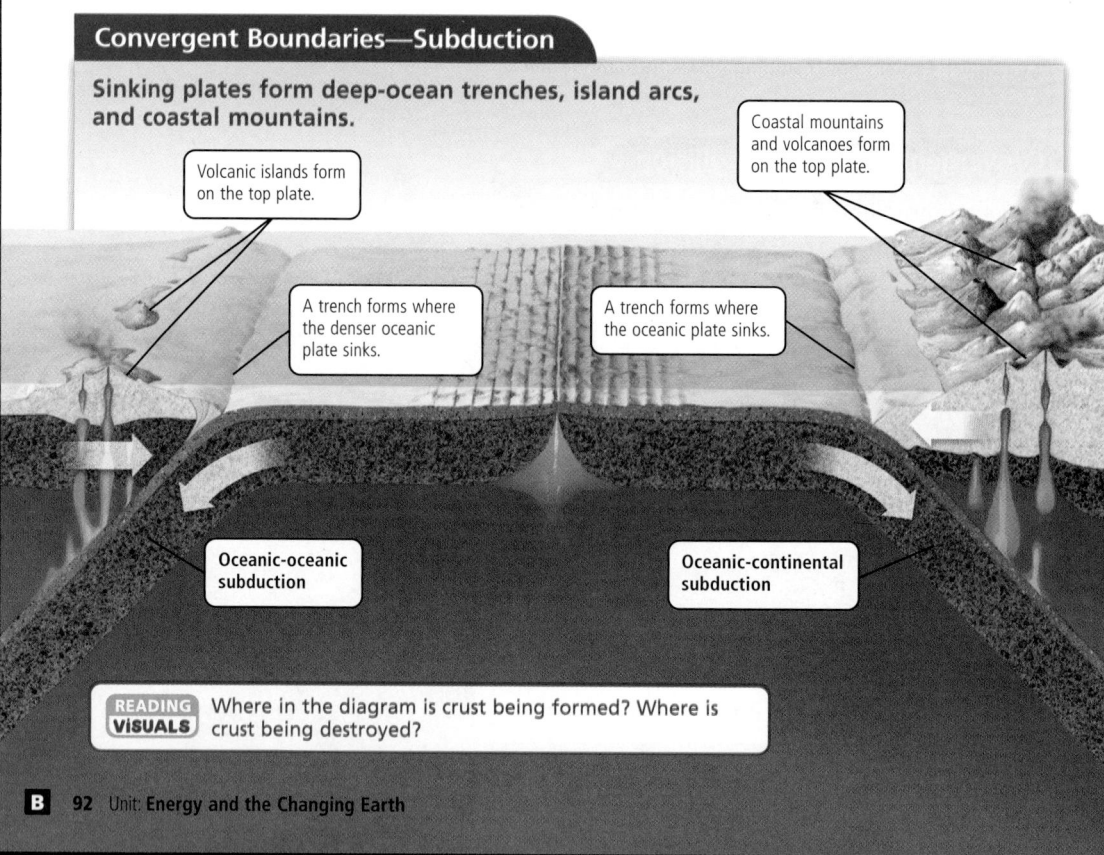

Convergent Boundaries—Subduction

Sinking plates form deep-ocean trenches, island arcs, and coastal mountains.

Volcanic islands form on the top plate.

Coastal mountains and volcanoes form on the top plate.

A trench forms where the denser oceanic plate sinks.

A trench forms where the oceanic plate sinks.

Oceanic-oceanic subduction

Oceanic-continental subduction

 **READING VISUALS** Where in the diagram is crust being formed? Where is crust being destroyed?

DIFFERENTIATE INSTRUCTION

? **More Reading Support**

C Does a lighter or denser plate sink? *the denser plate*

D Chains of volcanic islands that form parallel to a deep-ocean trench are called what? *island arcs*

Below Level Have students give an oral summary of what they just read about sinking plates and deep-ocean trenches. Explain that the melted rock of the sinking plate is lighter or less dense than the surrounding rock. It will rise up through cracks in the crust of the top plate and form either volcanic island arcs or coastal volcanoes.

Oceanic-Continental Subduction

An **oceanic-continental subduction** occurs when ocean crust sinks under continental crust, as shown in the diagram on page 92. The oceanic crust sinks because it is colder and denser than the continental crust. At these sites, deep-ocean trenches also form, along with coastal mountains.

Deep-Ocean Trenches Some of the world's youngest trenches are in the eastern Pacific Ocean. Here, for example, the Pacific Plate is sinking under the North American Plate. As the oceanic crust moves, it often causes underwater earthquakes.

Coastal Mountains As oceanic crust sinks under a continent, the continental crust buckles to form a range of mountains. These mountains, like island arcs, parallel a deep-ocean trench. As the diagram on page 92 shows, some of these mountains are volcanoes, which form as melted oceanic crust rises through the top plate.

The Cascade Mountains in Oregon and Washington are an example of coastal mountains. They began forming as the Juan de Fuca Plate began sinking under the North American Plate. Some of these peaks, such as Mount St. Helens in Washington, are active volcanoes.

VISUALIZATION
CLASSZONE.COM
Explore what happens along plate boundaries.

CHECK YOUR READING Why do deep-ocean trenches form at both types of subduction?

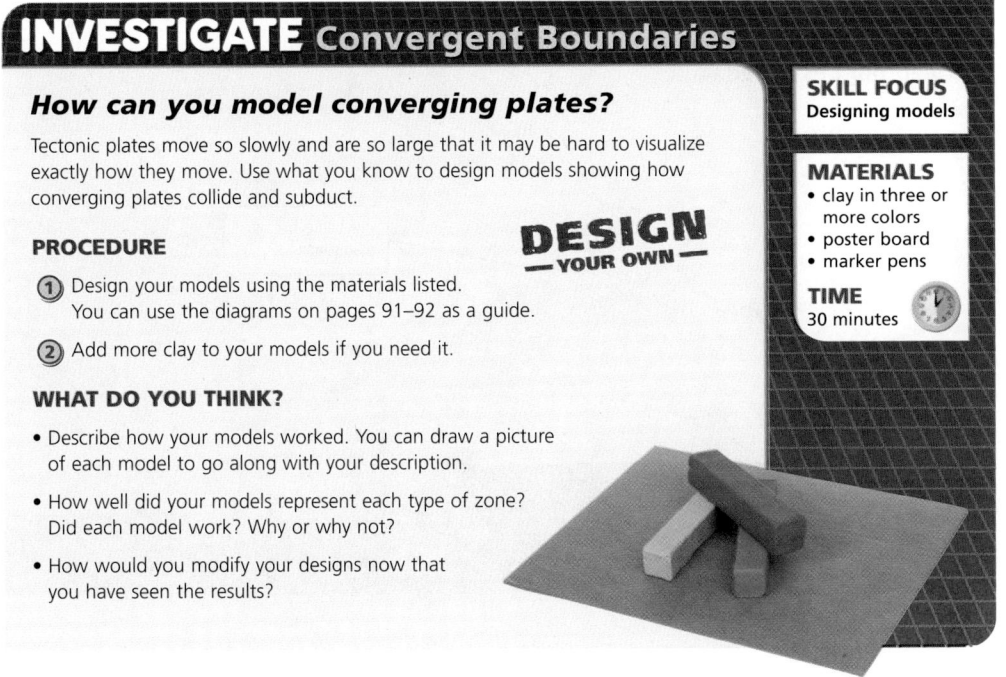

INVESTIGATE Convergent Boundaries

How can you model converging plates?

Tectonic plates move so slowly and are so large that it may be hard to visualize exactly how they move. Use what you know to design models showing how converging plates collide and subduct.

PROCEDURE

1. Design your models using the materials listed. You can use the diagrams on pages 91–92 as a guide.

2. Add more clay to your models if you need it.

DESIGN — YOUR OWN —

WHAT DO YOU THINK?

- Describe how your models worked. You can draw a picture of each model to go along with your description.

- How well did your models represent each type of zone? Did each model work? Why or why not?

- How would you modify your designs now that you have seen the results?

SKILL FOCUS
Designing models

MATERIALS
- clay in three or more colors
- poster board
- marker pens

TIME
30 minutes

Chapter 3: **Plate Tectonics** 93 **B**

INVESTIGATE Convergent Boundaries

PURPOSE To design models to show how plates collide and subduct in collision and subduction zones

TIP *30 min.* Have students label their models.

WHAT DO YOU THINK? *Student answers will vary.*

R Datasheet, Convergent Boundaries, p. 171

Technology Resources

Customize this student lab as needed or look for an alternative. Print rubrics to assess student lab reports.

Lab Generator CD-ROM

Metacognitive Strategy

Ask students to write down the most pressing question they have at this time about what happens at collision and subduction zones.

Teaching with Technology

Film groups of students showing and describing the models they created for the investigation on this page. Have the video available for parents to watch at conference time.

Ongoing Assessment

Identify what happens when an oceanic plate converges with another plate.

Ask: What causes volcanic islands and mountains to form? *Answer: The crust of the subducting plate melts and rises through cracks in the top plate, forming a series of volcanic islands or coastal volcanoes.*

CHECK YOUR READING *Answer: In both types of subduction, one plate sinks beneath another, forming a deep-ocean trench.*

Teacher Demo

To help students visualize the action at a transform boundary, demonstrate the action or have them demonstrate the action using two blocks of wood or two books.

Develop Critical Thinking

INFER Have students infer how scientists know that Los Angeles will be closer to where San Francisco is today in about 10 million years.

Teach from Visuals

To help students interpret the transform boundary diagram, ask:

What kind of movement occurs at a transform boundary? *Two plates slide past each other in opposite directions.*

What landform on the diagram shows how far the plates have moved? *The riverbed—as the plates move, the riverbed is offset along part of the fault.*

Ongoing Assessment

Explain what happens when one plate scrapes past another plate.

What happens as plates scrape past one another? *The rocks grind against each other, but no crust is formed or destroyed.*

CHECK YOUR READING *Answer: The Pacific Plate and North American Plate are scraping past each other along the San Andreas Fault. Crust is not being formed or destroyed.*

Tectonic plates scrape past each other at transform boundaries.

You learned that crust is formed at a divergent boundary and folded or destroyed at a convergent boundary. However, at a transform boundary, crust is neither formed nor destroyed. Here, two plates move past each other in opposite directions, as shown in the diagram below. As the plates move, their edges scrape and grind against each other. **?F**

Transform boundaries occur mostly on the sea floor near mid-ocean ridges. They also occur on land, where some are clearly visible as long cracks in Earth's surface. The San Andreas Fault in California is a transform boundary that runs from the Gulf of California through the San Francisco area. It marks where the Pacific Plate and part of the North American Plate are moving in opposite directions. If the plates keep moving at their present rate, Los Angeles will be a suburb of San Francisco in about 10 million years. **?G**

This long crack in the earth reveals the transform boundary known as the San Andreas Fault.

CHECK YOUR READING What makes the San Andreas Fault a transform boundary?

Transform Boundary

Plate edges grind and scrape past each other. Crust is neither formed nor destroyed.

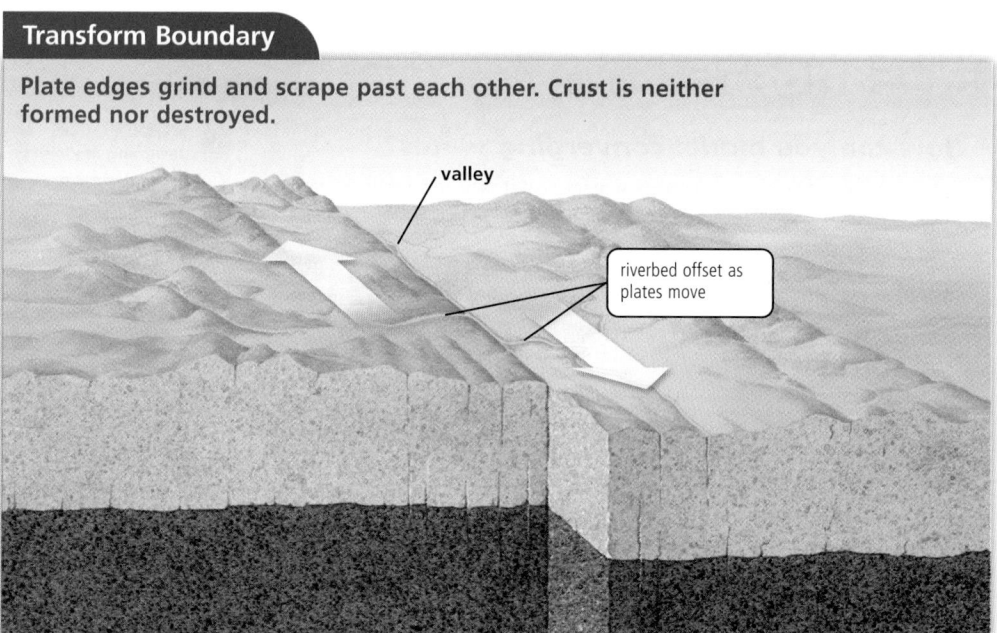

valley

riverbed offset as plates move

DIFFERENTIATE INSTRUCTION

? More Reading Support

F Where do two plates move past each other in opposite directions? *at a transform boundary*

G Where do transform boundaries occur? *on the sea floor and on land*

Advanced Have interested students learn about and report on current research on the San Andreas Fault.

R Challenge and Extension, p. 170

Tectonic Plate Boundaries

There are three types of plate boundaries: transform, divergent, and convergent. Major geologic events occur at all three types.

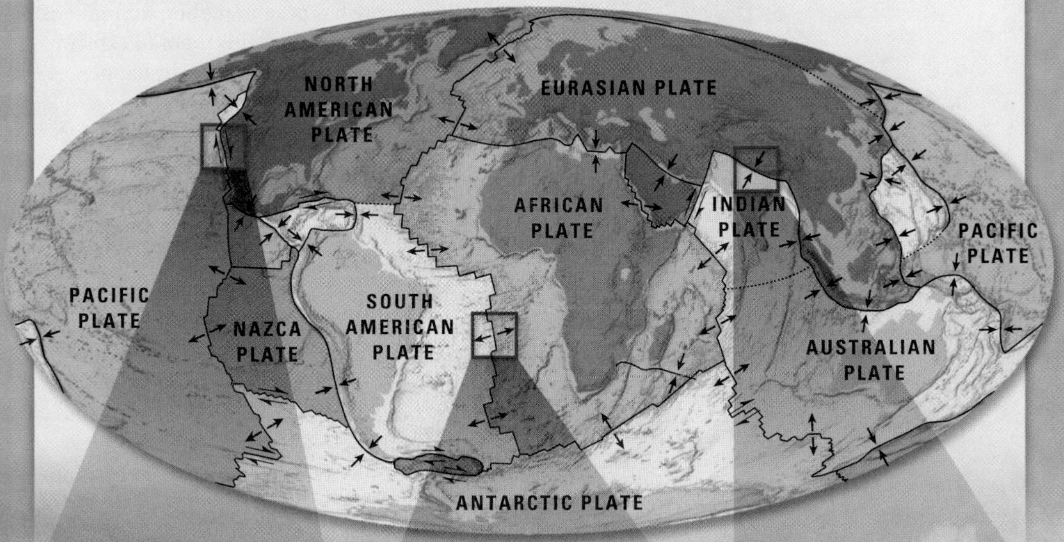

NORTH AMERICAN PLATE

EURASIAN PLATE

AFRICAN PLATE

INDIAN PLATE

PACIFIC PLATE

PACIFIC PLATE

NAZCA PLATE

SOUTH AMERICAN PLATE

AUSTRALIAN PLATE

ANTARCTIC PLATE

Transform Boundaries

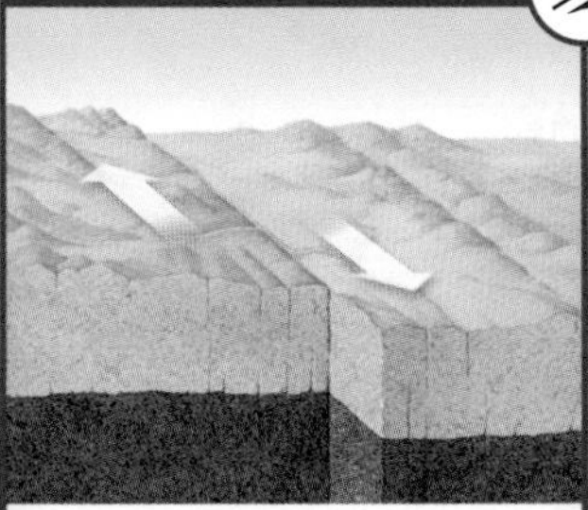

Plates scrape horizontally past each other. Crust is neither formed nor destroyed.

Divergent Boundaries

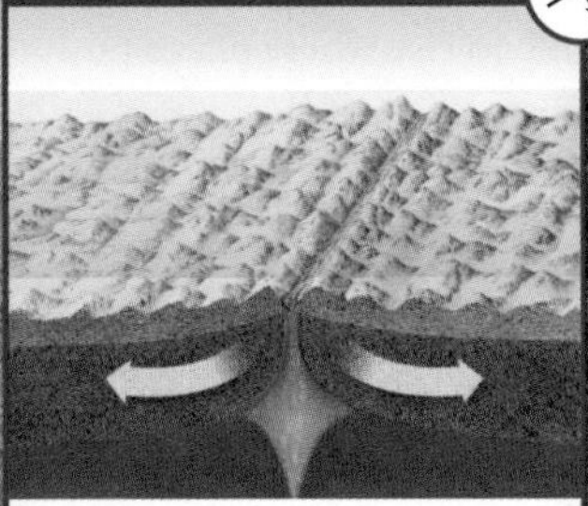

As plates move apart, new crust is built, forming mid-ocean ridges and rift valleys.

Convergent Boundaries

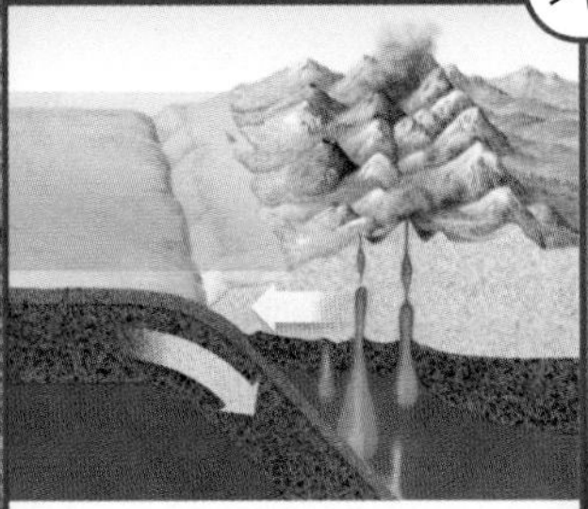

Crust is destroyed where plates subduct. It is folded where plates collide.

READING VISUALS Where else on the map above can you find a transform, divergent, and convergent boundary?

Chapter 3: **Plate Tectonics 95** **B**

Chapter 3 **95** **B**

Ongoing Assessment

History of Science

Although scientists can forecast the likelihood of an earthquake over a certain period of time, they cannot pinpoint exactly when and where an earthquake will occur. In 1990, an American scientist named Iben Browning predicted that a large earthquake would strike the New Madrid Fault Zone on about December 3, 1990. His prediction was widely publicized and taken seriously by many people in the region. Many people bought earthquake insurance policies; and hundreds of schools, shops, and businesses closed on that date. More than 10 years after the date, a large earthquake still had not hit the area.

Reinforce (the **BIG** idea)

Have students relate the section to the Big Idea.

 Reinforcing Key Concepts, p. 172

3.4 ASSESS & RETEACH

Assess

 Section 3.4 Quiz, p. 44

Reteach

Help students review this section's concepts by pairing the students and having them use the visual on p. 95 to quiz each other about the kind of movement and the types of features associated with each kind of tectonic plate boundary.

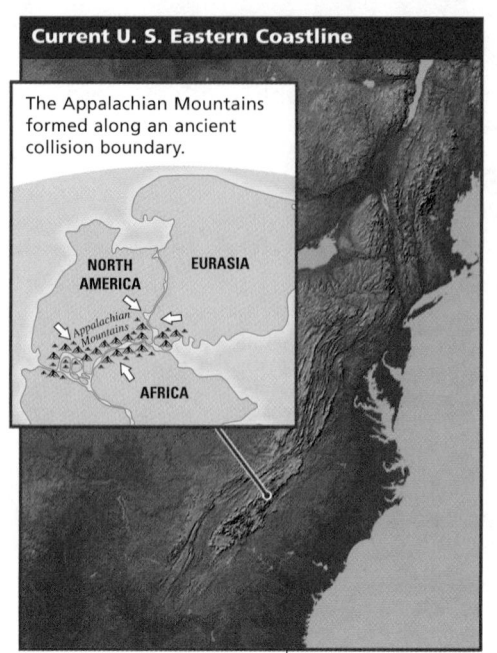

Current U. S. Eastern Coastline

The Appalachian Mountains formed along an ancient collision boundary.

NORTH AMERICA

EURASIA

Appalachian Mountains

AFRICA

The theory of plate tectonics helps geologists today.

The theory of plate tectonics changed the way that scientists view Earth. They learned that the planet's lithosphere has been in motion for millions of years. Today, the theory helps them to explain Earth's past and to predict what might happen along plate boundaries in the future.

By studying rock layers and using the theory, geologists can uncover the history of any region on Earth. For example, in the eastern United States, the deformed and folded rocks in the Appalachian Mountains are evidence of an ancient convergent boundary. Geologists discovered that these rocks are the same type and age as rocks in northwest Africa. These facts reveal that the mountains formed when North America collided with Africa and Eurasia as part of Pangaea. Where the plates eventually pulled apart, the rift valleys formed part of the current U. S. eastern coastline.

The theory of plate tectonics also gives scientists a way to study and predict geologic events. Scientists can predict, for example, that there are likely to be more earthquakes where plates slide past each other. They can look for volcanic activity where plates are sinking beneath other plates. And they can predict that mountains will continue to rise where plates push together.

CHECK YOUR READING What future events can scientists predict using the theory of plate tectonics? Give two examples.

 **Review**

KEY CONCEPTS

1. What are the three types of convergent boundaries?
2. Describe what happens at a transform boundary.
3. Why is the theory of plate tectonics so important to geologists?

CRITICAL THINKING

4. **Compare and Contrast** Use a Venn diagram to compare and contrast oceanic-oceanic and oceanic-continental subduction boundaries.
5. **Interpreting Visuals** Look again at the map on page 95. Identify the plates and type of boundary that formed the Andes Mountains on the west coast of South America.

⬥ CHALLENGE

6. **Synthesize** Sketch a diagram of the following landscape and label all the features. A plate with oceanic crust is sinking beneath a plate with continental crust. Further inland on the continent, a transform boundary can be seen in Earth's crust.

ANSWERS

1. where two continental plates meet, two oceanic plates meet, an oceanic and continental plate meet

2. Two plates move past each other in opposite directions.

3. gives geologists a new way to explain past and future geologic events; helps geologists understand why major geologic events happen along plate boundaries.

4. compare: both form trenches; contrast: oceanic–oceanic form volcanic islands, oceanic–continental form coastal mountains and volcanoes

5. South American and Nazca plates; convergent boundary

6. Sketches will vary, but should show a trench formed where the oceanic plate sinks under the continental plate, coastal mountains and volcanoes, and two inland plates scraping against each, moving in opposite directions.

Think SCIENCE

SKILL: EVALUATING CONCLUSIONS

What on Earth Is Happening Here?

When tectonic plates move, they cause major changes in Earth's surface. Among other things, the earth shakes, magma erupts on the surface, crust is built or destroyed, and mountains or islands form. Read the observations about plate movements below, then evaluate the conclusions given.

◉ Observations

Scientists made these observations about a region known for the movement of two major tectonic plates.

a. The region is on the coast of a landmass.
b. Along the coast is a deep-ocean trench.
c. The mountains on the coast are volcanic.
d. A line connecting these mountains is fairly straight.
e. The mountains are getting higher.
f. Far out at sea, a mid-ocean ridge is forming.

◉ Conclusions

Here are three possible conclusions about the movement of tectonic plates in the region.

- One plate is pulling away from the other.
- One plate is sinking under the other.
- One plate is scraping past the other.

◉ Evaluate Each Conclusion

On Your Own Decide how well the observations support each conclusion. Note any observations that indicate that a conclusion is not justified.

As a Group Decide which conclusion is most reasonable. Discuss your ideas in a small group, and see if the group can agree.

CHALLENGE What further observations would support or weaken each conclusion? How could you make these observations? What other phenomena might this conclusion help explain?

A volcanic coastal mountain spews out ash.

RESOURCE CENTER
CLASSZONE.COM

Learn more about the effects of plate movement.

Chapter 3: **Plate Tectonics** 97 **B**

Set Learning Goal

To read observations about plate movements and evaluate the conclusions that could be drawn from the data

Present the Science

Distinct geologic features occur at the three types of tectonic plate boundaries. In this activity, students will apply what they have learned about the geologic features associated with each type of boundary.

Guide the Activity

- Advise students to begin by making a list or chart of the geologic features associated with each type of plate boundary.
- Remind students that if any one of the observations does not fit with a conclusion, then the conclusion is not justified.

COOPERATIVE LEARNING STRATEGY

Divide the class into groups of 3–4 students. Tell groups to begin the discussion by allowing each group member to present his or her notes. Have each group select a reporter to present the group's opinion to the class.

Close

Ask: What is the name of the type of boundary that fits the observations? *convergent boundary—oceanic-continental subduction*

Technology Resources

Have students visit **ClassZone.com** to learn more about the effects of plate movement.

 RESOURCE CENTER

ANSWERS

On Your Own *Students should be able to support their choice of conclusions with observations.*
As a Group *Groups should be able to choose a logical conclusion based on the observations. If there are disagreements, ask students to draw a diagram based on the observations.*
CHALLENGE *Further observations might include: Is crust being formed or destroyed at the site? Are the volcanoes active? Are plates moving past each other? Observations could be made by measurement of plate movements, deep-sea explorations, and so on. Other phenomena might include earthquakes, hot springs, steam vents.*

BACK TO

the **BIG** idea

Refer students back to the photograph on pp. 66–67. Ask them to use what they have learned about tectonic plate movements to summarize what is happening to Iceland, as shown in this picture. *Sample answer: Iceland is located on the Mid-Atlantic Ridge, where two plates are moving apart. As the plates slowly move, the island country is being torn in two. The large crack represents where the divergent boundary appears on land.*

◖ KEY CONCEPTS SUMMARY

SECTION 3.1

What layers are the most dense? *inner and outer core*

What does the lithosphere include? *the crust and very top part of the mantle*

SECTION 3.2

What motions cause the tectonic plates to move? *convection currents, ridge push, and slab pull*

Why does Earth stay roughly the same size? *Crust is destroyed at about the same rate as it is formed.*

SECTION 3.3

Name the three types of plate boundaries. *divergent, convergent, and transform boundaries*

Where do most divergent boundaries occur? *in the oceans*

SECTION 3.4

Why does one plate sink beneath another at a subduction boundary? *The plate that sinks is more dense than the top plate.*

What is the main plate motion at a transform boundary? *Plates scrape past each other horizontally in opposite directions.*

Review Concepts

- Big Idea Flow Chart, p. T17
- Chapter Outline, pp. T23–T24

Chapter Review

the **BIG** idea

The movement of tectonic plates causes geologic changes on Earth.

CONTENT REVIEW
CLASSZONE.COM

◖ KEY CONCEPTS SUMMARY

3.1 Earth has several layers.

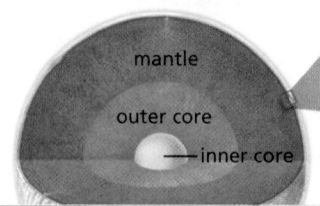
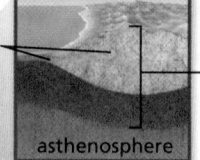

crust — lithosphere
mantle
asthenosphere
outer core
inner core

The lithosphere is made up of tectonic plates, which rest on the asthenosphere.

VOCABULARY
inner core p. 70
outer core p. 70
mantle p. 71
crust p. 71
lithosphere p. 71
asthenosphere p. 71
tectonic plate p. 72

3.2 Continents change position over time.

Gravity and motions in the asthenosphere move tectonic plates over Earth's surface.

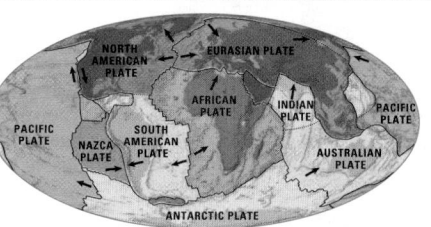

NORTH AMERICAN PLATE, EURASIAN PLATE, AFRICAN PLATE, INDIAN PLATE, PACIFIC PLATE, PACIFIC PLATE, NAZCA PLATE, SOUTH AMERICAN PLATE, AUSTRALIAN PLATE, ANTARCTIC PLATE

VOCABULARY
continental drift p. 74
Pangaea p. 76
mid-ocean ridge p. 76
convection p. 77
convection current p. 77
theory of plate tectonics p. 78

3.3 Plates move apart.

New crust is formed at divergent boundaries. Features include:
- mid-ocean ridges
- records of magnetic reversals
- rift valleys

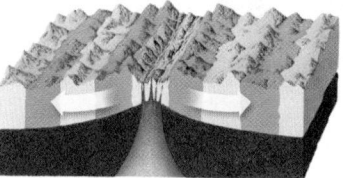

VOCABULARY
divergent boundary p. 82
convergent boundary p. 82
transform boundary p. 82
rift valley p. 83
magnetic reversal p. 84
hot spot p. 87

3.4 Plates converge or scrape past each other.

Crust is destroyed or folded at convergent boundaries.
- Subduction boundaries form island arcs, deep-ocean trenches, and coastal mountains.
- Collision boundaries can form mountains.

Crust is neither formed nor destroyed at transform boundaries.

VOCABULARY
subduction p. 90
continental-continental collision p. 91
oceanic-oceanic subduction p. 92
oceanic-continental subduction p. 93

B 98 Unit: **Energy and the Changing Earth**

Technology Resources

Have students visit **ClassZone.com** or use the CD-ROM for a cumulative review of concepts.

Engage students in a whole-class interactive review of Key Concepts. Edit content as you wish.

CONTENT REVIEW

CONTENT REVIEW CD-ROM

POWER PRESENTATIONS

Reviewing Vocabulary

Make a magnet word diagram for each of the vocabulary terms listed below. Write the term in the magnet. Write other terms or ideas related to it on the lines around the magnet.

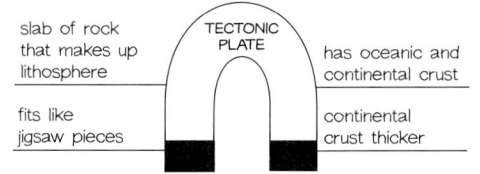

slab of rock that makes up lithosphere

TECTONIC PLATE

has oceanic and continental crust

fits like jigsaw pieces

continental crust thicker

1. mantle
2. lithosphere
3. mid-ocean ridge
4. convection current
5. divergent boundary
6. convergent boundary

Reviewing Key Concepts

Multiple Choice *Choose the letter of the best answer.*

7. Which of the following best describes Earth's mantle?
   a. the densest of Earth's layers
   b. the home of all life on Earth
   c. the thickest layer of hot rock
   d. the thinnest and hottest layer

8. Tectonic plates make up Earth's
   a. lower mantle
   b. lithosphere
   c. asthenosphere
   d. inner core

9. Why did many scientists reject Wegener's continental drift hypothesis?
   a. He could not explain how the continents moved.
   b. The geology of continents did not support his hypothesis.
   c. Fossil evidence showed that the continents were never joined.
   d. The climates of the continents have remained the same.

10. What evidence from the sea floor shows that tectonic plates move?
    a. The sea floor is much older than any of the continents.
    b. The sea floor is youngest near a mid-ocean ridge and older farther away.
    c. Mid-ocean ridges circle Earth like seams in a baseball.
    d. The sea floor is thinner than continental crust.

11. A mid-ocean ridge forms where plates
    a. move apart   c. scrape past each other
    b. push together   d. subduct

12. Plate motion is caused partly by
    a. magnetic reversals
    b. convection currents
    c. continental drift
    d. volcanic hot spots

13. Which of the following is formed at a collision zone?
    a. mountain range
    b. volcanic island chain
    c. deep-ocean trench
    d. continental rift valley

14. What happens when two oceanic plates meet?
    a. Both plates sink into the asthenosphere.
    b. The colder, denser plate sinks.
    c. Both plates fold the rock between them.
    d. One plate slides past the other.

15. Where is crust neither formed nor destroyed?
    a. mid-ocean ridge
    b. continental rift valley
    c. transform boundary
    d. subduction zone

Short Answer *Write a short answer to each question.*

16. How does the theory of plate tectonics help geologists predict future geologic events?

17. How do rocks record changes in Earth's magnetic field?

18. Explain what happens when a continental plate splits apart.

ASSESSMENT RESOURCES

UNIT ASSESSMENT BOOK
- Chapter Test A, pp. 45–48
- Chapter Test B, pp. 49–52
- Chapter Test C, pp. 53–56
- Alternative Assessment, pp. 57–58

SPANISH ASSESSMENT BOOK
Spanish Chapter Test, pp. 129–132

Technology Resources

Edit test items and answer choices.

 Test Generator CD-ROM

Visit **ClassZone.com** to extend test practice.

 Test Practice

Reviewing Vocabulary

Sample answers

1. mantle—thickest layer; hotter, denser near core; cooler, more rigid near top

2. lithosphere—crust plus topmost layer of mantle; made up of tectonic plates; home to all life

3. mid-ocean ridge—divergent boundary; new crust formed; rift valley; ridges circle Earth

4. convection current—a motion in which heated material rises, cools, sinks; explains partly how tectonic plates move

5. divergent boundary—two plates move apart; ocean—mid-ocean ridges, rift valleys; land—rift valleys, splits continents apart

6. convergent boundary—plates push together; crust is folded or destroyed; continent-continent collision—mountains; oceanic-oceanic subduction—trenches, island arcs; oceanic-continent subduction—trenches, coastal mountains

Reviewing Key Concepts

7. c	12. b
8. b	13. a
9. a	14. b
10. d	15. c
11. a	

16. Geologists can use the theory to predict where and when divergent, convergent, and transform boundaries are likely to be active, producing mountains, volcanoes, earthquakes, and other events.

17. Magnetic minerals in sea-floor rock line up with magnetic north and south like tiny compass needles. When the magnetic field reverses, the minerals in newly forming crust record the change.

18. A rising section in the mantle causes the plate above it to bulge. The crust splits and falls inward, forming a rift valley. As the valley widens, the floor thins and sinks below sea level. Water can enter to form a lake or sea.

Thinking Critically

19. *Answers will vary but should include oceanic-continental subduction, magma rising through cracks in the crust and forming volcanoes on the surface.*

20. *Yes, if the plates keep moving as they are, creating more melted rock. No, if the plates stop moving, which means the magma would also stop rising.*

21. *The bottom plate is sinking evenly along the coastline.*

22. *offshore, parallel to the coastline; this is where the oceanic plate is sinking beneath the continental plate.*

23. *reject; island arcs form where one oceanic plate sinks beneath another.*

24. *Students should draw a divergent boundary far out at sea, showing a mid-ocean ridge or spreading center.*

25. *If the South American and Pacific plates continue to converge, the Andes will grow taller in the future. If the plates stop moving, wind and water will wear down the mountains, making them shorter.*

26. *divergent*

27. *convergent—subduction*

28. *divergent*

29. *convergent—collision*

30. *convergent—subduction*

31. *none*

the BIG idea

32. *A divergent boundary may be splitting the land as two plates move apart.*

33. *Student diagrams will vary but should include one or two supercontinents with students' own labels for the landmasses.*

UNIT PROJECTS

Collect schedules, materials lists, and questions. Be sure dates and materials are obtainable and questions are focused.

 Unit Projects, pp. 5–10

Thinking Critically

Use the diagram to answer the questions below.

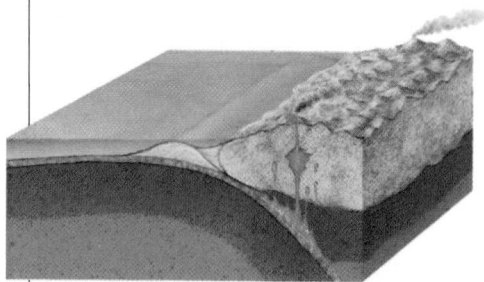

19. **ANALYZE** Write your own explanation of how the coastal mountains formed.

20. **PREDICT** Would you expect the volcanoes on this coastline to continue to be active? Why or why not?

21. **APPLY** Looking at the map above, why do you think the coastal mountains are in a fairly straight line?

22. **APPLY** On the map above, where would you expect to find a deep ocean trench? Why?

23. **APPLY** A friend looks at the diagram and tells you that there should be an island arc forming off the coast. Use your own knowledge and the map above to support or reject your friend's statement.

24. **SYNTHESIZE** On a separate piece of paper, extend the diagram to the left. Draw the type of plate boundary that someone might find far out at sea.

25. **PREDICT** Will the Andes Mountains on the west coast of South America become taller or shorter in the future? Use the theory of plate tectonics to explain your answer.

APPLY Copy the chart below. Fill in the type of boundary—divergent, convergent, or transform—where each formation is likely to appear.

Formation	Type of Boundary
26. Mid-ocean ridge	
27. Volcanic island arc	
28. Rift valley on land	
29. Mountains	
30. Deep-ocean trench	
31. Hot-spot volcano	

the BIG idea

32. **IDENTIFY CAUSE AND EFFECT** Look again at the photograph on pages 66 and 67. Now that you have finished the chapter, explain what may be forming this crack in Earth's surface.

33. **PREDICT** Use the map on page 79, which shows Earth's tectonic plates and the directions in which they are moving. Based on the plate movements, where do you think the continents might be in a few million years? Draw a map that illustrates your prediction. You might want to give your landmasses names.

UNIT PROJECTS

Check your schedule for your unit project. How are you doing? Be sure that you have placed data or notes from your research into your project folder.

MONITOR AND RETEACH

If students are having trouble using the concepts in Chapter Review items 19–25, ask them what kind of plate boundary is shown in the diagram. *convergent* Point out the two tectonic plates and discuss what is happening regarding these plates. *An oceanic plate is sinking beneath a continental plate.* Then have students review the discussion of oceanic-continental subduction on p. 93.

Students may benefit from summarizing one or more sections of the chapter.

 Summarizing the Chapter, pp. 198–199

Standardized Test Practice

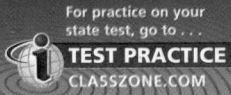 For practice on your state test, go to . . .
TEST PRACTICE
CLASSZONE.COM

Analyzing a Diagram

The diagram shows several tectonic plates. The arrows indicate the direction each plate is moving. Study the diagram and answer the questions below.

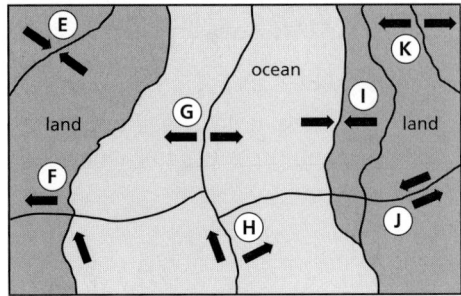

1. Where is an ocean trench most likely to form?
- **a.** F
- **b.** G
- **c.** H
- **d.** I

2. Where is a continental rift valley most likely to form?
- **a.** E
- **b.** F
- **c.** J
- **d.** K

3. Where would you find a convergent boundary?
- **a.** E
- **b.** F
- **c.** H
- **d.** K

4. Where is a mid-ocean ridge most likely to form?
- **a.** G
- **b.** H
- **c.** I
- **d.** F

5. What is a good example of a transform boundary?
- **a.** E
- **b.** I
- **c.** J
- **d.** K

6. Which is most likely to happen at I?
- **a.** Island arcs will form parallel to a trench.
- **b.** A spreading center will create a rift valley.
- **c.** Continental crust will be destroyed.
- **d.** Subduction will cause oceanic crust to melt.

7. Why are earthquakes likely to occur at J?
- **a.** Two plates are spreading away from each other.
- **b.** Two plates are colliding with each other.
- **c.** Two plates are scraping past each other.
- **d.** One plate is sliding under another plate.

8. Why are mountains likely to form at E?
- **a.** A rift valley is forming.
- **b.** Two plates are colliding.
- **c.** Magma is flowing upward.
- **d.** One plate is sinking.

9. Which is most likely to happen at G?
- **a.** Rising magma will create new crust.
- **b.** Subduction will cause a deep trench.
- **c.** Colliding plates will cause rocks to crumple.
- **d.** Moving plates will create island arcs.

Extended Response

Answer the two questions below in detail. Include some of the terms shown in the word box. In your answer, underline each term you use.

tectonic plates	subduction	magma	crust
continental drift	hot spot	mantle	

10. Two island chains are separated by a deep ocean trench. Although they are close to each other, the islands have very different fossils and types of rock. Explain why these island chains have such different geologic features.

11. Andrea lives near a chain of mountains located far from plate boundaries. The closest mountain is an active volcano. The other mountains used to be volcanoes. The farther away a mountain is in the chain, the older it is. Explain these facts.

Analyzing a Diagram

1. d	6. d
2. d	7. c
3. a	8. b
4. a	9. a
5. c	

Extended Response

10. RUBRIC

4 points for a response that correctly explains why the island chains have different geologic features and uses the following terms accurately:
- tectonic plates
- continental drift
- subduction

Sample answer: The trench between the island chains suggests that the chains are on different tectonic plates that are moving toward each other. These movements used to be called continental drift. One plate is now sinking under the other in a motion called subduction. The islands were once far apart, which explains why their geology differs greatly.

3 points provides an adequate explanation and uses two terms accurately
2 points provides a partial explanation and uses two terms accurately
1 point provides a partial explanation and uses one term accurately

11. RUBRIC

4 points for a response that correctly explains the facts and uses the following terms accurately:
- hot spot
- magma
- mantle
- crust

Sample answer: The mountain range is on a tectonic plate that is moving over a hot spot. As the plate moves, magma from the mantle melts the rock overhead and may form a new volcano on the crust. The mountains farthest away would be oldest because they were formed first.

3 points explains the facts adequately and uses three terms accurately
2 points explains the facts partially and uses two terms accurately
1 point explains the facts partially and uses one term accurately

METACOGNITIVE ACTIVITY

Have students answer the following questions in their **Science Notebook:**

1. What information in this chapter helped explain some of the geologic features of places you have visited or seen in pictures?

2. How did the models you made in the activities help you understand the concepts in the chapter?

3. What key concepts from this chapter will you use in your Unit Project?

CHAPTER 4 Earthquakes

Earth Science
UNIFYING PRINCIPLES

PRINCIPLE 1

Heat energy inside Earth and radiation from the Sun provide energy for Earth's processes.

PRINCIPLE 2

Physical forces, such as gravity, affect the movement of all matter on Earth and throughout the universe.

PRINCIPLE 3

Matter and energy move among Earth's rocks and soil, atmosphere, waters, and living things.

PRINCIPLE 4

Earth has changed over time and continues to change.

Unit: Energy and the Changing Earth
BIG IDEAS

CHAPTER 1
Energy

Energy has different forms, but it is always conserved.

CHAPTER 2
Temperature and Heat

Heat is a flow of energy due to temperature differences.

CHAPTER 3
Plate Tectonics

The movement of tectonic plates causes geologic changes on Earth.

CHAPTER 4
Earthquakes

Earthquakes release stress that has built up in rocks.

CHAPTER 5
Mountains and Volcanoes

Mountains and volcanoes form as tectonic plates move.

CHAPTER 4
KEY CONCEPTS

SECTION 4.1

Earthquakes occur along faults.

1. Rocks move along faults.

2. Faults are classified by how rocks move.

SECTION 4.2

Earthquakes release energy.

1. Energy from earthquakes travels through Earth.

2. Seismic waves can be measured.

SECTION 4.3

Earthquake damage can be reduced.

1. Earthquakes can cause severe damage and loss of life.

2. Scientists work to monitor and predict earthquakes.

3. Structures can be designed to resist earthquake damage.

 The Big Idea Flow Chart is available on p. T25 in the **UNIT TRANSPARENCY BOOK.**

Previewing Content

4.1 Earthquakes occur along faults.
pp. 105–110

1. Rocks move along faults.

The Earth's lithosphere contains huge breaks, or **faults,** along which movement of blocks of rock occurs. In some places along faults, movement is slow and continuous. In other places, movement stops because the blocks of rock on the two sides of the fault lock together. The pressure of the blocks of rock pushing or pulling on each other causes **stress** to build up. Eventually, the stored-up energy is released and causes an **earthquake,** a sudden ground motion, and the blocks of rock along the fault suddenly jerk past each other.

2. Faults are classified by how rocks move.

- Along a normal fault, the block of rock above the fault plane moves down relative to the other block. This motion is caused by the two blocks of rock being pulled apart. See the diagram below.

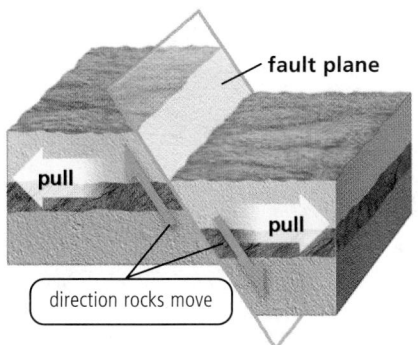

fault plane
pull
pull
direction rocks move

Normal Fault

- Along a reverse fault, the block of rock above the fault plane moves up relative to the other block. This motion is caused by the two blocks of rock being pushed together.
- Along a strike-slip fault, the blocks of rock move horizontally on either side of the fault plane. This motion is caused by the rocks being pushed horizontally.

4.2 Earthquakes release energy. pp. 111–119

1. Energy from earthquakes travels through Earth.

The location underground where an earthquake begins is the **focus** of the earthquake. The crust breaks at the focus, and the released energy radiates outward in all directions in the form of **seismic waves.** The point on Earth's surface directly above the focus is the **epicenter.** There are three types of seismic waves:

- Primary waves travel the fastest and therefore arrive first at any location. These waves can travel through any material.
- Secondary waves travel more slowly than primary waves and arrive second. They do not travel through liquids and gases. Both primary waves and secondary waves travel through Earth.
- Surface waves travel along the surface of the crust and cause the most damage. They arrive last.

2. Seismic waves can be measured.

- A **seismograph** is an instrument used to detect and record ground movements. When an earthquake occurs, the shaking of the ground is recorded on paper, magnetic tape, or some other recording material. Separate seismographs record horizontal and vertical movement. The two types are shown in the diagram.

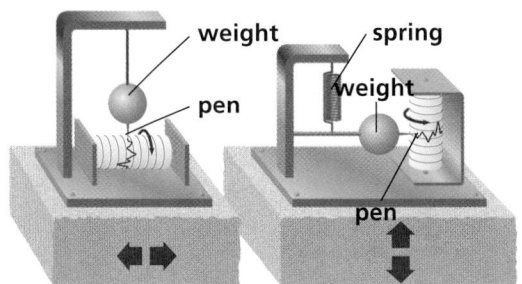

weight
spring
pen
weight
pen

This seismograph records side-to-side movements.

This seismograph records up-and-down movements.

- Seismograms recorded by seismographs at three different locations, or seismic stations, are needed to locate the epicenter of an earthquake. The difference in arrival time between primary and secondary waves is measured and used to calculate the distance to the epicenter. A circle with a radius corresponding to that distance is drawn around each seismic station, and the intersection of all three circles is the location of the epicenter.

Common Misconceptions

EFFECT OF POWERFUL EARTHQUAKES Students may think that a powerful earthquake could cause a landmass such as western California to break off and fall into the ocean. Landmasses do not float on the ocean—they are parts of Earth's surface at higher elevations. The ocean comprises land at lower elevations that is covered by seawater.

MISCONCEPTION DATABASE

CLASSZONE.COM Background on student misconceptions

 This misconception is addressed on p. 108.

Previewing Content

Earthquake damage can be reduced. pp. 120–129

1. Earthquakes can cause severe damage and loss of life.

- Earthquakes vary in size, or magnitude. Earthquake magnitude scales are used to describe the amount of energy an earthquake releases. Most scientists today prefer to use the moment magnitude scale.

- The movement of blocks of rock on opposite sides of a fault and the shaking of the ground can damage roads, dams, buildings, and other structures. Fires can break out, landslides often occur, and structures may sink or slide due to **liquefaction,** which causes soil to act like a liquid. Often, a strong earthquake is followed by weaker earthquakes, or **aftershocks.**

- Earthquakes may trigger water waves known as **tsunamis.** A tsunami moves quickly and may come ashore as a series of waves of varying heights.

2. Scientists work to monitor and predict earthquakes.

- Some of the signs that can help scientists predict the probability of a significant earthquake in a particular area include changes in the elevation of the ground, slow movement of blocks of rock, and the formation of small cracks in the ground.

- An area along an otherwise active fault where few or no earthquakes have occurred for a long time is known as a seismic gap. A gap may be an indicator that stress is building up and that a powerful earthquake might occur soon. The diagrams to the right show a seismic gap that was filled in by a large earthquake and its aftershocks.

3. Structures can be designed to resist earthquake damage.

- In areas where earthquakes are common, rules have been developed for building safer structures. For example, small buildings need to be firmly fastened to their foundations.

- Several methods are used to make large buildings more safe. Base isolators between a building and its foundation absorb much of the ground motion. An open space around a building lets the building shake more gently than the ground it is built on. Shear walls that contain steel supports add strength, as do cross braces, or X-shaped supports.

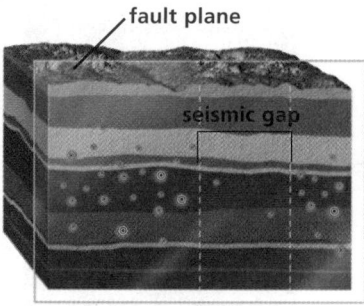

fault plane

seismic gap

① Over several years many earthquakes have occurred along this fault. However, one section of the fault has had little earthquake activity. Stress is building up along this section.

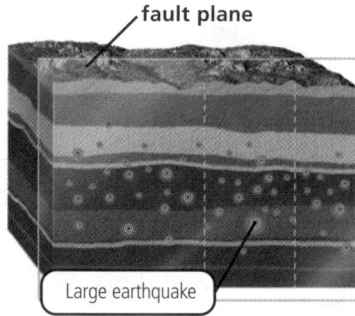

fault plane

Large earthquake

② A large earthquake and its aftershocks have occurred, releasing built-up stress. Over just a few weeks the seismic gap has been filled in.

Common Misconceptions

PREVENTING EARTHQUAKE DAMAGE Some students may think that it is now possible to construct earthquake-proof buildings. In reality, buildings can be designed and constructed to withstand some, but not all, earthquakes. Earthquake damage is always a possibility, especially in very strong earthquakes.

 This misconception is addressed on p. 126.

 MISCONCEPTION DATABASE
CLASSZONE.COM Background on student misconceptions

Previewing Labs

EXPLORE (the **BIG** idea)

Can You Bend Energy? p. 103
Students observe how light bends as it passes through air and water.

TIME 5 minutes
MATERIALS clear glass, water, flashlight

How Can Something Move Forward, Yet Sideways? p. 103
Students observe how individual cards in a stack and the whole stack can move in two directions at the same time.

TIME 5 minutes
MATERIALS stack of cards

Internet Activity: Earthquakes, p. 103
Students use the Internet to understand the frequency with which earthquakes occur.

TIME 20 minutes
MATERIALS computer with Internet access

SECTION 4.1

EXPLORE Pressure, p. 105
Students observe how a stick bends and then breaks in response to added pressure.

TIME 10 minutes
MATERIALS wooden craft stick

INVESTIGATE Faults, p. 107
Students use model blocks to explore how rocks can move along fault lines.

TIME 15 minutes
MATERIALS 2 triangular blocks of wood that fit together to form a rectangle, masking tape

---

SECTION 4.2

EXPLORE Movement of Energy, p. 111
Students use a spring toy to observe how energy moves through a solid material.

TIME 10 minutes
MATERIALS large spring toy

INVESTIGATE Subduction-Zone Earthquakes, p. 113
Students use an earthquake map and data to examine how earthquake depths change within a subduction zone.

R Earthquake Map, p. 220

TIME 20 minutes
MATERIALS Earthquake Map; three pieces of different colored string, 16 cm, 24 cm, and 60 cm long; scissors; ruler; tape

---

SECTION 4.3

EXPLORE Shaking, p. 120
Students use sand, a rock, and a washer to compare the reactions of various materials to shaking.

TIME 10 minutes
MATERIALS sand, newspaper, flat rock, washer

CHAPTER INVESTIGATION
How Structures React in Earthquakes, pp. 128–129
Students design and build a structure, attempting to make it earthquake resistant, and observe how long it can withstand shaking.

TIME 40 minutes
MATERIALS modeling clay, 20–30 stirrer straws, piece of thin cardboard 15 cm on each side, scissors, ruler, shake table

---

R **Additional INVESTIGATION,** Earthquake Depths, A, B, & C, pp. 249–257; Teacher Instructions, pp. 320–321

Previewing Chapter Resources

	INTEGRATED TECHNOLOGY	**LABS AND ACTIVITIES**

CHAPTER 4
Earthquakes

INTEGRATED TECHNOLOGY

 CLASSZONE.COM
- eEdition Plus
- EasyPlanner Plus
- Misconception Database
- Content Review
- Test Practice
- Visualizations
- Resource Centers
- Internet Activity: Earthquakes
- Math Tutorial

 SCILINKS.ORG
SCI LINKS

 CD-ROMS
- eEdition
- EasyPlanner
- Power Presentations
- Content Review
- Lab Generator
- Test Generator

AUDIO CDS
- Audio Readings
- Audio Readings in Spanish

LABS AND ACTIVITIES

P E EXPLORE the Big Idea, p. 103
- Can You Bend Energy?
- How Can Something Move Forward, Yet Sideways?
- Internet Activity: Earthquakes

R **UNIT RESOURCE BOOK**
Unit Projects, pp. 5–10

Lab Generator CD-ROM
Generate customized labs.

SECTION 4.1
Earthquakes occur along faults.
pp. 105–110

Time: 2 periods (1 block)
R Lesson Plan, pp. 200–201

 VISUALIZATION, Fault Motion

T **UNIT TRANSPARENCY BOOK**
- Big Idea Flow Chart, p. T25
- Daily Vocabulary Scaffolding, p. T26
- Note-Taking Model, p. T27
- 3-Minute Warm-Up, p. T28

P E
- EXPLORE Pressure, p. 105
- INVESTIGATE Faults, p. 107
- Extreme Science, p. 110

R **UNIT RESOURCE BOOK**
Datasheet, Faults, p. 209

SECTION 4.2
Earthquakes release energy.
pp. 111–119

Time: 2 periods (1 block)
R Lesson Plan, pp. 211–212

- **VISUALIZATION,** Primary-Wave and Secondary-Wave Motion
- **RESOURCE CENTER,** Seismology
- **MATH TUTORIAL**

T **UNIT TRANSPARENCY BOOK**
- Daily Vocabulary Scaffolding, p. T26
- 3-Minute Warm-Up, p. T28
- "Focus and Epicenter" Visual, p. T30

P E
- EXPLORE Movement of Energy, p. 111
- INVESTIGATE Subduction-Zone Earthquakes, p. 113
- Math in Science, p. 119

R **UNIT RESOURCE BOOK**
- Earthquake Map, p. 220
- Datasheet, Subduction-Zone Earthquakes, p. 221
- Math Support & Practice, pp. 238–239
- Additional INVESTIGATION, Earthquake Depths, A, B, & C, pp. 249–257

SECTION 4.3
Earthquake damage can be reduced.
pp. 120–129

Time: 4 periods (2 blocks)
R Lesson Plan, pp. 223–224

 RESOURCE CENTER, Explore Tsunamis

 UNIT TRANSPARENCY BOOK
- Big Idea Flow Chart, p. T25
- Daily Vocabulary Scaffolding, p. T26
- 3-Minute Warm-Up, p. T29
- Chapter Outline, pp. T31–T32

P E
- EXPLORE Shaking, p. 120
- CHAPTER INVESTIGATION, How Structures React in Earthquakes, pp. 128–129

R **UNIT RESOURCE BOOK**
CHAPTER INVESTIGATION, How Structures React in Earthquakes, A, B, & C, pp. 240–248

READING AND REINFORCEMENT

ASSESSMENT

STANDARDS

- Magnet Word, B24–25
- Main Idea and Detail Notes, C37
- Daily Vocabulary Scaffolding, H1–8

 UNIT RESOURCE BOOK
- Vocabulary Practice, pp. 235–236
- Decoding Support, p. 237
- Summarizing the Chapter, pp. 258–259

Audio Readings CD
Listen to Pupil Edition.

Audio Readings in Spanish CD
Listen to Pupil Edition in Spanish.

- Chapter Review, pp. 131–132
- Standardized Test Practice, p. 133

 UNIT ASSESSMENT BOOK
- Diagnostic Test, pp. 59–60
- Chapter Test, Levels A, B, & C, pp. 64–75
- Alternative Assessment, pp. 76–77

SP Spanish Chapter Test, pp. 133–136

Test Generator CD-ROM
Generate customized tests.

Lab Generator CD-ROM
Rubrics for Labs

National Standards
A.1–8. A.9.a–g, D.1.b, E.2–5, F.3.a, F.4.a

See p. 102 for the standards.

 UNIT RESOURCE BOOK
- Reading Study Guide, A & B, pp. 202–205
- Spanish Reading Study Guide, pp. 206–207
- Challenge and Extension, p. 208
- Reinforcing Key Concepts, p. 210

 Ongoing Assessment, pp. 105–107, 109

 Section 4.1 Review, p. 109

 UNIT ASSESSMENT BOOK
Section 4.1 Quiz, p. 61

National Standards
A.2–7, A.9.a–b. A.9.e–f, D.1.b

 UNIT RESOURCE BOOK
- Reading Study Guide, A & B, pp. 213–216
- Spanish Reading Study Guide, pp. 217–218
- Challenge and Extension, p. 219
- Reinforcing Key Concepts, p. 222

 Ongoing Assessment, pp. 112, 114–117

 Section 4.2 Review, p. 118

 UNIT ASSESSMENT BOOK
Section 4.2 Quiz, p. 62

National Standards
A.2–8, A.9.a–f

 UNIT RESOURCE BOOK
- Reading Study Guide, A & B, pp. 225–228
- Spanish Reading Study Guide, pp. 229–230
- Challenge and Extension, p. 231
- Reinforcing Key Concepts, p. 232
- Challenge Reading, pp. 233–234

 Ongoing Assessment, pp. 121–125, 127

 Section 4.3 Review, p. 127

 UNIT ASSESSMENT BOOK
Section 4.3 Quiz, p. 63

National Standards
A.1–7, A.9.a–b, A.9.d–g, E.2–5, F.3.a, F.4.a

Previewing Resources for Differentiated Instruction

CHAPTER INVESTIGATION

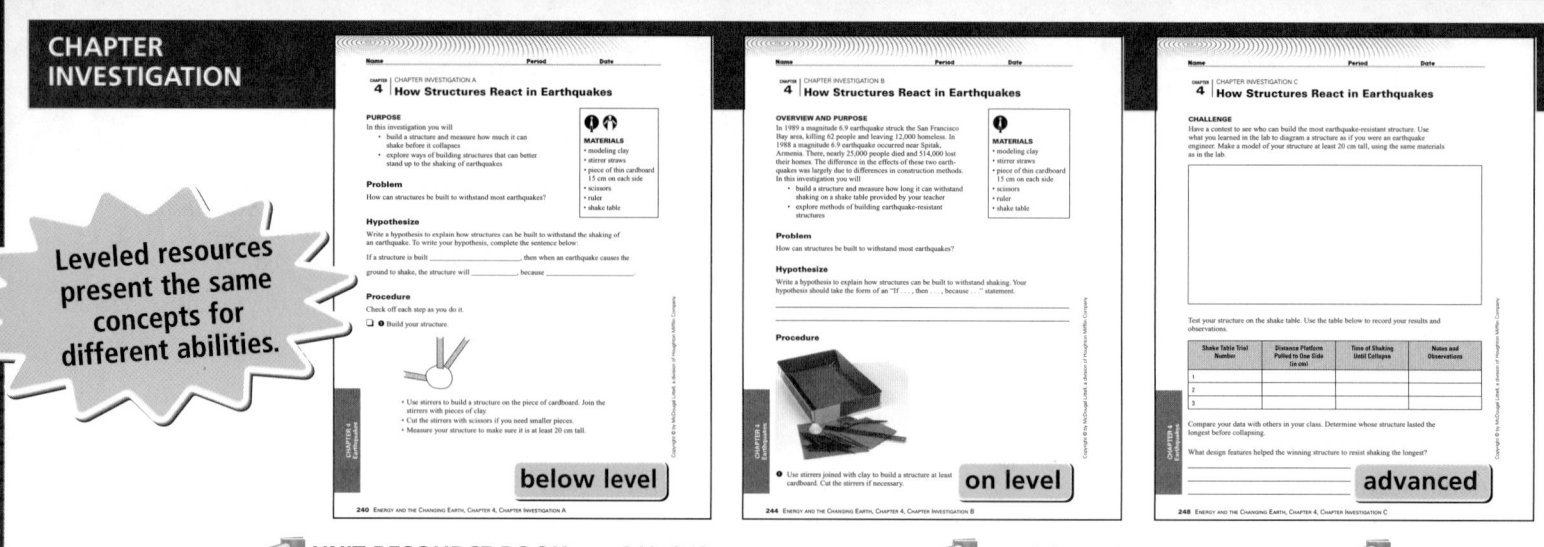

Leveled resources present the same concepts for different abilities.

below level

on level

advanced

R UNIT RESOURCE BOOK, pp. 240–243 · **R** pp. 244–247 · **R** pp. 244–248

READING STUDY GUIDE

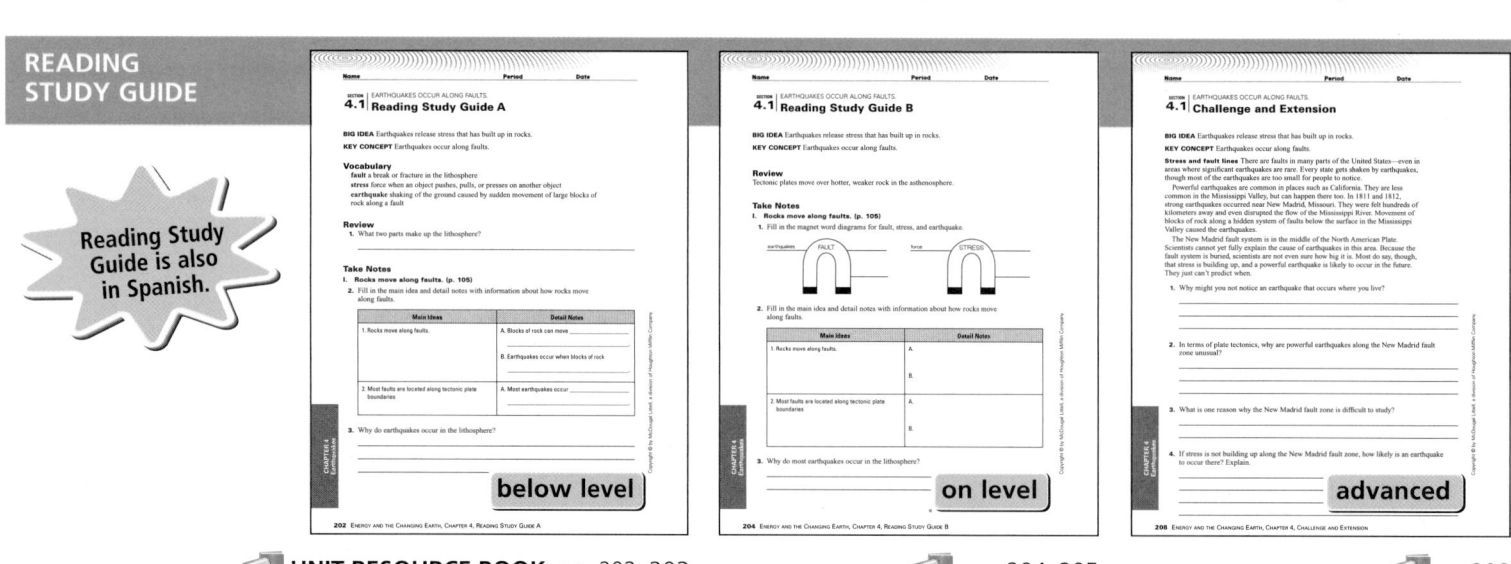

Reading Study Guide is also in Spanish.

below level

on level

advanced

R UNIT RESOURCE BOOK, pp. 202–203 · **R** pp. 204–205 · **R** p. 208

CHAPTER TEST

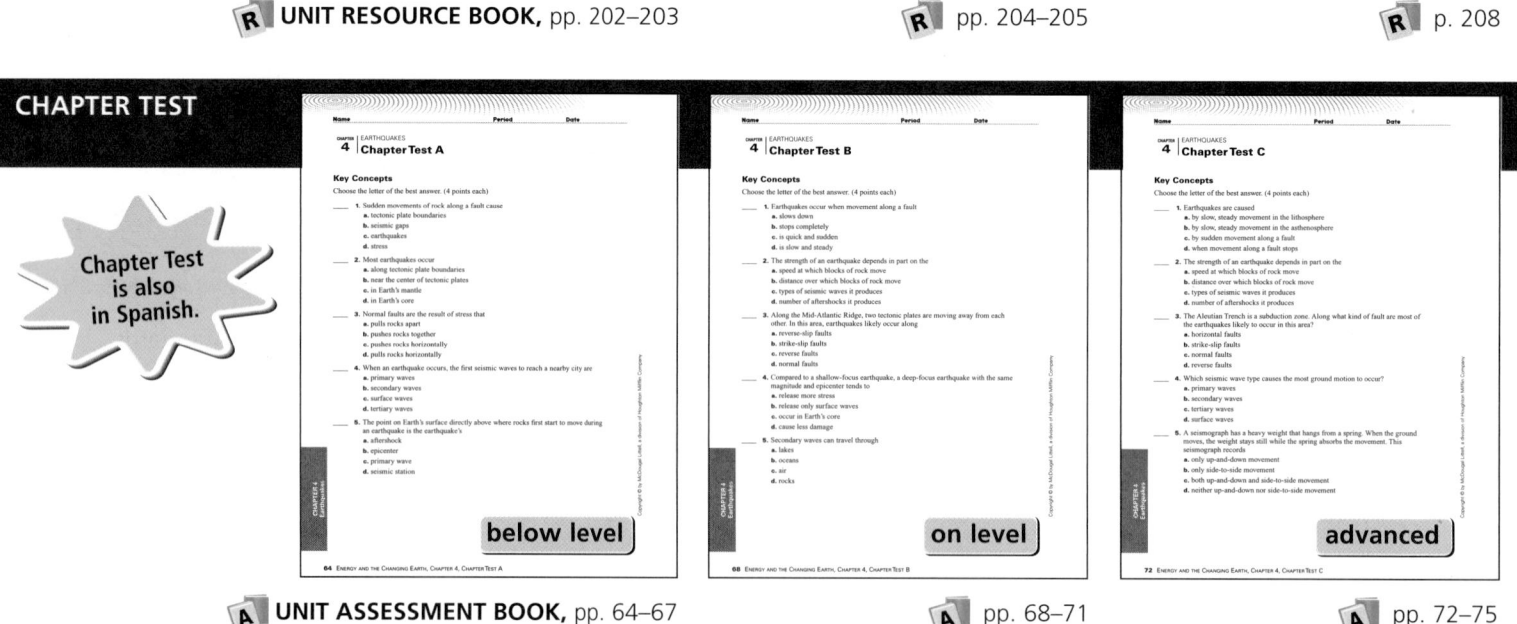

Chapter Test is also in Spanish.

below level

on level

advanced

A UNIT ASSESSMENT BOOK, pp. 64–67 · **A** pp. 68–71 · **A** pp. 72–75

TECHNOLOGY

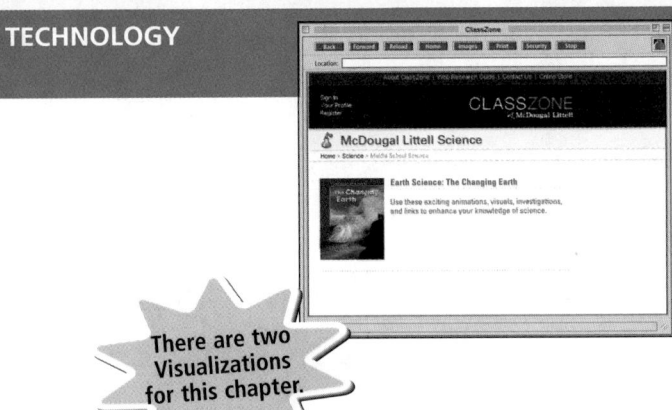

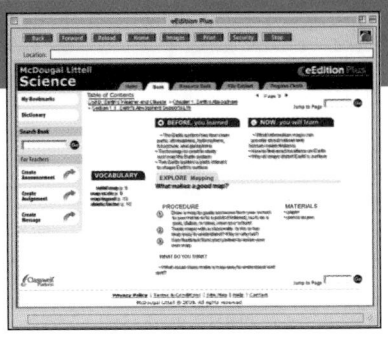

There are two Visualizations for this chapter.

CLASSZONE.COM　　　　**CD/CD-ROMS**　　　　**CLASSZONE.COM**

VISUAL CONTENT

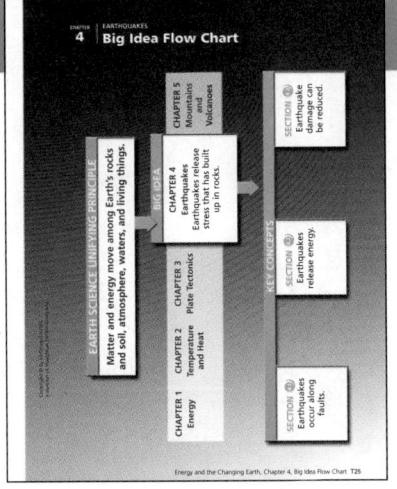

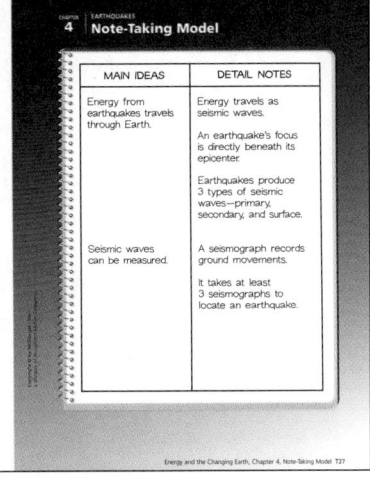

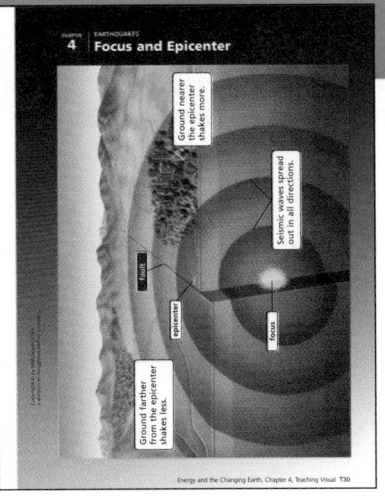

T **UNIT TRANSPARENCY BOOK,** p. T25　　　**T** p. T27　　　**T** p. T30

MORE SUPPORT

Reinforcing Key Concepts for each section

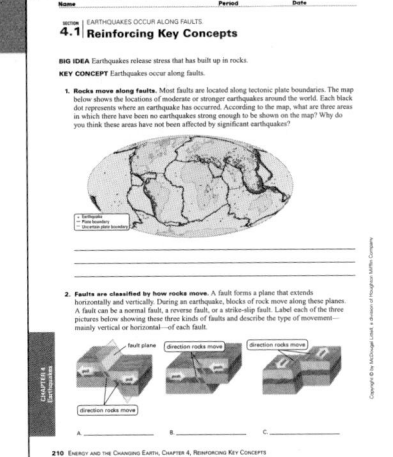

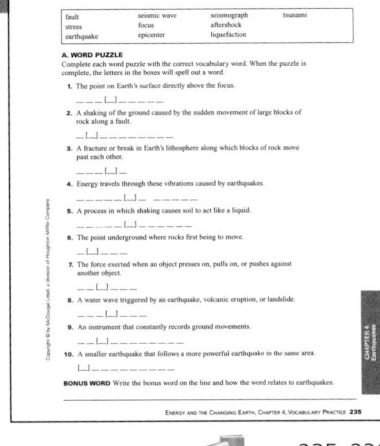

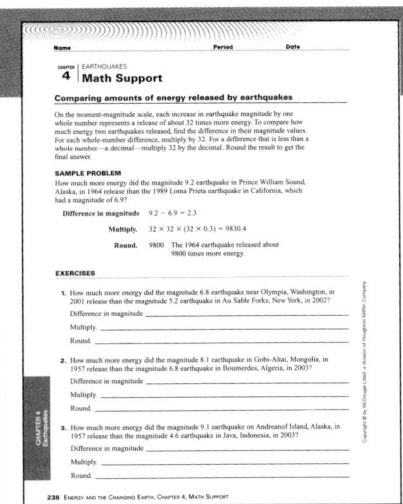

R **UNIT RESOURCE BOOK,** p. 210　　　**R** pp. 235–236　　　**R** p. 238

INTRODUCE

the BIG idea

Have students look at the photograph of a train derailment. The damage shown in the photograph was caused by a 1995 earthquake in Japan. The ground shook for 20 seconds.

Discuss how the question in the box links to the Big Idea.

- What was the source of the energy needed to bend the rails?
- What are other kinds of earthquake damage?

National Science Education Standards

Content

D.1.b Major geological events, such as earthquakes, result from tectonic plate motions.

F.3.a Internal and external processes of the earth system cause natural hazards, including earthquakes.

F.4.a Risk analysis is used to determine the options for reducing or eliminating risks.

Process

A.1–8 Identify questions that can be answered through scientific investigations; design and conduct an investigation; use tools; use evidence; think critically between evidence and explanation; recognize different explanations and predictions; communicate procedures and explanations; use mathematics.

A.9.a–g Understand scientific inquiry by using different investigations, methods, mathematics, technology, and explanations based on logic, evidence, and skepticism. Data often results in new investigations.

E.2–5 Design, implement, and evaluate a solution or product; communicate technological design.

---

the BIG idea

Earthquakes release stress that has built up in rocks.

Key Concepts

SECTION 4.1 Earthquakes occur along faults.
Learn how rocks move along different kinds of faults.

SECTION 4.2 Earthquakes release energy.
Learn how energy from an earthquake is used to determine its location and size.

SECTION 4.3 Earthquake damage can be reduced.
Learn how structures are built to better withstand earthquakes.

Internet Preview

CLASSZONE.COM
Chapter 4 online resources: Content Review, two Visualizations, three Resource Centers, Math Tutorial, Test Practice

B 102 Unit: **Energy and the Changing Earth**

What caused these rails to bend, and how long did it take?

INTERNET PREVIEW

CLASSZONE.COM For student use with the following pages:

Review and Practice
- Content Review, pp. 104, 130
- Math Tutorial: Multiplication, p. 119
- Test Practice, p. 133

Activities and Resources
- Internet Activity: Earthquakes, p. 103
- Visualizations: Fault Motion, p. 109; Wave Motion, p. 114. Resource Centers: Seismology, p. 116; Tsunamis, p. 123

NSTA scilinks.org SCiLINKS

Explore Earthquakes
Code: MDL053

EXPLORE (the BIG idea)

Can You Bend Energy?

Put a clear glass filled with water on a table. Holding a flashlight at an angle to the glass, shine light through the water so that an oval of light forms on the table.

Observe and Think Did the light, which is a form of energy, travel in a straight line through the layers of air and water? Do you think other forms of energy travel in straight lines through layers inside Earth?

How Can Something Move Forward, Yet Sideways?

Put a stack of cards on a table and hold them as shown in the photograph. Slide the entire stack forward, tilting your fingers from side to side to fan the cards back and forth.

Observe and Think Compare the direction of movement of the entire stack of cards with the directions of movement of individual cards. How might this be similar to how energy can travel in waves?

Internet Activity: Earthquakes

Go to **ClassZone.com** to see maps of recent earthquakes around the world, in the United States, and in your own area.

Observe and Think Where and when did the largest earthquakes occur?

NSTA
scilinks.org
SCiLINKS

Earthquakes **Code: MDL053**

CLASSZONE

McDougal Littell Science

Earth Science: The Changing Earth
Use these exciting animations, visuals, investigations, and links to enhance your knowledge of science.

Chapter 4: Earthquakes **103** **B**

TEACHING WITH TECHNOLOGY

Internet Search Engine After teaching p. 123, have students use a search engine and search the Internet to find an animation of a tsunami.

Presentation Software After teaching p. 126, have students use a computer with Internet access to find and download graphics of earthquake-resistant building structures. Have them use presentation software to present their findings to the class.

EXPLORE (the BIG idea)

These inquiry-based activities are appropriate for use at home or as a supplement to classroom instruction.

Can You Bend Energy?

PURPOSE To help students recognize that energy does not always travel in straight lines.

TIP *5 min.* Darken the room to make the beam of light more easily visible.

Answers will vary. Students should report that the light did not travel in a straight line through the water to the table. Other types of energy bend as they pass through boundaries between layers in Earth.

REVISIT after p. 114.

How Can Something Move Forward, Yet Sideways?

PURPOSE To prepare students for the idea that something can move in two directions at the same time.

TIP *5 min.* Move all the cards forward at the same time. Do not leave a trail of cards.

Answer: The entire deck moved in a direction perpendicular to the side-to-side movements of individual cards. Waves can move up and down and forward at the same time.

REVISIT after p. 115.

Internet Activity: Earthquakes

PURPOSE To help students understand that earthquakes happen every day somewhere on Earth.

TIP *20 min.* Revisit the map of recent earthquakes in a week or two and see how it has changed.

Sample answer: Where and when the largest earthquakes occur will change over time as new earthquakes are reported.

REVISIT after p. 125.

◐ CONCEPT REVIEW
Activate Prior Knowledge

Review what students have learned about tectonic plates. Ask:

- What kind of plates is Earth's lithosphere made of? *tectonic plates*
- How do tectonic plates move and interact? *pull apart, push together, scrape past one another*
- Where do most major geologic events happen? *along tectonic plate boundaries*

◑ TAKING NOTES

Main Idea and Detail Notes

Recording main ideas and details in a chart will help students organize and review key concepts and distinguish them from supporting details. Have students exchange charts and test each other.

Vocabulary Strategy

Students can include in their diagram as many other terms or ideas relating to the vocabulary term as they want.

Vocabulary and Note-Taking Resources

- Vocabulary Practice, pp. 235–236
- Decoding Support, p. 237

- Daily Vocabulary Scaffolding, p. T26
- Note-Taking Model, p. T27

- Magnet Word, B24–25
- Main Idea and Detail Notes, C37
- Daily Vocabulary Scaffolding, H1–8

◐ CONCEPT REVIEW

- Earth's lithosphere is broken into tectonic plates.
- Tectonic plates pull apart, push together, and scrape past one another.
- Major geologic events occur along tectonic plate boundaries.

◐ VOCABULARY REVIEW

lithosphere p. 71

tectonic plate p. 72

mid-ocean ridge p. 76

subduction p. 90

ⓘ CONTENT REVIEW
CLASSZONE.COM
Review concepts and vocabulary.

▶ TAKING NOTES

MAIN IDEA AND DETAIL NOTES

Make a two-column chart. Write the main ideas, such as those in the blue headings, in the column on the left. Write details about each of those main ideas in the column on the right.

VOCABULARY STRATEGY

For each vocabulary term, make a **magnet word** diagram. Write other terms or ideas related to that term around it.

See the Note-Taking Handbook on pages R45–R51.

SCIENCE NOTEBOOK

MAIN IDEAS	DETAIL NOTES
1. Rocks move along faults.	1. Blocks of rock can move past one another slowly and constantly.
	1. Blocks of rock can get stuck and then break free, causing earthquakes.
2. Most faults are located along tectonic plate boundaries.	2.
	2.
	2.

fracture in Earth   **FAULT**   moving rocks

earthquakes

CHECK READINESS

Administer the Diagnostic Test to determine students' readiness for new science content and their mastery of requisite math skills.

 Diagnostic Test, pp. 59–60

Technology Resources

Students needing content and math skills should visit **ClassZone.com**.

- **CONTENT REVIEW**
- **MATH TUTORIAL**

 CONTENT REVIEW CD-ROM

KEY CONCEPT

4.1 Earthquakes occur along faults.

◀ **BEFORE, you learned**

- The crust and uppermost mantle make up the lithosphere
- The lithosphere is cold and rigid
- Tectonic plates move over hotter, weaker rock in the asthenosphere

▶ **NOW, you will learn**

- Why earthquakes occur
- Where most earthquakes occur
- How rocks move during earthquakes

VOCABULARY

fault p. 105
stress p. 105
earthquake p. 105

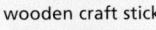

EXPLORE Pressure

How does pressure affect a solid material?

PROCEDURE

① Hold a wooden craft stick at each end.

② Bend the stick very slowly. Continue to put pressure on the stick until it breaks.

WHAT DO YOU THINK?
- How did the stick change before it broke?
- How might rocks react to pressure?

MATERIALS
wooden craft stick

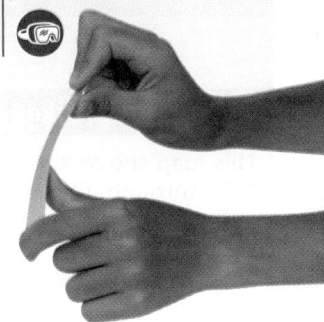

VOCABULARY
Add magnet word diagrams for *fault, stress,* and *earthquake* to your notebook.

Rocks move along faults.

Sometimes when you pull on a drawer, it opens smoothly. At other times, the drawer sticks shut. If you pull hard enough, the drawer suddenly flies open. Rocks along faults behave in a similar way. A **fault** is a fracture, or break, in Earth's lithosphere, along which blocks of rock move past each other.

Along some parts of a fault, the rock on either side may slide along slowly and constantly. Along other parts of the fault, the rocks may stick, or lock together. The rocks bend as stress is put on them. **Stress** is the force exerted when an object presses on, pulls on, or pushes against another object. As stress increases, the rocks break free. A sudden release of stress in the lithosphere causes an earthquake. An **earthquake** is a shaking of the ground caused by the sudden movement of large blocks of rock along a fault.

RESOURCES FOR DIFFERENTIATED INSTRUCTION

Below Level
UNIT RESOURCE BOOK
- Reading Study Guide A, pp. 202–203
- Decoding Support, p. 237

 AUDIO CDS

Advanced
UNIT RESOURCE BOOK
Challenge and Extension, p. 208

English Learners
UNIT RESOURCE BOOK
Spanish Reading Study Guide, pp. 206–207

 AUDIO CDS

- Audio Readings in Spanish
- Audio Readings (English)

⊙ Set Learning Goals

Students will

- Explain why earthquakes occur.
- Identify where most earthquakes occur.
- Describe how rocks move during earthquakes.
- Model how movement occurs along the three main types of faults.

◉ 3-Minute Warm-Up

Display Transparency 28 or copy this exercise on the board:

Decide if these statements are true. If not, correct them.

1. Earth's lithosphere consists of the uppermost mantle and core. *Earth's lithosphere consists of the crust and the uppermost mantle.*

2. Earth's lithosphere is hot and liquid. *Earth's lithosphere is cold and rigid.*

3. Tectonic plates move over the asthenosphere. *true*

 3-Minute Warm-Up, p. T28

4.1 MOTIVATE

EXPLORE Pressure

PURPOSE To introduce the concept that rocks can bend before they break

TIP *10 min.* Caution students to avoid injuries by pointing the stick away from themselves or other students as they bend it slowly.

WHAT DO YOU THINK? *Answers will vary, but may include that the stick bent and cracked. Students may suggest that rocks can also bend and then break when subjected to pressure.*

Ongoing Assessment

Explain why earthquakes occur.

Ask: What must happen along a fault for an earthquake to occur? *sudden movement of large blocks of rock*

Teach from Visuals

To help students interpret the map showing plate boundaries, ask:

• Where in the Atlantic Ocean do most earthquakes occur? Why? *Most occur in the middle of the ocean where there is a plate boundary, the mid-Atlantic Ridge.*

• Why are so few earthquakes shown along the eastern coast of North America? *There are no plate boundaries and therefore few earthquakes along that coast.*

Ongoing Assessment

Identify where most earthquakes occur.

Ask: Where on Earth do most earthquakes take place? *along tectonic plate boundaries*

 Answer: They are next to plate boundaries.

 Most faults are located along tectonic plate boundaries, so most earthquakes occur in these areas. However, the blocks of rock that move during an earthquake are much smaller than a tectonic plate. A plate boundary can be many thousands of kilometers long. During even a very powerful earthquake, blocks of rock might move only a few meters past each other along a distance of several hundred kilometers. The strength of an earthquake depends in part on

• how much stress builds up before the rocks move
• the distance the rocks move along the fault

 About 80 percent of all earthquakes occur in a belt around the edges of the Pacific Ocean. In the United States, the best-known fault in this belt is the San Andreas (san an-DRAY-uhs) Fault in California. It forms part of the boundary between the North American Plate and the Pacific Plate. Unlike many other faults, parts of the San Andreas Fault can be seen on the surface of the ground.

A small percentage of earthquakes occur along faults within plates. As you read in Chapter 1, a tectonic plate is rigid. Therefore, stress along a plate's boundary can cause rocks to break and move along weak areas toward the middle of the plate.

Where Earthquakes Occur

This map shows the locations of moderate to intense earthquakes from 1993 through 2002.

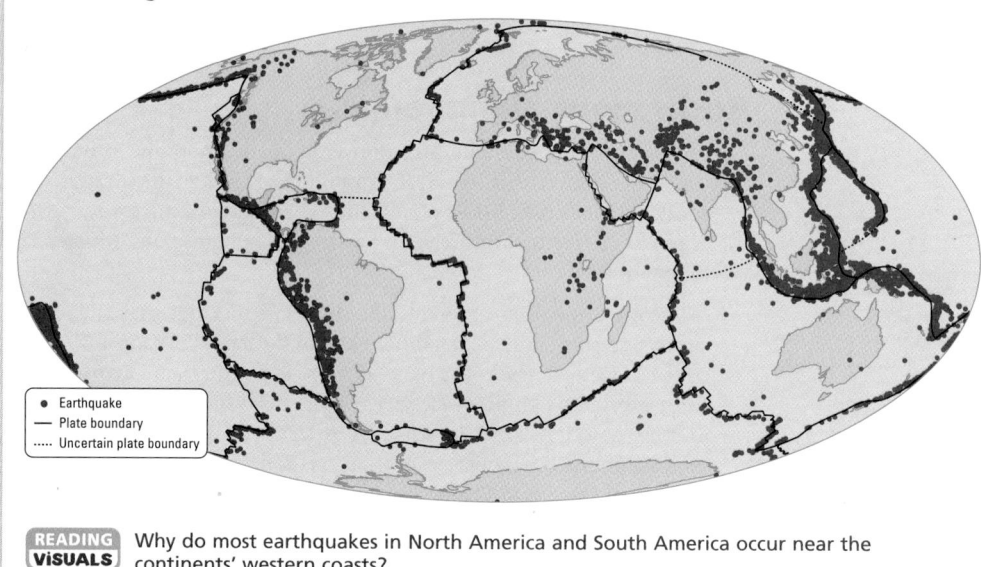

• Earthquake
— Plate boundary
····· Uncertain plate boundary

 Why do most earthquakes in North America and South America occur near the continents' western coasts?

DIFFERENTIATE INSTRUCTION

? More Reading Support

A Where are most faults located? *along plate boundaries*

B Where do most earthquakes occur? *in a belt around the edges of the Pacific Ocean*

Inclusion Enlarge the "Where Earthquakes Occur" illustration on a photocopy machine and give copies to students with visual impairments.

All earthquakes occur in the lithosphere. To understand why, you might compare a tectonic plate to a piece of cold, hard caramel. Like cold caramel, the plate is rigid and brittle. The rocks can break and move suddenly, causing an earthquake. Now compare the asthenosphere below the plate to warm, soft caramel. In the asthenosphere, hot rock bends and flows rather than breaks. A few earthquakes occur far below the normal depth of the lithosphere only because tectonic plates sinking in subduction zones are still cold enough to break.

 **CHECK YOUR READING** Why don't earthquakes occur in the asthenosphere?

Faults are classified by how rocks move.

The blocks of rock along different types of faults move in different directions, depending on the kinds of stress they are under. Scientists classify a fault according to the way the rocks on one side move with respect to the rocks on the other side.

The three main types of faults are normal faults, reverse faults, and strike-slip faults. More than one type of fault may be present along the same plate boundary. However, the type of fault that is most common along a boundary depends on whether plates are pulling apart, pushing together, or scraping past one another at that boundary.

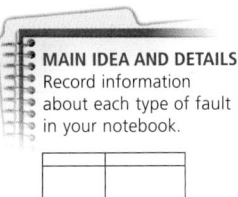

MAIN IDEA AND DETAILS Record information about each type of fault in your notebook.

INVESTIGATE Faults

How can rocks move along faults?

PROCEDURE

① Place one triangular block of wood against the other to form a rectangle.

② Put two pieces of masking tape across both blocks. Draw a different pattern on each piece of tape. Break the tape where it crosses the blocks.

③ Keep the blocks in contact and slide one block along the other.

④ Repeat step 3 until you find three different ways the blocks can move relative to each other. Draw diagrams showing how the blocks moved. Include the tape patterns.

WHAT DO YOU THINK?

• How can you use the tape patterns to find the relative directions in which the blocks were moved?

• In each case, what sort of stress (such as pulling) did you put on the blocks?

CHALLENGE Compare the ways you moved the blocks with the ways tectonic plates move at their boundaries.

SKILL FOCUS
Modeling

MATERIALS
• 2 triangular blocks of wood
• masking tape
• marker

TIME
15 minutes

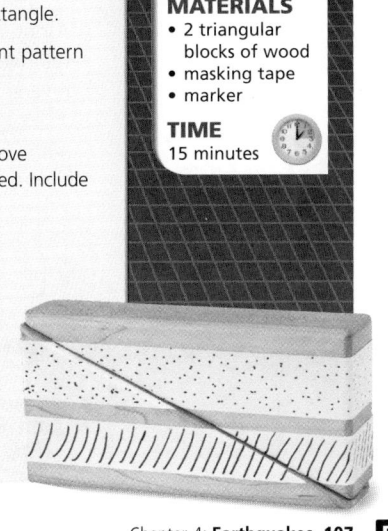

Chapter 4: **Earthquakes** 107 **B**

INVESTIGATE Faults

PURPOSE To model the three main types of faults

TIP *15 min.* Remind students to include in their drawings the patterns they draw on the masking tape.

WHAT DO YOU THINK? *by comparing how the layers are offset; pulling, pushing, sliding*

CHALLENGE *Pulling the blocks models the way plates move at a divergent boundary, pushing the blocks models the way plates move at a convergent boundary, and sliding the blocks models the way plates move at a transform boundary.*

 Datasheet, Faults, p. 209

Technology Resources

Customize this student lab as needed or look for an alternative. Print rubrics to assess student lab reports.

🧪 **Lab Generator CD-ROM**

Ongoing Assessment

CHECK YOUR READING *Answer: The rock is hot enough to bend and flow rather than break.*

DIFFERENTIATE INSTRUCTION

❓ More Reading Support

C How are faults classified? *by the way the rocks on one side of the fault move relative to the rocks on the other side*

Alternate Assessment Have students use the wood blocks to demonstrate for the class both physically and orally the answers to the questions in "Investigate Faults."

Advanced

R Challenge and Extension, p. 208

Teach from Visuals

To help students interpret the diagrams and photographs of normal and reverse faults and to compare and contrast block movement, ask:

- In each diagram on this page, how does the block on the left move relative to the block on the right? *For the normal fault, the block on the left moves up relative to the block on the right. For the reverse fault, the block on the left moves down relative to the block on the right.*

- In which type of fault are the blocks moving apart? *normal fault*

Address Misconceptions

IDENTIFY Point out the San Andreas Fault on a large map. Ask: What effects are likely as powerful earthquakes continue to occur in western California? Students who say that western California will fall into the ocean hold the misconception that a single earthquake can break off part of a continent, and that the surfaces of continents and adjacent ocean floors are not continuous.

CORRECT Show a cross-section of Earth that includes continental crust and oceanic crust. Point out that the edge of a continent is not a shelf of land extending over the ocean, so it cannot break off and fall in. Remind students that the San Andreas is a strike-slip fault, along which landmasses move past one another horizontally.

REASSESS Ask: What will happen to western California as movement continues along the San Andreas Fault? *It will slide northward relative to the rest of North America and may eventually become an island.*

READING TiP

The word *plane* comes from the Latin word *planum,* which means "flat surface."

The illustrations on this page and page 109 show that a fault forms a plane that extends both horizontally and vertically. Blocks of rock move along the fault plane during an earthquake. Along a normal or reverse fault, the movement of the blocks is mainly vertical—the blocks move up or down. Along a strike-slip fault, the movement is horizontal—the blocks move sideways.

Normal Faults

Along a normal fault, the block of rock above the fault plane slides down relative to the other block. Stress that pulls rocks apart causes normal faults. Earthquakes along normal faults are common near boundaries where tectonic plates are moving apart, such as in the Great Rift Valley of Africa.

READING TiP

Compare the directions of the arrows in the diagrams with the directions of the arrows on the photographs.

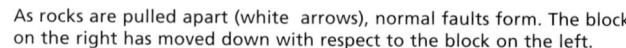
As rocks are pulled apart (white arrows), normal faults form. The block on the right has moved down with respect to the block on the left.

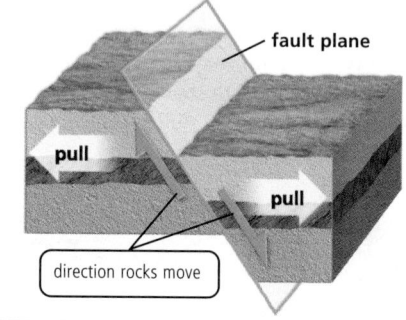
fault plane
pull
pull
direction rocks move

Normal Fault

Reverse Faults

Along a reverse fault, the block of rock above the fault plane moves up relative to the other block. Stress that presses rocks together causes reverse faults. These faults can occur near collision-zone boundaries

As rocks are pushed together (white arrows), reverse faults form. The block on the right has moved up with respect to the block on the left.

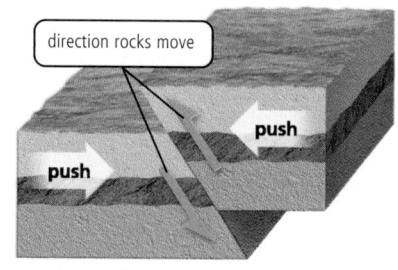
direction rocks move
push
push

Reverse Fault

DIFFERENTIATE INSTRUCTION

 **More Reading Support**

D Along a normal fault, how do the blocks move? *One slides down relative to the other.*

English Learners English learners may have difficulty with words that have more than one meaning. The terms *fault* and *stress* from this section have other, more common meanings that students may be familiar with. Have students look up the terms in the dictionary and read all the definitions for each one. Help students identify which definition is used here.

Make sure English learners understand the meaning of *along*—"over the length of," (pp. 105–109).

between plates. The Himalaya Mountains, which rise in the area where the Indian Plate is pushing into the Eurasian Plate, have many earthquakes along reverse faults.

 **CHECK YOUR READING** What type of stress produces reverse faults?

Strike-Slip Faults

Along a strike-slip fault, blocks of rock move sideways on either side of the fault plane. Stresses that push blocks of rock horizontally cause earthquakes along strike-slip faults. These faults can occur where plates scrape past each other. The San Andreas Fault is a strike-slip fault.

 **VISUALIZATION**
CLASSZONE.COM

Explore animations showing fault motion.

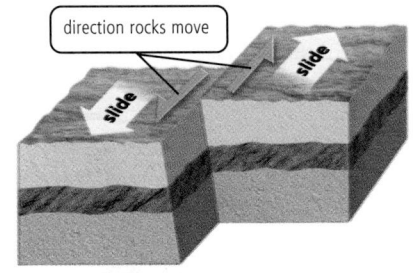

As rocks are pushed horizontally in opposite directions, strike-slip faults form. The block on the right has moved to the right with respect to the block on the left.

direction rocks move

slide

slide

Strike-Slip Fault

Over time, movement of rocks along normal and reverse faults can push up mountains and form deep valleys. As rocks move along strike-slip faults, rocks that were once in continuous layers can become separated by hundreds of kilometers.

4.1 Review

KEY CONCEPTS

1. What causes earthquakes?
2. Why do most earthquakes occur along tectonic plate boundaries?
3. What is the main direction of stress on blocks of rock at normal faults, reverse faults, and strike-slip faults?

CRITICAL THINKING

4. **Compare and Contrast** Make a chart showing the similarities and differences between normal and reverse faults.
5. **Connect** Japan is near a subduction zone. What type of faults would you expect to be responsible for many of the earthquakes there? Explain.

CHALLENGE

6. **Analyze** What evidence from rock layers could show a scientist that earthquakes had occurred in an area before written records were kept?

ANSWERS

1. sudden release of stress that had built up in rocks

2. Most faults are at or near plate boundaries.

3. normal faults: pulling apart; reverse faults: pressing together; strike-slip faults: horizontal sliding

4. similarities: movement of rock is mainly vertical, fault plane is at an angle, both are related to plate movements; differences: main direction of stress is opposite, direction of relative movement of blocks is opposite, each is common at a different type of plate boundary

5. reverse faults, because plates are pushing together along a subduction zone

6. Layers of rock that are broken and offset indicate that earthquakes have occurred.

Ongoing Assessment

Describe how rocks move during earthquakes.

Ask: How does movement along a reverse fault compare to movement along a strike-slip fault? *Movement along a reverse fault is mainly vertical whereas movement along a strike-slip fault is horizontal.*

 **CHECK YOUR READING** *Answer: stress that presses rocks together*

Reinforce (the **BIG** idea)

Have students relate the section to the Big Idea.

 R Reinforcing Key Concepts, p. 210

4.1 ASSESS & RETEACH

Assess

 A Section 4.1 Quiz, p. 61

Reteach

Help students review the three kinds of faults introduced in this section by creating on the board a three-column table with the following column heads: *Normal Fault, Reverse Fault,* and *Strike-Slip Fault.* In each column, have volunteers fill in how blocks of rock move along the fault and what kind of stress causes earthquakes along the fault. *Normal Fault: one block slides down relative to the other; stress: pulling. Reverse Fault: one block moves up relative to the other; stress: pushing together. Strike-Slip Fault: blocks move sideways; stress: pushing horizontally.*

Technology Resources

Have students visit **ClassZone.com** for reteaching of Key Concepts.

 CONTENT REVIEW

 CONTENT REVIEW CD-ROM

Purpose

To understand the incredible power of earthquakes

Present the Science

The ten largest earthquakes in the world since 1900 include the five listed in the chart and the following fire:

- Rat Islands, Alaska, 1965, 8.7
- India-China border, 1950, 8.6
- Kamchatka Peninsula, 1923, 8.5
- Banda Sea, Indonesia, 1938, 8.5
- Kuril Islands, 1963, 8.5

With the exception of the 1950 earthquake near the India-China border, all of these earthquakes occurred near subduction-zone boundaries. The 1950 earthquake was related to the convergence of India and Asia.

Discussion Questions

Ask: Where and when was the most powerful earthquake in the United States? *Prince William Sound, Alaska, 1964*

Ask: In this earthquake, how far did the plates move? *9 meters*

Ask: How high was the 1964 tsunami in Valdez Inlet, and what caused it? *67 meters—taller than a 20-story building; a landslide*

Ask: How strong was the most powerful earthquake ever recorded? *An earthquake in Chile in 1960 had about 10 times more energy than the Alaskan earthquake of 1964.*

Close

Ask students what they can conclude about earthquakes from their reading. *Earthquakes can be very powerful, can cause a great deal of destruction, and can be felt a long distance away. Such powerful earthquakes do not happen very often.*

EXTREME SCIENCE

INCREDIBLE EARTHQUAKES

When Earth Shakes

A landslide caused by the 1964 Alaskan earthquake tore this school in Anchorage apart. Fortunately, school was not in session.

In Anchorage, almost 120 km from the center of the earthquake, the ground shook for about three minutes, causing severe damage.

Alaskan Earthquake Sinks Louisiana Boats

The most powerful earthquake ever recorded in the United States struck Prince William Sound in Alaska on March 27, 1964. Plates that had been moving a few centimeters per year lurched 9 meters (30 ft), causing the ground to shake for more than three minutes. When energy from the earthquake reached Louisiana, more than 5000 kilometers (3000 mi) away, it caused waves high enough to sink fishing boats in a harbor.

Wall of Water Higher than 20-Story Building

The 1964 Alaskan earthquake caused buildings to crumble and collapse. It also produced tsunamis—water waves caused by a sudden movement of the ground during an earthquake, landslide, or volcanic eruption. In Alaska's Valdez Inlet, a landslide triggered by the earthquake produced a tsunami 67 meters (220 ft) high—taller than a 20-story building.

Missouri Earthquakes Ring Massachusetts Bells

Earthquakes near New Madrid, Missouri, in 1811 and 1812 caused church bells in Boston, Massachusetts—nearly 1600 kilometers (1000 mi) away—to ring.

Five Largest Earthquakes Since 1900		
Location	Date	Moment Magnitude
Off the coast of Chile	1960	9.5
Prince William Sound, Alaska	1964	9.2
Andreanof Islands, Alaska	1957	9.1
Kamchatka Peninsula, Russia	1952	9.0
Off the coast of Ecuador	1906	8.8

Largest Earthquake Ever

The most powerful earthquake ever recorded hit Chile in 1960. This earthquake released almost 10 times as much energy as the 1964 earthquake in Alaska—and about 600 times the energy of the earthquake that destroyed much of San Francisco in 1906.

EXPLORE

1. **EXPLAIN** How were the 1964 Alaskan earthquake and the 1960 Chilean earthquake related to movements along tectonic plate boundaries?
2. **CHALLENGE** An inlet is a narrow body of water connected to a lake or ocean. Why might a tsunami be higher in an inlet than along the coastline around it?

EXPLORE

1. *EXPLAIN* Both earthquakes occurred at subduction-zone boundaries where plates push together.
2. *CHALLENGE* The water cannot spread out, so it must rise higher.

KEY CONCEPT 4.2

Earthquakes release energy.

BEFORE, you learned

- Most earthquakes occur along tectonic plate boundaries
- Different directions of stress cause normal, reverse, and strike-slip faults

NOW, you will learn

- How energy from an earthquake travels through Earth
- How an earthquake's location is determined

VOCABULARY

seismic wave p. 111
focus p. 112
epicenter p. 112
seismograph p. 116

EXPLORE Movement of Energy

How does energy travel?

PROCEDURE

1. On a flat surface, hold one end of a spring toy while a partner holds the other end. Stretch the spring, then squeeze some coils together and release them.

2. Again, hold one end of the spring while your partner holds the other end. Shake your end of the spring back and forth.

WHAT DO YOU THINK?
- How did energy travel along the spring when you gathered and released some coils?
- How did energy travel along the spring when you shook one end back and forth?

MATERIALS
spring toy

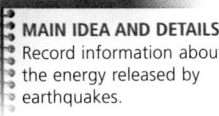
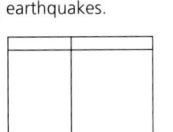

MAIN IDEA AND DETAILS
Record information about the energy released by earthquakes.

Energy from earthquakes travels through Earth.

When you throw a rock into a pond, waves ripple outward from the spot where the rock hits the water. The energy released by an earthquake travels in a similar way through Earth. Unlike the pond ripples, though, earthquake energy travels outward in all directions—up, down, and to the sides. The energy travels as **seismic waves,** (SYZ-mihk) which are vibrations caused by earthquakes. Seismic waves from even small earthquakes can be recorded by sensitive instruments around the world.

Chapter 4: **Earthquakes 111** **B**

RESOURCES FOR DIFFERENTIATED INSTRUCTION

Below Level

UNIT RESOURCE BOOK
- Reading Study Guide A, pp. 213–214
- Decoding Support, p. 237

 **AUDIO CDS**

R **Additional INVESTIGATION,**
Earthquake Depths, A, B, & C, pp. 249–257;
Teacher Instructions, pp. 320–321

Advanced

UNIT RESOURCE BOOK
Challenge and Extension, p. 219

English Learners

UNIT RESOURCE BOOK
Spanish Reading Study Guide, pp. 217–218

 AUDIO CDS

- Audio Readings in Spanish
- Audio Readings (English)

4.2 FOCUS

▶ Set Learning Goals

Students will

- Explain how energy from an earthquake travels through Earth.
- Understand how an earthquake's location is determined.
- Analyze in an experiment how the locations of earthquakes are related to structures and processes inside Earth.

◀ 3-Minute Warm-Up

Display Transparency 28 or copy this exercise on the board:

Choose the correct term to fill in the blank.

Terms
faults
plate boundaries
stress
earthquake

1. All earthquakes occur along ____ .
   faults

2. The force exerted when an object pushes, pulls, or presses against another object is called ____ . *stress*

3. Most faults are located along ____ . *plate boundaries*

T 3-Minute Warm-Up, p. T28

4.2 MOTIVATE

EXPLORE Movement of Energy

PURPOSE To model how energy travels in primary and secondary waves

TIP *10 min.* Ask students to think about how the movement they see might relate to earthquakes.

WHAT DO YOU THINK? *in a straight line down the spring; back and forth perpendicular to the spring*

Chapter 4 **111** **B**

Teach from Visuals

To help students interpret the visual showing the focus and epicenter, ask:

- Where is the fault in relation to the focus and the epicenter? *They are lined up in the same place.*

- What happens after an earthquake begins? *The seismic waves spread out in all directions from the focus.*

 This visual is also available as T30 in the Unit Transparency Book.

Mathematics Connection

Point out that a fault can be thought of as a plane on which the focus is located as a point.

Ongoing Assessment

READING VISUALS *Answer: The focus is where movement starts inside Earth; the epicenter is the point on Earth's surface above the focus.*

A

B

All earthquakes start beneath Earth's surface. The **focus** of an earthquake is the point underground where rocks first begin to move. Seismic waves travel outward from the earthquake's focus. The **epicenter** (EHP-ih-SEHN-tuhr) is the point on Earth's surface directly above the focus. Scientists often name an earthquake after the city that is closest to its epicenter.

In general, if two earthquakes of equal strength have the same epicenter, the one with the shallower focus causes more damage. Seismic waves from a deep-focus earthquake lose more of their energy as they travel farther up to Earth's surface.

The depths of earthquakes along tectonic plate boundaries are related to the directions in which the plates move. For example, an earthquake along a mid-ocean spreading center has a shallow focus. There, the plates are pulling apart, and the new crust that forms is thin. Subduction zones have a wide range of earthquake depths, from shallow to very deep. Earthquakes can occur anywhere along the sinking plates.

Focus and Epicenter

Seismic waves spread out from the focus of an earthquake.

Structures farther from the epicenter experience less shaking and less damage.

The **epicenter** is the point on the surface directly above the focus.

fault

Structures near the epicenter experience more shaking and more damage.

The earthquake begins at the **focus**.

Seismic waves spread out in all directions from the focus.

READING VISUALS What is the difference between the focus and the epicenter of an earthquake?

DIFFERENTIATE INSTRUCTION

? More Reading Support

A Where do all earthquakes start? *focus*

B Which causes more damage, a shallow- or deep-focus earthquake? *shallow*

Additional Investigation To reinforce Section 4.2 learning goals, use the following full-period investigation:

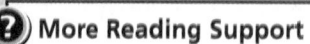 **Additional INVESTIGATION,** Earthquake Depths, A, B, & C, pp. 249–257, 320–321
(Advanced students should complete Levels B and C.)

English Learners To help students identify the subject of complicated sentences, have them find commas that separate introductory phrases and subordinate clauses from the main clause. For example, "When you throw a rock in a pond, waves ripple outward . . . " (p. 111).

INVESTIGATE Subduction-Zone Earthquakes

Why are some earthquakes deeper than others?

PROCEDURE

1. Cut the first string into 4 pieces that are 4 cm long. Cut the second string into 3 pieces that are 8 cm long, and the third string into 4 pieces that are 15 cm long.

2. Use the key on the Earthquake Map to match string lengths with earthquake depths.

3. Tape one end of the pieces of string to the map at the earthquake locations, as shown in the photograph. Always cover the same amount of string with tape.

4. Hold the map upside down, with the strings hanging down. Observe the patterns of earthquake locations and depths.

WHAT DO YOU THINK?

- What patterns among the strings do you observe? How do you explain them?
- How might the earthquake depths relate to the sinking of a tectonic plate in a subduction zone?

CHALLENGE
Draw a line on the map, showing where the subduction zone might be at Earth's surface. How might the depths of the earthquakes be different if the subduction zone were on the other side of the island?

> **SKILL FOCUS**
> Analyzing
>
> **MATERIALS**
> - different colors of string
> - ruler
> - scissors
> - Earthquake Map
> - tape
>
> **TIME**
> 20 minutes

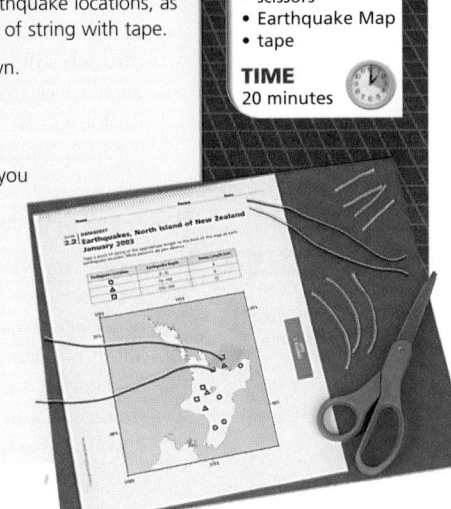

Waves and Energy

Waves are part of your everyday life. For example, music reaches your ears as sound waves. All waves, including seismic waves, carry energy from place to place. As a wave moves through a material, particles of the material move out of position temporarily, causing the particles next to them to move. After each particle moves, it returns to its original position. In this way, energy moves through the material, but matter does not.

On October 17, 1989, an earthquake stopped baseball's World Series at Candlestick Park in San Francisco. As the seismic waves arrived, fans heard a low rumble; then for about 15 seconds the stadium shook from side to side and up and down. About 20 minutes after the earthquake was felt at the stadium, the seismic waves had traveled to the other side of Earth. There, the waves did not shake the ground hard enough for people to notice. The waves could be detected only by scientific instruments.

Chapter 4: **Earthquakes** 113 **B**

INVESTIGATE Subduction-Zone Earthquakes

PURPOSE To examine how the locations of earthquakes are related to structures and processes inside Earth

TIPS *20 min.* Provide rulers for measuring the string. Tell students to be careful when using the scissors. Use pieces of string with obviously different colors (such as primary colors).

INCLUSION Use strings with different thicknesses for students who are color-blind or who have visual impairments.

WHAT DO YOU THINK? *Earthquakes are deeper on one side of the island and shallower on the other. Earthquakes are occurring along a tilted plane under the island; earthquakes get deeper as a plate sinks in a subduction zone.*

CHALLENGE *The line should be drawn to the east (right) of the island. The depths of earthquakes across the island would be reversed if the subduction zone were on the other side.*

- Earthquake Map, p. 220
- Datasheet, Subduction-Zone Earthquakes, p. 221

Technology Resources

Customize this student lab as needed or look for an alternative. Print rubrics to assess student lab reports.

 Lab Generator CD-ROM

Real World Example

Scientists have developed a system to provide a warning that seismic waves from an earthquake that just occurred are about to arrive, but the method's effectiveness depends on the location of earthquake sensors. If the sensors are at the epicenter, there can be no warning. But if the epicenter is, for example, 60 kilometers (37 mi) away from the sensors, there will be about 16 seconds' warning. This is enough time for automatic systems to shut off gas valves and for people to move to safer areas within buildings.

More Reading Support

C What do waves carry from place to place?
energy

Advanced Have students search in news sources or on the Internet for information about recent earthquakes. Have them identify the epicenter of each quake and the fault along which it occurred. Then ask them to use a large map of the world to present their findings to the class. Have them lead a discussion about where earthquakes are likely to occur.

 Challenge and Extension, p. 219

Integrate the Sciences

While discussing primary and secondary waves, remind students that solids, liquids, and gases are made up of tiny particles of matter. Particles of a solid are close together and have strong bonds between them. They vibrate in place but cannot overcome the bonds. Solids have a definite size and shape. Particles of a liquid are close together but move faster and overcome some of the forces of attraction between the particles. The particles slide past each other. Liquids have a definite size but not a definite shape. Particles of a gas are far apart, move very fast, and have very little or no attraction to other particles. Gases have no definite size or shape.

Develop Critical Thinking

COMPARE Have students make a chart in which they compare the similarities and differences of the three types of seismic waves. *Sample answer:*

Name	Primary	Secondary	Surface
Speed	Fastest	Medium	Slowest
Location	Earth's interior	Earth's interior	Earth's surface
Type of material	All	Solids	———
Type of movement	Push/pull	Up/down; side/side	Up/down; side/side
Damage	Some	Some	Most

EXPLORE (the BIG idea)

Revisit "Can You Bend Energy?" on p. 103. Have students relate their results to seismic wave movement.

Ongoing Assessment

CHECK YOUR READING *Answer: Particles in liquids and gases do not return to their original positions after being moved.*

Earthquakes produce three types of seismic waves: primary waves, secondary waves, and surface waves. Each type moves through materials differently. In addition, the waves can reflect, or bounce, off boundaries between different layers. The waves can also bend as they pass from one layer into another. Scientists learn about Earth's layers by studying the paths and speeds of seismic waves traveling through Earth.

READING TiP

One meaning of *primary* is "first." Primary waves arrive before secondary waves.

Primary Waves

The fastest seismic waves are called primary waves, or P waves. These waves are the first to reach any particular location after an earthquake occurs. Primary waves travel through Earth's crust at an average speed of about 5 kilometers per second (3 mi/s). Primary waves can travel through solids, liquids, and gases. As they pass through a material, the particles of the material are slightly pushed together and pulled apart. Buildings also experience this push and pull as primary waves pass through the ground they are built on.

VISUALIZATION
CLASSZONE.COM

Explore primary-wave and secondary-wave motion.

Secondary Waves

Secondary waves are the second seismic waves to arrive at any particular location after an earthquake, though they start at the same time as primary waves. Secondary waves travel through Earth's interior at about half the speed of primary waves. Secondary waves are also called S waves. As they pass through a material, the material's particles are shaken up and down or from side to side. Secondary waves rock small buildings back and forth as they pass.

Secondary waves can travel through rock, but unlike primary waves they cannot travel through liquids or gases. Look at the illustrations on page 55. As a primary wave passes through a material, the volume and density of the material change slightly. But as a secondary wave passes, the material changes slightly in shape. Liquids and gases do not have definite shapes. These materials flow—that is, particles in them do not return to their original positions after being moved. When scientists learned that secondary waves cannot pass through Earth's outer core, they realized that the outer core is not solid.

CHECK YOUR READING Why can't secondary waves travel through liquids or gases?

Surface Waves

Surface waves are seismic waves that move along Earth's surface, not through its interior. They make the ground roll up and down or shake from side to side. Surface waves cause the largest ground movements and the most damage. Surface waves travel more slowly than the other types of seismic waves.

DIFFERENTIATE INSTRUCTION

More Reading Support

D Which waves arrive first? *primary*

E Which waves do the most damage? *surface*

Alternative Assessment Modify the activity in "Develop Critical Thinking." Put students in groups and give each group a list, from the sample answer, of the main features of all waves. Then give them the chart without the wave labels. Have them figure out which wave is described in each column and complete the chart.

Seismic Waves

Earthquakes produce three types of seismic waves.

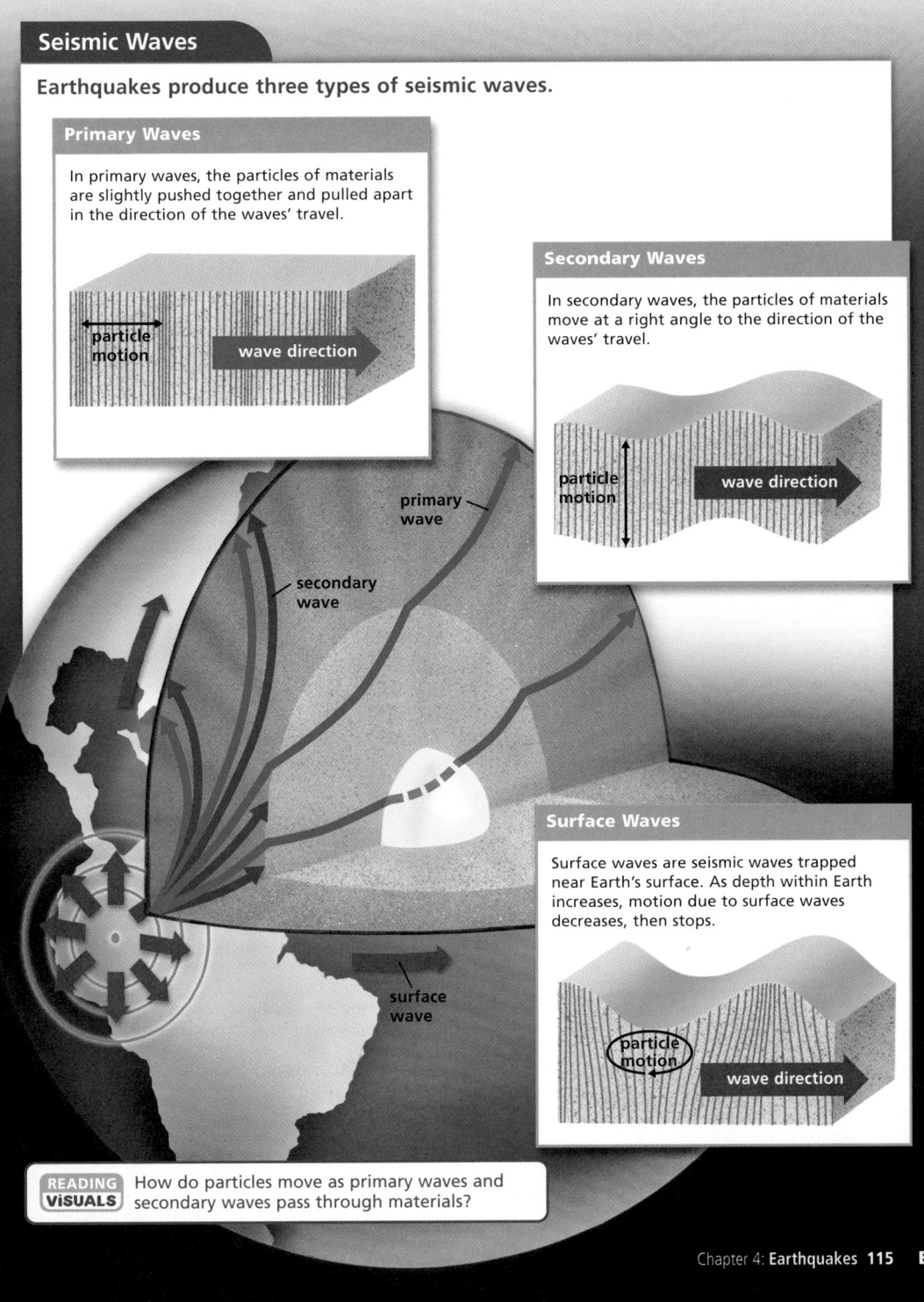

Primary Waves

In primary waves, the particles of materials are slightly pushed together and pulled apart in the direction of the waves' travel.

particle motion

wave direction

Secondary Waves

In secondary waves, the particles of materials move at a right angle to the direction of the waves' travel.

particle motion

wave direction

primary wave

secondary wave

surface wave

Surface Waves

Surface waves are seismic waves trapped near Earth's surface. As depth within Earth increases, motion due to surface waves decreases, then stops.

particle motion

wave direction

READING VISUALS How do particles move as primary waves and secondary waves pass through materials?

To help students with the visual on seismic waves, ask:

- How do particles move when primary waves pass through? *slightly pushed and pulled in direction the waves travel*
- How do particles move as secondary waves pass through? *at a right angle to direction the waves travel*
- How does depth affect motion due to surface waves? *As depth increases, motion decreases.*

Integrating Sciences

Seismic waves are just one kind of wave. Sound and light also move in waves. Different types of waves have similar traits.

Develop Geometry Skills

Draw several angles on the board. Include two right angles, but in different positions. Ask students to identify the right angles.

EXPLORE (the **BIG** idea)

Revisit "How Can Something Move Forward, Yet Sideways?" on p. 103. Have students relate their results to seismic wave movement.

Ongoing Assessment

Explain how energy from an earthquake travels through Earth.

Ask: What are three ways in which energy from an earthquake moves through Earth? *primary waves, secondary waves, surface waves*

READING VISUALS *Answer: Primary wave: particles are slightly pushed together and pulled apart in the direction the wave is moving. Secondary wave: particles move at a right angle to the direction the wave is moving.*

DIFFERENTIATE INSTRUCTION

Advanced Have students start a small wave in a pan of water that contains one or two objects. Then have them relate the reflections of the wave from the objects and the sides of the pan to the reflections of seismic waves inside Earth. Ask them to explain how reflections of seismic waves can be used to study Earth's structure.

Teacher Demo

Have two students hold a sheet of white cardboard vertically without moving it. Have another student place a marker against the cardboard and jump up and down to create a drawing like a seismogram. Ask: Which type of seismograph did we model? *one with a heavy weight hanging from a spring that bounces up and down as the ground moves and measures up-and-down movements* Ask: What would we need to do differently to model the other kind of seismograph? *Place the paper horizontally and hold the marker from above to measure side-to-side movements, as does a seismograph with a heavy weight suspended by a wire that stays still as the ground moves back and forth.*

Teach from Visuals

To help students interpret the visual showing two seismographs, ask:

* What do the seismographs measure? *ground movements*

* What is similar about the two seismographs? *Both have a weight with a pen attached for recording movements onto a paper.*

* What is different about the two seismographs? *One has a weight hanging from a wire, and the other has a weight hanging from a spring that absorbs Earth's up-and-down motion.*

Ongoing Assessment

CHECK YOUR READING *Answer: One type measures horizontal movements and another measures vertical movements.*

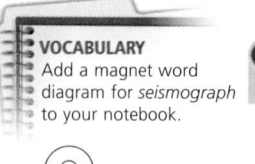

VOCABULARY
Add a magnet word diagram for *seismograph* to your notebook.

? **F**

RESOURCE CENTER
CLASSZONE.COM

Learn more about seismology.

Seismic waves can be measured.

Without listening to the news, scientists at seismic stations all over the world know when an earthquake occurs. Seismic stations are places where ground movements are measured. A **seismograph** (SYZ-muh-GRAF) is an instrument that constantly records ground movements. The recording of an earthquake looks like a group of wiggles in a line. The height of the wiggles indicates the amount of ground movement produced by seismic waves at the seismograph's location.

Using Seismographs

Separate seismographs are needed to record side-to-side movements and up-and-down movements. A seismograph that measures side-to-side movements has a heavy weight hanging from a wire. The weight remains almost still as the ground moves back and forth beneath it. A pen attached to the weight records the movements. A seismograph that records up-and-down movements has a heavy weight hanging from a spring. As the ground moves, the weight stays almost still as the spring absorbs the movement by getting longer or shorter. A pen attached to the weight records the changes in distance between the ground and the weight.

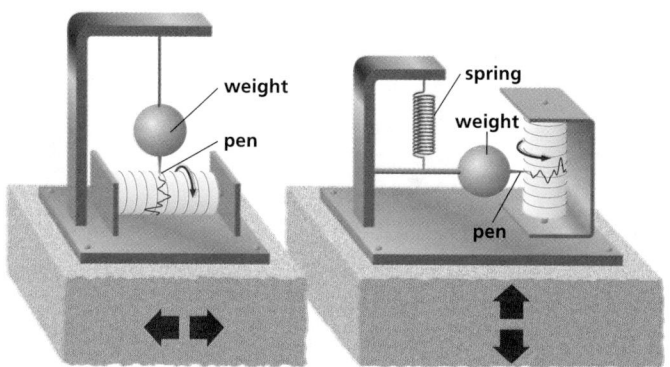

This seismograph records side-to-side movements.

This seismograph records up-and-down movements.

CHECK YOUR READING Why is more than one kind of seismograph needed to record all the movements of the ground during an earthquake?

? **G**

Scientists use seismographs to measure thousands of earthquakes, large and small, every year. Some seismographs can detect ground movements as small as one hundred-millionth of a centimeter. The recording produced by a seismograph is called a seismogram. By studying seismograms, scientists can determine the locations and strengths of earthquakes.

DIFFERENTIATE INSTRUCTION

? **More Reading Support**

F What instrument is used to measure ground movements? *seismograph*

G How many earthquakes are measured each year? *thousands*

Below Level Find a seismogram in a book or print one from the Internet. Have students first tell what it is and what instrument produced it. Then identify when the earthquake started and stopped. Ask them to identify what moved to cause the lines on the paper. *the ground*

Locating an Earthquake

To locate the epicenter of an earthquake, scientists must have seismograms from at least three seismic stations. The procedure for locating an epicenter has three steps:

1 Scientists find the difference between the arrival times of the primary and the secondary waves at each of the three stations.

2 The time difference is used to determine the distance of the epicenter from each station. The greater the difference in time, the farther away the epicenter is.

3 A circle is drawn around each station, with a radius corresponding to the epicenter's distance from that station. The point where the three circles meet is the epicenter.

Finding an Epicenter

Seismograms provide data used to find an earthquake's epicenter.

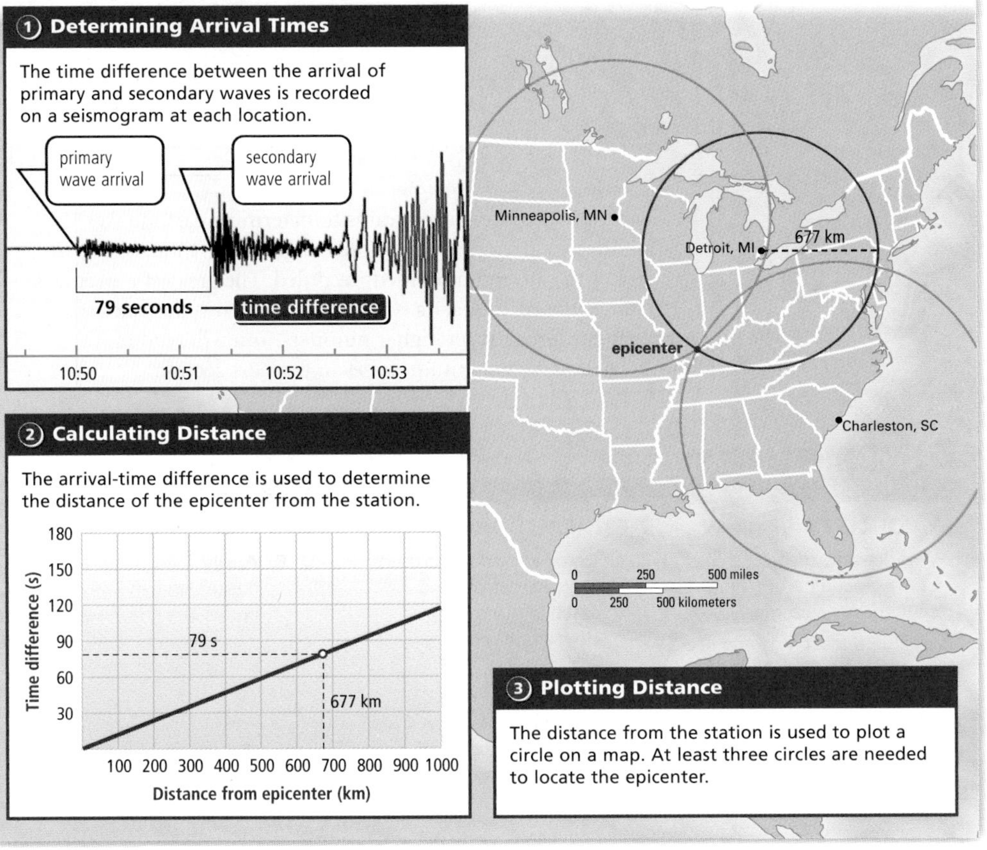

1 Determining Arrival Times

The time difference between the arrival of primary and secondary waves is recorded on a seismogram at each location.

primary wave arrival

secondary wave arrival

79 seconds — time difference

10:50   10:51   10:52   10:53

2 Calculating Distance

The arrival-time difference is used to determine the distance of the epicenter from the station.

180
150
120
90   79 s
60
30   677 km

Time difference (s)

100 200 300 400 500 600 700 800 900 1000
Distance from epicenter (km)

Minneapolis, MN

Detroit, MI — 677 km

epicenter

Charleston, SC

0   250   500 miles
0   250   500 kilometers

3 Plotting Distance

The distance from the station is used to plot a circle on a map. At least three circles are needed to locate the epicenter.

Chapter 4: **Earthquakes 117** **B**

History of Science

The first device for registering the occurrence of an earthquake was invented in about A.D. 132 by a Chinese scientist, Chang Heng. Heng's invention was called the dragon jar. The jar had eight dragon heads, each with a ball in its mouth, around the brim. Around the bottom of the jar were eight frogs. Each frog was directly beneath a dragon head. When an earthquake shook the ground, a ball dropped out of a dragon's mouth and fell into the mouth of a frog.

Reinforce (the BIG idea)

Have students relate the section to the Big Idea.

 Reinforcing Key Concepts, p. 222

Assess

 Section 4.2 Quiz, p. 62

Reteach

Write the following terms on the board in any order: *focus, epicenter, P wave, S wave, surface wave, seismograph,* and *seismogram.* Then create a three-column table with the following headings: *Location of Earthquake, Seismic Waves,* and *Measuring Earthquakes.*

- Invite students to place each of the terms from the list in the appropriate column. *Location of Earthquake: focus, epicenter; Seismic Waves: P wave, S wave, surface wave; Measuring Earthquakes: seismograph, seismogram*

- Have students explain why the terms belong in a particular column.

Technology Resources

Have students visit **ClassZone.com** for reteaching of Key Concepts.

 CONTENT REVIEW

 CONTENT REVIEW CD-ROM

Scientists can also use seismograph data to locate the focus of an earthquake. They study seismograms to identify waves that have reflected off boundaries inside Earth. Some of these waves help the scientists to determine the earthquake's depth.

A seismogram records the time when the first primary wave arrives. This wave travels by a direct path. The data also show when the first reflected primary wave arrives. After leaving the focus, this wave reflects from Earth's surface and then travels to the seismic station. The reflected wave takes a longer path, so it arrives slightly later. The difference in arrival times indicates the depth of the focus. Scientists can make the necessary calculations, but more commonly a computer is used to calculate the location of an earthquake's epicenter and focus.

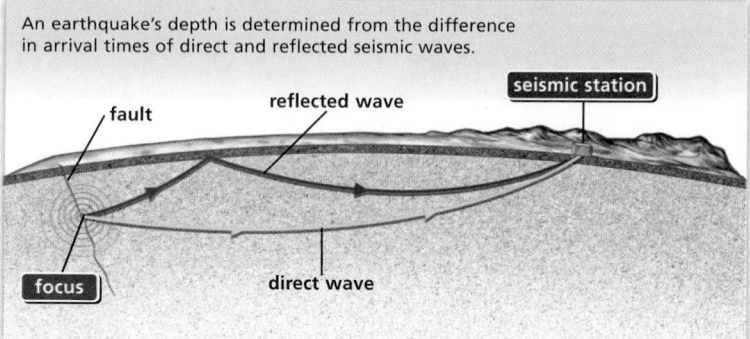

An earthquake's depth is determined from the difference in arrival times of direct and reflected seismic waves.

fault — reflected wave — seismic station

focus — direct wave

Scientists also use seismograms to determine earthquakes' magnitudes, or strengths. The more energy an earthquake releases, the greater the ground movement recorded. The greatest movement determines the earthquake's strength on a magnitude scale. Stronger earthquakes get higher numbers. You will read more about earthquake magnitude scales in the next section.

4.2 Review

KEY CONCEPTS

1. Why does the greatest shaking of the ground occur near an earthquake's epicenter?

2. What information do you need to completely describe where an earthquake started?

3. What types of information can a scientist get by studying seismograms?

CRITICAL THINKING

4. **Compare and Contrast** How are primary and secondary waves similar? How are they different?

5. **Apply** What information could you get about an earthquake's location from only two seismic stations' data? Explain.

CHALLENGE

6. **Apply** Why might an earthquake's primary waves, but not its secondary waves, reach a location on the other side of the world from the epicenter?

ANSWERS

1. Seismic waves lose more energy the farther they travel.

2. its epicenter and depth (focus)

3. where earthquakes start and how strong they are

4. Both travel out from the focus of an earthquake; both can travel through Earth's interior. Only primary waves can pass through areas inside Earth that are not solid.

5. Circles showing distances from two stations to the epi-center will usually intersect in two places, only one of which can be the actual epicenter.

6. Secondary waves cannot pass through Earth's outer core, but primary waves can.

MATH in SCIENCE

MATH TUTORIAL
CLASSZONE.COM
Click on Math Tutorial for more help with multiplication.

SKILL: MULTIPLICATION

Earthquake Energy

Seismologists use the moment magnitude scale to describe the energies of earthquakes. Because earthquakes vary from quite weak to very strong, the scale is designed to cover a wide range of energies. Each whole number increase in magnitude represents the release of about 32 times as much energy. For example, a magnitude 5 earthquake releases about 32 times as much energy as a magnitude 4 earthquake.

Magnitude	1	2	3	4	5	6	7	8	9	10
Energy		×32	×32	×32	×32	×32	×32	×32	×32	×32

Similarly, a magnitude 6 earthquake releases about 32 times as much energy as a magnitude 5 earthquake, and a magnitude 7 earthquake releases about 32 times as much energy as a magnitude 6 earthquake. You can use multiplication to compare the energies of earthquakes.

Example

Compare the energy of a magnitude 4 earthquake to the energy of a magnitude 7 earthquake. Give your answer to the nearest 1000.

SOLUTION

Magnitude	1	2	3	4	5	6	7	8	9	10
Energy		×32	×32	×32	×32	×32	×32	×32	×32	×32

(1) Multiply: $32 \times 32 \times 32 =$ 32,768

(2) Round your answer to the nearest 1000: **33,000**

ANSWER A magnitude 7 earthquake releases about 33,000 times as much energy as a magnitude 4 earthquake.

Compare the energies of two earthquakes:

1. Magnitude 4 and magnitude 6; give your answer to the nearest 100

2. Magnitude 5 and magnitude 9; give your answer to the nearest 100,000

3. Magnitude 3.3 and magnitude 4.3

CHALLENGE What is the magnitude of an earthquake that releases about 1000 times the energy of a magnitude 2 earthquake?

Chapter 4: **Earthquakes** 119 **B**

ANSWERS

1. *Magnitude 6 releases 1000 times as much energy as a magnitude 4:*
32 × 32 = 1024

2. *Magnitude 9 releases 1,000,000 times as much energy as a magnitude 5: 32 × 32 × 32 × 32 = 1,048,576*

3. *Magnitude 4.3 releases 32 times as much energy as magnitude 3.3.*

CHALLENGE A release of 1000 times more energy represents two steps higher on a magnitude scale; 2 + 2 = 4.

MATH IN SCIENCE
Math Skills Practice for Science

Set Learning Goal

To use multiplication to compare the energies of earthquakes

Present the Science

A magnitude scale compares the heights of waves on a seismogram. An increase of one unit of magnitude represents a 10-fold increase in wave height. The energy released by an earthquake can cause damage. An increase of one unit of magnitude represents a release of about 32 times more energy. An increase of 0.1 in magnitude represents a release of about 1.4 times more energy.

Develop Calculation Skills

- Remind students to multiply by 32 for each increase in magnitude of 1 unit.
- Remind students that digits of 5 or higher are rounded up.

DIFFERENTIATION TIP For visual learners, provide grid paper so that they can align their math calculations.

Close

Ask students to use what they have learned about the energy released by earthquakes to compare the destructive power of large- and small-magnitude earthquakes. *A large-magnitude earthquake will be much more destructive than a small-magnitude one because it releases so much more energy.*

- Math Support, p. 238
- Math Practice, p. 239

Technology Resources

Students can visit **ClassZone.com** to practice multiplying and rounding whole numbers.

 MATH TUTORIAL

Chapter 4 **119** **B**

◐ Set Learning Goals

Students will

- Explain how an earthquake's magnitude is related to the damage it causes.
- Describe how structures are built to withstand most earthquakes.
- Understand how scientists estimate the earthquake risk in an area.

◐ 3-Minute Warm-Up

Display Transparency 29 or copy this exercise on the board:

Decide if these statements are true. If not, correct them.

1. The epicenter is the point underground where rocks first begin to move. *The focus is the point underground where rocks first begin to move.*

2. Secondary waves move faster than primary waves. *Primary waves move faster than secondary waves.*

3. Three circles, each drawn around a different seismic station, meet at the epicenter of an earthquake. *true*

 3-Minute Warm-Up, p. T29

4.3 MOTIVATE

EXPLORE Shaking

PURPOSE To model how structures built on different types of ground behave during earthquakes

TIP *10 min.* Remind students to be careful that sand does not get in their eyes. Students should rinse their hands after working with sand.

WHAT DO YOU THINK? *Pieces of sand moved around and the washer sank down; the washer was less affected when it was on the rock. Buildings on loose soil are likely to be more damaged during earthquakes than are buildings on more stable surfaces such as rock.*

◀ **BEFORE, you learned**

- Seismic waves travel through Earth
- An earthquake's location and magnitude can be determined

▶ **NOW, you will learn**

- How an earthquake's magnitude is related to the damage it causes
- How structures are built to withstand most earthquakes
- How scientists estimate the earthquake risk in an area

VOCABULARY

aftershock p. 122
liquefaction p. 122
tsunami p. 122

EXPLORE Shaking

What happens as materials are shaken?

PROCEDURE

① Pour a pile of sand on a newspaper. Place a metal washer on top of the sand. Shake the paper and observe what happens to the sand and the washer.

② Now place the washer on top of a flat rock. Shake the rock and observe what happens.

MATERIALS
- sand
- newspaper
- flat rock
- washer

WHAT DO YOU THINK?
- How did the washer, the sand, and the rock react differently to shaking?
- How might the washer, the sand, and the rock model what happens to buildings and land during earthquakes?

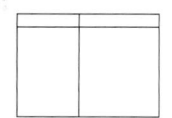

MAIN IDEA AND DETAILS
Record information about the effects of earthquakes in your notebook.

Earthquakes can cause severe damage and loss of life.

Every year, on average, an extremely powerful earthquake—one with a magnitude of 8 or higher—strikes somewhere on Earth. Such an earthquake can destroy almost all the buildings near its epicenter and cause great loss of life.

Earthquakes are most dangerous when they occur near areas where many people live. Most injuries and deaths due to earthquakes are not directly caused by the movement of the ground. They are caused by collapsing buildings and other structures and by fires. After an earthquake, fires may start due to broken natural-gas lines, broken electrical power lines, or overturned stoves.

RESOURCES FOR DIFFERENTIATED INSTRUCTION

Below Level
UNIT RESOURCE BOOK
- Reading Study Guide A, pp. 225–226
- Decoding Support, p. 237

 **AUDIO CDS**

Advanced
UNIT RESOURCE BOOK
- Challenge and Extension, p. 231
- Challenge Reading, pp. 233–234

English Learners
UNIT RESOURCE BOOK
Spanish Reading Study Guide, pp. 229–230

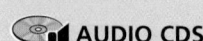 **AUDIO CDS**

- Audio Readings in Spanish
- Audio Readings (English)

Earthquake Magnitude

A very powerful earthquake can release more energy than 1 million weak earthquakes combined. Earthquake magnitude scales give scientists and engineers a simple way to describe this huge range in energy.

The first scale of earthquake magnitude was developed in California during the 1930s by the scientists Charles Richter (RIHK-tuhr) and Beno Gutenberg. In this scale, called the Richter scale, an earthquake's magnitude is based on how fast the ground moves at a seismic station. However, most scientists today prefer to use a newer, more accurate scale: the moment magnitude scale. This scale is based on the total amounts of energy released by earthquakes. The moment magnitude scale is used for all earthquake magnitudes given in this chapter.

Both the Richter scale and the moment magnitude scale are often shown with a top value of 10, but neither actually has a maximum value. On each scale, an increase of one whole number indicates an increase of 32 times more energy. For example, a magnitude 5 earthquake releases 32 times as much energy as a magnitude 4 earthquake and about 1000 times as much energy as a magnitude 3 earthquake.

Magnitude and Effects Near Epicenter

More powerful earthquakes have higher magnitude values.

Magnitude	Effects Near Epicenter
0–3.9 Very Minor to Minor	rarely noticed
4.0–4.9 Light	slight damage
5.0–5.9 Moderate	some structures damaged
6.0–6.9 Strong	major damage to structures
7.0–7.9 Major	some well-built structures destroyed
8.0 and above Great	major to total destruction

Damage from Powerful Earthquake

This road collapsed during a magnitude 6.9 earthquake in California on October 17, 1989. About 140 earthquakes with magnitudes of 6 or higher occur each year around the world.

Teach Difficult Concepts

Some students may have a hard time understanding liquefaction. Explain that the energy of the earthquake moves the soil particles apart; they no longer touch each other, so they lose their support. To help students understand this process, try the following demonstration.

Teacher Demo

Fill a loaf pan almost to the top with sand. Add water to just below the sand's surface. Push the narrow end of a brick into the sand so it stands up like a building. Wait a few minutes. Tap the side of the pan with a mallet. Have students observe what happens. Ask: What does pounding with the hammer represent? *an earthquake*

Explain that the energy from the hammer tries to push the sand particles together, but then the water needs to be pushed out. In an earthquake, seismic waves try to push soil particles together very fast, and the water doesn't have time to get out. The water pressure increases, decreasing the strength of the contact between the sand particles, so they can't hold up the building.

Develop Critical Thinking

APPLY Have students apply their knowledge of the ways in which earthquakes can cause damage by having them suggest ways people could help protect themselves if they are in an area where earthquakes are common. *Sample answer: Stay in open areas. Build strong buildings. Make strong, flexible water pipes or have alternate sources of water for fighting fires. Avoid hills covered with unstable rocks or soil.*

Ongoing Assessment

VOCABULARY
Add magnet word diagrams for *aftershock* and *liquefaction* to your notebook.

The moment magnitude scale is more accurate for larger earthquakes than the Richter scale. Another advantage of the moment magnitude scale is that it can be used for earthquakes that occurred before seismographs were invented. Geologists can measure the strength of the rocks and the length they moved along a fault to calculate a past earthquake's magnitude. This information is important for geologists to know when they determine an area's earthquake risk.

CHECK YOUR READING What are two advantages of the moment magnitude scale over the Richter scale?

Damage from Earthquakes

Movement of the blocks of rock on either side of a fault can crack roads, buildings, dams, and any other structures on the fault. As blocks of rock move, they can also raise, lower, or tilt the ground surface. Sometimes structures weakened by an earthquake collapse during shaking caused by aftershocks. An **aftershock** is a smaller earthquake that follows a more powerful earthquake in the same area. Also, fires that break out can cause great damage if broken water pipes keep firefighters from getting water. In the 1906 San Francisco earthquake, fires caused more than 90 percent of the building damage.

Earthquakes can cause major damage by affecting the soil and other loose materials. For example, landslides often occur as a result of earthquakes. A landslide is a movement of soil and rocks down a hill or mountain. Earthquakes can cause soil **liquefaction,** a process in which shaking of the ground causes soil to act like a liquid. For a short time the soil becomes like a thick soup. Liquefaction occurs only in areas where the soil is made up of loose sand and silt and contains a large amount of water. As the shaking temporarily changes the wet soil, structures either sink down into the soil or flow away with it. Shaking of the ground also affects areas that have mixtures of soils. Some soil types pack together more than others when shaken.

This building in Venezuela tilted and sank as the ground beneath it collapsed during an earthquake in 1967.

CHECK YOUR READING List five ways in which earthquakes can cause damage.

Damage from Tsunamis

If you sit on an ocean beach, you can watch the depth of the water change as waves come in. If you watch for a longer time, you may notice bigger changes as the tide rises or falls. A special type of wave, however, can make water rise more than the height of a 20-story building. This wave, known as a **tsunami** (tsu-NAH-mee), is a water wave triggered by an earthquake, volcanic eruption, or landslide. Tsunamis are

---

DIFFERENTIATE INSTRUCTION

More Reading Support

B What is a process in which shaking causes soil to act like a liquid? *liquefaction*

C What is a water wave triggered by an earthquake? *a tsunami*

Advanced Have students look for fact sheets and information about earthquake safety on the U.S. Geological Survey's Web site. Challenge them to explain how maps of expected ground-shaking intensity are made and used.

Below Level Ask students what the effects of earthquakes are and list their responses on the board. Have students discuss each effect and explain what happens as a result of it.

sometimes called tidal waves, but they are not caused by the forces that produce tides. A tsunami may not be a single wave but several waves that can have different heights and can arrive hours apart.

Tsunamis move quickly and can travel thousands of kilometers without weakening. In deep water, they can reach speeds of about 700 kilometers per hour (430 mi/h). A tsunami in the deep water of the open ocean may be less than one meter (3 ft) in height at the surface. As a tsunami reaches shallow water around an island or continent, however, it slows down, and its height greatly increases.

A 1946 earthquake on Alaska's coast caused a tsunami that swept across the entire Pacific Ocean. In Alaska the tsunami destroyed a new U.S. Coast Guard lighthouse that otherwise would have been able to send warnings to other areas. In less than five hours, the tsunami reached Hawaii as a series of waves. The highest wave was about 17 meters (55 ft) tall. Because people did not know of the danger, no one had evacuated, and 159 people were killed.

Many earthquakes occur around the edges of the Pacific Ocean. Therefore, Hawaii and other areas in and around this ocean are likely to be hit by tsunamis. The Pacific Tsunami Warning Center, located in Hawaii, was established in 1949. The center monitors earthquakes and issues warnings to areas that could be struck by tsunamis.

RESOURCE CENTER
CLASSZONE.COM
Explore tsunamis.

In 1993, a tsunami from a powerful earthquake in Japan threw boats onto land.

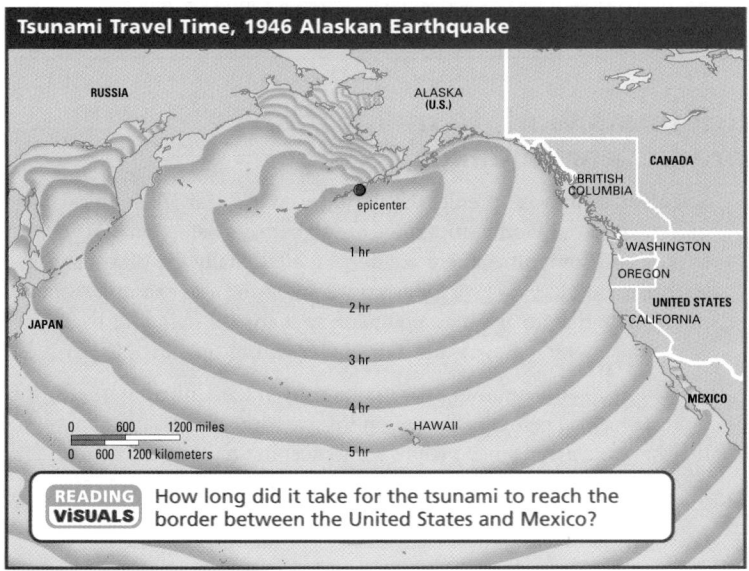

Tsunami Travel Time, 1946 Alaskan Earthquake

 How long did it take for the tsunami to reach the border between the United States and Mexico?

Chapter 4: **Earthquakes** 123 **B**

DIFFERENTIATE INSTRUCTION

? More Reading Support

D How many waves are in a tsunami? *more than one*

E Where are tsunamis most likely to hit? *areas in and around the Pacific Ocean*

Advanced Challenge students to explain why a powerful earthquake along a strike-slip fault under the ocean is unlikely to produce a tsunami, but a powerful earthquake along a reverse fault under the ocean might produce a large, destructive tsunami.
Answer: Only earthquakes that cause the sea floor to move vertically produce large tsunamis.

 Challenge and Extension, p. 231

Teach from Visuals

To help students interpret the visual showing the speed of a tsunami, ask:
- What does each circle represent? *the position of the tsunami a certain time after the earthquake*
- Where was the epicenter of the earthquake that caused this tsunami? *in the Alaskan islands*
- Where did people experience this tsunami? *all around the Pacific Ocean*

Teaching with Technology

Have students use a search engine and search the Internet to find an animation showing a tsunami in action.

Integrate the Sciences

The waves that are normally seen on a pond, lake, or ocean are generated by winds moving across the water. The water molecules stay in basically the same place, but the energy of the wave moves toward shore. These waves have a short wavelength (distance between wave crests). Tsunamis, by contrast, have a very long wavelength. Even in the deep ocean, their wavelength may be twice as long as the depth of the ocean. The speed at which a tsunami moves depends on the depth of the water—the shallower the water, the slower it moves.

Develop Critical Thinking

INFER Have students infer what a large tsunami looks like when it comes ashore and in what way tsunamis resemble tidal waves, though they are unrelated to tides. *A large tsunami often does not come ashore as a towering wave. Instead, it causes an increase in sea level like a very high and fast-moving high tide. (Students in hurricane-prone areas might compare a tsunami to a storm surge.)* Refer back to p. 110 and discuss why the 1964 tsunami in Valdez Inlet was described as "a wall of water." *This unusual tsunami was triggered in a narrow inlet, so the water was forced upward.*

Ongoing Assessment

 *Answer: 6 hours*

Chapter 4 **123** **B**

Teach from Visuals

To help students interpret the visual showing earthquake risk in the United States, ask:

• What are the areas with the greatest risk of earthquakes? *the West Coast, southern Alaska, Hawaii*

• What are the areas with the lowest risk of earthquakes? *mid–United States, southeastern coast*

Mathematics Connection

Discuss probabilities.

Ask: What does it mean when scientists give a percent chance that an area will be hit by an earthquake with a magnitude of 7 or higher within 25 years? *Scientists are giving a long-term prediction of the probability that such an earthquake will occur. The higher the percent given, the more likely that such an earthquake will occur within the time specified.*

Develop Critical Thinking

CONNECT Provide students with an outline map of the United States that shows the states. Have them shade their own state in one color. Have them shade the states with the highest and the lowest risk of earthquakes in two other colors. Then ask them to identify the area of the United States most at risk from earthquakes. What generalizations can they make? *Coastal and mountain regions in the West seem to have the greatest risk; the Great Plains, which are flat, seem to have the lowest.*

Ongoing Assessment

READING VISUALS *Answer: Answers will vary, depending on students' locations.*

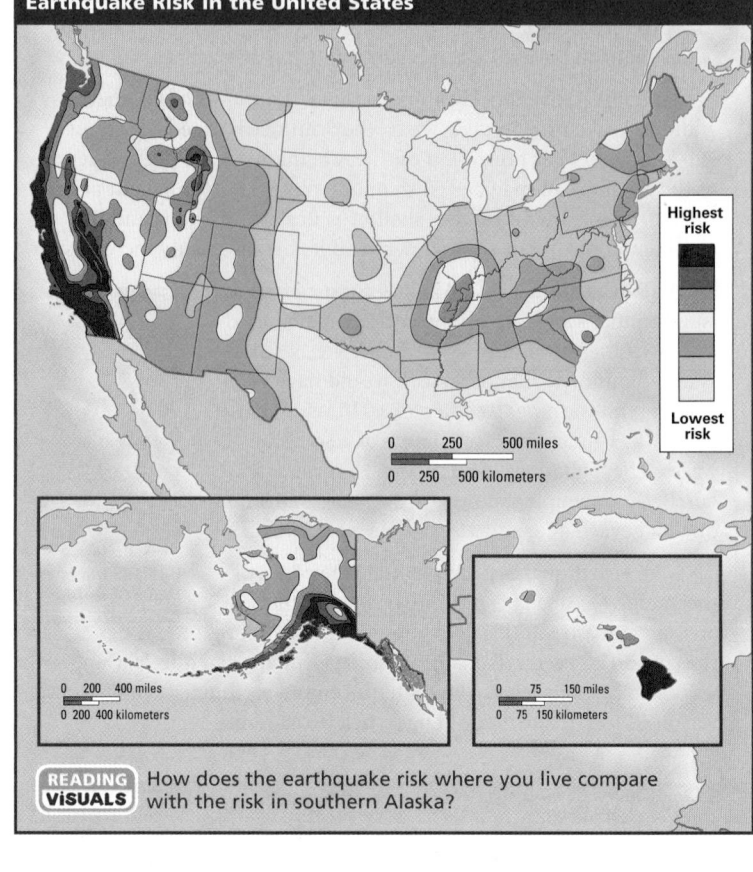

Earthquake Risk in the United States

Highest risk

Lowest risk

0   250   500 miles
0   250   500 kilometers

0   200   400 miles
0   200   400 kilometers

0   75   150 miles
0   75   150 kilometers

READING VISUALS How does the earthquake risk where you live compare with the risk in southern Alaska?

Scientists work to monitor and predict earthquakes.

F

READING TIP

A prediction is a statement about an event before it occurs. Scientists use their knowledge to make predictions about when earthquakes might occur.

Scientists cannot yet predict the day or even the year when an earthquake will occur. Sometimes there are signs years before an earthquake strikes, and sometimes there are none at all. Usually the best that scientists can do is to give long-term predictions. For example, they might state that an area has a 60 percent chance of being hit by an earthquake with a magnitude 7 or higher within the next 25 years.

The map above shows earthquake risks in the United States for the next 50 years. The map is based on information about earthquakes that have occurred since people began keeping records, along with evidence of earlier earthquakes preserved in rocks. Note that most areas with the highest earthquake risks are near the Pacific Ocean.

B   124   Unit: **Energy and the Changing Earth**

DIFFERENTIATE INSTRUCTION

? **More Reading Support**

F What kind of predictions can scientists make for earthquakes? *long-term predictions*

Inclusion As an auditory strategy for reading the map, read aloud the colors in the key and have students locate regions of the country that have the same color. As a visual aid, display a map of the United States with the state names written in.

To learn more about earthquakes and to find ways of predicting them, scientists all over the world study seismic activity along faults. They monitor whether stress is building up in the rocks along faults. Such signs include

- tilts or changes in the elevation of the ground
- slow movements or stretching in rock
- the development of small cracks in the ground

An increase in small earthquakes can be a sign that stress is building up along a fault and that a large earthquake is likely to occur. But an increase in small earthquakes can also be a sign that a fault is releasing stress bit by bit, decreasing the likelihood of a major earthquake.

Scientists also look for areas where earthquakes have not occurred along an otherwise active fault. They make diagrams in which they plot the locations where earthquakes have started, as shown below. Sometimes such a diagram shows an area of few or no earthquakes that is surrounded by many earthquakes. This area is called a seismic gap. A seismic gap can indicate a location where a fault is stuck. Movement along other parts of the fault can increase stress along the stuck part. This stress could be released by a major earthquake.

CHECK YOUR READING Why can a lack of earthquakes in an area near an active fault cause concern?

A seismic gap is a section of a fault with few earthquakes compared with sections of the fault on either side of the gap.

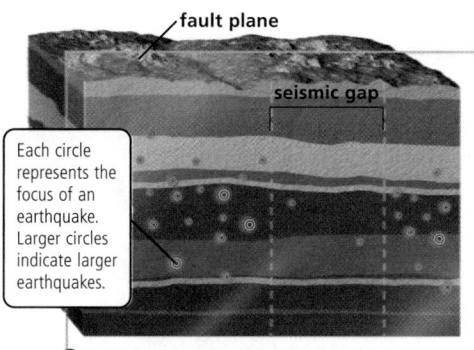

fault plane

seismic gap

Each circle represents the focus of an earthquake. Larger circles indicate larger earthquakes.

1 Over several years many earthquakes have occurred along this fault. However, one section of the fault has had little earthquake activity. Stress is building up along this section.

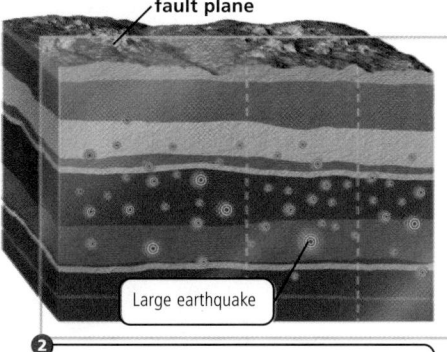

fault plane

Large earthquake

2 A large earthquake and its aftershocks have occurred, releasing built-up stress. Over just a few weeks the seismic gap has been filled in.

Chapter 4: **Earthquakes** 125 **B**

Teach from Visuals

To help students interpret the visual showing a seismic gap, ask:

- What does the illustration on the left show? *a fault along which many earthquakes have occurred, except for one section*
- What is important about the section with little earthquake activity? *It might be stuck. A lot of stress may be building up there.*
- What does the illustration on the right show? *A large earthquake and its aftershocks have filled in the gap.*

EXPLORE (the **BIG** idea)

Revisit "Internet Activity: Earthquakes" on p. 103. Have students relate their results to how earthquakes are predicted.

Ongoing Assessment

CHECK YOUR READING *Answer: Large amounts of stress could be building up along a fault.*

DIFFERENTIATE INSTRUCTION

 More Reading Support

G What do scientists monitor in order to predict earthquakes? *a buildup of stress along a fault*

Alternative Assessment Use a large book as a ramp and put a small box on it. Let pencils roll down and stack up against the box until it slides down the ramp. Have students explain how this relates to earthquakes and seismic gaps. *Each pencil represents an earthquake. The box represents a portion of the fault that is not moving—a seismic gap. When the stress on the box is great enough, it moves, causing a larger "earthquake."*

Address Misconceptions

IDENTIFY Ask: What is the purpose of specially designing and building structures in areas where earthquakes are likely? If students say that the purpose is to have structures that cannot be damaged during earthquakes, they hold the common misconception that people are capable of completely safeguarding themselves against natural disasters such as earthquakes.

CORRECT Tell students that designing structures to resist earthquake damage means that the amount of damage will likely be reduced but not eliminated. Refer back to the graphic on p. 121. Point out that even well-built structures can be damaged or destroyed by powerful earthquakes.

REASSESS Ask: Why can't any structure be made completely earthquake-proof? *A powerful earthquake causes so much shaking of the ground near its epicenter that even well-built structures will be affected.*

Teaching with Technology

Have students search the Internet for graphics of earthquake-safe building structures and then use presentation software to present their findings to the class.

Real World Example

The Federal Emergency Management Agency (FEMA) provides guidelines for homeowners about how to help make their homes as safe as possible during an earthquake. They also help with disaster relief after an earthquake.

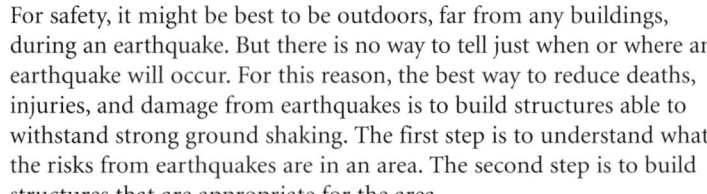

Structures can be designed to resist earthquake damage.

For safety, it might be best to be outdoors, far from any buildings, during an earthquake. But there is no way to tell just when or where an earthquake will occur. For this reason, the best way to reduce deaths, injuries, and damage from earthquakes is to build structures able to withstand strong ground shaking. The first step is to understand what the risks from earthquakes are in an area. The second step is to build structures that are appropriate for the area.

Scientists make maps of areas to show the locations of fault zones, past earthquakes, and areas likely to experience flooding, landslides, or liquefaction. In Japan, California, and other areas that have many earthquakes, planners use these maps to develop rules for building new structures and strengthening older ones. The maps are also used to select building locations that are stable—unlikely to experience landslides or liquefaction.

Earthquake damage to small buildings, such as most houses, often occurs when the buildings are shaken off their foundations. Small buildings are better protected when they are firmly fastened to their foundations. Also, their walls need to be strong. Some houses were built before modern safety rules were in place. The walls of these houses can be made stronger by adding supports. Supports are particularly important in brick walls, which can easily collapse in an earthquake. A special type of steel is commonly used for the supports because it is strong and is able to bend, then return to its original shape.

⚠ SAFETY TIPS

Earthquakes

Before

- Fasten heavy objects, such as bookcases, to floors or walls to keep them from falling.
- Put latches on cabinets to keep dishes from falling out.
- Identify safe spots in every room, such as the space under a strong table.
- Keep an emergency supply of bottled water.

During and After

- If you are inside a building, stay inside until the shaking stops. Objects falling from buildings cause many injuries.
- If you are outdoors, move away from buildings, poles, and trees.
- Make a family plan for contacting a person who lives in another town. As people call to say they are safe, this person can pass on the information.

DIFFERENTIATE INSTRUCTION

❓ More Reading Support

H What might be the safest place to be during an earthquake? *outside, away from buildings*

English Learners The words *should*, *would*, and *could* are not universal in all languages. Help students understand sentences that contain these words. For example, "What could you do to make your room safer during an earthquake?" The word *could* is used in this instance to indicate a hypothetical possibility.

Advanced

 Challenge Reading, pp. 233–234

Many of the methods used to make larger buildings and other structures safer are designed to reduce the amount they shake during an earthquake. One method is to use devices called base isolators, as shown in the illustration. Base isolators are placed between a building and its foundation. The isolators are made of flexible materials that are stacked in layers like pancakes. When an earthquake occurs, the isolators absorb much of the ground motion. Any shaking that does reach the building is slower and smoother.

A building may also have an open space, or moat, around it. The moat, which may be covered at the surface with sidewalks and landscaping, lets the building shake more gently than the ground during an earthquake.

Special walls, called shear walls, add strength to a structure. These walls contain steel supports. Shear walls in the center of a building are often built around a stairwell or an elevator shaft. These walls make up a part of the building known as the shear core.

Walls can also be made stronger by adding braces. Pairs of braces that form an **X** shape are called cross braces. They help a structure keep its shape while it is being shaken.

 **CHECK YOUR READING** Describe two methods used to make buildings stronger.

Earthquake-Resistant Building

cross braces

shear wall

shear core

moat

base isolator

 **4.3 Review**

KEY CONCEPTS

1. How is an earthquake magnitude scale related to the amounts of energy released by earthquakes?

2. What are the major dangers to people from an earthquake?

3. Name three methods of improving a building's safety before an earthquake.

CRITICAL THINKING

4. **Apply** What might people living next to the ocean do to protect themselves if they were given a two-hour warning of an approaching tsunami?

5. **Connect** If you lived in an area where earthquakes were common, what could you do to make your room safer?

CHALLENGE

6. **Analyze** Earthquakes release stress that has built up in rocks. Why do you think aftershocks occur?

ANSWERS

1. Each whole-number increase represents a release of about 32 times as much energy.

2. collapsing structures and fires

3. fastening a building to its foundation; adding wall supports; using base isolators, moats, shear walls, shear cores, and/or cross braces during original construction

4. go to a higher area

5. Fasten bookcases or other heavy furniture to the walls; identify the safest place to be in the room

6. Aftershocks occur because stress in the rock is still being released.

Focus

PURPOSE To tap into students' creativity as they examine ways to make buildings more earthquake resistant

OVERVIEW Students will explore ways of building earthquake-resistant structures by building a structure from modeling clay, stirrer straws, and cardboard and then observing how long it can withstand shaking. Students will find the following:

• Cross braces make structures sturdier.

• Putting similar materials together in different ways produces structures that react differently to shaking.

Lab Preparation

Construct a shake table.

• Materials: 2 large box lids, 40 marbles, 4 rubber bands, stapler

• Cut the bottom of one lid so that it is 4 cm shorter on all sides than the intact lid. Attach rubber bands to each corner.

• Put the marbles in the intact lid, then put the cut piece on top of them.

• Make small holes in the vertical corners of the intact lid. Pull the rubber bands through the holes. Staple the bands so they are somewhat stretched. The inner cardboard piece should shake when pulled to one side and then released.

• Prior to the investigation, have students read through the investigation, write a hypothesis, and prepare their data tables. Or you may wish to copy and distribute datasheets and rubrics.

 UNIT RESOURCE BOOK, pp. 240–248

SCIENCE TOOLKIT, F12

Lab Management

Limit the number of stirrers and amount of clay used to build each structure.

CHAPTER INVESTIGATION

How Structures React in Earthquakes

 DESIGN — YOUR OWN —

OVERVIEW AND PURPOSE

In 1989 a magnitude 6.9 earthquake struck the San Francisco Bay area, killing 62 people and leaving 12,000 homeless. In 1988 a magnitude 6.9 earthquake occurred near Spitak, Armenia. There, nearly 25,000 people died and 514,000 lost their homes. The difference in the effects of these two earthquakes was largely due to differences in construction methods. In this investigation you will

• build a structure and measure how long it can withstand shaking on a shake table provided by your teacher

• explore methods of building earthquake-resistant structures

MATERIALS
• modeling clay
• stirrer straws
• piece of thin cardboard 15 cm on each side
• scissors
• ruler
• shake table

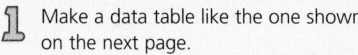 **Problem** Write It Up

How can structures be built to withstand most earthquakes?

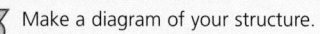 **Hypothesize** Write It Up

Write a hypothesis to explain how structures can be built to withstand shaking. Your hypothesis should take the form of an "If . . . , then . . . , because . . ." statement.

Procedure

1. Make a data table like the one shown on the next page.

2. Use stirrers joined with clay to build a structure at least 20 cm tall on top of the cardboard. Cut the stirrers if necessary.

step 2

3. Make a diagram of your structure.

INVESTIGATION RESOURCES

 CHAPTER INVESTIGATION, How Structures React in Earthquakes
• Level A, pp. 240–243
• Level B, pp. 244–247
• Level C, p. 248

Advanced students should complete Levels B & C.

Writing a Lab Report, D12–13

Technology Resources

Customize this student lab as needed or look for an alternative. Print rubrics to assess student lab reports.

 Lab Generator CD-ROM

4 Lift your structure by its cardboard base and place it on the shake-table platform. Pull the platform 2 centimeters to one side and release it.

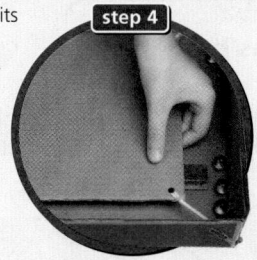

step 4

5 Repeat step 4 until the structure begins to collapse.

Observe and Analyze 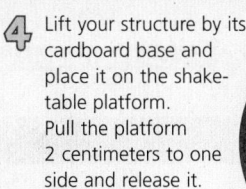 Write It Up

1. **RECORD** Complete your data table and make notes about the collapse, including areas of possible weakness in your structure.

2. **INFER** Use your observations to design a structure that will better withstand shaking.

Conclude Write It Up

1. **INTERPRET** Compare your results with your hypothesis. Do your observations support your hypothesis?

2. **INFER** How would you use the shake table to model earthquakes of different magnitudes?

3. **IDENTIFY VARIABLES** How might your results differ if you always pulled the platform to the same side or if you pulled it to different sides?

4. **IDENTIFY LIMITS** In what ways might a building's behavior during an earthquake differ from the behavior of your structure on the shake table?

5. **COMPARE** Examine the diagrams of the three structures that lasted longest in your class. What characteristics, if any, did they have in common?

6. **APPLY** Based on your results, write a list of recommendations for building earthquake-resistant structures.

▶ INVESTIGATE Further

CHALLENGE Have a contest to see who can build the most earthquake-resistant structure. Design your structure as if you were an earthquake engineer. Make a model of your structure at least 30 centimeters tall, using the types of materials you used in this investigation. Test the structure on the shake table. What design features helped the winning structure to resist shaking the longest?

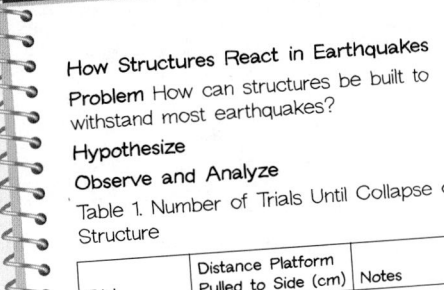

How Structures React in Earthquakes
Problem How can structures be built to withstand most earthquakes?

Hypothesize

Observe and Analyze
Table 1. Number of Trials Until Collapse of Structure

Trial	Distance Platform Pulled to Side (cm)	Notes
1	2	
2	2	
3	2	
4	2	

Conclude

▶ Observe and Analyze Write It Up

Sample Data: trial 1, 2 cm, structure tilts to one side after shaking; trial 2, 2 cm, structure completely collapses

1. *See students' data tables.*

2. *Sample answer: The new design will use more cross braces.*

▶ Conclude Write It Up

1. *Answers will vary, depending on students' results.*

2. *Pull the platform farther to one side before letting go.*

3. *A structure might have more weaknesses in one direction than another and so might collapse faster if shaken in different directions.*

4. *A real building would behave somewhat differently because seismic waves can cause the ground to move up and down as well as back and forth. An earthquake can cause the ground to shake longer than the platform shakes. Real buildings are more sturdy. But these buildings contain potentially dangerous materials such as sheets of glass, electrical wires, and natural gas lines that were not modeled in students' buildings.*

5. *Sample answer: They had more supports and cross braces.*

6. *Answers might include using strong, flexible materials and cross braces.*

▶ INVESTIGATE Further

CHALLENGE Student answers will vary.

Post-Lab Discussion

Ask: What differences did you observe among the buildings students created and their response to shaking? How can you explain these differences? *Answers will vary, depending upon their results.* Ask: How would you modify your design, now that you have seen the results? *Answers will vary depending on students' designs and results, but should suggest new designs that are markedly different and attempt to address limitations of the first design.*

BACK TO

the **BIG** idea

Ask students to summarize what happened during the 1989 San Francisco earthquake. *Rocks moved suddenly along a fault. Energy was released and spread out from the focus in seismic waves. The seismic waves were in the form of P waves, S waves, and surface waves. The waves made the ground shake, causing destruction of buildings and other structures.*

◀ KEY CONCEPTS SUMMARY

SECTION 4.1
Ask students to explain what is happening in each of the three diagrams. *Blocks of rock are pulling away from each other; blocks of rock are being pushed together; blocks of rock are moving past each other in opposite directions.*

SECTION 4.2
Ask students to describe the relationships among the focus, epicenter, and seismic waves shown in the diagram. *An earthquake begins underground at its focus. Vibrations called seismic waves travel out from the focus. The epicenter is the point on Earth's surface above the focus.*

SECTION 4.3
Have students explain the two ways earthquake damage can be reduced. *Scientists can predict where earthquakes are likely and make maps showing their predictions. Structures can be designed and built to resist earthquake damage.*

Review Concepts

- Big Idea Flow Chart, p. T25
- Chapter Outline, pp. T31–T32

 Chapter Review

the **BIG** idea

Earthquakes release stress that has built up in rocks.

CONTENT REVIEW
CLASSZONE.COM

◀ KEY CONCEPTS SUMMARY

4.1 Earthquakes occur along faults.

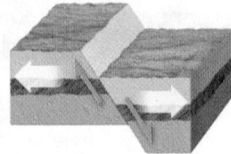 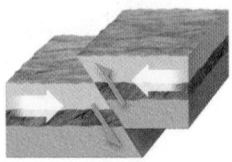 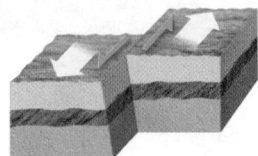

Normal faults form as rocks are pulled apart.

Reverse faults form as rocks are pushed together.

Strike-slip faults form as rocks are pushed horizontally in opposite directions.

VOCABULARY
fault p. 105
stress p. 105
earthquake p. 105

4.2 Earthquakes release energy.

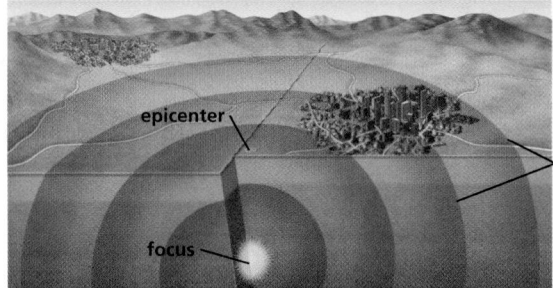

epicenter

Seismic waves move out from the focus in all directions.

focus

VOCABULARY
seismic wave p. 111
focus p. 112
epicenter p. 112
seismograph p. 116

4.3 Earthquake damage can be reduced.

A powerful earthquake releases more energy and causes more shaking of the ground than does a weak earthquake.

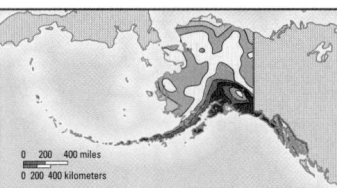 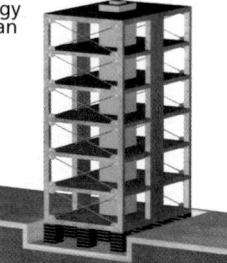

0 200 400 miles
0 200 400 kilometers

An area's risk of earthquakes can be predicted.

Structures can be designed for greater safety in an earthquake.

VOCABULARY
aftershock p. 122
liquefaction p. 122
tsunami p. 122

B 130 Unit: **Energy and the Changing Earth**

Technology Resources

Have students visit **ClassZone.com** or use the CD-ROM for a cumulative review of concepts.

 CONTENT REVIEW

 CONTENT REVIEW CD-ROM

Engage students in a whole-class interactive review of Key Concepts. Edit content as you wish.

 POWER PRESENTATIONS

Reviewing Vocabulary

On a separate sheet of paper, draw a diagram to show the relationships among each set of words. One set has been done as an example.

seismograph, seismic waves, seismogram

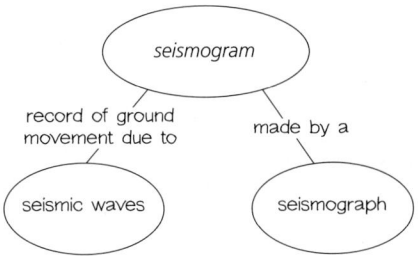

1. earthquake, epicenter, focus

2. earthquake, tsunami, liquefaction

3. fault, stress, earthquake, aftershock

4. tsunami, epicenter, seismogram

Reviewing Key Concepts

Multiple Choice *Choose the letter of the best answer.*

5. What causes an earthquake?
   a. a rise of magma in the mantle
   b. a sudden movement of blocks of rock
   c. a buildup of seismic waves
   d. a change in Earth's magnetic poles

6. Earthquakes release energy in the form of
   a. seismic waves
   b. faults
   c. stress lines
   d. seismograms

7. Most damage from an earthquake usually occurs
   a. below the focus
   b. far from the epicenter
   c. at the focus
   d. near the epicenter

8. To locate the epicenter of an earthquake, scientists need seismograms from at least _____ seismic stations.
   a. two   c. four
   b. three   d. five

9. The seismic waves that usually cause the most damage are
   a. surface waves
   b. tsunami waves
   c. primary waves
   d. secondary waves

10. Earthquakes release _____ that has built up in rocks.
    a. water   c. stress
    b. magnetism   d. electricity

11. About 80 percent of all earthquakes occur in a belt around the
    a. Pacific Ocean
    b. San Andreas Fault
    c. North American Plate
    d. African Rift Valley

12. In a strike-slip fault, blocks of rock move _____ along the fault plane.
    a. up
    b. down
    c. sideways
    d. up and down

13. One method of making a building earthquake resistant is to
    a. add sand under the foundation
    b. reduce the use of steel
    c. make the walls of brick
    d. use cross braces

Short Answer *Write a short answer to each question.*

14. Why do most earthquakes occur at or near tectonic plate boundaries?

15. How do data from seismic waves indicate that Earth's outer core is liquid?

16. What causes most of the injuries and deaths due to earthquakes?

ASSESSMENT RESOURCES

UNIT ASSESSMENT BOOK
- Chapter Test A, pp. 64–67
- Chapter Test B, pp. 68–71
- Chapter Test C, pp. 72–75
- Alternative Assessment, pp. 76–77

SPANISH ASSESSMENT BOOK
Spanish Chapter Test, pp. 133–136

Technology Resources

Edit test items and answer choices.

 Test Generator CD-ROM

Visit **ClassZone.com** to extend test practice.

 Test Practice

Reviewing Vocabulary

Sample answers:

1.
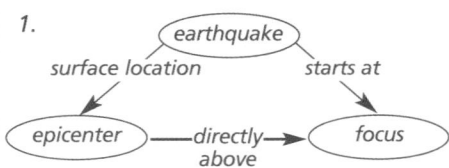

2.
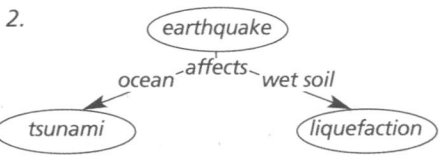

3.
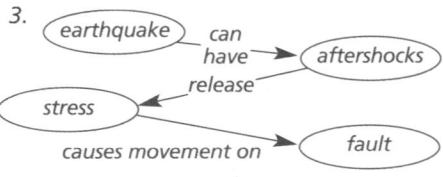

4.
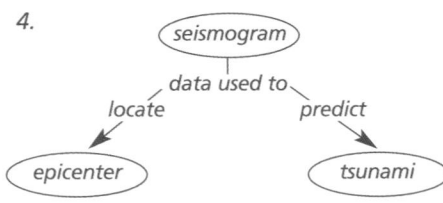

Reviewing Key Concepts

5. *b*

6. *a*

7. *d*

8. *b*

9. *a*

10. *c*

11. *a*

12. *c*

13. *d*

14. *Earthquakes occur along faults, and most faults are located at or near tectonic plate boundaries.*

15. *If the Earth's outer core were solid, secondary waves could pass through it. Since secondary waves cannot pass through the outer core, it must be liquid.*

16. *Collapsing buildings and outbreaks of fire cause most earthquake injuries and deaths.*

Thinking Critically

17. *reverse, because one block of rock has moved up the fault plane relative to the other*

18. *at the epicenter*

19. *seismic waves moving out from the focus*

20. *The arrival times will be closer together at A than at B.*

21. *The block to the right has moved up relative to the block to the left.*

22. *They are being pushed together.*

23. *Avoid areas where landslides or liquefaction are likely; use good building practices to make the house resistant to earthquake damage.*

24. *Students' answers should include two of these: Alaska, Washington, and California. All three states have or are near a plate boundary.*

25. *a lot of damage to buildings because the epicenter is nearby and the focus is shallow*

26. *They cause changes as large blocks of rock move up, down, or sideways.*

27. *2 minutes and 19 seconds*

the BIG idea

28. *Seismic waves travel out from an earthquake's focus in all directions. The greater the waves' energy at the surface, the more the ground shakes.*

29. *Heat inside Earth causes tectonic plates to move, and the movements of tectonic plates cause earthquakes to occur.*

UNIT PROJECTS

Students should have begun designing their models or presentations by this time. Remind them to continue researching as needed. Encourage them to try different solutions to any problems.

 Unit Projects, pp. 5–10

Thinking Critically

Study the illustration below, showing the epicenter and focus of an earthquake, then answer the following six questions.

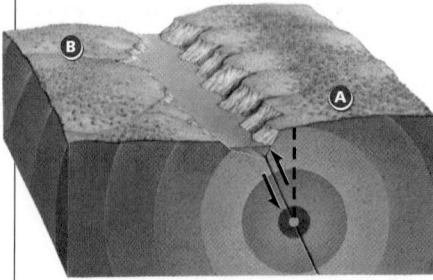

17. **APPLY** What type of fault is shown in the illustration? How do you know?

18. **APPLY** Where on the surface is the greatest shaking likely to occur?

19. **INFER** What does the set of circles around the focus represent?

20. **EXPLAIN** In what ways would the times of arrival of primary and secondary waves be different at points *A* and *B*?

21. **IDENTIFY EFFECTS** The land surface to the left of the fault is lower than the land surface to the right. How might this be related to movements along the fault?

22. **ANALYZE** What are the main directions of stress on the blocks of rock on either side of the fault?

23. **APPLY** A builder is planning to construct a new house near a fault along which earthquakes are common. Write a list of guidelines that the builder might use to decide where and how to build the house.

24. **ANALYZE** Identify two areas of the United States where earthquakes are most likely to occur. Explain your choices in terms of plate tectonics.

25. **IDENTIFY EFFECTS** A town has been struck by an earthquake with a magnitude of 5.8. The epicenter was 10 kilometers (6 mi) away, and the focus was shallow. What sort of damage would you expect to find in the town?

26. **ANALYZE** What role do earthquakes play in shaping Earth's surface?

27. **CALCULATE** If primary waves travel at a speed of about 5 kilometers per second, how long would it take them to arrive at a seismic station located 695 kilometers from an earthquake's focus?

the BIG idea

28. **CONNECT** Look again at the photograph of earthquake damage on pages 102 and 103. Explain how energy released by an earthquake can travel through rock and cause damage at Earth's surface.

29. **SYNTHESIZE** The illustration below shows convection in Earth's mantle. What are the relationships among the heat inside Earth, the movements of tectonic plates, and the occurrences of earthquakes?

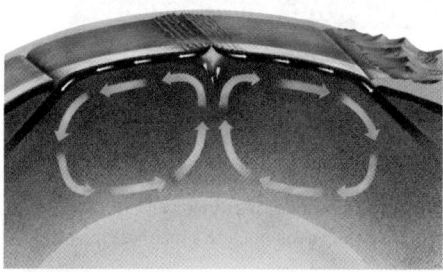

UNIT PROJECTS

If you need to create graphs or other visuals for your project, be sure you have grid paper, poster board, markers, or other supplies.

MONITOR AND RETEACH

If students have trouble applying the concepts in Chapter Review item 24, have them review the map on p. 106. Have them compare the locations of the plate boundaries and the earthquakes in North America.

Students may benefit from summarizing one or more sections of the chapter.

 Summarizing the Chapter, pp. 258–259

Standardized Test Practice

For practice on your state test, go to . . .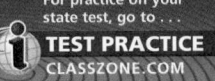
TEST PRACTICE
CLASSZONE.COM

Analyzing Data

The following tables show magnitudes and average numbers of earthquakes in the world per year, and states in which two or more major earthquakes have been recorded. Use the information in the tables to answer the questions below.

Earthquakes in the World per Year

Classification	Magnitude	Average Number per Year
Great	8.0 and higher	1
Major	7.0–7.9	18
Strong	6.0–6.9	120
Moderate	5.0–5.9	800
Light	4.0–4.9	6200
Minor	3.0–3.9	49,000

States That Have Recorded Two or More Major Earthquakes

State	Number of Major Earthquakes
Alaska	74
Arkansas	2
California	16
Hawaii	4
Missouri	2
Nevada	3

1. A major earthquake can have a magnitude of
- **a.** 6.0–6.9
- **b.** 6.0 and higher
- **c.** 7.4
- **d.** 8.2

2. The most major earthquakes have been recorded in which state?
- **a.** Arkansas
- **b.** Hawaii
- **c.** Missouri
- **d.** Nevada

3. A magnitude 3.2 earthquake is classified as
- **a.** major
- **b.** strong
- **c.** moderate
- **d.** minor

4. The world's most powerful earthquakes occur along reverse faults. In which state are reverse faults most likely to be common?
- **a.** Alaska
- **b.** California
- **c.** Hawaii
- **d.** Nevada

5. In which state is a tectonic plate boundary most likely to be located?
- **a.** Arkansas
- **b.** California
- **c.** Hawaii
- **d.** Nevada

6. Compared to the number of major earthquakes each year, the number of moderate earthquakes is
- **a.** about 40 times greater
- **b.** about 4 times greater
- **c.** about equal
- **d.** smaller

7. Alaska has recorded a total of 82 earthquakes with magnitudes of 7.0 and higher. How many of these earthquakes are classified as "great"?
- **a.** 0
- **b.** 8
- **c.** 56
- **d.** 74

8. An earthquake of which classification releases the most energy?
- **a.** great
- **b.** major
- **c.** strong
- **d.** minor

Extended Response

Answer the two questions below in detail. Include some of the terms shown in the word box. In your answers underline each term you use.

seismic waves	primary	secondary	surface
stress		fault	plate boundary

9. During an earthquake, Dustin felt a small amount of shaking. About 15 seconds later, he felt some more shaking. Then about 45 seconds later he felt the strongest shaking. Explain what happened.

10. The island of Sumatra is located in an area where the Pacific Plate sinks under the Eurasian Plate. Explain why Sumatra has many earthquakes.

Analyzing Data

1. c	5. b
2. b	6. a
3. d	7. b
4. a	8. a

Extended Response

9. RUBRIC

4 points for a good explanation that uses the following terms accurately:
- seismic waves
- primary
- secondary
- surface

Sample answer: The earthquake released energy as <u>seismic waves</u>. The fastest seismic waves are <u>primary</u> waves, so they arrived first. They caused a small amount of shaking. Then <u>secondary</u> waves arrived, which caused a bit more shaking. Finally, <u>surface</u> waves, which are the slowest, arrived. They caused the strongest shaking.

3 points correctly explains what happened and uses three terms accurately
2 points adequately answers the question and uses two terms accurately
1 point adequately answers the question and uses one term correctly

10. RUBRIC

4 points for a response that correctly answers the question and uses the following terms accurately:
- stress
- fault
- plate boundary

Sample answer: Sumatra has many earthquakes because it is along a <u>plate boundary</u>. As the plates push together, a lot of <u>stress</u> builds up in the rock along the boundary. When stress is released as blocks of rock move suddenly along a <u>fault</u>, an earthquake occurs.

3 points correctly answers the question and uses two terms accurately
2 points correctly answers the question and uses one term accurately
1 point correctly answers the question, but does not use the terms

---

METACOGNITIVE ACTIVITY

Have students answer the following questions in their **Science Notebook:**

1. What did you learn about earthquakes that surprised you?

2. What questions occurred to you that were not answered while you were reading the chapter? How might you seek answers to these questions?

3. What concepts from this chapter apply to your Unit Project?

Mountains and Volcanoes

Earth Science
UNIFYING PRINCIPLES

PRINCIPLE 1

Heat energy inside Earth and radiation from the Sun provide energy for Earth's processes.

PRINCIPLE 2

Physical forces, such as gravity, affect the movement of all matter on Earth and throughout the universe.

PRINCIPLE 3

Matter and energy move among Earth's rocks and soil, atmosphere, waters, and living things.

PRINCIPLE 4

Earth has changed over time and continues to change.

Unit: Energy and the Changing Earth
BIG IDEAS

CHAPTER 1
Energy

Energy has different forms, but it is always conserved.

CHAPTER 2
Temperature and Heat

Heat is a flow of energy due to temperature differences.

CHAPTER 3
Plate Tectonics

The movement of tectonic plates causes geologic changes on Earth.

CHAPTER 4
Earthquakes

Earthquakes release stress that has built up in rocks.

CHAPTER 5
Mountains and Volcanoes

Mountains and volcanoes form as tectonic plates move.

CHAPTER 5
KEY CONCEPTS

SECTION | SECTION |

Movement of rock builds mountains.

1. Most mountains form along plate boundaries.
2. Mountains can form as rocks fold.
3. Mountains can form as rocks move along faults.

Volcanoes form as molten rock erupts.

1. Volcanoes erupt many types of material.
2. Most volcanoes form along plate boundaries.
3. Volcanoes can have many shapes and sizes.
4. Scientists monitor volcanoes.

Volcanoes affect Earth's land, air, and water.

1. Volcanic eruptions affect the land.
2. Volcanic gases and ash affect the air.
3. Volcanic activity affects water.

T The Big Idea Flow Chart is available on p. T33 in the **UNIT TRANSPARENCY BOOK**.

Previewing Content

5.1 Movement of rock builds mountains. pp. 137–145

1. Most mountains form along plate boundaries.

The formation of most mountain ranges begins as a collision between tectonic plates and is followed by land being pushed up. In some cases, such as with the Himalayas, the collision continues today. In other cases, such as with the Appalachians, the collision boundary no longer exists.

While some processes push mountains up, other processes wear them down. Running water and wind constantly break rocks into pieces called sediment and carry them away. The sediment may settle in valleys or be carried to the ocean. In this way, tall jagged mountains eventually become low, rounded hills, then flat land.

2. Mountains can form as rocks fold.

Although rock is a hard, brittle material, it bends under certain conditions. When slowly subjected to pressure and high temperatures, rock can fold and crumple like soft modeling clay. **Folded mountains** form as an oceanic plate sinks under a continental plate or as two continental plates collide. The Himalayas are an example of folded mountains. Their development can be divided into different stages:

- 200 million years ago: India moves toward Eurasia, which was separated from India by an ocean. Folded mountains and volcanoes form at the convergent boundary where oceanic crust sinks beneath continental crust.
- 50 million years ago: India collides with Eurasia. Subduction stops. Volcanoes stop erupting. Crust along the edges of both continents continues folding into mountains.
- Today: India and Eurasia continue to collide, and the Himalayas continue to grow.

3. Mountains can form as rocks move along faults.

Whereas folded mountains form where continental crust is being pushed together, **fault-block mountains** form where continental crust is being pulled apart. As the crust is stretched, it breaks into blocks along fault lines. The tilting and dropping of the blocks in various ways creates mountains and valleys.

5.2 Volcanoes form as molten rock erupts. pp. 146–155

1. Volcanoes erupt many types of material.

A **volcano** is an opening in Earth's crust through which molten rock, rock fragments, and hot gases erupt.

- Molten rock, or magma, that is high in silica resists flowing and can prevent gases from escaping until the pressure builds and the gases blast out.
- Rock fragments can be as big as a house or as tiny as a speck of dust. Fragments form as **lava** cools in the air or as pieces of the volcano walls are ripped loose.
- The main gases from a volcano are water vapor and carbon dioxide. **Pyroclastic flows** are fast-moving mixtures of gases and ash that can sweep up and over hills, then race down a neighboring valley, causing deadly damage within minutes.

2. Most volcanoes form along plate boundaries.

Volcanoes, like earthquakes, are explained by plate tectonics. Volcanoes are commonly found at

- subduction zones where an oceanic plate is sinking beneath another plate
- spreading centers where plates are pulling apart
- hot spots where a plate is moving over an unusually hot area in the mantle

3. Volcanoes can have many shapes and sizes.

The size and shape of a volcano depends on the magma type feeding it. Eruptions form three basic kinds of volcanoes.

- A shield volcano is built from many eruptions of lava that is low in silica and flows easily. It is a broad, flat dome.
- A cinder cone is built of pieces of magma that harden in the air and fall to form a small, steep-sided volcano.
- A composite volcano is built of high-silica magma. The tall cone consists of layers of lava and layers of rock fragments.

4. Scientists monitor volcanoes.

Scientists monitor volcanoes to look for warning signs that an eruption may be coming. Warning signs include earthquakes, changes in the tilt of the ground, rising temperatures of openings, and changes in volcanic gases being released.

Common Misconceptions

MOUNTAIN RANGE Some students might think a mountain range is any expanse of western range land with mountains in the background, as is often seen in a Western movie. Other students may think that a mountain range includes all of the mountains within a large geographic area such as the Rockies or Appalachians. Actually, these mountains represent mountain belts, each made up of many mountain ranges.

 This misconception is addressed on p. 138.

MISCONCEPTION DATABASE
CLASSZONE.COM Background on student misconceptions

ORIGIN OF LAVA Many students might think that magma originates in Earth's core. Although the study of seismic, or earthquake, waves indicates that the outer core is liquid, magma originates in the upper portion of the mantle and even in the crust.

 This misconception is addressed on p. 147.

Previewing Content

Volcanoes affect Earth's land, air, and water. pp. 156–163

1. Volcanic eruptions affect the land.

Volcanic eruptions can be extremely destructive. The damage largely depends on how much and which types of material the volcano ejects.

- Lava flows can knock down and burn trees, fields, roads, and buildings.
- Volcanic ash can suffocate plants, people, and animals. It can collapse buildings and damage machinery.
- Mudflows have buried towns as a mixture of ash, rocks, soil, and water race down a mountain valley.
- Landslides occur when part of a volcano collapses. Landslides can change the landscape and cause tsunamis.
- Steam explosions occur when magma comes near or in contact with water, resulting in an explosion. These are not very common.

Some of the long-term effects of eruptions can be beneficial. Over many years, volcanic rock breaks down to form a rich soil. Highly productive farmland surrounds some volcanoes. Volcanoes can also create beautiful landscapes.

2. Volcanic gases and ash affect the air.

Volcanoes release gases before, during, and after eruptions. Sometimes these gases can be dangerous. Sudden releases of large amounts of carbon dioxide have been deadly. Sulfur dioxide and other gases mix with moisture in the air to form acids that add to **acid rain.** Large amounts of gases and ash from an eruption can travel around the world and affect weather for months or even years.

3. Volcanic activity affects water.

Volcanic activity is responsible for a variety of water-related features.

- Hot springs are pools that form when water moves underground near magma or hot rock. The water gets heated and rises to the surface.
- **Geysers** are similar to hot springs, but rather than flowing out gently, water shoots out into the air. A diagram of a geyser is shown on the right.
- Fumaroles release steam and other gases rather than liquid water.
- Deep-sea vents are hot springs that form at spreading centers in the ocean. Deep-sea vents support unusual life forms that do not exist anywhere else on Earth.

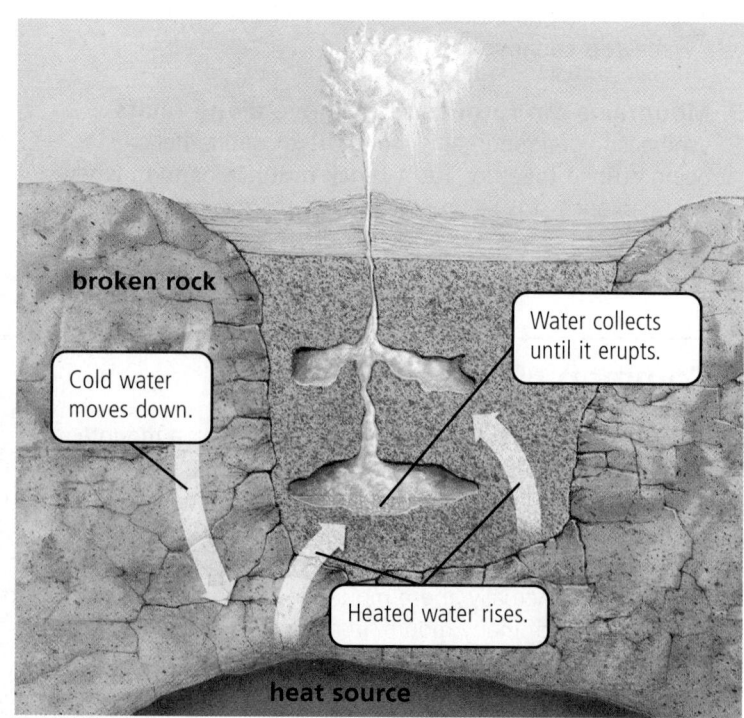

broken rock

Cold water moves down.

Water collects until it erupts.

Heated water rises.

heat source

Previewing Labs

Lab Generator CD-ROM
Edit these Pupil Edition labs and generate alternative labs.

EXPLORE (the BIG idea)

Making Mountains, p. 135
Students use checkers or coins to model how mountains form from tilted blocks of crust.

TIME 5 minutes
MATERIALS 10 checkers or coins

Under Pressure, p. 135
Students model how gas bubbles cause pressure to build up in magma.

TIME 10 minutes
MATERIALS 2 empty plastic bottles with caps, carbonated beverage, hot water, ice water

Internet Activity: Volcanoes, p. 135
Students are introduced to the roles that magma plays in the type of volcanic eruption.

TIME 20 minutes
MATERIALS computer with Internet access

SECTION

5.1

EXPLORE Folding, p. 137
Students use layers of modeling clay to show how solids can bend and fold.

TIME 10 minutes
MATERIALS 2 or 3 colors of modeling clay (1 stick or 1 cup of each color), ruler, 2 wooden blocks, newspaper

INVESTIGATE Fault-Block Mountains, p. 142
Students use wooden blocks to model how fault-block mountains form.

TIME 15 minutes
MATERIALS 3 triangular wooden blocks, 3 rectangular wooden blocks

---

SECTION

5.2

EXPLORE Eruptions, p. 146
Students use effervescent antacid tablets and film canisters to show how a buildup of pressure can lead to an eruption.

TIME 10 minutes
MATERIALS empty film canister with lid, 1/4 of an antacid tablet, 1/4 c water

CHAPTER INVESTIGATION
Make Your Own Volcanoes, pp. 154–155
Students build models by using plaster of Paris and gravel to relate volcanic materials to the type of volcano formed.

TIME 40 minutes
MATERIALS 375 mL plaster of Paris, 180 mL water, 500 mL gravel, 3 cardboard pieces (approximately 8 1/2" x 11"), two 250-mL paper cups, stirrer, ruler, protractor

---

SECTION

5.3

INVESTIGATE Mudflows, p. 159
Students analyze a map to discover how mudflows are affected by land shape.

R Map of Mount Ranier Mudflows, p. 290

TIME 25 minutes
MATERIALS Map of Mount Rainier Mudflows

R **Additional INVESTIGATION,** Modeling Magma Movement, A, B, & C, pp. 309–317; Teacher Instructions, pp. 320–321

Previewing Chapter Resources

| | **INTEGRATED TECHNOLOGY** | **LABS AND ACTIVITIES** |

CHAPTER 5
Mountains and Volcanoes

 CLASSZONE.COM
- eEdition Plus
- EasyPlanner Plus
- Misconception Database
- Content Review
- Test Practice
- Visualization
- Resource Centers
- Internet Activity: Volcanoes
- Math Tutorial

 SCILINKS.ORG
SCILINKS

 CD-ROMS
- eEdition
- EasyPlanner
- Power Presentations
- Content Review
- Lab Generator
- Test Generator

 AUDIO CDS
- Audio Readings
- Audio Readings in Spanish

 EXPLORE the Big Idea, p. 135
- Making Mountains
- Under Pressure
- Internet Activity: Volcanoes

 UNIT RESOURCE BOOK
Unit Projects, pp. 5–10

 Lab Generator CD-ROM
Generate customized labs.

SECTION
5.1 Movement of rock builds mountains.
pp. 137–145

Time: 2 periods (1 block)
 Lesson Plan, pp. 260–261

 MATH TUTORIAL

 UNIT TRANSPARENCY BOOK
- Big Idea Flow Chart, p. T33
- Daily Vocabulary Scaffolding, p. T34
- Note-Taking Model, p. T35
- 3-Minute Warm-Up, p. T36
- "Formation of Himalayas" Visual, p. T38

 EXPLORE Folding p. 137
- INVESTIGATE Fault-Block Mountains, p. 142
- Math in Science, p. 145

 UNIT RESOURCE BOOK
- Datasheet, Fault-Block Mountains, p. 269
- Math Support, p. 298
- Math Practice, p. 299

SECTION
5.2 Volcanoes form as molten rock erupts.
pp. 146–155

Time: 3 periods (1.5 blocks)
 Lesson Plan, pp. 271–272

 • **RESOURCE CENTER,** Historic/Current Volcanic Eruptions
- **VISUALIZATION,** Erupted Volcanic Material

 UNIT TRANSPARENCY BOOK
- Daily Vocabulary Scaffolding, p. T34
- 3-Minute Warm-Up, p. T36

 • EXPLORE Eruptions, p. 146
- CHAPTER INVESTIGATION, Make Your Own Volcanoes, pp. 154–155

 UNIT RESOURCE BOOK
- CHAPTER INVESTIGATION, Make Your Own Volcanoes, A, B, & C, pp. 300–308
- Additional INVESTIGATION, Modeling Magma Movement, A, B, & C, pp. 309–317

SECTION
5.3 Volcanoes affect Earth's land, air, and water.
pp. 156–163

Time: 3 periods (1.5 blocks)
 Lesson Plan, pp. 281–282

 RESOURCE CENTER, Effects of Volcanic Eruption

 UNIT TRANSPARENCY BOOK
- Big Idea Flow Chart, p. T33
- Daily Vocabulary Scaffolding, p. T34
- 3-Minute Warm-Up, p. T37
- Chapter Outline, pp. T39–T40

 • INVESTIGATE Mudflows, p. 159
- Science on the Job, p. 163

 UNIT RESOURCE BOOK
- Map of Mount Ranier Mudflows, p. 290
- Datasheet, Mudflows, p. 291

READING AND REINFORCEMENT

ASSESSMENT

STANDARDS

• Word Triangle, B18–19
• Content Frame, C35
• Daily Vocabulary Scaffolding, H1–8

UNIT RESOURCE BOOK
• Vocabulary Practice, pp. 295–296
• Decoding Support, p. 297
• Summarizing the Chapter, pp. 318–319

 Audio Readings CD
Listen to Pupil Edition.

 Audio Readings in Spanish CD
Listen to Pupil Edition in Spanish.

 • Chapter Review, pp. 165–166
• Standardized Test Practice, p. 167

 UNIT ASSESSMENT BOOK
• Diagnostic Test, pp. 78–79
• Chapter Test, A, B, & C, pp. 83–94
• Alternative Assessment, pp. 95–96
• Unit Test, A, B, C, pp. 97–108

 Spanish Chapter Test, pp. 137–140

 Test Generator CD-ROM
Generate customized tests.

 Lab Generator CD-ROM
Rubrics for Labs

National Standards
A.2–8, A.9.a–c, A.9.e–f, D.1.b–c, F.3.a, F.4.a–b

See p. 134 for the standards.

 UNIT RESOURCE BOOK
• Reading Study Guide, A & B, pp. 262–265
• Spanish Reading Study Guide, pp. 266–267
• Challenge and Extension, p. 268
• Reinforcing Key Concepts, p. 270

 Ongoing Assessment, pp. 139–143

 Section 5.1 Review, p. 144

 UNIT ASSESSMENT BOOK
Section 5.1 Quiz, p. 80

National Standards
A.2–8, A.9.a–c, A.9.e–f, D.1.b–c, F.3.a

 UNIT RESOURCE BOOK
• Reading Study Guide, A & B, pp. 273–276
• Spanish Reading Study Guide, pp. 277–278
• Challenge and Extension, p. 279
• Reinforcing Key Concepts, p. 280
• Challenge Reading, pp. 293–294

 Ongoing Assessment, pp. 147–149, 151, 153

 Section 5.2 Review, p. 153

 UNIT ASSESSMENT BOOK
Section 5.2 Quiz, p. 81

National Standards
A.2–7, A.9.a–b, A.9.e–f, D.1.b–c, F.3.a, F.4.a–b

 UNIT RESOURCE BOOK
• Reading Study Guide, A & B, pp. 283–286
• Spanish Reading Study Guide, pp. 287–288
• Challenge and Extension, p. 289
• Reinforcing Key Concepts, p. 292

 Ongoing Assessment, pp. 158, 160–162

 Section 5.3 Review, p. 162

 UNIT ASSESSMENT BOOK
Section 5.3 Quiz, p. 82

National Standards
A.2–7, A.9.a–b, A.9.e–f, D.1.b–c

Previewing Resources for Differentiated Instruction

CHAPTER INVESTIGATION

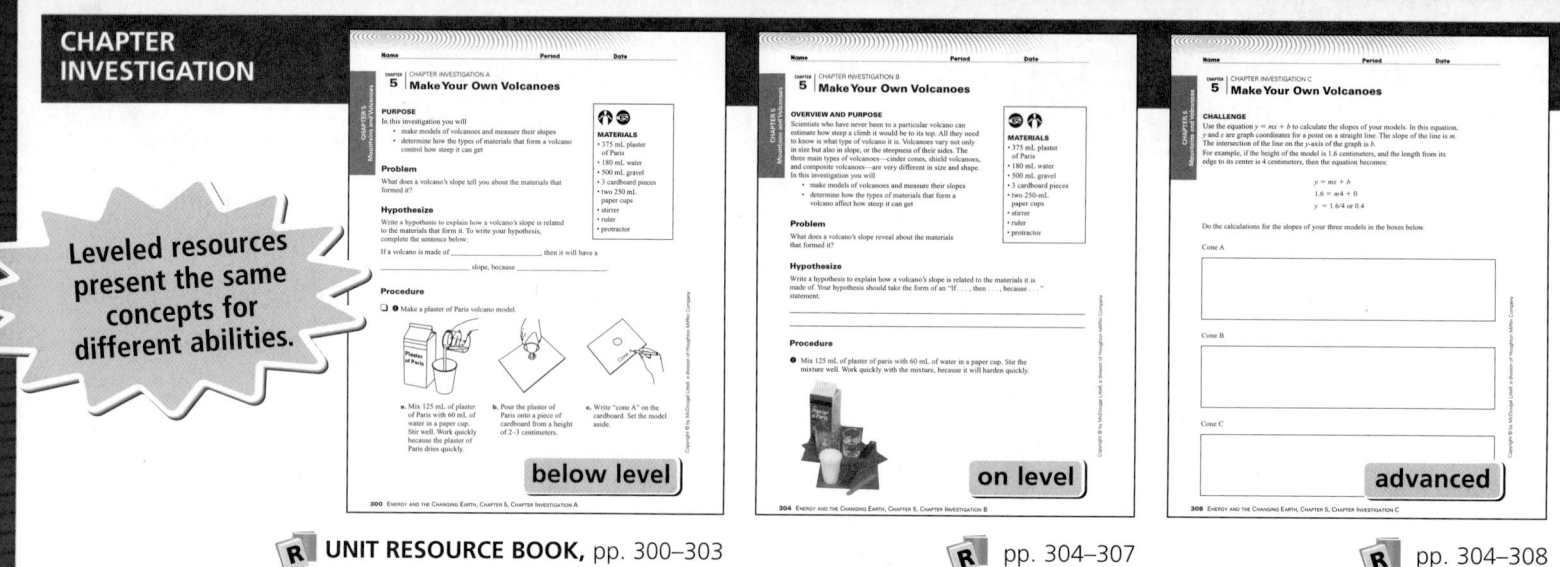

UNIT RESOURCE BOOK, pp. 300–303

pp. 304–307

pp. 304–308

> Leveled resources present the same concepts for different abilities.

READING STUDY GUIDE

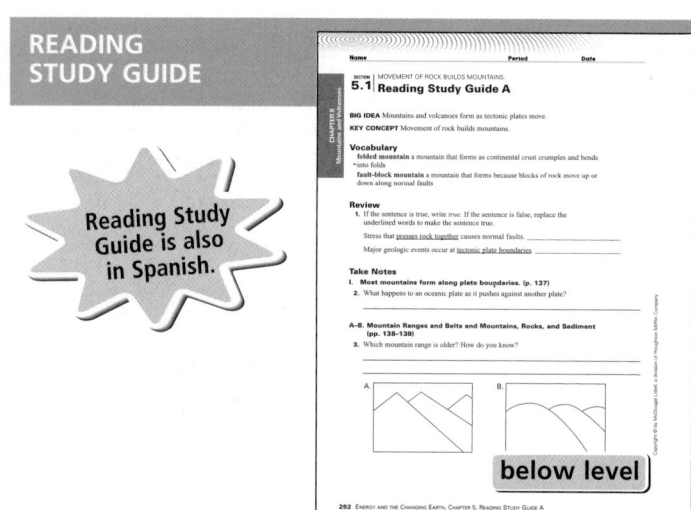

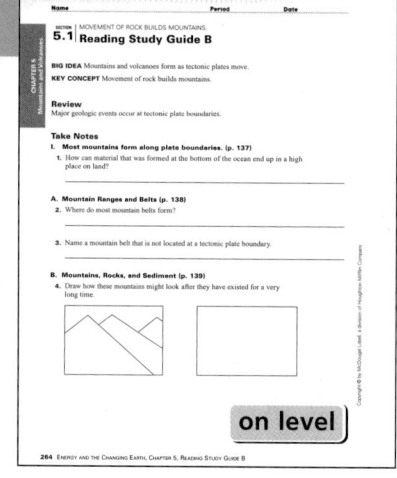

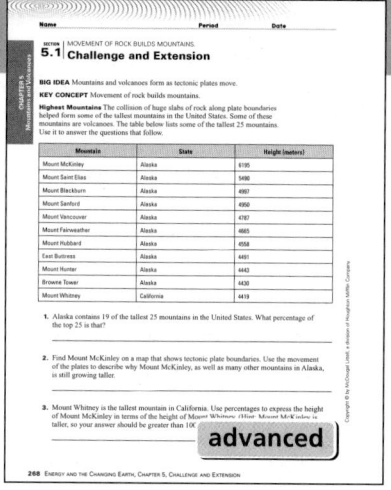

> Reading Study Guide is also in Spanish.

UNIT RESOURCE BOOK, pp. 262–263

pp. 264–265

p. 268

CHAPTER TEST

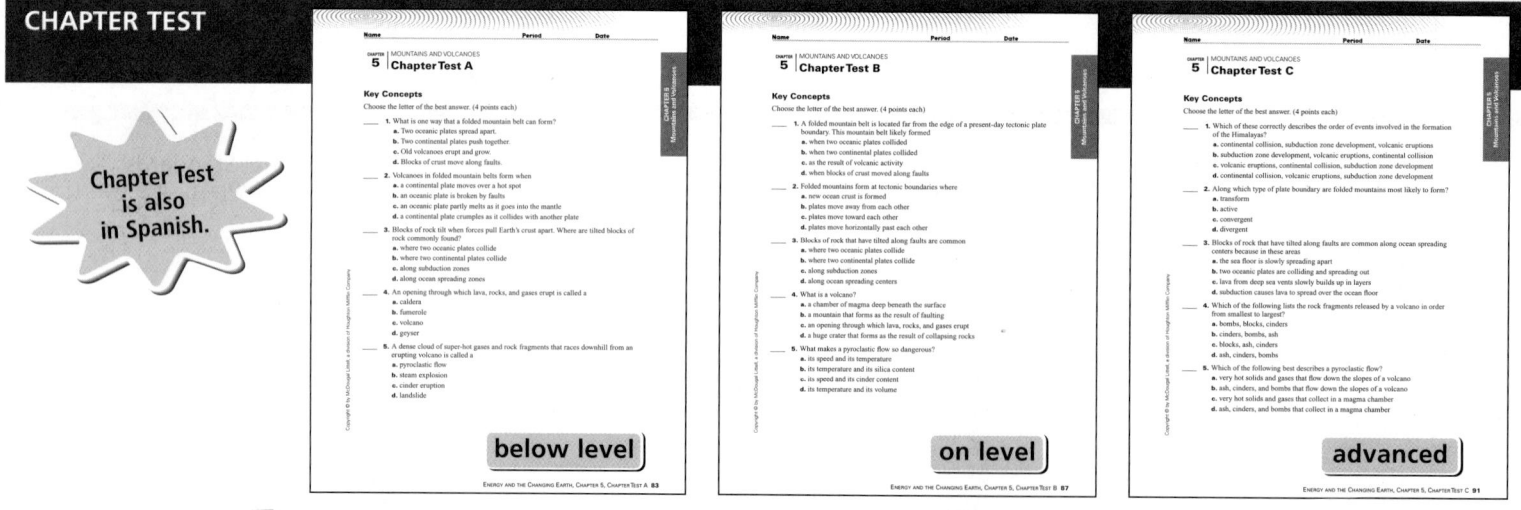

> Chapter Test is also in Spanish.

UNIT ASSESSMENT BOOK, pp. 83–86

pp. 87–90

pp. 91–94

TECHNOLOGY

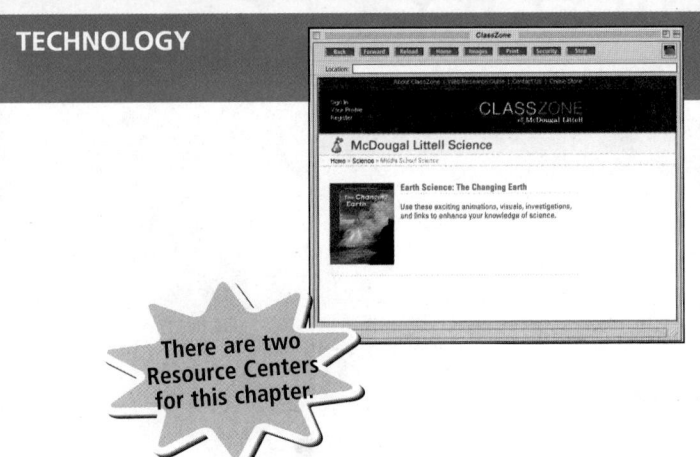

AUDIO READINGS

McDOUGAL LITTELL
LAB GENERATOR

Customize and edit labs with this easy-to-use CD-ROM
- Searchable database of all labs from the program
- Additional lab options
- Template for creating your own labs
- Rubrics and other resources

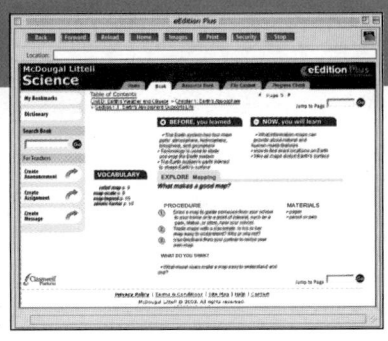

There are two Resource Centers for this chapter.

CLASSZONE.COM   **CD/CD-ROMS**   **CLASSZONE.COM**

VISUAL CONTENT

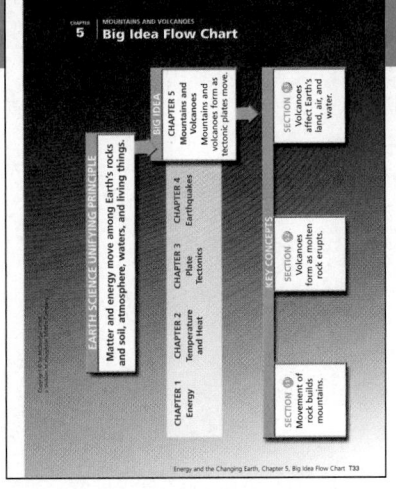

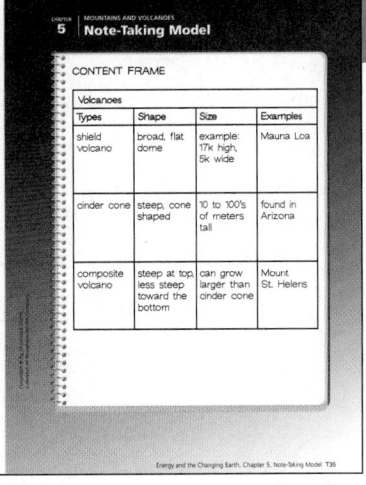

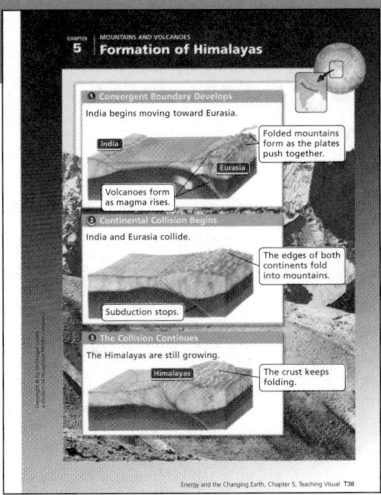

T UNIT TRANSPARENCY BOOK, p. T33   **T** p. T35   **T** p. T38

MORE SUPPORT

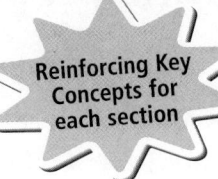

Reinforcing Key Concepts for each section

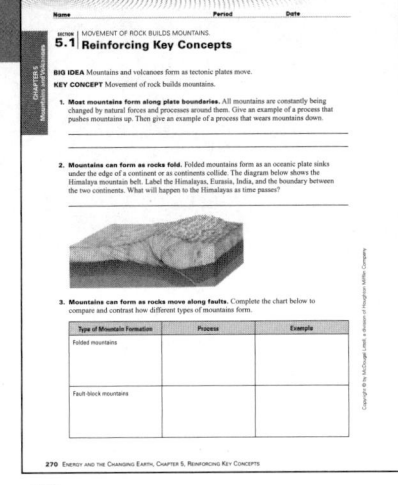

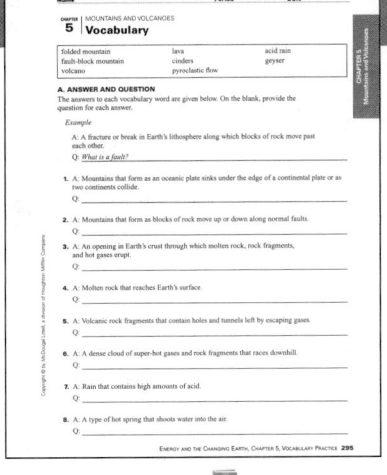

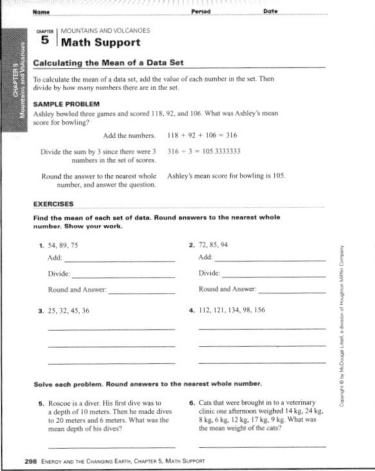

R UNIT RESOURCE BOOK, p. 270   **R** pp. 295–296   **R** p. 298

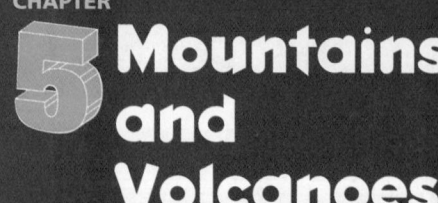
INTRODUCE

the **BIG** idea

Have students look at the photograph of the erupting volcano and discuss how the question in the box links to the Big Idea:

- What materials are coming from the volcano? What will happen to these materials?

- Where might this volcano be located? Might it be located any place in the world?

National Science Education Standards

Content

D.1.b Lithospheric plates constantly move at rates of centimeters per year in response to movements in the mantle, resulting in earthquakes, volcanic eruptions, and mountain building.

D.1.c Landforms are the result of a combination of constructive and destructive forces. Constructive forces include crustal deformation, volcanic eruption.

F.3.a Internal and external processes of the earth system cause natural hazards such as volcanic eruptions.

F.4.a Risk analysis considers how hazards will affect people and the options for reducing or eliminating risks.

Process

A.2–8 Design and conduct an investigation; use tools to gather and interpret data; use evidence to describe, predict, explain, model; think critically to make relationships between evidence and explanation; recognize different explanations and predictions; communicate scientific procedures and explanations; use mathematics.

A.9.a–c, A.9.e–f Understand scientific inquiry by using different investigations, methods, mathematics, and explanations based on logic, evidence, and skepticism.

F.4.b Know risks associated with natural disasters.

CHAPTER

Mountains and Volcanoes

the **BIG** idea

Mountains and volcanoes form as tectonic plates move.

> *How does new land form from molten rock?*

Key Concepts

SECTION 5.1 Movement of rock builds mountains. Learn how different types of mountains form.

SECTION 5.2 Volcanoes form as molten rock erupts. Learn why there are different types of volcanoes and volcanic eruptions.

SECTION 5.3 Volcanoes affect Earth's land, air, and water. Learn how volcanic eruptions affect land, air, and water.

Internet Preview

CLASSZONE.COM

Chapter 5 online resources: Content Review, Simulation, Visualization, two Resource Centers, Math Tutorial, Test Practice

INTERNET PREVIEW

CLASSZONE.COM For student use with the following pages:

Review and Practice
- Content Review, pp. 136, 164
- Math Tutorial: Finding the Mean, p. 145
- Test Practice, p. 167

Activities and Resources
- Internet Activity, p. 135
- Visualization: Erupted Volcanic Material, p. 148
- Resource Centers: Historic/Current Volcanic Eruptions, p. 150; Effects of Volcanic Eruptions, p. 158

NSTA
scilinks.org
SCiLINKS

Explore Volcanoes
Code: MDL054

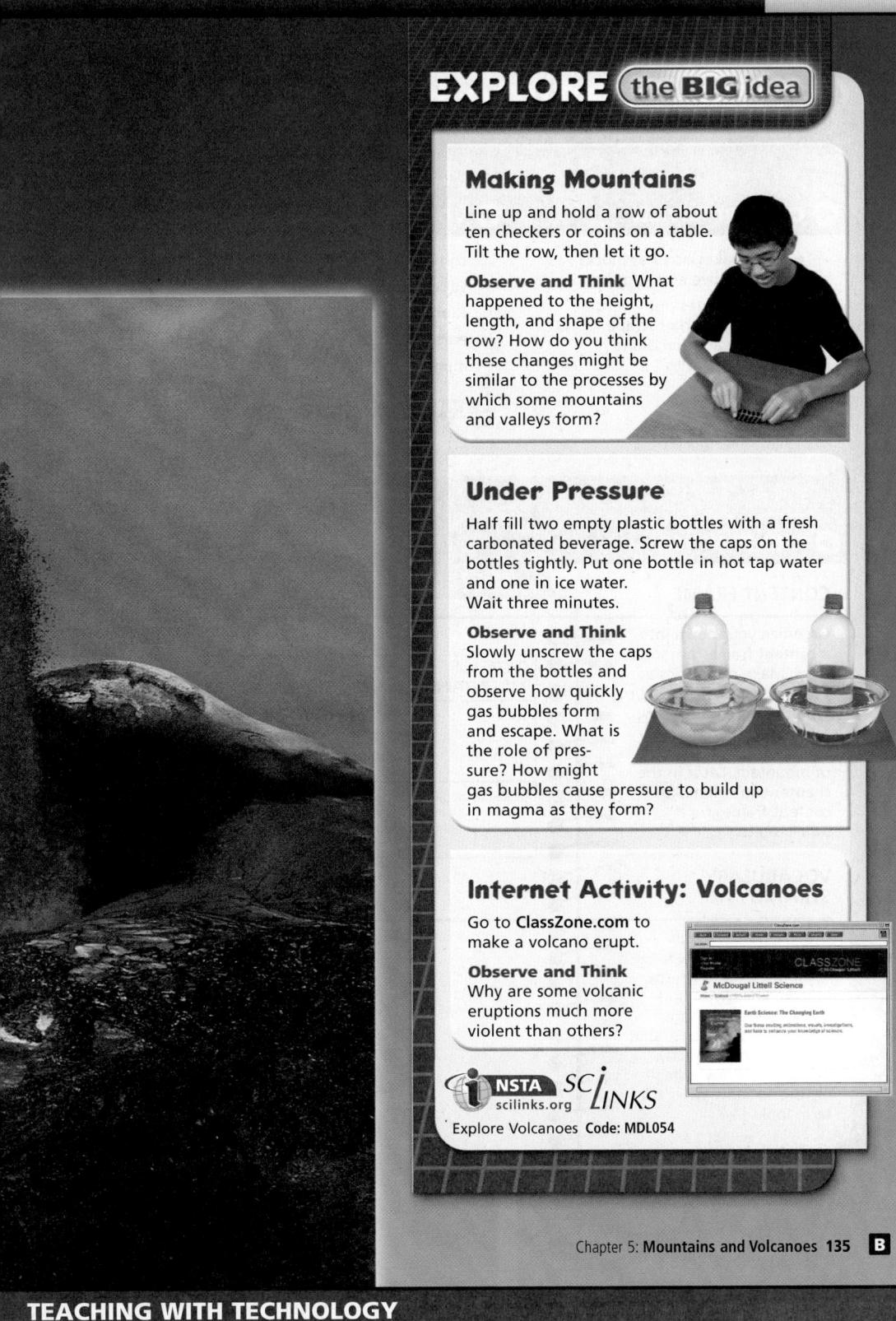

Making Mountains

Line up and hold a row of about ten checkers or coins on a table. Tilt the row, then let it go.

Observe and Think What happened to the height, length, and shape of the row? How do you think these changes might be similar to the processes by which some mountains and valleys form?

Under Pressure

Half fill two empty plastic bottles with a fresh carbonated beverage. Screw the caps on the bottles tightly. Put one bottle in hot tap water and one in ice water. Wait three minutes.

Observe and Think Slowly unscrew the caps from the bottles and observe how quickly gas bubbles form and escape. What is the role of pressure? How might gas bubbles cause pressure to build up in magma as they form?

Internet Activity: Volcanoes

Go to **ClassZone.com** to make a volcano erupt.

Observe and Think Why are some volcanic eruptions much more violent than others?

NSTA SCiLINKS
scilinks.org

Explore Volcanoes Code: MDL054

Chapter 5: **Mountains and Volcanoes** 135 **B**

EXPLORE the BIG idea

These inquiry-based activities are appropriate for use at home or as a supplement to classroom instruction.

Making Mountains

PURPOSE To introduce students to how mountains form from tilted blocks of crust.

TIP *5 min.* Suggest that students release the checkers or coins slowly so that the items remain in a fairly straight row.

Answer: The row's height decreases, its length increases, and the top of the row becomes uneven. Blocks of rock might break apart and tilt where the crust is being stretched, causing mountains and valleys to form.

REVISIT after p. 140.

Under Pressure

PURPOSE To introduce students to how the presence of gas increases pressure inside a volcano.

TIP *10 min.* During the three-minute wait, have students predict what will happen when they unscrew each lid.

Answer: Pressure is higher in the bottle of warm water, causing bubbles to escape more quickly. Gas bubbles that form in magma could cause pressure inside the magma to increase and perhaps lead to an eruption.

REVISIT after p. 147.

Internet Activity: Volcanoes

PURPOSE To introduce students to the role that the composition of magma plays in the type of volcanic eruption.

TIP *20 min.* Have students predict the answer to the question before they view the Internet page.

Answer: Eruptions of silica-rich magma tend to be much more violent than eruptions of silica-poor magma. Gas bubbles cannot easily escape from silica-rich magma, and as they expand, pressure within the magma increases.

REVISIT after p. 147.

TEACHING WITH TECHNOLOGY

Internet Search Engine After reading about the effects of volcanic eruptions on p. 157, students can use the Internet to find out about the most recent volcanic eruptions around the world. They can use the information for a bulletin board display or PowerPoint presentation.

Chapter 5 **135** **B**

◖ CONCEPT REVIEW

Activate Prior Knowledge

- Use two books to represent the basic movements of two adjacent tectonic plates: pulling apart, pushing together, or sliding past.
- Help students identify each kind of boundary as you demonstrate it.
- Discuss which geologic events occur at each of the boundaries.

▶ TAKING NOTES

Content Frame

Content frames are effective tools for comparing and contrasting characteristics of different items. At a glance, students can see, for example, the similarities between different kinds of mountains as well as what distinguishes one kind of mountain from another. Encourage students to use their content frames to organize the topics being described.

Vocabulary Strategy

Tell students that it will be helpful to include labels for some of their drawings. For example, they might label a fault in their drawing of a fault-block mountain. Suggest that students make the boundary lines of the triangle as they complete each section to ensure that they have enough space for their writing and drawing.

Vocabulary and Note-Taking Resources

- Vocabulary Practice, pp. 295–296
- Decoding Support, p. 297

- Daily Vocabulary Scaffolding, p. T34
- Note-Taking Model, p. T35

- Word Triangle, B18–19
- Content Frame, C35
- Daily Vocabulary Scaffolding, H1–8

CHAPTER 5
Getting Ready to Learn

◖ CONCEPT REVIEW

- Earthquakes occur as blocks of rock move along faults.
- Tectonic plates pull apart, push together, or scrape past one another along their boundaries.

◖ VOCABULARY REVIEW

convergent boundary p. 82

subduction p. 90

fault p. 105

earthquake p. 105

magma *See Glossary.*

 CONTENT REVIEW
CLASSZONE.COM
Review concepts and vocabulary.

▶ TAKING NOTES

CONTENT FRAME

Organize your notes into a **content frame** for mountains. Make categories at the top that describe their types, features, and how they form. Then fill in the boxes for each type of mountain. Later in the chapter you will make content frames for other topics.

SCIENCE NOTEBOOK

TYPE OF MOUNTAINS	CHARACTERISTIC	WHERE THEY FORM	EXAMPLES
folded	rocks bent and folded	at convergent plate boundaries	Appalachians Himalayas
fault-block			

VOCABULARY STRATEGY

Draw a **word triangle** diagram for each new vocabulary term. On the bottom line, write and define the term. Above that, write a sentence that uses the term correctly. At the top, draw a small picture to show what the term looks like.

Fault-block mountains form as continental crust is pulled apart.

fault-block mountain: a mountain pushed up or tilted along a fault

See the Note-Taking Handbook on pages R45–R51.

CHECK READINESS

Administer the Diagnostic Test to determine students' readiness for new science content and their mastery of requisite math skills.

 Diagnostic Test, pp. 78–79

Technology Resources

Students needing content and math skills should visit **ClassZone.com**.

- **CONTENT REVIEW**
- **MATH TUTORIAL**

 CONTENT REVIEW CD-ROM

KEY CONCEPT

5.1 Movement of rock builds mountains.

◀ **BEFORE, you learned**

- Major geologic events occur at tectonic plate boundaries
- Most faults are located along plate boundaries

▶ **NOW, you will learn**

- How the folding of rock can form mountains
- How movement along faults can form mountains

VOCABULARY

folded mountain p. 140
fault-block mountain p. 142

EXPLORE Folding

How does rock fold?

PROCEDURE

① Make three flat layers of clay on top of a sheet of newspaper. Put a block at either end of the clay.

② Hold one block still. Push on the other block to slowly bring the blocks closer together.

WHAT DO YOU THINK?

- What happened to the clay when you pushed on the block?
- What shape did the middle layer of clay form?
- If a large block of rock reacted to pressure in a similar way, what kind of landform would result?

MATERIALS
- 2 or 3 colors of modeling clay
- 2 blocks
- newspaper

Most mountains form along plate boundaries.

A shallow sea once covered the area that is now Mount Everest, Earth's tallest mountain. If you were to climb Mount Everest, you would be standing on rocks containing the remains of ocean animals. Mount Everest also contains rocks that formed far away at a spreading center on the sea floor. How can rocks from the sea floor be on top of a mountain on a continent? Plate tectonics provides the answer.

Recall that an oceanic plate sinks when it collides with a continental plate. Some sea-floor material scrapes off the sinking plate and onto the continent. As continental mountains form, material once at the bottom of an ocean can be pushed many kilometers high.

Chapter 5: **Mountains and Volcanoes** 137 **B**

5.1 FOCUS

▶ **Set Learning Goals**

Students will

- Describe how the folding of rock can form mountains.
- Recognize how movement along faults can form mountains.
- Model, in an experiment, how fault-block mountains form.

◀ **3-Minute Warm-Up**

Display Transparency 36 or copy this exercise on the board:

Draw a diagram that shows a convergent plate boundary. Include labels to show the major geologic events that occur at this type of boundary. *Diagrams should show magma, volcanoes and other mountains, and the crust of two colliding plates. If an oceanic plate is colliding with a continental plate, a trench should mark where the oceanic plate is moving beneath the continental plate.*

 3-Minute Warm-Up, p. T36

5.1 MOTIVATE

EXPLORE Folding

PURPOSE To introduce the concept that a solid can bend and fold

TIP *10 min.* Students can work in groups to conserve materials and share ideas, but encourage them to take turns pushing on the block. This will give them a better idea of the amount of stress and the length of time involved.

WHAT DO YOU THINK? *It bent and folded; an arch; a hill or mountain*

RESOURCES FOR DIFFERENTIATED INSTRUCTION

Below Level

UNIT RESOURCE BOOK
- Reading Study Guide A, pp. 262–263
- Decoding Support, p. 297

 **AUDIO CDS**

Advanced

UNIT RESOURCE BOOK
Challenge and Extension, p. 268

English Learners

UNIT RESOURCE BOOK
Spanish Reading Study Guide, pp. 266–267

 **AUDIO CDS**

- Audio Readings in Spanish
- Audio Readings (English)

Teach from Visuals

To help students connect the three images, ask:

- In which part of the Never Summer Mountain Range are the mountains in the photograph located? *They appear to be the center of the range.*

- In which part of the Rocky Mountain Belt is the Never Summer Mountain Range located? *southeastern*

Address Misconceptions

IDENTIFY Ask students to name a mountain range or point one out on a map. If they indicate a large mountain belt such as the Rockies or Appalachians or an expanse of range land that includes mountains, they may hold a misconception of what a mountain range is.

CORRECT Tell students that mountain belts are made up of different mountain ranges. Have students look on a map of the Rockies or Appalachians and find the names of various mountain ranges within these belts.

REASSESS Ask students how many mountain ranges they found. Then have them give a definition of a mountain range in their own words.

Technology Resources

Visit **ClassZone.com** for background on common student misconceptions.

 MISCONCEPTION DATABASE

Develop Critical Thinking

SEQUENCE Have students place *mountain range, mountain belt,* and *mountain* in a sequence of smallest to largest unit. *mountain, mountain range, mountain belt*

Mountain Ranges and Belts

 A A mountain is an area of land that rises steeply from the land around it. A single mountain is rare. Most mountains belong to ranges—long lines of mountains that were formed at about the same time and by the same processes. Ranges that are close together make up mountain belts. For example, the Rocky Mountain belt in western North America contains about 100 ranges.

① Mount Cumulus

② Mount Cumulus / Never Summer Mountain Range

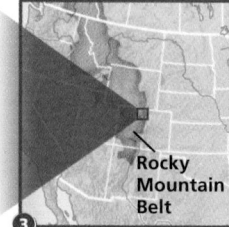

③ Rocky Mountain Belt

Mountains rise high above the land around them.

Most mountains are in groups called mountain ranges.

Closely spaced mountain ranges make up mountain belts.

 B Most of the world's major mountain belts are located along tectonic plate boundaries. But mountain belts like the Appalachians (AP-uh-LAY-chee-uhnz) in eastern North America are in the interior of plates. Mountains such as these were formed by ancient plate collisions that assembled the present-day continents.

Major Mountain Belts

Major mountain belts mark the locations of present or past plate boundaries.

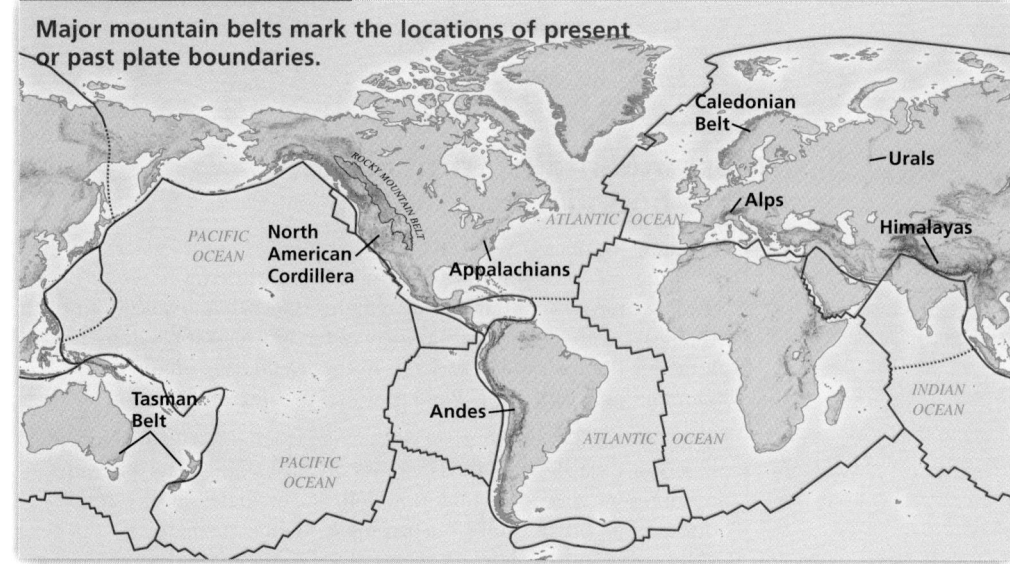

Caledonian Belt, Urals, Alps, Himalayas, ROCKY MOUNTAIN BELT, PACIFIC OCEAN, North American Cordillera, ATLANTIC OCEAN, Appalachians, INDIAN OCEAN, Tasman Belt, Andes, ATLANTIC OCEAN, PACIFIC OCEAN

DIFFERENTIATE INSTRUCTION

? More Reading Support

A What area of land rises steeply from the land around it? *a mountain*

B Where are most major mountain belts located? *along tectonic plate boundaries*

English Learners This section contains some phrasal verbs such as *make up* and *break down*. Help English learners understand that these phrases are the verbs of the sentence. Identify the following examples in the text:

1. Ranges that are close together *make up* mountain belts. (p. 138)

2. Rocks *break down* into loose pieces that can be carried by water or wind. (p. 139)

Inclusion Have students with visual impairments feel the patterns formed by mountain belts on a relief globe.

Mountains, Rocks, and Sediment

At the same time that some processes push mountains up, other processes wear them down. At Earth's surface, water and wind break rocks apart and move the pieces away. As long as mountains are pushed up faster than they wear down, they grow taller. For this reason, young mountains tend to be tall and steep. But eventually mountain-building processes slow, then end. Water and wind take over. Given enough time, all mountains become rounded hills, and then they are gone. Countless mountains have formed and worn away throughout Earth's long history.

Rocks break down into loose pieces that can be carried by water or wind. These pieces are called sediments. For example, sand on a beach is sediment. Thick layers of sediments can build up in low-lying areas, such as valleys, lakes, or the ocean. Pieces of sediments form sedimentary rock as they are pressed together or joined by natural cement.

The land becomes flatter as mountains wear down and valleys fill with sediments. If tectonic plates were to stop moving, eventually the surfaces of all the continents would be completely flat.

Mountains Wear Down

Mountains wear down as water and wind break their rocks into sediments and carry them away.

Young Mountains

Most young mountains are rugged. But even as they form, their rocks are being broken apart.

Old Mountains

Most old mountains are rounded. Lower areas around them contain thick layers of sediments.

READING VISUALS How do mountains wear away?

Chapter 5: **Mountains and Volcanoes 139** B

DIFFERENTIATE INSTRUCTION

? More Reading Support

C What do young mountains look like? *tall and steep*

D Sand on a beach is an example of what? *sediment*

Below Level Ask struggling readers for a definition of *sediment*. If they are having trouble, have them read the second sentence of the second paragraph that includes that word. Then they should read the sentence before and after that sentence as well as the caption for the photograph. Explain how these clues provide a context for the word *sediment* and help explain its meaning.

Real World Example

The sediment around your school is made up mostly of pieces of rock broken from larger pieces and carried by water or wind to the area.

Develop Critical Thinking

APPLY Ask students to apply what they have read on this page to explain why all the continents eventually would become completely flat if tectonic plates were to stop moving. *The processes that push mountains up would stop, but the processes that wear them down would continue.* Have students predict how long it would take for the continents to become flat. *Answers will vary, but students should recognize that the effects of such processes would take hundreds of millions of years to achieve.*

Teach from Visuals

To help students relate the diagrams of young and old mountains to the photograph, ask:

- In the bottom illustration, what has covered some of the lower peaks? *layers of sediment worn from the mountains*

- Where is the sediment shown in the photograph and how did it get there? *The mound fanning out at the base of the mountain is made of sediment. It moved down the mountain due to gravity.*

Ongoing Assessment

READING VISUALS *Answer: Water and wind break rock apart and carry the pieces away.*

Chapter 5 **139** B

Teacher Demo

Students may have a difficult time picturing a solid bending under stress. Demonstrate the ability of a candle to bend under stress, over time. Place a long, narrow candle across two piles of books so that it forms a "bridge." To accelerate the bending, hang a piece of string with several washers tied to it over the candle. Discuss other examples, such as a sagging bookshelf.

Develop Critical Thinking

IDENTIFY CAUSE AND EFFECT Ask students to identify cause-and-effect relationships in the development of the Himalayas. Provide students with the following example: cause—India moves northward; effect—oceanic lithosphere sinks under Eurasia.

EXPLORE (the BIG idea)

Revisit "Making Mountains" on p. 135. Have student discuss their observations.

Ongoing Assessment

Describe how the folding of rock can form mountains.

How is a crumpled rug caught behind an opening door similar to the way folded mountains form? *The opening door provides stress that pushes on the rug and folds it, just as a moving tectonic plate pushes on rock and folds it.*

CHECK YOUR READING *Answer: when stress is applied slowly and rocks are deep in the crust where temperature and pressure are high*

Mountains can form as rocks fold.

Though people usually do not think of rocks as being able to bend and fold, they can. Think of a wax candle. If you bend a candle quickly, it will break. If you leave a candle propped up at an angle, over many days it will bend. If the candle is in a warm area, it will bend more quickly. Rocks also bend when stress is applied slowly. Rocks deep in the crust are at high temperatures and pressures. They are particularly likely to bend rather than break.

 Under what conditions are rocks likely to bend and fold?

VOCABULARY
Make a word triangle for *folded mountain* in your notebook.

READING TiP
Eurasia is the landmass consisting of Europe and Asia.

Remember that tectonic plates move only a few centimeters each year. The edge of a continent along a convergent boundary is subjected to stress for a very long time as another plate pushes against it. Some of the continent's rocks break, and others fold. As folding continues, mountains are pushed up. A **folded mountain** is a mountain that forms as continental crust crumples and bends into folds.

Folded mountains form as an oceanic plate sinks under the edge of a continent or as continents collide. One example is the Himalaya (HIHM-uh-LAY-uh) belt, which formed by a collision between India and Eurasia. Its formation is illustrated on page 141.

① **Convergent Boundary Develops** At one time an ocean separated India and Eurasia. As India moved northward, oceanic lithosphere sank in a newly formed subduction zone along the Eurasian Plate. Along the edge of Eurasia, folded mountains formed. Volcanoes also formed as magma rose from the subduction zone to the surface.

② **Continental Collision Begins** Eventually the sea floor was completely destroyed, and India and Eurasia collided. Subduction ended. The volcanoes stopped erupting because they were no longer supplied with magma. Sea-floor material that had been added to the edge of Eurasia became part of the mountains pushed up by the collision.

③ **Collision Continues** India and Eurasia continue to push together. Their collision has formed the Himalayas, the world's tallest mountains. They grow even higher as rock is folded and pushed up for hundreds of kilometers on either side of the collision boundary.

Earthquakes can also be important to the upward growth of folded mountains. A great deal of rock in the Himalaya belt has been pushed up along reverse faults, which are common at convergent boundaries.

 140 Unit: Energy and the Changing Earth

DIFFERENTIATE INSTRUCTION

More Reading Support

E How far do tectonic plates move each year? *a few centimeters*

F What kind of mountains are the Himalayas? *folded mountains*

Inclusion Have students use their fingers to guide their reading on this page. As they read each numbered paragraph, have them point to the corresponding diagram on p. 141.

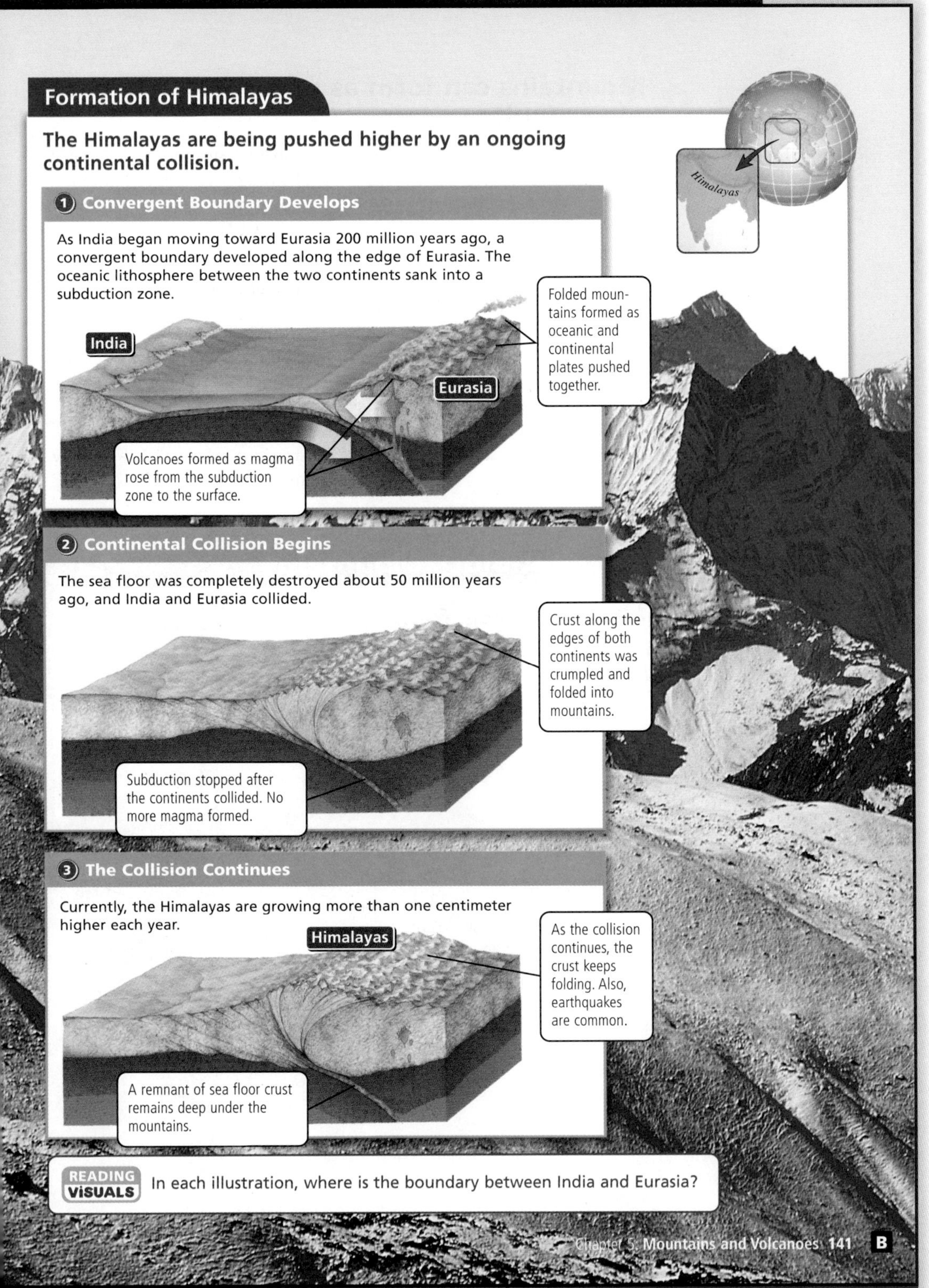
Formation of Himalayas
The Himalayas are being pushed higher by an ongoing continental collision.
Himalayas
1 Convergent Boundary Develops
As India began moving toward Eurasia 200 million years ago, a convergent boundary developed along the edge of Eurasia. The oceanic lithosphere between the two continents sank into a subduction zone.
India
Eurasia
Folded mountains formed as oceanic and continental plates pushed together.
Volcanoes formed as magma rose from the subduction zone to the surface.
2 Continental Collision Begins
The sea floor was completely destroyed about 50 million years ago, and India and Eurasia collided.
Crust along the edges of both continents was crumpled and folded into mountains.
Subduction stopped after the continents collided. No more magma formed.
3 The Collision Continues
Currently, the Himalayas are growing more than one centimeter higher each year.
Himalayas
As the collision continues, the crust keeps folding. Also, earthquakes are common.
A remnant of sea floor crust remains deep under the mountains.
READING VISUALS In each illustration, where is the boundary between India and Eurasia?
Chapter 5: Mountains and Volcanoes 141 B

Teach from Visuals

To help students interpret the diagrams of the formation of the Himalayas, ask:

- Where is the subduction zone in diagram 1? *on the right side where the oceanic plate is shown to be sinking beneath the continental plate*
- Why is there no magma in diagram 2? *Subduction has stopped, so crust is no longer sinking and melting to form magma.*
- What kind of crust is currently colliding under the Himalayas? *continental crust*
- Which diagram shows the most recent activity? *diagram 3*

T This visual is also available as T38 in the Unit Transparency Book.

Real World Example

While the Himalayas are, on average, growing more than 1 cm per year, individual mountains differ in their growth rate. Using the Global Positioning System to calculate elevation and movement, scientists measure the growth of Mt. Everest to be 5 to 8 mm (0.5 to 0.8 cm) per year. The Himalayas also are moving toward China. This rate is about 6 cm per year.

Ongoing Assessment

READING VISUALS *Answer: diagram 1: at the subduction zone; diagrams 2 and 3: near the edge of the mountains*

DIFFERENTIATE INSTRUCTION

Advanced Challenge students to choose a different folded mountain belt and create a poster similar to the one on this page that illustrates the formation of that belt or part of it. They might choose the Appalachians or the Andes.

R Challenge and Extension, p. 268

INVESTIGATE Fault-Block Mountains

PURPOSE To model how fault-block mountains form

TIPS *15 min.*

- Children's blocks work well for this activity.
- You might want to demonstrate the movements of both the triangular and rectangular blocks before students try it.

WHAT DO YOU THINK? *The edges of the blocks were left sticking up like mountains when the blocks were pulled apart or pulled apart and tilted; divergent, where plates are pulling apart*

CHALLENGE *No vertical movement occurs along strike-slip faults.*

 Datasheet, Fault-Block Mountains, p. 269

Technology Resources

Customize this student lab as needed or look for an alternative. Print rubrics to assess student lab reports.

 Lab Generator CD-ROM

Ongoing Assessment

CHECK YOUR READING *Answer: As blocks of rock move up or down along normal faults, mountains are formed.*

CONTENT FRAME
Add information about fault-block mountains to your content frame.

Mountains can form as rocks move along faults.

In the southwestern United States and northwestern Mexico, hundreds of mountain ranges line up in rows. The ranges, as well as the valleys between them, formed along nearly parallel normal faults. Mountains that form as blocks of rock move up or down along normal faults are called **fault-block mountains.**

CHECK YOUR READING How can the movement of rocks along faults lead to the formation of mountains?

Fault-block mountains form as the lithosphere is stretched and pulled apart by forces within Earth. The rocks of the crust are cool and rigid. As the lithosphere begins to stretch, the crust breaks into large blocks. As stretching continues, the blocks of rock move along the faults that separate them. The illustrations on page 83 show how this process forms fault-block mountains.

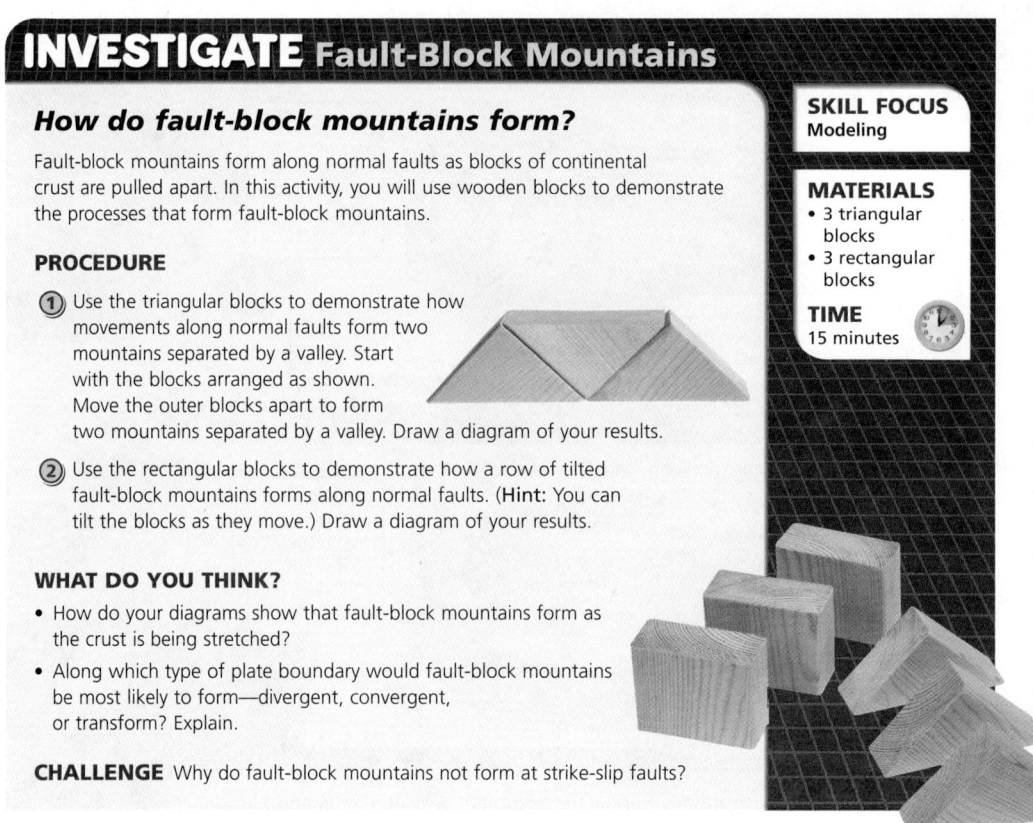

INVESTIGATE Fault-Block Mountains

How do fault-block mountains form?

Fault-block mountains form along normal faults as blocks of continental crust are pulled apart. In this activity, you will use wooden blocks to demonstrate the processes that form fault-block mountains.

PROCEDURE

1. Use the triangular blocks to demonstrate how movements along normal faults form two mountains separated by a valley. Start with the blocks arranged as shown. Move the outer blocks apart to form two mountains separated by a valley. Draw a diagram of your results.

2. Use the rectangular blocks to demonstrate how a row of tilted fault-block mountains forms along normal faults. (**Hint:** You can tilt the blocks as they move.) Draw a diagram of your results.

WHAT DO YOU THINK?

- How do your diagrams show that fault-block mountains form as the crust is being stretched?
- Along which type of plate boundary would fault-block mountains be most likely to form—divergent, convergent, or transform? Explain.

CHALLENGE Why do fault-block mountains not form at strike-slip faults?

SKILL FOCUS
Modeling

MATERIALS
- 3 triangular blocks
- 3 rectangular blocks

TIME
15 minutes

DIFFERENTIATE INSTRUCTION

More Reading Support

 G What do Earth's forces do to the lithosphere while a fault-block mountain is being formed? *stretch and pull it apart*

Alternative Assessment Suggest that students answer the Challenge question in "Investigate Fault-Block Mountains" by demonstrating with their blocks. *Students should demonstrate that strike-slip faults do not involve vertical movements, and therefore, do not cause mountains to form.*

❶ An area of the lithosphere can arch upward when, for example, it is heated by material rising in the mantle beneath it. As the crust stretches, it breaks into many blocks separated by faults.

❷ As the lithosphere is pulled apart, some blocks tilt. The edges of the blocks that tilt upward form mountains, and the edges that tilt downward form valleys. Other blocks drop down between faults, forming valleys. The edges of the blocks next to blocks that drop down are left standing high above the valleys as mountains.

Fault-block mountains form as stress repeatedly builds up in the crust and then is released during earthquakes. Even the most powerful earthquakes can move blocks of rock only a few meters up or down at one time. Fault-block mountains can be kilometers high. Millions of years and countless earthquakes are needed for them to form.

CHECK YOUR READING Describe two ways that blocks of rock can move along faults and form mountains.

Fault-Block Mountains

Fault-block mountains form as the crust stretches and breaks into blocks that move along faults.

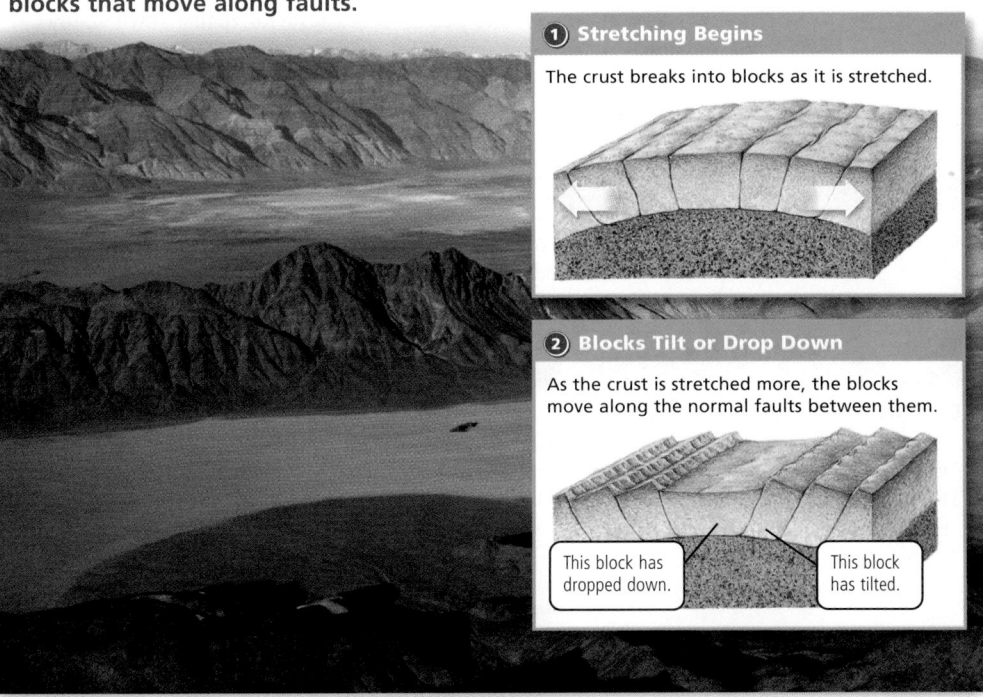

❶ Stretching Begins
The crust breaks into blocks as it is stretched.

❷ Blocks Tilt or Drop Down
As the crust is stretched more, the blocks move along the normal faults between them.

This block has dropped down.

This block has tilted.

Chapter 5: **Mountains and Volcanoes** 143 **B**

Develop Critical Thinking

COMPARE Ask students to compare folded mountains and fault-block mountains. Have them explain why the Himalayas have many reverse faults, while fault-block mountains are associated with normal faults. *The Himalayas have many reverse faults because two continents are pushing together there; fault-block mountains are associated with normal faults because they form where the crust is being pulled apart.*

Teach from Visuals

To help students interpret the images of fault-block mountains, ask:

• In diagram 1, where are the future faults going to develop? *where the cracks or fractures are forming*

• Which parts of diagram 2 look similar to parts in the photograph? Which parts look different? Why? *The rows of mountains and valleys are similar. The shape of the land, or landscape, looks different because parts of the exposed land in the photograph have been worn away, and sediments have partly filled in the valleys. The diagram just shows the structure of the rock layers without much erosion.*

Ongoing Assessment

Recognize how movement along faults can form mountains.

Which solid makes up mountains? What moves along faults to create fault-block mountains? *rock; large blocks of rock*

CHECK YOUR READING *Answer: A block can drop down, which creates an elevated edge in the block next to it, or a block can tilt upward.*

DIFFERENTIATE INSTRUCTION

❓ More Reading Support

H Which side of a block forms a valley in a fault-block mountain range? *the side that tilts downward*

Below Level Ask students why the term *fault-block* is appropriate for this kind of mountain. If students need help, break the term down into its two parts and show the role that each part plays in describing this kind of mountain.

Chapter 5 **143** **B**

Metacognitive Strategy

Have students look at the second paragraph on the page, then ask:

- What is the purpose of the paragraph? *to summarize*
- Is it helpful? *Sample answer: Yes, you can make sure you understand the main points of what you read.*

Reinforce the BIG idea

Have students relate the section to the Big Idea.

 Reinforcing Key Concepts, p. 270

5.1 ASSESS & RETEACH

Assess

 Section 5.1 Quiz, p. 80

Reteach

Point out that a summary, such as the one in the second paragraph, can be done for any kind of passage. Even a single paragraph can be summarized, usually in one sentence. After discussing what a summary is, have students summarize the main ideas, processes, and vocabulary terms that follow each blue heading:

- Most mountains form along plate boundaries.
- Mountains can form as rocks fold.
- Mountains can form as rocks move along faults.

If students need help getting started, ask them to identify or paraphrase a topic sentence in each paragraph.

The Sierra Nevada moved up along one side of the fault.

Approximate location of fault

The land on the other side of the fault dropped down.

The Sierra Nevada in California is a fault-block mountain range. The range moved up along a normal fault along its eastern edge. The block on the other side of the fault dropped down. This combination of upward and downward movement formed the steep eastern side of the Sierra Nevada. The western side of the range tilts down gently toward California's Central Valley.

In summary, both folded mountains and fault-block mountains form over millions of years. Folded mountains are pushed up by slow, continual stress that causes rock to gradually bend. Fault-block mountains form, earthquake by earthquake, as stress built up in the crust is released by the movement of rock. Folded mountains form where continental crust is being compressed, and fault-block mountains form where it is being stretched.

5.1 Review

KEY CONCEPTS

1. How is the formation of mountain belts related to tectonic plate boundaries?
2. How do folded mountains form?
3. How do fault-block mountains form?

CRITICAL THINKING

4. **Analyze** The Ural Mountain belt is no longer along the edge of a tectonic plate. Would you expect the Urals to be tall and steep or low and rounded? Why?
5. **Synthesize** How could it be possible for a mountain range to be continually pushed up but not get any higher?

◆ CHALLENGE

6. **Analyze** This graph shows how the heights of two mountains changed as they formed. Which line shows the formation of a folded mountain? a fault-block mountain? Explain.

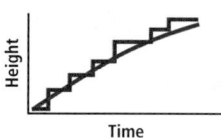

Height

Time

ANSWERS

1. *Mountain belts form along convergent plate boundaries.*

2. *as rocks fold where the crust is being pushed together*

3. *as blocks of rocks move up or down along normal faults where the crust is being stretched*

4. *low and rounded; because they are not near a modern plate boundary, they must have formed long ago, and undergone weathering and erosion*

5. *the rate of growth is equal to the rate of erosion*

6. *The curved line shows the formation of a folded mountain that was continually pushed up. The stepped line shows the formation of a fault-block mountain that was pushed up by a lot of individual earthquakes.*

MATH TUTORIAL
CLASSZONE.COM
Click on Math Tutorial for more help finding the mean.

SKILL: CALCULATING THE MEAN OF A DATA SET

Comparing Mountain Heights

How do the tallest mountains in the United States compare with the tallest mountains in the world? The table shows the heights of the five tallest mountains in the world. All five are in Asia.

Mountain	Height (meters)
Everest	8850
K2	8611
Kanchenjunga	8586
Lhotse	8516
Makalu	8463

To describe data, you can find their average, or mean. The **mean** of a data set is the sum of the values divided by the number of values.

Example

To find the mean height of the five tallest mountains in the world, first add the heights.

$$\begin{array}{r} 8{,}850 \\ 8{,}611 \\ 8{,}586 \\ 8{,}516 \\ +8{,}463 \\ \hline 43{,}026 \end{array}$$

Then divide by 5, the number of mountains.

$$\frac{43{,}026}{5} = 8605.2$$

Round your result to a whole number.

ANSWER The mean height of the five tallest mountains is 8605 meters.

Answer the following questions.

Mountain	Height (meters)
McKinley	6194
St. Elias	5489
Foraker	5304
Bona	5029
Blackburn	4996

1. The table to the left shows the heights of the five tallest mountains in the United States. All five are in Alaska. Find the mean of the data.

2. What is the difference between the mean height of the three tallest mountains in the world and the mean height of the three tallest mountains in the United States?

3. Suppose Mount Everest were in the United States. What would the mean of the three tallest mountains in the United States then be?

CHALLENGE The mean height of all the land in the United States is 763 meters. Does knowing the mean height help you describe the shape of the land in the United States? Explain why or why not.

Mount McKinley, Alaska, is the tallest mountain in North America.

Chapter 5: **Mountains and Volcanoes** 145 **B**

ANSWERS

1. $6194 + 5489 + 5304 + 5029 + 4996 = 27{,}102$
   $27{,}012/5 = 5402.4$; round to 5402 m

2. world: $8850 + 8611 + 8586 = 26{,}047$; $26{,}047/3 = 8682$
   U.S.: $6194 + 5489 + 5304 = 16{,}987$; $1{,}698{,}7/3 = 5662$
   $8682 - 5662 = 3020$ m

3. $8850 + 6194 + 5489 = 20{,}533$; $20{,}533/3 = 6844$ m

CHALLENGE No, you cannot tell the shape of the land. All the land could be at the same height of 763 m.

MATH IN SCIENCE
Math Skills Practice for Science

Set Learning Goal

To calculate the mean of a data set to compare mountain heights

Present the Science

Mount Everest's height of 8850 meters was determined by using the Global Positioning System (GPS). This system uses satellites to calculate information about a GPS receiver's exact location, including altitude. In 1999 an expedition placed a receiver on Everest's summit to track Everest's changing height.

Develop Number Sense

As you work through the example with students, point out that the average of this data set (8605 m) is not among the values for the set. Explain that a mean, or average, reduces a data set to one value that represents all values in the set.

DIFFERENTIATION TIP Below-level students may benefit from working through a simpler data set than the one given.

INCLUSION For visual learners, draw triangular mountains to scale on the board in the order given in the table. Ask a volunteer to draw another mountain that would best represent the mean height. The height should be between the lowest and tallest heights.

Close

Ask students to give an example of a height that would lower the mean if added to the data set for the world's five tallest mountains. *any number below the mean of 8605*

• Math Support, p. 298
• Math Practice, p. 299

Technology Resources

Students can visit **ClassZone.com** for more help finding the mean.

 MATH TUTORIAL

▶ Set Learning Goals

Students will

- Identify where most volcanoes are located.
- Explain how volcanoes erupt.
- Recognize different types of volcanoes.

◀ 3-Minute Warm-Up

Display Transparency 36 or copy this exercise on the board:

Match each definition with the correct term.

Definitions

1. motion that transfers heat within a material *d*
2. the layer formed by Earth's crust and the very top of the mantle *b*
3. underwater mountain ranges found where the ocean floor is spreading *a*

Terms

a. mid-ocean ridges
b. lithosphere
c. plate tectonics
d. convection current

T 3-Minute Warm-Up, p. T36

5.2 MOTIVATE

EXPLORE Eruptions

PURPOSE To model how a buildup of pressure due to the formation and expansion of gas bubbles can lead to an eruption

TIP *10 min.* Advise students to wear safety goggles. Have them do the activity with a very small piece of antacid tablet (1/8 of a tablet). They can repeat it while using slightly larger pieces but should not use pieces larger than 1/4 tablet because the lid might pop off too quickly.

WHAT DO YOU THINK? *The water bubbled and the lid popped off. Pressure from the gas of the bubbles built up inside the canister and pushed the lid off. Pressure from gases can build up inside a volcano until it erupts.*

KEY CONCEPT

5.2 Volcanoes form as molten rock erupts.

◀ **BEFORE, you learned**

- Magma is molten rock inside Earth
- Magma forms as a plate sinking in a subduction zone starts to melt
- Volcanoes can form over hot spots far from plate boundaries

▶ **NOW, you will learn**

- Where most volcanoes are located
- How volcanoes erupt
- What types of volcanoes there are

VOCABULARY

volcano p. 146
lava p. 147
pyroclastic flow p. 148

EXPLORE Eruptions

What happens when a volcano erupts?

PROCEDURE

1. Add water to an empty film canister until it is three-fourths full.
2. Drop an antacid tablet in the water and put the lid on the canister. Observe what happens.

WHAT DO YOU THINK?

- What happened to the water and to the canister lid?
- What caused the changes you observed?
- How might the events you observed be similar to the eruption of a volcano?

MATERIALS

- empty film canister
- effervescent antacid tablet
- water

 VOCABULARY
Make a word triangle for *volcano* in your notebook.

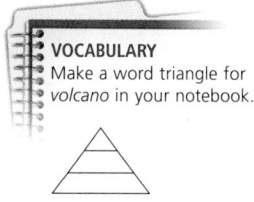

Volcanoes erupt many types of material.

Earth's thin outer layer is made of cool rock, but most of Earth is made of extremely hot rock and molten metal. Some of the heat inside Earth escapes to the surface through volcanoes. A **volcano** is an opening in Earth's crust through which molten rock, rock fragments, and hot gases erupt. A mountain built up from erupted material is also called a volcano.

A volcano may erupt violently or gently. A violent eruption can cause tremendous destruction even if not much molten rock reaches the surface. For example, a volcano might throw out huge amounts of rock fragments that start fires where they land or fall in thick layers on roofs, causing them to collapse. A volcano can erupt gently yet pour out rivers of molten rock that flow long distances. The violence of an eruption depends mainly on the type of magma feeding the volcano.

RESOURCES FOR DIFFERENTIATED INSTRUCTION

Below Level

UNIT RESOURCE BOOK
- Reading Study Guide A, pp. 273–274
- Decoding Support, p. 297

 AUDIO CDS

R **Additional INVESTIGATION,**
Modeling Magma Movement, A, B, & C, pp. 309–317; Teacher Instructions, pp. 320–321

Advanced

UNIT RESOURCE BOOK
- Challenge and Extension, p. 279
- Challenge Reading, pp. 293–294

English Learners

UNIT RESOURCE BOOK
Spanish Reading Study Guide, pp. 277–278

 **AUDIO CDS**

- Audio Readings in Spanish
- Audio Readings (English)

Magma

A major portion of all magma is silica, which is a compound of silicon and oxygen. Magma also contains gases, which expand as the magma rises. Magma that is high in silica resists flowing, so expanding gases are trapped in it. Pressure builds up until the gases blast out in a violent, dangerous explosion. Magma that is relatively poor in silica flows easily, so gas bubbles move up through it and escape fairly gently. Though an eruption of silica-poor magma can throw lava high into the air, forming lava fountains, visitors can usually watch safely nearby.

Magma rises toward Earth's surface as long as it is less dense than the surrounding rock. Once magma stops rising, it can collect in areas called magma chambers. Magma can remain in a chamber until it cools, forming igneous rock, or it can erupt. Volcanic eruptions occur when, for example, a chamber is not large enough to hold additional magma that pushes in. When magma erupts, it is called lava. **Lava** is magma that has reached Earth's surface.

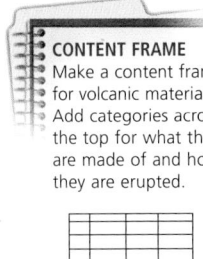
CONTENT FRAME
Make a content frame for volcanic materials. Add categories across the top for what they are made of and how they are erupted.

Structure of a Volcano

Magma collects in a magma chamber before erupting through a volcano.

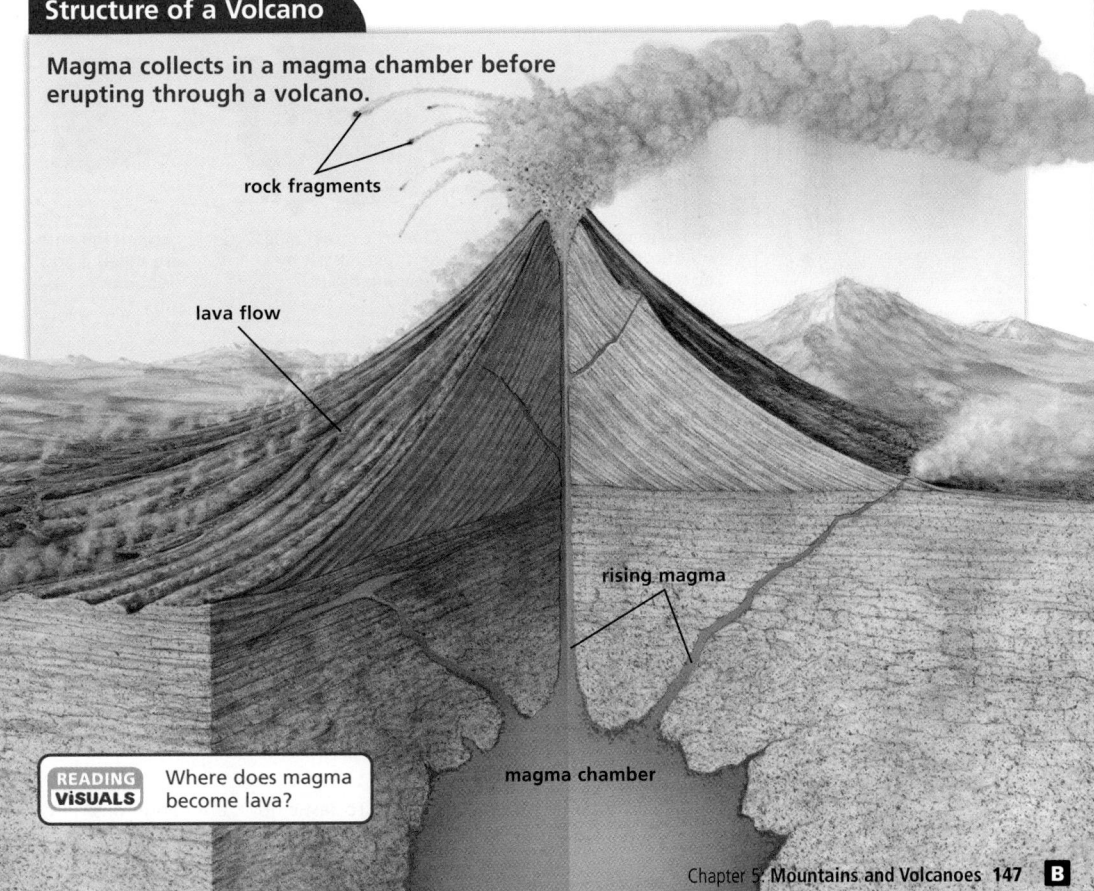

rock fragments

lava flow

rising magma

magma chamber

READING VISUALS Where does magma become lava?

DIFFERENTIATE INSTRUCTION

? More Reading Support

A Which flows more easily: magma with a lot of silica or magma with a small amount of silica? *small amount*

Additional Investigation To reinforce Section 5.2 learning goals, use the following full-period investigation:

R **Additional INVESTIGATION,** Modeling Magma Movement, A, B, & C, pp. 309–317, 320–321

English Learners English learners may not understand that bulleted text can be read as multiple endings to the same sentence. For example, on p. 148, "The fragments form as" is the beginning of a sentence. The clause after each bullet finishes the idea and completes the sentence.

EXPLORE the BIG idea

Revisit "Under Pressure" and "Internet Activity: Volcanoes" on p. 135. Have students explain their results and observations.

Address Misconceptions

IDENTIFY Ask students where they think the magma in the diagram comes from. If they say from Earth's core or the center of Earth, they may have misconceptions about the origins of magma.

CORRECT Tell students that magma forms in the lower crust and upper mantle. Minerals can melt in these regions if temperature and pressure conditions are favorable.

REASSESS Draw a cross-sectional diagram of Earth's crust, mantle, and core. Ask students to place an *x* where magma originates.

Technology Resources

Visit **ClassZone.com** for background on common student misconceptions.

MISCONCEPTION DATABASE

Teacher Demo

Students may have a difficult time understanding that magma rises only as long as it is less dense than the rock around it. When magma reaches an area of similar density, it stops rising. Demonstrate this concept with a cork, a glass marble, and vegetable oil. Show students the materials and ask them to predict the order of their densities. Place the marble and cork in a plastic container and fill it with vegetable oil. The marble will stay on the bottom, but the cork will rise to the top. Ask students what this shows about the order of their densities. *The most dense item is the marble, then the oil, then the cork.*

Ongoing Assessment

READING VISUALS *Answer: once it reaches the surface*

Teach Difficult Concepts

Some students may be confused by the names of some of the materials that erupt from a volcano. For example, volcanic ash does not come from the burning of rock, even though the word *ash* typically refers to the remains of burnt material. Explain that volcanic ash refers only to the size of rock fragments.

Teach from Visuals

To help students interpret the photographs of ash, cinders, and block, ask:

• What do these materials have in common? *They all were erupted from a volcano.*

• Which material has holes and tunnels left by escaping gases? *cinders*

Real World Example

The awesome power and danger of a pyroclastic flow was seen in the 1902 eruption of Mount Pelée on the Caribbean island of Martinique. On the morning of May 8, the volcano erupted, sending a pyroclastic flow of hot ash and gas plunging down the mountain. In one minute the flow reached the town of St. Pierre at the base of the mountain. The hot cloud burned everything in its path, and only two of the town's 29,000 inhabitants survived.

Ongoing Assessment

Explain how volcanoes erupt.

Name three types of materials that erupt from volcanoes. *molten rock, rock fragments, gases*

 *Answer: They are very hot and travel very fast.*

Watch clips of erupted volcanic material.

Rock Fragments

A great deal of material erupts from volcanoes as rock fragments. The fragments form as

• escaping gas bubbles pop, tearing magma apart
• larger pieces of lava are thrown into the air, cooling and hardening during their flight
• rocks of all sizes rip loose from volcanoes' walls during eruptions

B

Tiny rock fragments form volcanic ash, which consists of particles ranging from the size of dust to about the size of rice grains. Volcanic cinders are somewhat larger. The largest fragments are volcanic bombs and blocks. Bombs are molten when they are thrown out and often have streamlined shapes. Blocks, which can be the size of houses, erupt as solid pieces of rock. Large rock fragments fall quickly, but ash can be carried long distances by winds—even all the way around Earth.

C

Volcanic ash is made up of rock fragments less than 2 millimeters in diameter.

Cinders contain holes and tunnels left by escaping gases.

Large fragments are called blocks or bombs.

Volcanic Gases

What looks like smoke rising from a volcano is actually a mixture of ash and gases. The main gases in magma are water vapor and carbon dioxide. Some volcanic gases combine with water in the air to form acids—you will read about these in the next section.

READING TIP
The prefix *pyro-* means "heat," and *clastic* means "made up of rock fragments."

During an eruption, volcanic gases can mix with rock fragments and stay near the ground. The mixture forms a **pyroclastic flow** (PY-roh-KLAS-tihk), which is a dense cloud of superhot gases and rock fragments that races downhill. Such a flow can be as hot as 800°C (1500°F) and can travel faster than 160 kilometers per hour (100 mi/h). Pyroclastic flows are the most dangerous type of volcanic eruption.

 What are two reasons why pyroclastic flows are dangerous?

DIFFERENTIATE INSTRUCTION

? More Reading Support

B What are the smallest solid particles erupted from a volcano? *ash*

C Which rock fragments can be the size of a house? *blocks*

Inclusion To help students better understand the differences between rock fragments, obtain samples of volcanic ash, cinders, and blocks from a science supply company. Have students describe the texture of each. Then read the captions to the visual on this page and ask students to identify each sample.

Most volcanoes form along plate boundaries.

Volcanoes are common along tectonic plate boundaries where oceanic plates sink beneath other plates. As a plate sinks deep into a subduction zone, it heats and begins to melt, forming magma. If the magma reaches the surface it can build tall volcanic mountains.

Volcanoes are also common along tectonic boundaries where plates pull apart, allowing magma to rise from the mantle. Some of these volcanoes are in Africa's Great Rift Valley. However, much of Earth's volcanic activity takes place underwater. Magma erupts along spreading centers in the ocean and cools to form new lithosphere.

Less commonly, a volcano can form over a hot spot far from a plate boundary. Heat carried by material rising from deep in the mantle melts some of the rock in the lithosphere above it. Eruptions over a hot spot built the Hawaiian Islands.

More than 400 volcanoes—about 80 percent of all active volcanoes above sea level—are along subduction zones in the Pacific Ocean. An active volcano is one that is erupting or has erupted in recorded history. The volcanoes around the Pacific Ocean form a belt called the Ring of Fire. Some of these volcanoes are in the western United States.

Ring of Fire

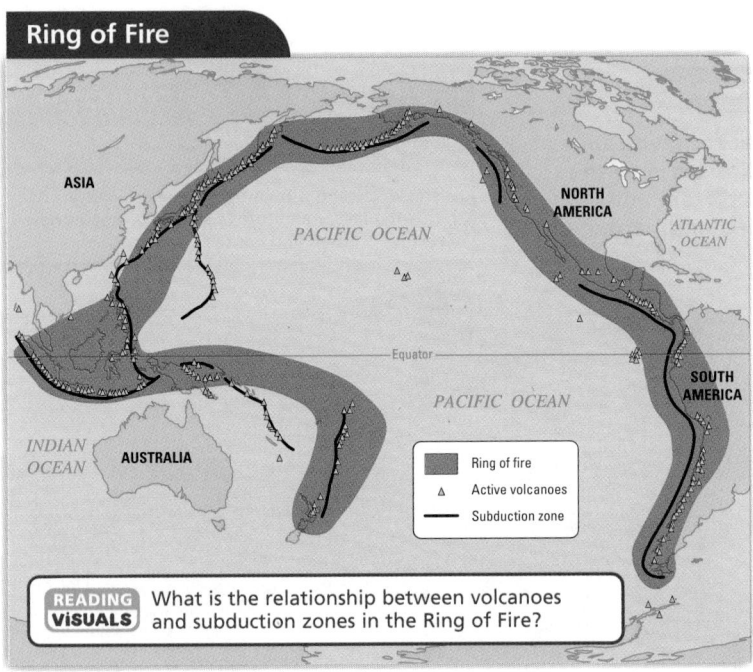

READING **ViSUALS** What is the relationship between volcanoes and subduction zones in the Ring of Fire?

Teach from Visuals

To help students interpret the map, ask:

- Which kind of plate boundary occurs most often along the edge of the Pacific Ocean? *convergent boundary*

- Which major geologic process is occurring at the trenches? *subduction of an oceanic plate beneath another plate*

- How do you think the islands stretching from the North American mainland in the north Pacific Ocean formed? *from the buildup of underwater volcanoes*

- What does the chain of volcanoes seem to form a ring around? *the Pacific Ocean*

Ongoing Assessment

Identify where most volcanoes are located.

Is a volcanic eruption possible where you live? Why or why not? *If your community is far from a plate boundary or a hot spot, students should recognize that active volcanoes do not exist there.*

READING **ViSUALS** *Answer: The volcanoes are caused by magma that forms because an oceanic plate is sinking beneath another plate. Therefore, volcanoes are near subduction zones.*

DIFFERENTIATE INSTRUCTION

? More Reading Support

D What is an active volcano? *one that is erupting or has erupted in recorded history*

Advanced Have students use the Internet or other sources to compile a list of at least five recent volcanic eruptions. Have them locate these eruptions on a world map and compare the locations to a map of plate boundaries.

R Challenge and Extension, p. 279

Inclusion Have students with visual impairments feel the raised surfaces on a relief globe to try and find the Ring of Fire. Tell them it is shaped more like a horseshoe than a ring.

Teach from Visuals

To help students summarize the three main types of volcanoes and the processes that form them, tell students that the landscape on pp. 150–151 does not represent a real area. Ask:

- In what way does a shield volcano look like a shield? *It looks like a shield that is lying face-up.*

- Which volcano is not shown near a plate boundary? *the shield volcano*

- Which colors represent magma? *red and yellow*

Develop Critical Thinking

INFER Have students infer answers to the following questions:

- How did the mountains shown to the left of the shield volcano form? *These are also probably volcanoes, built up as the plate moved over a hot spot.*

- Why does some of the magma in the shield volcano take different paths to the surface? *As the magma moves up the central path, it might be forced into cracks or other weakened areas of the rock layers.*

CONTENT FRAME
Make a content frame for types of volcanoes. Add categories for shape, size, makeup, and examples.

E

RESOURCE CENTER
CLASSZONE.COM

Learn more about historic and current volcanic eruptions.

Volcanoes can have many shapes and sizes.

Mount St. Helens is a cone-shaped volcano in Washington. Its eruption in 1980 killed 57 people. One side of the volcano exploded, blasting out a mixture of hot rock, ash, and gases that destroyed trees tens of kilometers away. Since 1980, this volcano has had many smaller eruptions.

Volcanoes can have many shapes, including steep cones and nearly flat land. Most volcanoes erupt from openings in bowl-shaped pits called craters. Some volcanoes erupt from long cracks in the ground. The type of magma feeding a volcano determines its shape.

① Shield Volcano A shield volcano is shaped like a broad, flat dome. It is built up by many eruptions of lava that is relatively low in silica and therefore flows easily and spreads out in thin layers. The largest volcano on Earth, Mauna Loa (MOW-nuh LOH-uh), is a shield volcano. It makes up much of the island of Hawaii. The total height of this volcano is about 17 kilometers (10.5 mi), but only about 4 kilometers (2.5 mi) are above sea level. At the top of Mauna Loa is a crater that is 5 kilometers (3 mi) across at its widest point. Mauna Loa is one of Earth's most active volcanoes.

F

② Cinder Cone A cinder cone is a steep, cone-shaped hill formed by the eruption of cinders and other rock fragments that pile up around

Three Types of Volcanoes

Two types of material form volcanoes: rock fragments that fall close to the openings they erupted from and lava flows that have cooled and hardened.

① Shield Volcano

A shield volcano is built up of many thin layers of hardened lava. Rangitoto, a shield volcano in New Zealand, is broad and has gently sloping sides.

shield volcano

DIFFERENTIATE INSTRUCTION

? More Reading Support

E What determines the shape of a volcano? *the type of magma*

F What is the silica content of lava that builds shield volcanoes? *low*

Advanced Have students research the 1980 eruption of Mount St. Helens and develop a presentation. Presentations should give background on the geology of the area, the sequence of events that led to the 1980 eruption, and the effects of the eruption.

a single crater. Cinders form as gas-rich magma erupts. Escaping gases throw small chunks of lava into the air, where they harden before landing. Cinder cones are tens to hundreds of meters tall. Many of them form on the sides of other types of volcanoes.

❸ Composite Volcano A composite volcano is a cone-shaped volcano built up of layers of lava and layers of rock fragments. Its magma is high in silica, and therefore is pasty. A composite volcano is steep near the top and flattens out toward the bottom. Because hardened lava flows add strength to the structure of a composite volcano, it can grow much larger than a cinder cone.

> **READING TiP**
> The word *composite* comes from a Latin word meaning "put together." Something that is composite is made of distinct parts.

G

Composite volcanoes have violent eruptions for two reasons. First, expanding gases trapped in rising magma tend to cause explosions. Second, hardened lava from earlier eruptions often plugs openings in these volcanoes. This rock must be blown out of the way before any more magma can escape. Mount St. Helens is a composite volcano. Though its 1980 eruption was devastating, many composite volcanoes have exploded with much greater power.

⬤ CHECK YOUR READING List the three main types of volcanoes. What questions do you have about how they form?

② Cinder Cone

A cinder cone, like this one in Arizona, has steep sides and is a loose pile of volcanic rock fragments.

③ Composite Volcano

A composite volcano is usually cone-shaped and is built up of layers of hardened lava and of rock fragments. Mount St. Helens is a typical composite volcano.

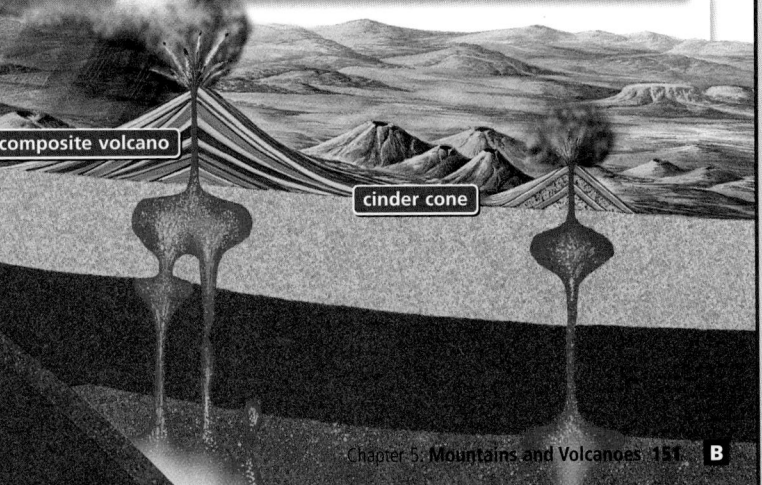
composite volcano

cinder cone

DIFFERENTIATE INSTRUCTION

? **More Reading Support**

G What plugs volcano openings? *hardened lava from earlier eruptions*

Below Level Have students make silhouettes of the three types of volcanoes out of dark construction paper, label them, and place them on a poster. Be sure they make the cinder cone smaller than the composite volcano, even though their shapes are similar. Encourage students to display their completed posters.

Have students who are interested in learning more about how scientists study volcanoes read the following article:

R Challenge Reading, pp. 293–294

Teach from Visuals

To continue helping students interpret the visuals of three volcano types, ask:

* Which underwater feature is shown just off the coast? *trench*
* Which tectonic phenomenon is happening at this feature? *A subduction zone is forming.*
* What is happening at the labeled composite volcano? *Gas, ash, and rock are erupting from the opening; magma is rising from under it.*
* Why are distinct layers shown in the composite volcano? *because it is built of layers of lava and rock fragments*

Develop Critical Thinking

INFER Ask students to infer how the drawing on this page would look if it extended several inches off the bottom of the page. You might want to make a simple reproduction of this drawing on the board or photocopy it at the top half of a piece of paper. Then let students draw how they think it would look. *The edge of the sinking oceanic plate would eventually break up and be incorporated into the mantle as it completely melts.*

Ongoing Assessment

Recognize different types of volcanoes.

Which volcano type does not contain layers of hardened lava flows? *cinder cone*

CHECK YOUR READING *Answer: shield, cinder cone, composite; questions will vary*

To help students interpret the visuals about Crater Lake, ask:

- From what type of volcano did Crater Lake form? *composite*
- Why did the volcano collapse? *After the eruption, there wasn't enough material left in the magma chamber to support the rock above it.*
- Why is the caldera filled with water? *It filled with rain and melting snow.*
- Why is there an island in the caldera? *It is a small volcano built from further eruptions over the years.*

Metacognitive Strategy

Ask students how diagrams and photographs, like those on this page, work together to help them understand something.

Social Studies Connection

In A.D. 79, Mount Vesuvius, on the southwest coast of Italy, erupted violently. Thousands of people perished in the nearby towns of Pompeii and Herculaneum. They were asphyxiated from the gases or suffocated from the ash and mud that completely buried these towns.

The towns and their inhabitants were forgotten until the mid-18th century when the excavation of Pompeii began. Since then, excavations have given archaeologists unprecedented opportunities to study daily life during the Roman Empire. Plaster casts have been made from many of the molds of victims' bodies preserved in the ash. The casts revealed information about what these individuals were doing at that fateful moment in history. The excavations have also shown that Pompeii's layout was in the form of an oval and that there were theaters and shops and public baths.

Formation of Crater Lake

Crater Lake fills the caldera of a composite volcano.

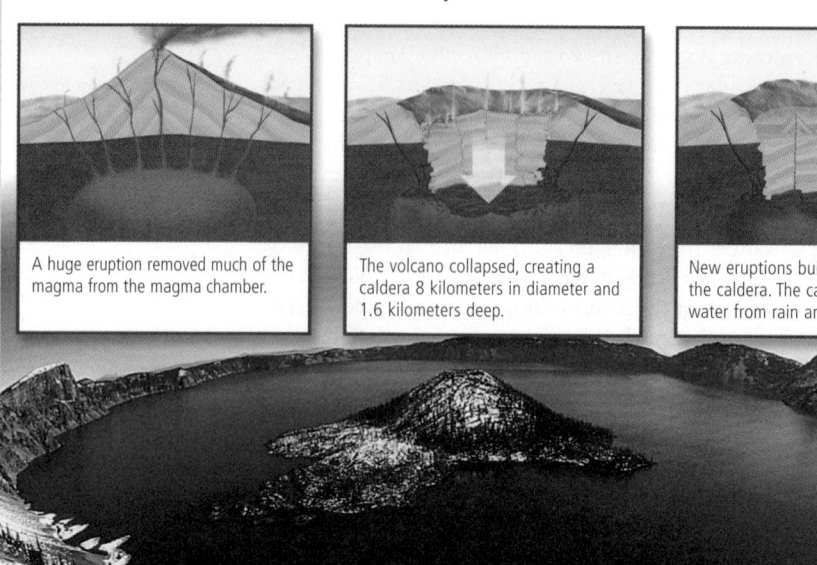

A huge eruption removed much of the magma from the magma chamber.

The volcano collapsed, creating a caldera 8 kilometers in diameter and 1.6 kilometers deep.

New eruptions built a small cone in the caldera. The caldera filled with water from rain and snow.

Both shield volcanoes and composite volcanoes can form features called calderas (kal-DAIR-uhz). A caldera is a huge crater formed by the collapse of a volcano when magma rapidly erupts from underneath it. The crater at the top of Mauna Loa in Hawaii is a caldera. Crater Lake in Oregon fills a caldera formed by a composite volcano about 7700 years ago. A violent eruption emptied much of its magma chamber, and the top of the volcano collapsed into it. The caldera now holds the deepest lake in the United States.

Scientists monitor volcanoes.

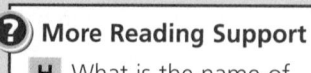

CONTENT FRAME
Make a content frame for types of data used to predict eruptions. Include categories for current activity and history.

Before Mount Pinatubo (PIHN-uh-TOO-boh) in the Philippines erupted in 1991, most people living in the area did not realize that it was a composite volcano. It had not erupted in about 500 years, and erosion had changed its shape. Fortunately, scientists in the Philippines knew that the volcano was becoming active months before it exploded. They were able to warn the government and ask people to leave the area. Their efforts probably saved tens of thousands of lives.

DIFFERENTIATE INSTRUCTION

? More Reading Support

H What is the name of the huge crater formed when a volcano collapses into a partly emptied magma chamber? *caldera*

Alternative Assessment Ask students to design a model of a volcano that forms a caldera by using a balloon, a square box (that a blownup balloon will fit in), and wooden craft sticks. *Students can blow up the balloon, tie it, put it upside down in the box, and arrange craft sticks in a bridge between the sides of the box, resting on top of the balloon. If a small hole is made at the top of the "volcano" (near the tied opening of the balloon), air will slowly escape, and without the support of the balloon, the craft sticks will sink or cave in.*

As the 1991 eruption of Mount Pinatubo shows, volcanoes can go hundreds of years between eruptions. Before Pinatubo's eruption, scientists noticed warning signs that included the occurrence of many small earthquakes followed by explosions of steam near the volcano's top. Researchers brought in equipment to monitor the volcano's activity. Although they could not stop the eruption, they were able to tell when people should leave.

Scientists monitor volcanoes around the world for signs of eruptions. Indications that magma is moving underneath a volcano include earthquake activity and changes in the tilt of the ground. Scientists also monitor the temperatures at openings, springs, and lakes on volcanoes, as well as the amounts and types of gases given off by the volcanoes. Rising temperatures and changes in volcanic gases can indicate that fresh magma has moved into a shallow magma chamber.

Scientists study the ages and types of volcanic rocks around a volcano to understand the volcano's history, including how much time has passed between eruptions and how violent the eruptions have been. This information gives clues about possible future eruptions.

Even with close monitoring, most property damage from volcanic eruptions cannot be prevented. But warning people to move away from a volcano that is about to erupt can save lives. Many of the active volcanoes that are closely monitored are located near major cities. Among these are Mount Rainier (ruh-NEER), which is near Seattle, Washington, and Mount Vesuvius (vih-SOO-vee-uhs), which is near Naples (NAY-puhlz), Italy.

The robot Dante II is about to enter the crater of Mt. Spurr, Alaska, where it will collect video data as well as water and gas samples.

 **CHECK YOUR READING** What is the purpose of monitoring volcanoes?

5.2 Review

KEY CONCEPTS
1. Where are most volcanoes located, and why are they located there?
2. How does the type of material that erupts from a volcano determine the shape of the volcano?
3. What conditions do scientists examine when they monitor volcanoes?

CRITICAL THINKING
4. **Compare and Contrast** How do the three main types of volcanoes differ?
5. **Infer** Volcanic ash can be deposited in areas many kilometers away from the volcano that produced it. What are two ways in which the ash can reach these areas?

CHALLENGE
6. **Analyze** Draw diagrams showing how a composite volcano might change in shape by getting larger or smaller with repeated eruptions.

Chapter 5: **Mountains and Volcanoes** 153 **B**

ANSWERS

1. at divergent and convergent boundaries because magma rises there

2. by whether it flows easily or resists flowing

3. increases in earthquakes, changes in the tilt of the ground, increases in temper- atures, and changes in volcanic gases given off

4. shield volcano: largest, flattest, and broadest; cinder cone: steep and small; composite volcano: large and cone-shaped

5. any two: mudflows, pyro- clastic flows, carried by winds

6. Drawings should show that the volcano becomes larger as new layers are added with repeated erup- tions or smaller due to large, violent eruptions that destroy part of its cone.

Teach from Visuals

To help students interpret the photo- graph of Dante II:

- Ask: Why is a robot being used to col- lect data? *It may be too dangerous for people to collect data inside the crater of an active volcano.*
- Tell students that Dante II was made by NASA. Then ask: Why do you think that NASA made this machine? *NASA has experience in making machines for exploring areas with extreme conditions.*

Reinforce **the BIG idea**

Have students relate the section to the Big Idea.

R Reinforcing Key Concepts, p. 280

5.2 ASSESS & RETEACH

Assess

A Section 5.2 Quiz, p. 81

Reteach

As a class, develop content frames to reteach volcanic materials, types of volca- noes, and how volcanoes are monitored. If students have already developed their own content frames, they can compare them with the ones the class develops, or suffice as models for the class.

Technology Resources

Have students visit **ClassZone.com** for reteaching of Key Concepts.

 CONTENT REVIEW

 CONTENT REVIEW CD-ROM

Chapter 5 **153** **B**

Focus

PURPOSE To find out how the type of materials that form a volcano determines its shape and size

OVERVIEW Students will use different materials to make models of volcanoes and then measure the slopes to find out how the shape relates to the materials that were used. Students will find that a combination of gravel and plaster of Paris builds the tallest volcano with the steepest slopes.

Lab Preparation

- Review with students how to use a protractor to measure angles. Then demonstrate how to measure the steepness of a slope of a model volcano. (Hold the straight edge of the protractor against the cardboard base so that the center point of the protractor is at the spot where the slope meets the base. Read the angle made by the slope in degrees).

- Prior to the investigation, have students read through the investigation and prepare their data tables. Or you may wish to copy and distribute datasheets and rubrics.

 UNIT RESOURCE BOOK, pp. 300–308

 SCIENCE TOOLKIT, F14

Lab Management

Emphasize to students that they should not pour any plaster of Paris down the drain. All cups used to mix the plaster should be thrown away.

INCLUSION Encourage students working together on activities to discuss in advance which tasks each will perform. Help students identify tasks that they can do well or alternative approaches that suit their abilities.

CHAPTER INVESTIGATION

Make Your Own Volcanoes

OVERVIEW AND PURPOSE Scientists who have never been to a particular volcano can estimate how steep a climb it would be to its top. All they need to know is what type of volcano it is. Volcanoes vary not only in size but also in slope, or the steepness of their sides. The three main types of volcanoes—cinder cones, shield volcanoes, and composite volcanoes—are very different in size and shape. In this activity you will
- make models of volcanoes and measure their slopes
- determine how the types of materials that form a volcano affect how steep it can get

▶ Problem

What does a volcano's slope reveal about the materials that formed it?

▶ Hypothesize

Write a hypothesis to explain how a volcano's slope is related to the materials it is made of. Your hypothesis should take the form of an "If . . . , then . . . , because . . ." statement.

▶ Procedure

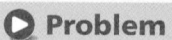

MATERIALS
- 375 mL plaster of Paris
- 180 mL water
- 500 mL gravel
- 3 cardboard pieces
- two 250 mL paper cups
- stirrer
- ruler
- protractor

1. Make a data table like the one shown in the sample notebook on page 155.

2. Mix 125 mL of plaster of Paris with 60 mL of water in a paper cup. Stir the mixture well. Work quickly with the mixture, because it will harden quickly.

3. Pour the mixture onto a piece of cardboard from a height of 2–3 cm. Write "cone A" on the cardboard and set it aside.

4. Fill another paper cup with gravel. Slowly pour the gravel onto a second piece of cardboard from a height of about 10 cm. Label this model "cone B" and set it aside.

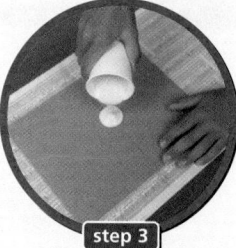
step 3

INVESTIGATION RESOURCES

 CHAPTER INVESTIGATION, Make Your Own Volcanoes
- Level A, pp. 300–303
- Level B, pp. 304–307
- Level C, p. 308

Advanced students should complete Levels B & C.

 Writing a Lab Report, D12–13

Technology Resources

Customize this student lab as needed or look for an alternative. Print rubrics to assess student lab reports.

 Lab Generator CD-ROM

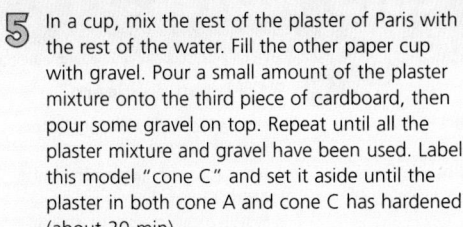

5. In a cup, mix the rest of the plaster of Paris with the rest of the water. Fill the other paper cup with gravel. Pour a small amount of the plaster mixture onto the third piece of cardboard, then pour some gravel on top. Repeat until all the plaster mixture and gravel have been used. Label this model "cone C" and set it aside until the plaster in both cone A and cone C has hardened (about 20 min).

Observe and Analyze Write It Up

1. **MEASURE** Use the protractor to measure the approximate slope of each cone.

2. **RECORD** Complete your data table.

3. **OBSERVE** Compare the appearances of the cone. Record your observations in your **Science Notebook.**

4. **COMPARE** How different are the slopes of the cones?

Conclude Write It Up

1. **CONNECT** Which volcanic materials do the plaster mixture and the gravel represent?

2. **IDENTIFY VARIABLES** What is the relationship between the cones' slopes and the materials they are made of?

3. **ANALYZE** Compare your results with your hypothesis. Do your data support your hypothesis?

4. **INTERPRET** Which type of volcano does each model represent?

5. **DRAW CONCLUSIONS** Which of your models represents a volcano that cannot grow as large as the others? Explain.

6. **APPLY** What factors might cause the slopes of real volcanoes to be different from those of your models?

7. **APPLY** If you were a scientist, what information, in addition to slope, might you need in order to determine a volcano's type?

8. **APPLY** How could the method you used to make a model of a cinder cone be used to show how the slope of a hill or mountain contributes to a landslide?

▶ INVESTIGATE Further

CHALLENGE Calculate the slopes of your models using the formula $y = mx + b$. In this formula, y and x are graph coordinates of a point on a straight line. The slope of the line is m. The intersection of the line with the y-axis of the graph is b. For example, if the height of a model is 1.6 cm, and the distance from its edge to its center is 4 cm, then the equation becomes $1.6 = m4 + 0$.
The slope is $\frac{1.6}{4}$, or 0.4.

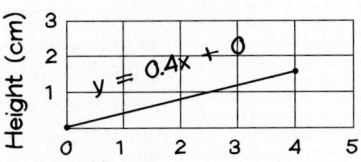

Distance from edge to center (cm)

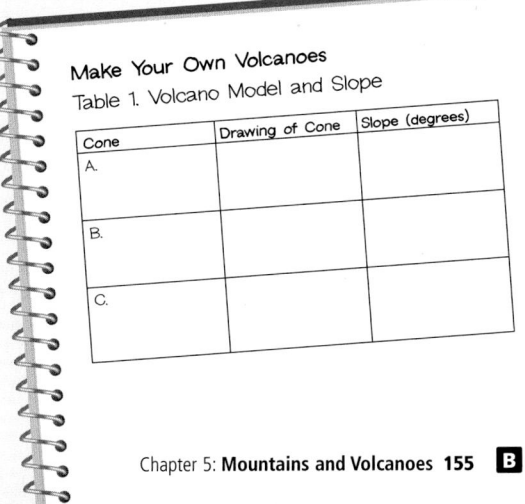

Make Your Own Volcanoes
Table 1. Volcano Model and Slope

Cone	Drawing of Cone	Slope (degrees)
A.		
B.		
C.		

▶ Observe and Analyze Write It Up

1. See students' data tables. You may choose to have students measure to the nearest one or two degrees.

2. See students' data tables.

3. lowest slope—shield volcano; small, steep slope—cinder cone; tall, steep slope—composite volcano

4. The slopes are noticeably different.

▶ Conclude Write It Up

1. plaster of Paris—molten rock; gravel—cinders and other cooled volcanic rocks

2. plaster of Paris only—low slope; gravel—steeper slopes

3. See students' hypotheses.

4. plaster of Paris only—shield volcano; gravel only—cinder cone; plaster of Paris and gravel—composite volcano

5. cinder cone, because it has no cooled lava flows (plaster of Paris) to help add strength to its structure

6. Plaster of Paris and magma have different properties. Material was poured from above rather than erupting from below. Volcanoes form from repeated eruptions rather than just one event.

7. the type of magma feeding it

8. As gravel is added, the cone gets steep enough that additional gravel falls down the sides rather than adding to the height.

▶ INVESTIGATE Further

CHALLENGE Answers will vary according to the measurements of students' models.

Post-Lab Discussion

Discuss why it is helpful to measure the angles of the slopes instead of just to observe and describe the slopes. *Descriptions are useful, but they are too subjective to be the only kind of data. Measurements clearly show differences in the slopes.*

▶ Set Learning Goals

Students will

- Describe how volcanic eruptions affect Earth's surface.
- Explain how volcanic gases affect the atmosphere.
- Describe how volcanic activity affects water.
- Analyze how the shape of land near Mount Rainier affects mudflows.

◀ 3-Minute Warm-Up

Display Transparency 37 or copy this exercise on the board:

Decide if these statements are true. If not, correct them.

1. The main gases in volcanic eruptions are water vapor and oxygen. *water vapor and carbon dioxide*

2. Much of Earth's volcanic activity takes place underwater along spreading centers in the oceans. *true*

3. Lava forms as tectonic plates sink into subduction zones. *Magma forms in this process.*

4. Pyroclastic flows are dense and dangerous clouds of superhot gases and rock fragments that race downhill during eruptions. *true*

 3-Minute Warm-Up, p. T37

5.3 MOTIVATE

THINK ABOUT

PURPOSE To think about the hazards posed by two different types of volcanoes

DISCUSS Ask students to compare and contrast the threats from ashes, gases, and lava from the two volcanoes.

Sample answer: Mt. Shasta erupts less often than Mauna Loa, but its explosions are much more violent due to built-up pressure. Volcanic gases from Mauna Loa are a constant danger to people with breathing difficulties such as asthma.

KEY CONCEPT

5.3 Volcanoes affect Earth's land, air, and water.

◀ **BEFORE, you learned**

- Rock fragments, lava, and gases erupt from volcanoes
- Some volcanoes have explosive eruptions

▶ **NOW, you will learn**

- How volcanic eruptions affect Earth's surface
- How volcanic gases affect the atmosphere
- How volcanic activity affects water

VOCABULARY

acid rain p. 160
geyser p. 161

THINK ABOUT

Which volcano is more dangerous?

Mauna Loa is a shield volcano that forms a large part of the island of Hawaii. It is one of the most active volcanoes on Earth, frequently producing large amounts of lava that flow long distances. Mount Shasta is a composite volcano in California. It has erupted at least once every 600 to 800 years for the past 10,000 years. Mount Shasta can erupt with devastating violence. Which volcano do you think it is more dangerous to live near. Why?

Mauna Loa

Mount Shasta

CONTENT FRAME
Add a content frame for how eruptions affect Earth's land and air. Include categories for what dangers are caused and how long the dangers last.

Volcanic eruptions affect the land.

A volcanic eruption can knock down forests and clog rivers with volcanic ash. Damage can occur far from the volcano. But volcanoes build as well as destroy. Material erupted from volcanoes can form new land. Over time, lava flows can form new, rich soil.

Many towns and cities are located close to volcanoes. The people of Goma in the eastern Democratic Republic of the Congo experienced an eruption of a nearby volcano in 2002. A lava flow cut the city in half and destroyed the homes of tens of thousands of people, either by flowing into the homes or by starting fires. Hilo (HEE-loh), the largest city on the island of Hawaii, is built in part on young lava flows. The city is at high risk from future volcanic activity.

RESOURCES FOR DIFFERENTIATED INSTRUCTION

Below Level
UNIT RESOURCE BOOK
- Reading Study Guide A, pp. 283–284
- Decoding Support, p. 297

 AUDIO CDS

Advanced
UNIT RESOURCE BOOK
Challenge and Extension, p. 289

English Learners
UNIT RESOURCE BOOK
Spanish Reading Study Guide, pp. 287–288

 AUDIO CDS

- Audio Readings in Spanish
- Audio Readings (English)

Immediate Effects

The effects of a volcanic eruption largely depend on how much material and what types of material the volcano ejects. Near a volcano, lava flows can cover the land with new rock. A much larger area can be affected by events such as ash falls, landslides, mudflows, pyroclastic flows, and steam explosions.

Lava Flows Most lava moves slowly enough that people can move away and not be hurt. But even a slow-moving lava flow will knock down, cover, or burn nearly everything in its path.

Volcanic Ash Near a volcanic eruption, the weight of fallen volcanic ash can cause the roofs of buildings to collapse. Volcanic ash is heavy because it is made of tiny pieces of rock. Ash makes roads slippery, and it clogs up machinery, including cars and airplanes. Large amounts of falling ash can suffocate plants, animals, and people.

Mudflows Mudflows are landslides that occur when loose rocks and soil are mixed with water. Heat from an eruption melts any ice and snow on the volcano very quickly. Mudflows form as the water mixes with volcanic ash and other loose particles. Mudflows also form as ash mixes into rivers flowing from a volcano. Fast-moving mudflows have buried entire towns tens of kilometers from an eruption.

Pyroclastic flows As a pyroclastic flow rushes downhill, it can knock down or burn everything in its way. Pyroclastic flows tend to follow valleys. However, a particularly fast-moving flow can sweep up and over hills, then race down a neighboring valley. As a flow passes, it can leave a thick layer of volcanic rock fragments. Pyroclastic flows are extremely dangerous. In 1902, a pyroclastic flow from an eruption in the West Indies completely destroyed the city of Saint Pierre (SAYNT PEER). Almost 30,000 people were killed within a few minutes.

Landslides Part of a volcano can collapse and start a landslide—a rapid downhill movement of rock and soil. The collapse may be caused by magma moving underground, an eruption, an earthquake, or even heavy rainfall. A landslide can cause a tsunami if a large amount of material falls into the ocean.

A

Lava Flow

Trees catch fire as a lava flow moves through a forest in Hawaii in 1999.

Volcanic Ash

Large piles of volcanic ash from the 1991 eruption of Mt. Pinatubo line a street in Olongapo, Philippines, at the start of the cleanup effort.

▼ REMINDER

A tsunami is a water wave caused by an earthquake, a volcanic eruption, or a landslide.

Chapter 5: **Mountains and Volcanoes** 157 **B**

DIFFERENTIATE INSTRUCTION

English Learners Help English learners recognize phrasal verbs that use prepositions as part of the verbs. Point out cases in which the prepositions should not be taken literally. For example, the phrase *break down* on p. 158 refers to rock weathering and breaking apart but not necessarily moving downhill. Similarly, the phrase *built up* on p. 159 refers to an increasing concentration of carbon dioxide in water, not an upward movement of carbon dioxide.

Teach from Visuals

To help students interpret the photographs showing effects of volcanic eruptions, ask:

• How might lava cause fires even before the main lava flow reaches the area? *Small amounts of lava ejected from a volcano or splattered from a lava flow can come into contact with trees and other objects before the main lava flow arrives.*

• What are some ways to clean the ash off this vehicle? *Push the top layer off with a broom and gently rinse the rest off with water so as not to scrape the paint off (because the ash is made of bits of rock).*

Develop Critical Thinking

RANK Ask students to rank the six possible effects of volcanic eruptions that are described from least dangerous to most dangerous. After five minutes ask them if this is an easy task. Ask what makes it somewhat difficult. Discuss how each event can be dangerous and devastating. *The danger associated with each event depends on factors such as the speed of a lava flow, the distance it covers, and the path it takes; the amount of ash produced by the eruption, wind speed and direction, and amount of water available to contribute to a mudflow; the shape of the land that a pyroclastic flow moves over; and the stability of the volcano's slopes. Only some of these events are likely to occur during a particular eruption.*

Teaching with Technology

Suggest that students use an Internet search engine to find out about the most recent volcanic eruptions around the world. They can use the information for a bulletin board display or PowerPoint presentation. Have students gather information about the locations of the eruptions and their relationships to plate tectonics. They should also find out and describe the events that accompanied the eruption such as lava flows, mudflows, pyroclastic flows, and ash falls.

Chapter 5 **157** **B**

Teach from Visuals

To help students interpret the photograph of the bus, ask: About how deep do you think the mudflow is in the photograph? *1–2 m (about 3–6 ft)*

Develop Critical Thinking

HYPOTHESIZE Ask students to hypothesize why people would choose to live near active volcanoes. To help students, have them consider which types of natural disasters are likely to occur in your area. (Examples include hurricanes, tornadoes, wildfires, earthquakes, flooding, and drought.) Then have them apply their knowledge of why these events do or do not cause people to avoid living in your area in order to form their hypotheses. *People get comfortable living near a volcano if the volcano hasn't erupted in many years; large cities—and jobs— happen to be located near some volcanoes; the rich soils near volcanoes provide good agriculture; volcanoes provide a natural beauty to the landscape.*

Ongoing Assessment

Describe how volcanic eruptions affect Earth's surface.

What are four kinds of events that can happen during a volcanic eruption? *any four of the following: lava flows, volcanic ash falls, landslides, mudflows, pyroclastic flows, steam explosions*

Answer: by causing heavy ash falls or tsunamis

Answer: Ash can mix with other loose materials and rainwater or floodwater to create dangerous mudflows.

RESOURCE CENTER
CLASSZONE.COM
Find out more about the effects of volcanic eruptions.

Steam Explosions Though relatively uncommon, steam explosions can be devastating. They occur when magma comes near water or into contact with it. A steam explosion may have caused the destruction of a volcanic island in Indonesia. The entire island of Krakatau (KRACK-uh-TOW) exploded in 1883, causing a tsunami that destroyed hundreds of towns and killed more than 36,000 people.

CHECK YOUR READING What are two ways a volcanic eruption can result in damage to areas hundreds of kilometers away?

Long-term Effects

Volcanic eruptions can be tremendously destructive. But even after an eruption ends, a volcano can remain dangerous for many years.

The explosive eruption of Mount Pinatubo in 1991 threw out huge amounts of volcanic ash and rock fragments. The area the volcano is in gets heavy rains each year. Mudflows have formed as large amounts of rainwater mixed with ash and other loose material on the sides of the volcano. Since the eruption, mudflows have destroyed the homes of more than 100,000 people.

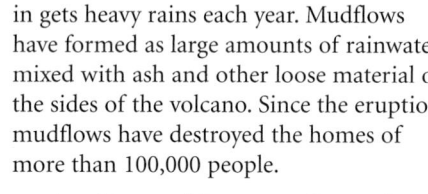
This school bus was partly buried by a mudflow from Mount St. Helens. No one was in the bus when the mudflow hit.

Another possible source of water for mudflows was a lake that began filling the volcano's crater. The upper part of the crater is weak, and the lake level was rising. A collapse of the crater could have emptied the lake of much of its water. In 2001, people dug a channel to lower the level of the lake, greatly decreasing the chance of a collapse.

CHECK YOUR READING Why can volcanic ash be dangerous for years after an eruption?

Even though volcanoes are dangerous, over time they can have positive effects. When a lava flow cools, it forms a layer of hard rock on which no plants can grow. However, over many years, this rock can break down to form rich soil. Volcanic ash can smother plants, but the tiny pieces of rock break down quickly and make soil richer. Highly productive farmland surrounds some active volcanoes.

Over time, repeated volcanic eruptions can build a magnificent landscape of mountains and valleys. People may choose to live in a volcanic area in part for its natural beauty. Many other people may visit the area, supporting a tourist industry.

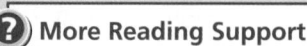

DIFFERENTIATE INSTRUCTION

More Reading Support

B What might happen when magma reaches an ocean? *steam explosion*

C Describe the soil that forms from lava. *rich or fertile*

Advanced Invite students to act as a reporter covering a famous past eruption. They can develop a report for a newspaper, radio broadcast, or TV broadcast. Suggest that they include maps and diagrams to accompany their report for a newspaper or TV broadcast. Students should provide background on the geology of the area and information on past eruptions. Other students can act as eyewitnesses and experts. Students also should research the effects of the eruption and provide this information to the eyewitnesses beforehand.

 Challenge and Extension, p. 289

INVESTIGATE Mudflows

How does the shape of the land affect mudflows?

PROCEDURE

① Look at the map of Mount Rainier mudflows. Observe the relationship between the paths of rivers and the paths of the mudflows.

② Write the number of towns shown within the boundaries of mudflow areas.

③ Write the differences in elevation between the following locations: the top of Mount Rainier and the point where the West Fork joins the White River, the point where the rivers join and the town of Buckley, and the towns of Buckley and Auburn. Where is the land steepest?

④ On the back of the paper, explain why in some areas mudflows have followed rivers and in other areas mudflows have spread out.

WHAT DO YOU THINK?

• What three factors are most important in causing mudflows to start near the top of Mount Rainier and flow long distances?

• How likely are future mudflows to follow the same paths as earlier mudflows?

CHALLENGE The largest mudflow starting on Mount Rainier moved at about 22 kilometers per hour (14 mi/h) and covered the land to an average depth of 6 meters (20 ft). Describe the steps you would take to protect people from a similar mudflow in the same area.

SKILL FOCUS
Analyzing

MATERIAL
Map of Mount Rainier Mudflows

TIME
25 minutes

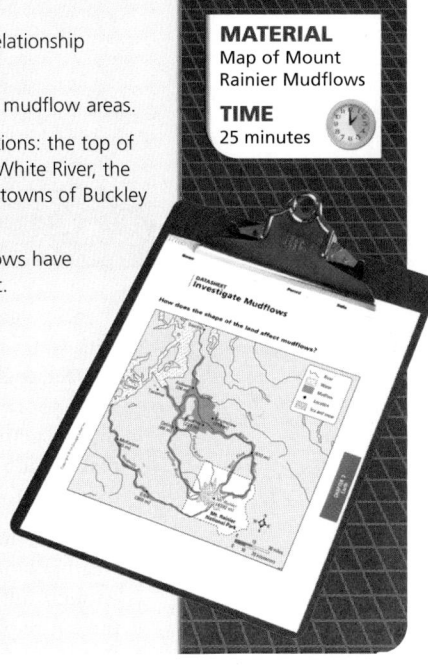

Volcanic gases and ash affect the air.

If you visit a volcano, you might notice some unpleasant odors. These odors come from gases released into the air from magma. Some of these gases contain the element sulfur. Hydrogen sulfide gas smells like rotten eggs. Sulfur dioxide gas is what you smell when you strike a match. The volcano might also be releasing carbon dioxide, a gas you would not notice because it has no color or odor. Volcanoes release gases before, during, and after eruptions.

Many gases from volcanoes are dangerous. They can make breathing difficult and damage the lungs of people and animals. Carbon dioxide can be fatal. In West Africa, a sudden release of carbon dioxide killed 1700 people in 1986. The gas came from a volcano at the bottom of a lake. Carbon dioxide built up in the water until a large amount escaped at once. Pipes are now being used to release carbon dioxide from the bottom of the lake so that the gas will not build up again.

READING TiP

An element is a substance that contains only one type of atom.

INVESTIGATE Mudflows

PURPOSE To analyze how the shape of land near Mount Rainier affects mudflows

TIPS *25 min.*

• Review the features of the map to make sure students are able to do the lab. Point out the rivers, mudflows, and towns.

• Make sure the mudflows show up clearly on the maps. You may have to outline the flows before photocopying the maps.

PROCEDURE *1. Mudflows tend to follow the paths of rivers. 2. Six towns 3. Mount Rainier–West Fork/White River: 3782 m; West Fork/White River–Buckley: 389 m; Buckley–Auburn: 195 m; The land is steepest between the top of Mount Rainier and the point at which the West Fork joins the White River. 4. Mudflows tend to follow the paths of rivers where the land is steep. They tend to spread out where the land is flatter.*

WHAT DO YOU THINK? *Three factors are the presence of ice and snow; heat from an eruption, which can quickly melt the ice and snow; the mountain's steepness. Future mudflows are very likely because mudflows move downhill along the lowest ground.*

CHALLENGE *Answers can include installing warning systems so people can move to higher ground, building barricades to slow or divert mudflows, building ditches to divert mudflows, and relocating towns.*

 • Map of Mount Rainier Mudflows, p. 290
• Datasheet, Mudflows, p. 291

Technology Resources

Customize this student lab as needed or look for an alternative. Print rubrics to assess student lab reports.

 Lab Generator CD-ROM

DIFFERENTIATE INSTRUCTION

 **More Reading Support**

D What are two gases released from a volcano?
any two of the following: carbon dioxide, hydrogen sulfide, sulfur dioxide

Below Level Have students make flash cards for the different effects of volcanic eruptions. They can write an effect, such as "lava flows" or "volcanic ash," on one side of a card and a brief description of that effect on the opposite side. For "lava flows," students might write "slow-moving" and "burn almost everything." Have students use the phrases as springboards to describe each type of effect to you or to a partner.

Integrate the Sciences

Sulfur dioxide from volcanic eruptions mixes with moisture in the air to form sulfuric acid. This acid mixes with rain or snow to form acid precipitation. The acidity of a substance is measured by its pH on a scale of 0 to 14. Distilled water, with a pH of 7, is neutral. The lower the number, the more acidic the substance. Tomato juice has a pH of 3 and lemon juice has a pH of 2. Normal precipitation is slightly acidic (pH: 5.5) because carbon dioxide dissolves in water in the air to produce a weak carbonic acid. Acid precipitation is defined as precipitation with a pH of less than 5.0, but it has been measured as being as low as 3.

Real World Example

Perhaps the best example of a volcanic weather changer is Mount Tambora, a volcano on Sumbawa Island in Indonesia. On April 5, 1815, Tambora erupted in an explosion that was heard up to 1400 km (870 mi.) away. An even larger eruption occurred less than one week later on April 10–11, 1815. Ash, dust, and gases from these eruptions blasted high into the atmosphere and were carried all around the world. These materials blocked significant amounts of sunlight throughout the rest of that year and the next. Unusual summer frosts, snowfalls, and wildly fluctuating temperatures took their toll on crops, especially during the following year of 1816. An estimated 80,000 people worldwide died of starvation and disease as a result of the crop failures and cold temperatures.

Ongoing Assessment

Explain how volcanic gases affect the atmosphere.

How do volcanic gases aid ash in blocking sunlight? *They lift ash high above an erupting volcano where winds can spread the ash and keep it suspended in the atmosphere, so it blocks sunlight.*

CHECK YOUR READING *Answer: by forming acid rain and by forming a haze that blocks sunlight*

A cloud of hot gases and ash rises high into the atmosphere during an eruption of Mount Etna in Italy.

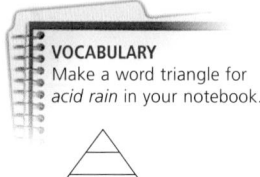
VOCABULARY
Make a word triangle for *acid rain* in your notebook.

Some gases, such as sulfur dioxide, form acids when they mix with water in the air. These acids fall to Earth's surface in rain, snow, or sleet. Rain that contains large amounts of acid is called **acid rain.** Volcanoes are sources of acid-forming gases, but a bigger source is human activity. For example, the burning of coal in electrical power plants adds acid-forming gases to the air. In some areas, acid rain has damaged forests and killed fish in lakes.

Large amounts of volcanic gases in the atmosphere can change weather worldwide. The 1991 eruption of Mount Pinatubo released enough sulfur dioxide to form a haze high in the atmosphere around the entire planet. The haze decreased the amount of sunlight reaching Earth's surface and lowered average world temperatures in 1992 and 1993.

Volcanic gases can lift ash high above an erupting volcano. Winds can then carry the ash far away. During the May 1980 eruption of Mount St. Helens, ash falling 400 kilometers (250 mi) away in Spokane, Washington, blocked so much sunlight that nighttime streetlights were turned on during the day. The smallest ash particles can remain in the air for years, circling Earth many times. These particles also reflect sunlight and can lower Earth's temperature.

 **CHECK YOUR READING** Describe two ways sulfur dioxide can affect the atmosphere.

Volcanic activity affects water.

Yellowstone National Park in the western United States is famous for its hot springs—places where heated water flows to Earth's surface. Yellowstone is a volcanic region, and its hot springs sit in a huge caldera. The springs' heat comes from a hot spot under the North American Plate.

 ? **E**

DIFFERENTIATE INSTRUCTION

? More Reading Support

E What causes the heat of the hot springs in Yellowstone National Park? *a hot spot under the North American Plate*

Alternative Assessment Have students use a world map to find the locations of all the places mentioned on p. 160: Mount Etna, Italy; Mount Pinatubo, Philippines; Mount St. Helens, Washington; and Yellowstone National Park, Wyoming. Have students discuss the relationship of these places to tectonic plates. *The first three places are near convergent plate boundaries; Yellowstone is above a hot spot far from plate boundaries.*

Geysers

Rainwater can sink through cracks in rock. If it is heated within Earth, it can rise to form hot springs and geysers.

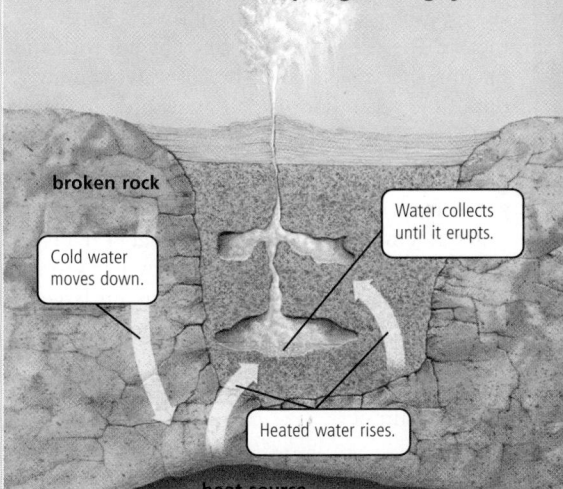

broken rock

Cold water moves down.

Water collects until it erupts.

Heated water rises.

heat source

Old Faithful geyser in Yellowstone National Park erupts more often than any other large geyser. Heated water is forced up into the air through a narrow channel.

Hot Springs, Geysers, and Fumaroles

Most hot springs are in areas where magma or hot rock is near Earth's surface. Water moves down through the ground, gets heated, and rises at a hot spring. At most hot springs, the water flows out into a calm pool. But at a type of hot spring called a **geyser**, water shoots into the air. A geyser forms where water collects in an underground chamber, then erupts through a narrow channel. Old Faithful, a geyser in Yellowstone National Park, erupts every 35 minutes to 2 hours. Most geysers erupt less predictably.

In addition to the United States, countries with many hot springs and geysers include New Zealand and Iceland. Beneath Iceland, which sits on an ocean spreading center, is magma that rises as plates pull apart. People in Iceland use hot underground water as an energy source to heat their capital city, Reykjavík (RAY-kyuh-VEEK).

A feature known as a fumarole (FYOO-muh-ROHL) is similar to a hot spring. Instead of liquid water, though, a fumarole releases steam and other gases. Changes in hot springs and fumaroles located on the sides of a volcano can show that the volcano is becoming more active. As magma moves close to the surface, water temperatures get higher, and fumaroles can release more or different gases.

CONTENT FRAME
Make a content frame for features formed by heated water. Include categories for how they form and where they form.

CHECK YOUR READING Why might fumaroles and hot springs be monitored?

DIFFERENTIATE INSTRUCTION

? More Reading Support

F What is the name of a hot spring that shoots water into the air? *geyser*

G Why does Iceland have many hot springs? *It is located on an ocean spreading center.*

Advanced Have students further analyze the diagram of a geyser to determine the role of a narrow, underground channel in the eruption of a geyser. *The narrower the channel, the more pressure builds up, and the higher the eruption of water.*

Teach from Visuals

To help students interpret the visuals of geysers, ask:

• Where does the cold water come from? *groundwater and surface water from rain and melting snow*

• How does the cold water reach the area of heat below ground? *through cracks in the rock*

• Why might Old Faithful be so named? *It erupts relatively regularly and predictably.*

Develop Critical Thinking

INFER Ask students to infer what caused the mound of materials around the geyser's opening? *Minerals dissolved in the hot water are deposited when the water cools or evaporates at the surface.*

Ongoing Assessment

Describe how volcanic activity affects water.

How are hot springs, geysers, and fumaroles similar? *They all form from water moving underground near magma or hot rock, then surfacing as a pool, a stream, or a fountain of hot water or steam.*

CHECK YOUR READING *Answer: to see if a volcano is becoming more active*

Integrate the Sciences

Most organisms ultimately depend on energy from the Sun for their food through the process of photosynthesis. At deep-sea vents, however, there is no sunlight. The food-making process in this environment is not photosynthesis but chemosynthesis. Bacteria use sulfur compounds ejected from the vents to make their food. These bacteria become the bottom link on a food chain that supports a community of organisms.

Reinforce (the **BIG** idea)

Have students relate the section to the Big Idea.

 Reinforcing Key Concepts, p. 292

Deep-Sea Vents

Deep-sea vents are hot springs that form at spreading centers in the ocean. In these places, the ocean floor has many cracks through which cold seawater sinks to depths of several kilometers. The sea water gets heated by hot rock and magma, then rises again. The hot water coming out of the ocean floor is rich in dissolved minerals and gases from the rock and magma.

At some deep-sea vents, warm water flows gently from cracks in the ocean floor. At others, water at temperatures that can be higher than 350°C (660°F) shoots out of chimney-like vents. The water looks black because it contains large amounts of dissolved minerals. As the hot water mixes with cold water, dissolved minerals form into solid minerals again, building up the vent chimneys.

Deep-sea vents support such unusual life forms as blind crabs and tubeworms that measure up to 3 meters (10 ft) long. These animals feed on one-celled organisms that get their energy from chemicals in the vent water. Unlike other one-celled organisms, these organisms do not need sunlight to make their food.

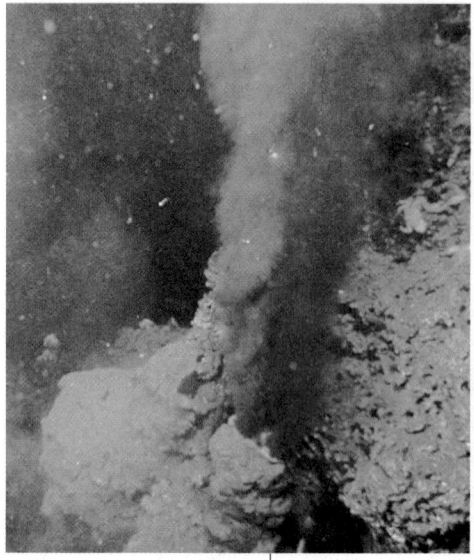
This deep-sea vent is more than 3 kilometers (2 mi) below the surface of the Atlantic Ocean. A black cloud of mineral-rich water rises from the vent.

CHECK YOUR READING Why do chimneys form around some deep-sea vents?

5.3 Review

KEY CONCEPTS

1. Describe how a heavy ash fall from a volcanic eruption can affect Earth's surface.

2. Describe how large amounts of volcanic gases can affect weather around Earth.

3. Why do hot springs occur in volcanic areas?

CRITICAL THINKING

4. **Compare and Contrast** What do geysers and deep-sea vents that form chimneys have in common? How are they different?

5. **Evaluate** Which is more dangerous, a pyroclastic flow or a mudflow? Explain.

CHALLENGE

6. **Analyze** Ice in Greenland and Antarctica contains layers of ash from eruptions that occurred many thousands of years ago. How do you think the ash reached the ice, and why is it preserved?

ANSWERS

1. It can cause collapse of roofs, suffocation of plants and animals, clogged machinery, slippery roads, mudflows, and richer soils over time.

2. Volcanic gases can form a haze that blocks sunlight and lowers average temperatures.

3. Magma and hot rock heat groundwater.

4. Very hot water shoots out of both. Geysers form on land, while deep-sea vents form in the ocean.

5. Both can be deadly. Given warning, people can leave the area to avoid pyroclastic flows during an eruption, but mudflows can occur for many years after an eruption.

6. Winds carried the ash to the ice, and new snow covered the ash and trapped it.

Rangers at Yellowstone

Rangers at Yellowstone National Park help monitor volcanic activity. The hot spot that is now under Yellowstone has powered some of the largest volcanic eruptions on Earth. The amount of volcanic ash and lava produced by Yellowstone's three giant eruptions could fill the Grand Canyon. The last giant eruption occurred 640,000 years ago. At least 30 smaller eruptions have occurred since. Most of Yellowstone's hot springs and geysers sit in the caldera produced by the last giant eruption.

Beware Volcanic Gases

Park rangers must be aware of the effects of volcanic gases given off by hot springs. Here, volcanic gases are bubbling up through mud. Carbon dioxide, a common volcanic gas, is heavier than air. It sinks and fills low areas. Rangers sometimes find the body of a small animal that entered a shallow cave and died for lack of oxygen.

On Thin Ground

It is dangerous to walk up to the edge of Yellowstone's springs, some of which contain scalding hot water. The ground might be a layer of rock too thin to support a person's weight. Park rangers make sure visitors know to stay on safe walkways, and they inform the public about the science of hot springs.

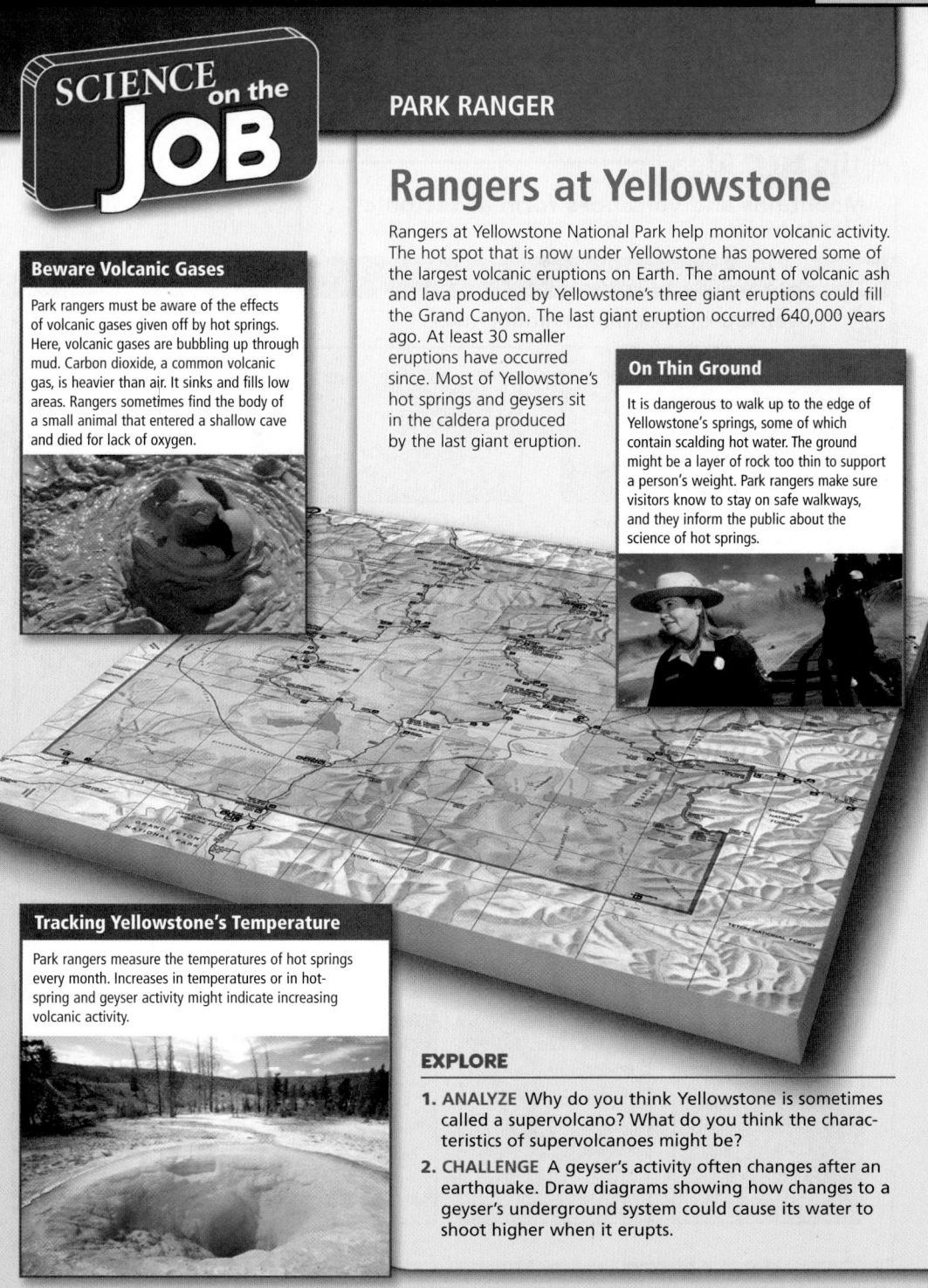

Tracking Yellowstone's Temperature

Park rangers measure the temperatures of hot springs every month. Increases in temperatures or in hot-spring and geyser activity might indicate increasing volcanic activity.

EXPLORE

1. **ANALYZE** Why do you think Yellowstone is sometimes called a supervolcano? What do you think the characteristics of supervolcanoes might be?
2. **CHALLENGE** A geyser's activity often changes after an earthquake. Draw diagrams showing how changes to a geyser's underground system could cause its water to shoot higher when it erupts.

Chapter 5: **Mountains and Volcanoes** 163 **B**

EXPLORE

1. *ANALYZE* because it has had such large eruptions; characteristics might be eruptions that release huge amounts of energy and produce tremendous amounts of ash and other volcanic materials
2. *CHALLENGE* Diagrams might show a narrowed geyser opening, which would allow pressure to build higher before an eruption; a larger collection area, which would allow more water to be available; a rise of magma toward the surface, which would heat the water more.

Set Learning Goal

To understand how rangers at Yellowstone National Park help to monitor volcanic activity

Present the Science

The three major eruptions at Yellowstone have occurred once every 600,000 to 800,000 years. With the last being 640,000 years ago, another eruption may be due. One possible sign of a future eruption is that parts of the caldera floor are rising about 20 mm each year. This may be because magma and related fluids are accumulating. Warning signs of an impending eruption would likely include an increase in hot-spring activity, dormant geysers reawakening, and more frequent minor earthquakes.

Discussion Questions

Ask: How does a caldera form? *A volcano collapses into a magma chamber that has been partly emptied after a huge eruption.*

Ask: What does 'an increase in volcanic activity' mean? *It could mean a rising of magma or a release of gases, which could mean an eruption is about to occur.*

DIFFERENTIATION TIP Challenge advanced students to research the Craters of the Moon National Monument southwest of Yellowstone and explain why the features there may be a result of the North American Plate's southwestward movement over the Yellowstone hot spot.

Close

Ask: Why must park rangers in Yellowstone have a good knowledge of the area's geology? *to keep themselves and visitors in the area safe; to collect data on volcanic features*

the BIG idea

Have students choose a type of mountain (folded, fault-block, or different types of volcanoes) and demonstrate how that mountain forms. They should relate the mountain formation to plate tectonics. Students can choose to use sheets of paper, clay, wooden blocks, coins, their hands, or other items for their demonstration.

○ KEY CONCEPTS SUMMARY

SECTION 5.1

Ask: Which rock movements occur to form each of the types of mountains shown? *Folded mountains: An oceanic plate pushes against and sinks beneath a continental plate or two continental plates collide. The pressure folds the continental crust and raises mountains. Fault-block mountains: The lithosphere is stretched and pulls apart, forming faults. Blocks of rock tilt and move along the faults, making parts of the blocks rise.*

SECTION 5.2

Ask: Why are the three types of volcanoes different shapes and sizes? *because each type erupts different kinds of materials such as low-silica lava, high-silica lava, cinders, and different amounts of gases*

SECTION 5.3

Ask students to write a sentence that relates each bulleted item to volcanic activity. Instead of separate sentences, students might write a brief paragraph for the set of items in each box. *During an eruption, part of a volcano can collapse and start a landslide. Large amounts of volcanic gases can produce a worldwide haze that decreases global temperatures. Hot springs form where water is heated near Earth's surface.*

Review Concepts

- Big Idea Flow Chart, p. T33
- Chapter Outline, pp. T39–T40

 # Chapter Review

the BIG idea

Mountains and volcanoes form as tectonic plates move.

 **CONTENT REVIEW**
CLASSZONE.COM

◁ KEY CONCEPTS SUMMARY

5.1 Movement of rock builds mountains.

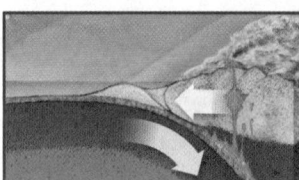

Folded mountains form as plates push together.

Fault-block mountains form as the lithosphere is stretched.

VOCABULARY
folded mountain
p. 140
fault-block mountain
p. 142

5.2 Volcanoes form as molten rock erupts.

Volcanoes erupt molten rock, rock fragments, and gases. Different types of erupted materials build up different types of volcanoes.

A cinder cone is made up of loose rock fragments and cinders that form as gas-rich magma erupts.

A shield volcano is made up of many layers of low-silica lava.

A composite volcano consists of layers of erupted rock fragments and cooled flows of high-silica lava.

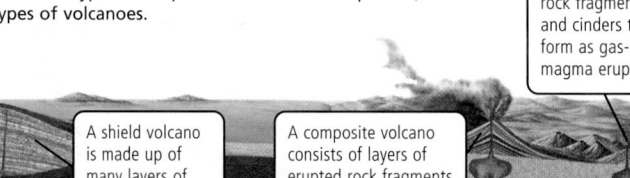

VOCABULARY
volcano p. 146
lava p. 147
pyroclastic flow p. 148

5.3 Volcanoes affect Earth's land, air, and water.

Materials erupted from volcanoes, as well as heat from molten rock underground, affect Earth's surface.

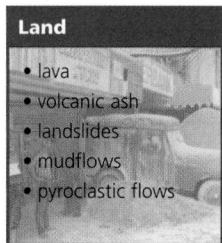

Land	Air	Water
• lava	• poisonous gases	• hot springs
• volcanic ash	• adds to acid rain	• geysers
• landslides	• haze	• fumaroles
• mudflows	• lower temperatures	• deep-sea vents
• pyroclastic flows		

VOCABULARY
acid rain p. 160
geyser p. 161

Technology Resources

Have students visit **ClassZone.com** or use the CD-ROM for a cumulative review of concepts.

 CONTENT REVIEW

 CONTENT REVIEW CD-ROM

Engage students in a whole-class interactive review of Key Concepts. Edit content as you wish.

 POWER PRESENTATIONS

Reviewing Vocabulary

Draw a Venn diagram to compare and contrast each pair of features. Example:

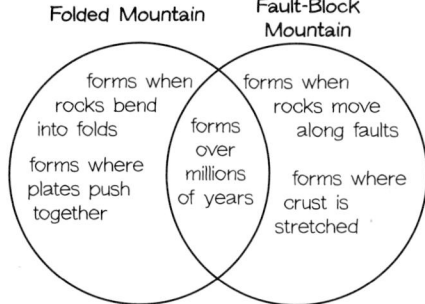

Folded Mountain — Fault-Block Mountain

forms when rocks bend into folds

forms where plates push together

forms over millions of years

forms when rocks move along faults

forms where crust is stretched

1. folded mountain, volcano

2. lava, pyroclastic flow

3. volcano, geyser

Reviewing Key Concepts

Multiple Choice *Choose the letter of the best answer.*

4. In areas where the lithosphere is being pulled apart, the crust
   a. folds and crumples into mountains
   b. breaks into blocks separated by faults
   c. slides down into the mantle
   d. develops a subduction zone

5. When two plates carrying continental crust collide, the rock of the continents
   a. folds
   b. melts
   c. expands
   d. stretches

6. The movement of huge blocks of rock along a fault can produce
   a. lava plugs
   b. volcanoes
   c. fault-block mountains
   d. folded mountains

7. Volcanoes in the Ring of Fire are supplied with magma rising from
   a. spreading centers
   b. hot spots
   c. rift valleys
   d. subduction zones

8. Before magma erupts it collects under a volcano in a
   a. chamber
   b. caldera
   c. crater
   d. vent

9. The explosiveness of a volcanic eruption depends mostly on the _____ of the magma.
   a. gas content
   b. silica content
   c. amount
   d. temperature

10. The type of magma erupting from a volcano determines the volcano's
    a. size
    b. age
    c. shape
    d. location

11. Volcanic ash can be carried thousands of kilometers from an eruption by
    a. lava flows
    b. pyroclastic flows
    c. landslides
    d. winds

12. In a volcanic region, water moving through the ground gets _____ by magma or hot rock.
    a. melted
    b. dissolved
    c. erupted
    d. heated

Short Answer *Write a short answer to each question.*

13. Describe how an old mountain belt located in the center of a continent most likely formed.

14. How are the locations of volcanoes related to tectonic plate boundaries?

15. What causes a shield volcano to be shaped like a broad dome?

16. By what processes can a volcanic eruption affect temperatures around the world?

Reviewing Vocabulary

1. *folded mountain: forms when rocks bend into folds, forms where plates collide; both: forms where an oceanic plate sinks under a continent; volcano: is built up of molten rock and rock fragments, forms where magma reaches the surface*

2. *lava: is molten rock at Earth's surface; both: erupts from a volcano, has very high temperatures, is dangerous; pyroclastic flow: is dense cloud of superhot volcanic gases and rock fragments*

3. *volcano: is built up of molten rock and rock fragments, forms where magma reaches the surface; both: erupts, has source of heat underneath it; geyser: is a hot spring that shoots water into the air*

Reviewing Key Concepts

4. *b*

5. *a*

6. *c*

7. *d*

8. *a*

9. *b*

10. *c*

11. *d*

12. *d*

13. *It most likely formed as different parts of the continent pushed together along a collision boundary.*

14. *Volcanoes commonly occur at divergent boundaries and subduction boundaries.*

15. *many layers of lava that was low in silica, so it flowed easily and spread out in thin layers*

16. *A volcanic eruption can release enough sulfur dioxide to form a haze around the planet as well as volcanic ash that stays in the air for a long time. The haze and/or ash can decrease the amount of sunlight reaching Earth's surface and cause average temperatures to drop.*

ASSESSMENT RESOURCES

UNIT ASSESSMENT BOOK
- Chapter Test A, pp. 83–86
- Chapter Test B, pp. 87–90
- Chapter Test C, pp. 91–94
- Alternative Assessment, pp. 95–96
- Unit Test A, B & C, pp. 97–108

SPANISH ASSESSMENT BOOK
Spanish Chapter Test, pp. 137–140

Technology Resources

Edit test items and answer choices.

 Test Generator CD-ROM

Visit **ClassZone.com** to extend test practice.

 Test Practice

Thinking Critically

17. *shield volcano, because the lava flows easily for long distances*

18. *no, because the eruptions of shield volcanoes are usually gentle and do not produce large amounts of ash*

19. *They might make breathing difficult and cause lung damage.*

20. *a steam explosion*

21. *It could cover farmland with lava. Over time, the lava could break down into rich soil.*

22. *increases in earthquakes, changes in the tilt of the ground, increases in temperatures on the volcano, changes in volcanic gases*

23. *folded mountains: stress is pushing the crust together; fault-block mountains: stress is pulling the crust apart*

24. *Diagrams should show a magma chamber beneath a shield volcano with a main conduit to the center and a side conduit to a small cinder cone on the side of the shield volcano.*

25. *composite volcanoes, because they are the most likely to erupt violently*

26. *The hot springs and geysers would cool over time and stop erupting.*

27. *The oceanic plate sinks, and magma forms and rises. Where two continents push together, neither plate sinks and no magma forms.*

28. *Different types and amounts of magma feed each volcano, causing various shapes to form as eruptions occur.*

the BIG idea

29. *An oceanic plate is sinking beneath a plate carrying continental crust.*

30. *A continental collision will occur. Folded mountains along the coast will be pushed up.*

UNIT PROJECTS

Have students present their projects. Use the appropriate rubrics from the URB to evaluate their work.

 Unit Projects, pp. 5–10

Thinking Critically

This photograph shows a volcanic eruption. The volcano produces rivers of lava that flow long distances. Use the photograph to answer the next six questions.

17. **INFER** What kind of volcano is shown in the photograph? How do you know?

18. **APPLY** Is this eruption likely to produce large amounts of ash that could lead to dangerous mudflows for many years afterward? Why or why not?

19. **IDENTIFY EFFECTS** How might volcanic gases affect the health of people and animals living near the volcano?

20. **ANALYZE** What would be likely to happen if a large amount of water reached the volcano's magma chamber?

21. **COMPARE AND CONTRAST** How could this volcano affect nearby farmland during the eruption? many years after the eruption?

22. **SYNTHESIZE** What types of changes would let scientists monitoring the volcano know that an eruption was likely to occur?

23. **COMPARE AND CONTRAST** How does the stress on continental crust in areas where folded mountains form differ from that in areas where fault-block mountains form?

24. **APPLY** Draw a diagram showing how one magma chamber can supply magma to a shield volcano and to a cinder cone on the side of the shield volcano.

25. **INFER** Many of the volcanoes in the Ring of Fire erupt explosively. Would you expect these volcanoes to be cinder cones, shield volcanoes, or composite volcanoes? Explain your answer.

26. **PREDICT** How might an area with many hot springs and geysers be affected as magma and hot rock near the surface cooled?

27. **ANALYZE** Why do volcanoes form along boundaries where oceanic plates are pushing into other plates but not along boundaries where continents are pushing together?

28. **APPLY** Explain why shield volcanoes, composite volcanoes, and cinder cones have different sizes and shapes.

the BIG idea

29. **INFER** How would you expect tectonic plates to be moving at a plate boundary where folded mountains are being pushed up and volcanoes are erupting?

30. **PREDICT** If tectonic plates continue to move as they are moving today, the continents of Australia and Antarctica will collide in the far future. What will happen after the sea floor that is now between the continents is destroyed?

UNIT PROJECTS

Evaluate all of the data, results, and information from your project folder. Prepare to present your project to the class. Be ready to answer questions posed by your classmates about your results.

MONITOR AND RETEACH

If students have trouble applying the concepts in items 15, 24, and 28, suggest that they review the visuals on pp. 150–151. Have them orally explain how each type of volcano forms. Then they can answer the questions by using the diagram.

Students may benefit from summarizing one or more sections of the chapter.

R Summarizing the Chapter, pp. 318–319

Standardized Test Practice

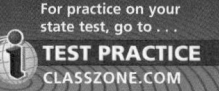

For practice on your state test, go to . . .
TEST PRACTICE
CLASSZONE.COM

Analyzing Data

The graph below shows the amounts of lava, rock, and other materials released in four large volcanic eruptions. Study the graph, then answer the questions below.

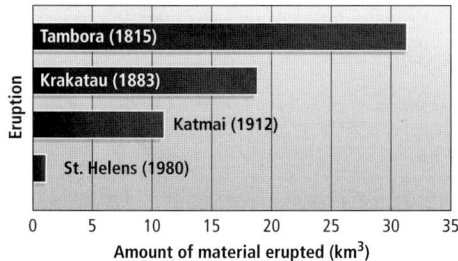

Eruption

- Tambora (1815)
- Krakatau (1883)
- Katmai (1912)
- St. Helens (1980)

0 5 10 15 20 25 30 35
Amount of material erupted (km³)

1. How much material did the eruption of Katmai release in 1912?
- **a.** 12 km³
- **b.** 17 km³
- **c.** 29 km³
- **d.** 41 km³

2. After 1850, which of these eruptions released the greatest amount of material?
- **a.** Krakatau
- **b.** Tambora
- **c.** Katmai
- **d.** St. Helens

3. About how much more material erupted from Krakatau in 1883 than from Katmai in 1912?
- **a.** 28 km³
- **b.** 12 km³
- **c.** 6 km³
- **d.** 2 km³

4. Katmai, a large mountain built of layers of hardened lava flows and of rock fragments, is a
- **a.** cinder cone
- **b.** shield volcano
- **c.** pyroclastic cone
- **d.** composite volcano

5. How much material did the 1815 eruption of Tambora produce compared with the 1883 eruption of Krakatau?
- **a.** less than one-half the amount
- **b.** a nearly equal amount
- **c.** almost two times the amount
- **d.** almost four times the amount

6. All of the eruptions shown in the graph created calderas—craters formed by the collapse of volcanoes—because the eruptions were large enough to
- **a.** mostly empty the volcanoes' magma chambers
- **b.** produce lava that flowed long distances
- **c.** produce lava that had a low silica content
- **d.** form dangerous pyroclastic flows and mudflows

7. The average temperature of Earth can decrease for several years when a huge volcanic eruption adds to the atmosphere large amounts of
- **a.** acid rain
- **b.** energy
- **c.** volcanic cinders
- **d.** volcanic gases

8. A thick layer of volcanic ash can be heavy enough to collapse the roofs of buildings because ash
- **a.** is produced as rocks burn
- **b.** is made up of tiny pieces of rock
- **c.** becomes heavier as it cools
- **d.** can hold large amounts of water

Extended Response

Answer the two questions below in detail. Include some of the terms shown in the word box. In your answers, underline each term you use.

boundaries	hot spots	rising
subduction	magma	heat
spreading centers		

9. Petra is marking the locations of active volcanoes on a map of the world. Explain how the locations of the volcanoes are related to the locations of tectonic plates.

10. Scientists regularly check the temperature of a lake on a volcano. Explain how this information might help them learn whether the volcano is becoming more active.

Chapter 5: **Mountains and Volcanoes** 167 **B**

Analyzing Data

1. a	3. c	5. c	7. d
2. a	4. d	6. a	8. b

Extended Response

9. RUBRIC

4 points for a response that correctly explains the relationship between volcanoes and tectonic plates and uses the following terms accurately:

- spreading centers
- hot spots
- boundaries
- subduction

Sample: Volcanoes are common at sub-duction zones along plate boundaries where an oceanic plate sinks beneath another plate. As the oceanic plate sinks, it partially melts into magma, which rises to form volcanoes. Volcanoes are also common at spreading centers where plates pull apart, allowing magma to rise from the mantle. Volcanoes can also form over hot spots far from plate boundaries as material rises from the mantle and melts the crust above it.

3 points correctly explains the relationship and uses three terms accurately
2 points correctly explains the relationship and uses two terms accurately
1 point correctly explains the relationship but does not use the terms

10. RUBRIC

4 points for a response that correctly explains the relationship between rising lake temperatures and increased volcanic activity and uses the following terms accurately:

- rising
- magma
- heat

Sample: Increased temperatures might mean that magma is rising under the volcano and heating lakes, springs, and other openings on the volcano.

3 points correctly explains the relationship and uses two terms accurately
2 points correctly explains the relationship and uses one term accurately
1 point correctly explains the relationship but does not use the terms

---

METACOGNITIVE ACTIVITY

Have students answer the following questions in their **Science Notebook:**

1. What did you find most difficult to understand about mountains and volcanoes?

2. What ideas did you have that you learned were incorrect?

3. How do the concepts of this chapter apply to your Unit Project?

Waves, Sound, and Light

transfer of energy

EM wave

MECHANICAL WAVE

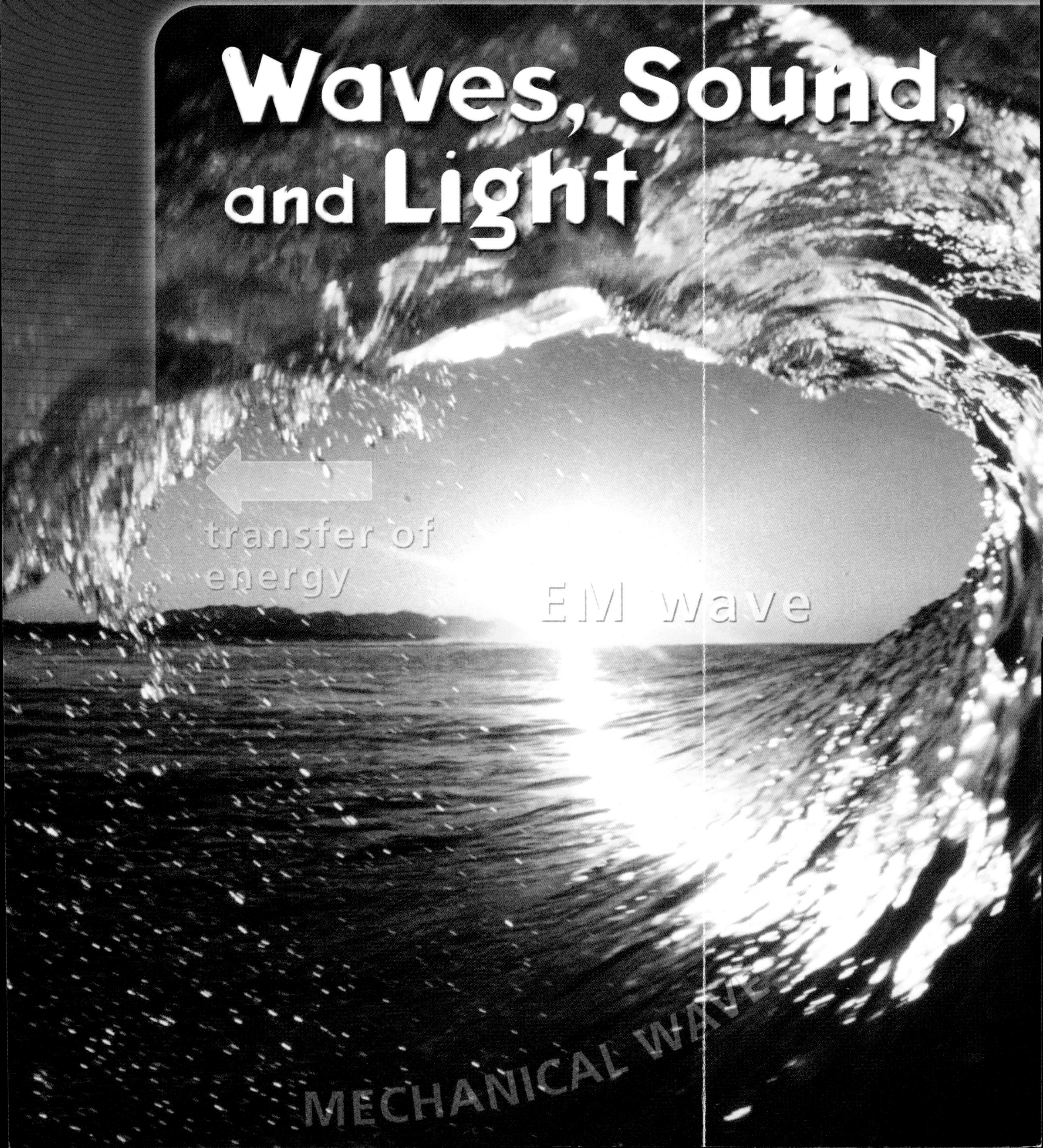

North Carolina Standards

In Unit C: Waves, Sound, and Light, students will learn and apply science concepts and skills related to the following goals from the North Carolina Standard Course of Study:

Competency Goal 1: The learner will design and conduct investigations to demonstrate an understanding of scientific inquiry. (Objectives 1.01–1.10)

Competency Goal 2: The learner will demonstrate an understanding of technological design. (Objectives 2.01–2.04)

Competency Goal 6: The learner will conduct investigations and examine models and devices to build an understanding of the characteristics of energy transfer and/or transformation.

6.01   Determine how convection and radiation transfer energy.

6.03   Analyze sound as an example that vibrating materials generate waves that transfer energy.

6.04   Evaluate data for qualitative and quantitative relationships associated with energy transfer and/or transformation.

6.05   Analyze the physical interactions of light and matter.

For a detailed lesson-by-lesson correlation of Unit C to the North Carolina Standard Course of Study, see Correlations pages 16–24 in the front of this Teacher's Edition.

Waves, Sound, and Light
Contents Overview

Unit Features

1 Waves   6

the **BIG** idea
Waves transfer energy and
interact in predictable ways.

2 Sound   34

the **BIG** idea
Sound waves transfer energy
through vibrations.

3 Electromagnetic Waves   70

the **BIG** idea
Electromagnetic waves transfer
energy through radiation.

4 Light and Optics   110

the **BIG** idea
Optical tools depend on
the wave behavior of light.

FRONTIERS in Science

VIDEO SUMMARY

SCIENTIFIC AMERICAN FRONTIERS

EACH SOUND IS A PRESENT "Each Sound Is a Present" is a segment of the Scientific American Frontiers series that aired on PBS stations. This segment focuses on Kelley Flynn, who suffered severe hearing damage from an infection. At seven, Kelley's hearing is becoming worse, and she will have cochlear implant surgery. The goal of the implant is to compensate for hair cells destroyed by Kelley's infection.

The human ear contains the cochlea, a spiral bone lined with thousands of tiny hairs that bend from sound vibrations. This movement triggers electrical signals along nerves to the brain, which receives and processes these signals as sound. Damaged hairs do not recover.

Kelley's surgeons replace cochlear hairs with electrodes connected to a magnet and an antenna implanted in her skull. After surgery, a transmitter is attached to the magnet inside her head. The transmitter is attached to a small computer that converts sounds collected by a microphone to electrical signals that are sent to the brain.

National Science Education Standards

A.9.a–d Understandings About Scientific Inquiry

E.6.a–f Understandings About Science and Technology

F.5.a–e Science and Technology in Society

G.1.a–b Science as a Human Endeavor

G.2.a Nature of science

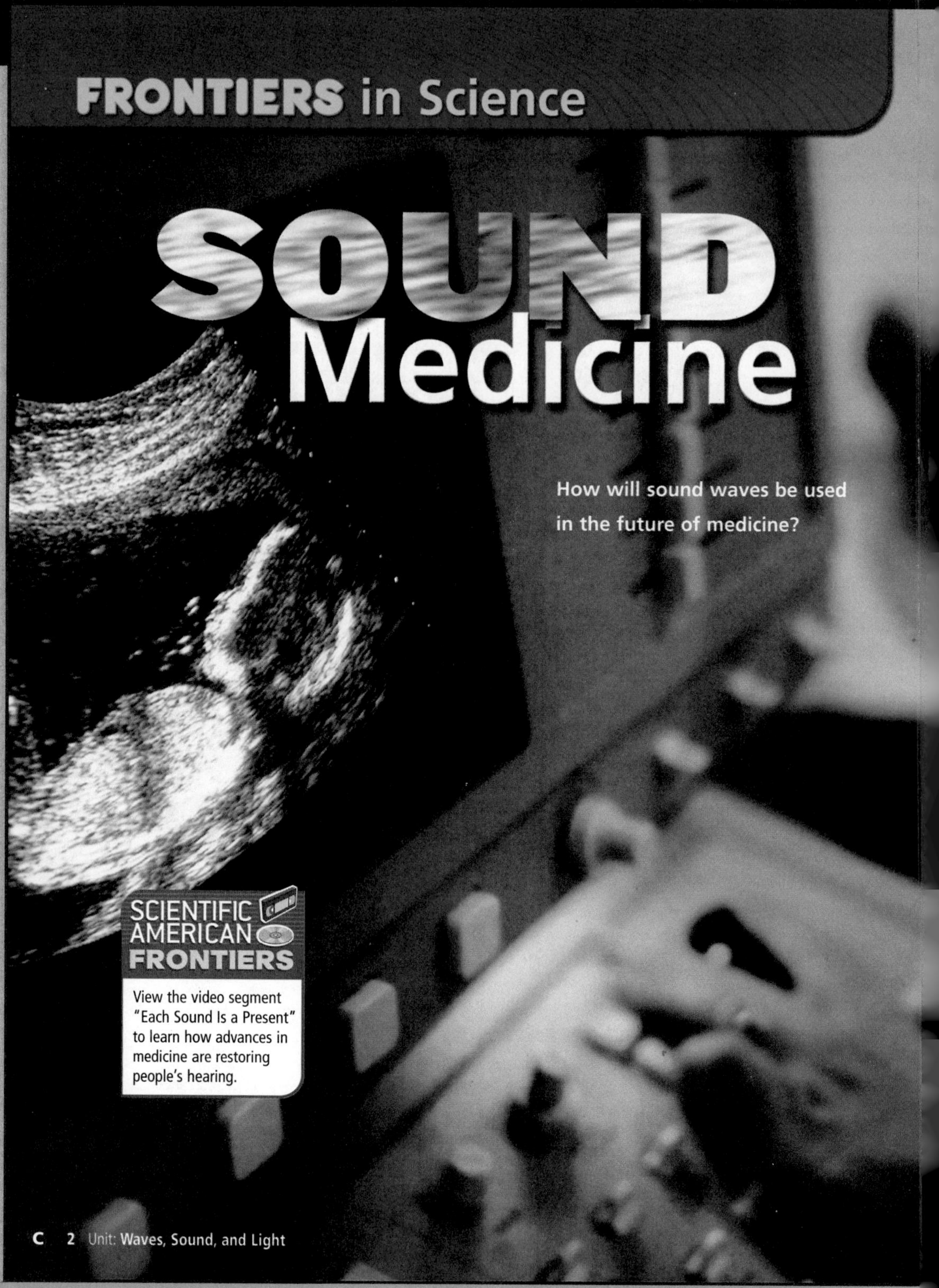

SOUND Medicine

How will sound waves be used in the future of medicine?

SCIENTIFIC AMERICAN FRONTIERS

View the video segment "Each Sound Is a Present" to learn how advances in medicine are restoring people's hearing.

C 2 Unit: Waves, Sound, and Light

ADDITIONAL RESOURCES

Technology Resources

 Scientific American Frontiers Video: *Each Sound Is a Present:* 7-minute video segment introduces the unit.

 ClassZone.com
CAREER LINK, careers in audiology

Guide student viewing and comprehension of the video:

 Frontiers in Science Teaching Guide, pp. 1–2; Viewing Guide, p. 3, Video Wrap-Up, p. 4

Scientific American Frontiers Video Guide, pp. 51–54

Unit project procedures and rubrics:

 Unit Projects, pp. 5–10

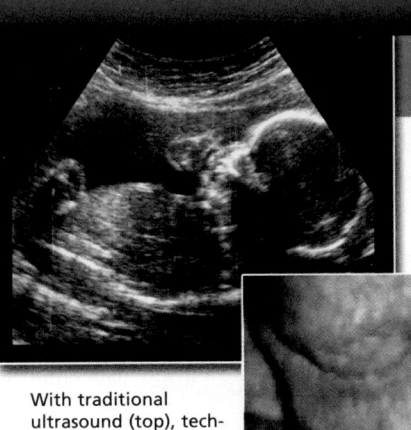

With traditional ultrasound (top), technicians interpret the image of the fetus. With the newer three-dimensional ultrasound (right), the image is much clearer.

Seeing Inside the Body

Have you ever wondered what the inside of your body looks like? Doctors have tried for many years to find ways of seeing what goes on inside a person's body that makes that person sick. Around 100 years ago, scientists found that a kind of wave called x-rays could be used to make images of the bones inside a person. This common method of seeing inside a body, is used mainly to show bones and teeth. However, repeated exposure to x-rays can be damaging to body cells. In the 1960s doctors started using a different kind of wave called ultrasound to make images of the organs inside the body.

Waves are now used in many medical applications. For example, cochlear implants use radio waves to help people hear. Ultrasound now has many new medical applications, from breaking up kidney stones to monitoring the flow of blood in the body.

Sound and Ultrasound

Sound is a type of wave, a vibration in the air. Humans can hear a wide range of different sounds, from very low pitches to very high. Sounds that are higher in pitch than humans can hear are referred to as ultrasound. They are no different from sounds we can hear, except they vibrate much faster than human ears can detect. Many animals can detect ultrasound; for example, dog whistles are in the ultrasound range.

(?) A

(?) B

▶ Set Learning Goals
Students will

- Observe practical uses of sound waves in medicine
- Compare technological uses of waves to similar uses in nature
- Design and produce a product that involves uses of waves

Remind students that frontiers are not totally unexplored areas; they are areas that are currently being explored and developed. Use the video segment "Each Sound Is a Present" to show that areas of science can have practical technologies yet still have new developments to come. Have students look at the ultrasound photographs and compare the effectiveness of the results shown.

INSTRUCT

Teach from Visuals

Have students examine the two ultrasound photographs and identify the heads and arms of the fetuses. Ask students if they know anyone who has had ultrasound tests or treatments. Emphasize that ultrasound is used for diagnosis of many diseases and disorders, including the presence and location of certain tumors.

Sharing Results

Ask: Why is it important that developments in medical research be shared among medical personnel? *Such developments are necessary for diagnosis and treatment of many diseases and disorders. The research that must be done is quite expensive and time-consuming, and specialized equipment is necessary. If the results of such research are not shared, the health of many people can be negatively affected.*

DIFFERENTIATE INSTRUCTION

(?) More Reading Support

A What type of wave is used to make images of bones inside a human body? *X-rays*

B Why can't humans hear ultrasound? *Its pitch is too high.*

Advanced Show students a copy of the electromagnetic spectrum. Point out the different types of electromagnetic waves. Ask: Why aren't ultrasound waves listed on the spectrum? *Ultrasound waves are sound waves, not electromagnetic waves.*

Teach from Visuals

Have students look at the figure of the dolphin and the sound waves reflecting off a fish, ask:

- Why do you think the process shown in this figure is called echolocation? *Sample answer: Dolphins use echoes to locate objects.*

- For what purposes other than finding food might a dolphin or bat use echolocation? *Sample answer: locate objects in its path*

Scientific Process

Emphasize to students that observations of wave behavior in nature were the bases for hypotheses regarding practical applications of waves. For example, observations of echolocation led to use of sound waves in ultrasound applications. By observing the results of these applications, further hypotheses can be made and conclusions can be drawn.

Asking a Question

Ask: In developing the technology that is used to help Kelley Flynn hear better, what questions might researchers have asked? *Sample answers: What part of the ear was damaged? What technology can duplicate the function of the damaged part of the ear?*

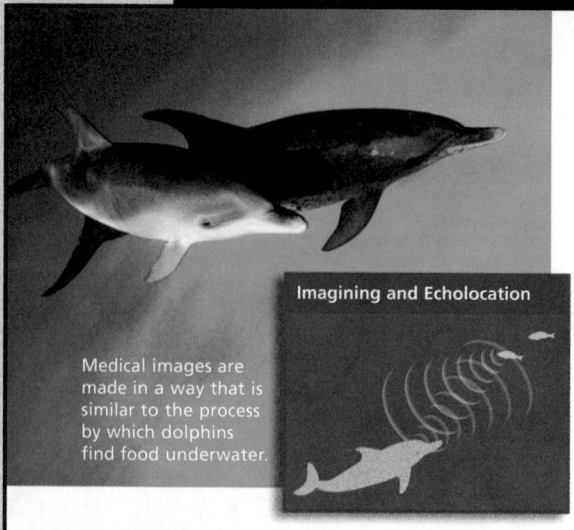

Imagining and Echolocation

Medical images are made in a way that is similar to the process by which dolphins find food underwater.

C

The technology of ultrasound in medicine is based upon a process similar to that used by bats and dolphins to find food, a process called echolocation. The animal emits an ultrasound click or chirp and then listens for an echo. The echo indicates that an object has reflected the sound back to the animal. Over time, these animals have evolved the ability to judge the distance of the object by noting the time required

for the sound to travel to the object and return. Echolocation enables bats to capture flying insects at night and dolphins to catch fish in the ocean depths, where light doesn't penetrate.

Similarly, in ultrasound imaging, a machine sends a beam of ultrasound into a person's body and detects any echoes. The waves reflect whenever they strike a boundary between two objects with different densities. A computer measures the time required for the wave to travel to the boundary and reflect back; this information is used to determine the location and shape of the organ. The computer can then generate a live image of the organ inside the body.

Ultrasound imaging has been used most often to monitor the development of a fetus inside its mother and to observe the valves of the heart. Blood flow can be color coded with faster flow in one color and slower flow in another color. The colors make it easier to see the location of blockages affecting the rate of flow in the blood vessels. This helps doctors detect blockages and diagnose heart problems.

?
D

SCIENTIFIC AMERICAN FRONTIERS

View the "Each Sound Is a Present" segment of your *Scientific American Frontiers* video to learn how a cochlear implant restores hearing to a young girl.

IN THIS SCENE FROM THE VIDEO ▶ A young girl's cochlear implant is turned on for the first time.

HEARING IS A GIFT A recent development in technology is about to give seven-year-old Kelly Flynn something she has always wanted—better hearing. Kelly has been almost completely deaf since she was two years old, and now she is losing the little hearing she does have. The development is a device called a cochlear

implant. Cochlear implants work inside the ear, stimulating the brain when a sound is detected.

Normally, sound travels as vibrations from the outer ear, through the middle ear to the inner ear, where thousands of tiny cells—called hair cells—register the quality of the sound and send a signal to the brain. In a cochlear implant, tiny electrical sensors, or electrodes, mimic the hair cells by registering the sound and sending a signal to the brain. The signals get to the electrodes through a system including a computer, microphone, and radio transmitter and receiver. Using this system, people with little or no hearing are able to sense sounds.

DIFFERENTIATE INSTRUCTION

? More Reading Support

C By what process do dolphins and bats locate food? *echolocation*

D What are two common medical uses of ultrasound? *studying a fetus and the heart*

Below Level Have each student write a short story about a bat on its nightly hunt for food. Stories should include how the bat uses echolocation to find food.

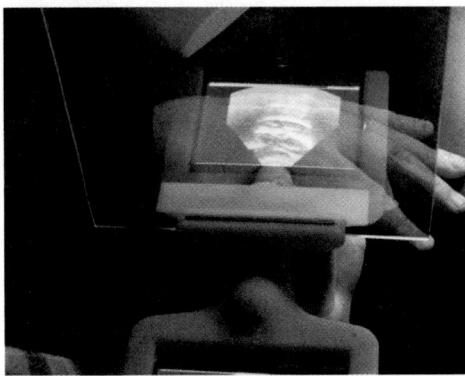

Recent advances in ultrasound technology include the development of portable devices that display images of the body, such as this hand-held device.

Advances in Ultrasound

Waves, including ultrasound, transfer energy. Physical therapists often use this fact when applying ultrasound to sore joints, heating the muscles and ligaments so they can move more freely. If the ultrasound waves are given stronger intensity and sharper focus, they can transfer enough energy to break up kidney stones in the body. The use of focused sound waves is now being tested for its ability to treat other problems, such as foot injuries.

Other recent advances in medical ultrasound include the development of devices that produce clearer images and use equipment that is smaller in size. In the late 1990's portable ultrasound devices were developed that allow the technology to be brought to the patient

UNANSWERED Questions

As scientists learn more about the use of sound and other types of waves, new questions will arise.

- Will new methods of imaging the body change the way diseases are diagnosed?
- How closely do sounds heard using a cochlear implant resemble sounds heard by the ear?

UNIT PROJECTS

As you study this unit, work alone or with a group on one of these projects.

Magazine Article

Write a magazine article about the medical uses of ultrasound.

- Collect information about medical ultrasound and take notes about applications that interest you.
- If possible, conduct an interview with a medical practitioner who uses ultrasound.
- Read over all your notes and decide what information to include in your article.

Make a Music Video

Make a music video for a song of your choice, and explain how the video uses sound waves and light waves.

- Plan the sound portion of the video, including how the music will be played and amplified.
- For the lighting, use colored cellophane or gels to mix different colors of light. Explain your choices.
- Rehearse the video. Record the video and present it to the class.

Design a Demonstration

Design a hands-on demonstration of echolocation.

- Research the use of echolocation by animals.
- Design a demonstration of echolocation using a tennis ball and an obstacle.
- Present your demonstration to the class.

 CAREER CENTER
CLASSZONE.COM

Learn more about careers in audiology.

Frontiers in Science **5** **C**

UNANSWERED Questions

Have students read the questions and think of some of their own. Remind them that scientists always end up with more questions—that inquiry is the driving force of science.

- With the class, generate on the board a list of new questions.
- Students can add to the list after they watch the Scientific American Frontiers Video.
- Students can use the list as a springboard for choosing their Unit Projects.

UNIT PROJECTS

Encourage students to pick the project that most appeals to them. Point out that each is long-term and will take several weeks to complete. You might group or pair students to work on projects and in some cases guide student choice.

Each project has two worksheet pages, including a rubric. Use the pages to guide students through criteria, process, and schedule.

R Unit Projects, pp. 5–10

Technology Resources

Visit **ClassZone.com** for project procedures and for science career direction.

 RESOURCE CENTER, Unit Projects

REVISIT concepts introduced in this article:

Chapter 1
- Properties of waves, pp. 16–23

Chapter 2
- Sound is a wave, pp. 37–43
- Uses of sound, pp. 58–63

Chapter 3
- Uses of electromagnetic waves, pp. 79–86

DIFFERENTIATE INSTRUCTION

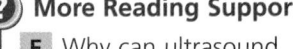

More Reading Support

E Why can ultrasound be used to break kidney stones? *It transfers energy.*

F What are two recent advances in ultrasound? *clearer images and smaller equipment*

Differentiate Unit Projects Projects are appropriate for varying abilities. Allow students to choose the ones that interest them most. Encourage them to vary the products they produce throughout the year. Encourage below-level students to try "Design a Demonstration." Challenge advanced students to complete the "Magazine Article."

Frontiers in Science **5** **C**

1 Waves

Physical Science
UNIFYING PRINCIPLES

PRINCIPLE 1

Matter is made of particles too small to see.

PRINCIPLE 2

Matter changes form and moves from place to place.

PRINCIPLE 3

Energy changes from one form to another, but it cannot be created or destroyed.

PRINCIPLE 4

Physical forces affect the movement of all matter on Earth and throughout the universe.

Unit: Waves, Sound, and Light
BIG IDEAS

CHAPTER 1
Waves

Waves transfer energy and interact in predictable ways.

CHAPTER 2
Sound

Sound waves transfer energy through vibrations.

CHAPTER 3
Electromagnetic Waves

Electromagnetic waves transfer energy through radiation.

CHAPTER 4
Light and Optics

Optical tools depend on the wave behavior of light.

CHAPTER 1
KEY CONCEPTS

SECTION 1.1

Waves transfer energy.

1. A wave is a disturbance.

2. Waves can be classified by how they move.

SECTION 1.2

Waves have measurable properties.

1. Waves have amplitude, wavelength, and frequency.

2. Wave speed can be measured.

SECTION 1.3

Waves behave in predictable ways.

1. Waves interact with materials.

2. Waves interact with other waves.

The Big Idea Flow Chart is available on p. T1 in the **UNIT TRANSPARENCY BOOK.**

Previewing Content

1.1 Waves transfer energy. pp. 9–15

1. A wave is a disturbance.

A **wave** is a disturbance that transfers energy from one place to another. **Mechanical waves** travel through a material, called a **medium,** transferring energy.

When a mechanical wave travels through a medium, such as water, ground, or air, the medium moves as the wave passes through it, but is not permanently moved. After the wave has passed, the medium returns to its former state.

2. Waves can be classified by how they move.

A **transverse wave** travels in the direction perpendicular to the disturbance that caused it. If you thrust your fist into a tub of water, waves travel out from the disturbance along the water's surface. These waves move at right angles to the downward force of your fist.

A **longitudinal wave** travels in the same direction as the disturbance that caused it. If you lay a spring toy on its side and push sharply on one end, waves will travel through the coils along the length of the spring toy. In this example, the disturbance—the push of your hand—is in the same direction in which the wave moves down the spring toy.

1.2 Waves have measurable properties. pp. 16–23

1. Waves have amplitude, wavelength, and frequency.

A wave has repeating **crests** and **troughs,** which alternate in a wave. **Amplitude** is either how high a wave peaks above level (at its crests) or how low it dips below level (at its troughs).

Wavelength is the distance from trough to trough or crest to crest. Wavelength can be measured from any part of one wave to the corresponding part on the next wave.

In a longitudinal wave such as in a spring toy, wavelength is the distance between compressions or rarefactions. Rarefactions are the spaces between compressions where the medium is spread out. Amplitude describes how tightly bunched the spring coils are in the wave.

Frequency is the number of wavelengths that pass a fixed point in a period of time—usually one second.

The graph below shows how wavelength, amplitude, and frequency are measured on a wave.

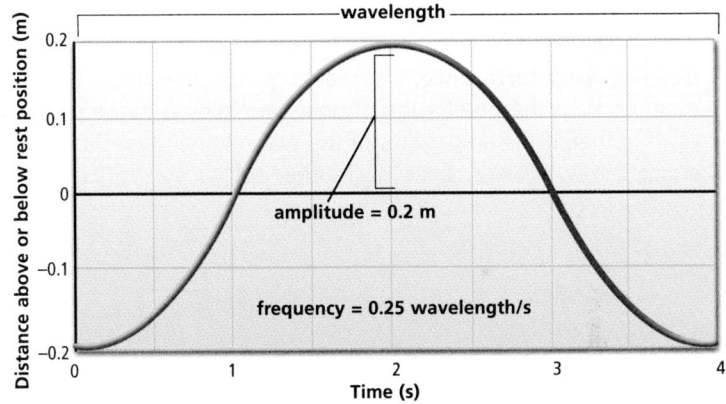

2. Wave speed can be measured.

The formula for calculating the speed of a wave is

$$S = \lambda \cdot f,$$

where S is speed, λ (lambda) is wavelength, and f is frequency.

Common Misconceptions

DISPLACEMENT OF MATTER Students may conceive of waves as the motion of matter from one place to another. Although matter can move in a wave, it is not permanently displaced. Rather, it is energy that is transferred in a wave.

[TE] This misconception is addressed on p. 12.

MISCONCEPTION DATABASE
CLASSZONE.COM Background on student misconceptions

Previewing Content

 Waves behave in predictable ways.
pp. 24–29

1. Waves interact with materials.

Waves behave predictably when they interact with barriers or other obstacles. Waves can undergo reflection, refraction, or diffraction.

- In **reflection,** waves meet a solid barrier and bounce back. For example, an echo occurs when a sound wave meets a wall and bounces back to the source of the sound.
- In **refraction,** waves move from one medium to another and bend, or refract. An example is a glass of water with a straw. Where the straw passes into the water, it looks broken. But the break is an illusion caused by refraction of light waves as they pass from air to water.
- In **diffraction,** waves interact with a partial barrier and a portion of the waves pass through and spread out. An example is the way sound waves spread around corners.

2. Waves interact with other waves.

In **constructive interference,** two waves combine in phase, so that a crest meets a crest or a trough meets a trough. In **destructive interference,** two waves of the same frequency meet up such that the trough of one wave joins with the crests of the other. If the amplitudes of the two original waves are equal, the two waves cancel each other out.

The following diagrams show how wave amplitudes can be added and subtracted as the waves interfere.

Constructive Interference   **Destructive Interference**

Previewing Labs

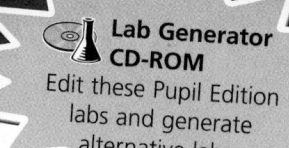

EXPLORE (the BIG idea)

How Can Energy Be Passed Along? p. 7
Students observe a domino effect and learn that energy can be transferred.

TIME 10 minutes
MATERIALS 4 video cassettes

How Can You Change a Wave? p. 7
Students make waves in a bowl and observe wave properties.

TIME 10 minutes
MATERIALS large bowl, half-full of water; pencil

Internet Activity: Waves, p. 7
Students find out how different forces start waves.

TIME 20 minutes
MATERIALS computer with Internet access

SECTION 1.1

EXPLORE Waves, p. 9
Students use a rope to find out how a wave travels.

TIME 5 minutes
MATERIALS 20 cm ribbon, 2 m rope, chair

INVESTIGATE Wave Types, p. 13
Students observe transverse and longitudinal waves in a spring toy.

TIME 10 minutes
MATERIALS spring toy

SECTION 1.2

INVESTIGATE Frequency, p. 20
Students vary the length of a pendulum to find out how length affects its frequency.

TIME 30 minutes
MATERIALS 3 metal washers, 60 cm string, 5 cm tape, stopwatch

CHAPTER INVESTIGATION Wavelength, pp. 22–23
Students vary the length of a pendulum to find out how it affects wavelength.

TIME 40 minutes
MATERIALS 1/2 sheet white paper, 16 cm tape, scissors, 80 cm string, meter stick, 40 mL fine sand, graduated cylinder, 2 sheets colored construction paper

SECTION 1.3

EXPLORE Reflection, p. 24
Students make ripples in water in a pan to find out how waves reflect.

TIME 10 minutes
MATERIALS wide, shallow pan, half-full of water; 3 drops food coloring; pencil

INVESTIGATE Diffraction, p. 26
Students manipulate water waves to go around an obstacle to learn about diffraction.

TIME 20 minutes
MATERIALS wide, shallow pan, half-full of water; 3 drops food coloring; plastic ruler; wooden block; sealable sandwich bag; 1–2 cups sand

R **Additional INVESTIGATION,** Tracking the Path of Light, A, B, & C, pp. 62–70; Teacher Instructions, pp. 284–285

Previewing Chapter Resources

	INTEGRATED TECHNOLOGY	LABS AND ACTIVITIES

CHAPTER 1
Waves

 CLASSZONE.COM
- eEdition Plus
- EasyPlanner Plus
- Misconception Database
- Content Review
- Test Practice
- Visualization
- Simulation
- Resource Centers
- Internet Activity: Waves
- Math Tutorial

 CD-ROMS
- eEdition
- EasyPlanner
- Power Presentations
- Content Review
- Lab Generator
- Test Generator

 AUDIO CDS
- Audio Readings
- Audio Readings in Spanish

 SCILINKS.ORG
SCILINKS

 Lab Generator CD-ROM
Generate customized labs.

PE EXPLORE the Big Idea, p. 7
- How Can Energy Be Passed Along?
- How Can You Change a Wave?
- Internet Activity: Waves

R **UNIT RESOURCE BOOK**
- Family Letter, p. vii
- Spanish Family Letter, p. viii
- Unit Projects, pp. 5–10

SECTION
 1.1 **Waves transfer energy.**
pp. 9–15

Time: 2 periods (1 block)
 R Lesson Plan, pp. 11–12

- **RESOURCE CENTER,** Waves
- **MATH TUTORIAL**

 T **UNIT TRANSPARENCY BOOK**
- Big Idea Flow Chart, p. T1
- Daily Vocabulary Scaffolding, p. T2
- Note-Taking Model, p. T3
- 3-Minute Warm-Up, p. T4

PE
- EXPLORE Waves, p. 9
- INVESTIGATE Wave Types, p. 13
- Math in Science, p. 15

R **UNIT RESOURCE BOOK**
- Datasheet, Wave Types, p. 20
- Math Support, p. 49
- Math Practice, p. 50

SECTION
 1.2 **Waves have measurable properties.**
pp. 16–23

Time: 3 periods (1.5 blocks)
 R Lesson Plan, pp. 22–23

- **VISUALIZATION,** Wave Graphing
- **RESOURCE CENTER,** Wave Speed

 T **UNIT TRANSPARENCY BOOK**
- Daily Vocabulary Scaffolding, p. T2
- 3-Minute Warm-Up, p. T4
- "Graphing a Wave" Visual, p. T6

PE
- INVESTIGATE Frequency, p. 20
- CHAPTER INVESTIGATION, Wavelength, pp. 22–23

R **UNIT RESOURCE BOOK**
- Datasheet, Frequency, p. 31
- Math Support & Practice, pp. 51–52
- CHAPTER INVESTIGATION, Wavelength, A, B, & C, pp. 53–61

SECTION
 1.3 **Waves behave in predictable ways.**
pp. 24–29

Time: 3 periods (1.5 blocks)
 R Lesson Plan, pp. 33–34

 T **UNIT TRANSPARENCY BOOK**
- Big Idea Flow Chart, p. T1
- Daily Vocabulary Scaffolding, p. T2
- 3-Minute Warm-Up, p. T5
- Chapter Outline, pp. T7–T8

PE
- EXPLORE Reflection, p. 24
- INVESTIGATE Diffraction, p. 26
- Connecting Sciences, p. 29

R **UNIT RESOURCE BOOK**
- Datasheet, Diffraction, p. 42
- Additional INVESTIGATION, Tracking the Path of Light, A, B, & C, pp. 62–70

READING AND REINFORCEMENT

ASSESSMENT

STANDARDS

- Four Square, B22–23
- Combination Notes, C36
- Daily Vocabulary Scaffolding, H1–8

R **UNIT RESOURCE BOOK**
- Vocabulary Practice, pp. 46–47
- Decoding Support, p. 48
- Summarizing the Chapter, pp. 71–72

 Audio Readings CD
Listen to Pupil Edition.

 Audio Readings in Spanish CD
Listen to Pupil Edition in Spanish.

PE
- Chapter Review, pp. 31–32
- Standardized Test Practice, p. 33

A **UNIT ASSESSMENT BOOK**
- Diagnostic Test, pp. 1–2
- Chapter Test, A, B, & C, pp. 6–17
- Alternative Assessment, pp. 18–19

 Spanish Chapter Test, pp. 281–284

 Test Generator CD-ROM
Generate customized tests.

 Lab Generator CD-ROM
Rubrics for Labs

National Standards
A.2–8, A.9.a–c, A.9.e–f, B.3.a, G.1.b

See p. 6 for the standards.

R **UNIT RESOURCE BOOK**
- Reading Study Guide, A & B, pp. 13–16
- Spanish Reading Study Guide, pp. 17–18
- Challenge and Extension, p. 19
- Reinforcing Key Concepts, p. 21
- Challenge Reading, pp. 44–45

TE Ongoing Assessment, pp. 9–14

PE Section 1.1 Review, p. 14

A **UNIT ASSESSMENT BOOK**
Section 1.1 Quiz, p. 3

National Standards
A.2–8, A.9.a–c, A.9.e–f, B.3.a, G.1.b

R **UNIT RESOURCE BOOK**
- Reading Study Guide, A & B, pp. 24–27
- Spanish Reading Study Guide, pp. 28–29
- Challenge and Extension, p. 30
- Reinforcing Key Concepts, p. 32

TE Ongoing Assessment, pp. 16–21

PE Section 1.2 Review, p. 21

A **UNIT ASSESSMENT BOOK**
Section 1.2 Quiz, p. 4

National Standards
A.2–8, A.9.a–c, A.9.e–f, G.1.b

R **UNIT RESOURCE BOOK**
- Reading Study Guide, A & B, pp. 35–38
- Spanish Reading Study Guide, pp. 39–40
- Challenge and Extension, p. 41
- Reinforcing Key Concepts, p. 43

TE Ongoing Assessment, pp. 24–25, 27–28

PE Section 1.3 Review, p. 28

A **UNIT ASSESSMENT BOOK**
Section 1.3 Quiz, p. 5

National Standards
A.2–8, A.9.a–c, A.9.e–f, G.1.b

Previewing Resources for Differentiated Instruction

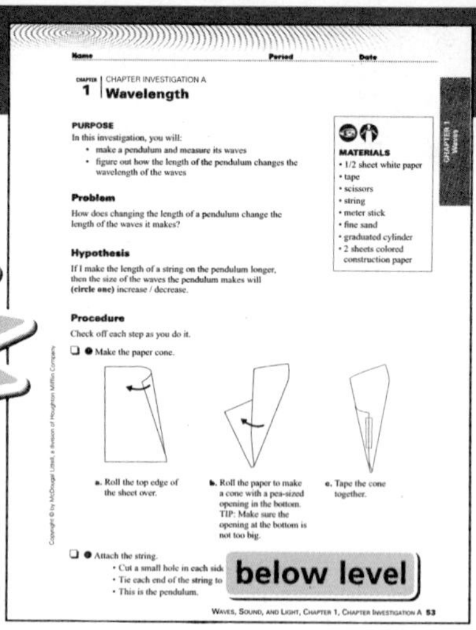

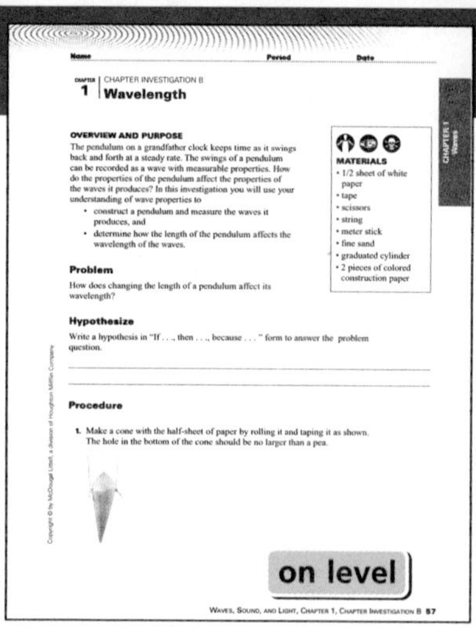

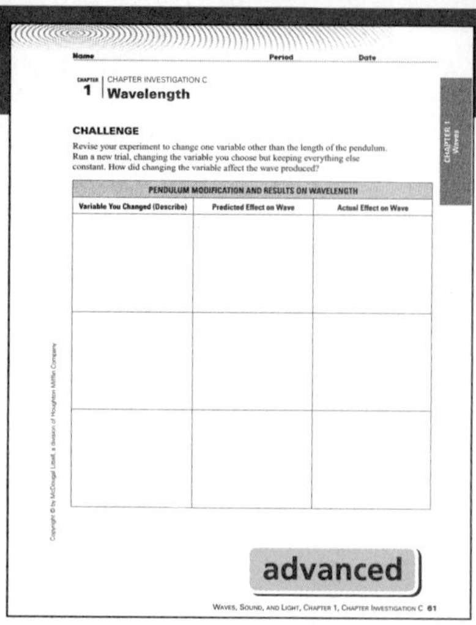

CHAPTER INVESTIGATION

Leveled resources present the same concepts for different abilities.

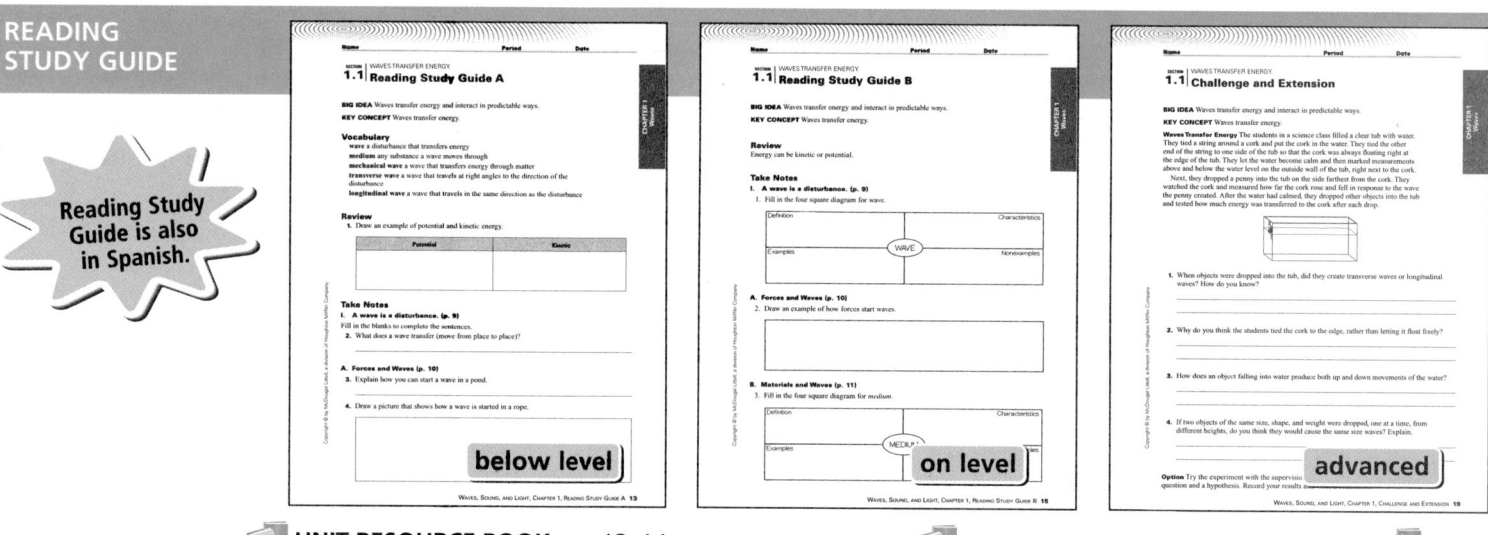

UNIT RESOURCE BOOK, pp. 53–56 · pp. 57–60 · pp. 57–61

below level · on level · advanced

READING STUDY GUIDE

Reading Study Guide is also in Spanish.

UNIT RESOURCE BOOK, pp. 13–14 · pp. 15–16 · p. 19

below level · on level · advanced

CHAPTER TEST

Chapter Test is also in Spanish.

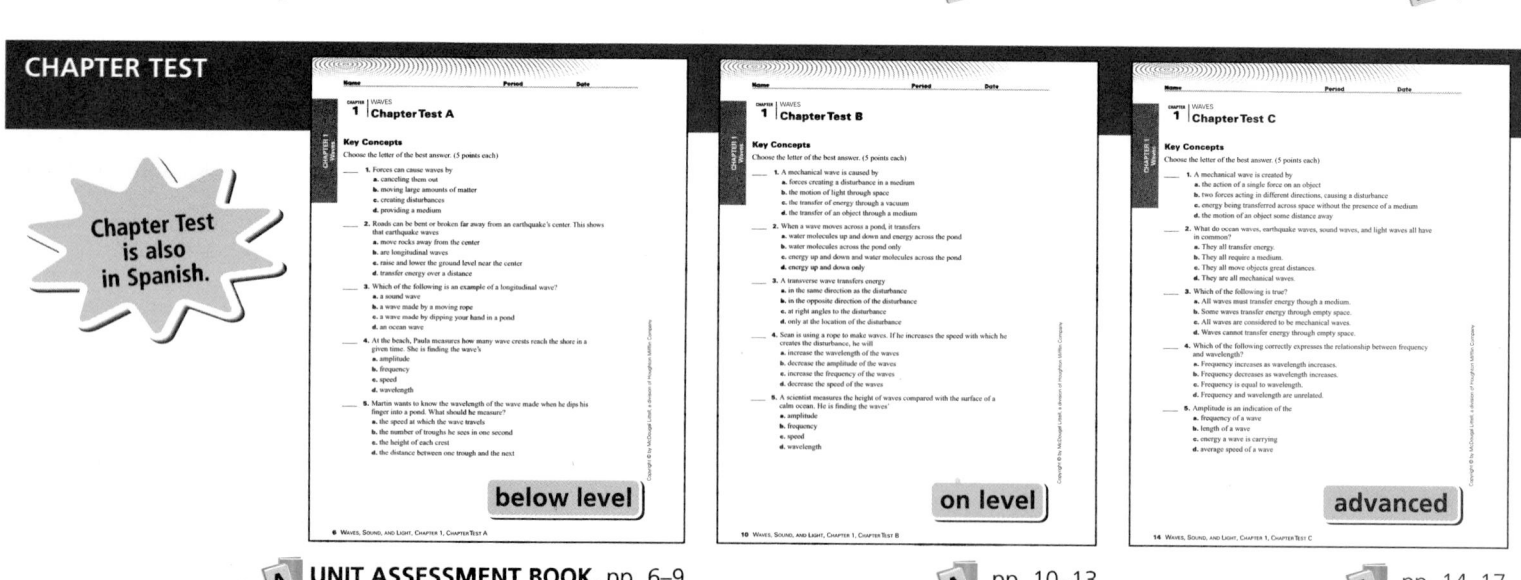

UNIT ASSESSMENT BOOK, pp. 6–9 · pp. 10–13 · pp. 14–17

below level · on level · advanced

TECHNOLOGY

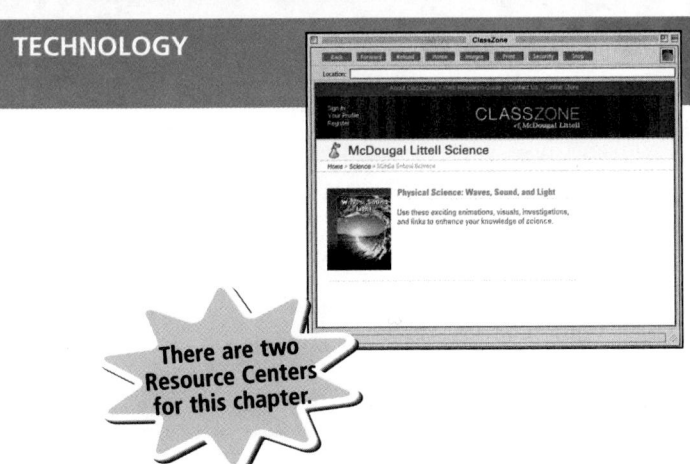

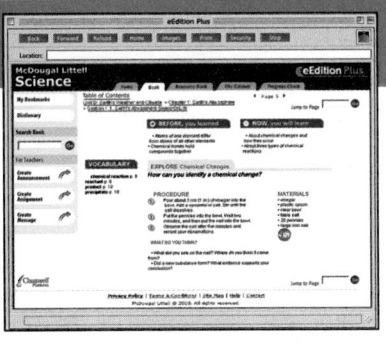

There are two Resource Centers for this chapter.

CLASSZONE.COM

CD/CD-ROMS

CLASSZONE.COM

VISUAL CONTENT

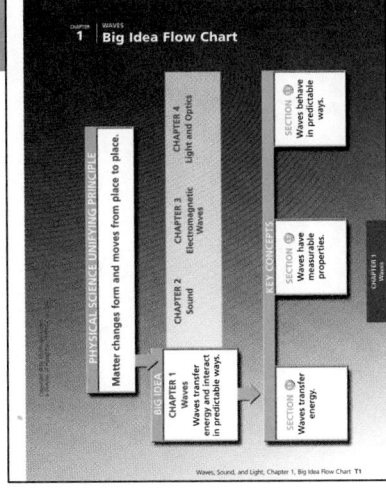

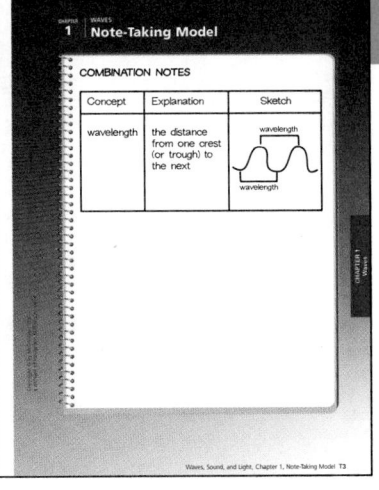

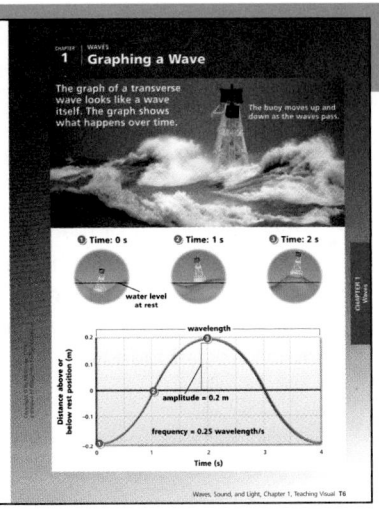

T **UNIT TRANSPARENCY BOOK,** p. T1

 **T** p. T3

 **T** p. T6

MORE SUPPORT

Reinforcing Key Concepts for each section

R **UNIT RESOURCE BOOK,** p. 21

R pp. 46–47

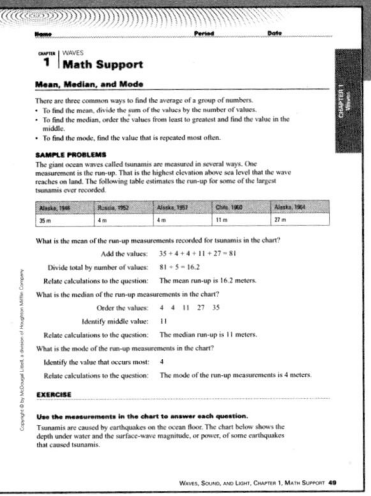 **R** p. 49

INTRODUCE

the **BIG** idea

Have students look at the photograph of the surfers riding the waves and discuss how the question in the box links to the Big Idea:

- What clues can you find that the wave carries energy?
- What parts of the wave can you see?
- What other kinds of waves can you think of?
- How do waves move from one place to another?

National Science Education Standards

Content

B.3.a Energy is a property of many substances and is associated with heat, light, electricity, mechanical motion, sound, nuclei, and the nature of a chemical. Energy is transferred in many ways.

Process

A.2–8 Design and conduct an investigation; use tools to gather and interpret data; use evidence to describe, predict, explain, model; think critically to make relationships between evidence and explanation; recognize different explanations and predictions; communicate scientific procedures and explanations; use mathematics.

A.9.a, A.9.c, A.9.e Understand scientific inquiry by using different investigations, methods, mathematics, and explanations based on logic, evidence, and skepticism.

G.1.b Science requires different abilities.

CHAPTER

1 Waves

the **BIG** idea

Waves transfer energy and interact in predictable ways.

> **What is moving these surfers?**

Key Concepts

SECTION
1.1 **Waves transfer energy.**
Learn about forces and energy in wave motion.

SECTION
1.2 **Waves have measurable properties.**
Learn how the amplitude, wavelength, and frequency of a wave are measured.

SECTION
1.3 **Waves behave in predictable ways.**
Learn about reflection, refraction, diffraction, and interference.

Internet Preview

CLASSZONE.COM

Chapter 1 online resources: Content Review, Simulation, Visualization, two Resource Centers, Math Tutorial, Test Practice

C 6 Unit: Waves, Sound, and Light

INTERNET PREVIEW

CLASSZONE.COM For student use with the following pages:

Review and Practice
- Content Review, pp. 8, 30
- Math Tutorial: Finding the Mean, Median, and Mode, p. 15
- Test Practice, p. 33

Activities and Resources
- Internet Activity: Waves, p. 7
- Resource Centers: Waves, p. 14; Wave Speed, p. 21
- Visualization: Wave Graphing, p. 18

NSTA scilinks.org SC*L*INKS

Seismic Waves **Code: MDL027**

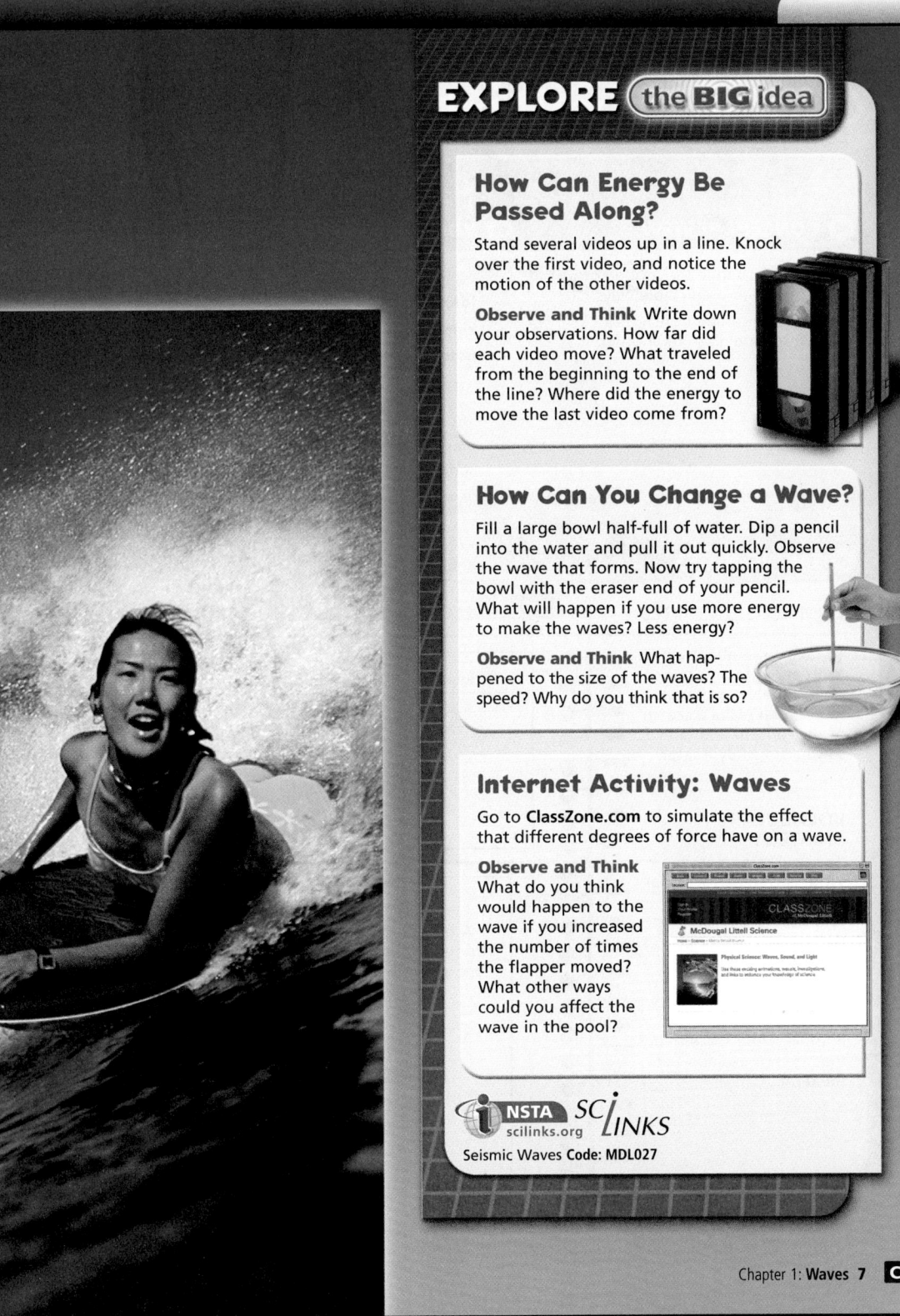

EXPLORE (the BIG idea)

How Can Energy Be Passed Along?

Stand several videos up in a line. Knock over the first video, and notice the motion of the other videos.

Observe and Think Write down your observations. How far did each video move? What traveled from the beginning to the end of the line? Where did the energy to move the last video come from?

How Can You Change a Wave?

Fill a large bowl half-full of water. Dip a pencil into the water and pull it out quickly. Observe the wave that forms. Now try tapping the bowl with the eraser end of your pencil. What will happen if you use more energy to make the waves? Less energy?

Observe and Think What happened to the size of the waves? The speed? Why do you think that is so?

Internet Activity: Waves

Go to **ClassZone.com** to simulate the effect that different degrees of force have on a wave.

Observe and Think What do you think would happen to the wave if you increased the number of times the flapper moved? What other ways could you affect the wave in the pool?

NSTA
scilinks.org

SCLINKS

Seismic Waves Code: MDL027

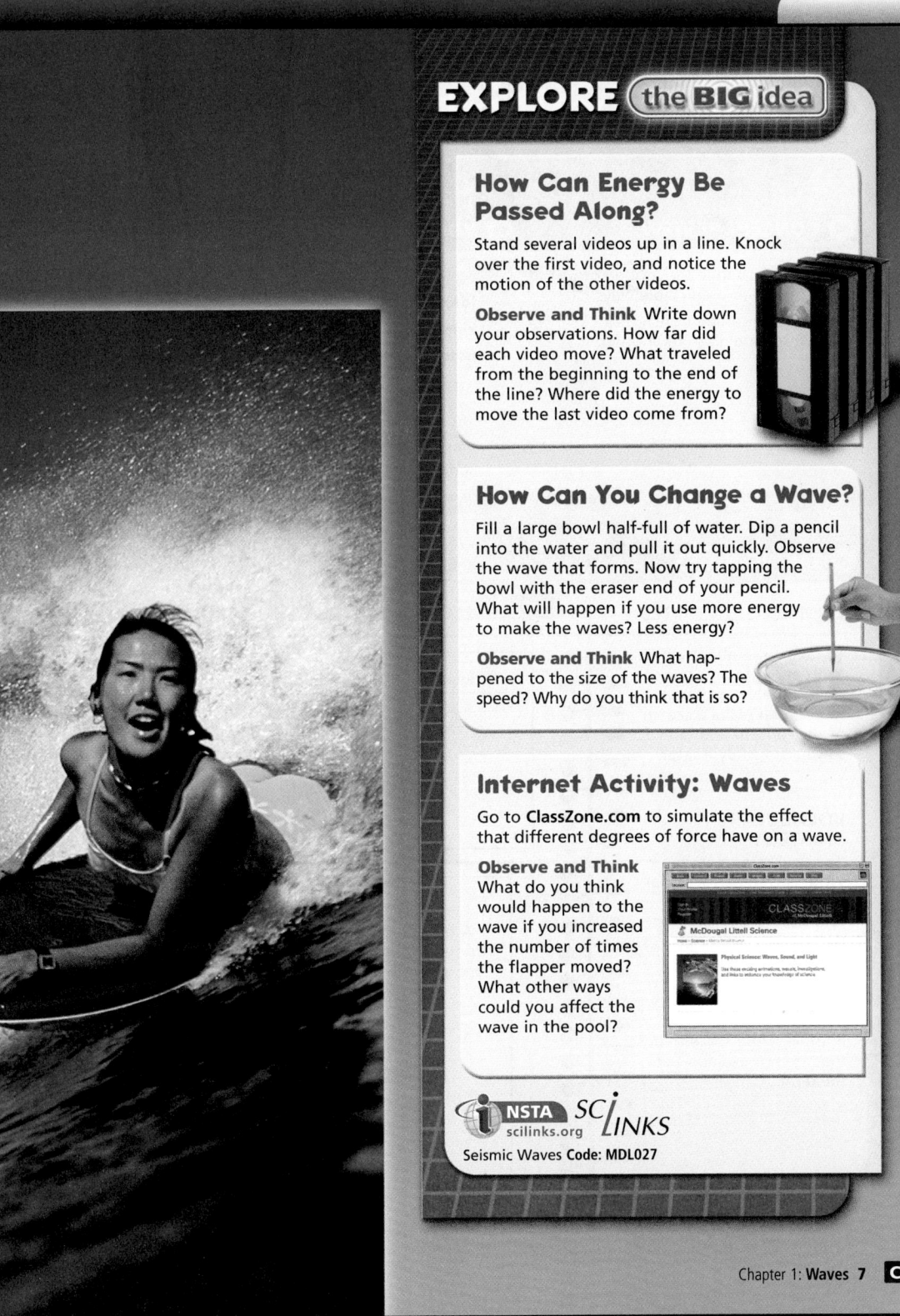

TEACHING WITH TECHNOLOGY

Computer Software and Overhead Projector Use a computer-generated wave to illustrate the form and motion of a transverse wave on p. 13. Help students identify crest, trough, amplitude, frequency, and wavelength in the wave.

Graphing Calculator Use a graphing calculator on p. 18 to graph sine and cosine functions. Graph $y = \sin x$ and $y = \cos x$, then point out to students that the graphs form a shape of a wave. Challenge students to alter the equations and report their findings. Ask them how the amplitude and wavelength vary.

EXPLORE (the BIG idea)

These inquiry-based activities are appropriate for use at home or as a supplement to classroom instruction.

How Can Energy Be Passed Along?

PURPOSE To introduce students to the idea that energy can be transferred. Students set up a row of video cassettes, push the first one, and observe as the whole row falls over.

TIP *10 min.* Students may use dominoes as an alternative to the video cassettes.

Answer: each video moved only to the next video; energy traveled from the beginning to the end of the line; the original source of energy could be the push, the first cassette falling, or the next to last cassette falling

REVISIT after p. 12.

How Can You Change a Wave?

PURPOSE To introduce students to wave properties such as amplitude and speed. Students generate and observe waves in a bowl.

TIP *10 min.* Only a small motion of the pencil is needed.

Answer: More energy produced larger waves; less energy produced smaller waves. The speed of the waves remained the same. Energy affects size of waves, but some other factor must affect speed of waves.

REVISIT after p. 21.

Internet Activity: Waves

PURPOSE To show how forces are involved in waves.

TIP *20 min.* Students observe waves produced by varying forces.

Answer: The waves would be produced at a higher rate if you increased the number of times the flapper moved. You could also affect the wave by moving the flapper slowly, or changing the amount of force applied by the flapper.

REVISIT after p. 10.

PREPARE

◐ CONCEPT REVIEW

Activate Prior Knowledge

Put two marbles on a flat surface. Flick one marble so that it strikes the other one. The first marble must move forcefully enough to move the second marble as well.

- Ask: How did force change the motion of the first marble? *The first marble went from rest to motion.*

- Ask: How was energy transferred to the second marble? *Energy was transferred from the first marble to the second marble when they hit.*

◐ TAKING NOTES

Combination Notes

Combining pictures with notes will help students connect abstract concepts with concrete examples. The three-column format allows students to write their notes in the first and second columns and draw their pictures in the third column.

Vocabulary Strategy

The four square diagram helps students organize complex information in a user-friendly, visual way. The format also prompts students to process more information for a concept than they might otherwise do.

Vocabulary and Note-Taking Resources

- Vocabulary Practice, pp. 46–47
- Decoding Support, p. 48

- Daily Vocabulary Scaffolding, p. T2
- Note-Taking Model, p. T3

- Four Square, B22–23
- Combination Notes, C36
- Daily Vocabulary Scaffolding, H1–8

◐ CONCEPT REVIEW

- Forces change the motion of objects in predictable ways.
- Energy can be transferred from one place to another.

◐ VOCABULARY REVIEW

See Glossary for definitions.

force

kinetic energy

potential energy

ⓘ CONTENT REVIEW
CLASSZONE.COM
Review concepts and vocabulary.

▶ TAKING NOTES

COMBINATION NOTES

To take notes about a new concept, write an explanation of the concept in a table. Then make a sketch of the concept and label it so you can study it later.

VOCABULARY STRATEGY

Write each new vocabulary term in the center of a **four square** diagram. Write notes in the squares around each term. Include a definition, some characteristics, and some examples of the term. If possible, write some things that are not examples of the term.

See the Note-Taking Handbook on pages R45–R51.

SCIENCE NOTEBOOK

Concept	Explanation	Sketch
Forces and waves	Forces move a medium up and down or back and forth. A wave moves forward.	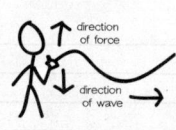

Definition	Characteristics
A disturbance that transfers energy from one place to another	Matter moves in place. Energy travels entire distance.

WAVE

Examples	Nonexamples
Water wave Sound wave	Ball rolling Water rushing downstream

CHECK READINESS

Administer the Diagnostic Test to determine students' readiness for new science content and their mastery of requisite math skills.

 Diagnostic Test, pp. 1–2

Technology Resources

Students needing content and math skills should visit **ClassZone.com**.

- **CONTENT REVIEW**
- **MATH TUTORIAL**

 CONTENT REVIEW CD-ROM

KEY CONCEPT

1.1 Waves transfer energy.

 BEFORE, you learned
- Forces can change an object's motion
- Energy can be kinetic or potential

▶ **NOW, you will learn**
- How forces cause waves
- How waves transfer energy
- How waves are classified

VOCABULARY

wave p. 9
medium p. 11
mechanical wave p. 11
transverse wave p. 13
longitudinal wave p. 14

EXPLORE Waves

How will the rope move?

PROCEDURE

① Tie a ribbon in the middle of a rope. Then tie one end of the rope to a chair.

② Holding the loose end of the rope in your hand, stand far enough away from the chair that the rope is fairly straight.

③ Flick the rope by moving your hand up and down quickly. Observe what happens.

MATERIALS
- ribbon
- rope
- chair

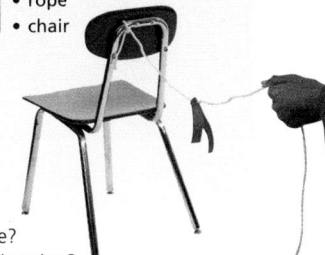

WHAT DO YOU THINK?
- How did the rope move? How did the ribbon move?
- What do you think starts a wave, and what keeps it going?

A wave is a disturbance.

You experience the effects of waves every day. Every sound you hear depends on sound waves. Every sight you see depends on light waves. A tiny wave can travel across the water in a glass, and a huge wave can travel across the ocean. Sound waves, light waves, and water waves seem very different from one another. So what, exactly, is a wave?

READING **TiP**

To *disturb* means to agitate or unsettle.

A **wave** is a disturbance that transfers energy from one place to another. Waves can transfer energy over distance without moving matter the entire distance. For example, an ocean wave can travel many kilometers without the water itself moving many kilometers. The water moves up and down—a motion known as a disturbance. It is the disturbance that travels in a wave, transferring energy.

 **CHECK YOUR READING** How does an ocean wave transfer energy across the ocean?

RESOURCES FOR DIFFERENTIATED INSTRUCTION

Below Level

UNIT RESOURCE BOOK
- Reading Study Guide A, pp. 13–14
- Decoding Support, p. 48

 **AUDIO CDS**

Advanced

UNIT RESOURCE BOOK
- Challenge and Extension, p. 19
- Challenge Reading, pp. 44–45

English Learners

UNIT RESOURCE BOOK
Spanish Reading Study Guide, pp. 17–18

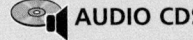 **AUDIO CDS**
- Audio Readings in Spanish
- Audio Readings (English)

1.1 FOCUS

▶ Set Learning Goals

Students will
- Explain how forces cause waves.
- Explain how waves transfer energy.
- Classify wave types.
- Compare and contrast different wave types in an experiment.

◀ 3-Minute Warm-Up

Display Transparency 4 or copy this exercise on the board:

1. Name two ways you can apply force to a soccer ball. *kicking with feet and hitting with hands*

2. Name two ways the force you apply can change the motion of the soccer ball. *The force changes the ball's speed and direction*

T 3-Minute Warm-Up, p. T4

1.1 MOTIVATE

EXPLORE Waves

PURPOSE To think of how wave motion starts and how a wave moves through a medium

TIP *5 min.* Jump ropes work well.

WHAT DO YOU THINK? *A wave moved through the rope; the ribbon moved up and down. Forces start a wave and keep it going through the material.*

Ongoing Assessment

CHECK YOUR READING *Answer: through a moving disturbance, which we see as a moving wave*

Teach from Visuals

To help students interpret the rope wave visual, ask:

- What represents the forces? *the up and down arrows*
- What produces the forces? *the person's hand and arm moving up and down*
- What is the result of the force? *a wave traveling down the rope*

Ask similar questions for the other visuals on the page.

Real World Example

A telephone cord wave can occur when you stretch out the cord and shake one end of the cord. The wave moves along the cord and reaches the handset.

EXPLORE (the BIG idea)

Revisit "Internet Activity: Waves" on p. 7. Have students explain the reasons for their results.

Ongoing Assessment

Explain how forces cause waves.

When a diver hits the smooth surface of water in a swimming pool, series of waves spread in all directions. Ask: How do forces make this happen? *The force of the diver striking the surface pushes water briefly out of the way; then the water rushes back in. These movements in the water set off the series of ripples, or waves, across the pool.*

Forces and Waves

You know that a force is required to change the motion of an object. Forces can also start a disturbance, sending a wave through a material. The following examples describe how forces cause waves.

READING TiP
As you read each example, think of how it is similar to and different from the other examples.

Example 1 Rope Wave Think of a rope that is tied to a doorknob. You apply one force to the rope by flicking it upward and an opposite force when you snap it back down. This sends a wave through the rope. Both forces—the one that moves the rope up and the one that moves the rope down—are required to start a wave.

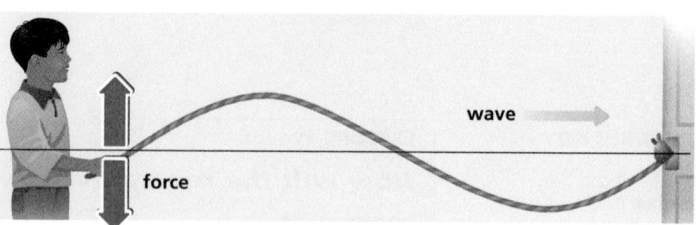

Example 2 Water Wave Forces are also required to start a wave in water. Think of a calm pool of water. What happens if you apply a force to the water by dipping your finger into it? The water rushes back after you remove your finger. The force of your finger and the force of the water rushing back send waves across the pool.

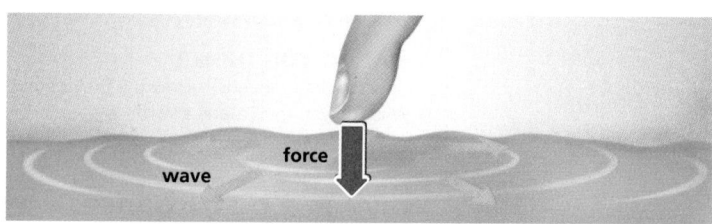

Example 3 Earthquake Wave An earthquake is a sudden release of energy that has built up in rock as a result of the surrounding rock pushing and pulling on it. When these two forces cause the rock to suddenly break, the energy is transferred as a wave through the ground.

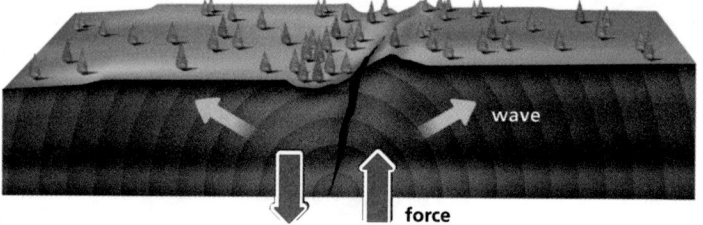

DIFFERENTIATE INSTRUCTION

More Reading Support

A What is required to make a disturbance that will set off a wave? *forces*

English Learners English learners may not always understand certain abbreviated instructions. For example, when a student is asked to "study a sketch," the word *study* is vague to an English learner. Use precise instructions like *examine*, *analyze*, or *compare*, and make sure students know the exact meaning of these instructions.

Materials and Waves

A rope tied to a doorknob, water, and the ground all have something in common. They are all materials through which waves move. A **medium** is any substance that a wave moves through. Water is the medium for an ocean wave; the ground is the medium for an earthquake wave; the rope is the medium for the rope wave. In the next chapter, you will learn that sound waves can move through many mediums, including air.

Waves that transfer energy through matter are known as **mechanical waves.** All of the waves you have read about so far, even sound waves, are mechanical waves. Water, the ground, a rope, and the air are all made up of matter. Later, you will learn about waves that can transfer energy through empty space. Light is an example of a wave that transfers energy through empty space.

VOCABULARY
Add a four square for *medium* to your notebook.

○ **CHECK YOUR READING** How are all mechanical waves similar?

Energy and Waves

The waves caused by an earthquake are good examples of energy transfer. The disturbed ground shakes from side to side and up and down as the waves move through it. Such waves can travel kilometers away from their source. The ground does not travel kilometers away from where it began; it is the energy that travels in a wave. In the case of an earthquake, it is kinetic energy, or the energy of motion that is transferred.

This photograph was taken after a 1995 earthquake in Japan. A seismic wave transferred enough energy through the ground to bend the railroad tracks, leaving them in the shape of a wave.

Develop Critical Thinking

CLASSIFY Write the following choices on the board:

- air
- water
- rocks and soil

State that these can all be mediums for different kinds of waves. Have students identify the medium for each of the following waves:

- ocean wave *water*
- seismic wave in an earthquake *rocks and soil*
- pulsating sound from a bell *air*

Ongoing Assessment

CHECK YOUR READING *Answer: All mechanical waves transfer energy through matter.*

DIFFERENTIATE INSTRUCTION

 **More Reading Support**

B What is the medium for an ocean wave? *water*

C Does a mechanical wave transfer material or energy? *energy*

Below Level Students may find the term *medium* confusing in the context of wave science. Students are likely to be familiar with *medium* meaning "halfway" or "in between."

Write the following sentences on the board:

- I like my steak medium rare.
- Water is the medium for an ocean wave . . . (p. 11).

Ask: Which of these sentences involves the scientific definition of *medium*? *the second sentence*

Address Misconceptions

IDENTIFY Ask students to imagine a wave in water. Ask: What moves from the beginning to the end of the wave? If students say water (or other matter), they may hold the misconception that matter is transferred in a wave.

CORRECT Have several students stand in a row. Have the first student tap the second on the shoulder, who in turn taps the third student, and so on. Notice that energy is transferred to the end of the row while each student stays in place.

REASSESS Ask: Why don't ocean waves that move toward the shore empty out the ocean? *Because waves transfer energy, not matter.*

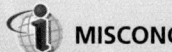
EXPLORE (the **BIG** idea)

Revisit "How Can Energy Be Passed Along?" on p. 7. Have students explain the reasons for their results.

Integrate the Sciences

Although ocean waves do not pile up water onshore, their energy dramatically shapes the coast. Examples of wave erosion on seacoasts include the formation of broad sandy beaches, sand spits and barrier islands, and stacks (rocky columns isolated in the water near the shoreline) or coves in stony coastlines.

Ongoing Assessment

Classify waves by how they move.

Ask: Name three directions waves can move. *up and down, side to side, or forward and backward*

READING VISUALS *Answer: The people move up and down. The wave moves around the stadium.*

CHECK YOUR READING *Answer: In an ocean wave, one part of the water pushes on the next. In the stadium wave, the people do not push on each other. Thus, the stadium wave is not a real wave because the energy is not transferred through a medium.*

C 12 Unit: **Waves, Sound, and Light**

A Wave Model

When these fans do "the wave" in a stadium, they are modeling the way a disturbance travels through a medium.

Each person only moves up and down.

The wave can move all the way around the stadium.

READING VISUALS In which direction do people move when doing the stadium wave? In which direction does the wave move?

Look at the illustration of people modeling a wave in a stadium. In this model, the crowd of people represents a wave medium. The people moving up and down represent the disturbance. The transfer of the disturbance around the stadium represents a wave. Each person only moves up and down, while the disturbance can move all the way around the stadium.

Ocean waves are another good example of energy transfer. Ocean waves travel to the shore, one after another. Instead of piling up all the ocean water on the shore, however, the waves transfer energy. A big ocean wave transfers enough kinetic energy to knock someone down.

 D

CHECK YOUR READING How does the stadium wave differ from a real ocean wave?

Waves can be classified by how they move.

? **E**

As you have seen, one way to classify waves is according to the medium through which they travel. Another way to classify waves is by how they move. You have read that some waves transfer an up-and-down or a side-to-side motion. Other waves transfer a forward-and-backward motion.

C 12 Unit: **Waves, Sound, and Light**

DIFFERENTIATE INSTRUCTION

? **More Reading Support**

D What does an ocean wave transfer? *energy*

E What are two ways to classify waves? *by medium and by how the wave moves*

Advanced Have students who are interested in learning about harnessing the energy of ocean waves read the following article:

 Challenge Reading, pp. 44–45

Transverse Waves

Think again about snapping the rope with your hand. The action of your hand causes a vertical, or up-and-down, disturbance in the rope. However, the wave it sets off is horizontal, or forward. This type of wave is known as a transverse wave. In a **transverse wave,** the direction in which the wave travels is perpendicular, or at right angles, to the direction of the disturbance. *Transverse* means "across" or "crosswise." The wave itself moves crosswise as compared with the vertical motion of the medium.

READING TiP

Perpendicular means at a 90° angle.

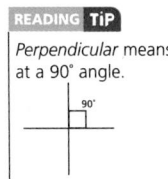

Transverse Wave

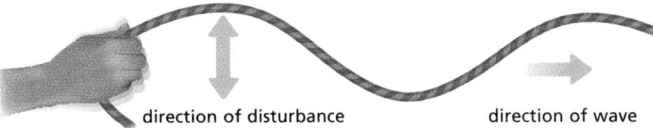

direction of disturbance   direction of wave

Water waves are also transverse. The up-and-down motion of the water is the disturbance. The wave travels in a direction that is perpendicular to the direction of the disturbance. The medium is the water, and energy is transferred outward in all directions from the source.

CHECK YOUR READING What is a transverse wave? Find two examples in the paragraphs above.

INVESTIGATE Wave Types

How do waves compare?

PROCEDURE

1. Place the spring toy on the floor on its side. Stretch out the spring. To start a disturbance in the spring, take one end and move it from side to side. Observe the movement in the spring. Remember that a transverse wave travels at right angles to the disturbance.

2. Put the spring toy on the floor in the same position as before. Think about how you could make a different kind of disturbance to produce a different kind of wave. (**Hint:** Suppose you push the spring in the direction of the wave you expect to make.) Observe the movement in the spring.

WHAT DO YOU THINK?
- Compare the waves you made. How are they alike? How are they different?
- What kind of wave did you produce by moving the spring from side to side?

CHALLENGE Can you think of a third way to make a wave travel through a spring?

SKILL FOCUS
Comparing

MATERIALS
spring toy

TIME
10 minutes

INVESTIGATE Wave Types

PURPOSE To observe a spring and explore the differences between transverse waves and longitudinal waves

TIPS *10 min.* Suggest the following:
- In step 1, make the shape of the spring toy look like a wavy line.
- In step 2, concentrate on what is happening inside the spring coils instead of the overall shape of the spring toy.

WHAT DO YOU THINK? *Both types travel from one end of the spring to the other. Transverse waves move the spring from side to side; longitudinal waves move the spring forward and backward.*

CHALLENGE *pinching together a bunch of coils and letting them go; moving the spring up and down*

R Datasheet, Wave Types, p. 20

Technology Resources

Customize this student lab as needed or look for an alternative. Print rubrics to assess student lab reports.

Lab Generator CD-ROM

Teaching with Technology

Use a computer-generated sine wave to illustrate the form and motion of a transverse wave. Use an overhead projector and ask students to identify the parts and properties of the wave.

Teach Difficult Concepts

Some students may have difficulty with the concept of a right angle in a three-dimensional context. Place a box on a tabletop. Help students identify the right angle between the vertical side of the box and the table surface. Have them think of other familiar examples.

Ongoing Assessment

CHECK YOUR READING *Answer: a wave that moves perpendicular to the direction of the disturbance; water waves and rope waves*

DIFFERENTIATE INSTRUCTION

More Reading Support

F What does transverse mean? *"across" or "crosswise"*

Inclusion Offer a wave model that is tailored to students with visual impairments. Ask students to imagine they are floating on an inner tube on a lake in which the water's surface is disturbed by waves. Ask how they would move with the waves. *They would bob up and down.* What types of waves are involved in this scenario? How do you know? *transverse; bobbing up and down is disturbance in a direction perpendicular to the direction of the wave.*

C 14   Unit: **Waves, Sound, and Light**

Longitudinal Waves

Another type of wave is a longitudinal wave. In a **longitudinal wave** (LAHN-jih-TOOD-n-uhl), the wave travels in the same direction as the disturbance. A longitudinal wave can be started in a spring by moving it forward and backward. The coils of the spring move forward and bunch up and then move backward and spread out. This forward and backward motion is the disturbance. Longitudinal waves are sometimes called compressional waves because the bunched-up area is known as a compression. How is a longitudinal wave similar to a transverse wave? How is it different?

Longitudinal Wave

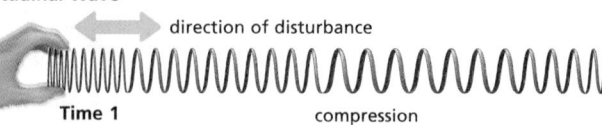

direction of disturbance

Time 1

compression

Time 2

direction of wave

Time 3

Sound waves are examples of longitudinal waves. Imagine a bell ringing. The clapper inside the bell strikes the side and makes it vibrate, or move back and forth rapidly. The vibrating bell pushes and pulls on nearby air molecules, causing them to move forward and backward. These air molecules, in turn, set more air molecules into motion. A sound wave pushes forward. In sound waves, the vibrations of the air molecules are in the same direction as the movement of the wave.

1.1 Review

KEY CONCEPTS

1. Describe how forces start waves.
2. Explain how a wave can travel through a medium and yet the medium stays in place. Use the term *energy* in your answer.
3. Describe two ways in which waves travel, and give an example of each.

CRITICAL THINKING

4. **Analyze** Does water moving through a hose qualify as a wave? Explain why or why not.
5. **Classify** Suppose you drop a cookie crumb in your milk. At once, you see ripples spreading across the surface of the milk. What type of waves are these? What is the disturbance?

○ CHALLENGE

6. **Predict** Suppose you had a rope long enough to extend several blocks down the street. If you were to start a wave in the rope, do you think it would continue all the way to the other end of the street? Explain why or why not.

C 14   Unit: Waves, Sound, and Light

Before going out on the water, boaters can check reports on wave conditions in their area.

Wave Heights

MATH TUTORIAL
CLASSZONE.COM
Click on Math Tutorial for more help with finding the mean, median, and mode.

Tracking stations throughout the world's oceans measure and record the height of water waves that pass beneath them. The data recorded by the stations can be summarized as average wave heights over one hour or one day.

How would you summarize the typical wave heights over one week? There are a few different ways in which data can be summarized. Three common ways are finding the mean, median, and mode.

Example

Wave height data for one week are shown below.

1.2 m	1.5 m	1.4 m	1.7 m	2.0 m	1.4 m	1.3 m

(1) Mean To find the mean of the data, divide the sum of the values by the number of values.

$$\text{Mean} = \frac{1.2 + 1.5 + 1.4 + 1.7 + 2.0 + 1.4 + 1.3}{7} = 1.5 \text{ m}$$

ANSWER The mean wave height is 1.5 m.

(2) Median To find the median of the data, write the values in order from least to greatest. The value in the middle is the median.

1.2 m   1.3 m   1.4 m   (1.4 m)   1.5 m   1.7 m   2.0 m

ANSWER The median wave height is 1.4 m.

(3) Mode The mode is the number that occurs most often.

ANSWER The mode for the data is also 1.4 m.

Use the data to answer the following questions.

The data below show wave heights taken from a station off the coast of Florida over two weeks.

Wk 1	1.2 m	1.1 m	1.1 m	1.5 m	4.7 m	1.2 m	1.1 m
Wk 2	0.7 m	0.8 m	0.9 m	0.8 m	1.0 m	1.1 m	0.8 m

1. Find the mean, median, and mode of the data for Week 1.

2. Find the mean, median, and mode of the data for Week 2.

CHALLENGE A storm carrying strong winds caused high waves on the fifth day of the data shown above for Week 1. Which of the following was most affected by the high value—the mean, median, or mode?

Set Learning Goal

To learn how to calculate three kinds of averages: mean, median, and mode

Present the Science

Point out that wave height measures from trough to crest.

Develop Estimation Skills

Students may wonder how to calculate median for an even number of data values. Inform students that they would find the two center values and calculate their mean value.

Make up a row of data with an even number of values and have students calculate the median.

Close

Present the following scenario: You are collecting and analyzing test scores for all sixth-grade students in the Centerville school system. What special insight would each of the three kinds of averages give you about students' test performance? *Sample answer: The mean will give an idea of the overall success of all the classes; the median will show approximately what the average student's score was; the mode will show where scores clustered.*

 • Math Support, p. 49
• Math Practice, p. 50

Technology Resources

Students can visit **ClassZone.com** for practice finding mean, median, and mode.

 MATH TUTORIAL

ANSWERS

1. mean (1.2 + 1.1 + 1.1 + 1.5 + 4.7 + 1.2 + 1.1) ÷ 7 = 1.7 m; mean = 1.7 m
median 1.1 m; 1.1 m; 1.1 m; (1.2 m); 1.2 m; 1.5 m; 4.7 m; median = 1.2 m;
mode = 1.1 m

2. mean (0.7 + 0.8 + 0.9 + 0.8 + 1.0 + 1.1 + 0.8) ÷ 7 = 0.9 m; mean = 0.9 m
median 0.7 m; 0.8 m; 0.8 m; (0.8 m); 0.9 m; 1.0 m; 1.1 m
median = 0.8 m; mode = 0.8 m

CHALLENGE the mean

● Set Learning Goals

Students will

- Learn how to measure amplitude, wavelength, and frequency.
- Calculate a wave's speed.
- Collect data to investigate how to change frequency in an experiment.

◀ 3-Minute Warm-Up

Display Transparency 4 or copy this exercise on the board:

How could you measure each of these things? What problems might you encounter in doing so?

1. width of a door opening
2. volume of liquid
3. length of time

Sample answers:

1. with measuring tape; keeping the tension in the tape across the door opening to get an accurate measurement

2. with a measuring cup; making sure liquid is stable

3. with a stopwatch; determining start and end time and variations in timing

 3-Minute Warm-Up, p. T4

1.2 MOTIVATE

THINK ABOUT

PURPOSE To think about different ways a wave can be measured

DISCUSS Have students look at the photograph and describe the scene. Solicit ideas for ways in which waves can be measured.

Ongoing Assessment

CHECK YOUR READING *Answer: amplitude, frequency, and wavelength*

◀ **BEFORE, you learned**

- Forces cause waves
- Waves transfer energy
- Waves can be transverse or longitudinal

▶ **NOW, you will learn**

- How amplitude, wavelength, and frequency are measured
- How to find a wave's speed

VOCABULARY

crest p. 17
trough p. 17
amplitude p. 17
wavelength p. 17
frequency p. 17

THINK ABOUT

How can a wave be measured?

This enormous wave moves the water high above sea level as it comes crashing through. How could you find out how high a water wave actually goes? How could you find out how fast it is traveling? In what other ways do you think a wave can be measured? Read on to find out.

Waves have amplitude, wavelength, and frequency.

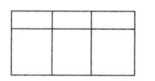

COMBINATION NOTES
Use combination notes in your notebook to describe how waves can be measured.

The tallest ocean wave ever recorded was measured from the deck of a ship during a storm. An officer on the ship saw a wave reach a height that was level with a point high on the ship, more than 30 meters (100 ft)! Height is a property of all waves—from ripples in a glass of water to gigantic waves at surfing beaches—and it can be measured.

The speed of a water wave is another property that can be measured—by finding the time it takes for one wave peak to travel a set distance. Other properties of a wave that can be measured include the time between waves and the length of a single wave. Scientists use the terms *amplitude*, *wavelength*, and *frequency* to refer to some commonly measured properties of all waves.

 **CHECK YOUR READING** What are three properties of a wave that can be measured?

C 16 Unit: Waves, Sound, and Light

RESOURCES FOR DIFFERENTIATED INSTRUCTION

Below Level

UNIT RESOURCE BOOK
- Reading Study Guide A, pp. 24–25
- Decoding Support, p. 48

 **AUDIO CDS**

Advanced

UNIT RESOURCE BOOK
Challenge and Extension, p. 30

English Learners

UNIT RESOURCE BOOK
Spanish Reading Study Guide, pp. 28–29

AUDIO CDS

- Audio Readings in Spanish
- Audio Readings (English)

Measuring Wave Properties

A

B

A **crest** is the highest point, or peak, of a wave. A **trough** is the lowest point, or valley, of a wave. Suppose you are riding on a boat in rough water. When the boat points upward and rises, it is climbing to the crest of a wave. When it points downward and sinks, the boat is falling to the trough of the wave.

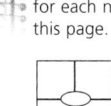

① **Amplitude** is the distance between a line through the middle of a wave and a crest or trough. In an ocean wave, amplitude measures how far the wave rises above, or dips below, its original position, or rest position.

Amplitude is an important measurement, because it indicates how much energy a wave is carrying. The bigger the amplitude, the more energy the wave has. Find amplitude on the diagram below.

② The distance from one wave crest to the very next crest is called the **wavelength.** Wavelength can also be measured from trough to trough. Find wavelength on the diagram below.

③ The number of wavelengths passing a fixed point in a certain amount of time is called the **frequency.** The word *frequent* means "often," so frequency measures how often one wavelength occurs. Frequency is often measured by counting the number of crests or troughs that pass by a given point in one second. Find frequency on the diagram below.

> **VOCABULARY**
> Remember to add a four square to your notebook for each new term on this page.

CHECK YOUR READING How is amplitude related to energy?

Wave Properties

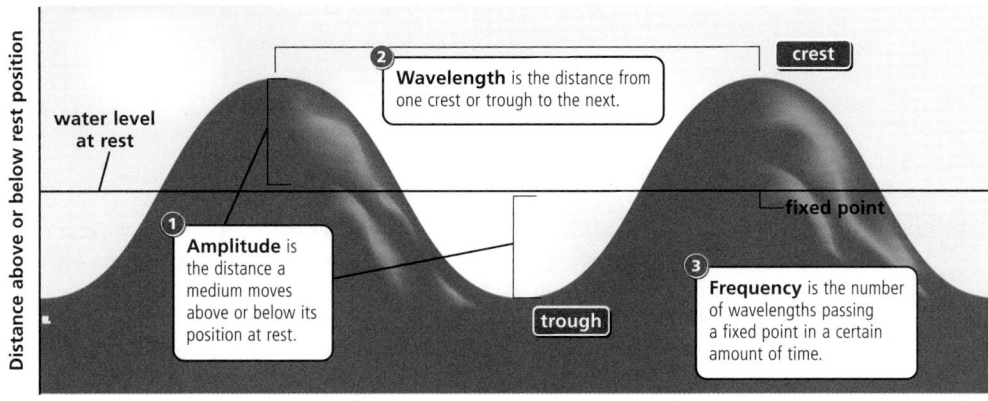

Distance above or below rest position

water level at rest

② **Wavelength** is the distance from one crest or trough to the next.

crest

① **Amplitude** is the distance a medium moves above or below its position at rest.

fixed point

trough

③ **Frequency** is the number of wavelengths passing a fixed point in a certain amount of time.

READING VISUALS How many wavelengths are shown in this diagram? How do you know?

Chapter 1: **Waves** **17** **C**

Develop Critical Thinking

EVALUATE Instruct students to think about two waves having equal frequencies and wavelengths. Ask them if that means the waves are identical. Have them draw a diagram to explain their answer. *Two waves can have the same frequency and wavelength without being identical if they have different amplitudes.*

Ongoing Assessment

Learn how to measure frequency.

Ask: How is frequency measured? *Frequency is measured by counting the number of crests or troughs that pass by a fixed point in one second.*

CHECK YOUR READING *Answer: The larger the amplitude, the more energy a wave carries.*

READING VISUALS *Answer: two wavelengths, shown from trough to trough*

DIFFERENTIATE INSTRUCTION

? More Reading Support

A What is the crest of a wave? *the highest point, or peak*

B What is the trough of a wave? *the lowest point, or valley*

English Learners Be aware that English learners do not always have the same background knowledge as the rest of the class. For example, this section's Investigate refers to small, metal rings called *washers.* English learners most likely won't connect the term *washer* to the metal rings in front of them. You may also want to point out the comparative structure of sentences such as: The bigger the amplitude, the more energy the wave has (p. 17).

Teach Difficult Concepts

Students may have trouble with the concept of wave frequency. Ask students to brainstorm examples of repetitive events. Students might think of natural cycles such as the sun rising and setting each day. Point out that the patterns change repeatedly with a particular frequency, or repeating time period. For example, the sun rises every 24 hours.

Relate examples to frequency in wave motion: in a transverse wave, the pattern is repeating crests or troughs; in a longitudinal wave, the pattern is repeating bunched-up areas. Emphasize that frequency describes *regular* repeating patterns.

Teach from Visuals

Draw attention to the visual of the spring toy. Ask:

• What repeating pattern do you observe? *bunching up/ spreading out*

• What part of the spring coil corresponds to the wave crest? *where the coils are spread out*

• What part corresponds to the wave trough? *where the coils are bunched up*

Teaching with Technology

On a graphing calculator, have students graph $y = \sin x$ and $y = \cos x$. Point out that the graphs form a shape of a wave. Ask students to alter the equations (for example, $y = 3 \sin x$, $y = \sin 2x$) and have them compare the different wavelengths and amplitudes.

Ongoing Assessment

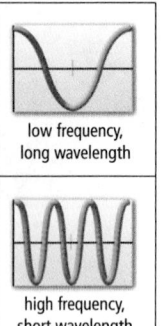

low frequency, long wavelength

high frequency, short wavelength

REMINDER
Frequency is the number of wavelengths that pass a given point in a certain amount of time.

VISUALIZATION
CLASSZONE.COM
Watch the graph of a wave form.

How Frequency and Wavelength Are Related

The frequency and wavelength of a wave are related. When frequency increases more wave crests pass a fixed point each second. That means the wavelength shortens. So, as frequency increases, wavelength decreases. The opposite is also true—as frequency decreases, wavelength increases.

Suppose you are making waves in a rope. If you make one wave crest every second, the frequency is one wavelength per second. Now suppose you want to increase the frequency to more than one wavelength per second. You flick the rope up and down faster. The wave crests are now closer together. In other words, their wavelengths have decreased.

Graphing Wave Properties

The graph of a transverse wave looks much like a wave itself. The illustration on page 19 shows the graph of an ocean wave. The measurements for the graph come from a float, or buoy (BOO-ee), that keeps track of how high or low the water goes. The graph shows the positioning of the buoy at three different points in time. These points are numbered. Since the graph shows what happens over time, you can see the frequency of the waves.

Unlike transverse waves, longitudinal waves look different from their graphs. The graph of a longitudinal wave in a spring is drawn below. The coils of the spring get closer and then farther apart as the wave moves through them.

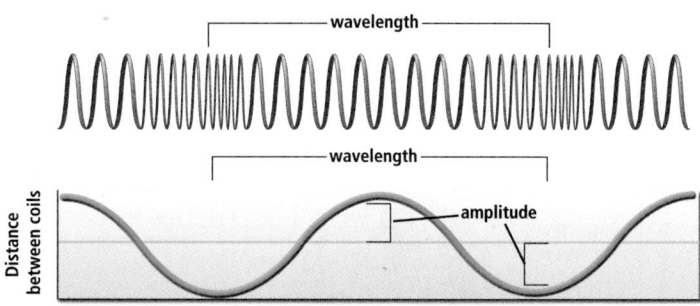

wavelength

wavelength

amplitude

Distance between coils

The shape of the graph resembles the shape of a transverse wave. The wavelength on a longitudinal wave is the distance from one compression to the next. The amplitude of a longitudinal wave measures how compressed the medium gets. Just as in a transverse wave, frequency in a longitudinal wave is the number of wavelengths passing a fixed point in a certain amount of time.

CHECK YOUR READING How are longitudinal waves measured?

DIFFERENTIATE INSTRUCTION

Below Level Draw two identical rectangular boxes far apart on the board, each about 65 cm wide and 25 cm deep. Ask two volunteers to each draw waves in one of the boxes. Have one student draw lazy, slow waves and the other fast-moving waves.

Ask: Which box has the most waves? Which box has the longest wavelengths? *Students should see that more waves mean shorter wavelengths (as in the box with fast-moving waves) and that fewer waves mean longer wavelengths (as in the box with slow waves).*

Graphing a Wave

The graph of a transverse wave looks like a wave itself. The graph shows what happens over time.

The buoy moves up and down as the waves pass.

1 **Time: 0 s** The buoy is below the rest position.

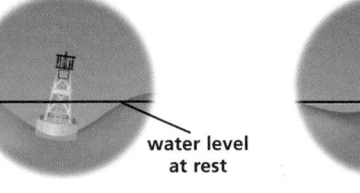

water level at rest

2 **Time: 1 s** The buoy is equal with the rest position.

3 **Time: 2 s** The buoy is above the rest position.

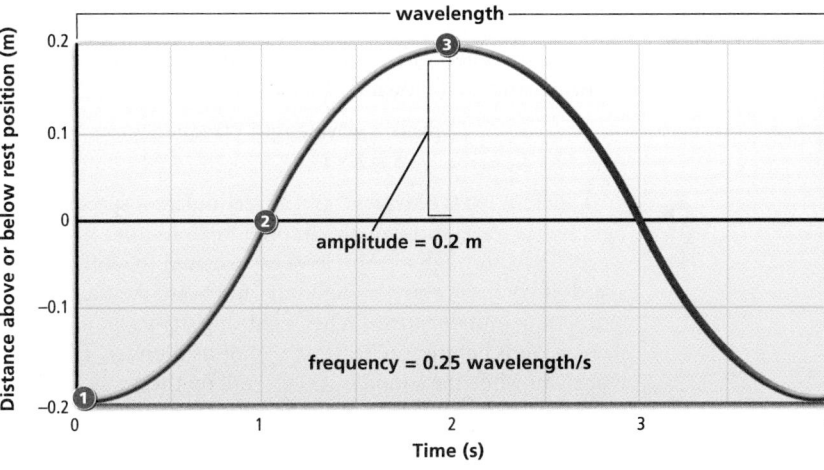

wavelength

amplitude = 0.2 m

frequency = 0.25 wavelength/s

Distance above or below rest position (m)

Time (s)

READING VISUALS How many seconds does it take for one wavelength to pass? How much of the wave passes in one second?

Chapter 1: **Waves** 19 **C**

DIFFERENTIATE INSTRUCTION

? **More Reading Support**

D Which type of wave has a graph that looks like the real wave—transverse or longitudinal? *transverse*

Advanced Instruct students to use the data in the graph on this page. Have them make a graph in which the frequency is doubled (0.5 wavelengths/second).

Have students write a sentence or two comparing their modified graph to the printed one.

R Challenge and Extension, p. 30

Teach from Visuals

To help students interpret the "Graphing a Wave" visual, ask:

- What are the different parts of the visual on this page? *a photo, three diagrams, and a graph*
- What does the curved line on the graph represent? *the wave in the photo*
- What do the *x*-axis and the *y*-axis represent? *time in seconds, and distance (amplitude) in meters*
- What do the bubble pictures above the graph show? Why are they important? *The buoy bobs up and down as a wave passes underneath; it is the fixed point from which frequency and other wave measurements can be taken.*

T The visual "Graphing a Wave" is available as T6 in the Unit Transparency Book.

Teacher Demo

Demonstrate wavelength and frequency in a wave. Tie a cord to a fixed object such as a doorknob; holding the other end, move back until the cord is taut. Pull up and down on the cord to set off waves, and then have students identify crests and troughs. Ask students how they could measure wavelength. Measure distance from one crest or trough to the next.

Place an object under the cord between you and the tied end. Prompt students to count waves passing this reference point as you call time. Say "start" when you set off the rope wave, time three seconds, and then say "stop." Get students' wave counts. Have students discuss how they counted the waves and how they could use their data to determine frequency.

Ongoing Assessment

READING VISUALS *Answer: 4 seconds; one-fourth of the wave*

INVESTIGATE Frequency

PURPOSE To investigate how changing the length of a pendulum affects wave frequency

TIPS *30 min.* If students have trouble with the technique, here are some suggestions.

- Tie the washers tightly together so that they will not shift weight.
- Make sure the washers swing freely, without bumping anything.
- Count one full swing each time the pendulum returns to the start position.

WHAT DO YOU THINK? *The longer the string, the lower the frequency. The swinging string is similar because it has frequency and amplitude. It is different because it does not transfer energy.*

CHALLENGE *Pulling the washers back farther would change the amplitude. Changing the amplitude does not change the frequency.*

 Datasheet, Frequency, p. 31

Technology Resources

Customize this student lab as needed or look for an alternative. Print rubrics to assess student lab reports.

 Lab Generator CD-ROM

History of Science

Scientists are continually refining measurement of the speed of sound. The standard speed of sound in air is measured at sea level at 0°C. In 1738, French scientists determined the speed of sound in air to be 332 m/s. In 1942, scientists made a more precise measurement: 331.45 m/s. As recently as 1986, scientists further refined the measurement to 331.29 m/s.

Ongoing Assessment

Calculate a wave's speed.

Ask: What measurements do you need to calculate a wave's speed? *wavelength and frequency*

INVESTIGATE Frequency

How can you change frequency?

PROCEDURE

1. Tie 3 washers to a string. Tape the string to the side of your desk so that it can swing freely. The swinging washers can model wave action.

2. Pull the washers slightly to the side and let go. Find the frequency by counting the number of complete swings that occur in 1 minute.

3. Make a table in your notebook to record both the length of the string and the frequency.

4. Shorten the string by moving and retaping it. Repeat for 5 different lengths. Keep the distance you pull the washers the same each time.

WHAT DO YOU THINK?

- How did changing the length of the string affect the frequency?
- How does this model represent a wave? How does it differ from a wave?

CHALLENGE How could you vary the amplitude of this model? Predict how changing the amplitude would affect the frequency.

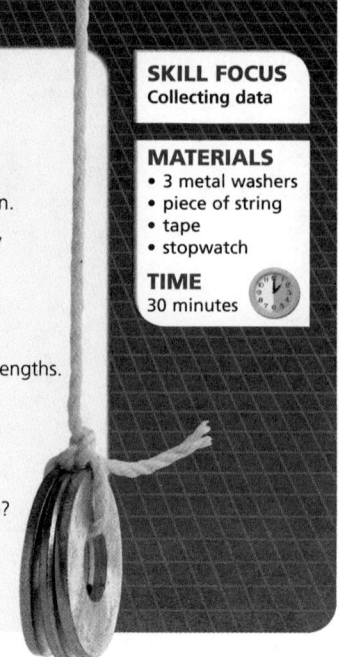

SKILL FOCUS
Collecting data

MATERIALS
- 3 metal washers
- piece of string
- tape
- stopwatch

TIME
30 minutes

Wave speed can be measured.

E

▼ **REMINDER**
The symbol λ represents wavelength.

?
F

In addition to amplitude, wavelength, and frequency, a wave's speed can be measured. One way to find the speed of a wave is to time how long it takes for a wave crest to get from one point to another. Another way to find the speed of a wave is to calculate it. The speed of any wave can be determined when both the frequency and the wavelength are known, using the following equation:

$$\text{Speed} = \text{wavelength} \cdot \text{frequency}$$
$$S = \lambda \cdot f$$

Different types of waves travel at very different speeds. For example, light waves travel through air almost a million times faster than sound waves travel through air. You have experienced the difference in wave speeds if you have ever seen lightning and heard the thunder that comes with it in a thunderstorm. When lightning strikes far away, you see the light seconds before you hear the clap of its thunder. The light waves reach you while the sound waves are still on their way.

How fast do you think water waves can travel? Water waves travel at different speeds. Use the equation for wave speed on the next page to find out how fast an ocean wave can travel.

DIFFERENTIATE INSTRUCTION

? **More Reading Support**

E Wavelength times frequency is the formula for which wave measurement? *wave speed*

F Do all kinds of waves travel at the same speed? *no*

Below Level Give this analogy for the formula for wave speed: To find the frequency of cars on a moving train, you could watch a moving train and count the number of railroad cars that pass in a certain length of time, such as 10 seconds, using a stopwatch. Wavelength is like the length of a railroad car. Frequency is the number of cars that pass in a certain length of time.

Calculating Wave Speed

▶ **Sample Problem**

An ocean wave has a wavelength of 16 meters and a frequency of 0.31 wavelengths per second. What is the speed of the wave?

What do you know?	1 wavelength = 16 m, frequency = 3 wavelengths/s
What do you want to find out?	Speed
Write the formula:	$S = \lambda \cdot f$
Substitute into the formula:	$S = 16 \dfrac{m}{wavelength} \cdot 0.31 \dfrac{wavelengths}{s}$
Calculate and simplify:	$16 \dfrac{m}{wavelength} \cdot 0.31 \dfrac{wavelengths}{s} = 5 \dfrac{m}{s}$
Check that your units agree:	Unit is m/s. Unit for speed is m/s. Units agree.
Answer:	$S = 5$ m/s

▶ **Practice the Math**

1. In a stormy sea, 2 waves pass a fixed point every second, and the waves are 10 m apart. What is the speed of the waves?
2. In a ripple tank, the wavelength is 0.1 cm, and 10 waves occur each second. What is the speed of the waves (in cm/s)?

Geologists use the wave speed equation to find oil deep underground. They send sound waves into the ground. The speed of the waves that bounce back indicates what the ground is made up of. This is possible because sound travels at different speeds through different kinds of rock. The geologists then use this information to determine where to drill for oil and how far down they will need to go.

 **CHECK YOUR READING** How do geologists use sound waves to find oil in the ground?

▶ **RESOURCE CENTER**
CLASSZONE.COM

Find out more about wave speed.

1.2 Review

KEY CONCEPTS

1. Make a simple diagram of a wave, labeling amplitude, frequency, and wavelength. For frequency, you will need to indicate a span of time, such as one second.
2. What two measurements of a wave do you need to calculate its speed?

CRITICAL THINKING

3. **Observe** Suppose you are watching water waves pass under the end of a pier. How can you figure out their frequency?
4. **Calculate** A wave has a speed of 3 m/s and a frequency of 6 wavelengths/s. What is its wavelength?

◔ CHALLENGE

5. **Apply** Imagine you are on a boat in the middle of the sea. You are in charge of recording the properties of passing ocean waves into the ship's logbook. What types of information could you record? How would this information be useful? Explain your answer.

Chapter 1: **Waves 21** **C**

ANSWERS

1. *See students' diagrams.*

2. *wavelength and frequency*

3. *Sample answer: Look at a fixed point below, and time how many waves pass that point within a unit of time.*

4. $S = \lambda \cdot f$
$\lambda = f \div s$
$\lambda = 6 \dfrac{wavelength}{s} \div 3$ m/s
$= 0.5$ m

5. *Sample answer: You could record the amplitude, wavelength, and frequency of waves at different times during the day. Changes in these measures could help indicate the approach of a storm.*

Focus

PURPOSE Students will learn how to measure waves produced by a pendulum and will investigate how the length of the pendulum affects wavelength.

OVERVIEW Students will:

• Make a pendulum from which sand drains.

• Record the pendulum's wave pattern with sand on construction paper.

• Repeat the activity with varying pendulum lengths.

• Evaluate the different waves produced.

Lab Preparation

• Students can prepare the paper cones ahead of time. Be sure students make the hole no larger than a pea. Have them make extra cones in case some perform poorly.

• For homework the night before, have students read the investigation, write their hypothesis, and draw their data table. Or you may wish to copy and distribute datasheets and rubrics.

 UNIT RESOURCE BOOK, pp. 53–61

SCIENCE TOOLKIT, F14

Lab Management

• Pair students. Have students choose roles: one partner will manipulate the pendulum, while the other will fill the pendulum with sand and then pull the paper under the swinging pendulum.

• The waves may not look like those in the text, but should have clear crests and troughs.

INCLUSION Encourage students working together to discuss in advance which tasks each will perform. Help students identify tasks that they can do well or alternate approaches that suit their abilities.

Wavelength

OVERVIEW AND PURPOSE The pendulum on a grandfather clock keeps time as it swings back and forth at a steady rate. The swings of a pendulum can be recorded as a wave with measurable properties. How do the properties of the pendulum affect the properties of the waves it produces? In this investigation you will use your understanding of wave properties to

• construct a pendulum and measure the waves it produces, and

• determine how the length of the pendulum affects the wavelength of the waves.

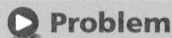 **Problem** Write It Up

How does changing the length of a pendulum affect the wavelength?

Hypothesize Write It Up

Write a hypothesis in "If . . . , then . . . , because . . ." form to answer the problem question.

Procedure

MATERIALS
• 1/2 sheet white paper
• tape
• scissors
• string
• meter stick
• fine sand
• graduated cylinder
• 2 sheets colored construction paper

1. Make a data table like the one shown on the sample notebook page.

2. Make a cone with the half-sheet of paper by rolling it and taping it as shown. The hole in the bottom of the cone should be no larger than a pea.

3. Cut a hole in each side of the cone and tie the ends of the string to the cone to make a pendulum.

4. Hold the string on the pendulum so that the distance from your fingers holding the string to the bottom of the cone is 20 cm.

5. Cover the bottom of the cone with your fingertip. While you hold the cone, have your partner pour about 40 ml of sand into the cone.

INVESTIGATION RESOURCES

 CHAPTER INVESTIGATION, Wavelength
• Level A, pp. 53–56
• Level B, pp. 57–60
• Level C, p. 61

Advanced students should complete Levels B & C.

Writing a Lab Report, D12–13

Technology Resources

Customize this student lab as needed or look for an alternative. Print rubrics to assess student lab reports.

 Lab Generator CD-ROM

6 Hold the pendulum about 5 cm above the construction paper as shown. Pull the pendulum from the bottom to one side of the construction paper. Be careful not to move the pendulum at the top, or to pull the pendulum over the edge of the paper.

7 Let the pendulum go while your partner gently pulls the paper forward so that the sand makes waves on the paper. Be sure to pull the paper at a steady rate. Let the remaining sand pile up on the end of the paper.

8 Measure the wavelength from crest to crest or trough to trough. Record the wavelength in your table.

9 Run two more trials, repeating steps 5–8. Be sure to pull the paper at the same speed for each trial. Calculate the average wavelength over all three trials, and record it in your table.

10 Repeat steps 4–8, changing the length of the pendulum to 30 cm and then to 40 cm.

▶ Observe and Analyze   Write It Up

1. **RECORD OBSERVATIONS** Draw the setup of your procedure. Be sure your data table is complete.

2. **IDENTIFY VARIABLES AND CONSTANTS** Identify the variables and constants that affected the wave produced by the moving pendulum. List them in your notebook.

3. **ANALYZE** What patterns can you find in your data? For example, do the numbers increase or decrease as you read down each column?

▶ Conclude   Write It Up

1. **INFER** Answer your problem question.

2. **INTERPRET** Compare your results with your hypothesis. Do your data support your hypothesis?

3. **IDENTIFY LIMITS** What possible limitations or sources of error could have affected your results?

4. **APPLY** Suppose you were examining the tracing made by a seismograph, a machine that records an earthquake wave. What would happen if you increased the speed at which the paper ran through the machine? What do you think the amplitude of the tracing represents?

▶ INVESTIGATE Further

CHALLENGE Revise your experiment to change one variable other than the length of the pendulum. Run a new trial, changing the variable you choose but keeping everything else constant. How did changing the variable affect the wave produced?

Wavelength

Problem How does changing the length of a pendulum affect the wavelength?

Hypothesize

Observe and Analyze

Table 1. Wavelengths Produced by Pendulums

Pendulum Length (cm)	Trial 1	Trial 2	Trial 3	Average Wavelength (cm)
20				
30				
40				

Conclude

Chapter 1: **Waves 23** **C**

▶ Observe and Analyze   Write It Up

SAMPLE DATA wavelength with 20-cm string: 3.5 cm; wavelength with 30-cm string: 5 cm; wavelength with 40-cm string: 8 cm

1. *See students' diagrams. See students' data tables.*

2. *The variable is the length of the pendulum. Ideally, constants will include the speed of the paper as the partner pulls it forward, the height of the pendulum above the table, the amount the pendulum is pulled back before letting go, and the amount of sand used in each trial.*

3. *Sample answer: Most of the numbers increase as you read down the columns.*

▶ Conclude   Write It Up

1. *Changing the length of the pendulum changes the wavelength of waves it produces.*

2. *Student answers will vary, depending on students' original hypotheses.*

3. *Sample answer: The speed at which the paper is pulled each time may have varied, affecting the results.*

4. *If you increase the speed of paper that runs through a seismograph, you would increase the wavelength. The amplitude represents the amount of energy carried by a seismic wave.*

▶ INVESTIGATE Further

CHALLENGE Students could choose to vary the weight of the pendulum, the size of the cone, the speed at which the paper is pulled under the pendulum, or the height of the pendulum above the paper. Any of these changes could affect the wave produced by the pendulum.

Post-Lab Discussion

• Discuss with students how the activity enabled them to graph the movement of a pendulum.

• Point out that almost any motion that is regular and repeating can be graphed as a wave. Challenge students to describe how the movement of a clock's minute hand could be interpreted and graphed as wave motion. You could graph the 12 o'clock position as the crest of the wave and the 6 o'clock position as the trough.

◉ Set Learning Goals

Students will

- Describe how waves change as they encounter a barrier.
- Explain what happens when waves enter a new medium.
- Identify ways in which waves interact with one another.
- Investigate in an experiment how waves behave when they meet a barrier.

◀ 3-Minute Warm-Up

Display Transparency 5 or copy this exercise on the board:

Draw a diagram that shows how a duck floats on waves. Use arrows to show how the waves move and how the duck moves. *Arrows for the duck should show it staying in the same position but bobbing up and down vertically; arrows for waves should point in a horizontal direction.*

 3-Minute Warm-Up, p. T5

1.3 MOTIVATE

EXPLORE Reflection

PURPOSE To introduce the concept that waves reflect off a barrier

TIP *10 min.* The waves will be circular.

WHAT DO YOU THINK? *The ripples travel back in the opposite direction after they encounter the side of the pan. Waves encounter a medium that they cannot travel through.*

Ongoing Assessment

 *Answer: reflection, refraction, diffraction*

KEY CONCEPT

1.3 Waves behave in predictable ways.

◀ **BEFORE, you learned**

- Waves transfer energy
- Amplitude, wavelength, and frequency can be measured

▶ **NOW, you will learn**

- How waves change as they encounter a barrier
- What happens when waves enter a new medium
- How waves interact with other waves

VOCABULARY

reflection p. 25
refraction p. 25
diffraction p. 26
interference p. 27

EXPLORE Reflection

How do ripples reflect?

PROCEDURE

① Put a few drops of food coloring into the pan of water.

② Dip the pencil in the water at one end of the pan to make ripples in the water.

③ Observe the ripples as they reflect off the side of the pan. Draw a sketch of the waves reflecting.

MATERIALS
- wide pan, half full of water
- food coloring
- pencil

WHAT DO YOU THINK?
- What happens when the waves reach the side of the pan?
- Why do you think the waves behave as they do?

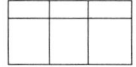 **COMBINATION NOTES** Use combination notes in your notebook to describe how waves interact with materials.

Waves interact with materials.

You have read that mechanical waves travel through a medium like air, water, or the ground. In this section, you will read how the motion of waves changes when they encounter a new medium. For instance, when an ocean wave rolls into a ship or a sound wave strikes a solid wall, the wave encounters a new medium.

When waves interact with materials in these ways, they behave predictably. All waves, from water waves to sound waves and even light waves, show the behaviors that you will learn about next. Scientists call these behaviors reflection, refraction, and diffraction.

CHECK YOUR READING What behaviors do all waves have in common?

RESOURCES FOR DIFFERENTIATED INSTRUCTION

Below Level
UNIT RESOURCE BOOK
- Reading Study Guide A, pp. 35–36
- Decoding Support, p. 48

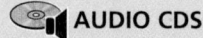 **AUDIO CDS**

 Additional INVESTIGATION, Tracking the Path of Light, A, B, & C, pp. 62–70; Teacher Instructions, pp. 284–285

Advanced
UNIT RESOURCE BOOK
Challenge and Extension, p. 41

English Learners
UNIT RESOURCE BOOK
Spanish Reading Study Guide, pp. 39–40

AUDIO CDS
- Audio Readings in Spanish
- Audio Readings (English)

Reflection

What happens to water waves at the end of a swimming pool? The waves cannot travel through the wall of the pool. Instead, the waves bounce off the pool wall. The bouncing back of a wave after it strikes a barrier is called **reflection.**

Remember what you have learned about forces. A water wave, like all waves, transfers energy. When the water wave meets the wall of the pool, it pushes against the wall. The wall applies an equal and opposite force on the water, sending the wave back in another direction. In the illustration on the right, you can see water waves reflecting off a barrier.

Sound and light waves reflect too. Sound waves reflecting off the walls of a canyon produce an echo. Light waves reflecting off smooth metal behind glass let you see an image of yourself in the mirror. The light waves bounce off the metal just as the water waves bounce off the pool wall. You will learn more about how sound and light waves reflect in the next chapters.

Reflection Water waves move in predictable ways. Here waves are shown from above as they reflect off a barrier.

CHECK YOUR READING How would you define *reflection* in your own words?

Refraction

Sometimes, a wave does not bounce back when it encounters a new medium. Instead, the wave continues moving forward. When a wave enters a new medium at an angle, it bends, or refracts. **Refraction** is the bending of a wave as it enters a new medium at an angle other than 90 degrees. Refraction occurs because waves travel at different speeds in different mediums. Because the wave enters the new medium at an angle, one side of the wave enters the new medium before the rest of the wave. When one side of a wave speeds up or slows down before the other side, it causes the wave to bend.

You have probably noticed the refraction of light waves in water. Objects half-in and half-out of water look broken or split. Look at the photograph of the straw in the glass. What your eyes suggest—that the straw is split—is not real, is it? You are seeing the refraction of light waves caused by the change of medium from air to water. You will learn more about the refraction of light waves in Chapter 4.

Refraction The light waves refract as they pass from air to water, making this straw look split.

Real World Example

Bands sometimes play on stages surrounded by a large curved backdrop. This curved backdrop, or shell, reflects sound waves out to the audience. Without the band shell, sound waves produced by the performers would shoot out in all directions in the open air, lost to listeners, and the music would sound faint and dull.

Integrate the Sciences

Seismologists—scientists who study earthquakes—measure seismic waves all over Earth. These waves, set off by earthquakes in Earth's crust, travel in all directions and eventually reach the surface. Surface stations make precise measurements of the seismic waves. By studying how these waves travel and are refracted by different materials, seismologists have learned much about the density and composition of Earth's core and mantle.

Ongoing Assessment

Describe how waves change as they encounter a barrier.

Ask: What happens when sound waves strike solid rock? Give an example. *They reflect from the rock, as in an echo.*

Explain what happens when waves enter a new medium.

Ask: Why do you see distorted shapes when you look into the water in a swimming pool? *Light waves bend, or undergo refraction, when they pass from the air into the water. This refraction distorts underwater objects.*

CHECK YOUR READING *Sample answer: waves bouncing off a barrier*

DIFFERENTIATE INSTRUCTION

More Reading Support

A What happens to a wave when it meets the wall of a pool? *It reflects.*

B What describes a wave moving into a new medium at an angle? *refraction*

Additional Investigation To reinforce Section 1.3 learning goals, use the following full-period investigation:

R **Additional INVESTIGATION,** Tracking the Path of Light, A, B, & C, pp. 62–70, 284–285 (Advanced students should complete Levels B and C.)

English Learners Providing models is an effective way to help English learners produce work that is representative of their abilities. For example, if a student is asked to write an explanatory paragraph, provide an appropriate model of one.

INVESTIGATE Diffraction

PURPOSE To investigate how waves behave when they meet a partial barrier

TIPS *20 min.* Allow students a few minutes to explore, then suggest the following:

- Make sure the block sticks out of the water.
- Use a gentle push on the ruler to create waves.

WHAT DO YOU THINK? *by putting a partial barrier in their path; students' answers will vary depending on their predictions.*

CHALLENGE *Sample answer: You could try blocks with different sizes and shapes to better diffract the waves.*

 Datasheet, Diffraction, p. 42

Technology Resources

Customize this student lab as needed or look for an alternative. Print rubrics to assess student lab reports.

 Lab Generator CD-ROM

Metacognitive Strategy

Ask students to write a paragraph describing the reasoning behind their prediction about what would happen when the waves hit the barrier in the pan.

Teach from Visuals

To help students interpret the visual of diffraction, ask:

- Through what medium are the waves moving? *water*
- From what perspective are you viewing the waves? *from above*
- What happens to the waves as they go through the opening? *The waves spread out.*

Diffraction

You have seen how waves reflect off a barrier. For example, water waves bounce off the side of a pool. But what if the side of the pool had an opening in it? Sometimes, waves interact with a partial barrier, such as a wall with an opening. As the waves pass through the opening, they spread out, or diffract. **Diffraction** is the spreading out of waves through an opening or around the edge of an obstacle. Diffraction occurs with all types of waves.

Look at the photograph on the right. It shows water waves diffracting as they pass through a small gap in a barrier. In the real world, ocean waves diffract through openings in cliffs or rock formations.

Similarly, sound waves diffract as they pass through an open doorway. Turn on a TV or stereo, and walk into another room. Listen to the sound with the door closed and then open. Then try moving around the room. You can hear the sound wherever you stand because the waves spread out, or diffract, through the doorway and reflect from the walls.

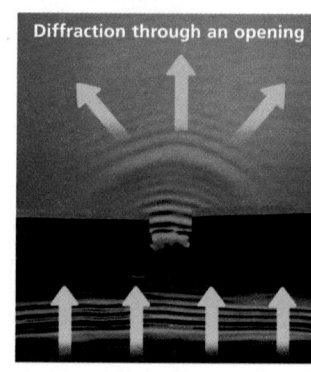
Diffraction through an opening

INVESTIGATE Diffraction

How can you make a wave diffract?

PROCEDURE

1. Put a few drops of food coloring into the container of water.
2. Experiment with quick motions of the ruler to set off waves in the container.
3. Place the block on its side in the center of the container. Set the bag of sand on the block to hold it down. Predict how the waves will interact with the barrier you have added.
4. Make another set of waves, and observe how they interact with the barrier.

WHAT DO YOU THINK?

- How did you make the waves diffract?
- How did your observations compare with your prediction?

CHALLENGE How could you change the experiment to make the effect of the diffraction more obvious?

SKILL FOCUS
Predicting

MATERIALS
- wide pan of water
- food coloring
- ruler
- wooden block
- bag of sand

TIME
20 minutes

DIFFERENTIATE INSTRUCTION

? More Reading Support

C What do waves do when they pass through an opening in a barrier? *They diffract.*

Below Level Students may have difficulty with the similar-sounding vocabulary in this lesson. Write "reflection," "refraction," and "diffraction" on the board, dividing them into syllables. Pronounce each word. Ask students to visually scan each word and find similarities and differences among them. *Reflection and refraction have identical prefixes and suffixes but different roots. Refraction and diffraction have identical roots and suffixes but different prefixes.*

Diffraction also occurs as waves pass the edge of an obstacle. The photograph at the right shows water waves diffracting as they pass an obstacle. Ocean waves also diffract in this way as they pass large rocks in the water.

Light waves diffract around the edge of an obstacle too. The edges of a shadow appear fuzzy because of diffraction. The light waves spread out, or diffract, around the object that is making the shadow.

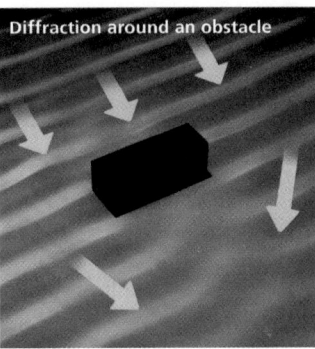
Diffraction around an obstacle

 Describe what happens when waves diffract.

Waves interact with other waves.

Just as waves sometimes interact with new mediums, they can also interact with other waves. Two waves can add energy to or take away energy from each other in the place where they meet. **Interference** is the meeting and combining of waves.

Waves Adding Together

Suppose two identical waves coming from opposite directions come together at one point. The waves' crests and troughs are aligned, which means they join up exactly. When the two waves merge, their amplitudes are added together, and the result is a bigger wave. After the waves have merged, they return to their original amplitudes and continue in their original directions.

The adding of two waves is called constructive interference. It builds up, or constructs, a larger wave out of two smaller ones. Look at the diagram at the right to see what happens in constructive interference.

Because the waves in the example joined together perfectly, the amplitude of the new wave equals the combined amplitudes of the 2 original waves. For example, if the crest of a water wave with an amplitude of 1 meter (3.3 ft) met up with the crest of another wave with an amplitude of 1 meter (3.3 ft), there would be a 2 meter (6.6 ft) crest in the spot where they met.

Constructive Interference

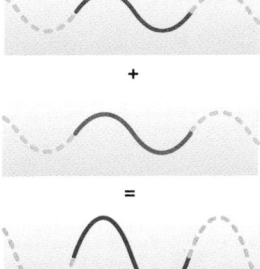

When two wave crests with amplitudes of 1 m each combine, a wave with an amplitude of 2 m is formed.

Chapter 1: **Waves 27** **C**

Ongoing Assessment

Sample answer: The amplitudes of waves can add or subtract when two waves with the same frequency meet.

Reinforce (the **BIG** idea)

Have students relate the section to the Big Idea.

 R Reinforcing Key Concepts, p. 43

1.3 ASSESS & RETEACH

Assess

A Section 1.3 Quiz, p. 5

Reteach

Present these four wave scenarios:

- You shout into a cave and hear an echo.
- Two people in a choir are singing slightly off-key, and their voices combine to produce loud, unpleasant beats.
- From shore, it looks like all of a bridge's pilings are broken at the water level, but trucks are safely driving over it.
- Before you reach the corner of a huge stone building, you hear a noisy parade approaching down the other street.

Have each student choose a scenario and find the appropriate presentation for that topic in the lesson. Have students diagram the wave scenario and write a scientific explanation for it.

Technology Resources

Have students visit **ClassZone.com** for reteaching of Key Concepts.

 CONTENT REVIEW

 CONTENT REVIEW CD-ROM

Waves Canceling Each Other Out

Imagine again that two very similar waves come together. This time, however, the crests of one wave join with the troughs of the other. The energy of one wave is subtracted from the energy of the other. The new wave is therefore smaller than the original wave. This process is called destructive interference. Look at the diagram below to see what happens in destructive interference.

For example, if a 2 meter (6.6 ft) crest met up with a 1 meter (3.3 ft) trough, there would be a crest of only 1 meter (3.3 ft) where they met. If the amplitudes of the 2 original waves are identical, the 2 waves can cancel each other out completely!

When identical waves meet, they are usually not aligned. Instead, the crests meet up with crests in some places and troughs in others. As a result, the waves add in some places and subtract in others. The photograph on the left shows a pattern resulting from waves both adding and subtracting on the surface of a pond. Have you ever listened to music on stereo speakers that were placed at a distance to each other? The music may have sounded loud in some places and soft in others, as the sound waves from the two speakers interfered with each other.

Wave interference produces this pattern on a pond as two sets of waves interact.

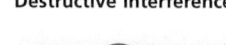
Destructive Interference

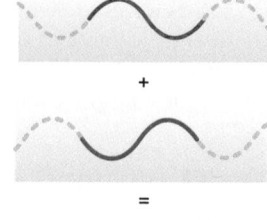

When a 1 m wave crest meets a 1 m wave trough, the amplitudes cancel each other out. A wave with an amplitude of 0 m is formed where they meet.

CHECK YOUR READING Summarize in your own words what happens during interference.

1.3 Review

KEY CONCEPTS

1. Explain what happens when waves encounter a medium that they cannot travel through.
2. Describe a situation in which waves would diffract.
3. Describe two ways that waves are affected by interference.

CRITICAL THINKING

4. **Synthesize** Explain how reflection and diffraction can happen at the same time in a wave.
5. **Compare** How is interference similar to net force? How do you think the two concepts might be related? **Hint:** Think about how forces are involved in wave motion.

⬤ CHALLENGE

6. **Predict** Imagine that you make gelatin in a long, shallow pan. Then you scoop the gelatin out of one end of the pan and add icy cold water to the exact same depth as the gelatin. Now suppose you set off waves at the water end. What do you think will happen when the waves meet the gelatin?

ANSWERS

1. *Waves reflect.*

2. *Sample answer: Ocean waves hit a spot of land.*

3. *Amplitudes can add up or cancel each other out.*

4. *When a wave hits a partial barrier, the part of the wave that hits the barrier reflects into the oncoming waves. The part of the wave that passes through the gap in the barrier diffracts.*

5. *Forces are responsible for moving a wave medium up and down as a wave passes through it. Forces can be added and subtracted on a wave medium just as they can on any object.*

6. *Answers could describe refraction, as waves meet and enter a new medium, or reflection, as waves encounter a barrier.*

Tsunamis!

Tsunamis (tsu-NAH-mees) are among the most powerful waves on Earth. They can travel fast enough to cross the Pacific Ocean in less than a day! When they reach shore, these powerful waves strike with enough force to destroy whole communities.

What Causes Tsunamis?

Tsunamis are caused by an undersea volcanic eruption, an earthquake, or even a landslide. This deep-sea event sends out a series of waves. Surprisingly, if you were out at sea, you would not even notice these powerful waves. The reason has to do with the physics of waves—their velocity, wavelength, and amplitude.

A tsunami generated by a powerful earthquake struck Japan in 1983. The photograph above shows a scene before the tsunami struck. What changes do you see in the picture below showing the scene after the tsunami struck?

Diagram of a Wave

1 open ocean

λ

A

2 near shore

λ

A

Amplitude (A) = 1 m
Wavelength (λ) = 200 km
Speed (S) = 1000 km/h

Amplitude = 30 m
Wavelength = 1.5 km
Speed = 80 km/h

The Changing Wave

1 On the open ocean, the waves of a tsunami are barely visible. The amplitude of the waves is less than a few meters, but the energy of the waves extends to the sea floor. The tsunami's wavelength is extremely long—up to 200 kilometers (120 mi). These long, low waves can travel as fast as a jet—almost 1000 kilometers per hour (600 mi/h).

2 Near shore, the waves slow down as they approach shallow water. As their velocity drops, their wavelengths get shorter, but their amplitude gets bigger. All the energy that was spread out over a long wave in deep water is now compressed into a huge wave that can reach a height of more than 30 meters (100 ft).

Individual tsunami waves may arrive more than an hour apart. Many people have lost their lives returning home between waves, making the fatal mistake of thinking the danger was over.

EXPLORE

1. **VISUALIZE** Look at **2** on the diagram. How tall is 30 meters (100 ft)? Find a 100-foot building or structure near you to visualize the shore height of a tsunami.

2. **CHALLENGE** Use library or Internet resources to prepare a chart on the causes and effects of a major tsunami event.

Set Learning Goal

To understand how the physics of waves applies to tsunamis

Present the Science

Share the following facts with students:

• The word *tsunami* is a Japanese word meaning "harbor wave."

• The most devastating tsunami occurred in Papua New Guinea in 1998.

• The states of Alaska and Hawaii have frequently felt tsunamis hitting their shores.

• Tsunamis are often confused with tidal waves, which are caused by the gravitational attraction of the Sun and Moon.

• Tsunamis are often called "seismic sea waves" because they are usually the result of "underwater earthquakes."

Discussion Questions

Ask: Why does the amplitude of the wave go up in shallow water? *It has nowhere else to go.*

Ask: Where will the energy of the wave go when it hits shore? *It will strike the shoreline with the force of the wave.*

Ask: How is the cause of a tsunami different from the cause of regular waves? *Regular waves are formed from wind and weather, while tsunamis develop from underwater volcanic eruptions or underwater earthquakes.*

Ask: Why do you think the waves slow down when they reach water that is more shallow? *They are slowed down by friction with the ocean floor.*

Close

Ask: How do tsunamis show that waves carry energy? *by the destruction they cause*

EXPLORE

1. *VISUALIZE Discuss with students the impact that 30 meters of water might have.*

2. *CHALLENGE While many pictures and Internet sites show the devastation caused by tsunamis, there are very few pictures of a tsunami in action. Artists have attempted to depict the phenomenon. Students should have no trouble finding information on tsunamis.*

PHOTO CAPTION Answer: There is a significant amount of water on the shore, the wall surrounding the water is destroyed, and the objects near the shore are pulled into the water by the force of the tsunami hitting the land.

BACK TO

the BIG idea

Ask students to describe a demonstration they could present to show that waves transfer energy. *Sample answer: You could go to the beach and put a plastic bucket in the sand a few centimeters out in the surf. The incoming waves would push the bucket, showing the transfer of energy.*

◯ KEY CONCEPTS SUMMARY

SECTION 1.1
For the picture on the left, have students describe the direction of the disturbance compared to the direction of the wave. *It is at right angles with the direction of the wave.* For the picture on the right, have students describe the direction of the disturbance compared to the direction of the wave. *They are both in the same direction.*

SECTION 1.2
Ask: What wave properties are identified in the picture? Which property indicates the amount of energy the wave has? *The wave properties are amplitude, wavelength, and frequency. Amplitude indicates the energy in the wave.*

SECTION 1.3
Have students describe the three wave behaviors pictured here. *In reflection, waves bounce off a solid barrier. In refraction, waves bend as they pass from one medium into another. In diffraction, waves pass by a barrier and spread out.*

Review Concepts

• Big Idea Flow Chart, p. T1
• Chapter Outline, pp. T7–T8

 # Chapter Review

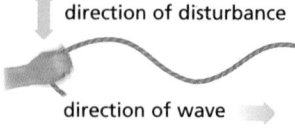 **the BIG idea**

Waves transfer energy and interact in predictable ways.

 **CONTENT REVIEW**
CLASSZONE.COM

◀ **KEY CONCEPTS SUMMARY**

 Waves transfer energy.

Transverse Wave	Longitudinal Wave
direction of disturbance	direction of disturbance
direction of wave	direction of wave
transfer of energy	transfer of energy

VOCABULARY
wave p. 9
medium p. 11
mechanical wave p. 11
transverse wave p. 13
longitudinal wave p. 14

1.2 Waves have measurable properties.

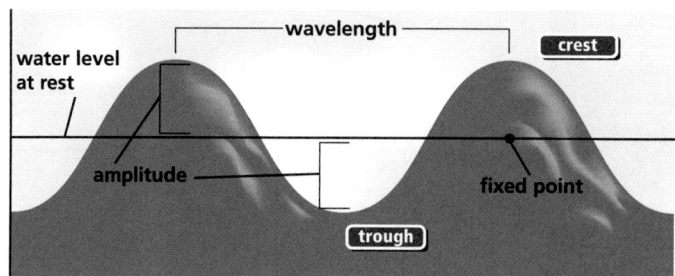

wavelength
crest
water level at rest
amplitude
fixed point
trough

Frequency is the number of wavelengths passing a fixed point in a certain amount of time.

VOCABULARY
crest p. 17
trough p. 17
amplitude p. 17
wavelength p. 17
frequency p. 17

1.3 Waves behave in predictable ways.

Reflection **Refraction** **Diffraction**

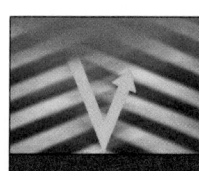  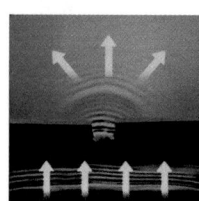

VOCABULARY
reflection p. 25
refraction p. 25
diffraction p. 26
interference p. 27

Technology Resources

Have students visit **ClassZone.com** or use the CD-ROM for a cumulative review of concepts.

Engage students in a whole-class interactive review of Key Concepts. Edit content as you wish.

 CONTENT REVIEW

 CONTENT REVIEW CD-ROM

 POWER PRESENTATIONS

Reviewing Vocabulary

Draw a triangle for each of the terms below. On the wide bottom of the triangle, write the term and your own definition of it. Above that, write a sentence in which you use the term correctly. At the top of the triangle, draw a small picture to show what the term looks like. The first triangle is completed for you.

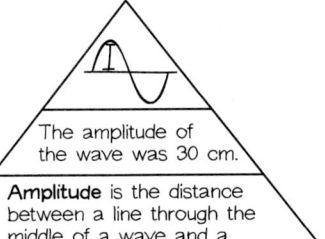

The amplitude of the wave was 30 cm.

Amplitude is the distance between a line through the middle of a wave and a crest or trough.

1. amplitude
2. diffraction
3. frequency
4. medium
5. crest
6. interference
7. reflection
8. trough
9. refraction
10. wavelength

Reviewing Key Concepts

Multiple Choice *Choose the letter of the best answer.*

11. The direction in which a transverse wave travels is
    a. in the same direction as the disturbance
    b. toward the disturbance
    c. from the disturbance downward
    d. at right angles to the disturbance

12. An example of a longitudinal wave is a
    a. water wave
    b. stadium wave
    c. sound wave
    d. rope wave

13. Which statement best defines a wave medium?
    a. the material through which a wave travels
    b. a point half-way between the crest and trough of a wave
    c. the distance from one wave crest to the next
    d. the speed at which waves travel in water

14. As you increase the amplitude of a wave, you also increase the
    a. frequency   c. speed
    b. wavelength   d. energy

15. To identify the amplitude in a longitudinal wave, you would look for areas of
    a. reflection   c. crests
    b. compression   d. refraction

16. Which statement describes the relationship between frequency and wavelength?
    a. When frequency increases, wavelength increases.
    b. When frequency increases, wavelength decreases.
    c. When frequency increases, wavelength remains constant.
    d. When frequency increases, wavelength varies unpredictably.

17. For wave refraction to take place, a wave must
    a. increase in velocity
    b. enter a new medium
    c. increase in frequency
    d. merge with another wave

18. Which setup in a wave tank would enable you to demonstrate diffraction?
    a. water only
    b. water and sand
    c. water and food coloring
    d. water and a barrier with a small gap

19. Two waves come together and interact to form a new, smaller wave. This process is called
    a. destructive interference
    b. constructive interference
    c. reflective interference
    d. positive interference

Reviewing Vocabulary

Sample definitions are given below.

1. Amplitude is how high or low a wave is from its test position.
2. Diffraction is the spreading of waves through a hole.
3. Frequency is the number of waves passing a fixed point in a certain time.
4. A medium is anything a wave travels through.
5. A crest is the highest point of a wave.
6. Interference is the meeting of two waves.
7. Reflection is the bouncing back of a wave after it meets a barrier.
8. A trough is the lowest point of a wave.
9. Refraction is the bending of a wave as it moves from one medium into another.
10. Wavelength is the distance from crest to crest.

Reviewing Key Concepts

11. d
12. c
13. a
14. d
15. b
16. b
17. b
18. d
19. a

ASSESSMENT RESOURCES

 UNIT ASSESSMENT BOOK
- Chapter Test A, pp. 6–9
- Chapter Test B, pp. 10–13
- Chapter Test C, pp. 14–17
- Alternative Assessment, pp. 18–19

 SPANISH ASSESSMENT BOOK
Spanish Chapter Test, pp. 281–284

Technology Resources

Edit test items and answer choices.

 Test Generator CD-ROM

Visit **ClassZone.com** to extend test practice.

 Test Practice

Thinking Critically

20. *a and b measure amplitude*

21. *wavelength*

22. *3 waves*

23. *frequency*

24. *3 wavelengths/s*

25. *No, it could be a liquid or gas.*

26. *By drawing the pendulum back farther; The swinging motion has amplitude, frequency, and wavelength.*

27. *It might diffract through the gap.*

28. *Sample answer: Yes, in each instance one wave meets another and changes it in some way.*

Using Math in Science

29. $S = \lambda \cdot f$

$S = 1.2 \; \dfrac{m}{\text{wavelength}} \cdot 2 \; \dfrac{\text{wavelength}}{s}$

$= 2.4 \; m/s$

30. $S = \lambda \cdot f$

$S = 9 \; \dfrac{m}{\text{wavelength}} \cdot 0.42 \; \dfrac{\text{wavelength}}{s}$

$= 3.78 \; m/s$

31. $S = \lambda \cdot f; \; \lambda = s \div f$

$\lambda = 340 \; m/s \div 10{,}000 \; \dfrac{\text{wavelength}}{s}$

$= 0.034 \; m, \text{ or } 3.4 \; cm$

32. $S = \lambda \cdot f; \; f = s \div \lambda$

$f = 2.5 \; m/s \div 4 \; \dfrac{m}{\text{wavelength}}$

$= 0.625, \text{ round to } 0.63 \; \dfrac{\text{wavelengths}}{s}$

the **BIG** idea

33. *Sample answer: The wave has transferred energy to a surfer.*

34. *Sample answer: (1) Sound in an empty room. (2) Ripples in a pond. (3) Waves in a swimming pool.*

35. *Students' paragraphs should demonstrate an understanding of the Big Idea.*

Thinking Critically

Use the diagram below to answer the next two questions.

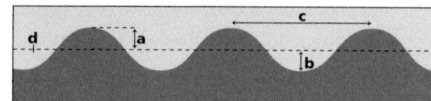

20. What two letters in the diagram measure the same thing? What do they both measure?

21. In the diagram above, what does the letter c measure?

Use the diagram below to answer the next three questions. The diagram shows waves passing a fixed point.

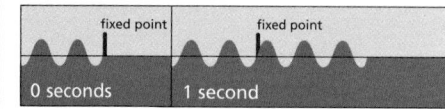

22. At 0 seconds, no waves have passed. How many waves have passed after 1 second?

23. What is the measurement shown in the diagram?

24. How would you write the measurement taken in the diagram?

25. **EVALUATE** Do you think the following is an accurate definition of medium? Explain your answer.

   A **medium** is any solid through which waves travel.

26. **APPLY** Picture a pendulum. The pendulum is swinging back and forth at a steady rate. How could you make it swing higher? How is swinging a pendulum like making a wave?

27. **PREDICT** What might happen to an ocean wave that encounters a gap or hole in a cliff along the shore?

28. **EVALUATE** Do you think *interference* is an appropriate name for the types of wave interaction you read about in Section 1.3? Explain your answer.

Using Math in Science

29. At what speed is the wave below traveling if it has a frequency of 2 wavelengths/s?

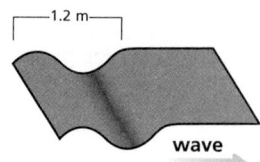

wave

30. An ocean wave has a wavelength of 9 m and a frequency of 0.42 wavelengths/s. What is the wave's speed?

31. Suppose a sound wave has a frequency of 10,000 wavelengths/s. The wave's speed is 340 m/s. Calculate the wavelength of this sound wave.

32. A water wave is traveling at a speed of 2.5 m/s. The wave has a wavelength of 4 m. Calculate the frequency of this water wave.

the **BIG** idea

33. **INTERPRET** Look back at the photograph at the start of the chapter on pages 6–7. How does this photograph illustrate a transfer of energy?

34. **SYNTHESIZE** Describe three situations in which you can predict the behavior of waves.

35. **SUMMARIZE** Write a paragraph summarizing this chapter. Use the big idea from page 6 as the topic sentence. Then write an example from each of the key concepts listed under the big idea.

MONITOR AND RETEACH

If students have difficulty answering questions 20 and 21, make flash cards for all the vocabulary words in the chapter. Draw a wave diagram on the board. Have students play a flash-card game. When a word and definition apply to some part of the diagram, have students identify it. For vocabulary words that are illustrated in the chapter, have students find a visual that depicts the vocabulary word.

Students may benefit from summarizing one or more sections of the chapter.

 Summarizing the Chapter, pp. 71–72

Standardized Test Practice

For practice on your state test, go to . . .

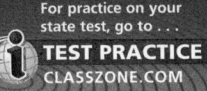 **TEST PRACTICE**
CLASSZONE.COM

Interpreting Diagrams

Study the illustration below and then answer the questions.

The illustration below shows a wave channel, a way of making and studying water waves. The motor moves the rod, which moves the paddle back and forth. The movement of the paddle makes waves, which move down the length of the channel. The material behind the paddle absorbs the waves generated in that direction.

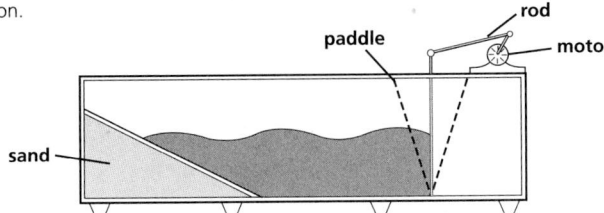

1. An experimenter can adjust the position of the rod on the arm of the motor. Placing it closer to the motor makes shallower waves. Placing it farther from the motor makes deeper waves. What property of waves does this affect?
   a. amplitude
   b. direction
   c. frequency
   d. wavelength

2. By changing motor speeds, an experimenter can make the paddle move faster or slower. What property of waves does this affect?
   a. amplitude
   b. direction
   c. trough depth
   d. wavelength

3. Sand is piled up in the channel at the end of the tank opposite the motor. When waves pass over this sand, their wavelengths shorten. Assuming that the speed of the waves stays the same, their frequency
   a. stays the same
   b. increases
   c. decreases
   d. cannot be predicted

4. Suppose there was no sand at the end of the tank opposite the paddle. In that case, the waves would hit the glass wall. What would they do then?
   a. stop
   b. reflect
   c. refract
   d. diffract

Extended Response

Answer the two questions below in detail.

5. Suppose temperatures in one 10-day period were as follows: 94°, 96°, 95°, 97°, 95°, 98°, 99°, 97°, 99°, and 98°. Make a simple line graph of the data. In what ways is the series of temperatures similar to a wave, and in what ways does it differ?

6. Lydia and Bill each drop a ball of the same size into the same tank of water but at two different spots. Both balls produce waves that spread across the surface of the water. As the two sets of waves cross each other, the water forms high crests in some places. What can you say about both waves? Explain your answer.

Interpreting Diagrams

1. a   3. c
2. d   4. b

Extended Response

5. RUBRIC
4 points for a response that correctly answers the question and uses the following terms accurately:
- amplitude
- frequency
- wavelength

Sample: The series of high temperatures is similar to a wave in that its graph has <u>amplitude</u>, <u>frequency</u>, *and* <u>wavelength</u>, *but it is different in that energy is not transferred from one place to another.*

3 points for a response that correctly answers the question and uses two terms accurately
2 points for a response that correctly uses one term accurately
1 point for a response that correctly answers the question but doesn't use the terms

6. RUBRIC
4 points for a response that correctly answers the question and uses the following terms accurately:
- amplitude
- crests
- trough

Sample: Both waves have the same <u>amplitude</u> *and cancel each other out because the* <u>crests</u> *and troughs were matched exactly. This is an example of destructive interference showing that when the two waves meet, the* <u>trough</u> *of one wave joins with the crest of the other.*

3 points for a response that correctly answers the question and uses two terms accurately
2 points for a response that correctly uses one term accurately
1 point for a response that correctly answers the question but doesn't use the terms

METACOGNITIVE ACTIVITY

Have students answer the following questions in their **Science Notebook:**

1. What did you find most surprising about how waves behave?

2. What questions do you still have about the ways waves interact?

3. What did you learn about waves that can be applied to your Unit Project?

Physical Science
UNIFYING PRINCIPLES

PRINCIPLE 1

Matter is made of particles too small to see.

PRINCIPLE 2

Matter changes form and moves from place to place.

PRINCIPLE 3

Energy changes from one form to another, but it cannot be created or destroyed.

PRINCIPLE 4

Physical forces affect the movement of all matter on Earth and throughout the universe.

Unit: Waves, Sound, and Light
BIG IDEAS

CHAPTER 1
Waves

Waves transfer energy and interact in predictable ways.

CHAPTER 2
Sound

Sound waves transfer energy through vibrations.

CHAPTER 3
Electromagnetic Waves

Electromagnetic waves transfer energy through radiation.

CHAPTER 4
Light and Optics

Optical tools depend on the wave behavior of light.

CHAPTER 2
KEY CONCEPTS

SECTION (2.1)

Sound is a wave.

1. Sound is a type of mechanical wave.

2. Sound waves vibrate particles.

3. The speed of sound depends on its medium.

SECTION (2.2)

Frequency determines pitch.

1. Pitch depends on the frequency of a sound wave.

2. The motion of the source of a sound affects its pitch.

SECTION (2.3)

Intensity determines loudness.

1. Intensity depends on the amplitude of a sound wave.

2. The intensity of sound can be controlled.

3. Intense sound can damage hearing.

SECTION (2.4)

Sound has many uses.

1. Ultrasound waves are used to detect objects.

2. Sound waves can produce music.

3. Sound can be recorded and reproduced.

T The Big Idea Flow Chart is available on p. T9 in the **UNIT TRANSPARENCY BOOK.**

Previewing Content

2.1 Sound is a wave. pp. 37–44

1. Sound is a type of mechanical wave.
Sound is a longitudinal wave. **Vibrations** in the wave move in the same direction as the wave. Because sound is a mechanical wave, it must travel through a medium.

Humans detect sound because of vibrations in the ear caused by sound waves.

2. Sound waves vibrate particles.
As sound waves push against molecules in the medium, they compress the molecules, creating bands of high and low pressure. These bands of pressure push and pull on the surrounding air, which then pushes and pulls on the air around that and so on. This creates a sound wave travelling through the air.

Materials and Sound Speeds		
Medium	**State**	**Speed of Sound**
Air (20°C)	Gas	344 m/s (769 mi/h)
Water (20°C)	Liquid	1,400 m/s (3,130 mi/h)
Steel (20°C)	Solid	5,000 m/s (11,200 mi/h)

Temperature and Sound Speeds		
Medium	**Temperature**	**Speed of Sound**
Air	0°C (32°F)	331 m/s (741 mi/h)
Air	100°C (212°F)	386 m/s (864 mi/h)

Sound waves can travel through mediums that are made up of particles, but sound waves cannot travel through a vacuum.

3. The speed of sound depends on its medium.
The speed of sound depends on the state and the temperature of the medium.
- Sound usually travels most quickly through a solid and most slowly through a gas.
- Sound travels more quickly through a specific medium at higher temperatures.

2.2 Frequency determines pitch. pp. 45–51

1. Pitch depends on the frequency of a sound wave.
Pitch is an indication of how high or how low a sound is. A high-frequency wave has a short wavelength and produces a high pitch. A low-frequency wave has a long wavelength and produces a low pitch.

Hertz is the unit used to measure frequency and therefore pitch. One hertz is one wavelength per second.

All objects have a natural frequency of vibrations. When a sound wave is produced that matches an object's natural frequency, its waves combine to create sound with a larger amplitude. This increase is **resonance.**

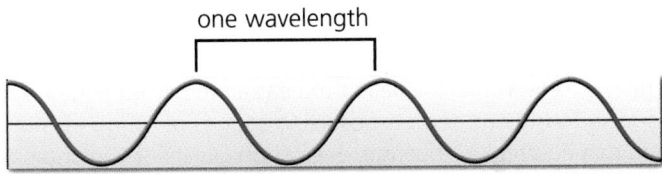

Low-frequency, low-pitched sound wave

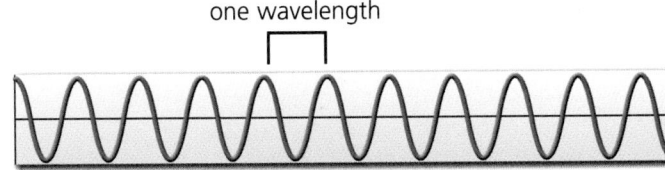

High-frequency, high-pitched sound wave

Timbre, or sound quality, is affected by
- the combination of waves produced by an object and
- how the sound starts and stops.

2. The motion of the source of a sound affects its pitch.
The **Doppler effect** is a change in pitch that occurs because the source or receiver of a sound is moving. Because the sound source is a little closer to the receiver each time it vibrates, it takes less time for the compression to reach the receiver. The decrease in distance makes the wavelength shorter, and the pitch rises.

Common Misconceptions

TYPES OF WAVES Students might think that all waves are the same. They should be aware that waves are classified according to whether they need a medium to travel or not. Electromagnetic waves do not need a medium, and mechanical waves do.

 This misconception is addressed on p. 38.

MISCONCEPTION DATABASE
CLASSZONE.COM Background on student misconceptions

SPEED OF SOUND The phrase "the speed of sound" might lead students to assume that sound always travels at the same speed. Mechanical waves, such as sound, travel at a speed that depends on the nature and temperature of the medium.

 This misconception is addressed on p. 42.

Previewing Content

SECTION

2.3 **Intensity determines loudness.**
pp. 52–57

1. Intensity depends on the amplitude of a sound wave.
Intensity is the amount of energy a sound wave has, measured in **decibels** (dB). Low-intensity sound waves are heard as quiet sounds. Louder sounds are produced by high-intensity sound waves.

2. The intensity of sound can be controlled.
Changing the amount of energy in a sound wave changes the sound's intensity without changing its pitch or quality.
• A muffler decreases intensity.
• An **amplifier** increases intensity.

3. Intense sound can damage hearing.
The hair cells in the cochlea in the ear are easily damaged by loud sounds. Long-term exposure to sounds of 90 dB or more can damage human hearing. Even short bursts of very intense sound can deafen a person.

SECTION

2.4 **Sound has many uses.** pp. 58–65

1. Ultrasound waves are used to detect objects.
Reflected ultrasound waves are used to detect the presence and location of objects.
• Some animals, such as bats, use **echolocation,** which involves sending out ultrasound signals and interpreting the returning sound echoes.
• Humans use **sonar,** a form of echolocation, to locate objects underwater.
• In medicine, **ultrasound** is used to treat stones that form in the human body and to scan internal organs.

2. Sound waves can produce music.
Noise is sound with no pattern. Music is sound with clear patterns of pitch and rhythm. Stringed, wind, and percussion instruments all produce vibrations in different ways, which accounts for their distinctive timbres.

3. Sound can be recorded and reproduced.
Vibrations can be changed to other types of signals or stored as reproducible information.
• Some methods of communication, such as the telephone, change sound waves into electrical signals. These signals travel to a receiver that changes them back into sound.
• Sound can be recorded as physical grooves (records) or pits (CDs) or as magnetic information (tapes) that can be changed back to sound waves.

Common Misconceptions

HEARING DAMAGE Students commonly assume that any hearing damage resulting from loud noises is temporary. Noises greater than 90 dB can cause permanent hearing damage.

 This misconception is addressed on p. 55.

 MISCONCEPTION DATABASE
CLASSZONE.COM Background on student misconceptions

Previewing Labs

Lab Generator CD-ROM
Edit these Pupil Edition labs and generate alternative labs.

EXPLORE the BIG idea

What Gives a Sound Its Qualities? p. 35
Students will explore sound to discover its properties.

TIME 5 minutes
MATERIALS table

How Does Size Affect Sound? p. 35
Students test three nails to find that the size of a sample affects its pitch.

TIME 10 minutes
MATERIALS 3 different-sized nails of the same material, string (at least 1 m), scissors, metal spoon

---

Internet Activity: Sound, p. 35
Students discover how air particles move as sound travels through air.

TIME 20 minutes
MATERIALS computer with Internet access

SECTION 2.1

EXPLORE Sound, p. 37
Students listen to sounds traveling via string to understand that sound travels through a medium.

TIME 10 minutes
MATERIALS 75 cm of string; large, metal spoon

INVESTIGATE Sound Energy, p. 41
Students observe that sound waves move salt, to find out that sound transfers energy.

TIME 10 minutes
MATERIALS clean jar, a pinch of table salt, balloon, scissors, rubber band, pencil with good eraser end

---

SECTION 2.2

EXPLORE Pitch, p. 45
Students observe sounds to find out what affects pitch.

TIME 5 minutes
MATERIALS ruler

INVESTIGATE Sound Frequency, p. 48
Students listen to rubber bands at differing tensions and infer the relationship between frequency and pitch.

TIME 20 minutes
MATERIALS two rubber bands of different sizes; small, open box; 16 cm tape

---

SECTION 2.3

INVESTIGATE Loudness, p. 53
Students pluck a rubber band to observe the relationship between amplitude and loudness.

TIME 15 minutes
MATERIALS piece of cardboard, 25 cm long; scissors; large rubber band; two pencils; ruler

---

SECTION 2.4

EXPLORE Echoes, p. 58
Students use sound to detect an object.

TIME 10 minutes
MATERIALS two cardboard tubes, 10 cm tape, book

CHAPTER INVESTIGATION
Build a Stringed Instrument, pp. 64–65
Students make a simple stringed instrument and find out how it can produce different pitches.

TIME 40 minutes
MATERIALS book, 3–5 rubber bands, two pencils, ruler, shoebox, scissors

---

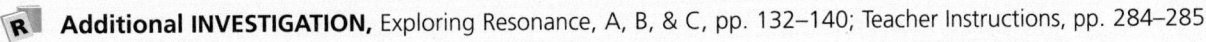 **Additional INVESTIGATION,** Exploring Resonance, A, B, & C, pp. 132–140; Teacher Instructions, pp. 284–285

Previewing Chapter Resources

	INTEGRATED TECHNOLOGY	LABS AND ACTIVITIES

CHAPTER 2
Sound

 CLASSZONE.COM
- eEdition Plus
- EasyPlanner Plus
- Misconception Database
- Content Review
- Test Practice
- Visualizations
- Resource Centers
- Internet Activity: Sound
- Math Tutorial

 CD-ROMS
- eEdition
- EasyPlanner
- Power Presentations
- Content Review
- Lab Generator
- Test Generator

 AUDIO CDS
- Audio Readings
- Audio Readings in Spanish

 SCILINKS.ORG
SCILINKS

PE EXPLORE the Big Idea, p. 35
- What Gives a Sound Its Qualities?
- How Does Size Affect Sound?
- Internet Activity: Sound

R **UNIT RESOURCE BOOK**
Unit Projects, pp. 5–10

 Lab Generator CD-ROM
Generate customized labs.

SECTION
2.1 **Sound is a wave.**
pp. 37–44

Time: 2 periods (1 block)
R Lesson Plan, pp. 73–74

 RESOURCE CENTER, Supersonic Aircraft

 UNIT TRANSPARENCY BOOK
- Big Idea Flow Chart, p. T9
- Daily Vocabulary Scaffolding, p. T10
- Note-Taking Model, p. T11
- 3-Minute Warm-Up, p. T12

PE
- EXPLORE Sound, p. 37
- INVESTIGATE Sound Energy, p. 41

R **UNIT RESOURCE BOOK**
Datasheet, Sound Energy, p. 82

SECTION
2.2 **Frequency determines pitch.**
pp. 45–51

Time: 2 periods (1 block)
R Lesson Plan, pp. 84–85

 VISUALIZATION, Doppler Effect

 UNIT TRANSPARENCY BOOK
- Daily Vocabulary Scaffolding, p. T10
- 3-Minute Warm-Up, p. T12
- "Sound Frequencies Heard by Animals" Visual, p. T14

PE
- EXPLORE Pitch, p. 45
- INVESTIGATE Sound Frequency, p. 48

R **UNIT RESOURCE BOOK**
- Datasheet, Sound Frequency, p. 93
- Additional INVESTIGATION, Exploring Resonance, A, B, & C, pp. 132–140

SECTION
2.3 **Intensity determines loudness.**
pp. 52–57

Time: 2 periods (1 block)
R Lesson Plan, pp. 95–96

 RESOURCE CENTER, Sound Safety
MATH TUTORIAL

 UNIT TRANSPARENCY BOOK
- Daily Vocabulary Scaffolding, p. T10
- 3-Minute Warm-Up, p. T13

PE
- INVESTIGATE Loudness, p. 53
- Math in Science, p. 57

R **UNIT RESOURCE BOOK**
- Datasheet, Loudness, p. 104
- Math Support, p. 121
- Math Practice, p. 122

SECTION
2.4 **Sound has many uses.**
pp. 58–65

Time: 4 periods (2 blocks)
R Lesson Plan, pp. 106–107

 RESOURCE CENTER, Musical Instruments

 UNIT TRANSPARENCY BOOK
- Big Idea Flow Chart, p. T9
- Daily Vocabulary Scaffolding, p. T10
- 3-Minute Warm-Up, p. T13
- Chapter Outline, p. T15–16

PE
- EXPLORE Echoes, p. 58
- CHAPTER INVESTIGATION, Build a Stringed Instrument, pp. 64–65

R **UNIT RESOURCE BOOK**
CHAPTER INVESTIGATION, Build a Stringed Instrument, A, B, & C, pp. 123–131

KEY TO ICONS

 **CD/CD-ROM**

 **INTERNET**   **Pupil Edition**

 Teacher Edition

 UNIT RESOURCE BOOK

T **UNIT TRANSPARENCY BOOK**

A **UNIT ASSESSMENT BOOK**

SP A **SPANISH ASSESSMENT BOOK**

SCIENCE TOOLKIT

READING AND REINFORCEMENT

ASSESSMENT

STANDARDS

- Description Wheel, B20–21
- Outline, C43
- Daily Vocabulary Scaffolding, H1–8

 UNIT RESOURCE BOOK
- Vocabulary Practice, pp. 118–119
- Decoding Support, p. 120
- Summarizing the Chapter, pp. 141–142

 Audio Readings CD
Listen to Pupil Edition.

Audio Readings in Spanish CD
Listen to Pupil Edition in Spanish

- Chapter Review, pp. 67–68
- Standardized Test Practice, p. 69

A **UNIT ASSESSMENT BOOK**
- Diagnostic Test, pp. 20–21
- Chapter Test, A, B, & C, pp. 26–37
- Alternative Assessment, pp. 38–39

SP A Spanish Chapter Test, pp. 285–288

 **Test Generator CD-ROM**
Generate customized tests.

Lab Generator CD-ROM
Rubrics for Labs

National Standards
A.1–8, A.9.a–g, E.2–5, F.5.a–d

See p. 34 for the standards.

 UNIT RESOURCE BOOK
- Reading Study Guide, A & B, pp. 75–78
- Spanish Reading Study Guide, pp. 79–80
- Challenge and Extension, p. 81
- Reinforcing Key Concepts, p. 83

 Ongoing Assessment, pp. 37–43

 Section 2.1 Review, p. 43

A **UNIT ASSESSMENT BOOK**
Section 2.1 Quiz, p. 22

National Standards
A.2–8, A.9.a–c, A.9.e–f, F.5.d

 UNIT RESOURCE BOOK
- Reading Study Guide, A & B, pp. 86–89
- Spanish Reading Study Guide, pp. 90–91
- Challenge and Extension, p. 92
- Reinforcing Key Concepts, p. 94
- Challenge Reading, pp. 116–117

 Ongoing Assessment, pp. 45–51

 Section 2.2 Review, p. 51

A **UNIT ASSESSMENT BOOK**
Section 2.2 Quiz, p. 23

National Standards
A.2–8, A.9.a–f, F.5.b

 UNIT RESOURCE BOOK
- Reading Study Guide, A & B, pp. 97–100
- Spanish Reading Study Guide, pp. 101–102
- Challenge and Extension, p. 103
- Reinforcing Key Concepts, p. 105

 Ongoing Assessment, pp. 52–56

 Section 2.3 Review, p. 56

A **UNIT ASSESSMENT BOOK**
Section 2.3 Quiz, p. 24

National Standards
A.2–8, A.9.a–f, F.5.a, F.5.c

 UNIT RESOURCE BOOK
- Reading Study Guide, A & B, pp. 108–111
- Spanish Reading Study Guide, pp. 112–113
- Challenge and Extension, p. 114
- Reinforcing Key Concepts, p. 115

 Ongoing Assessment, pp. 58, 60–63

 Section 2.4 Review, p. 63

A **UNIT ASSESSMENT BOOK**
Section 2.4 Quiz, p. 25

National Standards
A.1–7, A.9.a–b, A.9.d–g, E.2–5, F.5.a–c

Previewing Resources for Differentiated Instruction

CHAPTER INVESTIGATION

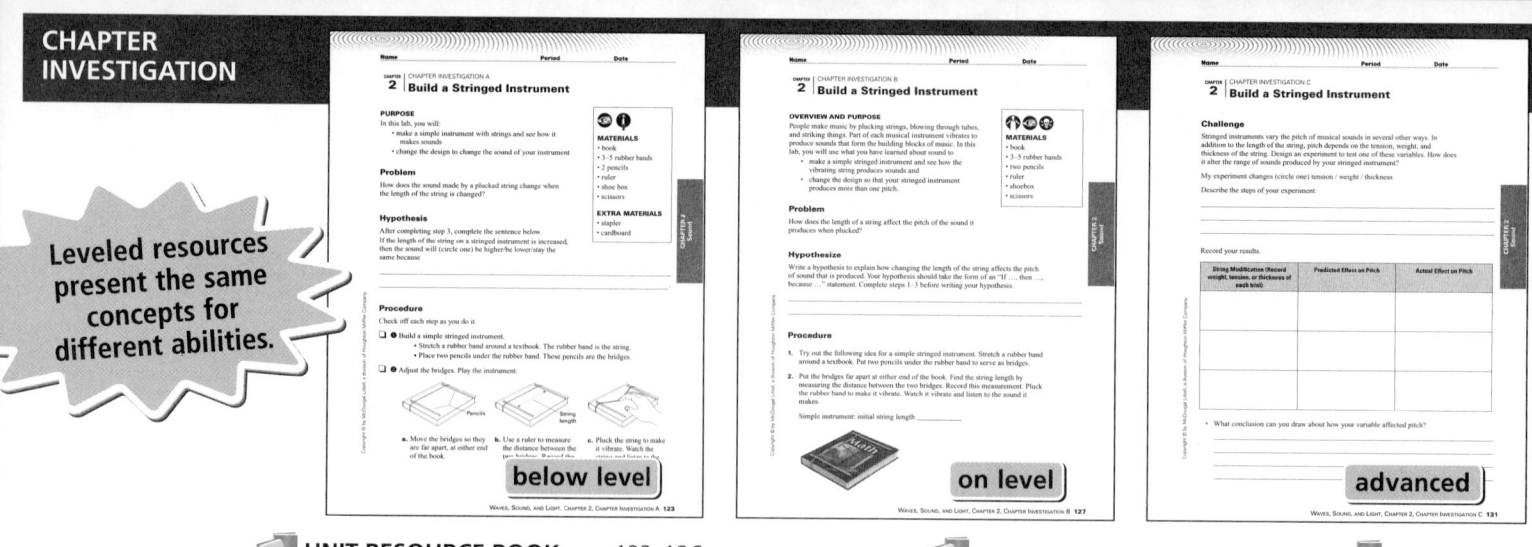

Leveled resources present the same concepts for different abilities.

below level

on level

advanced

R UNIT RESOURCE BOOK, pp. 123–126

R pp. 127–130

R pp. 127–131

READING STUDY GUIDE

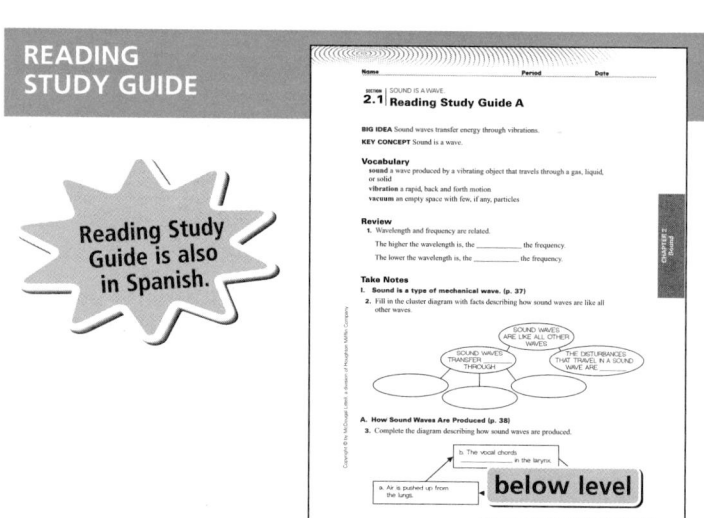

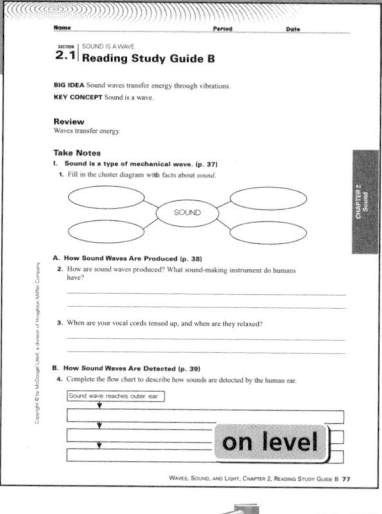

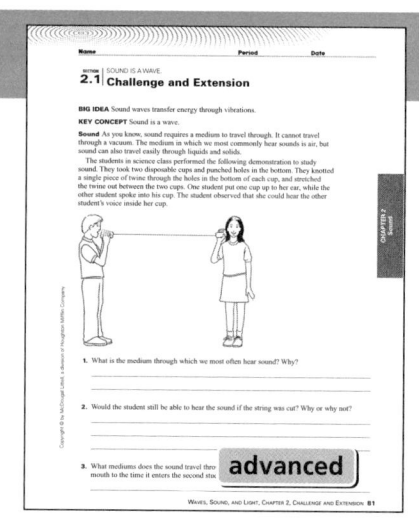

Reading Study Guide is also in Spanish.

below level

on level

advanced

R UNIT RESOURCE BOOK, pp. 75–76

R pp. 77–78

R p. 81

CHAPTER TEST

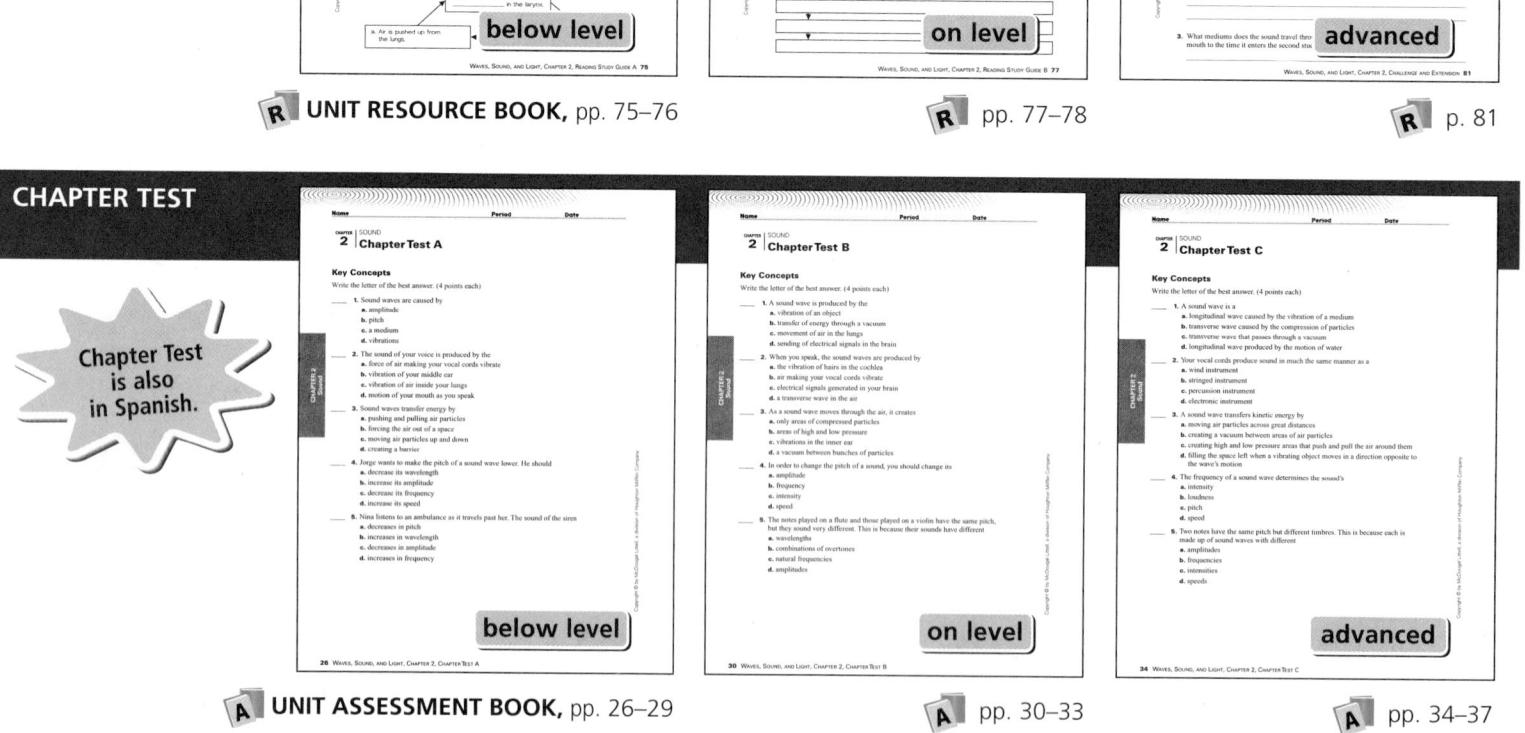

Chapter Test is also in Spanish.

below level

on level

advanced

A UNIT ASSESSMENT BOOK, pp. 26–29

A pp. 30–33

A pp. 34–37

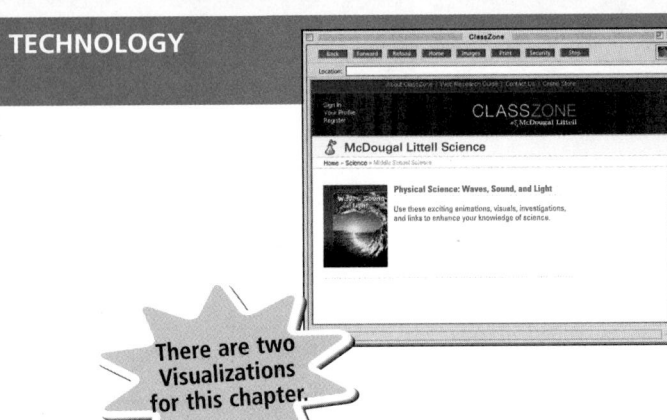

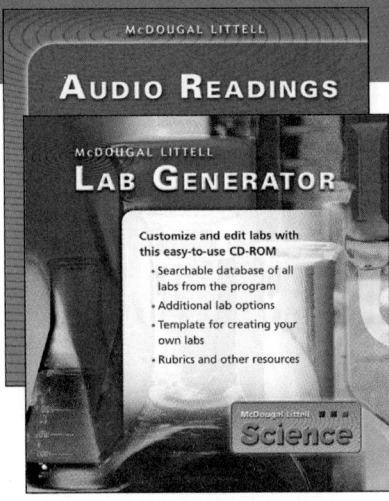

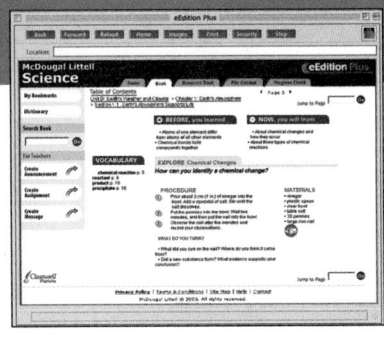

There are two Visualizations for this chapter.

CLASSZONE.COM   **CD/CD-ROMS**   **CLASSZONE.COM**

VISUAL CONTENT

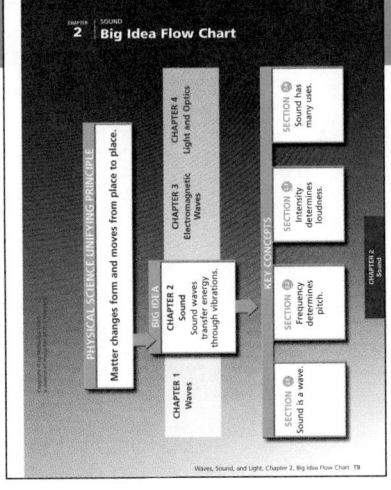

UNIT TRANSPARENCY BOOK, p. T9

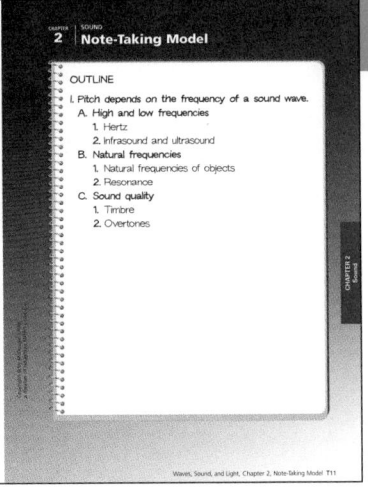

p. T11

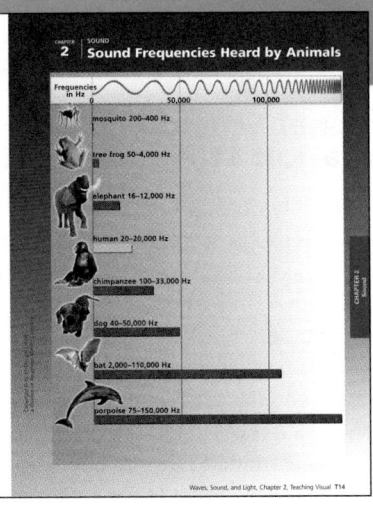

p. T14

MORE SUPPORT

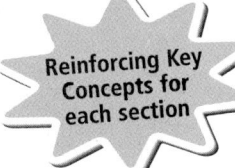

Reinforcing Key Concepts for each section

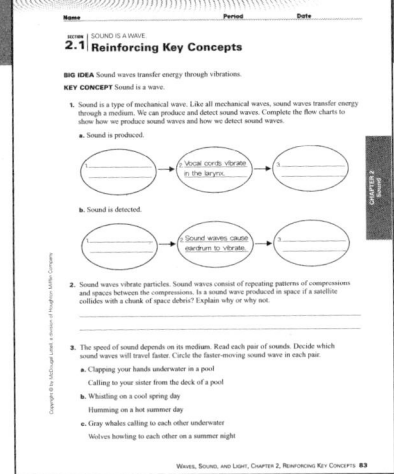

UNIT RESOURCE BOOK, p. 83

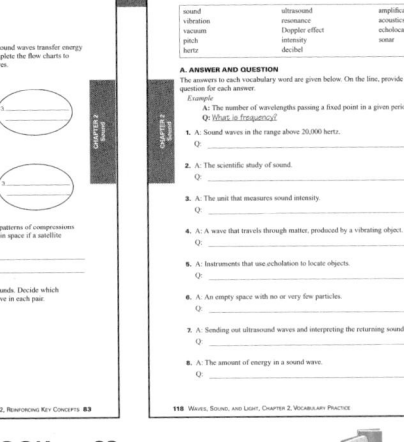

pp. 118–119

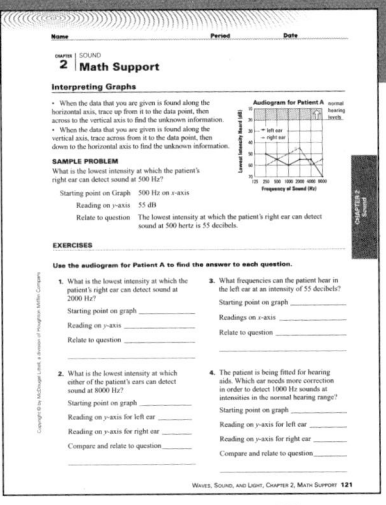

p. 121

CHAPTER

2 Sound

INTRODUCE

the BIG idea

Have students look at the photograph of the guitar player and discuss how the question in the box links to the Big Idea:

- What role do guitar strings play in producing vibrations?
- What role does the body of the guitar play in producing sound?
- What part of the human body receives the vibrations from the guitar?
- How are the vibrations from the guitar perceived as sound?

National Science Education Standards

A.1–8 Identify questions that can be answered through scientific investigations; design and conduct an investigation; use tools to gather and interpret data; use evidence to describe, predict, explain, model; think critically to make relationships between evidence and explanation; recognize different explanations and predictions; communicate scientific procedures and explanations; use mathematics.

A.9.a–g Understand scientific inquiry by using different investigations, methods, mathematics, technology, and explanations based on logic, evidence, and skepticism. Data often results in new investigations.

E.2-5 Design, implement, evaluate a solution or product; communicate technological design.

F.5.a–d Science and technology in society

CHAPTER

2 Sound

the BIG idea

Sound waves transfer energy through vibrations.

Key Concepts

SECTION 2.1 Sound is a wave. Learn how sound waves are produced and detected.

SECTION 2.2 Frequency determines pitch. Learn about the relationship between the frequency of a sound wave and its pitch.

SECTION 2.3 Intensity determines loudness. Learn how the energy of a sound wave relates to its loudness.

SECTION 2.4 Sound has many uses. Learn how sound waves are used to detect objects and to make music.

Internet Preview

CLASSZONE.COM
Chapter 2 online resources: Content Review, two Visualizations, three Resource Centers, Math Tutorial, Test Practice

> How is this guitar player producing sound?

INTERNET PREVIEW

CLASSZONE.COM For student use with the following pages:

Review and Practice
- Content Review, pp. 36, 66
- Math Tutorial: Interpreting Line Graphs, p. 57
- Test Practice, p. 69

Activities and Resources
- Internet Activity, p. 35
- Visualization: Doppler Effect, p. 51
- Resource Centers: Supersonic Aircraft, p. 44; Sound Safety, p. 56; Musical Instruments, p. 60

NSTA scilinks.org
What is Sound?
Code: MDL028

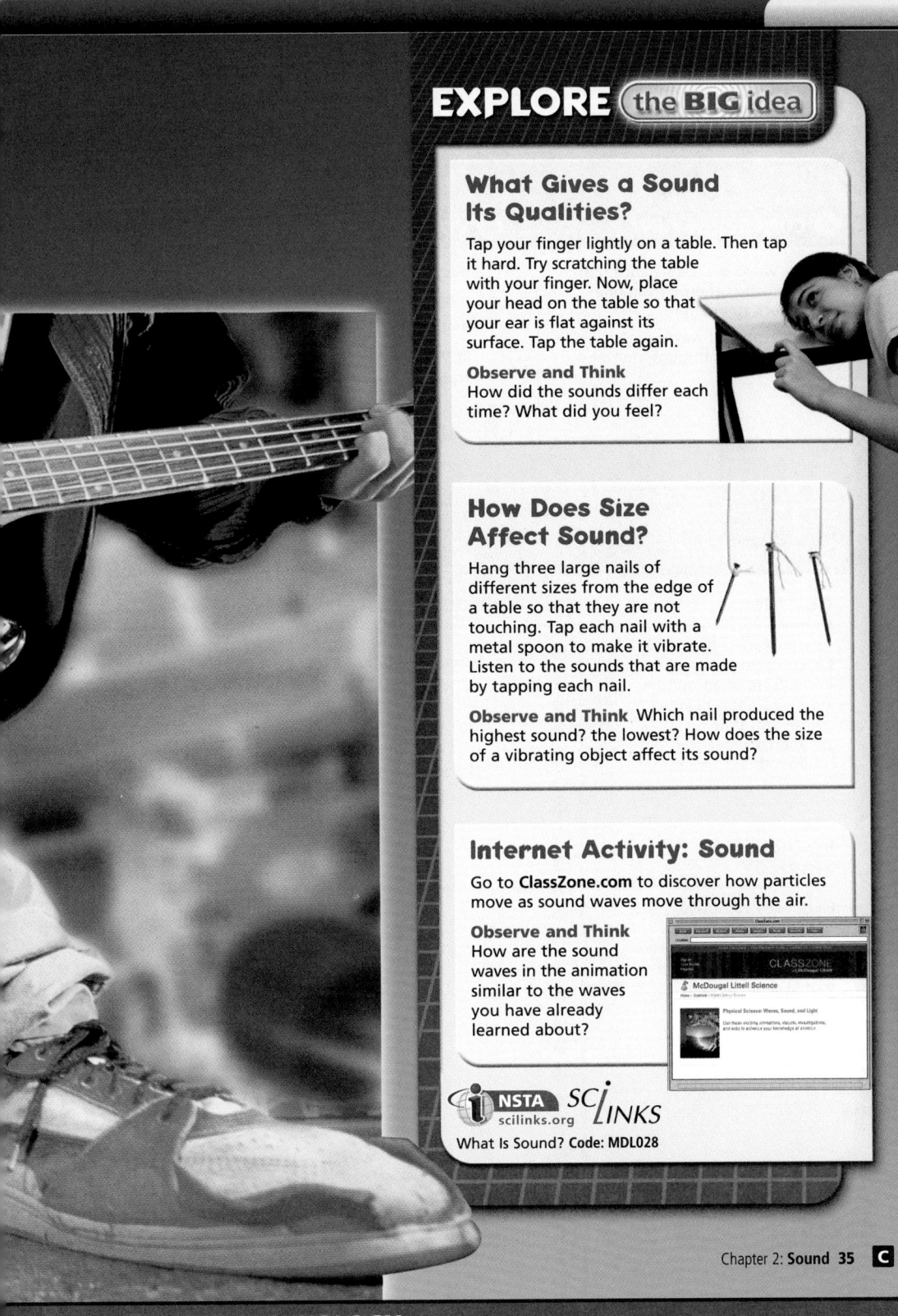

EXPLORE the BIG idea

What Gives a Sound Its Qualities?

Tap your finger lightly on a table. Then tap it hard. Try scratching the table with your finger. Now, place your head on the table so that your ear is flat against its surface. Tap the table again.

Observe and Think
How did the sounds differ each time? What did you feel?

How Does Size Affect Sound?

Hang three large nails of different sizes from the edge of a table so that they are not touching. Tap each nail with a metal spoon to make it vibrate. Listen to the sounds that are made by tapping each nail.

Observe and Think Which nail produced the highest sound? the lowest? How does the size of a vibrating object affect its sound?

Internet Activity: Sound

Go to **ClassZone.com** to discover how particles move as sound waves move through the air.

Observe and Think
How are the sound waves in the animation similar to the waves you have already learned about?

CLASSZONE
McDougal Littell Science

NSTA
scilinks.org
SCiLINKS

What Is Sound? Code: MDL028

Chapter 2: **Sound** 35 **C**

TEACHING WITH TECHNOLOGY

Tape Recorder Use a tape recorder to record the sounds of the stringed instruments the students build in the Chapter Investigation on pp. 64–65. Have students listen to the sounds so they can hear the differences in pitch between the different instrument designs.

CBL and Probeware If students have probeware, you might encourage them to use a microphone during activities and demonstrations throughout the chapter.

EXPLORE the BIG idea

These inquiry-based activities are appropriate for use at home or as a supplement to classroom instruction.

What Gives a Sound Its Qualities?

PURPOSE To introduce students to sound properties such as loudness, pitch, and general sound quality.

TIP *10 min.* Adapt the activity for students who might be hearing impaired. Depending on the degree of impairment, students might tap with an object that makes more noise than their fingernail.

Answer: The sounds each had a different quality. Students should feel the vibrations in the table.

REVISIT after p. 49.

How Does Size Affect Sound?

PURPOSE To show that the size of a nail affects the pitch produced by striking it. Students observe that the size and shape of an object affects the frequency of the vibration produced by the object.

TIP *10 min.* All nails must be made of the same material, so that comparison involves only the size and not the type of material.

Answer: The smallest nail produced the highest sound. The largest nail produced the lowest sound. The size of an object affects how high or low its sound is.

REVISIT after p. 61.

Internet Activity: Sound

PURPOSE To help students visualize sound moving through air as longitudinal waves.

TIP *20 min.* Ask students to predict the difference in the sound waves produced by a jet engine and those produced by a whisper. Have students keep their predictions for evaluation at the end of Section 3.

Answer: Accept any of the following: The sound waves in the animation have amplitude, frequency, and wavelength; transfer energy; are longitudinal waves.

REVISIT after p. 41.

Chapter 2 **35** **C**

◐ CONCEPT REVIEW

Activate Prior Knowledge

- Ask students to list examples of how waves transfer energy from one place to another. Examples include electromagnetic waves from the Sun warming Earth, and water waves moving a boat.

- Ask students to explain what a medium is.

- Review the concept of matter and that matter is present in a medium.

▶ TAKING NOTES

Outline

Outlining the chapter will help students pull together their ideas about sound and waves. Using the headings as a skeleton helps them identify the important points in the chapter.

Vocabulary Strategy

Students can use the description wheels not only to describe terms but also to differentiate between them.

Vocabulary and Note-Taking Resources

- Vocabulary Practice, pp. 118–119
- Decoding Support, p. 120

- Daily Vocabulary Scaffolding, p. T10
- Note-Taking Model, p. T11

- Description Wheel, B20–21
- Outline, C43
- Daily Vocabulary Scaffolding, H1–8

CHAPTER 2
Getting Ready to Learn

◐ CONCEPT REVIEW

- A wave is a disturbance that transfers energy from one place to another.
- Mechanical waves are waves that travel through matter.

◐ VOCABULARY REVIEW

medium p. 11
longitudinal wave p. 14
amplitude p. 17
wavelength p. 17
frequency p. 17

CONTENT REVIEW
CLASSZONE.COM
Review concepts and vocabulary.

▶ TAKING NOTES

OUTLINE

As you read, copy the headings on your paper in the form of an outline. Then add notes in your own words that summarize what you have read.

VOCABULARY STRATEGY

Place each vocabulary term at the center of a **description wheel** diagram. Write some words on the spokes describing it.

See the Note-Taking Handbook on pages R45–R51.

C 36 Unit: Waves, Sound, and Light

SCIENCE NOTEBOOK

I. Sound is a type of mechanical wave
  A. How sound waves are produced
    1.
    2.
    3.
  B. How sound waves are detected
    1.
    2.
    3.

rapid back-and-forth motion   can produce a sound

VIBRATION

usually too small to see   can make with vocal cords

CHECK READINESS

Administer the Diagnostic Test to determine students' readiness for new science content and their mastery of requisite math skills.

Diagnostic Test, pp. 20–21

Technology Resources

Students needing content and math skills should visit **ClassZone.com**.

- **CONTENT REVIEW**
- **MATH TUTORIAL**

CONTENT REVIEW CD-ROM

KEY CONCEPT

2.1 Sound is a wave.

◀ **BEFORE**, you learned
- Waves transfer energy
- Waves have wavelength, amplitude, and frequency

▶ **NOW**, you will learn
- How sound waves are produced and detected
- How sound waves transfer energy
- What affects the speed of sound waves

VOCABULARY

sound p. 37
vibration p. 37
vacuum p. 41

EXPLORE Sound

What is sound?

PROCEDURE

1. Tie the middle of the string to the spoon handle.

2. Wrap the string ends around your left and right index fingers. Put the tips of these fingers gently in your ears and hold them there.

3. Stand over your desk so that the spoon dangles without touching your body or the desk. Then move a little to make the spoon tap the desk lightly. Listen to the sound.

MATERIALS
- piece of string
- large metal spoon

WHAT DO YOU THINK?
- What did you hear when the spoon tapped the desk?
- How did sound travel from the spoon to your ears?

Sound is a type of mechanical wave.

OUTLINE
Start an outline for this heading. Remember to leave room for details.

I. Main idea
  A. Supporting idea
    1. Detail
    2. Detail
  B. Supporting idea

In the last chapter, you read that a mechanical wave travels through a material medium. Such mediums include air, water, and solid materials. Sound is an example of a mechanical wave. **Sound** is a wave that is produced by a vibrating object and travels through matter.

The disturbances that travel in a sound wave are vibrations. A **vibration** is a rapid, back-and-forth motion. Because the medium vibrates back and forth in the same direction as the wave travels, sound is a longitudinal wave. Like all mechanical waves, sound waves transfer energy through a medium.

CHECK YOUR READING What do sound waves have in common with other mechanical waves? Your answer should include the word *energy*.

Chapter 2: Sound 37 **C**

Chapter 2 **37** **C**

Address Misconceptions

IDENTIFY Ask: Do all waves have the same traits, or are there different types of waves? If students answer that all waves have the same traits, they hold the misconception that all waves are the same.

CORRECT Place a small amount of water in a flask. Attach a bell to a solid stopper with a wire and a thumbtack, so that it will hang in the middle of the flask when you insert the stopper. Shake the flask and listen to the bell. Shine a light through the flask against a dark surface.

Remove the stopper and heat the water to boiling. Immediately replace the stopper and allow the flask to cool. Shake the flask again, and note that the sound is much less. Shine a light through the flask again, and note that the intensity of the light is the same.

REASSESS Ask students to explain why sound decreased in intensity and light did not. *Sound is a mechanical wave and needs a medium. Heating the water causes the gases in the flask to expand. Cooling creates a partial vacuum, decreasing the amount of medium. Light is an electromagnetic wave that does not need a medium, so the partial vacuum does not affect its intensity.*

Technology Resources

Visit **ClassZone.com** for background on common student misconceptions.

 MISCONCEPTION DATABASE

Ongoing Assessment

CHECK YOUR READING *Answer: The vocal cords vibrate, producing sound waves.*

READING VISUALS *Answer: The vibrations start when air from the lungs passes through the vocal cords.*

READING TiP
When you see the words *push* or *pull*, think of force.

How Sound Waves Are Produced

The disturbances in a sound wave are vibrations that are usually too small to see. Vibrations are also required to start sound waves. A vibrating object pushes and pulls on the medium around it and sends out waves in all directions.

You have a sound-making instrument within your own body. It is the set of vocal cords within the voice box, or larynx, in your throat. Put several of your fingers against the front of your throat. Now hum. Do you feel the vibrations of your vocal cords?

Your vocal cords relax when you breathe to allow air to pass in and out of your windpipe. Your vocal cords tense up and draw close together when you are about to speak or sing. The illustration below shows how sound waves are produced by the human vocal cords.

❶ Your muscles push air up from your lungs and through the narrow opening between the vocal cords.

❷ The force of the air causes the vocal cords to vibrate.

❸ The vibrating vocal cords produce sound waves.

CHECK YOUR READING   How do human vocal cords produce sound waves?

How Vocal Cords Produce Sound

Sound waves are produced by vibrations.

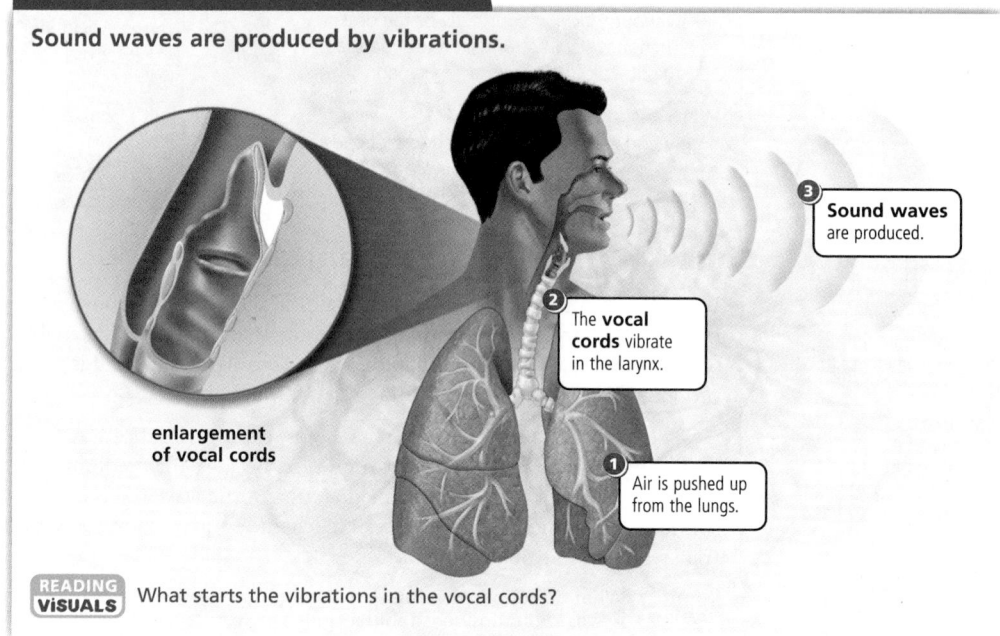

enlargement of vocal cords

3 **Sound waves** are produced.

2 The **vocal cords** vibrate in the larynx.

1 Air is pushed up from the lungs.

READING VISUALS   What starts the vibrations in the vocal cords?

C 38   Unit: Waves, Sound, and Light

DIFFERENTIATE INSTRUCTION

 More Reading Support

A What makes sounds in your throat? *the vibrations of vocal cords*

English Learners   Students new to English may be confused about what is required in review items, such as those on p. 43. For instructions such as "describe and explain," tell students exactly what each direction asks them to do.

- *describe:* Write as if drawing a picture. Give physical details.
- *explain:* Write as if listing steps in a process.

Students can practice both types of answers with simple questions, such as, "Describe and explain what happens in your classroom." It is also helpful to provide model answers.

How Sound Waves Are Detected

The shape of a human ear helps it collect sound waves. Picture a satellite dish. It collects radio waves from satellites. Your ear works in much the same way. Actually, what we typically call the ear is only the outer section of the ear. The illustration below shows the main parts of the human ear.

① Your outer ear collects sound waves and reflects them into a tiny tube called the ear canal. At the end of the ear canal is a thin, skin-like membrane stretched tightly over the opening, called the eardrum. When sound waves strike the eardrum, they make it vibrate.

② The middle ear contains three tiny, connected bones called the hammer, anvil, and stirrup. These bones carry vibrations from the eardrum to the inner ear.

③ One of the main parts of the inner ear, the cochlea, contains about 30,000 hair cells. Each of these cells has tiny hairs on its surface. The hairs bend as a result of the vibrations. This movement triggers changes that cause the cell to send electrical signals along nerves to your brain. Only when your brain receives and processes these signals do you actually hear a sound.

> **READING TiP**
> As you read each numbered description here, match it to the number on the illustration below.

How the Ear Detects Sound

Sound waves are detected in the human ear, beginning with vibrations of the eardrum.

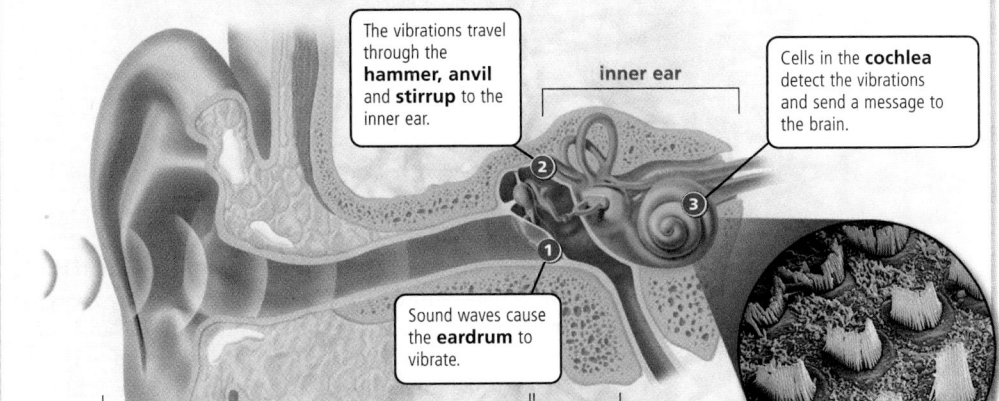

The vibrations travel through the **hammer, anvil** and **stirrup** to the inner ear.

inner ear

Cells in the **cochlea** detect the vibrations and send a message to the brain.

Sound waves cause the **eardrum** to vibrate.

outer ear

middle ear

Enlargement of hairs on a single cell in the cochlea (magnified 2185x)

READING VISUALS How do vibrations get from the eardrum to the cochlea?

Chapter 2: **Sound** 39 **C**

Integrate the Sciences

Although the ears detect sound and change it to electrical signals, the brain interprets the signals sent to it. One important function of the brain is to sort out unneeded noise, focusing on important or unusual sounds. This filtering occurs in a network of nerve cells in the brain stem, known as the reticular activating system (RAS). The action of the RAS enables you to study with the radio on or hear the sound of an announcer over the noise of a crowd.

Teach from Visuals

To help students interpret the visual of the ear, ask:

- What causes the eardrum to vibrate? *sound waves striking the eardrum*

- What effect would an inner ear infection, when the inner ear fills up with fluid, have on hearing? What might happen? *Students may infer that sound is blocked or it changes the perception of sounds. In fact, most ear infections block some vibrations from passing through the inner ear.*

Ongoing Assessment

Explain how sound waves are produced and detected.

Ask: If two people talk, how is sound produced and detected? *Air pushes between vocal cords to produce sound. The ear detects vibrations that enter it and interprets them as sound.*

READING VISUALS *Answer: The vibrations get to the cochlea by passing through the hammer, anvil, and stirrup.*

DIFFERENTIATE INSTRUCTION

 More Reading Support

B What happens when sound hits the eardrum? *The eardrum vibrates.*

Advanced

R Challenge and Extension, p. 81

Ask: What happens to the particles in a medium when sound waves pass through it? *The particles vibrate.*

CHECK YOUR READING *Sample answer: Sound travels as compressions in the particles that make up the air.*

Sound waves vibrate particles.

You can see the motion of waves in water. You can even ride them with a surfboard. But you cannot see air. How, then, can you picture sound waves moving through air? Sound waves transfer the motion of particles too small to see from one place to another.

For example, think about a drum that has been struck. What happens between the time the drum is struck and the sound is heard?

- The drum skin vibrates rapidly. It pushes out and then in, over and over again. Of course, this happens very, very fast. The vibrating drum skin pushes against nearby particles in the air. The particles in the air become bunched together, or compressed.

- When the drum skin pushes the opposite way, a space opens up between the drum's surface and the particles. The particles rush back in to fill the space.

- The back-and-forth movement, or vibration, of the particles is the disturbance that travels to the listener. Both the bunched up areas, or compressions, and the spaces between the compressions are parts of the wave.

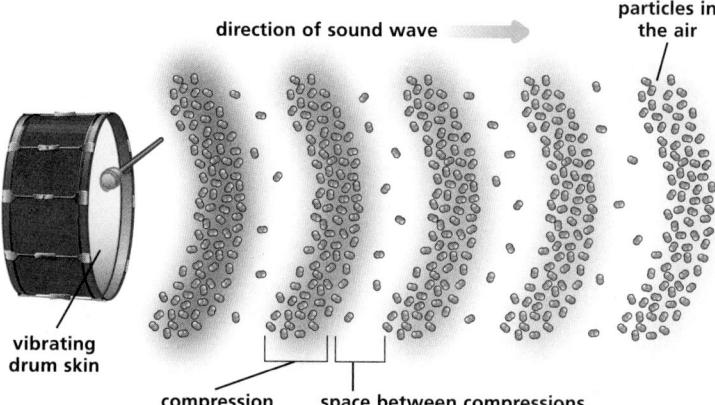

direction of sound wave ⟶   particles in the air

vibrating drum skin

compression   space between compressions

Notice that the waves consist of repeating patterns of compressions and spaces between the compressions. The compressions are areas of high air pressure. The spaces between the compressions are areas of low air pressure. The high- and low-pressure air pushes and pulls on the surrounding air, which then pushes and pulls on the air around that. Soon a sound wave has traveled through the air and has transferred kinetic energy from one place to another.

REMINDER
Kinetic energy is the energy of motion.

CHECK YOUR READING Summarize in your own words how sound travels through air.

DIFFERENTIATE INSTRUCTION

? More Reading Support

C What is the name for air particles bunching up in a sound wave? *compression*

Below Level Have two students model how a sound wave travels. Have them place a spring toy on the floor and stretch it between them until it is approximately 2 meters long. Have one student squeeze together about 20 coils on his or her end. They should see that the other coils become farther apart. When they release the coils, the compression travels down the spring.

In the middle 1600s, scientists began to do experiments to learn more about air. They used pumps to force the air out of enclosed spaces to produce a vacuum. A **vacuum** is empty space. It has no particles—or very, very few of them. Robert Boyle, a British scientist, designed an experiment to find out if sound moves through a vacuum.

Boyle put a ticking clock in a sealed jar. He pumped some air out of the jar and still heard the clock ticking. Then he pumped more air out. The ticking grew quieter. Finally, when Boyle had pumped out almost all the air, he could hear no ticking at all. Boyle's experiment demonstrated that sound does not travel through a vacuum.

The photograph at the right shows equipment that is set up to perform an experiment similar to Boyle's. A bell is placed in a sealed jar and powered through the electrical connections at the top. The sound of the loudly ringing bell becomes quieter as air is pumped out through the vacuum plate.

Sound is a mechanical wave. It can move only through a medium that is made up of matter. Sound waves can travel through air, solid materials, and liquids, such as water because all of these mediums are made up of particles. Sound waves cannot travel through a vacuum.

Sound Experiment

connections

sealed jar

bell

vacuum plate

INFER As air is pumped out of the jar, the sound of the bell becomes quieter. Why do you think the bell is suspended?

CHECK YOUR READING How did Boyle's experiment show that sound cannot travel through a vacuum?

INVESTIGATE Sound Energy

How does sound transfer energy?

PROCEDURE

1. Sprinkle a few grains of salt into the jar. Put the jar on a flat surface in a well-lit place.
2. Cut off the neck of the balloon with the scissors.
3. Stretch the balloon over the mouth of the jar and pull the sides down past the rim of the jar's mouth. Use a rubber band to make a tight fit.
4. Tap the balloon with the eraser end of the pencil. Observe what happens to the salt on the bottom of the jar.

WHAT DO YOU THINK?

- What happens to the salt?
- How can you explain what you observed?

CHALLENGE Suppose you could pump all the air out of the jar and could leave the salt grains in the jar and the tight rubber cover on top. If you repeated the experiment, do you think the results would be different? Explain your answer.

SKILL FOCUS
Observing

MATERIALS
- clean jar
- table salt
- balloon
- scissors
- rubber band
- pencil with good eraser end

TIME
10 minutes

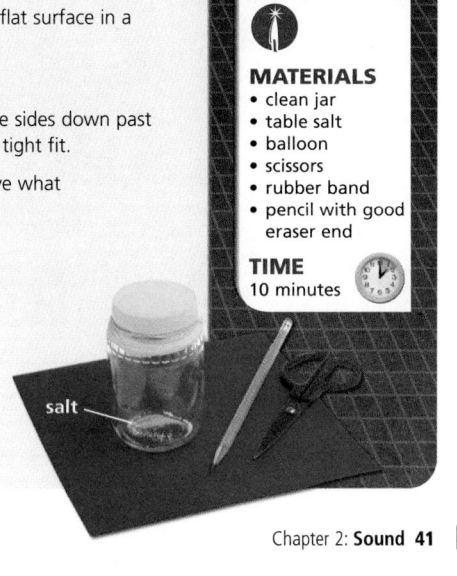

salt

Chapter 2: **Sound** 41 **C**

EXPLORE (the BIG idea)

Revisit "Internet Activity: Sound" on p. 35. Have students explain their results.

INVESTIGATE
Sound Energy

PURPOSE To observe how sound transfers energy from one place to another

TIPS *10 min.*
- Fine sand can be used instead of salt.
- Be sure all jars are completely dry.

WHAT DO YOU THINK? *The salt vibrates. The energy of vibration has traveled from the balloon to the salt.*

CHALLENGE *The salt would not vibrate because there would be no air to transfer the wave. Another acceptable answer is that the salt would still vibrate because the sound would travel through the glass.*

R   Datasheet, Sound Energy, p. 82

Technology Resources

Customize this student lab as needed or look for an alternative. Print rubrics to assess student lab reports.

Lab Generator CD-ROM

Ongoing Assessment

Observe that sound transfers energy.

Ask: Where did the energy that moved the salt come from? *from the sound waves*

CHECK YOUR READING *Answer: When air was removed from the jar, the sound was no longer heard, showing that sound cannot travel through a vacuum.*

DIFFERENTIATE INSTRUCTION

? More Reading Support

D Can sound travel through a vacuum? *No, it must have a medium.*

E What makes up mediums such as air and water? *particles or matter*

Alternative Assessment Have students perform the following activity and write a paragraph or draw a diagram that answers the question.
- Seal a bowl with plastic wrap and tape the wrap to the bowl.
- Tape a rubber band to the center of the plastic wrap.
- Snap the rubber band. Tape an identical rubber band to a table, and snap it against the table. Ask: Why do the sounds differ? *The surface, as well as particles in the air, vibrate. However, the wrap vibrates much more easily, so the sound is louder.*

Chapter 2 **41** **C**

The speed of sound depends on its medium.

Suppose you are in the baseball stands during an exciting game. A pitch flies from the mound toward home plate, and you see the batter draw back, swing, and hit the ball high. A split second later you hear the crack of the bat meeting the ball. You notice that the sound of the hit comes later than the sight. Just how fast does sound travel?

Sound travels more slowly than light, and it does not always travel at the same speed. Two main factors affect the speed of sound: the material that makes up the medium—such as air or water—and the temperature. If we know the medium and the temperature, however, we can predict the speed of sound.

CHECK YOUR READING Which two factors affect the speed of sound?

The Effect of the Material

You have probably heard sounds in more than one medium. Think about the medium in which you most often hear sound—air. You listen to a radio or a compact disk player. You hear the siren of a fire truck. These sound waves travel through air, a mixture of gases.

Now think about going swimming. You dip below the water's surface briefly. Someone jumps into the water nearby and splashes water against the pool wall. You hear strange underwater sounds. These sound waves travel through water, a liquid.

Sound travels faster through liquids than it does through gases because liquids are denser than gases. That means that the particles are packed closer together. It takes less time for a water particle to push on the water particles around it because the particles are already closer together than are the particles in air. As a result, divers underwater would hear a sound sooner than people above water would.

Sound can also travel through solid materials that are elastic, which means they can vibrate back and forth. In solid materials, the particles are packed even closer together than they are in liquids or gases. Steel is an example of an elastic material that is very dense. Sound travels very rapidly through steel. Look at the chart on the left. Compare the speed of sound in air with the speed of sound in steel.

These divers can hear the motor of a distant boat before their friends above water hear it.

Materials and Sound Speeds

Medium	State	Speed of Sound
Air (20°C)	Gas	344 m/s (769 mi/h)
Water (20°C)	Liquid	1,400 m/s (3,130 mi/h)
Steel (20°C)	Solid	5,000 m/s (11,200 mi/h)

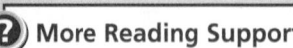

The Effect of Temperature

Sound also travels faster through a medium at higher temperatures than at lower ones. Consider the medium of air, a mixture of gases. Gas particles are not held tightly together as are particles in solids. Instead, the gas particles bounce all around. The higher the temperature, the more the gas particles wiggle and bounce. It takes less time for particles that are already moving quickly to push against the particles around them than it takes particles that are moving slowly. Sound, therefore, travels faster in hot air than in cold air.

Look at the picture of the snowboarders. The sound waves they make by yelling will travel more slowly through air than similar sounds made on a hot day. If you could bear to stand in air at a temperature of 100°C (212°F—the boiling point of water) and listen to the same person yelling, you might notice that the sound of the person's voice reaches you faster.

The chart on the right shows the speed of sound in air at two different temperatures. Compare the speed of sound at the temperature at which water freezes with the speed of sound at the temperature at which water boils. Sound travels about 17 percent faster in air at 100°C than in air at 0°C.

 These snowboarders' shouts reach their friends more slowly in this cold air than they would in hot air.

Temperature and Sound Speeds

Medium	Temperature	Speed of Sound
Air	0°C (32°F)	331 m/s (741 mi/h)
Air	100°C (212°F)	386 m/s (864 mi/h)

 **CHECK YOUR READING** What is the difference between the speed of sound in air at 0°C and at 100°C?

2.1 Review

KEY CONCEPTS

1. Describe how sound waves are produced.
2. Describe how particles move as energy is transferred through a sound wave.
3. Explain how temperature affects the speed of sound.

CRITICAL THINKING

4. **Predict** Would the sound from a distant train travel faster through air or through steel train tracks? Explain.
5. **Evaluate** Suppose an audience watching a science fiction movie hears a loud roar as a spaceship explodes in outer space. Why is this scene unrealistic?

⬥ CHALLENGE

6. **Evaluate** A famous riddle asks this question: If a tree falls in the forest and there is no one there to hear it, is there any sound? What do you think? Give reasons for your answer.

Chapter 2: Sound **43** **C**

ANSWERS

1. Sound waves are produced when an object vibrates.

2. Particles compress and then spread out as a sound wave passes through them.

3. the higher the temperature, the faster the speed of sound

4. The sound would travel faster through steel train tracks than through air because steel is a denser material than air.

5. Sound must travel through a material medium such as a gas, liquid, or solid. Outer

space is a vacuum, and so the sound of the explosion would not be heard.

6. Accept either of these answers if well-defended: The sole criterion for sound is the production of sound waves. The sound waves must be detected by some receiver to qualify as sound.

Set Learning Goal

To find out more about supersonic aircraft and the sonic booms they produce

Present the Science

A sonic boom is caused by an extremely high-pressure wave that is produced as an object accelerates to a speed faster than its sound waves and breaks through the pressure barrier.

The pressure from a sonic boom normally causes no damage on Earth. The energy range of a sonic boom is less than that of most industrial noise. Occasionally, minor damage such as broken glass results from a sonic boom.

Discussion Questions

Ask: How is the atmosphere different at the height of an airplane flying compared to close to Earth? *Air at the height of the plane is colder and less dense.*

Ask: Based on your answer to the first question, would the speed of sound be greater or less at Earth's surface? *greater*

Close

Ask: How do the sound waves produced by an airplane compare to the waves produced by the front of a ship as it moves through water? *The waves are similar because the moving object generates them. They collect at the front of the object, and the object passes through them.*

Technology Resources

Students can visit **ClassZone.com** to find out more about supersonic aircraft.

 RESOURCE CENTER

SURPASSING THE SPEED OF SOUND

 **RESOURCE CENTER**
CLASSZONE.COM
Find out more about supersonic aircraft.

This photograph may actually show the wake of a sonic boom. It was taken on a very humid day, and water vapor may have condensed in the low-pressure part of the sound wave.

Boom Notes

- The pilot of an airplane cannot hear the sonic boom because the sound waves are behind the plane.

- Lightning heats particles in the air so rapidly that they move faster than the speed of sound and cause a shock wave, which is what makes the boom of thunder. If a lightning strike is very close, you will hear a sharp crack.

- Large meteors enter the atmosphere fast enough to make a sonic boom.

Sonic Booms

Airplanes traveling faster than the speed of sound can produce an incredibly loud sound called a sonic boom. The sonic boom from a low-flying airplane can rattle and even break windows!

How It Works

Breaking the Barrier

| The sound waves produced by this airplane begin to pile up and produce a pressure barrier. | This airplane has broken through the pressure barrier and has produced a loud boom. |

When an airplane reaches extremely high speeds, it actually catches up to its own sound waves. The waves start to pile up and form a high-pressure area in front of the plane. If the airplane has enough acceleration, it breaks through the barrier, making a sonic boom. The airplane gets ahead of both the pressure barrier and the sound waves and is said to be traveling at supersonic speeds—speeds faster than the speed of sound.

Boom and It's Gone

If an airplane that produces a boom is flying very high, it may be out of sight by the time the sonic boom reaches a hearer on the ground. To make a sonic boom, a plane must be traveling faster than about 1240 kilometers per hour (769 mi/h)! The sound does not last very long—about one-tenth of a second for a small fighter plane to one-half second for a supersonic passenger plane.

EXPLORE

1. **PREDICT** Specially designed cars have traveled faster than the speed of sound. Would you expect them to produce a sonic boom?

2. **CHALLENGE** The space shuttles produce sonic booms when they are taking off and landing, but not while they are orbiting Earth, even though they are moving much faster than 1240 km/h. Can you explain why?

EXPLORE

1. *PREDICT* *Yes, a car traveling faster than the speed of sound would produce a sonic boom.*

2. *CHALLENGE* *Sonic waves would not be produced in space because there is no medium in which the sound can travel.*

KEY CONCEPT

2.2 Frequency determines pitch.

◀ **BEFORE, you learned**

• Sound waves are produced by vibrations
• Frequency measures the number of wavelengths passing a fixed point per second

▶ **NOW, you will learn**

• How the frequency of a wave affects the way it sounds
• How sound quality differs from pitch
• How the Doppler effect works

VOCABULARY

pitch p. 45
hertz p. 46
ultrasound p. 46
resonance p. 48
Doppler effect p. 50

EXPLORE Pitch

Why does the sound change?

PROCEDURE

① Hold the ruler flat on the edge of a desk so that it sticks out about 25 centimeters beyond the edge.

② With your free hand, push the tip of the ruler down and then let it go. As the ruler vibrates, slide it back onto the desk. Listen to the sounds the ruler makes.

WHAT DO YOU THINK?

• What happened to the sound as you slid the ruler back onto the desk?
• Describe the motion of the ruler.

MATERIALS
ruler

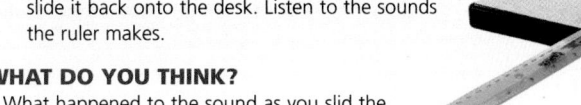

Pitch depends on the frequency of a sound wave.

VOCABULARY
Remember to add a description wheel in your notebook for each new term.

When you listen to music, you hear both high and low sounds. The quality of highness or lowness of a sound is called **pitch.** The frequency of a sound wave determines the pitch of the sound you hear. Remember that frequency is the number of wavelengths passing a fixed point in a given period of time. A high-frequency wave with short wavelengths, such as that produced by a tiny flute, makes a high-pitched sound. A low-frequency wave with long wavelengths, such as the one produced by the deep croak of a tuba, makes a low-pitched sound. An object vibrating very fast produces a high-pitched sound, while an object vibrating slower produces a lower-pitched sound.

 How is frequency related to pitch?

Chapter 2: **Sound** 45 **C**

RESOURCES FOR DIFFERENTIATED INSTRUCTION

Below Level

UNIT RESOURCE BOOK
• Reading Study Guide A, pp. 86–87
• Decoding Support, p. 120

AUDIO CDS

R **Additional INVESTIGATION,**
Exploring Resonance, A, B, & C, pp. 132–140;
Teacher Instructions, pp. 284–285

Advanced

UNIT RESOURCE BOOK
• Challenge and Extension, p. 92
• Challenge Reading, pp. 116–117

English Learners

UNIT RESOURCE BOOK
Spanish Reading Study Guide, pp. 90–91

AUDIO CDS
• Audio Readings in Spanish
• Audio Readings (English)

2.2 FOCUS

▶ Set Learning Goals
Students will

• Describe how the frequency of a wave affects the way it sounds.
• Describe how sound quality differs from pitch.
• Learn about the Doppler effect.
• Discover through an experiment how frequency and pitch are related.

◀ 3-Minute Warm-Up

Display Transparency 12 or copy this exercise on the board:

Decide if these statements are true. If not true, correct them.

1. In a longitudinal wave, the vibrations move perpendicular to the direction of the wave. *In a longitudinal wave, the vibrations move in the same direction as the wave.*

2. Sound is a type of electromagnetic wave. *Sound is a type of mechanical wave.*

3. Vibrations pass through many parts of the ear, not just the eardrum. *True*

T 3-Minute Warm-Up, p. T12

2.2 MOTIVATE

EXPLORE Pitch

PURPOSE To examine factors that affect the pitch of a sound

TIP *10 min.* Experiment with available rulers before class begins. Use those that produce the best results. Do not use plastic rulers that might break.

WHAT DO YOU THINK? *The sound became higher. The ruler moved up and down a greater distance when the ruler extended farther than when it was pulled back.*

Ongoing Assessment

CHECK YOUR READING *Answer: The higher the frequency of the sound wave, the higher pitched the sound.*

Chapter 2 **45** **C**

Teach from Visuals

To help students interpret the visual on frequency and pitch, have pairs of students prepare a series of flash cards, each of which contains a wave of a different wavelength. Have students work together, choosing two cards at a time and deciding which wave has a lower pitch. Have them identify the wavelength of each wave and compare their frequencies. You may want to remind students that wavelength and frequency are inversely related—the higher the frequency, the shorter the wavelength.

Develop Critical Thinking

APPLY Have students apply their knowledge of pitch by having them compare the length of vocal cords, based on the pitch of voices. Have them use the categories of male child, female child, male adult, and female adult. *In general, male adult vocal cords are longest, as indicated by the lower pitches of adult male voices. Female adult vocal cords are the next longest. The lengths of the vocal cords of a male and female child are about the same and are shorter than the vocal cords of a female adult.*

Ongoing Assessment

Describe the effect of frequency on how a wave sounds.

Ask: Does a wave with a high frequency have a high pitch or a low pitch? *a high pitch*

CHECK YOUR READING *Answer: Humans can hear frequencies between 20 hertz and 20,000 hertz.*

High and Low Frequencies

Frequency is a measure of how often a wavelength passes a fixed point. The unit for measuring frequency, and also pitch, is the hertz. A **hertz** (Hz) is one complete wavelength per second. For example, a wave with a frequency of 20 hertz has 20 wavelengths per second. In a wave with a frequency of 100 hertz, 100 wavelengths pass a given point every second. One complete wavelength can also be called a cycle. The diagram below shows how frequency and pitch are related.

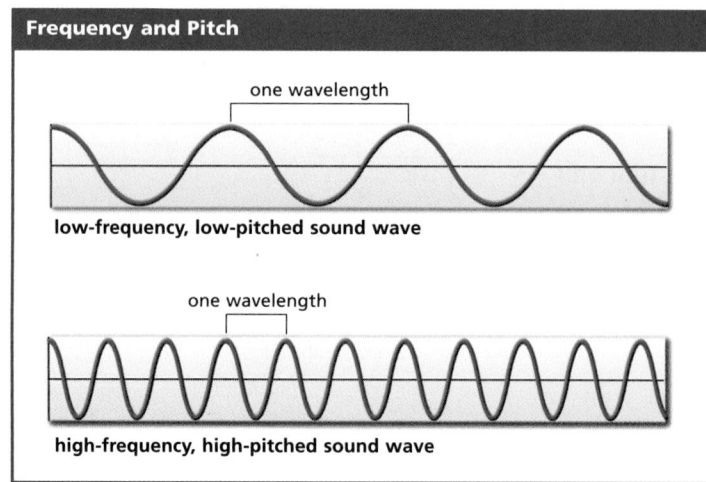

Frequency and Pitch

one wavelength

low-frequency, low-pitched sound wave

one wavelength

high-frequency, high-pitched sound wave

Human ears can hear a wide range of pitches. Most people with good hearing can hear sounds in the range of 20 hertz to 20,000 hertz. The note of middle C on a piano, for example, has a frequency of 262 hertz.

Sound waves with wavelengths below 20 hertz are called infrasound. People cannot hear sounds in this range. Infrasound waves have a very long wavelength and can travel great distances without losing much energy. Elephants may use infrasound to communicate over long distances. Some of the waves that elephants use travel through the ground instead of the air, and they may be detected by another elephant up to 32 kilometers (about 20 miles) away.

READING TiP

The prefix *infra* means "below," and the prefix *ultra* means "beyond."

The highest frequency that humans can hear is 20,000 hertz. Sound waves in the range above 20,000 hertz are called **ultrasound.** Though people cannot hear ultrasound, it is very useful. Later in this chapter, you will learn about some of the uses of ultrasound. Many animals can hear sound waves in the ultrasound range. The chart on the next page shows the hearing ranges of some animals.

CHECK YOUR READING What is the range of frequencies that humans can hear?

C 46 Unit: Waves, Sound, and Light

DIFFERENTIATE INSTRUCTION

? **More Reading Support**

A If a wave has a frequency of 16 Hz, how many wavelengths per second does it have? *16*

B What are sound waves above 20,000 Hz called? *ultrasound*

Inclusion If you have students in class who have visual impairments, sketch the waves in the figure on this page and glue yarn on the waves. Have students feel the difference in the high-frequency wave and the low-frequency wave.

English Learners Be aware that English learners do not always have necessary background knowledge. For example, English learners may not be familiar with some musical terminology, such as *cymbals* and *clarinet* (p. 49), and *middle C* and *piano* (above).

Sound Frequencies Heard by Animals

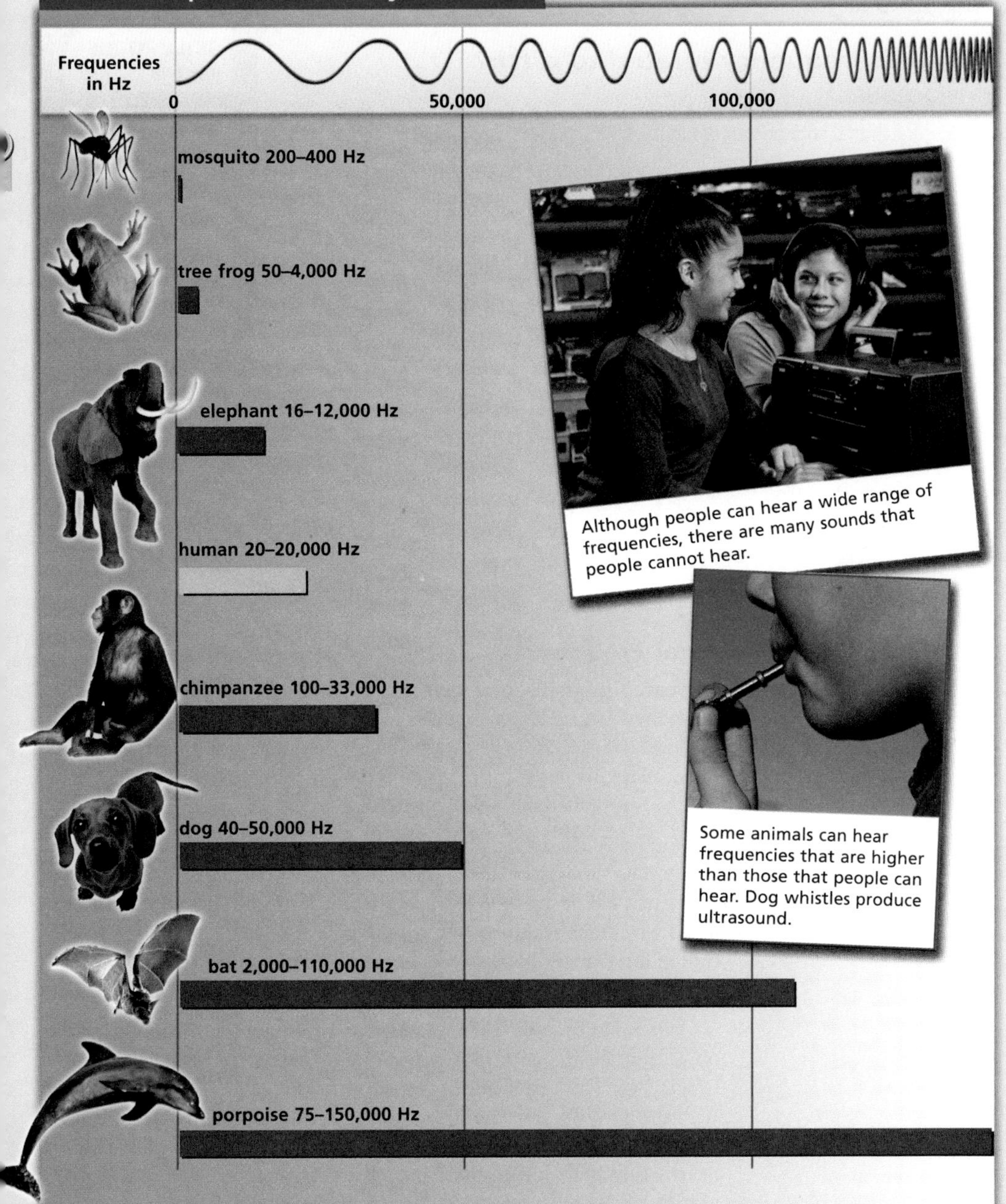

Frequencies in Hz

0   50,000   100,000

mosquito 200–400 Hz

tree frog 50–4,000 Hz

elephant 16–12,000 Hz

human 20–20,000 Hz

chimpanzee 100–33,000 Hz

dog 40–50,000 Hz

bat 2,000–110,000 Hz

porpoise 75–150,000 Hz

Although people can hear a wide range of frequencies, there are many sounds that people cannot hear.

Some animals can hear frequencies that are higher than those that people can hear. Dog whistles produce ultrasound.

READING VISUALS Which animals on this chart can hear frequencies above those that humans can hear?

Teach from Visuals

To help students interpret the sound frequency visual, ask:

- Why are devices that send out high-frequency sounds sometimes used as repellents for pests such as mice? (A mouse can hear frequencies from 1,000 to 90,000 hertz.) *Frequencies too high for human hearing can be heard by mice. Broadcasting upper frequencies that are uncomfortable for mice could repel them.*

- Why can't people hear the sound produced by a dog whistle? *The whistle sends out sound between 20,000 and 50,000 hertz. Dogs hear it, but it is barely audible to humans.*

- Cats have a hearing range from approximately 100 to 60,000 hertz. Where would cats be placed on the diagram on this page? *between dogs and bats*

T This visual is also available as T14 in the Unit Transparency Book.

Real World Example

Hearing aids amplify vibrations so that people with hearing loss can detect sound. However, hearing aids amplify all frequencies of sound. Very few people have equal hearing loss at all frequency levels. Some people have difficulty wearing hearing aids because, to make certain frequencies loud enough to hear, other frequencies become too loud.

Ongoing Assessment

READING VISUALS *Answer: chimpanzee, dog, bat, and porpoise*

DIFFERENTIATE INSTRUCTION

?) More Reading Support

C Which animals on the chart hear frequencies below those that humans can hear? *elephant*

Inclusion Have a group of students make a collage that represents the wavelengths heard by different animals. Have students use a variety of materials: yarn, cord, ribbon, paper, aluminum foil, etc. It should have enough texture so that students with visual impairments can feel the difference in ranges of frequencies.

Advanced

R Challenge Reading, pp. 116–117

INVESTIGATE Sound Frequency

PURPOSE To discover how frequency relates to pitch

TIP *20 min.* Students can use two identical rubber bands, pulling one tighter than the other, to show that the difference in pitch is from a difference in frequency, not a difference in rubber bands. Students may need to use tape to hold one or both of the rubber bands in place.

WHAT DO YOU THINK? *The tighter rubber band produces a higher pitch. The higher the frequency, the higher the pitch.*

CHALLENGE *To make a guitar string sound higher in pitch, tighten the string. A tighter string has a higher frequency and therefore higher pitch.*

 Datasheet, Sound Frequency, p. 93

Technology Resources

Customize this student lab as needed or look for an alternative. Print rubrics to assess student lab reports.

Lab Generator CD-ROM

Ongoing Assessment

Discover how frequency relates to pitch.

Ask: Does the tighter rubber band vibrate at a higher or lower frequency? *higher*

CHECK YOUR READING *Answer: Resonance is the adding of a sound wave with an object's natural frequency of vibration.*

INVESTIGATE Frequency

How is frequency related to pitch?

PROCEDURE

1. Stretch the rubber bands around the open box.
2. Pull one of the rubber bands tightly across the open part of the box so that it vibrates with a higher frequency than the looser rubber band. Tape the rubber band in place.
3. Pluck each rubber band and listen to the sound it makes.

WHAT DO YOU THINK?

- Which rubber band produces a sound wave with a higher pitch?
- How is frequency related to pitch?

CHALLENGE Suppose you are tuning a guitar and want to make one of the strings sound higher in pitch. Do you tighten or loosen the string? Explain your answer.

SKILL FOCUS
Inferring

MATERIALS
- 2 rubber bands of different sizes
- small open box
- tape

TIME
20 minutes

Natural Frequencies

You have read that sound waves are produced by vibrating objects. Sound waves also cause particles in the air to vibrate as they travel through the air. These vibrations have a frequency, or a number of wavelengths per second. All objects have a frequency at which they vibrate called a natural frequency.

You may have seen a piano tuner tap a tuning fork against another object. The tuner does this to make the fork vibrate at its natural frequency. He or she then listens to the pitch produced by the tuning fork's vibrations and tunes the piano string to match it. Different tuning forks have different frequencies and can be used to tune instrument to different pitches.

When a sound wave with a particular frequency encounters an object that has the same natural frequency, constructive interference takes place. The amplitude of the vibrating object adds together with the amplitude of the sound wave. The strengthening of a sound wave in this way is called **resonance.** When a tuning fork is struck, a nearby tuning fork with the same natural frequency will also begin to vibrate because of resonance.

?
D

CHECK YOUR READING How is natural frequency related to resonance?

DIFFERENTIATE INSTRUCTION

? More Reading Support

D What is produced when a sound wave combines with a natural vibration? *resonance*

Additional Investigation To reinforce Section 2.2 learning goals, use the following full-period investigation:

R **Additional INVESTIGATION,** Exploring Resonance, A, B, & C, pp. 132–140, 284–285 (Advanced students should complete Levels B and C.)

Below Level Make sure students understand how frequency is represented in the visuals *Frequency and Pitch* (p. 46) and *Sound Frequencies Heard by Animals* (p. 47).

Sound Quality

E

Have you ever noticed that two singers can sing exactly the same note, or pitch, and yet sound very different? The singers produce sound waves with their vocal cords. They stretch their vocal cords in just the right way to produce sound waves with a certain frequency. That frequency produces the pitch that the note of music calls for. Why, then, don't the singers sound exactly the same?

Each musical instrument and each human voice has its own particular sound, or quality. Another word for sound quality is timbre (TAM-buhr). Timbre can be explained by the fact that most sounds are not single waves but are actually combinations of waves. The pitch that you hear is called the fundamental tone. Other, higher-frequency pitches are called overtones. The combination of pitches is the main factor affecting the quality of a sound.

Another factor in sound quality is the way in which a sound starts and stops. Think about a musician who is crashing cymbals. The cymbals' sound blasts out suddenly. A sound produced by the human voice, on the other hand, starts much more gently.

CHECK YOUR READING What are two factors that affect sound quality? Which sentences above tell you?

F

The illustration below shows oscilloscope (uh-SIHL-uh-SKOHP) screens. An oscilloscope is a scientific instrument that tracks an electrical signal. The energy of a sound wave is converted into a signal and displayed on an oscilloscope screen. The screens below show sound waves made by musicians playing a piano and a clarinet. Both of these musical instruments are producing the same note, or pitch. Notice that the sound waves look slightly different from each other. Each has a different combination of overtones, producing a unique sound quality.

Oscilloscope Images

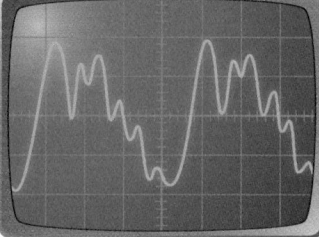
piano

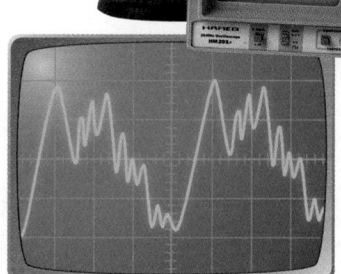
clarinet

Both oscilloscope images at left show sound waves of the same pitch produced on two different instruments. The waves, however, have different sound qualities.

Chapter 2 **49** **C**

Real World Example

At a band or orchestra concert, a single player plays a note before the concert starts. All the other players match that note, tuning their instruments. Although the sound quality of the instruments may vary considerably, the pitch of each instrument must blend harmoniously with the pitches of the other instruments.

Develop Critical Thinking

Encourage students to study the images on the oscilloscopes. Have students apply their knowledge about waves to answer the following questions.

- What property of the wave appears on the horizontal axis? *frequency and wavelength*

- What property of the wave appears on the vertical axis? *the height of the wave, or amplitude*

- If a sound with a higher pitch appeared on the scope, how would the picture change? *More waves would be visible.*

EXPLORE (the BIG idea)

Revisit "What Gives a Sound Its Qualities?" on p. 35. Have students explain their results.

Ongoing Assessment

Contrast sound quality and pitch.

Ask: If two people sing at the same pitch, why does the quality of the sound differ? *It differs because there are qualities of sound other than pitch, such as timbre (tone color).*

CHECK YOUR READING *Answer: Sound quality is affected by the combination of pitches (last sentence of paragraph 2) and the way sound starts and stops (first sentence of paragraph 3).*

DIFFERENTIATE INSTRUCTION

More Reading Support

E What is another name for sound quality? *timbre*

F What instrument is used to track electrical signals? *an oscilloscope*

Advanced Have interested students research how electronic displays of sound are used in voice identification. Topics to investigate include security systems that require voice identification for admittance to a secure area and using voice patterns to identify suspects in criminal investigations.

R Challenge and Extension, p. 92

Integrate the Sciences

Because the Doppler effect applies to all waves, astronomers can use it to determine the speed and direction of a galaxy's movement. If the galaxy is getting nearer, the light it generates will shift toward blue (shorter) wavelengths. If it is moving away, its light will shift toward red (longer) wavelengths.

Teach Difficult Concepts

Some students may have a hard time understanding the pattern of waves in the Doppler effect. To clarify the concept, have them visualize or recall the pattern of waves that surround a moving boat. Waves to the front of the boat are close together. To the back of the boat, the waves are farther apart.

Ongoing Assessment

Explain how the Doppler effect works.

Ask: As a siren moves away from you, does the pitch become higher or lower? *lower*

CHECK YOUR READING *Answer: If a sound moves toward the listener, the pitch rises. If it moves away from the listener, the pitch lowers.*

The motion of the source of a sound affects its pitch.

Sometimes in traffic, a screeching siren announces that an ambulance must pass through traffic. Drivers slow down and pull over to the side, leaving room for the ambulance to speed by. Suppose you are a passenger in one of these cars. What do you hear?

When the ambulance whizzes past you the pitch suddenly seems to drop. The siren on the ambulance blasts the same pitches again and again. What has made the difference in what you hear is the rapid motion of the vehicle toward you and then away from you. The motion of the source of a sound affects its pitch.

DESCRIPTION WHEEL
Make a description wheel in your notebook for the Doppler effect.

The Doppler Effect

In the 1800s an Austrian scientist named Christian Doppler hypothesized about sound waves. He published a scientific paper about his work. In it, he described how pitch changes when a sound source moves rapidly toward and then away from a listener. Doppler described the scientific principle we notice when a siren speeds by. The **Doppler effect** is the change in perceived pitch that occurs when the source or the receiver of a sound is moving.

Before long, a Dutch scientist learned of Doppler's work. In 1845 he staged an experiment to test the hypothesis that Doppler described. In the experiment, a group of trumpet players were put on a train car. Other musicians were seated beside the railroad track. Those musicians had perfect pitch—that is, the ability to identify a pitch just by listening to it. The train passed by the musicians while the trumpeters on the train played their instruments. The musicians recorded the pitches they heard from one moment to the next. At the end of the demonstration, the musicians reported that they had heard the pitch of the trumpets fall as the train passed. Their experiment showed that the Doppler effect exists.

? **G**

CHECK YOUR READING How does the motion of a sound affect its pitch?

To listeners outside the train, the noise made by this train sounds higher in pitch while it approaches them than while it speeds away.

C 50 Unit: Waves, Sound, and Light

DIFFERENTIATE INSTRUCTION

? **More Reading Support**

G When a siren approaches you, what happens to its pitch? *The pitch seems higher.*

English Learners English learners may have difficulty using the words *affect* and *effect* correctly. Explain that *affect* is a verb and *effect* is a noun. Compare the following two sentences from this page. *The motion of the source of a sound affects its pitch. The Doppler effect is the change in perceived pitch that occurs when the source or receiver of a sound is moving.* The first sentence uses the verb *affect*. The second sentence uses the noun *effect*.

The Doppler Effect

Sound waves moving toward a hearer have a different pitch from sound waves moving away from a hearer.

Sound waves arrive at these people farther apart, so the frequency is lower.

AMBULANCE

Sounds waves arrive at these people closer together, so the frequency is higher.

READING VISUALS Which people hear a higher pitch?

Frequency and Pitch

Again imagine sitting in a car as an ambulance approaches. The siren on the ambulance continually sends out sound waves. As the ambulance pulls closer to you, it catches up with the sound waves it is sending out. As a result, the sound waves that reach your ears are spaced closer together. The frequency, and therefore the pitch, is higher when it reaches you. As the ambulance continues, it gets farther and farther away from you, while the sound waves still move toward you. Now the waves arrive farther and farther apart. As the frequency decreases, you hear a lower pitch.

VISUALIZATION
CLASSZONE.COM
Explore the Doppler effect.

2.2 Review

KEY CONCEPTS

1. Describe what is different about the sound waves produced by a low note and a high note on a musical instrument.

2. Explain why two people singing the same pitch do not sound exactly the same.

3. How does perceived pitch change as a sound source passes a listener?

CRITICAL THINKING

4. **Apply** How could you produce vibrations in a tuning fork without touching it? Explain your answer.

5. **Predict** Suppose you could view the waves produced by a high-pitched and a low-pitched voice. Which wave would display the greater number of crests and troughs? Why?

⚠ CHALLENGE

6. **Infer** Offer a possible explanation for why no one noticed the Doppler effect before the 1800s.

Chapter 2: Sound **51** **C**

ANSWERS

1. The sound waves have different frequencies—high frequency for the high note and low frequency for the low note.

2. The quality, or timbre, of the sounds made by the voices is different, even though the pitch is the same.

3. The frequency changes as the source of the sound moves past a listener, changing the pitch.

4. by striking an identical tuning fork nearby; Resonance would cause the tuning fork to vibrate.

5. the high-pitched voice because the sound waves have higher frequency and thus more waves per unit of time

6. None of the modes of transportation went fast enough for the Doppler effect to happen.

Reinforce (the **BIG** idea)

Have students relate the section to the Big Idea.

R Reinforcing Key Concepts, p. 94

2.2 ASSESS & RETEACH

Assess

A Section 2.2 Quiz, p. 23

Reteach

Have students try the following activity:

- Tightly stretch a thread or light string about 50 cm long between two supports, parallel to the floor. There should be at least 25 cm of space beneath the string.

- Tie a piece of string to each of seven identical metal washers. Three pieces of string should be 20 cm long, two should be 15 cm, one 10 cm, and one 5 cm. Tie the strings evenly spaced on the long thread.

- Start swinging one washer. Notice that other washers on the same length of string will also swing because they have the same natural frequency. The other washers will not move.

- Repeat with each different length of string.

Technology Resources

Have students visit **ClassZone.com** for reteaching of Key Concepts.

 CONTENT REVIEW

 CONTENT REVIEW CD-ROM

○ Set Learning Goals

Students will

- Explain how the intensity of a wave affects its loudness.
- Describe how sound intensity can be controlled.
- Explain how loudness can affect hearing.
- Observe through an experiment how amplitude relates to loudness.

○ 3-Minute Warm-Up

Display Transparency 13 or copy this exercise on the board:

Match each of the definitions in the first column to one of the terms in the second column.

Definitions

1. sound waves with frequency greater than 20,000 hertz *c*
2. the measure of the height of a wave's crest *b*
3. how high or low a sound is *a*

Terms

a. pitch
b. amplitude
c. ultrasound

 3-Minute Warm-Up, p. T13

THINK ABOUT

PURPOSE To understand how to produce different types of sound

DISCUSS Ask: Which part of the drum vibrates? *all of it (especially the drum head)*

Answers: drumstick moving up and down; louder: move drumsticks with more energy; softer: with less energy

Ongoing Assessment

CHECK YOUR READING *Answer: the more energy, the louder the sound*

KEY CONCEPT

2.3 Intensity determines loudness.

◀ BEFORE, you learned	▶ NOW, you will learn
• Sound waves are produced by vibrations	• How the intensity of a wave affects its loudness
• Frequency determines the pitch of a sound	• How sound intensity can be controlled
• Amplitude is a measure of the height of a wave crest	• How loudness can affect hearing

VOCABULARY

intensity p. 52
decibel p. 52
amplification p. 55
acoustics p. 55

THINK ABOUT

What makes a sound louder?

A drum player has to play softly at some times and loudly at others. Think about what the drummer must do to produce each type of sound. If you could watch the drummer in the photograph in action, what would you see? How would the drummer change the way he moves the drumsticks to make a loud, crashing sound? What might he do to make a very soft sound?

Intensity depends on the amplitude of a sound wave.

OUTLINE
Make an outline for this heading. Remember to include main ideas and details.

I. Main idea
  A. Supporting idea
    1. Detail
    2. Detail
  B. Supporting idea

Earlier you read that all waves carry energy. The more energy a sound wave carries, the more intense it is and the louder it will sound to listeners. The **intensity** of a sound is the amount of energy its sound wave has. A unit called the **decibel** (dB) is used to measure sound intensity. The faint rustling of tree leaves on a quiet summer day can hardly be heard. Some of the softest sounds measure less than 10 decibels. On the other hand, the noise from a jet taking off or the volume of a TV set turned all the way up can hurt your ears. Very loud sounds measure more than 100 decibels. Remember that amplitude is also a measure of wave energy. The greater the amplitude, the more intensity a sound wave has and the louder the sound will be.

 How is energy related to loudness?

RESOURCES FOR DIFFERENTIATED INSTRUCTION

Below Level

UNIT RESOURCE BOOK
- Reading Study Guide A, pp. 97–98
- Decoding Support, p. 120

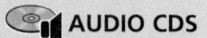 **AUDIO CDS**

Advanced

UNIT RESOURCE BOOK
Challenge and Extension, p. 103

English Learners

UNIT RESOURCE BOOK
Spanish Reading Study Guide, pp. 101–102

AUDIO CDS

- Audio Readings in Spanish
- Audio Readings (English)

INVESTIGATE Loudness

How is amplitude related to loudness?

PROCEDURE

① Cut a notch in the middle of both ends of the cardboard. Stretch the rubber band around the cardboard so that it fits into the notches as shown.

② Mark lines on the cardboard at one and four centimeters away from the rubber band.

③ Slide the pencils under the rubber band at each end.

④ Pull the rubber band to the one-centimeter line and let it go so that it vibrates with a low amplitude. Notice the sound it makes. Pull the rubber band to the four-centimeter line and let it go again. This time the amplitude is higher. Notice the sound it makes this time.

WHAT DO YOU THINK?

• How did the loudness of the sounds compare?

• How is amplitude related to loudness?

CHALLENGE Using what you learned from experimenting with the rubber band, explain why swinging a drumstick harder on a drum would make a louder sound than swinging a drumstick lightly.

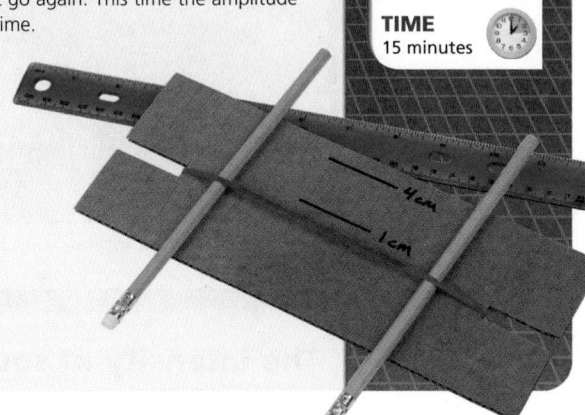

SKILL FOCUS
Observing

MATERIALS
• piece of cardboard
• scissors
• large rubber band
• 2 pencils
• ruler

TIME
15 minutes

The drummer varies the loudness of a sound by varying the energy with which he hits the drum. Loudness is also affected by the distance between the source and the listener.

Have you ever wondered why sound gradually dies out over distance? Think about someone walking away from you with a radio. When the radio is close, the radio seems loud. As the person walks away, the sound grows fainter and fainter. Sound waves travel in all directions from their source. As the waves travel farther from the radio, their energy is spread out over a greater area. This means that their intensity is decreased. The sound waves with lower intensities are heard as quieter sounds.

Other forces can take energy away from sound waves, too. The force of friction can act on the medium of a sound wave to decrease the intensity of the waves. This effect of friction on sound is probably a good thing. Imagine what the world would be like if every sound wave continued forever!

INVESTIGATE Loudness

PURPOSE To observe how amplitude relates to loudness

TIPS *15 min.*

• The cardboard must be thick. It should remain flat when the rubber band is stretched on it.

• Emphasize safety. The notch should be narrow and deep enough that the rubber band stays in the notch when stretched.

• It might be easier to use a knife to notch the cardboard before the lab.

• For accurate observations, students should pull the rubber bands from the middle.

WHAT DO YOU THINK? *The sound was louder when the rubber band was pulled back 4 cm than when it was pulled back 1 cm. The greater the amplitude, the louder the sound.*

CHALLENGE *Swinging a drumstick harder would make a louder sound because the drum skin would vibrate with greater amplitude.*

 Datasheet, Loudness, p. 104

Technology Resources

Customize this student lab as needed or look for an alternative. Print rubrics to assess student lab reports.

 Lab Generator CD-ROM

Ongoing Assessment

Explain the effect of intensity of a wave on its loudness.

Ask: Which sound will have greater intensity, a whisper or a yell? *a yell*

Observe how amplitude relates to loudness.

Ask: How can you make a sound louder? *by increasing the amplitude of the sound wave*

DIFFERENTIATE INSTRUCTION

 **More Reading Support**

A How does distance affect intensity? *the less distance, the more intensity*

English Learners Often readers are asked to imagine a situation and consider its implications. Consider the example from this page: *Have you ever wondered why sound gradually dies out over distance? Think about someone walking away from you with a radio.* These sentences require the reader to imagine a hypothetical scenario. When this occurs explain to English learners that they should imagine the situation. Also, tell students that the phrasal verb *dies out* means "fades."

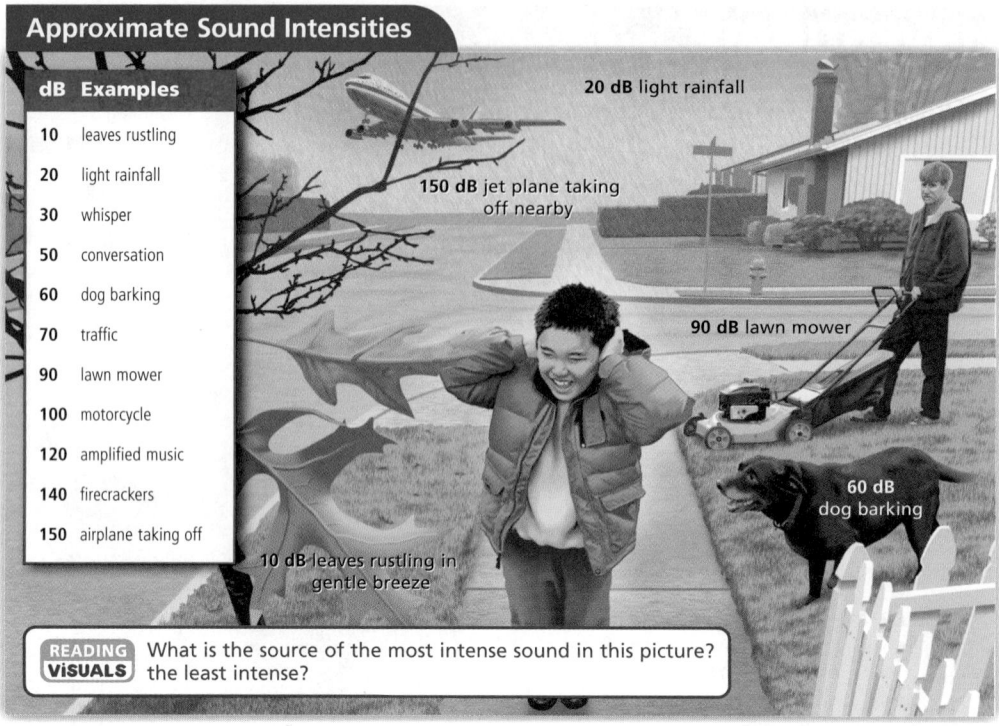

Approximate Sound Intensities

dB	Examples
10	leaves rustling
20	light rainfall
30	whisper
50	conversation
60	dog barking
70	traffic
90	lawn mower
100	motorcycle
120	amplified music
140	firecrackers
150	airplane taking off

20 dB light rainfall

150 dB jet plane taking off nearby

90 dB lawn mower

60 dB dog barking

10 dB leaves rustling in gentle breeze

READING VISUALS What is the source of the most intense sound in this picture? the least intense?

The intensity of sound can be controlled.

REMINDER
Remember, amplitude is a measure of wave energy.

Over time and distance, a sound wave gets weaker and weaker until the sound becomes undetectable. The pitch, however, does not typically change as the sound grows weaker. In other words, even as the amplitude decreases, the frequency stays the same.

Sometimes it is desirable to change sound intensity without changing the pitch and quality of a sound. We can do this by adding energy to or taking energy away from a sound wave. As you have already seen, intensity is the amount of energy in a sound wave. Changing the intensity of a sound wave changes its amplitude.

Sound intensity can be controlled in many ways. Mufflers on cars and trucks reduce engine noise. Have you ever heard a car with a broken muffler? You were probably surprised at how loud it was. Burning fuel in an engine produces hot gases that expand and make a very loud noise. A muffler is designed to absorb some of the energy of the sound waves and so decrease their amplitude. As a result, the intensity of the sound you hear is much lower than it would be without the muffler.

CHECK YOUR READING How could you change the intensity of a sound without changing the pitch?

DIFFERENTIATE INSTRUCTION

? More Reading Support

B Changing the intensity of sound also changes what else? *amplitude*

C What does a muffler in a car do? *reduces the sound of the engine*

Below Level Ask students what properties they think would be necessary for a device that could be worn over the ears to control sound intensity. *Sample answer: being made of dense material that would either absorb sound or keep vibrations from reaching the eardrums.* If possible, show students examples of such devices, such as earplugs or the devices used by people who work with loud industrial machinery or near airplanes at airports.

Amplification

In addition to being reduced, as they are in a muffler, sound waves can be amplified. The word *amplify* may remind you of *amplitude*, the measure of the height of a wave's crest. These words are related. To amplify something means to make it bigger. **Amplification** is the increasing of the strength of an electrical signal. It is often used to increase the intensity of a sound wave.

When you listen to a stereo, you experience the effects of amplification. Sound input to the stereo is in the form of weak electrical signals from a microphone. Transistors in an electronic circuit amplify the signals. The electrical signals are converted into vibrations in a coil in your stereo's speaker. The coil is attached to a cone, which also vibrates and sends out sound waves. You can control the intensity of the sound waves by adjusting your stereo's volume.

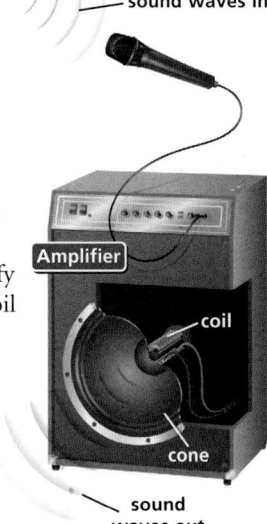

sound waves in

Amplifier

coil

cone

sound waves out

Acoustics

The scientific study of sound is called **acoustics** (uh-KOO-stihks). Acoustics involves both how sound is produced and how it is received and heard by humans and animals.

Acoustics also refers to the way sound waves behave inside a space. Experts called acoustical engineers help design buildings to reduce unwanted echoes. An echo is simply a reflected sound wave. To control sound intensity, engineers design walls and ceilings with acoustical tiles. The shapes and surfaces of acoustical tiles are designed to absorb or redirect some of the energy of sound waves.

The pointed tiles in this sound-testing room are designed to absorb sound waves and prevent any echoes.

The shapes and surfaces in this concert hall direct sound waves to the audience.

 READING VISUALS **COMPARE AND CONTRAST** Imagine sound waves reflecting off the surfaces in the two photographs above. How do the reflections differ?

Chapter 2: **Sound** 55 **C**

DIFFERENTIATE INSTRUCTION

 **More Reading Support**

D When sound is amplified, what happens to it? *It becomes bigger, or louder.*

E What is the study of sound called? *acoustics*

Alternative Assessment Have students sketch a room interior. Then have them draw arrows showing how sound reflects off surfaces in the room. Ask: How would the addition of sound-absorbing materials affect your drawing? *It would reduce reflected sound.*

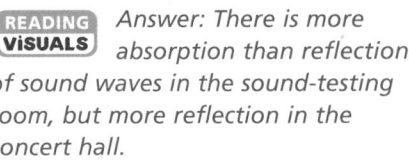

Chapter 2 **55** **C**

Intense sound can damage hearing.

healthy hair cells

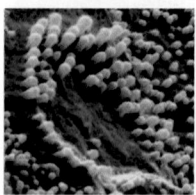
damaged hair cells

RESOURCE CENTER
CLASSZONE.COM
Find out more about sound and protecting your hearing.

When a train screeches to a stop in a subway station, the sound of the squealing brakes echoes off the tunnel walls. Without thinking about it, you cover your ears with your hands. This response helps protect your ears from possible damage.

In the first section of this chapter, you read about the main parts of the human ear. The part of the inner ear called the cochlea is lined with special cells called hair cells. As you have seen, these cells are necessary for hearing.

The hair cells are extremely sensitive. This sensitivity makes hearing possible, but it also makes the cells easy to damage. Continual exposure to sounds of 90 dB or louder can damage or destroy the cells. This is one reason why being exposed to very loud noises, especially for more than a short time, is harmful to hearing.

CHECK YOUR READING How do high-intensity sounds damage hearing?

Using earplugs can prevent damage from too much exposure to high-intensity sounds such as amplified music. The intensity at a rock concert is between 85 and 120 dB. Ear protection can also protect the hearing of employees in factories and other noisy work sites. In the United States, there are laws that require employers to reduce sounds at work sites to below 90 dB or to provide workers with ear protection.

Even a brief, one-time exposure to an extremely loud noise can destroy hair cells. Noises above 130 dB are especially dangerous. Noises above 140 dB are even painful. It is best to avoid such noises altogether. If you find yourself exposed suddenly to such a noise, covering your ears with your hands may be the best protection.

2.3 Review

KEY CONCEPTS

1. Explain how the terms *intensity, decibel,* and *amplitude* are related.

2. Describe one way in which sound intensity can be controlled.

3. How do loud sounds cause damage to hearing?

CRITICAL THINKING

4. **Synthesize** A wind chime produces both soft and loud sounds. If you could see the waves, how would they differ?

5. **Design an Experiment** How could you demonstrate that sound dies away over distance? Suppose you could use three volunteers, a boom box, and a tape recorder.

CHALLENGE

6. **Apply** Which of these acoustical designs would be best for a concert hall? Why?
a. bare room with hard walls, floor, and ceiling,
b. room padded with sound-absorbing materials such as acoustical tile,
c. room with some hard surfaces and some sound padding

 56 Unit: Waves, Sound, and Light

ANSWERS

1. The greater the amplitude, the more intensity the sound wave has, so it will have more decibels.

2. Sample answer: Sound intensities can be controlled with an amplifier.

3. Loud sounds damage the hair cells of the inner ear

which are necessary for hearing.

4. Sound waves of the soft sounds would have a low amplitude, and sound waves of the loud sounds would have a high amplitude.

5. One person could play the boom box. Another person

could go a certain distance away and record the sound with a tape recorder. The third person could do the same farther away.

6. c; design a would lead to an "echoey" room, and design b would deaden the sound too much. Design c is a good compromise.

This air traffic ground controller wears ear protection to prevent hearing loss.

MATH in SCIENCE

MATH TUTORIAL
CLASSZONE.COM
Click on Math Tutorial for more help with interpreting line graphs.

SKILL: INTERPRETING GRAPHS

Measuring Hearing Loss

An audiogram is a graph that can be used to determine if a patient has hearing loss. The vertical axis shows the lowest intensity, in decibels, that the patient can hear for each frequency tested. Notice that intensity is numbered from top to bottom on an audiogram.

To determine the lowest intensity heard at a given frequency, find the frequency on the horizontal axis. Follow the line straight up until you see the data points, shown as ✕ for the right ear and ● for the left ear. Look to the left to find the intensity. For example, the lowest intensity heard in both ears at 250 Hz is 10 dB.

Audiogram for Patient A

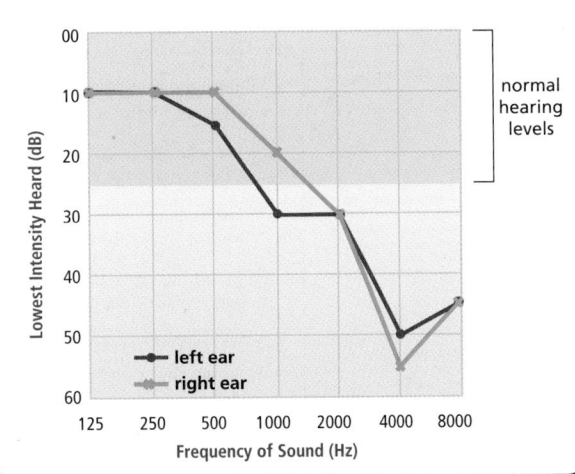

normal hearing levels

Lowest Intensity Heard (dB)

—●— left ear
—✕— right ear

Frequency of Sound (Hz)

Use the graph to answer the following questions.

1. What is the lowest intensity heard in the patient's left ear at 1000 Hz? the right ear at the same frequency?

2. At which frequencies are the data points for both ears within normal hearing levels?

3. Data points outside the normal hearing levels indicate hearing loss. At which frequencies are the data points for both ears outside the normal levels?

CHALLENGE A dip in the graph at 3000 to 4000 Hz is a sign that the hearing loss was caused by exposure to loud noises. The patient is referred to a specialist for further testing. Should Patient A get further testing? Why or why not?

Chapter 2: **Sound** 57 **C**

ANSWERS

1. *30 dB, 20 dB*

2. *from 125 Hz to about 750 Hz*

3. *1500 (also accept 2000) to 8000 Hz*

CHALLENGE *Yes; patient A should get further testing because a dip in this audiogram occurs between 2000 and 4000 Hz.*

MATH IN SCIENCE
Math Skills Practice for Science

Set Learning Goal
To interpret a graph that relates intensity heard to frequency of sound

Present the Science
Few people with hearing difficulties lose the same amount of hearing at all frequencies. If the hearing loss is a consequence of exposure to loud noises, the frequencies that show greatest loss depend on the frequency of the noise that caused the damage. Hair cells that are permanently damaged by noise of certain frequencies might never again respond to sounds of that frequency.

Develop Graphing Skills
The vertical axis of the graph is labeled in an unconventional manner that should be explained. Ask students how many examples they can think of where lower is better. *Examples might include a game of Crazy 8s or miniature golf scores.*

In the audiogram, the greater the intensity necessary for hearing, the more hearing loss is present. The scale produces a graph that gives the correct impression—patient A has lost hearing at high frequencies in both ears.

Close
Ask: Why might an audiogram show quite different hearing results for the right and left ear of a patient? *Answers might include that the patient was consistently exposed to different intensities of noise in different ears.*

 R
  • Math Support, p. 121
  • Math Practice, p. 122

Technology Resources

Students can visit **ClassZone.com** for practice interpreting graphs.

 MATH TUTORIAL

Set Learning Goals

Students will

- Describe how ultrasound is used.
- Observe how musical instruments work.
- Explain how sound can be recorded and reproduced.
- Build a stringed instrument in an experiment.

3-Minute Warm-Up

Display Transparency 13 or copy this exercise on the board:

You own a movie theater. Explain how you could control the loudness of the sound of movies. How would you eliminate as much audience noise as possible?

The intensity of the sound from the movie should be measured so that it is loud enough to be heard but not loud enough to damage hearing. Because sound reflects, using sound-absorbing materials would eliminate echoing and minimize audience noise.

 3-Minute Warm-Up, p. T13

2.4 MOTIVATE

EXPLORE Echoes

PURPOSE To introduce the concept that sound reflects from an object

TIP *10 min.* Have students trade places so both partners have the opportunity to whisper and to listen.

WHAT DO YOU THINK? *The sound was louder with the book than without the book. An echo can be used to detect an object by reflecting off the object. If there is no object to reflect off, there would be no echo.*

Ongoing Assessment

 CHECK YOUR READING *Acceptable answers include detecting objects, finding food, imaging the body.*

Sound has many uses.

 BEFORE, you learned

- Sound waves are produced by vibrations
- Sound waves have amplitude, frequency, and wavelength

NOW, you will learn

- How ultrasound is used
- How musical instruments work
- How sound can be recorded and reproduced

VOCABULARY

echolocation p. 59
sonar p. 59

EXPLORE Echoes

How can you use sound to detect an object?

PROCEDURE

1. Tape the two cardboard tubes onto your desk at a right angle as shown.
2. Put your ear up to the end of one of the tubes. Cover your other ear with your hand.
3. Listen as your partner whispers into the outside end of the other tube.
4. Stand the book upright where the tubes meet. Repeat steps 2 and 3.

MATERIALS
- 2 cardboard tubes
- tape
- book

WHAT DO YOU THINK?
- How did the sound change when you added the book?
- How can an echo be used to detect an object?

Ultrasound waves are used to detect objects.

A ringing telephone, a honking horn, and the sound of a friend's voice are all reminders of how important sound is. But sound has uses that go beyond communication. For example, some animals and people use reflected ultrasound waves to detect objects. Some animals, such as bats, use the echoes of ultrasound waves to find food. People use ultrasound echoes to detect objects underwater or even to produce images of the inside of the body.

 **CHECK YOUR READING** Other than communication, what are three uses of sound?

RESOURCES FOR DIFFERENTIATED INSTRUCTION

Below Level

UNIT RESOURCE BOOK
- Reading Study Guide A, pp. 108–109
- Decoding Support, p. 120

 **AUDIO CDS**

Advanced

UNIT RESOURCE BOOK
Challenge and Extension, p. 114

English Learners

UNIT RESOURCE BOOK
Spanish Reading Study Guide, pp. 112–113

 **AUDIO CDS**

- Audio Readings in Spanish
- Audio Readings (English)

Echolocation

Sending out ultrasound waves and interpreting the returning sound echoes is called **echolocation** (*echo* + *location*). Bats flying at night find their meals of flying insects by using echolocation. They send out as many as 200 ultrasound squeaks per second. By receiving the returning echoes, they can tell where prey is and how it is moving. They can also veer away from walls, trees, and other big objects.

VOCABULARY
Make description wheels for the terms *echolocation* and *sonar* to help you remember them later.

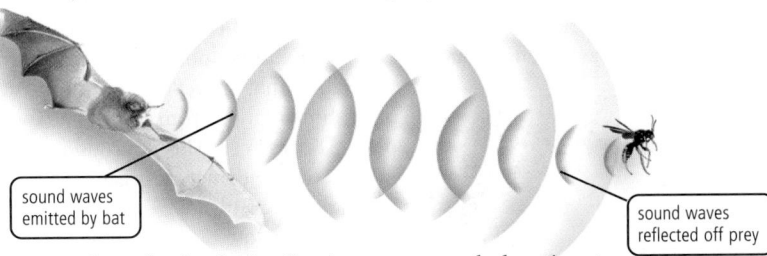

sound waves emitted by bat

sound waves reflected off prey

A number of animals that live in water use echolocation, too. Dolphins, toothed whales, and porpoises produce ultrasound squeaks or clicks. They listen to the returning echo patterns to find fish and other food in the water.

Sonar

People use the principles of echolocation to locate objects underwater. During World War I (1914–1918), scientists developed instruments that used sound waves to locate enemy submarines. Instruments that use echolocation to locate objects are known as **sonar.** Sonar stands for "sound navigation and ranging." The sonar machines could detect sounds coming from submarine propellers. Sonar devices could also send out ultrasound waves and then use the echoes to locate underwater objects. The information from the echoes could then be used to form an image on a screen.

Later, people found many other uses for sonar. Fishing boats use sonar to find schools of fish. Oceanographers—scientists who study the ocean—use it to map the sea floor. People have even used sonar to find ancient sunken ships in deep water.

This woman is using sonar to monitor for submarines.

Sonar is used to locate sunken ships. The image of the sunken ship above was produced on the basis of information from sonar.

DIFFERENTIATE INSTRUCTION

? More Reading Support

A What happens to a sound wave in an echo? *It bounces back to its source.*

B What is the main use of sonar? *to locate objects underwater*

English Learners It can be beneficial for English learners and their classmates to draw upon other cultures when learning new concepts. For example, students studying how a guitar generates sound may also learn about stringed instruments from South America or Asia. Make an effort to incorporate cultural references into classroom discussion.

2.4 INSTRUCT

Teach from Visuals

To help students interpret the visual of sound waves:

- Tell students that a bat bounces sound waves off an insect. Ask: What does it tell the bat if the sound waves take longer to return to the bat than they did a few seconds ago? *The insect is moving away.*

- Ask: Why is *echolocation* a good term for how animals use sound to locate food and other objects? *"Echo" indicates the bouncing back of sound, and "location" shows that the bouncing back reveals where the object is.*

Real World Example

Both shape and distance must be considered in using sonar to locate and describe objects underwater. For example, a shape might appear to be a sunken boat, but if it is not as deep as the seafloor, it might be a school of fish with a similar shape swimming higher in the water.

Teacher Demo

Model how sound waves are used in echolocation and in sonar. Stand a student in the front of the class. Have another student act as a timekeeper. Have the first student walk at a steady rate from the front to the middle of the room and back to the same spot again. Record the time it took on the board. Have the same student walk at the same rate to the back of the room and back to the same spot again. Point out that sound will travel at the same speed in the same medium at the same temperature, so the time it takes to return to its source is an indication of how far it traveled.

Teach from Visuals

Have students examine the photograph of the ultrasound image and share what they see. Ask them to identify the three fetuses and any features, such as the heads, that they can identify. If possible, make a transparency of the photograph so various features can be pointed out on an overhead projector.

Integrate the Sciences

Show students a tessellation to explain the difference between noise and music. A tessellation is a pattern formed by regular-shaped pieces, such as equilateral triangles, with no gaps or overlaps. Examples can be found in many algebra or geometry books or on the Internet. Show students that tessellations produce a nonrandom pattern. Then show students that some shapes, such as pentagons, will not form a regular pattern and are analogous to noise.

Ongoing Assessment

Describe how ultrasound is used.

Ask: How might ultrasound be used to examine a human liver? *Ultrasound waves bounce off the liver, producing an image.*

CHECK YOUR READING *Answer: Both use the reflection of ultrasound waves to detect objects.*

Medical Uses of Ultrasound

Ultrasound has many uses in medicine. Because ultrasound waves are not heard by humans, ultrasound can be used at very high intensities. For example, high-intensity vibrations from ultrasound waves are used to safely break up kidney stones in patients. The energy transferred by ultrasound waves is also used to clean medical equipment.

One of the most important medical uses of ultrasound is the ultrasound scanner. This device relies on the same scientific principle as sonar. It sends sound waves into a human body and then records the echoes that are reflected from inside the body. Information from the echoes forms a picture on a screen. The ultrasound scanner is used to examine internal organs such as the heart, pancreas, bladder, ovaries, and brain. Doppler ultrasound is a technology that can detect the movement of fluids through the body and is used to examine blood flow.

 **CHECK YOUR READING** How is an ultrasound scanner similar to sonar?

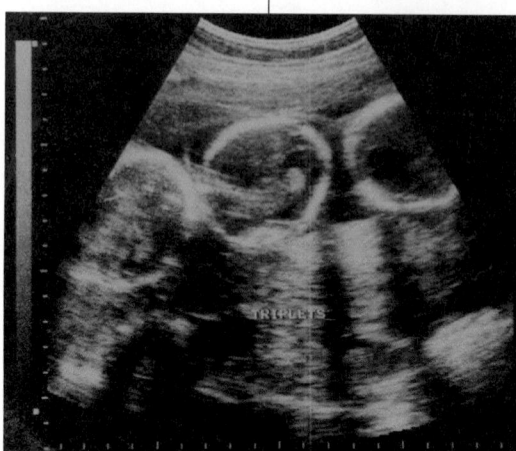

The image of these triplets was produced by reflected ultrasound waves.

One of the most well-known uses of ultrasound is to check on the health of a fetus during pregnancy. Problems that are discovered may possibly be treated early. The scan can also reveal the age and sex of the fetus and let the expecting parents know if they will be having twins or triplets. Ultrasound is safer than other imaging methods, such as the x-ray, which might harm the development of the fetus.

Sound waves can produce music.

Why are some sounds considered noise and other sounds considered music? Music is sound with clear pitches or rhythms. Noise is random sound; that means it has no intended pattern.

Musical instruments produce pitches and rhythms when made to vibrate at their natural frequencies. Some musical instruments have parts that vibrate at different frequencies to make different pitches. All of the pitches, together with the resonance of the instrument itself, produce its characteristic sound. The three main types of musical instruments are stringed, wind, and percussion. Some describe electronic instruments as a fourth type of musical instrument. Look at the illustration on the next page to learn more about how each type of musical instrument works.

RESOURCE CENTER CLASSZONE.COM

Explore instruments from around the world.

DIFFERENTIATE INSTRUCTION

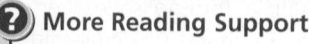

? More Reading Support

C What type of sound waves are used to check on the health of a fetus? *ultrasound*

D If sound is random, is it noise or music? *noise*

English Learners Discuss these words and their meanings with students: *scanner, fetus, expecting,* and *electronics.* Medical terms are often difficult for English learners because they usually are considerably different from one language to another. These terms also are not used frequently in everyday conversation. Use a bilingual dictionary to make a small medical dictionary of terms that might clarify the medical uses of ultrasound for English learners.

How Musical Instruments Work

The way a musical instrument vibrates when it is played determines the sound it produces.

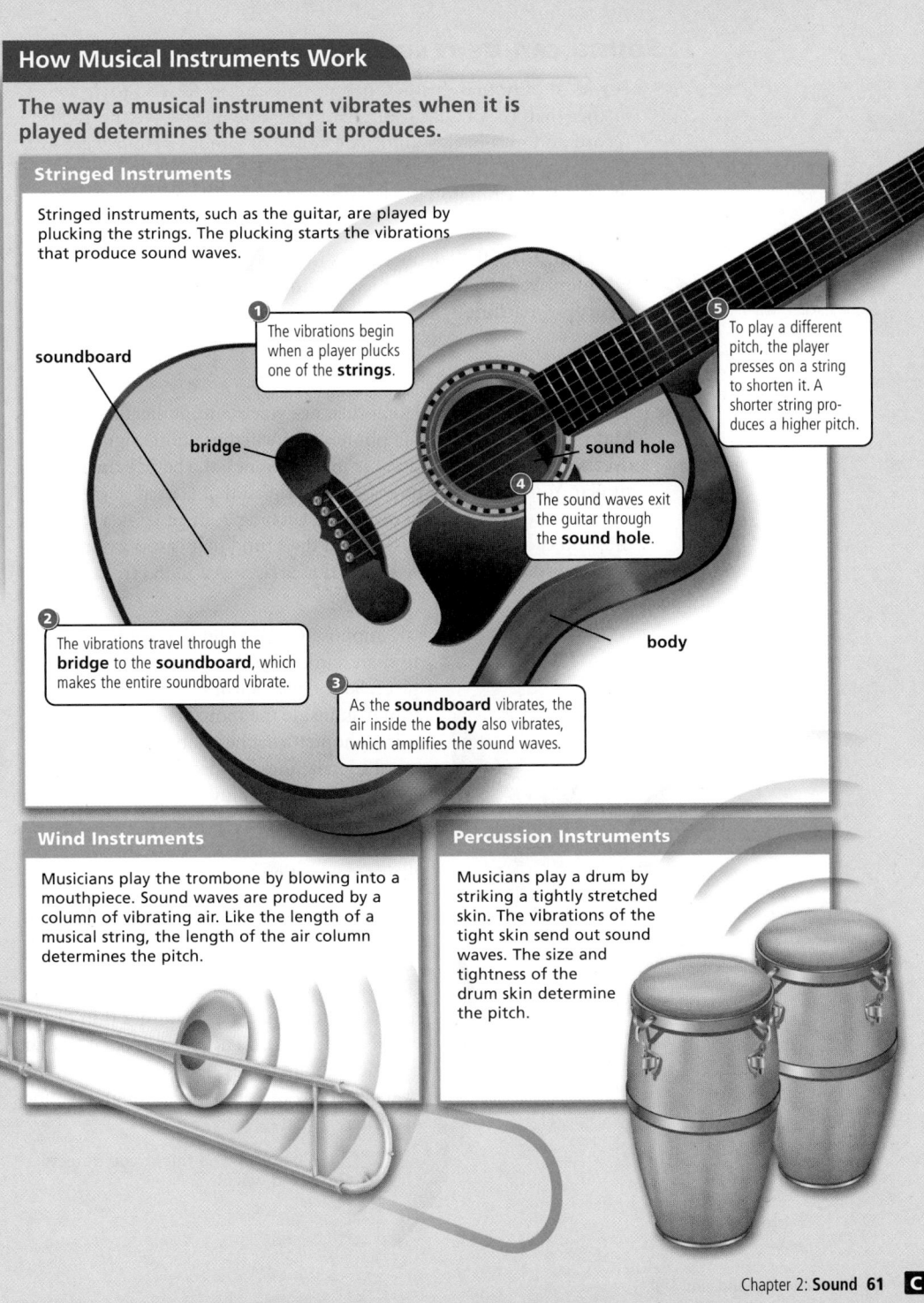

Stringed Instruments

Stringed instruments, such as the guitar, are played by plucking the strings. The plucking starts the vibrations that produce sound waves.

soundboard

1 The vibrations begin when a player plucks one of the **strings**.

5 To play a different pitch, the player presses on a string to shorten it. A shorter string produces a higher pitch.

bridge

sound hole

4 The sound waves exit the guitar through the **sound hole**.

2 The vibrations travel through the **bridge** to the **soundboard**, which makes the entire soundboard vibrate.

3 As the **soundboard** vibrates, the air inside the **body** also vibrates, which amplifies the sound waves.

body

Wind Instruments

Musicians play the trombone by blowing into a mouthpiece. Sound waves are produced by a column of vibrating air. Like the length of a musical string, the length of the air column determines the pitch.

Percussion Instruments

Musicians play a drum by striking a tightly stretched skin. The vibrations of the tight skin send out sound waves. The size and tightness of the drum skin determine the pitch.

Teach from Visuals

Have students examine the guitar in the visual. Explain that this acoustic guitar differs from an electric guitar. Show students an electric guitar or a picture of one.

- Ask them to predict the loudness of the electric guitar if the strings are plucked when it is not plugged in. *It will have a soft sound.*

- Ask students why an acoustic guitar is louder than the sound from an unamplified electric guitar. *It is designed to amplify the sound of the strings just the way it is.*

Teacher Demo

Use identical bottles, such as 1-liter or smaller transparent soft drink bottles, to make a wind instrument. Add different amounts of water to each bottle so that one bottle is nearly empty, one bottle is almost full, and the other bottles contain varying amounts of water. Blow across the mouth of each bottle, and ask students to explain their observations.

The pitch of the sound is lower as the amount of water decreases. The highest pitch comes from the bottle with the most water. Students should relate the pitch to the size of the column of air above the water.

EXPLORE (the BIG idea)

Revisit "How Does Size Affect Sound?" on p. 35. Have students explain their results.

Ongoing Assessment

Observe how musical instruments work.

Ask: What purpose does the bridge perform in a guitar? *It carries vibrations to the soundboard.*

DIFFERENTIATE INSTRUCTION

Alternative Assessment Have students label each of three pieces of paper with the name of a type of musical instrument. On half of the appropriate piece of paper, have them sketch an example of that type of instrument. Sketches should emphasize what part of the instrument is vibrating and producing sound. On the other half of the paper, have students list the characteristics and features of that type of instrument, and speculate as to how they determine pitch, quality, and intensity of sound.

Sound can be recorded and reproduced.

For most of human history, people had no way to send their voices farther than they could shout. Nor could people before the 1800s record and play back sound. The voices of famous people were lost when they died. Imagine having a tape or a compact disk recording of George Washington giving a speech!

 READING TiP
The prefix *phono* means "sound," and the suffix *graph* means "writing." **? E**

Then in the late 1800s, two inventions changed the world of sound. In 1876, the telephone was invented. And in 1877, Thomas Edison played the first recorded sound on a phonograph, or sound-recording machine.

The Telephone

The telephone has made long-distance voice communication possible. Many people today use cell phones. But whether phone signals travel over wires or by microwaves, as in cell phones, the basic principles are similar. You will learn more about the signal that is used in cell phones when you read about microwaves in Chapter 3. In general, a telephone must do two things. It must record the sound that is spoken into it, and it must reproduce the sound that arrives as a signal from somewhere else.

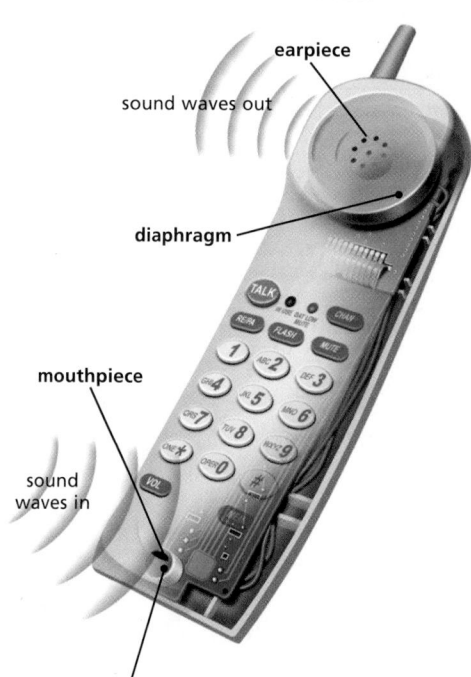

earpiece
sound waves out
diaphragm
mouthpiece
sound waves in

microphone

Suppose you are phoning your best friend to share some news. You speak into the mouthpiece. Sound waves from your voice cause a thin disk inside the mouthpiece to vibrate. A microphone turns these vibrations into electrical signals. Your handset sends these signals over wire to a switching station. Computers in the switching station connect phone callers and keep them connected until they finish their conversation. **? F**

Your friend receives the news by listening to the earpiece on his handset. There the process is more or less reversed. The electrical signals that arrive in the earpiece are turned into vibrations that shake another thin disk called a diaphragm. The vibrating diaphragm produces sound waves. The sound your friend hears is a copy of your voice, though it sounds like the real you.

 CHECK YOUR READING What part of a telephone detects sound waves?

DIFFERENTIATE INSTRUCTION

Recorded Sound

Sound occurs in real time, which means it is here for a moment and then gone. That is why Thomas Edison's invention of the phonograph—a way to preserve sound—was so important.

Edison's phonograph had a needle connected to a diaphragm that could pick up sound waves. The vibrations transferred by the sound waves were sent to a needle that cut into a piece of foil. The sound waves were translated into bumps along the grooves cut into the foil. These grooves contained all the information that was needed to reproduce the sound waves. Look at the image on top at the right to view an enlargement of record grooves. To play back the sound, Edison used another needle to track along the grooves etched in the foil. Later, phonographs were developed that changed sound waves into electrical signals that could be amplified.

Most people today listen to music on audio tapes or CDs. Tape consists of thin strips of plastic coated with a material that can be magnetized. Sounds that have been turned into electrical signals are stored on the tape as magnetic information. A CD is a hard plastic disc that has millions of microscopic pits arranged in a spiral. The bottom photograph at the right shows an enlargement of pits on the surface of a CD. These pits contain the information that a CD player can change into electrical signals, which are then turned into sound waves.

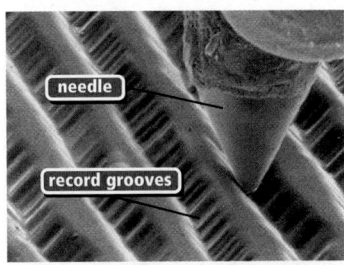

needle

record grooves

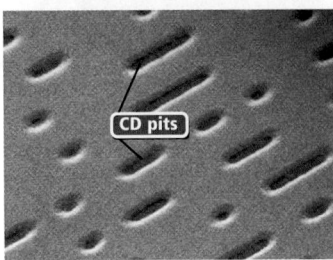

CD pits

The images above were taken by a scanning electron micrograph (SEM). Both the record grooves (top) and CD pits (bottom) store all of the information needed to reproduce sound.

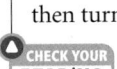 **CHECK YOUR READING** Describe three devices on which sound is recorded.

2.4 Review

KEY CONCEPTS

1. Describe one medical use of ultrasound.
2. How are vibrations produced by each of the three main types of musical instruments?
3. How does a telephone record and reproduce sound?

CRITICAL THINKING

4. **Model** Draw a simple diagram to show how telephone communication works. Begin your diagram with the mouthpiece and end with the earpiece.
5. **Classify** The pitch of a musical instrument is changed by shortening the length of a vibrating column of air. What type of instrument is it?

CHALLENGE

6. **Synthesize** How is the earpiece of a telephone similar to the amplifier you read about in Section 3? Look again at the diagram of the amplifier on page 55 to help you find similarities.

Chapter 2: **Sound 63** **C**

ANSWERS

1. Sample answer: to detect the health of a fetus

2. Strings: by plucking or bowing the strings; Winds: by blowing air into a column; Percussion: by striking a part of the instrument

3. The microphone changes the vibrations to electrical signals that travel to another phone. The other phone changes the signals back into vibrations.

4. Diagrams should include sound waves entering the mouthpiece and being converted into electrical signals; electrical signals traveling to switching station; electrical signals traveling to listener's end; electrical signals being converted into sound waves in listener's earpiece.

5. a wind instrument

6. In both, electrical signals are converted into vibrations that produce sound waves.

Focus

PURPOSE Students will make a stringed instrument and adjust it, so that changes in vibration produce two pitches.

OVERVIEW Students will observe how vibrations produce sound. They will build a stringed instrument and will find that

- the location of bridges on the instrument affects the pitch of its sound;
- cutting a hole in the instrument affects sound quality.

Lab Preparation

- Several days before performing the activity, have students bring appropriate boxes from home.
- Check rubber bands to be sure they are identical so that a difference in type or length of rubber band is not a variable.
- Prior to the investigation, have students read through the investigation, write their hypothesis, and prepare their data tables. Or you may wish to copy and distribute datasheets and rubrics.

 UNIT RESOURCE BOOK, pp. 123–131

 SCIENCE TOOLKIT, F14

Lab Management

SAFETY Emphasize the importance of using the rubber bands for their intended purpose only. Everyone in the classroom should wear safety goggles during the investigation.

INCLUSION Be sure any students who have hearing impairments are working with students who can describe the results to them. Have these students hold the sides of the box when the strings are plucked and note any differences in the vibrations they feel.

Teaching with Technology

Use a tape recorder to record the sounds of students' stringed instruments. Then play the tape back and ask students to recall what each pitch suggests about the instrument that made it.

CHAPTER INVESTIGATION

Build a Stringed Instrument

OVERVIEW AND PURPOSE

 DESIGN —YOUR OWN—

People make music by plucking strings, blowing through tubes, and striking things. Part of each musical instrument vibrates to produce sounds that form the building blocks of music. In this lab, you will use what you have learned about sound to

- make a simple stringed instrument and see how the vibrating string produces sounds and
- change the design so that your stringed instrument produces more than one pitch.

▶ Problem
Write It Up

How does the length of a string affect the pitch of the sound it produces when plucked?

▶ Hypothesize
Write It Up

Write a hypothesis to explain how changing the length of the string affects the pitch of sound that is produced. Your hypothesis should take the form of an "If . . . , then . . . , because . . ." statement. Complete steps 1–3 before writing your hypothesis.

MATERIALS
- book
- 3–5 rubber bands
- 2 pencils
- ruler
- shoebox
- scissors

▶ Procedure

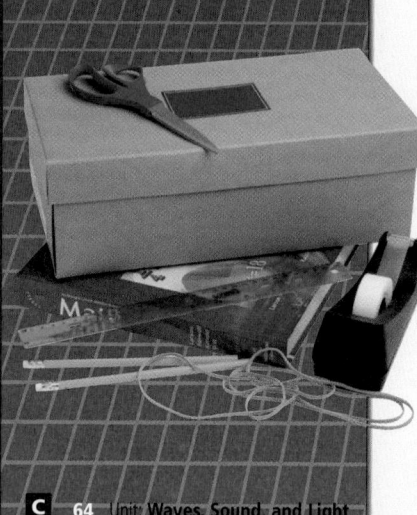

1. Make a data table like the one shown. Try out the following idea for a simple stringed instrument. Stretch a rubber band around a textbook. Put two pencils under the rubber band to serve as bridges.

2. Put the bridges far apart at either end of the book. Find the string length by measuring the distance between the two bridges. Record this measurement in your **Science Notebook.** Pluck the rubber band to make it vibrate. Watch it vibrate and listen to the sound it makes.

3. Move the bridges closer together. What effect does this have on the length of the string? Measure and record the new length. How does this affect the tone that is produced? Record your observations.

INVESTIGATION RESOURCES

 CHAPTER INVESTIGATION, Build a Stringed Instrument
- Level A, pp. 123–126
- Level B, pp. 127–130
- Level C, p. 131

Advanced students should complete Levels B & C.

 Writing a Lab Report, D12–13

Technology Resources

Customize this student lab as needed or look for an alternative. Print rubrics to assess student lab reports.

 Lab Generator CD-ROM

4. Make a musical instrument based on the principles you just identified. Begin by stretching rubber bands of the same weight or thickness over the box.

5. If necessary, reinforce the box with an extra layer of cardboard or braces so that it can withstand the tension of the rubber bands without collapsing.

6. Place pencils under the rubber bands at each end of the box. Arrange one pencil at an angle so that each string is a different length. Record the length of each string and your observations of the sounds produced. Experiment with the placement of the bridges.

7. You might also try putting one bridge at the center of the box and plucking on either side of it. How does this affect the range of pitches your instrument produces?

8. Experiment with the working model to see how you can vary the sounds. Try this variation: cut a hole in the center of the box lid. Put the lid back on the box. Replace the rubber bands and bridges. How does the hole change the sound quality?

▶ Observe and Analyze | Write It Up

1. **RECORD OBSERVATIONS** Draw a picture of your completed instrument design. Be sure your data table is complete.

2. **ANALYZE** Explain what effect moving the bridges farther apart or closer together has on the vibrating string.

3. **SYNTHESIZE** Using what you have learned from this chapter, write a paragraph that explains how your instrument works. Be sure to describe how sound waves of different frequencies and different intensities can be produced on your instrument.

▶ Conclude | Write It Up

1. **INTERPRET** Answer the question posed in the problem.

2. **ANALYZE** Compare your results with your hypothesis. Did your results support your hypothesis?

3. **EVALUATE** Describe any difficulties with or limitations of the materials that you encountered as you made your instrument.

4. **APPLY** Based on your experiences, how would you explain the difference between music and noise?

▶ INVESTIGATE Further

CHALLENGE Stringed instruments vary the pitch of musical sounds in several other ways. In addition to the length of the string, pitch depends on the tension, weight, and thickness of the string. Design an experiment to test one of these variables. How does it alter the range of sounds produced by your stringed instrument?

Build a Stringed Instrument

Problem How does the length of a string affect the pitch of the sound it produces when plucked?

Hypothesize

Observe and Analyze

Simple instrument: initial string length _____
Simple instrument: new string length _____

Table 1. Stringed Instrument Sound Observations

Stringed Instrument Designs	Length of Strings (cm)	Observations About Pitch and Sound Quality
Bridges at each end		
Bridge in middle		
After adding sound hole		

Conclude

▶ Observe and Analyze | Write It Up

1. See students' diagrams. See students' data tables.

2. The closer the bridges, the shorter the length of the vibrating band and the higher the pitch.

3. Sound waves of different frequencies can be produced by changing the length or tightness of the vibrating string. Sound waves of different intensities can be produced by varying the amplitude (or energy) with which the strings are plucked.

▶ Conclude | Write It Up

1. The longer the string is, the lower the pitch is.

2. Student answers will vary.

3. Answers might include incompatibility of the length of the rubber band and the size of the box.

4. Music is intended to include certain pitches and intensities; noise is random sound.

▶ INVESTIGATE Further

CHALLENGE Student results should include one of the following: tighter strings produce higher pitch, heavier and thicker strings produce lower pitch.

Post-Lab Discussion

• From the student instruments, choose one or two that have unique features. Discuss with the class the effect the features have on pitch and quality.

• Have students make a conclusion about the relationships between string length and pitch and about factors that affect sound quality.

• Ask students how they might revise their designs if they were to do a follow-up experiment to test another variable.

BACK TO

the **BIG** idea

Have students describe a situation that demonstrates the transfer of energy by a sound wave. *Students could use investigations in this chapter, the effect of vibrations on the human ear, or another example of how sound waves affect the medium they travel in.*

◖ KEY CONCEPTS SUMMARY

SECTION 2.1
Ask: If the drum were in a vacuum, would sound be produced when it was struck? *No; sound needs a medium, and a vacuum has no medium.*

Ask: What part of the drum vibrates, producing sound? *the drum skin*

SECTION 2.2
Ask: If the frequency of the top wave is 200 hertz, what is the frequency of the bottom wave? *600 Hz*

SECTION 2.3
The waves shown were originally identical, but one of the waves has been amplified. Ask: Which wave was amplified? How do you know? *The bottom wave was amplified; its amplitude is greater.*

Ask: If energy is removed from the top wave, will it be more similar to the bottom wave or more different from it? *different since amplitude will be less*

SECTION 2.4
Ask: How is sound being used in the picture on the left? *Sound bounces off an object and is used to determine its location.*

Ask: What is the term for this practice? *echolocation*

Review Concepts

• Big Idea Flow Chart, p. T9
• Chapter Outline, p. T15–T16

 # Chapter Review

the **BIG** idea

Sound waves transfer energy through vibrations.

 **CONTENT REVIEW**
CLASSZONE.COM

◖ KEY CONCEPTS SUMMARY

2.1 Sound is a wave.

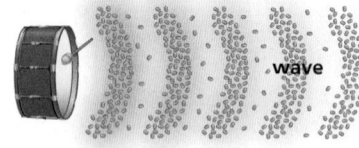
disturbance
wave

Sound is a longitudinal wave that travels through a material medium, such as air.

VOCABULARY
sound p. 37
vibration p. 37
vacuum p. 41

2.2 Frequency determines pitch.

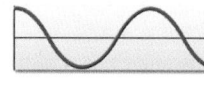
A sound wave with a lower frequency and longer wavelength is perceived to have a lower pitch.

A sound wave with a higher frequency and shorter wavelength is perceived to have a higher pitch.

VOCABULARY
pitch p. 45
hertz p. 46
ultrasound p. 46
resonance p. 48
Doppler effect p. 50

2.3 Intensity determines loudness.

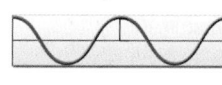
A sound wave with a lower amplitude and energy is perceived as a softer sound.

A sound wave with a higher amplitude and energy is perceived as a louder sound.

VOCABULARY
intensity p. 52
decibel p. 52
amplification p. 55
acoustics p. 55

2.4 Sound has many uses.

Human uses of sound:
sonar
ultrasound
music
telephone
recording

Bats use sound to locate objects.

VOCABULARY
echolocation p. 59
sonar p. 59

C 66 Unit: Waves, Sound, and Light

Technology Resources

Have students visit **ClassZone.com** or use the CD-ROM for a cumulative review of concepts.

 CONTENT REVIEW

 CONTENT REVIEW CD-ROM

Engage students in a whole-class interactive review of Key Concepts. Edit content as you wish.

 POWER PRESENTATIONS

Reviewing Vocabulary

Copy and complete the chart below by using vocabulary terms from this chapter.

Property of Wave	Unit of Measurement	Corresponding Quality of Sound
Frequency	1.	2.
3.	4.	loudness

Make a frame for each of the vocabulary words listed below. Write the word in the center. Decide what information to frame it with. Use definitions, examples, descriptions, parts, or pictures. An example is below.

5. resonance **8.** acoustics

6. Doppler effect **9.** echolocation

7. amplification **10.** sonar

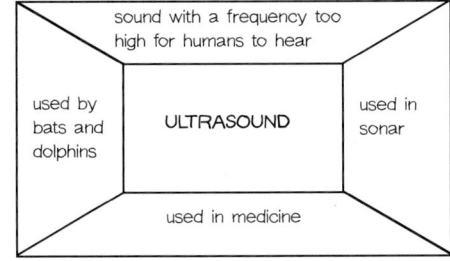

sound with a frequency too high for humans to hear

used by bats and dolphins

ULTRASOUND

used in sonar

used in medicine

Reviewing Key Concepts

Multiple Choice *Choose the letter of the best answer.*

11. Sound is a mechanical wave, so it always
   a. travels through a vacuum
   b. has the same amplitude
   c. is made by a machine
   d. travels through matter

12. Which unit is a measure of sound frequency?
   a. hertz
   b. decibel
   c. amp
   d. meters

13. In which of the following materials would sound waves move fastest?
   a. water
   b. cool air
   c. hot air
   d. steel

14. Which of the following effects is caused by amplification?
   a. wavelength increases
   b. amplitude increases
   c. frequency decreases
   d. decibel measure decreases

15. The frequency of a sound wave determines its
   a. pitch
   b. loudness
   c. amplitude
   d. intensity

16. As sound waves travel away from their source, their
   a. intensity increases
   b. energy increases
   c. intensity decreases
   d. frequency decreases

17. A telephone mouthpiece changes sound waves into
   a. electric signals
   b. vibrations
   c. CD pits
   d. grooves on a cylinder

Short Answer *Look at the diagrams of waves below. For the next two items, choose the wave diagram that best fits the description, and explain your choice.*

a.   **b.**   **c.**

18. the sound of a basketball coach blowing a whistle during practice

19. the sound of a cow mooing in a pasture

Reviewing Vocabulary

1. *hertz*

2. *pitch*

3. *intensity*

4. *decibel*

Sample answers:

5. resonance: *sound wave has the same frequency as an object's natural frequency; constructive interference; amplitudes combine with each other, sound wave is stronger*

6. Doppler effect: *lower pitch as source moves away; higher pitch as source approaches; pitch changes with movement of source; discovered by Christian Doppler*

7. amplification: *louder, greater intensity; greater height of sound wave; effect of an amplifier; used in TV, radio, stereo*

8. acoustics: *scientific study; study of sound; study of how sound is produced; study of how sound is detected*

9. echolocation: *use of sound; locates objects by reflection; used by bats; used by dolphins*

10. sonar: *used by humans to locate objects; used underwater; used in submarines, sound navigation, and mapping the sea floor*

Reviewing Key Concepts

11. *d*

12. *a*

13. *d*

14. *b*

15. *a*

16. *c*

17. *a*

18. *c; high frequency, pitch, and amplitude*

19. *a; low frequency, pitch, and amplitude*

Thinking Critically

20. By plucking the strings, which causes them to vibrate
21. by plucking the strings harder or more softly
22. The sound quality is different.
23. The order should be c, a, d, b.
24. Frequency and amplitude are both measures of a sound wave; frequency determines pitch, while amplitude determines loudness. Intensity and amplitude both relate to loudness of sound; intensity relates to amount of energy, while amplitude relates to the measure of wave energy. Pitch and quality concern an aspect of sound that we hear; pitch relates to the highness or lowness, while quality concerns other aspects of the sound. Fundamentals and overtones are pitches in a musical tone; the fundamental is the basic pitch we hear, while overtones are higher, fainter pitches that mix into the sound.

Using Math in Science

25. 7:45 A.M. to 8:00 A.M.
26. 103 dB; allow ±3 dB variance
27. yes, from about 7:30 A.M. to about 8:30 A.M.
28. You could use a bar to represent the noise-level "snapshot" at each quarter hour or half hour. The graph would not be as informative, because noise measures for times between would not be shown.

the **BIG** idea

29. by plucking the strings on the guitar; vibrations magnified by the amplifier; sound waves coming from the boom box; and sound caused by the shoes hitting the ground
30. Sample answer: Sound waves transfer energy through vibrations. Sound is a longitudinal wave that requires a medium. As frequency increases, pitch is higher. More intense sounds are louder.

UNIT PROJECTS

Collect schedules, materials lists, and questions. Be sure dates and materials are obtainable, and questions are focused.

 Unit Projects, pp. 5-10

Thinking Critically

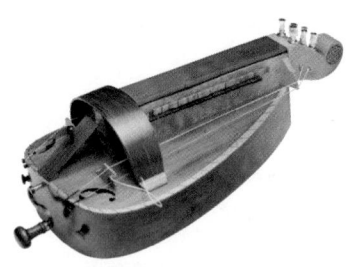

Look at the photograph of a lute above. Write a short answer to the next two questions.

20. **HYPOTHESIZE** How might sound waves be produced using the instrument in the photograph?

21. **APPLY** How might a person playing the instrument in the photograph vary the intensity?

22. **COMMUNICATE** Two people are singing at the same pitch, yet they sound different. Explain why.

23. **SEQUENCE** Copy the following sequence chart on your paper. Write the events in the correct sequence on the chart.

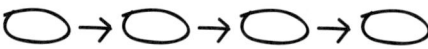

Events

a. Sound waves race out from the wind chime.
b. Air friction gradually weakens the chime sound.
c. A breeze makes a wind chime vibrate.
d. A person nearby hears the wind chime.

24. **COMPARE AND CONTRAST** Write a description of the similarities of and differences between each of the following pairs of terms: frequency—amplitude; intensity—amplitude; pitch—quality; fundamental tone—overtones.

Using Math in Science

Read the line graph below showing freeway noise levels at a toll collector's booth. Use the data in the graph to answer the next four questions.

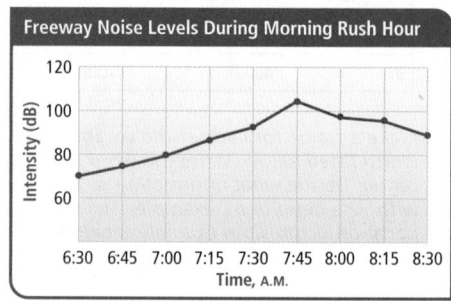

25. Which is the noisiest quarter-hour?

26. Estimate the loudest level of sound that the toll collector is exposed to.

27. If ear protection should be worn for a sound level above 90 dB, should the toll collector wear hearing protection? If so, during which times?

28. Describe how you could turn the line graph into a bar graph. Would the bar graph be as informative? Explain your answer.

the **BIG** idea

29. **ANALYZE** Look back at the picture at the start of the chapter on pages 34–35. How are sound waves being produced?

30. **SUMMARIZE** Write a paragraph summarizing this chapter. Use the Big Idea on page 34 as your topic sentence. Write examples of each key concept listed on page 34.

UNIT PROJECTS

Check your schedule for your unit project. How are you doing? Be sure that you've placed data or notes from your research in your project folder.

MONITOR AND RETEACH

If students have trouble applying the concepts in items 25-28, have them do the following activities:

• Make a bar graph as in problem 28 and compare the information.
• Trace the graph on a piece of paper. Use a ruler to carefully sketch grid lines on the graph, so that the numbers can be easily read.
• Make up additional questions about the graph. Trade questions, and answer someone else's questions.

Students may benefit from summarizing one or more sections of the chapter.

 Summarizing the Chapter, pp. 141–142

Standardized Test Practice

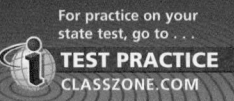

For practice on your state test, go to . . .

TEST PRACTICE
CLASSZONE.COM

Analyzing Experiments

Read the following description of the way scientists study animals' hearing. Then answer the questions below.

Scientists test the hearing ranges of a human by making a sound and asking the person to say whether it was heard. This cannot be done with animals. Scientists use different methods to find animals' hearing ranges. In some experiments, they train animals—by rewarding them with food or water—to make specific behaviors when they hear a sound. Another method is to study an animal's nervous system for electrical reactions to sounds.

Researchers have found that dogs and cats can hear a wide range of sounds. Both dogs and cats can hear much higher frequencies than humans can. Lizards and frogs can only hear sounds in a much narrower range than humans can. Elephants can hear a wider range than lizards and frogs but not as wide a range as dogs and cats. Elephants can hear the lowest frequency sounds of all these animals.

1. What type of behavior would be best for scientists to train animals to make as a signal they hear a sound?

 a. a typical motion that the animal makes frequently

 b. a motion that is difficult for the animal to make

 c. a motion the animal makes rarely but does make naturally

 d. a complicated motion of several steps

2. According to the passage, which animals can hear sounds with the highest frequencies?

 a. cats   **c.** frogs

 b. elephants   **d.** lizards

3. The high-pitched sounds of car brakes are sometimes more bothersome to pet dogs than they are to their owners. Based on the experimental findings, what is the best explanation for that observation?

 a. The dogs hear high-intensity sounds that their owners cannot hear.

 b. The dogs hear low-intensity sounds that their owners cannot hear.

 c. The dogs hear low-frequency sounds that their owners cannot hear.

 d. The dogs hear high-frequency sounds that their owners cannot hear.

4. Which animal will hear sounds with the longest wavelengths?

 a. cat   **c.** elephant

 b. dog   **d.** frog

Extended Response

Answer the two questions below in detail. Include some of the terms from the word box in your answer. Underline each term you use in your answer.

amplitude	distance	Doppler effect
frequency	pitch	wavelength

5. Suppose you are riding in a car down the street and pass a building where a fire alarm is sounding. Will the sound you hear change as you move up to, alongside, and past the building? Why or why not?

6. Marvin had six glass bottles that held different amounts of water. He blew air into each bottle, producing a sound. How would the sounds produced by each of the six bottles compare to the others? Why?

METACOGNITIVE ACTIVITY

Have students answer the following questions in their **Science Notebook:**

1. Was there a quality of sound that was new to you? If so, what?

2. What questions that you had about sound were answered in this chapter? What questions do you still have about sound?

3. Do the concepts in this chapter relate to your Unit Project? If so, how? If not, how might you revise your project to include sound?

Analyzing Experiments

1. c   3. d

2. a   4. c

Extended Response

5. RUBRIC

4 points for a response that correctly answers the question and uses the following terms accurately:

• pitch   • wavelength   • distance

Sample: The sound is higher in <u>pitch</u> *as the car moves closer to the alarm and becomes lower in pitch as it moves farther away. This is because sound changes with* <u>distance</u>. *When the distance decreases, the* <u>wavelength</u> *is shorter and the pitch is higher. When the distance increases, the wavelength is longer and the pitch lowers. A change in pitch occurs when either the source or the receiver of the sound is moving. This is known as the* <u>Doppler effect</u>.

3 points for a response that correctly answers the question and uses two terms accurately

2 points for a response that correctly answers the question and uses one term accurately

1 point for a response that correctly answers the question but does not use the terms

6. RUBRIC

4 points for a response that correctly answers the question and uses the following terms accurately:

• pitch   • frequency   • distance

Sample: The <u>pitch</u>, *or* <u>frequency</u>, *increases as the amount of water increases. So the bottles with more water would have a higher pitch than the bottles with less water. The reason for this is that the sound is traveling through a smaller* <u>distance</u> *since there is a smaller amount of air.*

3 points for a response that correctly answers the question and uses two terms accurately

2 points for a response that correctly answers the question and uses one term accurately

1 point for a response that correctly answers the question but does not use the terms

Electromagnetic Waves

Physical Science
UNIFYING PRINCIPLES

PRINCIPLE 1

Matter is made of particles too small to see.

PRINCIPLE 2

Matter changes form and moves from place to place.

PRINCIPLE 3

Energy changes from one form to another, but it cannot be created or destroyed.

PRINCIPLE 4

Physical forces affect the movement of all matter on Earth and throughout the universe.

Unit: Waves, Sound, and Light
BIG IDEAS

CHAPTER 1
Waves

Waves transfer energy and interact in predictable ways.

CHAPTER 2
Sound

Sound waves transfer energy through vibrations.

CHAPTER 3
Electromagnetic Waves

Electromagnetic waves transfer energy through radiation.

CHAPTER 4
Light and Optics

Optical tools depend on the wave behavior of light.

CHAPTER 3
KEY CONCEPTS

SECTION 3.1

Electromagnetic waves have unique traits.
1. An electromagnetic (EM) wave is a disturbance in a field.
2. EM waves can travel in a vacuum.
3. EM waves can interact with a material medium.

SECTION 3.2

Electromagnetic waves have many uses.
1. EM waves have different frequencies.
2. Long length, low frequency (radio waves, microwaves)
3. Mid-range length and frequency (infrared, visible and ultraviolet light)
4. Short length, high-frequency (x-rays, gamma rays)

SECTION 3.3

The Sun is the source of most visible light.
1. Light comes from the Sun and other natural sources.
2. Some living things produce visible light.
3. Human technologies produce visible light.

SECTION 3.4

Light waves interact with materials.
1. Light can be reflected, transmitted, or absorbed.
2. Wavelength determines color.

 The Big Idea Flow Chart is available on p. T17 in the **UNIT TRANSPARENCY BOOK.**

Previewing Content

3.1 Electromagnetic waves have unique traits. pp. 73–78

1. An electromagnetic wave is a disturbance in a field.

An **electromagnetic wave** is a disturbance that transfers energy through a field.

A **field** is the area around an object where the object applies force on another object without touching it. The two fields of an EM wave—electric and magnetic—vibrate at right angles to each other and are perpendicular to the direction the wave is moving (as illustrated in the visual below).

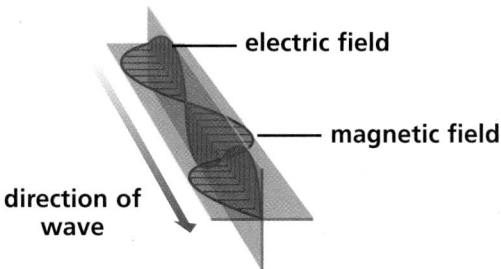

electric field

magnetic field

direction of wave

An EM wave is emitted whenever a charged atomic particle accelerates. The Sun and human technology are the two main sources of EM waves.

2. Electromagnetic waves can travel in a vacuum.

Once EM waves are produced, they travel on their own, independent of the source that emitted them. They don't need a medium and can travel in a vacuum at about 300,000 kilometers per second.

Radiation is the transfer of energy in the form of EM waves. EM waves do not lose energy as they travel in a vacuum. EM radiation from the Sun travels in a straight line through the vacuum of outer space.

3. Electromagnetic waves can interact with a material medium.

When EM waves encounter a material medium, they may transfer energy to it. Different mediums interact differently with EM waves, and can change the direction of the wave and affect energy transfer.

• In a vacuum, EM waves transfer energy by moving potential energy from one place to another.

• In a medium, an EM wave's potential energy can be converted into other forms, such as heat.

3.2 Electromagnetic waves have many uses. pp. 79–87

1. EM waves have different frequencies.

An EM wave's frequency determines the wave's characteristics. The higher the frequency, the more energy the wave carries. The **electromagnetic spectrum** is a continuum of waves from the lowest-frequency radio waves to the highest-frequency gamma waves.

2. Radio waves and microwaves have long wavelengths and low frequencies.

Radio waves are long, low-energy EM waves. They can be modified and converted into the sound and pictures of radios and TVs. **Microwaves** have more energy and shorter wavelengths than radio waves.

• In radar, microwaves are reflected off an object and returned to their source as a way of locating the object.

• Cell phone technology is like radio transmission but uses microwaves. A system of towers connects cell phones to each other and to the regular phone system.

3. Infrared, visible, and ultraviolet light have mid-range wavelengths and frequencies.

The range of frequencies that humans can see is just a tiny part of the EM spectrum.

• **Infrared waves** lie between visible light and microwaves. They are emitted by warm objects. Infrared technology is used to cook food, detect warm objects, and provide heat.

• **Ultraviolet light** carries more energy than visible light and can damage human tissue. It is used to sterilize medical equipment and kill bacteria in food.

4. X-rays and gamma rays have short wavelengths and high frequencies.

Because of their high frequencies, x-rays and gamma rays carry very high energies. They are naturally produced by stars.

• **X-rays** can penetrate soft tissues but not hard tissues of the body, making these waves useful for medical imaging.

• **Gamma rays** can penetrate all the tissues of the body, killing normal cells and causing cancer cells to grow.

Common Misconceptions

WAVE TRANSMISSION Students may think that EM waves must have a medium, or matter, to travel. EM waves can travel through matter, but do not need matter to travel.

 This misconception is addressed on p. 75.

MISCONCEPTION DATABASE
CLASSZONE.COM Background on student misconceptions

INFRARED LIGHT Students may think infrared light is part of the visible spectrum. Infrared light, however, is below the visible range and cannot be detected by the human eye.

 This misconception is addressed on p. 85.

Previewing Content

SECTION

3.3 The Sun is the source of most visible light. pp. 88–92

1. Light comes from the Sun and other natural sources.
Almost all organisms depend on light for survival. Virtually all light on Earth initiates in sunlight. Green plants use sunlight to synthesize food that both plants and animals depend on for energy. The Sun's intense heat produces light through **incandescence**. This light is the ultimate source of almost all energy on Earth.

2. Some living things produce visible light.
Chemical reactions in some living organisms produce **bioluminescence.** Unlike incandescence, luminescence produces light without the high temperatures that could harm organisms.

3. Human technologies produce visible light.
The discovery of electricity has led to several artificial lighting technologies.

- Most incandescent light bulbs use tungsten filaments and produce light and heat.
- Halogen lighting also produces lots of heat, but the tungsten filament lasts longer than in ordinary incandescent light bulbs and produces more light.
- Fluorescent lighting is cool and efficient. The bulb is coated with a phosphor, which glows when it absorbs the UV waves generated within the bulb.
- LEDs are semiconductors that produce light when electricity passes through. They are cool, efficient, and long-lasting. Light produced by LEDs has many advantages over other forms of lighting.

The visual below shows the different parts of incandescent, halogen, and fluorescent bulbs.

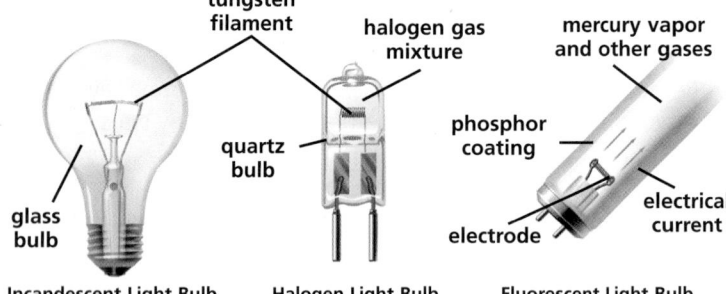

Incandescent Light Bulb   Halogen Light Bulb   Fluorescent Light Bulb

SECTION

3.4 Light waves interact with materials. pp. 93–101

1. Light can be reflected, transmitted, or absorbed.
EM waves can interact with a material medium in the same ways that mechanical waves do. The medium can reflect, transmit, or absorb the waves.

Most objects are visible because they reflect light. **Transmission** and **absorption** affect how objects look.

- Objects that transmit most of the light that strikes them appear transparent.
- Objects that transmit some of the light that strikes them but cause it to scatter appear translucent.
- Opaque objects do not transmit light.

Scattering from fine particles in a material sends light in all directions and creates diffuse light. **Polarization** reduces glare. When all of the electric fields of a group of light waves vibrate in the same direction, the light is polarized.

2. Wavelength determines color.
Visible light is a spectrum that is usually divided into seven colors. Visible light reflected from an object gives it color; a green leaf reflects green wavelengths and absorbs all other visible wavelengths.

The three **primary colors** are light of different wavelengths that produce white light when mixed equally. They are red, green, and blue.

The **primary pigments** reflect wavelengths of cyan, yellow, and magenta. When you mix pigments, the mixture absorbs more colors, and reflects fewer wavelengths.

The visual below shows primary pigments.

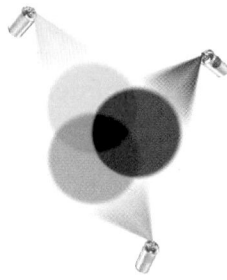

Common Misconceptions

BIOLUMINESCENCE Students commonly think that bioluminescence is an electrical process that occurs within an organism. In truth, bioluminescence is the result of chemical reactions that produce energy in the form of light.

 This misconception is addressed on p. 89.

MISCONCEPTION DATABASE

CLASSZONE.COM Background on student misconceptions

THE SKY'S COLOR It is commonly thought that the sky is blue because of the reflection of blue light from Earth's oceans. In fact, particles in the atmosphere scatter the blue wavelengths of sunlight more than they scatter other wavelengths, making the sky appear blue.

 This misconception is addressed on p. 95.

Previewing Labs

EXPLORE (the BIG idea)

What Melts the Ice Cubes? p. 71
Students will observe ice cubes melting to find out that black and white materials absorb different quantities of energy from light.

TIME 10 minutes
MATERIALS 2 ice cubes, 2 sandwich bags, sheet of white paper, sheet of black paper

What Is White Light Made Of? p. 71
Students will use a CD as a prism to find out that white light can separate into several colors.

TIME 10 minutes
MATERIALS compact disc, sheet of white paper, flashlight

Internet Activity: Electromagnetic Waves, p. 71
Students learn that the Sun emits different wavelengths.

TIME 20 minutes
MATERIALS computer with Internet access

SECTION 3.1

EXPLORE Electromagnetic Waves, p. 73
Students use a mirror to show that EM waves can be reflected.

TIME 10 minutes
MATERIALS TV with remote control unit, mirror with stand

INVESTIGATE Wave Behavior, p. 76
Students design an experiment to determine what makes the vanes of a radiometer move.

TIME 30 minutes
MATERIALS radiometer

SECTION 3.2

EXPLORE Radio Waves, p. 79
Students explore how radio waves form and how they are detected.

TIME 10 minutes
MATERIALS 25 cm copper wire (2 pieces), C or D battery, 5 cm electrical tape, metal fork, portable radio

INVESTIGATE The Electromagnetic Spectrum, p. 84
Students draw conclusions about the existence of invisible EM waves by measuring their temperature.

TIME 30 minutes
MATERIALS sheet of white paper, black marker, 3 thermometers, prism

SECTION 3.3

INVESTIGATE Artificial Lighting, p. 90
Students design an experiment to examine various kinds of bulbs.

TIME 30 minutes
MATERIALS a variety of bulb types and sizes

SECTION 3.4

EXPLORE Light and Matter, p. 93
Students observe the scattering of light in a translucent material.

TIME 10 minutes
MATERIALS clear plastic container with lid, 4–6 cups water, measuring spoons, 10 mL milk, flashlight

INVESTIGATE Mixing Colors, p. 98
Students discover the colors that make up black ink.

TIME 30 minutes
MATERIALS 3 coffee filters, scissors, 3 black felt-tip markers (different brands), 3 cups water

CHAPTER INVESTIGATION Wavelength and Color, pp. 100–101
Students use a light box to learn that an object's color is determined by the wavelengths of light it reflects.

TIME 40 minutes
MATERIALS sheets of acetate (red, blue, green), ruler, scissors, shoe box, masking tape, light source, solid-colored objects

R **Additional INVESTIGATION,** Seeing the Invisible, A, B, & C, pp. 203–211, Teacher Instructions, pp. 284–285

Previewing Chapter Resources

	INTEGRATED TECHNOLOGY	**LABS AND ACTIVITIES**

CHAPTER 3
Electro-magnetic Waves

 CLASSZONE.COM
- eEdition Plus
- EasyPlanner Plus
- Misconception Database
- Content Review
- Test Practice
- Visualization
- Resource Centers
- Internet Activity: EM Waves
- Math Tutorial

 SCILINKS.ORG
SCI**LINKS**

 CD-ROMS
- eEdition
- EasyPlanner
- Power Presentations
- Content Review
- Lab Generator
- Test Generator

 AUDIO CDS
- Audio Readings
- Audio Readings in Spanish

P·E EXPLORE the Big Idea, p. 71
- What Melts the Ice Cubes?
- What Is White Light Made Of?
- Internet Activity: Electromagnetic Waves

R **UNIT RESOURCE BOOK**
Unit Projects, pp. 5–10

 Lab Generator CD-ROM
Generate customized labs.

SECTION
3.1 Electromagnetic waves have unique traits.
pp. 73–78

Time: 2 periods (1 block)
 Lesson Plan, pp. 143–144

 • **VISUALIZATION,** EM Waves
- **MATH TUTORIAL**

 UNIT TRANSPARENCY BOOK
- Big Idea Flow Chart, p. T17
- Daily Vocabulary Scaffolding, p. T18
- Note-Taking Model, p. T19
- 3-Minute Warm-Up, p. T20

P·E
- EXPLORE Electromagnetic Waves, p. 73
- INVESTIGATE Wave Behavior, p. 76
- Math in Science, p. 78

R **UNIT RESOURCE BOOK**
- Datasheet, Wave Behavior, p. 152
- Math Support & Practice, pp. 192–193

SECTION
3.2 Electromagnetic waves have many uses.
pp. 79–87

Time: 2 periods (1 block)
 Lesson Plan, pp. 154–155

 RESOURCE CENTER, EM Spectrum

UNIT TRANSPARENCY BOOK
- Daily Vocabulary Scaffolding, p. T18
- 3-Minute Warm-Up, p. T20
- "The Electromagnetic Spectrum" Visual, p. T22

P·E
- EXPLORE Electromagnetic Waves, p. 79
- INVESTIGATE The EM Spectrum, p. 84
- Think Science, p. 87

R **UNIT RESOURCE BOOK**
- Datasheet, The EM Spectrum, p. 163
- Additional INVESTIGATION, Seeing the Invisible, A, B, & C, pp. 203–211

SECTION
3.3 The Sun is the source of most visible light.
pp. 88–92

Time: 2 periods (1 block)
 Lesson Plan, pp. 165–166

 RESOURCE CENTER, Visible Light

 UNIT TRANSPARENCY BOOK
- Daily Vocabulary Scaffolding, p. T18
- 3-Minute Warm-Up, p. T21

P·E INVESTIGATE Artificial Lighting, p. 90

R **UNIT RESOURCE BOOK**
Datasheet, Artificial Lighting, p. 174

SECTION
3.4 Light waves interact with materials.
pp. 93–101

Time: 4 periods (2 blocks)
 Lesson Plan, pp. 176–177

 UNIT TRANSPARENCY BOOK
- Big Idea Flow Chart, p. T17
- Daily Vocabulary Scaffolding, p. T18
- 3-Minute Warm-Up, p. T21
- Chapter Outline, pp. T23–T24

P·E
- EXPLORE Light and Matter, p. 93
- INVESTIGATE Mixing Colors, p. 98
- CHAPTER INVESTIGATION, Wavelength and Color, pp. 100–101

R **UNIT RESOURCE BOOK**
- Datasheet, Mixing Colors, p. 185
- CHAPTER INVESTIGATION, A, B, & C, pp. 194–202

 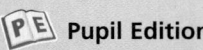
READING AND REINFORCEMENT

- Frame Game, B26–27
- Supporting Main Ideas, C42
- Daily Vocabulary Scaffolding, H1–8

 UNIT RESOURCE BOOK
- Vocabulary Practice, pp. 189–190
- Decoding Support, p. 191
- Summarizing the Chapter, pp. 212–213

 Audio Readings CD
Listen to Pupil Edition.

 Audio Readings in Spanish CD
Listen to Pupil Edition in Spanish.

ASSESSMENT

- Chapter Review, pp. 103–104
- Standardized Test Practice, p. 105

 UNIT ASSESSMENT BOOK
- Diagnostic Test, pp. 40–41
- Chapter Test, A, B, & C, pp. 46–51
- Alternative Assessment, pp. 58–59

 Spanish Chapter Test, pp. 289–292

 Test Generator CD-ROM
Generate customized tests.

 Lab Generator CD-ROM
Rubrics for Labs

STANDARDS

National Standards
A.2–8, A.9.a–f, B.3.c, B.3.f, E.2–5, F.4.c, F.5.c

See p. 70 for the standards.

 UNIT RESOURCE BOOK
- Reading Study Guide, A & B, pp. 145–148
- Spanish Reading Study Guide, pp. 149–150
- Challenge and Extension, p. 151
- Reinforcing Key Concepts, p. 153
- Challenge Reading, pp. 187–188

 Ongoing Assessment, pp. 74–77

 Section 3.1 Review, p. 77

 UNIT ASSESSMENT BOOK
Section 3.1 Quiz, p. 42

National Standards
A.2–8, A.9.a–f, E.2–5

 UNIT RESOURCE BOOK
- Reading Study Guide, A & B, pp. 156–159
- Spanish Reading Study Guide, pp. 160–161
- Challenge and Extension, p. 162
- Reinforcing Key Concepts, p. 164

 Ongoing Assessment, pp. 79, 81–82, 85

 Section 3.2 Review, p. 86

 UNIT ASSESSMENT BOOK
Section 3.2 Quiz, p. 43

National Standards
A.2–7, A.9.a–b, A.9.d–f, F.4.c, F.5.c

 UNIT RESOURCE BOOK
- Reading Study Guide, A & B, pp. 167–170
- Spanish Reading Study Guide, pp. 171–172
- Challenge and Extension, p. 173
- Reinforcing Key Concepts, p. 175

 Ongoing Assessment, pp. 88–92

 Section 3.3 Review, p. 92

 UNIT ASSESSMENT BOOK
Section 3.3 Quiz, p. 44

National Standards
A.2–7, A.9.a–b, A.9.d–f, B.3.f, E.2–5, F.5.c

 UNIT RESOURCE BOOK
- Reading Study Guide, A & B, pp. 178–181
- Spanish Reading Study Guide, pp. 182–183
- Challenge and Extension, p. 184
- Reinforcing Key Concepts, p. 186

 Ongoing Assessment, pp. 93–95, 97–99

 Section 3.4 Review, p. 99

 UNIT ASSESSMENT BOOK
Section 3.4 Quiz, p. 45

National Standards
A.2–7, A.9.a–b, A.9.e–f, B.3.c

Previewing Resources for Differentiated Instruction

CHAPTER INVESTIGATION

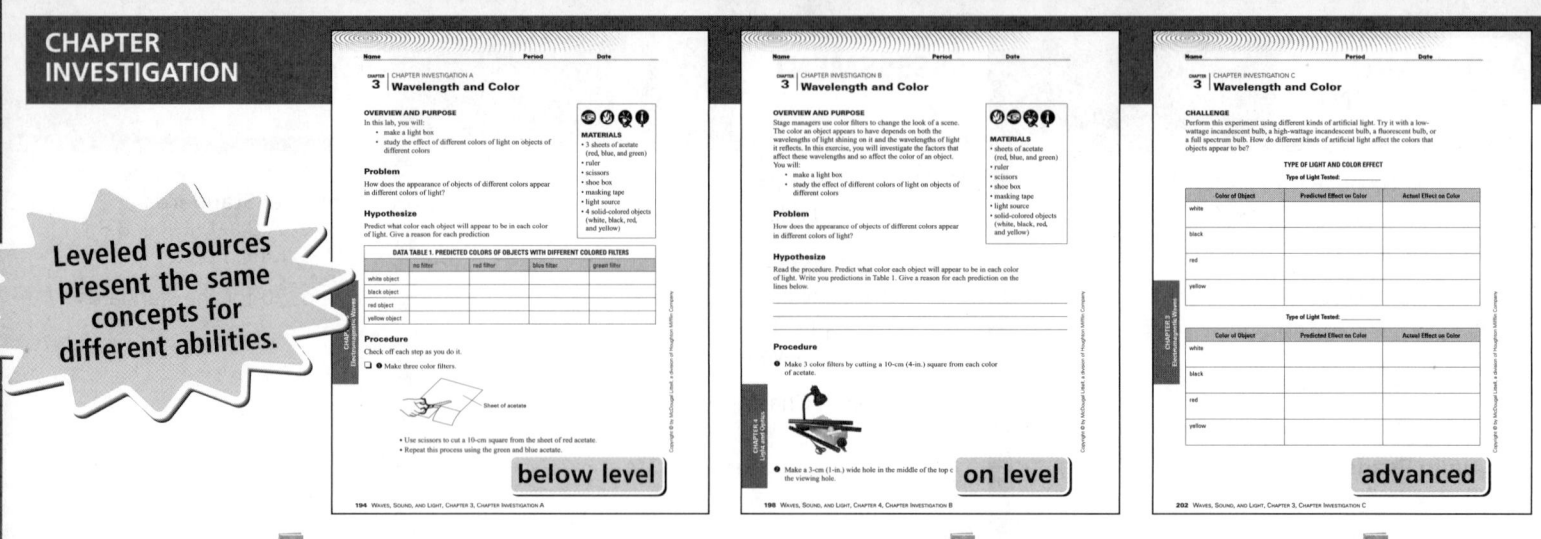

below level

on level

advanced

R **UNIT RESOURCE BOOK,** pp. 194–197 R pp. 198–201 R pp. 198–202

READING STUDY GUIDE

> Leveled resources present the same concepts for different abilities.

> Reading Study Guide is also in Spanish.

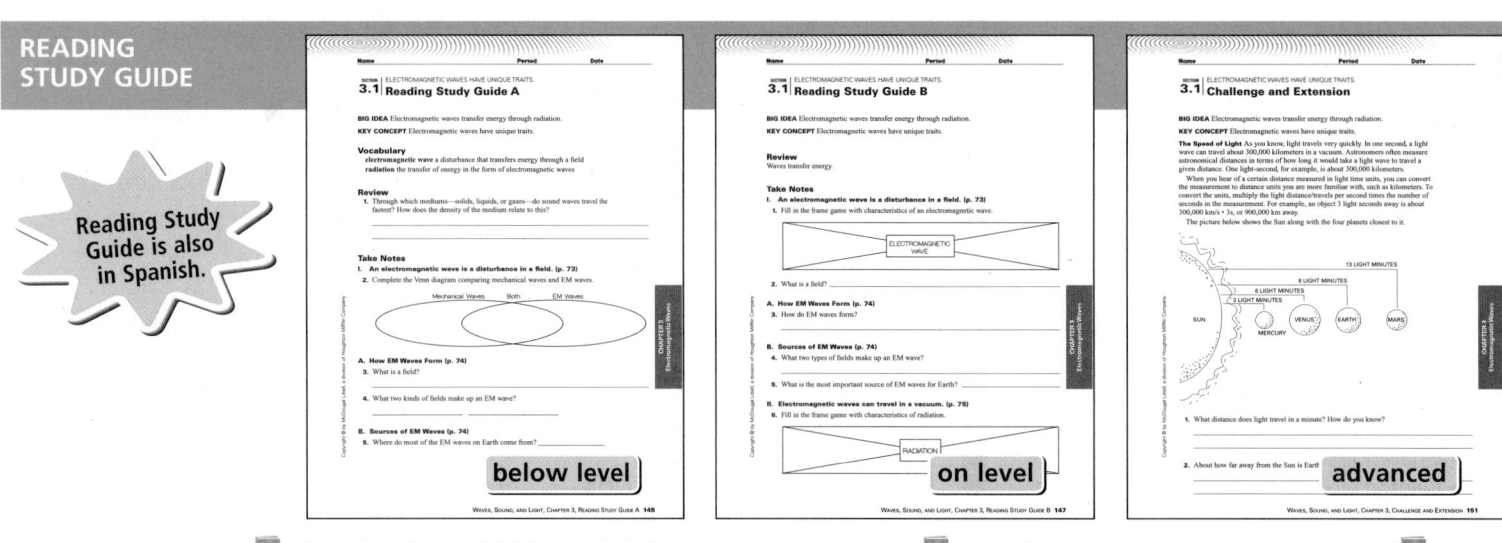

below level

on level

advanced

R **UNIT RESOURCE BOOK,** pp. 145–146 R pp. 147–148 R p. 151

CHAPTER TEST

> Chapter Test is also in Spanish.

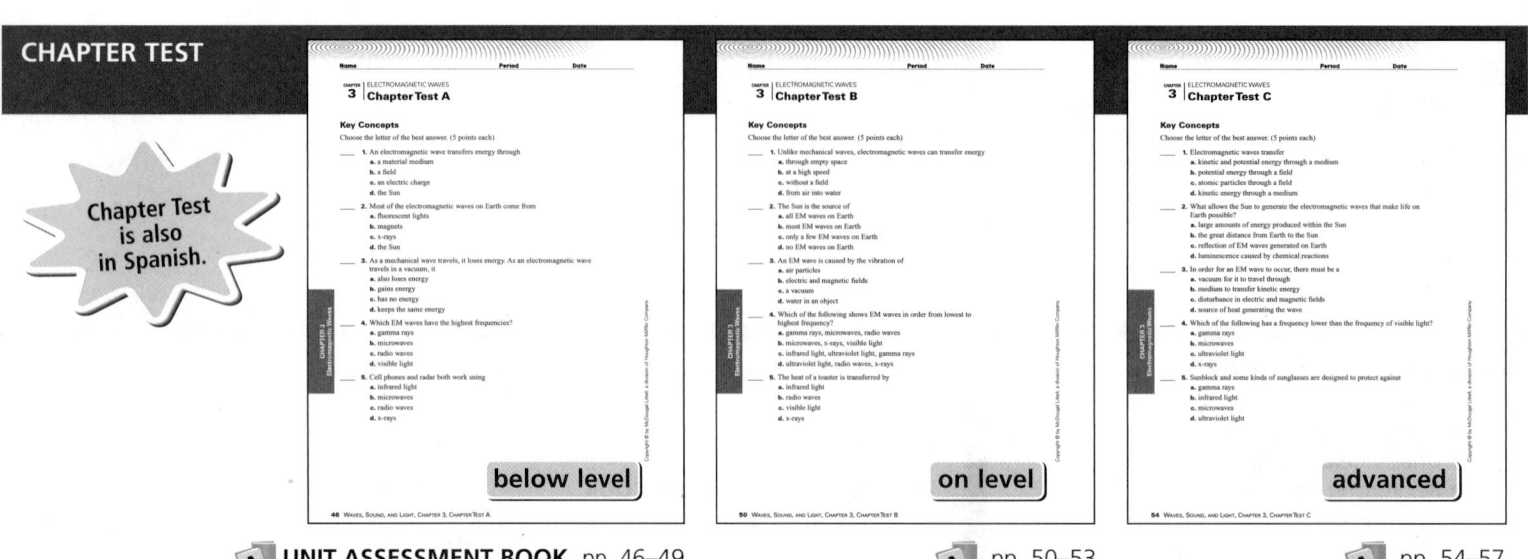

below level

on level

advanced

A **UNIT ASSESSMENT BOOK,** pp. 46–49 A pp. 50–53 A pp. 54–57

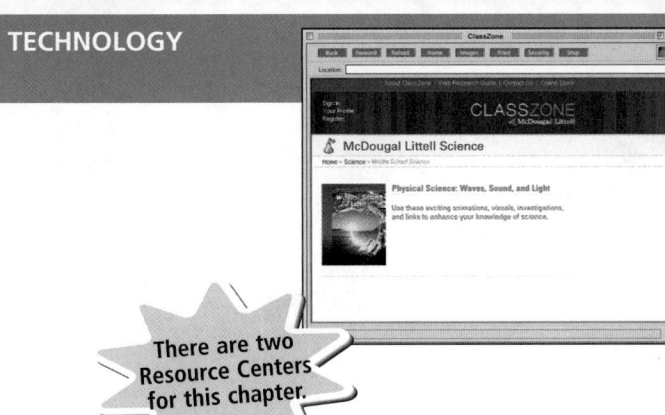

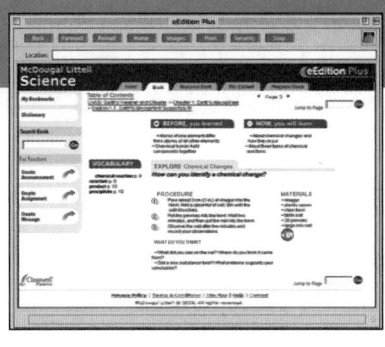

There are two Resource Centers for this chapter.

CLASSZONE.COM　　　　**CD/CD-ROMS**　　　　**CLASSZONE.COM**

VISUAL CONTENT

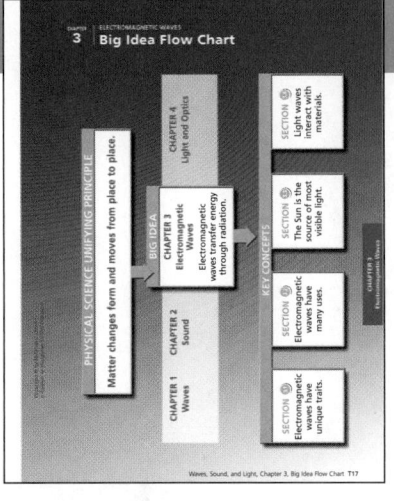

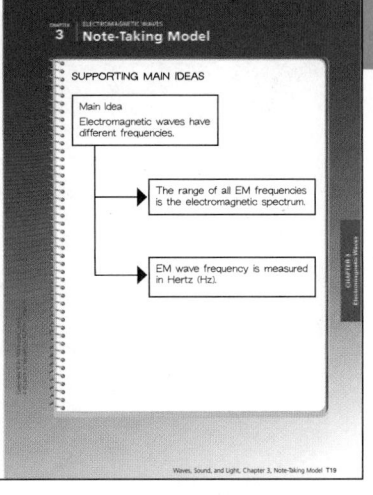

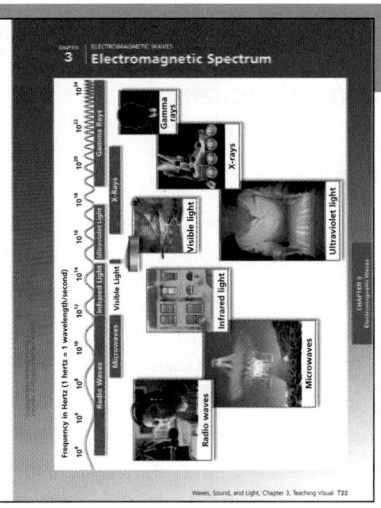

T **UNIT TRANSPARENCY BOOK,** p. T17　　　**T** p. T19　　　**T** p. T22

MORE SUPPORT

Reinforcing Key Concepts for each section

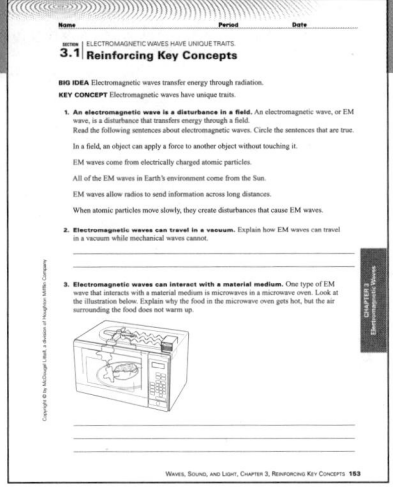

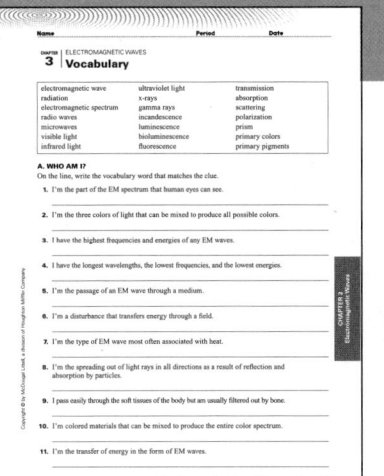

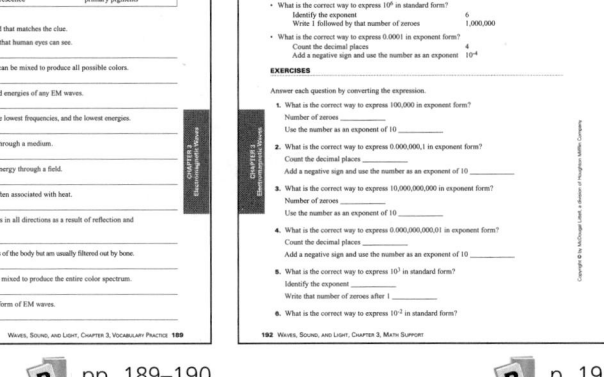

R **UNIT RESOURCE BOOK,** p. 153　　　**R** pp. 189–190　　　**R** p. 192

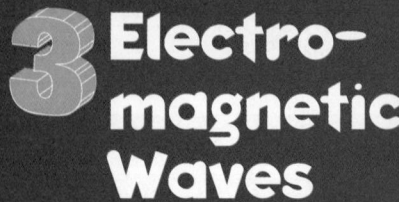
INTRODUCE

the BIG idea

Have students look at the photograph of the cell phone user and discuss how the question in the box links to the Big Idea:

• If waves are involved in cell phone technology, what kind of waves might they be?

• How can waves travel from one cell phone to another?

• What other devices use the same kind of waves as a cell phone?

National Science Education Standards

Content

B.3.c Light interacts with matter by transmission, absorption, and scattering.

B.3.f The Sun is a major source of energy for changes on Earth's surface. Energy from the Sun is transferred to Earth in the form of visible light, infrared, and ultraviolet radiation.

Process

A.2–8 Design and conduct an investigation; use tools to gather and interpret data; use evidence to describe, predict, explain, model; think critically to make relationships between evidence and explanation; recognize different explanations and predictions; communicate scientific procedures and explanations; use mathematics.

A.9.a–f Understand scientific inquiry by using different investigations, methods, mathematics, technology, and explanations based on logic, evidence, and skepticism.

E.2–5 Design, implement, and evaluate a solution or product; communicate technological design.

F.4.c–d Risks and benefits

F.5.c Science and technology in society

CHAPTER

Electromagnetic Waves

the BIG idea

Electromagnetic waves transfer energy through radiation.

How does this phone stay connected?

Key Concepts

**SECTION
3.1 Electromagnetic waves have unique traits.** Learn how electromagnetic waves differ from mechanical waves.

**SECTION
3.2 Electromagnetic waves have many uses.** Learn about the behaviors and uses of different types of electromagnetic waves.

**SECTION
3.3 The Sun is the source of most visible light.** Learn about the natural and artificial production of light.

**SECTION
3.4 Light waves interact with materials.** Learn how light waves behave in a material medium.

Internet Preview

CLASSZONE.COM

Chapter 3 online resources: Content Review, Simulation, Visualization, two Resource Centers, Math Tutorial, Test Practice.

INTERNET PREVIEW

CLASSZONE.COM For student use with the following pages:

Review and Practice
• Content Review, pp. 72, 102
• Math Tutorial: Positive and Negative Exponents, p. 78
• Test Practice, p. 105

Activities and Resources
• Internet Activity: EM Waves, p. 71
• Visualization: EM Waves, p. 74
• Resource Centers: EM Spectrum, p. 80; Visible Light, p. 88

NSTA scilinks.org *SCiLINKS*

Light and Color
Code: MDL029

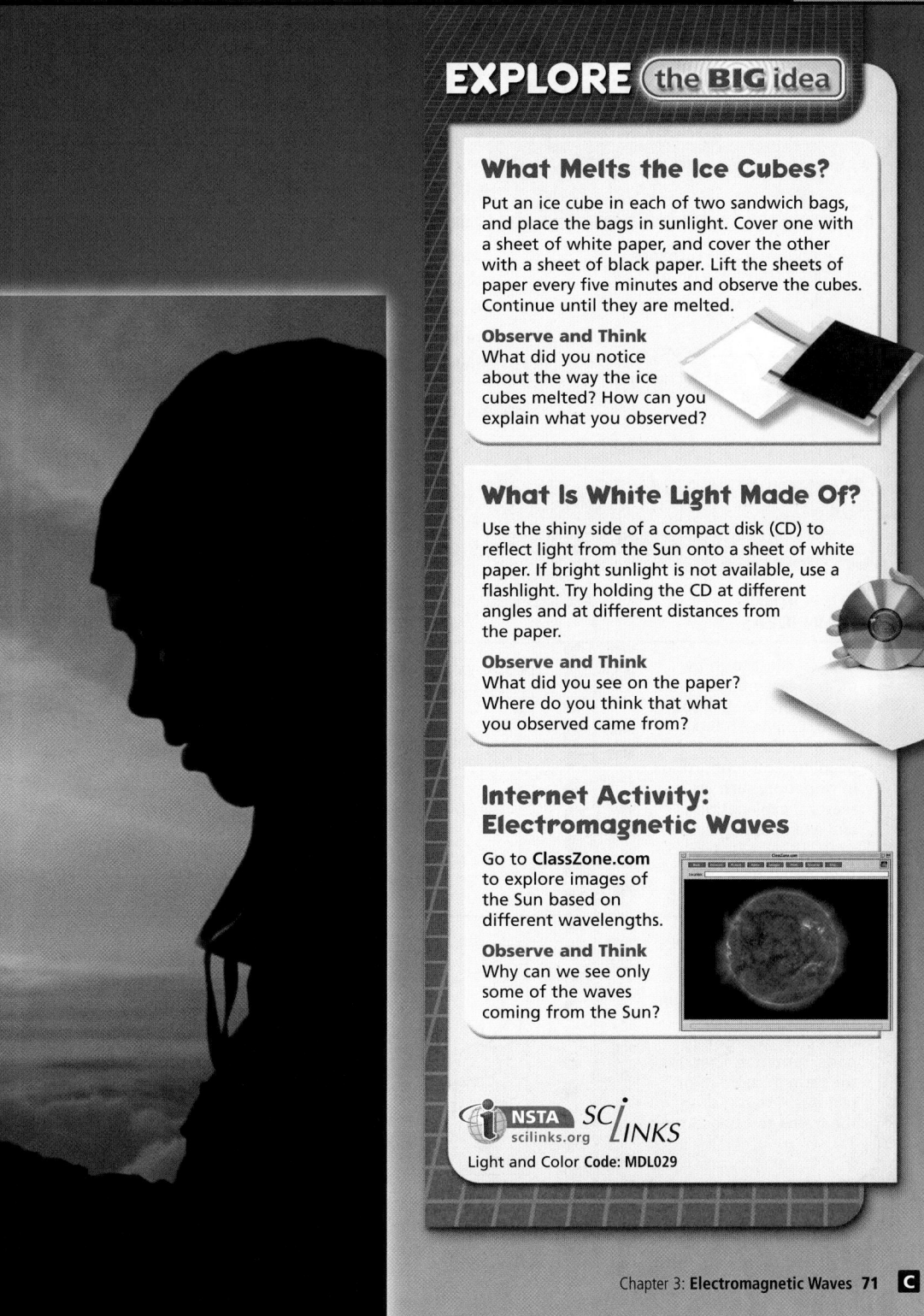

EXPLORE (the BIG idea)

What Melts the Ice Cubes?

Put an ice cube in each of two sandwich bags, and place the bags in sunlight. Cover one with a sheet of white paper, and cover the other with a sheet of black paper. Lift the sheets of paper every five minutes and observe the cubes. Continue until they are melted.

Observe and Think
What did you notice about the way the ice cubes melted? How can you explain what you observed?

What Is White Light Made Of?

Use the shiny side of a compact disk (CD) to reflect light from the Sun onto a sheet of white paper. If bright sunlight is not available, use a flashlight. Try holding the CD at different angles and at different distances from the paper.

Observe and Think
What did you see on the paper? Where do you think that what you observed came from?

Internet Activity: Electromagnetic Waves

Go to **ClassZone.com** to explore images of the Sun based on different wavelengths.

Observe and Think
Why can we see only some of the waves coming from the Sun?

NSTA
scilinks.org
SC_INKS

Light and Color **Code: MDL029**

TEACHING WITH TECHNOLOGY

CBL and Probeware If probeware is available, students can use temperature-sensing probes instead of thermometers for "Investigate the Electromagnetic Spectrum" on p. 84.

Digital Camera Take photographs of each step during "Investigate Mixing Colors" on p. 98 to document the activity. Use the camera to show time-elapsed images of the ink samples, taking photographs every few minutes to show how the samples have changed. Compare the final images.

EXPLORE (the BIG idea)

These inquiry-based activities are appropriate for use at home or as a supplement to classroom instruction.

What Melts the Ice Cubes?

PURPOSE To observe the difference between reflection and absorption of EM radiation. Students observe different amounts of light energy absorbed by black paper and white paper.

TIP *10 min.* The two ice cubes should be the same size when they are placed in the bags. Students can also try covering a bag with aluminum foil, shiny side out, and observe the rate of melting.

Answer: The cube under the black paper melts more quickly. The black paper gets hotter in the sun because it absorbs more light than the white paper.

REVISIT after p. 97.

What Is White Light Made Of?

PURPOSE To observe that white light is made up of different wavelengths and individual colors. Students use a CD as a prism to separate white light.

TIP *10 min.* Prompt students to think about why the silver CD reflects different colors and why the colors change as the CD moves.

Answer: A rainbow of colors from the light being reflected by the CD. The colors were part of the light.

REVISIT after p. 97.

Internet Activity: Electromagnetic Waves

PURPOSE To see that the Sun emits different wavelengths and that they must be detected and visualized in different ways.

TIP *20 min.* Before they use the simulation, have students predict how the different types of EM radiation coming from the Sun will look.

Answer: The human eye can detect waves only in the visible range.

REVISIT after p. 85.

PREPARE

○ CONCEPT REVIEW
Activate Prior Knowledge

- Give students a list of phrases or objects that waves travel through. Be sure to include "vacuum" or "outer space."
- Ask if there is any place or object on the list that a mechanical wave cannot travel through. *yes; vacuum*
- Ask how speed of sound is affected by different mediums on the list. *Answers should recognize that sound travels faster in denser materials and not at all in a vacuum.*

○ TAKING NOTES

Supporting Main Ideas

Making a chart of the main ideas will help students organize the material in the chapter. Using the section's heads is a good start; students can then add information, explanations, and examples that support these ideas.

Vocabulary Strategy

By surrounding each vocabulary term with examples and descriptions, students will develop a thorough understanding of the meaning of each term. Respellings should be included if appropriate.

Vocabulary and Note-Taking Resources

- Vocabulary Practice, pp. 189–190
- Decoding Support, p. 191

- Daily Vocabulary Scaffolding, p. T18
- Note-Taking Model, p. T19

- Frame Game, B26–27
- Supporting Main Ideas, C42
- Daily Vocabulary Scaffolding, H1–8

○ CONCEPT REVIEW

- A wave is a disturbance that transfers energy.
- Mechanical waves have a medium.
- Waves can be measured.
- Waves react to a change in medium.

○ VOCABULARY REVIEW

mechanical wave p. 11
wavelength p. 17
frequency p. 17
reflection p. 25
field *See Glossary.*

 CONTENT REVIEW
CLASSZONE.COM
Review concepts and vocabulary.

▶ TAKING NOTES

SUPPORTING MAIN IDEAS

Make a chart to show main ideas and the information that supports them. Copy each blue heading. Below each heading, add supporting information, such as reasons, explanations, and examples.

VOCABULARY STRATEGY

Write each new vocabulary term in the center of a **frame game** diagram. Decide what information to frame it with. Use examples, descriptions, parts, sentences that use the term in context, or pictures. You can change the frame to fit each term.

See the Note-Taking Handbook on pages R45–R51.

C 72 Unit: Waves, Sound, and Light

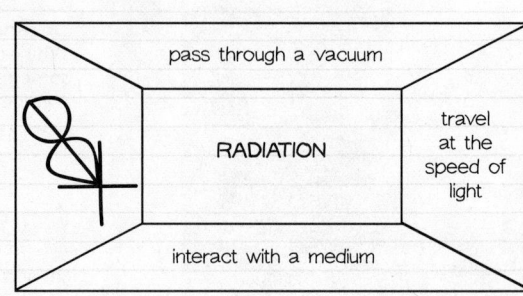

SCIENCE NOTEBOOK

MAIN IDEA
Electromagnetic waves have unique properties.

EM waves are disturbances in a field rather than in a medium.

EM waves can travel through a vacuum.

EM waves travel at the speed of light.

pass through a vacuum

RADIATION

travel at the speed of light

interact with a medium

CHECK READINESS

Administer the Diagnostic Test to determine students' readiness for new science content and their mastery of requisite math skills.

 Diagnostic Test, pp. 40–41

Technology Resources

Students needing content and math skills should visit **ClassZone.com**.

- CONTENT REVIEW
- MATH TUTORIAL

 CONTENT REVIEW CD-ROM

KEY CONCEPT

Electromagnetic waves have unique traits.

◀ **BEFORE, you learned**

- Waves transfer energy
- Mechanical waves need a medium to travel

▶ **NOW, you will learn**

- How electromagnetic waves differ from mechanical waves
- Where electromagnetic waves come from
- How electromagnetic waves transfer energy

VOCABULARY

electromagnetic
wave p. 73
radiation p. 75

EXPLORE Electromagnetic Waves

How does the signal from a remote control travel?

PROCEDURE

① Turn the TV on and off using the remote control.

② Work with a partner to try to turn on the TV by aiming the remote control at the mirror.

WHAT DO YOU THINK?
How did you have to position the remote control and the mirror in order to operate the TV? Why do you think this worked?

MATERIALS
- TV with remote control unit
- mirror with stand

An electromagnetic wave is a disturbance in a field.

Did you know that you are surrounded by thousands of waves at this very moment? Waves fill every cubic centimeter of the space around you. They collide with or pass through your body all the time.

Most of these waves are invisible, but you can perceive many of them. Light is made up of these waves, and heat can result from them. Whenever you use your eyes to see, or feel the warmth of the Sun on your skin, you are detecting their presence. These waves also allow radios, TVs, and cell phones to send or receive information over long distances. These waves have the properties shared by all waves, yet they are different from mechanical waves in important ways. This second type of wave is called an electromagnetic wave. An **electromagnetic wave** (ih-LEHK-troh-mag-NEHT-ihk) is a disturbance that transfers energy through a field. Electromagnetic waves are also called EM (EE-EHM) waves.

VOCABULARY
Create a frame game diagram for the term *electromagnetic wave.*

Chapter 3: Electromagnetic Waves **73** **C**

RESOURCES FOR DIFFERENTIATED INSTRUCTION

Below Level

UNIT RESOURCE BOOK
- Reading Study Guide A, pp. 145–146
- Decoding Support, p. 191

 **AUDIO CDS**

Advanced

UNIT RESOURCE BOOK
- Challenge and Extension, p. 162
- Challenge Reading, pp. 187–188

English Learners

UNIT RESOURCE BOOK
Spanish Reading Study Guide, pp. 149–150

 **AUDIO CDS**

- Audio Readings in Spanish
- Audio Readings (English)

◉ Set Learning Goals
Students will

- Explain how EM waves differ from mechanical waves.
- Identify the sources of EM waves.
- Recognize how EM waves transfer energy.
- Observe through an experiment how EM waves interact with matter.

◀ 3-Minute Warm-Up

Display Transparency 20 or copy this exercise on the board:

Are these statements true? If not, correct them.

1. Mechanical waves transfer energy through a vacuum. *Mechanical waves transfer energy through a medium.*

2. A wave is a disturbance that transfers energy. *true*

3. Most EM waves are invisible but detectable. *true*

 3-Minute Warm-Up, p. T20

3.1 MOTIVATE

EXPLORE Electromagnetic Waves

PURPOSE To show that EM waves can be reflected

TIP *10 min.* Stick a hand-held mirror into a blob of modeling clay if you don't have a mirror with a stand.

WHAT DO YOU THINK? *The remote control has to be aimed so that its beam reflects off the mirror in the same direction that light would, showing that EM waves can be reflected.*

Teach from Visuals

To help students interpret the visual of an electromagnetic wave, review the parts of a wave (such as trough and crest) and ask:

- How is the wavelength of the wave in the figure measured? *from one trough to another*

- What is the geometrical relationship between the magnetic and the electrical fields? *The fields are at right angles to each other.*

- How would a diagram of a wave with lower frequency differ from the wave in the figure? *The crests would be farther apart.*

Ongoing Assessment

Explain how EM waves differ from mechanical waves.

Ask: How do EM and mechanical waves differ in the way they form? *EM waves form when moving charged particles transfer energy through a field. Mechanical waves form when energy is transferred to particles of matter in a material medium.*

Identify the sources of EM waves.

Ask: Why do we receive so few EM waves from stars other than the Sun? *They are so far away from Earth.*

 **CHECK YOUR READING** *Answer: electric and magnetic*

 **CHECK YOUR READING** *Answer: the Sun and human technology*

A field is an area around an object where the object can apply a force—a push or a pull—to another object without touching it. You have seen force applied through a field if you have ever seen a magnet holding a card on the door of a refrigerator. The magnet exerts a pull on the door, even though it does not touch the door. The magnet exerts a force through the magnetic field that surrounds the magnet. When a disturbance occurs in a field rather than in a medium, the wave that results is an electromagnetic wave.

How EM Waves Form

 **VISUALIZATION** CLASSZONE.COM
Learn more about the nature of EM waves. **A**

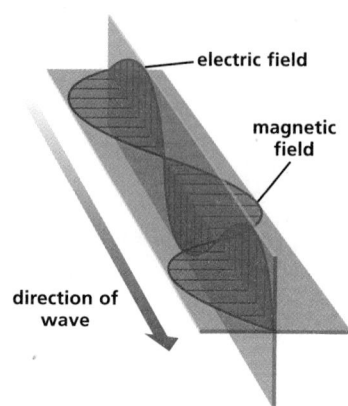

electric field

magnetic field

direction of wave

EM waves come from atomic particles that are electrically charged. Because of their charges, these particles can exert a force—a push or a pull—on one another through an electric field. These particles also create the magnetic fields that make magnets work.

When electrically charged particles move quickly, they can start a disturbance or vibration in their electric and magnetic fields. **B** The fields vibrate at right angles to each other, as shown in the diagram above. The EM wave travels in the form of these vibrating fields. As you read in Chapter 1, all waves have the properties of amplitude, wavelength, and frequency. In an EM wave, as the diagram shows, both the electric and the magnetic fields have these three properties.

 **CHECK YOUR READING** What are the two types of fields that make up an EM wave?

Sources of EM Waves

Many of the EM waves present in Earth's environment come from the Sun. The Sun's high energy allows it to give off countless EM waves. Other stars give off as many EM waves as the Sun, but because these bodies are so far away, fewer of their EM waves reach Earth. In addition to the Sun, technology is a source of EM waves that humans use for a wide variety of purposes.

When EM waves enter a material, the material often responds by giving off more EM waves. Many EM waves in the environment are given off by the surface of the Earth in response to EM waves from the Sun.

 **CHECK YOUR READING** What is the source of most EM waves in Earth's environment?

DIFFERENTIATE INSTRUCTION

 More Reading Support

A Where do EM waves come from? *electrically charged atomic particles*

B In what form does an EM wave travel? *as vibrating electric and magnetic fields*

English Learners English learners may have difficulty with nouns that are also used as adjectives. For example, "An EM wave can travel without any medium at all . . . " (p.75). Here, the word *medium* is used as a noun. Help English learners understand that for a word to be an adjective it must describe a noun.

Advanced Have students who are interested in the speed of light read the following article:

R Challenge Reading, pp. 187–188

Electromagnetic waves can travel in a vacuum.

The transfer of energy in the form of EM waves is called **radiation** (RAY-dee-AY-shuhn). Radiation is different from the transfer of energy through a medium by a mechanical wave. A mechanical wave must vibrate the medium as it moves, and this uses some of the wave's energy. Eventually, every mechanical wave will give up all of its energy to the medium and disappear. An EM wave can travel without any medium at all—that is, in a vacuum or space empty of matter—and does not lose energy as it moves. In theory, an EM wave can travel forever.

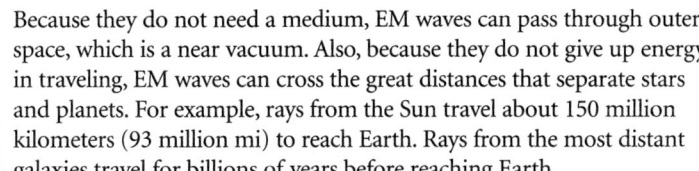

READING TiP

EM waves are also called rays. The words *radiation* and *radiate* come from the Latin word *radius*, which means "ray" or "spoke of a wheel."

How EM Waves Travel in a Vacuum

Because they do not need a medium, EM waves can pass through outer space, which is a near vacuum. Also, because they do not give up energy in traveling, EM waves can cross the great distances that separate stars and planets. For example, rays from the Sun travel about 150 million kilometers (93 million mi) to reach Earth. Rays from the most distant galaxies travel for billions of years before reaching Earth.

In a vacuum, EM waves spread outward in all directions from the source of the disturbance. The waves then travel in a straight line until something interferes with them. The farther the waves move from their source, the more they spread out. As they spread out, there are fewer waves in a given area and less energy is transferred. Only a very small part of the energy radiated from the Sun is transferred to Earth. But that energy is still a great amount—enough to sustain life on the planet.

The Speed of EM Waves in a Vacuum

In a vacuum, EM waves travel at a constant speed, and they travel very fast—about 300,000 kilometers (186,000 mi) per second. In 1 second, an EM wave can travel a distance greater than 7 times the distance around Earth. Even at this speed, rays from the Sun take about 8 minutes to reach Earth. This constant speed is called the speed of light. The vast distances of space are often measured in units of time traveled at this speed. For example, the Sun is about 8 light-minutes away from Earth. The galaxy shown in the photograph is 60 million light-years from Earth.

The light and other EM waves from this galaxy took approximately 60 million years to reach Earth.

CHECK YOUR READING How are EM waves used to measure distances in space?

Address Misconceptions

IDENTIFY Ask: What happens to an EM wave when it travels? If students respond that the EM wave must pass through matter, they may hold the misconception that a medium is necessary for an EM wave to continue through.

CORRECT Light waves from the Sun can travel through outer space to Earth, but sound waves, which need a medium, cannot. So we can see the Sun, but not hear it. (Actually, the Sun's sound waves are at frequencies too low for humans to hear.) Point out that light waves do not need matter to travel.

REASSESS Have students list examples of waves that need a medium to travel and waves that do not need a medium.

Technology Resources

Visit **ClassZone.com** for background on common student misconceptions.

MISCONCEPTION DATABASE

History of Science

In the nineteenth century, scientists believed that light must travel through a hypothetical substance called "ether" that filled space. It was not until 1887 that Albert Michelson and Edward Morley demonstrated that ether does not exist.

Ongoing Assessment

CHECK YOUR READING *Answer: by the time it takes an EM wave to travel at the speed of light from one place to another*

DIFFERENTIATE INSTRUCTION

More Reading Support

C Why can EM waves travel in a vacuum? *They do not need a medium.*

D What do we call the time it takes for the Sun's rays to hit Earth? *the speed of light*

Advanced Challenge students to use a calculator to answer: If light from a galaxy takes 60 million years to reach Earth, about how far away is it? *about 6×10^{20} km*

Calculations: First, find seconds in a year: $60 \cdot 60 = 3,600 \cdot 24 = 86,400 \cdot 365 = 31,536,000$ Second, find distance for 1 year: $300,000 \cdot 31,536,000 = 9.4608 \cdot 10^{12}$ Third, find distance for 60 million years: $(9.4608 \cdot 10^{12}) \cdot (6 \cdot 10^{7}) = 5.67648 \cdot 10^{20} = 6 \cdot 10^{20}$ km

Challenge and Extension, p. 151

INVESTIGATE Wave Behavior

PURPOSE To design an experiment to determine what makes a radiometer's vanes move

TIPS *30 min.* Allow students a few minutes to explore, then suggest the following:

• Aim a light at various parts of the radiometer.

• Remind students that the energy in light can be converted to heat.

WHAT DO YOU THINK? *The vanes turn with the white side forward and the black side on the back. Yes, light appears to push on the dark surfaces but not on the light surfaces. Answers will vary depending on student designs.*

CHALLENGE *The radiometer measures the relative brightness of the light falling on the radiometer. The brighter the light, the faster it spins.*

 Datasheet, Wave Behavior, p. 152

Metacognitive Strategy

Ask students if they are convinced that EM waves interact with matter. Have them write a paragraph that explains when they realized this interaction, or what doubts they still have and another experiment they would like to try.

Ongoing Assessment

Recognize how EM waves transfer energy.

Ask: What happens when EM waves encounter a material medium? *They transfer energy to the medium.*

CHECK YOUR READING *Answer: They transfer energy by moving potential energy from place to place.*

Electromagnetic waves can interact with a material medium.

When EM waves encounter a material medium, they can interact with it in much the same way that mechanical waves do. They can transfer energy to the medium itself. Also, EM waves can respond to a change of medium by reflecting, refracting, or diffracting, just as mechanical waves do. When an EM wave responds in one of these ways, its direction changes. When the direction of the wave changes, the direction in which the energy is transferred also changes.

Transferring Energy

▼ **REMINDER**
Potential energy comes from position or form; kinetic energy comes from motion.

A mechanical wave transfers energy in two ways. As it travels, the wave moves potential energy from one place to another. It also converts potential energy into kinetic energy by moving the medium back and forth.

In a vacuum, EM waves transfer energy only by moving potential energy from one place to another. But when EM waves encounter matter, their energy can be converted into many different forms.

▲ **CHECK YOUR READING** In what form do EM waves transfer energy in a vacuum?

INVESTIGATE Wave Behavior

How do EM waves interact with matter?

PROCEDURE

① Observe the radiometer on a table or desk.

② Write a hypothesis in the form of an "If . . . , then . . . , because . . ." statement to answer the question: What makes the radiometer vanes move?

③ Develop an experiment to test your hypothesis.

WHAT DO YOU THINK?

• How does light affect the vanes?

• Based on your observation of the vanes, does light affect the white and black surfaces differently? If so, how?

• How would you modify your design now that you have seen the results?

CHALLENGE Based on your observations, what does a radiometer measure? Explain your answer.

DESIGN
— YOUR OWN —
EXPERIMENT

SKILL FOCUS
Designing experiments

MATERIALS
radiometer

TIME
30 minutes

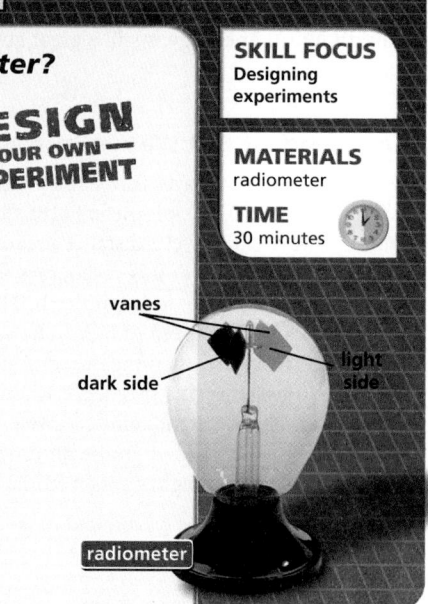

vanes

dark side

light side

radiometer

DIFFERENTIATE INSTRUCTION

? More Reading Support

E What does an EM wave transfer to the medium? *energy*

Below Level Students may have a hard time visualizing how a wave responds to a change of medium. Have them draw diagrams showing how a wave changes direction when it is reflected, refracted, and diffracted by a change of medium.

Converting Energy from One Form to Another

How EM waves interact with a medium depends on the type of the wave and the nature of the material. For example, a microwave oven uses a type of EM wave called microwaves. Microwaves pass through air with very little interaction. However, they reflect off the oven's fan and sides. But when microwaves encounter water, such as that inside a potato, their energy is converted into thermal energy. As a result, the potato gets cooked, but the oven remains cool.

reflecting fan

microwave source

microwaves

① A device on the oven produces microwaves and sends them toward the reflecting fan.

② Microwaves are reflected in many directions by the blades of the fan and then again by the sides of the oven.

③ Microwaves move through the air without transferring energy to the air.

④ Microwaves transfer energy to the water molecules inside the potato in the form of heat, cooking the potato.

EM waves usually become noticeable and useful when they transfer energy to a medium. You do not observe the microwaves in a microwave oven. All you observe is the potato cooking. In the rest of this chapter, you will learn about different types of EM waves, including microwaves, and about how people use them.

 **CHECK YOUR READING** How does microwave cooking depend on reflection?

3.1 Review

KEY CONCEPTS

1. How are EM waves different from mechanical waves?

2. What are two sources of EM waves in Earth's environment?

3. How can EM waves transfer energy differently in a material medium as compared to a vacuum?

CRITICAL THINKING

4. **Predict** What would happen to an EM wave that never came into contact with matter?

5. **Infer** What might be one cause of uneven heating in a microwave oven?

◯ CHALLENGE

6. **Synthesize** EM waves can interact with a medium. How might this fact be used to make a device for detecting a particular type of EM radiation?

ANSWERS

1. EM waves can travel through a vacuum, while mechanical waves need a material medium; EM waves travel at speed of light, while speed of mechanical waves varies and is slower.

2. the Sun and human technology

3. In a vacuum, EM waves move potential energy from one place to another. In a material medium, they can both move potential energy and convert energy into other forms.

4. It would continue to travel indefinitely.

5. uneven distribution of microwaves by the fan, or uneven reflection by sides of the oven

6. Sample answer: Since infrared rays warm things, a device with a thermometer could be used to detect infrared radiation.

Set Learning Goal

To gain skill in converting decimals to exponents and vice versa

Present the Science

The use of exponents makes working with very large and very small numbers easier. EM waves can have frequencies as great as a trillion trillion wavelengths per second and have wavelengths as small as trillionths of a centimeter. Working with so many zeros or decimal places is confusing and can lead to errors.

Develop Number Sense

Students should be proficient at using exponents before they begin the next section.

Emphasize that the final decimal place is counted when converting a decimal into exponent form and that the first integer of a large number is not counted when converting a large number.

DIFFERENTIATION TIP Demonstrate several conversion problems on the board before below-level students do the problems in the text.

Close

Ask: In what branches of science are numbers in exponent form used?
Sample answer: in astronomy to represent vast distances of space; in microbiology to count large numbers of microbes

• Math Support, p. 192
• Math Practice, p. 193

Technology Resources

Students can visit **ClassZone.com** for practice using exponents.

 MATH TUTORIAL

MATH in SCIENCE

MATH TUTORIAL
CLASSZONE.COM
Click on Math Tutorial for more help with positive and negative exponents.

The top photograph shows a visible-light image of the Crab Nebula. The bottom photograph shows the same nebula as it appears at higher x-ray frequencies.

SKILL: USING EXPONENTS

EM Frequencies

The Chandra X-Ray Observatory in the photograph is a space telescope that detects high-frequency EM waves called x-rays. A wave's frequency is the number of wavelengths that pass a given point in 1 second. EM frequencies usually run from about 100 wavelengths per second to about 1 trillion trillion wavelengths per second. If written in standard form (using zeros), 1 trillion trillion would look like this:

1,000,000,000,000,000,000,000,000

Because this number is hard to read, it would be helpful to write it more simply. Using exponents, 1 trillion trillion can be written as 10^{24}.

Exponents can also be used to simplify very small numbers. For example, the wavelength of a wave with a frequency of 10^{24} is about one ten-thousandth of one trillionth of a meter. That number can be written in standard form as **0.000,000,000,000,000,1 m.** Using exponents, the number can be written more simply as 10^{-16} **m.**

Examples

Large Numbers
To write a multiple of 10 in exponent form, just count the zeros. Then, use the total as the exponent.
(1) 10,000 has 4 zeros.
(2) 4 is the exponent.
ANSWER 10^4 is the way to write 10,000 using exponents.

Decimals
To convert a decimal into exponent form, count the number of places to the right of the decimal point. Then, use the total with a negative sign as the exponent.
(1) 0.000,001 has 6 places to the right of the decimal point.
(2) Add a negative sign to make the exponent –6.
ANSWER 10^{-6} is the way to write 0.000,001 using exponents.

Answer the following questions.

Write each number using an exponent.
1. 10,000,000	**3.** 100,000	**5.** 10,000,000,000
2. 0.000,01	**4.** 0.0001	**6.** 0.000,000,001

Write the number in standard form.
7. 10^8	**9.** 10^{11}	**11.** 10^{17}
8. 10^{-8}	**10.** 10^{-12}	**12.** 10^{-15}

CHALLENGE Using exponents, multiply 10^2 by 10^3. Explain how you got your result.

ANSWERS

1. 10^7	5. 10^{-4}	9. 100,000,000,000,000,000
2. 10^5	6. 10^{-9}	10. 0.000,000,01
3. 10^{10}	7. 100,000,000	11. 0.000,000,000,001
4. 10^{-5}	8. 100,000,000,000	12. 0.000,000,000,000,001

CHALLENGE *10^5; multiply powers of 10 by adding exponents.*

KEY CONCEPT

3.2 Electromagnetic waves have many uses.

◄ **BEFORE, you learned**
- EM waves transfer energy through fields
- EM waves have measurable properties
- EM waves interact with matter

▶ **NOW, you will learn**
- How EM waves differ from one another
- How different types of EM waves are used

VOCABULARY

electromagnetic spectrum p. 80
radio waves p. 82
microwaves p. 83
visible light p. 84
infrared light p. 84
ultraviolet light p. 85
x-rays p. 86
gamma rays p. 86

EXPLORE Radio Waves

How can you make radio waves?

PROCEDURE

1. Tape one end of one length of wire to one end of the battery. Tape one end of the second wire to the other end of the battery.

2. Wrap the loose end of one of the wires tightly around the handle of the fork.

3. Turn on the radio to the AM band and move the selector past all stations until you reach static.

4. Hold the fork close to the radio. Gently pull the free end of wire across the fork's prongs.

MATERIALS
- two 25 cm lengths of copper wire
- C or D battery
- electrical tape
- metal fork
- portable radio

WHAT DO YOU THINK?
- What happens when you stroke the prongs with the wire?
- How does changing the position of the dial affect the results?

▼ **REMINDER**
Remember that frequency is the number of wavelengths that pass a given point per second. The shorter the wavelength, the higher the frequency.

EM waves have different frequencies.

It might seem hard to believe that the same form of energy browns your toast, brings you broadcast television, and makes the page you are now reading visible. Yet EM waves make each of these events possible. The various types of EM waves differ from each other in their wavelengths and frequencies.

The frequency of an EM wave also determines its characteristics and uses. Higher-frequency EM waves, with more electromagnetic vibrations per second, have more energy. Lower-frequency EM waves, with longer wavelengths, have less energy.

Chapter 3: **Electromagnetic Waves** 79 **C**

RESOURCES FOR DIFFERENTIATED INSTRUCTION

Below Level
UNIT RESOURCE BOOK
- Reading Study Guide A, pp. 156–157
- Decoding Support, p. 191

 **AUDIO CDS**

 Additional INVESTIGATION,
Seeing the Invisible, A, B, & C, pp. 203–211; Teacher Instructions, pp. 284–285

Advanced
UNIT RESOURCE BOOK
Challenge and Extension, p. 162

English Learners
UNIT RESOURCE BOOK
Spanish Reading Study Guide, pp. 160–161

AUDIO CDS
- Audio Readings in Spanish
- Audio Readings (English)

3.2 FOCUS

◖ Set Learning Goals
Students will
- Distinguish how EM waves differ from one another.
- Describe how different types of EM waves are used.
- Observe how to detect invisible light.

◖ 3-Minute Warm-Up
Display Transparency 20 or copy this exercise on the board:

Match each definition to the correct term.

Definitions
1. The transfer of energy by EM waves *b*
2. A disturbance that transfers energy through a field *a*

Terms
a. electromagnetic wave   c. medium
b. radiation   d. vacuum

T 3-Minute Warm-Up, p. T20

3.2 MOTIVATE

EXPLORE Radio Waves
PURPOSE To introduce radio waves, how they are formed, and how they are detected

TIP *10 min.* Have students listen to the static as they vary the speed at which the wire is drawn across the fork.

WHAT DO YOU THINK? *Static is produced. The sound of the static may change from one frequency to another.*

Ongoing Assessment
Distinguish how EM waves differ from one another.

Ask: How does a radio wave differ from a microwave? *in wavelength and frequency*

Teach from Visuals

To help students interpret the diagram of the EM spectrum, point out the various parts. Ask:

- What is the smallest portion of the spectrum? *visible light*
- What is the frequency range of microwaves? *roughly 10^8 to 10^{12} hertz*
- Where do X-rays fall on the spectrum? *at the high-frequency end*

 The visual "The Electromagnetic Spectrum" is also available as T22 in the Unit Transparency Book.

RESOURCE CENTER
CLASSZONE.COM

Learn more about the electromagnetic spectrum.

The Electromagnetic Spectrum

The range of all EM frequencies is known as the **electromagnetic spectrum** (SPEHK-truhm), or EM spectrum. The spectrum can be represented by a diagram like the one below. On the left are the waves with the longest wavelengths and the lowest frequencies and energies. Toward the right, the wavelengths become shorter, and the frequencies and energies become higher. The diagram also shows different parts of the spectrum: radio waves, microwaves, infrared light, visible light, ultraviolet light, x-rays, and gamma rays.

The EM spectrum is a smooth, gradual progression from the lowest frequencies to the highest. Divisions between the different parts of the spectrum are useful, but not exact. As you can see from the diagram below, some of the sections overlap.

The Electromagnetic Spectrum

Frequency in Hertz (1 hertz = 1 wavelength/second)

| 10^4 | 10^5 | 10^6 | 10^7 | 10^8 | 10^9 | 10^{10} | 10^{11} | 10^{12} | 10^{13} |

Radio Waves | Infrared Light

Microwaves

This woman is speaking on the radio. **Radio waves** are used for radio and television broadcasts. They are also used for cordless phones, garage door openers, alarm systems, and baby monitors.

Not all astronomy involves looking at the sky. Telescopes like the one above pick up **microwaves** from space. Microwaves are also used for radar, cell phones, ovens, and satellite communications.

The amount of **infrared light** an object gives off depends on its warmth. Above, different colors indicate different amounts of infrared light.

DIFFERENTIATE INSTRUCTION

? More Reading Support

A Describe the EM waves at the left end of the EM spectrum. *They have the longest wavelengths and the lowest frequencies and energies.*

Inclusion Make a large copy of the EM spectrum on shelf paper and display it in the classroom.

Divide the class into seven groups. Have each group make a poster, containing information and examples about one type of EM wave shown on the spectrum. Students who are visually impaired can contribute ideas for tactile or aural representations of waves. Those with hearing impairments can create or obtain visuals of examples for each type. Display posters in their proper position on the spectrum.

Measuring EM Waves

B

All EM waves move at the same speed in a vacuum. The frequency of an EM wave is determined from its wavelength. EM wavelengths run from about 30 kilometers for the lowest-frequency radio waves to trillionths of a centimeter for gamma rays. EM waves travel so quickly that even those with the largest wavelengths have very high frequencies. For example, a low-energy radio wave with a wavelength of 30 kilometers has a frequency of 10,000 wavelengths per second.

C

EM wave frequency is measured in hertz (Hz). One hertz equals one wavelength per second. The frequency of the 30-kilometer radio wave mentioned above would be 10,000 Hz. Gamma ray frequencies reach trillions of trillions of hertz.

CHECK YOUR READING Why is wavelength all you need to know to calculate EM wave frequency in a vacuum?

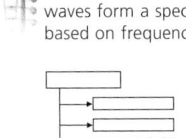

SUPPORTING MAIN IDEAS Write details that support the main idea that EM waves form a spectrum based on frequency.

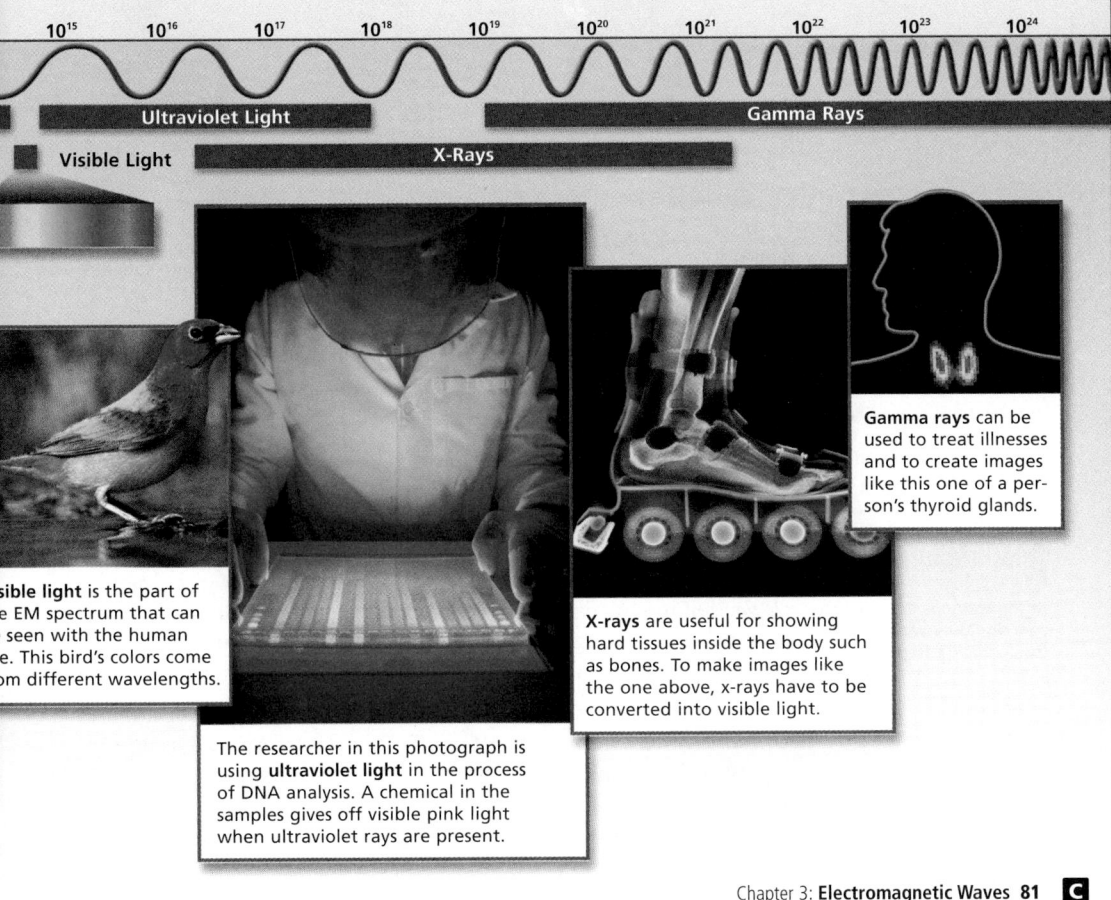

| 10^{15} | 10^{16} | 10^{17} | 10^{18} | 10^{19} | 10^{20} | 10^{21} | 10^{22} | 10^{23} | 10^{24} |

Ultraviolet Light

Gamma Rays

Visible Light

X-Rays

Gamma rays can be used to treat illnesses and to create images like this one of a person's thyroid glands.

X-rays are useful for showing hard tissues inside the body such as bones. To make images like the one above, x-rays have to be converted into visible light.

sible light is the part of e EM spectrum that can e seen with the human e. This bird's colors come om different wavelengths.

The researcher in this photograph is using **ultraviolet light** in the process of DNA analysis. A chemical in the samples gives off visible pink light when ultraviolet rays are present.

Chapter 3: **Electromagnetic Waves** 81 **C**

Integrate the Sciences

Many objects in space emit X-rays, radio waves, infrared light, or ultraviolet light as well as visible light. Newly developed devices can detect these EM waves and provide pictures of objects in the universe. You can see on the Internet some of the photographs that have been taken with these devices.

Develop Critical Thinking

APPLY Ask students to describe the mathematical relationship between frequency and wavelength. *As the frequency of a wave increases, its wavelength decreases. This is an inverse relationship. The frequency of any EM wave times its wavelength is always a constant—the speed of the wave in a vacuum (300,000 kilometers per second).*

Ongoing Assessment

CHECK YOUR READING *Answer: The speed of an EM wave in a vacuum is a constant. If you know the wavelength, you know both wavelength and speed, which are enough to calculate frequency.*

DIFFERENTIATE INSTRUCTION

 **More Reading Support**

B What part of the wave determines frequency? *wavelength*

C What is the unit of measurement of EM wave frequency? *hertz*

Alternative Assessment Give students copies of the EM spectrum that have the ranges marked but not labeled. Have students label each range of frequencies. The finished diagram should look like the spectrum on pp. 80 and 81.

Radio waves and microwaves have long wavelengths and low frequencies.

Radio waves are EM waves that have the longest wavelengths, the lowest frequencies, and the lowest energies. Radio waves travel easily through the atmosphere and many materials. People have developed numerous technologies to take advantage of the properties of radio waves.

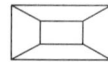

Radio Waves

Radio was the first technology to use EM waves for telecommunication, which is communication over long distances. A radio transmitter converts sound waves into radio waves and broadcasts them through the air in different directions. Radio receivers in many locations pick up the radio waves and convert them back into sound waves.

① Sound waves enter the microphone and are converted into electrical impulses.

② The electrical impulses are converted into radio waves and broadcast by the transmitter.

③ The radio waves reach a radio receiver and are converted back into sound.

Different radio stations broadcast radio waves at different frequencies. To pick up a particular station, you have to tune your radio to the frequency for that station. The numbers you see on the radio—such as 670 or 99.5—are frequencies.

Simply transmitting EM waves at a certain frequency is not enough to send music, words, or other meaningful sounds. To do that, the radio transmitter must attach information about the sounds to the radio signal. The transmitter attaches the information by modulating—that is, changing—the waves slightly. Two common ways of modulating radio waves are varying the amplitude of the waves and varying the frequency of the waves. Amplitude modulation is used for AM radio, and frequency modulation is used for FM radio.

You might be surprised to learn that broadcast television also uses radio waves. The picture part of a TV signal is transmitted using AM waves. The sound part is transmitted using FM waves.

AM Signal

Information is encoded in the signal by varying the radio wave's amplitude.

FM Signal

Information is encoded in the signal by varying the radio wave's frequency.

CHECK YOUR READING What two properties of EM waves are used to attach information to radio signals?

Microwaves

A type of EM waves called microwaves comes next on the EM spectrum. **Microwaves** are EM waves with shorter wavelengths, higher frequencies, and higher energy than other radio waves. Microwaves get their name from the fact that their wavelengths are shorter even than those of radio waves. Two important technologies that use microwaves are radar and cell phones.

Radar The term *radar* stands for "radio detection and ranging." Radar came into wide use during World War II (1939–1945) as a way of detecting aircraft and ships from a distance and estimating their locations. Radar works by transmitting microwaves, receiving reflections of the waves from objects the waves strike, and converting these reflections into visual images on a screen. Today, radar technology is used to control air traffic at airports, analyze weather conditions, and measure the speed of a moving vehicle.

Radar led to the invention of the microwave oven. The discovery that microwaves could be used to cook food was made by accident when radar waves melted a candy bar inside a researcher's pocket.

Cell Phones A cell phone is actually a radio transmitter and receiver that uses microwaves. Cell phones depend on an overlapping network of cells, or areas of land several kilometers in diameter. Each cell has at its center a tower that sends and receives microwave signals. The tower connects cell phones inside the cell to each other or to the regular wire-based telephone system. These two connecting paths are shown below.

READING TiP

As you read about the different categories of EM waves, refer to the diagram on pages 80 and 81.

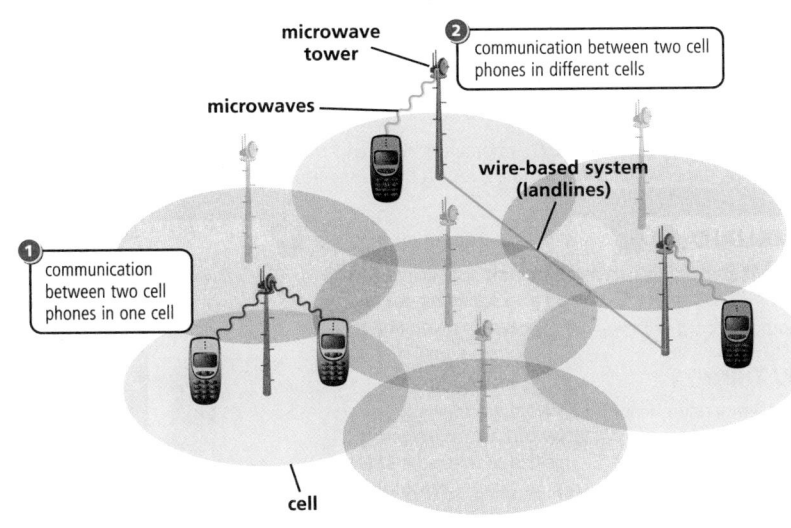

microwave tower

2 communication between two cell phones in different cells

microwaves

wire-based system (landlines)

1 communication between two cell phones in one cell

cell

History of Science

Radar, an acronym for radio detection and ranging, was first used during World War II to detect incoming enemy aircraft. A radar station sends out EM waves. Electronic equipment measures the time it takes for the waves to travel to the plane, reflect, and return to the station. The plane can then be located.

Teach from Visuals

To help students interpret the visual illustrating cellular communication, ask:

- What kind of waves are used in cell phones? *microwaves*

- How large is an overlapping network of cells? *several kilometers in diameter*

- What is the function of a tower in cell phone operation? *The tower receives microwave signals from the phone and sends the signal to another cell phone or to the wire-based telephone system.*

DIFFERENTIATE INSTRUCTION

More Reading Support

F What technologies use microwaves? *radar and cell phones*

G What connects cell phones to each other? *a tower that sends and receives signals*

Advanced Have interested students research and compare Doppler radar and conventional radar. Ask students to find out how Doppler radar is used and why it is used in weather prediction.

R Challenge and Extension, p. 162

INVESTIGATE The Electromagnetic Spectrum

PURPOSE To demonstrate the existence of invisible light waves

TIPS *30 min.* Suggest the following:

- Position the prism so that the spectrum is large enough to allow the thermometers not to touch each other.

- Use a glass or crystal optical-quality prism, the larger the better; don't use a plastic prism. The thermometers should show tenths of a degree.

- This activity will work best outdoors in bright sunlight. Window glass absorbs infrared radiation and will reduce results.

- The paper must be in the shade; students can put the paper in an open cardboard box in the shade of one side and mount the prism in a small rectangle cut into the upper edge.

WHAT DO YOU THINK? *The temperature in the shade was lower. The thermometers in the light, including the thermometer in the invisible infrared range, show higher temperatures because they absorb energy from EM radiation.*

CHALLENGE *Put three thermometers in different parts of the area outside the color spectrum next to the red area, and measure the temperatures.*

 Datasheet, The Electromagnetic Spectrum, p. 163

Technology Resources

Customize this student lab as needed or look for an alternative. Print rubrics to assess student lab reports.

 Lab Generator CD-ROM

Teaching with Technology

This investigate can be done using CBL probeware. Place temperature probes in different parts of the spectrum to measure the temperature of various wavelengths.

Infrared, visible, and ultraviolet light have mid-range wavelengths and frequencies.

H

Visible light is the part of the EM spectrum that human eyes can see. This part extends roughly from 10^{14} Hz, which we perceive as red, to 10^{15} Hz, which we perceive as violet. This narrow band is very small compared with the rest of the spectrum. In fact, visible light is only about 1/100,000 of the complete EM spectrum. Below visible light and above microwaves, is the infrared part of the EM spectrum. Above visible light is the ultraviolet part of the spectrum. You will read more about visible light in the next section.

READING TiP

Infrared means "below red." *Ultraviolet* means "beyond violet."

Infrared Light

I

The **infrared light** part of the spectrum consists of EM frequencies between microwaves and visible light. Infrared radiation is the type of EM wave most often associated with heat. Waves in this range are sometimes called heat rays. Although you cannot see infrared radiation, you can feel it as warmth coming from the Sun, a fire, or a radiator. Infrared lamps are used to provide warmth in bathrooms and to keep food warm after it is cooked. Infrared rays are also used to cook food—for example, in a toaster or over charcoal.

INVESTIGATE The Electromagnetic Spectrum

How can you detect invisible light?

PROCEDURE

1. Find a place that has both bright sunlight and shade, such as a window sill. Place the white paper in the shade.

2. Using the marker, paint the bulbs of the thermometers black and place one thermometer on the paper. After three minutes, record the temperature it shows.

3. Position the prism so that it shines a bright color spectrum on the white paper. Place the thermometers so that one bulb is in the blue area, one in the red, and one just outside the red.

4. After five minutes, record the three temperatures.

WHAT DO YOU THINK?

- How did the four temperature readings differ?
- How might you explain the temperature readings you noted?

CHALLENGE How could you modify the experiment to find the hottest part of the infrared range?

SKILL FOCUS
Drawing conclusions

MATERIALS
- white paper
- black marker
- 3 thermometers
- prism

TIME
30 minutes

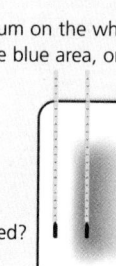

DIFFERENTIATE INSTRUCTION

?Reading Support

H How large is the visible light part of the spectrum? *very small*

I What EM waves are sometimes called heat rays? *infrared waves*

Additional Investigation To reinforce Section 3.2 learning goals, use the following full-period investigation:

 Additional INVESTIGATION, Seeing the Invisible, A, B, & C, pp. 203–211, 284–285 (Advanced students should complete Levels B and C.)

Alternative Assessment Have students draw a diagram showing how they would modify the experiment as described in the Challenge question. *The diagram should show three thermometers placed on a spectrum in different places to the left of the visible red waves.*

Some animals, such as pit viper snakes, can actually see infrared light. Normally, human beings cannot see infrared light. However, infrared scopes and cameras convert infrared radiation into visible wavelengths. They do this by representing different levels of infrared radiation with different colors of visible light. This technology can create useful images of objects based on the objects' temperatures.

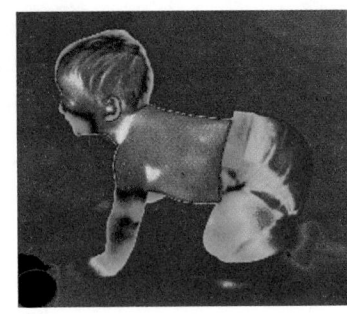

In this infrared photograph, warmer areas appear red and orange, while cooler ones appear blue, green, and purple.

 How do human beings perceive infrared radiation?

Ultraviolet Light

The **ultraviolet light** part of the EM spectrum consists of frequencies above those of visible light and below those of x-rays. Because ultraviolet (UV) light has higher frequencies than visible light, it also carries more energy. The waves in this range, having higher energies, can damage tissue, burning your skin or hurting your eyes. Sunblock and UV-protection sunglasses are designed to filter out these frequencies.

Ultraviolet light has beneficial effects as well. Because it can damage cells, UV light can be used to sterilize medical instruments and food by killing harmful bacteria. In addition, UV light causes skin cells to produce vitamin D, which is essential to good health. Ultraviolet light can also be used to treat skin problems and other medical conditions.

Like infrared light, ultraviolet light is visible to some animals. Bees and other insects can see higher frequencies than people can. They see nectar guides—marks that show where nectar is located—that people cannot see in visible light. The photographs below show how one flower might look to a person and to a bee.

This photograph shows the flower as it appears in visible light.

This photograph shows the flower as it might appear to a bee in ultraviolet light. Bees are able to see nectar guides in the UV range.

DIFFERENTIATE INSTRUCTION

English Learners Have English learners look up the word *radiation* in the dictionary. Explain to them that, although many people use the word to describe the energy given off during nuclear reactions, this is a very narrow interpretation of the word. Most EM waves are not involved in nuclear reactions. This explanation may also help to allay any fears that the activities in this chapter produce radioactivity.

Address Misconceptions

IDENTIFY Ask: Where does infrared light fall in the EM spectrum in relation to visible light? If students respond that infrared light falls within the visible range, they may hold the misconception that humans can see these EM waves.

CORRECT To help students see that infrared light is not visible, have them use a remote control to operate a TV or VCR in a dark room. Explain that most remote controls work using an infrared beam, but you cannot see it.

REASSESS Have students draw the EM spectrum and label visible light and infrared light.

Technology Resources
Visit **ClassZone.com** for background on common student misconceptions.

MISCONCEPTION DATABASE

Real World Example

Infrared detectors are used to find heat leaks in homes and buildings. A house is photographed on film that is sensitive to infrared waves. Places where heat is leaking out show up as bright spots on the film.

Ongoing Assessment

Draw conclusions about how to detect infrared radiation.

Ask: How can infrared radiation be detected if it cannot be seen? *when it is converted to a different form of energy*

Describe how different types of EM waves are used.

Ask: How is ultraviolet light used by animals? *Ultraviolet light helps skin cells make vitamin D. Insects that can see ultraviolet light use it to see nectar guides in flowers.*

 *Answer: as warmth*

X-rays and gamma rays have short wavelengths and high frequencies.

At the opposite end of the EM spectrum from radio waves are x-rays and gamma rays. Both have very high frequencies and energies. **X-rays** have frequencies from about 10^{16} Hz to 10^{21} Hz. **Gamma rays** have frequencies from more than 10^{19} Hz to more than 10^{24} Hz. Like other EM waves, x-rays and gamma rays are produced by the Sun and by other stars. People have also developed technologies that use these EM frequencies.

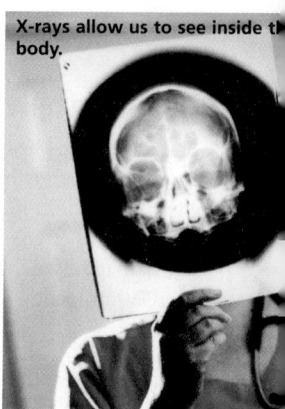

X-rays allow us to see inside the body.

X-rays pass easily through the soft tissues of the body, but many are filtered out by denser matter such as bone. If photographic film is placed behind the body and x-rays are aimed at the film, only the x-rays that pass through the body will expose the film. This makes x-ray images useful for diagnosing bone fractures and finding dense tumors. But too much exposure to x-rays can damage tissue. Even in small doses, repeated exposure to x-rays can cause cancer over time. When you have your teeth x-rayed, you usually wear a vest made out of lead to protect your organs. Lead blocks high-frequency radiation.

Gamma rays have the highest frequencies and energies of any EM waves. Gamma rays are produced by some radioactive substances as well as the Sun and other stars. Gamma rays can penetrate the soft and the hard tissues of the body, killing normal cells and causing cancer cells to develop. If carefully controlled, this destructive power can be beneficial. Doctors can also use gamma rays to kill cancer cells and fight tumors.

3.2 Review

KEY CONCEPTS

1. What two properties of EM waves change from one end of the EM spectrum to the other?
2. Describe two uses for microwave radiation.
3. How are EM waves used in dentistry and medicine?

CRITICAL THINKING

4. **Infer** Why do you think remote controls for TVs, VCRs, and stereos use infrared light rather than ultraviolet light?
5. **Apply** For a camera to make visible images of heat escaping from a building in winter, what type of EM wave would it need to photograph?

⚙ CHALLENGE

6. **Synthesize** When a person in a car is talking on a cell phone, and the car moves from one cell to another, the conversation continues without interruption. How might this be possible?

ANSWERS

1. *wavelength and frequency*

2. *Answers might include ovens to cook and heat food; radar to measure distance, location, or speed; cell phones to communicate.*

3. *Sample answer: X-rays are used to make images of hard tissues such as bones and teeth.*

4. *Infrared waves have low energies. They do not harm human tissue.*

5. *infrared light*

6. *The connection to the cell phone is switched from the microwave tower in the first cell to the microwave tower in the second cell without any disruption of the signal.*

Think SCIENCE

SKILL: DETERMINING RELEVANCE

Are Cell Phones Harmful?

In 1993, a man appearing on a popular television talk show claimed that cell phone radiation had caused his wife's brain cancer. Since that time, concerned scientists have conducted more than a dozen studies. None of them have shown clear evidence of a connection between cell phones and cancer. However, researchers have made a number of experimental observations.

▶ Experimental Observations

Here are some results from scientists' investigations.

1. Substances that cause cancer work by breaking chemical bonds in DNA.
2. Only EM radiation at ultraviolet frequencies and above can break chemical bonds.
3. Microwave radiation may make it easier for molecules called free radicals to damage DNA bonds.
4. Other factors such as psychological stress may cause breaks in DNA bonds.
5. Performing multiple tasks like driving and talking on the phone reduces the brain's ability to perform either task.
6. Exposing the brain to microwave radiation may slow reaction times.

▶ Hypotheses

Here are some hypotheses that could be used for further research.

A. Microwaves from cell phones can break DNA bonds.
B. Cell phones may contribute to cancer.
C. Holding and talking into a cell phone while driving increases a person's risk of having an accident.
D. Worrying about cell phones may be a health risk.

▶ Determining Relevance

On Your Own On a piece of paper, write down each hypothesis. Next to the hypothesis write each observation that you think is relevant. Include your reasons.

As a Group Discuss how each observation on your list is or is not relevant to a particular hypothesis.

CHALLENGE Based on the observations listed above, write a question that you think would be a good basis for a further experiment. Then explain how the answer to this question would be helpful.

Talking on a cell phone while driving may increase the risk of accidents.

ANSWERS

For hypothesis A, relevant observations are 1, 2, 3.

For hypothesis B, relevant observations are 1, 2, 3.

For hypothesis C, relevant observations are 5 and 6.

For hypothesis D, relevant observations are 1 and 4.

CHALLENGE *Qestions will vary. Sample question: Can DNA damage by free radicals cause cancer? If the answer is yes, then observation 3 supports the view that microwaves can contribute to cancer. If the answer is no, then observation 3 does not support the view that microwaves contribute to cancer.*

THINK SCIENCE
Scientific Methods of Thinking

Set Learning Goal

To evaluate hypotheses in terms of experimental observations

Present the Science

Scientists currently believe that a major cause of cancer is genetic, that is, breakage of the chemical bonds in the DNA molecule. Students will read about some of the facts related to the breaking of bonds in DNA and evaluate these facts to develop hypotheses about the safety of cell phones.

Guide the Activity

- Remind students that to evaluate means to judge a statement based on criteria.

- Ask students whether all four hypotheses listed are testable. *Hypothesis D would be difficult to test.*

- Ask students whether a hypothesis must explain all of the observations or just some of them. *A hypothesis must be supported by all of the observations. If some observations contradict a hypothesis, the hypothesis must be revised or discarded.*

COOPERATIVE LEARNING STRATEGY

Divide the class into small groups. In each group, assign a facilitator, a recorder, and a reporter. Assign each group one hypothesis to evaluate. The facilitator ensures that everyone has a chance to respond. The recorder writes the group's consensus. The reporter presents each observation in class.

Close

Ask: Why is it important to form hypotheses that are relevant to experimental observations? *You can build on information already acquired, instead of starting from scratch.*

3.3 FOCUS

◉ Set Learning Goals

Students will

- Explain how visible light is produced.
- Describe how living organisms produce light.
- Describe how humans produce light artificially.
- Observe in an experiment the different types of artificial light.

◑ 3-Minute Warm-Up

Display Transparency 21 or copy this exercise on the board:

Predict what would happen if you kept a green plant in the dark for one month. Explain why. *It would probably die. Plants require light from the Sun to survive.*

[T] 3-Minute Warm-Up, p. T21

3.3 MOTIVATE

THINK ABOUT

PURPOSE To understand why light is important to living organisms

DISCUSS Have students brainstorm the following scenario: What would happen to living things if the Sun suddenly went dark? *Everything on Earth would die. There would be no energy to produce food or, in the long run, to keep from freezing.*

Ongoing Assessment

CHECK YOUR READING *Answer: Green plants use light to make food. Plant material provides food, directly or indirectly, for most animals.*

---

 88 Unit: Waves, Sound, and Light

KEY CONCEPT

3.3 The Sun is the source of most visible light.

◀ **BEFORE, you learned**

- Visible light is part of the EM spectrum
- EM waves are produced both in nature and by technology

▶ **NOW, you will learn**

- How visible light is produced by materials at high temperatures
- How some living organisms produce light
- How humans produce light artificially

VOCABULARY

incandescence p. 89
luminescence p. 89
bioluminescence p. 89
fluorescence p. 91

THINK ABOUT

Why is light important?

This railroad worm has eleven pairs of green lights on its sides and a red light on its head. The animal probably uses these lights for illumination and to frighten away predators. Almost every living organism, including humans, depends on visible light. Think of as many different ways as you can that plants, animals, and people use light. Then, think of all the sources of visible light that you know of, both natural and artificial. Why is light important to living organisms?

Light comes from the Sun and other natural sources.

RESOURCE CENTER
CLASSZONE.COM

Learn more about visible light.

It is hard to imagine life without light. Human beings depend on vision in countless ways, and they depend on light for vision. Light is the only form of EM radiation for which human bodies have specialized sensory organs. The human eye is extremely sensitive to light and color and the many kinds of information they convey.

Most animals depend on visible light to find food and to do other things necessary for their survival. Green plants need light to make their own food. Plants, in turn, supply food directly or indirectly for nearly all other living creatures. With very few exceptions, living creatures depend on light for their existence.

CHECK YOUR READING How is plants' use of light important to animals?

RESOURCES FOR DIFFERENTIATED INSTRUCTION

Below Level

UNIT RESOURCE BOOK
- Reading Study Guide A, pp. 167–168
- Decoding Support, p. 191

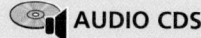 **AUDIO CDS**

Advanced

UNIT RESOURCE BOOK
Challenge and Extension, p. 173

English Learners

UNIT RESOURCE BOOK
Spanish Reading Study Guide, pp. 170–171

AUDIO CDS

- Audio Readings in Spanish
- Audio Readings (English)

Most of the visible light waves in the environment come from the Sun. The Sun's intense heat produces light of every wavelength. The production of light by materials at high temperatures is called **incandescence** (IHN-kuhn-DEHS-uhns). When a material gets hot enough, it gives off light by glowing or by bursting into flames.

Other than the Sun, few natural sources of incandescent light strongly affect life on Earth. Most stars give off as much light as the Sun, or even more, but little light from stars reaches Earth because they are so far away. Lightning produces bright, short-lived bursts of light. Fire, which can occur naturally, is a lower-level, longer-lasting source of visible light. The ability to make and use fire was the first light technology, making it possible for human beings to see on a dark night or inside a cave.

CHECK YOUR READING Why does little light reach Earth from stars other than the Sun?

Some living things produce visible light.

Many organisms produce their own visible light, which they use in a variety of ways. They produce this light through luminescence. **Luminescence** is the production of light without the high temperatures needed for incandescence. The production of light by living organisms is called **bioluminescence.** Bioluminescent organisms produce light from chemical reactions rather than from intense heat. Bioluminescence enables organisms to produce light inside their tissues without being harmed.

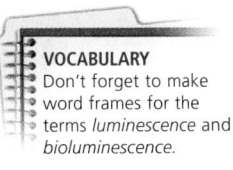

VOCABULARY
Don't forget to make word frames for the terms *luminescence* and *bioluminescence.*

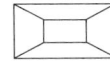

Bioluminescent organisms include insects, worms, fish, squid, jellyfish, bacteria, and fungi. Some of these creatures have light-producing organs that are highly complex. These organs might include light-producing cells but also reflectors, lenses, and even color filters.

The firefly, a type of beetle, uses bioluminescence to attract mates. A chemical reaction in its abdomen allows the firefly to glow at specific intervals. The pattern of glowing helps fireflies of the same species identify each other at night when they cannot see each other. Most often, the male flashes a specific signal while flying around. Females, usually sitting on vegetation near the ground, wait a certain amount of time and then respond with a flash. After they have identified each

---

Address Misconceptions

IDENTIFY Ask: Where does the energy for bioluminescence come from? If students respond that the light comes from heat or electricity produced by the organism, they may hold the misconception that bioluminescence is an electrical process rather than a chemical process.

CORRECT Have students experiment with a chemical glow stick (available at a hardware store). Show students that the stick is activated when a container inside the stick is broken. Have them observe that the stick remains cool to the touch. If possible, let them see a stick after it has stopped making light. Explain that the light in the stick comes from chemical reactions rather than heat or electricity.

REASSESS Ask students the following question: How does a glowstick model bioluminescence? *It glows because of a chemical reaction, not because of electricity.*

Technology Resources

Visit **ClassZone.com** for background on common student misconceptions.

 MISCONCEPTION DATABASE

Ongoing Assessment

Explain how visible light is produced.

Ask: How does the Sun produce light? *It emits radiation.*

Describe how living organisms produce light.

How do living things produce light? *chemicals in body*

CHECK YOUR READING *Answer: Except for the Sun, stars are too far away for much of their light to reach Earth.*

DIFFERENTIATE INSTRUCTION

 More Reading Support

A Where do most of the visible light waves in the environment come from? *the Sun*

English Learners English learners may be unfamiliar with some of the non-literal phrases used in the text. For example, the direction *Write up your experiment and carry it out* (p. 90) may be confusing to an English learner when taken literally. Be watchful for confusing language such as "carry it out," and explain unfamiliar phrases and idioms in clear terms.

INVESTIGATE Artificial Lighting

PURPOSE To examine properties of various types of artificial lighting

TIPS *30 min.* Allow students a few minutes to explore, then suggest the following:

• Use direct sunlight to test how different colored materials appear.

• Compare the properties of artificial lighting to those of natural sunlight.

WHAT DO YOU THINK? *Light qualities vary among different bulbs and lighting types. Light from any source can be broken up into a spectrum. One source's spectrum may be very different from another's. Answers will vary depending on student experiments.*

 Datasheet, Artificial Lighting, p. 174

Technology Resources

Customize this student lab as needed or look for an alternative. Print rubrics to assess student lab reports.

 Lab Generator CD-ROM

Metacognitive Strategy

Ask students to make a diagram of the experimental steps they tried and discarded. Have them write briefly about the problems that arose.

Ongoing Assessment

Design an experiment to compare different types of artificial light.

Ask: How could you compare the amount of heat given off by a halogen bulb and a regular incandescent bulb? *Measure the temperature at the same distance from two bulbs of equal wattage.*

CHECK YOUR READING *Incandescence is the production of light from high temperatures, or intense heat. Bioluminescence is the production of light from chemical reactions rather than from intense heat.*

A female firefly responds to a male's signal.

other, the fireflies may continue to exchange flashes until the male has located the female.

The process of bioluminescence is very efficient. Almost all of the energy released by the chemical reactions of bioluminescence is converted into light. Very little heat is produced. Researchers in lighting technology have wanted for years to imitate this efficiency, but that has become possible only in recent years.

 **CHECK YOUR READING** How is bioluminescence different from incandescence?

Human technologies produce visible light.

Human beings invented the first artificial lighting when they learned to make and control fire. For most of human history, people have made light with devices that use fire in some form, such as oil lamps, candles, and natural gas lamps. After the discovery of electricity, people began to make light through a means other than fire. However, the technique of using a very hot material as a light source stayed the same until the invention of fluorescent lighting. In recent years, "cool" lighting has become much more common.

INVESTIGATE Artificial Lighting

Is all artificial light the same?

Many types of artificial light sources are available. These sources differ in the amount of light they produce, the way the light beams are directed, and the quality of the light itself.

DESIGN —YOUR OWN— EXPERIMENT

SKILL FOCUS Designing experiments

MATERIALS Artificial lighting with a variety of bulb types and sizes

TIME 30 minutes

PROCEDURE

① Design a procedure to discover and record differences among several different types of artificial lighting. Your procedure should test how different colored materials appear in different types of lighting. You should compare the results with how these materials appear in direct sunlight.

② Write up your experiment and carry it out.

WHAT DO YOU THINK?

• What differences did you discover among bulbs of different types and sizes?

• How would you improve your design if you were to repeat your experiment?

DIFFERENTIATE INSTRUCTION

 More Reading Support

B What was the first artificial lighting used by humans? *fire*

Below Level Have students make a flow diagram showing how making light has changed throughout human history. *Diagrams should begin with fire, progress through oil lamps, candles, and natural gas, and end with electricity.*

Advanced

 Challenge and Extension, p. 173

Incandescent and Fluorescent Lighting

The development of the electric light bulb in the late 1800s made light available at the flip of a switch. An ordinary light bulb is a sealed glass tube with a thin tungsten wire running through it. This wire is called a filament. When electrical current passes through the filament, the tungsten gets hotter and begins to glow. Because these light bulbs need high temperatures to produce light, they are called incandescent bulbs.

Tungsten can become very hot—about 3500 degrees Celsius (6300°F)—without melting. At such high temperatures, tungsten can give off a bright light. However, the tungsten filament also produces much infrared radiation. In fact, the filament produces more infrared light than visible light. As a result, incandescent bulbs waste a lot of energy in the form of heat. At such high temperatures, tungsten also slowly evaporates and collects on the inside of the bulb. Eventually, the filament weakens and breaks, and the bulb burns out.

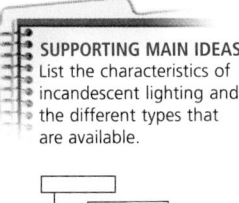

SUPPORTING MAIN IDEAS
List the characteristics of incandescent lighting and the different types that are available.

 What causes ordinary light bulbs to burn out?

Since the 1980s, halogen (HAL-uh-juhn) bulbs have come into wide use. Halogen bulbs have several advantages over ordinary incandescent bulbs. They contain a gas from the halogen group. This gas combines with evaporating tungsten atoms and deposits the tungsten back onto the filament. As a result, the filament lasts longer. The filament can also be raised to a higher temperature without damage, so it produces more light. Halogen bulbs, which are made of quartz, resist heat better than glass.

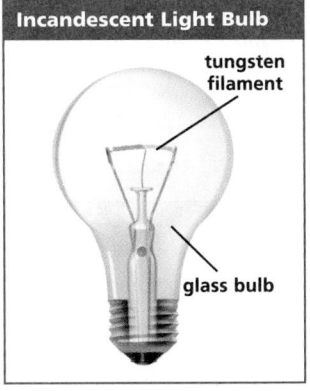

Incandescent Light Bulb

tungsten filament

glass bulb

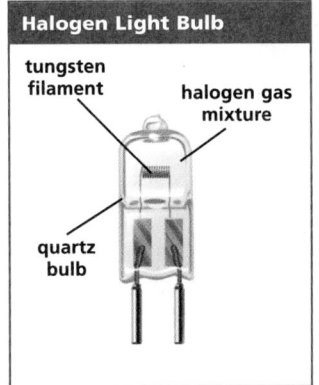

Halogen Light Bulb

tungsten filament

halogen gas mixture

quartz bulb

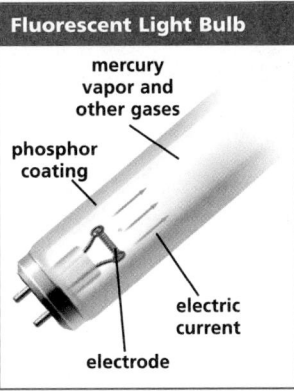

Fluorescent Light Bulb

mercury vapor and other gases

phosphor coating

electric current

electrode

Many electric lights in use today are fluorescent. **Fluorescence** (flu-REHS-uhns) occurs when a material absorbs EM radiation of one wavelength and gives off EM radiation of a different wavelength. Fluorescent bulbs are filled with a mixture of mercury vapor and other gases that give off ultraviolet light when an electric current passes

Chapter 3: **Electromagnetic Waves** 91 **C**

Chapter 3 **91** **C**

Ongoing Assessment

CHECK YOUR READING *Answer: Fluorescent light is cool and does not waste much energy as heat, unlike incandescent light.*

Reinforce (the **BIG** idea)

All students can benefit from the following worksheet:

 Reinforcing Key Concepts, p. 175

3.3 ASSESS & RETEACH

Assess

A Section 3.3 Quiz, p. 44

Reteach

Show students a regular incandescent light bulb and an LED. Have them list some visible differences between the two. Ask:

• What are the working elements of an incandescent bulb? *filament, vacuum or special gas enclosed in a bulb*

• Does the LED have these elements? What does it have instead? *no; semiconductor and wires*

• Compare heat, efficiency, and longevity of these two types of artificial lighting. *An LED lasts longer and is more efficient than an incandescent bulb; the incandescent bulb produces more heat.*

Technology Resources

Have students visit **ClassZone.com** for reteaching of Key Concepts.

 CONTENT REVIEW

 CONTENT REVIEW CD-ROM

---

through them. The insides of the bulbs are coated with a powder called phosphor that fluoresces. Phosphor absorbs ultraviolet light and gives off visible light. Because fluorescent light is cool and does not waste much energy as heat, it is more efficient, more economical, and safer than incandescent lighting.

 **CHECK YOUR READING** Why are fluorescent lights more efficient than incandescent lights?

Other Types of Artificial Lighting

LEDs are being used more and more in place of incandescent bulbs.

Like fluorescent lights, many other artificial light sources use a gas in place of a filament. For example, neon lights use gas-filled tubes to produce light. However, instead of ultraviolet light, the gas gives off visible light directly. The colors of neon lights come from the particular mixtures of gases used. Vapor lights, which are commonly used for street lights, work in a similar way. In a vapor light, a material such as sodium is heated until it becomes a gas, or vapor. The vapor responds to electricity by glowing brightly.

One of fastest-growing types of artificial lighting is the light emitting diode, or LED. LEDs do not involve bulbs, filaments, or gases. Instead, they produce light electronically. A diode is a type of semiconductor—a device that regulates the flow of electricity. An LED is a semiconductor that converts electricity directly into visible light.

LEDs have many advantages over traditional forms of lighting. They produce a very bright light, do not break easily, use little energy, produce little heat, can save money, and can last for decades. Some technologists believe that LEDs will eventually replace most traditional forms of artificial lighting.

3.3 Review

KEY CONCEPTS

1. Describe natural, nonliving sources of incandescent light.

2. What advantages does bioluminescence have over incandescence as a way for living organisms to produce light?

3. What are some advantages and disadvantages of artificial incandescent lighting?

CRITICAL THINKING

4. **Classify** Make a chart summarizing the different types of artificial lighting discussed in this section.

5. **Infer** Why do you think moonlight does not warm you, even though the Moon reflects light from the hot Sun?

CHALLENGE

6. **Compare and Contrast** What does LED lighting have in common with bioluminescence? How are the two different?

ANSWERS

1. *The Sun produces most of the natural light we use. Other sources are other stars, lightning, and fire.*

2. *Bioluminescence does not produce high temperatures, which could damage tissues.*

3. *advantages: give off bright light, no open flame; disad-* *vantages: can get very hot, wastes energy*

4. *Charts should summarize the information from pp. 90–92.*

5. *The Moon reflects mostly visible light and not much infrared light. Only a small* *part of the radiation from the Sun strikes the Moon.*

6. *Both do not involve bulbs, filaments, or gases. They produce cool light. LEDs produce light electronically, bioluminescence chemically.*

KEY CONCEPT

3.4 Light waves interact with materials.

◀ **BEFORE, you learned**

- Mechanical waves respond to a change in medium
- Visible light is made up of EM waves
- EM waves interact with a new medium in the same ways that mechanical waves do

▶ **NOW, you will learn**

- How the wave behavior of light affects what we see
- How light waves interact with materials
- Why objects have color
- How different colors are produced

VOCABULARY

transmission p. 93
absorption p. 93
scattering p. 95
polarization p. 96
prism p. 97
primary colors p. 98
primary pigments p. 99

EXPLORE Light and Matter

How can a change in medium affect light?

PROCEDURE

1. Fill the container with water.

2. Add 10 ml (2 tsp) of milk to the water. Put on the lid, and gently shake the container until the milk and water are mixed.

3. In a dark room, shine the light at the side of the container from about 5 cm (2 in.) away. Observe what happens to the beam of light.

WHAT DO YOU THINK?

- What happened to the beam of light from the flashlight?
- Why did the light behave this way?

MATERIALS

- clear plastic container with lid
- water
- measuring spoons
- milk
- flashlight

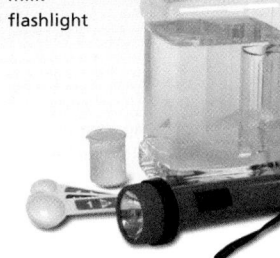

VOCABULARY
Don't forget to make word frames for *transmission* and *absorption*.

Light can be reflected, transmitted, or absorbed.

You have read that EM waves can interact with a material medium in the same ways that mechanical waves do. Three forms of interaction play an especially important role in how people see light. One form is reflection. Most things are visible because they reflect light. The two other forms of interaction are transmission and absorption.

Transmission (trans-MIHSH-uhn) is the passage of an EM wave through the medium. If the light reflected from objects did not pass through the air, windows, or most of the eye, we could not see the objects. **Absorption** (uhb-SAWRP-shun) is the disappearance of an EM wave into the medium. Absorption affects how things look, because it determines what light is available to be reflected or transmitted.

Chapter 3: **Electromagnetic Waves** 93 **C**

RESOURCES FOR DIFFERENTIATED INSTRUCTION

Below Level

UNIT RESOURCE BOOK
- Reading Study Guide A, pp. 178–179
- Decoding Support, p. 191

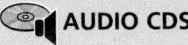 **AUDIO CDS**

Advanced

UNIT RESOURCE BOOK
Challenge and Extension, p. 184

English Learners

UNIT RESOURCE BOOK
Spanish Reading Study Guide, pp. 182–183

 **AUDIO CDS**

- Audio Readings in Spanish
- Audio Readings (English)

◉ Set Learning Goals

Students will

- Describe how the wave behavior of light affects what we see.
- Recognize how light waves interact with materials.
- Recognize why objects have color.
- Explain how colors are produced.
- Observe through an experiment what makes up the color black.

◀ 3-Minute Warm-Up

Display Transparency 21 or copy this exercise on the board:

Match each definition to the correct term.

Definitions

1. the production of light without high temperatures *a*
2. the production of light by living organisms *b*
3. the production of light with high temperatures *c*

Terms

a. luminescence   c. incandescence

b. bioluminescence

 3-Minute Warm-Up, p. T21

3.4 MOTIVATE

EXPLORE Light and Matter

PURPOSE To introduce the concept of light scattering

TIP *10 min.* Tell students that milk is composed of large molecules, like fats and proteins.

WHAT DO YOU THINK? *light spreads out inside the container; the color and direction of the light beam changes when light strikes the particles of milk*

Ongoing Assessment

Describe how the wave behavior of light affects what we see.

Ask: How does absorption of light waves affect how things look? *by what light it reflects or transmits*

History of Science

Not all glass is transparent to visible light. Opaque glass, often called milk glass, is creamy white and feels silky. It was first developed by the Egyptians about 1500 B.C., when they added chemicals to glass. The Chinese made milk-glass snuff bottles around 140 B.C., and the Persians kept their spices and medicines in milk-glass jars beginning in the eighth century. Today, opaque glass is made in all colors and textures.

Ongoing Assessment

Recognize how light waves interact with materials.

Ask: Why do some materials appear opaque? *All the light waves that strike them are reflected, absorbed, or both.*

CHECK YOUR READING *Answer: Translucent materials let some light pass through, causing it to spread out in all directions. Objects can be seen indistinctly through a translucent material. Opaque materials do not allow any light to pass through because they reflect light, absorb light, or both.*

How Materials Transmit Light

Materials can be classified according to the amount and type of light they transmit.

 1 Transparent (trans-PAIR-uhnt) materials allow most of the light that strikes them to pass through. It is possible to see objects through a transparent material. Air, water, and clear glass are transparent. Transparent materials are used for items such as windows, light bulbs, thermometers, sandwich bags, and clock faces.

 2 Translucent (trans-LOO-suhnt) materials transmit some light, but they also cause it to spread out in all directions. You can see light through translucent materials, but you cannot see objects clearly through them. Some examples are lampshades, frosted light bulbs, frosted windows, fluorescent light coverings, sheer fabrics, and notepaper.

3 Opaque (oh-PAYK) materials do not allow any light to pass through them, because they reflect light, absorb light, or both. Heavy fabrics, construction paper, and ceramic mugs are opaque. Shiny materials may be opaque mainly because they reflect light. Other materials, such as wood and rock, are opaque mainly because they absorb light.

CHECK YOUR READING What is the difference between translucent and opaque materials?

This stained-glass window contains transparent, translucent, and opaque materials.

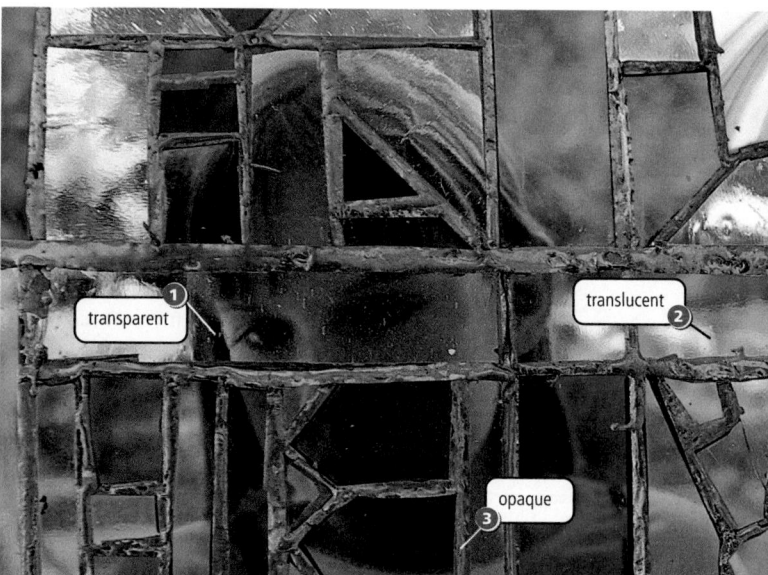

DIFFERENTIATE INSTRUCTION

? More Reading Support

A What two types of material transmit light? *transparent, translucent*

B What makes a material opaque? *no light passes through it*

English Learners Be aware that English learners do not always have the same background knowledge as the rest of the class. For example, the paragraph on scattering refers to what happens when students shine a flashlight into fog. Some students may have never had such an opportunity due to the climate in their native country or their lack of access to a flashlight.

A light filter is a material that is transparent to some kinds of light and opaque to others. For example, clear red glass transmits red light but absorbs other colors. Examples of light filters are the colored covers on taillights and traffic lights, infrared lamp bulbs, and UV-protected sunglasses. Filters that transmit only certain colors are called color filters.

Scattering

Sometimes fine particles in a transparent material interact with light passing through the material to cause scattering. **Scattering** is the spreading out of light rays in all directions, because particles reflect and absorb the light. Fog or dust in the air, mud in water, and scratches or smudges on glass can all cause scattering. Scattering creates glare and makes it hard to see through even a transparent material. Making the light brighter causes more scattering, as you might have noticed if you have ever tried to use a flashlight to see through fog.

Fine particles, such as those in fog, scatter light and reduce visibility.

Scattering is what makes the sky blue. During the middle of the day, when the Sun is high in the sky, molecules in Earth's atmosphere scatter the blue part of visible light more than they scatter the other wavelengths. This process gives the sky a blue tinge and makes it translucent. Light comes through the sky, but you cannot see through the sky. At dawn and dusk, light from the Sun must travel farther through the atmosphere before it reaches your eyes. By the time you see it, the greens and blues are scattered away and the light appears reddish. At night, because there is so little light, almost no scattering takes place, and you can see through the sky to the stars.

SUPPORTING MAIN IDEAS
Be sure to add to your chart the different ways light interacts with materials.

 **CHECK YOUR READING** How does scattering make the sky blue?

IDENTIFY Ask: Why does the sky appear blue? If students respond that the oceans reflect blue light, they may hold the misconception that the oceans are responsible for the sky's color.

CORRECT Point out that, if the oceans were responsible for the sky's blue color, the sky would be less blue farther inland. This is obviously not true.

REASSESS Ask students to recall their results for "Explore Light and Matter" on p. 93. Ask:

- Why did the milky water appear blue? *The milk particles scattered the blue wavelengths in the light.*

- How is the sky similar to the milk and water? *Particles in the atmosphere scatter the blue wavelengths in sunlight.*

Technology Resources

Visit **ClassZone.com** for background on common student misconceptions.

MISCONCEPTION DATABASE

Ongoing Assessment

CHECK YOUR READING *Answer: Particles in Earth's atmosphere scatter the blue part of the visible spectrum more than they scatter the other wavelengths. This makes the sky appear blue.*

DIFFERENTIATE INSTRUCTION

 More Reading Support

C What causes scattering of light? *fine particles in a transparent material*

Below Level Have students make a list of five materials that are transparent to visible light, five that are translucent, and five that are opaque. Ask students to write definitions of the three terms and to draw ray diagrams showing light rays being reflected, absorbed, or transmitted by each type of material.

To help students interpret the visual of light waves and filters, ask:

- In what direction are the light waves absorbed by the first filter? *horizontally*

- Why does no light pass through the second filter? *Only light waves vibrating vertically pass through the first filter. The second filter stops all waves except those vibrating horizontally.*

Teach Difficult Concepts

Students may have a hard time understanding polarization. It may help them visualize the process if they think of a polarizing filter as a picket fence. Only vertical objects can pass through an upright fence. If the fence were rotated to its side, only horizontal objects could pass through. To help students understand polarization, explain that light can become polarized when a nonmetallic surface reflects light. When the reflected light waves have a large concentration of horizontal vibrations, that is, in a plane parallel to the object's surface, they are called *glare*. Polarized sunglasses have microscopic vertical slits that block out the horizontally polarized light and therefore reduce glare. Have several pairs of polarized sunglasses available for students to take outdoors. Have students notice how the glare changes when they rotate the glasses.

Light reflecting off the surface of this pond causes glare.

A polarizing filter reduces glare, making it possible to see objects under the water.

Polarization

D

Polarization of light reduces glare and makes it easier to see objects. **Polarization** (POH-luhr-ih-ZAY-shuhn) is a way of filtering light so that all of its waves vibrate in the same direction. Remember that EM waves are made of electric and magnetic fields vibrating at right angles to each other. Polarization affects only the electric fields of a light wave. When all of the electric fields of a group of light waves vibrate in the same direction, the light is polarized.

Light can be polarized by a particular type of light filter called a polarizing filter. A polarizing filter acts on a light wave's electric field like the bars of a cage. The filter allows through only waves whose electric fields vibrate in one particular direction. Waves that pass through the filter are polarized. In the illustration below, these waves are shown in darker yellow.

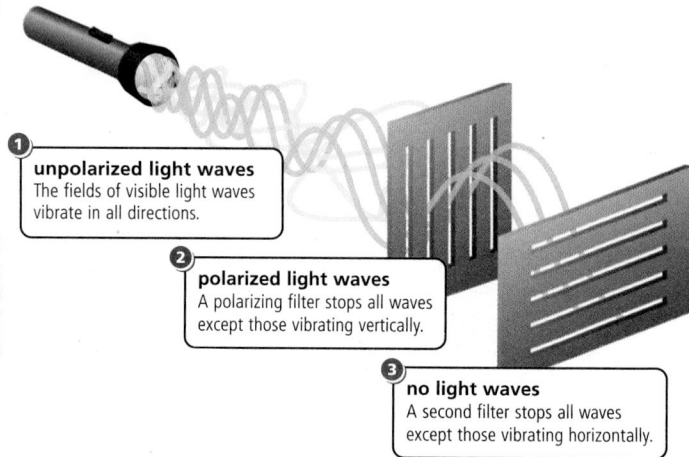

1 **unpolarized light waves**
The fields of visible light waves vibrate in all directions.

2 **polarized light waves**
A polarizing filter stops all waves except those vibrating vertically.

3 **no light waves**
A second filter stops all waves except those vibrating horizontally.

What do you think happens when polarized light passes into a second polarizing filter? If the direction of the bars in the second filter is the same as in the first, then all of the light will pass through the second filter. The light will still be polarized. If the direction of the bars in the second filter is at a right angle to the first, as in the illustration above, then no light at all will pass through the second filter.

Wavelength determines color.

The section of the EM spectrum called visible light is made up of many different frequencies and wavelengths. When all of these wavelengths are present together, as in light from the Sun or a light bulb, we see ordinary light, which is also called white light.

DIFFERENTIATE INSTRUCTION

? **More Reading Support**

D How do you make the electric fields of a wave vibrate in the same direction? *using polarization*

Advanced Unpolarized light (natural sunlight, for example) can become polarized to a certain degree when it is reflected from a flat surface such as a highway. This polarized light is termed glare and can be demonstrated by viewing the distant part of a highway on a sunny day. Have students make light diagrams showing how glare is formed. Have them investigate the conditions under which glare is formed, such as the angle at which the light approaches the surface, the time of day, and the material that is reflecting the light.

 Challenge and Extension, p. 184

Seen individually, the wavelengths appear as different colors of light. This fact can be demonstrated by using a prism. A **prism** is a tool that uses refraction to separate the different wavelengths that make up white light. The prism bends some of the wavelengths more than others. The lightwaves, bent at slightly different angles, form a color spectrum. The color spectrum could be divided into countless individual wavelengths, each with its own color. However, the color spectrum is usually divided into seven distinct color bands. In order of decreasing wavelength, the bands are red, orange, yellow, green, blue, indigo, and violet. You see a color spectrum whenever you see a rainbow.

Prisms split light into colors by refracting wavelengths in different amounts.

Color Reflection and Absorption

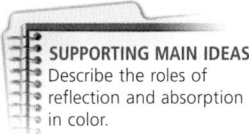

The color of an object or material is determined by the wavelengths it absorbs and those it reflects. An object has the color of the wavelengths it reflects. A material that reflects all wavelengths of visible light appears white. A material that absorbs all wavelengths of visible light appears black. A green lime absorbs all colors except green and reflects green, so the lime looks green, as shown below.

SUPPORTING MAIN IDEAS
Describe the roles of reflection and absorption in color.

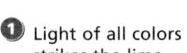

1 Light of all colors strikes the lime.

2 The lime absorbs all colors except green.

3 The lime reflects green, so it appears green.

The color that an object appears to the eye depends on another factor besides the wavelengths the object absorbs and reflects. An object can reflect only wavelengths that are in the light that shines on it. In white light, a white object reflects all the wavelengths of visible light and appears white. If you shine only red light on a white piece of paper, however, the paper will appear red, not white, because only red light is available to be reflected.

In summary, two factors determine the color of an object: first, the wavelengths that the object itself reflects or absorbs, and second, the wavelengths present in the light that shines on the object.

 What color wavelengths does a red apple absorb? What color wavelengths does a white flower absorb?

Chapter 3: **Electromagnetic Waves** 97 **C**

DIFFERENTIATE INSTRUCTION

Teach from Visuals

To help students interpret the visual of the prism, ask:

• What color would the lime seem to be if you shined a red light on it? Why? *It would appear black. The green lime absorbs red, so no light would be reflected.*

• What would have to happen for the lime to appear white? *The lime would have to reflect all the wavelengths of visible light.*

Teach Difficult Concepts

Some students may have a hard time understanding that matter can absorb light. Remind them of the ice cube melting under black and white paper. Ask:

• Where did the ice melt faster? *under the black paper*

• Why was black paper warmer than white? *It absorbs more light waves.*

• A ginger (orange) cat and a blue (dark gray) cat are sitting on a window sill. Which cat's fur will absorb more light? How could you tell? *The blue cat; it will feel warmer to the touch.*

EXPLORE (the **BIG** idea)

Revisit "What Melts the Ice Cubes?" and "What Is White Light Made Of?" on p. 71. Have students explain the reasons for their results.

Ongoing Assessment

Recognize why objects have color.

Ask: Why does an object appear black? *The object absorbs all wavelengths of light that strike it.*

CHECK YOUR READING *Answer: all visible wavelengths except red; no visible wavelengths*

INVESTIGATE Mixing Colors

PURPOSE To observe the colors that make up black ink

TIPS *30 min.* To get the best results in this lab:

- Use cups with wide mouths so students can cut a long flap in the filter. The farther the ink moves, the more clearly the colors will separate.

- Handle the filters as little as possible. Oils from skin interfere with the movement of pigments.

- The felt-tip markers must be water soluble (washable). Try to get pens made by different manufacturers.

WHAT DO YOU THINK? *The colors in black ink separated. Each brand of black ink is made of a different combination of colors.*

CHALLENGE *If black ink is put on a filter, then it will spearate into colors because black is a combination of different colors of pigments.*

 Datasheet, Mixing Colors, p. 185

Technology Resources

Customize this student lab as needed or look for an alternative. Print rubrics to assess student lab reports.

 Lab Generator CD-ROM

Teaching with Technology

You may wish to photograph this lab if you have access to a digital camera. Students can see how the ink samples change over time.

Ongoing Assessment

Observe what makes up the color black.

Ask: Why does black ink appear black? *It absorbs all wavelengths of light.*

CHECK YOUR READING *Answer: produces all possible colors*

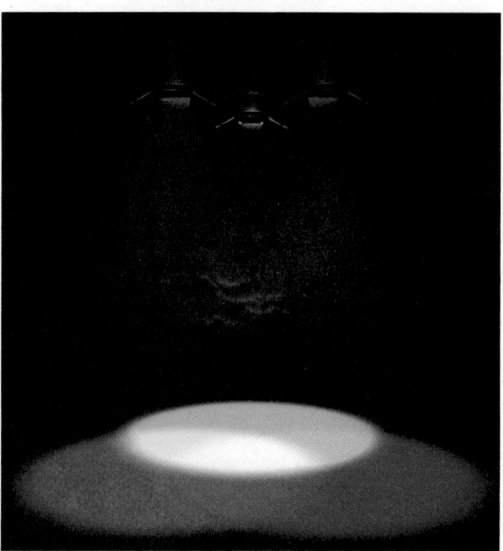

Primary colors of light combine to make the secondary colors yellow, cyan (light blue), and magenta (dark pink).

Primary Colors of Light

The human eye can detect only three colors: red, green, and blue. Your brain perceives these three colors and various mixtures of them as all the colors of the rainbow. These three colors of light, which can be mixed to produce all possible colors, are called **primary colors.** When all three colors are mixed together equally, they appear white, or colorless. Whenever colored light is added to a mixture, specific wavelengths are added. Mixing colors by adding wavelengths is called additive color mixing.

An example of the practical use of primary colors is a color television or computer monitor. The screen is divided into thousands of tiny bundles of red, green, and blue dots, or pixels. A television broadcast or DVD sends signals that tell the monitor which pixels to light up and when to do so. By causing only some pixels to give off light, the monitor can mix the three colors to create an amazing variety of colorful images.

 **CHECK YOUR READING** What does an equal mix of all three primary colors produce?

INVESTIGATE Mixing Colors

What is black ink made of?

PROCEDURE

① Trim each of the filter papers to a disk about 10 cm (4 in.) in diameter. Make two parallel cuts about 1 cm (.5 in.) apart and 5 cm (2 in.) long from the edge of each disk toward the center. Fold the paper to make a flap at a right angle.

② Use a different marker to make a dark spot in the middle of the flap on each disk.

③ Fill each of the cups with water. Set one of the disks on top of each cup so that the water covers the end of the flap but does not reach the ink spot.

④ After 15 minutes, examine each of the flaps.

WHAT DO YOU THINK?

- What did you observe about the effects of water on the ink spots?

- How do the three different samples compare?

CHALLENGE Write a hypothesis to explain what you observed about the colors in a black marker.

SKILL FOCUS
Observing

MATERIALS
- 3 coffee filters
- scissors
- 3 brands of black felt-tip marker
- 3 cups
- water

TIME
30 minutes

DIFFERENTIATE INSTRUCTION

? More Reading Support

G What are the three primary colors visible to human eyes? *red, green, and blue*

Alternative Assessment Have interested students videotape "Investigate Mixing Colors," then play back the tape at a slow speed. They can write and record a script to describe and explain what is happening as the separation of ink colors proceeds. The script should also explain why black ink has to be mixed this way.

Primary Pigments

Remember that two factors affect an object's color. One is the wavelengths present in the light that shines on the object. The other is the wavelengths that the object's material reflects or absorbs. Materials can be mixed to produce colors just as light can. Materials that are used to produce colors are called pigments. The **primary pigments** are cyan, yellow, and magenta. You can mix primary pigments just as you can mix primary colors to produce all the colors.

The primary pigment colors are the same as the secondary colors of light. The secondary pigment colors are red, blue, and green—the same as the primary colors of light.

The effect of mixing pigments is different from the effect of mixing light. Remember that a colored material absorbs all wavelengths except those of the color it reflects. Yellow paint absorbs all colors except yellow. Because pigments absorb wavelengths, whenever you mix pigments, you are subtracting wavelengths rather than adding them. Mixing colors by subtracting wavelengths is called subtractive color mixing. When all three primary pigments are mixed together in equal amounts, all wavelengths are subtracted. The result is black—the absence of color.

The inks used to make the circles on this page are primary pigments. They combine to make the secondary pigments red, blue, and green.

 **CHECK YOUR READING** How is mixing pigments different from mixing light?

3.4 Review

KEY CONCEPTS

1. What are some ways in which materials affect how light is transmitted?
2. How does a polarizing filter reduce glare?
3. In order for an object to appear white, which wavelengths must the light contain and the object reflect?

CRITICAL THINKING

4. **Apply** Imagine that you are a firefighter searching a smoke-filled apartment. Would using a stronger light help you see better? Explain your answer.
5. **Predict** Higher-energy EM waves penetrate farthest into a dense medium. What colors are more likely to penetrate to the bottom of a lake?

CHALLENGE

6. **Synthesize** If you focus a red light, a green light, and a blue light on the same part of a black curtain, what color will the curtain appear to be? Why?

ANSWERS

1. Reflection can diffuse light, as in translucent material. Absorption can filter out some wavelengths, as in a color filter, or all wavelengths, as in an opaque material.

2. A polarizing filter allows waves through only if their electric fields vibrate in the same direction, eliminating the random reflection and diffusion that cause glare.

3. all wavelengths of visible light

4. No; stronger light would cause more scattering and decrease visibility.

5. green, blue, indigo, and violet

6. The curtain will appear black because the black curtain absorbs all wavelengths.

Ongoing Assessment

Explain how different colors are produced.

Ask: How are secondary pigments produced? *by mixing primary pigments*

CHECK YOUR READING *Answer: Mixing colors of light produces new colors by the addition of wavelengths. Mixing pigments produces new colors by the subtraction of wavelengths.*

Reinforce (the **BIG** idea)

All students can benefit from the following worksheet:

R Reinforcing Key Concepts, p. 186

3.4 ASSESS & RETEACH

Assess

A Section 3.4 Quiz, p. 45

Reteach

Have each student or groups of students make a poster to review one of the main concepts of this section: reflection, transmission, absorption, scattering, polarization, color reflection and absorption, and how colors are mixed. Students can explain the concepts on their posters in oral presentations to the class.

Technology Resources

Have students visit **ClassZone.com** for reteaching of Key Concepts.

CONTENT REVIEW

CONTENT REVIEW CD-ROM

Focus

PURPOSE Students will learn that an object's color is determined by the wavelengths of light that shine upon it and those that it reflects.

OVERVIEW Students will make a light box and observe objects in blue, red, and green light. Students will find that

- a white object appears white in white light, red in red light, blue in blue light, and green in green light.
- a black object appears black in all colors of light.
- a red object appears red in white and red light, purple in blue light, and yellow in green light.
- a yellow object appears yellow in white light, orange in red light, green in blue light, and yellow-green in green light.

Lab Preparation

- Ask students to bring shoe boxes from home, or check with discount stores. Boxes without lids can be used upside down.
- Acetate sheets are available as report covers from school supply stores.
- Have students read the lab, write their hypotheses, and make data tables before class. Or copy and distribute datasheets and rubrics.

 UNIT RESOURCE BOOK, pp. 194–202

SCIENCE TOOLKIT, F14

Lab Management

- This investigation can be set up with four viewing stations, each with a box testing one color of light. Students can circulate to each box.
- Remind students that they should examine each of the four objects in four colors of light.

INCLUSION If you have physically challenged students in your class, you might make their boxes before class. Team up color-blind students with those who can distinguish colors.

CHAPTER INVESTIGATION

Wavelength and Color

OVERVIEW AND PURPOSE Stage managers use color filters to change the look of a scene. The color an object appears to have depends on both the wavelengths of light shining on it and the wavelengths of light it reflects. In this exercise, you will investigate the factors that affect these wavelengths and so affect the color of an object. You will

- make a light box
- study the effect of different colors of light on objects of different colors

Problem

How does the appearance of objects of different colors change in different colors of light?

Hypothesize

Read the procedure below and look at the sample notebook page. Predict what color each object will appear to be in each color of light. Give a reason for each prediction.

Procedure

1 Draw a data table like the one in the sample **Science Notebook.**

2 Make 3 color filters by cutting a 10 cm (4 in.) square from each color of acetate.

3 Make a 3 cm (1 in.) wide hole in the middle of the top of the box. This will be the viewing hole.

4 Make an 8 cm (3 in.) hole in one end of the box. This will be the light hole.

5 You will observe each of the four colored objects four times—with no filter and with the red, blue, and green filters. Use masking tape to position the filters in the light hole, as shown.

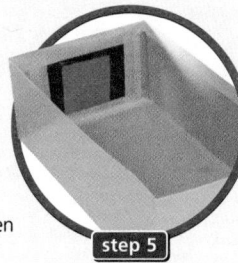

step 5

MATERIALS
- 3 sheets of acetate (red, blue, and green)
- ruler
- scissors
- shoe box
- masking tape
- light source
- 4 solid-colored objects (white, black, red, and yellow)

INVESTIGATION RESOURCES

 CHAPTER INVESTIGATION, Wavelength and Color
- Level A, pp. 194–197
- Level B, pp. 198–201
- Level C, p. 202

Advanced students should complete Levels B & C.

Writing a Lab Report, D12–13

Technology Resources

Customize this student lab as needed or look for an alternative. Print rubrics to assess student lab reports.

 Lab Generator CD-ROM

6 Place the light box on a flat surface near a strong white light source such as sunlight or a bright lamp. Position the box with the uncovered light hole facing the light source. Place the white object inside the box, look through the eye hole, and observe the object's color. Record your observations.

step 7

7 Use the light box to test each of the combinations of object color and filter shown in the table on the sample notebook page. Record your results.

▶ Observe and Analyze [Write It Up]

1. **RECORD OBSERVATIONS** Be sure your data table is complete.

2. **COMPARE** What color did the red object appear to be when viewed with a blue filter? a red filter?

▶ Conclude [Write It Up]

1. **INTERPRET** Answer your problem question.

2. **ANALYZE** Compare your results to your hypotheses. How do the results support your hypotheses?

3. **IDENTIFY VARIABLES** What different variables affected the outcome of your experiment?

4. **INFER** Why do colors of objects appear to change in different types of light?

5. **IDENTIFY LIMITS** What possible limitations or sources of error could have affected your results?

6. **APPLY** If you were going to perform on a stage that was illuminated using several different color filters, what color clothing should you wear in order to look as bright and colorful as possible?

▶ INVESTIGATE Further

CHALLENGE Perform this experiment using different kinds of artificial light. Try it with a low-wattage incandescent bulb, a high-wattage incandescent bulb, a fluorescent bulb, or a full-spectrum bulb. How do different kinds of artificial light affect the colors that objects appear to be?

Wavelength and Color

Problem

How does the appearance of objects of different colors change in different colors of light?

Hypothesize

Observe and Analyze

Table 1. Predicted and Observed Colors of Objects with Different Colored Filters

Predicted	no filter	red filter	blue filter	green filter
white object				
black object				
red object				
yellow object				
Observed	no filter	red filter	blue filter	green filter
white object				

▶ Observe and Analyze [Write It Up]

SAMPLE DATA White object: white in white light, red in red light, blue in blue light, green in green light; Black object: black in all colors of light; Red object: red in white and red light, purple in blue light, and yellow in green light; Yellow object: yellow in white light, orange in red light, green in blue light, and yellow-green in green light.

1. See students' data tables.

2. purple, red

▶ Conclude [Write It Up]

1. The color of an object depends both on the wavelengths of the light that shines on it and the wavelengths that it reflects.

2. Student answers will vary.

3. The variables are the color of the object and the color of the filter.

4. The color that an object reflects depends on the type of light shining on it.

5. Possible limitations or sources of error might include the shade of the colored acetate, the brightness of the light, leakage of white light into the box, and a person's sense of color.

6. You should wear white so your clothing will reflect any filter color.

▶ INVESTIGATE Further

CHALLENGE Results will vary depending on the type of light bulb tested. Different kinds of light bulbs emit different wavelengths of light.

Post-Lab Discussion

• Copy the data table onto the board. Have students fill in the object colors they observed. Discuss why results might have varied. Ask if other variables were introduced in the experiment.

• Ask students why it is wise to examine a paint sample in the same kind of light that it will be used in. Discuss how the objects appeared under various kinds of artificial lighting.

BACK TO

the **BIG** idea

Have students compare the frequency of the following EM waves: a burning ember glowing red, a yellow candle flame, the blue-white flame of a blow-torch. *The colors represent different frequencies of light. The red glowing ember has low frequency, the yellow candle flame has a higher frequency, and the blue-white flame of the blow-torch has the highest frequency.*

○ KEY CONCEPTS SUMMARY

SECTION 3.1
Ask: What is the spatial relationship between the electrical field and the magnetic field of an EM wave? *They are at right angles to each other.*

SECTION 3.2
Ask: What determines the characteristics of an EM wave? *frequency*

Ask: How would the wave pictured change if its frequency were increased? *The wavelength would be smaller.*

SECTION 3.3
Ask: What is the difference between the light produced from the two pictures? *The incandescent light bulb produces light from heat. The caterpillar produces light from chemical reactions.*

SECTION 3.4
Ask: What does a prism do? *separates white light into its component wavelengths*

Review Concepts

- Big Idea Flow Chart, p. T17

- Chapter Outline, p. T23–T24

---

3 Chapter Review

the **BIG** idea

Electromagnetic waves transfer energy through radiation.

CONTENT REVIEW
CLASSZONE.COM

◀ KEY CONCEPTS SUMMARY

3.1 Electromagnetic waves have unique traits.

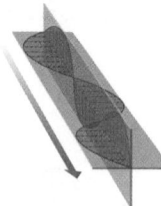

- Electromagnetic (EM) waves are made of vibrating electric and magnetic fields.
- EM waves travel at the speed of light through a vacuum.
- EM waves transfer energy and can interact with matter.

VOCABULARY
electromagnetic wave p. 73
radiation p. 75

3.2 Electromagnetic waves have many uses.

- EM waves are grouped by frequency on the EM spectrum.
- The EM spectrum is divided into radio waves, microwaves, infrared light, visible light, ultraviolet light, x-rays, and gamma rays.

VOCABULARY
EM spectrum p. 80
radio waves p. 82
microwaves p. 83
visible light p. 84
infrared light p. 84
ultraviolet light p. 85
x-rays p. 86
gamma rays p. 86

3.3 The Sun is the source of most visible light.

- Most visible light comes from the Sun.
- Many living organisms produce visible light for their own use.
- Humans produce visible light artificially.

VOCABULARY
incandescence p. 89
luminescence p. 89
bioluminescence p. 89
fluorescence p. 91

3.4 Light waves interact with materials.

- Reflection, transmission, and absorption affect what light we see.
- Light can be scattered and polarized.
- Visible light is made up of individual color wavelengths.
- The primary colors are red, blue, and green.
- The primary pigments are yellow, cyan, and magenta.

VOCABULARY
transmission p. 93
absorption p. 93
scattering p. 95
polarization p. 96
prism p. 97
primary colors p. 98
primary pigments p. 99

Technology Resources

Have students visit **ClassZone.com** or use the CD-ROM for a cumulative review of concepts.

Engage students in a whole-class interactive review of Key Concepts. Edit content as you wish.

CONTENT REVIEW

CONTENT REVIEW CD-ROM

POWER PRESENTATIONS

Reviewing Vocabulary

Make a four-square diagram for each of the listed terms. Write the term in the center. Define the term in one square. Write characteristics, examples, and nonexamples in other squares. A sample is shown below.

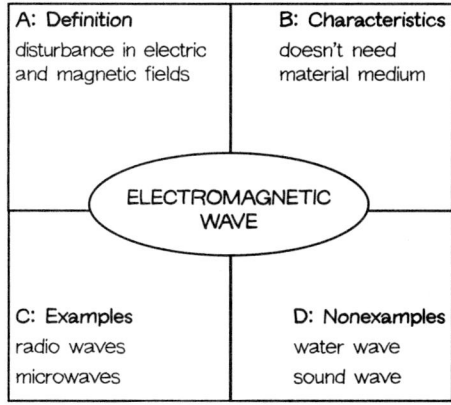

A: Definition	B: Characteristics
disturbance in electric and magnetic fields	doesn't need material medium

ELECTROMAGNETIC WAVE

C: Examples	D: Nonexamples
radio waves microwaves	water wave sound wave

1. gamma rays	6. radiation
2. infrared light	7. bioluminescence
3. transmission	8. EM spectrum
4. absorption	9. incandescence
5. pigment	10. polarization

Reviewing Key Concepts

Multiple Choice *Choose the letter of the best answer.*

11. An electromagnetic wave is a disturbance that transfers energy through a field. In this sense, a disturbance is the same as a
    a. confusion
    c. vibration
    b. magnification
    d. conflict

12. Unlike mechanical waves, EM waves can travel through
    a. a vacuum
    c. the ground
    b. water
    d. air

13. A light year is a measure of
    a. time
    c. speed
    b. distance
    d. wavelength

14. The Sun and a light bulb both produce light through
    a. bioluminescence
    c. luminescence
    b. incandescence
    d. polarization

15. Which of the following types of light bulb converts ultraviolet waves into visible light waves?
    a. incandescent
    c. halogen
    b. fluorescent
    d. tungsten

16. An object seen through a translucent material appears less clear than one seen through transparent material because the translucent material
    a. transmits none of the light coming from the object
    b. reflects all the light coming from the object
    c. transmits all the light coming from the object
    d. diffuses some light coming from the object

17. An object appears red because it
    a. reflects light waves of all colors
    b. reflects light waves of red
    c. absorbs light waves of red
    d. transmits light waves of all colors

18. Primary colors of light can combine to make
    a. black light
    c. primary pigments
    b. white light
    d. ultraviolet light

Short Answer *Write a short answer to each question.*

19. What parts of an EM wave have amplitude?

20. How can EM waves be used to measure distance in space?

21. Describe how microwaves are used in communications.

22. What two properties of an EM wave change as you move from one part of the EM spectrum to another?

23. How does visible light differ from other EM waves? How is it similar?

24. Explain briefly how an incandescent light bulb works.

ASSESSMENT RESOURCES

 UNIT ASSESSMENT BOOK
- Chapter Test A, pp. 46–49
- Chapter Test B, pp. 50–53
- Chapter Test C, pp. 54–57
- Alternative Assessment, pp. 58–59

 SPANISH ASSESSMENT BOOK
Spanish Chapter Test, pp. 289–292

Technology Resources

Edit test items and answer choices.

 Test Generator CD-ROM

Visit **ClassZone.com** to extend test practice.

 Test Practice

Reviewing Vocabulary

1. A: EM waves with highest frequencies and energies; B: 10^{19} Hz to 10^{24} Hz; C: the Sun; D: radio waves

2. A: EM frequencies between microwaves and visible light; B: invisible; C: lamps; D: x-rays

3. A: the passage of an EM wave through a medium; B: makes it possible to see through things; C: clear glass; D: wood

4. A: disappearance of an EM wave into the medium; B: causes materials to be opaque; C: wood; D: air

5. A: material used to mix colors; B: subtracts wavelengths rather than adding them; C: paint; D: colored light

6. A: transfer of energy in the form of EM waves; B: spreads outward in straight line from source; passes through vacuum; C: light from Sun; D: ocean waves

7. A: production of light by living organisms; B: light produced from chemical reactions; C: firefly; D: fire

8. A: range of all EM frequencies; B: smooth, gradual progression; C: microwaves, D: ultrasound

9. A: production of light from high temperatures; B: dangerous for living tissue; C: sunlight; D: firefly

10. A: filtering light so that all of its waves vibrate in the same direction; B: affects only electric fields of wave; C: sunglasses; D: glare

Reviewing Key Concepts

11. c	14. b	17. b
12. a	15. b	18. b
13. b	16. d	

19. electric and magnetic fields

20. by how far they travel in a certain amount of time

21. Cell phones and radar send and receive microwave signals.

22. wavelength and frequency

23. Visible light has different frequencies and wavelengths. Visible light, like all EM waves, is a disturbance in a field.

24. Electricity passes through the filament. Resistance causes the filament to heat up and glow.

Thinking Critically

25. absorption

26. Violet light should penetrate even deeper into the water than blue.

27. Objects near the ocean floor should appear blue.

28. when it interacts with a medium

29. The light source must contain red wavelengths and the object must reflect red light.

30. blue, all the other colors

31. Sample answer: Incandescent lighting wastes energy as heat, and lighting is more energy efficient.

32. The black numbers could be caused by polarizing filters at right angles that would screen out all light.

33. Like a sieve, a polarizing filter screens out certain kinds of light waves while letting others pass through. Unlike a sieve, a polarizing filter screens waves on the basis of orientation rather than size.

34. Fluorescent bulbs remain cooler than regular or halogen bulbs, so they waste less energy as heat.

35. blue, because only blue wavelengths pass through filter to your eye

the **BIG** idea

36. Sample answer: A cell phone uses microwaves. Cell phones depend on an overlapping network of cells. Each cell has a tower that sends and receives microwave signals. The tower connects cell phones to each other or the regular wired telephone system.

37. See students' summaries.

38. Infrared waves leave the radiator. They are transmitted by the air, which absorbs only a little of their energy. The kitten absorbs waves that travel toward it, and is warmed by energy transferred in the form of heat.

UNIT PROJECTS

Collect schedules, materials lists, and questions. Be sure dates and materials are obtainable, and questions are focused.

 Unit Projects, pp. 5–10

Thinking Critically

The diagram below shows how far different wavelengths of visible light penetrate into ocean water. Use information from this diagram to answer the next three questions.

25. **OBSERVE** An EM wave can interact with a material in different ways. Which type of interaction keeps some light waves from reaching the ocean floor?

26. **PREDICT** How would violet light behave in the same water? Think of where violet is on the color spectrum.

27. **SYNTHESIZE** How is the apparent color of objects near the ocean floor affected by the interactions shown in the diagram?

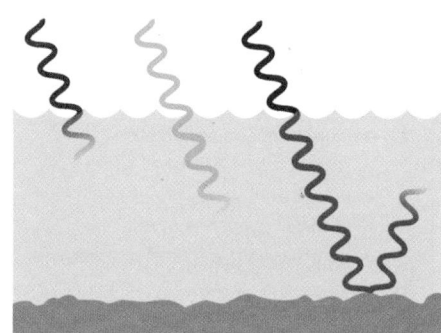

28. **ANALYZE** Under what circumstances can an EM wave begin to convert some of its electromagnetic energy into other forms of energy?

29. **ANALYZE** What two things must be true about the light source and the material of an object for you to see an object as red?

30. **PREDICT** If you shine a blue light on a white object, what color will the object appear to be? What color light would you need to add to make the white object appear white?

31. **APPLY** Why might incandescent lighting become less common in the future? Explain your reasoning.

---

32. **CAUSE AND EFFECT** Liquid crystal displays like the ones used in some calculators work by polarizing light. Describe how two polarizing filters could cause the numbers on the display panel to appear black.

33. **COMPARE AND CONTRAST** In what way would a sieve be a good model for a polarizing light filter? In what ways would it not be?

34. **CONTRAST** In what ways is a fluorescent bulb more efficient than incandescent and halogen bulbs?

35. **PREDICT** What color will a white object appear to be if you look at it through a blue filter?

the **BIG** idea

36. Return to the question on page 70. Answer the question again, using what you have learned in the chapter.

37. **SUMMARIZE** Write a summary of this chapter. Use the Big Idea statement from page 70 as the title for your summary. Use the Key Concepts listed on page 70 as the topic sentences for each paragraph. Provide an example for each key concept.

38. **ANALYZE** Describe all of the EM wave behaviors and interactions that occur when a radiator warms a kitten.

UNIT PROJECTS

Check your schedule for your unit project. How are you doing? Be sure that you've placed data or notes from your research in your project folder.

MONITOR AND RETEACH

If students have trouble applying the concepts in items 25–27, have them create a three-part visual aid showing how deeply various colors of light would penetrate the water.

Part 1 should show red, orange, yellow, green, blue, indigo, and violet light; **Part 2** should show relative frequencies of the various colors of light; **Part 3** should list the relative energies of the various colors of light. Students may benefit from summarizing one or more sections of the chapter.

 Summarizing the Chapter, pp. 212–213

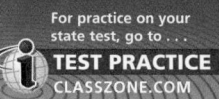
Interpreting Diagrams

1. c
2. d
3. a
4. c

Interpreting Diagrams

The diagram below shows part of the electromagnetic (EM) spectrum. The lower band shows frequency in hertz. The upper band shows part of the spectrum used by different technologies.

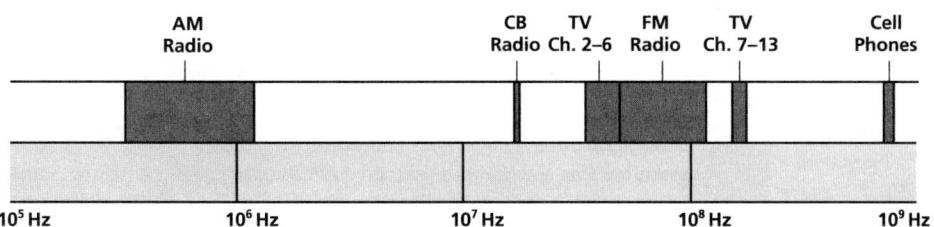

Use the diagram to answer the following questions.

1. Which of the technologies listed below uses the highest frequencies?

a. AM radio
b. CB radio
c. FM radio
d. TV channels 2–6

2. If you were receiving a signal at a frequency of nearly 10^9 Hz, what would you be using?

a. a CB radio
b. an AM radio
c. an FM radio
d. a cell phone

3. A television station broadcasts its video signal at 10^6 Hz and its audio signal at 10^8 Hz. To receive the broadcasts, your television would need to receive

a. both AM and FM radio
b. both CB and AM radio
c. both CB and FM radio
d. both CB radio and cell phone transmissions

4. Signals with similar frequencies sometimes interfere with each other. For this reason, you might expect interference in which of the following:

a. lower television channels from cell phones
b. upper television channels from FM radio
c. lower television channels from FM radio
d. upper television channels from cell phones

Extended Response

Answer the two questions below in detail. Include some of the terms from the word box. Underline each term you use in your answer.

frequency	energy	interaction
field	medium	vacuum

5. What are the similarities and differences between mechanical waves and electromagnetic waves?

6. What are some advantages and disadvantages of different types of artificial lighting?

Chapter 3: **Electromagnetic Waves 105** **C**

Extended Response

5. RUBRIC

4 points for a response that correctly answers the question and that uses the following terms accurately:

- wavelength
- amplitude
- frequency
- medium
- field

Sample: Mechanical and electromagnetic waves are disturbances that transfer energy. They have underline wavelength, amplitude, and frequency. Mechanical waves need a medium, while EM waves do not. EM waves are disturbances in electric and magnetic fields. Mechanical waves give up some energy when they travel, but EM waves can travel in a vacuum without losing energy.

3 points answers the question correctly and uses three of the listed terms accurately

2 points response is correct, but partial, and uses two terms correctly

1 point for a response that is partially correct, but contains some inaccuracies

6. RUBRIC

4 points for a response that correctly identifies advantages and disadvantages of the following types of artificial lighting:

- incandescent
- fluorescent
- halogen
- LED

Sample: Incandescent lighting is a good source of bright light, is relatively cheap, and is convenient to use. Fluorescent lights waste less energy than incandescent lights, because fluorescent bulbs produce less heat and they last longer. Halogen bulbs last longer than incandescent bulbs, but halogen bulbs are more of a fire and injury hazard because they get very hot. LEDs are very cheap, last a long time, are safe, and waste almost no energy.

3 points identifies advantages and disadvantages of three types of artificial lighting listed

2 points identifies advantages and disadvantages of two types of artificial lighting listed

1 point identifies advantages and disadvantages of one type of artificial lighting listed

METACOGNITIVE ACTIVITY

Have students answer the following questions in their **Science Notebook:**

1. What questions do you still have about electromagnetic waves?

2. What were you surprised to find out about visible light?

3. How do the concepts of this chapter relate to your Unit Project?

FOCUS

▶ Set Learning Goals

Students will

- Observe how scientists historically studied light.
- Examine how observations about the properties of light led to explanations of its behavior.
- Make a camera obscura and write a news article about a discovery regarding light.

National Science Education Standards

A.9.a–g Understandings About Scientific Inquiry

E.6.a–c Understandings About Science and Technology

F.5.a–e, F.5.g Science and Technology in Society

G.1.a–b Science as a Human Endeavor

G.2.a Nature of Science

G.3.a–c History of Science

INSTRUCT

History Connection

Point out to students that the top half of the timeline shows some major events in the scientific study of light that were historically recorded. The bottom half of the timeline illustrates advances in the technology that enables study of light and practical applications of the results of this study. The two gaps in the timeline represent periods of time in which no advances in the study of light are highlighted.

Technology

REFLECTING TELESCOPES The first telescope was a refractor, built by Galileo, and many current telescopes use lenses to refract light. When light travels through lenses, it bends. The amount it is bent depends on the shape, composition, and thickness of the lens. Many telescopes are both reflecting and refracting because they use both mirrors and lenses.

TIMELINES in Science

THE STORY OF LIGHT

Light has fascinated people since ancient times. The earliest ideas about light were closely associated with beliefs and observations about vision. Over the centuries, philosophers and scientists developed an increasingly better understanding of light as a physical reality that obeyed the laws of physics.

With increased understanding of the nature and behavior of light has come the ability to use light as a tool. Many applications of light technology have led to improvements in human visual abilities. People can now make images of a wide range of objects that were invisible to earlier generations. The study of light has also led to technologies that do not involve sight at all.

This timeline shows just a few of the many steps on the road to understanding light. The boxes below the timeline show how these discoveries have been applied and developed into new technologies.

400 B.C.
Light Travels in a Straight Line
Observing the behavior of shadows, Chinese philosopher Mo-Ti finds that light travels in a straight line. His discovery helps explain why light passing through a small opening forms an upside-down image.

300 B.C.
Reflection Obeys Law
Greek mathematician Euclid discovers that light striking mirrors obeys the law of reflection. The angle at which light reflects off a mirror is equal to the angle at which it strikes the mirror.

EVENTS

| 450 B.C. | 425 B.C. | 400 B.C. | 375 B.C. | 350 B.C. | 325 B.C. | 300 B.C. |

APPLICATIONS AND TECHNOLOGY

APPLICATION

Camera Obscura

The principle described by Mo-Ti in 400 B.C. led to the development of the camera obscura. When light from an object shines through a small hole into a dark room, an image of the object appears on the far wall. The darkened room is called, in Latin, *camera obscura*. Because light travels in a straight line, the highest points on the object appear at the lowest points on the image; thus, the image appears upside down. Room-sized versions of the camera obscura like the one shown here were a popular attraction in the late 1800s.

DIFFERENTIATE INSTRUCTION

Advanced Tell students that a line that is perpendicular to a flat surface is called the *normal*. Have students state generalizations about the following angles: the angle formed by the normal and a beam of light hitting a surface and the angle formed by the normal and the beam of light reflecting from the surface. *Sample answer: The angle formed by the normal and a beam of light hitting a surface is equal to the angle formed by the normal and the beam of light reflecting from the surface.*

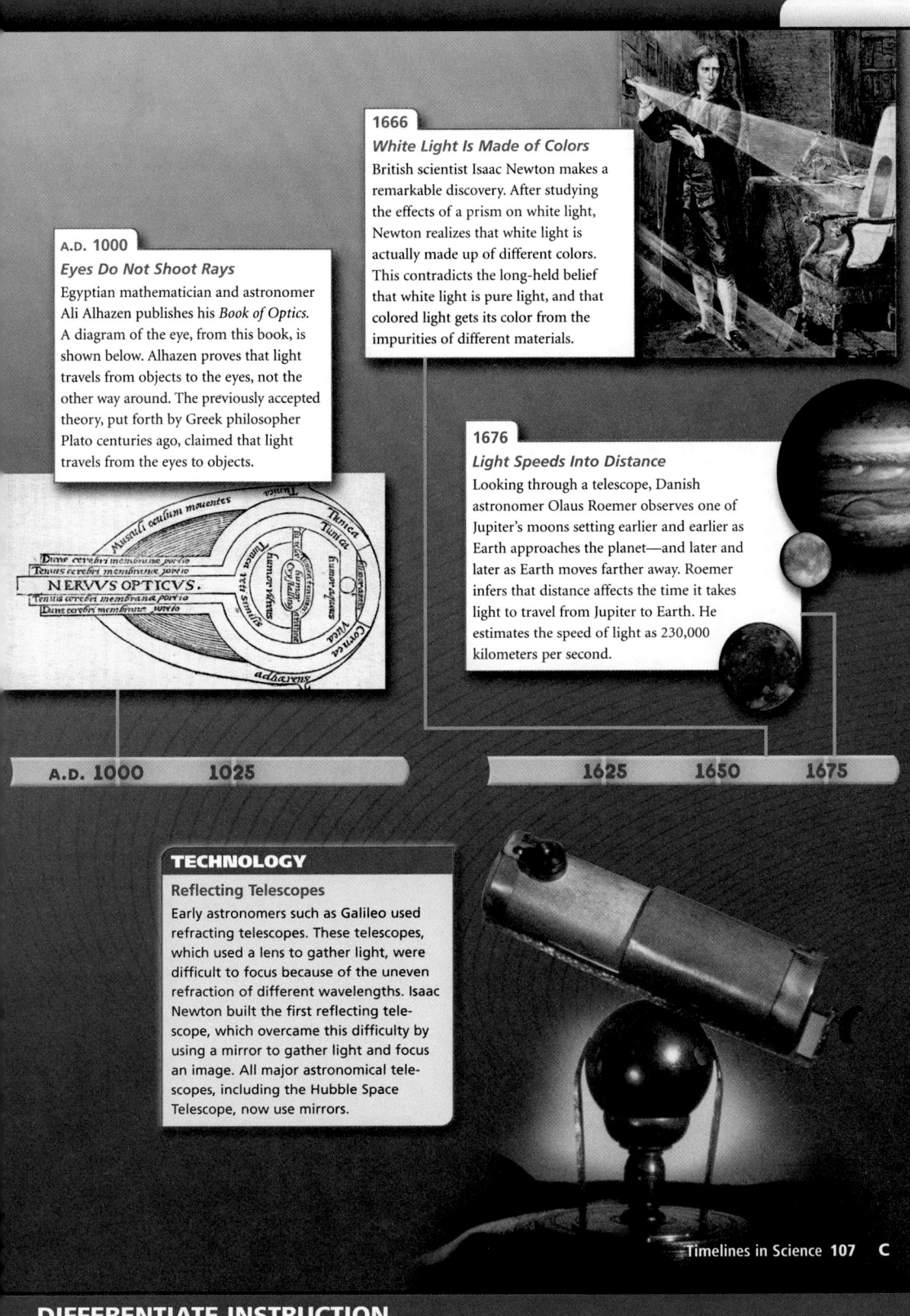

1666
White Light Is Made of Colors
British scientist Isaac Newton makes a remarkable discovery. After studying the effects of a prism on white light, Newton realizes that white light is actually made up of different colors. This contradicts the long-held belief that white light is pure light, and that colored light gets its color from the impurities of different materials.

A.D. 1000
Eyes Do Not Shoot Rays
Egyptian mathematician and astronomer Ali Alhazen publishes his *Book of Optics*. A diagram of the eye, from this book, is shown below. Alhazen proves that light travels from objects to the eyes, not the other way around. The previously accepted theory, put forth by Greek philosopher Plato centuries ago, claimed that light travels from the eyes to objects.

1676
Light Speeds Into Distance
Looking through a telescope, Danish astronomer Olaus Roemer observes one of Jupiter's moons setting earlier and earlier as Earth approaches the planet—and later and later as Earth moves farther away. Roemer infers that distance affects the time it takes light to travel from Jupiter to Earth. He estimates the speed of light as 230,000 kilometers per second.

| A.D. 1000 | 1025 | | 1625 | 1650 | 1675 |

TECHNOLOGY
Reflecting Telescopes
Early astronomers such as Galileo used refracting telescopes. These telescopes, which used a lens to gather light, were difficult to focus because of the uneven refraction of different wavelengths. Isaac Newton built the first reflecting telescope, which overcame this difficulty by using a mirror to gather light and focus an image. All major astronomical telescopes, including the Hubble Space Telescope, now use mirrors.

Mathematics Connection
1676 Working with the knowledge available in 1676, Roemer's estimated speed of light is relatively close to the currently accepted value of 3.00×10^8 m/s. The relationship among speed, frequency, and wavelength of light (or any other wave) can be expressed by the equation $S = f\lambda$, where S is the speed, f is the frequency, and λ is the wavelength.

Integrate the Sciences
Students are familiar with the spectrum of colors seen in a rainbow. This splitting of visible light into its various colors occurs when sunlight strikes droplets of water and light is refracted into different colors. Some of the light reflects off the back surface of the drop, and it refracts further when it leaves the water drop and reenters the air. Violet light is at one end of the visible spectrum, and it is seen coming from droplets lower in the atmosphere. Violet light emerges from the droplets at an angle of approximately 40°. Red light is at the opposite end of the visible spectrum, and it is seen coming from droplets higher in the air. Red light leaves the droplets at an angle of about 42°. The other colors of light are between these two extremes.

Language Arts Connection
All types of light make up the electromagnetic spectrum, of which visible light is only a small portion. Ask: Ultrasound is sound that is in a higher range than can be heard by humans. From this meaning of *ultra-*, what conclusion might you draw about ultraviolet light? *It has a frequency higher than that of violet light.* The prefix *infra-* has the opposite meaning of the prefix *ultra-*. Based on this information, where would infrared light be located in the electromagnetic spectrum? *It would have a frequency less than that of red light.*

DIFFERENTIATE INSTRUCTION

Advanced Have students use the mathematical relationship and the speed of light shown in the Mathematics Connection on this page to make the following calculations:

1. What is the wavelength of visible light that has a frequency of 5.0×10^{14} s? $(3.00 \times 10^8 \text{ m/s})(5.0 \times 10^{14}/\text{s}) = 6.0 \times 10^{-7}$ m

2. What is the frequency of x-rays that have a wavelength of 2.0×10^{-8} m? $(3.00 \times 10^8 \text{ m/s})(2.0 \times 10^{-8} \text{ m}) = 1.5 \times 10^{16}$ s

Scientific Process

Observations of light led to hypotheses that light is a wave. Observations also support light's being a particle. Experiments that test these hypotheses support both of them. As a result, light is considered to be both a wave and a particle made up of discrete packets of energy.

Application

HOLOGRAMS Because holograms look different from various angles, holograms are difficult to reproduce. As a result, they are used on certain credit cards and other documents to help prevent forgery.

Art Connection

Art forgery is a common problem for artists, art dealers, and art buyers. Some art forgeries are so well done that special technology is necessary to tell the real item from a forgery. What is done to tell forgeries from original art? There is a difference in modern paint and paints that were used years ago, but no one wants to chip off paint from an original painting to test it. One way to test a painting without damaging it is to use ultraviolet and infrared light and x-rays.

The human eye cannot see the varnish that is painted on the top of oil paintings, but it glows under ultraviolet light. Irregularities in the varnish and places that have had paint added show up as dark spots when this light is shined on it. Infrared light penetrates layers of oil paints, and if there is an image hidden under the surface oil paints, it shows up when infrared light is shined on the painting. X-rays show dense materials, such as metals and paints that contain metallic pigments. If metallic objects or materials that are inconsistent with when the painting was supposed to have been painted are seen, forgeries can be detected.

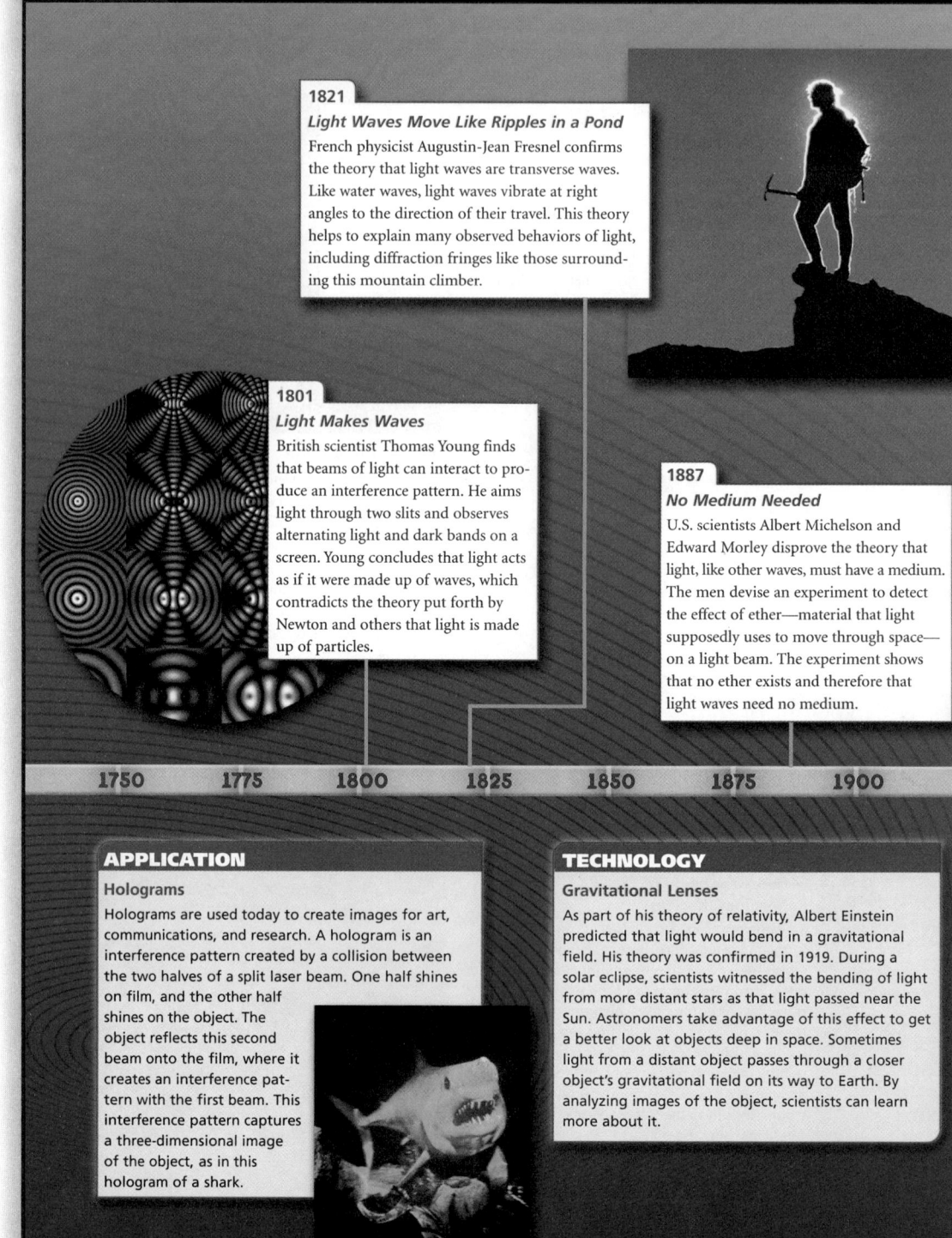

1821

Light Waves Move Like Ripples in a Pond

French physicist Augustin-Jean Fresnel confirms the theory that light waves are transverse waves. Like water waves, light waves vibrate at right angles to the direction of their travel. This theory helps to explain many observed behaviors of light, including diffraction fringes like those surrounding this mountain climber.

1801

Light Makes Waves

British scientist Thomas Young finds that beams of light can interact to produce an interference pattern. He aims light through two slits and observes alternating light and dark bands on a screen. Young concludes that light acts as if it were made up of waves, which contradicts the theory put forth by Newton and others that light is made up of particles.

1887

No Medium Needed

U.S. scientists Albert Michelson and Edward Morley disprove the theory that light, like other waves, must have a medium. The men devise an experiment to detect the effect of ether—material that light supposedly uses to move through space—on a light beam. The experiment shows that no ether exists and therefore that light waves need no medium.

| 1750 | 1775 | 1800 | 1825 | 1850 | 1875 | 1900 |

APPLICATION

Holograms

Holograms are used today to create images for art, communications, and research. A hologram is an interference pattern created by a collision between the two halves of a split laser beam. One half shines on film, and the other half shines on the object. The object reflects this second beam onto the film, where it creates an interference pattern with the first beam. This interference pattern captures a three-dimensional image of the object, as in this hologram of a shark.

TECHNOLOGY

Gravitational Lenses

As part of his theory of relativity, Albert Einstein predicted that light would bend in a gravitational field. His theory was confirmed in 1919. During a solar eclipse, scientists witnessed the bending of light from more distant stars as that light passed near the Sun. Astronomers take advantage of this effect to get a better look at objects deep in space. Sometimes light from a distant object passes through a closer object's gravitational field on its way to Earth. By analyzing images of the object, scientists can learn more about it.

DIFFERENTIATE INSTRUCTION

Below Level Have students show how light is separated into different colors by shining a light on bubbles made by using liquid dishwashing detergent. The colors can be seen better if this activity is done in a darkened room.

1960

Light Beams Line Up

U.S. inventor Theodore Harold Maiman builds a working laser by stimulating emission of light in a cylinder of ruby crystal. Laser light waves all have the same wavelength and their crests and troughs are lined up.

2001

Light Is Completely Stopped

After slowing light to the speed of a bicycle, Danish physicist Lene Vestergaard Hau brings it to a complete halt in a super-cold medium. Controlling the speed of light could revolutionize computers, communications, and other electronic technology.

 RESOURCE CENTER

CLASSZONE.COM

Learn more about current research involving light.

1925　　1950　　1975　　2000

APPLICATION

Lasers in Eye Surgery

For centuries, people have used corrective lenses to help their eyes focus images more clearly. Today, with the help of lasers, doctors can correct the eye itself. Using an ultraviolet laser, doctors remove microscopic amounts of a patient's cornea to change the way it refracts light. As a result, the eye focuses images exactly on the retina. For many nearsighted people, the surgery results in 20/20 vision or better.

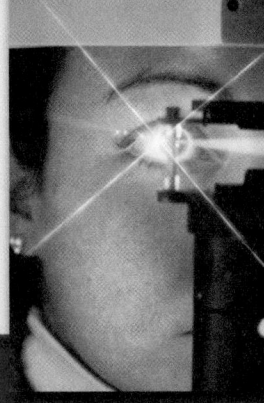

INTO THE **FUTURE**

Much of our current knowledge in science, from the workings of our bodies to the universe as a whole, is founded upon experiments that used light. Evidence from new light applications will continue to shape our knowledge. In the future, the nature of light, itself, may again come into question as new experiments are performed.

As new light microscopes are developed, scientists will gain more detailed information about how systems within our bodies work, such as how our brain cells interact with each other to perform a complex task. With powerful telescopes, scientists will gain a better understanding of the universe at its beginnings and how galaxies are formed.

Finally, as we continue to study the behavior of light, we may continue to modify its very definition. Sometimes considered a stream of particles, and other times considered waves, light is now understood to have qualities of both particles and waves.

ACTIVITIES

Make a Camera Obscura

Take a small box and paint the interior black. On one side, make a pinhole. On a side next to that one, make a hole about 5 cm in diameter.

On a bright, sunny day, hold the box so that sunlight enters the box through the pinhole. Fit your eye snugly against the larger hole and look inside.

Writing About Science

Lasers are currently used in entertainment, medicine, communication, supermarkets, and so on. Write a prediction about a specific use of lasers in the future. You might describe a new invention.

INTO THE **FUTURE**

Have students divide into two groups. Have one group list the ways they think that the use of light can provide information about the formation of the universe. Have the other group make a similar list that refers to using light to study the cells of the human body. Then have students in each group research actual scientific investigations in the area they have been assigned. Have each group prepare a presentation of their results. Presentations might consist of bulletin boards, videos done as news segments, or oral reports with visual aids.

ACTIVITIES

Make a Camera Obscura

Be sure the box does not allow any light to enter, other than the light that enters through the holes made in the box. A full-spectrum artificial light, such as a sunlamp, can be used instead of natural sunlight. Ask students to explain why a camera obscura might be a safe way to view a solar eclipse. *The gradual darkening of the Sun could be viewed on the side of the camera. Looking directly at the Sun can damage eyes, but the intensity of the light in the camera obscura is much less than direct sunlight.*

Writing About Science

Students can use Internet sources for information, as well as reference books. While writing their predictions, students should be aware of current uses of lasers.

Technology Resources

Students can visit **ClassZone.com** for current news about new advances in technology involving light.

DIFFERENTIATE INSTRUCTION

Inclusion Pair any visually impaired student with another student who can explain the timeline content to them. When making the camera, outline with yarn the area on the side of the camera where the image is shown. Have the visually impaired student feel the box, the two holes, and the area where the image is shown.

Light and Optics

Physical Science
UNIFYING PRINCIPLES

PRINCIPLE 1

Matter is made of particles too small to see.

PRINCIPLE 2

Matter changes form and moves from place to place.

PRINCIPLE 3

Energy changes from one form to another, but it cannot be created or destroyed.

PRINCIPLE 4

Physical forces affect the movement of all matter on Earth and throughout the universe.

Unit: Waves, Sound, and Light
BIG IDEAS

CHAPTER 1
Waves

Waves transfer energy and interact in predictable ways.

CHAPTER 2
Sound

Sound waves transfer energy through vibrations.

CHAPTER 3
Electromagnetic Waves

Electromagnetic waves transfer energy through radiation.

CHAPTER 4
Light and Optics

Optical tools depend on the wave behavior of light.

CHAPTER 4
KEY CONCEPTS

SECTION **4.1**

SECTION **4.2**

SECTION **4.3**

SECTION **4.4**

Mirrors form images by reflecting light.

1. Optics is the science of light and vision.

2. Mirrors use regular reflection.

3. Shape determines how mirrors form images.

Lenses form images by refracting light.

1. A medium can refract light.

2. Shape determines how lenses form images.

The eye is a natural optical tool.

1. The eye gathers and focuses light.

2. Corrective lenses can improve vision.

Optical technology makes use of light waves.

1. Mirrors and lenses can be combined to make more powerful optical tools.

2. Lasers use light in new ways.

(T) The Big Idea Flow Chart is available on p. T25 in the **UNIT TRANSPARENCY BOOK.**

Previewing Content

SECTION

4.1 Mirrors form images by reflecting light. pp. 113–118

1. Optics is the science of light and vision.
Optics is the study and application of visible light and its interaction with the eye to produce vision. Optical tools can improve vision or use light to do work.

2. Mirrors use regular reflection.
A mirror forms an image by reflecting light from an object. Light reflecting off a mirror follows the **law of reflection,** which states that the angle formed by a line perpendicular to the mirror and the light hitting the mirror (the incident ray) is equal to the angle formed by the perpendicular and the light leaving the mirror (the reflected ray).

3. Shape determines how mirrors form images.
Different mirror shapes produce different kinds of images.
- A flat mirror produces a virtual image. The image seems to come from behind the mirror.
- A **convex** mirror reflects light waves so that they spread out, never meeting at a focal point.
- A **concave** mirror reflects light waves so that they converge at a **focal point.**

Convex Mirror	Concave Mirror, Far Away	Concave Mirror, Up Close

The images formed in mirrors depend on the curve of the mirror's surface and the distance of the object from the mirror.

SECTION

4.2 Lenses form images by refracting light. pp. 119–125

1. A medium can refract light.
When a light wave moves into a new medium, it may change speed. If it hits the medium at an angle, one side of the wave changes speed before the other side, bending the wave. This is refraction.
- When light waves refract, they can bend toward or away from the normal.
- Refraction can occur when light moves from cool air in the sky to warmer air near the ground. Mirages occur in this way.

2. Shape determines how lenses form images.
Lenses produce predictable images when waves of light pass through the lens and refract. The shape of the lens determines the way objects look.
- A convex lens refracts parallel light waves so they meet at a focal point. As with a concave mirror, the type of image formed depends on the distance between the object and the lens.
- A concave lens spreads out light waves, which do not meet at a focal point. As with a convex mirror, the image formed is upright and reduced in size.

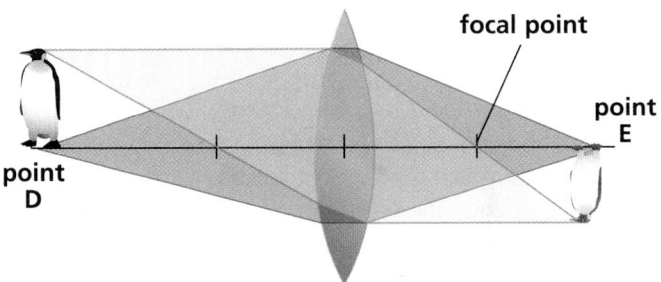

As the diagram shows, the image is inverted and reduced if the object is more than two focal lengths from the lens. Between one and two focal lengths from the lens, the image is inverted and enlarged. If the object is within one focal length from the lens, the image is virtual, upright, and enlarged.

Common Misconceptions

FULL-LENGTH REFLECTION Students might think that a flat mirror turns the image of a person's body around. Actually, in a mirror image a person's left hand still appears on the left. The image is reversed front to back, but not left to right.

 This misconception is addressed on p. 116.

MISCONCEPTION DATABASE
CLASSZONE.COM Background on student misconceptions

MAGNIFYING GLASSES Students may think that a magnifying glass always magnifies images of objects. However, a magnifying glass is simply a convex lens. It magnifies only when an object is the right distance from the lens.

 This misconception is addressed on p. 122.

Previewing Content

SECTION

4.3 **The eye is a natural optical tool.**
pp. 126–130

1. The eye gathers and focuses light.
Light travels through the eye from the **cornea,** through the **pupil,** through the lens, and hits the **retina.**
- The cornea and the lens are convex lenses that refract light in the eye.
- Pupil size, controlled by the iris, determines how much light enters.
- Light strikes the retina, forming a reduced, inverted image. The retina has cells called rods that distinguish brightness and cells called cones that detect color.

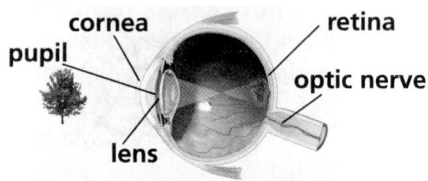

- The brain receives signals from the retina and interprets the image as an object that is right side up.

2. Corrective lenses can improve vision.
Vision is blurry if an image does not fall exactly on the retina. This occurs because the shape of the eye is imperfect or because the eye's lens does not work correctly. Corrective lenses, contact lenses, or surgery can correct these problems.
- Nearsightedness occurs when the image focuses in front of the retina. A corrective concave lens spreads out the light rays before they enter the eye and moves the image back toward the retina.
- Farsightedness occurs when the image focuses behind the retina. A corrective convex lens refracts the light rays inward before they enter the eye and moves the image forward toward the retina.
- Cornea shape can be changed by surgery so that the image will focus on the retina.
- Contact lenses correct vision by changing the way the cornea refracts light.

SECTION

4.4 **Optical technology makes use of light waves.** pp. 131–139

1. Mirrors and lenses can be combined to make more powerful optical tools.
Microscopes enlarge tiny objects by combining convex lenses. The objective lens produces an enlarged image. The eyepiece lens forms an enlarged virtual image of the first image.

A **refracting telescope** combines convex lenses. Because the object is more than two focal lengths from the objective lens, the first image is reduced. The eyepiece lens forms an enlarged virtual image of the first image.

A **reflecting telescope** has a concave mirror that focuses an image of the object. The eyepiece lens then forms a virtual enlarged image of the first image. A small flat mirror redirects the image to the telescope's side.

A **film camera** uses a convex lens to focus an image on light-sensitive film. A **digital camera** focuses the image on a sensor, which converts light waves into electrical charges and sends the information to a small computer. The computer reconstructs the image and displays it.

2. Lasers use light in new ways.
A **laser** is intense and concentrated light that carries a lot of energy. A laser beam has light waves with a single wavelength and a pure color. Lasers are made in tubes containing a stimulus that gives off light. The light is concentrated into a beam as it passes back and forth between two mirrors.

Fiber optics use total internal reflection to send signals through thin transparent fibers. Light reflects off the internal surface of a fiber. Fiber optic technology is important in communications and in medical imaging.

Common Misconceptions

REFRACTION IN THE EYE Students commonly think that refraction takes place only in the lens of the eye. Actually, most of the refraction takes place in the cornea, which is a membrane that covers the eye. The lens makes additional focusing adjustments so the image falls exactly on the retina.

 This misconception is addressed on p. 127.

 MISCONCEPTION DATABASE
CLASSZONE.COM Background on student misconceptions

REFRACTING TELESCOPES Some students may think that each lens of a refracting telescope enlarges the image of the object being observed and that the main function of a telescope is to produce an enlarged image. The main function of the objective lens is not to magnify the object, but to collect as much light from the faraway object as possible to clarify the object's details. The objective lens actually produces a slightly reduced image.

 This misconception is addressed on p. 133.

Previewing Labs

Lab Generator CD-ROM
Edit these Pupil Edition labs and generate alternative labs.

EXPLORE the BIG idea

How Does a Spoon Reflect Your Face? p. 111 Students observe their reflections in the concave and convex surfaces of a spoon.	**TIME** 10 minutes **MATERIALS** shiny metal spoon
Why Do Things Look Different Through Water? p. 111 Students examine objects while looking though a glass of water.	**TIME** 10 minutes **MATERIALS** glass jar filled with water
Internet Activity: Optics, p. 111 Students are introduced to the science of light and vision.	**TIME** 20 minutes **MATERIALS** computer with Internet access

SECTION 4.1

EXPLORE Reflection, p. 113 Students observe how different surface textures of aluminum foil affect reflection.	**TIME** 10 minutes **MATERIALS** one square sheet of new aluminum foil
INVESTIGATE The Law of Reflection, p. 115 Students make a periscope and analyze how light travels through it.	**TIME** 30 minutes **MATERIALS** quart-sized milk or juice carton, scissors, 0.5 m masking tape, 2 mirrors slightly smaller than the bottom of the carton, protractor

SECTION 4.2

EXPLORE Refraction, p. 119 Students explore refraction of light in water and in mineral oil.	**TIME** 10 minutes **MATERIALS** clear plastic cup, pencil, 0.25 L water, 0.25 L mineral oil
CHAPTER INVESTIGATION **Looking at Lenses,** pp. 124–125 Students use a convex lens to focus different types of images.	**TIME** 40 minutes **MATERIALS** index card, marker, 0.25 lbs. modeling clay, convex lens, meter stick, flashlight, 6 cm masking tape, white poster board

SECTION 4.3

EXPLORE Focusing Vision, p. 126 Students explore the way the eye focuses close and distant images.	**TIME** 10 minutes **MATERIALS** object to view
INVESTIGATE Vision, p. 128 Students use a magnifying glass to observe an image, as an analogy to the way an image forms in the eye.	**TIME** 10 minutes **MATERIALS** convex lens, index card, white paper plate, 0.25 kg modeling clay, lamp

SECTION 4.4

EXPLORE Combining Lenses, p. 131 Students determine how two convex lenses work together to focus different types of images.	**TIME** 10 minutes **MATERIALS** 2 convex lenses, 0.25 kg modeling clay, 2 index cards, object to view
INVESTIGATE Optical Tools, p. 134 Students make a model of a refracting telescope and determine how to position the lenses to produce a clear image.	**TIME** 30 minutes **MATERIALS** 2 convex lenses, 2 cardboard tubes, 0.5 m duct tape

R Additional **INVESTIGATION,** Bending Light, A, B, & C, pp. 273–281; Teacher Instructions, pp. 284–285

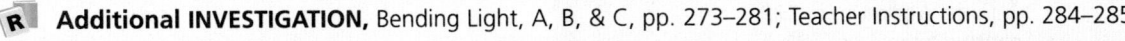

Previewing Chapter Resources

| | **INTEGRATED TECHNOLOGY** | **LABS AND ACTIVITIES** |

CHAPTER 4
Light and Optics

 CLASSZONE.COM
- eEdition Plus
- EasyPlanner Plus
- Misconception Database
- Content Review
- Test Practice
- Visualization
- Simulation
- Resource Centers
- Internet Activity: Optics
- Math Tutorial

 SCILINKS.ORG
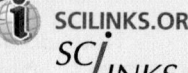 SCI*LINKS*

 CD-ROMS
- eEdition
- EasyPlanner
- Power Presentations
- Content Review
- Lab Generator
- Test Generator

 AUDIO CDS
- Audio Readings
- Audio Readings in Spanish

 EXPLORE the Big Idea, p. 111
- How Does a Spoon Reflect Your Face?
- Why Do Things Look Different Through Water?
- Internet Activity: Optics

 UNIT RESOURCE BOOK
Unit Projects, pp. 5–10

 Lab Generator CD-ROM
Generate customized labs.

SECTION
4.1 Mirrors form images by reflecting light.
pp. 113–118

Time: 2 periods (1 block)
 Lesson Plan, pp. 214–215

- **VISUALIZATION**, Reflection
- **MATH TUTORIAL**

 UNIT TRANSPARENCY BOOK
- Big Idea Flow Chart, p. T25
- Daily Vocabulary Scaffolding, p. T26
- Note-Taking Model, p. T27
- 3-Minute Warm-Up, p. T28

- EXPLORE Reflection, p. 113
- INVESTIGATE The Law of Reflection, p. 115
- Math in Science, p. 118

 UNIT RESOURCE BOOK
- Datasheet, The Law of Reflection, p. 223
- Math Support & Practice, pp. 262–263

SECTION
4.2 Lenses form images by refracting light.
pp. 119–125

Time: 3 periods (1.5 block)
 Lesson Plan, pp. 225–226

 SIMULATION, Using Lenses to Form Images

UNIT TRANSPARENCY BOOK
- Daily Vocabulary Scaffolding, p. T26
- 3-Minute Warm-Up, p. T28
- "How a Convex Lens Forms an Image" Visual, p. T30

- EXPLORE Refraction, p. 119
- CHAPTER INVESTIGATION, Looking at Lenses, pp. 124–125

 UNIT RESOURCE BOOK
- CHAPTER INVESTIGATION, Looking at Lenses, Levels A, B, & C, pp. 264–272
- Additional INVESTIGATION, Bending Light, A, B, & C, pp. 273–281

SECTION
4.3 The eye is a natural optical tool. pp. 126–130

Time: 2 periods (1 block)
 Lesson Plan, pp. 235–236

 UNIT TRANSPARENCY BOOK
- Daily Vocabulary Scaffolding, p. T26
- 3-Minute Warm-Up, p. T29

- EXPLORE Focusing Vision, p. 126
- INVESTIGATE Vision, p. 128

 UNIT RESOURCE BOOK
Datasheet, Vision, p. 244

SECTION
4.4 Optical technology makes use of light waves. pp. 131–139

Time: 3 periods (1.5 block)
 Lesson Plan, pp. 246–247

 RESOURCE CENTERS, Microscopes and Telescopes, Lasers

 UNIT TRANSPARENCY BOOK
- Big Idea Flow Chart, p. T25
- Daily Vocabulary Scaffolding, p. T26
- 3-Minute Warm-Up, p. T29
- Chapter Outline, pp. T31–T32

- EXPLORE Combining Lenses, p. 131
- INVESTIGATE Optical Tools, p. 134
- Science on the Job, p. 139

 UNIT RESOURCE BOOK
Datasheet, Optical Tools, p. 255

KEY TO ICONS

 CD/CD-ROM

 **INTERNET**    **Pupil Edition**

 Teacher Edition

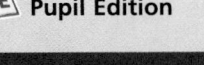 **UNIT RESOURCE BOOK**

T **UNIT TRANSPARENCY BOOK**

A **UNIT ASSESSMENT BOOK**

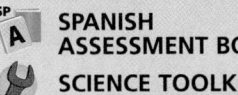 **SPANISH ASSESSMENT BOOK**

SCIENCE TOOLKIT

READING AND REINFORCEMENT

ASSESSMENT

STANDARDS

- Choose Your Own Strategy, B20–27
- Combination Notes, C36
- Daily Vocabulary Scaffolding, H1–8

 UNIT RESOURCE BOOK
- Vocabulary Practice, pp. 259–260
- Decoding Support, p. 261
- Summarizing the Chapter, pp. 282–283

Audio Readings CD
Listen to Pupil Edition

Audio Readings in Spanish CD
Listen to Pupil Edition in Spanish

- Chapter Review, pp. 141–142
- Standardized Test Practice, p. 143

 UNIT ASSESSMENT BOOK
- Diagnostic Test, pp. 60–61
- Chapter Test, Levels A, B, & C, pp. 66–77
- Alternative Assessment, pp. 78–79
- Unit Test, A, B, & C, pp. 80–91

- Spanish Chapter Test, pp. 241–244
- Spanish Unit Test, pp. 297–300

Test Generator CD-ROM
Generate customized tests.

Lab Generator CD-ROM
Rubrics for Labs

National Standards
A.2–8, A.9.a–f, B.3.c, E.2–5, E.6.a–f, F.5.a–c

See p. 110 for the standards.

 UNIT RESOURCE BOOK
- Reading Study Guide, A & B, pp. 216–219
- Spanish Reading Study Guide, pp. 220–221
- Challenge and Extension, p. 222
- Reinforcing Key Concepts, p. 224

 Ongoing Assessment, pp. 113, 114, 116

 Section 4.1 Review, p. 117

 UNIT ASSESSMENT BOOK
Section 4.1 Quiz, p. 62

National Standards
A.2–8, A.9.a–c, A.9.e–f, B.3.c

 UNIT RESOURCE BOOK
- Reading Study Guide, A & B, pp. 227–230
- Spanish Reading Study Guide, pp. 231–232
- Challenge and Extension, p. 233
- Reinforcing Key Concepts, p. 234

 Ongoing Assessment, pp. 120, 122–123

 Section 4.2 Review, p. 123

 UNIT ASSESSMENT BOOK
Section 4.2 Quiz, p. 63

National Standards
A.2–7, A.9.a–b, A.9.e–f, B.3.c

 UNIT RESOURCE BOOK
- Reading Study Guide, A & B, pp. 237–240
- Spanish Reading Study Guide, pp. 241–242
- Challenge and Extension, p. 243
- Reinforcing Key Concepts, p. 245
- Challenge Reading, pp. 257–258

 Ongoing Assessment, pp. 127–130

 Section 4.3 Review, p. 130

UNIT ASSESSMENT BOOK
Section 4.3 Quiz, p. 64

National Standards
A.2–7, A.9.a–b, A.9.d–f, B.3.c

 UNIT RESOURCE BOOK
- Reading Study Guide, A & B, pp. 248–251
- Spanish Reading Study Guide, pp. 252–253
- Challenge and Extension, p. 254
- Reinforcing Key Concepts, p. 256

 Ongoing Assessment, pp. 132–137

 Section 4.4 Review, p. 138

 UNIT ASSESSMENT BOOK
Section 4.4 Quiz, p. 65

National Standards
A.2–7, A.9.a–b, A.9.d–f, B.3.c, E.2–5, E.6.a–f, F.5.a–c

Previewing Resources for Differentiated Instruction

CHAPTER INVESTIGATION

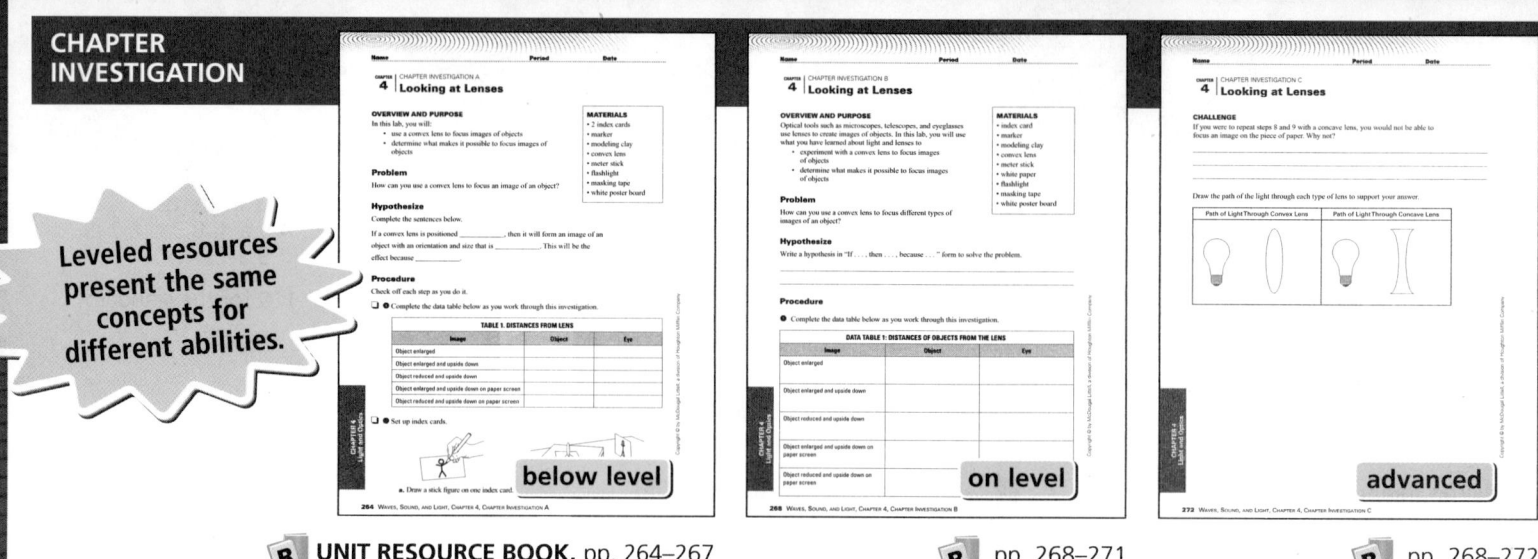

below level

on level

advanced

R **UNIT RESOURCE BOOK,** pp. 264–267

R pp. 268–271

R pp. 268–272

READING STUDY GUIDE

Leveled resources present the same concepts for different abilities.

Reading Study Guide is also in Spanish.

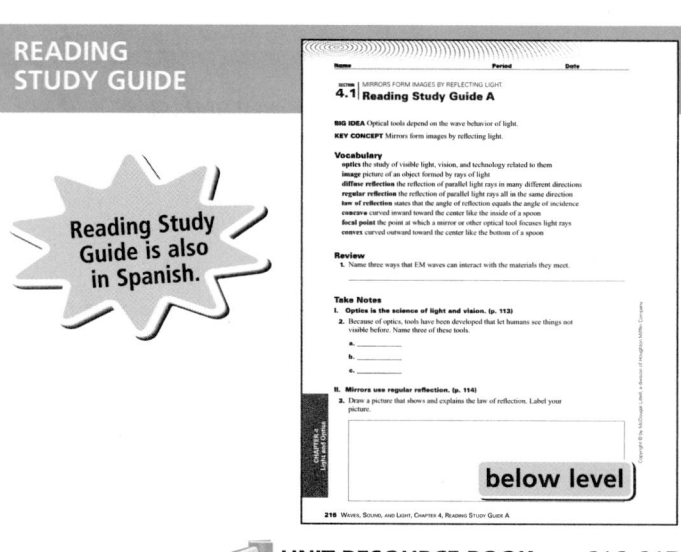

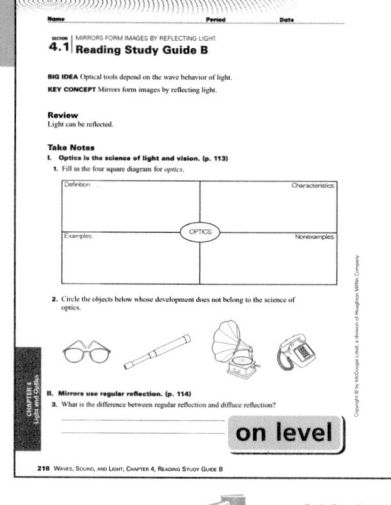

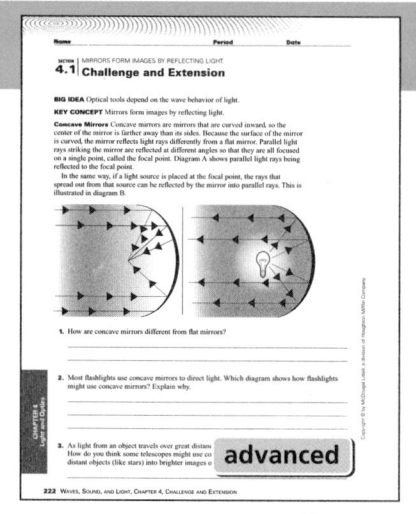

below level

on level

advanced

R **UNIT RESOURCE BOOK,** pp. 216–217

R pp. 218–219

R p. 222

CHAPTER TEST

Chapter Test is also in Spanish.

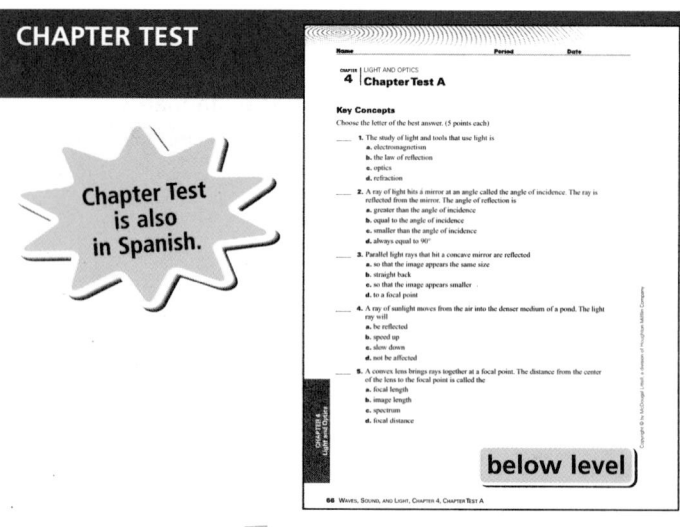

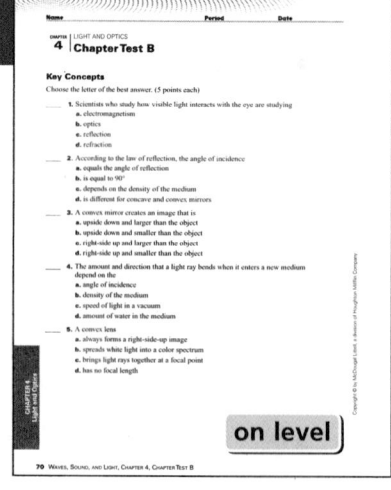

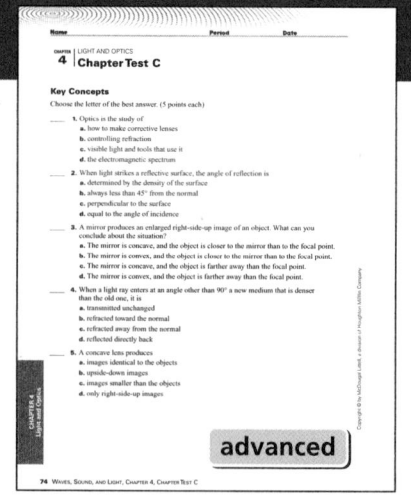

below level

on level

advanced

A **UNIT ASSESSMENT BOOK,** pp. 66–69

A pp. 70–73

A pp. 74–77

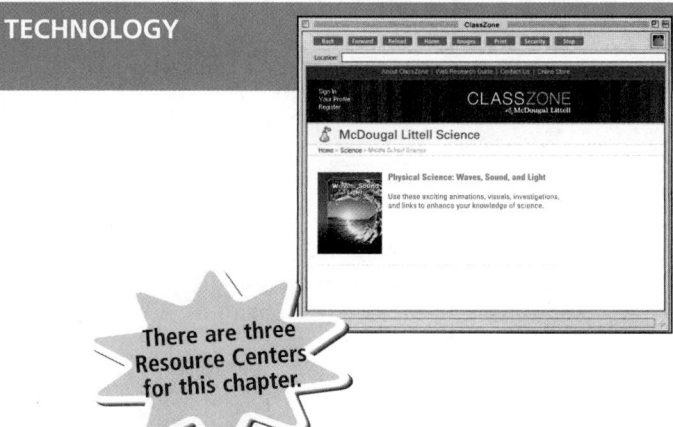

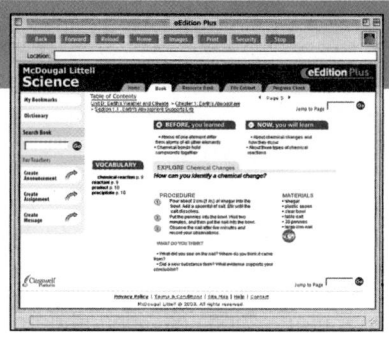

CLASSZONE.COM

CD/CD-Roms

CLASSZONE.COM

There are three Resource Centers for this chapter.

VISUAL CONTENT

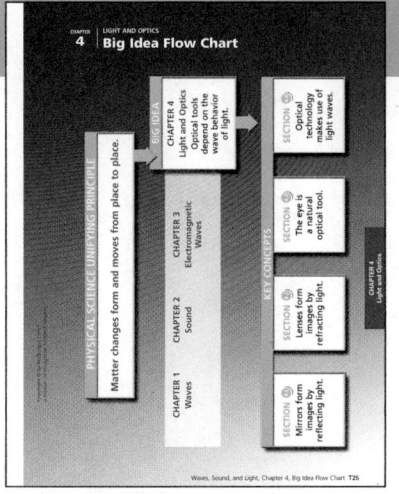

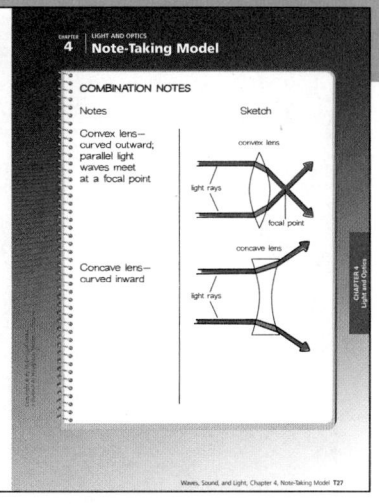

 **UNIT TRANSPARENCY BOOK,** p. T25

 p. T27

 p. T30

MORE SUPPORT

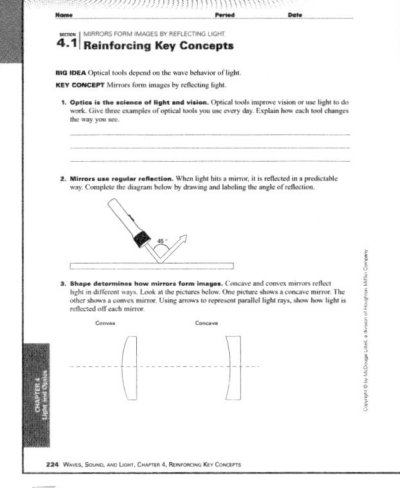

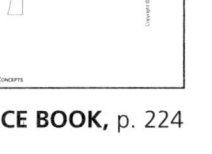

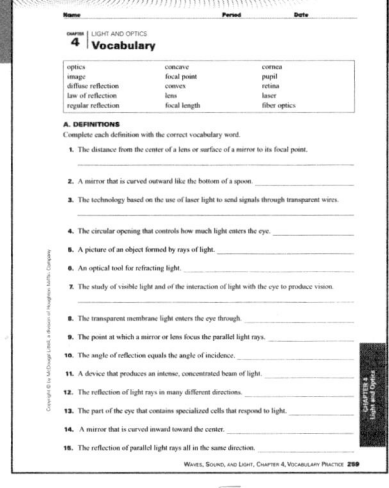

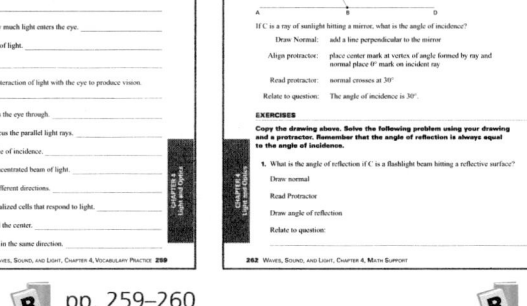

Reinforcing Key Concepts for each section

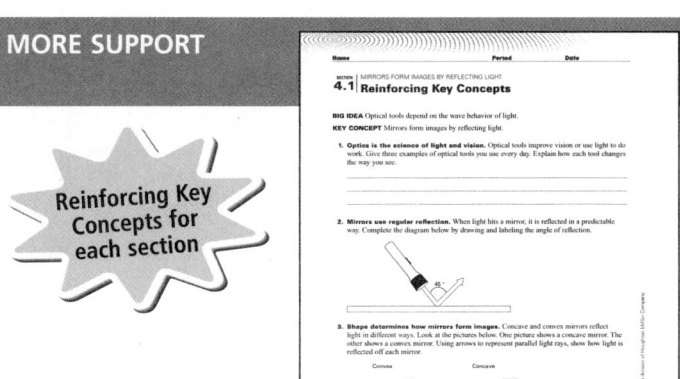 **UNIT RESOURCE BOOK,** p. 224

pp. 259–260

p. 262

INTRODUCE

the BIG idea

Have students look at the photograph of the optical refractor and discuss how the question in the box links to the Big Idea:

- How is the device in the photograph used?
- Why is the device called a refractor?

National Science Education Standards

Content

B.3.c Light interacts with matter by transmission (including refraction), absorption, or scattering (including reflection). To see an object, light from that object—emitted or scattered from it—must enter the eye.

Process

A.2–8 Design and conduct an investigation; use tools to gather and interpret data; use evidence to describe, predict, explain, model; think critically to make relationships between evidence and explanation; recognize different explanations and predictions; communicate scientific procedures and explanations; use mathematics.

A.9.a–f Understand scientific inquiry by using different investigations, methods, mathematics, technology, and explanations based on logic, evidence, and skepticism.

E.2–5 Design, implement, and evaluate a solution or product; communicate technological design.

E.6.a–f Understandings about science and technology

F.5.a–c Science influences society; societal challenges inspire scientific research; technology influences society through its products and processes.

CHAPTER

4 Light and Optics

the BIG idea

Optical tools depend on the wave behavior of light.

How can this device help a person to see better?

Key Concepts

SECTION
4.1 Mirrors form images by reflecting light.
Learn how mirrors use reflection to create images.

SECTION
4.2 Lenses form images by refracting light.
Learn how lenses use refraction to create images.

SECTION
4.3 The eye is a natural optical tool.
Learn about how eyes work as optical tools.

SECTION
4.4 Optical technology makes use of light waves.
Learn about complex optical tools.

Internet Preview

CLASSZONE.COM

Chapter 4 online resources: Content Review, Simulation, Visualization, three Resource Centers, Math Tutorial, Test Practice.

C   110   Unit: Waves, Sound, and Light

INTERNET PREVIEW

CLASSZONE.COM   For student use with the following pages:

Review and Practice
- Content Review, pp. 112, 140
- Math Tutorial: Measuring Angles, p. 118
- Test Practice, p. 143

Activities and Resources
- Internet Activity: Optics, p. 111
- Visualization: Reflection, p. 115; Simulation, p. 123
- Resource Centers: Microscopes and Telescopes, p. 132; Lasers, p. 136

Lenses **Code: MDL030**

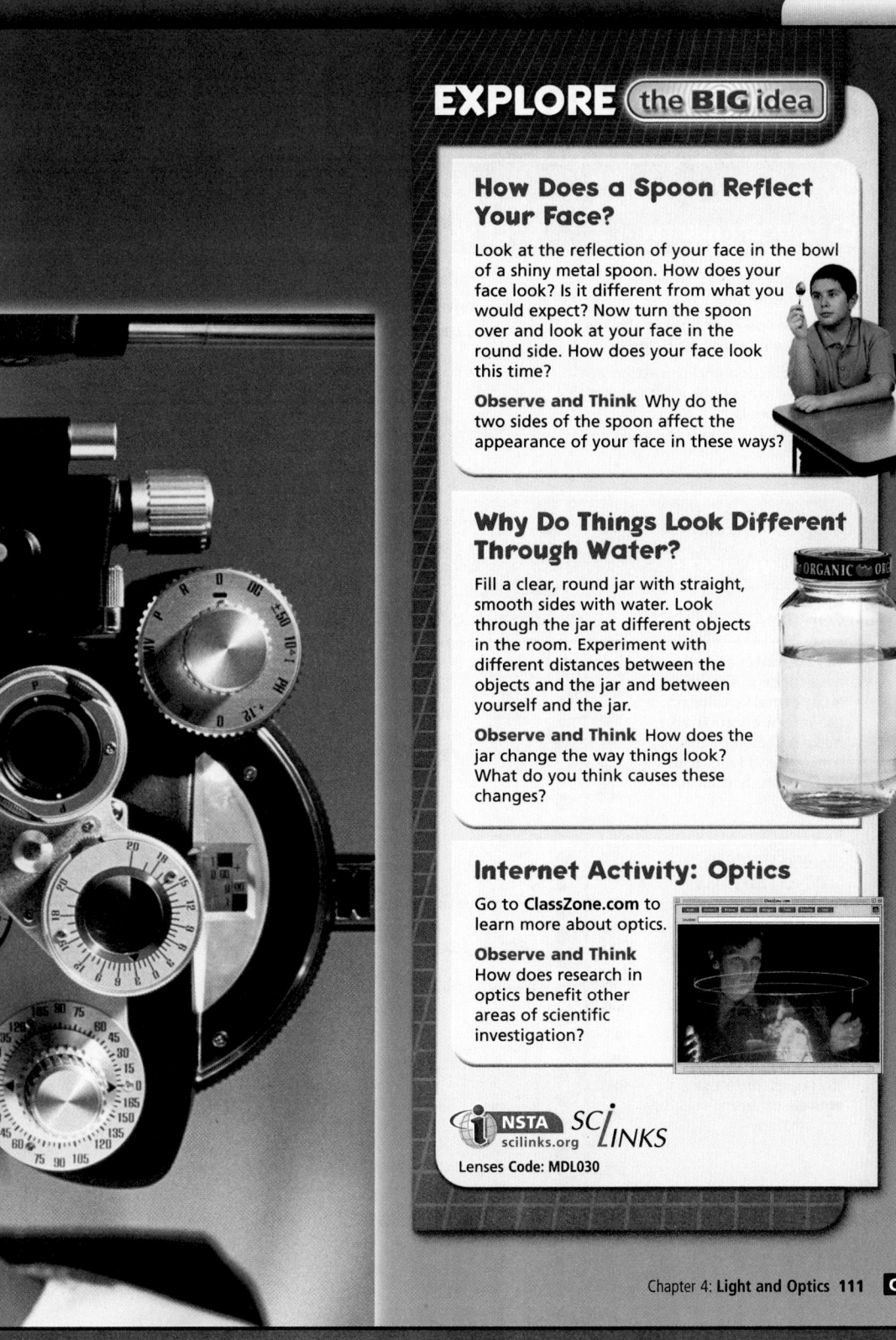

EXPLORE (the BIG idea)

How Does a Spoon Reflect Your Face?

Look at the reflection of your face in the bowl of a shiny metal spoon. How does your face look? Is it different from what you would expect? Now turn the spoon over and look at your face in the round side. How does your face look this time?

Observe and Think Why do the two sides of the spoon affect the appearance of your face in these ways?

Why Do Things Look Different Through Water?

Fill a clear, round jar with straight, smooth sides with water. Look through the jar at different objects in the room. Experiment with different distances between the objects and the jar and between yourself and the jar.

Observe and Think How does the jar change the way things look? What do you think causes these changes?

Internet Activity: Optics

Go to **ClassZone.com** to learn more about optics.

Observe and Think How does research in optics benefit other areas of scientific investigation?

NSTA
scilinks.org
SCI LINKS

Lenses Code: MDL030

EXPLORE (the BIG idea)

These inquiry-based activities are appropriate for use at home or as a supplement to classroom instruction.

How Does a Spoon Reflect Your Face?

PURPOSE To demonstrate that a mirror's shape affects the image it produces. Students observe the images that concave and convex mirrors produce.

TIP *10 min.* Students should think about why the image is inverted inside the spoon but not on the back.

Answer: The inside reflects an inverted image of a face because the reflected light rays cross each other. The back of the spoon reflects a right-side-up image because the reflected rays do not meet.

REVISIT after p. 117.

Why Do Things Look Different Through Water?

PURPOSE To see how refraction of light affects images. Students look at objects through a jar of water.

TIP *10 min.* Students can also try moving the jar as they look at an object to observe how the image of the object moves in relation to the object.

Answer: The jar appears to change the position and shape of objects. The water in the jar bends the light rays that make up images of objects.

REVISIT after p. 123.

Internet Activity: Optics

PURPOSE To examine how advances in optics affect other sciences.

TIP *20 min.* Ask students how research in optics can benefit other areas of scientific research.

Answer: Better microscopes or telescopes allow microbiology or astronomy researchers to see small or faraway objects more clearly. The invention of the laser benefits many areas of science.

REVISIT after p. 138.

TEACHING WITH TECHNOLOGY

CBL and Probeware If students have probeware, encourage them to use a light sensor with some of the activities in this chapter.

Telescope If you have access to a telescope, you may want to let students compare the images it shows to the images their telescope model from "Investigate Optical Tools" on p. 134 shows.

PREPARE

◖ CONCEPT REVIEW
Activate Prior Knowledge

- Cut three equal circles out of card-board and punch a pinhole in each.
- Cover a flashlight with one disk.
- Align the holes in the other two disks.
- Ask students why you can see the light only if the three pinholes and your eye are aligned.

▶ TAKING NOTES

Combination Notes

Making an outline of the main ideas of a concept will help students organize new material. Students who are visual learners will benefit by making a labeled sketch of a new concept.

Choose Your Own Strategy

Students can choose the strategies that best fit their individual learning styles. By surrounding a vocabulary term with information in a four square, description wheel, or frame game, students will develop a thorough understanding of the meaning of the term. Respellings should be included if appropriate.

Vocabulary and Note-Taking Resources

- Vocabulary Practice, p. 259–260
- Decoding Support, p. 261

- Daily Vocabulary Scaffolding, p. T26
- Note-Taking Model, p. T27

- Choose Your Own Strategy, B20–27
- Combination Notes, C36
- Daily Vocabulary Scaffolding, H1–8

CHAPTER 4
Getting Ready to Learn

◖ CONCEPT REVIEW

- Light tends to travel in a straight line.
- The speed of light is affected by a material medium.
- Reflection and refraction are two ways light interacts with materials.

◖ VOCABULARY REVIEW

reflection p. 25
refraction p. 25
visible light p. 84

CONTENT REVIEW
CLASSZONE.COM
Review concepts and vocabulary.

▶ TAKING NOTES

COMBINATION NOTES

To take notes about a new concept, first make an informal outline of the information. Then make a sketch of the concept and label it so you can study it later.

CHOOSE YOUR OWN STRATEGY

Take notes about new vocabulary terms, using one or more of the strategies from earlier chapters—**four square, description wheel,** or **frame game.** Feel free to mix and match the strategies, or to use an entirely different vocabulary strategy.

See the Note-Taking Handbook on pages R45–R51.

C 112 Unit: Waves, Sound, and Light

SCIENCE NOTEBOOK

NOTES
The angle of incidence (x) equals the angle of reflection (y).

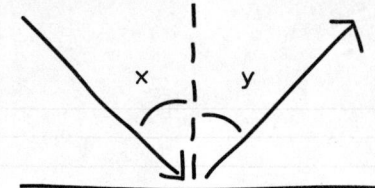

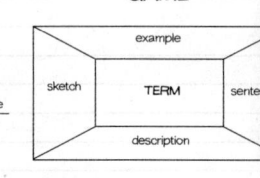

FOUR SQUARE

Definition	Characteristics
	TERM	
Examples	Nonexamples

DESCRIPTION WHEEL

feature — TERM — feature

FRAME GAME

	example	
sketch	TERM	senter
	description	

CHECK READINESS

Administer the Diagnostic Test to determine students' readiness for new science content and their mastery of requisite math skills.

 Diagnostic Test, pp. 60–61

Technology Resources

Students needing content and math skills should visit **ClassZone.com.**

- **CONTENT REVIEW**
- **MATH TUTORIAL**

 CONTENT REVIEW CD-ROM

KEY CONCEPT

Mirrors form images by reflecting light.

◀ **BEFORE, you learned**

• EM waves interact with materials
• Light can be reflected

▶ **NOW, you will learn**

• About the science of optics
• How light is reflected
• How mirrors form images

4.1 FOCUS

○ **Set Learning Goals**

Students will

• Summarize the science of optics.
• Describe how mirrors control reflection.
• Describe how mirrors produce images.
• Analyze through experimentation how mirrors direct the path of light through a periscope.

○ **3-Minute Warm-Up**

Display Transparency 28 or copy this exercise on the board:

Name the term described by each of the following:

1. How a light wave bends when it enters a new medium at an angle *refraction*

2. How a light wave bounces back when it hits a barrier *reflection*

3. The type of wave visible light is *electromagnetic wave*

 3-Minute Warm-Up, p. T28

VOCABULARY

optics p. 113
law of reflection p. 114
regular reflection p. 114
diffuse reflection p. 114
image p. 115
convex p. 116
concave p. 116
focal point p. 117

EXPLORE Reflection

How does surface affect reflection?

PROCEDURE

1. Tear off a square sheet of aluminum foil. Look at your reflection in the shiny side of the foil.

2. Turn the foil over and look at your reflection in the dull side.

3. Crumple up the piece of foil, then smooth it out again, shiny side up. Again, look at your reflection in the foil.

WHAT DO YOU THINK?
• How did the three reflections differ from one another?
• What might explain these differences?

MATERIALS
aluminum foil

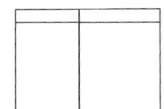

COMBINATION NOTES
Don't forget to include sketches of important concepts in your notebook.

Optics is the science of light and vision.

Optics (AHP-tihks) is the study of visible light and the ways in which visible light interacts with the eye to produce vision. Optics is also the application of knowledge about visible light to develop tools—such as eyeglasses, mirrors, magnifying lenses, cameras, and lasers—that extend vision or that use light in other ways.

Mirrors, lenses, and other optical inventions are called optical tools. By combining optical tools, inventors have developed powerful instruments to extend human vision. For example, the microscope uses a combination of mirrors and lenses to make very small structures visible. Telescopes combine optical tools to extend vision far into space. As you will see, some of the latest optical technology—lasers— use visible light in ways that do not involve human vision at all.

Chapter 4: **Light and Optics** 113 **C**

4.1 MOTIVATE

EXPLORE Reflection

PURPOSE To show that surface texture affects reflection

TIP *10 min.* Use a fresh piece of foil with no wrinkles. Remind students to smooth out the foil carefully to avoid tearing.

WHAT DO YOU THINK? *Students should see a recognizable image in the shiny side, but not in the dull side. The image in the crumpled foil should be less clear than before. Differences can be explained by the surface of the foil.*

RESOURCES FOR DIFFERENTIATED INSTRUCTION

Below Level

UNIT RESOURCE BOOK
• Reading Study Guide, A, pp. 216–217
• Decoding Support, p. 261

 **AUDIO CDS**

Advanced

UNIT RESOURCE BOOK
Challenge and Extension, p. 222

English Learners

UNIT RESOURCE BOOK
Spanish Reading Study Guide, pp. 220–221

 **AUDIO CDS**

• Audio Readings in Spanish
• Audio Readings (English)

Ongoing Assessment

Summarize the science of optics.

Ask: What are two parts of the definition of optics? *Sample answer: the study of light and how it interacts with the eye, and the application of that knowledge to develop tools that use light*

To help students interpret the mirror visual, ask:

• If the angle of incidence is 1 degree, what is the angle of reflection? *1 degree*

• How would a diagram of diffuse reflection look different from the diagram of regular reflection? *The angle of reflection of the light rays would not equal the angle of incidence. The reflected rays would go in different directions.*

Teacher Demo

To illustrate the law of reflection, set a protractor at right angles to the tabletop in a blob of clay. Place a mirror on the table in front of the protractor. Use a flashlight to make a beam of light visible to the class. Shine the flashlight at an angle to the surface of the mirror so that it strikes the mirror and is reflected onto a piece of paper or a wall. Point out the normal. Show that the angle of incidence equals the angle of reflection.

Ongoing Assessment

Describe how mirrors control reflection.

Ask: How do mirrors reflect light? *Parallel light rays reflected off the surface of mirrors remain parallel to each other.*

Mirrors use regular reflection.

You have read that when light waves strike an object, they either pass through it or they bounce off its surface. Objects are made visible by light waves, or rays, bouncing off their surfaces. In section 3 you will see how the light waves create images inside the human eye.

Light rays bounce off objects in a very predictable way. For example, look at the diagram on the left below. Light rays from a flashlight strike a mirror at an angle of 60° as measured from the normal, an imaginary line perpendicular to the surface of the mirror. This angle is called the angle of incidence. The angle at which the rays reflect off the mirror, called the angle of reflection, is also 60° as measured from the normal. The example illustrates the **law of reflection,** which states that the angle of reflection equals the angle of incidence. As you can see in the second diagram, holding the flashlight at a different angle changes both the angle of incidence and the angle of reflection. However, the two angles remain equal.

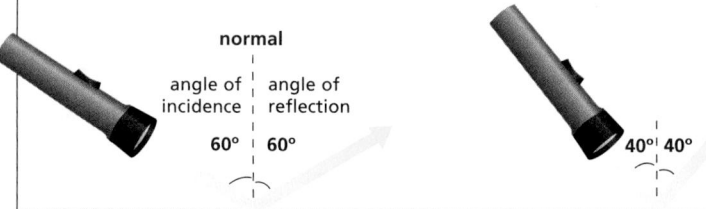

normal

angle of incidence 60° | angle of reflection 60°

40° 40°

The angle of reflection equals the angle of incidence.

The light rays striking the mirror bounce back by regular reflection. Rays striking everything else bounce back by diffuse reflection.

If the surface of an object is very smooth, like a mirror, light rays that come from the same direction will bounce off in the same new direction. The reflection of parallel light rays all in the same direction is called **regular reflection.**

If the surface is not very smooth—even if it feels smooth to the touch, like a piece of paper—light rays striking it from the same direction bounce off in many new directions. Each light ray follows the law of reflection, but rays coming from the same direction bounce off different bumps and hollows of the irregular surface. The reflection of parallel light rays in many different directions is called **diffuse reflection.**

DIFFERENTIATE INSTRUCTION

?) More Reading Support

A What is regular reflection? *the reflection of parallel light rays all in the same direction*

English Learners Help students with the two "if-then" situations on this page by setting them up as cause and effect. (Smooth surfaces cause regular reflection. Unsmooth surfaces cause diffuse reflection.) Help them use the same type of reasoning for the different shaped mirrors on pp. 115–117.

INVESTIGATE The Law of Reflection

How can you use mirrors to see around a corner?

PROCEDURE

1. To make a periscope, cut two flaps on opposite sides of the carton, one from the top and one from the bottom, as shown in the illustration.

2. Fold each flap inward until it is at a 45-degree angle to the side cuts and tape it into place.

3. Attach a mirror to the outside surface of each of the flaps.

4. Holding the periscope straight up, look through one of the openings. Observe what you can see through the other opening.

WHAT DO YOU THINK?

- Where are the objects you see when you look through the periscope?
- How does the angle of the mirrors affect the path of light through the periscope?

CHALLENGE How would it affect what you see through the periscope if you changed the angle of the mirrors from 45 degrees to 30 degrees? Try it.

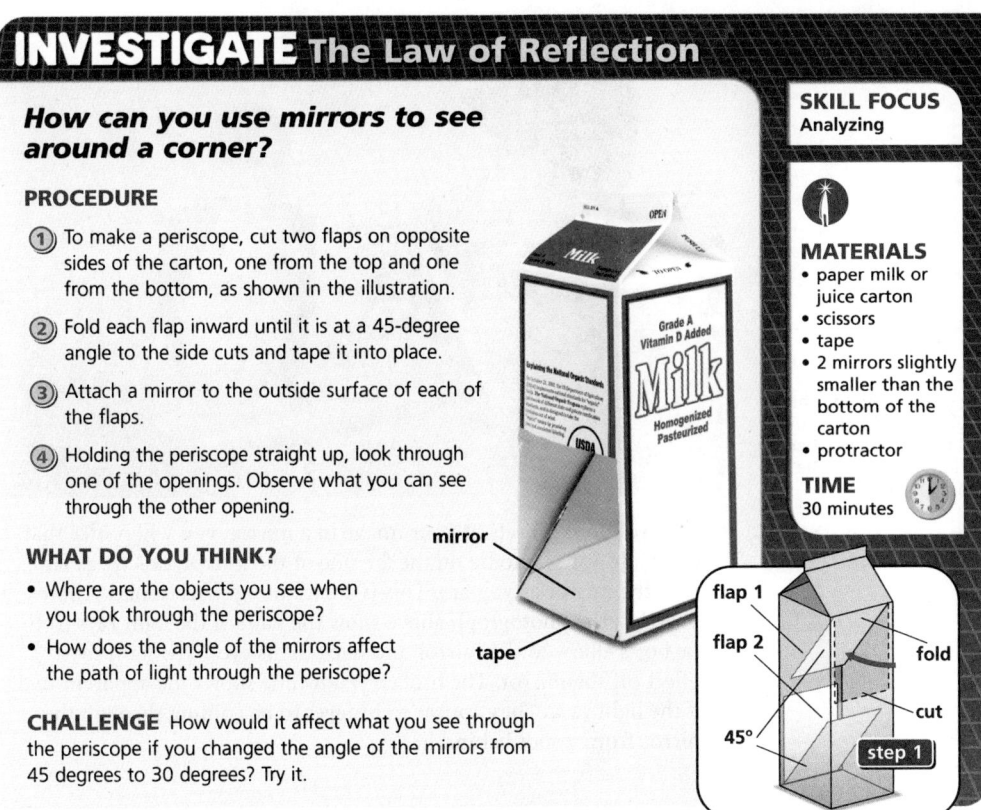

SKILL FOCUS
Analyzing

MATERIALS
- paper milk or juice carton
- scissors
- tape
- 2 mirrors slightly smaller than the bottom of the carton
- protractor

TIME
30 minutes

Shape determines how mirrors form images.

When you look in a mirror, you see an image of yourself. An **image** is a picture of an object formed by waves of light. The image of yourself is formed by light waves reflecting off you, onto the mirror, and back toward your eyes. Mirrors of different shapes can produce images that are distorted in certain ways.

See reflection in action.

Flat Mirrors

Your image in a flat mirror looks exactly like you. It appears to be the same size as you, and it's wearing the same clothes. However, if you raise your right hand, the image of yourself in the mirror will appear to raise its left hand. That is because you see the image as a person standing facing you. In fact, your right hand is reflected on the right side of the image, and your left on the left side.

 If you wink your left eye while looking in the mirror, which eye in the image of you will wink?

Chapter 4: **Light and Optics** 115 **C**

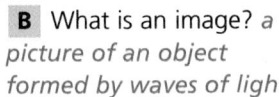
Alternative Assessment Have students make diagrams to answer the questions in "Investigate The Law of Reflection." Diagrams should show the shifted position of the object and the path of light through the periscope.

Advanced

 Challenge and Extension, p. 222

INVESTIGATE The Law of Reflection

PURPOSE To analyze the path of light through a periscope in order to learn about reflection

TIPS *30 min.* Suggest the following to students:

- Aluminum foil or squares of foil duct tape can be used in place of mirrors.
- Do not use the periscope to look at very bright light, including the Sun.

WHAT DO YOU THINK? *The objects are actually in front of and somewhat above the periscope. Having the mirrors aligned at 45 degrees means that the line of sight out of the periscope is parallel to the line of sight into the periscope.*

CHALLENGE *If the mirrors were positioned at an angle of 30 degrees, the line of sight out of the periscope would still be parallel to the line of sight into the periscope.*

 Datasheet, The Law of Reflection, p. 223

Technology Resources

Customize this student lab as needed or look for an alternative. Print rubrics to assess student lab reports.

 Lab Generator CD-ROM

Metacognitive Strategy

Ask students to write a paragraph describing a scenario in which a periscope would be useful.

Ongoing Assessment

 *Answer: The eye to the left in the mirror will blink; if you think of the image as a person facing you, it would appear that the image's right eye was blinking.*

Address Misconceptions

IDENTIFY Ask: Is a person's body turned around in a mirror image? If students answer yes, they may hold the misconception that what you see when you look at yourself in a mirror is the same as what you would see if your body were turned around to face you.

CORRECT Have students experiment by standing in front of a mirror, raising a hand on one side, and observing on which side the movement is reflected. The movement will be reflected on the same side as the hand that moves. Point out that if the mirror image were the same as one's body turned around, the movement would be reflected on the opposite side.

REASSESS Students should understand that the appearance that one's body is turned around in a mirror image is an illusion. Ask: If you wear a watch on your right wrist, which side of a mirror image will the watch appear on? *the right*

Technology Resources

Visit **ClassZone.com** for background on common student misconceptions.

MISCONCEPTION DATABASE

Teach from Visuals

To help students interpret the mirror visuals on pp. 116 and 117, ask:

- Where does the image appear to be in the flat mirror? *behind the mirror*

- How do images appear in a convex mirror? *always right-side up and smaller*

- Does the image in a concave mirror always appear the same? *No, the image may be inverted, smaller, right-side up, or larger. This depends on the position of the object relative to the focal point and the mirror.*

Ongoing Assessment

Describe how mirrors produce images.

Ask: In a concave mirror, where do parallel light rays meet after reflecting off the mirror? *at the focal point*

The solid line shows the actual path of light. The broken line shows where the light appears to be coming from.

If you look closely at your image in a mirror, you will notice that it actually appears to be on the far side of the mirror, exactly as far from the mirror as you are. This is a trick of light. The solid yellow arrows in the photograph above show the path of the light rays from the boy's elbow to the mirror and back to his eyes. The light rays reflect off the mirror. The broken yellow line shows the apparent path of the light rays. They appear to his eyes to be coming through the mirror from a spot behind it.

Concave and Convex Mirrors

VOCABULARY
Try making sketches to help you remember the new terms on this page.

Unlike light rays hitting a flat mirror, parallel light rays reflecting off a curved mirror do not move in the same direction. A **convex** mirror is curved outward, like the bottom of a spoon. In a convex mirror, parallel light rays move away from each other, as you can see in the diagram below on the left. A **concave** mirror is curved inward toward the center, like the inside of a spoon. Parallel light rays reflecting off a concave mirror move toward each other, as shown on the right.

D

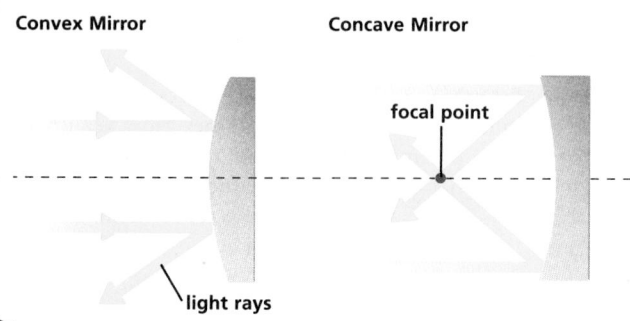

Convex Mirror   Concave Mirror

focal point

light rays

DIFFERENTIATE INSTRUCTION

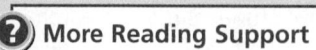

More Reading Support

D How is a convex mirror curved? *A convex mirror is curved outward, like the underside of a spoon.*

Below Level If some students have trouble distinguishing concave and convex mirrors, tell them that a conc*ave* mirror is shaped like a cave.

The rays striking a concave mirror cross and then move apart again. The point at which the rays meet is called the **focal point** of the mirror. The distance between the mirror and its focal point depends on the shape of the curve.

The images formed in these mirrors depend on the curve of the mirror's surface and the distance of the object from the mirror. Your image in a curved mirror may appear larger or smaller than you are, and it may even be upside down.

Convex Mirror

Your image in a convex mirror appears smaller than you.

Concave Mirror, Far Away

If you are standing far away, your image in a concave mirror appears upside down and smaller than you.

Concave Mirror, Up Close

If you are standing inside the focal point, your image in a concave mirror appears right-side up and larger.

All rays parallel to a line through the center of the mirror are reflected off the mirror and pass through the mirror's focal point. Rays from the top of the object are reflected downward and those from the bottom are reflected upward.

 CHECK YOUR READING How does your distance from the mirror affect the way your image appears in a concave lens?

4.1 Review

KEY CONCEPTS

1. Explain the term *optics* in your own words.

2. How is diffuse reflection similar to regular reflection? How is it different?

3. Describe the path that light rays take when they form an image of your smile when you look into a flat mirror.

CRITICAL THINKING

4. **Infer** Imagine seeing your reflection in a polished table top. The image is blurry and hard to recognize. What can you tell about the surface of the table from your observations?

5. **Analyze** Why do images formed by concave mirrors sometimes appear upside down?

CHALLENGE

6. **Synthesizing** Draw the letter *R* below as it would appear if you held the book up to (a) a flat mirror and (b) a convex mirror.

R

Chapter 4: Light and Optics 117 **C**

MATH IN SCIENCE
Math Skills Practice for Science

Set Learning Goal

To measure and calculate the angles of incidence and reflection in various situations

Present the Science

If you were trying to attract the attention of a search plane, you could use a mirror to reflect sunlight toward the plane and attract a pilot's attention.

Develop Measurement Skills

Students should measure the angles between the rays and the normal, not between the rays and the horizon.

Advise students to draw diagrams when answering the questions, especially the Challenge question.

DIFFERENTIATION TIP Below level: Review the definition of *normal* and the use of a protractor with students who need help.

Close

Ask: If you were lost in the desert but didn't have a mirror, what else could you use to signal a search plane? How could you tell if the object might work? *Anything shiny would reflect rays. If you can see your image in the object's surface, it might work as a mirror.*

• Math Support, p. 262
• Math Practice, p. 263

Technology Resources

Students can visit **ClassZone.com** for practice in measuring angles.

 MATH TUTORIAL

C **118** Unit: **Waves, Sound, and Light**

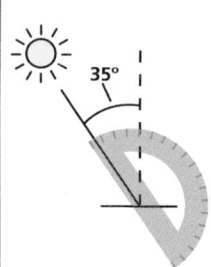 **MATH TUTORIAL**
CLASSZONE.COM
Click on Math Tutorial for more help with measuring angles.

A mirror can be used to signal for help.

C **118** Unit: Waves, Sound, and Light

SKILL: MEASURING ANGLES

Send Help!

Survival kits often contain a small mirror that can be used to signal for help. If you were lost in the desert and saw a search plane overhead, you could use the mirror to reflect sunlight toward the plane and catch the pilot's attention. To aim your signal, you would use the law of reflection. The angle at which a ray of light bounces off a mirror—the angle of reflection—is always equal to the angle at which the ray strikes the mirror—the angle of incidence.

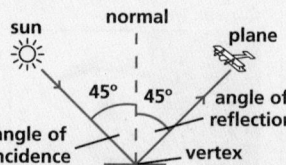

sun — normal — plane
45° 45° angle of reflection
angle of incidence — vertex

Example

35°

Measure the angle of incidence using a protractor as follows:

(1) Place the center mark of the protractor over the vertex of the angle formed by the incident ray and the normal.

(2) Place the left 0° mark of the protractor on the incident ray.

(3) Read the number where the normal crosses the scale (35°).

(4) The angle of incidence is 35°.

ANSWER Therefore, the angle of reflection will be 35°.

Copy each of the following angles of incidence, extend its sides, and use a protractor to measure it.

1.   2.   3.   4.

CHALLENGE Copy the drawing below. Use a protractor to find the angle of reflection necessary to signal the plane from point A.

• A

ANSWERS

1. 28°

2. 60°

3. 20°

4. 45°

CHALLENGE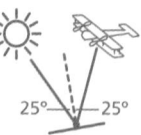
25° — 25°

KEY CONCEPT

4.2 Lenses form images by refracting light.

◀ **BEFORE,** you learned

- Waves can refract when they move from one medium to another
- Refraction changes the direction of a wave

▶ **NOW,** you will learn

- How a material medium can refract light
- How lenses control refraction
- How lenses produce images

VOCABULARY

lens p. 121
focal length p. 123

EXPLORE Refraction

How does material bend light?

PROCEDURE

1. Place the pencil in the cup, as shown in the photograph. Look at the cup from the side so that you see part of the pencil through the cup.

2. Fill the cup one third full with water and repeat your observations.

3. Gently add oil until the cup is two-thirds full. After the oil settles into a separate layer, observe.

MATERIALS
- clear plastic cup
- pencil
- water
- mineral oil

WHAT DO YOU THINK?
- How did the appearance of the pencil change when you added the water and the oil?
- What might explain these changes?

A medium can refract light.

When sunlight strikes a window, some of the light rays reflect off the surface of the glass. Other rays continue through the glass, but their direction is slightly changed. This slight change in direction is called refraction. Refraction occurs when a wave strikes a new medium—such as the window—at an angle other than 90° and keeps going forward in a slightly different direction.

Refraction occurs because one side of the wave reaches the new medium slightly before the other side does. That side changes speed, while the other continues at its previous speed, causing the wave to turn.

 **CHECK YOUR READING** How does the motion of a light wave change when it refracts?

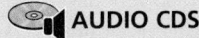 Chapter 4: **Light and Optics** 119 **C**

RESOURCES FOR DIFFERENTIATED INSTRUCTION

Below Level
UNIT RESOURCE BOOK
- Reading Study Guide A, pp. 227–228
- Decoding Support, p. 261

AUDIO CDS

R Additional **INVESTIGATION,**
Bending Light, A, B, & C, pp. 273–281
Teacher Instructions, pp. 284–285

Advanced
UNIT RESOURCE BOOK
Challenge and Extension, p. 233

English Learners
UNIT RESOURCE BOOK
Spanish Reading Study Guide, pp. 231–232

AUDIO CDS
- Audio Readings in Spanish
- Audio Readings (English)

4.2 FOCUS

▶ Set Learning Goals

Students will

- Identify how a material medium can refract light.
- Describe how lenses control refraction.
- Recognize how lenses produce images.
- Discover through experimentation how to use a convex lens to focus an image.

◀ 3-Minute Warm-Up

Display Transparency 28 or copy this exercise on the board:

Match each definition to the correct term.

Definitions
1. a picture of an object formed by light rays *e*
2. the point where parallel light rays striking a concave mirror meet *c*
3. a surface that curves out like the back of a spoon *b*

Terms
a. concave
b. convex
c. focal point
d. optics
e. image

T 3-Minute Warm-Up, p. T28

4.2 MOTIVATE

EXPLORE Refraction

PURPOSE To show how different materials bend light rays

TIP *10 min.* Have students think about their observations in terms of the direction of light waves.

WHAT DO YOU THINK? *The pencil appears to break where the water and air meet and where the water and the oil meet. The oil bends light more than the water does.*

 CHECK YOUR READING *Answer: Light waves change direction slightly when they refract.*

 Chapter 4 **119** **C**

Teach from Visuals

To help students interpret the diagram of alight wave passing through air and glass, ask:

- Does light move faster through air or through glass? *through air*

- Is glass a thin or a dense medium? *dense*

Develop Critical Thinking

APPLY Have students do the following experiment and apply their knowledge of refraction to explain the results. Put a penny in the bottom of a teacup. Lower your head until the penny just disappears from view behind the rim of the cup. Without moving your head or the cup, have a partner fill the cup with water. The penny will appear to float into view. *When you add water, rays of light reflected from the penny refract enough to reach your eye as they pass into the air from the water.*

Ongoing Assessment

Identify how a material medium can refract light.

Ask: In what direction does light turn when it refracts? *If the new medium slows the wave, the wave will turn toward the normal. If the new medium speeds the wave up, the wave will turn away from the normal.*

COMBINATION NOTES
Sketch the ways light is refracted when it moves into a denser medium and into a thinner medium.

READING TiP
A dense medium has more mass in a given volume than a thin medium.

?
A

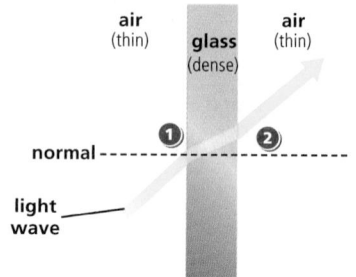
light
water droplet
color spectrum
Light passing through a droplet of water is refracted twice, forming a color spectrum.

Refraction of Light

Recall that waves travel at different speeds in different mediums. The direction in which a light wave turns depends on whether the new medium slows the wave down or allows it to travel faster. Like reflection, refraction is described in terms of an imaginary line—called the normal—that is perpendicular to the new surface. If the medium slows the wave, the wave will turn toward the normal. If the new medium lets the wave speed up, the wave will turn away from the normal. The wave in the diagram below turns toward the normal as it slows down in the new medium.

air (thin) — glass (dense) — air (thin)

normal

light wave

1 Waves moving at an angle into a denser medium turn toward the normal.

2 Waves moving at an angle into a thinner medium turn away from the normal.

Light from the Sun travels toward Earth through the near vacuum of outer space. Sunlight refracts when it reaches the new medium of Earth's upper atmosphere. Earth's upper atmosphere is relatively thin and refracts light only slightly. Denser materials, such as water and glass, refract light more.

By measuring the speed of light in different materials and comparing this speed to the speed of light in a vacuum, scientists have been able to determine exactly how different materials refract light. This knowledge has led to the ability to predict and control refraction, which is the basis of much optical technology.

Refraction and Rainbows

You've seen rainbows in the sky after a rainstorm or hovering in the spray of a sprinkler. Rainbows are caused by refraction and reflection of light through spherical water drops, which act as prisms. Just as a prism separates the colors of white light, producing the color spectrum, each water drop separates the wavelengths of sunlight to produce a spectrum. You can see the effect in the diagram on the left.

?
B

DIFFERENTIATE INSTRUCTION

? **More Reading Support**

A Can Earth's atmosphere refract light? *yes*

B How do spherical water drops cause rainbows? *act as prisms to separate wavelengths of white light*

Additional Investigation To reinforce Section 4.2 learning goals, use the following full-period investigation:

R **Additional INVESTIGATION,** Bending Light, A, B, & C, pp. 273–281, 284–285 (Advanced students should complete Levels B & C.)

Shape determines how lenses form images.

When you look at yourself in a flat mirror, you see your image clearly, without distortions. Similarly, when you look through a plain glass window, you can see what is on the other side clearly. Just as curved mirrors distort images, certain transparent mediums called lenses alter what you see through them. A **lens** is a clear optical tool that refracts light. Different lenses refract light in different ways and form images useful for a variety of purposes.

READING TiP

Distort means to change the shape of something by twisting or moving the parts around.

Convex and Concave Lenses

Like mirrors, lenses can be convex or concave. A convex lens is curved outward; a concave lens is curved inward. A lens typically has two sides that are curved, as shown in the illustration below.

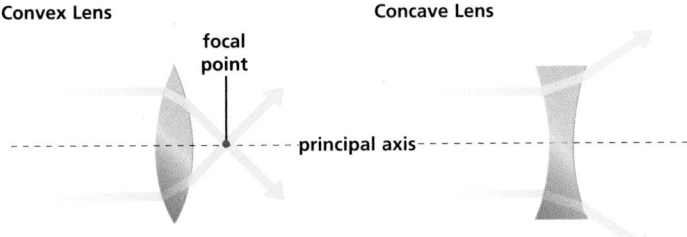

Convex Lens

focal point

principal axis

Concave Lens

A convex lens causes parallel light rays to meet at a focal point.

A concave lens causes parallel light rays to spread out.

Convex Parallel light rays passing through a convex lens are refracted inward. They meet at a focal point on the other side of the lens. The rays are actually refracted twice—once upon entering the lens and once upon leaving it. This is because both times they are entering a new medium at an angle other than 90 degrees. Rays closest to the edges of the lens are refracted most. Rays passing through the center of the lens—along the principal axis, which connects the centers of the two curved surfaces—are not refracted at all. They pass through to the same focal point as all rays parallel to them.

Concave Parallel light rays that pass through a concave lens are refracted outward. As with a convex lens, the rays are refracted twice. Rays closest to the edges of the lens are refracted most; rays at the very center of the lens pass straight through without being deflected. Because they are refracted away from each other, parallel light rays passing through a concave lens do not meet.

REMINDER

The focal point is the point at which parallel light rays meet after being reflected or refracted.

 **CHECK YOUR READING** Compare what happens to parallel light rays striking a concave mirror with those striking a concave lens.

Teach Difficult Concepts

Students often have a hard time understanding how light changes speed when it moves into a different medium. Use the analogy of a wagon with its two right wheels moving on a sidewalk and its two left wheels moving in mud. The wheels moving in mud will turn at a slower speed than the wheels on the sidewalk, and the wagon will turn toward the left.

Teach from Visuals

To help students interpret the lens diagram, ask:

• What happens at the focal point? *The refracted rays of light meet.*

• Do the light rays that pass through a concave lens ever meet? *no*

History of Science

The curved surface of a lens must be carefully shaped if it is to focus accurately. Early lens makers copied the shape of a mold onto a piece of glass. They ground and polished the lens using rouge, an abrasive powder made of iron oxide.

CHECK YOUR READING *Answer: A concave mirror causes parallel light waves to move towards each other so they meet at a focal point. Parallel light waves passing through a concave lens move away from each other and do not meet.*

DIFFERENTIATE INSTRUCTION

 **More Reading Support**

C How does a convex lens refract light? *It bends parallel light rays so that they meet at a focal point on the other side of the lens.*

English Learners Words that have multiple meanings may be confusing for English learners. For example, words like *vacuum* and *medium* are presented in a new context in this chapter. Have students write down each of these words and all their possible meanings. Then have them decide which meaning makes the most sense in the context of the sentence where it is found. To illustrate the concept of concave and convex lenses, put these terms on the Science Word Wall with visual reminders of how each lens refracts light.

Teach from Visuals

To help students interpret the lens diagrams, ask:

- Do the light waves passing through a convex lens move toward or away from each other? *toward each other*

- What is a focal length? *the distance from the center of a lens to its focal point*

- The images formed by a convex lens are similar to the images formed by what type of mirror? *concave*

 This visual is also available as T30 in the Unit Transparency Book.

Address Misconceptions

IDENTIFY Ask: Do magnifying glasses always enlarge images of an object, or can they form smaller images as well? If students say "enlarged images only," they may think that a magnifying glass is made with a special kind of lens that only magnifies.

CORRECT Pass out magnifying glasses and let students experiment with them. Students should discover that when the object is more than one focal length from the lens, a magnifying glass forms upside down images that can be enlarged, the same size as the object, or reduced.

REASSESS Ask students what a magnifying glass is. *A magnifying glass is simply a convex lens that is used in a particular way.*

Ongoing Assessment

Recognize how lenses form images.

Ask: Which types of lens forms images by causing light rays to meet at a focal point? *convex*

 *Answer: at the middle of the image of the penguin*

How a Convex Lens Forms an Image

A convex lens forms an image by refracting light rays. Light rays reflected from an object are refracted when they enter the lens and again when they leave the lens. They meet to form the image.

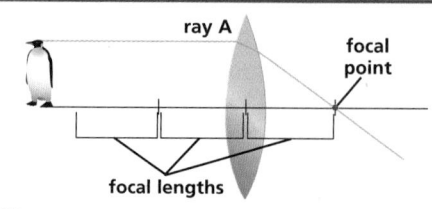

① Light rays reflect off the penguin in all directions and many enter the lens. Here a single ray (A) from the top of the penguin enters the lens and is refracted downward.

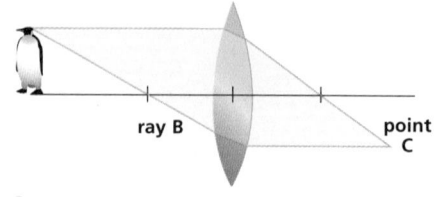

② Another light ray (B) from the top of the penguin passes through the lens at the bottom and meets the first ray at point C. All of the rays from the top of the penguin passing through the lens meet at this point.

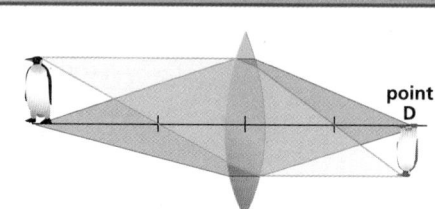

③ All of the light rays from the bottom of the penguin meet at a different point (D). Light rays from all parts of the penguin meet at corresponding points on the image.

READING VISUALS Where do light rays reflected from the middle of the penguin meet?

DIFFERENTIATE INSTRUCTION

Advanced If light is traveling in a direction that is perpendicular to the boundary between mediums, no refraction occurs even though the light's speed changes. Ask students to explain why this is so. *The light strikes the boundary at a right angle, so all sides of the wave enter the medium at the same time, all sides change speed at the same time, and no refraction occurs.*

 Challenge and Extension, p. 233

Images Formed by Lenses

When light rays from an object pass through a lens, an image of the object is formed. The type of image depends on the lens and, for convex lenses, on the distance between the lens and the object.

Notice the distance between the penguin and the lens in the illustration on page 122. The distance is measured in terms of a **focal length,** which is the distance from the center of the lens to the lens's focal point. The penguin is more than two focal lengths from the camera lens, which means the image formed is upside down and smaller.

If the penguin were between one and two focal lengths away from a convex lens, the image formed would be upside down and larger. Overhead projectors form this type of image, which is then turned right side up by a mirror and projected onto a screen for viewing.

Finally, if an object is less than one focal length from a convex lens, it will appear right side up and larger. In order to enlarge an object so that you can see details, you hold a magnifying lens close to the object. In the photograph, you see a face enlarged by a magnifying lens. The boy's face is less than one focal length from the lens.

If you look at an object through a concave lens, you'll see an image of the object that is right side up and smaller than the object normally appears. In the case of concave lenses, the distance between the object and the lens does not make a difference in the type of image that is formed. In the next section you'll see how the characteristics of the images formed by different lenses play a role in complex optical tools.

SIMULATION CLASSZONE.COM

Work with convex and concave lenses to form images.

 **CHECK YOUR READING** When will an image formed by a convex lens be upside down?

4.2 Review

KEY CONCEPTS
1. What quality of a material affects how much it refracts light?
2. How does the curve in a lens cause it to refract light differently from a flat piece of glass?
3. How does a camera lens form an image?

CRITICAL THINKING
4. **Infer** You look through a lens and see an image of a building upside down. What type of lens are you looking through?
5. **Make a Model** Draw the path of a light ray moving at an angle from air into water. Write a caption to explain the process.

CHALLENGE
6. Study the diagram on the opposite page. Describe the light rays that would pass through the labeled focal point. Where are they coming from, and how are they related to each other?

Chapter 4: **Light and Optics 123** **C**

ANSWERS
1. the speed of light in the material

2. Because the angle at which light strikes a curved surface varies across the surface, the amount of refraction for different light rays varies also.

3. A camera lens refracts light waves inward toward a focal point.

4. a convex lens

5. Diagrams should show the refracted light beam turning toward the normal. Sample

caption: Because water slows the light wave, the wave bends toward the normal.

6. All light rays reflected off the penguin that are parallel to the principal axis of the lens will pass through the focal point of the lens.

Ongoing Assessment

 CHECK YOUR READING Answer: The image will be upside down when the object is one or more focal lengths from the lens.

Teacher Demo

Students often learn best when they are allowed to make informal observations on their own. Pass out various lenses and let students discover for themselves how the image changes with the shape of the lens and with the focal length.

EXPLORE (the BIG idea)

Revisit "Why Do Things Look Different Through Water?" on p. 111. Have students explain the reasons for their results.

Reinforce (the BIG idea)

Have students relate the section to the Big Idea.

 Reinforcing Key Concepts, p. 234

4.2 ASSESS & RETEACH

Assess
 Section 4.2 Quiz, p. 63

Reteach

Have students make a table listing the shape of lenses and mirrors and the type, orientation, and size of images formed. Ask students to use the table to compare the images from mirrors to those from lenses.

Technology Resources

Have students visit **ClassZone.com** for reteaching of Key Concepts.

CONTENT REVIEW

CONTENT REVIEW CD-ROM

Focus

PURPOSE Students will focus images using a convex lens and determine the conditions that produce different kinds of images

OVERVIEW Students will examine the images formed by a convex lens as they vary the distance between the lens and the object. Students will see

- an enlarged, upright, virtual image when the distance between the object and the lens is less than one focal length

- an enlarged, inverted, real image when the distance between the object and the lens is between one and two focal lengths

- a reduced, inverted, real image when the distance between the object and the lens is more than two focal lengths

Lab Preparation

- Review the concepts of focal point and focal length.

- Prior to the investigation, have students read through the investigation and prepare their data tables. Or you may wish to copy and distribute datasheets and rubrics.

 UNIT RESOURCE BOOK, pp. 264–272

SCIENCE TOOLKIT, F15

Lab Management

- The lens can be mounted in an upright position in some modeling clay on the table surface.

- Students may need help setting up the lens and the light.

- Darken the room as much as possible. If the tape arrow does not produce clear images, have students make a light arrow by masking most of the flashlight cover instead.

SAFETY Caution students not to look directly into the flashlight.

INCLUSION Have students with visual impairments use large lenses and meter sticks with large numbers.

CHAPTER INVESTIGATION

Looking at Lenses

OVERVIEW AND PURPOSE Optical tools such as microscopes, telescopes, and eyeglasses use lenses to create images of objects. In this lab, you will use what you have learned about light and lenses to

- experiment with a convex lens to focus images of objects
- determine what makes it possible to focus images of objects.

▶ Procedure

PART A

1 Make a data table like the one shown on the sample notebook page.

2 Draw a stick figure on one index card. Assemble the cards, clay, and lens as shown in the photograph.

3 Position the convex lens so that you can see an enlarged, right-side up image of the stick figure. Measure the distances between the lens and the card, and between the lens and your eye. Record the distances in your data table.

4 Position the lens so that you can see an enlarged, upside down image of the stick figure. Measure the distances between the lens and the object, and between the lens and your eye. Record the distances in your data table.

5 Position the lens so that you can see a reduced, upside down image of the stick figure. Measure the distances between the lens and the object, and between the lens and your eye. Record the distances in your data table.

MATERIALS
- index card
- marker
- modeling clay
- convex lens
- meter stick
- flashlight
- masking tape
- white poster board

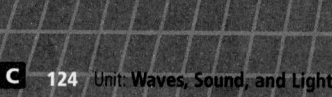

INVESTIGATION RESOURCES

 CHAPTER INVESTIGATION, Looking at Lenses
- Level A, pp. 264–267
- Level B, pp. 268–271
- Level C, p. 272

Advanced students should complete Levels B & C.

 Writing a Lab Report, D12–13

Technology Resources

Customize this student lab as needed or look for an alternative. Print rubrics to assess student lab reports.

Lab Generator CD-ROM

PART B

6 Put an arrow made of tape on the lens of the flashlight as shown.

step 6

7 Assemble poster board and clay to make a screen. Arrange the flashlight, lens, and screen as shown below right.

8 Shine the beam from the flashlight through the lens to form an enlarged, upside down image on the screen. Measure the distances between the lens and the flashlight and between the lens and the screen.

9 Position the light and screen to produce a reduced, upside down image. Measure the distances between the lens and the flashlight and between the lens and the screen.

10 Position the light and screen to produce an enlarged right-side up image.

▶ Observe and Analyze [Write It Up]

1. **RECORD OBSERVATIONS** Draw pictures of each setup in steps 3–9 to show what happened. Be sure your data table is complete.

2. **ANALYZE** What was the distance from the lens to the object in step 3? Answer this question for each of the other steps. How do the distances compare?

3. **ANALYZE** What happened when you tried to form the three types of images on the screen? How can you explain these results?

▶ Conclude [Write It Up]

1. **ANALYZE** What conclusions can you draw about the relationship between the distances you measured and the type of image that was produced?

2. **IDENTIFY LIMITS** Describe possible sources of error in your procedure or any places where errors might have occurred.

3. **APPLY** What kind of lenses are magnifying glasses? When a magnifying glass produces a sharp clear image, where is the object located in relation to the lens?

step 7

▶ INVESTIGATE Further

CHALLENGE If you were to repeat steps 8 and 9 with a concave lens, you would not be able to focus an image on the piece of paper. Why not?

Looking at Lenses

Problem How can you use a convex lens to focus different types of images of an object?

Hypothesize

Observe and Analyze

Table 1. Distances from Lens

Image	Object	Eye
Object enlarged and right-side up		
Object enlarged and upside down		
Object reduced and upside down	Flashlight	Screen
Object enlarged and right-side up		
Object enlarged and upside down		
Object reduced and upside down		

Conclude

Post-Lab Discussion

• Have students make ray diagrams to summarize their results. Diagrams should clearly show why images can be enlarged or reduced and inverted or upright when the object is at different distances.

• Describe this scenario: You are camping and want to start a fire, but you have no matches. You have a lens. Can you start a fire in a pile of dead leaves? What kind of lens would you need? *yes; convex* Where would the lens have to be? *exactly one focal length from the leaves. The Sun's rays would focus on the leaves, and the concentration of light could start a fire.*

▶ Observe and Analyze [Write It Up]

SAMPLE DATA Object enlarged, right-side up: 0–1 focal length from lens; Object enlarged, upside down: 1–2 focal lengths from lens; Object reduced, upside down: more than 2 focal lengths from lens; Lightbulb enlarged, right-side up: no image; Lightbulb image enlarged, upside down: 1–2 focal lengths from lens; Lightbulb image reduced, upside down: more than 2 focal lengths from lens.

1. See students' diagrams.

2. Step 3: less than one focal length; Steps 4 and 8: between one and two focal lengths; Steps 5 and 9: more than two focal lengths

3. Step 8: enlarged, upside down image appears on screen when distance from lens to screen is about twice the distance from light to lens. Step 9: reduced, upside down image is visible on screen when distance from lens to screen is about equal to the distance from light to lens. Step 10: enlarged, right side up image appears on screen when lens is very close to screen and the flashlight very close to the lens.

Explanation: Different images are formed when the screen is within one focal length, about one focal length, and outside one focal length from the lens.

▶ Conclude [Write It Up]

1. When the distance between an object and a convex lens is: 1. less than one focal length, an enlarged, upright image forms. 2. between one and two focal lengths, an enlarged, upside down image forms. 3. more than two focal lengths, a reduced, upside down image forms.

2. misidentifying the type of image, measuring incorrectly, and not having the lens in the correct position

3. convex lens; an object must be located less than one focal length in front of the lens.

▶ INVESTIGATE Further

CHALLENGE Answer: They do not cause light rays to meet at a focal point.

Set Learning Goals

Students will

- Recognize how the eye depends on natural lenses.
- Explain how artificial lenses can be used to correct vision problems.
- Observe and describe through an experiment how the eye focuses an image.

3-Minute Warm-Up

Display Transparency 29 or copy this exercise on the board:

Imagine a woman is spearfishing at a lake. She sees a fish through the water ahead of her and aims her spear directly at the image. Will she hit the fish? Explain your answer. *No; the image and the actual location of the fish are different because the light is refracted.*

If the woman is spearfishing underwater while scuba diving and she aims directly at a fish, will she hit it? Why? *Yes; because both the woman and the fish are underwater, there is no refraction.*

 3-Minute Warm-Up, p. T29

4.3 MOTIVATE

EXPLORE Focusing Vision

PURPOSE To investigate how the human eye focuses

TIP *10 min.* Students who cannot keep one eye closed should hold one hand over the eye.

WHAT DO YOU THINK? *The nearby object looks out of focus. The eye changes its focal point.*

KEY CONCEPT

4.3 The eye is a natural optical tool.

◀ **BEFORE, you learned**

- Mirrors and lenses focus light to form images
- Mirrors and lenses can alter images in useful ways

▶ **NOW, you will learn**

- How the eye depends on natural lenses
- How artificial lenses can be used to correct vision problems

VOCABULARY

cornea p. 127
pupil p. 127
retina p. 127

EXPLORE Focusing Vision

How does the eye focus an image?

PROCEDURE

1. Position yourself so you can see an object about 6 meters (20 feet) away.

2. Close one eye, hold up your index finger, and bring it as close to your open eye as you can while keeping the finger clearly in focus.

3. Keeping your finger in place, look just to the side at the more distant object and focus your eye on it.

4. Without looking away from the more distant object, observe your finger.

WHAT DO YOU THINK?

- How does the nearby object look when you are focusing on something distant?
- What might be happening in your eye to cause this change in the nearby object?

The eye gathers and focuses light.

The eyes of human beings and many other animals are natural optical tools that process visible light. Eyes transmit light, refract light, and respond to different wavelengths of light. Eyes contain natural lenses that focus images of objects. Eyes convert the energy of light waves into signals that can be sent to the brain. The brain interprets these signals as shape, brightness, and color. Altogether, these processes make vision possible.

In this section, you will learn how the eye works. You will also learn how artificial lenses can be used to improve vision.

RESOURCES FOR DIFFERENTIATED INSTRUCTION

Below Level

UNIT RESOURCE BOOK
- Reading Study Guide A, pp. 237–238
- Decoding Support, p. 261

 **AUDIO CDS**

Advanced

UNIT RESOURCE BOOK
- Challenge and Extension, p. 243
- Challenge Reading, pp. 257–258

English Learners

UNIT RESOURCE BOOK
Spanish Reading Study Guide, pp. 241–242

 **AUDIO CDS**

- Audio Readings in Spanish
- Audio Readings (English)

How Light Travels Through the Human Eye

① Light enters the eye through the **cornea** (KAWR-nee-uh), a transparent membrane that covers the eye. The cornea acts as a convex lens and does most of the refracting in the eye.

② The light then continues through the **pupil,** a circular opening that controls how much light enters the eye. The pupil is surrounded by the iris, which opens and closes to change the size of the pupil.

③ Next the light passes through the part of the eye called the lens. The lens is convex on both sides. It refracts light to make fine adjustments for near and far objects. Unlike the cornea, the lens is attached to tiny muscles that contract and relax to control the amount of refraction that occurs and to move the focal point.

④ The light passes through the clear center of the eye and strikes the **retina** (REHT-uh-nuh). The retina contains specialized cells that respond to light. Some of these cells send signals through the optic nerve to the brain. The brain interprets these signals as images.

> **READING TiP**
> The word *lens* can refer both to an artificial optical tool and to a specific part of the eye.

How the Human Eye Forms an Image

The cornea and lens together focus a reduced, inverted image on the retina.

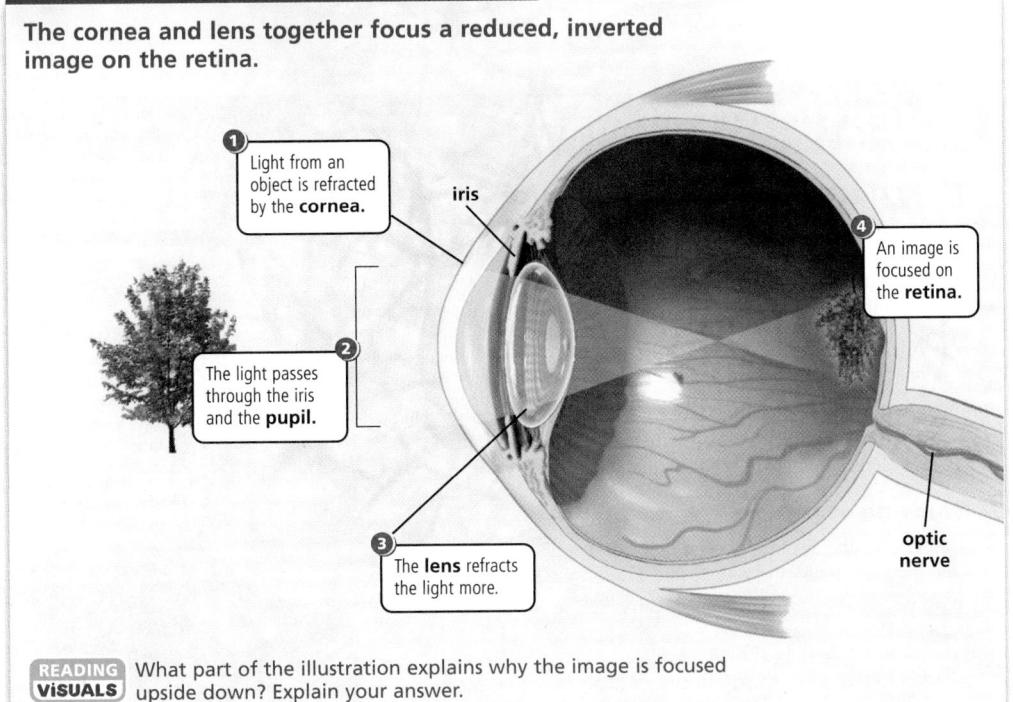

① Light from an object is refracted by the **cornea.**

iris

② The light passes through the iris and the **pupil.**

③ The **lens** refracts the light more.

④ An image is focused on the **retina.**

optic nerve

READING VISUALS What part of the illustration explains why the image is focused upside down? Explain your answer.

DIFFERENTIATE INSTRUCTION

More Reading Support

A What part of the eye does most light refraction? *the cornea*

B Where does the eye focus an image? *on the retina*

English Learners Developing a Science Word Wall in the classroom will help English learners learn new vocabulary. Offering a visual reminder with the word can reinforce meaning as well. Place the words *pupil, cornea,* and *retina* on the Science Word Wall and include a diagram of the eye showing the location of each part.

Address Misconceptions

IDENTIFY Ask: What is the main focusing part of the eye? If students say the lens, they may hold the misconception that most or all refraction occurs in the lens.

CORRECT Call students' attention to the diagram on this page. Point out that the cornea is shaped like a convex lens and does most of the refracting for the eye. Because the cornea covers the eye, most refraction actually takes place in the cornea rather than in the lens.

REASSESS Have students draw a diagram of light rays approaching an eye and being refracted by the cornea. The light should be further refracted by the lens.

> **Technology Resources**
> Visit **ClassZone.com** for background on common student misconceptions.
> **MISCONCEPTION DATABASE**

Teach from Visuals

To help students interpret the eye visual, ask:

- What is the shape of the cornea? *convex*
- Where is the focal point? *where the lines cross*
- What does the optic nerve do? *sends signals to the brain*

Ongoing Assessment

Recognize how the eye depends on natural lenses.

Ask: What two lenses are part of the eye? *the cornea and the lens*

READING VISUALS *Answer: The part that shows light rays crossing at a focal point so that the ones on top go to the bottom of the image and vice versa.*

How the Eye Forms Images

For you to see an object clearly, your eye must focus an image of the object on your retina. The light reflected from each particular spot on the object must converge on a matching point on your retina. Many such points make up an image of an entire object. Because the light rays pass through the lens's focal point, the image is upside down. The brain interprets this upside down image as an object that is right-side up.

For a complete image to be formed in the eye and communicated to the brain, more than the lens and the cornea are needed. The retina also plays an important role. The retina contains specialized cells that detect brightness and color and other qualities of light.

Rod Cells Rod cells distinguish between white and black and shades of gray. Rods respond to faint light, so they help with night vision.

Cone Cells Cone cells respond to different wavelengths of light, so they detect color. There are three types of cones, one for each of the colors red, blue, and green. Cones respond to other colors with combinations of these three, as the screen of a color monitor does. The brain interprets these combinations as the entire color spectrum.

 CHECK YOUR READING Which type of cell in the retina detects color?

 **COMBINATION NOTES** Make a chart showing how light interacts with different parts of the eye.

INVESTIGATE Vision

How does distance affect vision?

SKILL FOCUS Observing

PROCEDURE

1. Arrange the materials as shown so that the lamp shines through the lens onto the plate. The lens should be about $\frac{2}{3}$ a meter from the lamp.

2. Adjust the distance between the plate and the lens until you see a focused image of the bulb on the plate. Measure this distance.

3. Move the lens until it is about a meter and a half from the lamp. Adjust the plate once again to get a focused image, then measure the distance between the plate and the lens.

WHAT DO YOU THINK?

• How does the distance needed between the plate and the lens change when the lamp is farther from the lens?

• How is what happens in the eye different from what you did to refocus the image?

CHALLENGE How could you change the model to make it more like what happens in the eye?

MATERIALS
• convex lens
• index card
• modeling clay
• white paper plate
• lamp

TIME
10 minutes

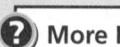
DIFFERENTIATE INSTRUCTION

 More Reading Support

C The eye forms what type of image? *upside down*

D What do rod cells do? *distinguish between black and white and shades of gray*

English Learners Some English learners may have never had a vision test or seen an optometrist. Go over the different ways a doctor can correct a person's vision. Explain how eyeglasses correct nearsightedness or farsightedness. Talk about how contact lenses are used. Encourage students to use the Internet to find out more about surgical methods of vision correction.

Advanced

 Challenge and Extension, p. 243

Corrective lenses can improve vision.

What happens when the image formed by the lens of the eye does not fall exactly on the retina? The result is that the image appears blurry. This can occur either because of the shape of the eye or because of how the lens works. Artificial lenses can be used to correct this problem.

Corrective Lenses

A person who is nearsighted cannot see objects clearly unless they are near. Nearsightedness occurs when the lens of the eye focuses the image in front of the retina. The farther away the object is, the farther in front of the retina the image forms. This problem can be corrected with glasses made with concave lenses. The concave lenses spread out the rays of light before they enter the eye. The point at which the rays meet then falls on the retina.

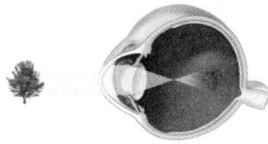

nearsighted eye

1 image in front of retina

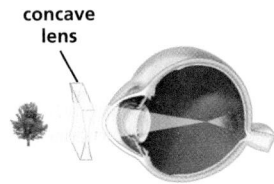

concave lens

2 image at retina

Objects are clearer to a farsighted person when the objects are farther away. Farsightedness occurs when the lens of the eye focuses an object's image behind the retina. This condition can result from aging, which may make the lens less flexible. The closer the object is, the farther behind the retina the image forms. Farsightedness can be corrected with glasses made from convex lenses. The convex lenses bend the light rays inward before they enter the eye. The point at which the rays meet then falls on the retina.

READING TiP

Nearsighted people can see objects near to them best. *Farsighted* people can see objects better when the objects are farther away.

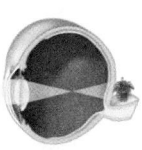

farsighted eye

1 image behind retina

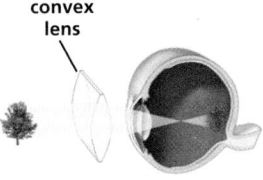

convex lens

2 image at retina

 **CHECK YOUR READING** What kind of lens is used for correcting nearsightedness?

To help students understand corrective lenses, ask:
- Where does the image form in a near-sighted eye? *in front of the retina*
- Where does the image form in a far-sighted eye? *behind the retina*

Integrate the Sciences

Perfect vision is measured at 20/20, which means that your eye sees at 20 feet what a normal eye can see at the same distance. The larger the second number, the blurrier the image. So 20/40 means that your eye sees at 20 feet what a normal eye can see at 40 feet. Legal blindness is 20/200 or worse in both eyes.

Ongoing Assessment

Explain how artificial lenses can be used to correct vision problems.

Ask: How does a concave lens correct nearsightedness? *By spreading out the light before it enters the eye, the lens lengthens the focal length in the eye, and the image focuses on the retina.*

CHECK YOUR READING *Answer: Nearsightedness can be corrected with a concave lens.*

DIFFERENTIATE INSTRUCTION

 More Reading Support

E What are corrective lenses? *artificial lenses that correct vision problems*

Inclusion Ray diagrams showing the path of light in the eye can be made for students with visual impairments. Use yarn or string to represent light rays. To represent the retina, use a heavier yarn. Use another three-dimensional material to represent the image.

Advanced Have students who are interested in why people have red eyes read the following article:

R Challenge Reading, pp. 257–258

4.3 ASSESS & RETEACH

Assess

 Section 4.3 Quiz, p. 64

Reteach

Ask students the following questions to extend their understanding of sight:

• Where are the images projected on the retina interpreted? *in the brain*

• What happens to the lens of the eye when light passes through? *It refracts light to make adjustments for near and far objects.*

Have students find their blind spot—the place where the retina joins the optic nerve.

• Make a diagram of an X and a black spot located about 6 cm apart.

• Close your left eye, look at the X, and gradually move the diagram away from the eye.

At a distance of about 25 cm, the spot will disappear.

Technology Resources

Have students visit **ClassZone.com** for reteaching of Key Concepts.

 CONTENT REVIEW

CONTENT REVIEW CD-ROM

Surgery and Contact Lenses

Wearing glasses is an effective way to correct vision. It is also possible to change the shape of the cornea to make the eye refract properly. The cornea is responsible for two-thirds of the refraction that takes place inside the eye. As you know, the eye's lens changes shape to focus an image, but the shape of the cornea does not ordinarily change.

However, using advanced surgical technology, doctors can change the shape of the cornea. By doing this, they change the way light rays focus in the eye so that the image lines up with the retina. To correct for nearsightedness, surgeons remove tissue from the center of the cornea. This flattens the cornea and makes it less convex so that it will refract less. To correct for farsightedness, surgeons remove tissue from around the edges of the cornea. This increases the cornea's curvature to make it refract more. Surgery changes the shape of the cornea permanently and can eliminate the need for eyeglasses.

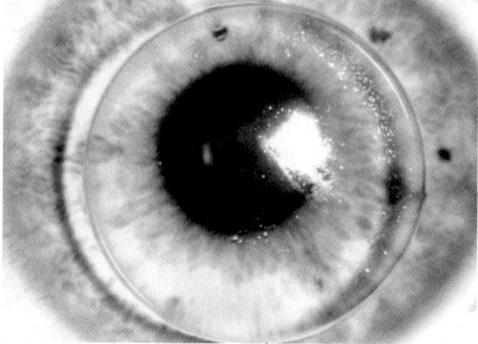

Contact lenses fit directly onto the cornea, changing the way light is refracted as it enters a person's eye.

Contact lenses also correct vision by changing the way the cornea refracts light. Contact lenses are corrective lenses that fit directly onto the cornea. The lenses actually float on a thin layer of tears. The moisture, the contact lens, and the cornea all function together as a single lens. Because the change is temporary, contacts, like eyeglasses, can be adapted to new changes in the eye.

CHECK YOUR READING What are two ways of changing the way the cornea refracts light to correct vision?

4.3 Review

KEY CONCEPTS

1. Where are images focused in an eye with perfect vision?

2. What causes people with nearsightedness to see blurry images of objects at a distance?

3. What kind of lens is used for correcting farsightedness? Why?

CRITICAL THINKING

4. **Make a Model** Draw a diagram to answer the following question: How does a convex lens affect the way a nearsighted eye focuses an image?

5. **Analyze** What distance would an eye doctor need to measure to correct a problem with nearsightedness or farsightedness?

◎ CHALLENGE

6. **Apply** A person alternates between wearing glasses and wearing contact lenses to correct farsightedness. Are the contact lenses more or less convex than the lenses of the glasses? Explain the reasoning behind your response.

C 130 Unit: Waves, Sound, and Light

KEY CONCEPT

4.4 Optical technology makes use of light waves.

◀ BEFORE, you learned

- Mirrors are optical tools that use reflection
- Lenses are optical tools that use refraction
- The eye is a natural optical tool
- Lenses can correct vision

▶ NOW, you will learn

- How mirrors and lenses can be combined to make complex optical tools
- How optical tools are used to extend natural vision
- How laser light is made and used in optical technology

VOCABULARY
laser p. 135
fiber optics p. 137

EXPLORE Combining Lenses

How can lenses be combined?

PROCEDURE

① Assemble the lenses, clay, and index cards as shown in the photograph.

② Line the lenses up so that you have a straight line of sight through them.

③ Experiment with different distances between
  - the lenses
  - the far lens and an object
  - the near lens and your eye
  Find an arrangement that allows you to see a clear image of an object through both lenses.

MATERIALS
- 2 convex lenses
- modeling clay
- 2 index cards

WHAT DO YOU THINK?
- What kind of image could you see? What arrangement or arrangements work best to produce an image?
- How do you think the lenses are working together to focus the image?

Mirrors and lenses can be combined to make more powerful optical tools.

COMBINATION NOTES
As you read this section, make a list of optical tools. Add sketches to help you remember important concepts.

If you know about submarines, then you know how much they depend on their periscopes to see above the water. Periscopes are made by combining mirrors. Lenses can also be combined. In the eye, for example, the cornea and the eye's lens work together to focus an image. Mirrors and lenses can be combined with each other, as they are in an overhead projector. Many of the most powerful and complex optical tools are based on different combinations of mirrors and lenses.

RESOURCES FOR DIFFERENTIATED INSTRUCTION

Below Level

UNIT RESOURCE BOOK
- Reading Study Guide A, pp. 248–249
- Decoding Support, p. 261

 **AUDIO CDS**

Advanced

UNIT RESOURCE BOOK
Challenge and Extension, p. 254

English Learners

UNIT RESOURCE BOOK
Spanish Reading Study Guide, pp. 252–253

 **AUDIO CDS**

- Audio Readings in Spanish
- Audio Readings (English)

○ Set Learning Goals

Students will

- Describe how mirrors and lenses can be combined to make complex optical tools.
- Explain how optical tools are used to extend natural vision.
- Recognize how laser light is made and used in optical technology.
- Design their own experiment by making a model of a telescope and explaining how it works.

○ 3-Minute Warm-Up

Display Transparency 29 or copy this exercise on the board:

Decide if these statements are true. If not true, correct them.

1. The lens of the human eye is concave on both sides. *The lens of the human eye is convex on both sides.*

2. Rods and cones, located in the retina, are important in night and color vision. *true*

3. The eyes convert the energy of light waves into nerve signals that travel to the brain. *true*

T 3-Minute Warm-Up, p. T29

4.4 MOTIVATE

EXPLORE Combining Lenses

PURPOSE To determine how two lenses work together to focus an image

TIP *10 min.* Use a protractor to ensure that the lenses are exactly vertical.

WHAT DO YOU THINK? *An enlarged image can be seen when the lenses are the distance of their combined focal lengths apart, the object is more than one focal length from the far lens, and the viewer is about one focal length from the near lens.*

History of Science

In the 17th century, Robert Hooke and Anton van Leeuwenhoek both developed microscopes and discovered the world of tiny living things. Although Hooke's microscope had two lenses and was similar to modern compound microscopes, poor-quality lenses provided little detail. Van Leeuwenhoek's microscope had only one lens, but it was good enough to show many details in cells and organisms.

Ongoing Assessment

Describe how mirrors and lenses can be combined to make complex optical tools.

Ask: What type of telescope combines mirrors and lenses? *a reflecting telescope*

CHECK YOUR READING *Answer: The objective lens forms an enlarged real image. The eyepiece forms an enlarged virtual image of the first image.*

CHECK YOUR READING *Answer: A reflecting telescope uses two mirrors and one lens to focus an image. A refracting telescope uses two lenses to focus an image.*

Microscopes

Microscopes are used to see objects that are too small to see well with the naked eye. An ordinary microscope works by combining convex lenses. The lens closer to the object is called the objective. The object is between one and two focal lengths from this lens, so the lens focuses an enlarged image of the object inside the microscope.

The other microscope lens—the one you look through—is called the eyepiece. You use this lens to look at the image formed by the objective. Like a magnifying glass, the eyepiece lens forms an enlarged image of the first image.

 **A**

Very small objects do not reflect much light. Most microscopes use a lamp or a mirror to shine more light on the object.

CHECK YOUR READING Which types of images do the lenses in a microscope form?

Telescopes

Telescopes are used to see objects that are too far away to see well with the naked eye. One type of telescope, called a refracting telescope, is made by combining lenses. Another type of telescope, called a reflecting telescope, is made by combining lenses and mirrors.

 **RESOURCE CENTER** CLASSZONE.COM
Find out more about microscopes and telescopes. **B**

Refracting telescopes combine convex lenses, just as microscopes do. However, the objects are far away from the objective lens instead of near to it. The object is more than two focal lengths from the objective lens, so the lens focuses a reduced image of the object inside the telescope. The eyepiece of a telescope then forms an enlarged image of the first image, just as a microscope does. This second image enlarges the object.

Reflecting telescopes work in the same way that refracting telescopes do. However, there is no objective lens where light enters the telescope. Instead, a concave mirror at the opposite end focuses an image of the object. A small flat mirror redirects the image to the side of the telescope. With this arrangement, the eyepiece does not interfere with light on its way to the concave mirror. The eyepiece then forms an enlarged image of the first image.

Both refracting and reflecting telescopes must adjust for the small amount of light received from distant objects. The amount of light gathered can be increased by increasing the diameter of the objective lens or mirror. Large mirrors are easier and less expensive to make than large lenses. So reflecting telescopes can produce brighter images more cheaply than refracting telescopes.

CHECK YOUR READING How is a reflecting telescope different from a refracting telescope?

DIFFERENTIATE INSTRUCTION

? More Reading Support

A What does the eyepiece of a microscope do? *forms an enlarged image of the first image*

B What type of telescope has two convex lenses? *refracting*

English Learners Label any refracting telescopes, reflecting telescopes, or microscopes in the classroom. English learners might be confused by phrasal verbs such as *made up* (p. 135). Tell students that in this context, "up" is not a literal direction, but rather a part of the verb. If students still have trouble, offer synonyms such as "composed" or "consists of."

Microscopes and Telescopes

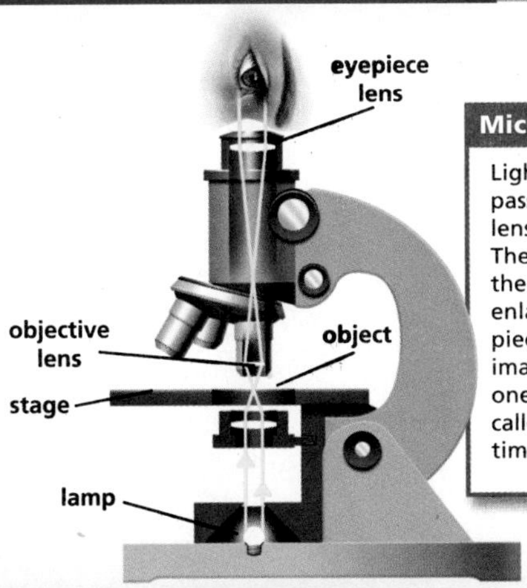

Microscope

eyepiece lens

objective lens

stage

lamp

object

Light from an object passes through a convex lens called an objective. The objective lens focuses the light to form an enlarged image. The eyepiece lens enlarges the image even more. The one-celled algae at right, called diatoms, appear 400 times their normal size.

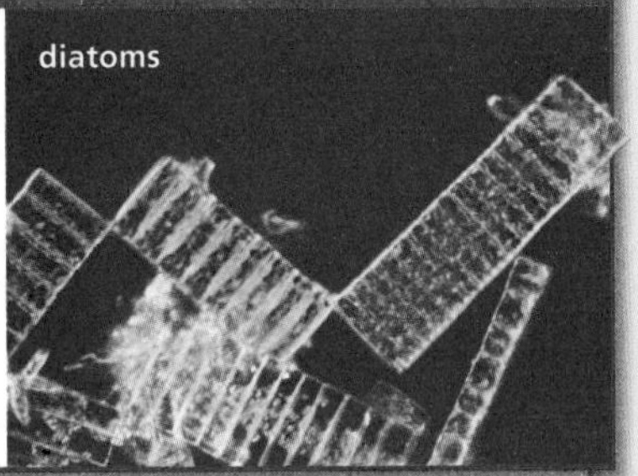

diatoms

Refracting Telescope

surface of the Moon

The objective lens gathers and focuses light from a distant object to form an image of the object. The eyepiece enlarges the image. The telescope image of the Moon at left shows fine details of the lunar surface.

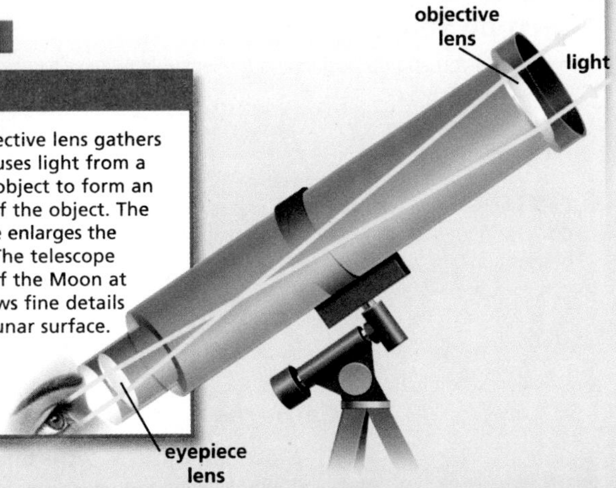

objective lens

light

eyepiece lens

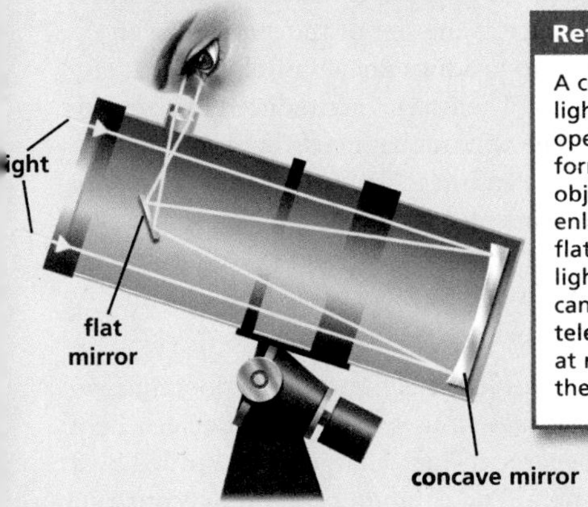

Reflecting Telescope

light

flat mirror

concave mirror

A concave mirror gathers light through a wide opening and focuses it to form an image of the object. The eyepiece lens enlarges the image. The flat mirror redirects the light so that the eyepiece can be out of the way. The telescope image of Saturn at right shows details of the planet's rings.

the planet Saturn

READING VISUALS Which type of telescope is similar in construction to a microscope?

DIFFERENTIATE INSTRUCTION

Advanced Have students investigate the focal lengths of the lenses in microscopes and refracting telescopes. Students should understand why lenses with long or short focal lengths are used. Students can make ray diagrams tracing the path of light through these instruments.
Microscopes use an objective lens with a very short focal length because the object being examined is very close to this lens. Telescopes use an objective lens with a very long focal length because the object being viewed is very far away.

 Challenge and Extension, p. 254

Teach from Visuals

To help students interpret the microscope and telescope visual:

- Both microscopes and refracting telescopes contain two lenses. Ask: How are these two instruments different? *The image in a microscope is enlarged twice. The refracting telescope enlarges the image once.*

- Ask: What is the advantage to having the eyepiece out of the way in a reflecting telescope? *The advantage of having the eyepiece out of the way is that it will not block light from entering the telescope.*

Address Misconceptions

IDENTIFY Ask: What is the function of each lens in a telescope? If students respond that both lenses produce enlarged images, they may hold the misconception that the only purpose of a telescope is to enlarge an image.

CORRECT Have students reexamine the visual on page 122, which shows that the image of an object located more than two focal lengths from a convex lens is reduced and inverted. Drawing a ray diagram will help reinforce this concept.

REASSESS Ask: What is the main function of an objective lens? *to collect as much light from the distant object as possible*

Technology Resources

Visit **ClassZone.com** for background on common student misconceptions.

 MISCONCEPTION DATABASE

Ongoing Assessment

READING VISUALS *Answer: a refracting telescope*

INVESTIGATE Optical Tools

PURPOSE To design and build a telescope to find out how two lenses work together

TIPS *30 min.* Let students explore for a few minutes. Offer these suggestions if necessary.

- The two lenses should be at a distance equal to the sum of the focal lengths of the two lenses.
- Use a large convex lens with a long focal length for the objective and a smaller convex lens with a short focal length for the eyepiece.

WHAT DO YOU THINK? *The object should be more than two focal lengths from the objective lens. Students will see an enlarged inverted image if their telescope works.*

CHALLENGE *The image is first upside down, because the objective lens forms an inverted image. The eyepiece then forms an upright image of the inverted image.*

 Datasheet, Optical Tools, p. 255

Technology Resources

Customize this student lab as needed or look for an alternative. Print rubrics to assess student lab reports.

 Lab Generator CD-ROM

Teaching with Technology

If you have access to a telescope, let students use it to compare its images with the images created by their homemade telescope.

Ongoing Assessment

Explain how optical tools are used to extend natural vision.

Ask: How do microscopes and telescopes extend natural vision? *They enlarge objects that are either too small or too far away to be seen with the naked eye.*

INVESTIGATE Optical Tools

How can you make a simple telescope?

Use what you have learned about how a telescope works to build one. Figure out how far apart the two lenses need to be and use that information to construct a working model.

 DESIGN —YOUR OWN—

PROCEDURE

1. Decide how the lenses should be positioned in relation to an object you select to view.
2. Adjust the lenses until you get a clear image.
3. Use the other materials to fix the lenses into place and to make it possible to adjust the distance between them.

WHAT DO YOU THINK?

- How did you end up positioning the lenses in relation to the object?
- Did your telescope work? Why do you think you got this result?

CHALLENGE Is your telescope image upside down or right-side up? How can you explain this observation?

SKILL FOCUS
Making models

MATERIALS
- 2 convex lenses
- 2 cardboard tubes
- duct tape

TIME
30 minutes

Cameras

Most film cameras focus images in the same way that the eye does. The iris of a camera controls the size of the aperture, an opening for light, just as the iris of an eye controls the size of the pupil. Like an eye, a camera uses a convex lens to produce images of objects that are more than two focal lengths away. The images are reduced in size and upside down. In the eye, an image will not be focused unless it falls exactly on the retina. In a camera, an image will not be focused unless it falls exactly on the film. The camera does not change the shape of its lens as the eye does to change the focal point. Instead, the camera allows you to move the lens nearer to or farther away from the film until the object you want to photograph is in focus.

A digital camera focuses images just as a film camera does. Instead of using film, though, the digital camera uses a sensor that detects light and converts it into electrical charges. These charges are recorded by a small computer inside the camera. The computer can then reconstruct the image immediately on the camera's display screen.

READING TiP
The term *digital* is often used to describe technology involving computers. Computers process information digitally, that is, using numbers.

C **134** Unit: Waves, Sound, and Light

DIFFERENTIATE INSTRUCTION

 More Reading Support

C What kind of an image is produced in a camera? *reduced in size and upside down*

Alternative Assessment Have students make diagrams showing how the lenses in a refracting telescope have to be positioned in relation to each other. Ask them to explain why the lenses have to be positioned in this way.

How Cameras Work

A camera focuses an image in the same way as an eye.

film camera

light lens iris aperture film

READING VISUALS What part of a camera corresponds to the pupil of an eye?

Eye and Camera

lens image

pupil retina

film iris lens aperture image

Digital Camera

A **digital camera** records images digitally, that is, using a computer.

Lasers use light in new ways.

A **laser** (LAY-zuhr) is a device that produces an intense, concentrated beam of light that is brighter than sunlight. The word *laser* means "light amplification by stimulated emission of radiation." Laser light has many uses. It carries a lot of energy and can be controlled precisely.

Ordinary visible light is made up of many different wavelengths. Even colored light usually contains many different wavelengths. But a laser beam is made up of light waves with a single wavelength and a pure color. In addition, the crests and troughs of the waves are in phase, which means that they are lined up so they match exactly.

▼ **REMINDER**
The crest of a wave is its highest point. The trough of a wave is its lowest point.

Visible light waves of different wavelengths

Light waves of a single wavelength

Single wavelength waves in phase

Chapter 4: **Light and Optics** 135 **C**

- What part of a camera corresponds to the retina of the eye? *the film*
- What replaces the film in a digital camera? *A small computer stores light waves from the object in the form of a digitized image.*

Teach Difficult Concepts

Some students may still be having trouble understanding where a lens focuses a real image. Remind them that the focal point of a lens is the point where parallel rays passing through the lens meet. Rays from different points on an object are not parallel and so meet a little beyond the focal point of the lens. Every point on the object has a corresponding point where light rays meet on the image.

Teacher Demo

Light a candle in a darkened room, and hold a magnifying glass between the candle and the wall. An inverted image of the candle will appear on the wall. If the light waves from a particular point on the object don't quite converge at the wall, the real image of the candle will not fall exactly on the wall, and it will be blurry. To focus the image, move the magnifying glass closer or farther away from the candle. When you focus a camera, you turn the lens to move it closer or farther away from the film surface. As you move the lens, you line up the focused real image of an object so it falls directly on the surface of the film.

Ongoing Assessment

READING VISUALS *Answer: the iris*

DIFFERENTIATE INSTRUCTION

(?) More Reading Support

D What is a laser? *a device that produces an intense, concentrated beam of light*

Below Level Ask students who have a hard time reading to describe and compare the path of light in a camera and in the human eye. Ask them to bring in a camera to show the class the different parts.

To help students interpret the laser visual, ask:

- What happens to the light as the mirrors reflect it back and forth? *It becomes stronger and more concentrated.*

- What do the light waves in a laser look like? *They are all one wavelength and parallel, and their troughs and crests line up.*

Real World Example

A bar code is a specific arrangement of bars and spaces. When a cashier moves a bar-coded item in front of a scanner, a laser scans the bar code. The white spaces between the bars reflect light in bursts through the scanner window, through a partial mirror, and onto a detector. The detector changes these light bursts into digital signals, which travel to a central computer. The computer processes the signals and sends information about the price of the item to the cash register.

Ongoing Assessment

Recognize how laser light is made and used in optical technology.

Ask: How is a laser beam made? *An energy source stimulates the atoms in a material to give off light waves of a single wavelength. Mirrors concentrate the light waves to produce a laser.*

Light waves in a laser beam are highly concentrated and exactly parallel. Ordinary light spreads out, growing more faint as it gets farther from its source. Laser light spreads out very little. After traveling 1 kilometer (0.6 mi), a laser beam may have a diameter of only one meter.

Making Laser Light

A laser is made in a special tube called an optical cavity. A material that is known to give off a certain wavelength of light, such as a ruby crystal, is placed inside the tube. Next, an energy source, such as a bright flash of light, stimulates the material, causing it to emit, or give off, light waves. Both ends of the crystal are mirrored so that they reflect light back and forth between them. One end is mirrored more than the other. As the light waves pass through the crystal, they cause the material to give off more light waves—all perfectly parallel, all with the same wavelength, and all with their crests and troughs lined up. Eventually the beam becomes concentrated and strong enough to penetrate the less-mirrored end of the crystal. What comes out of the end is a laser beam.

RESOURCE CENTER
CLASSZONE.COM

Learn more about lasers.

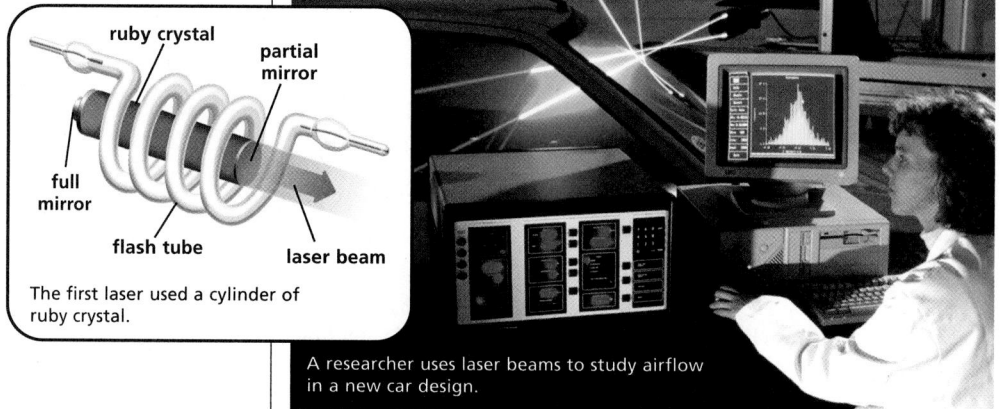

ruby crystal
partial mirror
full mirror
flash tube
laser beam

The first laser used a cylinder of ruby crystal.

A researcher uses laser beams to study airflow in a new car design.

Visual Uses of Lasers

Lasers are used today in an amazing variety of ways. One of these ways is to create devices that do the kind of work the human eye does—detecting and interpreting light waves. For example, surveyors once used telescopes to measure distances and angles. Now lasers can be used to take these measurements more precisely. Lasers are used to read bar codes, to scan images and pages of text, and to create holograms—three-dimensional images that appear to hover in the air. Holograms, which are hard to reproduce, are sometimes used in important documents so that the documents cannot be duplicated.

C 136 Unit: Waves, Sound, and Light

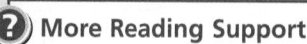

Fiber Optics

Some laser applications use visible light in ways that have nothing to do with vision. One of the fastest growing technologies is fiber optics. **Fiber optics** is technology based on the use of laser light to send signals through transparent wires called optical fibers. Fiber optics makes use of a light behavior called total internal reflection. Total internal reflection occurs when all of the light inside a medium reflects off the inner surface of the medium.

When light strikes the inner surface of a transparent medium, it may pass through the surface or it may be reflected back into the medium. Which one occurs depends on the angle at which the light hits the surface. For example, if you look through the sides of an aquarium, you can see what is behind it. But if you look at the surface of the water from below, it will act like a mirror, reflecting the inside of the aquarium.

Laser light is very efficient at total internal reflection. It can travel long distances inside clear fibers of glass or other materials. Light always travels in a straight line; however, by reflecting off the sides of the fibers, laser light inside fibers can go around corners and even completely reverse direction.

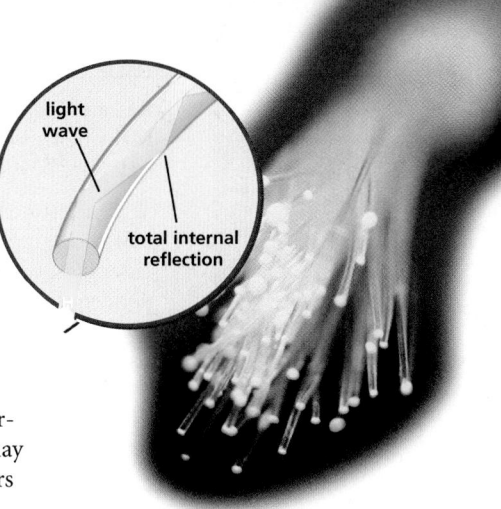

light wave

total internal reflection

optical fibers

CHECK YOUR READING What is total internal reflection? What questions do you have about this light behavior?

Fiber optics is important in communications, because it can be used to transmit information very efficiently. Optical fibers can carry more signals than a corresponding amount of electrical cable. Optical cables can be used in place of electrical wires for telephone lines, cable television, and broadband Internet connections.

Fiber optics also has visual uses. For example, fiber optics is used in medicine to look inside the body. Using optical cable, doctors can examine organs and diagnose illnesses without surgery or x-rays. Optical fibers can also deliver laser light to specific points inside the body to help surgeons with delicate surgery.

This surgeon uses fiber optics to see inside a patient's body.

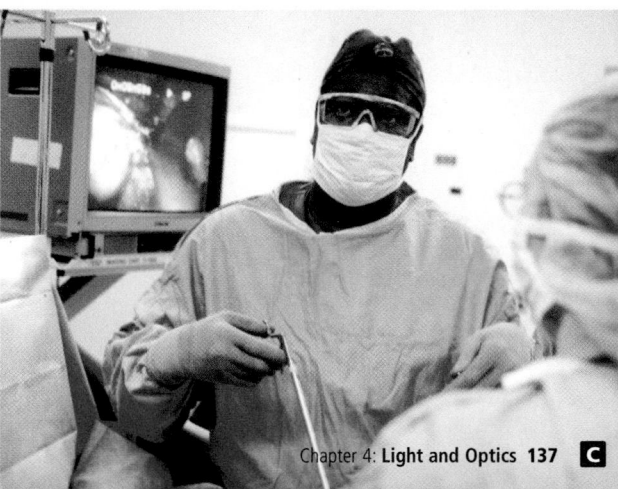

Chapter 4: **Light and Optics 137** **C**

Chapter 4 **137** **C**

Teach from Visuals

To help students interpret the fiber optics visual, ask:

What happens to light as it travels along an optical fiber? *It reflects off the inside surface of the fiber.*

Develop Critical Thinking

PROVIDE EXAMPLES Tell students that total internal reflection takes place only if the light is traveling within a more dense medium toward a less dense medium. Ask students for an example of this. *light traveling from water toward air*

Ongoing Assessment

CHECK YOUR READING *Answer: the reflection of the light from the inside surface of a transparent medium*

DIFFERENTIATE INSTRUCTION

More Reading Support

G How is fiber optics used in medicine? *to let doctors look inside the body*

Inclusion This activity can benefit students who are visually impaired as well as those who have learning disabilities. Have groups of students research the structure of an optical fiber and make a model, using any materials they wish. Several of these "optical fibers" can be bundled into a piece of PVC pipe, which can represent the outer jacket of an optical cable.

Integrate the Sciences

Because optical fibers are so flexible and can transmit and receive light, they are used in flexible digital cameras for medical imaging. An endoscope uses fiber optics and powerful lens systems to provide lighting and visualization of the interior of a body part. The endoscope uses two fiber-optic lines. One carries light into the body cavity, and the other carries the image of the body cavity back to the physician's viewing lens.

Reinforce

Have students relate the section to the Big Idea.

 Reinforcing Key Concepts, p. 256

 ASSESS & RETEACH

Assess

 Section 4.4 Quiz, p. 65

Reteach

Have groups each make a poster of an optical tool of their choosing. They should give a short history of the development of the tool, show a ray diagram explaining the optics of the tool, and include pictures of various types of the tool. If students choose optical tools that have not been covered in the text, you may want them to give reports to the class.

Technology Resources

Have students visit **ClassZone.com** for reteaching of Key Concepts.

 CONTENT REVIEW

CONTENT REVIEW CD-ROM

Drawing power from a laser beam, the space elevator climbs to an orbiting space station.

Future Uses of Lasers

Research involving new uses of lasers continues at an amazing pace. Many new discoveries and developments in science and technology today are possible only because of lasers.

One area of research in which lasers have made a big impact is nanotechnology—the development of super-tiny machines and tools. Laser light can be controlled very precisely, so scientists can use it to perform extremely fine operations. For example, lasers could be used to cut out parts to make molecule-size motors. Lasers can also be used as "optical tweezers" to handle extremely small objects such as molecules. Scientists are even beginning to use lasers to change the shape of molecules. They do this by varying the laser's wavelength.

Future applications of lasers are also sure to involve new ways of transferring energy. Remember that a wave is a disturbance that transfers energy. Laser light is made up of EM waves. EM waves can move energy over great distances without losing any of it. When EM waves encounter a material medium, their energy can then be converted into other forms and put to use.

One possible future use of lasers is to supply energy to spacecraft. Scientists imagine a day when orbiting space stations will make rockets unnecessary. A cable between the ground and the station will make it possible for a "space elevator" to escape Earth's gravity by climbing up the cable. The elevator will be powered by an Earth-based laser. A device on board the elevator will convert the laser's energy into electrical power.

4.4 Review

KEY CONCEPTS

1. How do refracting and reflecting telescopes use convex lenses and mirrors?
2. What is different about the way a camera focuses images from the way an eye focuses images?
3. How is laser light different from ordinary light?

CRITICAL THINKING

4. **Predict** What would happen to laser light if it passed through a prism?
5. **Analyze** What are two ways reflection is involved in fiber optics?

⚙ CHALLENGE

6. **Apply** How could the speed of light and a laser beam be used to measure the distance between two satellites?

C 138 Unit: Waves, Sound, and Light

C 138 Unit: Waves, Sound, and Light

ANSWERS

1. Refracting telescopes use one lens to focus and another to magnify the image; reflecting telescopes use a lens to magnify an image focused by a mirror.

2. The eye focuses by changing shape of the lens. A camera focuses by changing distance between the lens and the film.

3. Laser light is made up of a single wavelength and a pure color. Ordinary light is made up of many different wavelengths.

4. It would not produce a color spectrum, because all of it would be refracted the same amount.

5. to make a laser and to keep the laser light within optical fibers

6. One satellite could shine the beam at the other satellite. Measure the time it takes for the beam to reflect and return from the other satellite. Use the speed of light to calculate the distance.

Optics in Photography

Photographers use the science of optics to help them make the best photographs possible. For example, a portrait photographer chooses the right equipment and lighting to make each person look his or her best. A photographer needs to understand how light reflects, refracts, and diffuses to achieve just the right effect.

Using Reflection

A gold-colored reflector reflects only gold-colored wavelengths of light onto the subject. Photographers use these to fill in shadows and add warmth.

without gold reflector   **with gold reflector**

Using Diffusion

When light is directed toward a curved reflective surface, the light scatters in many directions. This diffused light produces a softer appearance than direct light.

direct light   **diffused light**

Using Refraction

Lenses refract light in different ways. A long lens makes the subject appear closer. A wide-angle lens includes more space around the subject.

long lens

wide-angle lens

EXPLORE

1. **COMPARE** Find photos of people and compare them to the photos above. Which would have been improved by the use of a gold reflector? a long lens? diffused light?

2. **CHALLENGE** Using a disposable camera and a desk lamp, experiment with photography yourself. Try using a piece of paper as a reflector and observe its effects on the photograph. What happens if you use more than one reflector? What happens if you use a different color of paper?

Chapter 4: **Light and Optics 139** **C**

EXPLORE

1. **COMPARE** *Sample Answer: A gold reflector will improve photographs by filling in shadows and adding warmth. A long lens enlarges details. Diffused light softens images.*

2. **CHALLENGE** *Multiple reflectors scatter the light coming from all directions and eliminate shadows. Colored reflectors absorb some wavelengths of light, changing the color of the light reflected off the subject.*

Set Learning Goal

To understand why photographers need a knowledge of optics

Present the Science

Photographers can choose from a wide variety of lenses.

- A **wide-angle lens** has a very short focal length, which takes in a wide field of view. Because of its short focal length, it must be close to the film to form a sharp image. Wide-angle lenses produce a relatively small image of the subject and include much of the background.

- **Telephoto lenses,** also called **long lenses,** have a long focal length and a narrow field of view. They must be relatively far from the film. They produce an enlarged image that seems closer than it really is.

- A **zoom lens** has a variable focal length. Many photographers like using this lens so they don't have to carry several lenses.

Discussion Question

Ask: Why must photographers understand how colors form from the interaction of different wavelengths of light? *Color affects the appearance of a photograph in subtle ways. Photographers can insert color filters in front of the camera lens to soften the image, create shadows and contrast, or tone down harsh colors.*

Close

Ask: When would a photographer want to use a wide-angle lens? a long lens? *Sample Answer: A wide-angle lens could be used for panoramic photographs of scenery or crowd scenes. Long lenses are useful for close-ups of small details or for blow-ups.*

BACK TO

the BIG idea

All optical technology uses reflection or refraction of light waves. Give students a list of optical tools and ask them to state which of these two phenomena are important for the operation of the tool. *refraction: microscope, camera, refracting telescope, contact lenses, corrective eyeglasses; reflection: lasers, periscope, fiber optics; both: reflecting telescope*

◀ KEY CONCEPTS SUMMARY

SECTION 4.1
Ask: How does regular reflection help mirrors form images? *Regular reflection causes the rays reflected from the mirror to keep the same arrangement as the rays coming from the object.*

SECTION 4.2
Ask: If the penguin is more than two focal lengths from the lens, what kind of image is formed? *a reduced inverted image*

Ask: If the penguin is between one and two focal lengths from the lens, what kind of image is formed? *an inverted image that is larger than the penguin*

SECTION 4.3
Ask: Does the eye shown need a corrective lens for normal sight? Why? *No; the image is focused directly on the retina.*

SECTION 4.4
Ask: Why does the tube have mirrors at both ends? *The mirrors reflect the light back and forth. One of the mirrors allows some of the light waves through, producing a laser beam.*

Review Concepts

- Big Idea Flow Chart, p. T25
- Chapter Outline, pp. T31–T32

 Chapter Review

the BIG idea

Optical tools depend on the wave behavior of light.

 **CONTENT REVIEW**
CLASSZONE.COM

◀ KEY CONCEPTS SUMMARY

4.1 Mirrors form images by reflecting light.

flat mirror

- Light rays obey the law of reflection.
- Mirrors work by regular reflection.
- Curved mirrors can form images that are distorted in useful ways.

VOCABULARY
optics p. 113
image p. 114
diffuse reflection p. 114
regular reflection p. 114
law of reflection p. 114
concave p. 116
focal point p. 116
convex p. 117

4.2 Lenses form images by refracting light.

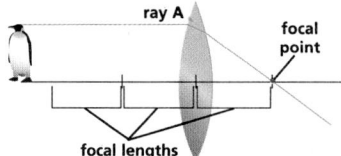
ray A
focal point
focal lengths

- Lenses have curved surfaces that refract parallel light waves in different amounts.
- Convex lenses bend light inward toward a focal point.
- Concave lenses spread light out.
- Lenses form a variety of useful images.

VOCABULARY
lens p. 121
focal length p. 123

4.3 The eye is a natural optical tool.

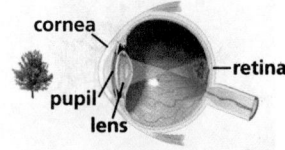
cornea
retina
pupil
lens

- The eyes of humans and many animals use lenses to focus images on the retina.
- The retina detects images and sends information about them to the brain.

VOCABULARY
cornea p. 127
pupil p. 127
retina p. 127

4.4 Optical technology makes use of light waves.

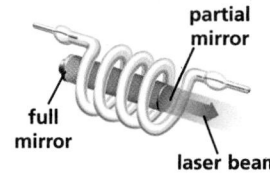
partial mirror
full mirror
laser beam

- Many optical tools are made by combining mirrors and lenses.
- Examples of optical tools include telescopes, microscopes, cameras, and lasers.
- Lasers have a wide variety of uses.

VOCABULARY
laser p. 135
fiber optics p. 137

C 140 Unit: Waves, Sound, and Light

Technology Resources

Have students visit **ClassZone.com** or use the CD-ROM for a cumulative review of concepts.

 CONTENT REVIEW

 CONTENT REVIEW CD-ROM

Engage students in a whole-class interactive review of Key Concepts. Edit content as you wish.

 POWER PRESENTATIONS

Reviewing Vocabulary

For each item below, fill in the blank. If the left column is blank, give a brief description or definition. If the right column is blank, give the correct term.

Term	Description
1.	shape like the inside of a bowl
2. convex	
3.	science of light, vision, and related technology
4.	picture of object formed by light rays
5. focal point	
6.	controls the amount of light entering the eye
7.	distance between mirror or lens and place where light rays meet
8. fiber optics	
9. law of reflection	
10.	concentrated, parallel light waves of a single wavelength

Reviewing Key Concepts

Multiple Choice *Choose the letter of the best answer.*

11. What shape is a mirror that reflects parallel light rays toward a focal point?
- **a.** convex
- **b.** flat
- **c.** concave
- **d.** regular

12. According to the law of reflection, a light ray striking a mirror
- **a.** continues moving through the mirror in the same direction
- **b.** moves into the mirror at a slightly different angle
- **c.** bounces off the mirror toward the direction it came from
- **d.** bounces off the mirror at the same angle it hits

13. Reflecting telescopes focus images using
- **a.** several mirrors
- **b.** several lenses
- **c.** both mirrors and lenses
- **d.** either a mirror or a lens, but not both

14. Ordinary light differs from laser light in that ordinary light waves
- **a.** all have the same wavelength
- **b.** tend to spread out
- **c.** stay parallel to each other
- **d.** all have their crests and troughs lined up

15. Nearsighted vision is corrected when lenses
- **a.** reflect light away from the eye
- **b.** allow light rays to focus on the retina
- **c.** allow light to focus slightly past the retina
- **d.** help light rays reflect regularly

16. Lasers do work similar to that of human vision when they are used to
- **a.** perform surgery
- **b.** send phone signals over optical cable
- **c.** scan bar codes at the grocery store
- **d.** change the shape of molecules

Short Answer *Write a short answer to each question.*

17. Name one optical tool, describe how it works, and explain some of its uses.

18. How are the images that are produced by a convex mirror different from those produced by a concave mirror?

19. Describe what typically happens to a ray of light from the time it enters the eye until it strikes the retina.

20. How do lenses correct nearsightedness and farsightedness?

21. What does a refracting telescope have in common with a simple microscope?

22. Describe two ways the distance of an object from a lens can affect the appearance of the object's image.

ASSESSMENT RESOURCES

UNIT ASSESSMENT BOOK
- Chapter Test A, pp. 66–69
- Chapter Test B, pp. 70–73
- Chapter Test C, pp. 74–77
- Alternative Assessment, pp. 78–79
- Unit Test, A, B, & C, pp. 80–91

SPANISH ASSESSMENT BOOK
- Spanish Chapter Test, pp. 293–296
- Spanish Unit Test, pp. 297–300

Technology Resources

Edit test items and answer choices.

 Test Generator CD-ROM

Visit **ClassZone.com** to extend test practice.

 Test Practice

Reviewing Vocabulary

1. concave
2. curved outward like the bottom of a spoon
3. optics
4. image
5. the point where a concave mirror focuses light rays
6. pupil
7. focal length
8. technology based on the use of laser light
9. states that the angle of reflection equals the angle of incidence
10. laser beam

Reviewing Key Concepts

11. c
12. d
13. c
14. b
15. b
16. c
17. Answers will vary. For example, students might name a microscope and describe how it uses lenses to make images of small objects.
18. Convex mirrors produce reduced, right-side up images. Concave mirrors can produce images that are reduced, enlarged, right-side up, or upside down.
19. Light first enters the eye through the cornea, where it is refracted. It then continues through the pupil, which controls how much light enters the eye. After the pupil, the light passes through the lens of the eye, where the light is refracted to make adjustments for nearby and distant objects.
20. by spreading out the rays of light for nearsightedness and bending light rays inward for farsightedness; in both cases, they cause the image to fall on the retina
21. Both use a convex lens to focus and enlarge an image.
22. The distance can change the image's size and determine whether the image is upside down or right side up.

Thinking Critically

23. C   24. D   25. A   26. B

For 27–32, sample answers are given.

27. reflect light; curved changes direction of light

28. bend light rays; convex bends rays inward, concave bends rays outward

29. involved in refraction of light by lenses; focal point is a point, focal length is a distance.

30. both are vision problems; nearsighted people can't see far objects clearly, farsighted people can't see near objects clearly

31. contain convex lenses; microscope focuses enlarged image, telescope focuses reduced image

32. involve reflection of light rays; in regular reflection parallel light rays reflect in the same direction, while in total internal reflection light inside a transparent medium reflects off the inner surface

33. distance from the lens to retina; image forms on the retina.

34. Laser light waves don't spread out; they stay parallel as they are reflected through the fiber.

35. more curved to shorten focal length

36. Lasers used in surgery have narrow beams that can be precisely controlled and carry energy to cut tissues and seal blood vessels.

the BIG idea

37. The refractor is used to test a person's eyesight. Light waves bend when they pass through the lens of a refractor. The patient benefits by having vision problems corrected with eyeglasses.

38. Sketches should show two mirrors at right angles and standing on a third mirror to form a half cube. Light rays bounce off each mirror at the same angle that they hit. Light striking the corner where mirrors meet is reflected from mirror to mirror, then reflected back parallel to original path.

UNIT PROJECTS

Have students present their projects. Use the appropriate rubrics from the URB to evaluate their work.

 Unit Projects, pp. 5–10

Thinking Critically

In the four diagrams below, light rays are shown interacting with a material medium. For the next four questions, choose the letter of the diagram that answers the question.

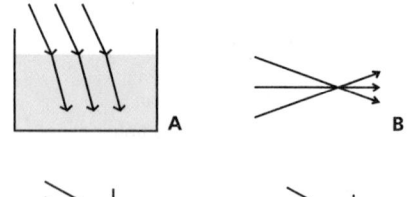

23. **INTERPRET** Which diagram shows regular reflection?

24. **INTERPRET** Which diagram shows diffuse reflection?

25. **INTERPRET** Which diagram shows refraction?

26. **INTERPRET** Which diagram shows light rays converging at a focal point?

Copy the chart below. For each pair of terms, write down one way they are alike (compare) and one way they are different (contrast).

Terms	Compare	Contrast
27. flat mirror, curved mirror		
28. convex lens, concave lens		
29. focal point, focal length		
30. nearsighted, farsighted		
31. simple microscope, refracting telescope		
32. regular reflection, total internal reflection		

33. **INFER** What is the approximate focal length of the eye's lens? How do you know?

34. **ANALYZE** Why is laser light used in fiber optics?

35. **APPLY** In order to increase the magnification of a magnifying glass, would you need to make the convex surfaces of the lens more or less curved?

36. **APPLY** Describe a possible use for laser light not mentioned in the chapter. What characteristics of laser light does this application make use of?

the BIG idea

37. **SYNTHESIZE** Using what you have learned in this chapter, describe two possible uses of an optical tool like the one shown on pages 110–111. Explain what wave behaviors of light would be involved in these uses. Then explain how these uses could benefit the person in the photo.

38. **APPLY** Make a sketch of an optical tool that would use 3 mirrors to make a beam of light return to its source. Your sketch should include:

   • the path of light waves through the tool
   • labels indicating the names of parts and how they affect the light.
   • 2 or 3 sentences at the bottom describing one possible use of the tool.

UNIT PROJECTS

Evaluate all the data, results, and information from your project folder. Prepare to present your project.

MONITOR AND RETEACH

If students have trouble applying the concepts in items 23–26, conduct a demonstration using a mirror, a flashlight, a prism, and a convex lens. Use the mirror to redirect a beam of light by reflection. Use the prism to redirect the beam by refraction. Use the lens to focus the beam into a concentrated spot. Then have students diagram the path of the light rays in each of the three events.

Students may benefit from summarizing sections of the chapter.

 Summarizing the Chapter, pp. 282–283

Standardized Test Practice

For practice on your state test, go to . . .
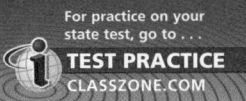
TEST PRACTICE
CLASSZONE.COM

Interpreting Diagrams

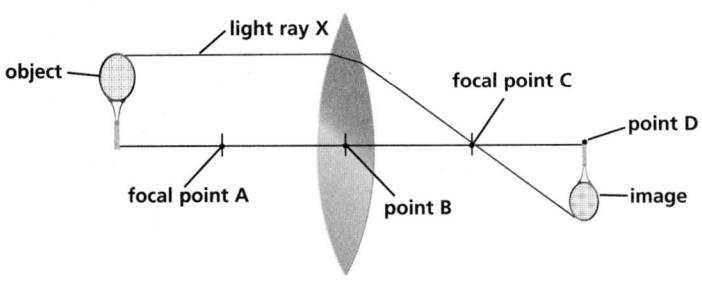

light ray X
object
focal point C
point D
focal point A
point B
image

Study the diagram above and then answer the questions that follow.

1. What kind of lens is shown in the diagram?
   a. concave   **c.** flat
   b. convex   **d.** prism

2. What happens to parallel light rays passing through this type of lens?
   a. They become polarized.
   b. They form a rainbow.
   c. They bend inward.
   d. They bend outward.

3. All light rays parallel to light ray X will pass through what point?
   a. point A   **c.** point C
   b. point B   **d.** point D

4. How far is the object in the diagram from the lens?
   a. less than one focal length
   b. one focal length
   c. about two focal lengths
   d. more than three focal lengths

5. Where would you position a screen in order to see the image in focus on the screen?
   a. at point A
   b. at point B
   c. at point C
   d. at point D

Extended Response

Answer the two questions below in detail. Include some of the terms from the word box. Underline each term you use in your answer.

concave	focal point	real image
convex	refraction	virtual image
flat mirror	reflection	magnifying glass

6. What kind of mirror would you use to see what is happening over a broad area? Why?

7. Choose one of the following optical tools and explain how it uses mirrors and/or lenses to form an image: camera, telescope, periscope, microscope

Chapter 4: **Optics** 143 **C**

METACOGNITIVE ACTIVITY

Have students answer the following questions in their **Science Notebook:**

1. How does what you learned about the eye relate to your life?
2. Describe a scenario in which you might use an optical tool.
3. Summarize the key concepts and main ideas of this chapter that apply to your Unit Project.

Interpreting Diagrams

1. *b*   3. *c*   5. *d*
2. *c*   4. *c*

Extended Response

6. RUBRIC

4 points for a response that thoroughly answers the question and uses the following terms accurately:

   • convex   • concave

Sample: I would use a <u>convex</u> mirror because parallel light rays move away from each other. My image in a convex mirror will appear smaller than me. You will be able to see a broad area because the images would look like they have shrunk. If I use a <u>concave</u> mirror and stand inside the focal point, my image will appear very large, and I would not be able to see a broad area.

3 points for a less thorough response that uses both terms accurately

2 points for a response that adequately answers the question and uses one term accurately

1 point for a response that adequately answers the question, but does not use the terms

7. RUBRIC

4 points for a response that correctly answers the question and uses the following terms accurately:

   • convex   • focal point   • real image

Sample: A film camera uses a <u>convex</u> lens to produce images of objects that are more than two focal lengths away. The images are reduced in size and upside down. The camera does not change the shape of its lens to change the <u>focal point</u>. Instead, you can move the lens nearer to or farther away from the film until the object you want to photograph is in focus. In a camera, the focal length is the distance between the lens and the <u>real image</u> of the object.

3 points for a response that correctly answers the question and uses two terms accurately

2 points for a response that uses one term accurately

1 point for a response that correctly answers the question, but does not use the terms

Ecology

symbiosis

Tickbird
(Buphagus erythrorhynchus)

Impala
(Aepyceros melampus)

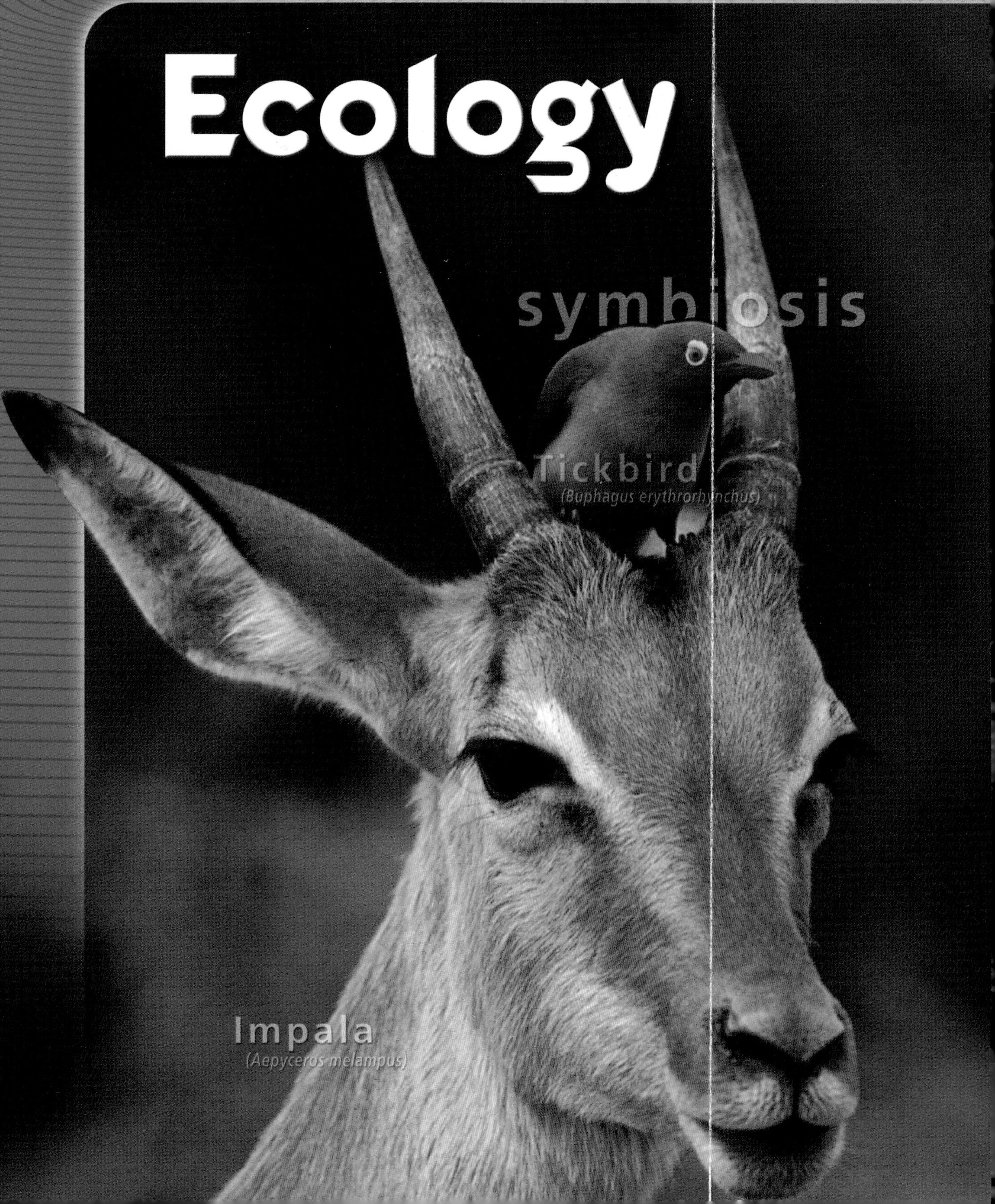

North Carolina Standards

In Unit D: Ecology, students will learn and apply science concepts and skills related to the following goals from the North Carolina Standard Course of Study:

Competency Goal 1: The learner will design and conduct investigations to demonstrate an understanding of scientific inquiry. (Objectives 1.01–1.10)

Competency Goal 2: The learner will demonstrate an understanding of technological design. (Objectives 2.01–2.04)

Competency Goal 3: The learner will build an understanding of the geological cycles, forces, process, and agents which shape the lithosphere.

3.06   Evaluate ways in which human activities have affected Earth's pedosphere and the measures taken to control the impact.

3.08   Conclude that the good health of environments and organisms requires monitoring of the pedosphere, taking steps to maintain soil quality, and stewardship.

Competency Goal 4: The learner will investigate the cycling of matter.

4.01   Describe the flow of energy and matter in natural systems.

4.02   Evaluate the significant role of decomposers.

4.03   Examine evidence that green plants make food.

4.04   Evaluate the significance of photosynthesis to other organisms.

4.05   Evaluate designed systems for ability to enable growth of certain plants and animals.

Competency Goal 6: The learner will conduct investigations and examine models and devices to build an understanding of the characteristics of energy transfer and/or transformation.

6.04   Evaluate data for qualitative and quantitative relationships associated with energy transfer and/or transformation.

Competency Goal 7: The learner will conduct investigations and use technologies and information systems to build an understanding of population dynamics.

7.01   Describe ways in which organisms interact with each other and with non-living parts of the environment.

7.02   Investigate factors that determine the growth and survival of organisms.

7.03   Explain how changes in habitat may affect organisms.

7.04   Evaluate data related to human population growth, along with problems and solutions.

7.05   Examine evidence that overpopulation by any species impacts the environment.

For a detailed lesson-by-lesson correlation of Unit D to the North Carolina Standard Course of Study, see Correlations pages 16–24 in the front of this Teacher's Edition.

North Carolina Handbook

The following sections of the North Carolina Handbook are also designed to be used in conjunction with this unit:

• Natural Selection (pp. NC2–NC6)
• Photosynthesis (pp. NC 12–NC13)
• Designed Systems (pp. NC14–NC15)

Ecology
Contents Overview

Unit Features

1 Ecosystems and Biomes   6

2 Interactions Within Ecosystems   42

3 Human Impact on Ecosystems   78

VIDEO SUMMARY

SCIENTIFIC AMERICAN FRONTIERS

"Prairie Comeback" is a segment of the Scientific American Frontiers series that aired on PBS stations. In this video, host Alan Alda visits the Tallgrass Prairie Preserve in northeastern Oklahoma. This is the location of an attempt to reconstruct a ecosystem that once covered more than a quarter of the continental United States. The Great Plains was once the largest grassland on Earth. Cultivation and the disappearance of wildlife, including buffalo herds, resulted in the prairie's disappearance. In 1989, the Nature Conservancy identified a large ranch that had never been farmed and therefore still had all the plants that grew on the original prairie. On 50 square miles of land, they have attempted to create a model of the prairie. They introduced a herd of buffalo to graze on the prairie plants. Today, a system based on controlled fires and grazing buffalo reproduces the life cycles of the original prairie.

National Science Education Standards

A.9.a–d Understandings about Scientific Inquiry

E.6.a–f Understandings about Science and Technology

F.5.a–e Science and Technology in Society

G.1.a–b Science as a Human Endeavor

G.2.a Nature of Science

FRONTIERS in Science

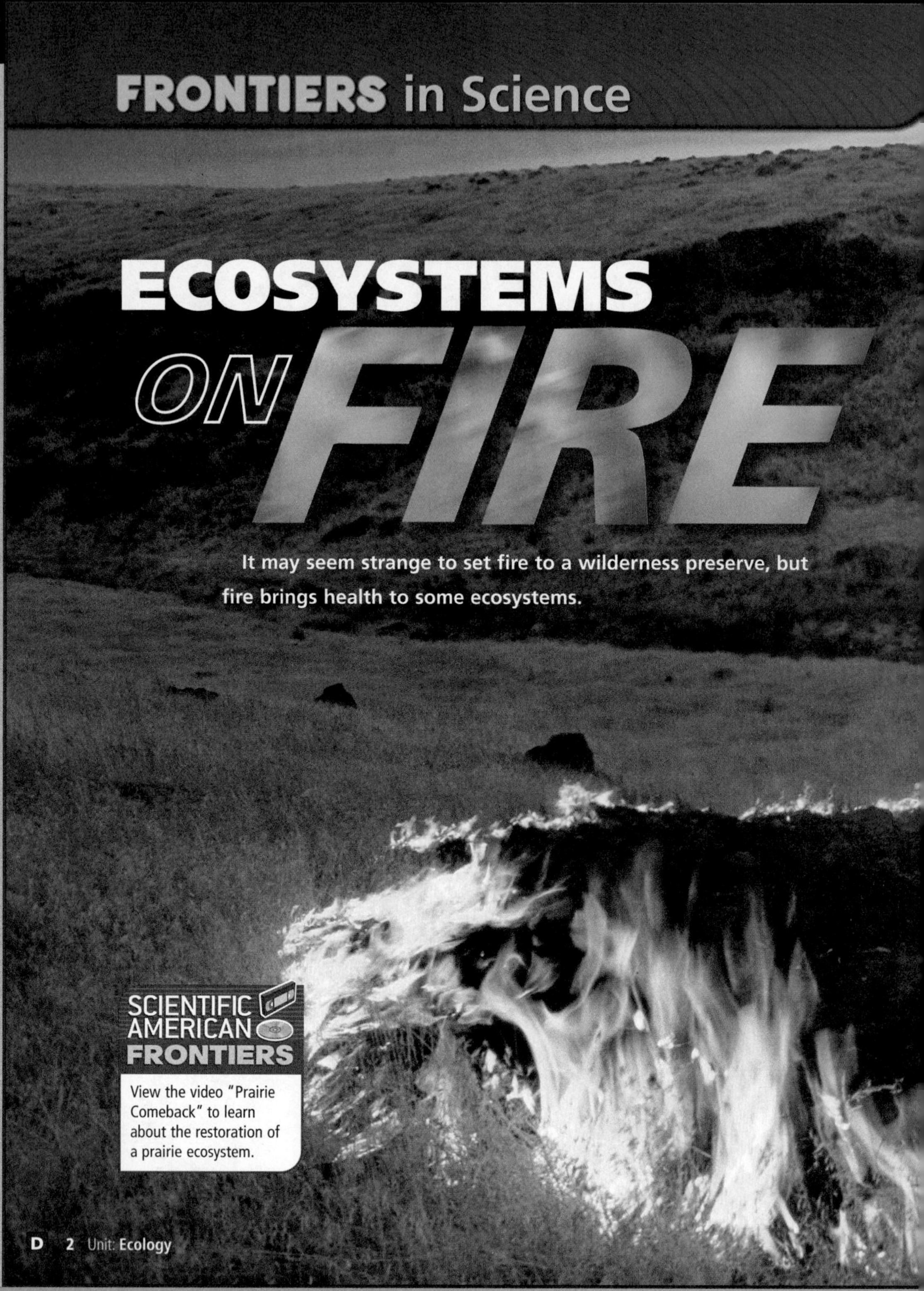

ECOSYSTEMS ON *FIRE*

It may seem strange to set fire to a wilderness preserve, but fire brings health to some ecosystems.

SCIENTIFIC AMERICAN FRONTIERS

View the video "Prairie Comeback" to learn about the restoration of a prairie ecosystem.

D 2 Unit: Ecology

ADDITIONAL RESOURCES

Technology Resources

 Scientific American Frontiers Video: *Ecosystems on Fire:* 8-minute video segment that introduces the unit.

 ClassZone.com
CAREER LINK, Ecologist

Guide student viewing and comprehension of the video:

 Video Teaching Guide, pp. 1–2; Video Viewing Guide, p. 3; Video Wrap-Up, p. 4

Scientific American Frontiers Video Guide, pp. 9–12

Unit projects procedures and rubrics:

 Unit Projects, pp. 5–10

An astonishing variety of plants blooms in this prairie in Missouri.

Fire and Life

Intense heat, smoke, the crackling of burning grasses, the crashing of flaming trees—all these characteristics of fire seem threatening. In recent years, forest fires have burned huge areas of forest and have endangered people and property nearby. But even though fire can be destructive, it can also be an agent of life. In fact, scientists are actively using fire to manage ecosystems—areas that contain specific groups of living and nonliving things. Prairies, forests, and woodlands are examples of ecosystems.

?
A

The fear of fire has led people to limit fires that are a natural part of some ecosystems. Preventing or putting out smaller fires in a forest ecosystem can mean trouble. Occasional small fires burn small amounts of material and cause only limited damage. Without these smaller fires, burnable materials may build up and lead to the outbreak of a catastrophic fire.

The species of living things in some ecosystems have adaptations that allow them to thrive on fire. In western forests in the United States trees such as lodgepole pine and jack pine depend upon flames to release seeds from their cones. Cape lilies lying under the forest floor blossom almost immediately after a forest fire. On prairies, flowers such as the rare coastal gayfeather in Texas or the fringed prairie orchid in Illinois benefit from prairie fires.

?
B

DIFFERENTIATE INSTRUCTION

Advanced Have students determine the locations of major forests, woodlands, and prairies in the United States. Ask them to indicate these locations on a blank map. Students may wish to look up statistics on occurrences of wildfires in the United States and draw a conclusion about the conditions of these forests and prairies.

FOCUS

▶ Set Learning Goals
Students will

• Observe positive and negative effects of prairie fires.

• Examine unanswered questions concerning ecosystem restoration.

• Explore the parts of an ecosystem.

Remind students that frontiers are undeveloped fields for discovery or research, and that the "Ecosystems on Fire" video shows real scientists gathering and analyzing data to find answers or solve problems. Have students look at the photographs and title on pp. 2–3 and predict what questions the scientists are trying to answer.

INSTRUCT

Scientific Process

Emphasize to students that understanding the effects of fires on ecosystems requires that scientists learn as much as they can about the plants and animals that live in the ecosystem. Have students review the parts of the scientific process on pages xxiv–xxv and ask what part this step falls under. *Determine what is known.*

Integrate the Sciences

Executing a controlled burn in an ecosystem requires attention to many details. Besides knowing how plants and animals will react to the effects of the fire, what other knowledge, skills, or personnel should scientists have before attempting a controlled burn? *They should know how to start fires and how fires spread.*

controlled burn

new growth

Seven months after a controlled burn, light shines on a new patch of wild hyacinth growing at the base of an oak tree.

Observing Patterns

Ecosystems include living things, such as plants and animals, and nonliving things, such as water and soil. Fires affect both the living and the nonliving. The photographs above show part of an oak woodland ecosystem. The photograph on the left shows a burn—a fire set deliberately by humans. The photograph on the right shows the same area seven months later.

Ashes left from fires add nutrients to the soil. Fire also opens space on the forest floor. Areas that were shaded by small trees, plants, and dead branches receive light. Over time, wild hyacinth and other new plants grow around the oak, and new insects and animals move into the area.

SCIENTIFIC AMERICAN FRONTIERS

View the "Prairie Comeback" segment of your Scientific American Frontiers video to see how understanding ecosystems can help bring a prairie into bloom.

IN THIS SCENE FROM THE VIDEO ▶ a bison grazes on new growth that appears after the prairie is burned.

BRINGING BACK THE PRAIRIE At one time natural events, such as lightning, along with human activity caused regular patterns of fire on the

prairie. Bison grazed on tender young plants that grew up after fires, and the plants that weren't eaten by the bison had room to grow. In 1989, an organization called The Nature Conservancy turned the Chapman-Barnard Cattle Ranch in Northeast Oklahoma into the Tall Grass Prairie Restoration Preserve.

Scientists at the preserve are using controlled fire and reintroducing bison to the area. Today there are more than 750 species of plants and animals growing in the preserve.

D 4 Unit: **Ecology**

Teach from Visuals

Have students look at the photos of the forest after the controlled burn and seven months after the burn. Ask students why the second photo shows a healthier ecosystem. *There is new, green vegetation and the trees have leaves in the second photo.*

Scientific Process

Ask students to identify the skill scientists use most in studying ecosystems. *observing*

Sharing Results

Ask students why it is even more crucial that scientists share what they learn from their observations of different ecosystems with other scientists. *The lives of people and animals depend upon the ecosystem. The better scientists understand an ecosystem, the better they help preserve the lives that depend on it.*

Social Studies Connection

The American bison, or buffalo, has had a troubled existence in the United States. Once it was a major source of food and clothing for many Native American tribes. However, increased settlement on the prairie brought increased hunting and near extinction for the buffalo as well as for the Native Americans that depended on them.

DIFFERENTIATE INSTRUCTION

More Reading Support

C What do ecosystems include? *living and nonliving things*

D Name one natural phenomenon that could start a prairie fire. *lightning*

Below Level Have students identify all of the words on this page that refer to protecting or safeguarding: *conservatory, restoration,* and *preserve.* Point out to students how the words *conservatory* and *preserve* share a stem, *–serve.* Have students think of another word that has this stem, like *reserve,* and ask if it has a similar meaning. *Yes. When you reserve something, you are protecting it in a way.*

In tall-grass prairie ecosystems, fire provides similar benefits. Fire burns away overgrown plants, enriches the soil, and clears the way for the growth of new plants. Bison prefer to graze on these new plants that appear after a fire.

A New Understanding

Although some of the benefits provided by ecosystems can't be measured, researchers are starting to measure the financial contributions of ecosystems. Ecosystems may help clean our water, balance gases in the atmosphere, and maintain temperature ranges.

Researchers today are studying these benefits. In fact, a new frontier in ecology, called ecosystem services, is emerging. This new study is gaining the attention of both scientists and economists.

Given our growing awareness of the importance of ecosystems, should humans deliberately set fire to areas in forests or prairies? The answer to this question requires an understanding of interactions among living and nonliving parts of ecosystems. Forest and prairie fires can be dangerous, but properly managed, they provide important benefits to society as well as to the natural world.

UNANSWERED Questions

Understanding the connections within ecosystems raises more questions. In the coming years, people will need to analyze the costs and benefits of ecosystem restoration.

- How will humans balance the need to feed the population with the cost of destroying ecosystems such as the prairie?
- How can scientists and wildlife managers protect people and property near forests while maintaining forest ecosystems?
- How do ecosystems protect natural resources, such as soil and water?

UNIT PROJECTS

As you study this unit, work alone or with a group on one of the projects listed below. Use the bulleted steps to guide your project.

Build an Ecosystem

Use an aquarium or other container to build an ecosystem such as an aquarium.

- Set up your ecosystem. Observe it daily, and record your observations.
- Bring your ecosystem into your classroom, or take photographs and make diagrams of it. Present the record of your observations along with the visual displays.

Conservation Campaign

Find out how much water, paper, and energy are used in a month at your school.

- Describe a plan for conserving resources.
- Present your plan. You might make posters, write announcements, perform a short skit.

Design a Park

You are part of a group that is planning a park near your school. Your group wants the park to include plants that lived in the area twenty-five years ago.

- Collect information from local museums, park districts, or botanic gardens. You can also visit Web sites sponsored by those organizations.
- Prepare a report and drawing of your park design.

CAREER CENTER
CLASSZONE.COM

Learn more about careers in ecology.

UNANSWERED Questions

Have students read the questions and think of some of their own. Remind them that scientists always end up with more questions—that inquiry is the driving force of science.

- With the class, generate on the board a list of new questions.
- Students can add to the list after they watch the Scientific American Frontiers Video.
- Students can use the list as a springboard for choosing their Unit Projects.

UNIT PROJECTS

Encourage students to pick the project that most appeals to them. Point out that each is long-term and will take several weeks to complete. You might group or pair students to work on projects and in some cases guide student choice. Each project has two worksheet pages, including a rubric to guide students through criteria, process, and schedule.

 Unit Projects, pp. 5–10

REVISIT concepts introduced in this article:

Chapter 1
- Ecosystems support life, pp. 9–15
- Living things depend on the environment, pp. 9–10
- All ecosystems need certain materials, p. 16

Chapter 2
- Groups of living things interact within ecosystems, pp. 45–51
- Ecosystems are always changing, pp. 63–69

Chapter 3
- Human activities affect the environment, pp. 89–97
- People are working to protect ecosystems, pp. 98–107

DIFFERENTIATE INSTRUCTION

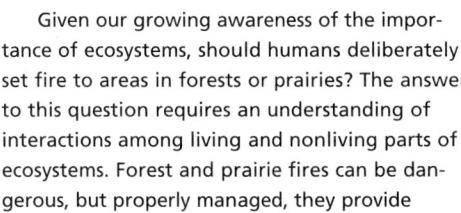

 More Reading Support

E Name one way ecosystems help us. *clean water, balance gases in the atmosphere*

F Who is interested in ecosystem services? *scientists and economists*

Differentiate Unit Projects Projects are appropriate for varying abilities. Allow students to choose the ones that interest them most and let them vary their product. Encourage below level students to give visual or oral presentations or to record audio presentations about their topic.

Below Level Encourage students to try "Build an Ecosystem."

Advanced Challenge students to complete "Design a Park."

1 Ecosystems and Biomes

Life Science
UNIFYING PRINCIPLES

PRINCIPLE 1

All living things share common characteristics.

PRINCIPLE 2

All living things share common needs.

PRINCIPLE 3

Living things meet their needs through interactions with the environment.

PRINCIPLE 4

The types and numbers of living things change over time.

Unit: Ecology
BIG IDEAS

CHAPTER 1
Ecosystems and Biomes

Matter and energy together support life within an environment.

CHAPTER 2
Interactions within Ecosystems

Living things within an ecosystem interact with each other and the environment.

CHAPTER 3
Human Impact on Ecosystems

Humans and human population growth affect the environment.

CHAPTER 1
KEY CONCEPTS

SECTION 1.1

Ecosystems support life.
1. Living things depend on the environment.
2. Biotic factors interact with an ecosystem.
3. Many abiotic factors affect ecosystems.

SECTION 1.2

Matter cycles through ecosystems.
1. All ecosystems need certain materials.
2. Water cycles through ecosystems.
3. Carbon cycles through ecosystems.
4. Nitrogen cycles through ecosystems.

SECTION 1.3

Energy flows through ecosystems.
1. Living things capture and release energy.
2. Models help explain feeding relationships.
3. Available energy decreases as it moves through an ecosystem.

SECTION 1.4

Biomes contain many ecosystems.
1. Regions of Earth are classified into biomes.
2. Water covers most of Earth's surface.

T The Big Idea Flow Chart is available on p. T1 in the **UNIT TRANSPARENCY BOOK.**

Previewing Content

1.1 Ecosystems support life. pp. 9–15

1. Living things depend on the environment.

An **ecosystem** comprises organisms and their physical environment. **Ecology** is the scientific study of how organisms interact with their environment and with other organisms.
- Natural ecosystems include water, air, and sunlight, as well as microorganisms, plants, and animals.
- **Biotic factors** are the living parts of an ecosystem.
- **Abiotic factors** are the nonliving parts.

2. Biotic factors interact with an ecosystem.

Every organism affects, and is affected by, other organisms in its ecosystem. Moles are a good example of this interrelatedness. They eat insects, worms, and grubs. They can severely damage plants, but moles help keep insect populations in check. Mole tunnels aerate soil, which is necessary for the growth of soil organisms and plant roots.

3. Many abiotic factors affect ecosystems.

Abiotic factors include any nonliving features of the environment, from soil fertility to climate characteristics—precipitation, temperature, air currents, and humidity. Here is a short list of the most influential factors.

- available water
- temperature
- available light
- soil content

The size of soil particles affects how much air and water the soil can hold.

1.2 Matter cycles through ecosystems. pp. 16–21

1. All ecosystems need certain materials.

Living things need certain materials, or matter, to meet their needs. This matter remains in the ecosystem, moving through it in continuous **cycles,** in which the matter changes form, but is never created or destroyed.

2. Water cycles through ecosystems.

All substances on Earth, including water, are repeatedly recycled. Five processes make up the **water cycle.**
- Condensation: water vapor condenses to liquid in the atmosphere.
- Precipitation: water falls back to Earth.
- Transpiration: plants take up water in their roots and release it from their leaves.
- Respiration: animals release water vapor as they exhale.
- Evaporation: heat changes liquid water to gaseous water vapor, which rises into the atmosphere.

3. Carbon cycles through ecosystems.

Life on Earth is based on carbon compounds. The **carbon cycle** includes several different processes.
- Photosynthesis removes carbon from the air.
- Animals obtain carbon by eating plants.
- Plants and animals release carbon dioxide during respiration.
- Carbon contained in fossil fuels and wood is released as carbon dioxide during combustion.

4. Nitrogen cycles through ecosystems.

Nitrogen is required for all life. Almost 78 percent of the air is nitrogen, but organisms cannot use nitrogen in gaseous form. In the **nitrogen cycle**, bacteria in soil and roots fix nitrogen by changing it from a gas to nitrate compounds that can be taken up by plants.

Common Misconceptions

PHOTOSYNTHESIS Students generally think that plants absorb food from the soil rather than manufacturing it. Through photosynthesis, plants make food—sugars—from sunlight, carbon dioxide, and water from the environment.

 This misconception is addressed on p. 12.

MISCONCEPTION DATABASE
CLASSZONE.COM Background on student misconceptions

WATER CYCLE Though students may be familiar with the water cycle, they often think that water gets added to the system from somewhere. Earth has a finite amount of water that cycles through living things and the environment continuously.

 This misconception is addressed on p. 17.

Previewing Content

SECTION

1.3 **Energy flows through ecosystems.**
pp. 22–29

1. Living things capture and release energy.

Energy and matter can move through an ecosystem as food.

- **Producers** capture energy from sunlight or, in a few cases, from chemicals in the deep sea.
- **Consumers** obtain food by eating producers or other consumers.
- **Decomposers** break down dead plant and animal matter into simpler compounds, returning them to the water or soil so that the matter may be used again.

2. Models help explain feeding relationships.

Food chains and food webs are models that show how energy and matter move through the organisms of an ecosystem.

- A **food chain** shows one path of energy movement through an ecosystem, from producer (e.g., grass) to herbivore or primary consumer (grasshopper), to a secondary consumer (robin), to a tertiary consumer (hawk).
- A **food web** shows many paths of energy movement through an ecosystem. It indicates that each organism eats and is eaten by several organisms.

3. Available energy decreases as it moves through an ecosystem.

An **energy pyramid** models the amount of energy available to producers and consumers in an ecosystem. At the bottom of the pyramid are the producers, which use the Sun's abundant energy to manufacture sugars. At the top of the pyramid are the tertiary consumers.

This model shows that the amount of available energy decreases with each succeeding layer.

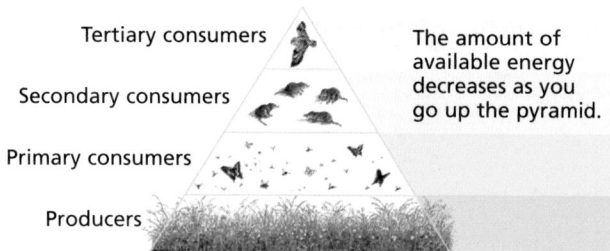

Tertiary consumers
Secondary consumers
Primary consumers
Producers

The amount of available energy decreases as you go up the pyramid.

SECTION

1.4 **Biomes contain many ecosystems.**
pp. 30–37

1. Regions of Earth are classified into biomes.

Earth's six terrestrial **biomes** are regions made up of ecosystems with similar plant life and climate.

- Tundra has little precipitation and lowest temperatures of all land biomes. Typical vegetation is lichens and mosses.
- Taiga has cold winters and short, cool summers. It supports **coniferous** trees with needlelike leaves.
- Desert has little precipitation and can be hot or cold. Typical vegetation is cacti and small plants.
- Grassland has rich soil but supports few shrubs and trees.
- Temperate forest includes mostly **deciduous** trees.
- Tropical rain forest is consistently warm and wet. Typical vegetation is broadleaf evergreen trees, with a huge number of species.

2. Water covers most of Earth's surface.

Freshwater biomes include

- rivers and streams, with high oxygen levels; plants are limited to shorelines and slow-moving shallows.
- lakes and ponds, with middling to very low oxygen levels; plants grow along the shoreline or float in upper layers.
- wetlands, such as swamps and bogs, that are wet most or all of the year; waterlogged soils limit plant species.
- **estuaries,** which are mixed fresh and salt water, where river meets ocean; fertile ecosystems act as nurseries for fish and other sea animals.

Marine biomes include

- coastal ocean, or seashore areas; many ecosystems, from sandy beaches to mud flats to rocky shores.
- open ocean to depths where sunlight stops penetrating; the plankton here serve as the basis of the ocean food web.
- deep ocean, where sunlight does not reach.

Common Misconceptions

FOOD CHAINS AND WEBS Students often think of feeding relationships as linear. They may misunderstand the food chain model in several ways: 1. They think arrows represent who eats whom rather than flow of energy; 2. They think organisms high up the chain eat everything that is lower on the chain; 3. They see only linear food chains as unconnected to a food web.

T E This misconception is addressed on p. 26.

🛈 MISCONCEPTION DATABASE
CLASSZONE.COM Background on student misconceptions

PYRAMID OF ENERGY Students commonly think that energy accumulates as it moves up a food chain or web. In reality, significant amounts of available energy are lost moving up a food chain or web. The least amount of energy is available and the fewest number of organisms are present at the top of an energy pyramid.

T E This misconception is addressed in the reteach on p. 28.

Previewing Labs

EXPLORE the BIG idea

How Do Plants React to Sunlight? p. 7 Students observe a plant's response to light.	**TIME** 10 minutes **MATERIALS** potted plant
What Is Soil? p. 7 Students determine what materials make up soil.	**TIME** 10 minutes **MATERIALS** garden soil, funnel, clear plastic bottle with cap, water
Internet Activity: A Prairie Ecosystem, p. 7 Students simulate a prairie ecosystem.	**TIME** 20 minutes **MATERIALS** computer with Internet access

SECTION 1.1

EXPLORE Your Environment, p. 9 Students measure the temperature in different places to discover variations in warmth.	**TIME** 10 minutes **MATERIALS** thermometer, stopwatch
CHAPTER INVESTIGATION **Soil Samples,** pp. 14–15 Students investigate the characteristics of three soil types.	**TIME** 40 minutes **MATERIALS** 50 mL each of clay, coarse sand, loam; 3 pieces of paper; spoon; hand lens; toothpick; eyedropper; 3 pieces of filter paper; 3 plastic funnels; 3 large beakers; small beaker; dropper; water; stopwatch

SECTION 1.2

EXPLORE The Water Cycle, p. 16 Students cover part of a plant and discover that plants give off water vapor.	**TIME** 10 minutes **MATERIALS** 1 small potted plant, 1 clear plastic bag, tape, water
INVESTIGATE Carbon, p. 19 Students observe how carbon is released in the ocean by adding vinegar to broken sea shells.	**TIME** 15 minutes **MATERIALS** whole seashell or fragments, mortar and pestle, white vinegar, small beaker

SECTION 1.3

EXPLORE Energy, p. 22 Students demonstrate energy conversion by using light to produce heat, which produces air movement.	**TIME** 10 minutes **MATERIALS** paper, marker, scissors, thread, tape, desk lamp
INVESTIGATE Decomposers, p. 25 Students observe the effect of decomposers on plant matter.	**TIME** 30 minutes **MATERIALS** clear soda bottle with cap, scissors, stones, garden soil, leaves, slices of fruit, masking tape, marker, water

SECTION 1.4

INVESTIGATE Climate, p. 35 Students collect and graph climate data for their area. Climate Graph, p. 52	**TIME** 20 minutes **MATERIALS** graph data, 2 colored pencils, Climate Graph

 Additional INVESTIGATION, The Water Cycle, A, B, & C, pp. 71–79; Teacher Instructions, pp. 200–201

Previewing Chapter Resources

	INTEGRATED TECHNOLOGY	LABS AND ACTIVITIES

CHAPTER 1

Ecosystems and Biomes

 CLASSZONE.COM
- eEdition Plus
- EasyPlanner Plus
- Misconception Database
- Content Review
- Test Practice
- Visualizations
- Simulations
- Resource Centers
- Internet Activity: A Prairie Ecosystem
- Math Tutorial

 SCILINKS.ORG
SCI LINKS

 CD-ROMS
- eEdition
- EasyPlanner
- Power Presentations
- Content Review
- Lab Generator
- Test Generator

 AUDIO CDS
- Audio Readings
- Audio Readings in Spanish

 PE EXPLORE the Big Idea, p. 7
- How Do Plants React to Sunlight?
- What Is Soil?
- Internet Activity: A Prairie Ecosystem

 R **UNIT RESOURCE BOOK**
- Family Letter, p. vii
- Spanish Family Letter, p. viii
- Unit Projects, pp. 5–10

 Lab Generator CD-ROM
Generate customized labs.

SECTION

 1.1
Ecosystems support life.
pp. 9–15

Time: 3 periods (1.5 blocks)

 R Lesson Plan, pp. 11–12

 RESOURCE CENTER, Ecosystems

T **UNIT TRANSPARENCY BOOK**
- Big Idea Flow Chart, p. T1
- Daily Vocabulary Scaffolding, p. T2
- Note-Taking Model, p. T3
- 3-Minute Warm-Up, p. T4

 PE
- EXPLORE Your Environment, p. 9
- CHAPTER INVESTIGATION Soil Samples, pp. 14–15

R **UNIT RESOURCE BOOK**
CHAPTER INVESTIGATION, Soil Samples, A, B, & C, pp. 62–70

SECTION

 1.2
Matter cycles through ecosystems.
pp. 16–21

Time: 2 periods (1 block)

 R Lesson Plan, pp. 21–22

 • **RESOURCE CENTER,** Cycles in Nature
- **VISUALIZATION,** Nitrogen Cycle
- **MATH TUTORIAL**

T **UNIT TRANSPARENCY BOOK**
- Daily Vocabulary Scaffolding, p. T2
- 3-Minute Warm-Up, p. T4

 PE
- EXPLORE The Water Cycle, p. 16
- INVESTIGATE Carbon, p. 19
- Math in Science, p. 21

R **UNIT RESOURCE BOOK**
- Datasheet, Carbon, p. 30
- Math Support and Practice, pp. 60–61
- Additional INVESTIGATION, The Water Cycle, A, B, & C, pp. 71–79

SECTION

1.3
Energy flows through ecosystems.
pp. 22–29

Time: 2 periods (1 block)

 R Lesson Plan, pp. 32–33

T **UNIT TRANSPARENCY BOOK**
- Daily Vocabulary Scaffolding, p. T2
- 3-Minute Warm-Up, p. T5
- "Energy Flows Through Ecosystems" Visual, p. T6

 PE
- EXPLORE Energy, p. 22
- INVESTIGATE Decomposers, p. 25
- Connecting Sciences, p. 29

R **UNIT RESOURCE BOOK**
Datasheet, Decomposers, p. 41

SECTION

1.4
Biomes contain many ecosystems.
pp. 30–37

Time: 3 periods (1.5 blocks)

 R Lesson Plan, pp. 43–44

 RESOURCE CENTER, Land and Aquatic Biomes

T **UNIT TRANSPARENCY BOOK**
- Big Idea Flow Chart, p. T1
- Daily Vocabulary Scaffolding, p. T2
- 3-Minute Warm-Up, p. T5
- Chapter Outline, pp. T7–T8

 PE INVESTIGATE Climate, p. 35

R **UNIT RESOURCE BOOK**
- Climate Graph, p. 52
- Datasheet, Climate, p. 53

KEY TO ICONS    **CD/CD-ROM**    **Teacher Edition**   **T** **UNIT TRANSPARENCY BOOK**   **SP A** **SPANISH ASSESSMENT BOOK**

 **INTERNET**   **PE** **Pupil Edition**   **R** **UNIT RESOURCE BOOK**   **A** **UNIT ASSESSMENT BOOK**   **SCIENCE TOOLKIT**

READING AND REINFORCEMENT

- Frame Game, B26–27
- Combination Notes, C40
- Daily Vocabulary Scaffolding, H1–8

R **UNIT RESOURCE BOOK**
- Vocabulary Practice, pp. 57–58
- Decoding Support, p. 59
- Summarizing the Chapter, pp. 80–81

 Audio Readings CD
Listen to Pupil Edition.

Audio Readings in Spanish CD
Listen to Pupil Edition in Spanish.

R **UNIT RESOURCE BOOK**
- Reading Study Guide, A & B, pp. 13–16
- Spanish Reading Study Guide, pp. 17–18
- Challenge and Extension, p. 19
- Reinforcing Key Concepts, p. 20

R **UNIT RESOURCE BOOK**
- Reading Study Guide, A & B, pp. 23–26
- Spanish Reading Study Guide, pp. 27–28
- Challenge and Extension, p. 29
- Reinforcing Key Concepts, p. 31

R **UNIT RESOURCE BOOK**
- Reading Study Guide, A & B, pp. 34–37
- Spanish Reading Study Guide, pp. 38–39
- Challenge and Extension, p. 40
- Reinforcing Key Concepts, p. 42
- Challenge Reading, pp. 55–56

R **UNIT RESOURCE BOOK**
- Reading Study Guide, A & B, pp. 45–48
- Spanish Reading Study Guide, pp. 49–50
- Challenge and Extension, p. 51
- Reinforcing Key Concepts, p. 54

ASSESSMENT

PE
- Chapter Review, pp. 39–40
- Standardized Test Practice, p. 41

A **UNIT ASSESSMENT BOOK**
- Diagnostic Test, pp. 1–2
- Chapter Test, A, B, & C, pp. 7–18
- Alternative Assessment, pp. 19–20

SP A Spanish Chapter Test, pp. 61–64

 Test Generator CD-ROM
Generate customized tests.

 Lab Generator CD-ROM
Rubrics for Labs

TE Ongoing Assessment, pp. 10–13

PE Section 1.1 Review, p. 13

A **UNIT ASSESSMENT BOOK**
Section 1.1 Quiz, p. 3

TE Ongoing Assessment, pp. 17–20

PE Section 1.2 Review, p. 20

A **UNIT ASSESSMENT BOOK**
Section 1.2 Quiz, p. 4

TE Ongoing Assessment, pp. 23–27

PE Section 1.3 Review, p. 28

A **UNIT ASSESSMENT BOOK**
Section 1.3 Quiz, p. 5

TE Ongoing Assessment, pp. 32, 34, 36

PE Section 1.4 Review, p. 37

A **UNIT ASSESSMENT BOOK**
Section 1.4 Quiz, p. 6

STANDARDS

National Standards
A.2–8, A.9.a–c, A.9.e–f, C.4.b–d, D.1.f

See p. 6 for the standards.

National Standards
A.2–7, A.9.a–b, A.9.e–f, C.4.c

National Standards
A.2–8, A.9.a–c, A.9.e–f, D.1.f

National Standards
A.2–7, A.9.a–b, A.9.e–f, C.4.b–c

National Standards
A.2–8, A.9.a–c, A.9.e–f, C.4.d

Previewing Resources for Differentiated Instruction

CHAPTER INVESTIGATION

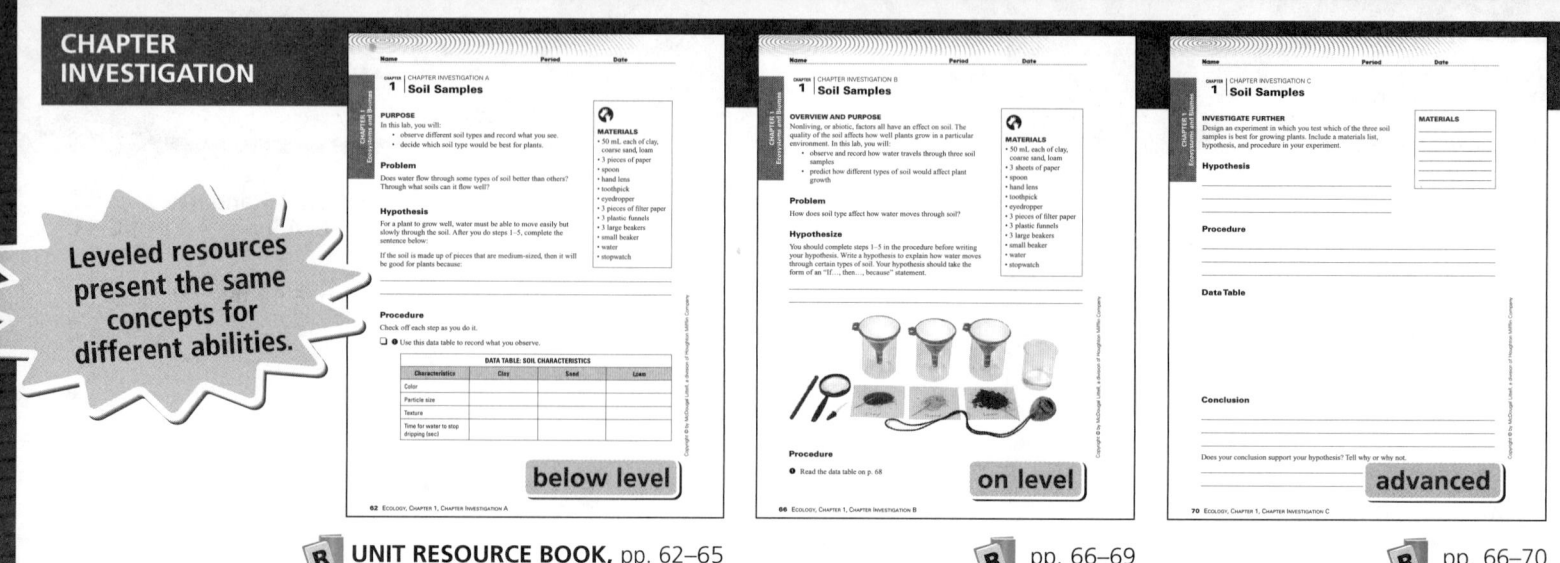

below level

on level

advanced

Leveled resources present the same concepts for different abilities.

R UNIT RESOURCE BOOK, pp. 62–65

R pp. 66–69

R pp. 66–70

READING STUDY GUIDE

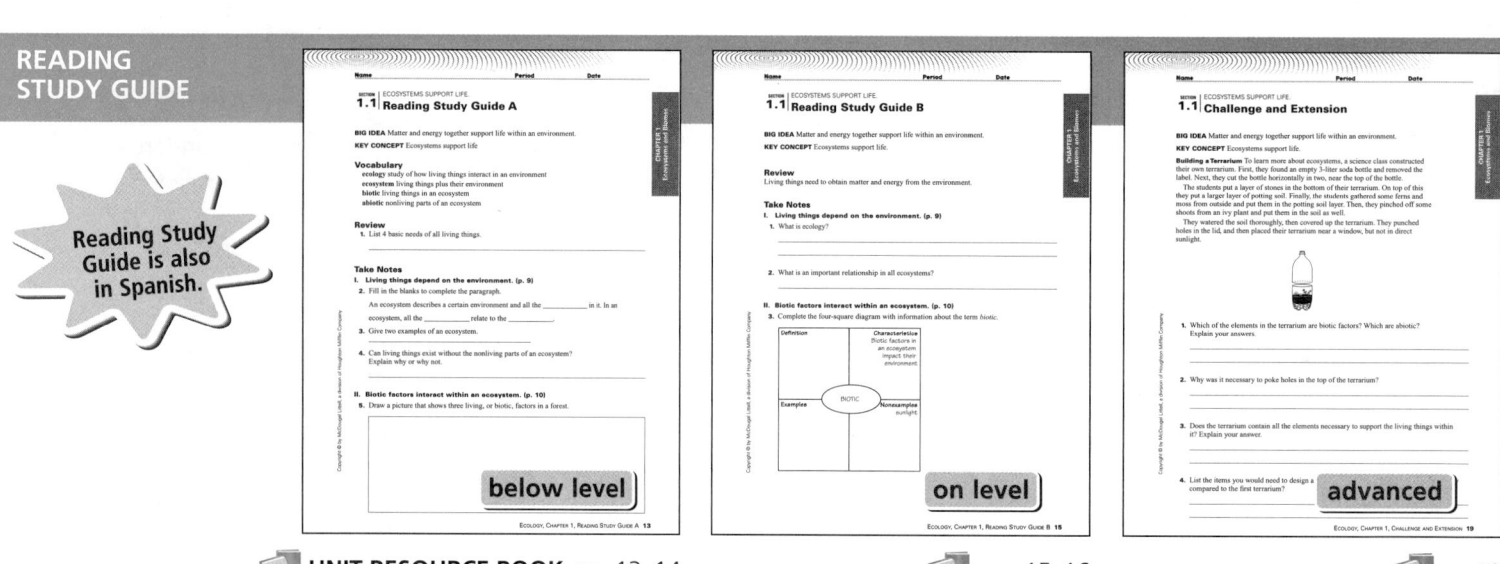

below level

on level

advanced

Reading Study Guide is also in Spanish.

R UNIT RESOURCE BOOK, pp. 13–14

R pp. 15–16

R p. 19

CHAPTER TEST

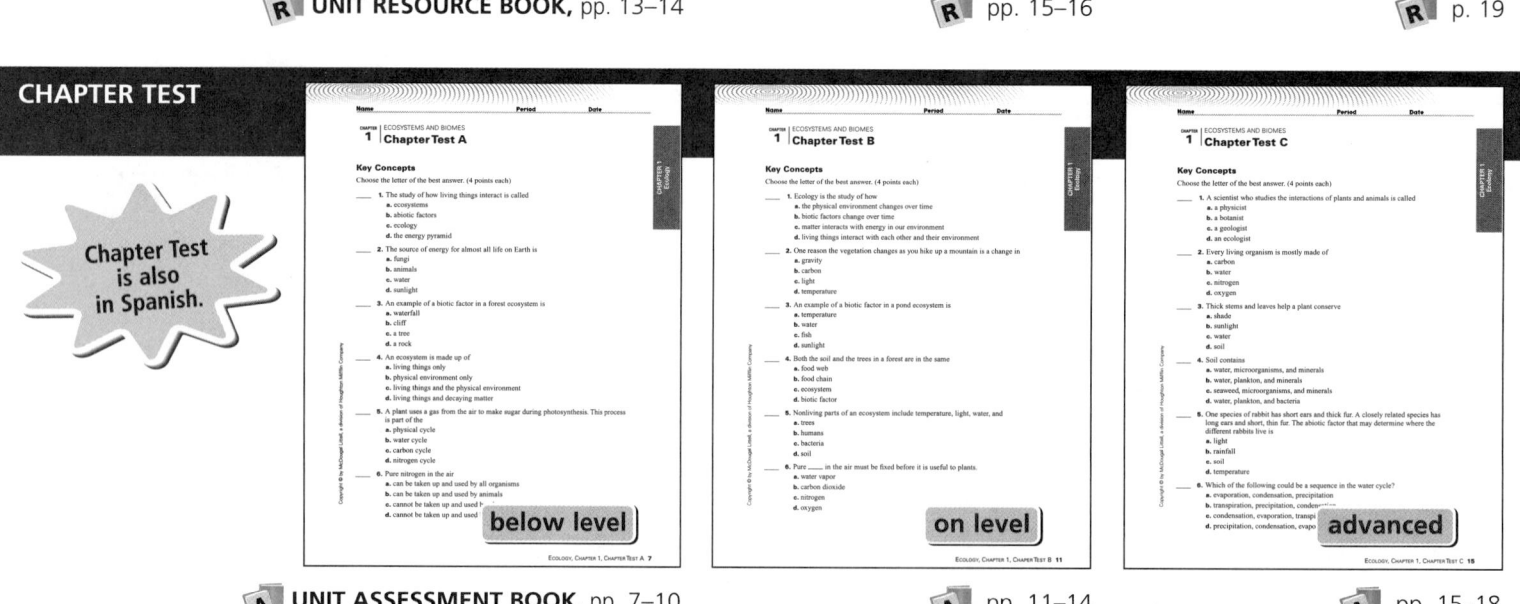

below level

on level

advanced

Chapter Test is also in Spanish.

A UNIT ASSESSMENT BOOK, pp. 7–10

A pp. 11–14

A pp. 15–18

TECHNOLOGY

There are two Resource Centers and a Visualization for this chapter.

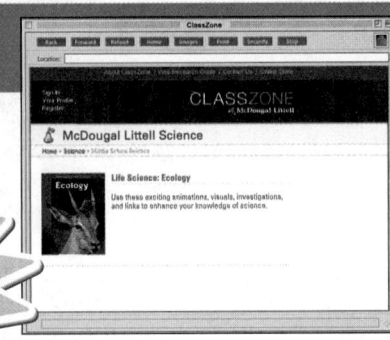

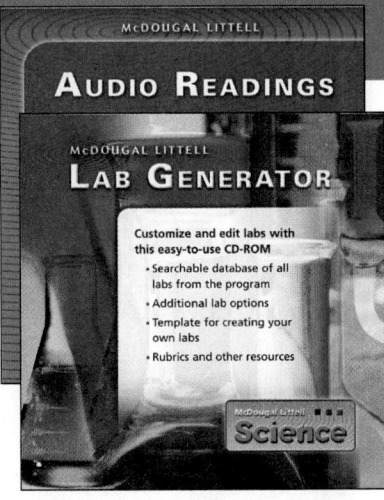

AUDIO READINGS

McDOUGAL LITTELL
LAB GENERATOR

Customize and edit labs with this easy-to-use CD-ROM

- Searchable database of all labs from the program
- Additional lab options
- Template for creating your own labs
- Rubrics and other resources

Science

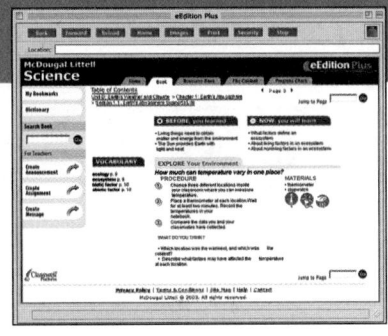

CLASSZONE.COM   **CD/CD-ROMS**   **CLASSZONE.COM**

VISUAL CONTENT

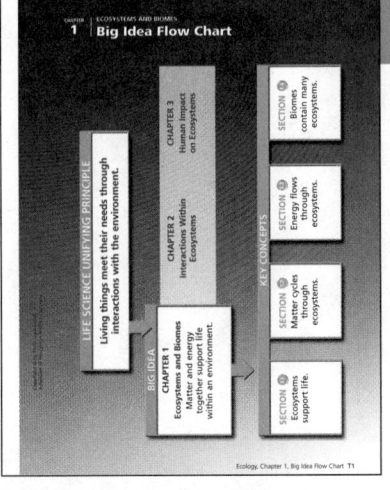

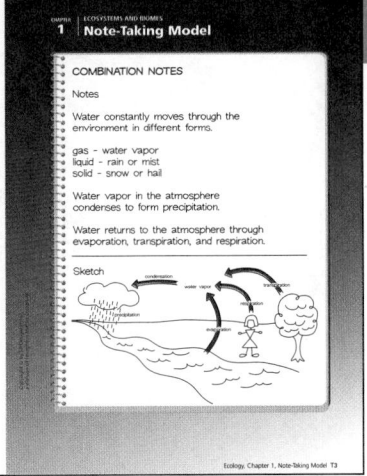

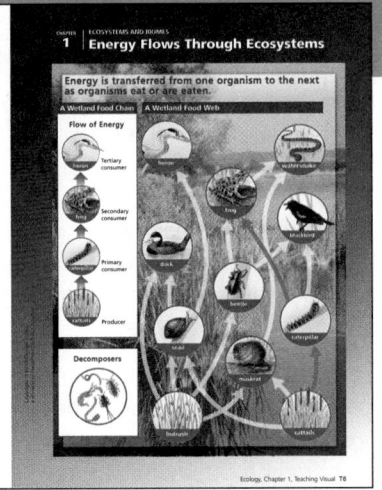

 **UNIT TRANSPARENCY BOOK,** p. T1

 p. T3

 p. T6

MORE SUPPORT

Reinforcing Key Concepts for each section

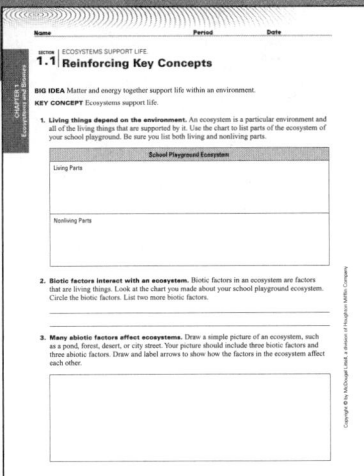

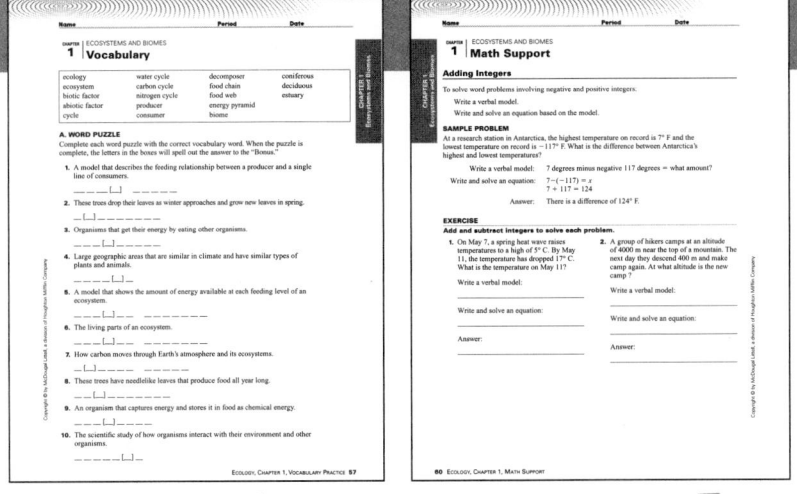

 **UNIT RESOURCE BOOK,** p. 20

pp. 57–58

p. 60

INTRODUCE

the **BIG** idea

Have students look at the photograph of Portage Lake, Alaska. Discuss how the question in the box relates to the Big Idea:

- What plants and animals are in the photograph?
- What might be keeping them alive?

National Science Education Standards

Content

C.4.b Populations of organisms can be categorized by the function they serve in an ecosystem. Plants and some microorganisms are producers. All animals are consumers. Decomposers consume waste materials and dead organisms for food. Food webs identify the relationships among producers, consumers, and decomposers in an ecosystem.

C.4.c Sunlight is transferred by producers into chemical energy through photosynthesis. That energy passes from organism to organism in food webs.

C.4.d The number of organisms an ecosystem can support depends on the resources available and abiotic factors.

D.1.f Water circulates through Earth's crust, oceans, and atmosphere in the "water cycle."

Process

A.2–8 Design and conduct a scientific investigation; use tools to gather and interpret data; use evidence to describe, predict, explain, model; use critical thinking to find relationships between results and interpretation; communicate results; use mathematics in investigations.

A.9.a–c, A.9.e–f Understand scientific inquiry by using different investigations, methods, mathematics, and explanations based on logic, evidence, and skepticism.

CHAPTER

1 Ecosystems and Biomes

the **BIG** idea

Matter and energy together support life within an environment.

> **How many living and nonliving things can you identify in this photograph?**

Key Concepts

SECTION
1.1 Ecosystems support life.
Learn about different factors that make up an ecosystem.

SECTION
1.2 Matter cycles through ecosystems.
Learn about the water, carbon, and nitrogen cycles.

SECTION
1.3 Energy flows through ecosystems.
Learn how energy moves through living things.

SECTION
1.4 Biomes contain many ecosystems.
Learn about different land and water biomes.

Internet Preview

CLASSZONE.COM

Chapter 1 online resources: Content Review, Simulation, Visualization, three Resource Centers, Math Tutorial, Test Practice

INTERNET PREVIEW

CLASSZONE.COM For student use with the following pages:

Review and Practice
- Content Review, pp. 8, 38
- Math Tutorial: Adding Integers, p. 21
- Test Practice, p. 41

Activities and Resources
- Internet Activity: A Prairie Ecosystem, p. 7
- Resource Centers: Ecosystem, p. 10; Cycles, p. 16; Biomes, p. 36
- Visualization: Nitrogen, p. 20

NSTA *SCI*LINKS
scilinks.org

Food Chains and Food Webs
Code: MDL001

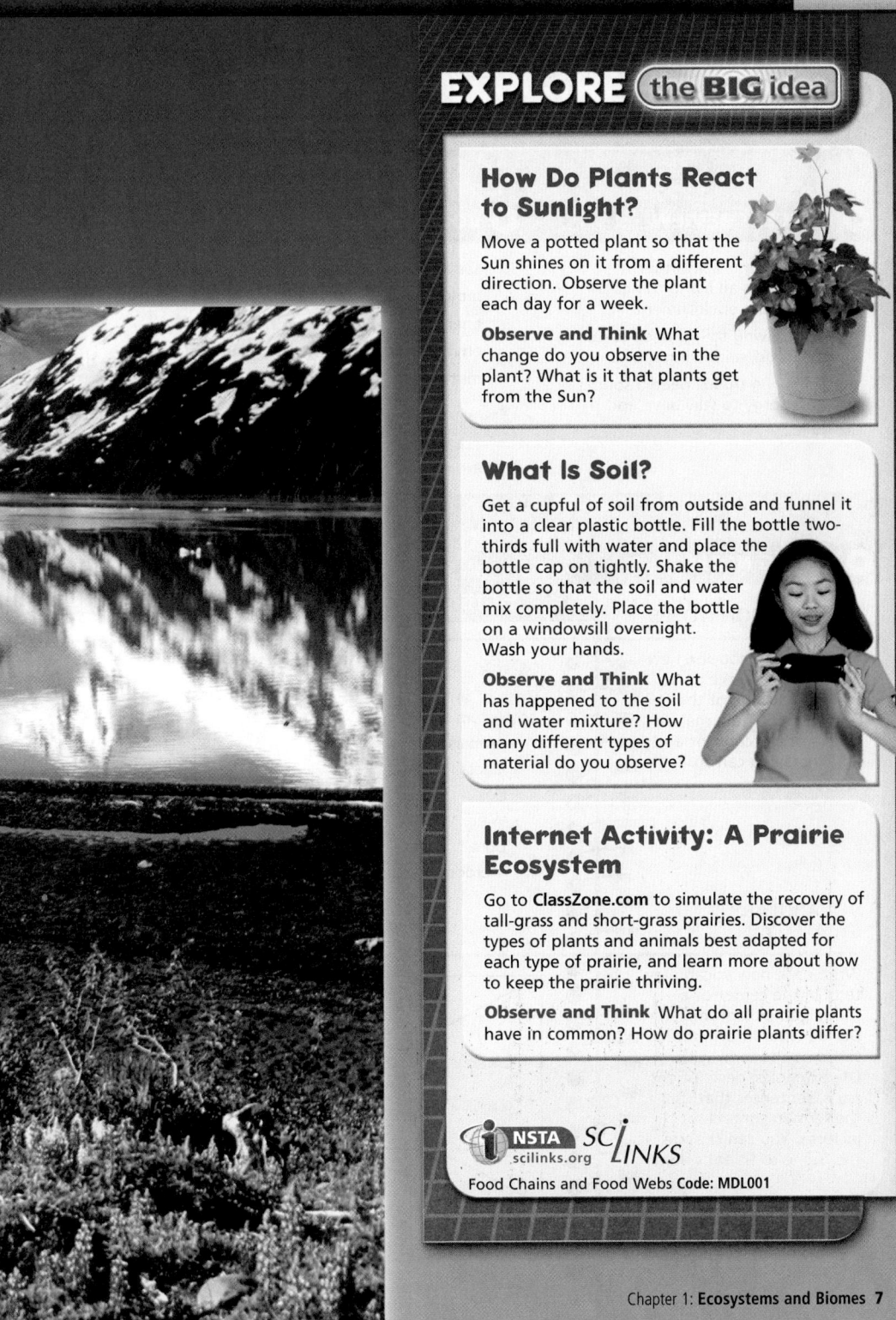

How Do Plants React to Sunlight?

Move a potted plant so that the Sun shines on it from a different direction. Observe the plant each day for a week.

Observe and Think What change do you observe in the plant? What is it that plants get from the Sun?

What Is Soil?

Get a cupful of soil from outside and funnel it into a clear plastic bottle. Fill the bottle two-thirds full with water and place the bottle cap on tightly. Shake the bottle so that the soil and water mix completely. Place the bottle on a windowsill overnight. Wash your hands.

Observe and Think What has happened to the soil and water mixture? How many different types of material do you observe?

Internet Activity: A Prairie Ecosystem

Go to **ClassZone.com** to simulate the recovery of tall-grass and short-grass prairies. Discover the types of plants and animals best adapted for each type of prairie, and learn more about how to keep the prairie thriving.

Observe and Think What do all prairie plants have in common? How do prairie plants differ?

NSTA
scilinks.org
SCiLINKS

Food Chains and Food Webs Code: MDL001

TEACHING WITH TECHNOLOGY

Digital Camera If a digital camera is available, students can photograph their potted plants (pp. 7, 16) each day. They can then assemble a series of still shots as a digital movie and dub sound over the image or add text screens to create a presentation.

Computer Microscope Have students use a computer microscope to examine particles in the Chapter Investigation on p. 14.

Spreadsheet Software Students can use graphing calculators or spreadsheet software to present their climate data on p. 35.

These inquiry-based activities are appropriate for use at home or as a supplement to classroom instruction.

How Do Plants React to Sunlight?

PURPOSE To demonstrate that plants respond to the presence of sunlight.

TIP *10 min.* Use plants with flexible, leafy stems. Bean, radish, or other seedlings will move toward light in a short time period.

Answer: Leaves and stems moved toward the sunlight; energy.

REVISIT after p. 12.

What Is Soil?

PURPOSE To introduce students to soil, a mixture of materials that support life within an environment.

TIP *10 min.* Have students compare their soil samples with those of their class-mates. They may observe that their region has more than one type of soil.

Answer: It has separated into layers. Number of types of material will vary depending on composition of soil used.

REVISIT after p. 13.

Internet Activity: A Prairie Ecosystem

PURPOSE To introduce students to factors that cause changes in an ecosystem.

TIP *20 min.* You might bring real samples of grasses into the classroom and compare them with the varieties on screen.

Answer: They are all grasses; some are low to ground, others tall.

REVISIT after p. 26.

PREPARE

◐ CONCEPT REVIEW

Activate Prior Knowledge

- Ask students to come to the board and draw familiar plants and animals in their natural environment.
- Ask students to name the living organisms shown in the environment and to suggest ways in which the organisms might interact with each other.
- Ask students to suggest possible ways in which each organism finds water, energy, and living space.

◑ TAKING NOTES

Combination Notes

Combining pictures with notes will help students connect abstract concepts with concrete examples. Later, students can fold over their two-column combination notes and quiz themselves based on thier pictures.

Vocabulary Strategy

Surrounding each term with a context helps students develop meaning.

Students can opt to use their frame game notes to create a guessing game with a partner. Partners fill in frames, but leave the "picture" or center-word blank, then trade with each other to "complete the picture."

Vocabulary and Note-Taking Resources

- Vocabulary Practice, pp. 57–58
- Decoding Support, p. 59

- Daily Vocabulary Scaffolding, p. T2
- Note-Taking Model, p. T3

- Frame Game, B26–27
- Combination Notes, C40
- Daily Vocabulary Scaffolding, H1–8

Getting Ready to Learn

◐ CONCEPT REVIEW

- The natural world that surrounds all living things is called the environment.
- Most living things need water, air, food, and living space.
- All living things need a source of energy to stay alive and grow.

◐ VOCABULARY REVIEW

See Glossary for definitions.

biology	nutrient
energy	photosynthesis
environment	respiration
matter	system

ⓘ CONTENT REVIEW
CLASSZONE.COM
Review concepts and vocabulary.

▶ TAKING NOTES

COMBINATION NOTES

To take notes about a new concept, first make an informal outline of the information. Then make a sketch of the concept and label it so you can study it later.

VOCABULARY STRATEGY

Write each new vocabulary term in the center of a **frame game** diagram. Decide what information to frame the term with. Use examples, descriptions, parts, sentences that use the term in context, or pictures. You can change the frame to fit each item.

See the Note-Taking Handbook on pages R45–R51.

D 8 Unit: Ecology

SCIENCE NOTEBOOK

NOTES

Parts of an ecosystem:
- Animals
- Plants
- Soil
- Water
- Light
- Microorganisms

	nonliving factors	
physical or chemical	ABIOTIC FACTOR	water, light, soil, temperature
	affected by living factors	

CHECK READINESS

Administer the Diagnostic Test to determine students' readiness for new science content and their mastery of requisite math skills.

 Diagnostic Test, pp. 1–2

Technology Resources

Students needing content and math skills should visit **ClassZone.com**.

- CONTENT REVIEW
- MATH TUTORIAL

 CONTENT REVIEW CD-ROM

KEY CONCEPT
1.1 Ecosystems support life.

◀ **BEFORE, you learned**
- Living things need to obtain matter and energy from the environment
- The Sun provides Earth with light and heat

▶ **NOW, you will learn**
- What factors define an ecosystem
- About living factors in an ecosystem
- About nonliving factors in an ecosystem

VOCABULARY
ecology p. 9
ecosystem p. 9
biotic factor p. 10
abiotic factor p. 10

EXPLORE Your Environment

How much can temperature vary in one place?

PROCEDURE

1. Choose three different locations inside your classroom where you can measure temperature.

2. Place a thermometer at each location. Wait for at least two minutes. Record the temperatures in your notebook.

3. Compare the data you and your classmates have collected.

MATERIALS
- thermometer
- stopwatch

WHAT DO YOU THINK?
- Which location was the warmest, and which was the coldest?
- Describe what factors may have affected the temperature at each location.

VOCABULARY
Add frame game diagrams for *ecology* and *ecosystem* to your notebook.

Living things depend on the environment.

You wouldn't find a kangaroo in the Arctic and you won't see a polar bear in Australia. Each of these organisms is suited to a certain environment. The kangaroo and the polar bear are able to survive despite the harsh conditions of their surroundings. **Ecology** is the scientific study of how organisms interact with their environment and all the other organisms that live in that environment.

Scientists use the word **ecosystem** to describe a particular environment and all the living things that are supported by it. An ecosystem can be as small as a pond or as large as a desert. What is important in an ecosystem is how the living parts of the ecosystem relate to the nonliving parts.

Chapter 1: **Ecosystems and Biomes** 9 **D**

RESOURCES FOR DIFFERENTIATED INSTRUCTION

Below Level
UNIT RESOURCE BOOK
- Reading Study Guide A, pp. 13–14
- Decoding Support, p. 59

 **AUDIO CDS**

Advanced
UNIT RESOURCE BOOK
Challenge and Extension, p. 19

English Learners
UNIT RESOURCE BOOK
Spanish Reading Study Guide, pp. 17–18

 **AUDIO CDS**

- Audio Readings in Spanish
- Audio Readings (English)

1.1 FOCUS

▶ **Set Learning Goals**
Students will
- Explain what factors define an ecosystem.
- Describe the living factors in an ecosystem.
- Describe the nonliving factors in an ecosystem.
- Measure different temperatures to discover variations in warmth.

◀ **3-Minute Warm-Up**

Display Transparency 4 or copy this exercise on the board:

Match the definitions to the correct terms.

Definitions

1. It surrounds all living things. *d*

2. All living organisms need it. *b*

3. It gives Earth most of its energy. *e*

Terms

a. organism

b. energy

c. the ocean

d. environment

e. the Sun

 3-Minute Warm-Up, p. T4

1.1 MOTIVATE

EXPLORE Your Environment

PURPOSE To demonstrate that micro-climates with different characteristics differ in temperature

TIP *10 min.* Students should select three locations that receive different amounts of sunlight, air exchange with the out-doors, or heat or air conditioning from indoor sources.

WHAT DO YOU THINK? *Sample answer: The location with the most sunlight was warmest; proximity to windows, doors, heat sources, air conditioning vents, number of people in the area, open windows or doors.*

Chapter 1 **9 D**

Teach from Visuals

To help students interpret the photograph of the pond ecosystem, ask:

• How do the living factors in this ecosystem depend on one another? *They depend on each other for food and shelter.*

• How do nonliving factors affect the living factors in this ecosystem? *They provide nutrients and energy for organisms.*

• Are there any living or nonliving factors that might be in this ecosystem but are not visible in the photograph? *living factors: fish, insects, microorganisms; nonliving factors: nutrients, oxygen, carbon dioxide, rocks*

History of Science

Biosphere 2 was built in the late 1980s with the intention of creating a closed system similar enough to Earth to be self-sustaining. The initial experiment lasted two years and yielded valuable information, but the system was not self-sustaining and could not be kept closed. Today, Biosphere 2's ecosystems are used for education and research.

A project in Japan called Mini Earth is attempting to pick up where Biosphere 2 left off. About half the size of Biosphere 2, Mini Earth is housed in three large buildings linked by stainless steel passageways. Scheduled to launch in 2005, the project will involve two scientists sealed inside along with plants and animals. It is intended to be self-sustaining, with no need for oxygen to be supplied from the outside. Developers of the project hope that the technologies used in Mini Earth will help future space exploration.

Ongoing Assessment

Explain what factors define an ecosystem.

Ask: What is the definition of an ecosystem? *living things and the physical environment around them*

RESOURCE CENTER
CLASSZONE.COM

Learn more about ecosystems.

A

Let's take a look at a pond. A pond ecosystem is more than just water and fish. Plants grow in and around the water, and animals feed on these plants. A variety of tiny microorganisms in the water are food for fish and for each other. These are just a few of the living parts, or **biotic factors** (by-AHT-ihk), of a pond ecosystem. The nonliving parts, or **abiotic factors** (AY-by-AHT-ihk), include the air that supplies oxygen and carbon dioxide, the soil that provides nutrients, the water in the pond, and the sunlight that plants need to grow.

CLASSIFY Name three living and three nonliving factors that are part of this pond ecosystem.

Biotic factors interact with an ecosystem.

B

Living things depend upon an ecosystem for food, air, and water, as well as other things they need for survival. In turn, living things have an impact on the ecosystem in which they live. Plants, as a biotic factor in land ecosystems, affect other biotic and abiotic parts of ecosystems. Plants are an important source of food. The types of plants found in a particular ecosystem will determine the types of animals that can live there. Plants can affect temperature by blocking sunlight. Plant roots hold soil in place. Even the atmosphere is affected by plants taking in carbon dioxide and releasing oxygen.

Animals, as biotic factors, also affect an ecosystem. A beaver that builds a dam changes the flow of a river and so affects the surrounding landscape. Large herds of cattle can overgraze a grassland ecosystem and cause the soil to erode. In an ocean biome, corals form giant reefs that provide food and shelter for marine organisms.

DIFFERENTIATE INSTRUCTION

 More Reading Support

A What two kinds of factors are in an ecosystem? *biotic and abiotic*

B Are plants abiotic or biotic factors? *biotic*

English Learners Have English learners write the definitions of *ecology* and *ecosystem* in their Science Word Dictionaries. Encourage students to look up *eco-* in the dictionary. Be certain that English learners understand the difference between *biotic factors* and *abiotic factors.* Ask them to list the different biotic and abiotic factors they see around them. Some biotic factors might be classmates, teachers, class pets, plants in the classroom or visible through a window. Abiotic factors might be desks, books, board, or lights.

Many abiotic factors affect ecosystems.

Abiotic factors include both the physical and chemical parts of an ecosystem. Physical factors are factors that you can see or feel, such as the temperature or the amount of water or sunlight. Important chemical factors include the minerals and compounds found in the soil and whether the ecosystem's water is fresh or salty. It is the combination of different abiotic factors that determines the types of organisms that an ecosystem will support.

READING TiP
The word *biotic* means "living." The prefix *a-* in *abiotic* means "not," so *abiotic* means "not living."

 List four different abiotic factors that can affect an ecosystem.

Temperature

Temperature is an important abiotic factor in any ecosystem. In a land ecosystem, temperature affects the types of plants that will do well there. The types of plants available for food and shelter, in turn, determine the types of animals that can live there. For example, a tropical rain forest has not only a lot of rain but it has consistently warm temperatures. The wide variety of plants that grow in a tropical rain forest supports a wide variety of monkeys, birds, and other organisms.

Animals are as sensitive to temperature as plants are. Musk oxen with their thick coat of fur can survive in very cold environments, where temperatures of –40°C (–40°F) are normal. The water buffalo, with its light coat, is better suited to warm temperatures. The wild water buffalo lives where temperatures can reach 48°C (118°F).

This musk ox's thick fur keeps it warm in the cold temperatures of northern Canada.

A water buffalo cools itself in a shallow stream during a hot day in India.

 COMPARE AND CONTRAST How are these animals alike? How are they different?

Chapter 1: **Ecosystems and Biomes** 11 **D**

DIFFERENTIATE INSTRUCTION

? More Reading Support

C What are physical abiotic factors? *light, temperature, amount of water*

D What determines the types of animals in an ecosystem? *plants*

Advanced Give students examples of three ecosystems of different sizes, such as an anthill, a one-acre meadow, and a continent. Have them describe the features that make each of these an ecosystem.

Teach from Visuals

Using the photgraphs, have students compare abiotic factors of the ecosystems in which musk oxen and water buffalo live. Ask:

- How does temperature affect the availability of water in each ecosystem? *Liquid water is present in the water buffalo's ecosystem, but water is often frozen in the musk ox's ecosystem.*

- How do temperature and water affect soil and plant life in each ecosystem? *Musk ox: Soil is often frozen, and vegetation is short and sparse. Water buffalo: Soil is often moist or muddy, and plant life is plentiful.*

Language Arts Connection

Help students understand the terms *ecology* and *ecosystem* by explaining the origin of the word root *ecos,* which means "house" or "place to live." Ecology then can be thought of as the study of places where organisms *live*; an ecosystem as the *system* of relationships among organisms and their *home* or surroundings.

Ongoing Assessment

Describe the living factors in an ecosystem.

Ask: Give some examples of the biotic factors in an ecosystem. *Sample answer: bacteria, insects, plants, algae, animals*

 *Answer: light, temperature, soil, water, air*

 *Answer: They both have similar sizes, similar bodies, and horns. In a warm climate, the musk ox's fur would make the animal too hot. The water buffalo has no protection from the cold.*

Address Misconceptions

IDENTIFY Ask: Where do green plants get their food? If students answer "from the soil," they might hold the misconception that plants obtain food from the environment rather than capturing energy from sunlight, and combining it with the chemicals in air.

CORRECT On the board, write an equation for photosynthesis: water + carbon dioxide + light = sugar + oxygen. Remind students that photosynthesis takes place in leaf cells and that sugar is food for the plant.

REASSESS Ask students where each item in the equation comes from. *water from soil, carbon dioxide from air, light from the Sun, sugar from all three combined, oxygen is left over*

EXPLORE (the **BIG** idea)

Revisit "How Do Plants React to Sunlight?" on p. 7. Have students explain their results.

Teach from Visuals

To help students interpret the soil visuals, explain the following interactions:

- Plant roots interact with soil. Roots take water from soil. Bacteria and fungi on plant roots help the roots absorb nutrients. Roots help hold soil in place.
- Air interacts with soil. Most soil organisms need air to survive. Their activity loosens soil, allowing air to circulate.
- Earthworms interact with soil. Worms digest organic matter, pass waste back into soil, and mix and aerate soil.

Ongoing Assessment

Describe the nonliving factors in an ecosystem.

Ask: What are some examples of abiotic factors in an ecosystem? *Sample answer: light, soil, water, temperature, minerals*

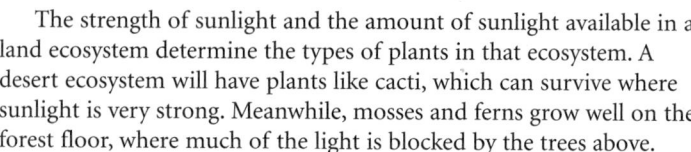

COMBINATION NOTES Remember to make notes and diagrams to show how abiotic factors affect biotic factors in an ecosystem.

Light

You can easily understand how abiotic factors work together when you think about sunlight and temperature. Sunlight warms Earth's surface and atmosphere. In addition, energy from sunlight supports all life on Earth. The Sun provides the energy that plants capture and use to produce food in a process called photosynthesis. The food produced by plants, and other photosynthetic organisms, feeds almost all the other living things found on Earth.

The strength of sunlight and the amount of sunlight available in a land ecosystem determine the types of plants in that ecosystem. A desert ecosystem will have plants like cacti, which can survive where sunlight is very strong. Meanwhile, mosses and ferns grow well on the forest floor, where much of the light is blocked by the trees above.

Light is a factor in ocean ecosystems as well. The deeper the water is, the less light there is available. In the shallow water near the shore, photosynthetic organisms can survive at the surface and on the ocean floor. In the open ocean, light is available for photosynthetic organisms only in the first hundred meters below the surface.

Soil

Soil, which is a mixture of small rock and mineral particles, is an important abiotic factor in land ecosystems. Organisms within the soil break down the remains of dead plants and animals. This process of decay provides important raw materials to the living plants and animals of an ecosystem.

The size of soil particles affects how much air and water the soil can hold.

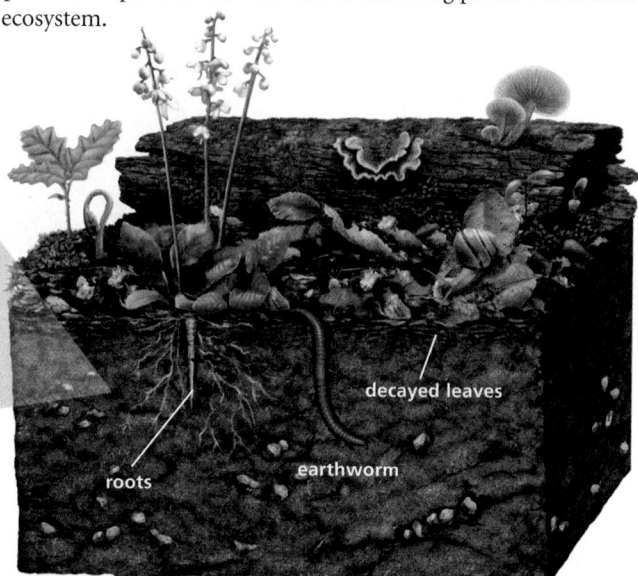

decayed leaves

roots   earthworm

DIFFERENTIATE INSTRUCTION

? **More Reading Support**

E Ecosystems need energy to function. Where does this energy come from? *the Sun*

F How do plants get energy? *by photosynthesis*

Advanced Invite students to observe small soil samples using a hand lens or dissecting microscope. Have them draw and identify the organisms they see, and use their research skills to find out more about them.

R Challenge and Extension, p. 19

Different ecosystems have different types of soil. The characteristics of the soil in an ecosystem affect plant growth. Soils that have a lot of decaying, or organic, matter can hold water well and allow air to reach the plant roots. Sandy soils usually do not hold water well because the water flows through too easily. Clay soil, which has small, tightly packed particles, will not allow water to move through easily at all. Minerals in the soil also affect plant growth.

 **CHECK YOUR READING** Explain how soil can affect plant life in an ecosystem.

Water

Another important abiotic factor in land ecosystems is the amount of water available to support life. All living things need water to carry out life processes. Plants need water as well as sunlight for photosynthesis. Animals need water to digest food and release the energy stored in the food. Look at the photograph to see the effect that an underground water source has on an otherwise dry, desert ecosystem. Trees could not survive there without a plentiful supply of water.

Ecosystems that have a lot of water can support a large number of different types of plants. These different types of plants can then support a large number of different types of animals. Tropical rain forests, the wettest of all ecosystems on land, are also the most diverse. Desert ecosystems, which are the driest land ecosystems, have far fewer types of plants and animals. The types and number of living things in a land ecosystem will always be related to the amount of fresh water available for its inhabitants.

INFER An oasis forms in the desert when underground water comes to the surface. How can you identify the boundary of this oasis?

1.1 Review

KEY CONCEPTS

1. Draw a diagram of an ecosystem near where you live. Label the factors "biotic" or "abiotic."

2. Give two examples of how plants and animals affect their environment.

3. Describe how temperature, light, and soil affect an ecosystem.

CRITICAL THINKING

4. **Predict** Think of a forest ecosystem. Now imagine that a large volcanic eruption throws large amounts of dust and ash into the air, blocking out sunlight. How might the forest ecosystem be affected if the sunlight is blocked for a day? For a year?

○ CHALLENGE

5. **Apply** Think of how you fit into your local environment. List ways in which you interact with biotic and abiotic factors within your ecosystem.

Chapter 1: Ecosystems and Biomes **13** **D**

CHAPTER INVESTIGATION

Focus

PURPOSE To observe the water-related characteristics of different types of soil

OVERVIEW Students will measure the rate at which water flows through three types of soil. They will find that the rate increases as the particle size increases. Water passes most quickly through coarse sand and most slowly through clay.

Lab Preparation

- Use coarse sand for this activity. The particle size of fine sand will produce slow percolation, too similar to clay.
- Use clear drinking glasses or clear plastic cups instead of beakers if you prefer.
- For homework the night before, have students read the investigation and draw their data table. Or you may wish to copy and distribute datasheets and rubrics.

 UNIT RESOURCE BOOK, pp. 62–70

 SCIENCE TOOLKIT, F14

Lab Management

- Be sure students can demonstrate how to operate the stopwatch before they begin the lab.
- Tell students to take care not to poke holes in the filters, as this will affect percolation rate.
- Remind students to start the stopwatch when the water begins to flow out the bottom of the funnel, even if the flow begins before all the water has been poured into the funnel.

SAFETY Emphasize that students should wash their hands after step 5 and again at the end of the activity.

Teaching with Technology

Students could use a computer microscope to examine soil particles, take pictures, and prepare slides for presenting data.

CHAPTER INVESTIGATION

Soil Samples

OVERVIEW AND PURPOSE Nonliving, or abiotic, factors all have an effect on soil. The quality of the soil affects how well plants grow in a particular environment. In this investigation, you will

- observe and record how water travels through three soil samples
- predict how different types of soil would affect plant growth

MATERIALS
- 3 pieces of paper
- spoon
- 50 mL each of clay, coarse sand, loam
- hand lens
- toothpick
- eyedropper
- water
- 3 pieces of filter paper
- 3 plastic funnels
- 3 large beakers
- small beaker
- stopwatch

▶ Problem
Write It Up

How does soil type affect how water moves through soil?

▶ Hypothesize
Write It Up

You should complete steps 1–5 in the procedure before writing your hypothesis. Write a hypothesis to explain how water moves through certain types of soil. Your hypothesis should take the form of an "If . . . , then . . . , because . . ." statement.

▶ Procedure

1. Make a data table in your **Science Notebook** like the one shown on page 15.

2. Label three sheets of paper "Clay," "Sand," and "Loam." Carefully place a spoonful of each sample on the appropriately labeled paper.

3. Carefully examine each of the soils, with and without the hand lens. Describe the color of each, and record the information in your data table.

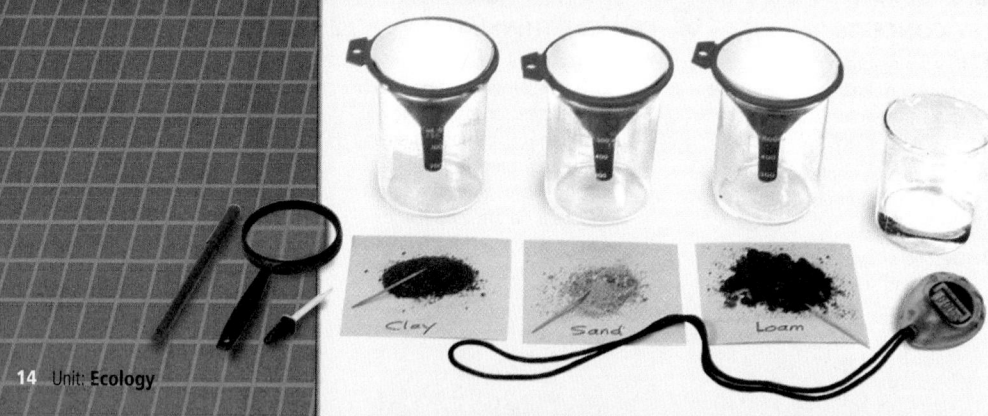

INVESTIGATION RESOURCES

 CHAPTER INVESTIGATION, Soil Samples
- Level A, pp. 62–65
- Level B, pp. 66–69
- Level C, p. 70

Advanced students should complete Levels B & C.

 Writing a Lab Report, D12–13

Technology Resources

Customize this student lab as needed or look for an alternative. Print rubrics to assess student lab reports.

 Lab Generator CD-ROM

4 Use a toothpick to separate the particles of each sample of soil. Record the size of the particles in the data table.

5 Put a small amount of each soil sample in the palm of your hand. Add a drop of water and mix the soil around with your finger. Write a description of the texture of each sample in your data table. Be sure to wash your hands after you finish. After you have recorded your observations, write your hypothesis.

6 Fold each piece of filter paper to form cones as shown in the diagram. Place one filter inside each funnel. Place one funnel in each large beaker. Measure 50 mL of each soil sample and place the sample in one of the funnels.

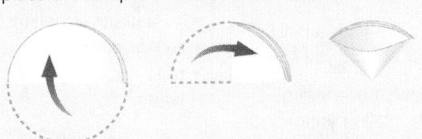

7 Measure 150 mL of water and pour it into the funnel containing the clay. Start the stopwatch when the water begins to drip out of the funnel. Stop the watch when the water stops dripping. Record the time in seconds in the data table.

8 Repeat step 7 for the sand and the loam. When you have finished with the activity, dispose of the materials according to your teacher's directions, and wash your hands.

 Observe and Analyze Write It Up

1. **INTERPRET DATA** Through which soil sample did the water move the fastest? The slowest?

2. **OBSERVE** What type of changes occurred in the soil as the water was added?

 Conclude Write It Up

1. **INTERPRET** Compare your results with your hypothesis. Does your data support your hypothesis?

2. **IDENTIFY LIMITS** What sources of error could have affected this investigation?

3. **EVALUATE** Based on your observations, what can account for the differences in the times recorded for the three soil samples?

4. **PREDICT** Based on your results, which of the soil samples would you expect to be the best type of soil in which to grow plants? Explain.

▶ **INVESTIGATE Further**

CHALLENGE Design an experiment in which you test which of the three soil samples is best for growing plants. Include a materials list, hypothesis, and procedure for your experiment.

Soil Samples
Table 1. Soil Characteristics

Characteristics	Clay	Sand	Loam
Color			
Particle size			
Texture			
Time for water to stop dripping (sec)			

 Observe and Analyze Write It Up

SAMPLE DATA *clay: grayish-brown, very fine, very soft; sand: light brown, coarse, rough; loam: black, fine, soft*

1. *fastest: sand; slowest: clay*

2. *Sample answer: All soils got darker; clay became muddy; the particles of loam floated; wet sand became hard, like beach sand.*

 Conclude Write It Up

1. *Answers will vary depending on observations and results in the investigation. Students should provide evidence or explanation for describing whether their hypotheses are correct or incorrect.*

2. *Errors might include procedural errors, sample inconsistencies, or inaccurate measurement, starting the stopwatch a little before or after flow begins, and so on.*

3. *Sample answer: Some soil particles were closer together or stuck to each other more than others. Some soil contains more moisture than others. (Clay has most, then loam, then sand.) The moisture (water) in the soil helps hold water that enters it.*

4. *Loam; sand does not store enough water, clay is too tightly packed for roots to get water easily.*

▶ **INVESTIGATE Further**

CHALLENGE Materials: plants, pots, soil, water, light source. Hypothesis should state which soil is best for plant growth. Procedure should include step-by-step instructions for setting up the experiment in such a way that the only variable is the soil and all other items (plant species, amount of water, soil, sunlight, air temperature, and so on) are constant.

Post-Lab Discussion

- On the board, make a chart correlating the three soil types with the characteristics students observed in steps 3–5. Have student teams write the flow rates from step 7 on the chart. Keep a tally from one class period to the next to show that larger data samples reveal more accurate trends.

- Discuss why permeability is an important property of soils.
  Permeability affects plant growth.

1.2 FOCUS

Set Learning Goals

Students will

- Explain how matter is exchanged between organisms and their environment.
- Describe the water, carbon, and nitrogen cycles.
- Observe carbon gas released from crushed seashells.

3-Minute Warm-Up

Display Transparency 4 or copy this exercise on the board:

Decide if these statements are true. If not true, correct them.

1. Organisms in soil are an example of abiotic factors. *Organisms in soil are an example of biotic factors.*
2. The amount of light available in an ecosystem affects the types and amount of plant life that will grow there. *true*
3. Plants use energy to make sugars through photosynthesis. *true*

3-Minute Warm-Up, p. T4

1.2 MOTIVATE

EXPLORE The Water Cycle

PURPOSE To introduce the concept that plants release water vapor (transpiration)

TIPS *10 min.* Put bags on a single stem to make them easier to seal. If possible, move the activity outdoors. Any lamp will work for this exploration.

SAFETY Have students place the lamp at a safe distance from the plant to avoid burning the leaves or melting the plastic bag.

WHAT DO YOU THINK? *Water condenses inside each bag. The plastic bag traps water vapor.*

Teaching with Technology

Students can use a digital camera as described on p. 7 to photograph plants.

KEY CONCEPT

1.2 Matter cycles through ecosystems.

BEFORE, you learned

- Ecosystems support life
- Living and nonliving factors interact in an ecosystem
- Temperature, light, soil, and water are important nonliving factors in ecosystems

NOW, you will learn

- How matter is exchanged between organisms and their environment
- About the water, carbon, and nitrogen cycles

VOCABULARY

cycle p. 16
water cycle p. 17
carbon cycle p. 18
nitrogen cycle p. 19

EXPLORE The Water Cycle

Do plants release water?

PROCEDURE

1. Cover a branch of the plant with a plastic bag. Tape the bag firmly around the stem.
2. Water the plant and place it in a sunny window or under a lamp. Wash your hands.
3. Check the plant after ten minutes, at the end of class, and again the next day.

WHAT DO YOU THINK?

- What do you see inside the plastic bag?
- What purpose does the plastic bag serve?

MATERIALS

- 1 small potted plant
- 1 clear plastic bag
- tape
- water

All ecosystems need certain materials.

RESOURCE CENTER
CLASSZONE.COM
Explore cycles in nature.

Living things depend on their environment to meet their needs. You can think of those needs in terms of the material, or matter, required by all living things. For example, all organisms take in water and food in order to survive. All of the materials an organism takes in are returned to the ecosystem, while the organism lives or after it dies.

The movement of matter through the living and nonliving parts of an ecosystem is a continuous process, a cycle. A **cycle** is a series of events that happens over and over again. Matter in an ecosystem may change form, but it never leaves the ecosystem, so the matter is said to cycle through the ecosystem. Three of the most important cycles in ecosystems involve water, carbon, and nitrogen.

RESOURCES FOR DIFFERENTIATED INSTRUCTION

Below Level

UNIT RESOURCE BOOK

- Reading Study Guide A, pp. 23–24
- Decoding Support, p. 59

AUDIO CDS

Additional INVESTIGATION, The Water Cycle, A, B, & C, pp. 71–79; Teacher Instructions, pp. 200–201

Advanced

UNIT RESOURCE BOOK

Challenge and Extension, p. 29

English Learners

UNIT RESOURCE BOOK

Spanish Reading Study Guide, pp. 27–28

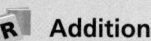

AUDIO CDS

- Audio Readings in Spanish
- Audio Readings (English)

Water Cycle

Different processes combine to move water through the environment.

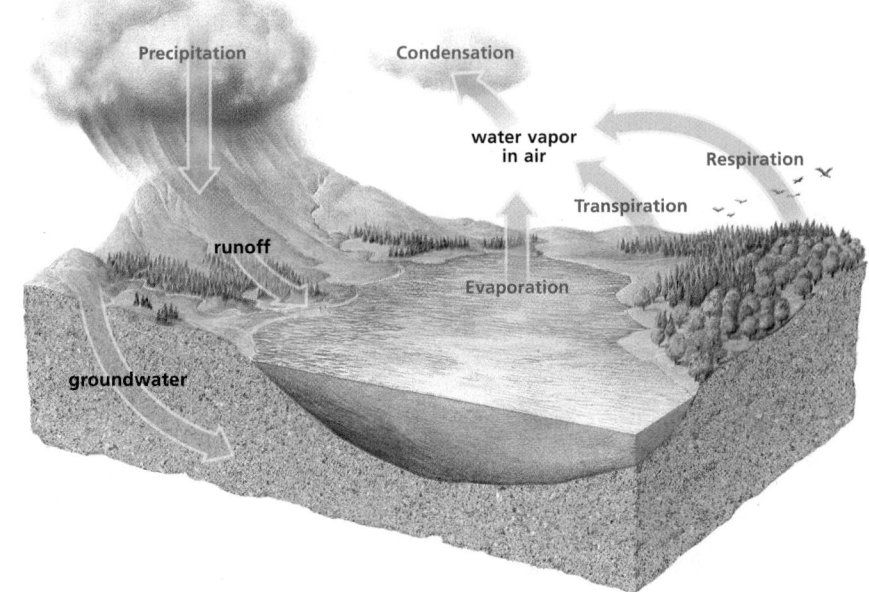

Precipitation
Condensation
water vapor in air
Respiration
Transpiration
runoff
Evaporation
groundwater

Water cycles through ecosystems.

Water is stored on Earth's surface in lakes, rivers, and oceans. Water is found underground, filling the spaces between soil particles and cracks in rocks. Large amounts of water are stored in glaciers and polar ice sheets. Water is also part of the bodies of living things. But water is not just stored, it is constantly moving. The movement of water through the environment is called the **water cycle.**

Water is made up of just two elements: oxygen and hydrogen. As water moves through an ecosystem, it changes in physical form, moving back and forth between gas, liquid, and solid. Water in the atmosphere is usually in gaseous form—water vapor. Water that falls to Earth's surface is referred to as precipitation. For precipitation to occur, water vapor must condense—it must change into a liquid or solid. This water can fall as rain, snow, sleet, mist, or hail.

A

COMBINATION NOTES Make notes and draw a diagram to show how water cycles through ecosystems.

CHECK YOUR READING What are the three physical forms of water in the water cycle?

B

Water returns to the atmosphere when heated, changing back into vapor, a process called evaporation. Living things also release water vapor. Animals release water vapor when they breathe, or respire. Plants release water vapor through a process called transpiration.

Chapter 1: **Ecosystems and Biomes 17** **D**

DIFFERENTIATE INSTRUCTION

? More Reading Support

A What is water made of? *oxygen and hydrogen*

B What process turns water to water vapor? *evaporation*

English Learners Place *water cycle, carbon cycle,* and *nitrogen cycle* on the Science Word Wall with abbreviated definitions. It may also be helpful for English learners to discuss each cycle with another English learner in their first language. Working out difficult concepts together in their first language can be beneficial to students. Encourage them to repeat or write down what they have learned in English afterwards.

Teach from Visuals

Remind students that the arrows in the diagram of the water cycle represent the movement of water molecules. Ask:

• What happens during condensation? *Water vapor becomes liquid water.*

• What happens during transpiration? *Water vapor is released from tiny openings in plant leaves.*

Language Arts Connection

On the board, write the verb form of each process in the water cycle next to its root meaning.

• <u>Evapor</u>ate: vapor: the gaseous form of a liquid

• Tran<u>spire</u>; respire: spiritus (Latin): breath

• Con<u>dense</u>: dense: crowded, thick, compact

Address Misconceptions

IDENTIFY Ask: Where does the water in Earth's water cycle come from? If students answer "oceans" or "atmosphere," they may think that water is added to or created within the water cycle.

CORRECT Create a demonstration using two beakers; fill one with water. Stopper the beakers and connect them with a rubber hose. Boil the water and have students observe as the water leaves one beaker and reappears in the other.

REASSESS Ask: Where did the water that appeared in the second beaker come from? *from the first beaker* How did it move? *Heating caused the water to change from liquid form into water vapor, which traveled through the hose. As water vapor cooled, it changed back into a liquid and collected in the second beaker.*

Technology Resources

Visit **ClassZone.com** for background on common student misconceptions.

 MISCONCEPTION DATABASE

Ongoing Assessment

CHECK YOUR READING *Answer: gas, liquid, and solid*

Teach from Visuals

To help students interpret the diagram of the carbon cycle, ask:

- How does carbon move from the air into plants and animals? *Carbon moves into plants by photosynthesis, and into animals by eating plants or other animals.*

- How does carbon move into the air from plants and animals? *The cells of plants and animals use oxygen to release the energy stored in food molecules. This process is called respiration. Carbon dioxide is released as a by-product of respiration.*

- How does carbon move into the air from fossil fuels? *Carbon is released as carbon dioxide when fossil fuels burn.*

History of Science

Recently, groups of college graduates in science were asked where a plant's mass comes from. Almost all of them answered sunlight, water, or soil. Few understood that carbon in the air was responsible.

In the 1640s, Jan Baptista van Helmont conducted an experiment that proved most of a plant's mass does not come from soil. Setting out to bolster his theory that everything is made of water, he placed 200 pounds of soil in a pot in which he planted a 5-pound willow tree. He watered the tree regularly and protected it from dust, but added no soil.

In five years, the tree gained 164 pounds, but the soil weighed 199 pounds.

The experiment showed that little of the tree's weight came from soil. Van Helmont thought the increase of weight was from water; in fact, it came from carbon dioxide.

Ongoing Assessment

CHECK YOUR READING *Answers should include three of the following: plants take in CO_2, animals release CO_2, carbon is deposited on seafloor when an organism dies, decaying matter releases CO_2, carbon in dead plants and animals becomes fossil fuel.*

Carbon cycles through ecosystems.

 C

Carbon is an element found in all living things. Carbon moves through Earth's ecosystems in a cycle referred to as the **carbon cycle.** It is through carbon dioxide gas found in Earth's atmosphere that carbon enters the living parts of an ecosystem.

 **READING TiP**
Notice that photosynthesis is a process that brings carbon into living matter and respiration is a process that releases carbon.

Plants use carbon dioxide to produce sugar—a process called photosynthesis. Sugars are carbon compounds that are important building blocks in food and all living matter. Food supplies the energy and materials living things need to live and grow. To release the energy in food, organisms break down the carbon compounds—a process called respiration. Carbon is released and cycled back into the atmosphere as carbon dioxide. When living things die and decay, the rest of the carbon that makes up living matter is released.

CHECK YOUR READING Name three ways that living things are part of the carbon cycle.

Earth's oceans contain far more carbon than the air does. In water ecosystems—lakes, rivers, and oceans—carbon dioxide is dissolved in water. Algae and certain types of bacteria are the photosynthetic organisms that produce food in these ecosystems. Marine organisms, too, release carbon dioxide during respiration. Carbon is also deposited on the ocean floor when organisms die.

Carbon Cycle

Different processes combine to move carbon through the environment.

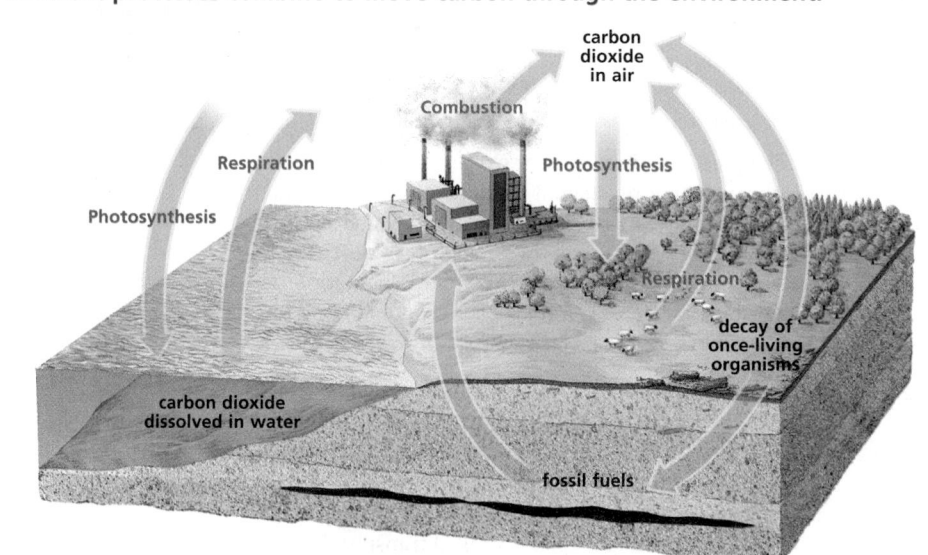

carbon dioxide in air

Combustion

Respiration

Photosynthesis

Photosynthesis

Respiration

decay of once-living organisms

carbon dioxide dissolved in water

fossil fuels

D 18 Unit: Ecology

DIFFERENTIATE INSTRUCTION

 More Reading Support

C All living things contain what chemical element? *carbon*

Below Level Encourage students to create their own color-coded diagrams of the carbon cycle. Have them use one color to represent carbon dioxide gas and another for solid carbon. Ask: Where is carbon dioxide gas found? *in the air and dissolved in oceans, lakes, streams* Ask: Where is solid carbon found? *in the bodies of plants and animals*

INVESTIGATE Carbon

What is one form in which carbon is stored on the ocean floor?

PROCEDURE

1. Use the mortar and pestle to crush the seashell into a powder.
2. Pour the powder into a small beaker.
3. Add enough white vinegar to cover the powder.

WHAT DO YOU THINK?

- What happens when white vinegar is added to the crushed shell?
- What is the material produced in the reaction and where did it come from originally?

CHALLENGE What type of reaction have you observed?

SKILL FOCUS
Observing

MATERIALS
- mortar and pestle
- whole seashell or fragments
- small beaker
- white vinegar

TIME
15 minutes

Large amounts of carbon are stored underground. The remains of plants and animals buried for millions of years decay slowly and change into fossil fuels, such as coal and oil. The carbon in fossil fuels returns to ecosystems in a process called combustion. As humans burn fossil fuels to release energy, dust particles and gases containing carbon are also released into the environment.

Nitrogen cycles through ecosystems.

Nitrogen is another element important to life that cycles through Earth in the **nitrogen cycle.** Almost four-fifths of the air you breathe is clear, colorless nitrogen gas. Yet, you cannot get the nitrogen you need to live from the air. All animals must get nitrogen from plants.

Plants cannot use pure nitrogen gas either. However, plants can absorb certain compounds of nitrogen. Plants take in these nitrogen compounds through their roots, along with water and other nutrients. So how does the nitrogen from the atmosphere get into the soil? One source is lightning. Every lightning strike breaks apart, or fixes, pure nitrogen, changing it into a form that plants can use. This form of nitrogen falls to the ground when it rains.

Chapter 1: **Ecosystems and Biomes** 19 **D**

TIPS *15 min.* Students should wear safety goggles or protective eyewear throughout the experiment. Calcium carbonate is also in the shells of birds' eggs. A similar test with an egg will have good results.

WHAT DO YOU THINK? *Answers: Gas bubbles form. CO_2 is produced; it originally came from the shells*

CHALLENGE *chemical*

 Datasheet, Carbon, p. 30

Technology Resources

Customize this student lab as needed or look for an alternative. Print rubrics to assess student lab reports.

Lab Generator CD-ROM

Real World Example

All living things contain carbon. People get carbon compounds from food. In the oceans, living things get carbon from carbon dioxide dissolved in water. Clams and oysters, for example, use carbon to make the hard calcium carbonate in their shells. To find out if an element, such as carbon, is present, scientists use chemical tests. In the case of carbon, an acid, such as vinegar, reacts with calcium carbonate to produce carbon dioxide gas.

Integrate the Sciences

Living organisms are made up of chemical compounds: carbohydrates, fats, and proteins. All of these compounds contain carbon, hydrogen, and oxygen. Proteins contain nitrogen as well.

Ongoing Assessment

Explain how matter is exchanged between organisms and their environment.

Ask: How does matter cycle between organisms and their environment? *Organisms take in water, carbon, and nitrogen; use them for life processes; and release them.*

DIFFERENTIATE INSTRUCTION

More Reading Support

D Where do animals get nitrogen? *from plants*

E Where do plants get the nitrogen they need? *from the soil*

Additional Investigation To reinforce Section 1.2 learning goals, use the following full-period investigation:

 **Additional INVESTIGATION,** The Water Cycle, A, B, & C, pp. 71–79, 200–201 (Advanced students should complete Levels B and C.)

Alternative Assessment Have students explain orally the findings of their investigation.

Challenge and Extension, p. 29

Chapter 1 **19** **D**

Ongoing Assessment

Describe the water, carbon, and nitrogen cycles.

Ask: How are the water, carbon, and nitrogen cycles alike? *Sample answer: All three pass into and out of the atmosphere, soil, and living organisms.*

Reinforce (the **BIG** idea)

Have students relate the section to the Big Idea.

 Reinforcing Key Concepts, p. 31

1.2 ASSESS & RETEACH

Assess

 Section 1.2 Quiz, p. 4

Reteach

Draw or have volunteers draw simple versions of the three cycle diagrams in Section 1.2 on the board. Next, have students describe similarities and differences in the water, carbon, and nitrogen cycles. Ask:

- How does water enter the atmosphere? Carbon? Nitrogen? *Water evaporates, is transpired by plants, and is exhaled by animals during respiration. Carbon is released during respiration and decay. Nitrogen is converted into gas by bacteria.*

- How does water leave the atmosphere? Carbon? Nitrogen? *Water vapor condenses and falls to the ground as precipitation. Carbon is fixed by plants during photosynthesis. Nitrogen is fixed by bacteria or by lightning.*

- Where is water stored? Carbon? Nitrogen? *water: oceans, lakes, groundwater; carbon: plant and animal bodies, ocean floor; nitrogen: plant and animal bodies*

Technology Resources

Have students visit **ClassZone.com** for reteaching of Key Concepts.

 CONTENT REVIEW

 CONTENT REVIEW CD-ROM

D **20** Unit: **Ecology**

Nitrogen Cycle

Different processes combine to move nitrogen through the environment.

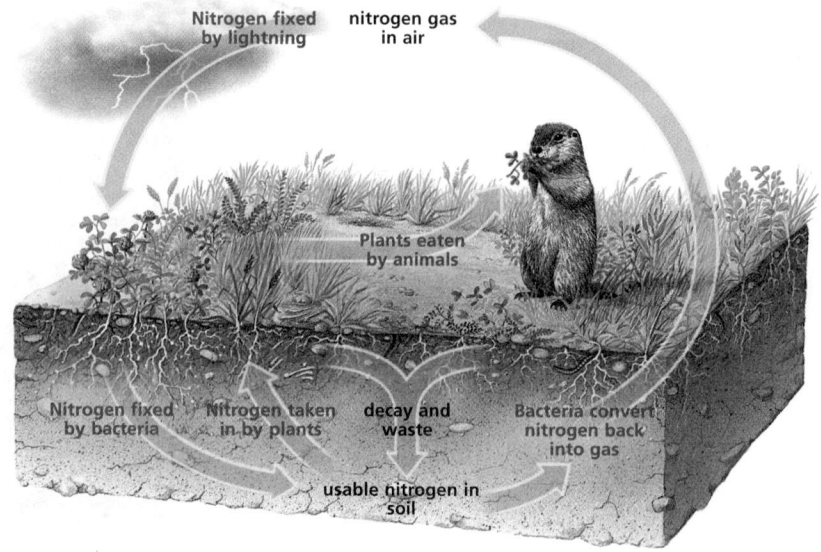

Nitrogen fixed by lightning

nitrogen gas in air

Plants eaten by animals

Nitrogen fixed by bacteria

Nitrogen taken in by plants

decay and waste

Bacteria convert nitrogen back into gas

usable nitrogen in soil

 **VISUALIZATION**
CLASSZONE.COM

Watch the nitrogen cycle in action.

A far greater source of nitrogen is nitrogen-fixing bacteria. These bacteria live in the oceans as well as the soil. Some even attach themselves to the roots of certain plants, like alfalfa or soybeans. When organisms die, decomposers in the ocean or soil break them down. Nitrogen in the soil or water is used again by living things. A small amount is returned to the atmosphere by certain bacteria that can break down nitrogen compounds into nitrogen gas.

1.2 Review

KEY CONCEPTS

1. Draw a diagram of the water cycle. Show three ways in which water moves through the cycle.

2. Summarize the main parts of the carbon cycle.

3. Explain two ways that nitrogen gas in the atmosphere is changed into nitrogen compounds that plants can use.

CRITICAL THINKING

4. **Predict** When people burn fossil fuels, carbon dioxide gas is added to the atmosphere. How might increased carbon dioxide affect plant growth?

5. **Compare and Contrast** Review the nitrogen and carbon cycles. How are these two cycles similar and different?

CHALLENGE

6. **Apply** Draw a cycle diagram that shows how water is used in your household. Include activities that use water, sources of water, and ways that water leaves your house.

D **20** Unit: **Ecology**

ANSWERS

1. Diagrams should include precipitation, evaporation, and condensation.

2. Green plants and algae remove CO_2 from air. Animals get carbon from food and release carbon as CO_2. The burning of fossil fuels, wood,

or other organisms and decay release carbon.

3. Bacteria break down nitrogen compounds into nitrogen gas. Lightning breaks apart pure nitrogen in the atmosphere.

4. Plants might grow larger or increase in numbers.

5. Both have a gaseous form. Plants make both elements available to animals. Decay returns both elements to the atmosphere.

6. Diagrams should include activity, source, and exit route.

MATH in SCIENCE

MATH TUTORIAL
CLASSZONE.COM

Click on Math Tutorial for more help with adding integers.

This iceberg is made up of fresh water, which freezes at 0°C. The surrounding ocean is salt water, which doesn't freeze at 0°C.

SKILL: ADDING INTEGERS

Temperature and the Water Cycle

Changes in temperature help water move through the environment. At freezing temperatures—below 32°F or 0°C for sea-level environments—water can begin to become solid ice. Ice starts to melt when the temperature rises above freezing, causing the water to become liquid again. Temperature change also causes water to become vapor, or gas, within the air.

Example

Suppose you are waiting for winter to come so you can skate on a small pond near your house. The weather turns cold. One day the temperature is 25°C, then the next day the air temperature drops by 35°C. What temperature is the air? If the air stays below 0°C, some of the water will begin to freeze.

(1) Write a verbal model:
25 degrees + a 35-degree drop = what temperature?

(2) Write an equation. Use negative and positive integers:
$25 + (-35) = ?$

(3) Solve the equation:
$25 - 35 = -10$

ANSWER −10°C.

[Thermometer diagram showing °C scale from −30 to 30 and °F scale from −20 to 80, with Freezing Point of Water marked at 0°C/32°F]

Answer the following questions.

1. A container of water is left out over night, when the temperature is −18°C. In the morning, the air temperature rises by 8°C. What temperature is the air? What will happen to the water?

2. An ice block sits in a field where the air is 0°C. The air temperature rises by 16°C, then it drops by 8°C. What temperature is the air in the field now? What will happen to the ice?

3. What happens to a block of ice after the temperature in the air follows this pattern: $-6 + 17 + 10 + 18 + (-5)$? What temperature has the air reached?

CHALLENGE Use a thermometer to measure the temperature of the air outside and indoors in degrees Celsius. Write two addition equations that show the temperature change between the two locations. One equation should show a rise, and one should show a drop.

ANSWERS

1. −18 + 8 = −10°C; the water will freeze.

2. 0 + 16 − 8 = 8°C; some of the ice block will melt.

3. It melts; 34°C

***CHALLENGE** Temperature figures should be recorded in degrees Celsius. The equations should show lower temperature + difference = higher temperature, and higher temperature + (− difference) = lower temperature.*

Set Learning Goal

To add positive and negative integers in situations involving temperature

Present the Science

Read the explanation with students. Make sure they understand the freezing point and boiling point of fresh water, and that a temperature below zero is preceded by a minus sign. Remind students that saltwater freezes at a lower temperature. The term "water" in this exercise refers to fresh water only.

Develop Algebra Skills

Go through the sample question with students. Ask:

• Why is a negative number (−35) used for the equation in step 2? *The temperature decreases so a negative number is used.*

• How do you subtract a larger number from a smaller number? *You can subtract the smaller number from the larger one, and then add a negative sign: 35 − 25 = 10; 25 − 35 = −10*

DIFFERENTIATION TIP Suggest that students use a number line. Demonstrate how to use the number line to figure rise and fall in temperatures.

Close

Ask: Name another example in the sciences where adding positive and negative integers is used. *elevations below sea level, dates B.C. and A.D.*

• Math Support, p. 60
• Math Practice, p. 61

Technology Resources

Students can visit **ClassZone.com** for practice in adding integers.

 MATH TUTORIAL

Students will

• Explain how living organisms move energy through an ecosystem.

• Explain how feeding relationships are important in an ecosystem.

• Explain how the amount of energy changes as it flows through an ecosystem.

• Observe plants decomposing with the help of microorganisms.

◉ **3-Minute Warm-Up**

Display Transparency 5 or copy this exercise on the board:

Serena puts a small amount of water in a saucer and leaves it on a sunny windowsill for several hours. What happens to the water? Why? *The water evaporates. Heat from the Sun changes liquid water into vapor, which escapes into the air. After several hours, the saucer may be completely dry.*

 3-Minute Warm-Up, p. T5

1.3 MOTIVATE

EXPLORE Energy

PURPOSE To demonstrate how energy changes form as it moves through an ecosystem

TIPS *10 min.* Cut spirals from circles or squares of paper about 8 centimeters square. Origami paper, construction paper, and Bristol board work well. As a control, hang one spiral in an area protected from air movement.

WHAT DO YOU THINK? *The spiral turned. Heat from the lamp is the energy source. It creates airflow.*

KEY CONCEPT

1.3 Energy flows through ecosystems.

◀ **BEFORE, you learned**

• Matter cycles continuously through an ecosystem

• Living things are part of the water, carbon, and nitrogen cycles

▶ **NOW, you will learn**

• How living things move energy through an ecosystem

• How feeding relationships are important in ecosystems

• How the amount of energy changes as it flows through an ecosystem

VOCABULARY

producer p. 23
consumer p. 24
decomposer p. 25
food chain p. 26
food web p. 26
energy pyramid p. 28

EXPLORE Energy

How can you observe energy changing form?

PROCEDURE

① Mark and cut a spiral pattern in a square piece of paper.

② Cut a 15-cm piece of thread and tape one end to the center of the spiral.

③ Adjust the lamp to shine straight at the ceiling. Turn the lamp on.

④ Hold the spiral by the thread and let it hang 10 cm above the light bulb.
CAUTION: Don't let the paper touch the bulb!

WHAT DO YOU THINK?

• What do you see happen to the spiral?

• In what sense has the energy changed form?

MATERIALS

• paper
• marker
• scissors
• thread
• tape
• desk lamp

Living things capture and release energy.

Everything you do—running, reading, and working—requires energy. The energy you use is chemical energy, which comes from the food you eat. When you go for a run, you use up energy. Some of that energy is released to the environment as heat, as you sweat. Eventually, you will need to replace the energy you've used.

Energy is vital to all living things. Most of that energy comes either directly or indirectly from the Sun. To use the Sun's energy, living things must first capture that energy and store it in some usable form. Because energy is continuously used by the activities of living things, it must be continuously replaced in the ecosystem.

D 22 Unit: Ecology

RESOURCES FOR DIFFERENTIATED INSTRUCTION

Below Level

UNIT RESOURCE BOOK

• Reading Study Guide A, pp. 34–35

• Decoding Support, p. 59

 **AUDIO CDS**

Advanced

UNIT RESOURCE BOOK

• Challenge and Extension, p. 40

• Challenge Reading, pp. 55–56

English Learners

UNIT RESOURCE BOOK

Spanish Reading Study Guide, pp. 38–39

AUDIO CDS

• Audio Readings in Spanish

• Audio Readings (English)

Producers

All of these producers capture energy from sunlight.

Plants

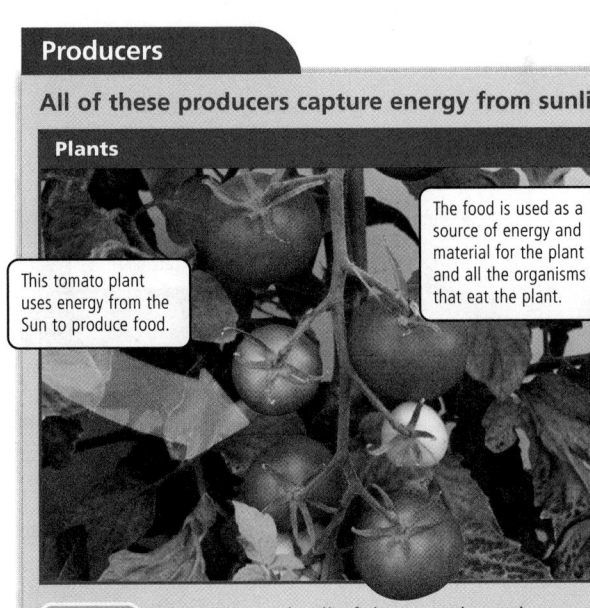

This tomato plant uses energy from the Sun to produce food.

The food is used as a source of energy and material for the plant and all the organisms that eat the plant.

READING VISUALS What process do all of these producers have in common?

Seaweed

Seaweed is a producer found in Earth's oceans and coastal zones.

Phytoplankton

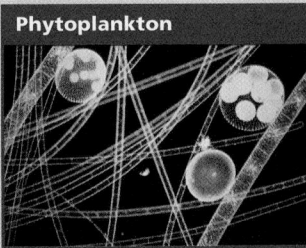

The most numerous producers are tiny organisms that live in water called phytoplankton.

Producers

A

B

A **producer** is an organism that captures energy and stores it in food as chemical energy. The producers of an ecosystem make energy available to all the other living parts of an ecosystem. Most energy enters ecosystems through photosynthesis. Plants, and other photosynthetic organisms, take water and carbon dioxide from their environment and use energy from the Sun to produce sugars. The chemical energy stored in sugars can be released when sugars are broken down.

 **CHECK YOUR READING** How does energy enter into the living parts of an ecosystem?

Plants are the most common producers found in land ecosystems. In water ecosystems, most food is produced by photosynthetic bacteria and algae. A few examples of producers that use photosynthesis are shown in the photographs above.

The Sun provides most of the energy that is stored in food. One exception is the unusual case of a type of bacteria that lives in the deep ocean, where there is no sunlight. These bacteria produce food using heated chemicals released from underwater vents. This process is called chemosynthesis. Whether producers use photosynthesis or chemosynthesis, they do just as their name suggests—they produce food for themselves and for the rest of the ecosystem.

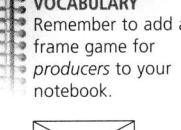 **VOCABULARY** Remember to add a frame game for *producers* to your notebook.

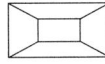

Chapter 1: **Ecosystems and Biomes 23** **D**

Teach from Visuals

To help students interpret the visual of consumers, ask:

- Why is the plant identified as the producer? *It is where photosynthesis takes place.*
- Why is the caterpillar identified as the primary consumer? *It eats the leaves of the plant (the producer).*
- Why is the bird identified as the secondary consumer? *The bird is second in the line of consumers—it eats a primary consumer.*

Develop Critical Thinking

CONNECT Have students discuss the transfer of energy and matter in the food chain represented in the illustration. Ask:

- Once the bird has eaten the caterpillar, what happens to the matter that made up the caterpillar and the energy that was stored in the caterpillar's cells? *It transfers to the body of the bird.*
- What kind of energy conversion is involved when a bird flies? *Chemical energy converts to mechanical energy.*

Integrate the Sciences

All matter on Earth is reused. Your body might contain carbon atoms that once were part of a dinosaur.

Energy cannot be recycled, but it is constantly converted from one form to another and transferred from place to place. For example, the Sun's radiation changes to heat energy as it shines on Earth. Chemical energy stored in wood changes to heat energy as it ignites and burns.

Ongoing Assessment

D 24 Unit: Ecology

Consumers

A consumer is an organism that gets energy by eating producers or other consumers.

Producer: tree

Primary consumer: caterpillar

Secondary consumer: bird

READING VISUALS How does the energy inside the leaf get transferred to the bird?

Consumers

Organisms that cannot produce their own food must get their food from other sources. **Consumers** are organisms that get their energy by eating, or consuming, other organisms. To understand how energy flows through an ecosystem, you have to study feeding relationships. A feeding relationship starts with a producer, followed by one and often many more consumers.

CHECK YOUR READING Describe the producer-consumer relationship in terms of energy.

Consumers are classified by their position in a feeding relationship. In a meadow ecosystem, animals such as antelopes and grasshoppers feed on grasses. They are primary consumers because they are the first link between the producers and the rest of the consumers in an ecosystem. The wolves that eat the antelopes and the meadowlarks that eat the grasshoppers are secondary consumers. There are also tertiary consumers, like the prairie falcon that eats the meadowlark. Ecosystems also have special consumers called scavengers, like the vulture or earthworm, which are consumers that feed on dead animals.

In the photograph above, energy enters the ecosystem through the tree, which is the producer. The caterpillar that gets its energy by feeding on the leaves is the first, or primary, consumer. The bird that gets its energy by feeding on the caterpillar is a secondary consumer.

READING TiP
Primary is a word that means "first in order," *secondary* means "second in order," and *tertiary* means "third in order."

D 24 Unit: Ecology

DIFFERENTIATE INSTRUCTION

More Reading Support

C What organisms get energy by eating other organisms? *consumers*

D What feed on dead animals? *scavengers*

Below Level Have students draw the organisms in the "Consumers" diagram as a food chain. Then have them draw a tertiary consumer, such as a fox or a hawk, in its appropriate place in the food chain.

Decomposers

If you've been for a hike through a forest, or a walk through a park, you have seen the interaction of producers and consumers. Tall trees and leafy shrubs are home to many insects and the birds that feed upon the insects. Also important to the maintenance of an ecosystem are decomposers, a group of organisms that often go unseen. **Decomposers** are organisms that break down dead plant and animal matter into simpler compounds.

You can think of decomposers as the clean-up crew of an ecosystem. In a forest, consumers such as deer and insects eat a tiny fraction of the leaves on trees and shrubs. The leaves that are left on the forest floor, as well as dead roots and branches, are eventually digested by fungi and bacteria living in the soil. Decomposers also break down animal remains, including waste materials. A pinch of soil may contain almost half a million fungi and billions of bacteria.

The energy within an ecosystem gets used up as it flows from organism to organism. Decomposers are the organisms that release the last bit of energy from once-living matter. Decomposers also return matter to soil or water where it may be used again and again.

mushrooms

Fungi, such as these mushrooms, are decomposers.

INVESTIGATE Decomposers

Where do decomposers come from?

PROCEDURE

1. Carefully use scissors to cut an opening across the middle of the bottle.

2. Place a handful of stones in the bottom of the bottle for drainage, and add enough soil to make a layer 10 cm deep.

3. Place some leaves and fruit slices on top of the soil.

4. Seal the cut you made with tape. Mark the date on the tape.

5. Add water through the top of the bottle to moisten the soil, and put the cap on the bottle. Wash your hands.

6. Observe the fruit slices each day for two weeks. Record your observations. Keep the soil moist.

WHAT DO YOU THINK?

- What do you observe happening to the fruit slices?
- Where do the decomposers in your bottle come from?

CHALLENGE Predict what would happen if you used potting soil instead of soil from outside.

SKILL FOCUS
Observing

MATERIALS
- clear soda bottle with cap
- scissors
- stones
- garden soil
- leaves
- slices of fruit
- masking tape
- marker
- water

TIME
30 minutes

25 **D**

INVESTIGATE Decomposers

PURPOSE To observe the effect of decomposers on plant matter

TIP *30 min.* You might want to start with rotting fruit rather than fresh fruit in this activity. It will speed the process, and you will avoid wasting food.

WHAT DO YOU THINK? *Answers: The fruit slices turn brown and rot; the decomposers come from the garden soil.*

CHALLENGE *The fruit would take longer to decay and not break down as well because potting soil does not have as many decomposers as garden soil.*

R Datasheet, Decomposers, p. 41

Technology Resources

Customize this student lab as needed or look for an alternative. Print rubrics to assess student lab reports.

Lab Generator CD-ROM

Ongoing Assessment

Explain how organisms move energy through an ecosystem.

Ask: How does the Sun's energy end up in the milk you drink at lunch? *Grasses (producers) convert the Sun's energy into food. Cows use matter and energy from grass to produce milk.*

DIFFERENTIATE INSTRUCTION

More Reading Support

E What kind of organism breaks down the bodies of dead plants and animals into simpler compounds? *decomposer*

Advanced Decomposers such as fungi and bacteria are continuously at work in ecosystems breaking down plant and animal wastes. Have students list and describe some specific processes of decomposition that benefit human beings.

Have students who are interested in ecosystem processes that benefit humans read the following article:

R Challenge Reading, pp. 55–56

IDENTIFY Ask: What do the arrows in the food web on p. 27 mean? If students answer that the arrows point from the eater to the eaten, they may hold the misconception that a food web is a linear model showing only which organism eats which.

CORRECT Create a food web bulletin board for an ecosystem in your area, using pictures of producers and consumers linked by arrows. Explain that the arrows show the flow of energy from one organism to another. Therefore, the arrows point from the eaten to the eater. Arrange the arrows so that they point in the opposite direction from the way they should. Have students explain the error.

REASSESS Ask: In a food web, what does an arrow pointing from a frog to a stork mean? *It means that energy flows from the frog to the stork when the stork eats the frog.*

EXPLORE (the **BIG** idea)

Revisit "Internet Activity: A Prairie Ecosystem" on p. 7. Have students explain the feeding relationships and other factors moving energy and water through that ecosystem.

Ongoing Assessment

 CHECK YOUR READING *Answer: A food chain shows only one set of feeding relationships in an ecosystem; a food web shows many different feeding relationships.*

COMBINATION NOTES
Remember to take notes and draw a diagram for *food chain* and *food web*.

Models help explain feeding relationships.

You have learned how energy is captured by producers and moved through ecosystems by consumers and decomposers. Scientists use two different models to show the feeding relationships that transfer energy from organism to organism. These models are food chains and food webs.

Food Chain

 A chain is made of links that are connected one by one. Scientists use the idea of links in a chain as a model for simple feeding relationships. A **food chain** describes the feeding relationship between a producer and a single chain of consumers in an ecosystem.

The illustration in the white box on page 27 shows a wetland food chain. The first link in the chain is a cattail, a primary producer that captures the Sun's energy and stores it in food. The second link is a caterpillar, a primary consumer of the cattail. The frog is the next link, a secondary consumer that eats the caterpillar. The final link is a heron, a tertiary consumer that eats the frog. Energy is captured and released at each link in the chain. The arrows represent the flow of energy from organism to organism. You can see that some of the energy captured by the cattail makes its way through a whole chain of other organisms in the ecosystem.

Food Web

 A **food web** is a model of the feeding relationships between many different consumers and producers in an ecosystem. A food web is more like a spiderweb, with many overlapping and interconnected food chains. It is a better model for the complex feeding relationships in an ecosystem, which usually has many different producers, with many primary and secondary consumers.

The illustration on page 27 also shows a wetland food web. You can see that the feeding relationships can go in several directions. For example, the food web shows that ruddy ducks eat bulrushes, which are producers. That makes ruddy ducks primary consumers. Ruddy ducks are also secondary consumers because they eat snails. A food web shows how one consumer can play several roles in an ecosystem.

 CHECK YOUR READING What is the difference between a food chain and a food web?

Both food chains and food webs show how different organisms receive their energy. They also show how different organisms depend on one another. If one organism is removed from the food web or food chain, it may affect many other organisms in the ecosystem.

READING TiP
Notice that the food chain described above is also a part of the food web described here. Follow the blue arrows in the diagram on page 27.

DIFFERENTIATE INSTRUCTION

? More Reading Support

F What are the links in a food chain or food web? *organisms and their feeding relationships*

G Which shows complex feeding relationships? *food web*

Below Level Have students create a simple food web with four to six organisms. Have them remove one of the organisms and explain some likely results for the rest of the organisms.

Inclusion Let students with cognitive disabilities use their bodies to represent the links in a food chain or food web. Have each student make and wear the name or picture of the organism he or she represents. Use yarn or string to show the links in the food web they are modeling.

Energy Flows Through Ecosystems

Energy is transferred from one organism to the next as organisms eat or are eaten.

A Wetland Food Chain

Flow of Energy
Energy flow starts at the bottom. Arrows represent energy moving from an organism that is eaten to the organism that eats it.

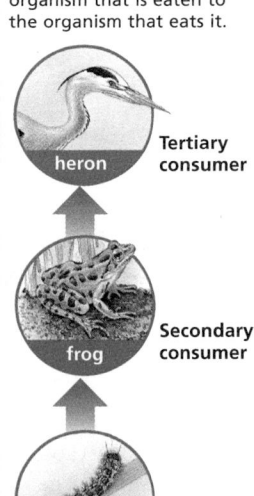

heron — **Tertiary consumer**

frog — **Secondary consumer**

caterpillar — **Primary consumer**

cattails — **Producer**

Decomposers
These tiny organisms recycle dead and decayed material.

A Wetland Food Web

heron

water snake

frog

blackbird

duck

beetle

snail

caterpillar

muskrat

bulrush

cattails

Chapter 1: **Ecosystems and Biomes** 27 **D**

To help students interpret the visual of energy flowing through an ecosystem:

- Ask: Why are there no arrows pointing away from the heron or the water snake? *Answer: because they are the tertiary consumers and they are not eaten by any organism shown in this food web*

- Have students list three different food chains that you can find in the food web shown here. *bulrush, beetle, blackbird; cattails, snail, duck; bulrush, snail, heron; cattails, muskrat, water snake*

 The visual "Energy Flows Through Ecosystems" is available as T6 in the Unit Transparency Book.

Develop Critical Thinking

CONNECT Have students apply their knowledge of a food web by asking them to create a food web for familiar organisms they observe in a local ecosystem, such as a park, garden, backyard, vacant lot, or urban neighborhood. *Sample answer: Aphids, crickets, and other insects feed on leaves of plants. Pigeons and sparrows eat insects. Falcons and hawks eat sparrows and pigeons.*

Ongoing Assessment

Explain how feeding relationships are important in an ecosystem.

Ask: What would happen to secondary consumers, such as cats, if primary consumers were eliminated from a food web? *Secondary consumers would starve unless they could eat and use producers or find another primary consumer on which to feed.*

DIFFERENTIATE INSTRUCTION

Below Level Have students work in pairs to identify the different food chains in the food web in the illustration. Assign each pair of students one of the organisms, and have them draw all of the food chains associated with that organism.

Advanced Have students hypothesize what would happen to the wetland food chain if one organism were removed.

R Challenge and Extension, p. 40

Teach from Visuals

To help students interpret the energy pyramid, ask:

- Which layer of the pyramid contains the most energy? *producers*
- Which layer of the pyramid contains the least energy? *tertiary consumers*
- Why is there less energy in the primary consumers than there is in the producers? *The life processes of the producers use up some of the energy before primary consumers eat the producers.*

Reinforce (the **BIG** idea)

Have students relate the section to the Big Idea.

 Reinforcing Key Concepts, p. 42

1.3 ASSESS & RETEACH

Assess

 Section 1.3 Quiz, p. 5

Reteach

Have students draw a food chain for one or more foods they've eaten. Ask them to indicate how energy travels in the chain and how much there is at each step. Ask:

- Did all of the Sun's energy absorbed by the producer in your food chain end up in your body? Why or why not? *No; some of the energy was used by the plant before it was eaten.*
- Describe your place in the food chain. *Answer should be a primary or higher consumer.*
- What other animals might take your place in this food chain? *other high-level consumers*

Technology Resources

Have students visit **ClassZone.com** for reaching of Key Concepts.

 CONTENT REVIEW

 CONTENT REVIEW CD-ROM

Available energy decreases as it moves through an ecosystem.

Another way to picture the flow of energy in an ecosystem is to use an energy pyramid. An **energy pyramid** is a model that shows the amount of energy available at each feeding level of an ecosystem. The first level includes the producers, the second level the primary consumers, and so on. Because energy is lost as it moves from producers to consumers, the bottom level is the largest. The available energy gets smaller and smaller the farther up the pyramid you go.

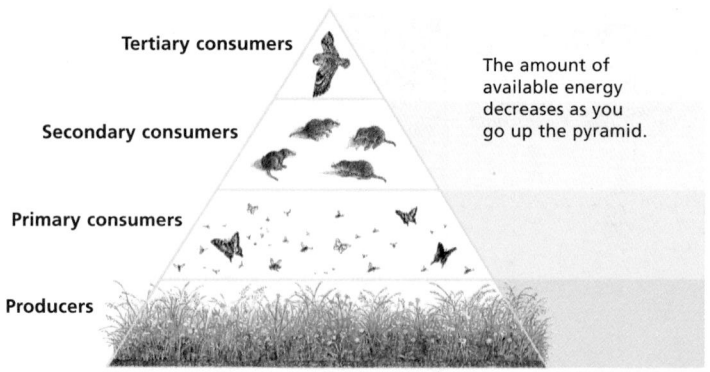

Tertiary consumers

Secondary consumers

Primary consumers

Producers

The amount of available energy decreases as you go up the pyramid.

READING TiP
Refer to the diagram above as you read the text. It is because some energy is lost at each level that the diagram takes the shape of a pyramid.

In the pyramid shown here, plants are the producers. They capture energy from the Sun, use some of it, then store the rest as food. The plants are eaten by insects, which also use up some of the energy before being eaten by shrews. The shrews use up energy before being eaten by the owl. You can see that it takes a lot of sunlight to support the producers and consumers in a food web that feeds an owl.

1.3 Review

KEY CONCEPTS

1. Describe the role of producers, consumers, and decomposers in an ecosystem.
2. Explain why a food web provides a better model of an ecosystem than a food chain does.
3. Explain how the amount of available energy changes as energy moves up a food chain.

CRITICAL THINKING

4. **Apply** Draw a food chain and a food web for an ecosystem near your home.
5. **Predict** Imagine that muskrats are removed from a wetland ecosystem. Predict what would happen both to producers and to secondary consumers.

CHALLENGE

6. **Synthesize** Explain how the carbon cycle is related to a food web. Describe how energy and matter move through the food web and the carbon cycle.

D 28 Unit: **Ecology**

ANSWERS

1. *Producers make sugars using sunlight. Consumers eat other consumers and producers. Decomposers break down dead producers and consumers.*

2. *Food webs show that one organism can have more than one role in an ecosystem.*

3. *Available energy decreases.*

4. *Food chains should show one energy path. Webs should show multiple paths.*

5. *Secondary consumers would disappear without having muskrats to eat.*

Producers would get more plentiful without the muskrats eating them.

6. *A food web shows movement of energy, but it also shows movement of matter. As consumers eat, carbon in plants and animals is transferred through the food web.*

Biomagnification

Matter moves through living things in an ecosystem. Some of it is used up, some of it is stored. Sometimes, a toxic, or poisonous, material can get into a food chain and be stored. The amount of poison increases over time, or is magnified. Biomagnification is the process by which matter becomes concentrated in living things in a food chain.

Moving up the Food Chain

DDT provides one example of the effects of biomagnification in an ecosystem. DDT is a chemical that was widely used to kill plant-eating insects. Some chemicals break down over time, but DDT does not. DDT collected in water and soil, was absorbed by living things, and moved up the food chain. The diagram shows how DDT became magnified in a wetland ecosystem. It entered through tiny organisms called zooplankton, which absorbed DDT from the water.

❶ The DDT in zooplankton was about 800 times greater than the DDT in the environment.

❷ Minnows fed on zooplankton. DDT was magnified 31 times so there was 24,800 times more DDT in minnows than in the environment: 800 x 31 = 24,800.

❸ Trout ate minnows. DDT was magnified 1.7 times so there was 42,160 times more DDT in trout than in the environment.

❹ Gulls ate trout. DDT was magnified 4.8 times so there was over 200,000 times more DDT in gulls than in the environment.

DDT is especially harmful to large birds such as osprey and eagles. The chemical made the shells of the eggs of these large birds so thin that the eggs did not survive long enough to hatch.

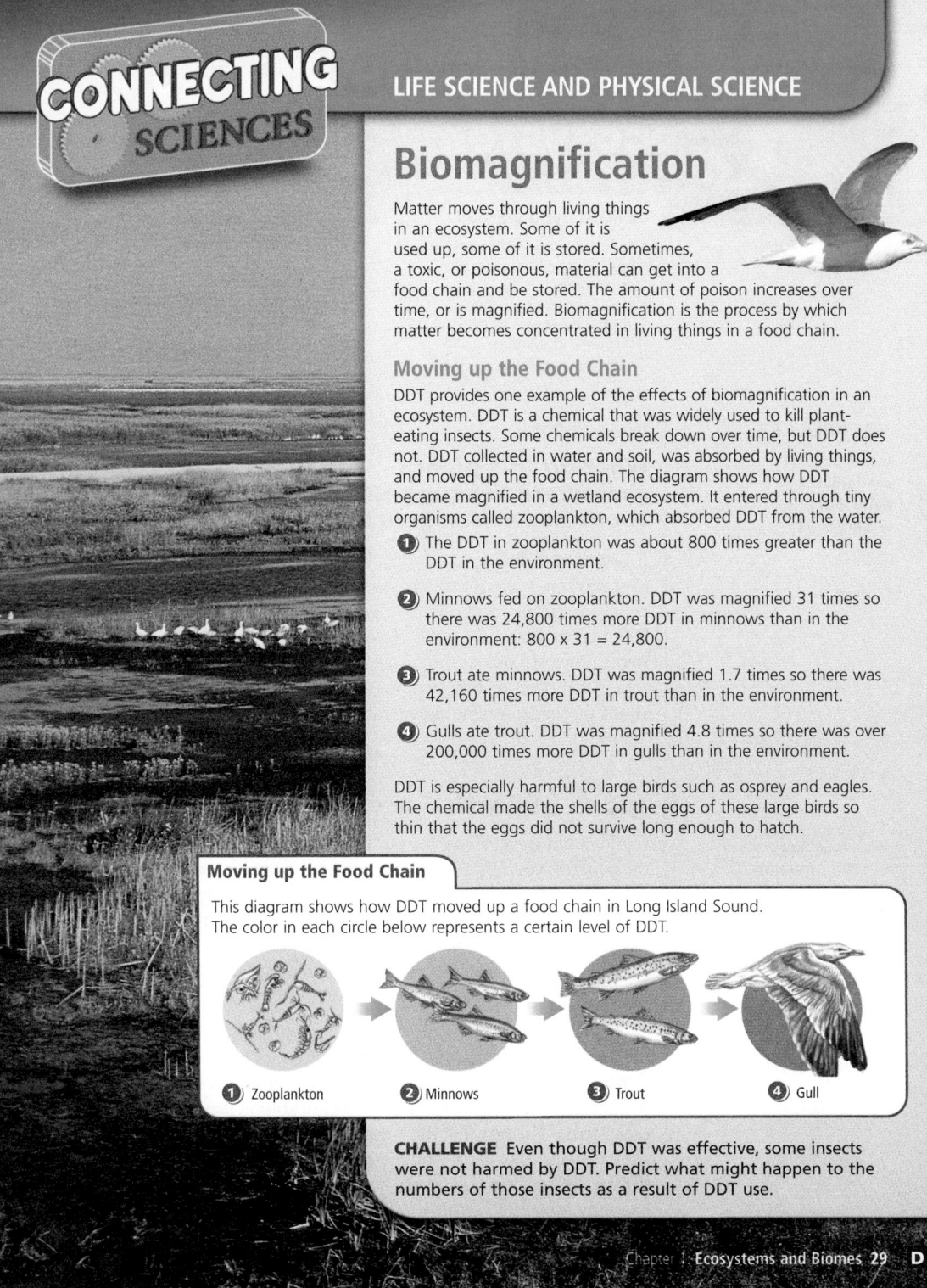

Moving up the Food Chain

This diagram shows how DDT moved up a food chain in Long Island Sound. The color in each circle below represents a certain level of DDT.

❶ Zooplankton ❷ Minnows ❸ Trout ❹ Gull

CHALLENGE Even though DDT was effective, some insects were not harmed by DDT. Predict what might happen to the numbers of those insects as a result of DDT use.

EXPLORE

CHALLENGE *Insects not affected by DDT might increase in numbers as living things that consume those insects might decrease in population.*

Set Learning Goal

To understand how chemicals in the environment can accumulate in organisms that feed high on the food chain

Present the Science

DDT is stored in fatty tissues. Accumulations of DDT in the body may not lead to death, but its gradual buildup can affect an animal's health and ability to reproduce. Although DDT was banned in the United States in 1972, it lingers in the environment. It is still used in some countries, especially to control malaria-carrying mosquitoes.

Discussion Questions

Go through the steps of the biomagnification food chain. Ask:

• How does DDT get into the bodies of zooplankton? *Runoff washes DDT into waterways, where zooplankton absorb it from the water.*

• How does an organism's place on the food chain relate to the concentration of DDT in its body? *Organisms higher on the food chain have higher concentrations of DDT.*

• How does the biomagnification of DDT affect reproduction in birds of prey? *It causes thin eggshells that break before young birds have a chance to hatch.*

Close

Ask: How does the biomagnification of nonbiodegradable chemicals show that matter moves through a food chain? *DDT is not broken down or used at each step in the food chain, so increasing amounts accumulate in the bodies of organisms that are higher on the chain.*

- Describe how biomes vary by region and how they are classified by the plant life they support.
- Explain that different ecosystems make up a biome.
- Describe different land and water biomes on Earth.
- Gather and graph local climate data.

◄ 3-Minute Warm-Up

Display Transparency 5 or copy the exercise on the board:

The organisms in a certain grassland ecosystem include grasses, insects, meadowlarks, mice, and owls. Draw a diagram that shows how these organisms depend on one another for food. Label each organism and use an arrow to show which organism(s) it feeds on. *Students should produce a simple food web with arrows from grasses to insects, insects to meadowlarks and mice, mice to owls.*

 3-Minute Warm-Up, p. T5

1.4 MOTIVATE

THINK ABOUT

PURPOSE To understand how a plant's characteristics are important for survival

DISCUSS What adaptations do cacti have? *thick green stems and spines* What do they do for the plants? *reduce water loss, perform photosynthesis, protect plant from herbivores.*

Answers: tubular stems and oval-shaped growth off stems; it has spines instead of leaves; its pads are stems; it flowers; it must conserve water; the environment is dry.

KEY CONCEPT

1.4 Biomes contain many ecosystems.

◄ **BEFORE, you learned**

- Feeding relationships describe how energy flows through ecosystems
- The amount of available energy decreases as it flows through ecosystems

► **NOW, you will learn**

- How biomes vary by region and by the plant life they support
- How different ecosystems make up a biome
- About the different land and water biomes on Earth

VOCABULARY

biome p. 30
coniferous p. 32
deciduous p. 33
estuary p. 36

THINK ABOUT

What do this plant's characteristics suggest about its environment?

A plant's overall shape and form help it to survive in its environment. Look closely at this plant in the photograph. Describe its shape. Does it have leaves? a stem? flowers? Look at the surrounding area. What do your observations suggest about the environment in general?

COMBINATION NOTES
Remember to take notes and draw a diagram for each of the six land biomes described in the text.

Regions of Earth are classified into biomes.

If you could travel along the 30° latitude line, either north or south of the equator, you'd notice an interesting pattern. You would see deserts give way to grasslands and grasslands give way to forests. Across Earth, there are large geographic areas that are similar in climate and that have similar types of plants and animals. Each of these regions is classified as a **biome** (BY-ohm). There are six major land biomes on Earth, as shown on the map on page 31.

Climate is an important factor in land biomes. Climate describes the long-term weather patterns of a region, such as average yearly rainfall and temperature ranges. Climate also affects soil type. Available water, temperature, and soil are abiotic factors important in ecosystems. The fact that the abiotic factors of a particular biome are similar helps to explain why the ecosystems found in these biomes are similar. Biomes represent very large areas, which means that there will be many ecosystems within a biome.

D 30 Unit: **Ecology**

RESOURCES FOR DIFFERENTIATED INSTRUCTION

Below Level
UNIT RESOURCE BOOK
- Reading Study Guide A, pp. 45–46
- Decoding Support, p. 59

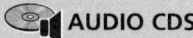 **AUDIO CDS**

Advanced
UNIT RESOURCE BOOK
Challenge and Extension, p. 51

English Learners
UNIT RESOURCE BOOK
Spanish Reading Study Guide, pp. 49–50

AUDIO CDS

- Audio Readings in Spanish
- Audio Readings (English)

Land Biomes

Each land biome is characterized by a particular climate, the quality of the soil, and the plant life found there.

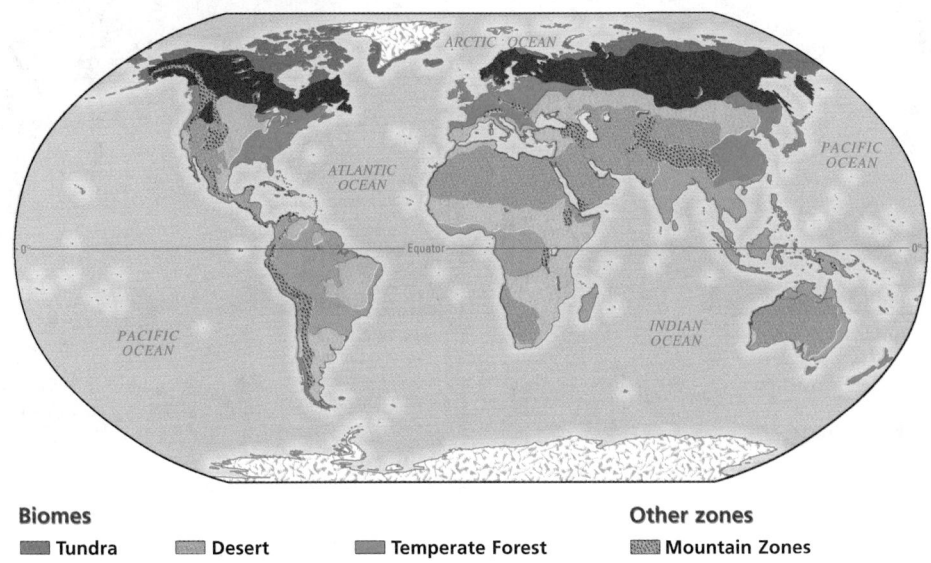

Biomes

- ▨ Tundra
- ▨ Taiga
- ▨ Desert
- ▨ Grassland
- ▨ Temperate Forest
- ▨ Tropical Forest

Other zones

- ▨ Mountain Zones
- ▨ Polar Ice

Taiga and Tundra

If you go to the northernmost regions of Earth, you will find two biomes—tundra and taiga—that are characterized by long cold winters and short cool summers. In the Arctic tundra, temperatures can go as low as –50°C, with a high of about 18°C. Temperature ranges in the taiga (TY-guh) are similar, –40°C to 20°C.

The tundra doesn't get much precipitation, less than 25 centimeters each year. Yet the area is wet because cold temperatures keep the water from evaporating. One of the important characteristics of tundra is permafrost, a deep layer of permanently frozen soil that lies just below the surface soil. Permafrost prevents trees from taking root in the tundra. Plants of the tundra are small and include mosses, grasses, and woody shrubs. Organisms called lichens also do well in the tundra.

The producers of tundra ecosystems support rodents, caribou, and musk oxen. Grizzly bears, white fox, and snowy owls are predators found there. Migrating birds come to nest in the tundra, feeding on insects that mature in summer.

snowy owl

Teach from Visuals

To help students interpret the map of land biomes, ask:

- How many of the six land biomes occur in North America? *all six*
- Which biomes occur in South America? *all except taiga and tundra*
- Which biome dominates Europe? *temperate forest*
- How do the biomes of Australia and southern Africa compare? *Both include desert and grassland and some tropical forest.*

Geography Connection

Remind students that latitude lines mark distance above and below the equator. Point out the location of the equator and the Arctic Circle on a world map or globe. Ask:

- In what latitudes does tundra occur? *around the Arctic Circle; in the Northern Hemisphere only*
- Why is there no tundra or taiga in the Southern Hemisphere? *No landmasses, other than the polar ice of Antarctica are close to the south pole.*
- Where do tropical forests occur on Earth? *near the equator, and spreading north and south*

DIFFERENTIATE INSTRUCTION

More Reading Support

A What two biomes are found in Earth's northernmost regions? *tundra and taiga*

B Which biome is drier than and nearly as cold as the taiga? *tundra*

English Learners Ask English learners to describe the climate, soil quality, and plant life found in their home country. Help them determine which type of biome they have described. Be certain that students understand that a country or region may have more than one type of biome. Have students write the definitions of *biome, coniferous, deciduous,* and *estuary* in their Science Word Dictionaries.

To help students compare and contrast the photographs of tundra and taiga, ask:

- What differences do you notice between the taiga and tundra? *Taiga has tall trees and bushes; tundra has only low-growing plants.*
- What is a primary reason for these differences? *Permafrost prevents the growth of the large, deep root systems of large plants in the tundra.*

Teach Difficult Concepts

Students may have difficulty remembering differences between taiga and tundra. Point out that tundra can be considered a kind of cold desert because it is cold, windy, and dry. The taiga, by contrast, is thickly forested with tall trees. Taiga receives more precipitation than tundra (30 to 60 cm compared to less than 25 cm) and has trees and no permafrost.

Teacher Demo

Show students what permafrost is like. Use a sharp spade or trowel to collect a block of turf or other soil that measures about 15 cm square. Keep the block intact and place it in a shallow container in the freezer for several hours. Remove the container from the freezer a few minutes before class so that the upper portion will begin to thaw. Let students use disposable chopsticks or other probes to explore the texture of the frozen soil. Students may find it helpful to know that *permafrost* is short for "permanent frost."

Ongoing Assessment

Describe how biomes vary by region and are classified according to the plant life they support.

Ask: Where do you find taiga and how do you recognize it? *It is in northern latitudes, has long winters and short summers, and is often dominated by coniferous trees.*

Tundra Only small plants and lichens grow in the tundra because the soil below the surface is frozen.

Taiga Evergreen trees grow in the taiga, where the ground is cold but not frozen.

Even though the temperatures of the taiga are similar to those of the tundra, the taiga has more precipitation, 30 to 60 centimeters a year. The effect of this is that there is more snow on the ground, which insulates the soil below, keeping it from freezing.

Taiga ecosystems are characterized by evergreen trees called **coniferous** (koh-NIHF-uhr-uhs) trees. These trees have needlelike leaves that produce food all year long. This is an advantage in taiga ecosystems because decomposers work slowly in the cold, so the soil is low in nutrients. The wood and leaves of these trees feed insects and their seeds feed birds and squirrels. Taiga ecosystems support deer, elk, snowshoe hares, and beavers. Predators include lynx, owls, bears, and wolves.

Desert and Grassland

collared lizard

Deserts and grasslands are biomes found toward the middle latitudes. You can see from the map on page 31 that a desert biome often leads into a grassland biome. What deserts and grasslands have in common is that they do not get enough precipitation to support trees.

Some deserts are cold and some deserts are hot, but all deserts are characterized by their dry soil. Less than 25 centimeters of rain falls each year in a desert. Desert plants, like the cactus, and desert animals, like the collared lizard, can get by on very little water. Small burrowing animals like the kangaroo rat and ground squirrel are part of desert ecosystems. Desert predators include snakes, owls, and foxes.

D 32 Unit: Ecology

DIFFERENTIATE INSTRUCTION

? **More Reading Support**

C What are evergreens in taiga ecosystems called? *coniferous*

D Which biome is defined by dry soil? *desert*

Inclusion For students who are still at a concrete stage of learning, model the rainfall amounts in this section either by filling a clear beaker or by displaying vertical strips of varying lengths. Explain how each amount represents the water that would collect in a rain gauge from falling precipitation.

Grassland ecosystems develop in areas of moderate rainfall, generally from 50 to 90 centimeters each year. There is enough rain to support grasses, but too little rain to support forests. Periodic wildfires and droughts keep smaller shrubs and tree seedlings from growing. Summers in grassland ecosystems are warm, up to 30°C, but winters are cold.

E

Grasses do well in large open areas. The more rain a grassland ecosystem gets, the higher the grasses grow. These ecosystems support seed-eating rodents that make their burrows in the grassland soil. There are also large grazing animals, like bison, wild horses, gazelle, and zebra. Predators include wolves, tigers, and lions.

Desert Plants of the desert are adapted to survive in dry soil. Many must also survive high daytime temperatures.

Grassland Grasslands receive enough rain to support grasses. Wildfires keep shrubs and trees from growing.

Temperate Forest and Tropical Forest

Trees need more water than smaller plants, shrubs, and grasses. So forest biomes are usually located in regions where more water is available. The taiga is a forest biome. There the coniferous trees survive on smaller amounts of precipitation because the cold weather limits evaporation. Across the middle latitudes, temperate forests grow where winters are short and 75 to 150 centimeters of precipitation fall each year. Near the equator, there are no winters. There, tropical forests grow where 200 to 450 centimeters of rain fall each year.

F

Most temperate forests are made up of deciduous trees, sometimes referred to as broadleaf trees. **Deciduous** (dih-SIHJ-oo-uhs) trees drop their leaves as winter approaches and grow new leaves in spring. The

---

Teach from Visuals

To help students compare and contrast the photographs of deserts and grasslands, ask:

- What differences do you notice between the desert and grassland? *Desert has bare soil with rocks and cacti; grassland soil is covered with grasses and wildflowers.*

- What are some primary reasons for these differences? *Grasslands receive more rain and have richer soil than deserts do.*

Teacher Demo

Compare features of grasses and broad-leaved plants for students. Carefully wash the soil from the roots of a sample of lawn grass and an uprooted broad-leaved plant. Show students the intact plants, including root system. Ask: Why can grass plants survive grazing and fire? *New leaves grow from an underground part of the plant that usually escapes damage from grazing or fire.*

Develop Critical Thinking

SYNTHESIZE Have students choose one animal from the taiga and suggest adaptations that animal would need to survive in the tundra. Students might choose other animals from other biomes as well. For example, what would make it hard for a snowy owl to survive in a grassland? What adaptations could increase its survival?

DIFFERENTIATE INSTRUCTION

? More Reading Support

E What kind of plant does well in large open areas? *grass*

F Which biome has trees that are bare of leaves in winter? *temperate forest*

Below Level Help students remember the differences among biomes by having them make flash cards. On one side of a card, have them write a biome name, and on the other side, one feature of that biome. Give students time to study their flash cards with the help of a partner.

Teach from Visuals

To help students compare and contrast the photographs of temperate and tropical forests, ask:

- What differences do you notice between the temperate and tropical forests? *Sample answer: more vines, greater number and variety of trees in the tropics*

- What do you notice about the variety of types of leaves in temperate and tropical forests? *A tropical forest has a greater variety of leaf types and sizes.*

Real World Example

The Alaskan forest contains cedar and spruce trees, salmon in rivers, sea lions, otters, and belugas in coastal waters. In 1989, the need to protect this bounty was magnified when the *Exxon Valdez* accidentally dumped 11 million gallons of oil on 15,000 miles of coastline. Wildlife like the otter, harbor seal, and harlequin duck still haven't recovered. Now the forest faces a greater threat: logging. Humans are leveling trees at a record rate. Some environmental groups are trying to preserve the rainforest. Oil-spill funds from the *Exxon Valdez* have added 66,000 acres of forest to the state-park system.

Ongoing Assessment

Explain that biomes are made up of several ecosystems.

Ask: What are some of the ecosystems in our biome? *Sample answer for temperate forest: deciduous forest, shrubland, marsh; grassland: meadow, field, banks of a stream*

CHECK YOUR READING *Answer: the greater the plant variety in a biome, the greater the variety of animals*

Temperate Forest
Temperate forests contain many trees with leaves that change color and fall as winter approaches.

Tropical Forest
Tropical forests are warm enough that trees stay green during the entire year.

most common broadleaf trees in North American deciduous forests are oak, birch, beech, and maple. Temperate forests support a wide variety of animals. Animals like mice, chipmunks, squirrels, raccoons, and deer live off seeds, fruit, and insects. Predators include wolves, bobcats, foxes, and mountain lions.

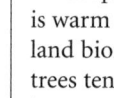

Most temperate forests in North America are deciduous. However, the wet winters and dry summers in the Pacific Northwest support forests made up mostly of coniferous trees—redwoods, spruce, and fir. These forests are referred to as temperate rain forests. The largest trees in the United States are found in these temperate rain forests.

Tropical forests are located near the equator, where the weather is warm all year, around 25°C. The tropical rain forest is the wettest land biome, with a rainfall of 250 to 400 centimeters each year. The trees tend to have leaves year round. This provides an advantage because the soil is poor in nutrients. High temperatures cause materials to break down quickly, but there are so many plants the nutrients get used up just as quickly.

More types of animals, plants, and other organisms live in the tropical rain forest than anywhere else on Earth. The trees grow close together and support many tree-dwelling animals like monkeys, birds, insects, and snakes. There are even plants, like orchids and vines, that grow on top of the trees.

 **CHECK YOUR READING** How does the variety of plants in a biome affect the variety of animals in a biome?

DIFFERENTIATE INSTRUCTION

 More Reading Support

G Which biome includes forests that are deciduous? *temperate forest*

H What is the wettest biome on Earth? *tropical forest*

Advanced Tropical rain forests contain most of Earth's species, yet they are rapidly disappearing. Challenge students to brainstorm products we use that come from the rain forest and explain why we rely on the rain forest in everyday life. Ask them to infer why use of each product would either help or harm rain forest conservation.

R Challenge and Extension, p. 51

INVESTIGATE Climate

How can you graph climate data for your area?

PROCEDURE

1. Gather local data on the average monthly precipitation and the average monthly temperature for a 12-month period.

2. On graph paper, mark off 12 months along the *x*-axis. Make a *y*-axis for each side of the graph, marking one "Temperature (°C)" and the other "Precipitation (mm)."

3. Plot the average precipitation for each month as a bar graph.

4. Plot the average temperature for each month as a line graph.

WHAT DO YOU THINK?

• How much precipitation did the area receive overall?

• What is the temperature range for the area?

CHALLENGE Collect data for the same location, going back 10, 20, and 30 years ago. Graph the data for each of these and compare these graphs to your original graph. Has the climate in your area changed? How might severe changes in climate affect the plant and animal life in your area?

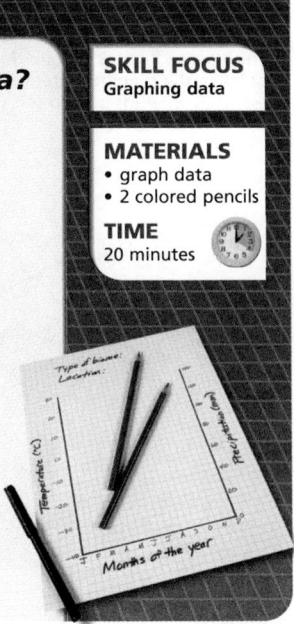

Water covers most of Earth's surface.

Close to three-quarters of Earth's surface is covered by water. Water, or aquatic, biomes can be divided into two broad categories: freshwater biomes and saltwater biomes. Plants have a role as producers in the water biomes that are closely surrounded by land—in ponds and streams and wetlands, and in coastal areas. The food chains of deepwater ecosystems depend on tiny photosynthetic microorganisms called phytoplankton.

leopard frog

Freshwater Biomes

The ecosystems of freshwater biomes are affected by the qualities of the landscape in which they are found. For example, the running water of streams and rivers results from differences in elevation. In shallow rivers, green algae and plants grow in from the banks, providing food for insects and snails that feed fish, salamanders, turtles, and frogs. Plants in a freshwater biome, like a stream or river, may take root in the soil under the water if the water is not too deep or moving too fast. Phytoplankton are not part of river ecosystems because of the moving water.

Chapter 1: **Ecosystems and Biomes** 35 **D**

Teaching with Technology

Students may use spreadsheets or graphing software to organize data and create their graphs.

Teach from Visuals

To help students understand the illustration and photographs of aquatic biomes, ask:

- What differences do you notice between the river and the lake or pond? *River has flowing water that travels a long way through the countryside. Ponds and lakes have still water that does not travel.*

- What differences do you notice between the estuary and the lake or pond? *There are no trees around the estuary. There is flowing water in the estuary. The pond is farther from the ocean.*

Integrating the Sciences

The biosphere is the part of Earth that supports life. It includes air, soil, and water. It extends from the bottom of the deepest ocean to high in the atmosphere, miles above Earth's surface. Just as biomes are made up of ecosystems, the biosphere is made up of biomes. In turn, the Earth as a system is made up of spheres. The spheres include the geosphere, the hydrosphere, the atmosphere, and the biosphere.

Ongoing Assessment

 *Answer: any two: lakes, ponds, estuaries, and rivers*

Aquatic Biomes

Freshwater biomes include the still water of lakes, the running water of rivers, and estuaries where fresh and salt waters mix.

Lakes and Ponds

Estuaries

Rivers and Streams

Ponds and lakes have still water. Ponds are shallow and support many plants as producers. The deeper lakes depend much more on phytoplankton. Ponds and lakes support many different insects, shellfish, snakes, fish, and the land animals that feed off them.

CHECK YOUR READING Name two types of freshwater biomes.

 J

Estuaries are water ecosystems that mark a transition between freshwater and saltwater biomes. An **estuary** is the lower end of a river that feeds into the ocean, where fresh water and salt water mix. Marshes and wetlands are two types of estuaries. Estuaries are sometimes referred to as the nurseries of the sea because so many marine animals travel into the calm waters of an estuary to reproduce. Seaweed, marsh grasses, shellfish, and birds all thrive in estuaries.

Marine Biomes

 K

Marine biomes are saltwater biomes. The three general marine biomes are coastal ocean, open ocean, and deep ocean. Beaches are part of the coastal ocean biome. Tidal pools also form along the coast as the tide comes in and goes out and the conditions constantly change. Organisms like crabs and clams are able to survive the ever-changing conditions to thrive in coastal areas.

RESOURCE CENTER CLASSZONE.COM

Find out more about land and aquatic biomes.

Organisms in the open ocean receive less sunlight than in the coastal ocean, and the temperatures are colder. Many types of fish and

DIFFERENTIATE INSTRUCTION

? More Reading Support

J Which biome combines fresh and saltwater? *estuary*

K Which biomes are in the ocean? *marine biomes; coastal, open ocean, deep ocean*

Advanced Have students select freshwater or marine ecosystems and draw or paint an ecosystem in that biome. If possible, use a technique called "crayon resist." Students draw organisms with oil pastels or crayons, then paint the watery surrounding using water-color paint. Ask them to use their drawings to create a classroom display that shows how the ecosystems combine to form different aquatic biomes.

Coastal

Open Ocean

Marine biomes include rocky and sandy shores as well as the open ocean and the deep waters below, where little or no light can reach.

Deep Ocean

other marine animals and floating seaweed live in the upper ocean. There are no plants in the open ocean. The producers at the bottom of the food chain are different types of phytoplankton.

The deep-ocean regions are much colder and darker than the upper ocean. In the deep ocean there is no sunlight available for photosynthesis. The animals in the deep ocean either feed on each other or on material that falls down from upper levels of the ocean. Many organisms in deep ocean biomes can only be seen with a microscope.

1.4 Review

KEY CONCEPTS

1. In biomes located on land, abiotic factors are used to classify the different biome types. What are these abiotic factors?

2. Name a characteristic type of plant for each of the six land biomes.

3. Name six different aquatic biomes.

CRITICAL THINKING

4. **Predict** If an ecosystem in the grassland biome started to receive less and less rainfall every year, what new biome would be established?

5. **Infer** Name some abiotic factors that affect aquatic biomes and ecosystems.

⏺ CHALLENGE

6. **Apply** Use the map on page 31 to list the following four biomes in the order you would find them moving from the equator to the poles.
   - desert
   - taiga
   - tropical Forest
   - tundra

Chapter 1: **Ecosystems and Biomes 37** **D**

ANSWERS

1. available water, temperature, soil

2. tundra: mosses, lichens; taiga: coniferous trees; desert: cacti; grassland: grasses; temperate forest: deciduous trees; tropical forest: plants grow on top of each other

3. rivers and streams, lakes and ponds, estuaries, coastal ocean, open ocean, deep ocean

4. desert

5. sunlight, water depth, temperature, nutrients

6. tropical forest, desert, taiga, tundra

Teach from Visuals

To help students understand marine biomes, ask:

- How are the coastal ocean and open ocean similar? *Both receive sunlight.*

- How does the deep ocean differ from the coastal and open ocean? *It is dark and cold.*

Reinforce (the **BIG** idea)

Have students relate the section to the Big Idea.

R Reinforcing Key Concepts, p. 54

1.4 ASSESS & RETEACH

Assess

A Section 1.4 Quiz, p. 6

Reteach

Start by listing the six land biomes on the board. Then list aquatic biomes.

Next, show pictures of landscapes and ask students to identify what biome they could be from. Have students point to details that support their identification. Discuss any landscapes that are difficult to categorize.

Technology Resources

Have students visit **ClassZone.com** for reteaching of Key Concepts.

ℹ CONTENT REVIEW

◎ CONTENT REVIEW CD-ROM

BACK TO

the BIG idea

Have students draw and label a diagram showing how matter and energy are both needed to support life in an ecosystem. *Drawings should show the movement of matter through an ecosystem and the movement of energy and matter through its food web.*

◀ KEY CONCEPTS SUMMARY

SECTION 1.1

Ask: What abiotic features are pictured? *temperature, sunlight, soil, water*

Ask: What biotic features are pictured? *tree, horse*

SECTION 1.2

Ask: What are the three important processes that take place in the water cycle? *evaporation, condensation, precipitation*

Ask: How does carbon move from air to plants to animals? *Plants absorb carbon dioxide from air, and animals eat plants.*

Ask: How does nitrogen move from air to plants to animals in an ecosystem? *Bacteria fix nitrogen gas into a compound that is taken up by plants. Animals eat plants.*

SECTION 1.3

Ask: Name one path that matter and energy take as they move through the food web shown in the picture on p. 27. *Sample answer: bulrush, snail, heron*

Ask: Which organisms are at the top of this ecosystem's energy pyramid? *heron, water snake*

SECTION 1.4

Ask: What are the chief factors that define a biome? *plant life and climate*

Review Concepts

- Big Idea Flow Chart, p. T1
- Chapter Outline, pp. T7–T8

---

1 Chapter Review

the BIG idea

Matter and energy together support life within an environment.

CONTENT REVIEW
CLASSZONE.COM

◀ KEY CONCEPTS SUMMARY

 Ecosystems support life.

Ecosystems are made up of living things (biotic) and nonliving things (abiotic).

plants   animals   temperature   Sun   soil   water

Biotic Factors   **Abiotic Factors**

VOCABULARY
ecology p. 9
ecosystem p. 9
biotic factor p. 10
abiotic factor p. 10

 Matter cycles through ecosystems.

Water, carbon, and nitrogen are materials that are necessary for life. They move through ecosystems in continuous cycles.

VOCABULARY
cycle p. 16
water cycle p. 17
carbon cycle p. 18
nitrogen cycle p. 19

 Energy flows through ecosystems.

Producers are the basis of feeding relationships in ecosystems.

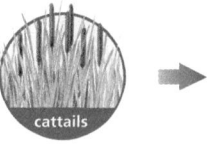  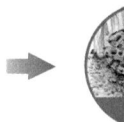

cattails   caterpillar   frog

Producer   **Primary consumer**   **Secondary consumer**

Food chains and food webs help show how energy moves through living things.

VOCABULARY
producer p. 23
consumer p. 24
decomposer p. 25
food chain p. 26
food web p. 26
energy pyramid p. 28

1.4 Biomes contain many ecosystems.

Ecosystems of land biomes
- are affected by climate
- are affected by conditions of the soil
- are characterized by types of plants

Ecosystems of water biomes
- can be freshwater or saltwater
- are affected by landscape if freshwater
- are affected by depth if marine

VOCABULARY
biome p. 30
coniferous p. 32
deciduous p. 33
estuary p. 36

D 38 Unit: Ecology

Technology Resources

Have students visit **ClassZone.com** or use the CD-ROM for a cumulative review of concepts.

 CONTENT REVIEW

 CONTENT REVIEW CD-ROM

Engage students in a whole-class interactive review of Key Concepts. Edit content as you wish.

 POWER PRESENTATIONS

Reviewing Vocabulary

Write a statement describing how the terms in each pair are similar and different.

1. biotic, abiotic

2. producer, consumer

3. food chain, food web

The table shows the meanings of word roots that are used in many science terms.

Root	Meaning
bio–	life
ecos–	house
–ogy	study of

Use the information in the table to write definitions for the following terms.

4. ecology

5. biome

6. ecosystem

Reviewing Key Concepts

Multiple Choice *Choose the letter of the best answer.*

7. Which best describes the components of an ecosystem?
   a. light, water, soil, and temperature
   b. autotrophs and heterotrophs
   c. biotic and abiotic factors
   d. producers, consumers, and decomposers

8. What is the primary source of energy for most ecosystems?
   a. water   c. carbon
   b. nitrogen   d. sunlight

9. What is the process by which the water in rivers, lakes, and oceans is converted to a gas and moves into the atmosphere?
   a. precipitation   c. condensation
   b. evaporation   d. transpiration

10. The process called nitrogen fixation is essential for life on Earth. Which of the following is an example of nitrogen fixation?
    a. Plants take in nitrogen gas from the atmosphere.
    b. Animals take in nitrogen gas from the atmosphere.
    c. Water absorbs nitrogen.
    d. Bacteria convert nitrogen gas into a form that plants can use.

11. Which organism is a decomposer?
    a. vulture   c. musk ox
    b. sunflower   d. fungi

12. How are decomposers important in an ecosystem?
    a. They make atmospheric nitrogen available to plants in a usable form.
    b. They convert organic matter into more complex compounds.
    c. They are an important source of food for scavengers.
    d. They break down organic matter into simpler compounds.

13. What factor is least important in determining the plant life in a biome?
    a. average annual rainfall
    b. average annual temperature
    c. the type of soil
    d. the type of animals living there

Short Answer *Write a short answer to each question.*

14. Write a paragraph to describe how carbon dioxide gas in the atmosphere can become part of the carbon compounds found inside animals.

15. Write a paragraph to explain how the amount of available energy changes as you move from producers to consumers in a food web.

16. Write a paragraph to describe one important way in which the flow of energy through ecosystems is different from the cycling of matter.

Reviewing Vocabulary

1. Both are parts of the ecosystem. Biotic are the living parts, and abiotic are the nonliving parts.

2. Producers and consumers are parts of the ecosystem. Consumers get their food from producers directly by eating them, or indirectly by eating other consumers that eat producers.

3. Both are feeding relationships. A food chain is a single relationship; food webs have many interconnected food chains in the same ecosystem.

4. ecology: from ecos– meaning "house" and –ology meaning "study of"—the scientific study of how organisms interact with their environment and all the other organisms in that environment.

5. biome: from bio– meaning "life"— a region on Earth with similar types of plants and animals.

6. ecosystem: from ecos– meaning "house" and system, parts that work together—a particular environment and all the living things supported by it.

Reviewing Key Concepts

7. c	11. d
8. d	12. d
9. b	13. d
10. d	

14. Plants use carbon dioxide in the air to produce sugars in a process called photosynthesis. Then animals eat the plants. The compounds in the plants become part of the animals.

15. Available energy decreases as you move from the bottom to the top of the energy pyramid. Each time energy moves from one level to the next, it changes form, and some energy is lost in that process. Some of the energy is also used by the organisms at each level.

16. Sample answers: Cycles involve movement of matter through the environment. A cycle happens over and over again. The flow of energy involves food webs in which energy and matter are transferred from one organism to the next as organisms eat and are eaten.

ASSESSMENT RESOURCES

UNIT ASSESSMENT BOOK
- Chapter Test A, pp. 7–10
- Chapter Test B, pp. 11–14
- Chapter Test C, pp. 15–18
- Alternative Assessment, pp. 19–20

SPANISH ASSESSMENT BOOK
Spanish Chapter Test, pp. 65–68

Technology Resources

Edit test items and answer choices.

 Test Generator CD-ROM

Visit **ClassZone.com** to extend test practice.

 Test Practice

Thinking Critically

17. a food web; a model of the feeding relationships in an ecosystem

18. producer: cattails; primary: mosquito, slug; secondary: frog; tertiary: water snake

19. shrew next to salamander, arrow from slug to shrew, arrow from salamander to shrew, arrow from shrew to water snake

20. about one-thousandth

21. Decomposers do not produce food. They break down dead plant and animal matter for food.

22. desert, taiga, grassland, deciduous forest, tropical rain forest

23. Climate, temperature, rainfall, and available water determine type of plants that will grow. Some animals migrate to different biomes during the year. In theory, this makes plants a more reliable indicator of difference.

24. Diagrams should show correct relationships among various aquatic biomes; saltiness of water and amount of oxygen available in water differ among these biomes.

25. Answers might include a description of the living and nonliving things in a home, home climate, and that a home environment is a controlled environment.

26. Sample answer: a summer drought killed grasses and plant life, which were food for small animals.

the BIG idea

27. Sample answer: I would add organisms you can't see such as decomposers and plankton. I would mention soil, air, and sunlight as well.

28. Student answers should use the eight listed terms correctly in a paragraph(s).

UNIT PROJECTS

Give students the appropriate Unit Project worksheets from the Unit Resource Book for their projects. Both directions and rubrics can be used as a guide.

 Unit Projects, pp. 5–10

Thinking Critically

Use the diagram to answer the next four questions.

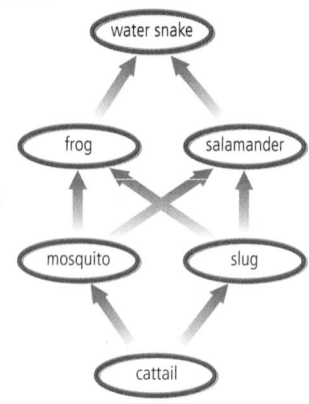

17. **CONNECT** What does the diagram above represent and how does it relate to energy in an ecosystem?

18. **CLASSIFY** Identify each of the animals in the diagram above as a producer, primary consumer, or secondary consumer or tertiary consumer.

19. **APPLY** Another animal that is found in many wetlands ecosystems is the shrew. The shrew eats salamanders and slugs and is eaten by water snakes. Copy the diagram above and show how you would add the shrew to the diagram.

20. **CONNECT** Use the diagram above to make an energy pyramid. If only one-tenth of the energy available at each level is passed on to the next higher level, how much of the energy in a cattail is transferred to a salamander?

21. **SYNTHESIZE** Why would it be difficult to show a decomposer as part of an energy pyramid?

22. **RANK** Arrange the following list of biomes according to the relative amounts of precipitation in each, going from the least amount to the most: grassland, desert, deciduous forest, taiga, tropical rain forest.

23. **SYNTHESIZE** Why are plants but not animals considered an important factor in classifying a land biome?

24. **SUMMARIZE** Draw a diagram that illustrates aquatic biomes. On your diagram label the following: freshwater river, freshwater lake, estuary, coastal zone, open ocean zone. How do abiotic factors differ among these biomes?

25. **COMPARE AND CONTRAST** In what ways is your home like an ecosystem? In what ways is it different?

26. **APPLY** Describe a change in an abiotic factor that affected living factors in an ecosystem near you.

the BIG idea

27. **CLASSIFY** Look again at the photograph on pages 6–7. Now that you have finished the chapter, how would you change or add details to your answer to the question on the photograph?

28. **SYNTHESIZE** Write one or more paragraphs describing how matter and energy together support life in an ecosystem. You may use examples from one specific ecosystem if you wish. In your description, use each of the following terms. Underline each term in your answer.

ecosystem	decomposer
food web	nitrogen cycle
producer	carbon cycle
primary consumer	secondary consumer

UNIT PROJECTS

If you are doing a unit project, make a folder for your project. Include in your folder a list of the resources you will need, the date on which the project is due, and a schedule to track your progress. Begin gathering data.

MONITOR AND RETEACH

If students have trouble with concepts in items 17–21, have them review the energy pyramid on p. 28, then make pie graphs with captions to show relative amount of energy available. Tell students the pie graphs are a visual memory device and the data is estimated.

Students may benefit from summarizing one or more sections of the chapter.

R Summarizing the Chapter, pp. 80–81

Standardized Test Practice

For practice on your state test, go to . . .
TEST PRACTICE
CLASSZONE.COM

Interpreting Graphs

Choose the letter of the best response.

The graphs below show average monthly temperature and precipitation for one year in Staunton, Virginia, an area located in a temperate deciduous forest biome.

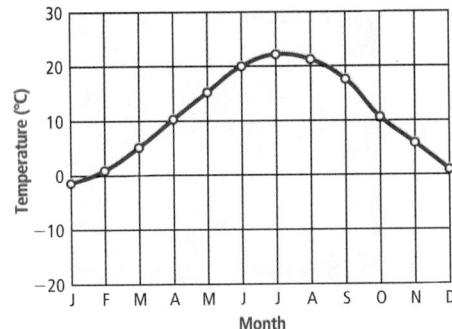

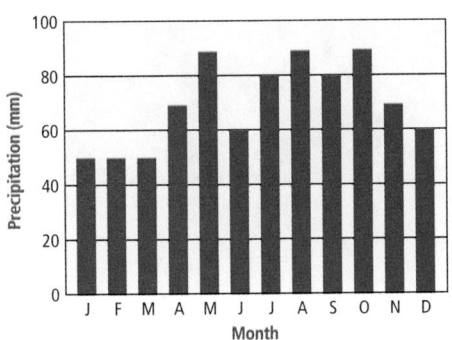

SOURCE: NASA

1. What was the average temperature during July?
- **a.** 20°
- **b.** 10°
- **c.** 23°
- **d.** 0°

2. Which months had the most precipitation?
- **a.** January, February, March
- **b.** May, August, October
- **c.** July, August, September
- **d.** December, January, February

3. What were conditions during May?
- **a.** warm and moist
- **b.** warm and dry
- **c.** cool and moist
- **d.** cool and dry

4. Which temperature is closest to the average temperature for the year shown?
- **a.** about 16°
- **b.** about 0°
- **c.** about 20°
- **d.** about 10°

5. How much precipitation would you estimate fell as snow in the year shown?
- **a.** less than 50 mm
- **b.** between 50 and 100 mm
- **c.** between 100 and 200 mm
- **d.** over 200 mm

Extended Response

6. Most of the United States is part of a temperate deciduous forest biome. The deciduous forest biome has four seasons. Trees in this biome lose their leaves yearly. Use this information, as well as the information in the graphs, to describe the seasons in the temperate deciduous forest biome.

7. Write a paragraph in which you describe a typical ecosystem in your city or town. In your answer include biotic factors such as plants, animals, and other organisms. Also include abiotic factors such as light, temperature, soil, and water. Finish your description by saying how you and other humans affect the ecosystem.

Interpreting Graphs

1. c	*4. d*
2. b	*5. b*
3. a	

Extended Response

6. RUBRIC

4 points for a response that includes complete sentences and temperature and precipitation information for a temperate deciduous forest and refers to information in both graphs:

Sample: This biome is characterized by trees that lose their leaves yearly. There are four seasons in this biome. Average precipitation is highest in the spring, summer, and autumn months, the months in which trees have their leaves. Average temperatures range from 20° C in summer months to around 0° C in winter.

3 points includes complete sentences and information about a temperate deciduous forest
2 points includes complete sentences and refers to information in the graphs
1 point attempts to accomplish the task, but does not meet the requirements

7. RUBRIC

4 points for a response that includes complete sentences and a description of biotic and abiotic factors, as well as human effects on the ecosystem:

Sample: In my town park there are ponds in the park that support fish, frogs, insects, and ducks. There are plants, shrubs, grass, and trees. Humans affect the ecosystem by walking on the grass and littering. Walking on the grass can kill the grass. Littering can affect the animals, plants, and water in the park. A piece of paper that is dropped can prevent a small plant from receiving enough light, and the plant may die.

3 points includes complete sentences and a description of biotic and abiotic factors
2 points includes complete sentences and human effect on the ecosystem
1 point attempts to accomplish the task, but does not meet the requirements

---

METACOGNITIVE ACTIVITY

Have students answer the following questions in their **Science Notebook:**

1. What ecosystems and biomes were you already familiar with? What new things have you learned about those places?

2. How do you see yourself taking part in an ecosystem?

3. What goals have you set for your Unit Project? What is the next step you will complete?

2 Interactions Within Ecosystems

Life Science
UNIFYING PRINCIPLES

PRINCIPLE 1 All living things share common characteristics.	**PRINCIPLE 2** All living things share common needs.	**PRINCIPLE 3** Living things meet their needs through interactions with the environment.	**PRINCIPLE 4** The types and numbers of living things change over time.

Unit: Ecology
BIG IDEAS

CHAPTER 1 **Ecosystems and Biomes** Matter and energy together support life within a certain environment.	**CHAPTER 2** **Interactions Within Ecosystems** Living things within an ecosystem interact with each other and the environment.	**CHAPTER 3** **Human Impact on Ecosystems** Humans and human population growth affect the environment.

CHAPTER 2
KEY CONCEPTS

SECTION **2.1**	SECTION **2.2**	SECTION **2.3**
Groups of living things interact within ecosystems. 1. Organisms occupy specific living areas. 2. The environment can be organized into five levels. 3. Patterns exist in populations.	**Organisms can interact in different ways.** 1. Organisms interact in different ways. 2. The survival of one species might depend on another species. 3. Interactions in an ecosystem are complex.	**Ecosystems are always changing.** 1. Populations change over time. 2. Ecosystems change over time.

 The Big Idea Flow Chart is available on p. T9 in the **UNIT TRANSPARENCY BOOK.**

Previewing Content

2.1 Groups of living things interact within ecosystems. pp. 45–53

1. Organisms occupy specific living areas.
Organisms are members of the same **species** if they are similar to each other and produce offspring that can breed. Members of the same species who live in a particular **habitat** constitute a **population.** The habitat provides everything the population needs to survive.

Organisms perform roles, called **niches,** in the habitat. For instance, grasses on a prairie anchor the topsoil and provide food for grazing animals. Populations that live together and interact form a **community.**

2. The environment can be organized into five levels.
Beyond the community are higher levels of organization.
- Organisms and their local environments constitute an **ecosystem.**
- Places that are similar in terms of climate and vegetation are called **biomes.** These are broadly defined and have world-wide distribution.

The diagram shows the levels of organization at a glance.

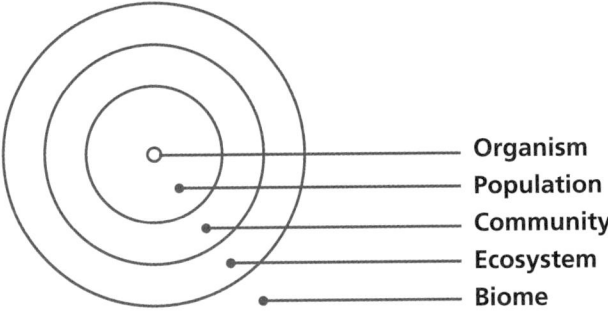

— Organism
— Population
— Community
— Ecosystem
— Biome

3. Patterns exist in populations.
The size of a population may change over time as a result of factors such as the change of seasons or interaction with another species. Spatial patterns of population distribution may result from the way organisms gather resources or from their need for mutual protection.

Common Misconceptions

HUMANS IN AN ECOSYSTEM Students commonly think that they themselves are not part of ecosystems. Many children view the lives of humans as separate and different from those of plants, animals, and microorganisms. Each species of living thing is unique, yet all share common needs and characteristics. All species—including humans—live and interact in ecosystems.

 This misconception is addressed on p. 49.

2.2 Organisms can interact in different ways. pp. 54–62

1. Organisms interact in different ways.
A food chain is made up of producers and consumers, although the distinction between the two groups is not always clear-cut. An animal, for example, could be predator, prey, or both.

When more than one organism, whether of the same species or not, needs the same resources, the organisms will **compete.** Some organisms, such as ants or packs of hunters, **cooperate** to improve their survival.

2. The survival of one species might depend on another.
Individuals of two species may have a close relationship called **symbiosis.** Three kinds of symbiosis are commonly recognized.
- **Mutualism** occurs when both species in the symbiosis benefit from the interaction.
- **Commensalism** occurs if one species benefits while the other is unharmed and unaffected.
- **Parasitism** occurs when one species is harmed while the other benefits.

The table shows how the three symbiotic relationships can be beneficial (**+**), neutral (**0**), or harmful (**−**).

Symbiosis		
Relationship Between Species	One Species	Other Species
mutualism	+	+
commensalism	0	+
parasitism	−	+

3. Interactions in an ecosystem are complex.
Relationships and interactions do not exist in isolation. Any one species can have a range of symbiotic or predatory relationships with many other species.

 MISCONCEPTION DATABASE
CLASSZONE.COM Background on student misconceptions

2.3 Ecosystems are always changing.
pp. 63–69

1. Populations change over time.
Population size changes in response to food supply, predation, the seasons, and birth rates. A **limiting factor,** such as water, light, or food, can affect population survival and growth. The **carrying capacity** of an environment is the maximum population it can support. At carrying capacity a population stops growing.

2. Ecosystems change over time.
Succession is a gradual series of changes that take place in an ecosystem after a disturbance.

- **Primary succession** starts from an environment that is mostly empty of life. After the retreat of a glacier, for example, or on new rock produced by a volcano, life can begin to return. **Pioneer species** move into the barren environment and begin the task of creating soil.
- **Secondary succession** occurs in areas that have soil with roots and seeds below the surface. In such cases, life already survives. Living things produce new generations and attract the return of diverse species. Secondary succession may begin after a fire or flood disturbs the ecosystem.

The pictures on the right show the difference at the start of two successional sequences. In both types of natural succession, plants may facilitate the establishment of other plants by creating a hospitable habitat. Some species, however, create conditions that prevent competitors from moving in.

Primary succession   Secondary succession

A key difference between primary and secondary succession is the presence of soil in the environment at the start of the series of changes.

Common Misconceptions

MATTER CHANGES FORM Most students think that matter can be destroyed. They often think that dead or decaying matter rots away to nothing. In fact, living and decaying matter is constantly transforming, changing from one form into another.

TE This misconception is addressed on p. 66.

Previewing Labs

EXPLORE the BIG idea

How Do Living Things Interact Where You Live? p. 43
Students observe how plants and animals interact in an environment.

TIME 10 minutes
MATERIALS notebook, outdoor area, hand lens (optional)

How Many Roles Can a Living Thing Have in an Ecosystem? p. 43
Students analyze how an organism fits with an environment.

TIME 10 minutes
MATERIALS notebook, outdoor area, hand lens (optional)

Internet Activity: Carrying Capacity, p. 43
Students change a population size in a virtual habitat to explore carrying capacity.

TIME 20 minutes
MATERIALS computer with Internet access

SECTION 2.1

EXPLORE Counting Animals, p. 45
Students use rice and graph paper to estimate population size.

TIME 10 minutes
MATERIALS handful of rice, large-grid graph paper, marker, calculator

---

CHAPTER INVESTIGATION
Estimating Populations, pp. 52–53
Students use beans in a paper bag to learn the mark-recapture method of estimating populations. They model the effects of disease on their populations and their estimates.

TIME 40 minutes
MATERIALS about 100 white kidney beans, paper bag, 2 colored markers, calculator

---

SECTION 2.2

INVESTIGATE Species Interactions, p. 57
Students use cardboard and paper pieces to analyze the effects of predators on prey and vice versa over 15 generations.

TIME 30 minutes
MATERIALS 20 10-cm squares of cardboard, 200 3-cm squares of paper, masking tape, graph paper, 2 colored pencils

---

SECTION 2.3

EXPLORE Population Growth, p. 63
Students observe the effects of different sugar concentrations on the growth of yeast.

TIME 20 minutes
MATERIALS 3 clear plastic cups, warm water, sugar, dry yeast, measuring spoons, measuring cup, stirring rod, marker, ruler

---

INVESTIGATE Limiting Factors, p. 65
Students design an experiment to test whether space is a limiting factor for the growth of radishes.

TIME 20 minutes
MATERIALS paper cups, potting soil, radish seeds, water, pencil, ruler

---

 Additional INVESTIGATION, Prey Survival, A, B, & C, pp. 130–138; Teacher Instructions, pp. 200–201

Previewing Chapter Resources

	INTEGRATED TECHNOLOGY	LABS AND ACTIVITIES

CHAPTER 2
Interactions Within Ecosystems

INTEGRATED TECHNOLOGY

 CLASSZONE.COM
- eEdition Plus
- EasyPlanner Plus
- Misconception Database
- Content Review
- Test Practice
- Resource Centers
- Internet Activity: Carrying Capacity
- Math Tutorial

 SCILINKS.ORG
SCLINKS

 CD-ROMS
- eEdition
- EasyPlanner
- Power Presentations
- Content Review
- Lab Generator
- Test Generator

AUDIO CDS
- Audio Readings
- Audio Readings in Spanish

LABS AND ACTIVITIES

PE EXPLORE the Big Idea, p. 43
- How Do Living Things Interact Where You Live?
- How Many Roles Can a Living Thing Have in an Ecosystem?
- Internet Activity: Carrying Capacity

R **UNIT RESOURCE BOOK**
Unit Projects, pp. 5–10

 Lab Generator CD-ROM
Generate customized labs.

SECTION
2.1 Groups of living things interact within ecosystems.
pp. 45–53

Time: 3 periods (1.5 blocks)
 Lesson Plan, pp. 82–83

 UNIT TRANSPARENCY BOOK
- Big Idea Flow Chart, p. T9
- Daily Vocabulary Scaffolding, p. T10
- Note-Taking Model, p. T11
- 3-Minute Warm-Up, p. T12
- "Levels in the Environment" Visual, p. T14

PE
- EXPLORE Counting Animals, p. 45
- CHAPTER INVESTIGATION, Estimating Populations, pp. 52–53

R **UNIT RESOURCE BOOK**
CHAPTER INVESTIGATION, Estimating Populations, A, B, & C, pp. 121–129

SECTION
2.2 Organisms can interact in different ways.
pp. 54–62

Time: 2 periods (1 block)
 Lesson Plan, pp. 92–93

 RESOURCE CENTER, Symbiotic Relationships

 UNIT TRANSPARENCY BOOK
- Daily Vocabulary Scaffolding, p. T10
- 3-Minute Warm-Up, p. T12

PE
- INVESTIGATE Species Interactions, p. 57
- Think Science, p. 62

R **UNIT RESOURCE BOOK**
- Datasheet, Species Interactions, p. 101
- Additional INVESTIGATION, Prey Survival, A, B, & C, pp. 130–138

SECTION
2.3 Ecosystems are always changing.
pp. 63–69

Time: 3 periods (1.5 blocks)
 Lesson Plan, pp. 103–104

- **RESOURCE CENTER,** Succession
- **MATH TUTORIAL**

 UNIT TRANSPARENCY BOOK
- Big Idea Flow Chart, p. T9
- Daily Vocabulary Scaffolding, p. T10
- 3-Minute Warm-Up, p. T13
- Chapter Outline, pp. T15–T16

PE
- EXPLORE Population Growth, p. 63
- INVESTIGATE Limiting Factors, p. 65
- Math in Science, p. 69

R **UNIT RESOURCE BOOK**
- Datasheet, Limiting Factors, p. 112
- Math Support, p. 119
- Math Practice, p. 120

41F D

READING AND REINFORCEMENT

- Four Square, B22–23
- Outline, C43
- Daily Vocabulary Scaffolding, H1–8

 UNIT RESOURCE BOOK
- Vocabulary Practice, pp. 116–117
- Decoding Support, p. 118
- Summarizing the Chapter, pp. 139–140

 Audio Readings CD
Listen to Pupil Edition.

 Audio Readings in Spanish CD
Listen to Pupil Edition in Spanish.

 UNIT RESOURCE BOOK
- Reading Study Guide, A & B, pp. 84–87
- Spanish Reading Study Guide, pp. 88–89
- Challenge and Extension, p. 90
- Reinforcing Key Concepts, p. 91

 UNIT RESOURCE BOOK
- Reading Study Guide, A & B, pp. 94–97
- Spanish Reading Study Guide, pp. 98–99
- Challenge and Extension, p. 100
- Challenge Reading, pp. 114–115
- Reinforcing Key Concepts, p. 102

 UNIT RESOURCE BOOK
- Reading Study Guide, A & B, pp. 105–108
- Spanish Reading Study Guide, pp. 109–110
- Challenge and Extension, p. 111
- Reinforcing Key Concepts, p. 113

ASSESSMENT

- Chapter Review, pp. 71–72
- Standardized Test Practice, p. 73

 UNIT ASSESSMENT BOOK
- Diagnostic Test, pp. 21–22
- Chapter Test, A, B, & C, pp. 26–37
- Alternative Assessment, pp. 38–39

 Spanish Chapter Test, pp. 69–70

 Test Generator CD-ROM
Generate customized tests.

 Lab Generator CD-ROM
Rubrics for Labs

 Ongoing Assessment, pp. 46–50

 Section 2.1 Review, p. 51

 UNIT ASSESSMENT BOOK
Section 2.1 Quiz, p. 23

 Ongoing Assessment, pp. 54, 56, 58–61

 Section 2.2 Review, p. 61

 UNIT ASSESSMENT BOOK
Section 2.2 Quiz, p. 24

 Ongoing Assessment, pp. 65, 67

 Section 2.3 Review, p. 68

 UNIT ASSESSMENT BOOK
Section 2.3 Quiz, p. 25

STANDARDS

National Standards
A.2–8, A.9.a–c, A.9.e–f, C.1.a, C.4.a, C.4.d, E.2, E.3, G.1.b

See p. 42 for the standards.

National Standards
A.2–7, A.9.a–c, A.9.e–f, C.1.a, C.4.a, G.1.b

National Standards
A.2–8, A.9.a–c, A.9.e–f, C.4.d, G.1.b

National Standards
A.2–8, A.9.a–c, A.9.e, C.4.d, E.2, E.3, G.1.b

Previewing Resources for Differentiated Instruction

CHAPTER INVESTIGATION

Leveled resources present the same concepts for different abilities.

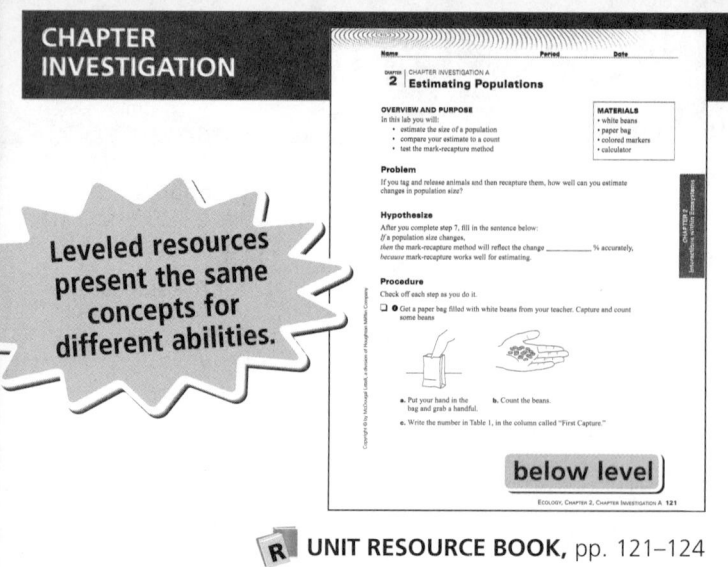

below level

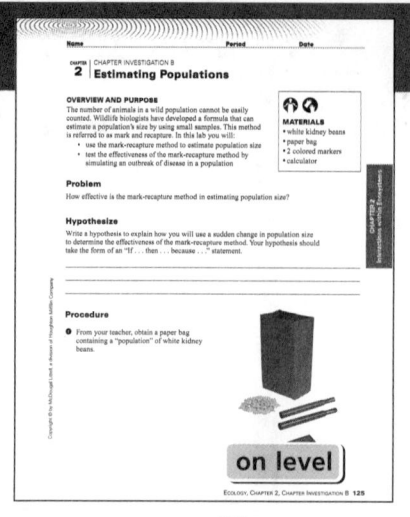

on level

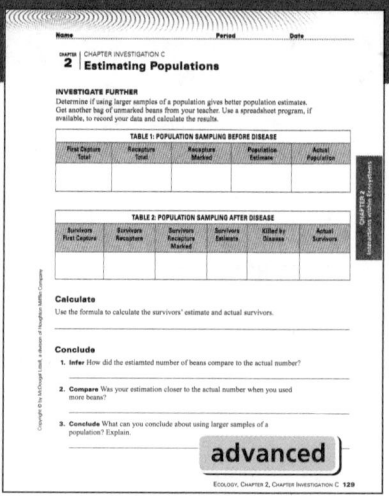

advanced

R UNIT RESOURCE BOOK, pp. 121–124

R pp. 125–128

R pp. 125–129

READING STUDY GUIDE

Reading Study Guide is also in Spanish.

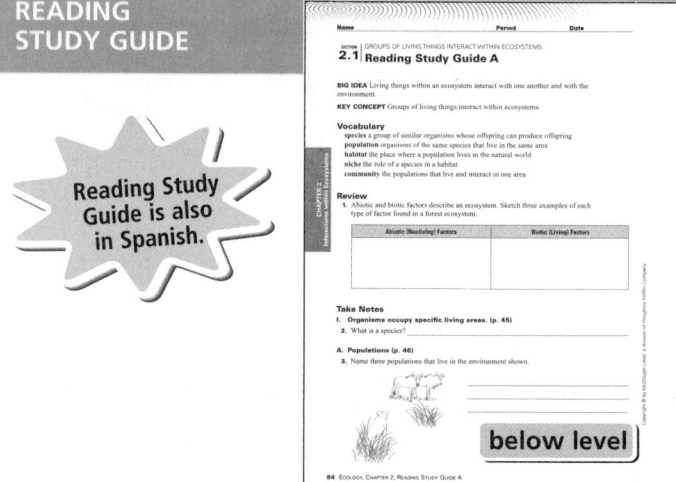

below level

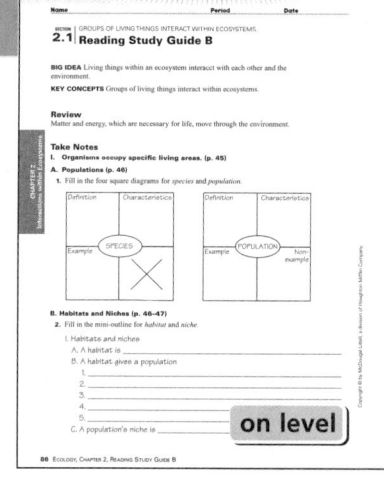

on level

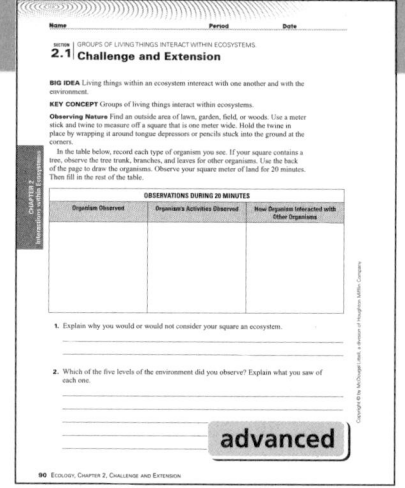

advanced

R UNIT RESOURCE BOOK, pp. 84–85

R pp. 86–87

R p. 90

CHAPTER TEST

Chapter Test is also in Spanish.

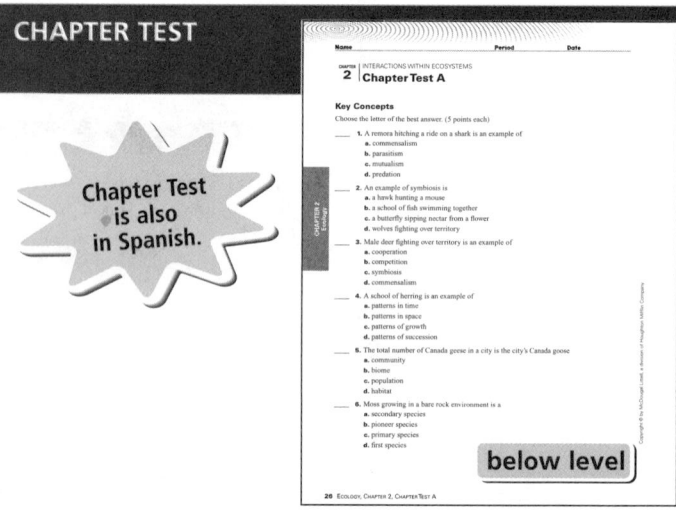

below level

on level

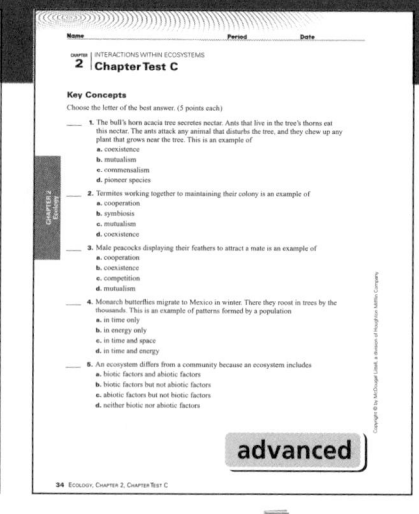

advanced

A UNIT ASSESSMENT BOOK, pp. 26–29

A pp. 30–33

A pp. 34–37

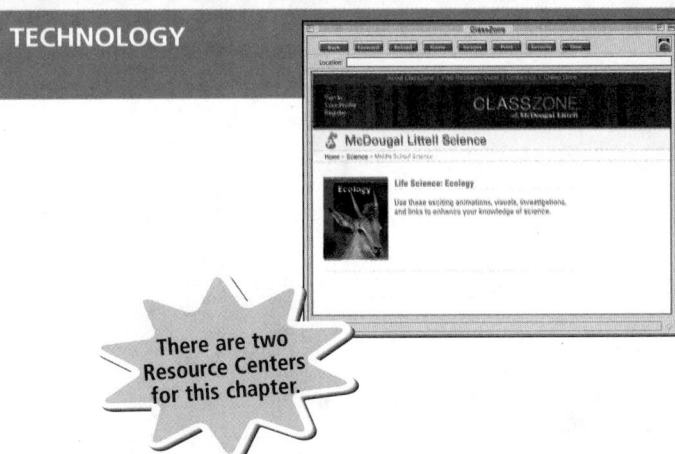

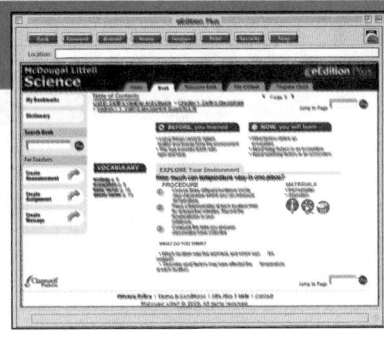

There are two Resource Centers for this chapter.

CLASSZONE.COM

CD/CD-ROMS

CLASSZONE.COM

VISUAL CONTENT

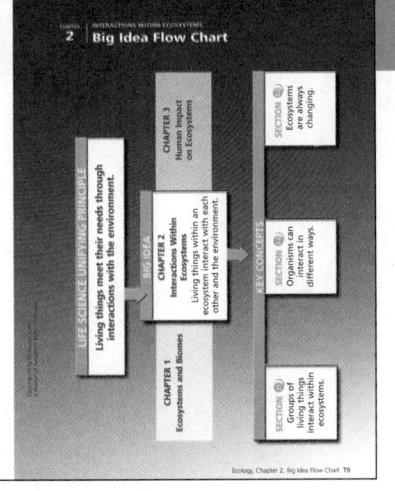

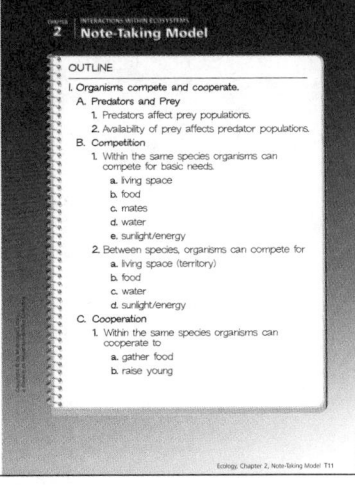

 **UNIT TRANSPARENCY BOOK,** p. T9

 p. T11

 p. T14

MORE SUPPORT

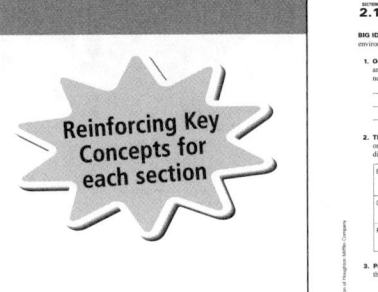

Reinforcing Key Concepts for each section

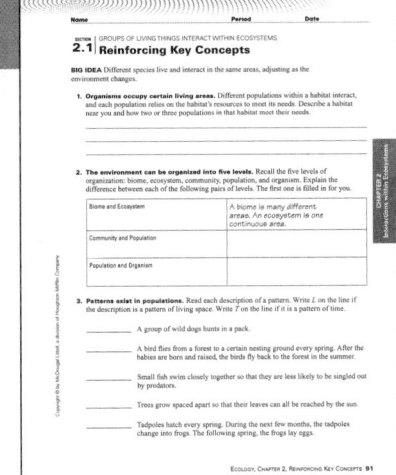

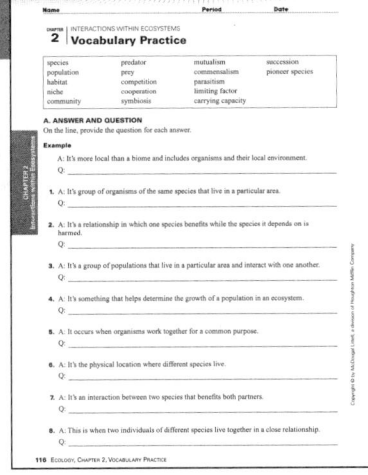

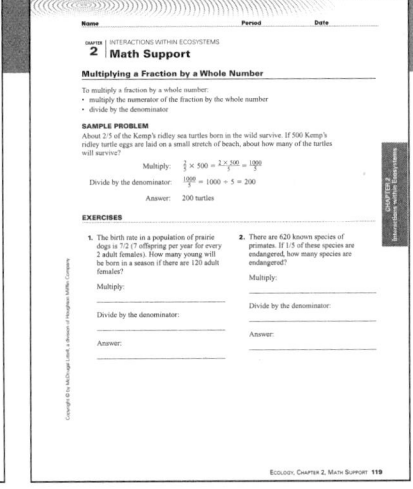

UNIT RESOURCE BOOK, p. 91

pp. 116–117

p. 119

INTRODUCE

the BIG idea

Have students look at the photograph of the reef lizardfish with the goby inside its mouth. Discuss how the question in the box links to the Big Idea:

- Ask: How does the reef lizardfish seem to be interacting with the goby?

- Have students brainstorm a quick class list of ways living things interact.

National Science Education Standards

Content

C.1.a Important levels of organization for living systems include cells, organs, tissues, organ systems, whole organisms, and ecosystems.

C.4.a A population consists of the individuals of a species together at a given place and time. All populations in an area and physical factors compose an ecosystem.

C.4.d The number of organisms an ecosystem can support depends on the resources available and abiotic factors.

Process

A.2–8 Design and conduct an investigation; use tools to gather and interpret data; use evidence to describe, predict, explain, model; think critically to make relationships between evidence and explanation; recognize different explanations and predictions; communicate scientific procedures and explanations; use mathematics.

A.9.a–c, A.9.e–f Understand scientific inquiry by using different investigations, methods, mathematics, and explanations based on logic and evidence.

E.2, E.3 Design a product or solution, implement a solution.

G.1.b Science requires different abilities.

D **42** Unit: Ecology

---

the BIG idea

Living things within an ecosystem interact with each other and the environment.

> **How do living things interact?**

Key Concepts

SECTION 2.1 Groups of living things interact within ecosystems. Learn about how different organisms share living areas, interact in larger communities, and show different patterns within those communities.

SECTION 2.2 Organisms can interact in different ways. Learn about the different types of interactions in an ecosystem, including competition, cooperation, and symbiosis.

SECTION 2.3 Ecosystems are always changing. Learn about the limits and boundaries of organisms within an ecosystem and how ecosystems may change over time.

Internet Preview

CLASSZONE.COM
Chapter 2 online resources: Content Review, Simulation, two Resource Centers, Math Tutorial, Test Practice

D 42 Unit: Ecology

INTERNET PREVIEW

CLASSZONE.COM For student use with the following pages:

Review and Practice
- Content Review, pp. 44, 70
- Math Tutorial: Multiplying Fractions and Whole Numbers, p. 69
- Test Practice, p. 73

Activities and Resources
- Internet Activity: Carrying Capacity, p. 43
- Resource Centers: Symbiotic Relationships, p. 59; Succession, p. 67

NSTA scilinks.org **SCiLINKS**

Populations and Communities
Code: MDL002

EXPLORE (the BIG idea)

How Do Living Things Interact Where You Live?

Take your notebook outside. Observe how different living things interact. Record your observations.

Observe and Think Do the interactions you see benefit both living things or just one? Do they involve just animals or plants and animals?

How Many Roles Can a Living Thing Have in an Ecosystem?

While you are outside, choose an organism within your view and think about how it fits into the ecosystem.

Observe and Think In what way does the organism fit into feeding relationships in the ecosystem? What are some other roles the organism plays?

Internet Activity: Carrying Capacity

Go to **ClassZone.com** to simulate the carrying capacity of an area for a population of deer.

Observe and Think What factors other than available food might affect the carrying capacity for a popuation of deer?

NSTA *sci*LINKS
scilinks.org
Populations and Communities **Code: MDL002**

TEACHING WITH TECHNOLOGY

Spreadsheets and Visual Displays Students could use a spreadsheet for recording data while investigating predator-prey relationships, p. 57. They could also enter and plot the data on a graphing calculator.

Digital Camera You might want to take daily photographs of the radish plants, p. 65. Students could use the photographs to construct a presentation of the experiment. They could create a time-lapse slideshow with fades.

EXPLORE (the BIG idea)

These inquiry-based activities are appropriate for use at home or as a supplement to classroom instruction.

How Do Living Things Interact Where You Live?

PURPOSE To demonstrate to students how plants and animals interact, and to have students recognize that they are part of the environment.

TIP *10 min.* If you need to do the activity indoors, students could observe interactions in a fish tank.

Answers should mention plants, animals, and resources, and should describe various behaviors.

REVISIT after p. 57.

How Many Roles Can a Living Thing Have in an Ecosystem?

PURPOSE To introduce students to the concept of roles in an ecosystem.

TIP *10 min.* If you cannot go outdoors, photographs or videotapes might help students examine one organism with many roles. It is important to view the organism in context.

Answers should mention feeding other organisms, and the various ways that the organism meets its own needs.

REVISIT after p. 47.

Internet Activity: Carrying Capacity

PURPOSE To model how carrying capacity can limit population size in an environment.

TIP *20 min.* You may wish to have students compare their results.

Answers might include predators, climate, human impact, and natural disasters.

REVISIT after p. 65.

PREPARE

◀ CONCEPT REVIEW

Activate Prior Knowledge

- Ask students to name some living and nonliving factors that make it possible to live in your town.
- Discuss how these factors affect different species in varying ways.
- Help students identify what biome they live in.

▶ TAKING NOTES

Outline

Students can rely on the blue and red headings in the textbook to form the basic structure of their outlines. In an outline, one idea hangs off another, which helps link the ideas in a student's memory. Encourage students to discuss how ideas in the outline are related. Encourage them to use their outlines to study.

Vocabulary Strategy

The four square diagram organizes all aspects of a word into a coherent pattern. By filling in their own words, students personalize their understanding. Be sure students know they can leave a square blank in the diagram. Many words, such as *species* and *habitat*, have no clear "Nonexamples."

Vocabulary and Note-Taking Resources

- Vocabulary Practice, pp. 116–117
- Decoding Support, p. 118

- Daily Vocabulary Scaffolding, p. T10
- Note-Taking Model, p. T11

- Four Square, B22–23
- Outline, C43
- Daily Vocabulary Scaffolding, H1–8

◀ CONCEPT REVIEW

- Ecosystems support life.
- Different ecosystems make up a biome.

◀ VOCABULARY REVIEW

producer p. 23   **food chain** p. 26
consumer p. 24   **food web** p. 26
interaction *See Glossary.*

CONTENT REVIEW
CLASSZONE.COM
Review concepts and vocabulary.

▶ TAKING NOTES

OUTLINE

As you read, copy the headings on your paper in the form of an outline. Then add notes in your own words that summarize what you read.

VOCABULARY STRATEGY

Write each new vocabulary term in the center of a **four square** diagram. Write notes in the squares around each term. Include definition, some characteristics, and some examples of the term. If possible, write some things that are not examples of the terms.

See the Note-Taking Handbook on pages R45–R51.

SCIENCE NOTEBOOK

I. Groups of living things interact within ecosystems.
  A. Organisms occupy specific living areas.
    1. populations: same species in one area
    2. habitat and niche: place where organisms live; role of organisms
    3. community: several populations living together

Definition	Characteristics
where something lives	supplies shelter and food
HABITAT	
Examples	Nonexamples
a tree is a habitat for a bird	(you won't always use this square)

CHECK READINESS

Administer the Diagnostic Test to determine students' readiness for new science content and their mastery of requisite math skills.

 Diagnostic Test, pp. 21–22

Technology Resources

Students needing content and math skills should visit **ClassZone.com**.

- **CONTENT REVIEW**
- **MATH TUTORIAL**
- **CONTENT REVIEW CD-ROM**

KEY CONCEPT

2.1 Groups of living things interact within ecosystems.

◀ **BEFORE, you learned**

- Abiotic and biotic factors interact in an ecosystem
- Matter and energy necessary for life move through the environment

▶ **NOW, you will learn**

- How groups of organisms interact in an ecosystem
- About levels of organization in an ecosystem
- About living patterns of different groups of organisms

VOCABULARY

species p. 45
population p. 46
habitat p. 46
niche p. 47
community p. 48

EXPLORE Counting Animals

How can you use a grid to estimate the number of animals in an area?

PROCEDURE

1. Mark off an area on the graph paper as shown. Count the number of large squares in that area.

2. Use a handful of rice to represent a group of animals. Spread the rice evenly within the area you marked. Count the number of "animals" inside one large square.

3. Use a calculator to multiply the counts from steps 1 and 2. This will give you an estimate of the total number of "animals." Check your answer by counting all the grains of rice.

MATERIALS

- handful of rice
- large-grid graph paper
- marker
- calculator

WHAT DO YOU THINK?

- How close was your estimate to the actual number?
- What would prevent a scientist from making an actual count of animals in an area?

Organisms occupy specific living areas.

On a walk through the woods, you may see many different plants and animals. These organisms, like all living things, depend on their environment to meet their needs. The particular types of living things you see will depend on the characteristics of the area you are visiting.

Scientists group living things according to their shared characteristics. The smallest grouping is the species. Scientists consider organisms to be members of the same **species** (SPEE-sheez) if the organisms are so similar that they can produce offspring that can also produce offspring. Members of a species can successfully reproduce.

READING TiP

The terms *species, specific,* and *special* come from the same Latin root meaning "kind." A species is a kind, or type, of organism.

Chapter 2: **Interactions Within Ecosystems** 45 **D**

2.1 FOCUS

◉ Set Learning Goals

Students will

- Describe how groups of organisms interact.
- Analyze different levels of organization in the environment.
- Recognize patterns found in groups of organisms.
- Use common items to estimate population size.

◀ 3-Minute Warm-Up

Display Transparency 12 or copy this exercise on the board:

Imagine that a pond in the park is a thriving ecosystem. A brick wall is built to separate the pond from a new playground. The wall is high enough to keep stray kickballs and other toys from falling into the pond. What might be the effect of the wall on the ecosystem of the pond? *Sample answer: The wall will reduce sunlight reaching the pond. Some organisms may die from lack of light; organisms that like shade may increase. The wall may also affect water runoff.*

 3-Minute Warm-Up, p. T12

2.1 MOTIVATE

EXPLORE Counting Animals

PURPOSE To introduce a scientific method for estimating populations

TIPS *10 min.* You might put sample counts for one column on the board. Prompt students to think about how this method would work for grasshoppers in a field.

WHAT DO YOU THINK? *Estimates should be within 80% accuracy or better. Possible limitations: vast numbers, motion, hidden locations of nests and homes, similar coloring, or similar appearance.*

2.1 INSTRUCT

Teach from Visuals

To help students connect the three photographs, remind them of what they learned in Chapter 1: matter cycles through ecosystems, and energy flows through ecosystems. Ask:

• What are some activities of the three species in the photographs? *growing, breathing, photosynthesis, getting water, eating, moving*

• How might the activities move and transform matter in the ecosystem? *Sample: drinking or absorbing water moves it inside an organism. The water can become part of that organism's structure.*

• What effect do you think these species might have on each other? *All use water; cacti release oxygen, which the crabs and the iguana breathe; iguana wastes fertilize the cacti; the crabs clean the beach.*

Ongoing Assessment

 CHECK YOUR READING *Answer: A population exists within a certain boundary. A species may exist in many places worldwide.*

Galápagos Island Populations

A population is a group of the same organisms that live in the same area.

 Cacti

 Crabs

 Iguanas

 VOCABULARY Add a four square for *population* to your notebook. Include the word *habitat* in your diagram.

Populations

 A Scientists use the term **population** to mean a group of organisms of the same species that live in a particular area. In a way, this is similar to the population of people who live in a particular city or town. You can then think of those people who live in different cities or towns as belonging to different populations. It is the boundary of an area that defines a population. In the study of ecology, members of the same species that live in different areas belong to different populations.

A biological population can be a group of animals or a group of plants. It can be a group of bacteria or fungi or any other living thing. Populations of many different species will be found living in the same area. For example, the photographs above show different populations of organisms that all live in the same place—on one of the Galápagos Islands. The island has a population of cacti, a population of crabs, and a population of iguanas.

 **CHECK YOUR READING** What is the difference between a species and a population?

Habitats and Niches

 B The Galápagos Islands are a small group of volcanic islands, off the coast of South America, that are famous for their unusual plant and animal life. These islands are the **habitat**—the physical location—where these plants and animals live. Island habitats have certain physical characteristics that describe them, including the amount of precipitation, a range of temperatures, and the quality of the soil. Different habitats have different characteristics.

DIFFERENTIATE INSTRUCTION

? More Reading Support

A How does a boundary define a population? *Members are within the boundary.*

B What is a habitat? *the natural home of a population*

English Learners Students new to English may find the following science words challenging: *environment, characteristics, offspring, reproduce, boundary (ies), precipitation, vegetation, fertilize, toxin.* Preview vocabulary by adding these words and their definitions to a Science Word Wall.

Students who are from South or Central America, Mexico, or the Southwest may be familiar with iguanas and cacti. They can share observations or knowledge.

Galápagos Island Habitat

This island habitat is home to many different populations.

Galápagos
Islands

cacti

crabs

iguanas

READING VISUALS What resources are available in this habitat?

A habitat is filled with different species, each of which depends on the habitat's resources to meet its needs. The characteristics of a habitat determine the species of plants that can grow there. The species of plants found in a habitat, in turn, determine the species of animals and other organisms that will do well there.

Different populations within a habitat interact. They are part of the flow of energy and matter through an ecosystem. For example, in the Galápagos Island scene above, the cacti capture the Sun's energy and store fresh water. They also provide food for the iguana, who eats the cactus leaves. The cactus is a producer and the iguana is a primary consumer. The crabs of the Galápagos are secondary consumers that feed on other shellfish. Each of these organisms has a role to play in the habitat, a role which is referred to as its **niche** (nihch).

The niche an organism fills in a habitat is not limited to its place in a food web. Plants provide nesting sites as well as food. The droppings left behind by animals fertilize soil and often spread seed. Generally, no two species will fill exactly the same niche in a habitat.

Chapter 2: **Interactions Within Ecosystems** 47 **D**

Teach from Visuals

To help students interpret the relationships shown in the illustration, ask:

• What niche do the crabs fill? *They pass matter and energy up the food chain to gulls and large fish. Some crabs clean the beach as they feed.*

• Which living thing in the picture might be a primary consumer? *iguanas* Why? *because they eat plants*

• Can you infer some animals or plants that aren't in the pictures but that you would expect to find in this habitat? *Sample answer: insects, birds, grasses, seaweed, fish*

Teach Difficult Concepts

Students may not fully understand the relationship between a species' habitat and its niche. Habitat is a location. Niche is a role. Different species may share a habitat, but each species fills a particular niche within that habitat. Using a familiar local habitat as an example, have students list elements of several species' niches.

EXPLORE the **BIG** idea

Revisit the activity and observations from "How Many Roles Can a Living Thing Have in an Ecosystem?" on p. 43. How have students' understandings changed?

Ongoing Assessment

Describe how groups of organisms interact.

Give an example of a population of organisms interacting with its habitat. *Sample answer: The cacti population stores fresh water and energy from sunlight.*

READING VISUALS *Answer: The cacti are green plants, so they are producers for this ecosystem. They are food and shelter for animals.*

DIFFERENTIATE INSTRUCTION

 **More Reading Support**

C What is a niche? *a species' role in a habitat*

D What things about an animal show us its niche? *what it eats or uses, what it is eaten by*

Advanced Have students name habitats other than those already listed—for example, rainforest or swamp. Challenge them to find plants, animals, or insects that live in these habitats, and to describe the niches of the organisms.

R Challenge and Extension, p. 90

Develop Critical Thinking

APPLY Have students discuss these examples of habitats: grassy field, pond, park. For each example, ask students to name some of the species that live in the habitat and to describe the niches they fill. *Sample answer: The meadow might contain grasses, worms, flowers, and insects. Insects feed on flowers and pollinate them. Worms loosen and fertilize the soil. Grasses anchor the soil and provide oxygen.*

Metacognitive Strategy

Ask students to restate the definitions for the five levels of organization in their own words. Encourage them to move from one to the next in order. What analogy or mnemonic device might help them recall the five levels?

Ongoing Assessment

Analyze different levels of organization in the environment.

Ask: Starting from an individual organism, describe the different levels into which scientists organize the environment. *An organism is a single living thing. Groups of individuals of the same species that live in the same area are a population. All living things within one ecosystem are a community. An ecosystem includes the living and nonliving factors in a local environment. A biome consists of similar places that have the same type of climate and vegetation.*

CHECK YOUR READING *Answer: A school community has many people that share the same space and use the same resources. A biological community has many organisms that share the same habitat and natural resources.*

Communities

Take a mental tour of your school. Note that you share space with people who do many different things—students, teachers, custodians, librarians, counselors, and many others. They all work together and help each other. We often say that a school is a community.

 E Scientists use the term *community* in a slightly different way. A biological **community** is a group of populations that live in a particular area and interact with one another. Cacti, iguanas, and crabs are part of the Galápagos Island community. This community also includes populations of tortoises, finches, fleas, bacteria, and many other species.

 **CHECK YOUR READING** How is a school community similar to a community of living things?

The environment can be organized into five levels.

OUTLINE Add the different levels of the environment to your outline. Make sure to explain each term in the supporting details.

? F The five terms—biome, ecosystem, community, population, and organism—describe the environment at different levels.

1 Biome A biome describes in very general terms the climate and types of plants that are found in similar places around the world.

2 Ecosystem Within each biome are many ecosystems. Inside an ecosystem, living and nonliving factors interact to form a stable system. An ecosystem is smaller than a biome and includes only organisms and their local environment.

3 Community A community is made up of the living components of the ecosystem. In a community, different plants, animals, and other organisms interact with each other.

4 Population A population is a group of organisms of the same species that live in the same area.

5 Organism An organism is a single individual animal, plant, fungus, or other living thing. As the picture on page 49 shows, an organism plays a part in each level of the environment.

Patterns exist in populations.

Members of a population settle themselves into the available living space in different ways, forming a pattern. Populations may be crowded together, be spread far apart, or live in small groups. A population may also show a pattern over time. The number of individuals in the population may rise and fall, depending on the season or other conditions, or as a result of interactions with other organisms.

DIFFERENTIATE INSTRUCTION

? More Reading Support

E What is a community? *many populations that interact in one area*

F Name 5 levels of the environment. *organism, population, community, ecosystem, biome*

English Learners Students will find the visual on p. 49 especially helpful. They can take notes in a step diagram, adding definitions in their own words.

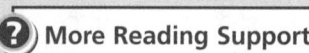

| biome |
| ecosystem |
| community |
| population |
| organism |

Levels in the Environment

Organisms living in an African savannah illustrate the different levels of the environment.

Grassland

① Biome
The African savannah is part of a grassland biome.

② Ecosystem
The community of organisms, along with water, soil, and other abiotic factors, make up an ecosystem.

③ Community
Populations of wildebeests, gazelles, lions, and grasses share the same living areas and resources. These and other populations form a savannah community.

④ Population
Gazelles travel together in herds looking for areas to graze in. The total number of gazelles in an ecosystem is called a population of gazelles.

⑤ Organism
The gazelle lives in various grassland habitats in eastern Africa and fills a particular niche.

READING ViSUALS Describe the gazelle's place in each level of the environment.

49 **D**

DIFFERENTIATE INSTRUCTION

Advanced Challenge advanced students to choose a different biome, and create a poster or illustration similar to the one on this page showing the relationship of one organism to its population, community, and larger environment.

For a further challenge, students could add more specific levels of organization within the organism, down to the cellular level.

Teach from Visuals

To help students interpret the levels in the environment illustration, ask:

• What is the most specific level pictured? *organism*

• What level of organization do we have in this classroom? *population*

• Is the water in the picture part of the ecosystem, population, or community? *ecosystem*

 The visual "Levels in the Environment" is available as T14 in the Unit Transparency Book.

Address Misconceptions

IDENTIFY Ask students to list the factors in a familiar local ecosystem. If they do not include human beings in their list, they may hold the common misconception that humans are not part of an ecosystem.

CORRECT Have students list the effects that human beings have had on the local ecosystem.

REASSESS Ask students to describe what the local ecosystem might be like if human beings were not part of it. *Descriptions may include the following: more animals; different types of plants; no pollution; no buildings, roads, or other structures; no cats, dogs, or other domestic animals; and so on.*

Technology Resources

Visit **ClassZone.com** for background on common student misconceptions.

 MISCONCEPTION DATABASE

Ongoing Assessment

READING ViSUALS *Answer: One gazelle is a single organism. A group of gazelles that live in one area is a population. All of the organisms that live in the same place as the gazelle population make up a community. These gazelles live within one African savannah ecosystem, made up of the community and its environment. Finally, gazelles are one kind of animal that lives in the grassland biome.*

To help students visualize population patterns in time and space, give a very dramatic example: Wildebeests show three unique patterns in populations:

- At night wildebeests sleep on the ground in rows, so they have the security of the large group and the space to run if necessary.

- Most calves are born within two to three weeks at the start of the rainy season. The huge number of calves increases an individual's chance of surviving, because predators can only kill so many prey at once.

- Wildebeest herds may grow to a million animals when they migrate in search of pasture.

Teacher Demo

Try using a game of jacks to demonstrate population patterns. It is easier to "pick off" individuals when they are spread out. It is easier to "wipe out" a group when it is closer together.

Ongoing Assessment

Recognize patterns found in groups of organisms.

Tell students about the three unique patterns shown by wildebeests, described above. Ask: Which are patterns in time, and which in space? *space, time, time and space*

CHECK YOUR READING *Answer: Different organisms meet their needs in different ways, so they need different amounts of space.*

READING VISUALS *Answer: The elephants are widely spread compared to the wildebeests.*

Patterns in Living Space

The patterns formed by a population often show how the population meets its needs. For example, in California's Mojave desert the pale soil is dotted with dark-green shrubs called creosote bushes. A surprising thing about the bushes is their even spacing. No human shaped this habitat, however. The bushes are the same distance from each other because the roots of each bush release a toxin, a type of poison, that prevents the roots of other bushes from growing.

The distribution of animals in a habitat is often influenced by how they meet their needs. Animals must be able to reach their food supply and have places to raise their young. If you put up bird houses for bluebirds on your property, they must be spaced at least a hundred meters apart. Bluebirds need a large area of their own around their nest in order to collect enough insects to feed their young.

Sometimes, the particular pattern of individuals in a living space helps a population survive. Herring swim in schools, with the individual fish spaced close together. Wildebeests roam African grasslands in closely packed herds. These animals rely on the group for their safety. Even if one member of the group is attacked, many more will survive.

READING TIP
As you read this paragraph, note the pattern of wildebeests and elephants in the photograph.

CHECK YOUR READING What are some reasons for the spacing patterns observed in different populations?

elephant

wildebeest

READING VISUALS COMPARE AND CONTRAST How would you describe the spacing of these elephants and wildebeests?

DIFFERENTIATE INSTRUCTION

 More Reading Support

G Is the herd a pattern in space or in time? *space*

H How does living in large herds meet animals' needs? *protects them from predators*

Below Level When geese migrate or fly south for the winter, they travel in a "V" formation. This example contains within it both a pattern in time and a pattern in space. Ask students to tell how the example shows both patterns. *time: seasonal movement, southward in winter; space: flying in formation*

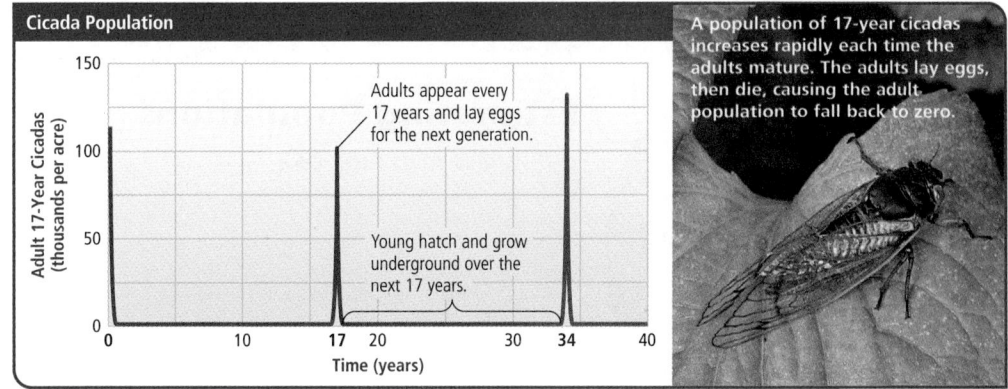

Cicada Population

Adult 17-Year Cicadas (thousands per acre)

Adults appear every 17 years and lay eggs for the next generation.

Young hatch and grow underground over the next 17 years.

Time (years)

A population of 17-year cicadas increases rapidly each time the adults mature. The adults lay eggs, then die, causing the adult population to fall back to zero.

Patterns in Time

At a spring picnic, you would rarely see the wasps called yellow jackets. At a fall picnic, however, they swarm to the food. This is an example of a population whose size changes with time. In spring, the queen wasp lays eggs and new wasps hatch. She continues to lay eggs all summer and the population grows. When winter comes, all the wasps except the queen die, and the population decreases.

Many birds that nest in North America in summer fly south to Central and South America in winter. There they find enough food and good nesting sites. In North America, this seasonal pattern leads to small bird populations in winter and large ones in summer.

The graph above shows an unusual pattern of population growth. Certain species of cicadas appear only every 17 years. Because no other species can rely on these insects as their main source of food, the cicadas survive long enough to lay eggs when they do appear.

2.1 Review

KEY CONCEPTS

1. What are two characteristics of a population?
2. Order these terms from the simplest to the most complex: biome, community, ecosystem, organism, population.
3. How do the terms *habitat* and *niche* relate to each other?

CRITICAL THINKING

4. **Apply** Choose a biological community in your region. Describe some of the populations that make up that community.
5. **Infer** How might the seasonal patterns of insect populations relate to the seasonal patterns of bird populations?

⚠ CHALLENGE

6. **Apply** The Explore activity on page 45 shows one way in which scientists sample a population to determine its total size. Would this method work for estimating the size of a population of 17-year cicadas? Why or why not?

Chapter 2: **Interactions Within Ecosystems 51** **D**

ANSWERS

1. organisms of same species; living in same area

2. organism, population, community, ecosystem, biome

3. Habitat refers to the physical setting a population lives in; niche is the role any one

population fills in that habitat.

4. Sample answer: Pond will have fish, insects, frogs, birds, and surrounding plants.

5. Population booms for insects would allow bird

populations to thrive and vice versa.

6. Yes, only during the few weeks the adults are above ground; or No, it would give deceptive results if the population was young.

Teach from Visuals

To help students interpret the cicada population graph, ask:

- What is represented on the vertical axis? *thousands of adult cicadas in a given area*
- What is represented on the horizontal axis? *time in years*
- How many complete population cycles are shown on the graph? *two*

Reinforce (the **BIG** idea)

Have students relate the section to the Big Idea.

R Reinforcing Key Concepts, p. 91

2.1 ASSESS & RETEACH

Assess

A Section 2.1 Quiz, p. 23

Reteach

Have students identify an animal in their neighborhood. Ask for volunteers to explain

- the animal's niche *Answers should include what the animal eats and whether another animal eats it.* (Point out that a niche is the animal's role in the transfer of matter and energy though the entire system.)
- any patterns in space or in time that it fits. Does it migrate? Does it flock? Are groups spaced closely together or far apart? *Answers will vary.*
- how it fits into scientific organization of the environment *Answers should show levels of organism, population, community, ecosystem, and biome.*

Technology Resources

Have students visit **ClassZone.com** for reteaching of Key Concepts.

 CONTENT REVIEW

 CONTENT REVIEW CD-ROM

Focus

PURPOSE To learn how scientists estimate animal populations and how to use estimates to reflect a change in the ecosystem

OVERVIEW Students will use marked white beans to generate data, which they will record and analyze. Students will determine the following:

• an actual population total

• an estimated population total

• the effectiveness of the estimate

Lab Preparation

• The day before doing the lab, have volunteers make up the bags. Bags should contain around 100 beans, but the number should vary.

• Prior to the investigation have students read through the investigation and prepare their data tables. Or you may wish to copy and distribute datasheets and rubrics.

 UNIT RESOURCE BOOK, pp. 121–129

SCIENCE TOOLKIT, F14

Lab Management

• Have students work in pairs, with one student handling the beans and the other recording the data. Have them switch roles throughout the lab.

• Tell students to take small handfuls, or demonstrate what a "handful" means here.

• White beans work well for marking. Avoid pinto or other spotted beans.

INCLUSION If students have learning disabilities, have them handle and count the "population" samples, while a partner reads directions and records data. If a student has poor fine motor control and is physically unable to perform the population counts, he or she could read and record the procedure aloud, and could present the results. You might use a tape recorder for results if writing is problematic. If a student is colorblind, be sure the two markers are not red and green.

Estimating Populations

OVERVIEW AND PURPOSE The number of animals in a wild population cannot be easily counted. Wildlife biologists have developed a formula that can estimate a population's size by using small samples. This method is referred to as mark and recapture. In this investigation you will

• use the mark-recapture method to estimate population size
• test the effectiveness of the mark-recapture method by simulating an outbreak of disease in a population

▶ Problem

How effective is the mark-recapture method in estimating population size?

▶ Hypothesize

Write a hypothesis to explain how you will use a sudden change in population size to determine the effectiveness of the mark-recapture method. Your hypothesis should take the form of an "If . . . , then . . . , because . . ." statement.

MATERIALS
• paper bag
• white kidney beans
• 2 colored markers
• calculator

▶ Procedure

1. Make two data tables in your **Science Notebook,** like the ones shown on page 53.

2. From your teacher, obtain a paper bag containing a "population" of white kidney beans.

3. Remove a small handful of beans. Count the sample and record the count in Table 1, under First Capture Total.

4. Use a colored marker to mark your sample population. Return the beans to the bag, and gently shake the bag to mix all the beans.

5. Remove and count a second sample of beans. Record the count in Table 1, under Recapture Total.

6. Count the number of beans from this sample that were marked from the first capture. Record this number in Table 1, under Recapture Marked. Return all the beans to the bag.

INVESTIGATION RESOURCES

 CHAPTER INVESTIGATION, Estimating Populations
• Level A, pp. 121–124
• Level B, pp. 125–128
• Level C, p. 129

Advanced students should complete Levels B & C.

 Writing a Lab Report, D12–13

Technology Resources

Customize this student lab as needed or look for an alternative. Print rubrics to assess student lab reports.

 Lab Generator CD-ROM

7 Use a calculator and the following formula to estimate the population size. Record the estimate in Table 1 as the Calculated Population Estimate.

$$\frac{\text{First Capture Total} \times \text{Recapture Total}}{\text{Recapture Marked}} = \text{Population Estimate}$$

8 Disease strikes. Remove a small handful of beans from the bag. Count the beans, and record this count in Table 2, under Killed by Disease. Set these beans aside.

9 Repeat steps 3–7 to mark and recapture your survivor population. This time use a different colored marker to mark your sample population, and only include the beans marked in the second color in your counts.

10 Fill in Data Table 2 for the survivor population. Use the formula from step 7 to calculate your estimate of the survivor population.

11 Once you have calculated your estimate of survivors, dump out the paper bag and count all the beans that were inside. Record this count in Table 2, under Actual Survivors Total.

▶ Observe and Analyze `Write It Up`

1. CALCULATE From Table 2 add together the number of actual survivors and the number killed by disease. Put this in Table 1, under Actual Population Total.

2. CALCULATE Find the percentage of the population affected by disease using the following formula:

$$\frac{\text{Killed by disease} \times 100}{\text{Actual Population Total}} = \text{Percentage affected}$$

▶ Conclude `Write It Up`

1. INFER How did the estimated number of beans compare with the actual number?

2. IDENTIFY LIMITS What aspects of this investigation most likely would not be possible in a natural habitat? Why not?

3. EVALUATE Compare your results with your hypothesis. Do your data support your hypothesis?

▶ INVESTIGATE Further

CHALLENGE Determine if using larger samples of a population gives better population estimates. Get another bag of unmarked beans from your teacher. Use a spreadsheet program, if available, to record your data and calculate the results.

▶ Observe and Analyze `Write It Up`

1. *SAMPLE DATA Table 1: First Capture Total, 22; Recapture Total, 28; Recapture Marked, 6; Calculated Population Estimate, 102; Actual Population Total, 100.*

2. *SAMPLE DATA Table 2: Survivors First Capture Total, 26; Survivors Recapture Total, 22; Survivors Recapture Marked, 4; Calculated Survivors Estimate, 71; Killed by Disease, 14; Actual Survivors Total, 86 (Percentage affected, 16%).*

▶ Conclude `Write It Up`

1. *SAMPLE DATA The estimate should be within 20% of the actual number.*

2. *It might not be possible to know exactly when disease strikes a population. Also, capturing the required number of animals would be difficult. It most likely would not be possible to catch them all at once. When they are released, they likely would not all stay in one small area.*

3. *Answers will vary. Students who predicted effective correlation (80% or better) between the estimated and actual count will say the hypothesis was supported by the results.*

▶ INVESTIGATE Further

CHALLENGE Answers will vary, but results should indicate that the larger samples are more effective.

Estimating Populations
Table 1. Population sampling before disease

First Capture Total	Recapture Total	Recapture Marked	Calculated Population Estimate	Actual Population Total

Table 2. Population sampling after disease

Survivors First Capture Total	Survivors Recapture Total	Survivors Recapture Marked	Calculated Survivors Estimate	Killed by Disease	Actual Survivors Total

Post-Lab Discussion

- Discuss whether the percent difference between the estimate and the actual counts would be acceptable or not to working ecologists. *The small difference would be acceptable in most cases. Ecologists can not possibly track every member of a population. Accuracy to 100% becomes more important in small endangered populations.*

- Discuss how the mark-recapture method might be used to study different populations. What data could be collected? *migration patterns, birth rates, predator-prey interactions*

⊙ Set Learning Goals

Students will

* Describe the different types of interactions in an ecosystem.
* Describe symbiotic relationships in which one or more species benefits.
* Describe symbiotic relationships in which one species is harmed.

◑ 3-Minute Warm-Up

Display Transparency 12 or copy this exercise on the board:

Decide if these statements are true. If not true, correct them.

1. An ecosystem is composed of biotic factors. *An ecosystem is composed of both biotic and abiotic factors.*

2 In a species, the organisms' offspring must be able to breed. *true*

3. The same niche in a habitat may be occupied by more than one species. *Different species never occupy exactly the same niche.*

 3-Minute Warm-Up, p. T12

2.2 MOTIVATE

THINK ABOUT

PURPOSE To understand ways people interact

DISCUSS Brainstorm situations in which two or more people transact. Begin with a game, a group project, a purchase, and so on. Then revisit the list and discuss whether the interaction is competitive or cooperative.

Sample answer: Players on opposite teams compete to score points. Players on the same team pass the ball to each other and divide the field to defend it. Fans give energy by cheering. Both cooperative and competitive relationships are shown in the picture.

Ongoing Assessment

 *Sample answer: sharing food, a water source, living in the same place*

KEY CONCEPT

2.2 Organisms can interact in different ways.

◀ **BEFORE, you learned**

* Different populations live together in a habitat
* Different species fill different niches in a habitat
* There are patterns in the ways organisms interact with each other and their environment

▶ **NOW, you will learn**

* About different types of interactions in an ecosystem
* How some species benefit from interactions
* How some species are harmed by interactions

VOCABULARY

predator p. 55
prey p. 55
competition p. 55
cooperation p. 57
symbiosis p. 58
mutualism p. 58
commensalism p. 59
parasitism p. 59

THINK ABOUT

What are some of the ways people interact?

People in a community interact with each other in many ways. An interaction is the way a person behaves toward or responds to another person. This photo-

graph shows groups of people at a soccer game. There are players from two teams and fans who are watching the game. How would you describe the interactions between the people in this photograph?

Organisms interact in different ways.

The photograph above shows how members of a human community both compete and cooperate. Different members of the populations of a biological community also compete and cooperate. They not only share a habitat, but they also share the resources in that habitat. How different organisms interact depends on their relationship to each other.

   A robin in a meadow picks at the soil, pulls out an earthworm, and swallows it. This is one obvious way organisms in an ecosystem interact—one eats, and the other gets eaten. Organisms also compete. The robin may have to compete with a chickadee to get the earthworm. And organisms can cooperate. Ants work together to build a nest, collect food, and defend their colony.

⊙ **CHECK YOUR READING** Name three ways organisms may interact with each other in an ecosystem.

RESOURCES FOR DIFFERENTIATED INSTRUCTION

Below Level

UNIT RESOURCE BOOK
* Reading Study Guide A, pp. 94–95
* Decoding Support, p. 118

 **AUDIO CDS**

R Additional INVESTIGATION,
Prey Survival, A, B, & C, pp. 130–138;
Teacher Instructions, pp. 200–201

Advanced

UNIT RESOURCE BOOK
* Challenge and Extension, p. 100
* Challenge Reading, pp. 114–115

English Learners

UNIT RESOURCE BOOK
Spanish Reading Study Guide, pp. 98–99

AUDIO CDS

* Audio Readings in Spanish
* Audio Readings (English)

Predator and Prey

Many interactions between organisms in an ecosystem involve food. A food chain shows the feeding relationships between different species. There are producers and consumers. Another way to look at a food chain is through the interactions of predators and prey. The **predator** is an animal that eats another. The **prey** is an animal that is eaten by a predator. In a food chain, an organism can be both predator and prey. A meadowlark that feeds on a grasshopper is, in turn, eaten by a prairie falcon.

Predators can affect how members of their prey populations are distributed. Herring move together in a school and wildebeests travel in herds to protect themselves. It is the sick or older members of the population that will most likely be eaten by predators. Species of prey may also have adaptations that relate to the behavior of predators. This is true of cicadas and their long reproductive cycles.

Prey populations, in turn, affect the location and number of predator populations. For example some birds are predators feeding on insects. One factor that may affect movement of birds from one location to another is the availability of insects.

▼ REMINDER
A *producer* is an organism that makes its own food; a *consumer* is an organism that eats another organism for food.

Competition

In a team game, two teams compete against each other with the same goal in mind—to win the game. In a biological community, competition is for resources, not wins. **Competition** is the struggle between individuals or different populations for a limited resource.

In an ecosystem, competition may occur within the same species. Individual plants compete with each other for light, space, and nutrients. For example, creosote bushes compete with other creosote bushes for the same water supply. The toxins produced by the roots of one creosote bush prevent other creosote bushes from growing.

Competition also occurs between members of different species. In the tropical rain forests of Indonesia, vines called strangler figs compete with trees for water, light, and nutrients. The vine attaches itself to a host tree. As it grows, the vine surrounds and eventually kills the tree by blocking out sunlight and using up available water and nutrients.

INFER Do you think a strangler fig could survive on its own?

host tree

strangler fig

Chapter 2: **Interactions Within Ecosystems** 55 **D**

Teach from Visuals

To help students interpret the photograph of the strangler fig and the host tree, ask:
- What is it like on the floor of the rain forest? *deep shade, damp, moist*
- What is at the top of the rainforest? *lots of sunlight, leafy*
- What does the tree give to the fig vine? *support so it can grow up towards the sunlight*

Teach Difficult Concepts

Predator-prey relationships are not the only sort of feeding relationships in ecosystems. Point out that predators and prey are both always animal species. Foraging is another type of interaction. It takes place when an organism eats a producer, such as a plant, protist, bacteria, or fungus.

Social Studies Connection

In order to link the concept of competition among species in an ecosystem with social studies curriculum, discuss with students how competition functions in a free enterprise economic system.

As in an ecosystem, a decrease in the supply of a resource results in an increase in competition. In an economic system, for example, when the need for workers is greater than the supply, employers compete with one another by paying workers higher wages. On the other hand, when the number of workers exceeds the number of available jobs, wages usually fall and workers must compete with one another for a limited supply of jobs.

DIFFERENTIATE INSTRUCTION

More Reading Support

A Is a robin a predator? If so, what is its prey? *yes; earthworms*

B What do plants compete for? *light, space, nutrients, water*

English Learners Have students write the definitions for *symbiosis, mutualism, commensalism,* and *parasitism* in their Science Word Dictionaries. English learners probably do have prior knowledge of soccer which is pictured on p. 54. Ask students to think of predator-prey relationships between animals found in their home countries.

Teach from Visuals

To help students interpret the photographs of interspecies and intraspecies competition, ask:

- In what ways do organisms of the same or different species compete? *for food, space, water, other resources*
- What groups of organisms compete for mates? *males or females of the same species*

Develop Critical Thinking

INFER Ask students to decide whether they think competing for mates or competing for food is more common within a species and which is more common between species.

Ongoing Assessment

Describe the different types of interaction in an ecosystem.

Ask: When animals mark their territory, how are they relating to other members of their species? *They are competing.* How are they relating when they hunt in packs? *They are cooperating within their species, and they are preying on another species.*

 **CHECK YOUR READING** *Answer: space, light, water, nutrients*

Competition

Competition between species Two different species, hyenas and vultures, compete for the remains of a dead animal.

Competition within species Two male deer lock horns as they battle over territory.

 C

Competition occurs between species and within species. For example, vultures and hyenas will compete over the food left in the remains of a dead animal. Wolves will compete with one another over territory. A wolf will mark its territory by urinating on trees and so warn off other wolves. Animals also compete over territory by fighting, using threatening sounds, and putting on aggressive displays.

Competition within species often occurs during the mating season. Male birds use mating songs and displays of feathers to compete for the attention of females. Male hippopotamuses fight to attract female hippopotamuses. Male crickets chirp to attract female crickets.

 **CHECK YOUR READING** What sorts of resources do plants and animals compete for?

READING TiP

Compare and contrast the meanings of *competition* and *coexistence.*

Competition does not occur between all populations that share the same resources. Many populations can coexist in a habitat—different species can live together without causing harm to one another. Many different populations of plants coexist in a forest. Maple trees, beech trees, and birch trees can live side by side and still have enough water, nutrients, and sunlight to meet their needs.

D 56 Unit: Ecology

DIFFERENTIATE INSTRUCTION

 More Reading Support

C What are examples of competition among animals? *marking territory, fighting for mates*

Advanced Have students search news sources for stories about interactions between species. Encourage them to generate new questions about species interactions that might be appropriate for current science research.

Have students who are interested in interactions between species read the following article:

 Challenge Reading, pp. 114–115

INVESTIGATE Species Interactions

How do predator-prey populations interact?

Use these rules for predator-prey interaction for each round. If a predator card touches three or more prey cards, remove the prey cards touched. If the predator card does not touch at least three prey cards, remove the predator card and leave the prey cards. Predator cards are large, prey cards are small.

PROCEDURE

(1) Use masking tape to mark a boundary on a table top.

(2) Scatter five prey cards into the area. Take a predator card and toss it, trying to get it to land on the prey.

(3) According to the rules above, remove the predators and prey that have "died." Record the number of predators and prey that have

"survived." This represents one generation.

(4) Double the populations of predators and prey—they have "reproduced."

(5) Scatter the prey cards into the area and then toss the predator cards as before. Repeat steps 3 and 4 for a total of 15 rounds (generations).

WHAT DO YOU THINK?

- How does the size of the prey population affect the predator population?
- How might the size of a habitat affect the interaction of predators and prey?

CHALLENGE Use graph paper and colored pencils to make a graph of your results. Or use a spreadsheet program if one is available to you.

SKILL FOCUS
Analyzing data

MATERIALS
- 20 10 × 10 cm cardboard squares—predators
- 200 3 × 3 cm paper squares—prey
- masking tape
for Challenge:
- graph paper
- 2 colored pencils

TIME
30 minutes

Cooperation

Not all interactions in an ecosystem involve competition. **Cooperation** is an interaction in which organisms work in a way that benefits them all. Some predators cooperate when they hunt. Although individual lions may hunt on their own, they also hunt in packs to kill large prey.

Killer whales also cooperate when they hunt. The whales swim in packs called pods. The pod swims in circles around a school of fish, forcing the fish close together so they are easier to catch. Pod members may also take turns chasing a seal until it gets tired and is easily killed. The pod may even work together to attack larger species of whales.

Ants, bees, and termites are social insects. Members of a colony belong to different groups, called castes, and have different responsibilities. Some groups gather food while others defend the colony. Other animals, like apes and monkeys, live in family groups. Members of the family cooperate to care for their young.

Cooperation
Driver ants work together to bring food to their nest.

INVESTIGATE Species Interactions

PURPOSE Simulate predator-prey relationships to generate and analyze data

TIPS *30 min.* Limit area to two feet by two feet, perhaps by using tape to mark boundaries. You might use sticky notepads and cut off the sticky side of the pad instead of cutting squares individually.

WHAT DO YOU THINK? *Results should show a cycle, with the number of prey increasing for several generations, then predators increasing, then prey decreasing, and repeating.*

CHALLENGE Student graphs will vary but should show the trends described above.

R Datasheet: Species Interactions, p. 101

Technology Resources

Customize this student lab as needed or look for an alternative. Print rubrics to assess student lab reports.

Lab Generator CD-ROM

Teaching with Technology

If spreadsheet software is available, have students use it to record data for the investigation. They can also use a graphing calculator to show the data visually.

EXPLORE (the BIG idea)

Revisit "How Do Living Things Interact Where You Live?" on p. 43. Now that students have studied the basic types of interactions between and within species, have them explain their observations.

DIFFERENTIATE INSTRUCTION

? More Reading Support

D Besides competition, what is another way for animals to interact?
cooperation

Additional Investigation To reinforce Section 2.2 learning goals, use the following full-period investigation:

R **Additional INVESTIGATION,** Prey Survival, A, B, & C, pp. 130–138; 200–201
(Advanced students should complete Levels B and C.)

To help students interpret the photograph of the hummingbird, ask:

- Which structures and behaviors of the hummingbird enable it to get nectar from the flower? *It has a long thin beak and can hover.*

- How is the structure of the flower suited to its interaction with the hummingbird? *Its blooms are deep; it is colorful, bright, and produces sweet food; its pollen can be spread by the interaction helping it to reproduce.*

- Why is this a good example of mutualism? *Two different species interact. They each get a different need met.*

Ongoing Assessment

Describe a symbiotic relationship in which one species benefits from another.

Ask: What is the difference between a mutualistic relationship and a commensal relationship between species? *In a mutualistic relationship both species get something they need. In a commensal relationship, only one species gets something, but the other is unharmed.*

OUTLINE
Add a sentence about *symbiosis* to your outline and define the three types of symbiosis in the supporting details.

The survival of one species might depend on another species.

You have learned that many different organisms live together in a habitat. The fact that organisms live together forces them to interact in different ways. For example, an organism preys upon another for food. Or perhaps there is competition among organisms over resources such as food, water, and territory.

The actions of different organisms can be so closely related that the survival of one species depends on the action or presence of another. In such a relationship, at least one of the species is getting a resource that it needs to survive. Benefits of the relationship may include food, reproductive help, or protection.

The relationship between individuals of two different species who live together in a close relationship is called **symbiosis** (SIHM-bee-OH-sihs). This word means "living together." A symbiotic relationship may affect the partners in different ways.

?
E

- Both species benefit from the relationship.
- One species benefits while the other is not affected.
- One species benefits while the other is harmed.

Here are some examples for each of the three types of symbiosis.

Mutualism The interaction between the hummingbird and the flower benefits both.

Both Species Benefit

Stroll through a garden on a sunny day and notice the bees buzzing from flower to flower. Look closely at a single bee and you may see yellow pollen grains sticking to its hairy body. The relationship between the flower and the bee is an example of **mutualism** (MYOO-choo-uh-LIHZ-uhm)—an interaction between two species that benefits both. The bees get food in the form of nectar, and the flowers get pollen from other flowers, which they need to make seeds.

?
F

Many plants rely on mutualism to reproduce. The pollen needed to make seeds must be spread from flower to flower. The birds and insects that feed on the nectar in these flowers transfer pollen from one flower to the next. The seeds produced are then moved to new ground by animals that eat the seeds or the fruits that hold the seeds. This form of mutualism doesn't benefit the individual flower but instead ensures the survival of the species.

DIFFERENTIATE INSTRUCTION

? **More Reading Support**

E What does *symbiosis* mean? *living together*

F What happens when two species act in mutualism? *They interact in a way that is good for both partners.*

Below Level Struggling readers may not know the words *benefit* and *mutual*. Both words are key to understanding the material on pp. 58–61. Define these words for students (*benefit* = have some need met, have some help; *mutual* = shared, equally taking part in). Then have them make their own word webs, in which *mutual* is the central word and *benefit* is one of the many related words.

In some cases, mutualism is necessary for the survival of the organisms themselves. For example, termites are able to live off a food that most animals cannot digest: wood. The termites, in fact, can't digest wood either. However, they have living in their guts tiny single-celled organisms, protozoans, that can break the wood down into digestible components. The protozoans get a safe place to live, and the termites can take advantage of a plentiful food source.

 **RESOURCE CENTER**
CLASSZONE.COM
Explore symbiotic relationships.

 **CHECK YOUR READING** Describe how a bee and a flower benefit from a symbiotic relationship.

One Species Benefits

G

Commensalism (kuh-MEHN-suh-LIHZ-uhm) is a relationship between two species in which one species benefits while the other is not affected. Orchids and mosses are plants that can have a commensal relationship with trees. The plants grow on the trunks or branches of trees. They get the light they need as well as nutrients that run down along the tree. As long as these plants do not grow too heavy, the tree is not affected.

Commensal relationships are very common in ocean ecosystems. Small fish called remoras use a type of built-in suction cup to stick to a shark's skin and hitch a ride. When the shark makes a kill, the remora eats the scraps. The shark makes no attempt to attack the remora. The remora benefits greatly from this commensal relationship; the shark is barely affected.

Not all commensal relationships involve food. Some fish protect themselves by swimming among the stinging tentacles of a moon jellyfish. The fish benefit from the relationship because the tentacles keep them safe from predators. The jellyfish is not helped or hurt by the presence of the fish. As in this example, it is common in commensal relationships for the species that benefits to be smaller than the species it partners with.

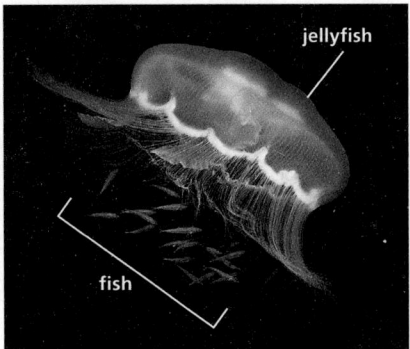
jellyfish

 fish

Commensalism The interaction between the jellyfish and the fish benefits the fish only.

One Species Is Harmed

H

There is one symbiotic relationship in which a small partner can harm a much larger host. **Parasitism** (PAR-uh-suh-TIHZ-uhm) is a relationship between two species in which one species benefits while the species it depends on, its host, is harmed. Parasites are often tiny organisms that feed off, and weaken, their hosts. Ticks, lice, and mites are external parasites that live on or attach to their host's skin. Other parasites, like tapeworms and ringworms, are internal parasites that live inside their hosts.

Chapter 2: **Interactions Within Ecosystems 59** **D**

Real World Example

All humans have resident populations of bacteria, fungi, and protozoans. These are called the "normal flora" of the body, and an average body has more of them than it has cells. Normal flora live on the skin, in the eyes, nose, mouth, upper throat, urethra, and small intestine, and in especially high numbers in the large intestine. The relationships of these species to humans are mainly commensal. In some cases they are mutualistic. Some flora compete with disease-causing microorganisms.

Teach from Visuals

To help students interpret the photograph of the moon jellyfish, ask:

Why is the size of the fish a factor in this method of protection? *The fish have to be small enough to swim among the tentacles. If the fish were larger, they might not need this type of protection.*

Teach Difficult Concepts

The three types of relationships can be hard to remember, especially mutualism and commensalism. Ask the class to bring in pictures of examples for display on a bulletin board that you have started.

Ongoing Assessment

CHECK YOUR READING *Answer: A bee gets food from a flower, and the flower's pollen is carried by the bee to other flowers.*

DIFFERENTIATE INSTRUCTION

? **More Reading Support**

G How are species affected in commensalism? *one species gains; one is not affected*

H How are species affected in parasitism? *one gains; one is harmed*

Below Level Have students make a two-column chart with the types of relationships in one column. In the other column, have them draw a picture or paste a photograph of animals and plants that illustrate each relationship.

Teach from Visuals

To help students interpret the illustration of symbiotic relationships, ask:

- What are the parasites shown in the image? *mistletoe and ticks*

- In the commensal relationships shown, which species benefit? Which species are unaffected? *Lichens and mice benefit; trees and humans are unaffected.*

- What might be another example of mutualism that you would find in this environment? *Sample answer: Bees feed on nectar and help flowers pollinate.*

Ongoing Assessment

Describe symbiotic relationships where one species is harmed.

Ask: What are some ways that one plant can be a parasite of another plant? *Sample answer: A vine might climb a taller or stronger plant to get light and choke or shade the stronger plant; one plant might take nutrients from another plant.*

Symbiotic Relationships

Mutualism
Both species benefit from the relationship.

Commensalism
One species benefits while the other is not affected.

Parasitism
One species benefits while the other is harmed.

Parasitism
Mistletoe is a plant that takes nourishment from a tree, causing damage to the tree.

Mutualism
Aphids are insects that provide ants with a sweet liquid. Ants live alongside the aphids, protecting them from predators.

Commensalism
Lichens benefit from living on a tree, but the tree is not harmed.

Parasitism
Ticks are animals that attach to their hosts, feeding on the host's blood.

Mutualism
Nitrogen-fixing bacteria get their nourishment from the roots of certain plants, providing the plants with nitrogen in return.

Commensalism
Mice do well living near humans, living off the food scraps humans leave behind.

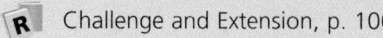

D 60 Unit: Ecology

DIFFERENTIATE INSTRUCTION

Advanced Have students choose one of the relationships in the Symbiotic Relationships illustration, p. 60, and find out more about it. Ask them to consider just one of these three issues:

- Do organisms shown on p. 60 participate in a parasitic relationship?

- Where do disruptions of a mutualistic relationship occur?

- How could a commensal relationship become parasitic?

R Challenge and Extension, p. 100

The relationship between cowbirds and warblers is an unusual type of association called nest or brood parasitism. Female cowbirds never build their own nests or rear their own young. Instead, they lay their eggs in warbler nests. Although nest parasitism does not harm the host warbler, it does harm the warbler species because either warblers eggs do not hatch, or the chicks do not survive. The warbler species is often harmed because cowbirds push most warbler eggs from the nest in order to make room for their own eggs. Once the cowbird chicks hatch, their larger size helps them to outcompete the smaller warbler chicks for food, so that the host's chicks starve.

host warbler

warbler chick

cowbird chick

Parasitism The larger cowbird chick is cared for by a warbler at the expense of the smaller warbler chick.

 **CHECK YOUR READING** How is parasitism different from commensalism?

Interactions in an ecosystem are complex.

Different types of symbiosis occur throughout an ecosystem and often overlap. They may occur in the same locations, and the same species might be involved in more than one symbiotic relationship. The illustration on page 60 shows different symbiotic relationships that may occur in a backyard.

Symbiosis is just one of many interactions that take place in an ecosystem. The yard may have a garden, with individual tomato plants competing for water and nutrients; it may have ants cooperating to maintain a successful colony. An ecosystem is more than just a collection of biotic and abiotic factors. Interactions within an ecosystem help explain how resources are shared and used up and how energy flows through the system.

2.2 Review

KEY CONCEPTS

1. Name two ways in which members of the same species interact.

2. In what ways do members of different species interact?

3. Give an example of each type of symbiotic relationship: mutualism, commensalism, and parasitism.

CRITICAL THINKING

4. **Apply** Think of a biological community near you, and give an example of how one population has affected another.

5. **Compare and Contrast** Explain how symbiotic relationships are similar to and different from predator-prey interactions.

CHALLENGE

6. **Synthesize** Mutualism is more common in tropical ecosystems such as rain forests and coral reefs than in other ecosystems. Why do you think this is so?

ANSWERS

1. compete for mates, cooperate for resources

2. compete, cooperate, or form symbiotic relationships

3. Sample answer: mutualism—bee and flower; commensalism—fish and jellyfish; parasitism—tapeworms in humans

4. Sample answer: Bittersweet competes with trees for space and sunlight, and has stunted their growth.

5. In a predator-prey relationship, one species benefits and the other is harmed. Parasitism is similar, but the effect is more dramatic

because the parasite relies on its host for survival.

6. Sample answer: Tropical rainforests and coral reefs have many more species than other ecosystems; more opportunities for mutualism.

Set Learning Goal

To make inferences by combining new knowledge with past knowledge

Present the Science

Salamanders absorb water through their skin. These amphibians generally live in freshwater wetlands and damp woods. They range from 5 cm to 1.5 m long, and are bright orange or yellow with stripes or spots. They feed on insects, worms, snails, and other small animals.

Guide the Activity

- Remind students that an inference is a statement that is probably true, based on other information. It must be supported by prior knowledge and observations or data.

- The first notebook contains evidence. Ask: Which statements are qualitative observations—those that must be described? (*b, e*) Which are quantitative—those that can be counted, measured, or calculated? (*a, c, d*)

- The second notebook shows inferences that may or may not be supported. They have not been directly observed or measured. Explain that students must decide which ones are reasonable.

COOPERATIVE LEARNING STRATEGY

Divide the class into groups of five. Have each group brainstorm inferences. A time keeper can keep track of 10 minutes, while a recorder quickly writes all suggestions. Group members suggest which inferences to keep, and which to cross out. They must support their choices.

Close

Ask: Why is it important to study what killed the salamanders? *Sample answer: All organisms have a niche, and their disappearance can affect the entire community. It may be possible to prevent spread of the disease to other populations.*

This barred tiger salamander can be found in many wetlands in the Great Plains.

Think SCIENCE

Where Are the Salamanders?

At the Cottonwood Lake Study Area in rural Stutsman County, North Dakota, U.S. Fish and Wildlife Service biologists have been studying wetland ecosystems for more than 30 years. Salamanders are one of the most abundant species in these wetlands. But in May 2000, the researchers started noticing sick salamanders in one wetland. By July, most salamanders had died. What killed them?

◉ Observations

a. In the past, cold winter weather and food shortages have killed salamanders at Cottonwood Lake.

b. The sick salamanders had discolored skin and enlarged livers.

c. The previous year, leopard frogs in a nearby wetland were found dying from a contagious fungal infection.

d. A viral disease has killed tiger salamanders elsewhere in the West.

e. Both large, well-fed salamanders and small, poorly nourished salamanders died.

◉ Inferences

The following statements are possible inferences:

a. A food shortage caused salamanders to starve.

b. The fungal disease that killed leopard frogs also killed the salamanders

c. Salamanders were killed by a viral disease.

◉ Evaluate Inferences

On Your Own Which of the inferences are supported by the observations? Write the observations that support each of the inferences you identify.

As a Group Discuss your decisions. Come up with a list of reasonable inferences.

CHALLENGE What further observations would you make to test any of these inferences?

ANSWERS

Inference a is not supported. Large well-fed salamanders died off. This does not support the animals starving to death.

Inference b is partly supported. Frogs and salamanders share many traits. It is reasonable to think that they could be killed by the same infection. But, they also have differing traits. They may be unharmed by it.

Inference c is supported. The exact same species of salamanders died in both locations. Viral diseases can spread over large areas.

CHALLENGE Study other tiger salamanders for symptoms of the virus, and leopard frogs for symptoms of the fungal infection. Dissect dead salamanders for clues.

KEY CONCEPT

2.3 Ecosystems are always changing.

◀ **BEFORE, you learned**

- Populations in an ecosystem interact in different ways
- Organisms can benefit from interactions in an ecosystem
- Organisms can be harmed by interactions in an ecosystem

▶ **NOW, you will learn**

- How different factors affect the size of a population
- How biological communities get established
- How biological communities change over time

VOCABULARY

limiting factor p. 64
carrying capacity p. 65
succession p. 66
pioneer species p. 66

EXPLORE Population Growth

How does sugar affect the growth of yeast?

PROCEDURE

① Use a marker to label the cups A, B, C. Pour 150 mL of warm water into each cup. Mark the water level with the marker.

② Add 1/2 teaspoon of dry yeast to each plastic cup and stir.

③ Add 1/4 teaspoon of sugar to cup B. Add 1 teaspoon of sugar to cup C. Stir.

④ Wait 15 minutes. Measure the height of the foam layer that forms in each cup.

WHAT DO YOU THINK?
- Which cup had the most foam, which cup had the least?
- Describe the effect of sugar on a population of yeast.

MATERIALS
- 3 clear plastic cups
- warm water
- sugar
- dry yeast
- measuring spoons
- measuring cup
- stirring rod
- marker
- ruler

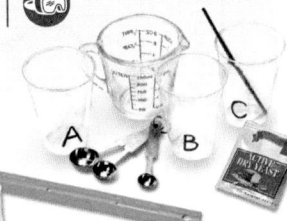

Populations change over time.

> **REMINDER**
>
> A *population* is a group of organisms of the same species that live together in the same habitat.

You may have a strong memory of a park you visited as a little child. You remember collecting pine cones, listening to woodpeckers, and catching frogs. Then you visit again, years later, and the park has changed. Maybe more land has been added, there are more birds and trees. Or maybe the area around the park has been developed. There seem to be fewer woodpeckers, and you can't find any frogs. The community has changed. There are a lot of factors that affect the populations within a biological community. Some have to do with the organisms themselves. Others relate to the habitat.

Chapter 2: **Interactions Within Ecosystems 63** **D**

RESOURCES FOR DIFFERENTIATED INSTRUCTION

Below Level

UNIT RESOURCE BOOK
- Reading Study Guide A, pp. 105–106
- Decoding Support, p. 118

🎧 **AUDIO CDS**

Advanced

UNIT RESOURCE BOOK
Challenge and Extension, p. 111

English Learners

UNIT RESOURCE BOOK
Spanish Reading Study Guide, pp. 109–110

🎧 **AUDIO CDS**
- Audio Readings in Spanish
- Audio Readings (English)

2.3 FOCUS

◉ Set Learning Goals

Students will

- Explain what affects the size of a population.
- Explore ways that biological communities are established.
- Describe how ecosystems change over time.
- Observe the effects of sugar on the growth of yeast.

◀ 3-Minute Warm-Up

Display Transparency 13 or copy this exercise on the board:

Match the definitions to the words.

Definitions

1. a relationship in which two organisms both try to get the same thing *d*
2. a relationship in which both of the organisms benefit *e*
3. the role a species fills in a habitat *b*

Terms

a. parasitism
b. niche
c. habitat
d. competition
e. mutualism

T 3-Minute Warm-Up, p. T13

2.3 MOTIVATE

EXPLORE Population Growth

PURPOSE To introduce students to limiting factors affecting growth of a population of yeast

TIP *20 min.* Check the yeast before the lab to make sure it's alive.

WHAT DO YOU THINK? *Cup C had the most foam; cup A had the least; yeast feeds on sugar, so the more food, the more foam.*

Teach from Visuals

To help students interpret the graphs, ask:

- What was the moose population in 1970? *about 1,300* The wolf population in 1970? *20*

- How did the moose population change between 1970 and 1975? How did the wolf population change in the same period? *The moose population peaked. The wolf population grew.*

- What time period did the wolf population decrease as the moose population decreased? *1980–1982*

Real World Example

In the United States, many animal populations are endangered as a result of human use of their habitat. Whooping cranes are endangered because their wetland habitat has been drained for farmland. The endangered sawback turtle's food (snails and insects) has been reduced by flood controls, siltation, and pollution.

Population Growth and Decline

One factor that obviously affects population size is how often organisms reproduce. Birth rate is a measure of the number of births in an animal population. It can also be a measure of the stability of an ecosystem. For example, black bears reproduce once every two years. If there is not enough food available, however, the female bear's reproductive cycle is delayed, and the bear population does not grow.

 A

Predator-prey interactions also affect population size. The graphs show how an increase in the moose population—the prey—in Isle Royale National Park was followed by an increase in the island's population of wolves—the predators. The wolves preyed upon the moose, the moose population decreased, then the wolf population decreased.

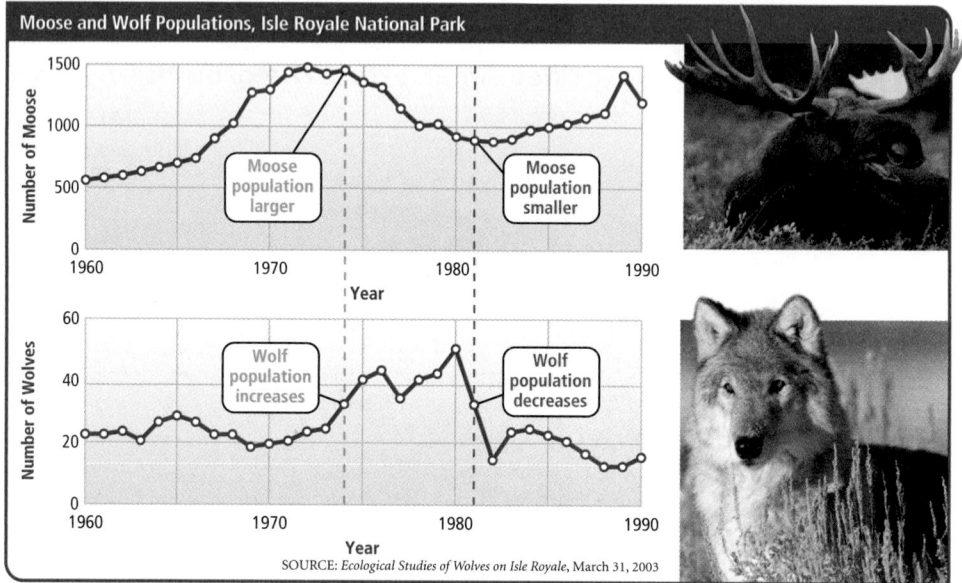

Moose and Wolf Populations, Isle Royale National Park

Moose population larger — Moose population smaller

Wolf population increases — Wolf population decreases

SOURCE: *Ecological Studies of Wolves on Isle Royale*, March 31, 2003

READING TiP
Note in the graphs above that it can take some time for the size of one population to affect the size of the other.

 B

Any factor or condition that limits the growth of a population in an ecosystem is called a **limiting factor.** A large population of predators will limit the population of prey; a small population of prey will limit the population of predators. Too much or too little of any biotic or abiotic factor—like food, water, or light—makes an ecosystem unstable and brings about change.

A lack of nutrients in the soil is a limiting factor for plants. That is why farmers fertilize their crops. That same fertilizer, if it runs off into a lake, can increase the population of algae, another photosynthetic organism. A large population of algae can cover a lake with scum and use up oxygen needed by fish. This then limits the fish population.

DIFFERENTIATE INSTRUCTION

? More Reading Support

A What can cause a population to grow? *fewer predators*

B What does a limiting factor do? *limits the growth of a population*

English Learners There are many different kinds of charts and graphs. English learners may be unfamiliar with some uncommon types. Help students understand how to read the population chart on the page above.

INVESTIGATE Limiting Factors

What effect does spacing have upon a population of plants?

DESIGN — YOUR OWN — EXPERIMENT

Using the materials listed, design an experiment to test this hypothesis: "If plants grow too close together, the health of the population will be affected because the individual plants do not get enough of the nutrients and water that they need."

PROCEDURE

1. Decide how to use the seeds, cups, and soil to test the hypothesis.

2. Write up your experimental procedure. Include safety tips.

WHAT DO YOU THINK?

- What are the variables in your experiment?
- What evidence would you expect to see if your hypothesis is true?

CHALLENGE Conduct your experiment. Note that seeds must be planted near the top of the soil. A good measure for this is the tip of a pencil. Measure and record the growth of the seedlings. Allow the seedlings to grow for two weeks before drawing your conclusions.

SKILL FOCUS
Designing experiments

MATERIALS
- paper cups
- potting soil
- radish seeds
- water
- pencil
- ruler

TIME
20 minutes

Maintaining a Balance

Living things have certain minimum requirements for food, water, and living space. When a population reaches a state where it can no longer grow, the population has reached its **carrying capacity,** the maximum number of individuals that an ecosystem can support. You can see on page 64 that the graph for the moose population does appear to peak around 1500. Even if there were no wolves on the island of Isle Royale, the population of moose would still be limited because there is only so much food and space available.

CHECK YOUR READING Explain the term *carrying capacity*.

VOCABULARY
Remember to make a four square diagram for *carrying capacity* in your notebook. Try to use *limiting factor* in your diagram.

An ecosystem's carrying capacity is different for each population. A meadow ecosystem will support many more bees and ants than bluebirds, for example. Isle Royale supports many more moose than wolves. The moose is a primary consumer of plants. It is at a lower level of the energy pyramid than the wolf, a secondary consumer.

Biotic factors can be limiting factors. These factors include the interactions between populations, such as competition, predation, and parasitism. Abiotic factors, such as temperature, availability of water or minerals, and exposure to wind, are also limiting.

Chapter 2: **Interactions Within Ecosystems** 65 **D**

INVESTIGATE Limiting Factors

PURPOSE To observe how space can be a limiting factor for plants

TIPS *20 min.*

- Do not plant seeds any deeper than twice their length.
- To accentuate the effects of limited space, crowd the 20 seeds closely together. Using 3-oz. cups for this experiment will dramatize the results.

WHAT DO YOU THINK?

- *The space given to the radish seeds should be the only variable.*
- *Radish seeds given less space would grow less successfully. There would be fewer and/or smaller plants.*

R Datasheet, Limiting Factors, p. 112

Technology Resources

Customize this student lab as needed or look for an alternative. Print rubrics to assess student lab reports.

Lab Generator CD-ROM

Teaching with Technology

Use a digital camera to take daily photos of the plants. Students can use them in a presentation of the experiment.

EXPLORE (the **BIG** idea)

Revisit "Internet Activity: Carrying Capacity" on p. 43. Have students explain how limiting factors affected carrying capacity in their simulations.

Ongoing Assessment

Explain what affects the size of a population.

Ask: What factors affect the carrying capacity of a population of trees? *nutrients, space, light, and water; disease, competition, predation*

CHECK YOUR READING *Answer: Carrying capacity is the maximum population that an environment can support.*

DIFFERENTIATE INSTRUCTION

? More Reading Support

C What's the name for the largest population that an environment can support? *carrying capacity*

Below Level Students may have trouble with the concept of carrying capacity. Use the analogy of a group of people on a boat. Ask: What are the factors that limit the number of people that can safely board the boat? *buoyancy of the boat relative to weight of passengers and supplies; space available to fit people without hurting each other; also could be food and water available for a trip* What are factors that limit the number of organisms that can survive in a population? *food, water, space, light*

Chapter 2 **65** **D**

Address Misconceptions

IDENTIFY Ask: What happens to organic material as it decays? If students answer that it "disappears" or "is destroyed," they may hold the misconception that decay causes matter to break down into nothing.

CORRECT Direct students to the primary succession diagram on p. 66. Explain that the broken-down rocks contribute to the mineral content of soil. As the first plants that grow on the thin, rocky soil die and decay, the materials that made up their living tissues become the soil's organic content. As this process continues, the soil layer eventually becomes deep enough to support trees.

REASSESS Ask: What else besides plants and rock particles contributes to soil content? *dead and decaying animal matter* What happens to the decaying organic matter after it becomes part of the soil? *Living organisms eat or absorb the nutrients it contains to carry on their life processes; organic matter becomes part of the life cycle in an altered form.*

Integrate the Sciences

In 1980 Mount St. Helens in Washington erupted, causing a blast of hot gas and debris that reached 300°C. The surface was new rock or scorched ash. Soon after the eruption, the Forest Service reported seeing long earth cores on top of the ash layer. The northern pocket gopher had made tunnels in the snow and filled them with fertile soil from underground burrows. The soil mixture became a seed bed for new plant life.

Teach from Visuals

To help students interpret the sequence of illustrations, ask:

- How is the underground different in the three pictures? *It is rock; then partly rock, partly soil; then soil.*

- What caused this difference? *Pioneering species broke down rock and contributed organic material.*

Ecosystems change over time.

Take a walk in a New Hampshire woods and you may see the remains of old stone walls scattered about. A hundred years ago this land was mostly farmland. The farms were abandoned. And now, new trees have grown where farm animals once grazed.

Succession (suhk-SEHSH-uhn) is the gradual change in an ecosystem in which one biological community is replaced by another. The change from field to forest is an example of succession. Over time the grasses of open farmland are slowly replaced by small plants and shrubs, then trees.

Primary Succession

READING TIP
Succeed and *succession* come from the same Latin root word, *succedere*, meaning to go up or to follow after.

Very few places on Earth are without some form of life. Even when a lava flow covers an area or a glacier retreats and leaves behind an empty and barren environment, plants will move into the area and bring it back to life. These are examples of primary succession, the establishment of a new biological community.

Pioneer species are the first living things to move into a barren environment. In the illustration below, moss and lichen move in after a glacier retreats. There is little or no topsoil. Moss and lichen are common pioneers because they have tiny rootlike structures that can take hold on exposed rock.

Primary Succession

Primary succession can occur after a glacier retreats, when little topsoil is present.

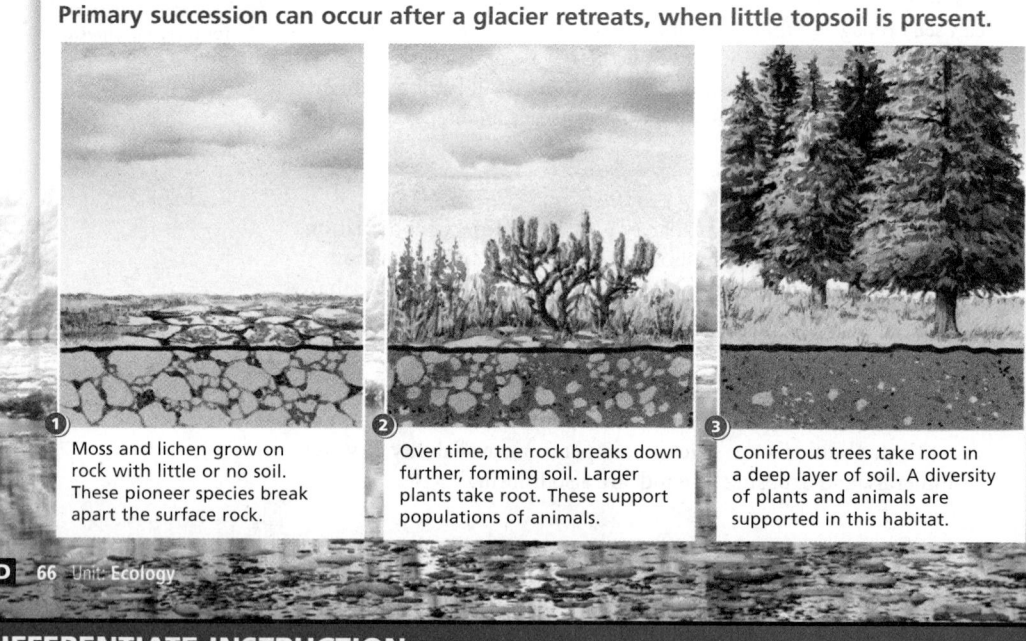

1. Moss and lichen grow on rock with little or no soil. These pioneer species break apart the surface rock.

2. Over time, the rock breaks down further, forming soil. Larger plants take root. These support populations of animals.

3. Coniferous trees take root in a deep layer of soil. A diversity of plants and animals are supported in this habitat.

DIFFERENTIATE INSTRUCTION

 More Reading Support

D What is succession? *a gradual change in the plant and animal communities in an area*

E Give an example of a pioneer species. *moss, lichens*

Advanced Challenge students to come up with examples of how secondary succession could be followed by primary succession in a particular environment.

R Challenge and Extension, p. 111

As the pioneers grow, they gradually weaken the rock surface. The rock breaks down and weathers over time. Decaying plant matter adds nutrients, forming soil. Now a variety of small plants and shrubs can take root. These plants, in turn, support insects, birds, and small rodents. Eventually there is enough soil to support coniferous trees. Forests grow, providing a stable habitat for larger animals.

RESOURCE CENTER
CLASSZONE.COM

Learn more about succession.

Secondary Succession

?
F

Secondary succession takes place after a major disturbance to the biological community in a stable ecosystem. Despite the disturbance, the soil remains. A community can be disturbed by a natural event, like fire or flood, or it can be disturbed by human activity. A forest cleared or farmland abandoned can lead to secondary succession.

?
G

The illustration below shows secondary succession following a forest fire. The damage, as bad as it is, is surface damage. Below the surface, seeds and plant roots survive. After a time, grasses and small shrubs grow up among the decaying remains of the original plants. Birds, insects, and rodents return. Alder trees take root—alders are trees that put nutrients into the soil. Over time, a variety of trees and plants grow, providing food for a variety of animals.

CHECK YOUR READING What is the difference between primary and secondary succession?

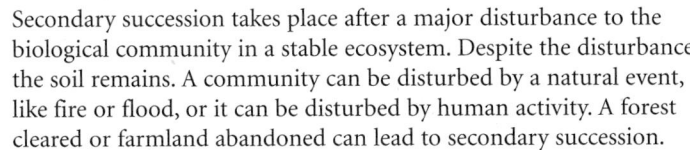

Secondary Succession

Secondary succession occurs if soil remains after a disturbance, such as a forest fire.

① Plants at the surface are burned; however, below the surface seeds and some plant roots survive.

② Grasses and small shrubs sprout among the charred trees and vegetation. Smaller animals return.

③ Deciduous trees like elm and maple grow and mature. A forest habitat is reestablished. More animals are supported.

Chapter 2: Interactions Within Ecosystems 67 **D**

DIFFERENTIATE INSTRUCTION

Below Level Use a table to help students understand the different ways ecosystems change over time.

Type of change	Soil	Cause	Pioneer species
primary succession	no	lava flow, glacier movement, landslide	need to move in via seeds and spores
secondary succession	yes	fire, flooding, land-use change	survive in soil

Teach from Visuals

To help students interpret the sequence of illustrations, ask:

- What kind of soil is still on the surface in the first image? *topsoil*
- Why are some plants able to grow back quickly? *because some roots and seeds survive below the surface*
- What lures animals and insects back to the area? *new plant life*

Teach Difficult Concepts

Give more extreme examples to help students distinguish between primary and secondary succession. Primary succession examples: the surface of new construction such as a building or wall, a sterilized canning jar. Secondary succession examples: ice-scoured riverbank, scrubbed footstep, a rinsed-out cup. To help students understand, try the following demonstration.

Teacher Demo

Collect a newly broken rock and a moss- or lichen-covered stone from an old wall, or a new brick and a mossy one. Show them to the class and point out the totally bare sharp surface of the new rock. Describe the succession that could lead to the lichen-covered rock. Pioneer species trap dirt and litter and provide hiding places for small organisms and rooting material for plants.

Ongoing Assessment

Describe how ecosystems change over time.

Ask: When a glacier retreats or a forest burns, how does the ecosystem recover? *After a glacier retreats, primary succession occurs. Pioneer species add soil, small plants and animals move in, then large plants and animals arrive. After a fire, secondary succession occurs. Small plants and shrubs grow from roots and seeds that survived underground. Large plants and animals return.*

CHECK YOUR READING *Answer: Primary succession occurs when life moves to a barren, soilless area. In secondary succession, the ecosystem changes after a disturbance, when there is still soil for life to gain a foothold.*

Chapter 2 **67** **D**

Reinforce (the **BIG** idea)

Have students relate the section to the Big Idea.

 Reinforcing Key Concepts, p. 113

 **ASSESS & RETEACH**

Assess

A Section 2.3 Quiz, p. 25

Reteach

Write the following terms on the board:

- carrying capacity
- limiting factors
- pioneer species
- predator-prey interaction
- primary succession
- secondary succession

Have students tell whether each term relates more closely to the concept of "population change" or the concept of "ecosystem change." Encourage them to explain their answers. Then discuss how population changes cause overall ecosystem changes and vice versa. Point out that the ecosystem includes all the populations within it.

Technology Resources

Have students visit **ClassZone.com** for reaching of Key Concepts.

 CONTENT REVIEW

 CONTENT REVIEW CD-ROM

Patterns of Change

All types of ecosystems go through succession. Succession can establish a forest community, a wetland community, a coastal community, or even an ocean community. Succession can happen over tens or hundreds of years. The pattern is the same, however. First a community of producers is established. These are followed by decomposers and consumers, then more producers, then more decomposers and consumers. Over time, a stable biological community develops.

In a way, the establishment of a biological community is like planting a garden. You first prepare the soil. Perhaps you add compost. This adds organic matter and nutrients to the soil, which helps the soil hold water. With the right preparation, your vegetables and flowers should grow well.

Pioneer species can function in one of two ways in an ecological succession. They can help other species to grow or they can prevent species from getting established.

READING TiP

As you read about the two ways plant species function in succession, think in terms of cooperation and competition.

- Some plant species function a bit like gardeners. Trees such as alders have nitrogen-fixing bacteria on their roots that improve the nutrient content of the soil and allow other tree seedlings to grow. Pioneering species may also stabilize the soil, shade the soil surface, or add nutrients to the soil when they die and decay.

- Other plant species produce conditions that keep out other plants. The plants may release chemicals that keep other plants from taking root. Or a new species may outcompete other species by using up resources or better resisting a disease.

Such interactions between living things help to determine succession in an ecosystem.

2.3 Review

KEY CONCEPTS

1. Describe three factors that could limit the size of a population in a habitat.
2. List two natural disturbances and two human-made disturbances that can lead to succession.
3. What role do pioneer species play in succession?

CRITICAL THINKING

4. **Infer** How and why would secondary succession in a tundra habitat differ from secondary succession in a rainforest habitat?
5. **Predict** Suppose you are clearing an area in your yard to construct a small pond. Sketch the stages of succession that would follow this disturbance.

CHALLENGE

6. **Synthesize** Imagine you are the wildlife manager for a forest preserve that supports both moose and wolves. What types of information should you collect to determine the carrying capacity for each species?

ANSWERS

1. predators, parasites, food, space, nutrients, disease, etc.

2. volcanic eruptions, glacier retreat, fire, flooding, abandoned fields

3. Moss, lichen, and plants can move into a barren area on the wind. Over time they help break rock into soil, die into the soil, and attract insects and other animals.

4. Succession occurs more slowly in the tundra because of cold temperatures and a short growing season.

5. Sketches could include pioneering seeds, insects, and small lifeforms in the pond.

Vegetation and larger animals might be shown around an older pond.

6. Sample answer: a census of animals, including their sex; plants; food sources; breeding sites; human factors that may affect population

MATH in SCIENCE

MATH TUTORIAL
CLASSZONE.COM

Click on Math Tutorial for more help with multiplying fractions and whole numbers.

SKILL: MULTIPLYING A FRACTION BY A WHOLE NUMBER

Birth Rates and Populations

Ecologists pay careful attention to the yearly birth rates of endangered species. A birth rate is usually expressed as a fraction. It is the number of births divided by the number of adult females. A 2/5 birth rate for a population means that there are 2 births for every 5 adult females.

Example

Suppose at a national park in Borneo, there is a 2/5 birth rate among orangutans. There are 150 adult females in the park. Estimate how many young will be born. To find out, multiply the fraction by the number of adult females.

(1) Multiply the numerator of the fraction by the whole number.

$$150 \text{ females} \times \frac{2 \text{ births}}{5 \text{ females}} = \frac{150 \times 2}{5} = \frac{300}{5}$$

(2) Divide by the denominator.

$$\frac{300}{5} = 300 \div 5 = 60$$

ANSWER 60 young

Answer the following questions.

1. In 2001, there were about 72 adult female right whales. Scientists observing the whales reported a 1/3 birth rate. About how many right whales were born in 2001?

2. Giant pandas are severely endangered. Currently about 140 giant pandas live in captivity, in zoos and parks. About 3/5 of these were born in captivity. How many is that?

3. The orangutan population of the world has decreased sharply. At one time there were over 100,000 ranging across Asia. Now there may be 21,000, of which, 2/3 live in Borneo. About how many orangutans live in Borneo?

CHALLENGE Suppose 1/1 is given as the desired birth rate to save an endangered population. If the population is currently at 4 births per 20 adult females, by how many times does the rate need to increase to reach the desired rate?

ANSWERS

1. $\frac{72}{3}$ = 24 calves

2. $\frac{140 \times 3}{5} = \frac{420}{5}$ = 84 pandas

3. $\frac{21,000 \times 2}{3} = \frac{42,000}{3}$ = 14,000 orangutans

CHALLENGE The rate is 20% of what is desired. The desired rate represents 100%. It needs to increase by 5 times its current rate.

MATH IN SCIENCE
Math Skills Practice for Science

Set Learning Goal

To calculate birth rates and populations by multiplying fractions and whole numbers

Present the Science

Animals become endangered for various reasons. Right whales were hunted to near extinction, not only because they had thick blubber and valuable baleen, but also because they swam slowly and floated when killed.

Develop Calculation Skills

Remind students that the numerator of the fraction is above the line, and the denominator is below.

To help them remember which part of the fraction to multiply, emphasize that they can think of "below the line" as "division." If you multiply "below the line," you are really dividing, making the total decrease: $\frac{1}{16}$ is less than $\frac{1}{2}$.

DIFFERENTIATION TIP Use grid paper or graph paper to model some simple problems multiplying friendly fractions such as $\frac{1}{2}$, $\frac{3}{4}$, $\frac{2}{3}$ by small whole numbers, such as 4, 5, 6. In each case, shade squares that show the fraction as a portion of a larger square. Students will see that repeated addition gets the same result as multiplying.

Close

Ask students to brainstorm how scientists can increase the population of an endangered species. *Raise birth rates by encouraging captive breeding, restore habitat, protect animals from hunting.*

 • Math Support, p. 119
 • Math Practice, p. 120

Technology Resources

Students can visit **ClassZone.com** to practice multiplying fractions and whole numbers.

 MATH TUTORIAL

BACK TO

the BIG idea

Have students choose one of the habitats discussed in the chapter and give examples of the different types of relationships found there. Ask them to propose a natural disaster that could occur in that habitat and to explain how the habitat will recover.

○ KEY CONCEPTS SUMMARY

SECTION 2.1

Ask students to describe the habitat in which the crabs live, as shown in the picture on the right. *The crabs live in a rocky, beach habitat, next to the ocean. Based on the crabs' habitat, what niche do you think the crabs fill? Crabs gather food from the beach and the ocean. They use the beach and the ocean for reproduction and shelter. The crabs are also food for other animals in the habitat.*

SECTION 2.2

Ask students to explain how the faces represent the different symbiotic relationships. *For mutualism, both faces are smiles, meaning both benefit. For commensalism, one face is smiling and one is blank, meaning one benefits and the other is not affected. For parasitism, one face is smiling and the other is frowning, meaning one benefits and the other is harmed.*

SECTION 2.3

Ask: What types of succession are shown? *primary and secondary* What is the main difference between them? *In secondary succession, there is soil that remains.*

Review Concepts

- Big Idea Flow Chart, p. T9
- Chapter Outline, pp. T15–T16

---

2 Chapter Review

the BIG idea

Living things within an ecosystem interact with each other and the environment.

CONTENT REVIEW
CLASSZONE.COM

◖ KEY CONCEPTS SUMMARY

2.1 Groups of living things interact within ecosystems.

- Members of the same species form a population within a habitat.
- Each species has a distinct role within a habitat. This is its niche.

Population of Crabs   **Island Habitat for Crabs**

VOCABULARY
species p. 45
population p. 46
habitat p. 46
niche p. 47
community p. 48

2.2 Organisms can interact in different ways.

Organisms within a community interact with each other in many ways. Some are predators, some are prey. Some compete with one another, some cooperate. Some species form symbiotic relationships with other species:

Mutualism
benefits both

Commensalism
benefits one, other unaffected

Parasitism
benefits one, harms other

VOCABULARY
predator p. 55
prey p. 55
competition p. 55
cooperation p. 57
symbiosis p. 58
mutualism p. 58
commensalism p. 59
parasitism p. 59

2.3 Ecosystems are always changing.

Primary Succession

In a barren area, a new community is established with pioneer species, like mosses, that do well with little or no soil. Mosses eventually give way to coniferous trees.

Secondary Succession

When a disturbance damages a community but soil remains, the community gets reestablished from seeds and roots left behind. Grasses grow, then small shrubs, and eventually trees.

VOCABULARY
limiting factor p. 64
carrying capacity p. 65
succession p. 66
pioneer species p. 66

D 70 Unit: Ecology

Technology Resources

Have students visit **ClassZone.com** or use the CD-ROM for a cumulative review of concepts.

Engage students in a whole-class interactive review of Key Concepts. Edit content as you wish.

  CONTENT REVIEW

  CONTENT REVIEW CD-ROM

  POWER PRESENTATIONS

Reviewing Vocabulary

Draw a Venn diagram for each pair of terms. Put shared characteristics in the overlap area, put differences to the outside. A sample diagram is provided.

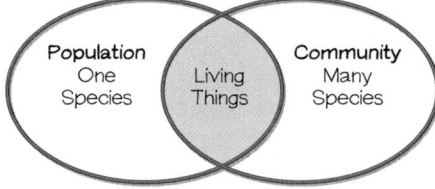

Population
One Species

Living Things

Community
Many Species

1. habitat, niche

2. mutualism, commensalism

3. mutualism, parasitism

4. competition, cooperation

5. primary succession, secondary succession

Reviewing Key Concepts

Multiple Choice *Choose the letter of the best answer.*

6. What is carrying capacity?
   a. the largest population an ecosystem can support
   b. the smallest population an ecosystem can support
   c. the number of species an ecosystem can support
   d. the number of habitats in an ecosystem

7. A new species of bird moves into a habitat. The birds feed on a particular caterpillar, so that the resulting population of butterflies is small. What can be said of the relationship between the birds and the butterflies?
   a. The birds and the butterflies have a commensal relationship.
   b. The birds and butterflies compete.
   c. The birds are a limiting factor for the butterflies.
   d. The birds and butterflies coexist.

8. Certain types of worms live in the mud at the bottom of lakes. What does the mud represent for the worm?
   a. an ecosystem   **c.** a community
   b. a niche   **d.** a habitat

9. What is a pioneer species?
   a. a species that travels within an ecosystem
   b. a species that is among the first to move into an area after a natural disaster
   c. a species that depends upon animal life
   d. a species that cannot return after a natural disaster

10. Which is an example of competition within the same species?
   a. whales in a pod
   b. wildebeests in a herd
   c. creosote bushes in a desert
   d. birds that fly south

11. Which is an example of parasitism?
   a. dog and tick
   b. termite and protozoans
   c. shark and remora
   d. flower and hummingbird

12. Which is an example of secondary succession?
   a. succession after a forest fire
   b. succession after a large volcanic lava flow devastates an area
   c. succession after a glacier retreats, leaving bare rock
   d. succession after a hurricane washes away all the sand from a beach

Short Answer *Write a short answer to each question.*

13. Put the terms in order, starting with the term that includes the largest number of individuals and ending with the group containing the fewest individuals: community, population, ecosystem, biome.

14. List four ways in which members of the same species can cooperate with each other.

15. Describe three different types of symbiosis.

Reviewing Vocabulary

1. habitat: environment surrounding a living thing;
both: within a boundary; relate to matter and energy;
niche: role of one type of living thing in moving matter and energy

2. mutualism: two species benefit by interactions;
both: symbiotic relationships; benefit at least one species; neither is harmed;
commensalism: one species benefits from an interaction, the other remains neutral.

3. mutualism: two species benefit by an interaction;
both: symbiotic relationships, benefit at least one species;
parasitism: one species benefits from an interaction, the other is harmed.

4. competition: two living things are in conflict or oppose each other;
both: types of interactions, can be between or within species;
cooperation: two living things work together or help each other.

5. primary succession: takes place in a barren landscape;
both: series of changes in an ecosystem; take place after disaster or erosion;
secondary succession: takes place after most living things have died, soil remains

Reviewing Key Concepts

6. a   *10. c*

7. c   *11. a*

8. d   *12. a*

9. b

13. biome, ecosystem, community, population

14. hunt together (whales), move together for protection (wildebeest, herring), share different tasks (ants), care for young (primates)

15. benefits to both species (mutualism), benefits one, but harms another (parasitism), benefits one while other is unaffected (commensalism)

Thinking Critically

16. Years 1–7: steady increase in both; Years 8–10: a decline in both.

17. It is reasonable to infer that the larger a population of lynx or hare, the more pelts traders would sell. The data given is not for populations, but it does suggest increase and decrease in the populations.

18. limiting factors for hares: predator, food, weather, and area of habitat

19. No. Trees function in similar ways, but each species has its niche. Birds, insects, and mammals feed on different trees; shade and nutrients vary plants and fungi around trees.

20. All plants need sunlight. In early stages of succession, small plants grow fastest. Eventually, shrubs, then trees grow, blocking light for smaller plants. Large trees limit growth of small trees.

21. any three: clearing land for development, abandoning farmland, logging, fires, flooding from dams

22. Creosotes are part of a desert community in which populations compete for limited resources. They spread widely and evenly. The roots release a toxin that is a limiting factor for other bushes. Thus, each creosote gets the resources it needs.

23. It would cause populations that rely on those trees for food or shelter to decrease; however, open space might increase low bushes, grasses, and animals that feed on them.

the BIG idea

24. One fish eating another is a predator-prey interaction. Fish may clean, protect, or attract food to one another.

25. Answers should use correct terms in ecology, and should address interactions and carrying capacity.

UNIT PROJECTS

Collect schedules, materials lists, and questions. Be sure dates and materials are obtainable, and questions are focused.

 Unit Projects, pp. 5–10

Thinking Critically

The data in the table below come from the records of a Canadian trading company that, in the late 1800s, bought lynx and hare pelts from hunters and trappers. The Canadian lynx and varying hare share the same habitat. The lynx relies on the hare as a food source. Use the table to answer the next three questions.

Year	Lynx	Hare
1	2	30
2	15	55
3	65	90
4	75	160
5	100	200
6	95	140
7	75	80
8	40	35
9	20	3
10	3	4
11	30	40
12	55	95

16. **ANALYZE** How would you describe the pattern that emerges between the two populations in years 1–7? How does the pattern change in years 8–10?

17. **EVALUATE** The data on the lynx and hare pelts have been used to suggest the sizes of the lynx and hare populations. Is this a reasonable approach to take? Why or why not?

18. **ANALYZE** Scientists have observed that hare populations will go through cycles of increasing and decreasing populations even when the lynx is not part of the habitat. How would you explain this observation?

19. **APPLY** A forest has pine trees, along with oak trees and birch trees. All the trees provide shelter and food for different animals in the habitat. Do these trees occupy the same niche? Explain.

20. **INFER** Explain why low-growing plants like mosses are eventually replaced by shrubs, and shrubs replaced by trees, in both primary and secondary successions.

21. **PROVIDE EXAMPLES** List three human activities that could lead to secondary succession.

22. **ANALYZE** Creosote bushes in the Mojave desert are spread out, so that each plant is about an equal distance from another. Write a short paragraph to describe the interaction of the creosote bushes, using the terms from the table.

competition	population pattern
limiting factor	community

23. **APPLY** How might building homes in a wooded area affect carrying capacity of different populations in the area?

the BIG idea

24. **SUMMARIZE** Look again at the photograph on pages 42–43. How would you change or add details to your answer to the question on the photograph?

25. **APPLY** Imagine that you are an ecologist from another galaxy who arrives on Earth. Describe a human community using the terms that an Earth ecologist would use to describe a natural community. Your description should include at least three examples of interactions between individuals (whether the same or different species). Identify the biotic or abiotic factors that serve as limiting factors to human population growth. Also state whether you think the human population is at or below its carrying capacity—and why.

UNIT PROJECTS

By now you should have completed the following items for your unit project.
- questions that you have asked about the topic
- schedule showing when you will complete each step of your project
- list of resources including Web sites, print resources, and materials

---

MONITOR AND RETEACH

If students are having trouble using the concepts in Chapter Review items 2, 3, 15, and 24, suggest that they review the visual on p. 60. Have them answer the questions using the illustration of the backyard habitat and the organisms that are pictured.

Students may benefit from summarizing one or more sections of the chapter.

 Summarizing the Chapter, pp. 139–140

Standardized Test Practice

For practice on your state test, go to . . .

TEST PRACTICE
CLASSZONE.COM

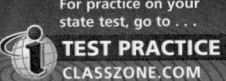

Understanding Symbiosis

Read the following description of the strangler fig and the relationship it has with other species in a rain forest. Then answer the questions that follow.

Strangler figs are part of many symbiotic relationships in a rain-forest ecosystem. In some cases, the symbiotic relationship benefits both the fig and an animal. Fig wasps lay their eggs in the fruit of the strangler fig and, in turn, pollinate it. Many birds feed on the fruit of the strangler fig and, in doing so, spread the seeds of the plant. The fig does not benefit from its interactions with all species. For example, certain butterflies feed on juice from the fruit without affecting the tree in any way.

The symbiotic relationship that gives the strangler fig its name is that between the strangler fig and its host tree. Birds drop seeds onto the top of a tree, and vines of the fig grow downward. Eventually, the vines of the strangler fig touch the ground and join with the roots of the host tree. The host tree is harmed because the leaves of the strangler fig block sunlight and its vines take root, using up nutrients the host tree needs.

1. Which feeding relationship is a form of mutualism in which both species benefit?

a. the strangler fig and its host tree
b. the strangler fig and the butterflies
c. the strangler fig and the birds
d. the strangler fig and the fig wasp

2. Which symbiotic relationship is a form of parasitism in which one species benefits and the other is harmed?

a. the strangler fig and its host tree
b. the strangler fig and the butterflies
c. the strangler fig and the birds
d. the strangler fig and the fig wasp

3. Which symbiotic relationship is a commensal relationship in which one species benefits without affecting the other?

a. the strangler fig and its host tree
b. the strangler fig and the butterflies
c. the strangler fig and the birds
d. the strangler fig and the fig wasp

4. Which word best describes the interaction between the strangler fig and its host?

a. coexistence
b. cooperation
c. competition
d. community

Extended Response

5. Strangler figs attach to trees that are sometimes cut for lumber. Write a paragraph that describes how removal of the host trees would affect these populations.

- butterflies
- birds
- wasps
- strangler figs

6. Write a paragraph describing some of the different roles played by a strangler fig in the rain forest. Use the vocabulary terms listed below in your answer.

habitat	niche	populations
community	ecosystem	

Understanding Symbiosis

1. c   2. a   3. b   4. c

Extended Response

5. RUBRIC
4 points for a response that correctly identifies the following effects:

- on butterflies: food lost
- on birds: food lost
- wasps: nesting area lost
- strangler fig: access to sunlight lost

Sample answer: The populations of birds and butterflies will be affected since the strangler fig provides them with food. How much they are affected depends on if they have other food sources. The population of wasps will decrease in the next generation because wasps need the fig to reproduce. The figs will get cut down with the host trees. The strangler fig grows well by reaching the tops of trees for sunlight. It may not grow as well on the ground.

3 points correctly identifies how three populations are affected
2 points correctly identifies how two populations are affected
1 point correctly identifies how one population is affected

6. RUBRIC
4 points for a response that correctly describes the role and uses four of the following terms accurately:

- habitat
- niche
- populations
- community
- ecosystem

Sample answer: The strangler fig fills an important <u>niche</u> in a rainforest <u>habitat</u>. <u>Populations</u> of birds and butterflies depend upon it for food. The fig wasp uses the fruit as part of its reproductive cycle. The wasp in turn helps the reproductive cycle of the fig. Figs are part of a diverse <u>community</u> in a rainforest <u>ecosytem</u>.

3 points describes role adequately and uses three terms accurately
2 points describes role partially and uses two terms accurately
1 point describes role partially and uses 1 term accurately

METACOGNITIVE ACTIVITY

Have students answer the following questions in their **Science Notebook:**

1. What did you find the most surprising about interactions in ecosystems?

2. What questions do you still have about interactions in ecosystems?

3. What are the strongest pieces right now in your Unit Project?

TIMELINES in Science

FOCUS

⬤ Set Learning Goals

Students will

- Examine historical steps people have taken to protect ecosystems.
- Learn about some of the tools people have used to study and preserve ecosystems.
- Write a proposal for protecting the ecosystem.

National Science Education Standards

A.9.a–b, A.9.d–g Understandings about Scientific Inquiry

E.6.a–c Understandings about Science and Technology

F.5.a–e, F.5.g Science and Technology in Society

G.1.a–b Science as a Human Endeavor

G.2.a Nature of Science

G.3.a–c History of Science

INSTRUCT

History Connection

Point out to students that the top half of the timeline shows major events in wilderness conservation in the United States starting in the1870s. The bottom half of the timeline illustrates advances in technology and the application of wilderness conservation. The gap between 1910 and 1950 represents a block of time that has been omitted.

Technology

PHOTOGRAPHY First sold in 1888, the Kodak Camera was simple: press a button to expose the film, then turn a key to advance the film. Ask students how this new camera influenced the way conservationists were able to work. *Both conservationists and wildlife photographers could move freely with a lightweight camera to capture images in the environment.*

D **74** Unit: Ecology

WILDERNESS CONSERVATION

The idea of wilderness conservation would have seemed strange to anyone living before the 1800s. The wilderness was vast and much of the wildlife in it dangerous to humans.

In the late 1800s, as smoke from railroads and factories rose in American skies, scientists, artists, even presidents began the work of setting aside land as parks and reservations to protect natural landscapes. Forestry, unpracticed in the U.S. before the 1890s, became a priority of the federal government as the new century dawned. Industries learned to harvest and nurture forests rather than clearing them. Next came the protection of animal species along with a call to control the pollution and depletion caused by human activity.

1872

National Parks Protect Resources

On March 1, 1872, President Ulysses S. Grant signs a law declaring Yellowstone's 2 million acres in northwest Wyoming as the country's first national park. Yellowstone serves as a model, and by 1887, about 45 million acres of forest have been set aside.

EVENTS

1870

APPLICATIONS and TECHNOLOGY

TECHNOLOGY

Seeing the Wilderness

The development of photography in 1839, and its spread during the Civil War, led to adventurous mobile photographers in the late 1800s. In the early 1860s Mathew Brady and other photographers took mobile studios to the battlefields to bring war news to the public. By the late 1860s and early 1870s the wagonload shrank to a pack load. In 1871, William Henry Jackson balanced his tripod in Yellowstone, as the official photographer of the region's first U.S. Geological Survey.

D **74** Unit: Ecology

DIFFERENTIATE INSTRUCTION

Below Level For those students who may have difficulty understanding how information is organized on a timeline, call their attention to the dates on the yellow center line.

Point out how the dates become more recent as they move from left to right. Call attention also to the lines connecting the event boxes to specific dates in the timeline. Emphasize how timelines are a good way of showing quickly a brief or selected history of any subject.

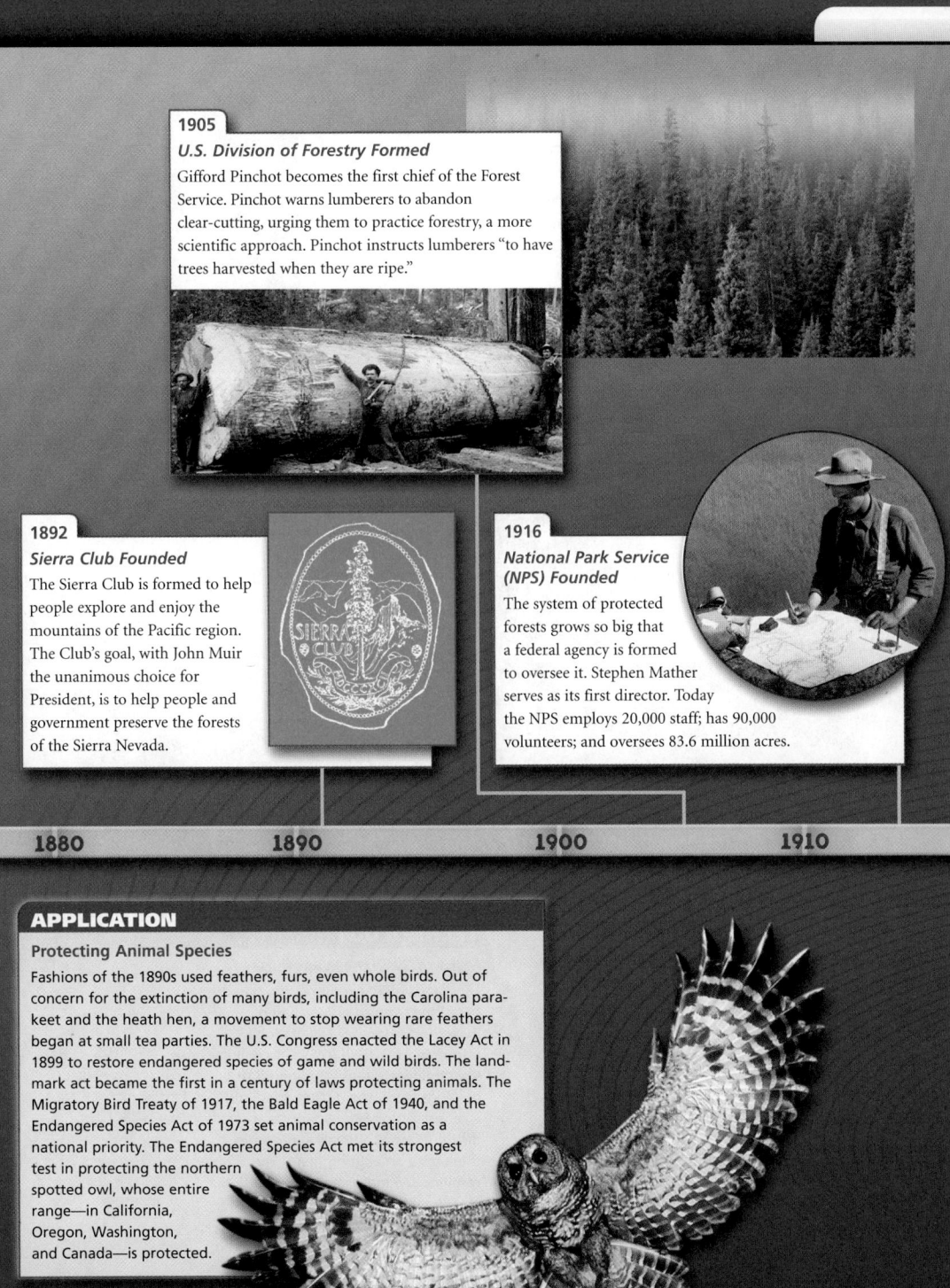

1905

U.S. Division of Forestry Formed

Gifford Pinchot becomes the first chief of the Forest Service. Pinchot warns lumberers to abandon clear-cutting, urging them to practice forestry, a more scientific approach. Pinchot instructs lumberers "to have trees harvested when they are ripe."

1892

Sierra Club Founded

The Sierra Club is formed to help people explore and enjoy the mountains of the Pacific region. The Club's goal, with John Muir the unanimous choice for President, is to help people and government preserve the forests of the Sierra Nevada.

1916

National Park Service (NPS) Founded

The system of protected forests grows so big that a federal agency is formed to oversee it. Stephen Mather serves as its first director. Today the NPS employs 20,000 staff; has 90,000 volunteers; and oversees 83.6 million acres.

1880   1890   1900   1910

APPLICATION

Protecting Animal Species

Fashions of the 1890s used feathers, furs, even whole birds. Out of concern for the extinction of many birds, including the Carolina parakeet and the heath hen, a movement to stop wearing rare feathers began at small tea parties. The U.S. Congress enacted the Lacey Act in 1899 to restore endangered species of game and wild birds. The landmark act became the first in a century of laws protecting animals. The Migratory Bird Treaty of 1917, the Bald Eagle Act of 1940, and the Endangered Species Act of 1973 set animal conservation as a national priority. The Endangered Species Act met its strongest test in protecting the northern spotted owl, whose entire range—in California, Oregon, Washington, and Canada—is protected.

Scientific Process

Testing hypotheses in ecology takes a long time. A conservationist has no way to be certain about the long-term results of the actions he or she supports. Ecosystems are always larger and more complex than laboratories. When a conservationist takes an action to preserve the environment, he or she must often wait years to fully understand the results. Similarly, the environmental impacts of other human activity, such as industry and agriculture, often take years to truly be felt. As scientists, ecologists have to balance the two.

Art Connection

1892 The Sierra Club has had several logos in its history. The current logo features a giant sequoia tree and the peak of Yosemite's Half Dome mountain. Although the Sierra Club is now a nationwide organization, these symbols were chosen then to symbolize the distinctive beauty of the Sierra Nevada Mountain range. Students may wish to design their own conservation logo. Tell students to think about which natural resources of their region (trees, water, etc.) are most important to preserve and incorporate these into their logos.

Application

PROTECTING ANIMAL SPECIES

The Lacey Act eventually led to the Endangered Species Act, which set up two classes of protected species: *threatened* and *endangered.* The act covers all species of plants and animals. Species classified as threatened are not as in danger of dying out as species classified as endangered. The Fish and Wildlife Service monitors the populations of threatened and endangered species as steps are taken to preserve their habitats. Ask students why they think certain species of plants and animals are threatened. *loss of food and habitat due to human beings' actions on the environment*

DIFFERENTIATE INSTRUCTION

Advanced Students can visit the website of the U.S. Fish and Wildlife Service and learn about other endangered and threatened species. They can also find out which species have been taken off the endangered list—the success stories.

Students might then select one species and report on what actions are recommended for that species' future. Encourage students to suggest things anyone could do to help ensure the species is protected in a balanced or ecological way.

Social Studies Connection

1960s The 1960s was both an exciting and troubling time in American history. The decade saw the assassinations of President John F. Kennedy in 1963 and civil rights leader Dr. Martin Luther King, Jr. in 1968. College students in the '60s held peaceful protests against American foreign and domestic policies and succeeded in getting much legislation passed by Congress. Some of this legislation eventually led to significant environmental initiatives like the Endangered Species Act and establishment of the Environmental Protection Agency. **Ask:** Why do you think environmental issues would have concerned people at this time? *Sample answer: People were concerned about their country and wanted to protect it from threats; or People were disappointed by human activities and wanted to focus on nature and wildlife.*

Language Arts Connection

1962 Many people consider the publication of *Silent Spring* to be the start of the environmentalist movement. More than simply calling for a stop to the use of pesticides, Carson urged that people needed to adopt a different view of their place in the world. People needed to see themselves as part of nature, not as masters of nature. Ask students why they think this change in view would give people a greater respect for nature. *Sample answer: If people are part of nature, they will want to protect it.*

Social Studies Connection

1968 The Grand Canyon has been considered a sacred site by the Hopi of the southwestern United States. Hopi mythology holds that the first people emerged from inside the Earth through the Grand Canyon.

1951

Nature Conservancy Established

The Nature Conservancy is formed to preserve plants, animals, and natural communities that represent Earth's biological diversity.

1962

Glen Canyon Destroyed

Completion of the Glen Canyon dam causes flooding in Glen Canyon, an immense area north of the Grand Canyon. Many groups fight to close the dam, but it is too late. The canyon is destroyed as Lake Powell forms.

1962

Silent Spring *Breaks Silence*

Biologist and science writer Rachel Carson publishes *Silent Spring.* Chemical pesticides have been widely used and publicized, but Carson uses scientific evidence to show that many of these chemicals harm people and the environment.

1968

Grand Canyon Dam Plans Squashed

Plans to dam the Grand Canyon are withdrawn as a result of public outcry. Recalling what happened to Glen Canyon, organizers ran national newspaper ads in 1966 making the public aware of plans to dam the Canyon.

1950   1960   1970

TECHNOLOGY

Maps to Save the Wilderness

Land and wildlife conservation has benefited from computer-based mapping technology called global information systems (GIS). GIS compiles satellite photographs, temperature readings, and other information into a central set of data. Scientists enter distributions of animals and overlay these data on existing maps. The resulting GIS maps show the gap in an animal's range and the quality of its habitat. Government efforts to restore the habitat of the endangered San Joaquin Kit Fox relied on GIS maps.

DIFFERENTIATE INSTRUCTION

English Learners English learners may not know the expression *public outcry* (1968). Students may also need help with words such as *pesticides, publishes,* and *evidence* (1962). You might point out the connection between the terms: *publishes, publicized,* and *public.* Write such terms on the board and put reminder sketches beside them.

Encourage students with limited English to focus mainly on understanding the red headings in the event boxes.

1990 to present

Reservation vs. Resource

In 1990, President George H.W. Bush expands the Arctic National Wildlife Refuge (ANWR) to more than twice its 1980 size. In 2001, President George W. Bush proposes limited oil drilling within the range. Today, debate continues over how to manage its resources and wildlife.

RESOURCE CENTER
CLASSZONE.COM
Read more about current conservation efforts.

1990   2000

APPLICATION

Selling a Service

In New York City in 1996, the water department spent $1.5 billion to protect natural watersheds rather than build a $6 billion water treatment plant. In 2001, a group of scientists met to promote the value that ecosystems bring to society—benefits that include pest control, air purification, and water treatment. For example, dragonflies can eat 300 mosquitoes in a single day. Toads and bats can eat a thousand or more mosquitoes in a single day or night.

INTO THE FUTURE

Society has long put a price on natural resources—minerals, water, timber, and so on. But how much is an ecosystem worth? Communities have begun to look at the dollar values of "ecosystem services," the ongoing activities in nature that keep our environment healthy. Data is needed on ecosystem processes. Such data can be compared to the services of human-made treatment plants and agriculture.

Other questions arise with protecting species. Many species, such as wild turkeys and bald eagles, once endangered have come back in great numbers. When a protected species thrives it may endanger another species or bump up against the human landscape and human activity. How can managers of resources set priorities?

ACTIVITIES

Ecosystem Services Proposal

What services to the human population are provided by your local ecosystem? Choose one service and describe how natural processes and interactions within the ecosystem provide the benefits you've identified. What processes are involved?

Write a proposal for protecting the ecosystem. Include a comparison of the estimated cost of protecting the ecosystem and the cost of human services that provide a similar benefit.

Writing Project: The Story Behind the News

Research one of the events described on the timeline. Then write the story behind that event.

DIFFERENTIATE INSTRUCTION

Advanced Encourage motivated students to submit their proposals to their local town or neighborhood board. Tell students that the reports do not need to be comprehensive and numbers exact, but that they should be able to justify how they arrived at the values.

Health Connection

Ask students how the health of our environment and wildlife population affects the health of the human population. Have them to give examples of this interconnectedness. *Sample answer: Fish living in polluted water become contaminated; human beings eat the contaminated fish.*

INTO THE FUTURE

Make three columns on the board. Label the columns *Conservation Activities, Positive Results,* and *Difficulties.* In the first column, have students list ways they can help preserve the ecosystem they live in. *clean up fields, prevent the dumping of trash in water* In the second, have students list the positive impacts of the action. *animal survival, less pollution* In the third, have students identify at least one difficulty they would need to address when taking the action. *waste collecting, effect different animals in the ecosystem*

ACTIVITIES

Ecosystem Services Proposal

Students could get help with this project by contacting their local 4-H, Sierra Club, or chapter of the Forestry Service. Remind students that they need to write persuasively and present their cost estimates clearly when writing their proposals.

Writing Project: The Story Behind the News

Suggest to students that they write their stories from the point of view of one of the participants. If reporting on the founding of the Sierra Club, for example, students could write from the perspective of John Muir, as if he were telling it to a newspaper reporter.

Technology Resources

Students can visit **ClassZone.com** for current news about conservation.

CHAPTER

3 Human Impact on Ecosystems

Life Science
UNIFYING PRINCIPLES

PRINCIPLE 1

All living things share common characteristics.

PRINCIPLE 2

All living things share common needs.

PRINCIPLE 3

Living things meet their needs through interactions with the environment.

PRINCIPLE 4

The types and numbers of living things change over time.

Unit: Ecology
BIG IDEAS

**CHAPTER 1
Ecosystems and Biomes**
Matter and energy together support life within a certain environment.

**CHAPTER 2
Interactions Within Ecosystems**
Living things within an ecosystem interact with each other and the environment.

**CHAPTER 3
Human Impact on Ecosystems**
Humans and human population growth affect the environment.

CHAPTER 3
KEY CONCEPTS

SECTION 3.1

Human population growth presents challenges.

1. The human population is increasing.

2. Human populations can put pressure on ecosystems.

SECTION 3.2

Human activities affect the environment.

1. Humans use many resources.

2. Pollution endangers biodiversity.

3. Habitat loss endangers biodiversity.

SECTION 3.3

People are working to protect ecosystems.

1. Environmental awareness is growing.

2. Conserving resources protects ecosystems.

3. Think globally, act locally.

The Big Idea Flow Chart is available on p. T17 in the **UNIT TRANSPARENCY BOOK.**

Previewing Content

 3.1 Human population growth presents challenges. pp. 81–88

1. The human population is increasing.

Earth's human population was 6 billion in 1999 and is expected to be 9 billion by 2050. Part of the reason for growth is longer life spans, and another reason is the high birth rate.

The human population is not following the usual pattern of leveling off at carrying capacity.

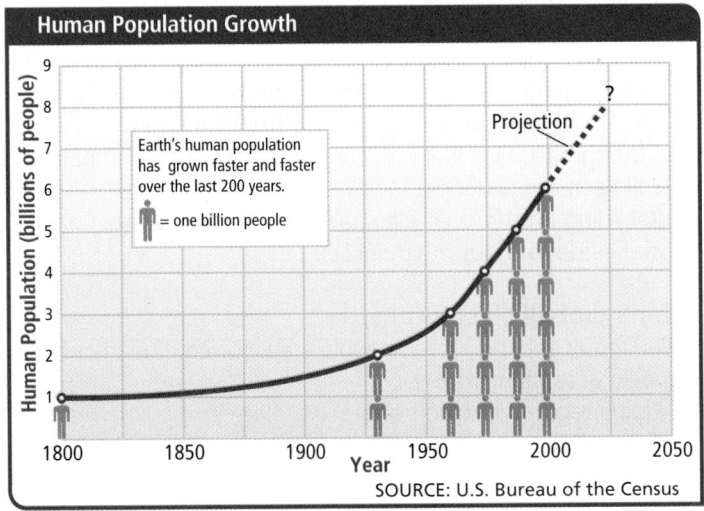

Human Population Growth

Earth's human population has grown faster and faster over the last 200 years.

🚶 = one billion people

SOURCE: U.S. Bureau of the Census

2. Human populations can put pressure on ecosystems.

The pressures humans cause to ecosystems arise from waste, resource use, and land-use changes.

- Waste fills up land with toxic garbage. Sewage releases contaminants into the environment.
- **Natural resources** are not evenly distributed. Much of the world's population lives in Asia and Africa, where natural resources are often exported for commercial interests.
- High demand for water is difficult to meet, especially in arid regions. Water is a finite resource.
- A high **population density** contributes to overuse of resources and disturbance or destruction of natural habitats.

 3.2 Human activities affect the environment. pp. 89–97

1. Humans use many resources.

- Renewable resources include trees, sunlight, and water.
- Nonrenewable resources include fossil fuels (coal, oil, natural gas) and minerals such as copper and gold.

2. Pollution endangers biodiversity.

Biodiversity describes the number and variety of life in an ecosystem. Ecosystems with a variety of species are healthier and more able to recover from problems such as disease.

- Air and water **pollution** affect entire ecosystems.
- Use of fossil fuels causes acid rain, which destroys trees, kills fish, and damages soil.
- Water pollution is caused by oil spills, soil erosion, waste-water, and chemical and waste runoff from farm fields, animal feedlots, and landfills. Water pollution poisons fish, causes algal blooms, and damages the entire food web.
- Pollution moves across systems.

3. Habitat loss endangers biodiversity.

If living space is limited or a food source is removed, then the number of organisms in a biological community will be reduced. Human actions remove habitat, for example, by clear-cutting forests.

Invasive species change habitat. An invasive species is a nonnative species that is introduced by humans or moves in and supplants native species.

Common Misconceptions

POLLUTION Most students hold the misconception that air pollution and water pollution affect a limited area. In fact, air pollution can fall to the ground in precipitation, seep into watersheds, and run into bodies of water. Water pollution can evaporate into the air, all the while being carried to larger and larger areas.

 This misconception is addressed on p. 92.

 MISCONCEPTION DATABASE
CLASSZONE.COM Background on student misconceptions

BIODIVERSITY Students sometimes think that changes in population of an organism may not affect an ecosystem because some organisms are not important. They may think that one population can change and have limited or no effects on an ecosystem. In fact, all populations are important and affect the entire ecosystem.

 This misconception is addressed on p. 93.

Previewing Content

People are working to protect ecosystems. pp. 98–107

1. Environmental awareness is growing.

Awareness of the environment and environmental protection have slowly progressed since the nineteenth century in the United States. Some milestones are

- Yellowstone National Park, created in 1872, is the first U.S. national park.
- *Silent Spring,* by Rachel Carson, a book about toxic chemical use published in 1962, raised public awareness about how pollution spreads throughout ecosystems. The author's research on the toxicity of DDT in the environment led to U.S. laws banning its use.
- Citizen efforts to preserve biodiversity included the founding of the Nature Conservancy and the National Wildlife Federation.
- More recent government efforts to protect ecosystems have included the Endangered Species Act, the Clean Air Act, Clean Water Act, and the National Environmental Policy Act.

Discontinuing DDT use has permitted several raptors to recover from drastically low populations.

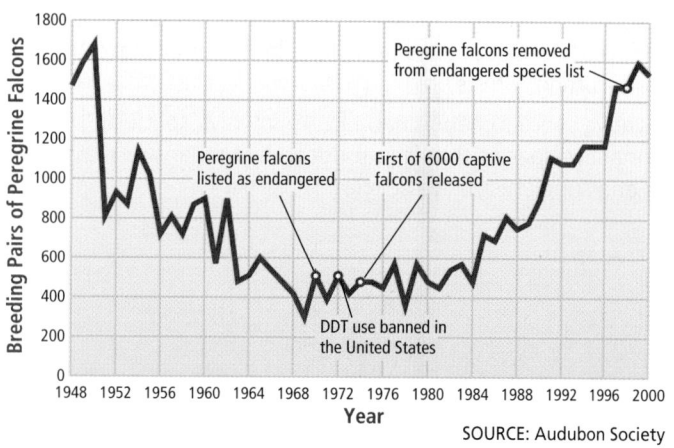

SOURCE: Audubon Society

2. Conserving resources protects ecosystems.

Sustainable practices are ways to use resources without using them up. They include the following established practices:

- U.S. farms practice conservation tillage and use natural fertilizers such as compost and natural pest controls like ladybugs.
- Forestry practices are changing to strip and selective cutting, which improve regrowth and help prevent erosion.
- Energy companies are exploring alternative sources of energy like hydropower (energy generated by the force of flowing water), geothermal power (energy from the heat at Earth's core), and wind power (generated from windmills).
- Cutting back on fossil-fuel consumption in cars and homes will decrease pollution.
- Recycling efforts keep glass, aluminum, some plastic, paper, and cardboard out of landfills.

3. Think globally, act locally.

Working at the local level, people are involved in many efforts to help ecosystems recover.

- Prairie recovery projects are taking place in the Midwest.
- The United States and Canada have worked together to clean up Lake Erie, which was heavily polluted by phosphorus.
- River and watershed restoration takes place in areas throughout the U.S., largely through local community efforts. Businesspeople, economists, and urban planners are also beginning to look at ecosystems as service-providers, with economic value to the community.

Common Misconceptions

INVASIVE SPECIES Some students may think that all plant and animal species, including invasive species, benefit the environment. In fact, because invasive species often have no local predators, they can cause decreases in populations of native organisms through competition. They can use up resources and become difficult to remove or control.

 This misconception is addressed on p. 96.

MISCONCEPTION DATABASE
CLASSZONE.COM Background on student misconceptions

SCIENTIFIC MODELS Middle-school students generally think of the world concretely, and often interpret a scientific model too literally. They often believe that scientific models are exact representations of the world. Every model is in some way different from that which it represents.

 This misconception is addressed on p. 107.

Previewing Labs

EXPLORE (the BIG idea)

How Many Is Six Billion? p. 79
Students count rice grains and calculate how much space 6 billion grains would occupy.

TIME 10 minutes
MATERIALS uncooked rice, paper, scissors, tape, ruler, calculator

How Easily Does Polluted Water Move Through Plants? p. 79
Students observe that dye moves through plants, to discover how pollution could affect plants.

TIME 10 minutes
MATERIALS bowl of water, food coloring, stalk of celery

Internet Activity: The Environment, p. 79
Students use the Internet to explore how humans can change ecosystems.

TIME 20 minutes
MATERIALS computer with Internet access

SECTION 3.1

EXPLORE Sharing Resources, p. 81
Students divide objects among members of a group and discover how difficult it is to share unequal resources.

TIME 15 minutes
MATERIALS bag; assorted unlike objects such as pennies, blocks, pencils

INVESTIGATE Resources, p. 84
Students use a map to interpret where their community gets resources and where it disposes of waste.

TIME 30 minutes
MATERIALS recent map of your county, city, or town; tracing paper, ruler

---

SECTION 3.2

INVESTIGATE Particles in the Air, p. 91
Students collect and observe samples of local air pollution.

TIME 30 minutes
MATERIALS 2 index cards, marker, hole punch, transparent tape, string, scissors, petroleum jelly, hand lens

---

SECTION 3.3

EXPLORE Environmental Impacts, p. 98
Students add water to compressed and uncompressed soil to see how trampling could affect water absorption.

TIME 15 minutes
MATERIALS 2 plant pots with trays, potting soil, measuring cups, stopwatch, water

CHAPTER INVESTIGATION Oil Spills, pp. 106–107
Students create and clean up an oil spill, exploring different methods of cleanup.

TIME 40 minutes
MATERIALS small beaker, vegetable oil, turmeric, spoon, aluminum baking pan, sand, large beaker, water, sponge, dish soap, rubbing alcohol, paper towels, cotton balls, cornstarch, yarn, feather, seaweed

---

R **Additional INVESTIGATION,** Pollutants on the Move, A, B, & C, pp. 189–197; Teacher Instructions, pp. 200–201

Previewing Chapter Resources

	INTEGRATED TECHNOLOGY	LABS AND ACTIVITIES

Chapter 3
Human Impact on Ecosystems

 CLASSZONE.COM
- eEdition Plus
- EasyPlanner Plus
- Misconception Database
- Content Review
- Test Practice
- Visualizations
- Resource Centers
- Internet Activity: The Environment
- Math Tutorial

 **SCILINKS.ORG**
SCiLINKS

 CD-ROMS
- eEdition
- EasyPlanner
- Power Presentations
- Content Review
- Lab Generator
- Test Generator

 AUDIO CDS
- Audio Readings
- Audio Readings in Spanish

PE EXPLORE the Big Idea, p. 79
- How Many Is Six Billion?
- How Easily Does Polluted Water Move Through Plants?
- Internet Activity: The Environment

R **UNIT RESOURCE BOOK**
Unit Projects, pp. 5–10

 Lab Generator CD-ROM
Generate customized labs.

SECTION

3.1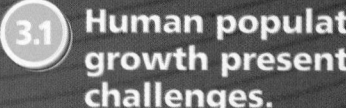
Human population growth presents challenges.
pp. 81–88

Time: 2 periods (1 block)
 Lesson Plan, pp. 141–142

 • **VISUALIZATION,** Population Growth
• **RESOURCE CENTER,** Urban Expansion

 UNIT TRANSPARENCY BOOK
- Big Idea Flow Chart, p. T17
- Daily Vocabulary Scaffolding, p. T18
- Note-Taking Model, p. T19
- 3-Minute Warm-Up, p. T20
- "Landfill Cross-Section" Visual, p. T22

PE • EXPLORE Sharing Resources, p. 81
• INVESTIGATE Resources, p. 84
• Science on the Job, p. 88

R **UNIT RESOURCE BOOK**
Datasheet, Resources, p. 150

SECTION

3.2
Human activities affect the environment.
pp. 89–97

Time: 2 periods (1 block)
 Lesson Plan, pp. 152–153

 • **RESOURCE CENTER,** Natural Resources
• **MATH TUTORIAL**

T **UNIT TRANSPARENCY BOOK**
- Daily Vocabulary Scaffolding, p. T18
- 3-Minute Warm-Up, p. T20

PE • INVESTIGATE Particles in the Air, p. 91
• Math in Science, p. 97

R **UNIT RESOURCE BOOK**
- Datasheet, Particles in the Air, p. 161
- Math Support, p. 178
- Math Practice, p. 179
- Additional INVESTIGATION, Pollutants on the Move, A, B, & C, pp. 189–197

SECTION

3.3
People are working to protect ecosystems.
pp. 98–107

Time: 4 periods (2 blocks)
 Lesson Plan, pp. 163–164

 RESOURCE CENTER, Ecosystem Recovery

T **UNIT TRANSPARENCY BOOK**
- Big Idea Flow Chart, p. T17
- Daily Vocabulary Scaffolding, p. T18
- 3-Minute Warm-Up, p. T21
- Chapter Outline, pp. T23–T24

PE • EXPLORE Environmental Impacts, p. 98
• CHAPTER INVESTIGATION, Oil Spills, pp. 106–107

R **UNIT RESOURCE BOOK**
CHAPTER INVESTIGATION, Oil Spills, A, B, & C, pp. 180–188

READING AND REINFORCEMENT

ASSESSMENT

STANDARDS

- Magnet Words, B24–25
- Supporting Main Idea Notes, C37
- Daily Vocabulary Scaffolding, H1–8

 UNIT RESOURCE BOOK
- Vocabulary Practice, pp. 175–176
- Decoding Support, p. 177
- Summarizing the Chapter, pp. 198–199

 Audio Readings CD
Listen to Pupil Edition.

 Audio Readings in Spanish CD
Listen to Pupil Edition in Spanish.

- Chapter Review, pp. 109–110
- Standardized Test Practice, p. 111

 UNIT ASSESSMENT BOOK
- Diagnostic Test, pp. 40–41
- Chapter Test, A, B, & C, pp. 45–56
- Alternative Assessment, pp. 57–58
- Unit Test, A, B, & C, pp. 59–70

- Spanish Chapter Test, pp. 65–68
- Spanish Unit Test, pp. 77–80

 Test Generator CD-ROM
Generate customized tests.

 Lab Generator CD-ROM
Rubrics for Labs

National Standards
A.2–8, A.9.a–c, A.9.e–f, E.2–5, E.6.d–f, F.1.g, F.2.a–b

See p. 78 for the standards.

 UNIT RESOURCE BOOK
- Reading Study Guide A & B, pp. 143–146
- Spanish Reading Study Guide, pp. 147–148
- Challenge and Extension, p. 149
- Reinforcing Key Concepts, p. 151

 Ongoing Assessment, pp. 82–83, 85–87

 Section 3.1 Review, p. 87

 UNIT ASSESSMENT BOOK
Section 3.1 Quiz, p. 42

National Standards
A.2–7, A.9.a–b, A.9.e–f, F.2.a

 UNIT RESOURCE BOOK
- Reading Study Guide A & B, pp. 154–157
- Spanish Reading Study Guide, pp. 158–159
- Challenge and Extension, p. 160
- Reinforcing Key Concepts, p. 162
- Challenge Reading, pp. 173–174

 Ongoing Assessment, pp. 90, 92–95

 Section 3.2 Review, p. 96

UNIT ASSESSMENT BOOK
Section 3.2 Quiz, p. 43

National Standards
A.2–8, A.9.a–c, A.9.e–f, F.2.b

 UNIT RESOURCE BOOK
- Reading Study Guide A & B, pp. 165–168
- Spanish Reading Study Guide, pp. 169–170
- Challenge and Extension, p. 171
- Reinforcing Key Concepts, p. 172

 Ongoing Assessment, pp. 99–100, 102–104

 Section 3.3 Review, p. 105

 UNIT ASSESSMENT BOOK
Section 3.3 Quiz, p. 44

National Standards
A.2–7, A.9.a–b, A.9.d–f, E.2–5, E.6.d–e, F.1.g

Previewing Resources for Differentiated Instruction

CHAPTER INVESTIGATION

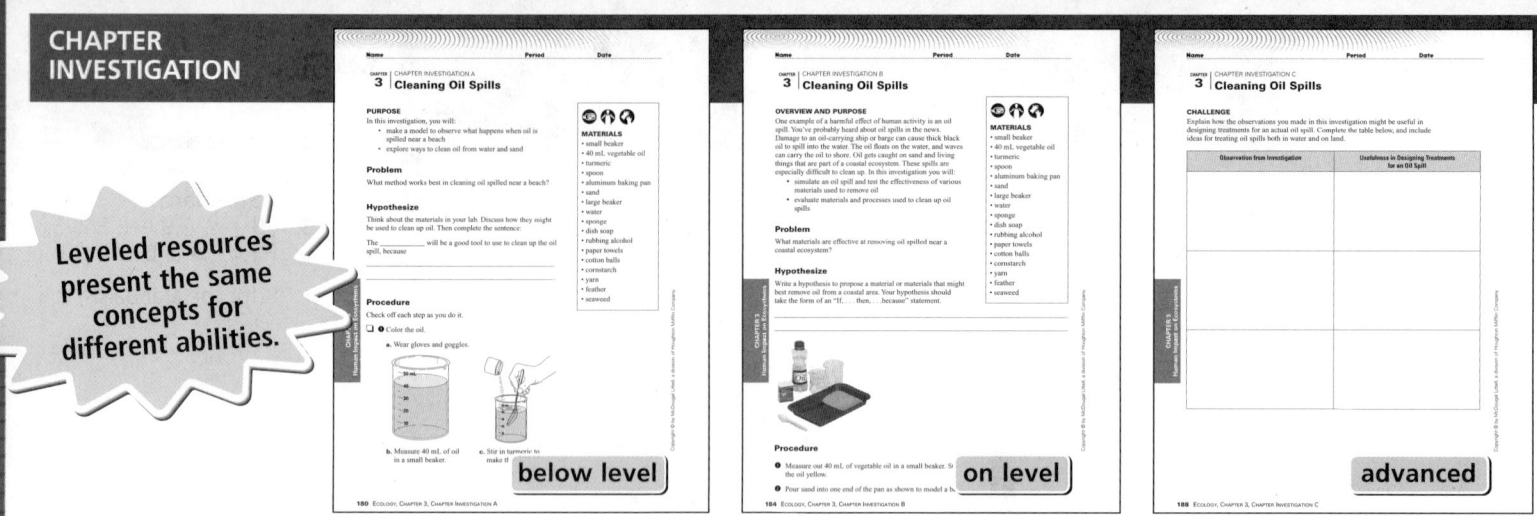

Leveled resources present the same concepts for different abilities.

below level

on level

advanced

UNIT RESOURCE BOOK, pp. 180–183   pp. 184–187   pp. 184–188

READING STUDY GUIDE

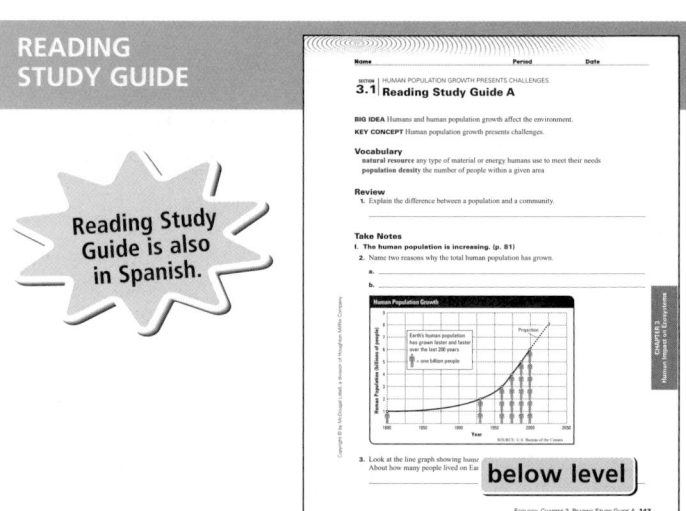
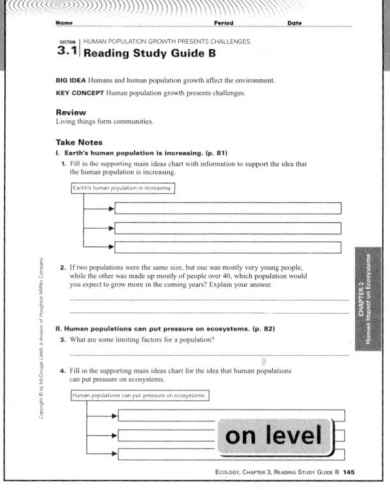
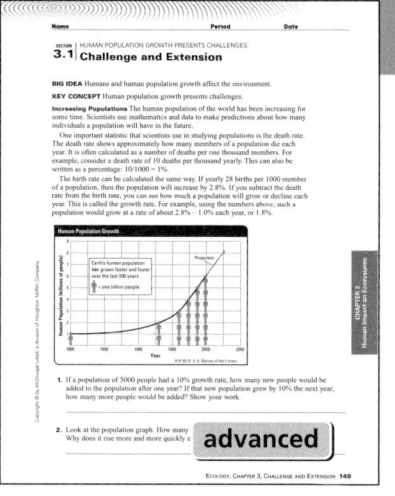

Reading Study Guide is also in Spanish.

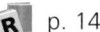

below level

on level

advanced

UNIT RESOURCE BOOK, pp. 143–144   pp. 145–146   p. 149

CHAPTER TEST

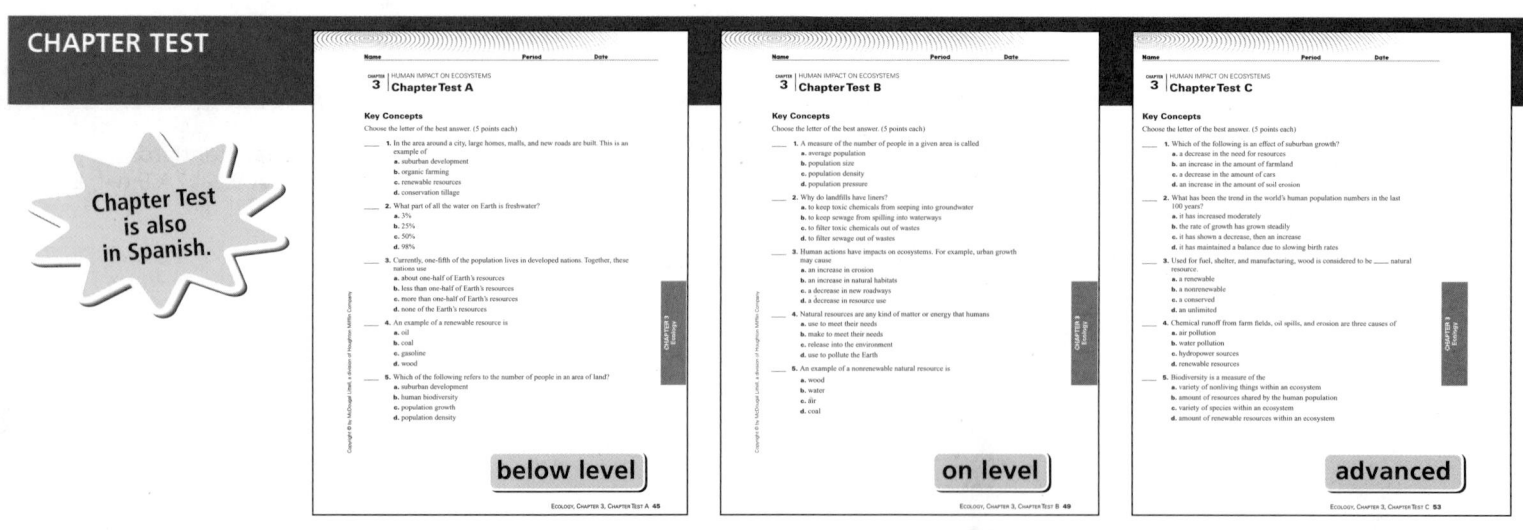

Chapter Test is also in Spanish.

below level

on level

advanced

UNIT ASSESSMENT BOOK, pp. 45–48   pp. 49–52   pp. 53–56

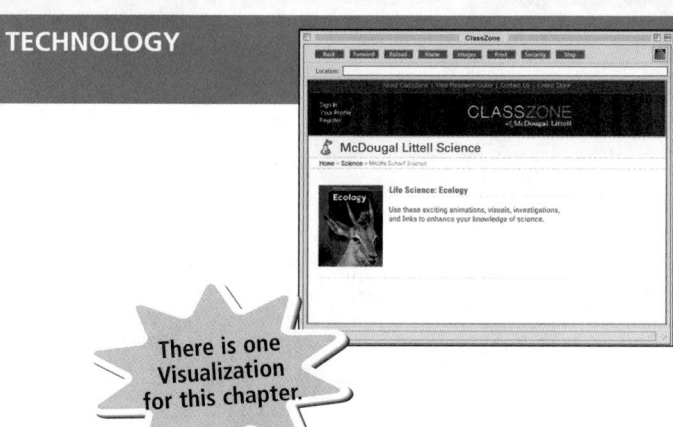

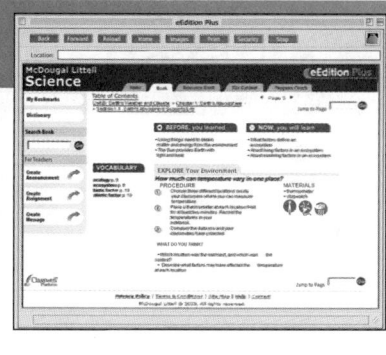

CLASSZONE.COM

CD/CD-ROMS

CLASSZONE.COM

There is one Visualization for this chapter.

VISUAL CONTENT

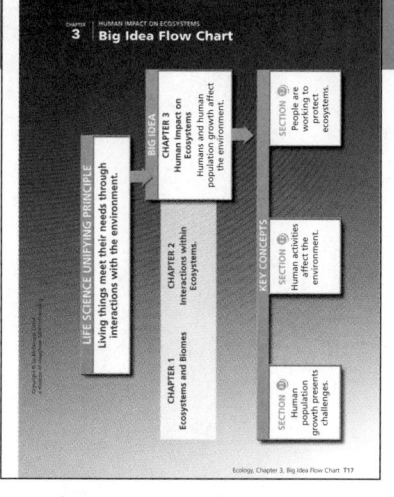

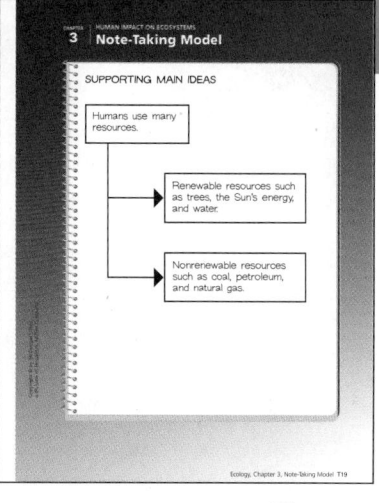

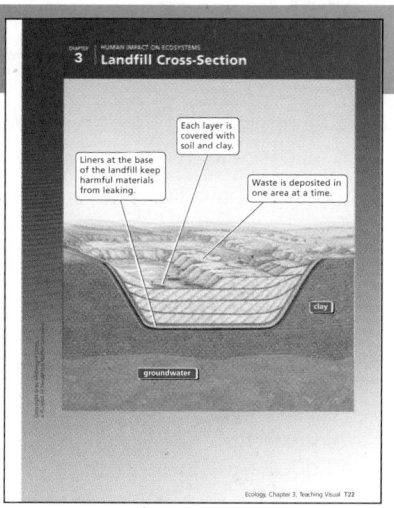

T **UNIT TRANSPARENCY BOOK,** p. T17

T p. T19

T p. T22

MORE SUPPORT

Reinforcing Key Concepts for each section

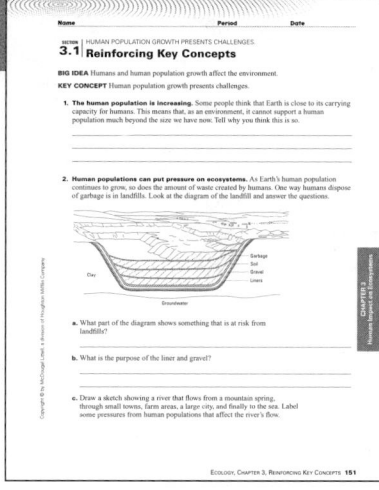

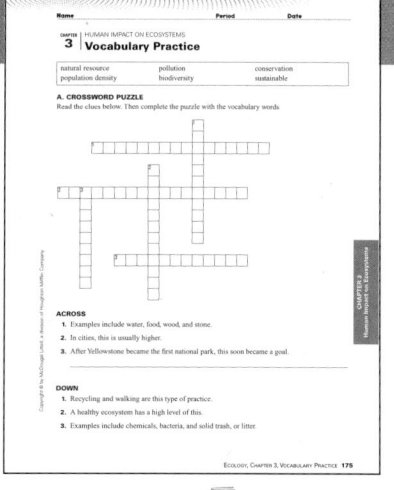

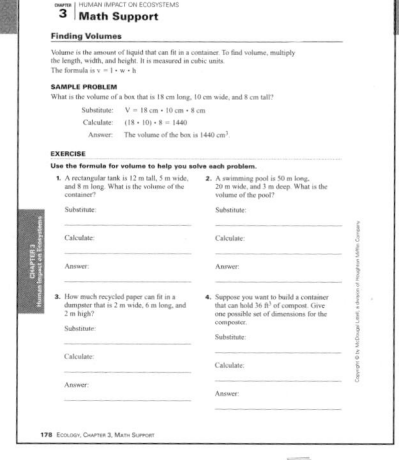

R **UNIT RESOURCE BOOK,** p. 151

R pp. 175–176

R p. 178

INTRODUCE

the **BIG** idea

Have students look at the photograph of cars on a freeway system and discuss how the question in the box links to the Big Idea:

- What items did humans add to this landscape?
- How do you think humans altered the original landscape?

National Science Education Standards

Content

E.6.d All technology has risks and trade-offs such as cost, safety, and efficiency.

E.6.e All designs have limits including availability, safety, and environmental impact.

F.1.g Environmental health relies on monitoring the use of soil, water, and air, as well as the use of harmful substances.

F.2.a When an area becomes overpopu-lated, the environment will become degraded due to the increased use of resources.

F.2.b Causes of environmental degradation and resource depletion vary in regions and in countries.

Process

A.2–8 Design and conduct an investiga-tion; use tools to gather and interpret data; use evidence to describe, predict, explain, model; think critically to make relationships between evidence and explanation; recognize different explana-tions and predictions; communicate scientific procedures and explanations; use mathematics.

A.9.a–c, A.9.e–f Understand scientific inquiry by using different investigations, methods, mathematics, and explanations based on logic, evidence, and skepticism.

E.2–5 Design a solution, implement solution, evaluate a solution, and com-municate the design process.

D **78** Unit: **Ecology**

CHAPTER

Human Impact on Ecosystems

the **BIG** idea

Humans and human population growth affect the environment.

> **How have humans affected this landscape?**

Key Concepts

SECTION 3.1 Human population growth presents challenges. Learn how the increasing human population must share land and resources and dispose of its wastes.

SECTION 3.2 Human activities affect the environment. Learn how humans may affect natural resources, air and water quality, and biodiversity.

SECTION 3.3 People are working to protect ecosystems. Learn about federal, local, and scientific efforts to improve resource use and protect ecosystems.

Internet Preview

CLASSZONE.COM

Chapter 3 online resources: Content Review, Visualization, four Resource Centers, Math Tutorial, Test Practice

D **78** Unit: **Ecology**

INTERNET PREVIEW

CLASSZONE.COM For student use with the following pages:

Review and Practice
- Content Review, pp. 80, 108
- Math Tutorial: Finding Volumes, p. 97
- Test Practice, p. 111

Activities and Resources
- Internet Activity: The Environment, p. 79
- Resource Centers: Urban Expansion p. 86; Natural Resources, p. 90; Recovery, p. 99
- Visualization: Population Growth, p. 82

NSTA scilinks.org

Population Growth
Code: MDL003

EXPLORE (the BIG idea)

How Many Is Six Billion?

Use a piece of paper, scissors, and some tape to make a box that measures 1 cm by 1 cm by 1 cm. Fill the box with rice. Use the number of grains of rice in 1 cm^3 to calculate the volume of 6,000,000,000 grains of rice.

Observe and Think How many grains of rice are in a cubic centimeter? Do 6 billion grains take up more or less space than you expected?

How Easily Does Polluted Water Move Through Plants?

Place a few drops of food coloring in a half cup of water. Take a leafy stalk of celery and make a fresh cut across the bottom. Place the celery in the water overnight.

Observe and Think What do you observe about the celery and its leaves? What do your observations suggest about plants growing near polluted water?

Internet Activity: The Environment

Go to **ClassZone.com** to explore the effects of human activities on the environment.

Observe and Think How are people working to protect the environment?

NSTA
scilinks.org
SCiLINKS

Population Growth **Code: MDL003**

Chapter 3: **Human Impact on Ecosystems 79** **D**

TEACHING WITH TECHNOLOGY

Online Government Many maps showing land use with community resource data are available at county, city, and town websites. For the Resources activity on p. 84, bookmark these sites or help students find them.

Documentary Film You may wish to introduce the Investigation on p. 106 with a video documentary about oil spills.

EXPLORE (the BIG idea)

These inquiry-based activities are appropriate for use at home or as a supplement to classroom instruction.

How Many Is Six Billion?

PURPOSE To promote students' understanding of the magnitude of 6 billion.

TIP *10 min.* Make a box template or model to show students.

Typically students relate the volume of 6 billion rice grains to something familiar, like a cereal box. They find that 6 billion is quite a large number.

REVISIT after p. 82.

How Easily Does Polluted Water Move Through Plants?

PURPOSE To introduce students to the way plants absorb pollution from water. Students observe how food coloring moves into celery.

TIP *10 min.* Students will not see the liquid moving. Have them wait until the next class period to observe results.

Answer: The food coloring moved up into the celery. Plants near polluted water would take the pollution into their bodies.

REVISIT after p. 93.

Internet Activity: The Environment

PURPOSE To explore how humans can change ecosystems.

TIP *20 min.* Students can think about steps they can take to protect the environment.

Sample answer: People are building awareness, passing laws, and conserving resources.

REVISIT after p. 105.

◀ CONCEPT REVIEW

Activate Prior Knowledge

- Ask students to list some factors that make up an ecosystem.
- Ask: What would happen if you eliminated light from an ecosystem? If you doubled the light?
- Discuss how changing other factors might affect an ecosystem.

▶ TAKING NOTES

Supporting Main Ideas

Having students take notes as main ideas and supporting details enables students to make connections and see relationships. Remind students to use the blue headings for main ideas and to include only the most important details.

Vocabulary Strategy

Students can use the magnet word strategy for any word or phrase that poses a challenge to them. They do not need to stick to the listed vocabulary items. The strategy can be especially helpful for students learning English.

Vocabulary and Note-Taking Resources

- Vocabulary Practice, pp. 175–176
- Decoding Support, p. 177

- Daily Vocabulary Scaffolding, p. T18
- Note-Taking Model, p. T19

- Magnet Words, B24–25
- Main Idea and Supporting Details Notes, C37
- Daily Vocabulary Scaffolding, H1–8

◀ CONCEPT REVIEW

- Both living and nonliving factors affect ecosystems.
- Populations can grow or decline over time.
- Matter and energy move through the environment.

◀ VOCABULARY REVIEW

species p. 45
habitat p. 46

See Glossary for definitions.
diversity, urban

CONTENT REVIEW
CLASSZONE.COM
Review concepts and vocabulary.

▶ TAKING NOTES

SUPPORTING MAIN IDEAS

Make a chart to show main ideas and the information that supports them. Copy each blue heading; then add supporting information, such as reasons, explanations, and examples.

VOCABULARY STRATEGY

Think about a vocabulary term as a **magnet word** diagram. Write the other terms or ideas related to that term around it.

See the Note-Taking Handbook on pages R45–R51.

SCIENCE NOTEBOOK

Human populations can put pressure on ecosystems.

→ Humans produce waste that must be disposed of.

→ Resources must be shared among a growing human population.

→ Human population centers are expanding.

diversity — populations — life — **BIODIVERSITY** — habitats — variety — species

CHECK READINESS

Administer the Diagnostic Test to determine students' readiness for new science content and their mastery of requisite math skills.

 Diagnostic Test, pp. 40–41

Technology Resources

Students needing content and math skills should visit **ClassZone.com**.

- **CONTENT REVIEW**
- **MATH TUTORIAL**

 CONTENT REVIEW CD-ROM

KEY CONCEPT

Human population growth presents challenges.

 BEFORE, you learned

- Populations have boundaries and are affected by limiting factors
- Living things form communities

 NOW, you will learn

- How a growing human population puts pressure on ecosystems
- How sharing resources can be difficult

VOCABULARY

natural resource p. 84
population density p. 86

EXPLORE Sharing Resources

How can you model resource distribution?

PROCEDURE

1. You will work in a group of several classmates. One member of your group gets a bag of objects from your teacher.

2. Each object in the bag represents a necessary resource. Divide the objects so that each member of the group gets the resources he or she needs.

3. After 10 minutes, you may trade resources with other groups.

MATERIALS
bag containing an assortment of objects

WHAT DO YOU THINK?
- Did you get a fair share of your group's objects?
- How does the number of people in each group affect the outcome?
- Was the job made easier when trading occurred across groups?

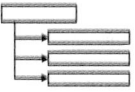

SUPPORTING MAIN IDEAS
Make a chart to show information that supports the first main idea presented: *The human population is increasing.*

The human population is increasing.

According to the United Nations, on October 12, 1999, Earth's human population reached 6 billion. Until 300 years ago, it had never grown beyond a few hundred million people. Only 200 years ago, the population reached 1 billion. So the increase to 6 billion people has occurred in a very short time. About one-third of all humans alive today are 14 years old or younger. Partly for this reason, experts predict Earth's population will keep growing—to 9 billion or more by the year 2050.

Chapter 3: **Human Impact on Ecosystems 81**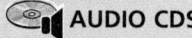

RESOURCES FOR DIFFERENTIATED INSTRUCTION

Below Level

UNIT RESOURCE BOOK
- Reading Study Guide A, pp. 143–144
- Decoding Support, p. 177

 **AUDIO CDS**

Advanced

UNIT RESOURCE BOOK
Challenge and Extension, p. 149

English Learners

UNIT RESOURCE BOOK
Spanish Reading Study Guide, pp. 147–148

 **AUDIO CDS**

- Audio Readings in Spanish
- Audio Readings (English)

3.1 FOCUS

▶ Set Learning Goals
Students will

- Describe how a growing human population puts pressure on ecosystems.
- Explain how sharing resources can be difficult.
- Interpret through maps where the local community gets resources and where it disposes of waste.

◀ 3-Minute Warm-Up

Display Transparency 20 or copy this exercise on the board:

Which of the following are populations and which are communities? Write "P" beside a description of a population. Write "C" beside a description of a community.

- group of elephants living in the same grassland *P*
- iguanas and crabs interacting with one another *C*
- group of grasses living on a prairie *P*
- group of fungi living in a pond *P*

[T] 3-Minute Warm-Up, p. T20

3.1 MOTIVATE

EXPLORE Sharing Resources

PURPOSE To experience the difficulty of sharing unequal resources

TIPS *15 min.* 4–5 students per group is suggested. Representative or symbolic objects can include: drinking straws for water, kidney beans for food, birthday candles for fuel, and so on.

WHAT DO YOU THINK? *Sample answer: No; group members could not figure out a fair distribution. (Most groups will be unable to divide the objects fairly throughout the exercise.)*

Teach from Visuals

To help students interpret the human population growth graph, ask:

• What is measured on the *x*-axis? *years*

• What is measured on the *y*-axis? *population in billions of people*

• What does the slope of the line tell you? *Human population is growing faster than it used to.*

• What is one problem with using only a mathematical projection for predicting population growth? *Mathematical projection does not account for other factors that might affect future population growth. It only uses current growth rate.*

EXPLORE (the **BIG** idea)

Revisit "How Many Is Six Billion?" on p. 79. Have students relate the activity to human population growth.

Ongoing Assessment

CHECK YOUR READING *Answer: The population will continue to grow, threatening the limit of Earth's carrying capacity. Some students may add that population will level off due to carrying capacity.*

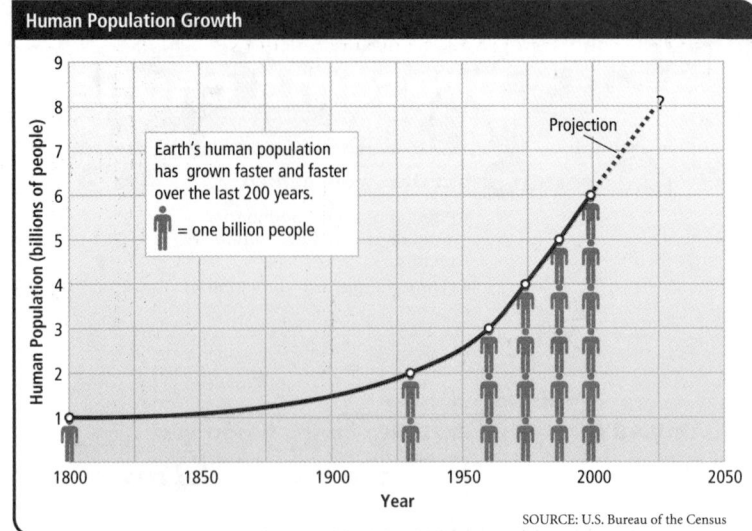

Human Population Growth

Earth's human population has grown faster and faster over the last 200 years.

= one billion people

Projection

SOURCE: U.S. Bureau of the Census

PREDICT The graph shows actual population growth through 2000. Predict how the population will grow in the future.

The graph above shows how the human population has grown in the last 200 years. You can see from the way the graph gets noticeably steeper after 1950 how quickly the population has increased in just the last 50 years. It is not just the number of babies being born that contributes to Earth's large human population. People are living longer as a result of improving health care and nutrition.

The dotted line on the graph shows a projection, which helps us predict what the population would be if it continues to grow at the rate it is growing today. However, remember that an ecosystem has a carrying capacity for any given population. At some point, Earth will reach its carrying capacity for the human population. Today, many people think that our planet is close to—if not already at—its carrying capacity for humans.

CHECK YOUR READING How might Earth's carrying capacity affect human population growth?

Human populations can put pressure on ecosystems.

VISUALIZATION
CLASSZONE.COM
Examine how the human population has grown.

If your family has guests for the weekend, you may find that you run out of hot water for showers or do not have enough milk for everyone's breakfast. The resources that would ordinarily be enough for your family are no longer enough.

DIFFERENTIATE INSTRUCTION

 More Reading Support

A Why has the population grown so fast? *longer lifespans, high birth rates*

B Why is part of the graph dotted? *It is a future prediction.*

English Learners Help English learners realize that *may* and *might* indicate that an event is uncertain or hypothetical. For example, if guests visit for the weekend, you *might* run out of hot water for showers. Or you *might* not have enough milk for everyone's breakfast. Have students practice writing science statements using *may* or *might*.

Help English learners visualize the "football field" estimate on p. 83. They can use the trucks in the illustration as a more familiar size reference. For instance, about 15 trucks equal 1 football field.

C

You read in Chapter 2 that resources such as food, water, and space can be limiting factors for biological populations. These same resources limit Earth's human population. As the human population grows, it uses more resources—just as your weekend visitors used more of your home's resources. The activities of the growing human population are putting pressure on Earth's ecosystems.

> ⬤ **REMINDER**
>
> A *limiting factor* is something that prevents a population from continuing to grow.

Pressures of Waste Disposal

As Earth's human population grows, so does the amount of waste produced by humans. Humans, like all living things, produce natural waste. Often, the water that carries this waste is treated to remove harmful chemicals before being cycled back to the environment. However, some of these materials still make it into lakes, rivers, and oceans, harming these ecosystems.

Much of the waste material produced by humans is the result of human activity. Some of this waste is garbage, or food waste. The rest of it is trash, or nonfood waste. In the United States, huge amounts of trash are thrown out each year. Most garbage and trash ends up in landfills.

D

Landfills take up a lot of space. The Fresh Kills Landfill in Staten Island, New York, is 60 meters (197 ft) high and covers an area as big as 2200 football fields. Decomposing trash and garbage can release dangerous gases into the air as well as harmful chemicals into the ground. Liners, which are layers of plastic or packed clay, are used to keep chemicals from leaking into surrounding land and water.

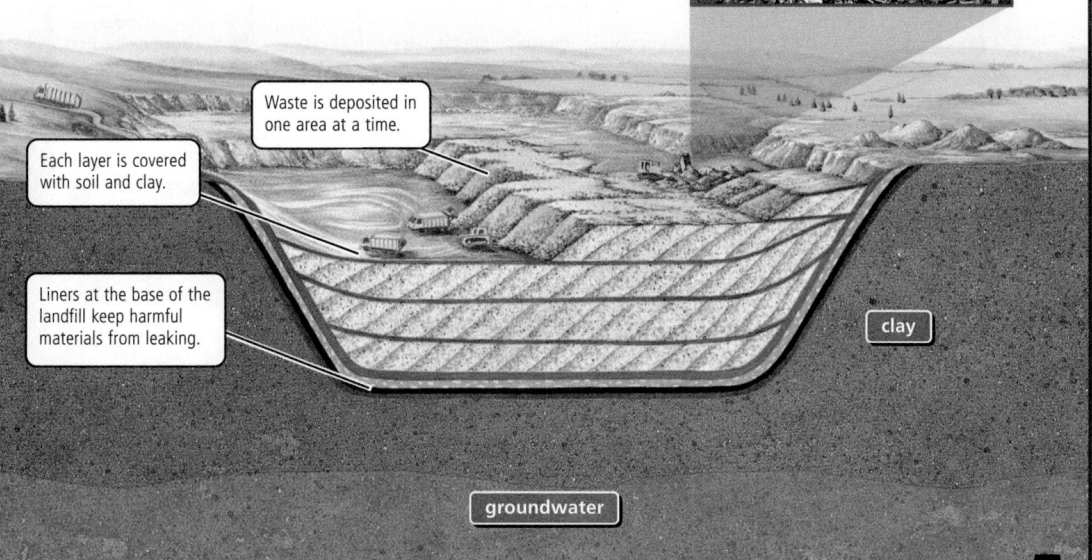

Waste is deposited in one area at a time.

Each layer is covered with soil and clay.

Liners at the base of the landfill keep harmful materials from leaking.

clay

groundwater

Chapter 3: **Human Impact on Ecosystems** 83 **D**

DIFFERENTIATE INSTRUCTION

 More Reading Support

C What resources limit human population? *food, water, space*

D What is one pressure of disposing garbage in landfills? *It takes up lots of space.*

Below Level Have students make a list of things that they regularly throw away in the trash. Ask them to sort the items or materials in their lists into ones that will probably stay in the environment a long time and ones that will break down quickly.

Develop Critical Thinking

EVALUATE To help students evaluate a problem and solution:

- Tell students that landfills do not actually destroy trash and garbage. Why, then, have they become a widely used method of dealing with solid waste? *They provide a place to store solid waste in a restricted area so that it will have the least impact on the environment. Landfills are also designed to provide a barrier between the solid waste and the soil and groundwater.*

- Ask: What problems with destroying solid waste do landfills avoid? *Landfills eliminate the need to burn solid waste, and so they avoid the air pollution that is produced by burning.*

- Ask: What are some drawbacks of landfills? *Pollutants may leak out and contaminate the soil and groundwater. Landfills may also make an area permanently unsuitable for other uses.*

Teach from Visuals

To help students interpret the drawing of the landfill, ask:

- What is used to cover each layer? *soil and clay*

- What protects chemicals from leaking into the landfill and surrounding areas? *liners made of plastic*

- What lies between the landfill and the groundwater? *clay*

  T The visual "Landfill Cross-Section" is available as T22 in the Unit Transparency Book.

Ongoing Assessment

Describe how a growing human population puts pressure on ecosystems.

Ask: Why can't the human population just keep growing forever? *There are limited amounts of food, water, and space for humans, as well as limited space for human waste.*

INVESTIGATE Resources

PURPOSE To interpret local maps identifying local resources and refuse facilities

TIP *30 min.* Contact your local city hall, town hall, or county agency for maps.

WHAT DO YOU THINK? *Sample answers: The water reservoir is in another town. A neighboring town uses our landfill and electricity.*

 Datasheet, Resources, p. 150

Teaching with Technology

Land-use maps and city plans may be available on your city, town, or county website. Show students how this site is set up, and the variety of resources, including e-mail contact with local officials.

Teach Difficult Concepts

Students may have difficulty grasping how much pressure a large population puts on Earth. Give them a simple example, such as foot traffic on a path. If someone occasionally walks across vegetation, the mosses, lichens, and plants can continue to live there. If many people walk on vegetation, vegetation will not grow.

Integrate the Sciences

Glaciers lock up water both as ice and behind glacial dams. When a glacial dam bursts or the glacier melts quickly, the result is a catastrophic flood, called a jökulhlaup. *Jökulhlaup* is an Icelandic word meaning "glacier burst." Iceland has many glaciers with volcanoes underneath. These volcanoes sometimes send out hot emissions that melt a big part of the glacier, causing a flood. In Nepal, glaciers often form dams on streams or lakes. The meltwater rises until the glacier gives way.

 Another way to get rid of trash and garbage is to incinerate it—burn it. The problem with incineration is that it releases harmful gases and chemicals into the air. To prevent the release of these harmful substances, incinerator smokestacks have filters. To prevent further environmental contamination, used filters must be disposed of safely.

Pressures on Resources

VOCABULARY
Add a magnet word diagram for *natural resource* to your notebook.

You have seen that a growing human population puts pressure on ecosystems by the amount of waste it leaves behind. Human populations also put pressure on ecosystems by what they take away. Humans depend on the environment for resources. A **natural resource** is any type of material or energy that humans use to meet their needs. Natural resources that humans take from their environment include water, food, wood, stone, metal, and minerals.

Clean fresh water is an important resource. Only 3 percent of Earth's water supply is fresh water—and two-thirds of that small amount is locked up in polar ice caps, glaciers, and permanent snow. As the human population grows, sharing this important resource will become more difficult.

INVESTIGATE Resources

How does your community meet its needs?

PROCEDURE

1. Obtain a recent map of your county, city, or town.
2. Using the map, try to identify where your community gets its electricity and water and how it disposes of trash and garbage.
3. Identify locations where food is grown.

WHAT DO YOU THINK?

- How much does your community rely on other communities for resources?
- What resources does your community share with other communities?
- Where does your community dispose of its own waste materials?

CHALLENGE Draw a grid on a piece of tracing paper and place it on top of the map. Use your grid to estimate what percentage of land in your city or town is used for housing and what percentage is used for governmental, agricultural, and commercial purposes.

SKILL FOCUS
Interpreting

MATERIALS
- map of your county, city, or town
For Challenge:
- tracing paper
- pencil
- ruler

TIME
30 minutes

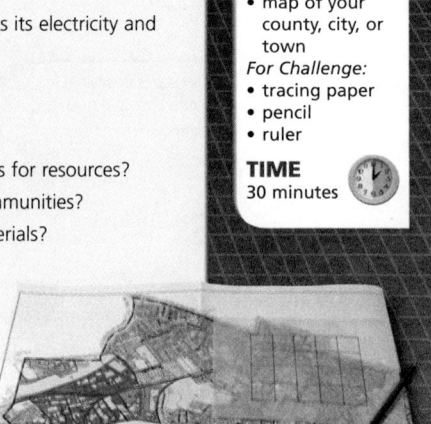

DIFFERENTIATE INSTRUCTION

 More Reading Support

E What are problems with burning trash? *harmful gases, chemicals*

F What are examples of natural resources? *water, food, wood, metal*

Inclusion As you obtain local maps from government agencies, ask if Braille maps are available. Also request the largest format and type size available. You may need to emphasize the labels, colors, and locations of certain resources, using bold, colored markers.

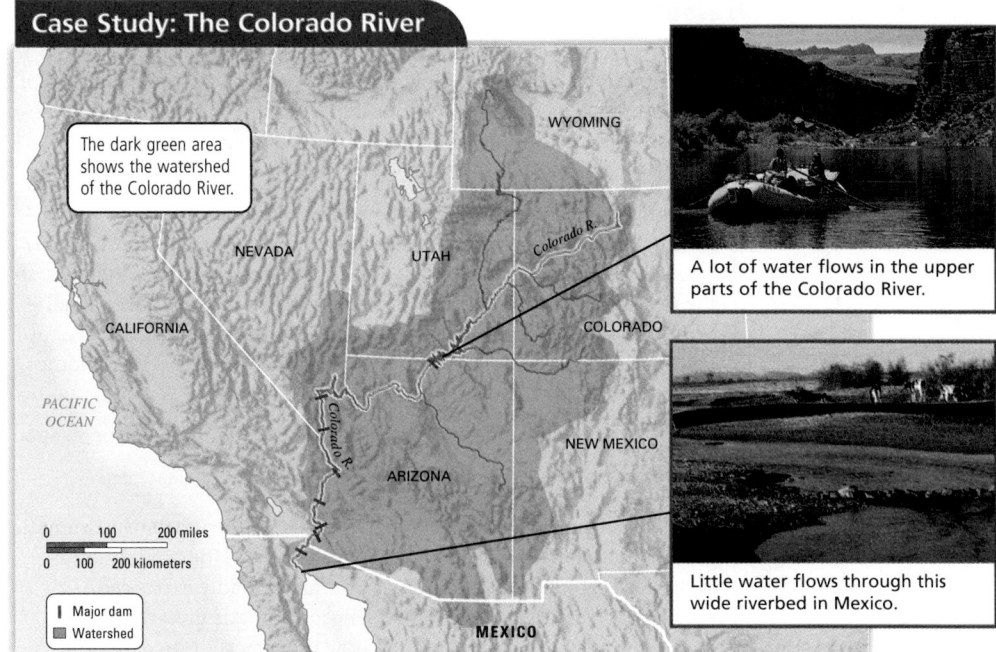

Case Study: The Colorado River

The dark green area shows the watershed of the Colorado River.

WYOMING

NEVADA

UTAH

Colorado R.

CALIFORNIA

COLORADO

PACIFIC OCEAN

Colorado R.

ARIZONA

NEW MEXICO

0   100   200 miles
0   100   200 kilometers

| Major dam
▬ Watershed

MEXICO

A lot of water flows in the upper parts of the Colorado River.

Little water flows through this wide riverbed in Mexico.

A case study that involves the Colorado River shows how a growing human population puts pressures on natural resources. This example also shows that sharing resources isn't easy. The watershed of this major Western river extends into seven U.S. states and parts of Mexico. The watershed includes all the smaller rivers and streams that flow into the Colorado River. In a region where little rain falls each year, these streams and rivers are an important source of water for drinking and agriculture.

As the West was settled, people in the downstream states of California, Arizona, and Nevada worried that the people in the upstream states of Colorado, Utah, Wyoming, and New Mexico would drain too much water from the river. In 1922 the seven states signed an agreement that divided the water between the two groups.

Problems with this agreement soon became apparent. First, the needs of Native American and Mexican populations were not considered. Second, the dams and channels built to prevent floods and transport water harmed river ecosystems. And third, the seven states planned to use more water than the river usually holds. As a result, the river often runs nearly dry at its mouth, in Mexico.

READING TiP
As you read about the Colorado River, refer to the map above to see where the river flows and the states that use the Colorado River's water.

CHECK YOUR READING List three problems that developed after people made a plan to share Colorado River water. **G**

DIFFERENTIATE INSTRUCTION

? More Reading Support

G What happens to the Colorado River when it reaches Mexico? *It runs nearly dry.*

Advanced Have a student bring in a cardboard box large enough to hold the paper that is thrown away in one classroom. Ask them to figure the approximate volume of trash that the class generates each day. Have them use the daily total to estimate the volume of paper waste generated in a year. Have students calculate how many classrooms the trash would fill.

R Challenge and Extension, p. 149

Teach from Visuals

To help students interpret the map of the Colorado River, ask:

- What is the relationship between the large map and the two small inset photographs? *The small photographs describe details of the large map.*
- If you trace the Colorado River with your finger, how many states and countries do you move through? *five states, two countries*
- Where does more water flow—in the northern parts or toward Mexico? *The amount of water is much greater in the north.*

Geography Connection

You can assess the learning goals for this section by having students work cooperatively to draft and present a plan for sharing the resources of the Colorado River watershed. Be sure they include the interests of the seven states and Mexico, and address ways to solve each of the three problems the original plan encountered.

Ongoing Assessment

Explain how sharing resources can be difficult.

Ask: Why are there international treaties that regulate such things as water rights, fishing, and land boundaries? *Sample answer: Because resources are scarce and people compete for them. Some resources are found in more than one country.*

CHECK YOUR READING *Answer: The agreement ignored Native Americans and Mexicans, the dams and reservoirs destroyed river ecosystems, and there was not enough water in the river to meet the amounts each state wanted to withdraw.*

Teach Difficult Concepts

Some students may have a hard time understanding the concept of density. Ask them to imagine two pictures: twenty cows in a field and twenty cows in a barn. Have them contrast the pictures. Point out that density is greater in the barn. To help students understand you might try the demo.

Teacher Demo

Give students the measurements of the classroom and ask them to compute area and number of students. Compare the density of students during class to the density during recess or lunch, when the classroom is mostly empty.

Develop Geometry Skills

Population density is the number of people in a particular area. Students may need a refresher on area calculations.

- Area is expressed in square feet, square miles, square meters, and so forth.
- Area of a square or rectangle, equals length times width or $A = lw$.
- Area of a circle equals πr^2.

Teach from Visuals

To help students interpret the aerial photograph and satellite photographs of Las Vegas:

- Ask: In 1972, about how much of Las Vegas was developed land? *no more than one-third*
- Ask: In 1997, about how much of Las Vegas was developed land? *more than one-half*
- Explain that the largest photograph shows Las Vegas in 2000. Ask students to infer what may have changed for the city between 1997 and 2000. *greater diversity at the city center and outskirts, greater resource use*

Ongoing Assessment

CHECK YOUR READING *Answer: Population density is greater in a city than in suburbs because there are more people in a smaller place.*

RESOURCE CENTER
CLASSZONE.COM
Learn more about urban expansion.

Pressures of Urban Growth

Until recently, the majority of Earth's population was spread out, so the population density was low. **Population density** is the measure of the number of people in a given area. Generally, the lower the population density, the less pressure there is on the environment.

Today, about half of the world's population lives in urban, or city, areas. People are attracted to these areas to live and to work. Over time, suburban areas around a city develop as more and more people look for a place to live. In cities, buildings are spaced close together, so the population density is high. A large number of people in a small area changes the landscape. The local environment can no longer support the number of people living there, and so resources must come from outside.

CHECK YOUR READING How does population density in a city differ from the population density of a suburb?

In recent years, some people have raised concern over the dramatic growth in and around urban areas. Los Angeles; Houston; Atlanta; and Washington, D.C. are all cities that have rapidly expanded. Another urban area that has experienced dramatic growth is Las Vegas, Nevada. The images below show the effects of increasing

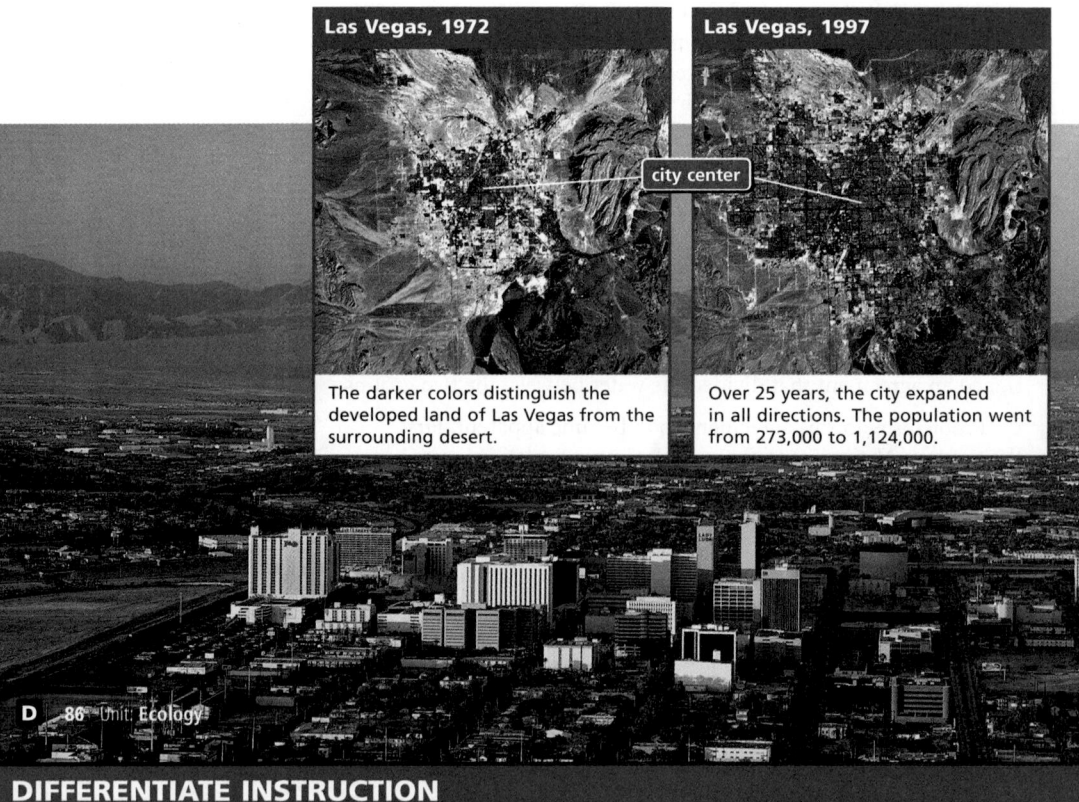

Las Vegas, 1972

Las Vegas, 1997

city center

The darker colors distinguish the developed land of Las Vegas from the surrounding desert.

Over 25 years, the city expanded in all directions. The population went from 273,000 to 1,124,000.

DIFFERENTIATE INSTRUCTION

More Reading Support

H Where does half of the world's population live? *in cities*

I What has happened to cities in recent years? *Some have grown very fast.*

English Learners Have students write definitions for *population density* and *natural resource* in their Science Word Dictionaries. English learners may not have prior knowledge of the terms *suburban* and *suburb* on this page. Use the aerial photograph of Las Vegas to explain the terms. Students may be unfamiliar with the concept of the mouth of a river on p. 85. Students' abilities to read the text on a map in "Investigate Resources," p. 84, will vary. Encourage students to learn and use the visual key and color codes.

population density around the city between 1972 and 1997. Located in the middle of the desert, Las Vegas depends upon the Colorado River for water and energy. As the population grows, so does the need for natural resources.

Pressures of Expanding Land Use

An increasing demand for resources in a particular area is one consequence of urban growth. But as communities around cities expand onto surrounding land, the environment is affected. Natural habitats, such as forests, are destroyed. Because forests cycle carbon through the environment, cutting down trees affects the carbon cycle. Soil that was held in place by tree roots may wash into lakes and rivers.

INFER What do you think this ecosystem looked like a hundred years ago? two hundred years ago?

Another consequence of widespread development is the loss of productive farmland. Development replaces more than 2.5 million acres of farmland each year in the United States. This means less land is available locally to produce food for the growing population. The result is that food is often transported great distances.

Unlike compact city development, widespread suburban development also increases the need for residents to have cars. This is because most people in suburban areas live farther from where they work, shop, or go to school. A greater number of cars decreases the air quality in communities and requires additional road construction, which can interrupt natural habitats and endanger wildlife.

 **CHECK YOUR READING** Describe some ways that development harms natural ecosystems.

3.1 Review

KEY CONCEPTS

1. Identify four pressures placed on ecosystems by an increasing human population.

2. Give an example that shows how resources can be difficult to share.

CRITICAL THINKING

3. **Apply** Describe an example of sharing resources that occurs in your home.

4. **Infer** How would a city's population density change if the city increased in area and the number of people in it remained the same?

CHALLENGE

5. **Evaluate** Imagine that you lived along the Colorado River. What information would you need if you wanted to evaluate a water-sharing agreement.

ANSWERS

1. *Natural habitats are destroyed, carbon cycle affected, erosion, loss of productive farmland, decreased air quality, construction interrupts habitats and can endanger wildlife.*

2. *Colorado River case study shows how the use of river*

water at one location can remove resources from another location.

3. *Sample answer: Telephone time is a limited resource. We share by setting a limit on how long one person can use the phone.*

4. *The population density would decrease.*

5. *Important information would include how many communities depend on one source, how much water is affected by dams, how much water a town needs.*

Ongoing Assessment

Explain how a growing population puts pressure on an ecosystem.

Ask: What happens when the human population grows too fast? *There may be stresses due to increased need for garbage disposal, water, or transport.*

CHECK YOUR READING *Sample answer: Natural habitats disappear, the carbon cycle is interrupted, local climate may change, and erosion occurs.*

Reinforce (the **BIG** idea)

Have students relate the section to the Big Idea.

R Reinforcing Key Concepts, p. 151

3.1 ASSESS & RETEACH

Assess

A Section 3.1 Quiz, p. 42

Reteach

Refer to the graph on p. 82. Have students compare the curve to the moose and wolf graphs on p. 64. Ask:

- How do the graphs differ? *Humans show steady increase, moose and wolf go up and down.*

- Why does the wolf population go down after the moose population does? *The moose provide food for the wolves. When there are too few moose, the wolves do not have enough food.*

- Will the human population have enough or too little food if it continues to grow? *There may be too little.*

Technology Resources

Have students visit **ClassZone.com** for reteaching of Key Concepts.

 CONTENT REVIEW

 CONTENT REVIEW CD-ROM

Set Learning Goal

To interest students in a specific use of
the science of ecology

Present the Science

Urban planning began with an emphasis
on physical factors, but now includes
social, economic, and political issues.
Urban planners balance economic
progress with preserving open spaces
and natural habitats. They also consider
social goals such as access to education,
transportation, and medicine.

Discussion Questions

Ask: What needs are filled by the area in
the upper right corner of the urban diagram? *Sample: shelter, jobs, and places
to buy, sell, and produce goods.* Does
this area address ecological needs? Why
or why not? *No; the area meets humans'
social and economic needs. Natural features are absent. Or, Yes; all parts are
planned with awareness of pollution,
waste, and environmental impact.*

Which area of the diagram balances the
needs of human beings and of the natural environment? Why? *The lower right
corner; it fills humans' need for open
spaces and provides other species a
habitat. Live plants benefit air quality.*

Ask: What kind of information might an
ecologist provide to an urban planner
who is designing a railway system to
connect a city with its suburbs? *Sample:
the types of wild places that may be
affected, the species that live there, the
presence of watersheds and wetlands*

DIFFERENTIATION TIP Pair some strong
readers with students who need support
understanding the text. Partners can
take turns reading aloud and summarizing as they go along.

Close

Ask: What ecological factors do you
think an urban planner should pay most
attention to? *Sample answer: environmental impact, safety, availability of
resources to all neighborhoods*

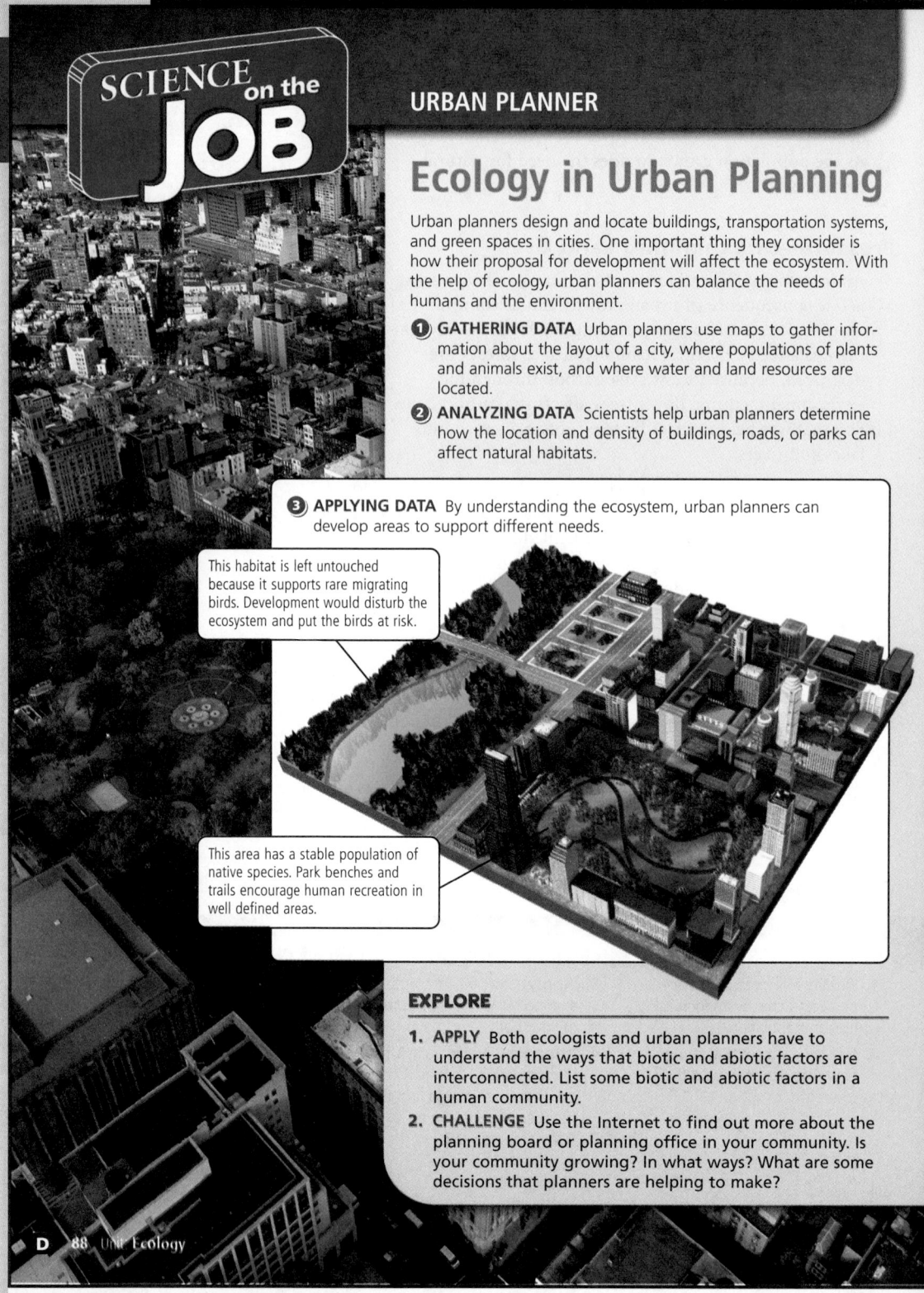

SCIENCE on the JOB

URBAN PLANNER

Ecology in Urban Planning

Urban planners design and locate buildings, transportation systems,
and green spaces in cities. One important thing they consider is
how their proposal for development will affect the ecosystem. With
the help of ecology, urban planners can balance the needs of
humans and the environment.

1 GATHERING DATA Urban planners use maps to gather information about the layout of a city, where populations of plants
and animals exist, and where water and land resources are
located.

2 ANALYZING DATA Scientists help urban planners determine
how the location and density of buildings, roads, or parks can
affect natural habitats.

3 APPLYING DATA By understanding the ecosystem, urban planners can
develop areas to support different needs.

This habitat is left untouched
because it supports rare migrating
birds. Development would disturb the
ecosystem and put the birds at risk.

This area has a stable population of
native species. Park benches and
trails encourage human recreation in
well defined areas.

EXPLORE

1. **APPLY** Both ecologists and urban planners have to
understand the ways that biotic and abiotic factors are
interconnected. List some biotic and abiotic factors in a
human community.

2. **CHALLENGE** Use the Internet to find out more about the
planning board or planning office in your community. Is
your community growing? In what ways? What are some
decisions that planners are helping to make?

EXPLORE

1. ***APPLY*** *Biotic factors could be population density, park areas, other
animals, trees and other plants. Abiotic factors could be light,
roads, climate, wind.*

2. ***CHALLENGE*** *Answers should clearly say whether the community is
growing and what the planning office is doing to plan for change
in population, land use, and so on.*

3.2 Human activities affect the environment.

◀ **BEFORE, you learned**

- Human populations are increasing
- Human population growth causes problems

▶ **NOW, you will learn**

- How natural resources are classified
- How pollution affects the environment
- How a loss of diversity affects the environment

VOCABULARY

pollution p. 91
biodiversity p. 91

THINK ABOUT

How do you use water?

Think of the number of times you use water every day. Like all living things, you need water. In fact, more than half of the material that makes up your body is water.

No matter where you live, most of the time you can turn on a faucet and clean water flows out the spout. You use water when you take a shower, fix a snack, or wash a dish. If you've ever lost water service to your home, you've probably been reminded how much you depend upon it. No doubt about it, our need for water is serious.

SUPPORTING MAIN IDEAS
Make a chart to show information that supports the main idea: *Humans use many resources.*

Humans use many resources.

Throughout history, people around the world have relied on natural resources for survival. Ancient civilizations used stone to create tools and weapons. And wood was an important fuel for cooking and keeping warm. Today, humans continue to rely on the environment and have discovered additional resources to meet their needs. In Section 3.1 you read about sharing natural resources. Scientists classify these resources into two categories:

- renewable resources
- nonrenewable resources

▶ **Set Learning Goals**

Students will

- Classify natural resources.
- Explain how pollution affects the environment.
- Describe how a loss of biodiversity affects the environment.
- Collect and observe air-pollution samples.

◀ **3 Minute Warm-Up**

Display Transparency 20 or copy this exercise on the board:

Suppose that next week our school had to accept enough new students to double the student population. List five changes that would occur and explain how they would affect you. *Sample answer: The hallways would be much more crowded, so it would be harder to get to class on time. Lunch time would have to last longer to accommodate more students in the same space; I could end up eating lunch at 10:00 in the morning. Classes would be twice as large, and teachers would spend less time with each student. The books and supplies available would become scarce, and we would have to share them. There would be more competition to get on a sports team.*

 3-Minute Warm-Up, p. T20

3.2 MOTIVATE

THINK ABOUT

PURPOSE To understand the importance of water in everyday life

DISCUSS Have students discuss where water comes from at their home. Ask:

- Where is the water that comes from a faucet stored?
- How does it get into the storage tank?
- Does it come from a well, reservoir, or river?
- Under what circumstances could we run out of clean water?

Sample answer: water heater in basement; from pipes from city water source; reservoir; drought

---

RESOURCES FOR DIFFERENTIATED INSTRUCTION

Below Level

UNIT RESOURCE BOOK
- Reading Study Guide A, pp. 154–155
- Decoding Support, p. 177

 AUDIO CDS

R Additional INVESTIGATION,
Pollutants on the Move, A, B, & C, pp. 189–197;
Teacher Instructions, pp. 200–201

Advanced

UNIT RESOURCE BOOK
- Challenge and Extension, p. 160
- Challenge Reading, pp. 173–174

English Learners

UNIT RESOURCE BOOK
Spanish Reading Study Guide, pp. 158–159

AUDIO CDS
- Audio Readings in Spanish
- Audio Readings (English)

Develop Critical Thinking

INFER Ask students to compare the description of the Northeast 200 years ago to developed areas of the country as they are today.

- What has likely happened to the woodlots of 200 years ago? *They may have been cleared for development or for agriculture.*
- What has happened to pastures and fields? *Many have forests on them. Some have been built on as cities, industry, and highways.*

Teacher Demo

Bring in fresh, living blades of grass and dry, dead ones. Pass the living and dead blades around the class, encouraging students to notice differences in color, texture, flexibility, and overall feel. Help them understand that withdrawal of water results in the dry, dead blade.

Teach from Visuals

To help students interpret the visual of renewable and nonrenewable resources, ask:

- Which two resources are renewable? *trees, water*
- Which two resources are nonrenewable? *oil, coal*
- Are there endless supplies of oil and coal? *No, supplies are limited.*

Ongoing Assessment

Categorize natural resources.

Ask: Coal and oil originally were plant matter. Plants are renewable resources, so why are coal and oil nonrenewable? *Creating coal and oil takes a long time and special geological circumstances.*

CHECK YOUR READING *Answer: trees (they can be planted or regrow); sunlight (Earth receives continuous sunlight); water (water cycle replenishes water in lakes and groundwater)*

 **RESOURCE CENTER**
CLASSZONE.COM

Find out more about natural resources.

Renewable Resources

Two hundred years ago, most small towns in the Northeastern part of the United States included farm fields, pasture, and woods. The wooded areas that weren't farmed were used as wood lots. The wood from these lots supplied firewood for towns and was often exported for income.

Trees are an example of a renewable resource—a resource that can be used over and over again. The Sun's energy is another important renewable resource. Because the Sun is expected to supply energy for another five billion years, its energy is considered essentially unlimited. As you read earlier in your study of the water cycle, water can be classified as a renewable resource. Renewable resources can be replaced naturally or by humans in a short amount of time, but they may run out if they are overused or managed poorly.

? **A**

CHECK YOUR READING Give three examples of renewable resources. Explain why each one is considered renewable.

Nonrenewable Resources

? **B**

Nonrenewable resources are resources that cannot be replaced. In some cases, they may be replenished by natural processes, but not quickly enough for human purposes. Nonrenewable resources are often underground, making them more difficult to reach. But technology has enabled humans to locate and remove nonrenewable resources from places that used to be impossible to reach.

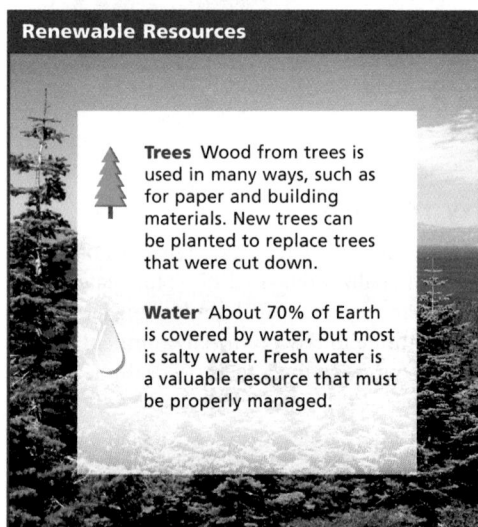

Renewable Resources

Trees Wood from trees is used in many ways, such as for paper and building materials. New trees can be planted to replace trees that were cut down.

Water About 70% of Earth is covered by water, but most is salty water. Fresh water is a valuable resource that must be properly managed.

Nonrenewable Resources

OIL Oil and oil products provide energy. Because it takes millions of years to form, oil is considered a nonrenewable resource.

Coal Coal is the decayed remains of organisms that lived millions of years ago. It is burned to provide heat and energy.

DIFFERENTIATE INSTRUCTION

? **More Reading Support**

A What is a renewable resource? *a resource that can be replenished*

B What is a nonrenewable resource? *a resource that cannot be replaced*

English Learners Encourage English learners to write down the definitions of *renewable* and *nonrenewable resources* in their personal dictionaries. Have students draw a T-chart and list different renewable and nonrenewable resources under the correct heading. Let students compare lists and add new examples like the one shown to their own.

renewable	nonrenewable

Coal, petroleum, and natural gas are nonrenewable resources that are removed from underground by mining or drilling. Also called fossil fuels, they are the main energy source for heating, industry, and transportation and are used to make many products. Many minerals, like copper and gold, are also considered nonrenewable resources.

Pollution endangers biodiversity.

As you walk along a city street, you may smell exhaust or see litter. These are examples of pollution. **Pollution** is the addition of harmful substances to the environment. Many of the ways humans use natural resources cause pollution to be released into the soil, air, and water. Pollutants include chemicals, bacteria, and dirt. Even materials that are ordinarily not harmful can cause pollution when they build up in one location.

As pollution becomes common in an ecosystem, living things may be threatened. Plant and animal populations may decrease and biodiversity may decline. **Biodiversity** is the number and variety of life forms within an ecosystem. Healthy ecosystems support a variety of species. An ecosystem with a variety of organisms can recover more easily from disturbances than an ecosystem that has fewer species.

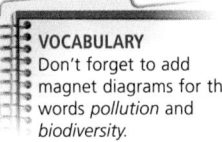

VOCABULARY
Don't forget to add magnet diagrams for the words *pollution* and *biodiversity*.

INVESTIGATE Particles in the Air

Where do you find air pollution?

PROCEDURE

1. Use a hole punch to make holes at the ends of two index cards. Cut two pieces of string 30 cm long and tie one string to each card.

2. Choose a different location for each card. Mark the card with its location and the date.

3. Spread a thin film of petroleum jelly on a 3 cm² area on each card and hang each card at the location you've chosen.

4. Collect the cards in one week and examine them with the hand lens.

WHAT DO YOU THINK?
- Identify the types of particles collected at each location.
- Do you think of all of the particles collected as pollution?
- Which location had the most pollution?

CHALLENGE Hypothesize why certain locations have more particles in the air than others.

SKILL FOCUS
Observing

MATERIALS
- 2 index cards
- marker
- hole punch
- string
- scissors
- petroleum jelly
- hand lens

TIME
30 minutes

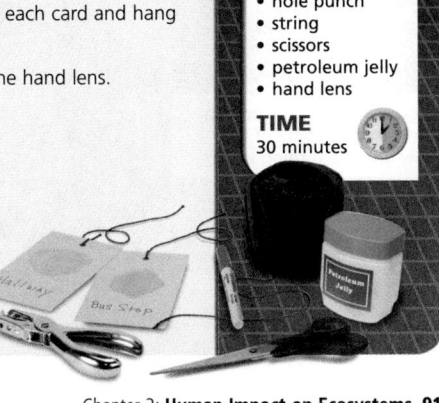

Integrate the Sciences

Fossil fuels are formed from remains of living things 50 to 350 million years ago. Coal was formed in great swamps, where plant remains first formed peat, which was later covered by sand and mud. Oil began as sediment formed from the remains of plants and animals living in shallow seas. Over thousands of centuries, heat and pressure cause chemical changes that form both coal and petroleum.

INVESTIGATE Particles in the Air

PURPOSE To observe air pollution

TIPS *30 min.* The longer you can hang the cards, the better. Some pollutants take a full week to appear. Premake cards for disabled students.

WHAT DO YOU THINK? *Sample answers: dust, dirt, exhaust, pollen, etc.; answers will vary depending on the locations from which samples were collected.*

CHALLENGE *Possibilities include better ventilation or air circulation, proximity to sources of pollution, location inside or outside, amount of people who use the area.*

Technology Resources

Customize this student lab as needed or look for an alternative. Print rubrics to assess student lab reports.

Lab Generator CD-ROM

DIFFERENTIATE INSTRUCTION

More Reading Support

C What is pollution? *substances that harm air, water, or land*

D What is biodiversity? *number and variety of species of living things in an ecosystem*

Below Level To help students distinguish between renewable and nonrenewable resources, have them construct a collage for each category with pictures of examples that they draw or cut from magazines. Display the collages on posters or a bulletin board.

Address Misconceptions

IDENTIFY Ask students to describe or draw the way pollution spreads in water, in air, or on land. If students answer by describing small or isolated areas, they may hold the misconception that air pollution and water pollution affect only limited areas.

CORRECT Demonstrate evaporation by heating a small amount of water on a burner until it boils away. Have students discuss where the water has gone. Pour another pot of water in the sink or on the ground, and discuss where it moved to.

REASSESS Ask: What is likely to happen to pollutants that enter a lake? *Some pollutants would enter the soil around the lake; others might affect living things in the lake. Other pollutants might enter the water cycle through evaporation, move throughout the atmosphere, and fall back to Earth. Evaporated pollutants would enter the air. Precipitation would bring the pollution back down to Earth again.* How would you describe the movement of pollutants through a system? *They move in a cycle, from air to water and soil, into bodies of water, and back to air again.*

Teach from Visuals

To help students interpret the photographs of acid-rain damage, ask: Why are the spruce needles discolored? *They have been exposed to acid rain.*

Ongoing Assessment

Answer: motor vehicles, factory exhaust, and power plant exhaust

---

Air Quality

Air quality affects entire ecosystems. For example, in 1980, Mount St. Helens erupted on the West Coast of the United States. Hot ash was blown 15 miles up into the air. Three days later some of that ash reached the East Coast. Although natural events occasionally release air pollutants, human activities pollute every day.

Today in the United States, motor vehicles, factories, and power plants are the main sources of air pollution. The fossil fuels they burn release sulfur dioxide, nitrogen dioxide, and carbon monoxide into the air. These pollutants affect humans and animals and are the main cause of acid rain, a serious problem affecting ecosystems.

CHECK YOUR READING What air pollutants contribute to acid rain problems in the United States?

Acid rain occurs when air pollutants such as sulfur dioxide and nitrogen dioxide mix with water in the atmosphere to form acid droplets of rain, ice, snow, or mist. Just as the wind carried ash from Mount St. Helens, wind can carry these droplets for very long distances before they fall as rain.

Acid rain has been very harmful in areas without rich soil to help correct the rain's acidity. In New York's Adirondack Mountains, acid rain has killed all the fish in some lakes. The photograph below shows the impact of acid rain on trees in the Adirondacks. Where acid rain falls, it damages leaves and soil. This damage destroys both habitats and food sources for many animals, eventually reducing biodiversity.

Acid-Rain Damage

A close look at the branch reveals that some of the needles are turning brown.

Air Quality Spruce trees in the Adirondacks show damage caused when pollutants in the air mix with rain.

DIFFERENTIATE INSTRUCTION

Additional Investigation To reinforce Section 3.2 learning goals, use the following full-period investigation:

R Additional **INVESTIGATION,** Pollutants on the Move, A, B, & C, pp. 189–197, 200–201 (Advanced students should complete Levels B and C.)

Water Quality

Water quality is another factor that affects biodiversity in ecosystems. Forty years ago, newspaper headlines announced that Lake Erie was "dead" because of pollution. Almost every living thing in the lake had died. Lake Erie suffered for years from pollution by neighborhoods, industries, and farms along its banks. Rivers that emptied into the lake also carried pollution with them.

The pollution found in Lake Erie is common in communities across the United States. Chemicals or waste that drain off of farm fields, animal feedlots, and landfills all cause water pollution. So do oil spills, soil erosion, and the discharging of wastewater from towns and industries.

 **Name four different sources of water pollution.**

Like air pollution, water pollution affects entire ecosystems. One river that suffers from heavy pollution is the Duwamish River in Washington. Over 600 million gallons of untreated waste and storm water drain off the land into the river. As a result, large amounts of bacteria and harmful chemicals contaminate the water, killing fish and putting humans at risk.

When fish and amphibians in aquatic ecosystems are exposed to pollution, the entire food web is affected. If fish become scarce, some birds may no longer find enough food. The bird population may decrease as birds die or move to a new habitat. The result is that biodiversity in the ecosystem decreases.

Water Quality A scientist tests the water of the Duwamish River after chemicals were released into the river.

Chemical Pollution

Pollution that flows into aquatic ecosystems can harm—even kill—organisms like these fish.

DIFFERENTIATE INSTRUCTION

? More Reading Support

G What killed Lake Erie? *water pollution*

H How much of an ecosystem can water pollution affect? *all of it*

Advanced Tell students that scientists have found amphibians with mutations in aquatic ecosystems. Scientists have identified several possible causes such as chemical pollution, UV radiation, disease, and parasites. Have students research and debate whether pollution caused the deformities.

Have students who are interested in amphibians with mutations read the following article:

R Challenge Reading, pp. 173–174

Teach from Visuals

To help students interpret the photographs of chemical pollution, ask:

• Why is the scientist testing the water? *because chemicals were released into the water*

• How does chemical pollution harm fish? *It can kill them.*

Address Misconceptions

IDENTIFY Ask: What types of populations can change without affecting the rest of the ecosystem they are part of? If students name any type of organism, they may hold the misconception that some organisms do not affect the health of an ecosystem. On the contrary, each type of organism is important and affects the entire ecosystem.

CORRECT Use one of the students' answers as an example to illustrate the importance of all organisms to an ecosystem. A sudden decrease in the mosquito population, for example, may cause a decrease in the populations of animals that feed on mosquitoes, such as swallows and bats. The effects continue to move up the food chain.

REASSESS Ask: What species can be removed from an ecosystem without affecting it? *None; all species eat or consume something. Even fleas are predators and serve the purpose of thinning host populations.*

Technology Resources

Visit **ClassZone.com** for background on common student misconceptions.

MISCONCEPTION DATABASE

EXPLORE (the **BIG** idea)

Revisit "How Easily Does Polluted Water Move Through Plants?" on p. 79. Have students explain how the activity relates to plants near polluted water.

Ongoing Assessment

 *Answer: oil spills, soil erosion, wastewater, chemical runoff*

Teach from Visuals

To help students interpret the diagrams of water and air pollution, ask:

- In the picture on the left, how does pollution move from one place to another? *by water*

- In the picture on the right, how does pollution move from one place to another? *by evaporating into the air*

- How do these pictures suggest a cycle? *the arrows suggest that pollution moves from land to water*

- What might be the next part of the cycle? *pollution in the air might move back to the land by rain or snow*

Integrate the Sciences

Pollutants can move large distances and end up hundreds or thousands of miles away from their source. This "jumping" from one location to another is sometimes referred to as the grasshopper effect. The pollutants move by water or by air. For example, PCBs and mercury can exist as tiny particles that are carried by winds through Earth's atmosphere. These same pollutants can fall to Earth's surface in drops of rain or in snow, where they can enter streams and lakes. Warm temperatures can cause pollutants in the water to vaporize and move back into Earth's atmosphere. The air and the water each represent a different medium that carries the pollutants. This type of interaction is described as cross-media contamination.

Metacognitive Strategy

Ask students to reflect on what they knew about pollution before they studied it in class. Ask them to recall where they got their information, and to assess the reliability of their sources. Have them describe how their thinking has changed.

Ongoing Assessment

Explain how pollution endangers the environment.

Ask: How do air and water pollution harm Earth? *Air pollution causes acid rain and irritation; water pollution poisons fish and other species.*

 94 Unit: **Ecology**

Pollution Across Systems

As you have learned, pollution can be spread among ecosystems by abiotic factors. For example, wind carried ash from Mount St. Helens to different ecosystems. Wind also carries acid rain to forest ecosystems. Pollution can also move between air and water. For example, some chemical pollutants can run off land and into a body of water. As this polluted water evaporates and cycles through the environment, some of the pollutants may be transported with it.

① Runoff containing harmful chemicals flows into this pond.

② Water evaporates, taking some of the harmful chemicals into the air.

Habitat loss endangers biodiversity.

Scientists know that an ecosystem with many different species of plants and animals can withstand the effects of flooding, drought, and disease more effectively than an ecosystem with fewer species. But for biodiversity to be maintained, a habitat must be able to support a large number of different species. If living space is limited or a food source is removed, then the number of species in a biological community will be reduced.

Removing Habitat

One way human activities affect habitats is by reducing the amounts of natural resources available to living things. When this occurs, populations that rely on those resources are less likely to survive. For example, if you trim all the dead branches off the trees in your yard and remove them, insects that live in rotting wood will not settle in your yard. As a result, woodpeckers that may have nested in the area will lose their source of food. By removing this food source, you might affect the biodiversity in your backyard.

Now consider altering an ecosystem much larger than your backyard. Instead of removing a single resource, imagine removing a large area of land that is a habitat to many different species. Disturbing habitats removes not only food but space, shelter, and protection for living things.

D 94 Unit: **Ecology**

DIFFERENTIATE INSTRUCTION

❓ More Reading Support

I How does pollution move from land to water? *It dissolves in rainwater or gets eroded in runoff.*

Alternative Assessment Have students design an experiment to test human impact on an ecosystem. Have them study how paving areas affects soil and water in the region. Refer them to the Nature of Science pp. xxii–xxv. Have students identify the information they will need, the way that they can measure results, and the observations they would use.

Removing Habitat

A clear-cut forest provides a dramatic example of habitat loss.

Forest Habitat The forest provides food and shelter for many organisms.

Deforestation Removing all the trees from an area removes habitat that other species depend on.

Because of land development, forests that once stretched for hundreds of miles have been fragmented, or broken apart into small patches. Organisms that depend on trees cannot live in woods that have large areas that have been clear-cut. Their habitat is removed or reduced so there is a greater risk of attack by predators. Skunks, raccoons, and crows, which eat the eggs of forest songbirds, will not travel deep into large forests. However, they can reach nests more easily when forests are broken into small areas.

CHECK YOUR READING Why is biodiversity important and how can human activities affect it?

Changing Habitat

Another kind of habitat loss occurs when humans move species into new habitats, either on purpose or by accident. Some species, when released in a new place, successfully compete against the native species, crowding them out. Over time, these species, called invasive species, may replace the native species.

One example of an invasive plant is purple loosestrife. In the 1800s loosestrife from Europe was brought to the United States to use as a garden plant and medicinal herb. One loosestrife plant can make about 2 million seeds a year. These seeds are carried long distances by wind, water, animals, and humans. Loosestrife sprouts in wetlands, where it can fill in open-water habitat or replace native plants such as goldenrod. Most ducks and fish do not feed on purple loosestrife.

Chapter 3: **Human Impact on Ecosystems** 95 **D**

Teach from Visuals

To help students interpret the photograph of a clear-cut forest, ask:

- What has happened in the foreground of the picture? *The forest has been clear-cut.*
- How is the light in the background different from the foreground? *There is much more light in the foreground.*
- How might the ecosystem change from the foreground to the background? *Foreground has dry soil with very little life. Background has variety of life in and under trees; soil is not eroded.*

Real World Example

There are many examples of invasive species. Imported red fire ants were accidentally introduced into Alabama in the ballast of merchant ships. The ants have spread throughout the South. Fire ants are aggressive, their stings are painful, and mainly their mounds can ruin fields of crops. Also in the South, the kudzu vine, imported from Japan, now runs wild, covering small houses and killing trees. Zebra mussels from Europe cover piers, boats, machinery, and clog water supply pipes in the Great Lakes. In Australia, European rabbits have wiped out some native vegetation, severely stressing the local species.

Ongoing Assessment

Describe how loss of diversity affects the environment.

Ask: When land is cleared with a bulldozer, how does loss of diversity affect the environment? *Soil is removed and may become too thin or dry for plants to grow. Plants, insects, and other living things are removed. Many larger animals can no longer live in this habitat. They lose the food and living space they depend on.*

CHECK YOUR READING *Answer: Biodiversity is important because it measures the richness and variety of life in an ecosystem. Human activities can reduce biodiversity by decreasing the amount of land in an ecosystem.*

Chapter 3 **95 D**

Address Misconceptions

IDENTIFY Ask students to explain why they think ecologists should or should not work to reduce the growth of some plants. Students may think that all species are beneficial to an environment, and that there is no need to control growth of an invasive species.

CORRECT Have volunteers add steps to a flow chart on the board that illustrates what might happen to the monarch butterfly if the only food source for its larvae were replaced by an invasive plant species.

REASSESS Explain how the growth of a population of a non-native species might limit the growth of another species. *through competition or the destruction of a living area*

Reinforce (the BIG idea)

Have students relate the section to the Big Idea.

 Reinforcing Key Concepts, p. 162

3.2 ASSESS & RETEACH

Assess

 Section 3.2 Quiz, p. 43

Reteach

Create a three-column chart for students titled "Human Activities Affect the Environment." Use these headings:

- Use Resources
- Release Waste and Pollution
- Alter Habitats

Under each heading have students cite specific activities. Discuss the effects on biodiversity and efficiency of the ecosystem. Have students brainstorm activities that minimize impacts.

Technology Resources

Have students visit **ClassZone.com** for reteaching of Key Concepts.

 CONTENT REVIEW

 CONTENT REVIEW CD-ROM

D **96** Unit: Ecology

Changing Habitat

Habitat loss occurs when purple loosestrife fills in open water or crowds out goldenrod.

Invasive Species Purple loosestrife fills in wetlands and crowds out native species, disturbing organisms that rely on native species for food or living space.

Native Species Goldenrod is a native species that is a food source for many wetland populations.

When the native plants that wetland animals depend on are crowded out by loosestrife, the animals disappear, too.

Scientists estimate that Earth supports more than 10 million different species. They also estimate that thousands of species are threatened, and over a hundred species of plants and animals become extinct every year. By protecting biodiversity we can help ecosystems thrive and even recover more quickly after a natural disturbance such as a hurricane. And biodiversity directly benefits humans. For example, many medications are based on natural compounds from plants that only grow in certain types of ecosystems.

3.2 Review

KEY CONCEPTS

1. List some renewable and nonrenewable resources that you need to survive.
2. Describe two ways in which pollution can move through ecosystems.
3. Explain what scientists mean by *biodiversity*.

CRITICAL THINKING

4. **Explain** Under some circumstances, valuable natural resources can be considered pollutants. Explain this statement, giving two examples.
5. **Compare** Identify two natural habitats in your area, one with high biodiversity and one with low biodiversity. Describe the biodiversity of each.

CHALLENGE

6. **Hypothesize** When lakes are polluted by acid rain, the water appears to become clearer, not cloudier. Why do you think this is the case?

D **96** Unit: Ecology

ANSWERS

1. renewable: air, water, wood, crops; nonrenewable: oil, coal, minerals, metals

2. Wind can carry acid rain; chemical pollutants run off land into groundwater.

3. number and variety of life forms in an ecosystem

4. Sample: Natural resources can be pollutants when they end up where they don't belong. Example: when erosion washes soil into streams; carbon from forest fire pollutes the air.

5. Sample: low biodiversity: grass field with insects,

worms; high biodiversity: a forest with variety of plant and animal life

6. Acidic water slows the growth of producers in the lake. With fewer producers and less food available, the water appears clearer because there is less life in it.

SKILL: FINDING VOLUMES

How Much Water?

When you take a 10-minute shower, you are using about 190 liters of water. How much is that? Liters are a metric unit of capacity—the amount of liquid that can fit into a container of a certain size. The liter is based on a metric unit of volume. One liter is equal to 1000 cubic centimeters.

Example

A rectangular tank holds the amount of water used for a 10-minute shower. The dimensions of the tank are 250 cm × 40 cm × 19 cm. What is the volume of the tank?

Volume = **length** × **width** × height
$$V = l \times w \times h$$

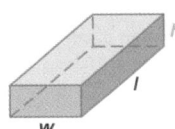

(1) Use the formula for volume.
Replace variables with actual dimensions.
$V = 250 \text{ cm} \times 40 \text{ cm} \times 19 \text{ cm}$

(2) Calculate by multiplying.
$(250 \times 40) \times 19$
$10{,}000 \quad \times 19 = 190{,}000$

(3) Check units:
cm × cm × cm = cm³ (cubic centimeters)

ANSWER 250 cm × 40 cm × 19 cm = 19,000 cm³

Find the following volumes or dimensions.

1. Brushing your teeth with the water running uses the water in a tank 14 cm by 45 cm by 12 cm. Sketch an aquarium that holds exactly this amount. Label the dimensions. What is the volume?

2. If you turn off the water while you brush, you use only about half as much water. Sketch a rectangular tank that holds this volume. Label the dimensions. What is the volume?

3. A typical toilet flush uses the water in a 50 cm by 20 cm by 20 cm space. Find the volume in cubic centimeters. Sketch a model of this volume.

CHALLENGE An Olympic swimming pool is 50 m by 25 m by 3 m. What is its volume? There are approximately 5678 cubic meters of water in the water tower shown. How many Olympic pools of water would it take to fill the tower?

ANSWERS

1. *Aquariums should have length, width, and height labeled correctly; 7,560 cm³*

2. *Sample answer: 14 cm · 45 cm · 6 cm = 3780 cm³*

3. *50 cm · 20 cm · 20 cm = 20,000 cm³*

CHALLENGE *50 m · 25 m · 3 m = 3750 m³;* $\dfrac{5678 \text{ cm}^3}{3750 \text{ cm}^3} = 1.5$

MATH IN SCIENCE
Math Skills Practice for Science

Set Learning Goal

To calculate volumes for various scenarios of water usage

Present the Science

From 50–90 percent of the weight of all living things is water. The basic material of cells, protoplasm, is a solution of water and substances like fats, proteins, and salts. Water transports, breaks down, and dissolves these substances.

Develop Geometry Skills

• Remind students that volume adds the third dimension to area.

• Point out that, if a shape is irregular, the standard formula *(lwh)* does not apply.

• Point out that problems asking for volume are easier to solve if you set them up as equations before trying to answer. Have students begin each problem with writing out the $V = l \cdot w \cdot h$ equation.

DIFFERENTIATION TIP Have students who have trouble with the formula keep a cube or rectangular small empty box on their desks as a reminder that volume takes up space, and that it has three dimensions: length, width, and height.

Close

Have students use amounts given in the problems to estimate the volume of water they use in a total day. *Sample answer: 188,500 cm³ for a shower, 5 flushes at 18,850 cm³ per flush, 2 tooth brushings at 950 cm³ each Total = 208,300 cm³ per day*

 • Math Support, p. 178
• Math Practice, p. 179

Technology Resources

Students can visit **ClassZone.com** for practice in finding volumes.

 MATH TUTORIAL

▶ Set Learning Goals

Students will

- Consider laws that have been passed to help protect the environment.
- Describe the efforts that are being made to conserve natural resources.

◯ 3-Minute Warm-Up

Display Transparency 21 or copy this exercise on the board:

Match the definition to the correct term.

Definitions

1. something from the environment that humans use *c*
2. number of people in a given area *b*
3. the variety of life in an ecosystem *e*

Terms

a. pollution   d. invasive species

b. population density   e. biodiversity

c. natural resource

 3-Minute Warm-Up, p. T21

3.3 MOTIVATE

EXPLORE Environmental Impacts

PURPOSE To demonstrate how foot traffic might affect water absorption by soil

TIPS *15 min.* Pots about 4 inches in diameter work well. You do not have to use potting soil. Any soil will do.

WHAT DO YOU THINK? *The pot with the compressed soil took longer to absorb the water; soil that is walked on quite a bit will hold less water, making it more difficult for grass or other plants to get water.*

People are working to protect ecosystems.

◁ **BEFORE, you learned**

- Human activities produce pollutants
- Human activity is depleting some natural resources

▷ **NOW, you will learn**

- About some of the laws that have been passed to help protect the environment
- About efforts that are being made to conserve natural resources

VOCABULARY

conservation p. 99
sustainable p. 102

EXPLORE Environmental Impacts

What happens when soil is compressed?

PROCEDURE

1. Fill two pots with 1 cup each of potting soil.
2. Compress the soil in the second pot by pushing down hard upon it with your hand.
3. Pour 1 cup of water into the first pot. Start the stopwatch as soon as you start pouring. Stop the watch as soon as all the water has been absorbed. Record the time.
4. Pour 1 cup of water into the second pot and again record how long it takes for the water to be absorbed. Wash your hands.

MATERIALS

- 2 plant pots with trays
- measuring cups
- potting soil
- water
- stopwatch

WHAT DO YOU THINK?

- What effect does compressing the soil have upon how quickly the water is absorbed?
- What might happen to water that is not absorbed quickly by soil?

Environmental awareness is growing.

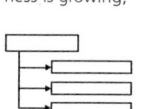

SUPPORTING MAIN IDEAS Make a chart to list some of the activities that show that environmental awareness is growing.

As people moved westward across grassy plains and steep mountain ranges of the United States, many believed our nation's resources were endless. Midwestern prairies were converted to farmland. Forests were clear-cut for lumber. Land was mined for coal.

By the 1800s, foresters and naturalists began to take interest in preserving the wild areas they saw rapidly disappearing. In 1872 our nation's outlook started to change when Yellowstone, the world's first national park, was established. It wasn't long before conservation of

D 98 Unit: Ecology

RESOURCES FOR DIFFERENTIATED INSTRUCTION

Below Level

UNIT RESOURCE BOOK

- Reading Study Guide A, pp. 165–166
- Decoding Support, p. 177

 **AUDIO CDS**

Advanced

UNIT RESOURCE BOOK

Challenge and Extension, p. 171

English Learners

UNIT RESOURCE BOOK

Spanish Reading Study Guide, pp. 169–170

AUDIO CDS

- Audio Readings in Spanish
- Audio Readings (English)

wild places became a goal. **Conservation** is the process of saving or protecting a natural resource.

The movement to protect our environment grew rapidly in the 1960s. *Silent Spring*, a book that raised public awareness of the effect of harmful chemicals in the environment, sparked debate about serious pollution problems. As local efforts for environmental protection grew, the United States government responded. Throughout the 1970s important laws were passed to preserve and protect the environment. Today small groups of citizens, along with local and national government efforts, protect America's natural resources.

RESOURCE CENTER
CLASSZONE.COM
Discover how people help ecosystems recover.

CHECK YOUR READING List three events in the history of the environmental movement in the United States.

Volunteers work to clean up a stream.

Local Efforts

Maybe you have heard the expression "Think globally, act locally." It urges people to consider the health of the entire planet and to take action in their own communities. Long before federal and state agencies began enforcing environmental laws, individuals were coming together to protect habitats and the organisms that depend on them. These efforts are often referred to as grassroots efforts. They occur on a local level and are primarily run by volunteers.

Often the efforts of a few citizens gather the support and interest of so many people that they form a larger organization. These groups work to bring about change by communicating with politicians, publishing articles, or talking to the news media. Some groups purchase land and set it aside for preservation.

3.3 INSTRUCT

Social Studies Connection

President Theodore Roosevelt is depicted on Mount Rushmore because, more than any other president, he supported conservation. Because of him, Congress created the Forest Service in 1905 to manage federal forest. He set aside about 200 million acres as public lands, protecting them from commercial exploitation. He designated 150 national forests, the first 51 federal bird reservations, and 5 national parks. He pushed for the Reclamation Act of 1902, which established irrigation and other services for western lands. In 1911, the Reclamation Service completed Roosevelt Dam, near Phoenix, Arizona.

History of Science

Rachel Carson wrote four books about the connection between living things and their environment. The most important of these books is *Silent Spring.* Published in 1962, *Silent Spring* exposed the danger of the pesticide DDT. The book depicted how DDT entered the food chain and affected entire ecosystems. Carson kept careful notes and her hard work paid off. Today, *Silent Spring* is credited with starting the environmental movement in the United States.

Ongoing Assessment

CHECK YOUR READING *Answer: creation of first national park (1872), publication of* Silent Spring *(1962), passage of major environmental laws in the 1970s*

DIFFERENTIATE INSTRUCTION

? More Reading Support

A When did the movement to protect the environment catch on in a big way? *1960s*

English Learners Encourage English learners to share environmental issues from their native countries. Also encourage them to discuss any local or community conservation efforts.

To help students interpret the graph of peregrine falcon pairs, ask:

- What was happening to the peregrine falcon population until 1968? *The overall trend was that the population declined.*

- In what year was DDT banned? *1972*

- In what year were the first captive falcons released? *1974*

- What has been happening to the peregrine falcon population since 1985? *The number of breeding pairs has risen steeply.*

Real World Example

DDT was once considered very beneficial. After World War II, it was used heavily throughout the world to control the insects that carry life-threatening diseases such as malaria, yellow fever, typhus, and elephantiasis. In the 1950s in India, the use of DDT decreased the number of malaria cases from 75 million to 5 million. Further, crops sprayed with DDT sometimes doubled their yields.

By 1962, however, DDT's damaging effects were being identified. Because DDT is a very stable chemical, it accumulated in the birds and fish that ate the insects, poisoning them and causing reproductive problems. Many insects developed resistance to DDT, and these populations grew unchecked while their natural predators were killed. For these reasons, DDT was banned in the United States in 1972 except for use in extreme health emergencies. Developing countries, such as those in Africa, continue to use DDT to control mosquitoes that can carry malaria.

Ongoing Assessment

CHECK YOUR READING *Answer: the National Environmental Policy Act (NEPA), the Endangered Species Act, the Clean Air Act, and Clean Water Act*

Federal Efforts

B

You have probably heard of the Endangered Species Act or the Clean Air Act. You might wonder, though, exactly what these laws do. The United States government works with scientists to write laws that ensure that companies and individuals work together to conserve natural resources and maintain healthy ecosystems.

In the late 1960s the National Environmental Policy Act, known as NEPA, made the protection of natural ecosystems a national goal. Several important laws followed. For example, the Clean Air Act and Clean Water Act improved the control of different kinds and amounts of pollutants that can be put into the air and water. The Environmental Protection Agency (EPA) enforces all federal environmental laws.

C

CHECK YOUR READING Identify two federal environmental laws.

Over the past decades, chemical waste from factories has piled up in landfills and polluted water sources. These wastes can threaten ecosystems and human health. In 1980, citizen awareness of the dangers led to the Superfund Program. The goal of the program is to identify dangerous areas and to clean up the worst sites.

Helping Endangered Species

Government and private groups have helped peregrine falcon populations to recover.

Peregrine falcons removed from endangered species list

Peregrine falcons listed as endangered

First of 6000 captive falcons released

DDT use banned in the United States

Breeding Pairs of Peregrine Falcons (vertical axis: 0–1800)
Year (horizontal axis: 1948–2000)

SOURCE: Audubon Society

D 100 Unit: Ecology

DIFFERENTIATE INSTRUCTION

? More Reading Support

B What do the Clean Air and Clean Water Acts do? *give government control over pollution*

C What does the EPA do? *enforces all federal environmental laws*

Advanced Suggest that students create political cartoons depicting pollution issues and/or government or civilian responses.

R Challenge and Extension, p. 171

English Learners There are many different types of graphs. Review the graph on endangered species with English learners. Help them understand how the information is arranged and how to interpret it. Encourage them to generate questions that can be answered by the graph.

Ecosystem Recovery

A growing awareness of the importance of healthy ecosystems is inspiring restoration projects.

Wetland

Restoration efforts in Galveston Bay, Texas, focus on bringing back the sea-grass meadows near the coast.

Volunteers help replant sea grass around Galveston Island State Park. Sea grass is a major habitat for birds, fish, and crabs and helps prevent erosion by holding bottom sediments in place.

Desert

Members of a restoration group work to restore desert plants and soil in Red Rock Canyon State Park, California.

1 A power auger is used to break up severely compacted soil and prepare it for planting.

2 Seedlings of native species, like the saltbush, are grown off site. Once they reach a more mature size, they are brought in to be planted.

3 Plastic cones are used to protect plants from being disturbed by severe weather or predators.

Teach from Visuals

Ecosystem recovery projects are underway in many areas, including Galveston Island State Park in Texas and Red Rock Canyon State Park in California.

To help students interpret the photographs of wetland and desert, ask:

- How do the seagrass meadows help the marine ecosystem? *Sea grass holds soil in place and keeps the water clear.*
- What were plastic cones used for? *to protect new plants*
- Why did vegetation need to be restored in Red Rock Canyon? *Soil had been compacted and vegetation stripped by vehicles and mining.*

Real World Example

To restore the Galveston Island seagrass meadows—which broke up because of shrimp trawling and pumping groundwater for industrial, commercial, and residential use—an offshore oyster reef had to be replaced. The oyster reef had protected the wetlands from the waves. To replace it, 13,500 geotubes were installed in open water offshore to simulate the reef. Geotubes use a special fabric that contains fill material while allowing water through. These geotubes have helped minimize erosion and improve water clarity.

DIFFERENTIATE INSTRUCTION

Below Level Create a two-column chart on a bulletin board or dry-erase board. Use the column headings: "Sustainable Practices" and "Renewable Resources." Have students brainstorm specific examples of each. Write any "non-examples" off to the side to discuss as a contrast.

Integrate the Sciences

One use for recycled newspapers is cellulose insulation. Newspaper is turned into a pulp, which is sprayed into the walls of houses and under rooftops. It fills cavities and so stops air filtration better than fiberglass batting does. Cellulose-insulated buildings may use 20–40 percent less energy than conventional insulated buildings. And it takes less energy to make the insulation than to make fiberglass insulation. Cellulose insulation also increases the fire resistance of a house.

Ongoing Assessment

Consider the kinds of laws that have been passed to help protect the environment.

Ask: What is the goal of the National Environmental Policy Act? *to protect natural ecosystems from damage or destruction*

CHECK YOUR READING *Answer: Sustainable practices use natural resources without using them up.*

INFER At this Superfund site, the chemical cadmium pollutes the soil. Why does this worker need to wear a face mask?

Federal agencies oversee the Superfund Program and other environmental laws. In addition to federal laws protecting the environment, there are state laws. Companies must follow all the laws that apply in each state where they do business. The same company may need to follow different laws in different states.

The United States is just one of many countries learning to deal with the effects of their human population on the environment. Dozens of countries have already met to discuss concerns about clear-cutting, water pollution, and endangered species. At this international level, the United Nations Environment Programme encourages sound environmental practices worldwide.

Conserving resources protects ecosystems.

 D

Around the world, individuals and companies are expressing more interest in **sustainable** practices—ways of living and doing business that use natural resources without using them up. Sustainable development allows people to enjoy a high quality of life while limiting harm to ecosystems. Developing new technologies, reducing resource use, and creating less waste are three ways to practice sustainability.

 **CHECK YOUR READING** What are sustainable practices?

Improving Resource Use

As you read in Chapter 2, many different interactions take place in ecosystems. Some organisms form close relationships with one other and their environment. Humans are like other organisms. We depend on the environment to help meet our requirements for life. Because many of the resources we rely on are limited, businesses and governments are changing the way they manage farms, forests, and energy resources. They are adopting sustainable practices.

 E

Some farmers are practicing sustainable methods that protect land and provide nutritious food. Nearly one-third of U.S. farms practice conservation tillage, a method that involves planting seeds without plowing the soil. This technique can cut soil erosion by more than 90 percent. Organic farmers reject fertilizers and pesticides made from fossil fuels. Instead they use natural fertilizers, like compost, and natural pest controls, like ladybugs, which eat aphids.

DIFFERENTIATE INSTRUCTION

? More Reading Support

D Describe one sustainable practice. *reduce use of resources; lessen waste*

E Name one way organic farms control pests. *use ladybugs to eat aphids*

English Learners English learners may be unfamiliar with words that have multiple meanings. Explain the multiple meanings of the following words in the section. On p. 100, *private* is used to mean non-governmental. On p. 102, *adopting* is used to indicate something being put to use. On p. 102, *practice* is used to mean a policy or way of doing things. On p. 104, *pool* in *carpooling* is used to mean a group.

Forestry practices are also changing. Cutting selectively instead of clear-cutting reduces soil erosion and encourages rapid regrowth. The U.S. Forest Service has adopted an ecosystem-management approach that tries to balance the need for timber with the need to conserve soil and water and preserve wildlife and biodiversity.

 CHECK YOUR READING Give two examples of sustainable practices.

Energy companies are also promoting sustainability by developing alternative energy sources that do not come from fossil fuels. By the time you buy your first car, it may run on fuel cells, and the electricity in your house may be generated by a solar power plant.

Commercial geothermal power plants are a renewable energy source that uses the heat of molten rock in the Earth's interior. Geothermal power already supplies electricity to households in New Zealand, Japan, the United States, and elsewhere.

The energy of falling or flowing water can also be used to generate electricity in a hydropower plant. Commercial hydropower plants generate over half of the alternative energy used in the United States. Like solar and geothermal power, hydropower releases no pollutants. But hydropower often requires dams, which are expensive to build and can flood wildlife habitats and interfere with fish migration.

Wind is another source of energy that is clean and renewable. Large open areas with relatively constant winds are used as wind farms. Wind turbines are spread across these farms and convert the energy of moving air into electricity. Wind-generating capacity has increased steadily around the world in just the last ten years.

Solar Energy These mirrors collect and concentrate sunlight, which will be used to generate electricity.

Chapter 3: **Human Impact on Ecosystems** 103 **D**

DIFFERENTIATE INSTRUCTION

❓ More Reading Support

F Name an energy supply other than fossil fuels. *sunlight, geothermal, hydropower*

G What do windfarms do? *generate electricity from wind power*

Real World Example

Several cities have innovative ways to decrease traffic and pollution. Singapore created a drivable city center by constructing a ring of tollbooths around the city. The toll that people pay varies according to when they are driving and how much pollution there is. It costs more to drive into the city during rush hour than during off-peak periods, and more when pollution is high than when it is low. Licenses for cars are also different prices, depending on how much the car is driven. A license to drive only on weekends costs less than one to drive every day. London uses congestion charging, which charges drivers five pounds a day to drive in central London. This policy is encouraging other modes of transportation such as buses and trains.

Art Connection

In 1970, Container Corporation of America (CCA) sponsored a nationwide contest for students to create a design that would symbolize the paper recycling process. At that time CCA, a paperboard company, was the largest user of recycled fiber in the United States, and it wanted a symbol to identify packages made from recycled materials. Gary Anderson, an architecture student, designed the three-arrow symbol we see so many places today, and won the contest. You may wish to ask students to design a logo for another sustainable practice, such as organic farming.

Ongoing Assessment

Describe the efforts that are being made to conserve natural resources.

Ask: What are some ways that people conserve fossil fuels in their daily transportation to work and school? *carpooling, mass transit, bicycling, and walking*

INFER What benefits do people get from using mass transit? Why might some people be reluctant to use mass transit?

READING **TIP**
The prefix *re–* means *again*, so to *recycle* a resource is to use it again.

Reducing Waste and Pollution

Perhaps you are one of the many students who take a bus to school. Buses and trains are examples of mass transit, which move large groups of people at the same time. When you travel by mass transit, you are working to reduce waste and pollution. The photograph to the left shows a light rail train that carries commuters from downtown Portland, Oregon, into suburbs an hour away. In Portland, mass transit like this light rail helps reduce traffic congestion, air pollution, and noise pollution.

Another way to reduce pollution is by carpooling. Many states encourage carpools by reducing tolls or reserving highway lanes for cars carrying more than one person. Traffic is also reduced when workers telecommute, or work from home, using computers and telephones. Of course a telecommuter uses energy at home. But there are many ways to reduce home energy use. You can install compact fluorescent light bulbs, which use less electricity than a regular light bulb. And you can choose energy-efficient appliances.

CHECK YOUR READING How does mass transit benefit the environment?

Most homes are heated with oil or natural gas, two nonrenewable resources. To use less of these resources, you lower your thermostat in winter or add insulation around doors and windows to keep heat inside. Many power companies offer a free energy audit, to show how you can use less energy at home.

Recycling is a fairly new idea in human communities, but if you think about it, it's what biological communities have always done to reduce waste and pollution. Resources are used again and again as they move through the water, nitrogen, and carbon cycles. Materials

These students are participating in a local recycling program.

DIFFERENTIATE INSTRUCTION

? **More Reading Support**

H Name some ways to reduce the use of cars. *mass transit, carpool, bike*

I Name some things that are recycled. *glass, aluminum, plastic, paper, cardboard*

Below Level Have students review the ways to conserve natural resources on pp. 104–105 and give an example of each that is practiced in their local neighborhood. Ask for an example of: reducing waste (using a lunch box or canvas grocery bag rather than throw-away packaging), recycling (returning bottles), conserving energy use (lowering heat or air-conditioner use), and reducing air pollution (walking or biking).

that people now commonly recycle include glass, aluminum, certain types of plastic, office paper, newspaper, and cardboard.

Sometimes materials are recycled into the same product. Cans and glass bottles are melted down to make new cans and bottles. Materials can also be recycled into new products. Your warm fleece jacket might be made from recycled soda bottles. The cereal box on your breakfast table might be made from recycled paper.

 **CHECK YOUR READING** Name three things people can do at home that reduce waste and pollution.

Think globally, act locally.

Visitors to an ocean beach may find signs like the one on the right. Such signs remind people that small actions—like protecting the nests of sandpipers—make a difference in the preservation of ecosystems.

The challenges facing society are great. Providing Earth's growing population with clean water and air and with energy for warmth and transportation are only some of the many tasks. Scientists continue to learn about the interactions in ecosystems and how important ecosystems are to humans. As you have read about the interactions in ecosystems, you have probably realized that humans—including you—have a large effect on the natural world.

In the coming years, protection of ecosystems will remain a major challenge. By thinking globally, you will be able to understand the effects of society's decisions about resources, development, and transportation. By acting locally you can become involved in efforts to reduce the use of limited resources and to restore ecosystems.

BIRDS ONLY
Beyond
This
Sign

EXPLORE (the BIG idea)

Revisit "Internet Activity: The Environment" on p. 79. Have students explain their results.

Reinforce (the BIG idea)

Have students relate the section to the Big Idea.

R Reinforcing Key Concepts, p. 172

3.3 ASSESS & RETEACH

Assess

A Section 3.3 Quiz, p. 44

Reteach

Have the class add to a natural resources problem/possible solutions chart. Students can brainstorm actions that can be taken for the following problems:
- polluted water
- endangered species
- polluted air
- use of nonrenewable energy sources like fossil fuels

Technology Resources

Have students visit **ClassZone.com** for reteaching of Key Concepts.

 CONTENT REVIEW

 CONTENT REVIEW CD-ROM

3.3 Review

KEY CONCEPTS

1. List at least five ways that you can reduce your use of natural resources.

2. Describe three ways that resources can be managed in a sustainable way.

CRITICAL THINKING

3. **Infer** Controlling air and water pollution and protecting endangered species usually require the involvement of the federal government. Why can't state or local governments do this on their own?

CHALLENGE

4. **Apply** Explain how efforts to protect endangered species relate to restoration of ecosystems.

ANSWERS

1. volunteer clean up, mass transit, practice sustainable farming, recycling, alternative energy sources

2. Farms can use conservation tillage and natural pest control. Strip cutting and selective cutting can maintain

forests. Renewable sources such as wind, solar, and hydropower are alternatives to fossil fuels.

3. Animals migrate; water flows from one state to the next; and pollution created in one state can travel, so

the federal government needs to be involved to solve problems and set policies.

4. When efforts to protect or bring back endangered species are successful, more balance and more biodiversity are brought to the ecosystem.

Focus

PURPOSE Hypothesize the effects of various methods for containing and cleaning up an oil spill, and design an experimental model to test the effects of a spill on a beach environment

OVERVIEW Using sand and water, students will construct a model of a beach. They will add oil to their "coastal area" and then use materials and solutions to try to remove the oil. Students will find that cotton balls are most absorbent, and detergent most effective at breaking down oil. They will analyze the difference between their models and real oil-spill situations.

Lab Preparation

• Square cake pans work well.

• Prior to the investigation have students read through the investigation and prepare their data tables. Or you may wish to copy and distribute datasheets and rubrics.

 UNIT RESOURCE BOOK, pp. 180–188

 SCIENCE TOOLKIT, F12

Lab Management

• Ensure that all students wear gloves and aprons.

• Spread newspapers on desks to protect from spills.

• Students may dampen the sand for the beach so that it stays where they want it.

Teaching with Technology

You may wish to introduce this activity with a video documentary on cleaning up oil spills.

CHAPTER INVESTIGATION

Cleaning Oil Spills

DESIGN —YOUR OWN—

OVERVIEW AND PURPOSE

One example of a harmful effect of human activity is an oil spill. You've probably heard about oil spills in the news. Damage to an oil-carrying ship or barge can cause thick black oil to spill into the water. The oil floats on the water, and waves can carry the oil to shore. Oil gets caught on sand and living things that are part of a coastal ecosystem. These spills are especially difficult to clean up. In this investigation you will

• simulate an oil spill and test the effectiveness of various materials used to remove oil
• evaluate materials and processes used to clean up oil spills

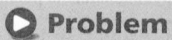 **Problem** Write It Up

What materials are effective at removing oil spilled near a coastal ecosystem?

Hypothesize Write It Up

Write a hypothesis to propose a material or materials that might best remove oil from a coastal area. Your hypothesis should take the form of an "If . . . , then . . . , because . . ." statement.

Procedure

1. Measure out 40 mL of vegetable oil in a small beaker. Stir in turmeric to make the oil yellow.

2. Pour sand into one end of the pan as shown to model a beach.

3. Carefully pour enough water into the pan so that it forms a model ocean at least 2 cm deep. Try not to disturb the sand pile.

4. Use the yellow-colored oil to model an oil spill. Pour the oil onto the slope of the sand so that it runs off into the water.

step 4

MATERIALS

• small beaker
• 40 mL vegetable oil
• turmeric
• spoon
• aluminum baking pan
• sand
• large beaker
• water
• sponge
• dish soap
• rubbing alcohol
• paper towels
• cotton balls
• cotton rag
• cornstarch
• yarn
• feather
• seaweed

INVESTIGATION RESOURCES

 CHAPTER INVESTIGATION, Oil Spills
• Level A, pp. 180–183
• Level B, pp. 184–187
• Level C, p. 188

Advanced students should complete Levels B & C.

 Writing a Lab Report, D12–13

Technology Resources

Customize this student lab as needed or look for an alternative. Print rubrics to assess student lab reports.

 Lab Generator CD-ROM

5 Test the materials for effectiveness in removing the oil from the sand and the water.

6 Place the feather and the seaweed on the beach or in the water, where the oil is. Test materials for effectiveness in removing oil from the feather and seaweed.

7 Make a table in your **Science Notebook** like the one below. Record your observations on the effectiveness of each material.

8 Using your observations from step 7, design a process for removing oil from sand and water. This process may involve several materials and require a series of steps.

▶ Observe and Analyze [Write It Up]

1. **RECORD** Write up your procedure for cleaning oil from sand and water. You may want to include a diagram.

2. **EVALUATE** What, if any, difficulties did you encounter in carrying out this experiment?

▶ Conclude [Write It Up]

1. **INTERPRET** How do your results compare with your hypothesis? Answer the problem statement.

2. **EVALUATE** Which materials were most useful for cleaning the water? Were they the same materials that were most useful for cleaning the sand?

3. **EVALUATE** Suppose you are trying to clean oil off of living things, such as a bird or seaweed. What process would you use?

4. **IDENTIFY LIMITS** In which ways did this demonstration fail to model a real oil spill?

▶ INVESTIGATE Further

CHALLENGE Explain how the observations you made in this investigation might be useful in designing treatments for an actual oil spill.

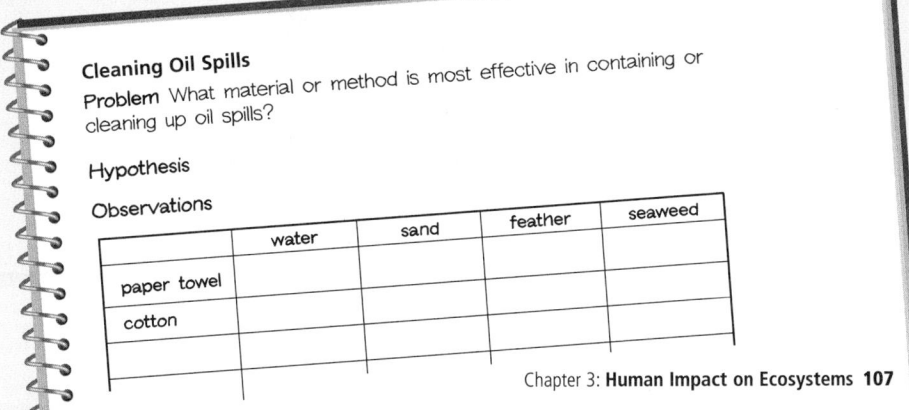

Cleaning Oil Spills

Problem What material or method is most effective in containing or cleaning up oil spills?

Hypothesis

Observations

	water	sand	feather	seaweed
paper towel				
cotton				

Chapter 3: **Human Impact on Ecosystems** 107 D

▶ Observe and Analyze [Write It Up]

1. *Student answers will vary.*

2. *Student answers will vary.*

▶ Conclude [Write It Up]

1. *Answers should detail comparisons between hypothesis and results.*

2. *Sample: Cotton balls were most useful to clean water. The sand had soaked up most of the oil, so we needed soap to clean the sand.*

3. *Sample: I would remove as much of the oil surrounding the plant or animal and then clean it. Some animals can be removed immediately and cleaned first.*

4. *Sample: We've created a model of a controlled environment. In real life, oil sinks into the ground and groundwater, making it harder to clean up. In a real ecosystem, you need to worry about the effects of chemicals like detergents on living things.*

▶ INVESTIGATE Further

CHALLENGE Answer: You need something porous and absorbent to clean oil spills on water. On land, you need to get to the oil as soon as possible before the oil sinks into the soil. Soap or detergent is needed to clean the ground.

Address Misconceptions

IDENTIFY Ask: What can be learned about cleaning real oil spills from making a model? Students may think that the techniques that work in a model would hold true for the real environment. Many students think that scientific models are exact representations.

CORRECT Discuss with students the differences between a real oil spill cleanup and a model oil spill cleanup. Explain that using detergent in a real cleanup could harm living things. Although oil is cleaned from the top layer of sand, oil could seep into lower layers. Also point out that cotton balls and sponges are not available on a large scale.

REASSESS Review students' answers to question 4. Point out that detergent is one method used to clean oil spills, but is much less effective in a real oil spill.

Post-Lab Discussion

• With modern technology, why are oil spills a problem? *People can't completely clean up an oil spill, and cleanup operations can pollute the environment.*

• During a real oil spill, how do you think bad weather might affect the cleanup? *Bad weather could spread the oil, interfere with cleanup boats, and add to wildlife stress.*

• What might help prevent an oil spill? *safer ships, safety programs for crew*

BACK TO

the BIG idea

Use a hypothetical scenario to demonstrate the statement, "Humans and human population growth affect the environment."

Mineral ore is discovered near a small town out in the desert. Quickly, companies arrive to mine for and process the ore, bringing their employees, which in turn attract other businesses (stores, gas stations, restaurants, etc.) to serve them. Explain three ways that this will affect the desert ecosystem. *There will be more waste to dispose of. The limited water supply may run out. Expanding land use will destroy habitats.*

▶ KEY CONCEPTS SUMMARY

SECTION 3.1
Ask: What does the steep curve on the graph imply for the challenges posed by population growth? *We might run out of natural resources.*

SECTION 3.2
Ask: How can pollution change systems? *It can make them unfit for inhabitants and fit for new organisms.*

Ask: How do humans cause habitat loss? *by developing pastures and farms, by clearcutting forests, and by introducing nonnative species*

SECTION 3.3
Ask: What federal laws in the U.S. protect ecosystems? *NEPA, Clean Air and Clean Water Acts, Superfund Program*

Ask students to list some alternative energy resources that lessen impact on the environment. *wind power, hydropower, geothermal power, solar power*

Review Concepts

- Big Idea Flow Chart, p. T17
- Chapter Outline, pp. T23–T24

---

3 Chapter Review

the BIG idea

Humans and human population growth affect the environment.

 **CONTENT REVIEW**
CLASSZONE.COM

◀ KEY CONCEPTS SUMMARY

 Human population growth presents challenges.
As the population continues to grow, there is a greater demand for natural resources. Cities and countries share many resources. Increasing populations put pressure on ecosystems.

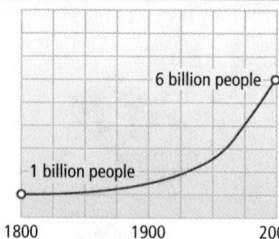
6 billion people
1 billion people
1800   1900   2000

VOCABULARY
natural resource p. 84
population
density p. 86

 Human activities affect the environment.
Pollution and habitat loss make it difficult for plants and animals to survive. Without the necessary resources, biodiversity of living things decreases, and ecosystems become less stable.

Pollution   Habitat Loss

VOCABULARY
pollution p. 91
biodiversity p. 91

 Humans are working to protect ecosystems.
Working at local and governmental levels, humans are helping ecosystems recover.

Laws protect endangered species.   Researchers are investigating alternative resources.

VOCABULARY
conservation p. 99
sustainable p. 102

Technology Resources

Have students visit **ClassZone.com** or use the CD-ROM for a cumulative review of concepts.

Engage students in a whole-class interactive review of Key Concepts. Edit content as you wish.

 CONTENT REVIEW

 CONTENT REVIEW CD-ROM

 POWER PRESENTATIONS

Reviewing Vocabulary

Place each vocabulary term at the center of a description wheel diagram. Write some words describing it on the spokes.

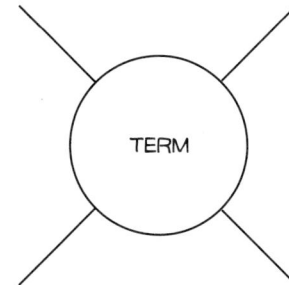

TERM

1. population density
2. natural resources
3. pollution
4. biodiversity
5. sustainable
6. conservation

Reviewing Key Concepts

Multiple Choice *Choose the letter of the best answer.*

7. In 2000, how big was Earth's human population?
   a. 1 billion   c. 6 billion
   b. 3 billion   d. 9 billion

8. Experts predict that by the year 2050, Earth's population will reach what number?
   a. 3 billion   c. 9 billion
   b. 6 billion   d. 12 billion

9. Which statement best explains why Earth's population has grown very rapidly in the last 100 years?
   a. On average, women are having children at an older age.
   b. People live longer because of improved health care and nutrition.
   c. Global warming has enabled farmers to grow more food.
   d. More land has been developed for housing.

10. Which of the four natural resources listed is likely to be used up the soonest?
    a. petroleum   c. sunlight
    b. water   d. wood

11. Which of the following is an example of increasing biodiversity?
    a. A forest is clear-cut for its wood, leaving land available for new uses.
    b. New species of animals and plants appear in a wildlife preserve.
    c. A new species of plant outcompetes all of the others around a lake.
    d. A cleared rain forest results in a change to a habitat.

12. Which represents a sustainable practice?
    a. conservation tillage and use of natural fertilizers
    b. more efficient removal of oil
    c. allowing unlimited use of water for higher fees
    d. restocking a lake with fish every year

13. What environmental problem does the Superfund Program address?
    a. habitat loss
    b. land development
    c. biodiversity
    d. pollution

Short Answer *Write a short answer to each question.*

14. List four ways increased population density affects ecosystem.

15. Three ways that humans dispose of waste are landfills, incineration, and wastewater treatment plants. List one advantage and one disadvantage of each.

16. Write a paragraph to describe how an increase in population density affects land development.

Reviewing Vocabulary

1–6. *Answers will vary, but all of the vocabulary terms listed should be used properly.*

Reviewing Key Concepts

7. c

8. c

9. b

10. a

11. b

12. a

13. d

14. *more pollution, greater demand on limited natural resources like water, destruction of habitats, death of plants and animals*

15. *Landfill disposal is generally cheap, but trash and materials may stay there for a long time. Incineration reduces the amount of material that needs to stay in the ground, but leads to air pollution. Sewage treatment plants clean water that is released into the environment, but there is still a lot of sludge that must be disposed of.*

16. *When a population grows to the point that the local environment becomes stressed, people look for other places to live. Land gets developed—forests, farms, and grasslands are destroyed—as roads and buildings are built to create a place for people to live.*

ASSESSMENT RESOURCES

UNIT ASSESSMENT BOOK
- Chapter Test A, pp. 45–48
- Chapter Test B, pp. 49–52
- Chapter Test C, pp. 53–56
- Alternative Assessment, pp. 57–58
- Unit Test, A,B, & C, pp. 59–70

SPANISH ASSESSMENT BOOK
- Spanish Chapter Test, pp. 65–68
- Spanish Unit Test, pp. 77–80

Technology Resources

Edit test items and answer choices.

  Test Generator CD-ROM

Visit **ClassZone.com** to extend test practice.

  Test Practice

Thinking Critically

17. *The population of Atlanta in 2000 was 4 million while that of Las Vegas was 1.5 million. The rate of growth in Atlanta between 1990 and 2000 was about twice that of Las Vegas. At current rates of increase, the population of Las Vegas will not get bigger than the population of Atlanta.*

18. *No; area of both cities*

19. *Sample answer: Carrying capacity is higher in Atlanta as available water sources are greater in a temperate forest biome than in a desert.*

20. *More water would be available for Mexican use and for Mexican wildlife near the mouth of the river.*

21. *Trees are generally considered a renewable resource because a properly managed or natural forest will have new trees grow to replace dead or removed ones. If the land is destroyed or new trees aren't planted, then trees from a forest are a nonrenewable resource.*

22. *RENEWABLE: water, wood, sunlight, soil; NONRENEWABLE: copper, aluminum, petroleum, coal*

23. *3600 kg less carbon dioxide*

the BIG idea

24. *Answers should show a deeper understanding of, not just what was added to the landscape in physical structures, but what was taken away, as well as the pollution and environmental pressures created.*

25. *Answers should list varieties of plants and animals, and should include at least four sustainable practices, including conservation of resources and reduction of waste.*

UNIT PROJECTS

Have students present their projects. Use the appropriate rubrics from the Unit Resource Book to evaluate their work.

R Unit Projects, pp. 5–10

Thinking Critically

Use the graph to answer the next three questions.

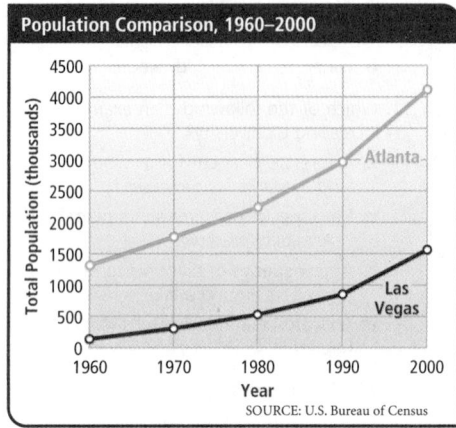

Population Comparison, 1960–2000

Total Population (thousands) vs. Year — Atlanta and Las Vegas

SOURCE: U.S. Bureau of Census

17. **COMPARE AND CONTRAST** Describe the population size and rate of growth for the cities of Atlanta and Las Vegas. Would you expect the population of Las Vegas to ever get bigger than that of Atlanta based on the data supplied?

18. **EVALUATE** Is it possible to determine from the data shown whether the population density is higher in Atlanta than Las Vegas? What other information would you need?

19. **CONNECT** Atlanta is located in a temperate-forest biome and Las Vegas is located in a desert biome. How might the characteristics of these biomes affect the carrying capacity of the human populations in these cities?

20. **PREDICT** If states in the U.S. used less water from the Colorado River, how would the depth of the river in Mexico be affected?

21. **COMPARE AND CONTRAST** Explain why trees are generally considered a renewable resource. Now describe circumstances under which they could be considered a nonrenewable resource.

---

22. **CLASSIFY** Sort the resources below into the correct categories:

Resource	Renewable	Nonrenewable
Water		
Coal		
Soil		
Wood		
Copper		
Petroleum		
Aluminum		
Sunlight		

23. **CALCULATE** A compact fluorescent bulb uses less energy than a regular bulb. It is estimated that a coal-burning power plant would release 72 kilograms more carbon dioxide (CO_2) a year to power one regular bulb than it would to power one fluorescent bulb. If you replace five regular bulbs with five compact bulbs, how much less CO_2 would be released in a 10-year period?

the BIG idea

24. **PROVIDE EXAMPLES** Look again at the photograph on pages 78–79. How would you change or add details to your answer to the question on the photograph?

25. **APPLY** You are on the town council of a community located on a small island. The council has decided to make a brochure for the town's citizens. In your brochure, describe the island habitat. Include information about natural resources, such as water and soil. List the plants and animals that live there. Establish four rules that the community should follow to preserve the local habitat.

UNIT PROJECTS

Evaluate the materials in your project folder. Finish your project and get ready to present it to your class.

MONITOR AND RETEACH

If students have trouble applying the concepts in items 17–19, explain that upward-trending lines in the graph show that the populations of the two cities have increased steadily over the past 40 years. Ask: What does it mean that Las Vegas is lower on the graph? *The population numbers are less.* Review the impacts of population growth.

Students may benefit from summarizing sections of the chapter.

R Summarizing the Chapter, pp. 198–199

Standardized Test Practice

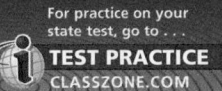

For practice on your state test, go to . . .
TEST PRACTICE
CLASSZONE.COM

Analyzing Data

Nowhere is the impact of human population growth more obvious than in the growth of urbanized areas. Buildings, parking lots, and roads are replacing forests, farmland, and wetlands. The table below shows the growth of urbanized areas around 10 cities in the United States during a 20-year period.

1. What patterns can you see in the way information is presented from the top of the table to the bottom?
   a. Cities are arranged alphabetically.
   b. Cities are arranged by growth in population over 20 years.
   c. Cities are arranged by the growth in land area over 20 years.
   d. Cities are arranged by size of urban area.

2. How would you describe the change in the land around Atlanta between 1970 and 1990?
   a. In 1990, more land was used for farming.
   b. The number of buildings and roads increased.
   c. The urbanized area decreased.
   d. Natural habitats for birds increased.

3. Which type of graph would be best for displaying the data in the table?
   a. a bar graph
   b. a circle graph
   c. a line graph
   d. a double bar graph

4. How many square kilometers around Philadelphia were affected by urbanization between 1970 and 1990?
   a. 1116 km^2 **c.** 1068 km^2
   b. 1166 km^2 **d.** 1020 km^2

Growth in land area, 1970-1990

Location	Growth in Land Area (km²)
Atlanta, GA	1816
Houston, TX	1654
New York City–N.E. New Jersey	1402
Washington, D.C.–MD–VA	1166
Philadelphia, PA	1068
Los Angeles, CA	1020
Dallas–Fort Worth, TX	964
Tampa–St. Petersburg–Clearwater, FL	929
Phoenix, AZ	916
Minneapolis–Saint Paul, MN	885

SOURCE: U.S. Bureau of Census data on Urbanized Areas

Extended Response

5. Write a paragraph to describe how a rural area would change if the land were developed and the area became more urban. Use the vocabulary words listed below in your answer.

population density	biodiversity
renewable resources	nonrenewable resources

6. If you were an urban designer working for a small city that expected to expand rapidly in the next 10 years, what recommendations would you make to the city council on how the land should be developed?

Chapter 3: **Human Impact on Ecosystems** 111 **D**

Analyzing Data

1. c   2. b   3. a   4. c

Extended Response

5. RUBRIC

4 points for a response that uses at least three vocabulary words and offers an accurate description of urbanization.

Sample: If a rural area were developed to become more urban, many changes would occur to natural resources. As trees and other vegetation would need to be cleared, available <u>renewable resources</u> would be altered. <u>Nonrenewable resources</u> such as air and water would be affected because construction creates <u>pollution</u>. Many animal species would lose their habitat due to urbanization so there would be a change in <u>biodiversity</u> as well.

3 points description is realistic and uses at least two vocabulary words
2 points description is realistic and uses at least one vocabulary word
1 point attempts to describe the urban area; does not use any vocabulary words

6. RUBRIC

4 points for a response that addresses the following topics:
   • wildlife and/or ecosystems
   • traffic, transportation, and/or development
   • sewage and/or water supply
   • waste disposal and/or pollution

Sample: The council should consider any endangered wildlife in the outlying areas. They should preserve open spaces, both for wildlife and for people. They should plan the growth so that traffic heading toward and away from the city doesn't back up. Alternative modes of transportation such as bike paths, trains, buses, and carpool lanes should be planned. Sewage and water supply should not overwork the environment. Recycling should be used to address the extra burden on the landfills.

3 points for a response that correctly addresses the topic and uses three of the topics above
2 points for a response that correctly addresses the topic and uses two of the topics above
1 point for a response that attempts to address the question and uses one of the topics above

METACOGNITIVE ACTIVITY

Have students answer the following questions in their **Science Notebook:**

1. How has reading the chapter made you think about your own impact on ecosystems?

2. What activity in the chapter posed the biggest challenge? What was important to you about that activity?

3. What have you learned from your research on your Unit Project?

Chapter 3 **111** **D**

UNIT E

Space Science

comet

UNIVERSE

electromagnetic
radiation

telescope

North Carolina Standards

In Unit E: Space Science, students will learn and apply science concepts and skills related to the following goals from the North Carolina Standard Course of Study:

Competency Goal 1: The learner will design and conduct investigations to demonstrate an understanding of scientific inquiry. (Objectives 1.01–1.10)

Competency Goal 2: The learner will demonstrate an understanding of technological design. (Objectives 2.01–2.04)

Competency Goal 4: The learner will investigate the cycling of matter.
4.05   Evaluate designed systems for ability to enable growth of certain plants and animals.

Competency Goal 5: The learner will build an understanding of the Solar System.
5.01   Analyze the components and cycles of the solar system.
5.02   Compare and contrast the Earth to other planets.
5.03   Relate the influence of the sun and the moon's orbit to the gravitational effects produced on Earth.
5.04   Describe space explorations and the understandings gained from them.
5.05   Describe the setting of the solar system in the universe.
5.06   Analyze the spin-off benefits generated by space exploration technology.

For a detailed lesson-by-lesson correlation of Unit E to the North Carolina Standard Course of Study, see Correlations pages 16–24 in the front of this Teacher's Edition.

Space Science
Contents Overview

Unit Features

1 Exploring Space

the BIG idea

People develop and use technology
to explore and study space.

2 Earth, Moon, and Sun

the BIG idea

Earth and the Moon move in predictable
ways as they orbit the Sun.

3 Our Solar System

the BIG idea

Planets and other objects form a
system around our Sun.

4 Stars, Galaxies, and the Universe

the BIG idea

Our Sun is one of billions of stars
in one of billions of galaxies in the
universe.

FRONTIERS in Science

FRONTIERS in Science

VIDEO SUMMARY

SCIENTIFIC AMERICAN FRONTIERS

"Big Dish," a segment of the *Scientific American Frontiers* series that aired on PBS stations, takes viewers to the mountains of Puerto Rico to visit the Arecibo Observatory. This is the site of the largest, most powerful radio telescope in the world. Astronomer Jim Cordes explains how radio waves are collected from space and then analyzed. Objects millions of miles away can be detected and tracked around the clock. Their radio waves, or signals, are collected in the telescope's big dish. Then they are concentrated and reflected until they are ten times stronger. At that point the signals reach a receiver and are analyzed by computers. The observatory not only receives radio signals but also transmits them in the form of radar. Radar bouncing back from objects in space helps scientists identify, measure, and track any asteroids that might be on a collision course with our planet. As part of this detection effort, scientists at the Arecibo Observatory have begun to catalog and record information on all asteroids that are potentially hazardous to Earth.

National Science Education Standards

A.1–8 Abilities Necessary to Do Scientific Inquiry

A.9.a–b, A.9.d–g Understandings about Scientific Inquiry

F.5.e Science and Technology in Society

G.1.a–b Science as a Human Endeavor

G.2.a, G.2.c Nature of Science

DANGER from the Sky

How can astronomers find out whether a large object from space is going to strike our planet?

SCIENTIFIC AMERICAN FRONTIERS

View the video segment "Big Dish" to learn how astronomers use the largest radio telescope on Earth.

ADDITIONAL RESOURCES

Technology Resources

 Scientific American Frontiers Video: *Big Dish:* 8-minute video segment that introduces the unit.

 ClassZone.com
CAREER LINK, Astronomer

Guide student viewing and comprehension of the video:

 Video Teaching Guide, pp. 1–2; Video Viewing Guide, p. 3; Video Wrap-Up, p. 4

Scientific American Frontiers Video Guide, pp. 35–38

Unit projects procedures and rubrics:

 Unit Projects, pp. 5–10

The streak of light in the photograph above was produced by a tiny particle from space burning up in Earth's atmosphere. Shown to the left is Barringer Crater in Arizona.

Collisions in Space

In the summer of 1994, telescopes all over the world were aimed at Jupiter. For the first time in history, astronomers had warning of a collision in space. Jupiter's gravity had split a comet named Shoemaker-Levy 9 into more than 20 large pieces. As the rocky objects collided with Jupiter's atmosphere, they exploded spectacularly.

Astronomers have found evidence of impacts closer to home. The craters that cover much of the Moon's surface were caused by collisions with space objects billions of years ago. In 1953 an astronomer even caught on film the bright flash of an object hitting the Moon. Other solid bodies in space also have impact craters. Little evidence of impacts remains on Earth because its surface is always changing. Fewer than 200 craters are still visible.

Earth's atmosphere protects us from collisions with small objects, which burn up in the air. However, when a large object strikes Earth, the atmosphere can spread the effects of the impact far beyond the crater. A large collision may throw dust high into the air, where it can be carried around the globe. The dust can block sunlight for months and sharply lower global temperatures.

About 65 million years ago, a large space object struck Earth. The dust from this collision can be found around the world in a layer of rock that was forming at the time. At about the same time, most species of organisms died out, including the dinosaurs. Many scientists think that the collision caused this global devastation.

FOCUS

⊙ Set Learning Goals
Students will
- Recognize that collisions with space objects can affect Earth.
- Assess the risk of different types of collisions.
- Describe how scientists track space objects.
- Observe and model objects in the night sky.

Before students view the video "Big Dish," have them define the word *frontier* in their own words. *an area that is not yet completely explored* Ask: How does the meaning of *frontier* relate to science? *A frontier in science may be a topic that is not yet completely explored or is just beginning to be explored.*

INSTRUCT

Scientific Process
Point out the question that this feature addresses. Ask: Why do scientists think an impact is possible? *because of evidence of past Earth impacts and craters on other planets and the Moon*

Asking a Question
After students have read about the large space object that may have led to the extinction of the dinosaurs, ask them what more they would like to know about this topic. Have them develop a list of questions for further research.

DIFFERENTIATE INSTRUCTION

? More Reading Support

A What causes craters on the Moon's surface? *collisions*

B What protects us from collisions with small space objects? *Earth's atmosphere*

Below Level Have students drop marbles or other small objects into a pan of sand or flour to model impact craters. Remind them that wind, water, and other agents of erosion constantly change Earth's surface—that is why so few impact craters are visible on Earth. Using their model craters, have students demonstrate how different types of erosion affect impact craters.

Scientific Process

Tell students to imagine that they are scientists who have been asked to assess the risk of a meteorite strike. Based on the facts on p. 4, have them describe the likelihood of a collision with worldwide effects. *Major collisions that affect the entire world are rare, so the likelihood of such a collision is small.*

Technology Design

Have students make a table called "Tracking Asteroids" with two columns: "Technological Challenges" and "Technological Solutions." Have students read the text on pp. 4–5, then fill in the appropriate columns with the challenges and solutions involved with tracking asteroids. *Sample answer: challenges: identifying asteroids, predicting path of asteroids, gathering information about the characteristics of asteroids; solutions: studies that use telescopes, computer models, and tests with real materials*

Teach from Visuals

Have students compare the two photographs on this page. The dome in the lower photograph can be seen above the dish in the upper photograph. The dome's shadow is visible near the center of the dish. The catwalk (bridge) near the upper left of the close-up can help students get a sense of the sizes.

The Risk of a Major Collision

When will the next space object hit Earth? A collision is probably occurring as you read this sentence. Tiny particles hit Earth's atmosphere all the time. Some of these particles have enough mass to make it through the atmosphere. Objects that reach Earth's surface are called meteorites. Most meteorites splash harmlessly into the ocean or hit unpopulated areas. Every few years a meteorite damages a home or other property. However, there is no known case of a meteorite's killing a person.

Collisions that cause widespread damage happen less often because the solar system contains fewer large objects. In 1908 a large object from space exploded above a remote region of Russia. The explosion knocked down trees across an area more than half the size of Rhode Island. Even this impact was small in comparison with major collisions that affect the entire world. Such collisions happen on average about twice every million years. Events that kill off many species occur even less often.

Tracking Asteroids

Although Earth is unlikely to have a major collision with a space object anytime soon, the danger is too great to ignore. Scientists are using telescopes to find large, rocky space objects called asteroids. After locating an asteroid, they use computer models to predict its path centuries into the future. Scientists expect that by 2008 they will have found almost all of the asteroids that could cause global devastation on Earth.

Locating objects that may threaten life on Earth is just the first step. Scientists also want to

SCIENTIFIC AMERICAN FRONTIERS

View the "Big Dish" segment of your *Scientific American Frontiers* video to learn how astronomers are using the giant Arecibo radio telescope to explore the universe.

IN THIS SCENE FROM THE VIDEO ▶

You see a close-up of the Arecibo telescope's dome and one of its antennas.

EXPLORING ASTEROIDS An asteroid's crashing into Earth may seem like the subject of a science fiction movie. Yet asteroids pose a real danger to humans. Some asteroids could cause widespread destruction if they struck our planet.

Astronomers are tracking these asteroids to determine how close they will pass to Earth in the future.

Asteroids are too faint to be viewed clearly with optical telescopes on Earth. However, radio telescopes can provide detailed images of asteroids. Inside the dome of the Arecibo telescope is the world's most powerful radar transmitter. The transmitter can bounce a beam of radio waves off the telescope's dish to reach an asteroid millions of miles away. The telescope picks up returning signals, which are converted into images.

DIFFERENTIATE INSTRUCTION

? More Reading Support

C What do you call space objects that reach Earth's surface? *meteorites*

D What do you call large, rocky space objects that could strike Earth? *asteroids*

Advanced Tell students that in 2001, the NEAR spacecraft landed on the asteroid Eros. The landing was not part of the spacecraft's original mission. Ask students to infer why NASA decided, very near the end of the mission, to land the spacecraft on the asteroid. *Close-up images of Eros provided NASA with valuable information about the physical characteristics of asteroids. The landing was also a test run: NASA now knows it can direct a spacecraft to land on any asteroid set on a collision course with Earth.*

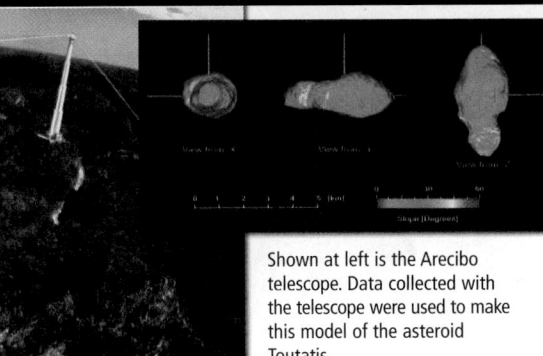

Shown at left is the Arecibo telescope. Data collected with the telescope were used to make this model of the asteroid Toutatis.

learn about the characteristics of asteroids. The Arecibo telescope in Puerto Rico is an important tool for studying asteroids. The largest radio dish in the world, it allows scientists to determine the **②** **E** motions and shapes of asteroids. Computer models and tests with real materials provide additional information about the mass, materials, and structure of each asteroid.

If scientists ever find an asteroid headed toward Earth, these studies may help us change the asteroid's course safely. Remember the comet that struck Jupiter in many pieces? If an asteroid broke apart before reaching Earth, pieces hitting different locations could cause even more damage than a single impact. Before using a bomb or laser to change the course of an asteroid, govern- **②** ments must make sure that the asteroid will not **F** break apart. Fortunately, scientists would have decades to study a dangerous asteroid and figure out what action to take.

② UNANSWERED Questions

Scientists are learning about the risk of an asteroid's colliding with Earth. The more we learn about collisions in space, the more questions we have.

• What methods can be used to change the course of an asteroid that threatens Earth?

• How can we make sure that an asteroid will not break apart because of our efforts to change its course?

• How many smaller but still dangerous objects may be headed toward Earth?

UNIT PROJECTS

As you study this unit, work alone or with a group on one of these projects.

Observe the Sky

Choose a space object or part of the distant sky to observe over a month. Keep an observation journal of what you see and think.

• Pay special attention to any changes relative to other objects in the sky.

• Look up information or construct tools to help you observe.

• Copy your best drawings for a display board. Explain your observations.

Multimedia Presentation

The Arecibo telescope is not used only for studying asteroids. Prepare a multimedia presentation on other research that is being carried out with the giant radio telescope.

• Find information about the research from Internet sites and other sources.

• Prepare both audio and visual components for your presentation.

Map a Space Object

Use a large potato to represent a newly explored space object. Draw lines of latitude and longitude. Then identify features, and make a flat map.

• Use roller-ball pens to mark poles, an equator, and lines of longitude and latitude. Try not to pierce the potato's skin.

• Do the potato's eyes seem like craters or volcanoes? Decide how to name the different types of features.

• Make a flat map of the space object.

CAREER CENTER
CLASSZONE.COM
Learn about careers in astronomy.

Have students read the questions and think of some of their own. Remind them that scientists always end up with more questions—that inquiry is the driving force of science.

• With the class, generate on the board a list of new questions.

• Students can add to the list after they watch the Scientific American Frontiers Video.

• Students can use the list as a springboard for choosing their Unit Projects.

UNIT PROJECTS

Encourage students to pick the project that most appeals to them. Point out that each is one will take several weeks to complete. You might group or pair students to work on projects and in some cases guide student choice. Some of the projects have student-choice built into them. Each project has two worksheet pages, including a rubric. Use the pages to guide students through criteria, process, and schedule.

R Unit Projects, pp. 5–10

REVISIT concepts introduced in this article:

Chapter 1
• Telescopes and space exploration, pp. 15–20
• Society and space exploration, pp. 31–34

Chapter 2
• Earth's movements, pp. 43–49
• The Moon, pp. 52–57

Chapter 3
• Objects in the solar system, pp. 79–83
• Composition of space objects, pp. 100–105

DIFFERENTIATE INSTRUCTION

② More Reading Support

E What type of telescope is the Arecibo?
a radio telescope

F What could governments use to change the course of an asteroid?
bombs or lasers

Differentiate Unit Projects Projects are appropriate for varying abilities. Allow students to choose the ones that interest them most and let them vary their product. Encourage below-level students to give visual or oral presentations or to record audio presentations about their topic.

Below Level Encourage students to try "Observe the Sky" concentrating on the Moon.

Advanced Challenge students to complete "Map a Space Object."

CHAPTER 1 Exploring Space

Earth Science
UNIFYING PRINCIPLES

PRINCIPLE 1

Heat energy inside Earth and radiation from the Sun provide energy for Earth's processes.

PRINCIPLE 2

Physical forces, such as gravity, affect the movement of all matter on Earth and throughout the universe.

PRINCIPLE 3

Matter and energy move among Earth's rocks and soil, atmosphere, waters, and living things.

PRINCIPLE 4

Earth has changed over time and continues to change.

Unit: Space Science
BIG IDEAS

CHAPTER 1
Exploring Space

People develop and use technology to explore and study space.

CHAPTER 2
Earth, Moon, and Sun

Earth and the Moon move in predictable ways as they orbit the Sun.

CHAPTER 3
Our Solar System

Planets and other objects form a system around our Sun.

CHAPTER 4
Stars, Galaxies, and the Universe

Our Sun is one of billions of stars in one of billions of galaxies in the universe.

CHAPTER 1
KEY CONCEPTS

SECTION 1.1

Some space objects are visible to the human eye.

1. We see patterns in the universe.
2. The sky seems to turn as Earth rotates.
3. The movements of planets and other nearby objects are visible from Earth.

SECTION 1.2

Telescopes allow us to study space from Earth.

1. Light and other forms of radiation carry information about space.
2. Astronomers use telescopes to collect information about space.

SECTION 1.3

Spacecraft help us explore beyond Earth.

1. Astronauts explore space near Earth.
2. Spacecraft carry instruments to other worlds.

SECTION 1.4

Space exploration benefits society.

1. Space exploration has given us new viewpoints.
2. Space technology has practical uses.

 The Big Idea Flow Chart is available on p. T1 in the **UNIT TRANSPARENCY BOOK.**

Previewing Content

SECTION 1.1 Some space objects are visible to the human eye. pp. 9–14

1. We see patterns in the universe.

For most of history, people knew very little about space. In the past few hundred years, new technology and scientific theories have taught us about the properties of objects in space and how they relate to one another. Gravity causes space objects to be grouped together in several basic structures:

- Earth **orbits** the Sun.
- The **solar system** contains the Sun as well as the planets and other objects that orbit the Sun.
- Our solar system and billions of stars are grouped together in a **galaxy** called the Milky Way.
- Billions of galaxies are spread throughout the **universe.**

A **constellation** is a group of stars that form a pattern in the sky. Although the stars in a constellation appear close together when viewed from Earth, they are often far apart from one another.

2. The sky seems to turn as Earth rotates.

Throughout the night, the constellations move across the sky from east to west. The apparent motion of the stars is caused by Earth's rotation. Polaris, the North Star, does not show this apparent motion because it is directly over the North Pole. Time-lapse photography shows that the other stars in the sky seem to travel in circles around Polaris.

3. The movements of planets and other nearby objects are visible from Earth.

Stars are always moving, but they are so far away that you cannot notice their movements. Therefore, the patterns of the constellations gradually change, but the change is too slight to notice for many thousands of years. The movements of objects closer to Earth, such as the Moon and planets, are noticeable over short periods of time.

SECTION 1.2 Telescopes allow us to study space from Earth. pp. 15–21

1. Light and other forms of radiation carry information about space.

Scientists can gain information about a space object by studying its electromagnetic radiation. The full range of **electromagnetic radiation** includes radio waves, microwaves, infrared radiation, visible light, ultraviolet radiation, x-rays, and gamma rays. These forms are listed here in the order of their wavelengths, from longest to shortest. **Wavelength**—the distance between one wave peak and the next wave peak—indicates the level of a wave's energy. Shorter waves have higher energy than longer waves. Visible light is made up of various colors that differ in wavelength.

2. Astronomers use telescopes to collect information about space.

A **telescope** gathers electromagnetic radiation. The most familiar kinds of telescopes are those that gather visible light. There are two types of visible-light telescopes:

- A reflecting telescope uses a mirror to collect light.
- A refracting telescope uses a lens to collect light.

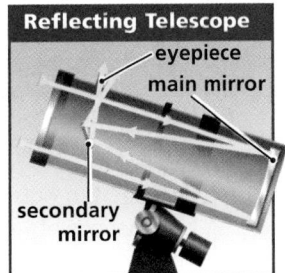
Reflecting Telescope — eyepiece, main mirror, secondary mirror

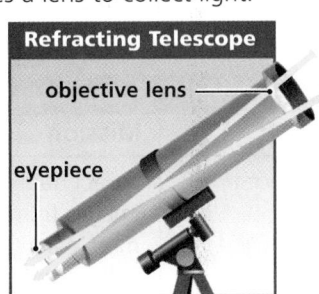
Refracting Telescope — objective lens, eyepiece

Other telescopes gather radio waves, infrared radiation, and other forms of radiation. Some telescopes, such as the Hubble Space Telescope, are located in orbit around Earth. Because space telescopes operate without interference from Earth's atmosphere, they have provided some of the clearest images of distant objects.

Common Misconceptions

MISCONCEPTION DATABASE
CLASSZONE.COM Background on student misconceptions

MOTIONS OF EARTH Some students may think that the Sun orbits Earth because of the apparent motion of the Sun across the sky from sunrise to sunset. However, it is Earth's rotation from west to east that makes the Sun appear to move across the sky.

 This misconception is addressed on p. 10.

GRAVITY IN SPACE Students might think that gravity is present only on Earth and does not relate to objects in space. Gravity, however, is a universal force and is responsible for the grouping of objects in space.

 This misconception is addressed on p. 11.

LIGHT Many students do not understand that their eyes receive light when they look at an object and that this is why they are able to see the object. Misconceptions about the relationship between light and vision vary. Some students think that light travels from their eyes to an object, making it visible.

 This misconception is addressed on p. 16.

Previewing Content

 SECTION

1.3 Spacecraft help us explore beyond Earth. pp. 22–30

1. Astronauts explore space near Earth.

For over 40 years astronauts have been exploring space. The earliest explorations were driven by a rivalry between the United States and the Soviet Union to reach the Moon. NASA achieved six moon landings between 1969 and 1972, and U.S. astronauts set up experiments and brought back samples of the Moon's rocks and soil.

In the 1970s, both the United States and the Soviet Union launched the first **space stations.** These missions paved the way for the International Space Station (ISS)—a project involving 17 countries, including the United States and Russia. Most crews fly to the ISS aboard space shuttles. While such flights have been numerous, they remain a dangerous activity that involves careful planning, training, and advanced technology.

2. Spacecraft carry instruments to other worlds.

Currently it is too difficult and dangerous to send humans to other planets. Most research of other planets is accomplished through the use of spacecraft without astronauts aboard. The following chart details three stages of space exploration.

Space Exploration		
Spacecraft	**Mission**	**Duration**
flyby spacecraft	collect data and images from one or more planets without orbiting them	can last for decades, but only brief periods of time near any one planet
orbiter	study one planet's surface or atmosphere while orbiting it	several months to several years
lander or probe	land on a planet's surface or drop into its atmosphere to measure properties and provide close-up images	hours to years

 SECTION

1.4 Space exploration benefits society. pp. 31–35

1. Space exploration has given us new viewpoints.

As we study other worlds, we learn more about our own planet. Exploration of the Moon and other bodies in space helps scientists understand how Earth has developed.

Impact craters form when a space object strikes the surface of another object. Earth has few remaining impact craters because its surface undergoes constant change. However, much more evidence of impacts remains on the Moon and other bodies. The diagrams below show two stages in the formation of an impact crater.

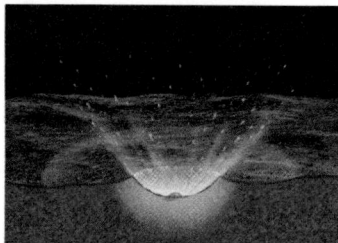 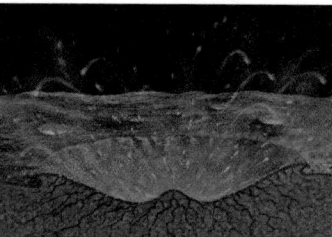

The object explodes as it strikes the surface, compressing and fracturing the rock underneath.

As the rock springs back from the impact, material is thrown out of the crater.

Scientists have gained knowledge of how liquid water affects Earth's atmosphere by comparing Earth with the two nearest planets, Venus and Mars, which have no liquid water on their surfaces.

2. Space technology has practical uses.

Every day, we probably use some material or product that was first developed for the space program. From satellite technology to tools for diagnosing disease to fire-resistant materials, space technology benefits us all.

Previewing Labs

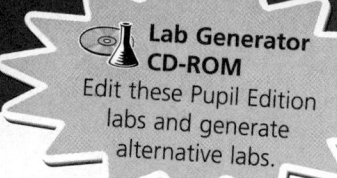

Lab Generator CD-ROM
Edit these Pupil Edition labs and generate alternative labs.

EXPLORE (the BIG idea)

Why Does the Sun Appear to Move Around Earth? p. 7
Students turn before a lamp to model the Sun's apparent motion around Earth.

TIME 5 minutes
MATERIALS floor lamp

What Colors Are in Sunlight? p. 7
Students construct a simple prism and use it to observe a spectrum.

TIME 5 minutes
MATERIALS clear plastic pen, small box

Internet Activity: Universe, p. 7
Students use the Internet to visualize different levels of scale in the universe.

TIME 20 minutes
MATERIALS computer with Internet access

SECTION 1.1

EXPLORE Distance, p. 9
Students create a model to visualize the relative distance between Earth and the Moon compared with their sizes.

TIME 10 minutes
MATERIALS tennis ball, 5-cm strip of aluminum foil, 250 cm of string, felt marker

---

INVESTIGATE Constellation Positions, p. 13
Students use a constellation wheel to observe how time of day affects the positions of constellations.

R Constellation Wheel Sheet, p. 20

TIME 20 minutes
MATERIALS Constellation Wheel Sheet, scissors, brass fastener

---

SECTION 1.2

EXPLORE Distortion of Light, p. 15
Students create a model to observe how particles in the atmosphere distort light.

TIME 10 minutes
MATERIALS flashlight; drinking glass; water; sheet of white paper; spoon; spoonful of salt

---

CHAPTER INVESTIGATION
Observing Spectra, pp. 20–21
Students build a spectroscope to observe spectra from different light sources.

TIME 40 minutes
MATERIALS shoebox with lid, ruler, scissors, diffraction grating, tape, index card, colored pencils or markers, incandescent light, fluorescent light, cellophane in several colors

---

SECTION 1.3

EXPLORE Viewing Space Objects, p. 22
Students sketch to observe how objects appear at different distances.

TIME 10 minutes
MATERIALS paper, pencils

INVESTIGATE Launch Planning, p. 25
Students model how Earth's rotation affects launches into space.

TIME 10 minutes
MATERIALS 14 sheets of paper, small bucket, large bucket, meter stick

---

SECTION 1.4

INVESTIGATE Weathering, p. 33
Students make models of impact craters to observe how weather affects evidence of impacts on Earth.

TIME 30 minutes
MATERIALS 2 shoebox lids, about 2 liters of sand, ruler, golf ball, meter stick

---

 Additional INVESTIGATION, A Simple Refracting Telescope, A, B, & C, pp. 71–79; Teacher Instructions, pp. 287–288

Previewing Chapter Resources

	INTEGRATED TECHNOLOGY	LABS AND ACTIVITIES

CHAPTER 1
Exploring Space

CLASSZONE.COM
- eEdition Plus
- EasyPlanner Plus
- Misconception Database
- Content Review
- Test Practice
- Visualization
- Simulation
- Resource Centers
- Internet Activity: Universe
- Math Tutorial

SCILINKS.ORG

CD-ROMS
- eEdition
- EasyPlanner
- Power Presentations
- Content Review
- Lab Generator
- Test Generator

AUDIO CDS
- Audio Readings
- Audio Readings in Spanish

EXPLORE the Big Idea, p. 7
- Why Does the Sun Appear to Move Around Earth?
- What Colors Are in Sunlight?
- Internet Activity: Universe

UNIT RESOURCE BOOK
- Family Letter, p. vii
- Spanish Family Letter, p. viii
- Unit Projects, pp. 5–10

Lab Generator CD-ROM
Generate customized labs.

SECTION 1.1
Some space objects are visible to the human eye.
pp. 9–14

Time: 2 periods (1 block)
Lesson Plan, pp. 11–12

VISUALIZATION, The Night Sky

UNIT TRANSPARENCY BOOK
- Big Idea Flow Chart, p. T1
- Daily Vocabulary Scaffolding, p. T2
- Note-Taking Model, p. T3
- 3-Minute Warm-Up, p. T4
- "Structures in the Universe" Visual, p. T6

- EXPLORE Distance, p. 9
- INVESTIGATE Constellation Positions, p. 13

UNIT RESOURCE BOOK
- Constellation Wheel Sheet, p. 20
- Datasheet, Constellation Positions, p. 21

SECTION 1.2
Telescopes allow us to study space from Earth.
pp. 15–21

Time: 3 periods (1.5 blocks)
Lesson Plan, pp. 23–24

RESOURCE CENTER, Telescopes

UNIT TRANSPARENCY BOOK
- Daily Vocabulary Scaffolding, p. T2
- 3-Minute Warm-Up, p. T4

- EXPLORE Distortion of Light, p. 15
- CHAPTER INVESTIGATION, Observing Spectra, pp. 20–21

UNIT RESOURCE BOOK
- Additional INVESTIGATION, A Simple Refracting Telescope, A, B, & C, pp. 71–79
- CHAPTER INVESTIGATION, Observing Spectra, A, B, & C, pp. 62–70

SECTION 1.3
Spacecraft help us explore beyond Earth. pp. 22–30

Time: 2 periods (1 block)
Lesson Plan, pp. 33–34

- **RESOURCE CENTER,** Space Exploration
- **MATH TUTORIAL**

UNIT TRANSPARENCY BOOK
- Daily Vocabulary Scaffolding, p. T2
- 3-Minute Warm-Up, p. T5

- EXPLORE Viewing Space Objects, p. 22
- INVESTIGATE Launch Planning, p. 25
- Math in Science, p. 30

UNIT RESOURCE BOOK
- Datasheet, Launch Planning, p. 42
- Math Support, p. 60
- Math Practice, p. 61

SECTION 1.4
Space exploration benefits society.
pp. 31–35

Time: 3 periods (1.5 blocks)
Lesson Plan, pp. 44–45

UNIT TRANSPARENCY BOOK
- Big Idea Flow Chart, p. T1
- Daily Vocabulary Scaffolding, p. T2
- 3-Minute Warm-Up, p. T5
- Chapter Outline, pp. T7–T8

- INVESTIGATE Weathering, p. 33
- Connecting Sciences, p. 35

UNIT RESOURCE BOOK
Datasheet, Weathering, p. 53

KEY TO ICONS    **CD/CD-ROM**   **Teacher Edition**   **T** **UNIT TRANSPARENCY BOOK**   **SP A** **SPANISH ASSESSMENT BOOK**

 INTERNET   **PE** **Pupil Edition**   **R** **UNIT RESOURCE BOOK**   **A** **UNIT ASSESSMENT BOOK**   **SCIENCE TOOLKIT**

READING AND REINFORCEMENT

ASSESSMENT

STANDARDS

- Magnet Word, B24–25
- Main Idea Web, C38–39
- Daily Vocabulary Scaffolding, H1–8

 UNIT RESOURCE BOOK
- Vocabulary Practice, pp. 57–58
- Decoding Support, p. 59
- Summarizing the Chapter, pp. 80–81

 Audio Readings CD
Listen to Pupil Edition.

 Audio Readings in Spanish CD
Listen to Pupil Edition in Spanish.

 PE
- Chapter Review, pp. 37–38
- Standardized Test Practice, p. 39

 A **UNIT ASSESSMENT BOOK**
- Diagnostic Test, pp. 1–2
- Chapter Test, A, B, & C, pp. 7–18
- Alternative Assessment, pp. 19–20

SP A Spanish Chapter Test, pp. 193–196

Test Generator CD-ROM
Generate customized tests.

Lab Generator CD-ROM
Rubrics for Labs

National Standards
A.2–8, A.9.a–f, B.3.f, F.5.c, G.1.a–b

See p. 6 for the standards.

 UNIT RESOURCE BOOK
- Reading Study Guide, A & B. pp. 13–16
- Spanish Reading Study Guide, pp. 17–18
- Challenge and Extension, p. 19
- Reinforcing Key Concepts, p. 22

 TE Ongoing Assessment, pp. 10–14

PE Section 1.1 Review, p. 14

A **UNIT ASSESSMENT BOOK**
Section 1.1 Quiz, p. 3

National Standards
A.2–7, A.9.a–b, A.9.d–f

 UNIT RESOURCE BOOK
- Reading Study Guide, A & B. pp. 25–28
- Spanish Reading Study Guide, pp. 29–30
- Challenge and Extension, p. 31
- Reinforcing Key Concepts, p. 32

 TE Ongoing Assessment, pp. 16, 18–19

PE Section 1.2 Review, p. 19

A **UNIT ASSESSMENT BOOK**
Section 1.2 Quiz, p. 4

National Standards
A.2–7, A.9.a–b, A.9.d–f, B.3.f, F.5.c, G.1.a–b

 UNIT RESOURCE BOOK
- Reading Study Guide, A & B. pp. 35–38
- Spanish Reading Study Guide, pp. 39–40
- Challenge and Extension, p. 41
- Reinforcing Key Concepts, p. 43
- Challenge Reading, pp. 55–56

 TE Ongoing Assessment, pp. 24–27, 29

PE Section 1.3 Review, p. 29

A **UNIT ASSESSMENT BOOK**
Section 1.3 Quiz, p. 5

National Standards
A.2–8, A.9.a–f, F.5.c, F.5.e, G.1.a–b

R **UNIT RESOURCE BOOK**
- Reading Study Guide, A & B. pp. 46–49
- Spanish Reading Study Guide, pp. 50–51
- Challenge and Extension, p. 52
- Reinforcing Key Concepts, p. 54

TE Ongoing Assessment, pp. 31–32, 34

PE Section 1.4 Review, p. 34

A **UNIT ASSESSMENT BOOK**
Section 1.4 Quiz, p. 6

National Standards
A.2–7, A.9.a–b, A.9.d–f, F.5.c, G.1.a–b

Previewing Resources for Differentiated Instruction

CHAPTER INVESTIGATION

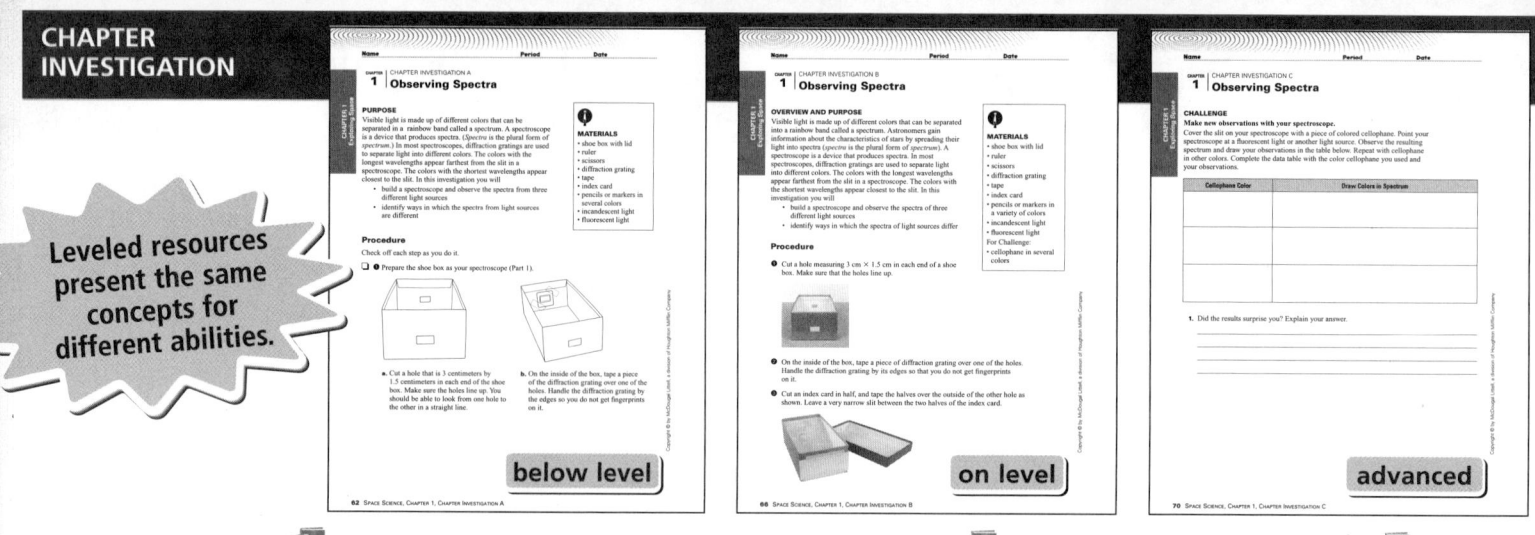

UNIT RESOURCE BOOK, pp. 62–65

pp. 66–69

pp. 66–70

> Leveled resources present the same concepts for different abilities.

READING STUDY GUIDE

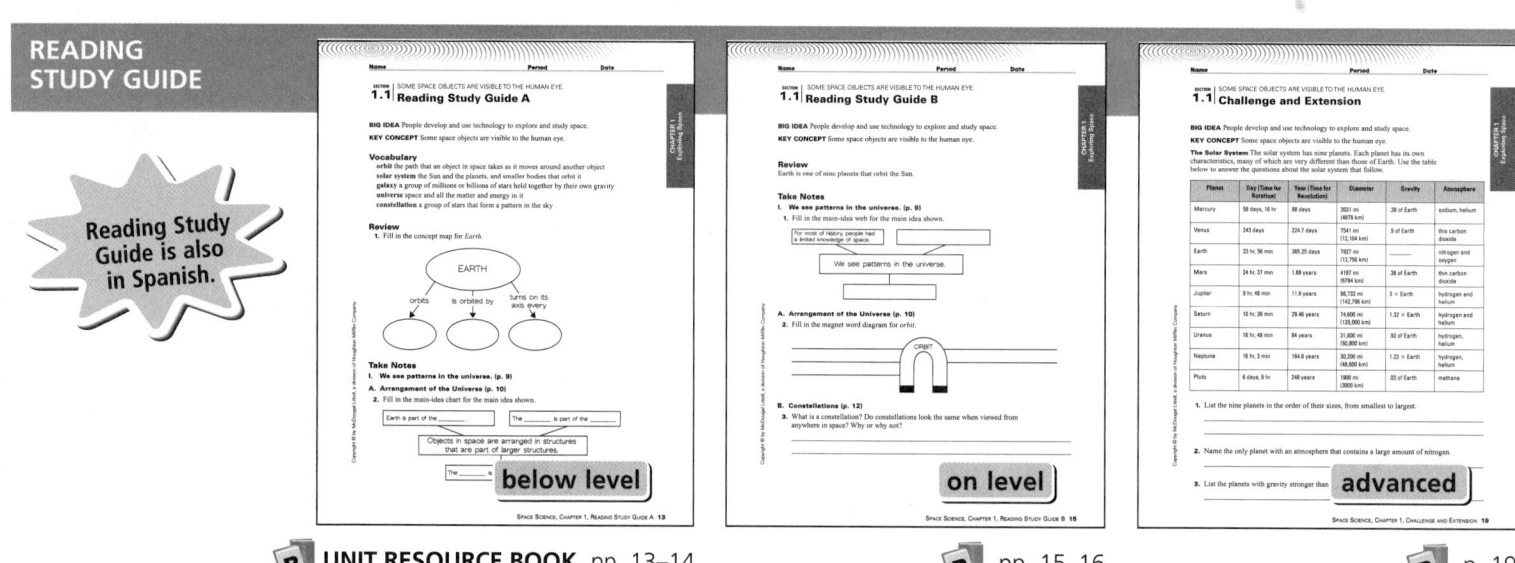

UNIT RESOURCE BOOK, pp. 13–14

pp. 15–16

p. 19

> Reading Study Guide is also in Spanish.

CHAPTER TEST

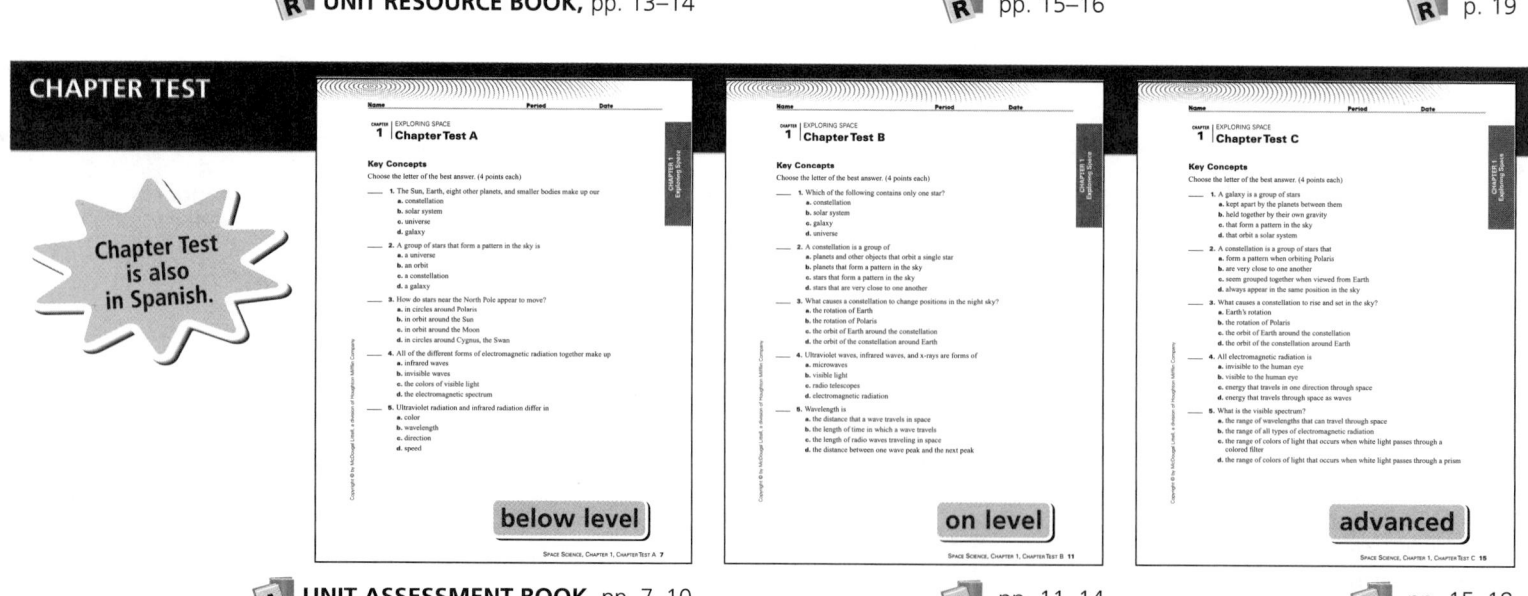

UNIT ASSESSMENT BOOK, pp. 7–10

pp. 11–14

pp. 15–18

> Chapter Test is also in Spanish.

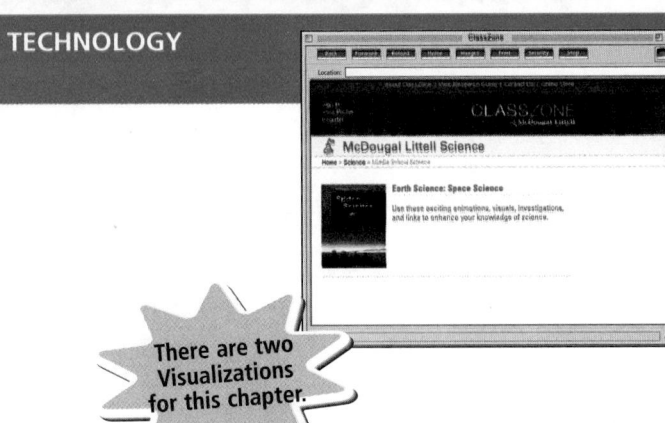

There are two Visualizations for this chapter.

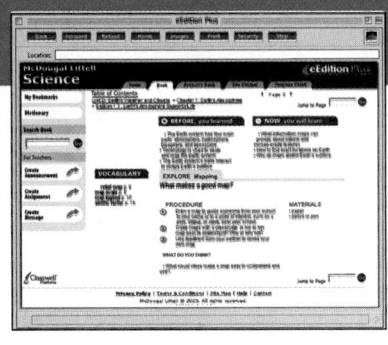

 CLASSZONE.COM

 CD/CD-ROMS

 CLASSZONE.COM

VISUAL CONTENT

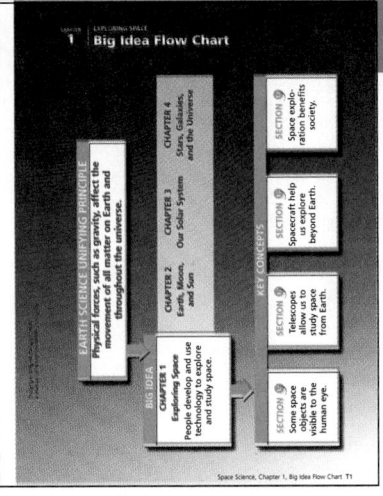

UNIT TRANSPARENCY BOOK, p. T1

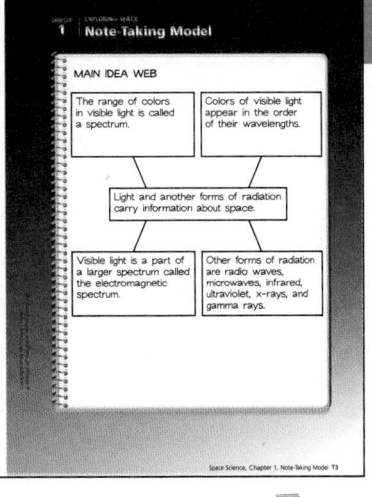

p. T3

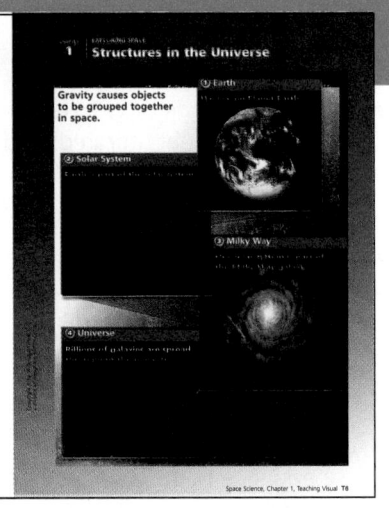

p. T6

MORE SUPPORT

Reinforcing Key Concepts for each section

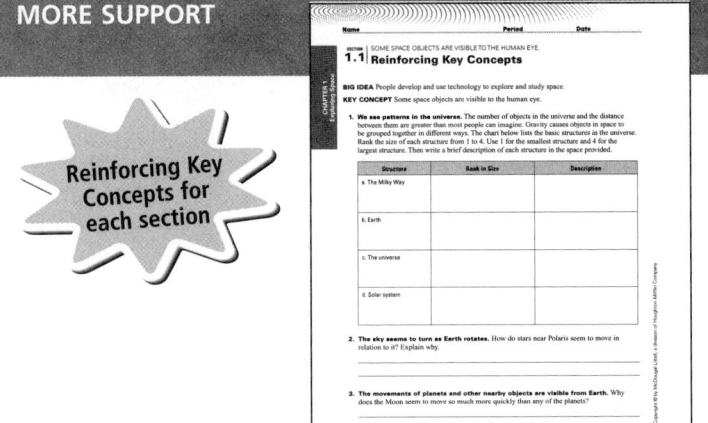

UNIT RESOURCE BOOK, p. 22

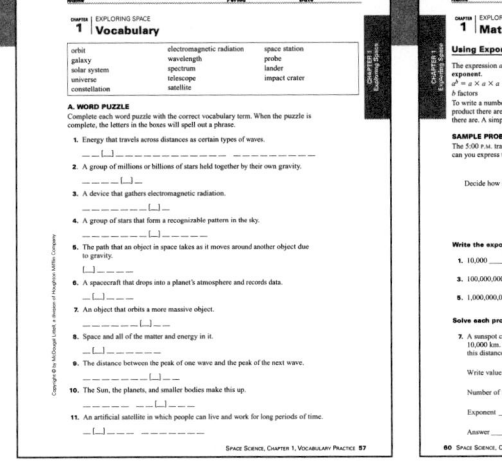

pp. 57–58

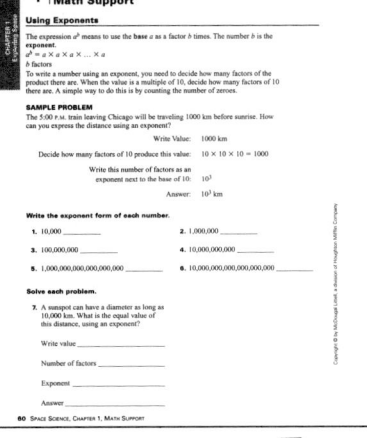

p. 60

INTRODUCE

the BIG idea

Have students look at the photograph of the astronaut in space and discuss how the question in the box links to the Big Idea:

- Why is it necessary for the astronaut to wear the space suit?
- What does the space suit provide?

National Science Education Standards

Content

B.3.f The Sun is a major source of energy that has a range of wavelengths, consisting of visible light, infrared, and ultraviolet radiation.

F.5.c Technology influences society through its products and processes and influences the quality of life and the ways people act and interact.

Process

A.2–8 Design and conduct an investigation; use tools to gather and interpret data; use evidence to describe, predict, explain, model; think critically to make relationships between evidence and explanation; recognize different explanations and predictions; communicate scientific procedures and explanations; use mathematics.

A.9.a–f Understand scientific inquiry by using different investigations, methods, mathematics, technology, and explanations based on logic, evidence, and skepticism.

F.5.e Scientists work in different settings.

G.1.a–b Science as a human endeavor

CHAPTER

Exploring Space

the BIG idea

People develop and use technology to explore and study space.

What challenges must be overcome in space exploration?

Key Concepts

SECTION
1.1 Some space objects are visible to the human eye.
Learn about views of space from Earth and about the arrangement of the universe.

SECTION
1.2 Telescopes allow us to study space from Earth.
Learn how astronomers gather information about space from different kinds of radiation.

SECTION
1.3 Spacecraft help us explore beyond Earth.
Learn how astronauts and instruments provide information about space.

SECTION
1.4 Space exploration benefits society.
Learn about the benefits of space exploration.

Internet Preview

CLASSZONE.COM

Chapter 1 online resources: Content Review, Simulation, Visualization, two Resource Centers, Math Tutorial, Test Practice

INTERNET PREVIEW

CLASSZONE.COM For student use with the following pages:

Review and Practice
- Content Review, pp. 8, 36
- Math Tutorial: Powers and Exponents, p. 30
- Test Practice, p. 39

Activities and Resources
- Internet Activity: Universe, p. 7
- Resource Centers: Telescopes, p. 18; Space Exploration, p. 22
- Visualization: The Night Sky Throughout the Year, p. 12

NSTA scilinks.org **SCiLINKS**
Space Probes **Code: MDL057**

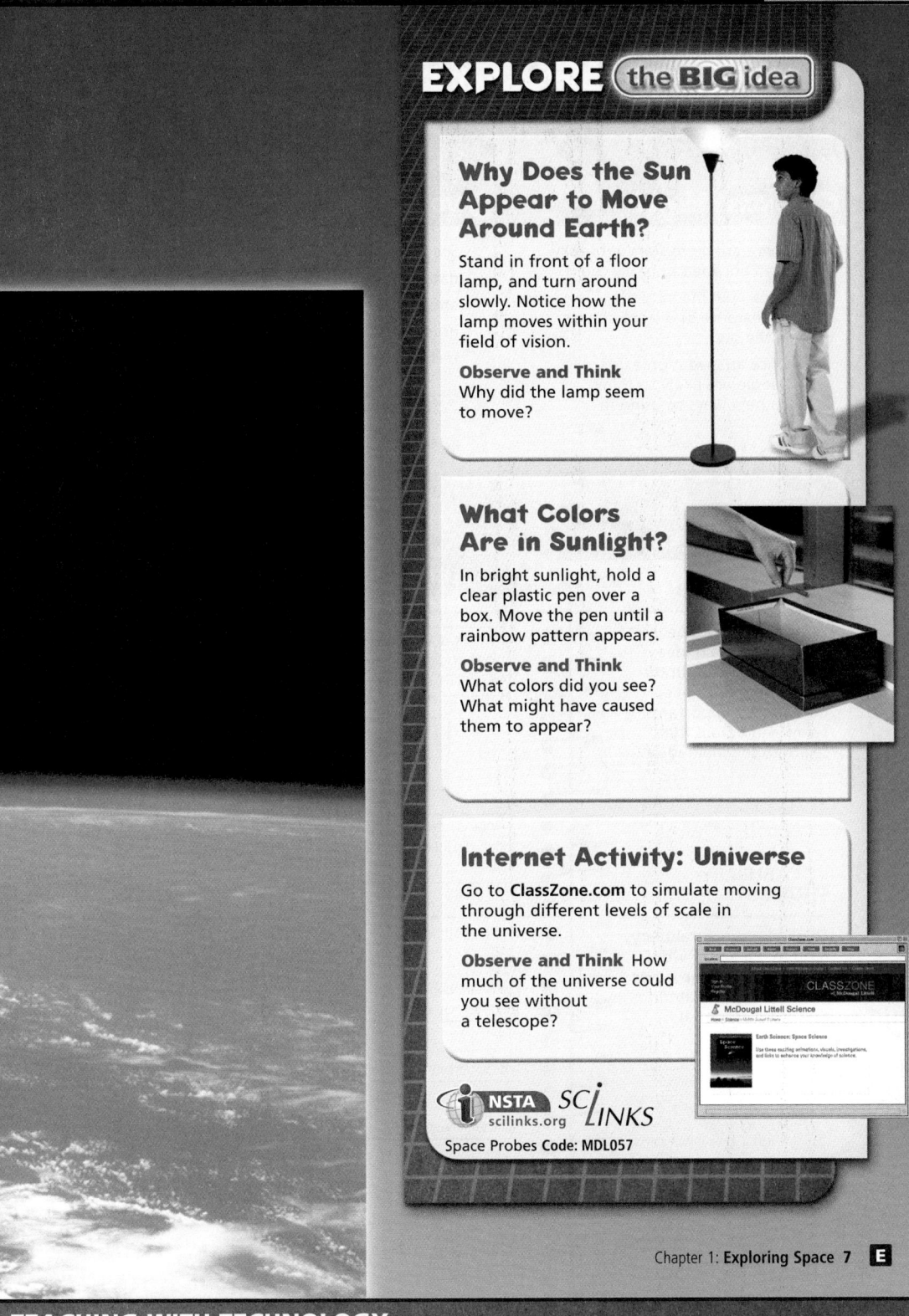

EXPLORE (the BIG idea)

Why Does the Sun Appear to Move Around Earth?

Stand in front of a floor lamp, and turn around slowly. Notice how the lamp moves within your field of vision.

Observe and Think
Why did the lamp seem to move?

What Colors Are in Sunlight?

In bright sunlight, hold a clear plastic pen over a box. Move the pen until a rainbow pattern appears.

Observe and Think
What colors did you see? What might have caused them to appear?

Internet Activity: Universe

Go to **ClassZone.com** to simulate moving through different levels of scale in the universe.

Observe and Think How much of the universe could you see without a telescope?

NSTA
scilinks.org
SCLINKS

Space Probes **Code: MDL057**

TEACHING WITH TECHNOLOGY

Turbidity Sensor You might want students to use a turbidity probe and a CBL unit to measure the water's lack of clarity in "Explore Distortion of Light" on p. 15.

Spectroscope You might want students to compare the results they get from their home-made spectroscopes on pp. 20–21 with the results from a professionally designed and built spectroscope.

EXPLORE (the BIG idea)

These inquiry-based activities are appropriate for use at home or as a supplement to classroom instruction.

Why Does the Sun Appear to Move Around Earth?

PURPOSE To demonstrate to students why the Sun appears to move around Earth.

TIP *5 min.* The floor lamp can be replaced with any tall object, such as a coat stand.

Answer: The lamp seemed to move because it crossed the student's field of vision as the student turned.

REVISIT after p. 10.

What Colors Are in Sunlight?

PURPOSE To introduce students to the concept that white light is composed of light of various colors.

TIP *5 min.* Students might have to tilt the box or move it up or down to get a clear pattern.

Answer: Most of the colors of the rainbow should be discernable, including red, orange, yellow, green, blue, and violet. Indigo is difficult to distinguish from blue and violet. Students should understand that the colors appeared because sunlight passed through the clear plastic.

REVISIT after p. 16.

Internet Activity: Universe

PURPOSE To visualize different levels of scale in the universe.

TIP *20 min.* Have students compare the images of the universe in the simulation with those on p. 11.

Answer: You could see only a part of the Milky Way galaxy, which is a very small portion of the universe.

REVISIT after p. 18.

PREPARE

◔ CONCEPT REVIEW
Activate Prior Knowledge

• Draw a circle on the board with five dots in it. Tell students that this represents stars that you might see in a small portion of the sky with your eyes only.

• Draw a similar circle to represent the view of the same part of the sky through a telescope. Then ask students to fill in the circle showing how the view might be different.

▶ TAKING NOTES

Main Idea Web

Each blue heading, written in a complete sentence, provides a clear statement of the main idea for the text that follows. Remind students that the boxes surrounding the main idea can be used for both vocabulary and details. Periodically, review students' webs and discuss how their detailed notes relate to the main idea.

Vocabulary Strategy

Point out that the magnet word diagram for *orbit* is filled in with a variety of items: a definition, sentences that use the term, descriptions, and related ideas. Encourage students to use such variety when filling in their diagrams. This variety provides a more complete meaning of the word than just a definition.

Vocabulary and Note-Taking Resources

• Vocabulary Practice, pp. 57–58
• Decoding Support, p. 59

• Daily Vocabulary Scaffolding, p. T2
• Note-Taking Model, p. T3

• Magnet Word, B24–25
• Main Idea Web, C38–39
• Daily Vocabulary Scaffolding, H1–8

◔ CONCEPT REVIEW

• There are more stars in the sky than anyone can easily count.

• Telescopes magnify the appearance of distant objects in the sky.

• Once an invention exists, people are likely to think up new ways of using it.

◔ VOCABULARY REVIEW

See Glossary for definitions.

data

energy

gravity

technology

 CONTENT REVIEW
CLASSZONE.COM
Review concepts and vocabulary.

▶ TAKING NOTES

MAIN IDEA WEB

Write each new blue heading, or main idea, in the center box. In the boxes around it, take notes about important terms and details that relate to the main idea.

VOCABULARY STRATEGY

Think about a vocabulary term as a **magnet word** diagram. Write the other terms or ideas related to that term around it.

See the Note-Taking Handbook on pages R45–R51.

E 8 Unit: Space Science

SCIENCE NOTEBOOK

| The constellations change position in the night sky as Earth rotates. | Polaris is located straight over the North Pole. |

The sky seems to turn as Earth rotates.

| Polaris can help you figure out direction and location. | |

ORBIT

path around another object — influence of gravity

Moon orbits Earth — planets orbit Sun

space telescopes — satellites

CHECK READINESS

Administer the Diagnostic Test to determine students' readiness for new science content and their mastery of requisite math skills.

 Diagnostic Test, pp. 1–2

Technology Resources

Students needing content and math skills should visit **ClassZone.com**.

• **CONTENT REVIEW**
• **MATH TUTORIAL**

 CONTENT REVIEW CD-ROM

KEY CONCEPT

Some space objects are visible to the human eye.

◀ **BEFORE,** you learned

- Earth is one of nine planets that orbit the Sun
- The Moon orbits Earth
- Earth turns on its axis every 24 hours

▶ **NOW,** you will learn

- How the universe is arranged
- How stars form patterns in the sky
- How the motions of bodies in space appear from Earth

VOCABULARY

orbit p. 10
solar system p. 10
galaxy p. 10
universe p. 10
constellation p. 12

EXPLORE Distance

How far is the Moon from Earth?

PROCEDURE

1. Tie one end of the string around the middle of the tennis ball. The tennis ball will represent Earth.

2. Wrap the string 9.5 times around the tennis ball, and make a mark on the string at that point. Wrap the aluminum foil into a ball around the mark. The foil ball will represent the Moon.

3. Stretch out the string to put the model Moon and Earth at the right distance compared to their sizes.

MATERIALS
- tennis ball
- aluminum foil (5 cm strip)
- string (250 cm)
- felt marker

WHAT DO YOU THINK?
- How does the scale model compare with your previous idea of the distance between Earth and the Moon?
- How many Earths do you estimate would fit between Earth and the Moon?

We see patterns in the universe.

MAIN IDEA WEB
Record details about patterns in space.

For most of history, people had very limited knowledge of space. They saw planets and stars as points of light in the night sky. However, they did not know how far those bodies were from Earth or from each other. Early observers made guesses about planets and stars on the basis of their appearance and the ways they seemed to move in the sky. Different peoples around the world connected the patterns they saw in the sky with stories about imaginary beings.

Chapter 1: Exploring Space **9** **E**

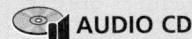

▶ **Set Learning Goals**

Students will

- Recognize how the universe is arranged.
- Explain how stars form patterns in the sky.
- Describe how the motions of bodies in space appear from Earth.
- Analyze in an experiment how the rotation of Earth affects the positions of constellations.

◀ **3-Minute Warm-Up**

Display Transparency 4 or copy this exercise on the board:

Decide if each statement is true. If not, correct it.

1. There are 11 planets in our solar system. *There are 9 planets in our solar system.*

2. The stars in the sky are all the same distance from Earth. *The stars are different distances from Earth.*

3. It takes Earth one year to orbit the Sun. *true*

 3-Minute Warm-Up, p. T4

1.1 MOTIVATE

EXPLORE Distance

PURPOSE To create a model for visualizing the relative distance between Earth and the Moon compared with their sizes

TIPS *10 min.*

- Clarify that the 9.5 times the string is wrapped around the ball does not include the amount of string that was used to tie the string to the ball.

- If students have trouble tying the string to the ball, they can use tape.

WHAT DO YOU THINK? *Students might respond that they were surprised by the large distance between Earth and the Moon; the distance is about 30 Earth diameters (accept reasonable estimates).*

Address Misconceptions

IDENTIFY Ask: Why does the Sun rise in one part of the sky and set in another part of the sky? If students respond that the Sun moves, they may hold the misconception that the Sun orbits Earth.

CORRECT Remind students that when they look out a window while traveling in a car, trees and other stationary objects outside might seem to move because they change position in the window as the car rolls forward. Explain that the turning of Earth has the same effect on our view of the Sun.

REASSESS Ask: Why does the Sun appear to move across the sky? *The Sun appears to move because Earth is turning.*

Technology Resources

Visit **ClassZone.com** for background on common student misconceptions.

 MISCONCEPTION DATABASE

EXPLORE (the BIG idea)

Revisit "Why Does the Sun Appear to Move Around Earth?" on p. 7. Have students explain their observations based on what they now understand.

Ongoing Assessment

Recognize how the universe is arranged.

Place the following structures in order from largest to smallest: galaxy, universe, planet, solar system. *universe, galaxy, solar system, planet*

 *Answer: The solar system lies within the Milky Way.*

We still have much to learn about the universe. Within the last few hundred years, however, new tools and scientific theories have greatly increased our knowledge. In this chapter you will learn about the arrangement of planets and stars. You will also learn about the ways in which astronomers explore and study space.

Arrangement of the Universe

If you look up at the sky on a clear night, you will see only a tiny fraction of the planets and stars that exist. The number of objects in the universe and the distances between them are greater than most people can imagine. Yet these objects are not spread around randomly. Gravity causes objects in space to be grouped together in different ways.

 The images on page 11 show some basic structures in the universe. Like a camera lens zooming out, the images provide views of space at different levels of size.

1 Earth Our planet's diameter is about 13,000 kilometers (8000 mi). This is almost four times the diameter of the Moon, which orbits Earth. An **orbit** is the path of an object in space as it moves around another object because of gravity.

2 Solar System Earth and eight other major planets orbit the Sun. The Sun, the planets, and various smaller bodies make up the **solar system.** The Sun is about 100 times greater in diameter than Earth. You could fit more than 4000 bodies the size of the Sun between the Sun and the solar system's outermost planet at its average distance from the Sun. The Sun is one of countless stars in space. Astronomers have detected planets orbiting some of these other stars.

3 The Milky Way Our solar system and the stars you can see with your bare eyes are part of a galaxy called the Milky Way. A **galaxy** is a group of millions or billions of stars held together by their own gravity. If the solar system were the size of a penny, the Milky Way would stretch from Chicago to Dallas. Most stars in the Milky Way are so far away that our galaxy appears to us as a hazy band of light.

4 The Universe The **universe** is everything—space and all the matter and energy in it. The Milky Way is just one of many billions of galaxies in the universe. These galaxies extend in all directions.

Astronomers study space at each of these different levels. Some focus on planets in the solar system. Other astronomers study distant galaxies. To learn how the universe formed, astronomers even study the smallest particles that make up all matter.

 **CHECK YOUR READING** What is the relationship between the solar system and the Milky Way?

READING TiP
The word *orbit* can be a noun or a verb.

DIFFERENTIATE INSTRUCTION

? More Reading Support

A What force causes objects in space to be grouped together? *gravity*

B A galaxy is a group of what? *stars*

English Learners This section has a variety of introductory clauses and phrases. For example, "To learn how the universe formed, astronomers even study the smallest particles that make up all matter" (p. 10). Have students find the comma that separates the introductory clause or phrase from the rest of the sentence. Then help them locate the subject of the sentence. *In this sentence, astronomers is the subject.*

Structures in the Universe

Gravity causes objects to be grouped together in space.

① Earth

We live on Earth, a planet that orbits the Sun.

② Solar System

The solar system contains the Sun, nine major planets, and many smaller objects.

③ Milky Way

The Sun and billions of other stars are grouped together in a galaxy called the Milky Way.

④ Universe

Billions of galaxies are spread throughout the universe.

READING VISUALS How are these structures different from one another? How are they similar?

Chapter 1 Exploring Space **11** **E**

DIFFERENTIATE INSTRUCTION

Advanced The Milky Way is a spiral galaxy, which is only one of several types of galaxies. Have students find out the other types and make a chart comparing and contrasting them. The chart should include examples and characteristics of each type.

R Challenge and Extension, p. 19

Alternative Assessment Have students write an extended version of their home address in which they include structures of the universe. ("Earth," "the Solar System," and "the Milky Way.")

Teach from Visuals

To help students interpret the visual:

- Ask: How does each diagram relate to the next? *It is a much smaller part of the structure that follows in the next diagram.*
- Ask: Where is our solar system located in the Milky Way galaxy? *on one of the spiraling arms*

  T This visual is also available as T6 in the Unit Transparency Book.

Teach Difficult Concepts

Some students may not understand why we don't see the Milky Way galaxy as it is shown here. Explain that our solar system is located on one of the galaxy's spiral arms. From Earth we only have an edge-on view of the galaxy, which appears as a hazy band of light. Tell students that it is similar to the view of someone observing a marching-band formation from the football field. That point of view is very different from the view high up in the bleachers.

Address Misconceptions

IDENTIFY Ask: What holds the planets in the solar system in orbit around the Sun? If students' responses do not include the concept of gravity, they may think that gravity is present only on Earth.

CORRECT Tell students to imagine twirling a ball attached to a rope over their head. Ask them to think about why the ball twirls in a circle. Point out that the Sun's gravity pulls the planets into orbits in a similar way.

REASSESS Ask: What would happen if you suddenly let go of the rope? *The rope and ball would fly off in a straight line.* What would happen to the planets if gravity suddenly were "turned off"? *They would fly off into space and no longer orbit the Sun.*

Technology Resources

Visit **ClassZone.com** for background on common student misconceptions.

MISCONCEPTION DATABASE

Ongoing Assessment

READING VISUALS *Answer: They vary in size. All are affected by gravity.*

Chapter 1 **11** **E**

Teach from Visuals

To help students interpret the visual of Cygnus, ask:

- About how far away is the star Deneb from the grouping of Gienah Cygni and Delta Cygni? *about 1500 light-years*

- Which stars look about equally spaced from each other when viewed from the young woman's position (as if from Earth)? *Deneb, Delta Cygni, Sadr, Gienah Cygni*

- Are those stars equally spaced in outer space? *no*

Teacher Demo

Students may have difficulty seeing the relationship between the constellation pattern in the illustration and the projected positions of the stars in space. Create a three-dimensional model of Cygnus or an imaginary constellation that shows the stars at different distances from the viewer. You can attach small balls of clay to the ends of toothpicks attached to a shoe box lid. Let students view the constellation head-on, then turn the lid sideways to reveal the stars' true positions in space.

Ongoing Assessment

Explain how stars form patterns in the sky.

What does it mean to say that a star is located in Cygnus? *The star is found in that part of the sky. It may or may not be part of the swan pattern.*

 *Answer: Deneb and Gienah Cygni*

 *Answer: The stars seem to be grouped together when viewed from Earth.*

E 12 Unit: **Space Science**

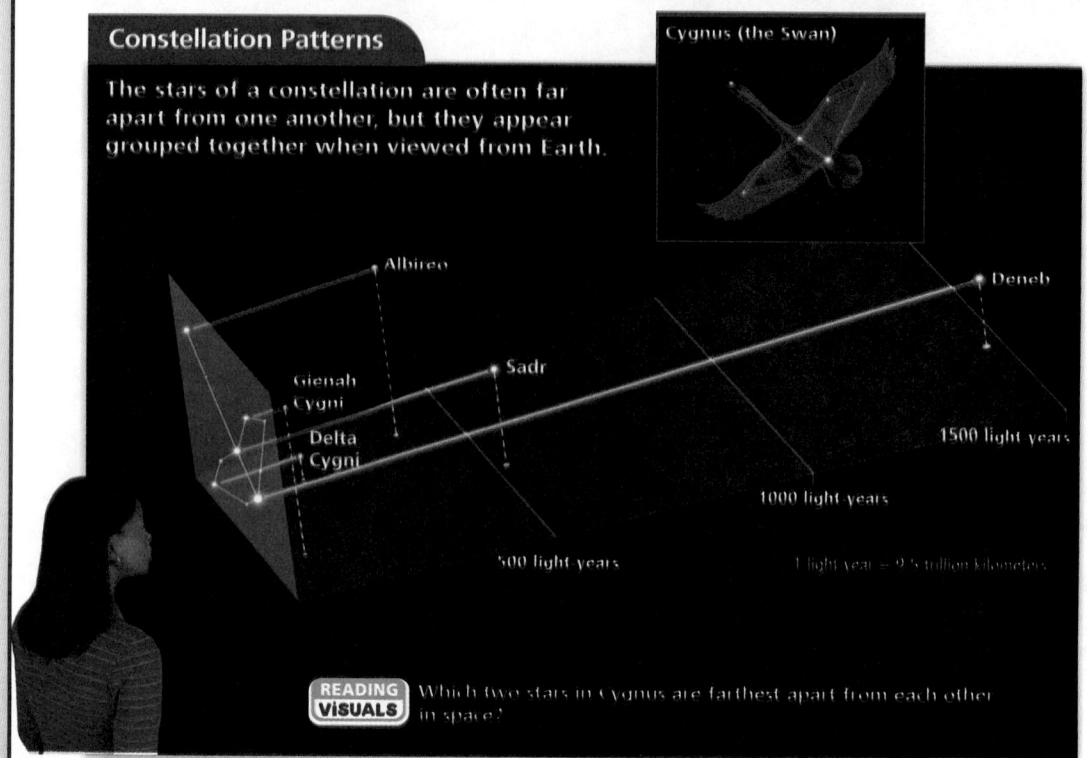

Constellation Patterns

The stars of a constellation are often far apart from one another, but they appear grouped together when viewed from Earth.

Cygnus (the Swan)

Albireo

Deneb

Gienah Cygni

Sadr

Delta Cygni

1500 light-years

1000 light-years

500 light-years

1 light year = 9.5 trillion kilometers

 Which two stars in Cygnus are farthest apart from each other in space?

Constellations

If you want to find a particular place in the United States, it helps to know the name of the state it is in. Astronomers use a similar system to describe the locations of objects in the sky. They have divided the sky into 88 areas named for the constellations.

A **constellation** is a group of stars that form a pattern in the sky. In the constellation Cygnus, for example, a group of bright stars form the shape of a flying swan. Any other objects in that area of the sky, such as galaxies, are said to be located in Cygnus, even if they are not parts of the swan pattern. The ancient Greeks named many of the constellations for animals and imaginary beings.

Unlike the planets in the solar system, the stars in a constellation are usually not really close to each other. They seem to be grouped together when viewed from Earth. But as the illustration above shows, you would not see the same pattern in the stars if you viewed them from another angle.

 What relationship exists among the stars in a constellation?

E 12 Unit: Space Science

 **DIFFERENTIATE INSTRUCTION**

? More Reading Support

C What is a group of stars that form a pattern in the sky called? *a constellation*

Inclusion Describe the visual "Constellation Patterns" to tactile learners and students with vision impairments. See if they can construct a model like that in the Teacher Demo using poster board, toothpicks, tape, and balls of clay or foil. Tell them the distance in light years between the stars and ask: If Sadr is one toothpick away from the cardboard, how many toothpicks should you tape together to approximate Deneb's distance from the board? *three*

The sky seems to turn as Earth rotates.

?
D

You cannot see all of the constellations at once, because Earth blocks half of space from your view. However, you can see a parade of constellations each night as Earth rotates. As some constellations slowly come into view over the eastern horizon, others pass high in the sky above you, and still others set at the western horizon. Throughout the ages, many peoples have observed these changes and used them to help in navigation and measuring time.

?
E

If you extended the North Pole into space, it would point almost exactly to a star called Polaris, or the North Star. If you were standing at the North Pole, Polaris would be directly over your head. As Earth rotates through the night, the stars close to Polaris seem to move in circles around it. Although not the brightest star in the sky, Polaris is fairly bright and easy to find. You can use Polaris to figure out direction and location.

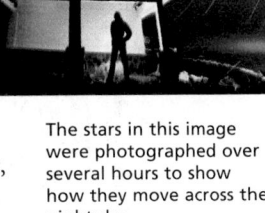

The stars in this image were photographed over several hours to show how they move across the night sky.

CHECK YOUR READING What causes constellations to change positions during the night?

INVESTIGATE Constellation Positions

How does time of day affect the positions of constellations?

PROCEDURE

1. Cut out both diagrams on the Constellation Wheel Sheet and assemble them as shown.

2. Rotate the wheel so that the current month is aligned with 9 P.M. Observe the positions of the constellations.

3. Align the current month with other times to determine how the positions of the constellations change during the night.

WHAT DO YOU THINK?

- How do the positions of the constellations change during the night?
- In which direction does the northern sky seem to turn?

CHALLENGE Earth's rotation makes the sky seem to turn. What does the model tell you about the direction of Earth's rotation?

SKILL FOCUS
Analyzing

MATERIALS
- Constellation Wheel Sheet
- scissors
- brass fastener

TIME
20 minutes

Chapter 1: **Exploring Space** 13 **E**

History of Science

Many ancient cultures used their observations of the sky to mark the seasons, develop calendars, and plan when to plant crops. The ancient Egyptians, for example, noted that the brightest star in the sky, Sirius, appeared in the east at dawn shortly before the flooding of the Nile River. They would plant at this time to take advantage of the floodwaters.

INVESTIGATE Constellation Positions

PURPOSE To analyze the positions of the constellations in relation to the rotation of Earth

TIPS *20 min.*

- You can glue or photocopy the wheel sheets onto tag board to make the wheel easier to manipulate and more durable.

- Students should push the brass fastener through Polaris.

WHAT DO YOU THINK? *The constellations move from east to west. The sky seems to turn from east to west.*

CHALLENGE *Earth turns from west to east.*

- Constellation Wheel Sheet, p. 20
- Datasheet, Constellation Positions, p. 21

Technology Resources

Customize this student lab as needed or look for an alternative. Print rubrics to assess student lab reports.

Lab Generator CD-ROM

Ongoing Assessment

CHECK YOUR READING *Answer: Earth's rotation*

DIFFERENTIATE INSTRUCTION

? **More Reading Support**

D In what direction do stars move across the sky? *from east to west*

E If you stood at the North Pole, what star would be directly overhead? *Polaris*

Advanced Have interested students investigate a constellation other than Cygnus. They should find out where it is located in the sky, and what stars form it, then construct a model.

Chapter 1 **13** **E**

Ongoing Assessment

Describe how the motions of bodies in space appear from Earth.

Why does the Moon appear to move faster than the planets? *The Moon is closer to us.*

Reinforce (the BIG idea)

Have students relate the section to the Big Idea.

 Reinforcing Key Concepts, p. 22

1.1 ASSESS & RETEACH

Assess

 Section 1.1 Quiz, p. 3

Reteach

Have students examine the time-lapse photograph of stars on p. 13. Ask for volunteers to explain

- where the stars are located in the universe *the Milky Way galaxy*
- why the stars are moving in circles *Earth's rotation makes the sky seem to turn.*
- how the movement of the stars differs from the movement of objects such as the Moon and the planets *The stars only appear to be moving in circles because of Earth's rotation, but we can see the actual movements of closer objects such as the Moon.*

Technology Resources

Have students visit **ClassZone.com** for reteaching of Key Concepts.

 CONTENT REVIEW

 CONTENT REVIEW CD-ROM

The movements of planets and other nearby objects are visible from Earth.

A jet plane travels at a greater speed and altitude than a bird. Yet if a bird and a plane flew overhead at the same time, you might think that the bird was faster. You would have this impression because the farther away a moving object is from you, the less it seems to move.

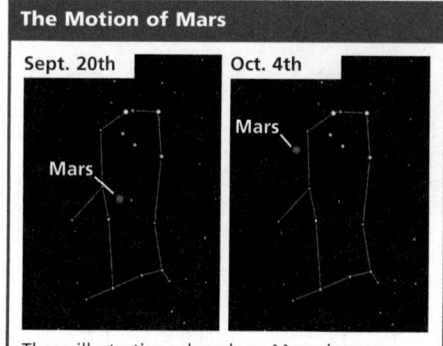

The Motion of Mars

Sept. 20th — Mars

Oct. 4th — Mars

These illustrations show how Mars changes positions in the constellation Gemini over a period of two weeks.

Stars are always moving, but they are so far away that you cannot see their movements. Observers have seen the same constellation patterns for thousands of years. Only over a much longer period does the motion of stars gradually change constellation patterns.

By contrast, the Moon moves across the star background a distance equal to its width every hour as it orbits Earth. The Moon is our closest neighbor. The planets are farther away, but you can see their gradual movements among the constellations over a period of weeks or months.

Planet comes from a Greek word that means "wanderer." Ancient Greek astronomers used this term because they noticed that planets move among the constellations. It is easiest to see the movements of Venus and Mars, the two planets closest to Earth. They change their positions in the sky from night to night.

The apparent movement of the sky led early astronomers to believe that Earth was at the center of the universe. Later astronomers discovered that Earth and the other planets orbit the Sun. The timeline on pages 72–75 introduces some of the astronomers who helped discover how planets really move in the solar system.

1.1 Review

KEY CONCEPTS

1. What are the basic structures in which objects are grouped together in space?
2. What is a constellation?
3. How does Earth's rotation affect our view of stars?

CRITICAL THINKING

4. **Compare and Contrast** How is the grouping of stars in a constellation different from the grouping of planets in the solar system?
5. **Apply** The planet Jupiter is farther than Mars from Earth. Which planet seems to move faster when viewed from Earth? Explain.

⬥ CHALLENGE

6. **Predict** Suppose that you are standing at the North Pole on a dark night. If you keep turning clockwise at the same speed as Earth's rotation, how would your movement affect your view of the stars?

ANSWERS

1. the solar system, galaxies, and the universe

2. a group of stars that form a pattern in the sky, which astronomers use to describe locations

3. It makes them appear to move across the night sky.

4. Stars in a constellation only appear to be grouped together when viewed from Earth. Planets really are grouped together.

5. Mars, because it is easier to see the motion of nearer objects than farther objects.

6. The stars would appear to remain still instead of circling around Polaris.

1.2 Telescopes allow us to study space from Earth.

◀ **BEFORE,** you learned

- Objects in the universe are grouped together in different ways
- The motions of planets and other nearby objects are visible from Earth

▶ **NOW,** you will learn

- About light and other forms of radiation
- How astronomers gather information about space

VOCABULARY

electromagnetic radiation p. 15

spectrum p. 16

wavelength p. 16

telescope p. 17

EXPLORE Distortion of Light

How can light become distorted?

PROCEDURE

① Place a white sheet of paper behind a glass filled with plain water. Shine a flashlight through the glass, and observe the spot of light on the paper.

② Pour a spoonful of salt into the water. Stir the water, and observe the spot of light.

WHAT DO YOU THINK?

- How did the spot of light change after you mixed the salt into the water?
- How could Earth's atmosphere cause similar changes in light from space?

MATERIALS

- flashlight
- glass filled with water
- sheet of white paper
- spoon
- salt

Light and other forms of radiation carry information about space.

VOCABULARY
Add a magnet word diagram for *electromagnetic radiation* to your notebook.

When you look at an object, your eyes are gathering light from that object. Visible light is a form of **electromagnetic radiation** (ih-LEHK-troh-mag-NEHT-ihk), which is energy that travels across distances as certain types of waves. There are other forms of electromagnetic radiation that you cannot see directly, such as radio waves and x-rays. Scientists have developed instruments to detect these other forms.

Electromagnetic radiation travels in all directions throughout space. Almost everything we know about the universe has come from our study of radiation. Astronomers can often learn about the size, distance, and movement of an object by studying its radiation. Radiation can also reveal what an object is made of and how it has changed.

Chapter 1: **Exploring Space** 15 **E**

RESOURCES FOR DIFFERENTIATED INSTRUCTION

Below Level

UNIT RESOURCE BOOK

- Reading Study Guide A, pp. 25–26
- Decoding Support, p. 59

AUDIO CDS

R **Additional INVESTIGATION,**
A Simple Refracting Telescope, A, B, & C, pp. 71–79; Teacher Instructions, pp. 287–288

Advanced

UNIT RESOURCE BOOK
Challenge and Extension, p. 31

English Learners

UNIT RESOURCE BOOK
Spanish Reading Study Guide, pp. 29–30

AUDIO CDS

- Audio Readings in Spanish
- Audio Readings (English)

1.2 FOCUS

▶ Set Learning Goals

Students will

- Identify light and other forms of radiation.
- Explain how astronomers gather information about space.

◀ 3-Minute Warm-Up

Display Transparency 4 or copy this exercise on the board:

Draw a diagram showing how the following structures are related:

- Milky Way galaxy
- Earth
- solar system
- universe

Diagram should illustrate that Earth is part of the solar system, the solar system is part of the Milky Way, and the Milky Way is part of the universe.

T 3-Minute Warm-Up, p. T4

1.2 MOTIVATE

EXPLORE Distortion of Light

PURPOSE To model how particles in the atmosphere can distort light from stars

TIP *10 min.* Use a clear glass so that there is as little distortion of light as possible before adding the salt.

WHAT DO YOU THINK? *The spot of light became fuzzier because the salt particles blocked some of the light from shining through the water. The atmosphere has many particles suspended in it that can block light entering from space.*

Teaching with Technology

If a turbidity probe and a CBL unit are available, have students use them to measure the water's lack of clarity after salt is added. This will give students quantified data to compare with their qualitative description.

Teach from Visuals

To help students interpret the illustration of the electromagnetic spectrum, ask:

• Which kind of radiation has the longest wavelength? *radio waves*

• Which has the shortest wavelength? *gamma rays*

Address Misconceptions

IDENTIFY Ask: How does light allow us to see an object? If students don't say that light reflects from objects and travels to our eyes, they may have misconceptions about how light allows us to see.

CORRECT Draw a diagram on the board using arrows to show light going from a light bulb to an object to a person's eyes. Trace this path as you point out how the light reflects off the object and reaches the person's eyes, allowing him or her to see the object.

REASSESS Present a similar diagram and have students draw the arrows and explain how light allows us to see.

EXPLORE (the BIG idea)

Revisit "What Colors Are in Sunlight?" on p. 7. Have students explain their results.

Ongoing Assessment

Identify light and other forms of radiation.

Name four forms of electromagnetic radiation. *any four of the following: radio waves, microwaves, infrared waves, visible light, ultraviolet waves, x-rays, gamma rays*

CHECK YOUR READING *Answer: It differs in wavelength and we can see it.*

The Electromagnetic Spectrum

The different forms of electromagnetic radiation vary in their wavelengths.

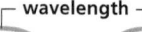

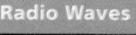

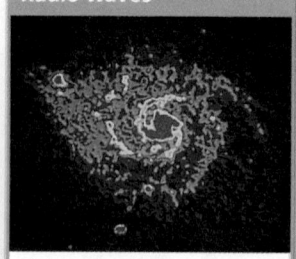

Radio Waves

This image of a galaxy shows where radio waves are emitted.

Visible Light

Visible light is the only form of radiation our eyes can detect.

X-Rays

This image shows where the same galaxy emits x-rays.

READING TIP
A prism is a transparent object that is used to separate the wavelengths of light.

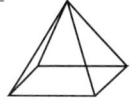

If you shine a flashlight through a prism, the beam of white light will separate into a range of colors called a **spectrum** (SPEHK-truhm). The colors that make up visible light are red, orange, yellow, green, blue, indigo, and violet. These are the colors in a rainbow, which appears when light spreads out as it passes through raindrops.

In a spectrum, the colors of visible light appear in the order of their wavelengths. **Wavelength** is the distance between one wave peak and the next wave peak. Red light has the longest wavelength. Violet light has the shortest.

As you can see in the illustration above, visible light is just a tiny part of a larger spectrum called the electromagnetic spectrum. The electromagnetic spectrum includes all the forms of electromagnetic radiation. Notice that the wavelength of infrared radiation is longer than the wavelength of visible light but not as long as the wavelength of microwaves or radio waves. The wavelength of ultraviolet radiation is shorter than the wavelength of visible light but not as short as the wavelength of x-rays or gamma rays.

CHECK YOUR READING How is visible light different from other forms of electromagnetic radiation?

DIFFERENTIATE INSTRUCTION

? More Reading Support

A What makes up white light? *a range of colors called a spectrum*

B What does the electromagnetic spectrum include? *all forms of electromagnetic radiation*

English Learners Have students write the definitions for *electromagnetic radiation, wavelength, spectrum,* and *telescope* in their Science Word Dictionaries. When discussing the colors that make up visible light, note that not all cultures separate the colors the same way. For instance, some cultures have only one word for indigo and violet.

Astronomers use telescopes to collect information about space.

A **telescope** is a device that gathers electromagnetic radiation. If you have ever looked through a telescope, it was probably one that gathers visible light. Such telescopes provide images that are much clearer than what is seen with the naked eye. Images from other types of telescopes show radiation that your eyes cannot detect. Each form of radiation provides different information about objects in space.

Astronomers usually record images from telescopes electronically, which allows them to use computers to analyze images. Different colors or shades in an image reveal patterns of radiation. For example, in the right-hand image on page 16, the colors yellow and red indicate where the galaxy is emitting large amounts of x-rays.

Most types of telescopes gather radiation with a glass lens or a reflecting surface, such as a mirror. Larger lenses and reflecting surfaces produce brighter and more detailed images. You can magnify an image from a telescope to any size. However, enlarging an image will not bring out any more details of an object. If the image is fuzzy at a small size, it will remain fuzzy no matter how much it is enlarged.

Visible-Light, Infrared, and Ultraviolet Telescopes

There are two types of visible-light telescopes: reflecting telescopes and refracting telescopes. Reflecting telescopes can also be built to gather infrared or ultraviolet radiation.

- **Reflecting Telescope** This type of telescope has a curved mirror that gathers light. The image comes into focus in front of the mirror. Many reflecting telescopes have a second mirror that reflects the image to recording equipment or to a lens called an eyepiece.

- **Refracting Telescope** This type of telescope has an objective lens, or curved piece of glass, at one end of a long tube. The lens gathers light and focuses it to form an image near the other end of the tube. An eyepiece magnifies this image.

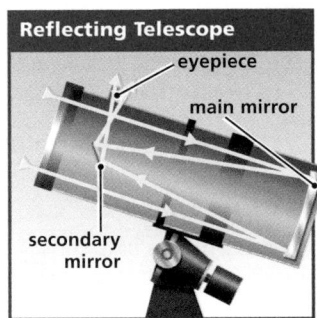

Reflecting Telescope
eyepiece
main mirror
secondary mirror

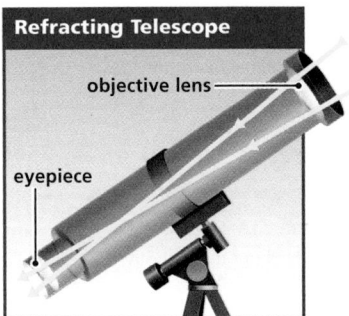

Refracting Telescope
objective lens
eyepiece

Metacognitive Strategy

Ask students to think of some tactics to easily remember the order of the different forms of radiation and the order of the colors in the spectrum. Tell them that acronyms or other mnemonic devices might help.

History of Science

Galileo Galilei built one of the earliest telescopes in 1609. He continued to improve the design of his refracting telescope, and by 1610 he was using it to make astronomical discoveries. Galileo was the first to notice that the Moon has craters, mountains, and valleys. It is not the perfectly smooth sphere people had thought it was. Galileo also discovered the four largest moons of Jupiter. He used these findings to support Copernicus's earlier assertion that Earth and the planets orbit the Sun, a claim that opposed the common belief that the Sun and planets orbit Earth.

Teach from Visuals

To help students interpret the diagrams of telescopes, ask:

- How are reflecting and refracting telescopes similar? *They both gather and focus light and magnify an image.*

- How are reflecting and refracting telescopes different? *A reflecting telescope uses a curved mirror to gather light. A refracting telescope uses an objective lens for this purpose.*

- How does the path of light differ between the two telescopes? *Light bounces off two different mirrors in the reflecting telescope but travels in straight lines in the refracting telescope.*

DIFFERENTIATE INSTRUCTION

More Reading Support

C What does a telescope do? *gathers electromagnetic radiation*

D What part of a visible-light telescope magnifies the image? *eyepiece*

Additional Investigation To reinforce Section 1.2 learning goals, use the following full-period investigation:

R **Additional INVESTIGATION,** A Simple Refracting Telescope, A, B, & C, pp. 71–79, 287–288 (Advanced students should complete Levels B and C.)

Advanced Have interested students work in a group to compare a visible-light telescope to a camera and an eye.

R Challenge and Extension, p. 31

A familiar type of radio telescope is a satellite TV dish. A satellite dish collects radio waves from satellites in space. These satellites relay signals that are converted into television images and sounds.

EXPLORE (the **BIG** idea)

Revisit "Internet Activity: Universe" on p. 7. Have students discuss their answers.

Teach from Visuals

To help students interpret the diagram and photograph of radio dishes, ask:

- What do the yellow lines in the diagram show? *the path of radio waves gathered by the telescope*

- How does the arrangement of the telescopes in the photograph allow them to provide a combined image? *They are all aimed in the same direction.*

Ongoing Assessment

Explain how astronomers gather information about space.

What helps astronomers improve the quality of radio telescope images? *aiming a group of radio telescopes at the same object*

CHECK YOUR READING *Answer: to gather radio waves and focus them on the antenna*

Most powerful visible-light telescopes are built on mountaintops in rural areas. Rural areas offer a much better view of the night sky than cities do, because the many electric lights in cities make dim space objects hard to see. By locating telescopes on mountaintops, astronomers reduce problems caused by Earth's atmosphere. The atmosphere interferes with light coming in from space. In fact, movements of the air are what make stars appear to twinkle. At high altitudes there is less air above the ground to interfere with light.

Radio Dish

Radio Telescopes

Radio telescopes show where radio waves are being emitted by objects in space. A radio telescope has a curved metal surface, called a dish, that gathers radio waves and focuses them onto an antenna. The dish works in the same way as the main mirror of a reflecting telescope. Some radio telescopes have dishes made of metal mesh rather than solid metal.

Because radio waves are so long, a single radio telescope must be very large to produce useful images. To improve the quality of images, astronomers often aim a group of radio telescopes at the same object. Signals from the telescopes are combined and then converted into an image. Groups of radio telescopes, like the Very Large Array in New Mexico, can show more detail than even the largest single dish.

Signals from these radio telescopes in New Mexico can be combined to produce clearer images.

Unlike visible-light telescopes, radio telescopes are not affected by clouds or bad weather. They even work well in daylight. In addition, radio telescopes can be located at low altitudes because most radio waves pass freely through Earth's atmosphere.

CHECK YOUR READING What is the function of the dish in a radio telescope?

RESOURCE CENTER CLASSZONE.COM
Find out more about telescopes.

Telescopes in Space

Many exciting images have come from the Hubble Space Telescope and other telescopes in space. The Hubble telescope is a reflecting telescope. It was placed in orbit around Earth in 1990. Astronomers operate it from the ground, although astronauts have visited it to make repairs and improvements. The telescope sends images and measurements back to Earth electronically.

E 18 Unit: **Space Science**

DIFFERENTIATE INSTRUCTION

? **More Reading Support**

E Telescopes built on mountaintops in rural areas are able to avoid what two things? *city lights and atmospheric interference*

Below Level Have students revisit "Explore Distortion of Light" on p. 15 to recall their firsthand experience of how particles can distort light and thus interfere with the viewing of objects.

The Hubble Space Telescope produced this image of a part of a galaxy where new stars are appearing.

Because the Hubble telescope is located in space, Earth's atmosphere does not interfere with light from objects the telescope is aimed at. This lack of interference allows it to obtain clearer images than ground-based telescopes with much larger mirrors. In addition to collecting visible light, the Hubble telescope produces images of ultraviolet and infrared radiation.

The Hubble Space Telescope is part of a group of telescopes that orbit Earth. The telescopes allow astronomers to gain information from the full range of electromagnetic radiation. The Compton Gamma-Ray Observatory was sent into orbit in 1991. The Chandra X-Ray Observatory was launched eight years later. These telescopes were placed in space because Earth's atmosphere blocks most x-rays and gamma rays.

 **CHECK YOUR READING** Why does the Hubble telescope produce clearer images than a telescope of the same size on Earth?

1.2 Review

KEY CONCEPTS

1. How are visible light, radio waves, and other forms of electromagnetic radiation different from each other?

2. What function do mirrors serve in reflecting telescopes?

3. Why are some telescopes placed on mountains or in orbit around Earth?

CRITICAL THINKING

4. **Compare and Contrast** What are the similarities and differences between refracting telescopes and reflecting telescopes?

5. **Analyze** Why would it be difficult to build radio telescopes if they did not work well at low altitudes?

CHALLENGE

6. **Analyze** Why might astronomers use different types of telescopes to obtain images of the same object in space?

ANSWERS

1. They have different wavelengths. Some can pass freely through Earth's atmosphere, while others cannot.

2. They gather and focus light.

3. because this diminishes or eliminates the interference from Earth's atmosphere

4. Both produce images by gathering and focusing light. Refractors use lenses to gather light. Reflectors gather light with mirrors.

5. Radio telescopes must be very large to produce images. If they had to be located on mountains or

in space, they would be extremely expensive and difficult to build.

6. Each type of telescope would provide different information about the object, allowing astronomers to gain a greater understanding of its structure and features.

CHAPTER INVESTIGATION

Focus

PURPOSE To construct a simple spectroscope and view spectra from different light sources

OVERVIEW Students will use diffraction grating to construct a spectroscope. Students will observe and compare the spectra from the following: sunlight, incandescent light, and fluorescent light.

Lab Preparation

- Cut 3 cm by 1.5 cm rectangles from pieces of paper, and give them to students to use as stencils for cutting out the holes in step 1. You might also have volunteers cut the holes in the shoeboxes the day before the lab.

- Prior to the investigation, have students read through the investigation and prepare their data tables. Or you may wish to copy and distribute datasheets and rubrics.

 UNIT RESOURCE BOOK, pp. 62–70

 SCIENCE TOOLKIT, F15

Lab Management

- In step 3, students should use the precut sides of the index cards to form the slit.
- The spectroscope will not work if the diffraction grating is placed incorrectly. Tell students that when they tape the diffraction grating onto the box, the writing on the diffraction grating card should be horizontal.
- Tell students that they may need to look around the box to find a spectrum. One should appear on each side of the slit.

SAFETY Emphasize in step 5 that students should not look directly at the Sun when aiming their spectroscope through the window.

Teaching with Technology

If possible, have students view the light sources through a purchased spectroscope. They can then compare the results to those obtained with their homemade spectroscopes.

 E 20 Unit: **Space Science**

MATERIALS
- shoebox with lid
- ruler
- scissors
- diffraction grating
- tape
- index card
- pencils or markers in a variety of colors
- incandescent light
- fluorescent light
for Challenge:
- cellophane in several colors

CHAPTER INVESTIGATION

Observing Spectra

OVERVIEW AND PURPOSE Visible light is made up of different colors that can be separated into a rainbow band called a spectrum. Astronomers gain information about the characteristics of stars by spreading their light into spectra (*spectra* is the plural form of *spectrum*). A spectroscope is a device that produces spectra. In most spectroscopes, diffraction gratings are used to separate light into different colors. The colors with the longest wavelengths appear farthest from the slit in a spectroscope. The colors with the shortest wavelengths appear closest to the slit. In this investigation you will

- build a spectroscope and observe the spectra of three different light sources
- identify ways in which the spectra of light sources differ

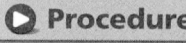 Procedure

1 Cut a hole measuring 3 cm by 1.5 cm in each end of a shoebox. Make sure that the holes line up.

2 On the inside of the box, tape a piece of diffraction grating over one of the holes. Handle the diffraction grating by its edges so that you do not get fingerprints on it.

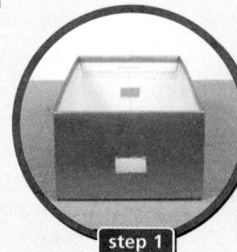
step 1

3 Cut an index card in half, and tape the halves over the outside of the other hole as shown. Leave a very narrow slit between the two halves of the index card.

INVESTIGATION RESOURCES

 CHAPTER INVESTIGATION, Observing Spectra
- Level A, pp. 62–65
- Level B, pp. 66–69
- Level C, p. 70

Advanced students should complete Levels B & C.

 Writing a Lab Report, D12–13

Technology Resources

Customize this student lab as needed or look for an alternative. Print rubrics to assess student lab reports.

Lab Generator CD-ROM

4. Put the lid on the shoebox. Then turn off the overhead lights in the classroom.

5. Look through the hole covered with the diffraction grating, aiming the spectroscope's slit at the sky through a window. **Caution:** *Never look directly at the Sun.* Observe the spectrum you see to the left of the slit.

step 5

6. Repeat step 5 while aiming the spectroscope at an incandescent light and then at a fluorescent light.

Observe and Analyze
Write It Up

1. **RECORD OBSERVATIONS** For each light source, draw in your data table the spectrum you see to the left of the slit. Describe the colors and patterns in the spectrum, and label the light source.

2. **IDENTIFY LIMITS** What problems, if any, did you experience in observing the spectra? Why was it important to turn off overhead lights for this activity?

Conclude
Write It Up

1. **COMPARE AND CONTRAST** How did the spectra differ from one another? Which light sources produced bands of colors with no breaks in them? Which source produced a band of colors broken by dark stripes?

2. **ANALYZE** On the basis of your observations, which color has the shortest wavelength? Which color has the longest wavelength?

3. **INFER** How might the spectra look different if the slit at the end of the spectroscope were curved instead of a straight line?

INVESTIGATE Further

CHALLENGE Cover the slit on your spectroscope with a piece of colored cellophane. Aiming the spectroscope at the sky or at an incandescent lamp, observe and draw the resulting spectrum. Then repeat with cellophane of other colors. List the colors that each piece of cellophane transmitted. Did these results surprise you? If so, why?

Observing Spectra
Observe and Analyze
Table 1. Spectra of Different Light Sources

Light Source	Drawing	Description

Conclude

Observe and Analyze
Write It Up

SAMPLE DATA Sunlight: even stripes of red, orange, yellow, green, blue, indigo, and violet that blend into each other, some faint dark lines; incandescent: even stripes of same colors listed above; fluorescent: some color stripes are much brighter and narrower than others.

1. *Students should provide accurate drawings and complete tables.*

2. *Students might have difficulty viewing spectra if the rectangles cut into the box do not line up or the slit is too wide. Some students might have difficulty identifying colors. It is important to turn off the overhead lights so that the spectroscope does not produce spectra from different light sources mixed together.*

Conclude
Write It Up

1. *The spectra from sunlight and incandescent light should look similar, but students may see faint lines separating some colors in the sunlight spectrum. In the fluorescent spectrum, some colors are much brighter and narrower than others.*

2. *Red has the longest wavelength because it appears farthest from the slit. Violet has the shortest wavelength because it appears closest to the slit.*

3. *The stripes of color within the spectra would be curved instead of straight.*

INVESTIGATE Further

CHALLENGE The filter blocks out colors other than the color of the filter. This effect is easiest to see with the fluorescent light.

Post-Lab Discussion

Ask students to discuss why different light sources might produce different spectra. *Different sources emit light through different processes. For example, sunlight is produced by extremely hot gases inside the Sun, incandescent light is produced by hot wire coils inside a light bulb, and fluorescent light is produced by electric current that passes through a gas-filled bulb coated on the inside with powder.*

○ Set Learning Goals

Students will

- Describe how astronauts explore space near Earth.
- Explain how different types of space-craft are used in exploration.
- Identify variables in an experiment about launch planning.

◐ 3-Minute Warm-Up

Display Transparency 5 or copy this exercise on the board:

Match each definition to the correct term.

Definitions

1. radiation with the longest wavelength
   b

2. an orbiting telescope that produces images from visible light, ultraviolet radiation, and infrared radiation *e*

3. all the separate colors of visible light *c*

Terms

a. Chandra X-Ray Observatory

b. radio waves

c. spectrum

d. microwaves

e. Hubble Space Telescope

 3-Minute Warm-Up, p. T5

1.3 MOTIVATE

EXPLORE Viewing Space Objects

PURPOSE To demonstrate how space missions to other planets help us gain knowledge

TIP *10 min.* Tell students to include as many details in their sketches as they can see.

WHAT DO YOU THINK? *The close-up drawing should show more details, such as wrinkles and grooves in the paper; clouds, mountains, valleys, the presence of water or ice*

KEY CONCEPT

1.3 Spacecraft help us explore beyond Earth.

◀ **BEFORE, you learned**

- The motions of planets and other nearby objects are visible from Earth
- Light and other forms of radiation carry information about the universe

▶ **NOW, you will learn**

- How astronauts explore space near Earth
- How different types of space-craft are used in exploration

VOCABULARY

satellite p. 23
space station p. 24
lander p. 28
probe p. 29

EXPLORE Viewing Space Objects

How do objects appear at different distances?

PROCEDURE

1. Crumple the paper into a ball and place it on your desk.

2. Sketch the ball at the same time as another student sketches it. One of you should sketch it from a distance of 1 m. The other should sketch it from 5 m away.

WHAT DO YOU THINK?

- How do the details in the two drawings compare?
- What details might be easier to see on a planet if you were orbiting the planet?

MATERIALS
- paper
- pencils

Astronauts explore space near Earth.

RESOURCE CENTER
CLASSZONE.COM

Learn more about space exploration.

Space travel requires very careful planning. Astronauts take everything necessary for survival with them, including air, water, and food. Spacecraft need powerful rockets and huge fuel tanks to lift all their weight upward against Earth's gravity. The equipment must be well designed and maintained, since any breakdown can be deadly.

Once in space, astronauts must get used to a special environment. People and objects in an orbiting spacecraft seem to float freely unless they are fastened down. This weightless condition occurs because they are falling in space at the same rate as the spacecraft. In addition, to leave their airtight cabin, astronauts must wear special protective suits. Despite these conditions, astronauts have managed to perform experiments and make important observations about space near Earth.

E **22** Unit: Space Science

RESOURCES FOR DIFFERENTIATED INSTRUCTION

Below Level
UNIT RESOURCE BOOK
- Reading Study Guide A, pp. 35–36
- Decoding Support, p. 59

 **AUDIO CDS**

Advanced
UNIT RESOURCE BOOK
- Challenge and Extension, p. 41
- Challenge Reading, pp. 55–56

English Learners
UNIT RESOURCE BOOK
Spanish Reading Study Guide, pp. 39–40

AUDIO CDS

- Audio Readings in Spanish
- Audio Readings (English)

Moon Missions

For about a decade, much of space exploration was focused on a race to the Moon. This race was driven by rivalry between the United States and the Soviet Union, which included Russia. In 1957 the Soviet Union launched the first artificial satellite to orbit Earth. A **satellite** is an object that orbits a more massive object. The Soviet Union also sent the first human into space in 1961. Although the United States lagged behind in these early efforts, it succeeded in sending the first humans to the Moon.

Preparation Many steps had to be taken before astronauts from the United States could visit the Moon. The National Aeronautics and Space Administration (NASA) sent spacecraft without crews to the Moon to find out whether it was possible to land on its surface. NASA also sent astronauts into space to practice important procedures.

Landings The NASA program to reach the Moon was called Apollo. During early Apollo missions, astronauts tested spacecraft and flew them into orbit around the Moon. On July 20, 1969, crew members from *Apollo 11* became the first humans to walk on the Moon's surface. NASA achieved five more Moon landings between 1969 and 1972. During this period, the Soviet Union sent spacecraft without crews to get samples of the Moon's surface.

Scientific Results The Apollo program helped scientists learn about the Moon's surface and interior. Much of the information came from 380 kilograms (weighing 840 lb) of rock and soil that astronauts brought back to Earth. These samples are still being studied.

Powerful booster rockets were used to launch the Apollo spacecraft. Beginning with *Apollo 15*, astronauts rode in lunar roving vehicles to explore greater areas of the Moon's surface.

1.3 INSTRUCT

Integrate the Sciences

Astronauts floating in a spaceship are often said to be experiencing weightlessness or zero gravity. Actually, the spaceship and its contents are not weightless at all, and there's plenty of gravity. Astronauts feel weightless because they, and the spaceship, are continually falling together toward Earth. This falling produces the condition known as microgravity, in which it seems as if gravity is absent. The combination of gravity pulling the spaceship toward Earth and the spaceship tending to move in a straight line away from Earth keeps the spaceship in an orbit.

Develop Critical Thinking

HYPOTHESIZE Point out the footprints in the photograph. Remind students that the footprints were made in the early 1970s. Have students hypothesize how the footprints look today and why. *They look the same because there is no weather on the Moon to erode them.*

Teach from Visuals

To help students interpret the photograph of the Moon's surface, ask:

- How does the surface of the Moon look? *dusty, powdery*
- What was the advantage of having a lunar rover on Moon missions? *Astronauts could explore a much greater area than just by walking.*

DIFFERENTIATE INSTRUCTION

? More Reading Support

A What is an object that orbits a more massive object? *a satellite*

B What were crew members of *Apollo 11* the first to do? *walk on the Moon*

English Learners Place the terms *satellite, space station, lander,* and *probe* on the classroom's Science Word Wall, along with a brief definition of each. Make sure students understand that the noun *breakup* used on p. 24 is different from the verbal phrase "break up." Students may take the phrase "carry out" literally on pp. 24 and 26. Explain that this idiom means "do" or "conduct" in this context. On p. 27, tell students that *since* means "because" and does not indicate the passage of time.

Integrate the Sciences

Microgravity—the condition in which it seems as if there is no gravity present—affects the human body in several ways. Astronauts grow about an inch in space because gravity does not compress their spine. Blood moves from the legs toward the head, resulting in a stuffed-up nose. Astronauts drink extra fluids to maintain a balance as body fluids are redistributed. The heart and other muscles become smaller because they have less work to do. All these conditions eventually go back to normal with proper care upon returning to Earth.

Teach from Visuals

To help students interpret the visual of the ISS, ask:

- What makes up the largest area of the ISS? *the solar panels*

- Do you think the solar panels are moveable? If so, for what purpose? *yes, so that they can be turned toward the Sun to provide energy*

Ongoing Assessment

Describe how astronauts explore space near Earth.

Why is the ISS an important mission? *It involves many nations; some experiments are more effective when performed there.*

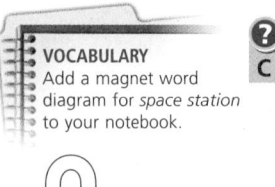

VOCABULARY
Add a magnet word diagram for *space station* to your notebook.

C

D

Orbiting Earth

A **space station** is a satellite in which people can live and work for long periods. The United States and the Soviet Union launched the first space stations in the early 1970s. After the breakup of the Soviet Union in 1991, the Russian space agency and NASA began to act as partners rather than rivals. Russian and U. S. astronauts carried out joint missions aboard *Mir* (meer), the Russian space station.

The *Mir* missions helped prepare for the International Space Station (ISS). The United States, Russia, and 15 other nations are working together to build the ISS. When completed, it will cover an area about as large as two football fields. The ISS is too large to launch into space in one piece. Instead, sections of the space station are being launched separately and assembled in orbit over a period of years.

Construction of the ISS began in 1998. The first three-member crew arrived at the station in 2000. In addition to constructing the station, crew members make observations of Earth and perform experiments. Some experiments are much more effective when they are performed in space, where gravity affects them differently. For example, scientists can grow cell tissue more easily in space than they can on Earth. Research on cell tissue grown in space may increase our understanding of cancer and other diseases.

International Space Station

Each section of the space station has a specific function.

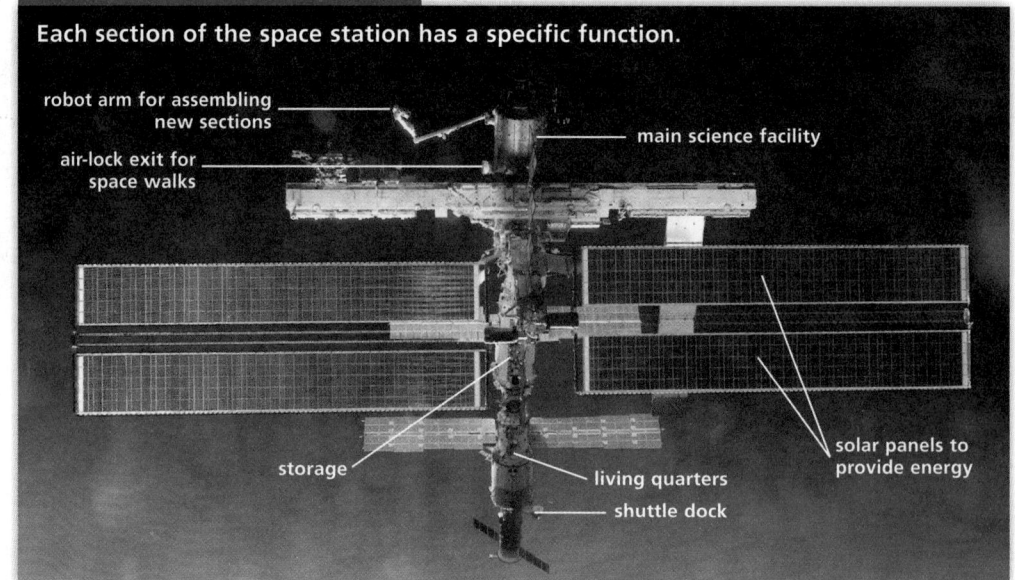

robot arm for assembling new sections

air-lock exit for space walks

main science facility

storage

living quarters

shuttle dock

solar panels to provide energy

DIFFERENTIATE INSTRUCTION

? More Reading Support

C What is a satellite in which scientists can live called? *a space station*

D What is the latest space station being built? *International Space Station*

Alternative Assessment Show a video of the history of space exploration or of the Apollo program specifically. Afterwards, have students create a timeline of space exploration. They should choose key events, including those discussed in the text.

Research and technological advances from the space station may lay the groundwork for new space exploration. ISS crew members study how living in space affects the human body over long periods. This research may provide useful information for future efforts to send astronauts to other planets.

Most crews have flown to the ISS aboard space shuttles. Unlike earlier spacecraft, a space shuttle can be used again and again. At the end of a mission, it reenters Earth's atmosphere and glides down to a runway. The large cargo bay of a space shuttle can carry satellites, equipment, and laboratories.

NASA has launched space shuttles more than 100 times since 1981. Space shuttles are much more sophisticated than the Apollo spacecraft that carried astronauts to the Moon. However, space travel remains a dangerous activity.

Two booster rockets and an external fuel tank are needed to lift a space shuttle into orbit.

CHECK YOUR READING Why might some researchers choose to perform experiments aboard a space station rather than on Earth?

INVESTIGATE Launch Planning

How does Earth's rotation affect launches of spacecraft?

PROCEDURE

① Tightly wad 14 sheets of paper into balls, and place the balls in a small bucket.

② Stand 1.5 m away from a large bucket placed on a desk. Try tossing 7 balls into the bucket.

③ While turning slowly, try tossing the remaining 7 balls into the bucket.

WHAT DO YOU THINK?

• How much more difficult was it to toss the paper balls into the bucket while you were turning than when you were standing still?

• Why does Earth's rotation make launching rockets into space more complicated?

CHALLENGE How would you design an experiment to show the variables involved in a launch from Earth toward another rotating body in space, such as the Moon?

SKILL FOCUS
Identifying variables

MATERIALS
• paper
• small bucket
• large bucket

TIME
10 minutes

Chapter 1: Exploring Space 25 **E**

Teach from Visuals

To help students interpret the photograph of the space shuttle, tell students that the shuttle boosters are retrieved in the ocean and reused. Then ask: What else in this photograph is reusable? *The shuttle itself is reusable.*

INVESTIGATE Launch Planning

PURPOSE To identify variables that affect launches into space

TIPS *10 min.*

• You may want to have students perform this investigation in groups of four to limit the number of buckets used and paper balls being tossed.

• If necessary, review with students that a variable is any factor that can change in an experiment. After students perform the activity, ask them to name the variables. *Students representing planets are variables in this activity.*

WHAT DO YOU THINK? *Most students will find it more difficult to toss balls into the bucket while turning. There is only a limited time period when the rockets can be launched in the right direction.*

CHALLENGE *The large bucket could be held by another student who was also turning.*

 Datasheet, Launch Planning, p. 42

Technology Resources

Customize this student lab as needed or look for an alternative. Print rubrics to assess student lab reports.

 Lab Generator CD-ROM

Ongoing Assessment

CHECK YOUR READING *Answer: Some experiments are more effective in an environment where gravity affects objects differently than on Earth.*

DIFFERENTIATE INSTRUCTION

? More Reading Support

E What is an advantage of space shuttles over earlier spacecraft? *They can be reused.*

Inclusion Put an electronic device that emits a mild sound (such as a metronome or portable radio at a low volume) in the bucket so students with visual impairments can identify the target and take part in "Investigate Launch Planning."

Advanced Have students who are interested in learning about space junk read the following article:

 Challenge Reading, pp. 55–56

Chapter 1 **25 E**

Teach Difficult Concepts

Some students may not understand the statement "Some planets do not even have surfaces to land on." Point out that most of the outer planets are referred to as "gas giants" and are made mostly of gas and liquid.

Develop Critical Thinking

EVALUATE Ask students to evaluate whether or not NASA should send astronauts on a mission to Mars. Begin discussion by creating a class chart on which are listed advantages and disadvantages of missions that do and do not include astronauts. This chart can become the basis for further discussion. Be sure students support their points with facts from the text or other sources.

Ongoing Assessment

CHECK YOUR READING *Sample answer: What conditions on Mars would make it difficult for astronauts to explore the planet?*

Spacecraft carry instruments to other worlds.

Currently, we cannot send humans to other planets. One obstacle is that such a trip would take years. A spacecraft would need to carry enough air, water, and other supplies needed for survival on the long journey. Another obstacle is the harsh conditions on other planets, such as extreme heat and cold. Some planets do not even have surfaces to land on.

Because of these obstacles, most research in space is accomplished through the use of spacecraft without crews aboard. These missions pose no risk to human life and are less expensive than missions involving astronauts. The spacecraft carry instruments that test the compositions and characteristics of planets. Data and images are sent back to Earth as radio signals. Onboard computers and radio signals from Earth guide the spacecraft.

 F Spacecraft have visited all the major planets in our solar system except Pluto. NASA has also sent spacecraft to other bodies in space, such as comets and moons. Scientists and engineers have designed different types of spacecraft to carry out these missions.

 **CHECK YOUR READING** What questions do you still have about space exploration?

Flybys

 G The first stage in space exploration is to send out a spacecraft that passes one or more planets or other bodies in space without orbiting them. Such missions are called flybys. After a flyby spacecraft leaves Earth's orbit, controllers on Earth can use the spacecraft's small rockets to adjust its direction. Flyby missions may last for decades. However, because a spacecraft flies by planets quickly, it can collect data and images from a particular planet only for a brief period.

As a flyby spacecraft passes a planet, the planet's gravity can be used to change the spacecraft's speed or direction. During the flyby of the planet, the spacecraft can gain enough energy to propel it to another planet more quickly. This method allowed *Voyager 2* to fly past Saturn, Uranus, and Neptune, even though the spacecraft left Earth with only enough energy to reach Jupiter.

Many complex mathematical calculations are needed for a flyby mission to be successful. Experts must take into account Earth's rotation and the positions of the planets that the spacecraft will pass. The period of time when a spacecraft can be launched is called a launch window.

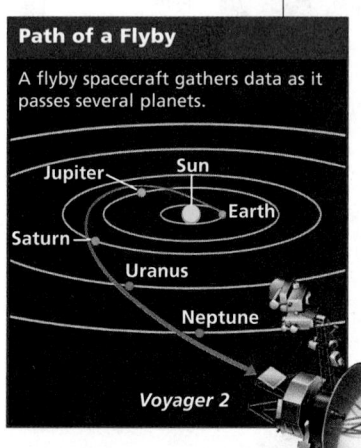

Path of a Flyby

A flyby spacecraft gathers data as it passes several planets.

Jupiter
Sun
Earth
Saturn
Uranus
Neptune
Voyager 2

E 26 Unit: **Space Science**

DIFFERENTIATE INSTRUCTION

 More Reading Support

F What major planets have we sent spacecraft to? *all except Pluto*

G What type of mission is the first stage in space exploration? *a flyby*

Advanced Have students pool their questions from Check Your Reading and brainstorm ideas for how to answer them. Plans might include research through the library and Internet, contacting NASA, visiting a planetarium, or designing experiments. Encourage students to follow through with their plan.

R Challenge and Extension, p. 41

Orbiters

The second stage in space exploration is to study a planet over a long period of time. Spacecraft designed to accomplish this task are called orbiters. As an orbiter approaches its target planet, rocket engines are fired to slow the spacecraft down. The spacecraft then goes into orbit around the planet.

In an orbiter mission, a spacecraft orbits a planet for several months to several years. Since an orbiter remains near a planet for a much longer period of time than a flyby spacecraft, it can view most or all of the planet's surface. An orbiter can also keep track of changes that occur over time, such as changes in weather and volcanic activity.

Orbiters allow astronomers to create detailed maps of planets. Most orbiters have cameras to photograph planet surfaces. Orbiters may also carry other instruments, such as a device for determining the altitudes of surface features or one for measuring temperatures in different regions.

Some orbiters are designed to explore moons or other bodies in space instead of planets. It is also possible to send a spacecraft to orbit a planet and later move it into orbit around one of the planet's moons.

▼ REMINDER
Remember that objects orbit, or move around, other objects in space because of the influence of gravity.

CHECK YOUR READING What is the main difference between a flyby spacecraft and an orbiter?

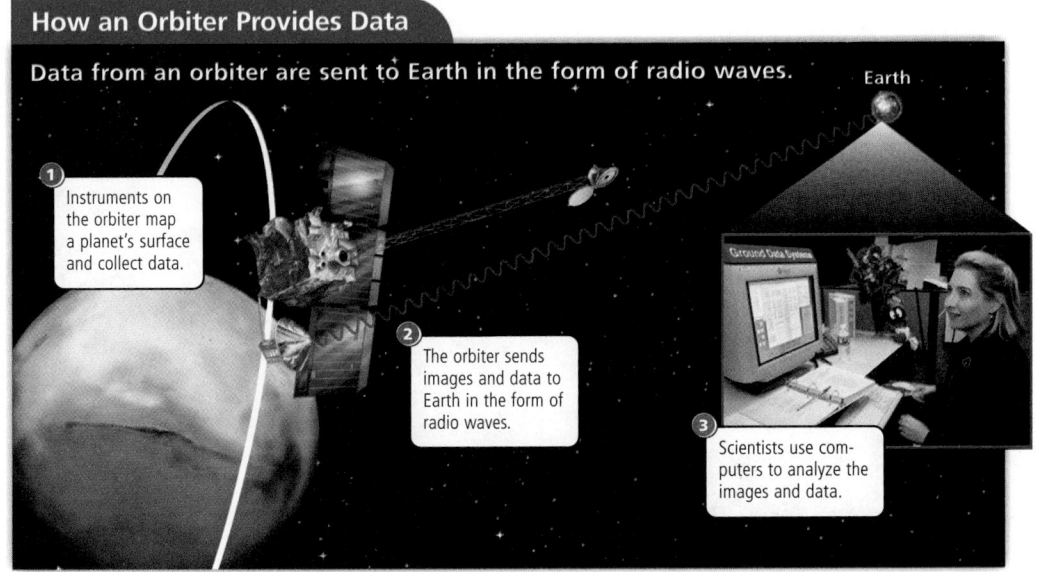

How an Orbiter Provides Data

Data from an orbiter are sent to Earth in the form of radio waves.

Earth

1. Instruments on the orbiter map a planet's surface and collect data.

2. The orbiter sends images and data to Earth in the form of radio waves.

Ground Data System

3. Scientists use computers to analyze the images and data.

DIFFERENTIATE INSTRUCTION

? More Reading Support

H What slows down an orbiter as it approaches a target planet? *rocket engines*

English Learners Pair two or three English learners who speak the same native language. Have them study the "Landing Sequence" diagram on p. 28. After discussing the steps together in their native language, they should each write a short paragraph in English describing the steps of the landing sequence. They may also repeat the steps aloud in English. Then pair English learners with more advanced students so they can learn and practice model English.

Language Arts Connection

Students may be confused by the word *orbit* because it is used as both a noun and a verb. Also, some students may have difficulty distinguishing the word *orbiter.* Clarify by holding a model orbiter, such as a coin, in one hand and a model planet, such as a globe, in the other. Move the orbiter toward the planet but not in orbit. Ask: Is the orbiter orbiting the planet? *no* Is the orbiter in orbit? *no* Then move the orbiter in orbit around the planet and repeat each question.

Teach from Visuals

To help students interpret the diagram of an orbiter mission, ask:

• What form of electromagnetic radiation is used to communicate between the spacecraft and people on Earth? *radio waves*

• How does the path of the orbiter in this diagram differ from the path of the flyby in the diagram on p. 26? *The orbiter is moving around one planet; the flyby is passing several planets.*

• Why is there only one planet in this diagram, while there are several planets in the diagram for a flyby on p. 26? *Orbiters remain near one planet for a length of time.*

Ongoing Assessment

Explain how different types of spacecraft are used in exploration.

Why is using an orbiter a good way to analyze weather? *Orbiters can track changes that occur over time because they can orbit a planet for several years.*

CHECK YOUR READING *Answer: A flyby spacecraft passes several planets and does not remain near one for long; an orbiter remains near one planet for a long period of time.*

Develop Critical Thinking

PROVIDE EXAMPLES Have students provide examples of why it is important to first do flyby and orbiting missions before sending a lander mission to a planet. *The planet may have features or conditions that would doom a landing mission to failure unless they were known and prepared for. Also, flyby and orbiting missions let scientists know where the lander should land and what types of experiments to design for the lander to conduct.*

Teach from Visuals

To help students interpret the diagram of a lander, ask:

- How does a planet's atmosphere slow down a spacecraft? *The gas particles in the atmosphere cause friction on the spacecraft.*

- How does the lander survive the bouncy landing? *Air bags are inflated before landing.*

- What are some things that can go wrong with a lander during a mission? *The parachute might not deploy, air bags might not inflate, some air bags might be punctured upon landing, the air bags might not deflate and release the lander, the rover might be damaged during the flight or landing.*

Landers and Probes

The third stage in space exploration is to land instruments on a planet or to send instruments through its atmosphere. Such a mission can tell us more about the features and properties of a planet. It can also provide clues to what the planet was like in the past.

A **lander** is a craft designed to land on a planet's surface. After a lander touches down, controllers on Earth can send it commands to collect data. Landers have been placed successfully on the Moon, Venus, and Mars. Some have operated for months or years at a time.

The images taken by a lander are more detailed than those taken by an orbiter. In addition to providing close-up views of a planet's surface, a lander can measure properties of the planet's atmosphere and surface. A lander may have a mechanical arm for gathering soil and rock samples. It may also contain a small vehicle called a rover, which can explore beyond the landing site.

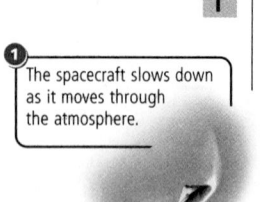

1 The spacecraft slows down as it moves through the atmosphere.

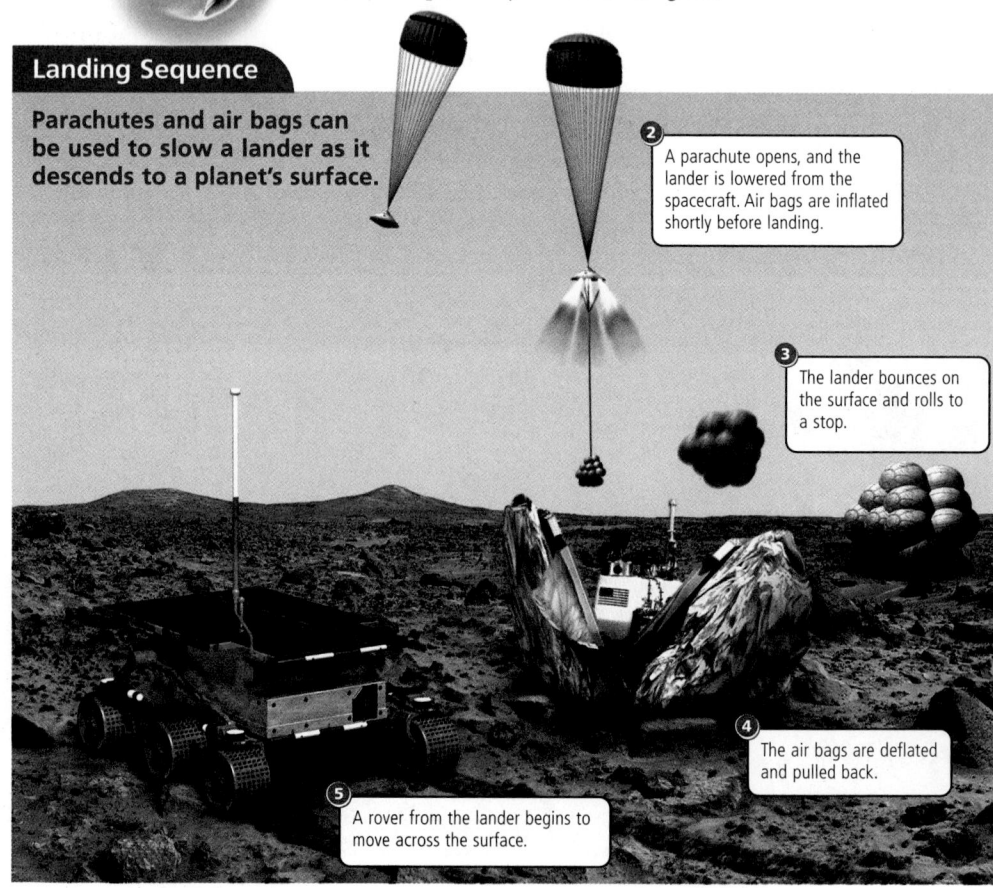

Landing Sequence

Parachutes and air bags can be used to slow a lander as it descends to a planet's surface.

2 A parachute opens, and the lander is lowered from the spacecraft. Air bags are inflated shortly before landing.

3 The lander bounces on the surface and rolls to a stop.

4 The air bags are deflated and pulled back.

5 A rover from the lander begins to move across the surface.

DIFFERENTIATE INSTRUCTION

? More Reading Support

I What bodies in space have been reached by landers? *the Moon, Venus, and Mars*

Advanced Challenge students to design part of a training mission for a future lander. They might use a remote-controlled car as a model rover and devise a way of collecting samples or drilling in rock to get deeper samples. Have students design solutions to any obstacles their rover encounters, such as uneven terrain.

One of the most successful space missions was that of *Mars Pathfinder*, which landed on Mars in 1997. *Mars Pathfinder* and its rover sent back thousands of photographs. These images provided evidence that water once flowed over the surface of Mars. Unfortunately, another lander, sent two years later, failed to work after it reached Mars.

Some spacecraft are designed to work only for a short time before they are destroyed by conditions on a planet. The term **probe** is often used to describe a spacecraft that drops into a planet's atmosphere. As the probe travels through the atmosphere, its instruments identify gases and measure properties such as pressure and temperature. Probes are especially important for exploring the deep atmospheres of giant planets, such as Jupiter.

 **CHECK YOUR READING** What is the difference between a probe and a lander?

Combining Missions

A lander or a probe can work in combination with an orbiter. For example, in 1995 the orbiter *Galileo* released a probe into Jupiter's atmosphere as it began orbiting the planet. The probe sent data back to the orbiter for nearly an hour before it was destroyed. The orbiter passed the data on to Earth. *Galileo* continued to orbit Jupiter for eight years.

Future space missions may involve even more complex combinations of spacecraft. Planners hope to send groups of landers to collect soil and rock samples from the surface of Mars. A rocket will carry these samples to an orbiter. The orbiter will then bring the samples to Earth for study.

1.3 Review

KEY CONCEPTS

1. Why are space stations important for scientific research?
2. How is information sent between Earth and a spacecraft?
3. What are the three main stages in exploring a planet?

CRITICAL THINKING

4. **Analyze** Why is most space exploration accomplished with spacecraft that do not have astronauts on board?
5. **Infer** Why is it important to map a planet's surface before planning a lander mission?

CHALLENGE

6. **Predict** Early space exploration was influenced by political events, such as the rivalry between the United States and the Soviet Union. What circumstances on Earth might interfere with future space missions?

Chapter 1: **Exploring Space 29** **E**

ANSWERS

1. Space stations allow astronauts to conduct experiments in space for long periods.

2. through radio waves

3. sending spacecraft to fly by the planet, moving a spacecraft into orbit around the planet, and landing a spacecraft on the planet or sending a probe through its atmosphere

4. A spacecraft without a crew is less expensive and safer to operate, and it can visit planets where humans cannot go.

5. The mapping identifies locations that allow for a safe landing and that have interesting features to study.

6. Political conflict might discourage nations from cooperating in projects; economic problems might make it harder to fund space exploration.

Ongoing Assessment

 Answer: A probe travels through a planet's atmosphere until it is destroyed. A lander is designed to land safely on a planet.

Reinforce (the BIG idea)

Have students relate the section to the Big Idea.

R Reinforcing Key Concepts, p. 43

 **1.3 ASSESS & RETEACH**

Assess

A Section 1.3 Quiz, p. 5

Reteach

Have students work in pairs to develop headlines for news stories on each of the accomplishments described in the text. For example,

- The Space Age Begins
- We Reach the Moon
- Cooperation in Space
- A New Look at Mars

Collect the headlines and write some on the board. Discuss which accomplishment is being proclaimed. Then have students add a topic sentence for each headline. Topic sentences should summarize the text and grab the attention of a reader.

Technology Resources

Have students visit **ClassZone.com** for reteaching of Key Concepts.

 CONTENT REVIEW

 CONTENT REVIEW CD-ROM

Chapter 1 **29** **E**

MATH IN SCIENCE
Math Skills Practice for Science

Set Learning Goal
To use exponents to represent the large distances in space

Present the Science
Explain that exponents are used in a method of expressing values called scientific notation. Scientists often use this method as a shorthand way of writing very large numbers (such as distances in space) or very small numbers (such as diameters of atoms).

Develop Number Sense
Suggest that students count the zeroes in groups of three, starting from the far right. They should double-check their counts because it is easy to make an error when counting so many zeroes.

DIFFERENTIATION TIP Explain that the complete form of scientific notation uses a number between one and ten multiplied by a power of ten in exponential form. So 10,000 or 10^4 is written as 1×10^4. Challenge students to write these numbers in full scientific notation:

40,000,000 4×10^7

12,300,000 1.23×10^7

800,780,000,000,000 8.0078×10^{14}

Close
What are the advantages of using exponents? *It is easier and less time-consuming than writing out strings of zeroes.*

- Math Support, p. 60
- Math Practice, p. 61

Technology Resources
Students can visit **ClassZone.com** to practice using exponents.

 MATH TUTORIAL

MATH in SCIENCE

MATH TUTORIAL
CLASSZONE.COM
Click on Math Tutorial for more help with powers and exponents.

Galaxy M83, which is roughly the same size as the Milky Way, has a diameter of about 10^{18} kilometers.

SKILL: USING EXPONENTS

Distances in Space

Astronomers often deal with very large numbers. For example, the planet Venus is about 100 million kilometers from the Sun. Written out, 100 million is 100,000,000. To use fewer zeros and to make the number easier to write and read, you could write 100 million as 10^8, which is the same value in exponent form.

> #### Example
>
> **PROBLEM** Write 1000 km, using an exponent.
>
> To find the exponent of a number, you can write the number as a product. For example,
>
> **1000 km = 10 × 10 × 10 km**
>
> This product has 3 factors of 10. When whole numbers other than zero are multiplied together, each number is a factor of the product. To write a product that has a repeated factor, you can use an exponent. The exponent is the number of times the factor is repeated. With factors of 10, you can also determine the exponent by counting the zeros in the given number.
>
> There are 3   The factor 10 is
> zeros in 1000.   repeated 3 times.
>
> **1000 = 10 × 10 × 10**
>
> **ANSWER** The exponent form of 1000 km is 10^3 km.

Write each distance, using an exponent.

1. 10,000 km

2. 1,000,000 km

3. 100,000,000,000 km

4. 10,000,000,000,000 km

5. 100,000,000,000,000,000 km

6. 10 km

CHALLENGE The galaxy shown on this page is about 10^{18} kilometers across. Write the value of 10^{18} without using an exponent.

ANSWERS

1. 10^4 km

2. 10^6 km

3. 10^{11} km

4. 10^{13} km

5. 10^{17} km

6. 10^1 km

CHALLENGE $10 \times 10 \times 10 \times 10 \times 10 \times 10 \times 10 \times 10 \times 10 \times 10 \times 10 \times 10 \times 10 \times 10 \times 10 \times 10 \times 10 \times 10 = 1,000,000,000,000,000,000$

KEY CONCEPT

1.4 Space exploration benefits society.

◀ **BEFORE, you learned**

- Light and other radiation carry information about space
- Astronauts explore space near Earth

▶ **NOW, you will learn**

- How space exploration has helped us to learn more about Earth
- How space technology is used on Earth

VOCABULARY

impact crater p. 32

THINK ABOUT

How does Earth look from space?

This photograph of Earth over the Moon was taken by the crew of *Apollo 8*. The Apollo missions provided the first images of our planet as a whole. What do you think we can learn about Earth from photographs taken from space?

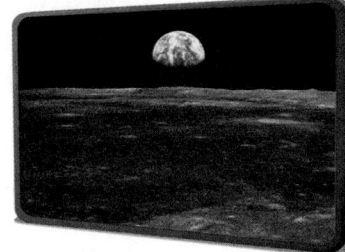

MAIN IDEA WEB

Record in your notes important information that space exploration has provided about Earth.

Space exploration has given us new viewpoints.

Space exploration enriches us in many ways. Throughout history, the study of stars and planets has inspired new ideas. As we meet the challenges of space exploration, we gain valuable technology. Space exploration is also an exciting adventure.

Space science has advanced knowledge in other scientific fields, such as physics. For example, observations of the Moon and other bodies in space helped scientists understand how gravity works. Scientists figured out that the same force that causes an object to fall to the ground causes the Moon to orbit Earth.

Finally, the study of other worlds can teach us about our own. Earth has changed considerably since its formation. By comparing Earth with different worlds, scientists can learn more about the history of Earth's surface features and atmosphere.

 **CHECK YOUR READING** Identify some benefits of space exploration.

Chapter 1: **Exploring Space** 31 **E**

1.4 FOCUS

▶ **Set Learning Goals**

Students will

- Explain how space exploration has helped us to learn more about Earth.
- Identify how space technology is used on Earth.
- Predict the effects of weathering in an experiment.

◀ **3-Minute Warm-Up**

Display Transparency 5 or copy this exercise on the board:

Identify the purpose of each type of mission.

- flyby *pass by one or more planets*
- orbiter *orbit a planet and study it over a long period*
- lander *land instruments on a planet*
- space station *allow people to live and work in space*

T 3-Minute Warm-Up, p. T5

1.4 MOTIVATE

THINK ABOUT

PURPOSE To introduce the idea that we can learn about Earth by viewing it from space

DISCUSS Show students other pictures of Earth taken from space. Ask students to identify the noticeable features such as oceans and continents as well as clouds and storms.

Possible answer: Photographs can provide information about weather, such as the location and path of storms. They can show how changes on Earth—such as the smoke from a volcanic eruption or forest fire—might affect areas far away.

Ongoing Assessment

 CHECK YOUR READING *Answer: inspired new ideas, given us valuable technology, enhanced knowledge in various scientific fields, and helped us learn about Earth's development*

RESOURCES FOR DIFFERENTIATED INSTRUCTION

Below Level

UNIT RESOURCE BOOK

- Reading Study Guide A, pp. 46–47
- Decoding Support, p. 59

 **AUDIO CDS**

Advanced

UNIT RESOURCE BOOK

Challenge and Extension, p. 52

English Learners

UNIT RESOURCE BOOK

Spanish Reading Study Guide, pp. 50–51

 **AUDIO CDS**

- Audio Readings in Spanish
- Audio Readings (English)

Teach from Visuals

To help students interpret the visuals of a crater, ask:

• What happens to the object as it strikes the surface? *It explodes.*

• What processes are involved in the formation of a crater after the object hits the surface? *exploding, compressing, fracturing, springing back, material being thrown off*

• What can you compare Wolf Creek Crater with in order to get a better idea of its size? *It is more than nine times longer than a football field.*

Develop Critical Thinking

COMPARE AND CONTRAST Have students contrast an impact crater and a crater caused by a volcano. *Craters of volcanoes are caused by eruptions of material from beneath Earth's surface or by the collapse of part of the volcano, not by an impact from above.*

Ongoing Assessment

Explain how space exploration has helped us to learn more about Earth.

Why do you think the blue heading for this section includes the word *viewpoints*? *Space exploration has allowed us to look at Earth in new ways.*

CHECK YOUR READING *Answer: They have learned about impact craters, the effect of liquid water on the development of the atmosphere, and how changes visible on the Sun's surface can cause periods of cooling.*

Formation of a Crater

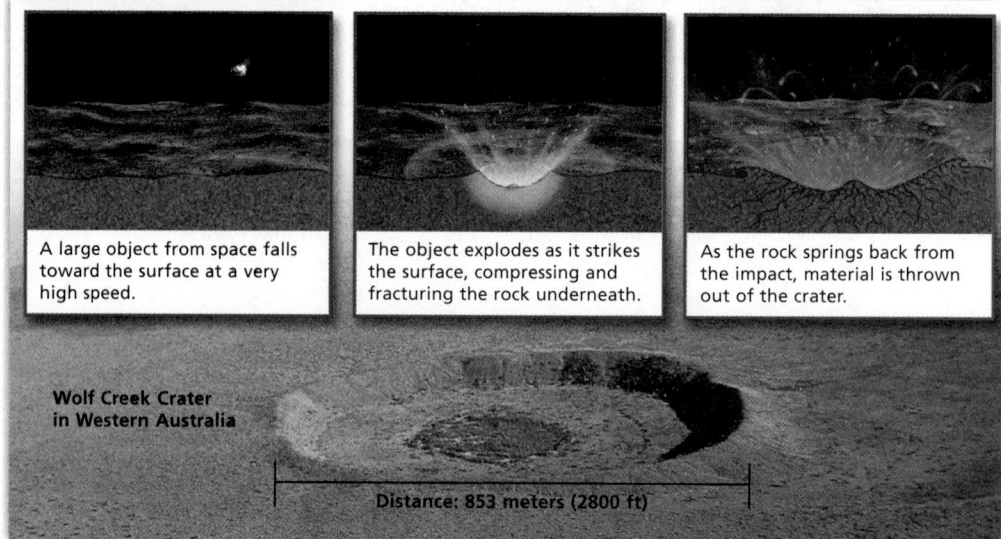

A large object from space falls toward the surface at a very high speed.

The object explodes as it strikes the surface, compressing and fracturing the rock underneath.

As the rock springs back from the impact, material is thrown out of the crater.

Wolf Creek Crater in Western Australia

Distance: 853 meters (2800 ft)

Surface Features

Exploration of other worlds has helped us learn about the impacts of space objects. When an object strikes the surface of a larger object in space, it explodes and leaves behind a round pit called an **impact crater.** The illustration above shows how an impact crater forms.

 Earth has little evidence of impacts because its surface is constantly being worn down by wind and water and altered by forces beneath the surface. However, impact craters remain on the Moon, Mercury, and many other bodies that have no wind or liquid water.

Atmosphere

We are also learning about Earth's atmosphere from space exploration. Earth's temperature allows liquid water to remain on the surface. Mars and Venus, the planets closest to Earth, have no liquid water on their surfaces. By comparing Earth with those planets, we can see how liquid water has affected the development of Earth's atmosphere.

 Another area of study involves the energy Earth receives from the Sun. Many scientists think that small changes visible on the Sun's surface can affect weather on Earth. These changes may have caused periods of cooling in Earth's atmosphere.

 **CHECK YOUR READING** What have scientists learned about Earth's past from studying bodies in space?

 **More Reading Support**

A What has Earth's weather prevented? *evidence of impact*

B From where does Earth receive energy? *the Sun*

English Learners Make sure students understand the imperative mood used in "Investigate Weathering" on p. 33 and recognize that "you" is the subject of the sentence even if only implied. If students have trouble following directions, have them read each step out loud, preceding it with "You." For example, "You fill a shoebox lid halfway . . ." (p. 33) and so on.

INVESTIGATE Weathering

How does weather affect evidence of impacts on Earth?

PROCEDURE

1. Fill a shoebox lid halfway with sand, and smooth the surface with a ruler.

2. Create three craters by dropping a golf ball into the sand from a height of 70 cm. Remove the ball carefully. Leave the lid inside the classroom.

3. Repeat steps 1 and 2 outdoors, leaving the lid in an area where it will be exposed to the weather.

4. Check both lids after 24 hours. Observe changes in each one.

WHAT DO YOU THINK?

- How did the craters in the sand that you left outdoors differ in appearance from the craters in the sand that remained inside?

- What aspect of weather caused any differences you observed?

CHALLENGE What natural processes besides weather can affect evidence of impacts from space objects on Earth?

SKILL FOCUS
Predicting

MATERIALS
- 2 shoebox lids
- sand
- ruler
- golf ball

TIME
30 minutes

Space technology has practical uses.

Space exploration has done more than increase our knowledge. It has also provided us with technology that makes life on Earth easier. Each day you probably benefit from some material or product that was developed for the space program.

Satellite Views of Earth

One of the most important benefits of space exploration has been the development of satellite technology. Satellites collect data from every region of our planet. The data are sent to receivers on Earth and converted into images. Scientists have learned from the space program how to enhance such images to gain more information.

Weather satellites show conditions throughout Earth's atmosphere. Images and data from weather satellites have greatly improved weather forecasting. Scientists can now provide warnings of dangerous storms long before they strike populated areas.

Other satellites collect images of Earth's surface to show how it is being changed by natural events and human activity. Satellite data are also used for wildlife preservation, conservation of natural resources, and mapping.

PURPOSE To predict how weathering affects evidence of impacts from space objects on Earth

TIPS *30 min.*

- A small ball or large marble can be substituted for the golf ball.

- Be sure students do not put their heads close to the sand when the ball is being dropped so that sand doesn't splash into their eyes.

- The lids both indoors and outdoors should be placed where no one will disturb them.

WHAT DO YOU THINK? *Weather will probably have at least partially worn away the craters in the lid left outdoors, but the craters that remained indoors will not have changed. Wind and precipitation could have caused differences in the outdoor craters.*

CHALLENGE *Volcanoes, earthquakes, and other tectonic forces can affect craters on Earth.*

 Datasheet, Weathering, p. 53

Technology Resources

Customize this student lab as needed or look for an alternative. Print rubrics to assess student lab reports.

Lab Generator CD-ROM

Real World Example

One example of the benefits of satellite technology is the Global Positioning System (GPS). This system uses 24 satellites, enough so that several of them are always in range of a GPS receiver. By timing how long it takes to receive signals from different satellites, the receiver can calculate its own position anywhere on Earth. GPS was originally developed to track military positions, but it is now also used by mapmakers, fire and police departments for rescue, public transportation systems, trucking companies, taxis, fishing boats, and hikers.

DIFFERENTIATE INSTRUCTION

More Reading Support

C Name at least two uses of satellite technology.
weather forecasting, protection of wildlife, conservation, mapping

Alternative Assessment Instead of writing answers to the questions for "Investigate Weathering," students can draw before and after views of the craters in both lids.

Advanced

 Challenge and Extension, p. 52

Ongoing Assessment

Identify how space technology is used on Earth.

How have satellites affected life on Earth? *Satellites provide information for forecasting weather, for detecting atmospheric changes and trends, for mapping, and for monitoring hazards.*

Reinforce (the **BIG** idea)

Have students relate the section to the Big Idea.

 Reinforcing Key Concepts, p. 54

1.4 ASSESS & RETEACH

Assess

 Section 1.4 Quiz, p. 6

Reteach

Revisit the list of space missions in the warm-up exercise at the beginning of this section. Ask students to explain how each type of space mission could provide a benefit on Earth. Have students cover the following benefits:

• knowledge about Earth's surface features and atmosphere
• satellite technology
• technology spinoffs

Technology Resources

Have students visit **ClassZone.com** for reteaching of Key Concepts.

 CONTENT REVIEW

 CONTENT REVIEW CD-ROM

Technology Spinoffs

Have you ever come up with a new way to use something that was designed for a different purpose? NASA often creates advanced technology to meet the special demands of space travel. Many spinoffs of technology from the space program can be found in homes, offices, schools, and hospitals.

NASA designers helped develop a system that allows this boy to communicate by using eye movements.

Everything on a spacecraft must be as small and lightweight as possible because the heavier a spacecraft is, the more difficult it is to launch. Design techniques developed to meet this need have improved devices used on Earth, such as tools for diagnosing diseases and devices that help people overcome disabilities.

Materials and parts on a spacecraft have to endure harsh conditions, such as extreme heat and cold. Many new homes and buildings contain fire-resistant materials developed for the space program. Firefighters wear protective suits made from fabric originally used in space suits. NASA has also helped design devices that allow firefighters to avoid injury from inhaling smoke.

Humans need a safe environment in spacecraft and space stations. NASA has developed systems for purifying air, water, and food. These systems now help protect people on Earth as well as in space.

1.4 Review

KEY CONCEPTS

1. How has space exploration helped us learn about impacts of space objects on Earth?
2. How do satellites provide images of Earth's surface and atmosphere?
3. Give two examples of technology we use on Earth that is a result of space exploration.

CRITICAL THINKING

4. **Infer** Hurricanes form in the middle of the ocean. Why would satellites be useful in tracking hurricanes?
5. **Apply** What space-technology spinoffs might be used in a school?

⚫ CHALLENGE

6. **Predict** It takes over a year for a spacecraft to reach Mars and return to Earth. If astronauts ever travel to Mars, they will need a spacecraft that can recycle air and water. How might such technology be adapted for use on Earth?

E 34 Unit: **Space Science**

ANSWERS

1. Other worlds that lack wind and water have much more evidence of impacts than Earth does.

2. They collect data from Earth's surface and send the data to receivers on Earth, where the data are converted to images.

3. Answers might include satellites, medical devices, fire-resistant materials, fire-fighting equipment, and purification systems.

4. Satellites can monitor activity in unpopulated areas.

5. Answers should reflect an understanding of the qualities that are important in technology used in space.

6. The technology might be used to solve pollution problems and water scarcities in parts of the world.

How Earth's Gravity Affects Plants

One of the most important issues in biology is understanding how plants grow. By applying the results of research on this issue, American farmers now grow twice as much food as they did 50 years ago.

One aspect of plant growth is the direction in which plants grow. After a plant sprouts from a seed, some of its cells form a shoot that grows upward. Other cells grow downward, becoming roots. How does this happen? Biologists think that plants usually respond to signals from the Sun and from the force of gravity.

Gravity and Plant Growth

To test the importance of sunlight, biologists can grow plants in the dark on Earth. Testing the impact of gravity, though, is more difficult. In 1997, a space shuttle carried moss plants into space. The plants grew for two weeks in microgravity, an environment in which objects are almost weightless. When the shuttle returned the plants to Earth, biologists studied how they had grown.

Prediction

Biologists had predicted that the moss would grow randomly. They expected that without signals from sunlight or the force of gravity, the moss would grow in no particular pattern.

Results

The biologists were surprised by what they saw. The moss had not grown randomly. Instead, the plants had spread out in a clear pattern. Each plant had formed a clockwise spiral.

The left-hand photograph shows moss growing on Earth. The right-hand photograph shows the same variety of moss growing in space. How do the mosses differ?

Significance

The moss experiment may be important for future space exploration. Can plants provide the food and oxygen that astronauts will need on long voyages to other planets? Experiments with moss are among the first steps in finding out.

EXPLORE

1. **PROVIDE EXAMPLES** Make a list of other spiral formations that occur in nature. Discuss why spirals may be common.
2. **CHALLENGE** Use library or Internet resources to learn about other experiments that test the effects of microgravity on plants and seeds.

Set Learning Goal

To explore the significance of doing experiments with plants in space

Present the Science

Scientists can create microgravity situations for research by using drop facilities. These enclosed towers allow objects to be in free fall for 5 to 10 seconds. Specially equipped airplanes create microgravity for 15 seconds at a time when they climb and descend steeply in a curved pattern. But these conditions do not last long enough to carry out long-term experiments involving plant growth.

Discussion Questions

- Ask: Why is it difficult to do experiments on Earth that involve microgravity and plant growth? *It is difficult to create conditions of microgravity on Earth for long enough to run experiments that involve plant growth.*

- How might plant experiments in space be helpful in planning a long space voyage? *Experiments may show whether plants can grow well enough to provide food and oxygen for astronauts on long voyages.*

DIFFERENTIATION TIP Some students may not understand the concept of microgravity. Ask if they have ever felt a sudden drop while in a fast-moving elevator, while driving over a small hill on the road, or while jumping off a diving board. If so, they have experienced to some degree the feeling of "weightlessness" that occurs in microgravity.

Close

What other kinds of experiments do you think would be interesting to conduct in the microgravity of space? *experiments involving the manufacture of materials, the growth of crystals, and the effects of gravity on the human body*

EXPLORE

1. *PROVIDE EXAMPLES Galaxies, tornadoes, whirlpools, DNA molecules, snail shells, and some flowers have spiral shapes. They might result from an interaction between two forces, one pushing outward and one pushing inward.*

2. *CHALLENGE Some experiments have tested the effects of microgravity on the growth of potatoes, mutations in seeds, and the ability of wheat to produce oxygen.*

BACK TO

the BIG idea

Have students choose one of the technological developments discussed in the chapter and explain how this development has improved our knowledge of space. *Sample answer: The development of space telescopes has allowed us to obtain clearer images of space objects because Earth's atmosphere does not interfere with light that the telescopes gather.*

◐ KEY CONCEPTS SUMMARY

SECTION 1.1
Ask: How would the stars that form the shape in this constellation appear if viewed from a different angle? *They would not appear grouped together in the same pattern.*

SECTION 1.2
Ask: How are the two telescopes alike? *Both produce images by gathering electromagnetic radiation from space.* How do they differ from each other? *The reflecting telescope on the left gathers visible light, infrared radiation, or ultraviolet radiation with a curved mirror. The radio telescope on the right gathers radio waves with a metal dish.*

SECTION 1.3
Ask: What explorations are usually done before a rover can be landed on another planet? *A spacecraft gains information about the planet while passing it on a flyby mission, and an orbiter maps the planet's surface.*

SECTION 1.4
Ask: What are some ways that space technology helps us on Earth? *improving and developing devices to diagnose diseases and to help people overcome disabilities; fire-resistant materials; systems for purifying air, water, and food*

Review Concepts

- Big Idea Flow Chart, p. T1
- Chapter Outline, pp. T7–T8

---

1 Chapter Review

the BIG idea
People develop and use technology to explore and study space.

 **CONTENT REVIEW**
CLASSZONE.COM

◐ KEY CONCEPTS SUMMARY

 Some space objects are visible to the human eye.

- Gravity causes objects in space to be grouped together in different ways.
- Stars form patterns in the sky.
- The sky seems to turn as Earth rotates.

VOCABULARY
orbit p. 10
solar system p. 10
galaxy p. 10
universe p. 10
constellation p. 12

 Telescopes allow us to study space from Earth.

Each form of electromagnetic radiation provides different information about objects in space. Astronomers use different types of telescopes to gather visible light and other forms of radiation.

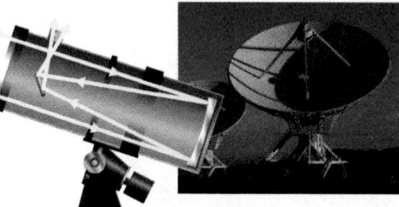

VOCABULARY
electromagnetic radiation p. 15
spectrum p. 16
wavelength p. 16
telescope p. 17

 Spacecraft help us explore beyond Earth.

Astronauts can explore space near Earth. Spacecraft without crews carry instruments to other worlds. A flyby mission usually provides data from several bodies in space. Orbiters, landers, and probes gather data from one planet or body.

VOCABULARY
satellite p. 23
space station p. 24
lander p. 28
probe p. 29

 Space exploration benefits society.

Space exploration has taught us about Earth's development. It has also provided technology that has important uses on Earth.

VOCABULARY
impact crater p. 32

Technology Resources

Have students visit **ClassZone.com** or use the CD-ROM for a cumulative review of concepts.

 CONTENT REVIEW

 CONTENT REVIEW CD-ROM

Engage students in a whole-class interactive review of Key Concepts. Edit content as you wish.

 POWER PRESENTATIONS

Reviewing Vocabulary

Write a definition of each word. Use the meaning of the underlined word part to help you.

Word	Root Meaning	Definition
EXAMPLE <u>satell</u>ite	person of lesser rank	an object that orbits a more massive object
1. <u>orb</u>it	circle	
2. <u>sol</u>ar system	Sun	
3. <u>uni</u>verse	one	
4. constel<u>lation</u>	star	
5. electromagnetic <u>radiation</u>	to emit rays	
6. <u>spect</u>rum	to look at	
7. <u>prob</u>e	test	
8. impact <u>crater</u>	bowl	

Reviewing Key Concepts

Multiple Choice *Choose the letter of the best answer.*

9. Stars in a galaxy are held together by
   a. light
   b. radiation
   c. gravity
   d. satellites

10. Astronomers use constellations to
    a. locate objects in the sky
    b. calculate the distances of objects
    c. calculate the masses of objects
    d. classify spectra

11. Stars rise and set in the night sky because
    a. Earth orbits the Sun
    b. Earth rotates
    c. the North Pole points toward Polaris
    d. the stars are moving in space

12. In the electromagnetic spectrum, different forms of radiation are arranged according to their
    a. colors
    b. distances
    c. wavelengths
    d. sizes

13. Astronomers often locate telescopes on mountains to
    a. lessen the interference of Earth's atmosphere
    b. save money on land
    c. keep their discoveries secret
    d. get closer to space objects

14. A reflecting telescope gathers light with a
    a. lens
    b. eyepiece
    c. refractor
    d. mirror

15. What was the goal of the Apollo program?
    a. to view Earth from space
    b. to explore the Sun
    c. to explore the Moon
    d. to explore other planets

16. Which type of mission produces detailed maps of a planet?
    a. flyby
    b. orbiter
    c. lander
    d. probe

17. What causes an impact crater to form on a planet's surface?
    a. Gravity pulls soil and rock downward.
    b. Wind and water wear away the surface.
    c. Forces beneath the surface push upward.
    d. An object from space strikes the surface.

Short Answer *Write a short answer to each question.*

18. Why is it easier to see the motions of planets than to see the motions of stars?

19. How do astronomers obtain most of their information about space?

20. How does the size of a telescope's main lens or mirror affect its performance?

21. Why have lightweight materials been developed for space travel?

Reviewing Vocabulary

1. the path of an object in space as it moves around another object due to gravity
2. the Sun and the planets, moons, and other objects that orbit it
3. space and all the matter and energy in it
4. a group of stars that form a pattern in the sky
5. energy that travels across distances as certain types of waves
6. the range of colors that appears in a beam of visible light when it passes through a prism
7. a spacecraft that drops into a planet's atmosphere
8. a round pit left behind when a smaller object strikes the surface of a larger object in space

Reviewing Key Concepts

9. c
10. a
11. b
12. c
13. a
14. d
15. c
16. b
17. d
18. It is easier to see the motions of nearby objects than those of distant objects.
19. by gathering electromagnetic radiation with telescopes
20. The larger the lens or mirror, the sharper and brighter the image.
21. It is expensive and difficult to lift heavy objects into space.

ASSESSMENT RESOURCES

UNIT ASSESSMENT BOOK
- Chapter Test, Level A, pp. 7–10
- Chapter Test, Level B, pp. 11–14
- Chapter Test, Level C, pp. 15–18
- Alternative Assessment, pp. 19–20

SPANISH ASSESSMENT BOOK
Spanish Chapter Test, pp. 193–196

Technology Resources

Edit test items and answer choices.

 Test Generator CD-ROM

Visit **ClassZone.com** to extend test practice.

 Test Practice

Thinking Critically

22. *both: gather radiation with curved surfaces; radio dish: gathers radio waves with a large, metal dish, can be combined to make clearer images; reflecting telescope: gathers visible light with a mirror, is affected by Earth's atmosphere*

23. *radio dish, because clouds do not block radio waves*

24. *Both are forms of radiation. Radio waves have longer wavelengths.*

25. *People in earlier times had no artificial lighting to interfere with their view of the night sky.*

26. *wouldn't have to be at the telescope's location to obtain an electronically recorded image, could analyze the data using computers*

27. *the risk to the lives of the astronauts and the greater expense of human exploration of space*

28. *The United States and the Soviet Union competed in Moon exploration. The United States, Russia, and other countries have worked together on the ISS.*

29. *Designers of space technology make extremely reliable devices that are as small as possible. These qualities would be desirable in such a medical device.*

30. *Students should provide logical reasons for their opinions.*

31. *Flyby: gathers information as it flies past each of the planets; Orbiter: goes into orbit around one of the planets and maps it; Lander or probe: lands on the surface or drops into the atmosphere*

the BIG idea

32. *Student responses should reflect what they have learned.*

33. *Students should provide logical reasons for their opinions.*

UNIT PROJECTS

Give students the appropriate Unit Project worksheets from the URB for their projects. Both directions and rubrics can be used as a guide.

 Unit Projects, pp. 5–10

Thinking Critically

Copy the Venn diagram below, and use it to help you answer the next two questions.

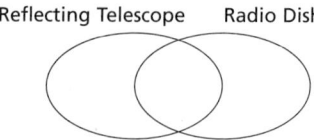

Reflecting Telescope   Radio Dish

22. **COMPARE AND CONTRAST** Fill in the Venn diagram to show similarities and differences between a reflecting telescope and a radio dish.

23. **APPLY** Suppose that you live in an area that has frequent storms. Which would be more suitable for your location, a reflecting telescope or a radio dish? Explain.

24. **COMPARE AND CONTRAST** What are the similarities and differences between visible light and radio waves?

25. **HYPOTHESIZE** Many of the constellations named by ancient peoples are now hard to see from populated areas. Why might it have been easier to see them hundreds or thousands of years ago?

26. **ANALYZE** What may be the advantages of electronically recording an image from a telescope instead of looking at the object directly through the telescope's eyepiece?

27. **SYNTHESIZE** Suppose it became possible to send astronauts to explore a nearby planet. What concerns would need to be taken into account before deciding whether to send a spacecraft with astronauts or a spacecraft with no crew aboard?

28. **COMPARE AND CONTRAST** Compare and contrast the development of the International Space Station with the Apollo missions to the Moon.

29. **ANALYZE** If you were designing a medical device to be implanted in a patient's body, why might you seek help from designers of space technology?

30. **EVALUATE** Do you think that the United States should continue to maintain its own space program, or should it combine its space program with the programs of other nations? Explain.

31. **SEQUENCE** Astronomers have learned that some stars other than the Sun have planets orbiting them. Imagine that you are planning a program to explore one of these planet systems. Copy the chart below. Use the chart to identify stages in the exploration of the system and to describe what would occur during each stage.

Stage of Exploration	Description

the BIG idea

32. **PROVIDE EXAMPLES** Look again at the photograph on pages 6–7. Now that you have finished the chapter, how would you change your response to the question on the photograph?

33. **EVALUATE** In the United States billions of dollars are spent each year on space exploration. Do you think that this expense is justified? Why or why not?

UNIT PROJECTS

If you are doing a unit project, make a folder for your project. Include in your folder a list of the resources you will need, the date on which the project is due, and a schedule to track your progress. Begin gathering data.

MONITOR AND RETEACH

If students have trouble applying the concepts in question 29, have them first consider what qualities an implanted medical device must have. Then have students review and summarize the material on p. 34.

Students may benefit from summarizing one or more sections of the chapter.

R Summarizing the Chapter, pp. 80–81

Standardized Test Practice

For practice on your state test, go to . . .
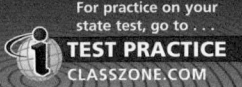
TEST PRACTICE
CLASSZONE.COM

Analyzing a Star Map

Use the star map to answer the next five questions.

1. Constellations are represented on the map as dots that are
   a. surrounded by planets
   b. grouped in a spiral pattern
   c. connected by lines
   d. scattered in a random pattern

2. How would a map showing the same portion of the sky two hours later compare with the map above?
   a. Almost all the space objects would have changed position noticeably.
   b. No space objects would have changed position.
   c. Only the moon would have changed position.
   d. Only the planets would have changed position.

3. Why would the map for two hours later be different from this map?
   a. The Moon is rotating on its axis.
   b. Earth is rotating on its axis.
   c. The solar system is part of the Milky Way.
   d. The planets move in relation to the stars.

4. A map showing the same portion of the sky exactly one year later would look very similar to this map. What would probably be different?
   a. the shapes of the constellations
   b. the names of the constellations
   c. the positions of the Moon and the planets
   d. the radiation of the stars

5. Which statement best describes the location of the stars shown on the map?
   a. They are outside the solar system but within the Milky Way galaxy.
   b. They are within the solar system.
   c. They are outside the Milky Way galaxy but within the universe.
   d. They are outside the universe.

Extended Response

Answer the two questions below in detail. Include some of the terms shown in the word box. In your answer, underline each term you use.

electromagnetic radiation	solar system
Milky Way	radio waves
universe	visible light

6. What is the relationship between Earth, our solar system, the Milky Way, and the universe?

7. What do visible-light telescopes and radio telescopes have in common? How are they different?

Analyzing a Star Map

1. *c*   3. *b*   5. *a*
2. *a*   4. *c*

Extended Response

6. RUBRIC
4 points for a response that correctly answers the question and uses the following terms accurately:
   • Milky Way
   • universe
   • solar system

Sample: Earth is one of nine major planets in the <u>solar system</u>, which is part of the <u>Milky Way</u>, which is one of billions of galaxies in the <u>universe</u>.

3 points correctly answers the question and uses two terms accurately
2 points partially answers the question and uses one term accurately
1 point partially answers the question, but does not use the terms

7. RUBRIC
4 points for a response that gives similarities and differences and uses the following terms accurately:
   • electromagnetic radiation
   • radio waves
   • visible light

Sample: Similarities: Visible-light telescopes and radio telescopes both collect <u>electromagnetic radiation</u>. Both also use curved surfaces that focus the waves being collected. Differences: Visible-light telescopes collect <u>visible light</u>, whereas radio telescopes collect <u>radio waves</u>. Radio telescopes can be grouped together to make images.

3 points correctly answers the question and uses two terms accurately
2 points partially answers the question and uses one term accurately
1 point partially answers the question, but does not use the terms

---

METACOGNITIVE ACTIVITY

Have students answer the following questions in their **Science Notebook:**

1. What further questions do you have about space exploration? What material in this chapter sparked these questions?

2. How do the concepts in this chapter relate to your life?

3. What topics in this chapter would you like to learn more about in your Unit Project?

CHAPTER 2 Earth, Moon, and Sun

Earth Science
UNIFYING PRINCIPLES

PRINCIPLE 1
Heat energy inside Earth and radiation from the Sun provide energy for Earth's processes.

PRINCIPLE 2
Physical forces, such as gravity, affect the movement of all matter on Earth and throughout the universe.

PRINCIPLE 3
Matter and energy move among Earth's rocks and soil, atmosphere, waters, and living things.

PRINCIPLE 4
Earth has changed over time and continues to change.

Unit: Space Science
BIG IDEAS

CHAPTER 1
Exploring Space
People develop and use technology to explore and study space.

CHAPTER 2
Earth, Moon, and Sun
Earth and the Moon move in predictable ways as they orbit the Sun.

CHAPTER 3
Our Solar System
Planets and other objects form a system around our Sun.

CHAPTER 4
Stars, Galaxies, and the Universe
Our Sun is one of billions of stars in one of billions of galaxies in the universe.

CHAPTER 2
KEY CONCEPTS

SECTION 2.1

Earth rotates on a tilted axis and orbits the Sun.

1. Earth's rotation causes day and night.

2. Earth's tilted axis and orbit cause seasons.

SECTION 2.2

The Moon is Earth's natural satellite.

1. The Moon rotates as it orbits Earth.

2. The Moon's craters show its history.

3. The Moon has layers.

SECTION 2.3

Positions of the Sun and Moon affect Earth.

1. Phases are different views of the Moon's sunlit half.

2. Shadows in space cause eclipses.

3. The Moon's gravity causes tides on Earth.

T The Big Idea Flow Chart is available on p. T9 in the **UNIT TRANSPARENCY BOOK.**

Previewing Content

2.1 Earth rotates on a tilted axis and orbits the Sun. pp. 43–51

1. Earth's rotation causes day and night.

Earth's gravity pulls objects nearby toward Earth's center. This defines the directions "up" and "down" locally—there is no natural up and down in the universe. Earth turns on an imaginary line through its center called an **axis of rotation.** Earth's rotation is used to define north and south (the poles), east, and west. At any one time, about half of Earth is in sunlight. Earth takes 24 hours to rotate once in an easterly direction, producing day and night.

2. Earth's tilted axis and orbit cause seasons.

At any given time, sunlight strikes different parts of Earth's curved surfaces at different angles. Sunlight is most concentrated where it strikes perpendicular to Earth's surface and least concentrated where it strikes almost parallel to Earth's surface, such as near the poles.

A **revolution** is the motion of one object around another. It takes Earth a year to revolve around, or orbit, the Sun. Earth's axis is tilted 23° relative to a line perpendicular to its orbit. Earth's axis points in a constant direction as Earth orbits the Sun.

The tilted axis and orbit cause **seasons,** or yearly patterns of temperature changes and other weather trends. When Earth is on one side of the Sun, the Northern Hemisphere (NH) receives more sunlight and experiences spring and summer. When Earth is on the other side of the Sun, the Southern Hemisphere (SH) receives more sunlight. The amount of sunlight is characterized by the length of daylight and the height of the Sun at noon. You might share the chart at right with students.

	December solstice	June solstice
Beginning of	winter in NH summer in SH	summer in NH winter in SH
Sunlight is more in	SH	NH
North Pole leans	away from the Sun	toward the Sun
North Pole is in	darkness	sunlight
In NH, days are	shorter	longer
In NH, noon Sun is	lower	higher

	September equinox	March equinox
Beginning of	fall in NH spring in SH	spring in NH fall in SH
Sunlight is	half in each hemisphere	
North Pole is	perpendicular to direction of the Sun	
North Pole enters	darkness	sunlight
Length of day is	about equal to length of night	
Noon Sun is	in the middle of its annual range	

Common Misconceptions

ABSOLUTE DIRECTION IN SPACE Students often think that "down" is a single uniform direction in space. Absolute directions do not exist in space. "Up" and "down" are based on the local direction of gravitational pull.

 This misconception is addressed in Teach Difficult Concepts on p. 45.

 MISCONCEPTION DATABASE
CLASSZONE.COM Background on student misconceptions

SEASONS Students may think that seasons are caused by Earth's changing distance from the Sun. Actually, Earth is closest to the Sun in January, when the Northern Hemisphere experiences winter. Seasons are caused by a combination of Earth's motion around the Sun and the tilt of Earth's axis.

 This misconception is addressed on p. 46.

Previewing Content

1. The Moon rotates as it orbits Earth.
The Moon rotates once on its axis each time it completes one revolution around Earth. Because the Moon's period of rotation and revolution are equal, only one side of the Moon can be seen from Earth.

2. The Moon's craters show its history.
Much of the Moon's surface consists of ancient, light-colored highlands. Some of the rock is as old as the Moon itself, about 4.5 billion years. Impacts from objects in space have formed craters on the Moon's surface, compressed or melted some rock, and produced finely broken rock called lunar soil. This breaking of rock on the Moon is called weathering in analogy to processes on Earth. Many large impacts occurred during a period early in the Moon's history. Later, smaller impacts softened or erased earlier craters.

The large, dark-colored areas of the Moon are lunar maria (singular *mare*). During a period from 3.8 to 3.1 billion years ago, molten rock from beneath the Moon's surface formed the maria. The molten rock, called lava at the surface, filled huge impact craters, cooled, and solidified into flat plains. The rock is basalt, similar to that beneath Earth's oceans.

3. The Moon has layers.
The Moon has a crust of relatively low-density rock, a mantle of more dense rock, and a small dense core that may consist largely of iron. The Moon may have formed when a smaller space body struck the young Earth. The material from both bodies formed a new Earth and an orbiting Moon, but little material from the original cores ended up in the Moon.

1. Phases are different views of the Moon's sunlit half.
The moon shines because its surface reflects sunlight. The position of the Moon relative to the Sun and Earth affects how it appears to an observer on Earth. During the first half of its monthly cycle, the Moon waxes from new, through increasing crescents, to first quarter, through increasing gibbous phases, to full. Then the Moon wanes from full, through gibbous, to third quarter, through crescent, to new. First quarter and third quarter describe points in the cycle rather than shapes.

The amount of the Moon seen from Earth depends on the angle between the Moon and the Sun. When the angle is small, only a small part of the moon is visible from Earth. A thin crescent moon appears near the Sun and thus is up mostly during daylight hours. When the angle is large, a large part of the Moon is visible from Earth. A full moon appears opposite the Sun and thus is up mostly at night.

2. Shadows in space cause eclipses.
An **eclipse** occurs when a shadow makes the Sun or the Moon seem to grow dark. During a lunar eclipse, the Moon becomes dark because it passes through Earth's shadow. The darkest part of the shadow is the **umbra.** The **penumbra** is the lighter shadow around the umbra. During a solar eclipse, the Sun appears to darken because the Moon's shadow falls onto part of Earth.

3. The Moon's gravity causes tides on Earth.
Tides occur because the Moon's gravity changes the shape of Earth's oceans. As a result, water level rises slowly, then sinks. The highest level is called high tide. The lowest level is called low tide. In a cycle that lasts a little more than 24 hours, most shorelines experience two high tides and two low tides.

Common Misconceptions

LUNAR PHASES Students may think that lunar phases are caused by Earth's shadow. They may not realize that moonlight is sunlight reflected by the Moon's surface and that the Moon's position in its monthly orbit determines how it appears from Earth.

 This misconception is addressed on p. 60.

 MISCONCEPTION DATABASE
CLASSZONE.COM Background on student misconceptions

Previewing Labs

Lab Generator CD-ROM
Edit these Pupil Edition labs and generate alternative labs.

EXPLORE (the BIG idea)

How Do Shadows Move? p. 41 Students observe shadows to see how the angle of sunlight changes throughout the day.	**TIME** 10 minutes **MATERIALS** sticky note, pencil, paper
What Makes the Moon Bright? p. 41 Students use a round object to see that sunlight illuminates that object and the Moon in the same way.	**TIME** 10 minutes **MATERIALS** round object
Internet Activity: Seasons, p. 41 Students use the Internet to investigate the causes and effects of seasons.	**TIME** 20 minutes **MATERIALS** computer with Internet access

SECTION 2.1

EXPLORE Time Zones, p. 43 Students identify and compare time zones. R Time Zone Map, p. 91	**TIME** 15 minutes **MATERIALS** Time Zone Map
INVESTIGATE Rotation, p. 44 Students model to observe how Earth's rotation to understand what causes day and night.	**TIME** 15 minutes **MATERIALS** lamp
CHAPTER INVESTIGATION **Modeling Seasons,** pp. 50–51 Students model seasons to determine how the angle of sunlight changes throughout a year.	**TIME** 40 minutes **MATERIALS** graph paper, flashlight, meter stick, protractor, globe, stack of books, sticky note

SECTION 2.2

EXPLORE The Moon's Motion, p. 52 Students model the Moon's movement around Earth.	**TIME** 15 minutes **MATERIALS** paper, magnetic compass
INVESTIGATE Moon Features, p. 55 Students infer how the Moon's features formed.	**TIME** 20 minutes **MATERIALS** 1/8 cup of liquid gelatin, clear plastic cup, paper towel, bowl of ice

SECTION 2.3

INVESTIGATE Phases of the Moon, p. 62 Students model phases of the Moon.	**TIME** 20 minutes **MATERIALS** foam ball, stick, lamp

R **Additional INVESTIGATION,** Making an Equatorial Sundial, A, B, & C, pp. 133–141; Teacher Instructions, pp. 287–288

Previewing Chapter Resources

	INTEGRATED TECHNOLOGY	LABS AND ACTIVITIES

CHAPTER 2
Earth, Moon, and Sun

 CLASSZONE.COM
- eEdition Plus
- EasyPlanner Plus
- Misconception Database
- Content Review
- Test Practice
- Visualizations
- Resource Centers
- Internet Activity: Seasons
- Math Tutorial

 SCILINKS.ORG
SCI LINKS

 CD-ROMS
- eEdition
- EasyPlanner
- Power Presentations
- Content Review
- Lab Generator
- Test Generator

 AUDIO CDS
- Audio Readings
- Audio Readings in Spanish

PE EXPLORE the Big Idea, p. 41
- How Do Shadows Move?
- What Makes the Moon Bright?
- Internet Activity: Seasons

R **UNIT RESOURCE BOOK**
Unit Projects, pp. 5–10

 Lab Generator CD-ROM
Generate customized labs.

SECTION
2.1 Earth rotates on a tilted axis and orbits the Sun.
pp. 43–51

Time: 3 periods (1.5 blocks)
 Lesson Plan, pp. 82–83

 RESOURCE CENTER, Seasons

T **UNIT TRANSPARENCY BOOK**
- Big Idea Flow Chart, p. T9
- Daily Vocabulary Scaffolding, p. T10
- Note-Taking Model, p. T11
- 3-Minute Warm-Up, p. T12
- "Seasons" Visual, p. T14

PE
- EXPLORE Time Zones, p. 43
- INVESTIGATE Rotation, p. 44
- CHAPTER INVESTIGATION, Modeling Seasons, pp. 50–51

R **UNIT RESOURCE BOOK**
- Time Zone Map, p. 91
- Datasheet, Rotation, p. 92
- CHAPTER INVESTIGATION, Modeling Seasons, A, B, & C, pp. 124–132
- Additional INVESTIGATION, Making an Equatorial Sundial, A, B, & C, pp. 133–141

SECTION
2.2 The Moon is Earth's natural satellite.
pp. 52–58

Time: 2 periods (1 block)
 Lesson Plan, pp. 94–95

 MATH TUTORIAL

T **UNIT TRANSPARENCY BOOK**
- Daily Vocabulary Scaffolding, p. T10
- 3-Minute Warm-Up, p. T12

PE
- EXPLORE The Moon's Motion, p. 52
- INVESTIGATE Moon Features, p. 55
- Math in Science, p. 58

R **UNIT RESOURCE BOOK**
- Datasheet, Moon Features, p. 103
- Math Support, pp. 121–122
- Math Practice, p. 123

SECTION
2.3 Positions of the Sun and Moon affect Earth.
pp. 59–67

Time: 3 periods (1.5 blocks)
 Lesson Plan, pp. 105–106

- **VISUALIZATION,** Lunar Phases
- **RESOURCE CENTER,** Tides

T **UNIT TRANSPARENCY BOOK**
- Big Idea Flow Chart, p. T9
- Daily Vocabulary Scaffolding, p. T10
- 3-Minute Warm-Up, p. T13
- Chapter Outline, pp. T15–T16

PE
- INVESTIGATE Phases of the Moon, p. 62
- Science on the Job, p. 67

R **UNIT RESOURCE BOOK**
Datasheet, Phases of the Moon, p. 114

READING AND REINFORCEMENT

ASSESSMENT

STANDARDS

- Frame Game, B26–27
- Combination Notes, C36
- Daily Vocabulary Scaffolding, H1–8

 UNIT RESOURCE BOOK
- Vocabulary Practice, pp. 118–119
- Decoding Support, p. 121
- Summarizing the Chapter, pp. 142–143

 Audio Readings CD
Listen to Pupil Edition.

 Audio Readings in Spanish CD
Listen to Pupil Edition in Spanish.

- Chapter Review, pp. 69–70
- Standardized Test Practice, p. 71

 UNIT ASSESSMENT BOOK
- Diagnostic Test, pp. 21–22
- Chapter Test, A, B, & C, pp. 26–37
- Alternative Assessment, pp. 38–39

 Spanish Chapter Test, pp. 197–200

 Test Generator CD-ROM
Generate customized tests.

 Lab Generator CD-ROM
Rubrics for Labs

National Standards
A.2–8, A.9.a–c, A.9.e–f, D.3.b–d

See p. 40 for the standards.

 UNIT RESOURCE BOOK
- Reading Study Guide, A & B. pp. 84–87
- Spanish Reading Study Guide, pp. 88–89
- Challenge and Extension, p. 90
- Reinforcing Key Concepts, p. 93

 Ongoing Assessment, pp. 43–44, 46–48

 Section 2.1 Review, p. 49

 UNIT ASSESSMENT BOOK
Section 2.1 Quiz, p. 23

National Standards
A.2–8, A.9.a–c, A.9.e–f, D.3.b–d

 UNIT RESOURCE BOOK
- Reading Study Guide, A & B. pp. 96–99
- Spanish Reading Study Guide, pp. 100–101
- Challenge and Extension, p. 102
- Reinforcing Key Concepts, p. 104
- Challenge Reading, pp. 116–117

 Ongoing Assessment, p. 53–57

 Section 2.2 Review, p. 57

 UNIT ASSESSMENT BOOK
Section 2.2 Quiz, p. 24

National Standards
A.2–8, A.9.a–c, A.9.e–f, D.3.b–c

 UNIT RESOURCE BOOK
- Reading Study Guide, A & B, pp. 107–110
- Spanish Reading Study Guide, pp. 111–112
- Challenge and Extension, p. 113
- Reinforcing Key Concepts, p. 115

 Ongoing Assessment, p. 59–63, 65–66

 Section 2.3 Review, p. 66

 UNIT ASSESSMENT BOOK
Section 2.3 Quiz, p. 25

National Standards
A.2–7, A.9.a–b, A.9.e–f, D.3.b–c

Previewing Resources for Differentiated Instruction

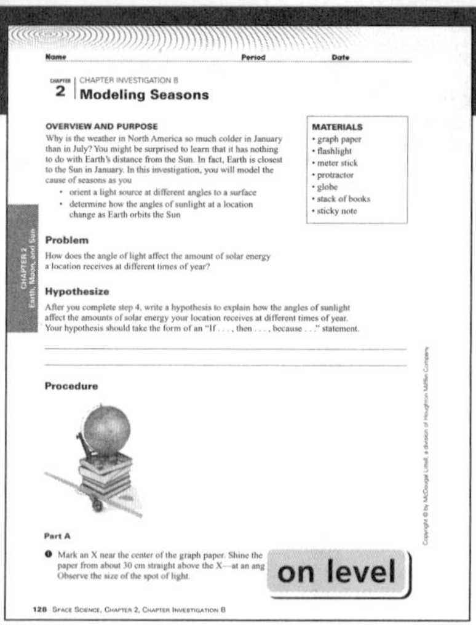

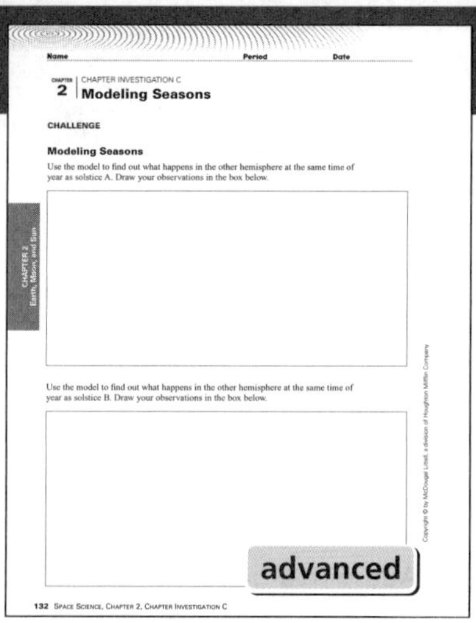

CHAPTER INVESTIGATION

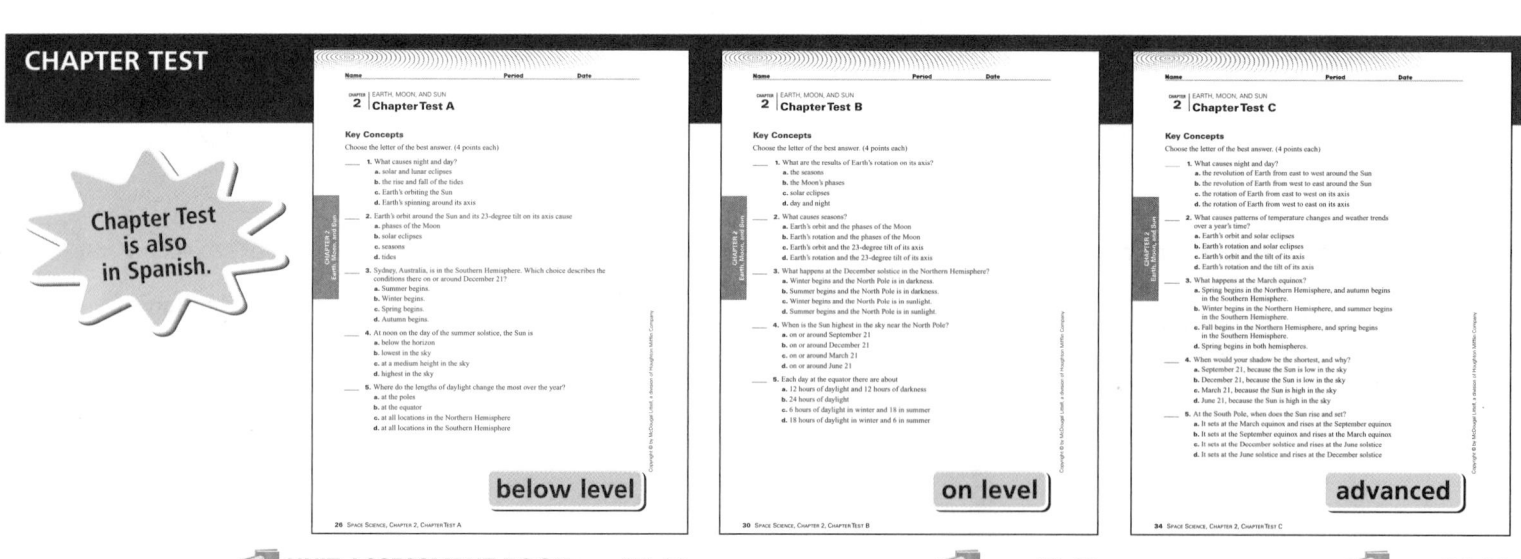

below level

on level

advanced

R **UNIT RESOURCE BOOK,** pp. 124–127   R pp. 128–131   R pp. 128–132

> Leveled resources present the same concepts for different abilities.

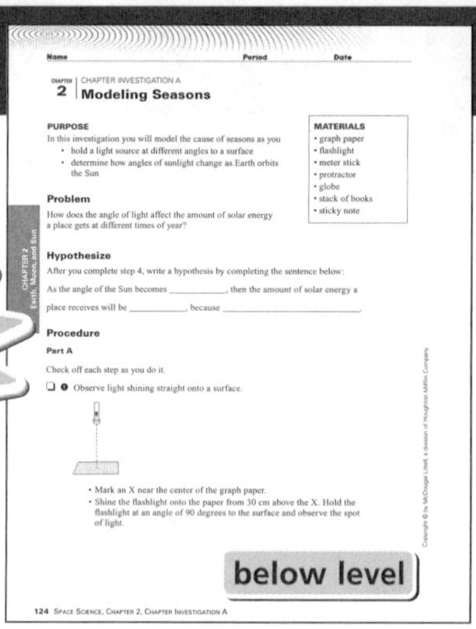

READING STUDY GUIDE

below level

on level

advanced

R **UNIT RESOURCE BOOK,** pp. 84–85   R pp. 86–87   R p. 90

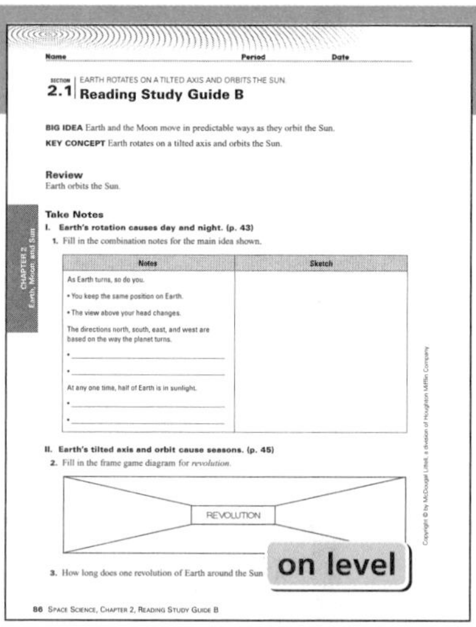

> Reading Study Guide is also in Spanish.

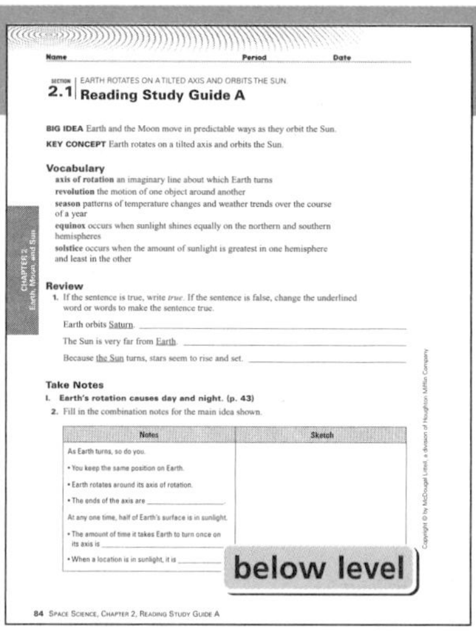

CHAPTER TEST

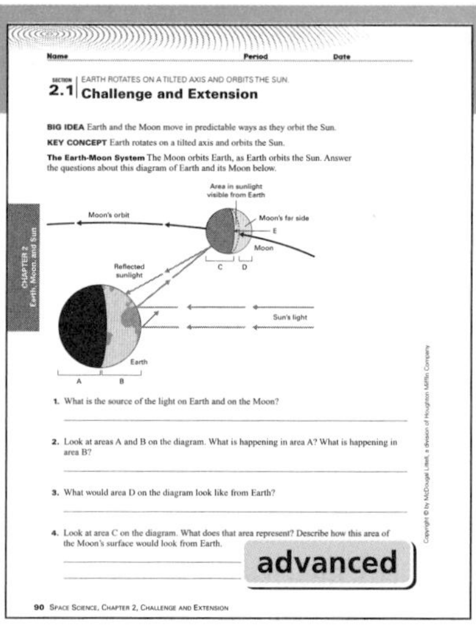

below level

on level

advanced

A **UNIT ASSESSMENT BOOK,** pp. 26–29   A pp. 30–33   A pp. 34–35

> Chapter Test is also in Spanish.

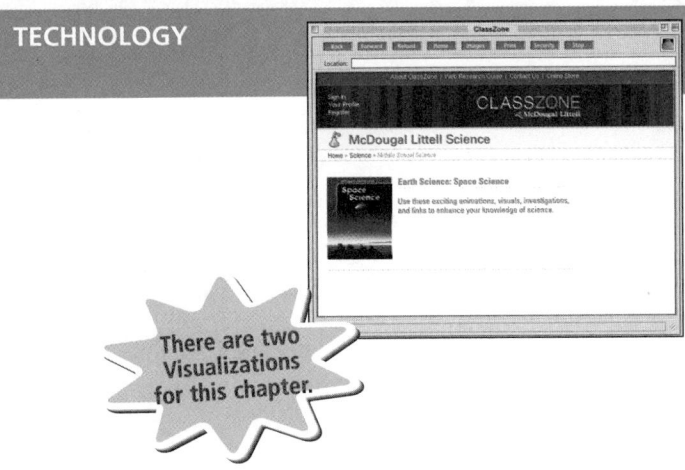

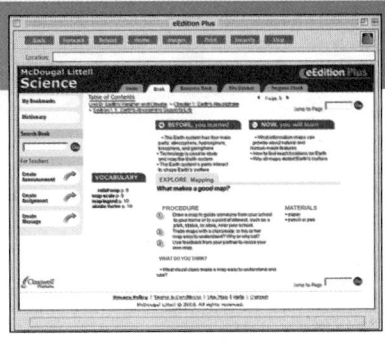

There are two Visualizations for this chapter.

CLASSZONE.COM   **CD/CD-ROMS**   **CLASSZONE.COM**

VISUAL CONTENT

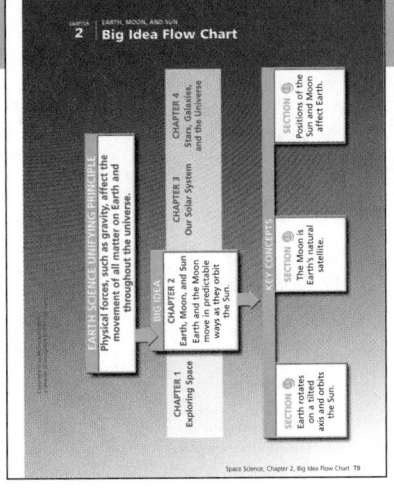

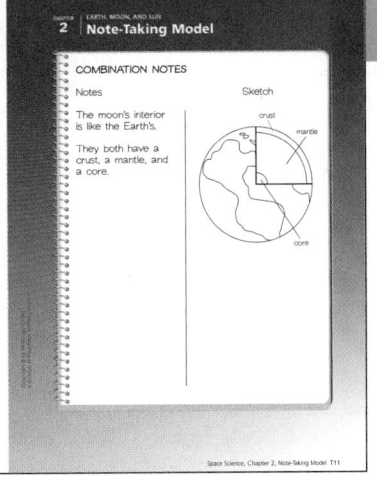

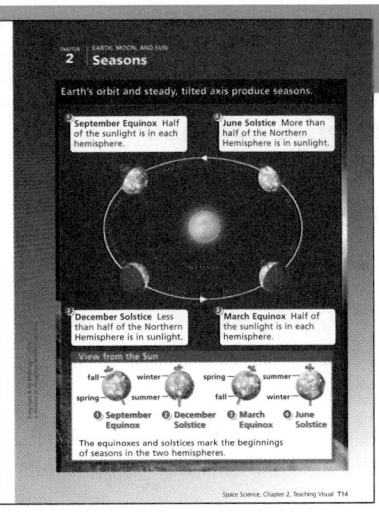

 **UNIT TRANSPARENCY BOOK**, p. T9

 p. T11

 p. T14

MORE SUPPORT

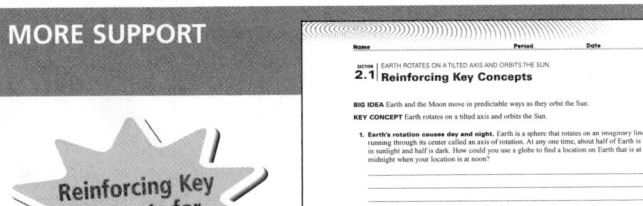

Reinforcing Key Concepts for each section

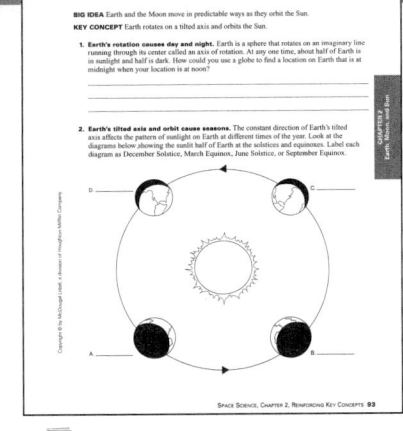

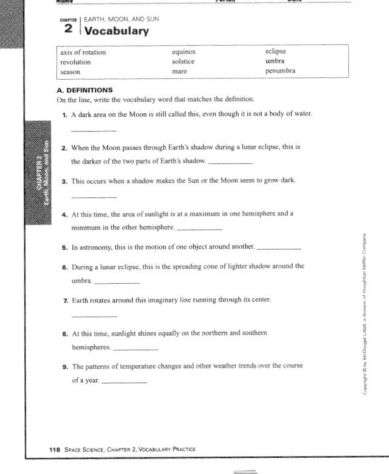

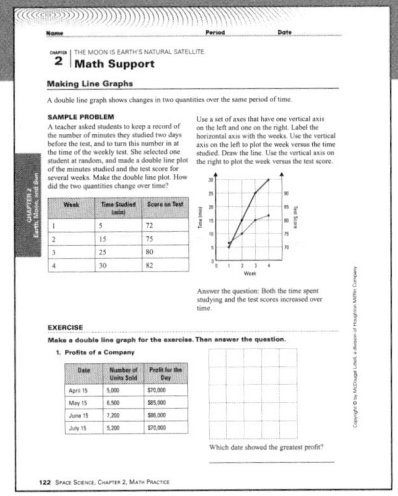

UNIT RESOURCE BOOK, p. 93

pp. 118–119

p. 122

INTRODUCE

the **BIG** idea

Have students look at the photograph of the telescope on Earth and the Moon in the sky. Discuss how the Moon's appearance links to the Big Idea:

- How does the Moon look in the photograph?
- What has the Moon looked like when you have seen it in the sky?
- How do you think the Sun affects how the Moon appears?

National Science Education Standards

Content

D.3.b Most objects in the solar system are in regular and predictable motion. Those motions explain such phenomena as the day, the year, phases of the Moon, and eclipses.

D.3.c Gravity alone holds us to Earth's surface and explains the phenomena of the tides.

D.3.d Seasons result from variations in the amount of the Sun's energy hitting the surface, due to the tilt of Earth's rotation on its axis and the length of the day.

Process

A.2–8 Design and conduct an investigation; use tools to gather and interpret data; use evidence to describe, predict, explain, model; think critically to make relationships between evidence and explanation; recognize different explanations and predictions; communicate scientific procedures and explanations; use mathematics.

A.9.a–c, A.9.e–f Understand scientific inquiry by using different investigations, methods, mathematics, and explanations based on logic, evidence, and skepticism.

CHAPTER

Earth, Moon, and Sun

the **BIG** idea

Earth and the Moon move in predictable ways as they orbit the Sun.

What would you see if you looked at the Moon through a telescope?

Key Concepts

SECTION 2.1 Earth rotates on a tilted axis and orbits the Sun. Learn what causes day and night and why there are seasons.

SECTION 2.2 The Moon is Earth's natural satellite. Learn about the structure and motion of Earth's Moon.

SECTION 2.3 Positions of the Sun and Moon affect Earth. Learn about phases of the Moon, eclipses, and tides.

Internet Preview

CLASSZONE.COM
Chapter 2 online resources: Content Review, two Visualizations, two Resource Centers, Math Tutorial, Test Practice

E 40 Unit: **Space Science**

INTERNET PREVIEW

CLASSZONE.COM For student use with the following pages:

Review and Practice
- Content Review, pp. 42, 68
- Math Tutorial: Line Graphs, p. 58
- Test Practice, p. 71

Activities and Resources
- Internet Activity: Seasons, p. 41
- Resource Centers: Seasons, p. 48, Tides, p. 66
- Visualization: Lunar Phases, p. 60

NSTA SCiLINKS
scilinks.org
The Moon **Code: MDL058**

EXPLORE (the BIG idea)

How Do Shadows Move?

Place a small sticky note on a window that sunlight shines through. At several different times of day, sketch the location of the note's shadow in the room.

Observe and Think
Does the shadow move in a clockwise or counterclockwise direction? Does the shadow's distance from the window change?

What Makes the Moon Bright?

On a day when you see the Moon in the sky, compare it with a round object. Hold the object in line with the Moon. Make sure that your hand does not block the sunlight. Notice the part of the object that is bright.

Observe and Think
How does the sunlight on the object compare with the light on the Moon?

Internet Activity: Seasons

Go to **ClassZone.com** to explore seasons. Find out how sunlight affects the temperature in different places at different times of year.

Observe and Think
Does the picture show Earth in June or in December?

NSTA
sclinks.org
SCLINKS
The Moon **Code: MDL058**

Chapter 2: **Earth, Moon, and Sun** 41 **E**

EXPLORE (the BIG idea)

These inquiry-based activities are appropriate for use at home or as a supplement to classroom instruction.

How Do Shadows Move?

PURPOSE To introduce students to the changes in sunlight angle that occur throughout the day.

TIP *10 min.* Have students record the time as they complete each sketch.

Answer: Generally, the shadow will move clockwise, and its distance from the window will change.

REVISIT after p. 48.

What Makes the Moon Bright?

PURPOSE To introduce students to the concept of reflected sunlight.

TIP *10 min.* Look for times of moonrise and moonset in the weather section of a newspaper.

Answer: Sunlight illuminates the object and the Moon in exactly the same way.

REVISIT after p. 62.

Internet Activity: Seasons

PURPOSE To introduce students to the relationship between sunlight and seasons.

TIP *20 min.* Use a globe to help students better visualize the illustration. Tell them to imagine they are looking at Earth from the Sun.

Answer: The picture shows Earth in December because Antarctica and the South Pole are in sunlight.

REVISIT after p. 47.

TEACHING WITH TECHNOLOGY

Camera If you have computer access to a rooftop camera, especially one pointing due east or west, collect images of shadows. Take images that show the lengths and directions of shadows at different times during the day. Alternatively, take images around solar noon on several days over the course of a week or more. Students can draw lines to show the angles of sunlight after reading p. 48.

PREPARE

◖ CONCEPT REVIEW

Activate Prior Knowledge

- What objects in space are visible from Earth?
- Which of these objects seem the closest to Earth?
- Based on what you know about gravity, do you think that the closest space objects exert a force on Earth? Do you think Earth exerts a force on these objects? Explain your answer.

▶ TAKING NOTES

Combination Notes

Before students write combination notes about a new concept, have them read the text and identify supporting ideas. The blue and red headings can help students identify important concepts to include in their notes.

Vocabulary Strategy

Because many of the terms involve geometry, encourage students to use diagrams and sketches to visually describe the vocabulary term in their frame game diagrams.

Vocabulary and Note-Taking Resources

  • Vocabulary Practice, pp. 118–119
  • Decoding Support, p. 120

  • Daily Vocabulary Scaffolding, p. T10
  • Note-Taking Model, p. T11

  • Frame Game, B26–27
  • Combination Notes, C36
  • Daily Vocabulary Scaffolding, H1–8

Getting Ready to Learn

◖ CONCEPT REVIEW

- The sky seems to turn as Earth rotates.
- The motions of nearby space objects are visible from Earth.
- Light and other radiation carry information about space.

◖ VOCABULARY REVIEW

orbit p. 10
electromagnetic radiation p. 15
satellite p. 23
See Glossary for definitions.
force, gravity, mass

 CONTENT REVIEW
CLASSZONE.COM
Review concepts and vocabulary.

▶ TAKING NOTES

COMBINATION NOTES

To take notes about a new concept, first make an informal outline of the information. Then make a sketch of the concept and label it so you can study it later.

VOCABULARY STRATEGY

Write each new vocabulary term in the center of a **frame game** diagram. Decide what information to frame the term with. Use examples, descriptions, pictures, or sentences in which the term is used in context. You can change the frame to fit each term.

See the Note-Taking Handbook on pages R45–R51.

E 42 Unit: Space Science

SCIENCE NOTEBOOK

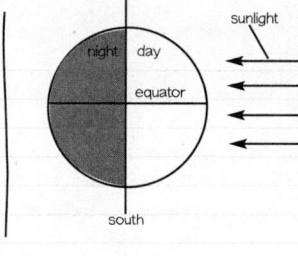

NOTES

Earth turns.
- It turns on an imaginary axis.
  - Poles are ends of axis.
  - Equator is halfway.
- Rotation takes 24 hours.
- Sun shines on one side only.
  - Light side is daytime.
  - Dark side is night.

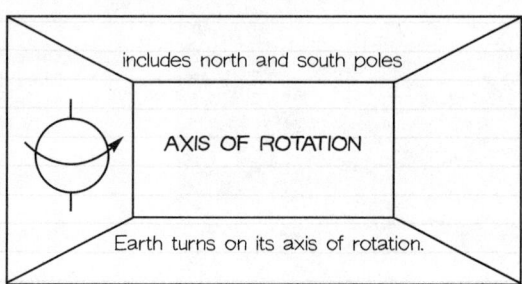

includes north and south poles

AXIS OF ROTATION

Earth turns on its axis of rotation.

CHECK READINESS

Administer the Diagnostic Test to determine students' readiness for new science content and their mastery of requisite math skills.

  Diagnostic Test, pp. 21–22

Technology Resources

Students needing content and math skills should visit **ClassZone.com**.

 • CONTENT REVIEW
  • MATH TUTORIAL
 CONTENT REVIEW CD-ROM

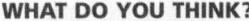

KEY CONCEPT

2.1 Earth rotates on a tilted axis and orbits the Sun.

◀ **BEFORE, you learned**
- Stars seem to rise, cross the sky, and set because Earth turns
- The Sun is very large and far from Earth
- Earth orbits the Sun

▶ **NOW, you will learn**
- Why Earth has day and night
- How the changing angles of sunlight produce seasons

VOCABULARY
axis of rotation p. 44
revolution p. 45
season p. 46
equinox p. 46
solstice p. 46

EXPLORE Time Zones

What time is it in Iceland right now?

PROCEDURE

① Find your location and Iceland on the map. Identify the time zone of each.

② Count the number of hours between your location and Iceland. Add or subtract that number of hours from the time on your clock.

WHAT DO YOU THINK?
- By how much is Iceland's time earlier or later than yours?
- Why are clocks set to different times?

MATERIAL
time zone map

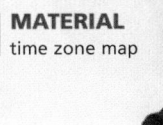

Earth's rotation causes day and night.

When astronauts explored the Moon, they felt the Moon's gravity pulling them down. Their usual "down"—Earth—was up in the Moon's sky.

As you read this book, it is easy to tell which way is down. But is down in the same direction for a person on the other side of Earth? If you both pointed down, you would be pointing toward each other. Earth's gravity pulls objects toward the center of Earth. No matter where you stand on Earth, the direction of down will be toward Earth's center. There is no bottom or top. Up is out toward space, and down is toward the center of the planet.

As Earth turns, so do you. You keep the same position with respect to what is below your feet, but the view above your head changes.

 **CHECK YOUR READING** In what direction does gravity pull objects near Earth?

Chapter 2: **Earth, Moon, and Sun 43** **E**

RESOURCES FOR DIFFERENTIATED INSTRUCTION

Below Level

UNIT RESOURCE BOOK
- Reading Study Guide A, pp. 84–85
- Decoding Support, p. 120

 AUDIO CDS

R **Additional INVESTIGATION,**
Making an Equatorial Sundial, A, B, & C, pp. 133–141;
Teacher Instructions, pp. 287–288

Advanced

UNIT RESOURCE BOOK
Challenge and Extension, p. 90

English Learners

UNIT RESOURCE BOOK
Spanish Reading Study Guide, pp. 88–89

 AUDIO CDS

- Audio Readings in Spanish
- Audio Readings (English)

2.1 FOCUS

▶ **Set Learning Goals**
Students will
- Explain why Earth has day and night.
- Recognize how the changing angles of sunlight produce seasons.
- Model Earth's rotation in an experiment.

◀ **3-Minute Warm-Up**
Display Transparency 12 or copy this exercise on the board:

Decide if each statement is true. If not, correct it.

1. The sky seems to turn because Earth stays still. *The sky seems to turn because Earth rotates.*

2. Mass is the force that keeps a satellite in orbit around an object in space. *Gravity is the force that keeps a satellite in orbit around an object.*

3. Earth is a satellite of the Sun. *true*

 3-Minute Warm-Up, p. T12

2.1 MOTIVATE

EXPLORE Time Zones
PURPOSE To introduce students to different time zones

TIP *15 min.* A globe with a time disk can be used as a supplement to the time zone maps in the Appendix and the datasheet. Tell students to ignore daylight-savings time.

WHAT DO YOU THINK? *The time in Iceland is five hours later than Eastern Standard Time (add 5h to EST). Clocks are set so that noon will be approximately in the middle of a period of daylight.*

 Time Zone Map, p. 91

Ongoing Assessment

 **CHECK YOUR READING** *Answer: toward the center of Earth*

Chapter 2 **43** **E**

2.1 INSTRUCT

INVESTIGATE Rotation

PURPOSE To model Earth's rotation in order to understand what causes day and night

TIPS *15 min.*

• Darken the room somewhat before beginning the activity.

• Remind students that Earth rotates in an easterly direction.

WHAT DO YOU THINK? *In step 2, the time was midnight; in step 3, it was sunrise, or about 6 A.M; in step 4, it was sunset, or about 6 P.M; it is about 6 A.M.*

CHALLENGE *Shortly after sunset, the location on the ground may have rotated out of the sunlight while the cloud high above is still in sunlight.*

 Datasheet, Rotation, p. 92

Technology Resources

Customize this student lab as needed or look for an alternative. Print rubrics to assess student lab reports.

 Lab Generator CD-ROM

Metacognitive Strategy

Ask: Imagine that you are performing "Investigate Rotation" in your living room. A family member enters the room and watches with a puzzled expression. How would you explain the activity to your relative? For example, what are you using your hands to represent? *the horizon*

Ongoing Assessment

Recognize why Earth has day and night.

Ask: Why does Earth have day and night? *because it turns on its axis*

CHECK YOUR READING *Answer: midnight*

The directions north, south, east, and west are based on the way the planet rotates, or turns. Earth rotates around an imaginary line running through its center called an **axis of rotation.** The ends of the axis are the north and south poles. Any location on the surface moves from west to east as Earth turns. If you extend your right thumb and pretend its tip is the North Pole, then your fingers curve the way Earth rotates.

At any one time, about half of Earth is in sunlight and half is dark. However, Earth turns on its axis in 24 hours, so locations move through the light and darkness in that time. When a location is in sunlight, it is daytime there. When a location is in the middle of the sunlit side, it is noon. When a location is in darkness, it is night there, and when the location is in the middle of the unlit side, it is midnight.

❓ A
❓ B

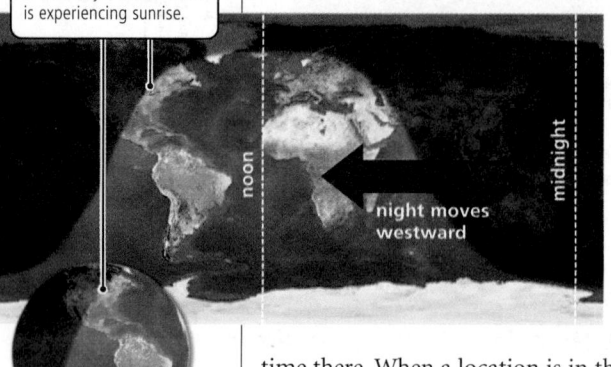

The globe and the flat map show the progress of daylight across Earth in two ways. This location is experiencing sunrise.

noon ← *night moves westward* *midnight*

CHECK YOUR READING If it is noon at one location, what time is it at a location directly on the other side of Earth?

INVESTIGATE Rotation

What causes day and night?

In this model the lamp represents the Sun, and your head represents Earth. The North Pole is at the top of your head. You will need to imagine locations on your head as if your head were a globe.

PROCEDURE

① Face the lamp and hold your hands to your face as shown in the photograph. Your hands mark the horizon. For a person located at your nose, the Sun would be high in the sky. It would be noon.

② Face away from the lamp. Determine what time it would be at your nose.

③ Turn to your left until you see the lamp along your left hand.

④ Continue turning to the left, through noon, until you just stop seeing the lamp.

WHAT DO YOU THINK?

• What times was it at your nose in steps 2, 3, and 4?

• When you face the lamp, what time is it at your right ear?

CHALLENGE How can a cloud be bright even when it is dark on the ground?

SKILL FOCUS
Making models

MATERIALS
lamp

TIME
15 minutes

DIFFERENTIATE INSTRUCTION

❓ More Reading Support

A About how much of Earth is in sunlight at any one time? *half*

B How long does it take Earth to make one turn on its axis? *24 hours*

English Learners English learners might expect that sentences beginning with *If* always contain a clause beginning with *then:* "If you extend your right thumb…, then your fingers curve the way Earth rotates" (p. 44). Make sure students understand that *then* can be implied rather than stated explicitly and that the meaning of the sentence remains the same: "If they did, Earth's equator would be in the same plane as Earth's orbit" (p. 45).

Earth's tilted axis and orbit cause seasons.

Just as gravity causes objects near Earth to be pulled toward Earth's center, it also causes Earth and other objects near the Sun to be pulled toward the Sun's center. Fortunately, Earth does not move straight into the Sun. Earth moves sideways, at nearly a right angle to the Sun's direction. Without the Sun's gravitational pull, Earth would keep moving in a straight line out into deep space. However, the Sun's pull changes Earth's path from a straight line to a round orbit about 300 million kilometers (200,000,000 mi) across.

Just as a day is the time it takes Earth to rotate once on its axis, a year is the time it takes Earth to orbit the Sun once. In astronomy, a **revolution** is the motion of one object around another. The word *revolution* can also mean the time it takes an object to go around once.

Earth's rotation and orbit do not quite line up. If they did, Earth's equator would be in the same plane as Earth's orbit, like a tiny hoop and a huge hoop lying on the same tabletop. Instead, Earth rotates at about a 23° angle, or tilt, from this lined-up position.

READING TiP

Use the second vowel in each word to help you remember that an object rot<u>a</u>tes on its own <u>a</u>xis, but rev<u>o</u>lves around another <u>o</u>bject.

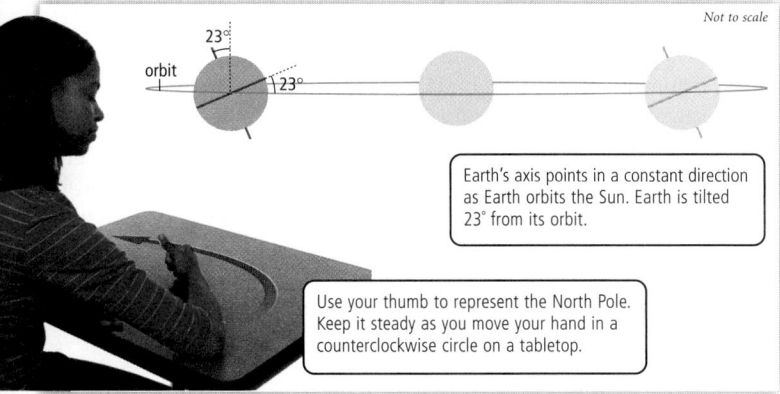

Not to scale

Earth's axis points in a constant direction as Earth orbits the Sun. Earth is tilted 23° from its orbit.

Use your thumb to represent the North Pole. Keep it steady as you move your hand in a counterclockwise circle on a tabletop.

As Earth moves, its axis always points in the same direction in space. You could model Earth's orbit by moving your right fist in a circle on a desktop. You would need to point your thumb toward your left shoulder and keep it pointing that way while moving your hand around the desktop.

Earth's orbit is not quite a perfect circle. In January, Earth is about 5 million kilometers closer to the Sun than it is in July. You may be surprised to learn that this distance makes only a tiny difference in temperatures on Earth. However, the combination of Earth's motion around the Sun with the tilt of Earth's axis does cause important changes of temperature. Turn the page to find out how.

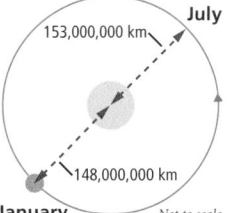

July

153,000,000 km

January

148,000,000 km

Not to scale

Earth's orbit is almost a circle. Earth's distance from the Sun varies by only about 5,000,000 km—about 3%—during a year.

DIFFERENTIATE INSTRUCTION

? More Reading Support

C How long does it take Earth to orbit the Sun once? *a year*

D What happens to Earth's axis during an orbit? *It doesn't change.*

Below Level Have students sit at their desks and use a fist to model Earth's orbit around the Sun, as shown in the visual on this page. Erasers can be placed in the center of students' desktops to represent the Sun. Students can use the diagram in the margin to estimate Earth's position in January and July. Help students keep their thumbs pointing in the same direction relative to the desk and themselves, not the eraser.

Teach Difficult Concepts

Remind students that absolute directions do not exist in space; "up" and "down" are based on local direction of gravitational pull. Students can develop a more complete understanding of seasons if they are able to imagine different points of view. Have students use the diagram and picture on this page. Tell them to imagine standing at the equator near the label 23°. Ask:

• What on this page would be straight overhead? *the bottom of the Reading Tip in the right margin*

• In which directions would the horizon be? *to the lower right (a corner of the desk in the photograph) and to the upper left (the highlighted word* revolution*); also, straight into and out of the page*

• How high would the Sun be? *close to (about 23° from) overhead*

Teach from Visuals

To help students interpret the visual of Earth's orbit around the Sun, ask:

• What does the girl's thumb represent? *the North Pole*

• Why does the girl move her fist in a counterclockwise direction? *to model the direction of Earth's orbit*

• Why is the girl's thumb pointed toward her left shoulder? *to model the tilt of Earth's axis*

• Why doesn't the model of Earth's axis change direction as it moves? *Earth's axis always points in the same direction in space.*

Social Studies Connection

Ask students if they can relate the term *revolution* as it is used in astronomy to how it often is used in social studies. Point out that in social studies, revolution is the overturning of a nation's government, usually by force, and the establishment of a new government. Discuss how the Latin derivation—*re-* ("back") + *volvere* ("to roll")—applies to both the astronomical and social studies meanings.

Address Misconceptions

IDENTIFY Ask: What causes seasons? If students say that seasons are caused by Earth's changing distance from the Sun, they may hold misconceptions about the role of Earth's tilted axis and seasonal changes.

CORRECT Ask students whether it is winter or summer at their location when Earth is closest to the Sun (January). Then have students use a physical model to see how the angle of sunlight, not distance from the Sun, produces seasons. (You might discuss the diagram or perform the Alternative Assessment on p. 47, or conduct "Modeling Seasons" on pp. 50–51.)

REASSESS Ask students to describe the conditions that produce summer weather in December in New Zealand, which is in the Southern Hemisphere. *In December, the Southern Hemisphere is at an angle where it receives more sunlight, so it becomes warmer there. (Acknowledge that distance from a hot object matters in everyday experiences.)*

Real World Example

Scientists estimate that solar energy— energy from the Sun—can meet current global energy needs many times over. However, the amount of sunlight received by most areas on Earth varies on a daily and seasonal basis. Technology to harness solar energy continues to improve. Devices that use solar energy include solar cells, which convert sunlight directly into electrical energy; dark-colored tanks that absorb sunlight and heat water; and solar ovens, which are used in equatorial areas that receive plenty of sunlight.

Ongoing Assessment

 *Answer: June*

VOCABULARY
Remember to put each new term into a frame game diagram.

READING TiP
The positions and lighting can be hard to imagine, so you might use a model as well as the diagram on the next page to help you understand.

 E

Seasonal Patterns

Most locations on Earth experience **seasons,** patterns of temperature changes and other weather trends over the course of a year. Near the equator, the temperatures are almost the same year-round. Near the poles, there are very large changes in temperatures from winter to summer. The temperature changes occur because the amount of sunlight at each location changes during the year. The changes in the amount of sunlight are due to the tilt of Earth's axis.

Look at the diagram on page 47 to see how the constant direction of Earth's tilted axis affects the pattern of sunlight on Earth at different times of the year. As Earth travels around the Sun, the area of sunlight in each hemisphere changes. At an **equinox** (EE-kwuh-NAHKS), sunlight shines equally on the northern and southern hemispheres. Half of each hemisphere is lit, and half is in darkness. As Earth moves along its orbit, the light shifts more into one hemisphere than the other. At a **solstice** (SAHL-stihs), the area of sunlight is at a maximum in one hemisphere and a minimum in the other hemisphere. Equinoxes and solstices happen on or around the 21st days of certain months of the year.

① **September Equinox** When Earth is in this position, sunlight shines equally on the two hemispheres. You can see in the diagram that the North Pole is at the border between light and dark. The September equinox marks the beginning of autumn in the Northern Hemisphere and of spring in the Southern Hemisphere.

② **December Solstice** Three months later, Earth has traveled a quarter of the way around the Sun, but its axis still points in the same direction into space. The North Pole seems to lean away from the direction of the Sun. The solstice occurs when the pole leans as far away from the Sun as it will during the year. You can see that the North Pole is in complete darkness. At the same time, the opposite is true in the Southern Hemisphere. The South Pole seems to lean toward the Sun and is in sunlight. It is the Southern Hemisphere's summer solstice and the Northern Hemisphere's winter solstice.

③ **March Equinox** After another quarter of its orbit, Earth reaches another equinox. Half of each hemisphere is lit, and the sunlight is centered on the equator. You can see that the poles are again at the border between day and night.

④ **June Solstice** This position is opposite the December solstice. Earth's axis still points in the same direction, but now the North Pole seems to lean toward the Sun and is in sunlight. The June solstice marks the beginning of summer in the Northern Hemisphere. In contrast, it is the winter solstice in the Southern Hemisphere.

 CHECK YOUR READING In what month does winter begin in the Southern Hemisphere?

DIFFERENTIATE INSTRUCTION

 More Reading Support

E What causes the changes in the amount of sunlight at a location during the year? *the tilt of Earth's axis*

Advanced Have students discuss what changes might occur if Earth's axis were not tilted relative to its orbit. Ask: What would seasons be like? *There would be no seasonal changes.* How would the lack of tilt affect temperatures at the poles and the equator? *The poles would still be cold year-round; the equator would be hotter.*

 **R** Challenge and Extension, p. 90

Seasons

Earth's orbit and steady, tilted axis produce seasons.

① **September Equinox** Half of the sunlight is in each hemisphere. The strongest sunlight is on the equator.

④ **June Solstice** More than half of the Northern Hemisphere is in sunlight. The strongest sunlight is north of the equator, so the Northern Hemisphere grows warmer.

August

July

October

November

May

April

January

February

Not to scale

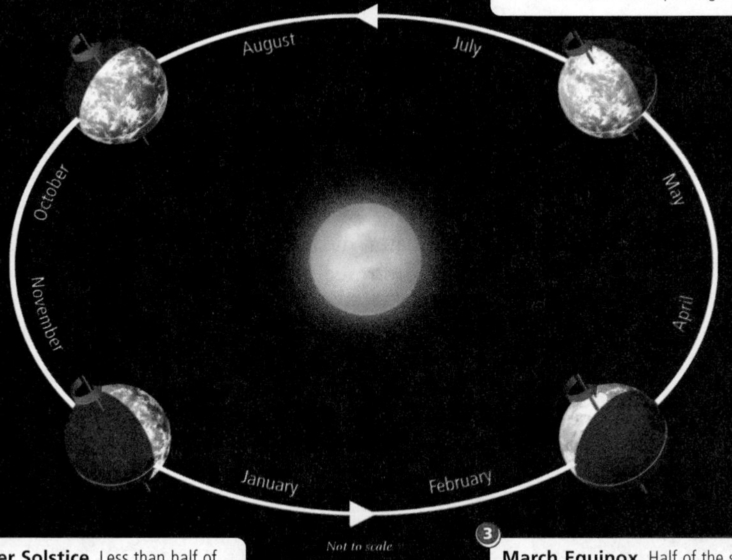

② **December Solstice** Less than half of the Northern Hemisphere is in sunlight. The strongest sunlight is south of the equator, so the Southern Hemisphere grows warmer.

③ **March Equinox** Half of the sunlight is in each hemisphere. The strongest sunlight is on the equator.

View from the Sun

If you could stand on the Sun and look at Earth, you would see different parts of Earth at different times of year.

fall — spring —

winter — summer —

spring — fall —

summer — winter —

① September Equinox   **②** December Solstice   **③** March Equinox   **④** June Solstice

The equinoxes and solstices mark the beginnings of seasons in the two hemispheres. Warmer seasons occur when more of a hemisphere is in sunlight.

READING VISUALS Look at the poles to help you see how each hemisphere is lit. When is the South Pole completely in sunlight?

Chapter 2: **Earth, Moon, and Sun** 47 **E**

DIFFERENTIATE INSTRUCTION

Alternative Assessment In groups of four, have students tilt their bodies toward one wall of the classroom as they stand in a circle around an object representing the Sun. Each student represents Earth at a different time of year. Tell students their head represents the North Pole and their waist the equator. Have each student orient the visual on this page to match their model and to identify the month that he or she represents. *The upper left corner points toward the chosen wall; months roughly match diagram.*

Teach from Visuals

To help students interpret the visual on seasons:

- Remind students that the Sun's diameter is about 100 times bigger than Earth's diameter. Then ask them why "Not to scale," is written on the diagram. *It tells readers that the size and distance relationships between the image of the Sun and the images of Earth are not accurate.*

- Ask: When does the Northern Hemisphere get the most sunlight? *the June solstice*

- Ask: How are the two diagrams of the June solstice different? *They show Earth from two different directions. The orbit diagram shows Earth from outside Earth's orbit, while the "View from the Sun" diagram shows Earth as it would be seen from the Sun.*

- Ask: Does more of the Southern or Northern Hemisphere face the Sun during the December solstice? *Southern* What does this account for? *Summer in December in southern latitudes*

Have students model Earth by making a fist and using their right thumb to represent Earth's North Pole. For each season, have students move their hand to the position pictured in the orbit diagram and then compare the result with the matching "View from the Sun." Allow students time to work out how sunlight is distributed on Earth for each position. The orbit diagram shows the position of Earth and its axis during the year, while the "View from the Sun" diagram shows how sunlight is distributed relative to the poles and equator.

 The "Seasons" visual is also available as T14 in the Unit Transparency Book.

EXPLORE the BIG idea

Revisit "Internet Activity: Seasons" on p. 41. Have students describe what the picture would look like if it showed Earth in June.

Ongoing Assessment

 *Answer: in December*

Chapter 2 **47** **E**

Teach Difficult Concepts

Some students may have a hard time understanding the effects of sunlight's various angles. Point out that the angle of sunlight changes throughout the day as well as throughout the seasons. In the early morning, sunlight strikes the ground at a slant and does not seem very warm. In all cases, the angle of light affects temperature. You can do the following demonstration to help students better understand angles of sunlight.

Teacher Demo

Tie a dozen pencils into a loose bundle so they can slide. Tell students that the bundle represents sunlight. Hold the pencils vertically on a sheet of paper to model concentrated sunlight striking Earth's surface. Ask: Where would the Sun be in this model? *high in the sky* What season might it be? *summer* Next, hold the bundle at an angle while keeping all pencil tips on the paper. Ask: Where would the Sun be in this model? *low in the sky* What time of day might it be? *sunset* What season would most likely have this angle of sunlight at noon? *winter*

Teaching with Technology

If you have computer access to a rooftop camera, collect images of the lengths and directions of shadows at different times. Students can draw lines to show the angles of sunlight.

EXPLORE (the BIG idea)

Revisit "How Do Shadows Move?" on p. 41. Have students describe how the shadow changed throughout the day.

Ongoing Assessment

CHECK YOUR READING *Answer: Temperatures rise when the angle of sunlight is greater.*

 **48** Unit: **Space Science**

 **RESOURCE CENTER** CLASSZONE.COM

Learn more about seasons.

Angles of Sunlight

You have seen that seasons change as sunlight shifts between hemispheres during the year. On the ground, you notice the effects of seasons because the angle of sunlight and the length of daylight change over the year. The effects are greatest at locations far from the equator. You may have noticed that sunshine seems barely warm just before sunset, when the Sun is low in the sky. At noon the sunshine seems much hotter. The angle of light affects the temperature.

When the Sun is high in the sky, sunlight strikes the ground at close to a right angle. The energy of sunlight is concentrated. Shadows are short. You may get a sunburn quickly when the Sun is at a high angle. When the Sun is low in the sky, sunlight strikes the ground at a slant. The light is spread over a greater area, so it is less concentrated and produces long shadows. Slanted light warms the ground less.

Near the equator, the noonday Sun is almost overhead every day, so the ground is warmed strongly year-round. In the middle latitudes, the noon Sun is high in the sky only during part of the year. In winter the noon Sun is low and warms the ground less strongly.

 **CHECK YOUR READING** How are temperatures throughout the year affected by the angles of sunlight?

Sun Height and Shadows

Winter Solstice, 12 P.M.

Winter shadows are long because sunlight is spread out. The Sun appears low in the sky even at noon.

location on Earth

Spring Equinox, 12 P.M.

Spring and fall shadows are of medium length, and the noon Sun appears higher in the sky.

Summer Solstice, 12 P.M.

Summer shadows are short because the light is concentrated in a small area. The noon Sun appears high in the sky.

E 48 Unit: **Space Science**

DIFFERENTIATE INSTRUCTION

 **More Reading Support**

F Where is the Sun when shadows are shortest? *high in the sky*

G Where is the noonday Sun almost overhead every day? *near the equator*

Additional Investigation To reinforce Section 2.1 learning goals, use the following full-period investigation:

R Additional **INVESTIGATION,** Making an Equatorial Sundial, A, B, & C, pp. 133–141, 287–288 (Advanced students should complete Levels B and C.)

Alternative Assessment Have students make a sketch for one of the three seasons in the diagram "Sun Height and Shadows." The sketch should show how the height of the Sun affects the shadows of objects. Have students exchange sketches to identify the season shown in another's sketch.

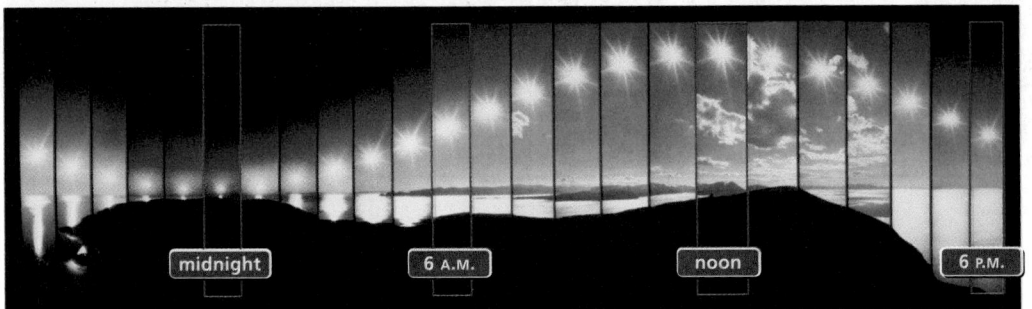

midnight 6 A.M. noon 6 P.M.

Near the pole in the summer, the Sun stays above the horizon, so there is no night. This series of photographs was taken over the course of a day.

Lengths of Days

Seasonal temperatures depend on the amount of daylight, too. In Chicago, for example, the summer Sun heats the ground for about 15 hours a day, but in winter there may be only 9 hours of sunlight each day. The farther you get from the equator, the more extreme the changes in day length become. As you near one of the poles, summer daylight may last for 20 hours or more.

Very close to the poles, the Sun does not set at all for six months at a time. It can be seen shining near the horizon at midnight. Tourists often travel far north just to experience the midnight Sun. At locations near a pole, the Sun sets on an equinox and then does not rise again for six months. Astronomers go to the South Pole in March to take advantage of the long winter night, which allows them to study objects in the sky without the interruption of daylight.

Very near the equator, the periods of daylight and darkness are almost equal year-round—each about 12 hours long. Visitors who are used to hot weather during long summer days might be surprised when a hot, sunny day ends suddenly at 6 P.M. At locations away from the equator, daylight lasts 12 hours only around the time of an equinox.

> **READING TiP**
>
> *Equinox* means "equal night"—daylight and nighttime are equal in length.

2.1 Review

KEY CONCEPTS

1. What causes day and night?
2. What happens to Earth's axis of rotation as Earth orbits the Sun?
3. How do the areas of sunlight in the two hemispheres change over the year?

CRITICAL THINKING

4. **Apply** If you wanted to enjoy longer periods of daylight in the summertime, would you head closer to the equator or farther from it? Why?
5. **Compare and Contrast** How do the average temperatures and the seasonal changes at the equator differ from those at the poles?

◑ CHALLENGE

6. **Infer** If Earth's axis were tilted so much that the North Pole sometimes pointed straight at the Sun, how would the hours of daylight be affected at your location?

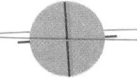

Chapter 2: **Earth, Moon, and Sun** 49 **E**

ANSWERS

1. Earth's rotation

2. It points in a constant direction.

3. At an equinox, the areas of sunlight are equal in the two hemispheres. At a solstice, the area of sunlight is at a maximum in one hemisphere and at a minimum in the other hemisphere.

4. farther, because the Sun would set at about 6 P.M. at the equator

5. In general, seasonal changes are slight at the equator, and average temperatures are high year-round. At the poles, temperatures are much lower, but seasonal changes are more extreme.

6. Most locations would experience daylight patterns similar to those that exist at the poles. Around the summer solstice, the Sun would be above the horizon for many days. Around the winter solstice, the Sun would be below the horizon for many days.

Ongoing Assessment

Recognize how the changing angles of sunlight produce seasons.

Ask: For places in the middle latitudes, where is the noon Sun during winter, and how does its position affect temperature? *The sun is low in the sky, causing the ground to be cooler than when the Sun is higher.*

Reinforce (the **BIG** idea)

Have students relate the section to the Big Idea.

R Reinforcing Key Concepts, p. 93

2.1 ASSESS & RETEACH

Assess

 Section 2.1 Quiz, p. 23

Reteach

Take students outside on a sunny day. Hold a globe in the sunlight so that your location is at the top and the North Pole points north. Sunlight will fall on the globe exactly as it falls on Earth at that instant. Point out the distribution of sunlight between hemispheres and the location of the pole relative to the day and night sides of the globe. *In October, for example, more of the Southern Hemisphere is lit, and the North Pole points slightly into the night side.*

Technology Resources

Have students visit **ClassZone.com** for reteaching of Key Concepts.

 CONTENT REVIEW

 CONTENT REVIEW CD-ROM

Focus

PURPOSE To model the cause of seasons

OVERVIEW Students will observe different angles of light on graph paper. Students will find the following:

- Angles of sunlight affect the amount of solar energy a location receives throughout the year.
- Changing angles of sunlight cause seasons.

Lab Preparation

- Make sure all students know how to use a protractor before beginning the lab. Review its use, if necessary.
- Have students read through the investigation and prepare their data tables. (Make sure they leave space before their data table for notes from Part A.) Or you may wish to copy and distribute datasheets and rubrics.

 UNIT RESOURCE BOOK, pp. 124–132

 SCIENCE TOOLKIT, F14

Lab Management

In Part A, students may move the flashlight through a range of angles several times in order to determine what happens to the light.

In Part B, the fold of the sticky note should run north-south. For solstice B, the marked location will likely be closer to the tabletop. Have students adjust the number of books so that the center of the flashlight beam shines on the location in each case. If students have trouble estimating the angle of light, have one student hold a pencil horizontally, similar to the red dashed line in the photograph, while another estimates the angle.

CHAPTER INVESTIGATION

Modeling Seasons

OVERVIEW AND PURPOSE Why is the weather in North America so much colder in January than in July? You might be surprised to learn that it has nothing to do with Earth's distance from the Sun. In fact, Earth is closest to the Sun in January. In this lab, you will model the cause of seasons as you
- orient a light source at different angles to a surface
- determine how the angles of sunlight at a location change as Earth orbits the Sun

▶ Problem

How does the angle of light affect the amount of solar energy a location receives at different times of year?

▶ Hypothesize

After performing step 3, write a hypothesis to explain how the angles of sunlight affect the amounts of solar energy your location receives at different times of year. Your hypothesis should take the form of an "If . . . , then . . . , because . . ." statement.

▶ Procedure

MATERIALS
- graph paper
- flashlight
- meter stick
- protractor
- globe
- stack of books
- sticky note

PART A

1. Mark an *X* near the center of the graph paper. Shine the flashlight onto the paper from about 30 cm straight above the X—at an angle of 90° to the surface. Observe the size of the spot of light.

2. Shine the flashlight onto the X at different angles. Keep the flashlight at the same distance. Write down what happens to the size of the spot of light as you change angles.

3. Repeat step 2, but observe just one square near the X. Write down what happens to the brightness of the light as you change the angle. The brightness shows how much energy the area receives from the flashlight.

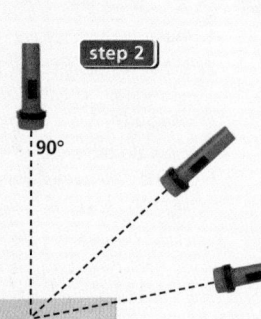
step 2
90°

4. Think about the temperatures at different times of year at your location, then write your hypothesis.

 E 50 Unit: Space Science

INVESTIGATION RESOURCES

 CHAPTER INVESTIGATION, Modeling Seasons
- Level A, pp. 124–127
- Level B, pp. 128–131
- Level C, p. 132

Advanced students should complete Levels B & C.

 Writing a Lab Report, D12–13

Technology Resources

Customize this student lab as needed or look for an alternative. Print rubrics to assess student lab reports.

💿 **Lab Generator CD-ROM**

PART B

5 Set up the globe, books, and flashlight as shown in the photograph. Point the globe's North Pole to the right. This position represents solstice A.

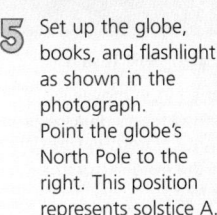
solstice A

6 Find your location on the globe. Place a folded sticky note onto the globe at your location as shown in the photograph. Rotate the globe on its axis until the note faces toward the flashlight.

7 The flashlight beam represents noonday sunlight at your location. Use the protractor to estimate the angle of the light on the surface.

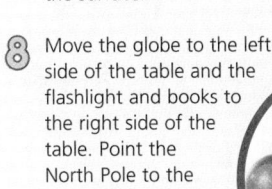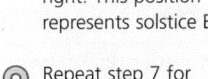
light
steps 6–7

8 Move the globe to the left side of the table and the flashlight and books to the right side of the table. Point the North Pole to the right. This position represents solstice B.

9 Repeat step 7 for solstice B.

solstice B

▶ Observe and Analyze   Write It Up

1. **RECORD** Draw the setup of your materials in each part of the investigation. Organize your notes.

2. **ANALYZE** Describe how the angle of the flashlight in step 2 affected the area of the spot of light. Which angle concentrated the light into the smallest area?

3. **EVALUATE** At which angle did a square of the graph paper receive the most energy?

4. **COMPARE** Compare the angles of light in steps 7 and 9. In which position was the angle of light closer to 90°?

▶ Conclude   Write It Up

1. **EVALUATE** How did the angle of sunlight at your location differ at the two times of year? At which position is sunlight more concentrated at your location?

2. **APPLY** The amount of solar energy at a location affects temperature. Which solstice—A or B—represents the summer solstice at your location?

3. **INTERPRET** Do your results support your hypothesis? Explain why or why not.

▶ INVESTIGATE Further

CHALLENGE What happens in the other hemisphere at the two times of year? Use the model to find out.

Modeling Seasons

Problem How does the angle of light affect the amount of solar energy a location receives at different times of year?

Hypothesize

Observe and Analyze

Table 1. Solstices A and B

	Solstice A	Solstice B
Drawing		
Angle of light (°)		
Observations		

Conclude

Chapter 2: **Earth, Moon, and Sun 51** **E**

▶ Observe and Analyze   Write It Up

SAMPLE DATA Solstice A: angle of light, 30°; observations, the light was spread out over a large area. Solstice B: angle of light, 80°; observations, the light was more concentrated.

1. *Drawings should include information in the photographs.*

2. *The spot was largest at low angles. It was concentrated into the smallest area at a 90° angle.*

3. *A square received the most energy when the angle of light was 90°.*

4. *solstice B (Northern Hemisphere)*

▶ Conclude   Write It Up

1. *(Northern Hemisphere) The angle was smaller for solstice A and greater for solstice B. Sunlight was more concentrated for solstice B.*

2. *B represents the summer solstice for the Northern Hemisphere.*

3. *Sample answer: Data supported the hypothesis that slanted light means less concentrated solar energy (and cooler weather) in winter because the energy from sunlight is more spread out.*

▶ INVESTIGATE Further

CHALLENGE Answer: The results would be reversed. The angle of light would be lower for solstice B in the Southern Hemisphere. It would be winter there.

Post-Lab Discussion

- Help students see the meaning of the angles they measured. The zero line of the protractor should have been parallel to the surface, so they measured the angle from the horizon up to the direction of the Sun.

- Students can compare their answers with ideal results. Subtract your latitude from the following to get the angle of the noon Sun: winter solstice 67°, summer solstice 113° (equinox 90°).

2.2 FOCUS

2.2 FOCUS

◯ Set Learning Goals

Students will

- Explain how the Moon moves.
- Describe the Moon's dark-colored and light-colored features.
- Describe the inside structure of the Moon.
- Infer in an experiment how the Moon's features formed.

◯ 3-Minute Warm-Up

Display Transparency 12 or copy these questions on the board:

1. How long does it take Earth to turn once on its axis? *one day or 24 hours*

2. What is this motion called? *rotation*

3. How long does it take Earth to move once around the Sun? *a year*

4. What is this motion called? *revolution or orbit*

 3-Minute Warm-Up, p. T12

2.2 MOTIVATE

EXPLORE The Moon's Motion

PURPOSE To introduce students to the motion of the Moon

TIP *15 min.* Many students have trouble understanding that the Moon turns because their reference point is Earth rather than a fixed point in space. Use the compass needle to help students see that they have to turn the compass relative to the direction north.

WHAT DO YOU THINK? *It must change relative to a point in outer space. The Moon must turn to keep the same side toward Earth.*

KEY CONCEPT

2.2 The Moon is Earth's natural satellite.

◀ **BEFORE, you learned**

- Earth turns as it orbits the Sun
- The day side of Earth is the part in sunlight
- The Moon is the closest body to Earth

▶ **NOW, you will learn**

- How the Moon moves
- What the Moon's dark-colored and light-colored features are
- About the inside structure of the Moon

VOCABULARY

mare p. 53

EXPLORE The Moon's Motion

How much does the Moon turn?

PROCEDURE

1. Draw a circle to represent the Moon's orbit with Earth at the center. The compass represents the Moon.

2. Move the compass around the circle. Keep the side of the compass marked *E* always facing Earth.

3. Observe the positions of the *E* and the compass needle at several positions on the circle.

WHAT DO YOU THINK?
What does the model tell you about the Moon's motion?

MATERIALS
- paper
- magnetic compass

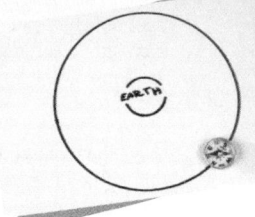

The Moon rotates as it orbits Earth.

When you look at the disk of the Moon, you may notice darker and lighter areas. Perhaps you have imagined them as features of a face or some other pattern. People around the world have told stories about the animals, people, and objects they have imagined while looking at the light and dark areas of the Moon. As you will read in this chapter, these areas tell a story to scientists as well.

The pull of gravity keeps the Moon, Earth's natural satellite, in orbit around Earth. Even though the Moon is Earth's closest neighbor in space, it is far away compared to the sizes of Earth and the Moon.

The Moon's diameter is about 1/4 Earth's diameter, and the Moon is about 30 Earth diameters away.

Earth   Moon

RESOURCES FOR DIFFERENTIATED INSTRUCTION

Below Level

UNIT RESOURCE BOOK
- Reading Study Guide A, pp. 96–97
- Decoding Support, p. 120

 **AUDIO CDS**

Advanced

UNIT RESOURCE BOOK
- Challenge and Extension, p. 102
- Challenge Reading, pp. 116–117

English Learners

UNIT RESOURCE BOOK
Spanish Reading Study Guide, pp. 100–101

AUDIO CDS

- Audio Readings in Spanish
- Audio Readings (English)

The distance between Earth and Moon is roughly 380,000 kilometers (240,000 mi) —about a hundred times the distance between New York and Los Angeles. If a jet airliner could travel in space, it would take about 20 days to cover a distance that huge. Astronauts, whose spaceships traveled much faster than jets, needed about 3 days to reach the Moon.

You always see the same pattern of dark-colored and light-colored features on the Moon. Only this one side of the Moon can be seen from Earth. The reason is that the Moon, like many other moons in the solar system, always keeps one side turned toward its planet. This means that the Moon turns once on its own axis each time it orbits Earth.

 **CHECK YOUR READING** Why do you see only one side of the Moon?

Moon

The side of the Moon that constantly faces Earth has large, dark areas called maria.

Mass 1% of Earth's mass
Diameter 27% of Earth's diameter
Average distance from Earth 380,000 km
Orbits in 27.3 Earth days
Rotates in 27.3 Earth days

The Moon's craters show its history.

A

The half of the Moon's surface that constantly faces Earth is called the near side. The half that faces away from Earth is called the far side. Much of the Moon's surface is light-colored. Within the light-colored areas are many small, round features. There are also dark-colored features, some of which cover large areas. Much of the near side of the Moon is covered with these dark-colored features. In contrast, the far side is mostly light-colored with just a few of the darker features.

Just as on Earth, features on the Moon are given names to make it easier to discuss them. The names of the larger surface features on the Moon are in the Latin language, because centuries ago scientists from many different countries used Latin to communicate with one another. Early astronomers thought that the dark areas might be bodies of water, so they used the Latin word for "sea." Today, a dark area on the Moon is still called a lunar **mare** (MAH-ray). The plural form is *maria* (MAH-ree-uh).

The maria are not bodies of water, however. All of the features that can be seen on the Moon are different types of solid or broken rock. The Moon has no air, no oceans, no clouds, and no life.

?
B

READING TiP

Lunar means "having to do with the Moon." The word comes from *luna*, the Latin word for the Moon.

Integrate the Sciences

Since the 1960s, when astronauts first began traveling in space, scientists have studied the effects of space travel on the human body. On Earth, gravity pulls astronauts to the floor of the spaceship. In space, the pull of Earth's gravity causes both astronauts and the spaceship to change their paths together. Without stress on their bones from standing and sitting up, astronauts may lose bone mass. To keep their bones healthy, astronauts may do special exercises while in space. Muscles can atrophy in a low-gravity environment. Again, low-intensity exercise helps counter this effect.

Language Arts Connection

Call attention to the fact that Latin was used by early scientists to name parts of the Moon. Encourage students to look for Latin root words when they are looking up words in the dictionary. The meaning of a Latin root word can help them understand the definition of a term.

Ongoing Assessment

Explain how the Moon moves.

Ask: How long does it take for the Moon to orbit Earth? *27.3 Earth days*

CHECK YOUR READING *Answer: because the Moon turns once on its axis each time it orbits Earth*

DIFFERENTIATE INSTRUCTION

 **More Reading Support**

A What do we call the Moon's surface that faces Earth? *the near side*

B What is a dark area on the Moon called? *a lunar mare*

English Learners The directions in "Investigate Moon Features" (p. 55) and other instructions use the imperative mood; "you" is eliminated from the directions. For example, "Pour about 1 cm of partly cooled liquid gelatin" means "You pour about 1 cm . . ." Be sure that English learners can understand and follow the directions.

Craters and Maria

The light-colored areas of the Moon are higher—at greater altitudes—than the maria, so they are called the lunar highlands. The ground of the lunar highlands is rocky, and some places are covered with a powder made of finely broken rock.

The highlands have many round features, called impact craters, that formed when small objects from space hit the Moon's surface. Long ago, such collisions happened more often than they do today. Many impact craters marked the surfaces of the Moon, Earth, and other bodies in space. On Earth, however, most craters have been worn away by water and wind. On the dry, airless Moon, impact craters from a long time ago are still visible.

Long ago, some of the largest craters filled with molten rock, or lava, that came from beneath the Moon's surface. The lava filled the lowest areas and then cooled, forming the large, flat plains called maria. Smaller impacts have continued to occur, so the dark plains of the maria do contain some craters. Most of the large maria are on the near side of the Moon. However, the widest and deepest basin on the Moon is on the far side, near the Moon's south pole.

CHECK YOUR READING How did the maria form? List the steps.

Lunar Map

Light-colored highlands and dark maria form a familiar pattern on the near side of the Moon and a very different pattern on the far side.

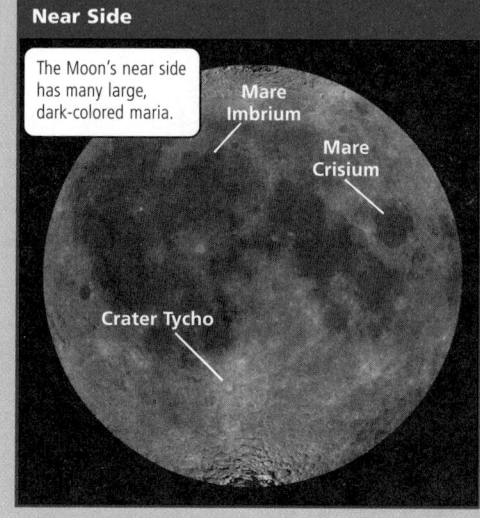

Near Side

The Moon's near side has many large, dark-colored maria.

Mare Imbrium

Mare Crisium

Crater Tycho

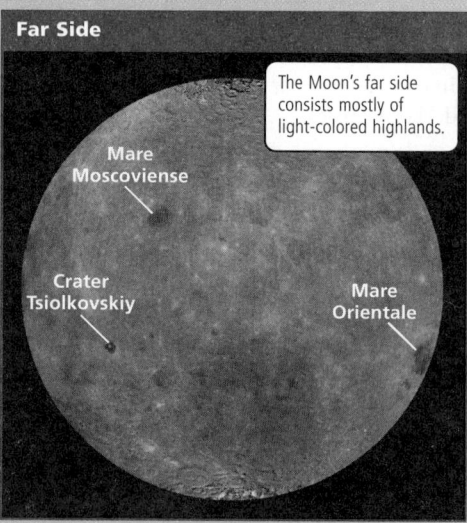

Far Side

The Moon's far side consists mostly of light-colored highlands.

Mare Moscoviense

Crater Tsiolkovskiy

Mare Orientale

DIFFERENTIATE INSTRUCTION

INVESTIGATE Moon Features

How did the Moon's features form?

In this model, you will use a paper napkin to represent the Moon's surface and gelatin to represent molten rock from inside the Moon.

PROCEDURE

1. Pour about 1 cm of partly cooled liquid gelatin into the cup.

2. Hold the paper towel by bringing its corners together. Push the towel into the cup until the center of the towel touches the bottom of the cup. Open the towel slightly.

3. Place the cup in the bowl of ice, and allow the gelatin time to solidify.

WHAT DO YOU THINK?

- What part of the towel did the gelatin affect?
- When you look down into the cup, what can the smooth areas tell you about heights?

CHALLENGE Early astronomers thought there might be oceans on the Moon. How does your model lava resemble an ocean?

SKILL FOCUS
Inferring

MATERIALS
- liquid gelatin
- clear plastic cup
- paper towel
- bowl of ice

TIME
20 minutes

Moon Rocks

Moon rocks have different ages. Some of the surface rock of the Moon is about 4.5 billion years old—as old as the Moon itself. This very old rock is found in the lunar highlands. The rock in the maria is younger because it formed from lava that solidified later, 3.8–3.1 billion years ago. These two main types of rock and their broken pieces cover most of the Moon's surface. Astronauts explored the Moon and brought back samples of as many different types of material as they could.

Impacts from space objects leave craters, and they also break the surface material into smaller pieces. This breaking of material is called weathering, even though it is not caused by wind and water. Weathered material on the Moon forms a type of dry, lifeless soil. The lunar soil is more than 15 meters (50 ft) deep in some places. Impacts can also toss lunar soil into different places, compact it into new rocks, or melt it and turn it into a glassy type of rock.

The dark-colored rock that formed from lava is called basalt (buh-SAWLT). Lunar basalt is similar to the rock deep beneath Earth's oceans. The basalt of the lunar maria covers large areas but is often only a few hundred meters in depth. However, the basalt can be several kilometers deep at the center of a mare, a depth similar to that of Earth's oceans.

Almost 400 kg (weighing more than 800 lb) of Moon rocks and soil were collected and brought back to Earth by astronauts.

highland rock

basalt

Chapter 2: **Earth, Moon, and Sun** 55 **E**

INVESTIGATE Moon Features

PURPOSE To infer how the Moon's maria formed

TIP *20 min.* Prepare double-strength unflavored gelatin and allow it to cool to a safe temperature before beginning the activity.

WHAT DO YOU THINK? *The gelatin covered the lowest part of the towel. The smooth areas indicate places of low elevation.*

CHALLENGE *The "maria" that formed from the model lava were smooth and flat, like the surface of an ocean.*

R Datasheet, Moon Features, p. 103

Technology Resources

Customize this student lab as needed or look for an alternative. Print rubrics to assess student lab reports.

Lab Generator CD-ROM

Develop Critical Thinking

INFER Ask students why astronauts who explored the Moon had to have some knowledge of geology. *They needed some geological training in order to know what kinds of rocks to bring back to Earth.* Ask students where on the Moon they would land if their mission was to gather as many different types of Moon rocks as they could. They should use the map on p. 54. *Sample answer: on the edge of a mare, in order to get at least two types of rock*

Ongoing Assessment

Describe the Moon's dark-colored and light-colored features.

Ask: What are the two main types of lunar surface, and what are they like? *Maria are dark-colored, flat plains. Lunar highlands are light-colored areas located at high altitudes.*

DIFFERENTIATE INSTRUCTION

? More Reading Support

E Where are the oldest lunar rocks? *in the highlands*

F What produces lunar soil? *impacts from space objects*

Inclusion Encourage students working together on activities to discuss in advance which tasks each will perform. Help students identify tasks that they can do well, or suggest alternative approaches that will suit their abilities. For example, in "Investigate Moon Features," students with visual impairments might arrange the paper towel or describe how parts of the resulting model feel.

Develop Critical Thinking

HYPOTHESIZE Tell students that the crust on the near side of the Moon is about 65 km thick. In contrast, the crust on the far side of the Moon is more than 100 km thick. Remind students that there are very few maria on the Moon's far side. Have them develop a hypothesis that relates the crustal thickness of the far side to its lack of maria. *There are few maria on the far side of the Moon because it is more difficult for molten rock to move the greater distance through a thicker crust.*

Teach from Visuals

To help students interpret the visual of the Moon's interior:

- Have students sequence the layers of the Moon from outermost to innermost. *crust, mantle, core*
- Ask: Which layer is thickest? *mantle*
- Ask: How does the size of the core compare with the overall size of the Moon? *The core is small compared with the overall size of the Moon. It makes up only a tiny fraction of the Moon's mass.*

Ongoing Assessment

CHECK YOUR READING *Sample answer: Why did impacts happen more often early in the Moon's history?*

COMBINATION NOTES Remember to take notes and make diagrams when you read about new ideas and terms.

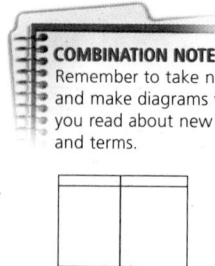

The Moon's interior resembles Earth's interior in several ways.

crust

mantle

core

The Moon has layers.

Scientists on Earth have analyzed the lunar rocks and soil to determine their ages and materials. These results told scientists a story about how the Moon changed over time. During an early stage of the Moon's history, impacts happened often and left craters of many different sizes. That stage ended about 3.8 billion years ago, and impacts have happened much less often since then. The highland rocks and soil come from the original surface and impacts. Shortly after the impacts slowed, lava flooded the low-lying areas and formed the maria. Then the flooding stopped. During the last 3 billion years, the Moon has gained new impact craters from time to time but has remained mostly unchanged.

Structure

Scientists have used information from lunar rocks and other measurements to figure out what is inside the Moon. Beneath its thin coating of crushed rock, the Moon has three layers—a crust, a mantle, and a core. As on Earth, the crust is the outermost layer. It averages about 70 kilometers (about 40 mi) thick and contains the least dense type of rock.

Beneath the crust is a thick mantle that makes up most of the Moon's volume. The mantle is made of dense types of rock that include the elements iron and magnesium. The basalt on the lunar surface contains these same elements, so scientists infer that the material of the basalt came from the mantle.

In the middle of the Moon is a small core, approximately 700 kilometers (400 mi) across. Although dense, it makes up only a tiny fraction of the Moon's mass. Scientists have less information about the core than the mantle because material from the core did not reach the Moon's surface. The core seems to consist of iron and other metals.

CHECK YOUR READING What are your own questions about the Moon?

Formation

Scientists develop models to help them understand their observations, such as the observed similarities and differences between Earth and the Moon. The two objects have similar structures and are made of similar materials. However, the materials are in different proportions. The Moon has more materials like Earth's crust and mantle and less material like Earth's core.

Scientists have used these facts to develop models of how the Moon formed. A widely accepted model of the Moon's origin involves a giant collision. In this model, an early version of Earth was hit by a

---

DIFFERENTIATE INSTRUCTION

? More Reading Support

G What did scientists use to model the Moon's formation? *similar structures and materials found on Earth*

Alternative Assessment Tell students that the Moon's crust is an average of 70 km thick, its mantle is roughly 1000 km thick, and its core is about 700 km in diameter. Have students draw a model of the Moon's interior, using a scale of 1 cm = 50 km. *Based on this scale, the crust would be 1.4 cm thick; the mantle, 20 cm thick; and the core, 14 cm across.*

Advanced Have students who are interested in the Moon's origin read the following article:

 Challenge Reading, pp. 116–117

Formation of the Moon

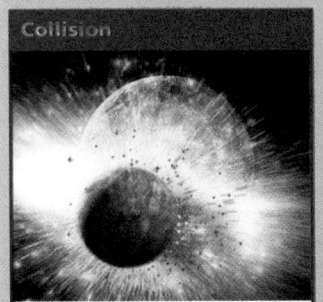

Collision

An early version of Earth is struck by a slightly smaller space body.

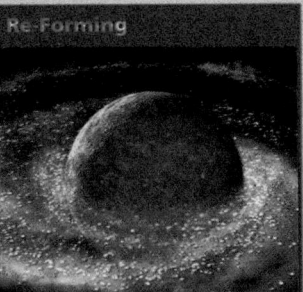

Re-Forming

The many pieces pull each other into orbits. Most of the material forms a new version of Earth.

Earth and Moon

The Moon forms from material that orbits the new version of Earth.

smaller space body. Much of the material from both bodies, especially the cores, combined to form a new version of Earth. The energy of the collision also threw material out, away from Earth. Bits of material from the crusts and mantles of both bodies went into orbit around the new Earth. Much of this orbiting material clumped together and became the Moon. Computer simulations of these events show that the Moon may have formed quickly—perhaps within just one year.

Evidence from fossils and rocks on Earth show that, whether the Moon formed from a giant collision or in some other way, it was once much closer to Earth than it is today. The Moon has been moving slowly away from Earth. It now moves 3.8 centimeters (1.5 in.) farther from Earth each year. However, this change is so slow that you will not notice any difference in your lifetime.

2.2 Review

KEY CONCEPTS

1. How many times does the Moon rotate on its axis during one trip around Earth?

2. What are the dark spots and the light areas on the Moon called?

3. Describe the Moon's layers.

CRITICAL THINKING

4. **Compare and Contrast** How are the Moon's dark-colored areas different from its light-colored areas?

5. **Draw Conclusions** How have the Moon rocks that astronauts brought back to Earth helped scientists understand the history of the Moon?

CHALLENGE

6. **Analyze** Scientists use indirect methods to learn about the cores of Earth and the Moon. Imagine you have several Styrofoam balls, some with steel balls hidden inside. WIthout breaking a ball open, how might you tell whether it contains a steel ball?

ANSWERS

1. once

2. dark spots: maria; light spots: lunar highlands

3. The Moon has a small core that seems to consist of metal, a mantle of dense rock, and a crust of rock that is less dense.

4. Both are made of rock or broken rock. The light areas are covered with craters. The dark areas are smooth and have few craters.

5. The rocks helped scientists compare the materials of the Moon and Earth. Scientists

developed models to explain their observations.

6. A ball with a metal core would feel heavier than a ball that contained only Styrofoam.

Ongoing Assessment

Describe the inside structure of the Moon.

Ask: Which layer of the Moon is most like a layer of Earth's? Explain your answer. *Accept all supported answers. Example: the mantle, because the Moon's core is small and the Moon's surface has no life*

Reinforce (the **BIG** idea)

Have students relate the section to the Big Idea.

 Reinforcing Key Concepts, p. 104

2.2 ASSESS & RETEACH

Assess

Section 2.2 Quiz, p. 24

Reteach

Reinforce that the Moon rotates once on its axis each time it orbits Earth, causing the same side of the Moon to always face Earth. Place a basketball on a table—the basketball represents Earth. Place an X on a small Styrofoam ball—this ball represents the Moon. Have students take turns holding the "Moon" and orbiting "Earth" so that the X always faces Earth. To accomplish this, students will find that they must rotate the Moon once. To help them understand, have them orbit Earth without rotating the Moon at all relative to the classroom. They will find that different parts of the Moon face Earth throughout the orbit. Ask: Why do we see only one side of the Moon from Earth? *because the Moon turns once on its axis each time it orbits Earth*

Technology Resources

Have students visit **ClassZone.com** for reteaching of Key Concepts.

 CONTENT REVIEW

 CONTENT REVIEW CD-ROM

Set Learning Goal

To make line graphs showing changing patterns of sunlight

Present the Science

Changes in temperature from summer to winter are produced by the changing amount of energy from sunlight in an area. The amount of energy from sunlight depends on both the angle of sunlight, which is at its maximum around noon, and the duration of sunlight, or hours of daylight. A high noon Sun means the ground receives more energy in the middle of the day. A long day means more energy per 24 hours. However, it takes time for an area to heat up or cool down.

Develop Graphing Skills

Copy the graph onto the board, using colored chalk for the red labels. Plot the first two months of data, using regular chalk for sunlight and colored chalk for angle. Tell students that color helps them match the axis to the data set.

DIFFERENTIATION TIP Create a graph and mount it on posterboard. Then use pushpins to plot data, so students with visual impairments can connect the points by wrapping yarn around them.

Close

Have students compare the two lines, noting the maximum and minimum values. Ask: Do the two aspects of solar energy strengthen each other or cancel out? *strengthen, because their maximums occur at the same time.*

 • Math Support, pp. 121–122
• Math Practice, p. 123

Technology Resources

Students can visit **ClassZone.com** for practice with graphs.

 MATH TUTORIAL

 MATH TUTORIAL
CLASSZONE.COM
Click on Math Tutorial for more help with line graphs.

Washington, D.C.

Month	Sunlight Each Day (h)	Angle of Sun at Noon (°)
Jan.	9.9	31.4
Feb.	11.0	40.8
Mar.	12.2	51.6
Apr.	13.5	63.2
May	14.5	71.4
June	14.9	74.6
July	14.5	71.4
Aug.	13.5	63.0
Sept.	12.2	51.6
Oct.	11.0	40.2
Nov.	9.9	31.1
Dec.	9.5	27.7

This is a series of images of the Sun photographed at exactly the same time of day every few days over most of a year. The bottom of the photograph is from just one of the days and includes a stone circle calendar.

SKILL: MAKING LINE GRAPHS

Graphing Sunlight

The location of the Moon and the Sun in the sky depend on your location on Earth and when you look. In summer, the noon Sun is at a greater angle above the horizon—closer to 90°—than it is in winter. In summer, the Sun rises earlier and sets later than in winter. Longer days and steeper angles of sunlight combine to make summer days much warmer than winter days. Plot the data for Washington, D.C. (latitude 39° N) to see the changing patterns of sunlight.

Example

You can make a double line graph to see patterns in the data. Use a colored pencil to label the second y-axis.

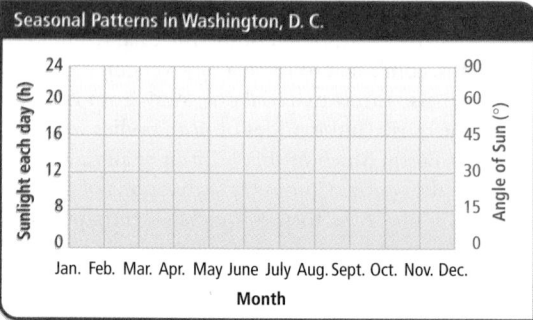

Seasonal Patterns in Washington, D. C.

(1) Copy all three graph axes onto graph paper.

(2) Use the y-axis on the left to plot the data for the hours of daylight. Draw line segments to connect the points.

(3) Use the y-axis on the right and a colored pencil to plot the data for the angle of the Sun. Draw line segments to connect the points.

Answer the following questions.

1. During which time period do days get shorter?

2. About how many degrees higher in the sky is the noon Sun in June than in December? About how many more hours of sunlight are there each day in June than in December?

3. Does the angle of the Sun change more quickly between June and July or between September and October? How can you tell from the graph?

CHALLENGE Copy the axes again, then graph the data your teacher gives you for a location near the North Pole. Use your graphs to compare daylight patterns at the two latitudes.

ANSWERS

1. from June to December

2. nearly 50°; about 5 hours

3. The angle changes more quickly between September and October. You can tell from the graph because the slope is steeper.

CHALLENGE *Challenge data for 68°N latitude: Jan. 4.2 h, 2°; Feb. 8.7 h, 12°; Mar. 12.4 h, 22°; Apr. 16.5 h, 34°; May 21.6 h, 42°; June 24 h, 46°; July 22 h, 43°; Aug. 16.6 h, 34°; Sept. 12.5 h, 23°; Oct. 8.6 h, 11°; Nov. 4.2 h, 2°; Dec. 0 h, −1°. Answer: daylight: 0–24h, angle: 0°–46°, more extreme than those for Washington, D.C.*

KEY CONCEPT

2.3 Positions of the Sun and Moon affect Earth.

◀ **BEFORE, you learned**

- The Moon orbits Earth
- Sunlight shines on Earth and the Moon

▶ **NOW, you will learn**

- Why the Moon has phases
- What causes eclipses
- Why Earth's oceans have tides

VOCABULARY

eclipse p. 63
umbra p. 63
penumbra p. 63

THINK ABOUT

Have you seen the Moon in daylight?

Many people think that the Moon is visible only at night. This idea is not surprising, because the Moon is the brightest object in the sky at night. In the daytime the Moon is only as bright as a tiny, thin cloud. It is easy to miss, even in a cloudless blue sky. You can see the Moon sometimes in the daytime, sometimes at night, often at both times, and sometimes not at all. Why does the Moon sometimes disappear from view?

COMBINATION NOTES
Use the blue heading to start a new set of notes.

Phases are different views of the Moon's sunlit half.

What you see as moonlight is really light from the Sun reflected by the Moon's surface. At any time, sunlight shines on half of the Moon's surface. Areas where sunlight does not reach look dark, just as the night side of Earth looks dark from space. As the Moon turns on its axis, areas on the surface move into and out of sunlight.

When you look at the Moon, you see a bright shape that is the lit part of the near side of the Moon. The unlit part is hard to see. Lunar phases are the patterns of lit and unlit portions of the Moon that you see from Earth. It takes about a month for the Moon to orbit Earth and go through all the phases.

CHECK YOUR READING Why do you sometimes see only part of the near side of the Moon?

Chapter 2: Earth, Moon, and Sun 59 **E**

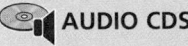

2.3 FOCUS

◗ Set Learning Goals
Students will

- Determine why the Moon has phases.
- Explain what causes eclipses.
- Explain why Earth's oceans have tides.
- Make an experimental model of Moon phases.

◖ 3-Minute Warm-Up

Display Transparency 13 or copy this exercise on the board:

Think about a time you have seen the Moon in the sky. Draw the Moon the way you have seen it. Add labels or sentences to help describe what you saw. *Encourage students to include shape, brightness, location, and any other details they recall.*

T 3-Minute Warm-Up, p. T13

2.3 MOTIVATE

THINK ABOUT

PURPOSE To realize that the Moon can sometimes be seen in daylight

DISCUSS Remind students that the Sun also disappears from view each day. Have them remember why this happens. *The Sun disappears when it is below the horizon.* Tell students that the Moon is not visible when it is below the horizon and that they will learn other reasons the Moon may not be visible.

Ongoing Assessment

CHECK YOUR READING *Answer: Areas where sunlight does not reach—the unlit parts—look dark and are difficult to see.*

Address Misconceptions

IDENTIFY Ask: What causes lunar phases? If students say that lunar phases are caused by Earth's shadow, they may hold misconceptions about the Moon's movements and why the Moon shines.

CORRECT Have students use models to see that half the Moon is lit by the Sun at any given time, but only part of it may be visible from our point of view on Earth. If time allows, have students record their observations of the Moon for two weeks or more to see that lunar phases involve small changes from day to day.

REASSESS Tell students that if phases were caused by Earth's shadow, the Moon would look the same for most of the month and not have the phases that it does. Have students demonstrate three or more Moon phases using a model (such as that from "Investigate Phases of the Moon" on p. 62). *Demonstrations should include direction of sunlight and position of the Moon relative to Earth.*

Technology Resources

Visit **ClassZone.com** for background on common student misconceptions.

 MISCONCEPTION DATABASE

Real World Example

The month is based, historically, on the motion of the Moon. The Moon takes 27.3 days to go around Earth. Because Earth moves about 30° around the Sun during this time, the Moon has to go somewhat more than once around Earth to complete a cycle of phases, so a lunar month takes about 29 days.

Ongoing Assessment

 *Answer: that is when less than half of its near side is in sunlight*

 **VISUALIZATION**
CLASSZONE.COM
Explore lunar phases.

READING TiP
Use the red dashed lines at each position in the diagram on page 61 to determine what part of the Moon is visible from Earth.

READING TiP
Crescent and *gibbous* describe the shape, while *waxing* and *waning* describe the changes— growing or shrinking.

The Moon's position in its monthly orbit determines how it appears from Earth. The diagram on page 61 shows how the positions of the Moon, the Sun, and Earth affect the shapes you see in the sky.

Waxing Moon

First Week The cycle begins with a new moon. From Earth, the Moon and the Sun are in the same direction. If you face a new moon, you face the Sun. Your face and the far side of the Moon are in sunlight. The near side of the Moon is unlit, so you do not see it. During a new moon, there appears to be no Moon.

? A

As the Moon moves along its orbit, sunlight begins falling on the near side. You see a thin crescent shape. During the first week, the Moon keeps moving farther around, so more of the near side becomes lit. You see thicker crescents as the Moon waxes, or grows.

Second Week When half of the near side of the Moon is in sunlight, the Moon has completed one-quarter of its cycle. The phase is called the first quarter, even though you might describe the shape as a half-moon. You can see in the diagram that the Moon is 90 degrees—at a right angle—from the Sun. If you face the first-quarter moon when it is high in the sky, sunlight will shine on the right side of your head and the right side of the Moon.

You see more of the Moon as it moves along its orbit during the second week. The phase is called gibbous (GIHB-uhs) when the near side is more than half lit but not fully lit. The Moon is still waxing, so the phases during the second week are called waxing gibbous moons.

? B

 **CHECK YOUR READING** Why does the Moon sometimes seem to have a crescent shape?

Waning Moon

Third Week Halfway through its cycle, the whole near side of the Moon is in sunlight—a full moon. You might think of it as the second quarter. Viewed from Earth, the Moon and the Sun are in opposite directions. If you face a full moon at sunset, sunlight from behind you lights the back of your head and the near side of the Moon.

As the Moon continues around during the third week, less and less of the near side is in sunlight. The Moon seems to shrink, or wane, so these phases are called waning gibbous moons.

Fourth Week When the near side is again only half in sunlight, the Moon is three-quarters of the way through its cycle. The phase is called the third quarter. The Moon is again 90 degrees from the Sun. If you face the third-quarter moon when it is high in the sky, sunlight will shine on the left side of your head and the left side of the Moon.

DIFFERENTIATE INSTRUCTION

? More Reading Support

A During which phase does the Moon seem to disappear? *new moon*

B What happens to the Moon during the first two weeks? *It waxes, or grows.*

English Learners This section includes sentences with a variety of introductory clauses and phrases. Point out common introductory phrases to watch for, and help students distinguish between them and the main clause, which contains the subject of the sentence. Write the following example from this page on the board. Underline the introductory phrase and circle the subject.

 As the Moon moves along its orbit, (sunlight) begins falling on the near side.

Lunar Phases

The appearance of the Moon depends on the positions of the Sun, Moon, and Earth.

If you could watch the Moon from high above its pole, you would always see half the Moon in sunlight and half in darkness.

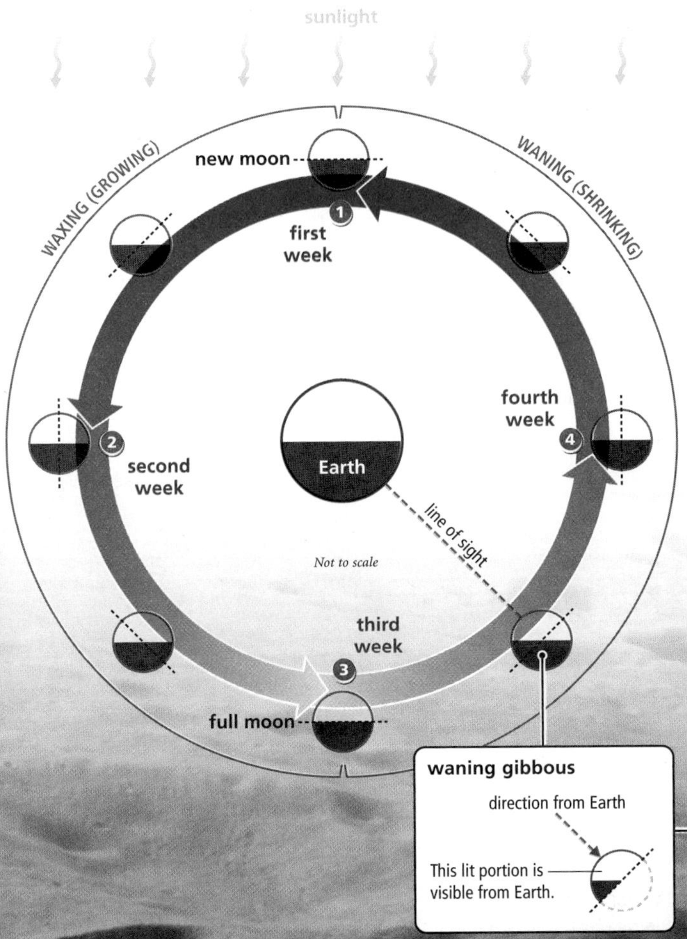

sunlight

WAXING (GROWING)

WANING (SHRINKING)

new moon

first week

fourth week

Earth

second week

line of sight

Not to scale

third week

full moon

waning gibbous

direction from Earth

This lit portion is visible from Earth.

View from Earth

Viewed from Earth, the Moon's shape seems to change.

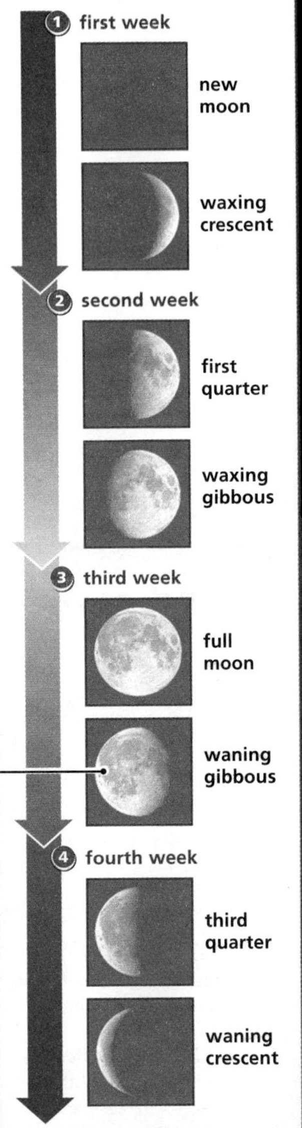

1 **first week**
- new moon
- waxing crescent

2 **second week**
- first quarter
- waxing gibbous

3 **third week**
- full moon
- waning gibbous

4 **fourth week**
- third quarter
- waning crescent

READING VISUALS COMPARE How are the sunlit portions alike in the image and the diagram of the waning gibbous moon?

Chapter 2: Earth, Moon, and Sun **61** E

INVESTIGATE Phases of the Moon

PURPOSE To model Moon phases

TIPS *20 min.*

• Darken the room before beginning this activity.

• Try to position the lamp as high as possible so that students' heads do not block the light for a full moon. Students may need to hold the balls high.

WHAT DO YOU THINK? *The right side of the ball was lit, because the lamp was to the right of the ball. The drawings have the same shape as the Moon phases shown in the photographs. Step 2 resembles a waxing crescent; step 3 resembles the Moon in first quarter; step 4 resembles a full moon, third-quarter moon, and waning crescent.*

CHALLENGE *Sunlight reflects off Earth and can then reflect off the near side of the Moon.*

 Datasheet, Phases of the Moon, p. 114

Technology Resources

Customize this student lab as needed or look for an alternative. Print rubrics to assess student lab reports.

 Lab Generator CD-ROM

Metacognitive Strategy

Tell students to close their eyes and imagine they are viewing the Moon from different places in space. What do they see? How does it differ from what they see from Earth? What did they do to change their perspective?

EXPLORE (the BIG idea)

Revisit "What Makes the Moon Bright?" on p. 41. Have students describe their observations.

Ongoing Assessment

 **CHECK YOUR READING** *Answer: crescent*

E **62** Unit: Space Science

As the Moon continues to move around Earth during the fourth week, less and less of the near side is in sunlight. The waning crescent moon grows thinner and thinner. At the end of the fourth week, the near side is again unlit, and the new moon begins a new cycle.

Crescent and Gibbous Moons

Think through the waxing lunar phases again. The Moon waxes from new to crescent to gibbous during the first half of its cycle. Then it wanes from full to gibbous to crescent during the second half of its cycle.

 The amount of the Moon that you see from Earth depends on the angle between the Moon and the Sun. When this angle is small, you see only a small amount of the Moon. Crescent moons occur when the Moon appears close to the Sun in the sky. As a result, they are visible most often in the daytime or around the time of sunrise or sunset. When the angle between the Sun and the Moon is large, you see a large amount of the Moon. Gibbous and full moons appear far from the Sun in the sky. You may see them in the daytime, but you are more likely to notice them at night.

 What shape does the Moon appear to be when it is at a small angle to the Sun?

INVESTIGATE Phases of the Moon

Why does the Moon seem to change shape?

PROCEDURE

① Place the ball on the stick, which will act as a handle. The ball will represent the Moon, and your head will represent Earth.

② Hold the ball toward the light, then move it to your left until you see a bright edge. Draw what you see.

③ Move the ball farther around until half of what you see is lit. Draw it.

④ Keep moving the ball around to your left until the side you see is fully lit, then half lit, then lit only a little bit. Each time, face the ball and draw it.

WHAT DO YOU THINK?

• In step 2, which side of the ball was lit? Explain why.

• How are your drawings like the photographs of the Moon's phases? Label each drawing with the name of the corresponding lunar phase.

CHALLENGE When the Moon is a crescent, sometimes you can dimly see the rest of the Moon if you look closely. Where might the light that makes the darker part of the Moon visible come from?

SKILL FOCUS Making models

MATERIALS
• foam ball
• stick
• lamp

TIME 20 minutes

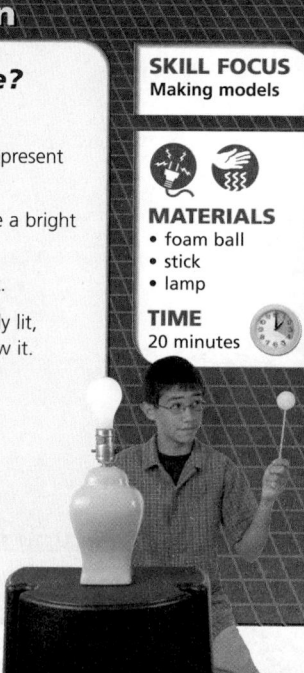

E **62** Unit: Space Science

DIFFERENTIATE INSTRUCTION

 More Reading Support

C When do you see a small amount of the Moon? *when it is crescent and appears close to the Sun*

Below Level While doing the investigation, students may lose track of the model Moon's orbit when they pause to do their sketches. Have them work with partners. One student can hold the ball and keep track of the step number while the other sketches; then they can switch roles.

Shadows in space cause eclipses.

Sunlight streams past Earth and the Moon, lighting one side of each body. Beyond each body is a long, thin cone of darkness where no sunlight reaches—a shadow in space. The two bodies are far apart, so they usually miss each other's shadow as the Moon orbits Earth. However, if the Moon, the Sun, and Earth line up exactly, a shadow crosses Earth or the Moon. An **eclipse** occurs when a shadow makes the Sun or the Moon seem to grow dark. In a lunar eclipse, the Moon darkens. In a solar eclipse, the Sun seems to darken.

VOCABULARY
Remember to record vocabulary terms.

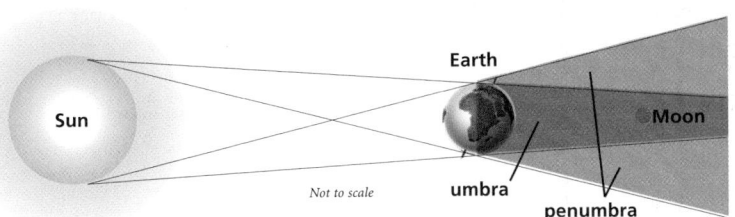

Earth

Sun

Moon

Not to scale   umbra

penumbra

Lunar Eclipses

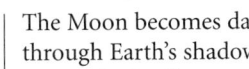

The Moon becomes dark during a lunar eclipse because it passes through Earth's shadow. There are two parts of Earth's shadow, as you can see in the diagram above. The **umbra** is the darkest part. Around it is a spreading cone of lighter shadow called the **penumbra.**

Just before a lunar eclipse, sunlight streaming past Earth produces a full moon. Then the Moon moves into Earth's penumbra and becomes slightly less bright. As the Moon moves into the umbra, Earth's dark shadow seems to creep across and cover the Moon. The entire Moon can be in darkness because the Moon is small enough to fit entirely within Earth's umbra. After an hour or more, the Moon moves slowly back into the sunlight that is streaming past Earth.

A total lunar eclipse occurs when the Moon passes completely into Earth's umbra. If the Moon misses part or all of the umbra, part of the Moon stays light and the eclipse is called a partial lunar eclipse.

Earth's shadow

The Moon starts getting dark on one side as it passes into Earth's umbra. Even when the Moon is completely within Earth's umbra, some red sunlight, bent by Earth's atmosphere, may still reach the Moon.

Chapter 2: **Earth, Moon, and Sun** 63   **E**

DIFFERENTIATE INSTRUCTION

 More Reading Support

D What becomes dark during a lunar eclipse? *the Moon*

E What is the darkest part of Earth's shadow? *the umbra*

Advanced Have students refer back to the visual of lunar phases on p. 61. Then have them reexamine the visual of a lunar eclipse on this page. Ask: During which lunar phase or phases can a lunar eclipse occur? Explain your answer. *A lunar eclipse can only occur during a full moon because during that phase the Sun, Earth, and the Moon are properly lined up.*

 Challenge and Extension, p. 113

Teach from Visuals

To help students interpret the diagram of a lunar eclipse:

- Have them compare and contrast the Earth's umbra and penumbra. *Both are parts of Earth's shadow. The umbra is the darkest part. The penumbra is a spreading cone of lighter shadow around the umbra.*

- Ask: Where is Earth in relation to the Sun and Moon? *in between them*

- Ask: How would the diagram change to show a partial lunar eclipse? *the Moon would be only partially in Earth's umbra.*

History of Science

From ancient times, educated people have known that Earth was round. The famous Greek philosopher Aristotle (384–322 BC.) observed lunar eclipses and noted that Earth's shadow on the Moon was curved—only a round object would cast a curved shadow. Later, the Greek mathematician Eratosthenes measured Earth's circumference by using shadows.

Ongoing Assessment

Explain what causes eclipses.

Ask: What causes eclipses? *A shadow makes the Sun or the Moon seem to grow dark.*

Health Connection

The retina, located near the back of the eye, is made up of two kinds of cells—rods and cones. Both types are extremely sensitive to light and can be easily damaged by staring directly at the Sun. This can lead to temporary or permanent blindness. Because the retina has no pain receptors, the damage may not be apparent until several hours later. Therefore, no one should ever look directly at the Sun's disk, even when the Sun appears mostly hidden during a solar eclipse.

Teach from Visuals

To help students interpret the diagram of a solar eclipse, ask:

- In what phase is the Moon during a solar eclipse? *new moon*

- This diagram and the one on p. 63 both say "Not to scale." How would the diagrams be different if they were to scale? Could they be shown in this book? *The Sun would be much larger and the distances between the Sun and Earth and between the Moon and Earth would be much greater, too great to fit in this book.*

Teach Difficult Concepts

Students may question why eclipses do not happen every month. Explain that the Moon's orbit is slightly tilted with respect to Earth's orbit around the Sun. Most times, the Moon is not in the same plane as Earth's orbit. Both solar and lunar eclipses can only occur when the Sun, the Moon, and Earth are aligned.

Solar Eclipses

 F In a solar eclipse, the Sun seems to darken because the Moon's shadow falls onto part of Earth. Imagine that you are in the path of a solar eclipse. At first, you see a normal day. You cannot see the dark Moon moving toward the Sun. Then part of the Sun seems to disappear as the Moon moves in front of it. You are in the Moon's penumbra. After several hours of growing darkness, the Moon covers the Sun's disk completely. The sky becomes as dark as night, and you may see constellations. In place of the Sun is a black disk—the new moon—surrounded by a pale glow. You are in the Moon's umbra, the darkest part of the shadow, experiencing a total solar eclipse. After perhaps a minute, the Sun's bright surface starts to appear again.

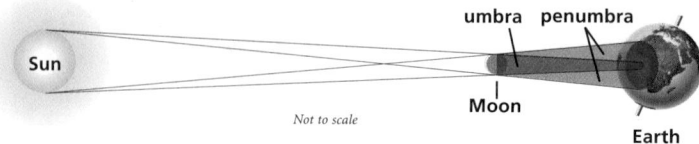

Sun · umbra · penumbra · Moon · Earth · *Not to scale*

A solar eclipse occurs when the Moon passes directly between Earth and the Sun. As you can see in the diagram above, the side of the Moon that faces Earth is unlit, so solar eclipses occur only during new moons.

If you could watch a solar eclipse from space, it might seem more like a lunar eclipse. You would see the Moon's penumbra, with the dark umbra in the center, move across Earth's daylight side. However, the Moon is smaller than Earth, so it casts a smaller shadow. As you can see in the diagram above, the Moon's umbra covers only a fraction of Earth's surface at a time. **G**

June 21, 2001 Eclipse

total eclipse

In this time-lapse photograph, the Sun's disk appears darker as the Moon passes in front. When the Moon is exactly in front of the Sun, the sky grows as dark as night.

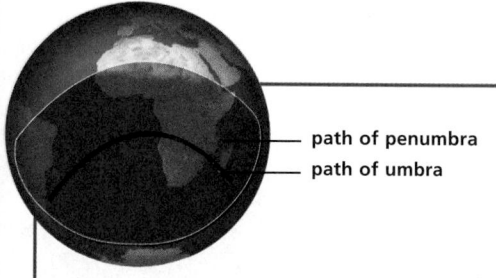

path of penumbra
path of umbra

Path of June 21, 2001 Eclipse Only locations along the thin central path of the shadow experience a total eclipse. Other locations experience a partial eclipse.

DIFFERENTIATE INSTRUCTION

? **More Reading Support**

F What casts a shadow on Earth during a solar eclipse? *the Moon*

G Why does the Moon cast a smaller shadow than Earth? *The Moon is smaller.*

Below Level Place students into groups of three. One student should represent the Sun, another should represent Earth, and the third should represent the Moon. Have the students line up in proper order to model the positions of the Sun, Earth, and Moon during both a lunar and a solar eclipse. Students representing the Moon and Earth can use their arms to represent the edges of their shadows. *During a lunar eclipse, Earth is between the Sun and the Moon. During a solar eclipse, the Moon is between the Sun and Earth.*

Only locations in the path of the Moon's shadow experience a solar eclipse. Some people travel thousands of miles to be in the thin path of the Moon's umbra so that they can experience a total solar eclipse. Locations near the path of the umbra get an eclipse that is less than total. If only the penumbra moves over your location, you experience a partial solar eclipse. The Moon covers just part of the Sun.

Bright light from the Sun's disk can damage your eyes if you look directly at it. The Sun is unsafe to look at even when the Moon covers most of the Sun's disk. If you have the chance to experience a solar eclipse, use a safe method to view the Sun.

 **CHECK YOUR READING** Where is the Moon during a solar eclipse? Find a way to remember the difference between the two types of eclipses.

The Moon's gravity causes tides on Earth.

If you have spent time near an ocean, you may have experienced the usual pattern of tides. At first, you might see dry sand that slopes down to the ocean. Then, waves creep higher and higher onto the sand. The average water level rises slowly for about 6 hours. The highest level is called high tide. Then the water level slowly drops for about 6 hours. The lowest level is called low tide. Then the water level rises and falls again. The entire pattern—two high tides and two low tides—takes a little more than 24 hours.

In areas with tides, the water generally reaches its lowest level twice a day and its highest level twice a day.

 **CHECK YOUR READING** How many high tides do you expect per day?

Tides occur because the Moon's gravity changes the shape of Earth's oceans. The Moon pulls on different parts of Earth with different amounts of force. It pulls hardest on the side of Earth nearest it, a little less hard on the center of Earth, and even less hard on the farthest side of Earth. If Earth were flexible, it would be pulled into a football shape. Earth's crust is hard enough to resist being pulled into a different shape, but Earth's oceans do change shape.

 Chapter 2: **Earth, Moon, and Sun** 65 **E**

Real World Example

There are safe ways to view a solar eclipse. One method is pinhole projection. Use a pin to poke a small hole in the center of a large piece of cardboard. Outside, stand on a smooth surface. Hold the cardboard at shoulder height and look at the middle of the cardboard's shadow to see the image of the round or partially eclipsed Sun. More complex arrangements, also suitable for viewing sunspots, can be found in libraries and on the Internet. Specially designed glasses can also be used to view solar eclipses. These glasses are covered with a thin film of aluminum or a similar substance that filters out the Sun's harmful rays.

Teach from Visuals

To help students interpret the two photographs of the tides, ask:

- What is the main difference between these two photographs? *The water covers the shore in the bottom photograph.*

- Which photograph shows high tide? *the bottom photograph*

- What helps you tell about how high the tide is in this inlet? *The people in the top photograph provide a scale.*

Ongoing Assessment

CHECK YOUR READING *Answer: The Moon is between the Sun and Earth. Students may suggest remembering that the name of the eclipse describes the object that darkens or seems to disappear.*

CHECK YOUR READING *Answer: two*

DIFFERENTIATE INSTRUCTION

 **More Reading Support**

H Why do tides occur? *because the Moon's gravity changes the shape of Earth's oceans*

Alternative Assessment Tell students that *tidal range* refers to the difference in water level between high tide and low tide. Have them obtain tide data from the Internet or from a newspaper located in a coastal area. The tide data (a table or graph) should show water levels for a tidal day, which corresponds to slightly more than 24 hours. Have students describe any patterns they observe. *Students should note that over the course of most tidal days, there are two peaks, or high tides, and two troughs, or low tides.*

Ongoing Assessment

Explain why Earth's oceans have tides.

Ask: What effect does the Moon have on Earth's oceans? *It produces two bulges of water.*

 **Answer:** *It takes 24 hours for Earth to complete one rotation.*

Real World Example

The tidal range—the difference in water level between high tide and low tide—depends partly on the shape of the shoreline. The range is highest in small, narrow inlets. At the narrow end of Nova Scotia's long, V-shaped Bay of Fundy, for example, high tide is as much as 15 meters above low tide.

Reinforce (the **BIG** idea)

Have students relate the section to the Big Idea.

 Reinforcing Key Concepts, p. 115

2.3 ASSESS & RETEACH

Assess

 Section 2.3 Quiz, p. 25

Reteach

Place students in groups of three—two to represent Earth and the Moon, and one to keep track of where sunlight falls. Students should imagine sunlight coming from one wall of the classroom. Have the teams model the positions that produce different lunar phases. *Positions should match the diagram on p. 61.* Students may use a piece of cloth to cover the unlit half of the Moon.

Technology Resources

Have students visit **ClassZone.com** for reteaching of Key Concepts.

 CONTENT REVIEW

 CONTENT REVIEW CD-ROM

E 66 Unit: **Space Science**

Cause of Tides

The Moon's gravity changes the shape of Earth's oceans.

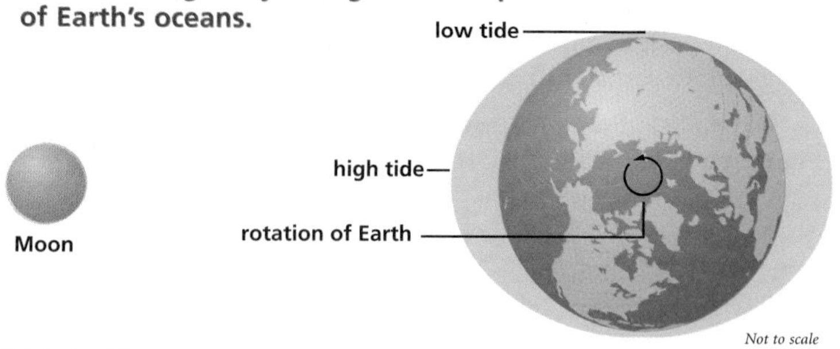

low tide

high tide

rotation of Earth

Moon

Not to scale

 **RESOURCE CENTER** CLASSZONE.COM
Learn more about tides.

The diagram above shows what would happen if Earth were covered with a thick layer of water. The Moon's pull produces a bulge of thicker ocean water on the side of Earth nearest the Moon. Another bulge of water is produced on the side of Earth farthest from the Moon because the Moon pulls the center of Earth away from that side. The layer of water is thinnest in the middle, between the bulges.

A location moves past different thicknesses of water as Earth turns on its axis. As a result, the water level there rises and falls. The thickest water produces the highest level, which is high tide. A quarter of a rotation—6 hours—later, the location has moved to the thinnest layer of water, or low tide. Another high tide and low tide complete the cycle. Because the Moon is orbiting while Earth is turning, the cycle takes a little longer than the 24 hours in a day.

 Why does a cycle of tides take about 24 hours?

2.3 Review

KEY CONCEPTS

1. When the Moon is full, where is it in its orbit around Earth?
2. Where is the Moon in its orbit at the time of a solar eclipse?
3. If it is high tide where you are, is the tide high or low on the side of Earth directly opposite you?

CRITICAL THINKING

4. **Apply** If you were on the Moon's near side during a new moon, how much of the side of Earth facing you would be sunlit?
5. **Predict** If Earth did not turn, how would the pattern of tides be affected?

CHALLENGE

6. **Predict** Would we see lunar phases if the Moon did not rotate while it orbits Earth?

E 66 Unit: **Space Science**

ANSWERS

1. The full moon is opposite the Sun from Earth.

2. The Moon is in front of the Sun.

3. The tide is high.

4. All of the side of Earth facing the Moon would be sunlit.

5. A cycle of tides would take about a month, rather than a day. Students may reasonably predict unchanging water heights.

6. Yes; lunar phases would occur regardless of the Moon's period of rotation.

ARCHAEOLOGIST

Antikythera Computer

A device with gears and dials was found in an ancient Greek shipwreck. While examining the device, a scientist noticed terms, patterns, and numbers from astronomy. These observations led him to form a hypothesis that ancient Greeks used the instrument to calculate the positions of the Sun, Moon, and other bodies in space. Gamma-ray images of the instrument's interior later supported this hypothesis.

Chimney Rock

Chimney Rock, in Colorado, is topped by two natural pillars of rock. The Moon appears to rise between the pillars under special circumstances that happen about every 18 years. Near the pillars are ruins of buildings of the Anasazi people. In order to construct the buildings and live here, the builders had to haul materials and water much farther than was usual. Some archaeologists hypothesize that the Anasazi built here in order to watch or celebrate special events in the sky.

Astronomy in Archaeology

In order to understand how people lived and thought long ago, archaeologists study the buildings and other physical remains of ancient cultures. Archaeologists often think about what needs people had in order to figure out how they used the things they built. For example, people needed to know the time of year in order to decide when to plant crops, move to a different location for winter, or plan certain ceremonies.

Archaeologists can use their knowledge about objects in the sky to hypothesize about the purpose of an ancient structure. They can also use knowledge and models from astronomy to test their hypotheses. For example, archaeologists found some structures at Chimney Rock that were built at times of special events in the sky.

Stonehenge

Stonehenge is an arrangement of stones in Britain. The first stones were placed there around 3100 B.C. The way that the Sun and Moon line up with the stones has led some archaeologists to think that they were designed to help people predict solstices and eclipses. Solstices tell people the time of year, so Stonehenge has sometimes been called a calendar.

path of rising Sun on solstice

Stonehenge as seen from above

EXPLORE

1. **COMPARE** How is each archaeological example related to astronomy?
2. **CHALLENGE** Make a list of five print or television advertisements that feature the Sun or other objects in the sky. Bring in copies of the advertisements if you can. Why might the advertisers have chosen these objects?

Ruins of buildings were found on a high, narrow ridge at Chimney Rock.

Chapter 2: **Earth, Moon, and Sun** 67 **E**

EXPLORE

1. **COMPARE** *The Antikythera computer may have helped people to calculate the positions of bodies in space. At Chimney Rock, the Moon appears to rise between two natural pillars of rock every 18 years; people may have used the site to celebrate special events in the sky. At Stonehenge, the arrangement of the stones may have helped people predict solstices and eclipses.*

2. **CHALLENGE** *Lists should contain specific advertisements. Objects in the sky, such as the Sun, Moon, and stars, can communicate ideas such as daytime, mystery, or great size.*

Chapter 2 **67** **E**

BACK TO

the BIG idea

Refer students back to the photograph on pp. 40–41. Ask: What effects does the Moon have on Earth? *phases (light), tides, eclipses, people's knowledge of space and lunar events*

◀ KEY CONCEPTS SUMMARY

SECTION 2.1

Ask: In the globe on the left, where is sunrise occurring? *along the line between dark and light*

Ask: In the series of four globes, what does the last image show? *the June solstice*

Ask: Which hemisphere receives less sunlight at this time? *Southern*

SECTION 2.2

Ask: Which Moon features are large, flat plains? *maria*

Ask: Why do the materials of the Moon resemble those of Earth? *Sample answer: They probably formed from the same material.*

SECTION 2.3

Ask: During which part of its monthly cycle does the Moon appear to wax, or grow? *the first half*

Ask: Based on the positions of the Sun, the Moon, and Earth, during which lunar phase can a lunar eclipse occur? *full moon*

Review Concepts

- Big Idea Flow Chart, p. T9
- Chapter Outline, pp. T15–T16

 # Chapter Review

the BIG idea

Earth and the Moon move in predictable ways as they orbit the Sun.

CONTENT REVIEW
CLASSZONE.COM

◀ KEY CONCEPTS SUMMARY

2.1 Earth rotates on a tilted axis and orbits the Sun.

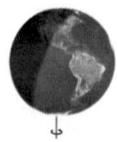   

Earth's rotation in sunlight causes day and night.

The changing angles of sunlight on Earth cause seasons.

VOCABULARY
axis of rotation p. 44
revolution p. 45
season p. 46
equinox p. 46
solstice p. 46

2.2 The Moon is Earth's natural satellite.

Dark-colored maria formed from lava-filled craters.

Light-colored highlands are old and cratered.

The Moon's near side always faces Earth.

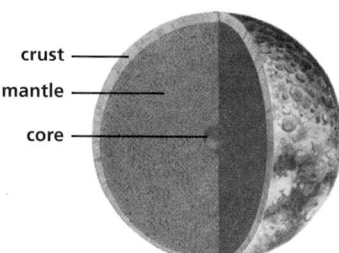
crust
mantle
core

VOCABULARY
mare p. 53

2.3 Positions of the Sun and Moon affect Earth.

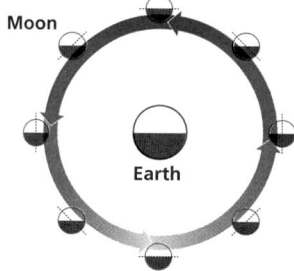
Moon

Earth

Lunar phases are different views of the Moon's sunlit half.

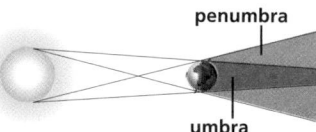
penumbra
umbra

Shadows cause eclipses.

The Moon's gravity causes tides as Earth turns.

VOCABULARY
eclipse p. 63
umbra p. 63
penumbra p. 63

Technology Resources

Have students visit **ClassZone.com** or use the CD-ROM for a cumulative review of concepts.

Engage students in a whole-class interactive review of Key Concepts. Edit content as you wish.

 CONTENT REVIEW

 CONTENT REVIEW CD-ROM

 POWER PRESENTATIONS

Reviewing Vocabulary

Use words and diagrams to show the relationship between the terms in each the following pairs. *Underline the two terms in each answer.*

1. revolution, rotation
2. revolution, season
3. solstice, equinox
4. mare, impact crater
5. eclipse, umbra
6. umbra, penumbra

Reviewing Key Concepts

Multiple Choice *Choose the letter of the best answer.*

7. How long does it take Earth to turn once on its axis of rotation?
   a. an hour   c. a month
   b. a day   d. a year

8. How long does it take Earth to orbit the Sun?
   a. an hour   c. a month
   b. a day   d. a year

9. About how long does it take the Moon to revolve once around Earth?
   a. an hour   c. a month
   b. a day   d. a year

10. Why is it hotter in summer than in winter?
    a. Earth gets closer to and farther from the Sun.
    b. Sunlight strikes the ground at higher and lower angles.
    c. Earth turns faster in some seasons.
    d. Earth revolves around the Sun more times in some seasons.

11. The dark maria on the Moon formed from
    a. dried-up seas
    b. finely-broken rock
    c. large shadows
    d. lava-filled craters

12. The lunar highlands have more impact craters than the maria, so scientists know that the highlands
    a. are older than the maria
    b. are younger than the maria
    c. are flatter than the maria
    d. are darker than the maria

13. Why is just one side of the Moon visible from Earth?
    a. The Moon does not rotate on its axis as it orbits Earth.
    b. The Moon rotates once in the same amount of time that it orbits.
    c. Half of the Moon is always unlit by the Sun.
    d. Half of the Moon does not reflect light.

14. Why does the Moon seem to change shape from week to week?
    a. Clouds block part of the Moon.
    b. The Moon moves through Earth's shadow.
    c. The Moon is lit in different ways.
    d. Different amounts of the dark-colored side of the Moon face Earth.

15. Which words describe the different shapes that the Moon appears to be?
    a. waning and waxing
    b. waning and crescent
    c. waxing and gibbous
    d. crescent and gibbous

16. During a total eclipse of the Moon, the Moon is
    a. in Earth's umbra
    b. in Earth's penumbra
    c. between Earth and the Sun
    d. casting a shadow on Earth

Short Answer *Write a short answer to each question.*

17. What motion produces two high tides in a day? Explain your answer.

18. How are the structure of the Moon and the structure of Earth similar?

Reviewing Vocabulary

1. A <u>revolution</u> describes how an object moves around another object. A <u>rotation</u> describes how an object turns on its axis.

2. <u>Seasons</u> occur at different positions in Earth's <u>revolution</u> around the Sun.

3. At an <u>equinox,</u> sunlight shines equally on the northern and southern hemispheres. At a <u>solstice,</u> the area of sunlight is at a maximum in one hemisphere and a minimum in the other hemisphere.

4. A <u>mare</u> is a large <u>impact crater</u> that filled with lava.

5. A total <u>eclipse</u> occurs when one body's <u>umbra</u> falls on another body.

6. An <u>umbra</u> is the darkest part of a shadow. The <u>penumbra</u> is the spreading cone of lighter shadow around the umbra.

Reviewing Key Concepts

7. b
8. d
9. c
10. b
11. d
12. a
13. b
14. c
15. d
16. a
17. Earth's rotation produces two high tides as a location moves past two bulges of water.
18. Earth and the Moon each have a core, mantle, and crust.

ASSESSMENT RESOURCES

 UNIT ASSESSMENT BOOK
- Chapter Test A, pp. 26–29
- Chapter Test B, pp. 30–33
- Chapter Test C, pp. 34–37
- Alternative Assessment, pp. 38–39

 SPANISH ASSESSMENT BOOK
Spanish Chapter Test, pp. 197–200

Technology Resources

Edit test items and answer choices.

 Test Generator CD-ROM

Visit **ClassZone.com** to extend test practice.

 Test Practice

Thinking Critically

19. *Points B and D are at higher elevations. Lunar highlands are light-colored.*

20. *Point B will be in sunlight.*

21. *All four points will be in darkness. A and B will be briefly in Earth's shadow; C and D will be unlit.*

22. *A and B will be unlit and in darkness.*

23. *one year, because the Moon orbits Earth, which orbits the Sun in a year*

24. *The mantle and maria both contain iron and magnesium.*

25. *It is midnight.*

26. *Near the poles temperatures change the most from summer to winter.*

27. *It is the summer solstice in Sydney, Australia.*

28. *The seasons would be the same as they are now. Distance from the Sun is not the cause of seasons on Earth.*

29. *There would be no seasonal changes if Earth's axis were not tilted. The poles, however, would be cold, and the equator would be warm year-round.*

30. *Sample answer: Tides affect sailing and fishing. Seasons, which depend on angles of sunlight, affect farming and some recreational activities.*

31. *Crescent moons are most likely to be seen during daylight hours.*

32. *Scientists use data about the ages and composition of lunar rocks and soil. They also compare the Moon's structure and composition to Earth's.*

33. *South Pole is in sunlight, so date is around December solstice.*

the BIG idea

34. *cratered highlands and smoother, dark maria on the Moon's surface*

35. *The ground would be in sunlight. The side of Earth facing the Moon would be unlit.*

UNIT PROJECTS

Check to make sure students are working on their projects. Check schedules and work in progress.

 Unit Projects, pp. 5–10

Thinking Critically

Use the lunar map below to answer the next four questions.

Near Side   **Far Side**

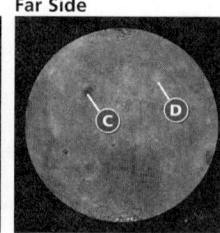

19. **APPLY** Which points are at higher elevations? Explain how you know.

20. **COMPARE** During a first-quarter moon, will point A, point B, both, or neither be in sunlight? **Hint:** Use the diagram on page 61.

21. **INFER** During a total lunar eclipse, which points will be in darkness?

22. **INFER** During a total solar eclipse, the Moon is new. Which points will be in darkness?

23. **CONNECT** Use your knowledge of the motions of Earth and the Moon to determine how long it takes the Moon to travel once around the Sun.

24. **ANALYZE** Which two parts of the Moon have important chemical elements in common? Choose from the following: core, mantle, crust, maria, highlands.

25. **APPLY** If it is noon for you, what time is it for someone directly on the opposite side of Earth?

26. **CLASSIFY** On what part or parts of Earth are winter and summer temperatures the most different from each other?

27. **APPLY** If it is the winter solstice in New York, what solstice or equinox is it in Sydney, Australia, in the Southern Hemisphere?

28. **PREDICT** If Earth stayed exactly the same distance from the Sun throughout the year, would the seasons be different? Explain what you think would happen.

29. **PREDICT** If Earth's axis were not tilted with respect to the orbit, would the seasons be different? Explain what you think would happen.

30. **PROVIDE EXAMPLES** How do the positions of the Sun and the Moon affect what people do? Give three examples of the ways that people's jobs or other activities are affected by the positions of the Sun, the Moon, or both.

31. **PREDICT** Which shape of the Moon are you most likely to see during the daytime? **Hint:** Compare the directions of the Sun and Moon from Earth in the diagram on page 61.

32. **CLASSIFY** What types of information have scientists used to make inferences about the Moon's history?

South Pole

33. **ANALYZE** The photograph above shows the side of Earth in sunlight at a particular time. The location of the South Pole is indicated. Was the photograph taken in March, in June, in September, or in December?

the BIG idea

34. **APPLY** Look again at the photograph on pages 40–41. Now that you have finished the chapter, how would you change your response to the question on the photograph?

35. **SYNTHESIZE** If you were an astronaut in the middle of the near side of the Moon during a full moon, how would the ground around you look? How would Earth, high in your sky, look? Describe what is in sunlight and what is in darkness.

UNIT PROJECTS

If you need to do an experiment for your unit project, gather the materials. Be sure to allow enough time to observe results before the project is due.

MONITOR AND RETEACH

If students have trouble applying the concepts in items 19–22, have them study the visuals on pp. 54 and 61. For questions 20–22, you might also use objects to model the positions of the Sun, the Moon, and Earth. For a lunar eclipse, put Earth in the middle; for a solar eclipse put the Moon in the middle. Put the first-quarter moon 90° counterclockwise from the Sun. You might add labels A–D to the Moon.

Students may benefit from summarizing one or more sections of the chapter.

 Summarizing the Chapter, pp. 142–143

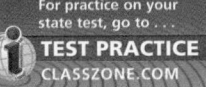

Analyzing a Diagram

The sketches show the phases of the Moon one week apart. The diagram shows the Moon's orbit around Earth. Use the diagram and the sketches to answer the questions below.

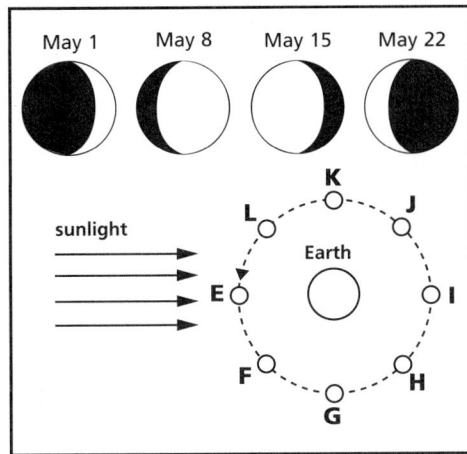

1. At which letter on the diagram might a full moon occur?

  a. E   **c.** I

  b. G   **d.** J

2. Which letter on the diagram shows the position of the Moon on May 8?

  a. E   **c.** G

  b. F   **d.** H

3. Approximately when was the Moon full?

  a. May 4   **c.** May 18

  b. May 11   **d.** May 29

4. At which letter on the diagram might a solar eclipse occur?

  a. E   **c.** I

  b. H   **d.** L

5. How much of the sunlit part of the Moon was visible from Earth on May 8?

  a. None of the sunlit part was visible.

  b. About one-quarter of the sunlit part was visible.

  c. About three-quarters of the sunlit part was visible.

  d. All of the sunlit part was visible.

6. Which of these sketches show Earth's shadow on the Moon?

  a. those for May 1 and May 22

  b. those for May 8 and May 15

  c. all 4 of them

  d. none of them

7. Which factor is most directly responsible for determining how often a full moon appears?

  a. the size of the Moon

  b. the size of Earth

  c. how quickly the Moon orbits Earth

  d. how quickly the Moon turns on its axis

Extended Response

Answer the two questions below in detail. A diagram may help you to answer.

8. The Moon was once much closer to Earth. What effect do you think that this distance had on eclipses?

9. What do you think would happen to tides on Earth if Earth stopped rotating? Why?

Analyzing a Diagram

1. c   3. b   5. c   7. c

2. d   4. a   6. d

Extended Response

8. RUBRIC

4 points for a response that answers the question completely and accurately

Sample answer: When the Moon was closer, Earth and the Moon cast larger umbras upon one another. Eclipses of both types happened more often and lasted longer.

3 points for a response that answers the question correctly but incompletely

2 points for a response that answers the question with some errors, or that includes an accurate and relevant diagram but does not draw conclusions

1 point for a response that addresses the question in words or with a diagram but is mostly incomplete or incorrect

9. RUBRIC

4 points for a response that correctly and completely answers the question

Sample answer: Without Earth's rotation, there would not be two high tides in 24 hours because the two bulges of water would stay in the same location on Earth.

3 points for a response that answers the question correctly but incompletely, or completely but with minor errors

2 points for a response that misses either the two bulges or the effect of rotation, or that includes an accurate and relevant diagram but does not draw conclusions

1 point for a response that addresses the question in words or with a diagram but is mostly incomplete or incorrect

METACOGNITIVE ACTIVITY

Have students answer the following questions in their **Science Notebook:**

1. When you were studying seasons and Moon phases, what helped you the most? Think about reading paragraphs, drawing and looking at diagrams, using models, moving your hands or body, making calculations, or other things you might have done to learn.

2. What did you learn about the Moon that you did not know before?

3. List the concepts from this chapter that apply to your Unit Project.

◉ Set Learning Goals

Students will

- Describe the history of astronomy.
- Describe the technology used to study space.
- Discuss applications of space technology.
- Observe patterns in the movements and appearance of the Moon.

National Science Education Standards

A.9.a–g Understandings about Scientific Inquiry

E.6.a–c Understandings about Science and Technology

F.5.a–e, F.5.g Science and Technology in Society

G.1.a–b Science as a Human Endeavor

G.2.a Nature of Science

G.3.a–c History of Science

The top half of the timeline shows major developments in the study of astronomy. The bottom half discusses technological advances and applications. Point out that some of the greatest theories in science, such as Isaac Newton's laws of motion and Albert Einstein's general theory of relativity, played direct roles in advancing the study of astronomy.

Scientific Process

One of the problems Copernicus solved with the Sun-centered model of the solar system was disagreement about the order of the planets relative to Earth. Putting the Sun in the center solved that problem but created others. Ask: How could astronomers test the Sun-centered model? *Sample answer: Collect data that fit the Sun-centered model but not the Earth-centered model.*

TIMELINES in Science

THE STORY OF ASTRONOMY

Around the year A.D. 140, an astronomer named Ptolemy wrote down his ideas about the motion of bodies in space. Ptolemy shared the view of many Greek astronomers that the Sun, the Moon, and the planets orbit Earth in perfect circles. The Greeks had observed that planets sometimes seem to reverse direction in their motion across the sky. Ptolemy explained that the backward movements are smaller orbits within the larger orbits. For 1400 years, Europeans accepted this Earth-centered model. In the mid-1500s, however, astronomers began to challenge and then reject Ptolemy's ideas.

The timeline shows a few events in the history of astronomy. Scientists have developed special tools and procedures to study objects in the sky. The boxes below the timeline show how technology has led to new knowledge about space and how that knowledge has been applied.

1543

Sun Takes Center Stage

Nicolaus Copernicus, a Polish astronomer, proposes that the planets orbit the Sun rather than Earth. His Sun-centered model shocks many because it conflicts with the traditional belief that Earth is the center of the universe.

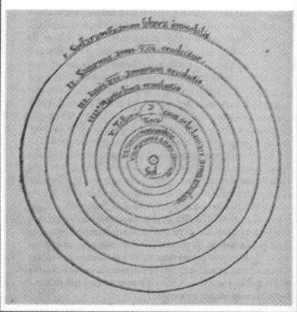

EVENTS

| 1500 | 1520 | 1540 | 1560 |

APPLICATIONS AND TECHNOLOGY

APPLICATION

Navigating by Sunlight and Starlight

For thousands of years, sailors studied the sky to find their way at sea. Because the Sun and stars move in predictable ways, sailors used them to navigate across water. During the 1400s, sailors began to use a device called a mariner's astrolabe to observe the positions of the Sun and stars. Later devices allowed sailors to make more accurate measurements.

This mariner's astrolabe was made in the 1600s.

DIFFERENTIATE INSTRUCTION

Below Level Have students use adding machine tape to recreate the timeline. Students can mark 20-year intervals on the tape, beginning with the year 1540. After students have plotted important events and advances on the tape, have them identify gaps of activity in the timeline as well as periods of increased activity. Ask: Does the timeline show everything that happened during this period? *No, it shows only a few events.*

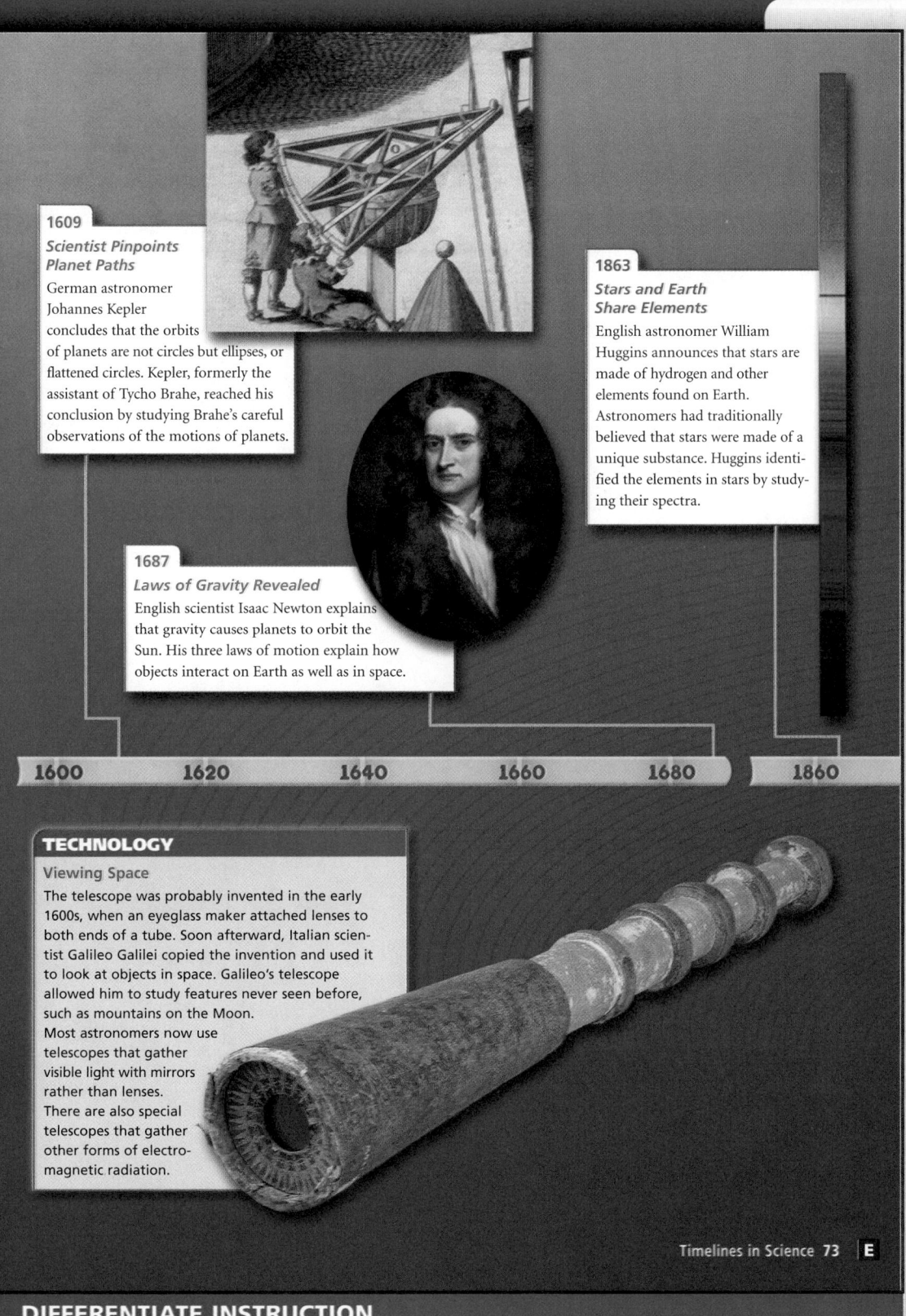

1609

Scientist Pinpoints Planet Paths

German astronomer Johannes Kepler concludes that the orbits of planets are not circles but ellipses, or flattened circles. Kepler, formerly the assistant of Tycho Brahe, reached his conclusion by studying Brahe's careful observations of the motions of planets.

1863

Stars and Earth Share Elements

English astronomer William Huggins announces that stars are made of hydrogen and other elements found on Earth. Astronomers had traditionally believed that stars were made of a unique substance. Huggins identified the elements in stars by studying their spectra.

1687

Laws of Gravity Revealed

English scientist Isaac Newton explains that gravity causes planets to orbit the Sun. His three laws of motion explain how objects interact on Earth as well as in space.

| 1600 | 1620 | 1640 | 1660 | 1680 | 1860 |

TECHNOLOGY

Viewing Space

The telescope was probably invented in the early 1600s, when an eyeglass maker attached lenses to both ends of a tube. Soon afterward, Italian scientist Galileo Galilei copied the invention and used it to look at objects in space. Galileo's telescope allowed him to study features never seen before, such as mountains on the Moon. Most astronomers now use telescopes that gather visible light with mirrors rather than lenses. There are also special telescopes that gather other forms of electro-magnetic radiation.

Scientific Process

Have students read about the major developments that took place in the study of astronomy between 1543 and 1863. Ask: What ideas were changed during this time? *The model of an Earth-centered universe was replaced by Copernicus' Sun-centered model. Kepler showed that the planets orbit in ellipses, not circles. Huggins demonstrated that stars are not made of unique substances—they are made of elements that are found on Earth.*

Technology

VIEWING SPACE Help students see that technology often advances in a logical manner—the invention of a simple product may spark the invention of increasingly complex products. For example, the invention of eyeglasses that magnified letters eventually led to the invention of telescopes to magnify objects in space. Visible light telescopes have given rise to telescopes that gather radiation from other parts of the electro-magnetic spectrum as well.

Mathematics Connection

1687 Newton's law of gravity states that all objects in the universe have a gravitational force between them. The gravitational force, F_g, between two objects is equal to the product of their masses, m, and the inverse square of the distance between them, r. With G equal to a gravitational constant, the law can be written $F_g = G(m_1m_2/r^2)$.

DIFFERENTIATE INSTRUCTION

Advanced Review Newton's first law of motion, which states that an object will remain at rest or in uniform motion unless acted upon by an external force. Ask students to infer how the planets would move if gravity did not exist. *in a straight line*

Application

1912 Describe how astronomers can use a Cepheid variable to compute the intrinsic brightness of a star. They do this by comparing the light from a Cepheid star whose distance from Earth is known with the visibility of the star whose distance is unknown. Since we know how fast light travels, the difference in light between the two stars can be calculated to learn the distance of the second star.

Scientific Process

Have students relate research on the big bang to scientific processes. Ask:

* What problem are scientists attempting to solve with their research on the big bang? *What were conditions like at the beginning of the universe?*

* What is one way that scientists gather data? *by conducting tests with particle accelerators*

* What do scientists do with the data? *develop models of conditions immediately following the big bang*

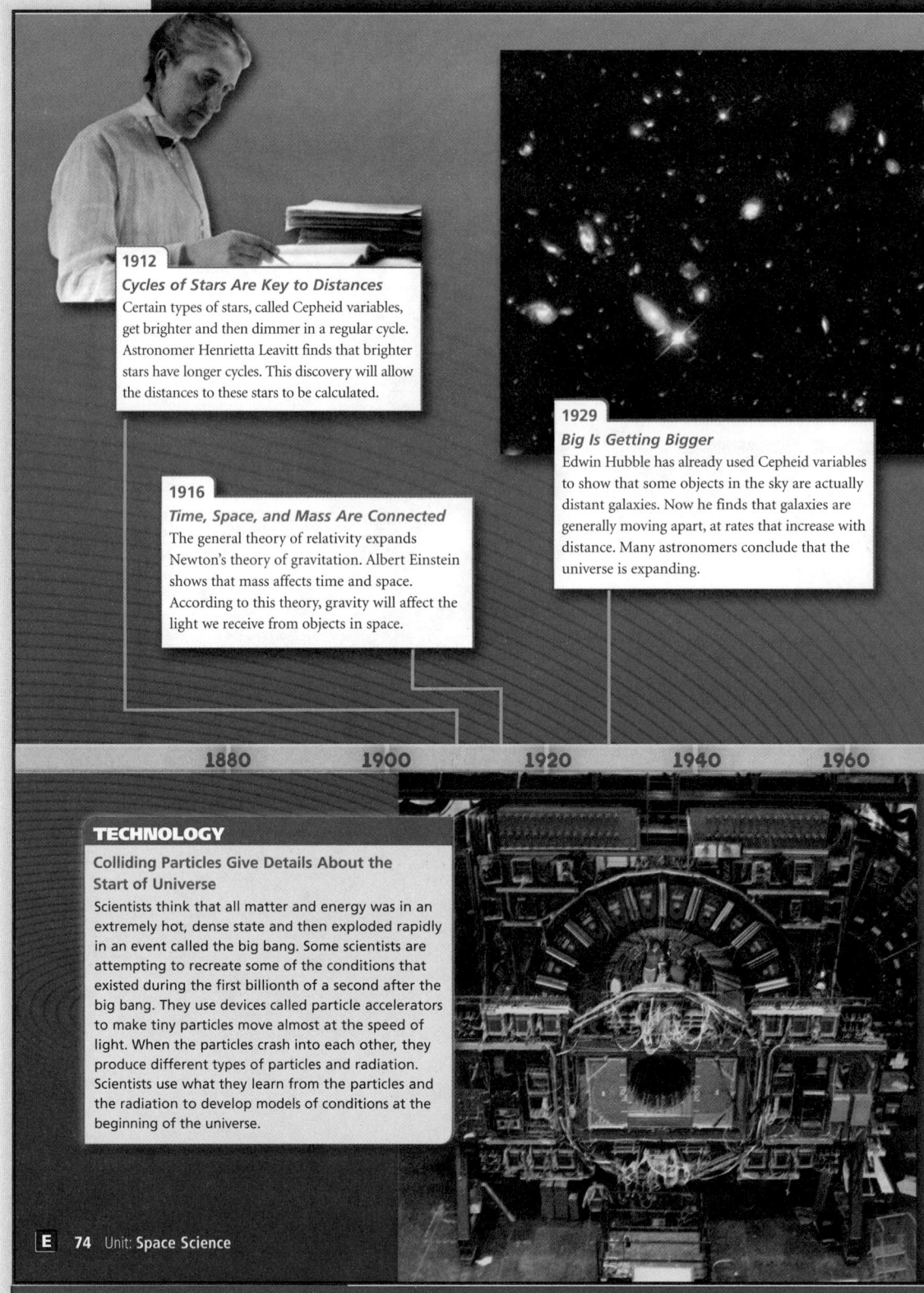

1912

Cycles of Stars Are Key to Distances
Certain types of stars, called Cepheid variables, get brighter and then dimmer in a regular cycle. Astronomer Henrietta Leavitt finds that brighter stars have longer cycles. This discovery will allow the distances to these stars to be calculated.

1929

Big Is Getting Bigger
Edwin Hubble has already used Cepheid variables to show that some objects in the sky are actually distant galaxies. Now he finds that galaxies are generally moving apart, at rates that increase with distance. Many astronomers conclude that the universe is expanding.

1916

Time, Space, and Mass Are Connected
The general theory of relativity expands Newton's theory of gravitation. Albert Einstein shows that mass affects time and space. According to this theory, gravity will affect the light we receive from objects in space.

1880   1900   1920   1940   1960

TECHNOLOGY

Colliding Particles Give Details About the Start of Universe
Scientists think that all matter and energy was in an extremely hot, dense state and then exploded rapidly in an event called the big bang. Some scientists are attempting to recreate some of the conditions that existed during the first billionth of a second after the big bang. They use devices called particle accelerators to make tiny particles move almost at the speed of light. When the particles crash into each other, they produce different types of particles and radiation. Scientists use what they learn from the particles and the radiation to develop models of conditions at the beginning of the universe.

E 74 Unit: Space Science

DIFFERENTIATE INSTRUCTION

English Learners Students may be unfamiliar with some of the words and phrases used in this timeline, such as *particle accelerator* and *gravitation*. Give them opportunities to see the words in context. Bring in magazines, reference books, and age-appropriate novels that deal with astronomy. You can set aside time for students to read independently in class or allow them to borrow the reading materials for a specified period.

1998

Fast Is Getting Faster

Two groups of astronomers studying exploding stars called supernovae come to the same remarkable conclusion. Not only is the universe expanding, but the rate of expansion is increasing. In the diagram below, the rate of expansion is shown by the distances between rings and between galaxies.

The expanding universe

Present

Expansion slows down Expansion speeds up

Big Bang

Farthest supernova

~15 billion years

RESOURCE CENTER
CLASSZONE.COM
Learn more about current advances in astronomy.

1980   2000

TECHNOLOGY

Measuring the Big Bang

In 1965 two researchers noticed radio waves that came from all directions instead of from just one direction, like a signal from a space object. They inferred that the radiation was left over from the big bang. In 1989 and again in 2001, NASA launched spacecraft to study the radiation. Data gathered using these telescopes in space are still being used to test different models of the big bang, including the arrangement of matter in the universe. In this map of the sky, red and yellow show the areas that were hottest after the big bang.

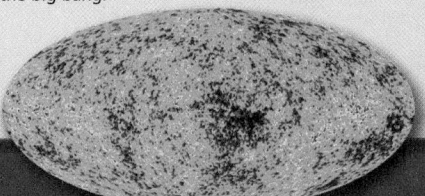

INTO THE FUTURE

Throughout history, people have learned about the universe from visible light and other radiation. New and better measurements have been made as technologies improved. Better and more complex models are filling in details that cannot be measured directly. In the future, improvements will continue. Computers, telescopes in space, and other instruments will allow astronomers to collect better data and make better models.

Some matter in the universe does not give off or reflect any detectable radiation. This is called dark matter. Astronomers infer its existence from its effects on matter that is detected. In the future, astronomers hope to determine what dark matter is, exactly where it is, and how it moves in the universe. In a similar way, astronomers will learn more about why the universe is expanding faster with time and what energy is involved in this acceleration.

ACTIVITIES

Reliving History

Some early astronomers observed the Moon in order to develop and test their ideas about space. For two weeks or more, make frequent observations of the Moon and keep your notes, sketches, and thoughts in a notebook. You might look for the Moon at a certain time each day or night or perhaps record the direction in which the Moon sets. A newspaper may list the times of moonrise and moonset for your location.

Compare your observations and thoughts with those of other students. You might also find out what people in other cultures thought of the patterns of change they saw in the Moon.

Writing About Science

Choose one of these famous astronomers and research his or her story. Write a biographical profile or an imaginary interview with that person.

INTO THE FUTURE

Have students discuss the future of space technology. Do they think that spacecraft will one day travel to other galaxies? *No, it would take many years just to reach the nearby stars in our galaxy.* Encourage students to use scientific reasoning to back up their opinions.

ACTIVITIES

Reliving History

After students have several sketches, display a diagram of Moon phases. Have students compare their sketches with the diagram, and then label each drawing according to which Moon phase it represents. Ask students if they noticed any pattern in the time of day or night that they saw different phases

Writing About Science

Encourage students to research their subject and find some human-interest details about the astronomer. Suggest that students look for controversy related to their astronomer's views.

Technology Resources

Students can visit **ClassZone.com** for information about astronomy.

DIFFERENTIATE INSTRUCTION

Alternative Writing Project Have students write a dialogue between two scientists who have just discovered a new planet in a distant solar system. Each speaker's words should be in quotation marks.

Inclusion Students with physical disabilities may have difficulty sketching and writing. Allow these students to use tape recorders to describe their observations of the Moon orally or let them use clay or another medium to represent what they saw.

 **Our Solar System**

Earth Science
UNIFYING PRINCIPLES

PRINCIPLE 1

Heat energy inside Earth and radiation from the Sun provide energy for Earth's processes.

PRINCIPLE 2

Physical forces, such as gravity, affect the movement of all matter on Earth and throughout the universe.

PRINCIPLE 3

Matter and energy move among Earth's rocks and soil, atmosphere, waters, and living things.

PRINCIPLE 4

Earth has changed over time and continues to change.

Unit: Space Science
BIG IDEAS

CHAPTER 1
Exploring Space
People develop and use technology to explore and study space.

CHAPTER 2
Earth, Moon, and Sun
Earth and the Moon move in predictable ways as they orbit the Sun.

CHAPTER 3
Our Solar System

Planets and other objects form a system around our Sun.

CHAPTER 4
Stars, Galaxies, and the Universe
Our Sun is one of billions of stars in one of billions of galaxies in the universe.

CHAPTER 3
KEY CONCEPTS

SECTION **3.1**	SECTION **3.2**	SECTION **3.3**	SECTION **3.4**
Planets orbit the Sun at different distances.	**The inner solar system has rocky planets.**	**The outer solar system has four giant planets.**	**Small objects are made of ice and rock.**
1. Planets have different sizes and distances.	1. The terrestrial planets have rocky crusts.	1. The gas giants have very deep atmospheres.	1. Pluto and most objects in the outer solar system are made of ice and rock.
2. The solar system formed from a swirling cloud of gas and dust.	2. Craters cover the surface of Mercury.	2. Jupiter is a world of storms and clouds.	2. Asteroids and comets orbit the Sun.
	3. Volcanoes shape the surface of Venus.	3. Saturn has large rings.	
	4. Erosion changes the appearance of Mars.	4. Uranus and Neptune are extremely cold.	

⊤ The Big Idea Flow Chart is available on p. T17 in the **UNIT TRANSPARENCY BOOK.**

Previewing Content

3.1 Planets orbit the Sun at different distances. pp. 79–84

1. Planets have different sizes and distances.

The planets and other objects that orbit the Sun vary greatly in size. The smallest objects, such as asteroids, may be about 1/1000 Earth's diameter. The largest planets are Jupiter and Saturn, which are each about 10 Earth diameters across.

The distances of planets and other objects from the Sun are so huge that astronomers use **astronomical units** to compare them. One AU is the average distance of Earth from the Sun. In the inner solar system are four planets relatively close to the Sun, while the outer solar system has planets that are more spread out. The shape of each orbit is an **ellipse,** a flattened circle or oval. Most planets have orbits that are very nearly circles, though for some, the Sun is clearly not at the center. Pluto's orbit has the Sun noticeably off center, so Pluto's distance from the Sun changes a lot during an orbit.

2. The solar system formed from a swirling cloud of gas and dust.

Planets and other objects in the solar system form an organized system around the Sun. Many of the objects are arranged in a flat disk rather than in a cloud around the Sun. All of the planetary orbits and many other motions are in the same direction—counterclockwise as viewed from far above Earth's North Pole.

The composition of objects also fits a pattern. Objects in the inner solar system are made mostly of rock and metal. Objects in the outer solar system, aside from the gas giants, are made mostly of ices and rock. Asteroids are mostly rock and metal, while comets, in the outer solar system, are mostly ice and rock.

These patterns, along with other information, have led scientists to hypothesize that the solar system formed from a cloud of gas and dust. The cloud flattened into a disk of material whirling in one direction. Solid material collided and formed larger and larger clumps. Massive objects became round because their gravity pulled down the parts that stuck out. Many objects still move in the same direction as the motion of the original disk.

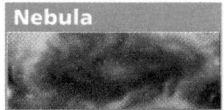
Nebula

Disk

Solar System

3.2 The inner solar system has rocky planets. pp. 85–93

1. The terrestrial planets have rocky crusts.

The **terrestrial planets** are Mercury, Venus, Earth, and Mars. These planets are closest to the Sun and have rocky crusts and dense mantles and cores. The surface of each planet has been shaped by four types of processes. The first two occur only while the mantle is hot.

- **Tectonics** is the wrinkling, twisting, or stretching of the crust by motions of the hot mantle. Earth has a special type of tectonics called plate tectonics.
- **Volcanism** delivers molten rock to a planet's surface from below. Lava may build up volcanic mountains or spread into flat volcanic plains.
- **Weathering** breaks down rocks, and erosion moves the material. These processes are driven largely by water and wind on Earth but can be caused by heating and cooling and by gravity on airless worlds.
- **Impact cratering** occurs when a small object hits a planet's surface and produces an explosion. Most of Earth's craters are erased.

Surface temperatures depend on energy from sunlight. An atmosphere can slow the loss of energy from a planet's surface and can also redistribute that energy.

2. Craters cover the surface of Mercury.

Cratering, along with slow weathering and erosion, is the main process on Mercury today. Mercury has no atmosphere.

3. Volcanoes shape the surface of Venus.

Venus shows the effects of a hot mantle—volcanoes and tectonic features. Venus's thick atmosphere retains energy and spreads it to produce relatively uniform temperatures.

4. Erosion changes the appearance of Mars.

Features from all four types of processes are seen on Mars. Features show the effects of weathering and erosion from wind in the thin atmosphere and also from water in the past.

Common Misconceptions

SHAPES OF ORBITS Students often have the impression that orbits are very elongated ovals. Most planets orbit in ellipses that are very nearly circles, although the Sun is significantly off center for some planets' orbits.

 MISCONCEPTION DATABASE
CLASSZONE.COM Background on student misconceptions

 This misconception is addressed on p. 81.

Previewing Content

 3.3 **The outer solar system has four giant planets.** pp. 94–99

1. The gas giants have very deep atmospheres.
Jupiter, Saturn, Uranus, and Neptune are the **gas giants** in the outer solar system. These planets are made mainly of hydrogen, helium, and other gases. The planets have so much mass that gravity pulls the particles in close, making the gases and hence the planets very dense. Gases are as dense as familiar liquids in the outside layers of each planet. The materials become more dense and extremely hot toward the planets' centers.

2. Jupiter is a world of storms and clouds.
Jupiter is the largest planet in the solar system. What looks like a surface is actually clouds in the atmosphere. High clouds of ice crystals look white. Lower layers of clouds have different colors. Jupiter rotates much faster than Earth does. This fast rotation produces strong winds, alternating bands of which blow eastward and westward. Storms form, and they can last a long time because there is no land to slow them.

3. Saturn has large rings.
Saturn is only a little smaller than Jupiter, but it has much less mass and is not as dense. Although all the gas giants have planetary rings, scientists first noticed Saturn's. A planetary **ring** is a wide, flat zone of small particles around a planet's equator. Saturn's rings are made of chunks of water ice the size of a building or smaller that orbit the planet. Very large chunks, considered small moons, orbit the planet within the ring zones.

4. Uranus and Neptune are extremely cold.
Both Uranus and Neptune are about one-third the size of Jupiter, but they are more dense. Most of their mass is from heavier gases, such as methane, ammonia, and water. The small numbers of particles of these heavier gases have more total mass than the greater numbers of hydrogen and helium particles in the two planets. The methane causes Uranus and Neptune to appear bluish because it absorbs visible light in the red-to-yellow range. Uranus has its axis of rotation almost in the plane of its orbit.

 3.4 **Small objects are made of ice and rock.** pp. 100–107

1. Pluto and most objects in the outer solar system are made of ice and rock.
Pluto and other objects that formed far away from the Sun are made mostly of ice, with some rock and a little metal. Pluto is the smallest of the nine planets and is so far away that no spacecraft has been sent to it. Scientists infer that it has a crust, a mantle, a core, and a thin atmosphere that grows and shrinks as Pluto's distance from the Sun changes along its elongated orbit. All the bodies in a system of a planet and moons revolve around a central point; for most systems that point is within the planet. For Pluto and its moon Charon, the point is between the two bodies, so the two objects are often considered a double planet.

All the giant planets have systems of moons; six of their moons are larger than Pluto. The four types of processes that affect the terrestrial planets affect these other solid objects. The smaller moons have irregular shapes and surfaces marked mostly by impact cratering, weathering, and erosion.

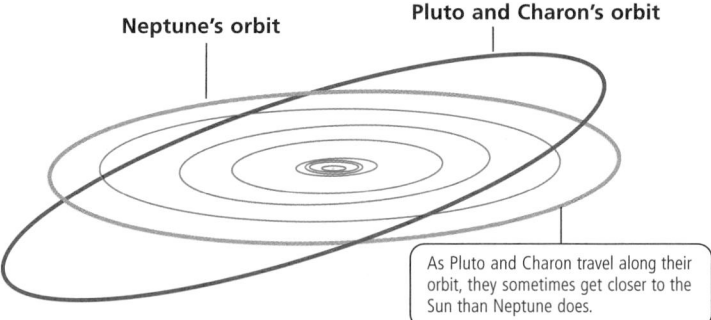

Neptune's orbit   **Pluto and Charon's orbit**

As Pluto and Charon travel along their orbit, they sometimes get closer to the Sun than Neptune does.

2. Asteroids and comets orbit the Sun.
Asteroids are small, solid, rocky bodies in the inner solar system, mostly orbiting in the asteroid belt between Mars and Jupiter. Scientists think that an asteroid that hit Earth 65 million years ago might have contributed to the mass extinction that ended the age of dinosaurs. A **comet** is a small, icy body from the outer solar system that produces a coma and tails if its orbit carries it near the Sun. Most comet orbits are elongated; they may carry the comets many thousands of AU from the Sun. Small pieces from asteroids and comets constantly collide with Earth, but most are destroyed by its atmosphere. A brief streak of light, or a **meteor,** can be seen when this happens. Larger particles that actually reach Earth's surface are called **meteorites.**

Common Misconceptions

GASES Students may think that gases are not forms of matter and have no mass. Gases consist of the same types of atoms and

 MISCONCEPTION DATABASE
CLASSZONE.COM Background on student misconceptions

molecules that make up liquids and solids, though these particles are often more spread out when in gaseous form.

 This misconception is addressed on p. 95.

Previewing Labs

EXPLORE the BIG idea

How Big Is Jupiter? p. 77
Students compare the sizes of Jupiter and Earth by creating a scale model.

TIME 10 minutes
MATERIALS graduated cylinder or eyedropper, two 2-liter plastic bottles, 2 liters and 22 drops water

How Round Is an Orbit? p. 77
Students construct a model to learn about the shape of Pluto's orbit.

TIME 10 minutes
MATERIALS 20 cm of string, 2 thumbtacks, metric ruler, sheet of paper, pencil

Internet Activity: Spacing, p. 77
Students are introduced to the distances between planets.

TIME 20 minutes
MATERIALS computer with Internet access

SECTION 3.1

EXPLORE Planet Formation, p. 79
Students observe the movement of wax pieces in swirling water to understand how planets formed.

TIME 10 minutes
MATERIALS bowl, water, spoon, wax pieces

INVESTIGATE Distances, p. 82
Students use a model to compare distances between planets.
R Distance Table, p. 153

TIME 30 minutes
MATERIALS roll of toilet paper, felt-tipped pen, Distance Table

---

SECTION 3.2

EXPLORE Surfaces, p. 85
Students infer the effect that a planet's mantle has on its surface.

TIME 15 minutes
MATERIALS 2 blocks, paper towel, water, newspaper

INVESTIGATE Layers, p. 88
Students construct a model to infer how a solid planet's layers form.

TIME 40 minutes
MATERIALS small clear container, spoon, pieces of firm gelatin to fill one-quarter of container, spoonful of sand, spoonful of small wax pieces, bowl (large enough for container and hot water to fit inside), about half a bowl of hot tap water (about 70°C)

SECTION 3.3

INVESTIGATE Giant Planets, p. 97
Students observe how Saturn's rings appear to change size.

TIME 20 minutes
MATERIALS ice-cream stick, paper plate, scissors, 1 stick of clay

---

SECTION 3.4

CHAPTER INVESTIGATION
Exploring Impact Craters, pp. 106–107
Students design an experiment to explore the effects of one variable on impact craters.

TIME 40 minutes
MATERIALS newspapers, baking dish or large box lid, 4–6 cups of flour, 1 cup colored powder, variety of objects, meter stick, ruler, balance, graph paper

---

R **Additional INVESTIGATION,** Exploring Ellipses, A, B, & C, pp. 204–212; Teacher Instructions, pp. 287–288

Previewing Chapter Resources

| | INTEGRATED TECHNOLOGY | LABS AND ACTIVITIES |

CHAPTER 3
Our Solar System

 CLASSZONE.COM
- eEdition Plus
- EasyPlanner Plus
- Misconception Database
- Content Review
- Test Practice
- Visualization
- Resource Centers
- Internet Activity: Spacing
- Math Tutorial

 SCILINKS.ORG
SCILINKS

 CD-ROMS
- eEdition
- EasyPlanner
- Power Presentations
- Content Review
- Lab Generator
- Test Generator

 AUDIO CDS
- Audio Readings
- Audio Readings in Spanish

P E EXPLORE the Big Idea, p. 77
- How Big Is Jupiter?
- How Round Is an Orbit?
- Internet Activity: Spacing

R **UNIT RESOURCE BOOK**
Unit Projects, pp. 5–10

 Lab Generator CD-ROM
Generate customized labs.

SECTION
3.1 Planets orbit the Sun at different distances.
pp. 79–84

Time: 2 periods (1 block)
 Lesson Plan, pp. 144–145

 MATH TUTORIAL

 UNIT TRANSPARENCY BOOK
- Big Idea Flow Chart, p. T17
- Daily Vocabulary Scaffolding, p. T18
- Note-Taking Model, p. T19
- 3-Minute Warm-Up, p. T20

P E
- EXPLORE Planet Formation p. 79
- INVESTIGATE Distances, p. 82
- Math in Science, p. 84

R **UNIT RESOURCE BOOK**
- Distance Table, p. 153
- Datasheet, Distances, p. 154
- Additional INVESTIGATION, Exploring Ellipses, A, B, & C, pp. 204–212
- Math Support & Practice, pp. 193–194

SECTION
3.2 The inner solar system has rocky planets. pp. 85–93

Time: 2 periods (1 block)
 Lesson Plan, pp. 156–157

 RESOURCE CENTER, Impact Craters

 UNIT TRANSPARENCY BOOK
- Daily Vocabulary Scaffolding, p. T18
- 3-Minute Warm-Up, p. T20
- "Features of Rocky Planets" Visual, p. T22

P E
- EXPLORE Surfaces, p. 85
- INVESTIGATE Layers, p. 88
- Think Science, p. 93

R **UNIT RESOURCE BOOK**
Datasheet, Layers, p. 165

SECTION
3.3 The outer solar system has four giant planets.
pp. 94–99

Time: 2 periods (1 block)
 Lesson Plan, pp. 167–168

 UNIT TRANSPARENCY BOOK
- Daily Vocabulary Scaffolding, p. T18
- 3-Minute Warm-Up, p. T21

P E INVESTIGATE, Giant Planets, p. 97

R **UNIT RESOURCE BOOK**
Datasheet, Giant Planets, p. 176

SECTION
3.4 Small objects are made of ice and rock.
pp. 100–107

Time: 4 periods (2 blocks)
 Lesson Plan, pp. 178–179

 RESOURCE CENTER, Moons of Giant Planets

UNIT TRANSPARENCY BOOK
- Big Idea Flow Chart, p. T17
- Daily Vocabulary Scaffolding, p. T18
- 3-Minute Warm-Up, p. T21
- Chapter Outline, pp. T23–T24

P E CHAPTER INVESTIGATION, Exploring Impact Craters, pp. 106–107

R **UNIT RESOURCE BOOK**
CHAPTER INVESTIGATION, Exploring Impact Craters, A, B, & C, pp. 195–203

KEY TO ICONS

 CD/CD-ROM

 **INTERNET** 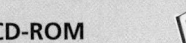 **Pupil Edition**

TE Teacher Edition

R **UNIT RESOURCE BOOK**

T **UNIT TRANSPARENCY BOOK**

A **UNIT ASSESSMENT BOOK**

SP A **SPANISH ASSESSMENT BOOK**

 **SCIENCE TOOLKIT**

READING AND REINFORCEMENT

ASSESSMENT

STANDARDS

- Word Triangle, B18–19
- Main Idea and Detail Notes, C37
- Daily Vocabulary Scaffolding, H1–8

 UNIT RESOURCE BOOK
- Vocabulary Practice, pp. 190–191
- Decoding Support, p. 192
- Summarizing the Chapter, pp. 213–214

 Audio Readings CD
Listen to Pupil Edition.

 Audio Readings in Spanish CD
Listen to Pupil Edition in Spanish.

- Chapter Review, pp. 109–110
- Standardized Test Practice, p. 111

 UNIT ASSESSMENT BOOK
- Diagnostic Test, pp. 40–41
- Chapter Test, A, B, & C, pp. 46–57
- Alternative Assessment, pp. 58–59

 Spanish Chapter Test, pp. 201–204

 Test Generator CD-ROM
Generate customized tests.

 Lab Generator CD-ROM
Rubrics for Labs

National Standards
A.2–8, A.9.a–b, A.9.e–f, D.1.a, D.2.a, D.3.a, G.1.a–b

See p. 76 for the standards.

 UNIT RESOURCE BOOK
- Reading Study Guide, A & B, pp. 146–149
- Spanish Reading Study Guide, pp. 150–151
- Challenge and Extension, p. 152
- Reinforcing Key Concepts, p. 155
- Challenge Reading, pp. 188–189

 Ongoing Assessment, pp. 79, 81, 83

 Section 3.1 Review, p. 83

 UNIT ASSESSMENT BOOK
Section 3.1 Quiz, p. 42

National Standards
A.2–8, A.9.a–c, A.9.e–f, D.3.a, G.1.a–b

 UNIT RESOURCE BOOK
- Reading Study Guide, A & B, pp. 158–161
- Spanish Reading Study Guide, pp. 162–163
- Challenge and Extension, p. 164
- Reinforcing Key Concepts, p. 166

 Ongoing Assessment, pp. 86–89, 91–92

 Section 3.2 Review, p. 92

 UNIT ASSESSMENT BOOK
Section 3.2 Quiz, p. 43

National Standards
A.2–7, A.9.a–b, A.9.e–f, D.1.a, D.2.a, D.3.a, G.1.a–b

 UNIT RESOURCE BOOK
- Reading Study Guide, A & B, pp. 169–172
- Spanish Reading Study Guide, pp. 173–174
- Challenge and Extension, p. 175
- Reinforcing Key Concepts, p. 177

 Ongoing Assessment, pp. 94–99

 Section 3.3 Review, p. 99

 UNIT ASSESSMENT BOOK
Section 3.3 Quiz, p. 44

National Standards
A.2–7, A.9.a–b, A.9.e–f, D.3.a, G.1.a–b

 UNIT RESOURCE BOOK
- Reading Study Guide, A & B, pp. 180–183
- Spanish Reading Study Guide, pp. 184–185
- Challenge and Extension, p. 186
- Reinforcing Key Concepts, p. 187

 Ongoing Assessment, pp. 100–105

 Section 3.4 Review, p. 105

 UNIT ASSESSMENT BOOK
Section 3.4 Quiz, p. 45

National Standards
A.2–7, A.9.a–b, A.9.e–f, D.2.a, D.3.a, G.1.a–b

Previewing Resources for Differentiated Instruction

CHAPTER INVESTIGATION

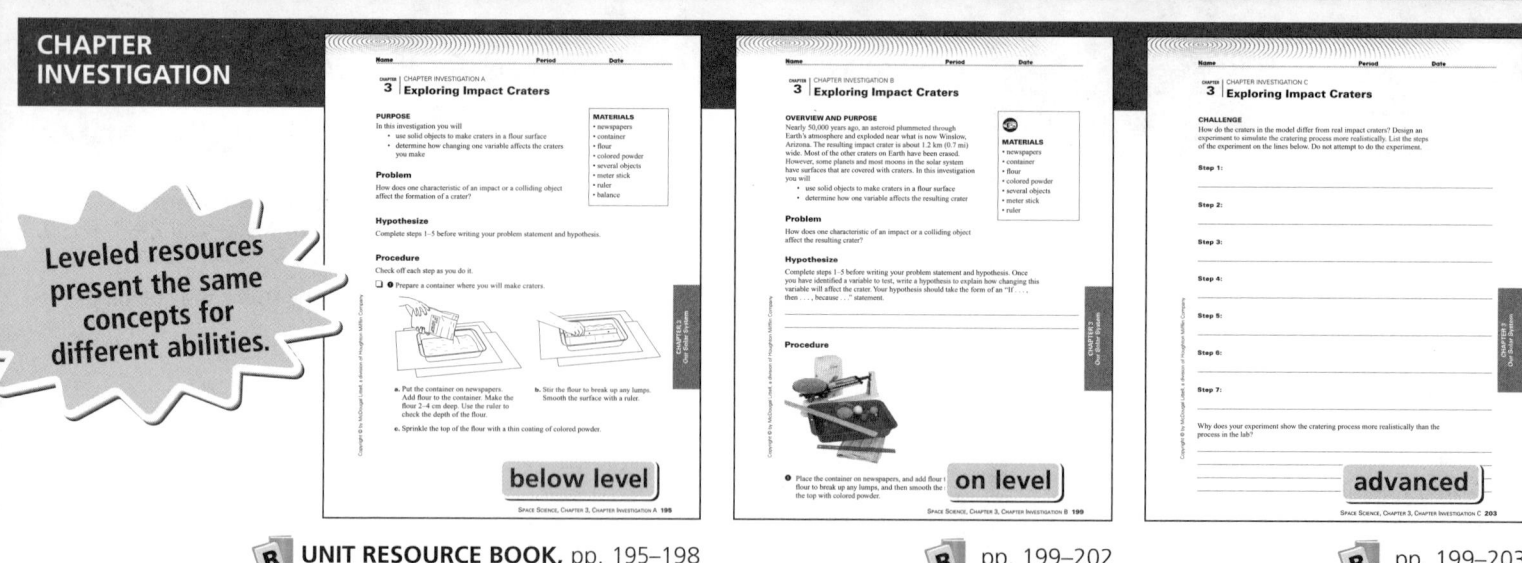

Leveled resources present the same concepts for different abilities.

below level

on level

advanced

R **UNIT RESOURCE BOOK,** pp. 195–198

R pp. 199–202

R pp. 199–203

READING STUDY GUIDE

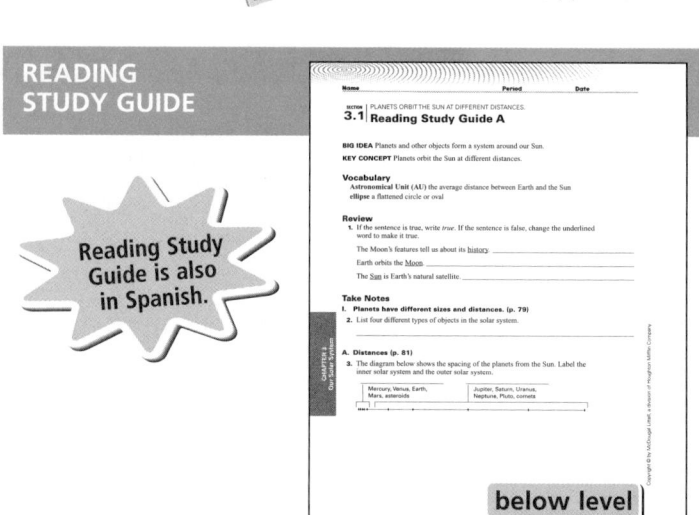

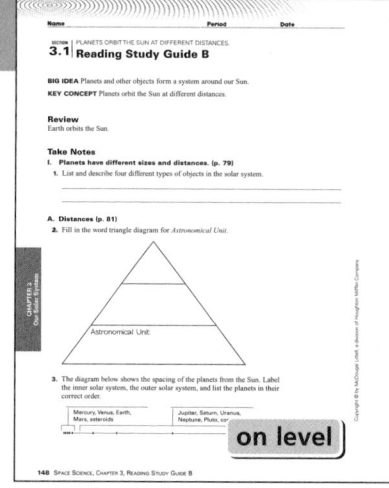

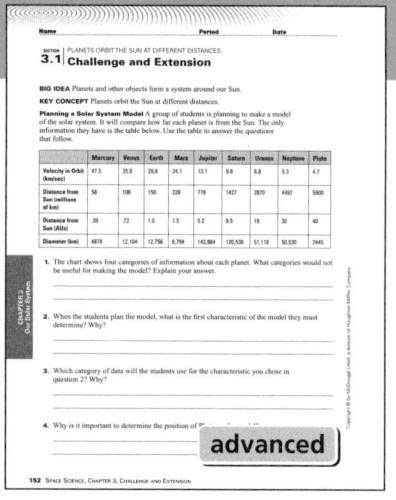

Reading Study Guide is also in Spanish.

below level

on level

advanced

R **UNIT RESOURCE BOOK,** pp. 146–147

R pp. 148–149

R p. 152

CHAPTER TEST

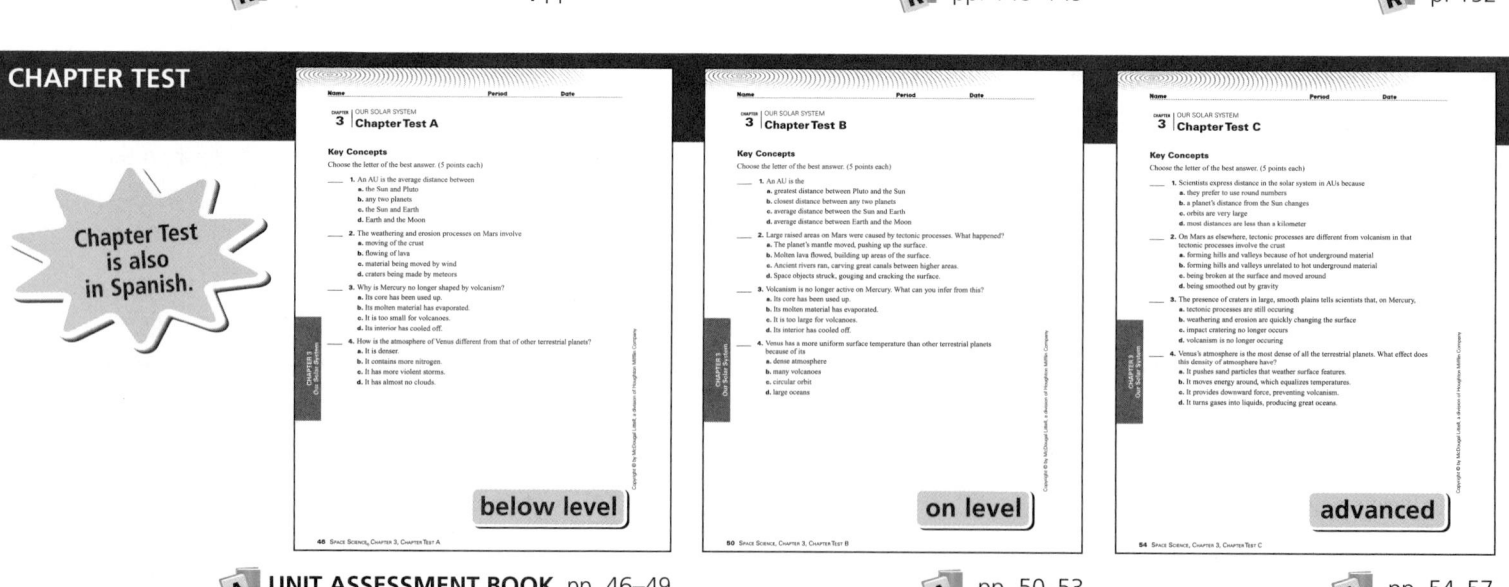

Chapter Test is also in Spanish.

below level

on level

advanced

A **UNIT ASSESSMENT BOOK,** pp. 46–49

A pp. 50–53

A pp. 54–57

TECHNOLOGY

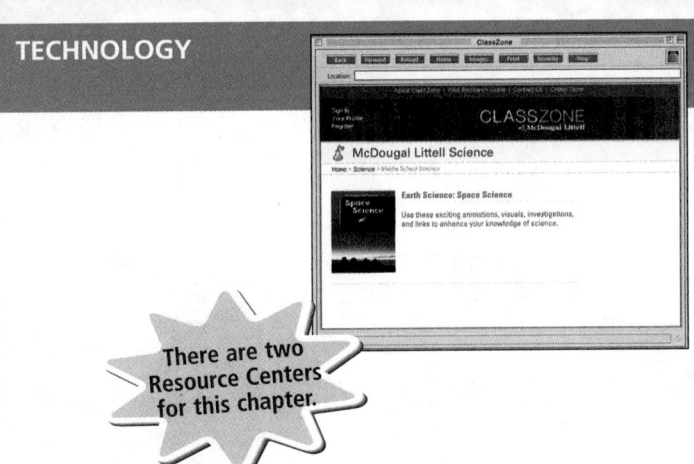

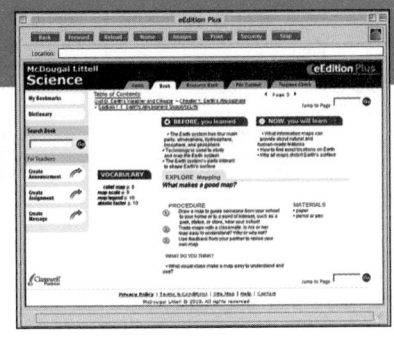

CLASSZONE.COM   CD/CD-ROMS   CLASSZONE.COM

VISUAL CONTENT

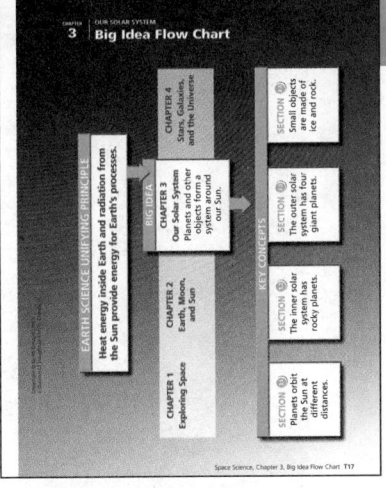

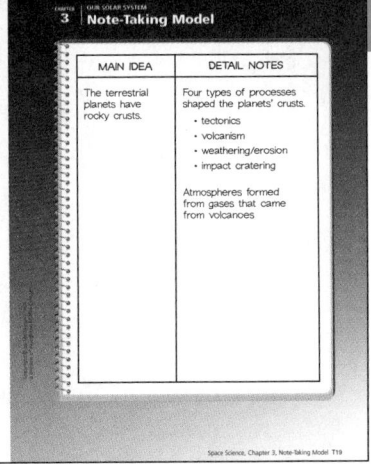

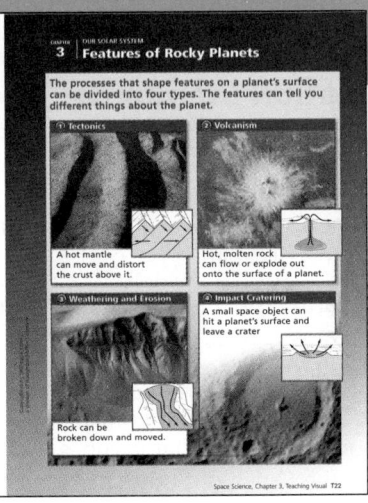

 **UNIT TRANSPARENCY BOOK,** p. T17

 p. T19

 p. T22

MORE SUPPORT

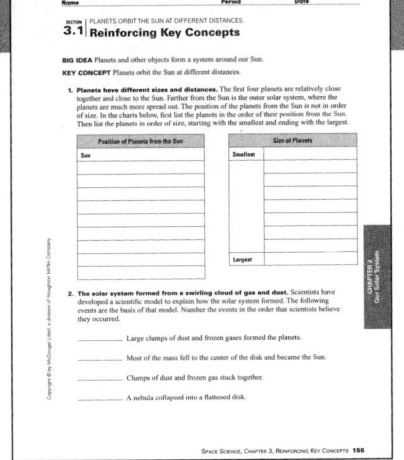

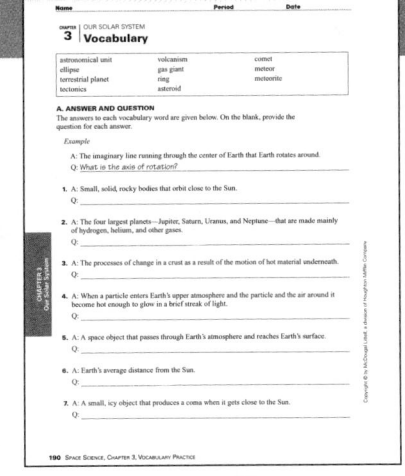

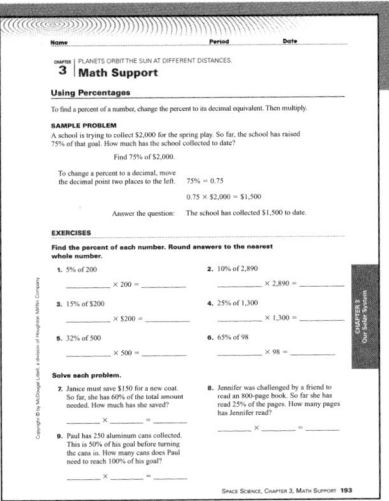

UNIT RESOURCE BOOK, p. 155

pp. 190–191

p. 193

INTRODUCE

the **BIG** idea

Have students look at the image of Jupiter and one of its large moons and discuss how the question in the box links to the Big Idea. For further discussion:

- Ask: How does the idea of a system apply to a planet and one of its moons?

- Have the class brainstorm a list of what they already know about the solar system. Accept all answers but then discuss them.

National Science Education Standards

Content

D.1.a The solid Earth is layered with a lithosphere; hot, convecting mantle; and dense, metallic core.

D.2.a Earth history is influenced by occasional catastrophes, such as the impact of an asteroid or comet.

D.3.a The Earth is the third planet from the Sun in a system that includes the Moon, the Sun, eight other planets and their moons, and smaller objects, such as asteroids and comets. The Sun, an average star, is the central and largest body in the solar system.

Process

A.2–8 Design and conduct an investigation; use tools to gather and interpret data; use evidence to describe, predict, explain, model; think critically to make relationships between evidence and explanation; recognize different explanations and predictions; communicate scientific procedures and explanations; use mathematics.

A.9.a–c, A.9.e–f Understand scientific inquiry by using different investigations, methods, mathematics, and explanations based on logic, evidence, and skepticism.

G.1.a–b Science as a human endeavor

CHAPTER

Our Solar System

the **BIG** idea

Planets and other objects form a system around our Sun.

This image shows Jupiter with one of its large moons. How big are these objects compared with Earth?

Key Concepts

SECTION 3.1 Planets orbit the Sun at different distances. Learn about the sizes and the distances of objects in the solar system and about its formation.

SECTION 3.2 The inner solar system has rocky planets. Learn about the processes that shape Earth and other planets.

SECTION 3.3 The outer solar system has four giant planets. Learn about the largest planets.

SECTION 3.4 Small objects are made of ice and rock. Learn about moons, asteroids, and comets.

 Internet Preview

CLASSZONE.COM

Chapter 3 online resources: Content Review, Visualization, two Resource Centers, Math Tutorial, Test Practice

E 76 Unit: **Space Science**

INTERNET PREVIEW

CLASSZONE.COM For student use with the following pages:

Review and Practice
- Content Review, pp. 78, 108
- Math Tutorial: The Percent Equation, p. 84
- Test Practice, p. 111

Activities and Resources
- Internet Activity: Spacing, p. 77
- Resource Centers: Impact Craters, p. 86; Moons of Giant Planets, p. 102

The Solar System
Code: MDL059

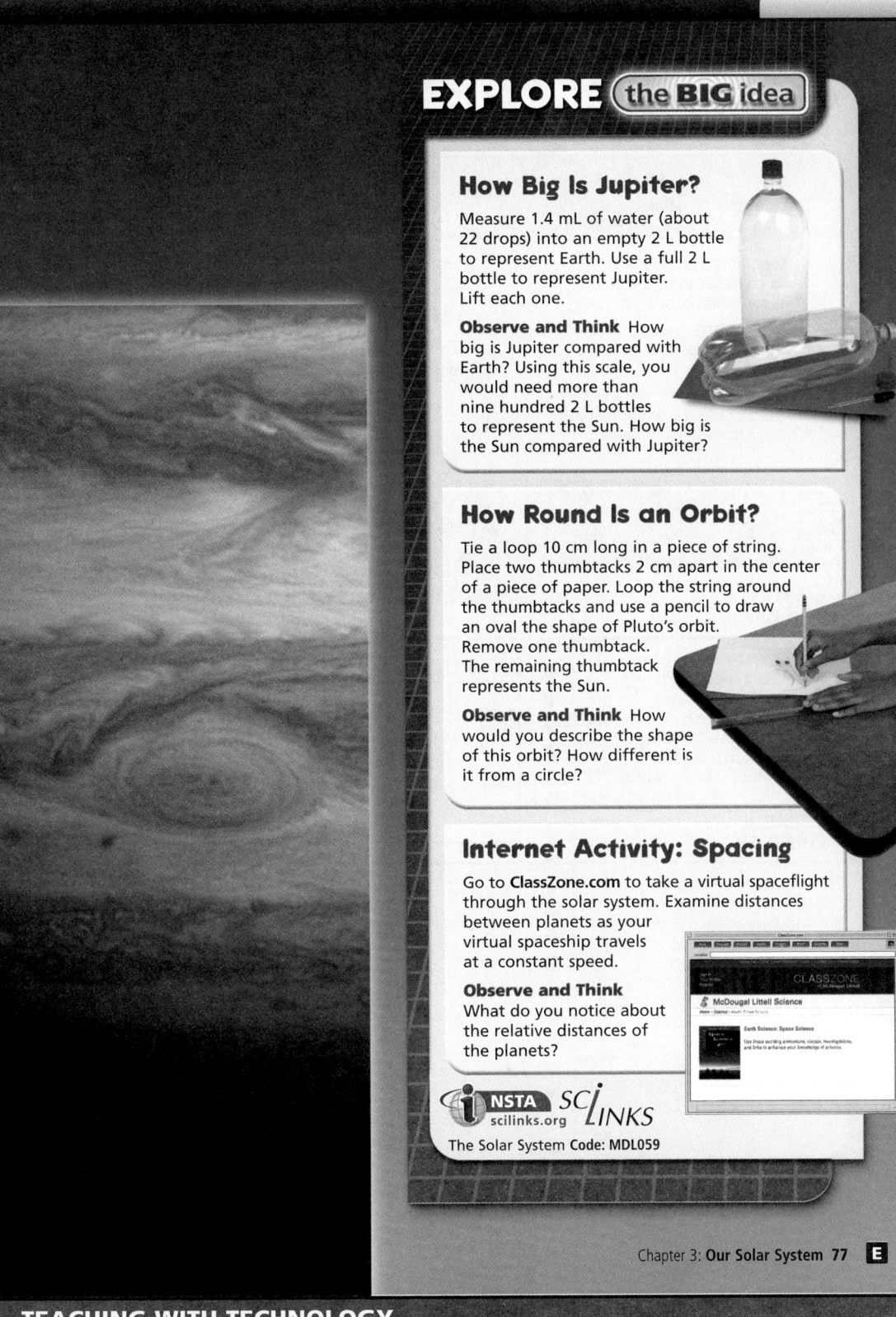

EXPLORE (the BIG idea)

How Big Is Jupiter?

Measure 1.4 mL of water (about 22 drops) into an empty 2 L bottle to represent Earth. Use a full 2 L bottle to represent Jupiter. Lift each one.

Observe and Think How big is Jupiter compared with Earth? Using this scale, you would need more than nine hundred 2 L bottles to represent the Sun. How big is the Sun compared with Jupiter?

How Round Is an Orbit?

Tie a loop 10 cm long in a piece of string. Place two thumbtacks 2 cm apart in the center of a piece of paper. Loop the string around the thumbtacks and use a pencil to draw an oval the shape of Pluto's orbit. Remove one thumbtack. The remaining thumbtack represents the Sun.

Observe and Think How would you describe the shape of this orbit? How different is it from a circle?

Internet Activity: Spacing

Go to **ClassZone.com** to take a virtual spaceflight through the solar system. Examine distances between planets as your virtual spaceship travels at a constant speed.

Observe and Think What do you notice about the relative distances of the planets?

NSTA scilinks.org SCI**LINKS**

The Solar System Code: MDL059

EXPLORE (the BIG idea)

These inquiry-based activities are appropriate for use at home or as a supplement to classroom instruction.

How Big Is Jupiter?

PURPOSE To model and compare the sizes of Jupiter and Earth.

TIP *10 min.* Have students imagine the 900 bottles that would model the size of the Sun by putting 15 bottles in a row. Then have students imagine a solid square of bottles that is 15 bottles on each side and imagine stacking 4 such squares.

Answer: Jupiter's volume is huge compared with that of Earth, and the Sun is enormous compared with Jupiter.

REVISIT after p. 95.

How Round Is an Orbit?

PURPOSE To introduce students to the shape of Pluto's orbit.

TIP *10 min.* Students can make models of other orbits, using the following spacings for the thumbtacks: Mercury, 1.7 cm; Venus and Neptune, 0.1 cm; Earth, 0.2 cm; Mars, 0.9 cm; Jupiter and Saturn, 0.5 cm; Uranus, 0.4 cm; comet Halley, 4.9 cm. The thumbtacks are the foci, or two central points, of the ellipse. For orbits, the Sun is always at one focus.

Answer: a circle or near circle

REVISIT after p. 81.

Internet Activity: Spacing

PURPOSE To introduce students to the distances between planets.

TIP *20 min.* Because the imaginary spaceship travels at a constant speed, the time it takes to travel between planets is proportional to the distance between orbits.

Answer: Planets get farther apart as you travel outward through the solar system.

REVISIT after p. 80.

TEACHING WITH TECHNOLOGY

Video Camera Students can tape the impacts and resulting craters in the Chapter Investigation on pp.106–107 and slow down the action.

Digital Camera Students can record the craters in the Chapter Investigation or the different views of the model rings on p. 97.

Remote-Access Telescope With access to a remote telescope, students can analyze images of objects in the solar system. Venus, Saturn, Jupiter and its moons (p. 96), and comets (p. 104) can show shapes or changes.

◑ CONCEPT REVIEW

Activate Prior Knowledge

Display a model or poster of the solar system.

- Ask: What makes up the solar system? *the Sun, planets, and smaller objects such as moons, asteroids, and comets*
- Ask: How are planets you can see in the night sky different from stars in constellations? *Planets are much closer; they reflect sunlight and shine.*

◑ TAKING NOTES

Main Idea and Details

Writing detail notes about each main idea can help students understand and remember the main ideas. Help students look for important details in topic and summary sentences. Students can use their notes to test themselves by covering up one-half of the chart as they study.

Vocabulary Strategy

Encourage students to write sentences in their own words instead of copying sentences from the text. Point out that students can use symbols, arrows, and labels in their drawings. By using a word in a sentence and drawing a picture, students personalize their understanding. The word triangles become easy study devices when students look back through their notes.

Vocabulary and Note-Taking Resources

- Vocabulary Practice, pp. 190–191
- Decoding Support, p. 192

- Daily Vocabulary Scaffolding, p. T18
- Note-Taking Model, p. T19

- Word Triangle, B18–19
- Main Idea and Detail Notes, C37
- Daily Vocabulary Scaffolding, H1–8

E 78 Unit: **Space Science**

◑ CONCEPT REVIEW

- The planets we see are much closer than the stars in constellations.
- The Sun, the planets, and smaller bodies make up the solar system.
- Scientists observe different types of electromagnetic radiation from space objects.

◑ VOCABULARY REVIEW

orbit p. 10

solar system p. 10

satellite p. 23

impact crater p. 32

axis of rotation p. 44

ⓘ CONTENT REVIEW
CLASSZONE.COM
Review concepts and vocabulary.

▶ TAKING NOTES

MAIN IDEA AND DETAILS

Make a two-column chart. Write main ideas, such as those in the blue headings, in the column on the left. Write details about each of those main ideas in the column on the right.

VOCABULARY STRATEGY

Draw a **word triangle** diagram for each new vocabulary term. In the bottom row write and define the term. In the middle row, use the term correctly in a sentence. At the top, draw a small picture to help you remember the term.

See the Note-Taking Handbook on pages R45–R51.

E 78 Unit: Space Science

SCIENCE NOTEBOOK

MAIN IDEAS	DETAIL NOTES
1. Planets have different sizes and distances.	1. Objects in the solar system • Sun • planets • moons • comets and asteroids
2.	2.

Jupiter is about 5 AU from the Sun.

astronomical unit (AU): Earth's average distance from the Sun

CHECK READINESS

Administer the Diagnostic Test to determine students' readiness for new science content and their mastery of requisite math skills.

 Diagnostic Test, pp. 40–41

Technology Resources

Students needing content and math skills should visit **ClassZone.com**.

- **CONTENT REVIEW**
- **MATH TUTORIAL**
- **CONTENT REVIEW CD-ROM**

KEY CONCEPT

3.1 Planets orbit the Sun at different distances.

 BEFORE, you learned

- Earth orbits the Sun
- The Moon is Earth's natural satellite
- The Moon's features tell us about its history

 NOW, you will learn

- What types of objects are in the solar system
- About sizes and distances in the solar system
- How the solar system formed

VOCABULARY

astronomical unit (AU) p. 81
ellipse p. 81

EXPLORE Planet Formation

How do planets form?

PROCEDURE

1. Fill the bowl about halfway with water.
2. Stir the water quickly, using a circular motion, and then remove the spoon.
3. Sprinkle wax pieces onto the swirling water.

WHAT DO YOU THINK?

- In what direction did the wax move?
- What else happened to the wax?

MATERIALS

- bowl
- water
- spoon
- wax pieces

 MAIN IDEA AND DETAILS
Put sizes and distances in the solar system into a chart.

Planets have different sizes and distances.

You may have seen some planets in the sky without realizing it. They are so far from Earth that they appear as tiny dots of light in the darkened sky. If you have seen something that looks like a very bright star in the western sky in the early evening, you have probably seen the planet Venus. Even if you live in a city, you may have seen Mars, Jupiter, or Saturn but thought that you were seeing a star. Mercury is much more difficult to see. You need a telescope to see three of the planets in our solar system—Uranus, Neptune, and Pluto.

Like the Moon, planets can be seen because they reflect sunlight. Planets do not give off visible light of their own. Sunlight is also reflected by moons and other objects in space, called comets and asteroids. However, these objects are usually too far away and not bright enough to see without a telescope.

 **CHECK YOUR READING** Why do planets look bright?

Chapter 3: **Our Solar System** 79 **E**

RESOURCES FOR DIFFERENTIATED INSTRUCTION

Below Level

UNIT RESOURCE BOOK
- Reading Study Guide A, pp. 146–147
- Decoding Support, p. 192

 **AUDIO CDS**

R **Additional INVESTIGATION,**
Exploring Ellipses, A, B, & C, pp. 204–212;
Teacher Instructions, pp. 287–288

Advanced

UNIT RESOURCE BOOK
- Challenge and Extension, p. 152
- Challenge Reading, pp. 188–189

English Learners

UNIT RESOURCE BOOK
Spanish Reading Study Guide, pp. 150–151

 **AUDIO CDS**

- Audio Readings in Spanish
- Audio Readings (English)

Set Learning Goals

Students will

- Identify the types of objects in the solar system.
- Compare sizes and distances in the solar system.
- Describe how the solar system formed.
- Use models in an experiment to compare distances.

3-Minute Warm-Up

Display Transparency 20 or copy this exercise on the board:

Draw a diagram showing the orbit of Earth and the orbit of Earth's Moon. Label the Sun, Earth, the Moon, Earth's orbit, and the Moon's orbit. *Diagrams should show Earth orbiting the Sun and the Moon orbiting Earth. Call attention to the scale.*

T 3-Minute Warm-Up, p. T20

3.1 MOTIVATE

EXPLORE Planet Formation

PURPOSE To model how a system of planets can form

TIP *10 min.* Use a potato peeler or grater with large holes to get wax pieces. Prepare the pieces for the lab on p. 88 at the same time.

WHAT DO YOU THINK? *The wax moved, and clumps spun the way the water was stirred. The wax gathered into spinning clumps.*

Ongoing Assessment

CHECK YOUR READING *Answer: Planets reflect sunlight.*

Teach from Visuals

To help students interpret the diagram of objects in the solar system, ask them to divide the objects shown into groups based on size. *extra-large: Sun; large: Jupiter, Saturn, Uranus, Neptune; medium: remaining planets and larger moons; small: asteroids, comets, remaining objects*

Teach Difficult Concepts

Students often have difficulty understanding and distinguishing between large numbers. Point out that scientists sometimes use comparisons that are easier to understand than very large numbers. Scientists use an AU to compare distances, an Earth mass to gauge the masses of other worlds, and a standard Earth gravitational constant to compare the surface gravities of other worlds. For further student help, you might discuss the following information.

Develop Critical Thinking

COMPARE Write this information on the board and discuss:

- It would take about 30 Earths to span the distance to the Moon.
- Jupiter is about 10 Earths across.
- The Sun is about 100 Earths across (about 10 Jupiters across).
- It would take roughly 100 Suns to span the distance between Earth and the Sun.

EXPLORE (the **BIG** idea)

Revisit "Internet Activity: Spacing" on p. 77. Have students describe what they noticed about the relative distances of the planets.

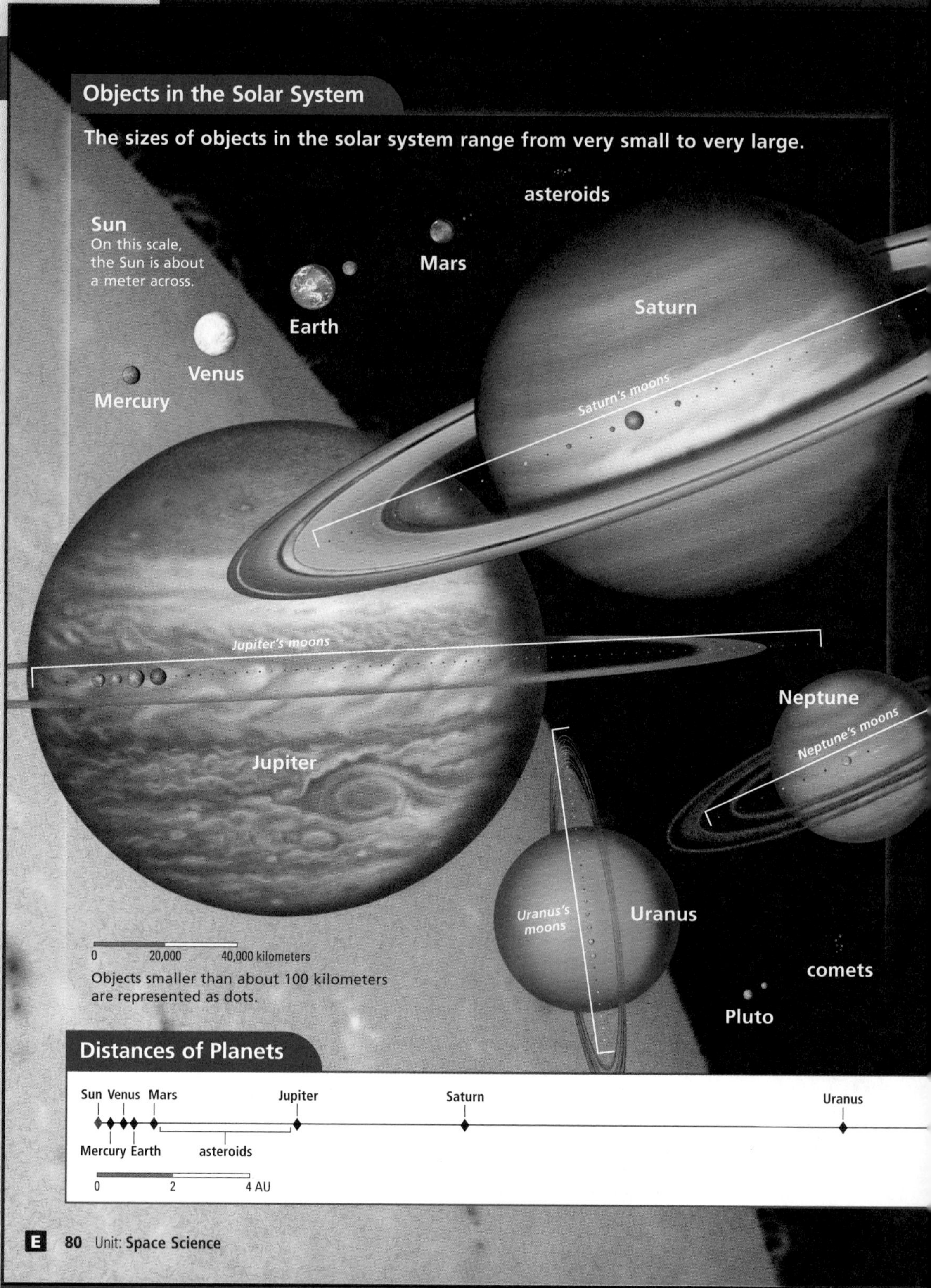

Objects in the Solar System

The sizes of objects in the solar system range from very small to very large.

Sun On this scale, the Sun is about a meter across.

Mercury

Venus

Earth

Mars

asteroids

Saturn

Saturn's moons

Jupiter

Jupiter's moons

Uranus's moons

Uranus

Neptune

Neptune's moons

comets

Pluto

| 0 | 20,000 | 40,000 kilometers |

Objects smaller than about 100 kilometers are represented as dots.

Distances of Planets

| Sun | Venus | Mars | Jupiter | Saturn | Uranus |

Mercury Earth   asteroids

| 0 | 2 | 4 AU |

DIFFERENTIATE INSTRUCTION

English Learners Make sure students understand the context of words with multiple meanings. For example, in the statement "Pluto gets nearly 50 AU from the Sun" on p. 81, students may think *gets* means "receives." Likewise, *tell* does not mean "communicate verbally" in "You can tell a little bit about the size . . ." (p. 83) but rather means "interpret."

Advanced Have students who are interested in learning about the farthest and faintest objects in our solar system read the following article:

 Challenge Reading, pp. 188–189

Objects in the solar system have very different sizes. An asteroid may be as small as a mountain, perhaps 1/1000 Earth's diameter. In contrast, the largest planets are about 10 Earth diameters across. The Sun's diameter is about 100 times Earth's. If the planets were the sizes shown on page 80, the Sun would be about a meter across.

Distances

The distances between most objects in space are huge in comparison with the objects' diameters. If Earth and the Sun were the sizes shown on page 80, they would be more than 100 meters from each other.

Astronomers understand huge distances by comparing them with something more familiar. One **astronomical unit,** or AU, is Earth's average distance from the Sun. An AU is about 150 million kilometers (93 million mi). Mercury is less than 0.5 AU from the Sun, Jupiter is about 5 AU from the Sun, and Pluto gets nearly 50 AU from the Sun at times. You can use the diagram at the bottom of pages 80–81 to compare these distances. However, the planets are not arranged in a straight line—they move around the Sun.

VOCABULARY
Draw word triangles in your notebook for new terms.

You can see that the planets are spaced unevenly. The first four planets are relatively close together and close to the Sun. They define a region called the inner solar system. Farther from the Sun is the outer solar system, where the planets are much more spread out.

 What are the two regions of the solar system?

Orbits

More than 99 percent of all the mass in the solar system is in the Sun. The gravitational pull of this huge mass causes planets and most other objects in the solar system to move around, or orbit, the Sun.

The shape of each orbit is an **ellipse**—a flattened circle or oval. A circle is a special type of ellipse, just as a square is a special type of rectangle. Most of the planets' orbits are very nearly circles. Only one planet—Pluto—has an orbit that looks a little flattened instead of round.

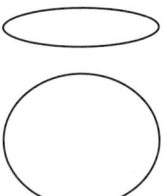

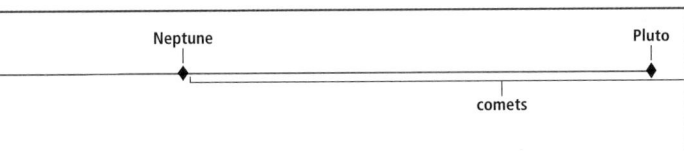
Neptune   Pluto
comets

DIFFERENTIATE INSTRUCTION

 More Reading Support

A How do distances between objects in the solar system compare with their diameters? *much greater*

B What is the shape of planets' orbits? *ellipses*

Additional Investigation To reinforce Section 3.1 learning goals, use the following full-period investigation:

R **Additional INVESTIGATION,** Exploring Ellipses, A, B, & C, pp. 204–212, 287–288 (Advanced students should complete Levels B and C.)

Below Level Point out that the planets are not in one straight line but in various spots in their orbits around the Sun. Have students examine or make a model of planets orbiting the Sun. Orbits can be approximated as circles in this model.

Address Misconceptions

IDENTIFY Tell students to imagine a tiny version of the Sun and Earth on their desktop. Ask them to draw Earth's orbit as seen from above this model. Students with the misconception that orbits are very elongated ovals may draw an elongated shape.

CORRECT Point out that orbits are often drawn at an angle, like a disk looked at from just above an edge. Have students examine or make drawings of orbits as if they were looking down on the solar system, perhaps using "How Round Is an Orbit?" on p. 77 as a model. The orbits are almost circles, but the Sun is clearly off center for some orbits.

REASSESS Ask students to describe the orbit of any of the planets. *Description should indicate a round, not elongated, shape (even for Pluto).*

Technology Resources

Visit **ClassZone.com** for background on common student misconceptions.

MISCONCEPTION DATABASE

EXPLORE (the BIG idea)

Revisit "How Round Is an Orbit" on p. 77. Have students explain their results.

Ongoing Assessment

Identify the types of objects in the solar system.

Ask: What types of objects in the solar system reflect sunlight? *planets, moons, comets, and asteroids*

Compare sizes and distances in the solar system.

Ask: How do the distances between the inner planets compare with those between the outer planets? *The outer planets are much farther apart than the inner planets.*

CHECK YOUR READING *Answer: the inner solar system and the outer solar system*

INVESTIGATE Distances

PURPOSE To use a model to compare distance between planets

TIPS *30 min.* Caution students to be careful so that the paper does not tear. You might want to have clear tape available to repair any tears.

WHAT DO YOU THINK? *The distance between Saturn and Uranus is much greater (roughly 20 times). The planets that are relatively close together form the inner solar system, and the ones that have huge distances between them form the outer solar system.*

CHALLENGE *about 6 times as long, or about 12 years (Actual time was 10 years.)*

- Distance Table, p. 153
- Datasheet, Distances, p. 154

Teach Difficult Concepts

Reinforce the idea that the solar system is a system and that its parts formed as a system. Ask students to cite evidence in the text to challenge the hypothesis that the Sun formed alone as a star, then later captured planets and other objects as it moved through space. *Most of the objects' orbits are very nearly in a plane (p. 82, second sentence); planets orbit the Sun in the same direction, counterclockwise as seen from above Earth's North Pole (p. 82, third sentence). Some students may already know that there is a pattern in the composition of objects also.*

INVESTIGATE Distances

How far apart are the planets?
PROCEDURE

1. Mark one sheet from the end of the roll of paper as the location of the Sun. Mark an *X* and write the word *Sun* with dots rather than lines.

2. Use the Distance Table data sheet to mark the distances for the rest of the solar system. Count sheets and estimate tenths of a sheet as necessary. Re-roll or fold the paper neatly.

3. Go to a space where you can unroll the paper. Compare the distances of planets as you walk along the paper and back again.

WHAT DO YOU THINK?
- How does the distance between Earth and Mars compare with the distance between Saturn and Uranus?
- How would you use the spacing to sort the planets into groups?

CHALLENGE If it took two years for the *Voyager 2* spacecraft to travel from Earth to Jupiter, about how long do you think it took for *Voyager 2* to travel from Jupiter to Neptune?

SKILL FOCUS
Using models

MATERIALS
- roll of toilet paper
- felt-tipped pen
- Distance Table

TIME
30 minutes

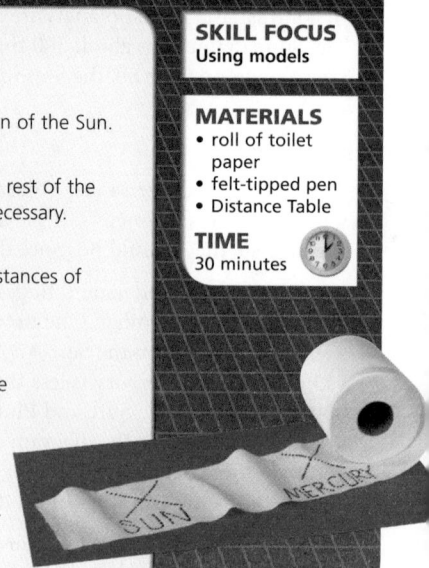

The solar system formed from a swirling cloud of gas and dust.

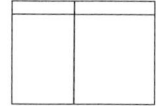
MAIN IDEA AND DETAILS
Remember to take notes about how the solar system formed.

The planets orbit the Sun in similar ways. Their paths are almost in a flat plane, like the rings of a target. They all orbit the Sun in the same direction—counterclockwise as seen from above Earth's North Pole. Most of the planets rotate on their axes in this direction, too. Many other objects in the solar system also orbit and rotate in this same direction. These similar motions have given scientists clues about how the solar system formed.

According to the best scientific model, the solar system formed out of a huge cloud of different gases and specks of dust. The cloud flattened into a disk of whirling material. Most of the mass fell to the center and became a star—the Sun. At the same time, tiny bits of dust and frozen gases in the disk stuck together into clumps. The clumps stuck together and became larger. Large clumps became planets. They moved in the same direction that the flat disk was turning.

Not all the clumps grew big enough to be called planets. However, many of these objects still orbit the Sun the same way that planets orbit. Some of the objects close to the Sun are like rocks or mountains in space and are called asteroids. Other objects, farther from the Sun, are more like enormous snowballs or icebergs. They are called comets.

DIFFERENTIATE INSTRUCTION

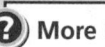 **More Reading Support**

C What is similar about the planets' orbits and many other motions in the solar system? *They are in the same direction.*

Advanced Students can see how much each planet's distance from the Sun changes over an orbit. Using the "Investigate Distances" model on this page, students should subtract and add the following number of sheets from each planet's average distance to get the minimum and maximum distances: Mercury, 0.4; Venus, 0.03; Earth, 0.9; Mars, 0.7; Jupiter, 1.2; Saturn, 2.7; Uranus, 4.4; Neptune, 1.5; Pluto, 49.0.

 Challenge and Extension, p. 152

Formation of the Solar System

The Sun and other objects formed out of material in a flat disk.

① Nebula	② Disk	③ Solar System
Part of a huge cloud of material, called a nebula, collapsed into a flattened disk.	The Sun formed at the center of the disk. Other objects formed from the whirling material of the disk.	Much of the material was cleared away. The Sun, planets, and other objects remained.

Some objects orbit planets instead of orbiting the Sun directly, so they are considered moons. You will read more about asteroids, comets, and moons in Section 3.4.

You can tell a little bit about the size of an object in space from its shape. Lumpy objects are usually much smaller than round objects. As a space object starts to form, the clumps come together from many directions and produce an uneven shape. The gravity of each part affects every other part. The pieces pull each other closer together. When an object has enough mass, this pulling becomes strong enough to make the object round. Any parts that would stick far out are pulled in toward the center until the object becomes a sphere.

 **CHECK YOUR READING** Why do planets and large moons have a spherical shape?

3.1 Review

KEY CONCEPTS

1. What are the types of space objects in the solar system?

2. Why is the unit of measurement used for the distances of planets from the Sun different from the unit used for their sizes?

3. How did planets and other objects in the solar system form out of material in a disk?

CRITICAL THINKING

4. **Analyze** Why do the planets all orbit in one direction?

5. **Infer** Which of the two moons below has more mass? Explain why you think so.

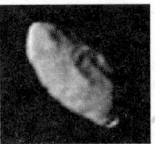 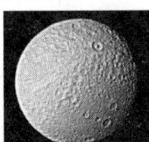

⬤ CHALLENGE

6. **Apply** Could you model all the sizes of objects in the solar system by using sports balls? Explain why or why not.

Chapter 3: **Our Solar System** 83 **E**

ANSWERS

1. one star, planets, moons, asteroids, and comets

2. Distances of the planets from the Sun are much greater than their diameters. The distances in kilometers would be too large to be useful.

3. The solid material stuck together in clumps, and the clumps stuck together and became larger.

4. The planets formed out of material that was moving around in one direction.

5. The moon on the right has more mass. Its gravity pulled it into a sphere.

6. No, because if the largest ball were used for the Sun, no ball would be small enough for the smallest objects.

Set Learning Goal

To use percentages to calculate weights in newtons on other planets and moons

Present the Science

Mass is the measure of the amount of matter making up an object. The kilogram is a unit of mass. Weight is the measure of the gravitational force between a massive object, such as a planet, and a much less massive object. Newtons and pounds are both units of force. An object has the same mass no matter where it is located, but the same object weighs different amounts on different worlds because the gravitational force depends on the world's mass as well as the object's mass. The gravitational force also depends on distance—approximately the distance between the centers of the objects, or the radius of the world. The percentages given in the table can be applied to weights measured in either newtons or pounds.

Develop Number Sense

- Ask: Why do you need to multiply to find a percentage of a number? *"Of" means "multiply."*

- Have students convert a percentage to a decimal fraction by moving the decimal point two places to the left.

Close

Ask students to summarize how gravity affects weight. Have students compare the three weights in question 1. *The backpack would be heaviest on Jupiter, lightest on Io.* Then have them compare the three weights in question 2. *The student would weigh slightly more on Earth, and almost the same on Venus and Saturn, despite the very different radii and masses of those two planets.*

- Math Support, p. 193
- Math Practice, p. 194

Technology Resources

Students can visit **ClassZone.com** for practice in using percentages.

 MATH TUTORIAL

MATH in SCIENCE

MATH TUTORIAL
CLASSZONE.COM
Click on Math Tutorial for more help with the percent equation.

This picture of Buzz Aldrin on the Moon was taken by Neil Armstrong, who can be seen reflected in Aldrin's helmet.

E 84 Unit: **Space Science**

SKILL: USING PERCENTAGES

How Much Would You Weigh on Other Worlds?

When astronauts walked on the Moon, they felt much lighter than they felt when they were on Earth. Neil Armstrong's total mass—about 160 kilograms with space suit and backpack—did not change. However, the Moon did not pull as hard on him as Earth did, so he weighed less on the Moon. At the surface, the Moon's gravitational pull is only 17% of Earth's gravitational pull. You can use percentages to calculate Neil Armstrong's weight on the Moon.

Example

On Earth, with his heavy space suit and backpack, Neil Armstrong weighed about 1600 newtons (360 lb). To calculate his weight on the Moon, find 17% of 1600 newtons.

"Of" means "multiply."   17% of 1600 N = 17% × 1600 N

Change the percent to a decimal fraction.   = 0.17 × 1600 N

Simplify.   = 272 N

ANSWER With his suit and backpack, Neil Armstrong weighed about 270 newtons on the Moon.

Use the percentages in the table to answer the following questions.

1. A backpack weighs 60 newtons (13 lb) on Earth. **(a)** How much would it weigh on Jupiter? **(b)** How much would it weigh on Jupiter's moon Io?

2. **(a)** How much would a student weighing 500 newtons (110 lb) on Earth weigh on Saturn? **(b)** on Venus?

3. On which planet or moon would you be lightest?

CHALLENGE A pencil weighs 0.3 newtons (1 oz) on Earth. How much would it weigh on the Moon? If an astronaut let go of the pencil on the Moon, would the pencil fall? Explain.

Percent of Weight on Earth	
Planet or Moon	**%**
Mercury	38
Venus	91
Earth	100
Moon (Earth)	17
Mars	38
Jupiter	236
Io (Jupiter)	18
Europa (Jupiter)	13
Ganymede (Jupiter)	15
Callisto (Jupiter)	13
Saturn	92
Titan (Saturn)	14
Uranus	89
Neptune	112
Triton (Neptune)	8.0
Pluto	6.7
Charon (Pluto)	2.8

ANSWERS

1. 141.6, or 142, N (2.36 × 60 N); 10.8, or 11, N (0.18 × 60 N)

2. 460 N (0.92 × 500 N); 455 N (0.91 × 500 N)

3. Charon (Pluto's moon)

CHALLENGE 0.05 N (0.17 × 0.3 N); yes, the pencil would fall because the Moon's gravity would pull it down.

3.2 The inner solar system has rocky planets.

◀ BEFORE, you learned

- Planets are closer together in the inner solar system than in the outer solar system
- Planets formed along with the Sun
- Gravity made planets round

▶ NOW, you will learn

- How four processes change the surfaces of solid planets
- How atmospheres form and then affect planets
- What the planets closest to the Sun are like

VOCABULARY

terrestrial planet p. 85
tectonics p. 86
volcanism p. 86

EXPLORE Surfaces

How does a planet's mantle affect its surface?

PROCEDURE

1. Dampen a paper towel and place it on top of two blocks to model a crust and a mantle.

2. Move one block. Try different amounts of motion and different directions.

WHAT DO YOU THINK?
- What happened to the paper towel?
- What landforms like this have you seen?

MATERIALS
- 2 blocks
- paper towel
- newspaper

The terrestrial planets have rocky crusts.

Scientists study Earth to learn about other planets. They also study other planets to learn more about Earth. The **terrestrial planets** are Mercury, Venus, Earth, and Mars—the four planets closest to the Sun. They all have rocky crusts and dense mantles and cores. Their insides, surfaces, and atmospheres formed in similar ways and follow similar patterns. One planet—Earth—can be used as a model to understand the others. In fact, the term *terrestrial* comes from *terra*, the Latin word for Earth.

Earth

Most of Earth's rocky surface is hidden by water. More details about Earth and other planets are listed in the Appendix at the back of this book.

Mass 6×10^{24} kg
Diameter 12,800 km
Average distance from Sun 1 AU

Orbits in 365 days
Rotates in 24 hours

RESOURCES FOR DIFFERENTIATED INSTRUCTION

Below Level
UNIT RESOURCE BOOK
- Reading Study Guide A, pp. 158–159
- Decoding Support, p. 192

🎧 **AUDIO CDS**

Advanced
UNIT RESOURCE BOOK
Challenge and Extension, p. 164

English Learners
UNIT RESOURCE BOOK
Spanish Reading Study Guide, pp. 162–163

🎧 **AUDIO CDS**
- Audio Readings in Spanish
- Audio Readings (English)

3.2 FOCUS

◉ Set Learning Goals

Students will
- Explain how four processes change the surfaces of solid planets.
- Identify how atmospheres form and then affect planets.
- Describe what the planets closest to the Sun are like.
- Experiment using a model to see why layers formed in solid planets.

◉ 3-Minute Warm-Up

Display Transparency 20 or copy this exercise on the board:

Decide if these statements are true. If not, correct them.

1. The planets that are the closest together are the planets in the outer solar system. *The planets that are the closest together are the planets in the inner solar system.*

2. Planets and the Sun formed from the same cloud of material. *true*

3. Planets are round because of their orbits. *Planets are round because of their gravity.*

🅣 3-Minute Warm-Up, p. T20

3.2 MOTIVATE

EXPLORE Surfaces

PURPOSE To model the effect that the motion of a solid planet's mantle has on its surface

TIP *15 min.* Have students squeeze out the paper towels by folding and pressing them. Use newspaper underneath to catch drips.

WHAT DO YOU THINK? *It wrinkled, tore, or became distorted in other ways; mountains, valleys, or other landforms*

History of Science

Pioneer 10 was launched in 1972, and *Pioneer 11* was launched in 1973. *Voyager 1* and *2* were both launched in 1977. The Pioneer and Voyager spacecraft changed astronomers' view when they took close-up images that showed that other planets and moons had geological features much like Earth's.

Integrate the Sciences

Geology is the science that deals with the compositions of Earth and other planets and the processes that formed them. Meteorology is the science that deals with the atmosphere and weather. Physics is the science that deals with matter and energy and the relationship between them. The rules and scientific principles learned through these fields of study on Earth apply to other space bodies.

Real World Example

Most volcanoes on Earth tend to form near the edges of tectonic plates. On most other planets, there are no plate edges, so volcanoes form along cracks, at hot spots, and at places where the crust is thin or heated more. On Earth, volcanoes do sometimes form in the middle of a continent or ocean. The Hawaiian Islands are a chain of many islands that formed from volcanoes in the Pacific Ocean far from any plate edges. The Hawaiian volcanoes were produced by the Hawaiian hot spot. At the present time, three of the Hawaiian volcanoes are active. The volcano Kilauea has been erupting since 1983.

Ongoing Assessment

CHECK YOUR READING *Answer: tectonics, volcanism, weathering and erosion, and impact cratering*

READING TiP

Compare what you read about each type of feature with the pictures and diagrams on page 87.

A

RESOURCE CENTER
CLASSZONE.COM

Find out more about impact craters on Earth and other space objects.

Processes and Surface Features

All terrestrial planets have layers. Each planet gained energy from the collisions that formed it. This energy heated and melted the planet's materials. The heaviest materials were metals, which sank to the center and formed a core. Lighter rock formed a mantle around the core. The lightest rock rose to the surface and cooled into a crust.

Four types of processes then shaped each planet's rocky crust. The processes acted to different extents on each planet, depending on how much the crust and inside of the planet cooled.

① **Tectonics** Earth's crust is split into large pieces called tectonic plates. These plates are moved by Earth's hot mantle. Mountains, valleys, and other features form as the plates move together, apart, or along each other. The crusts of other terrestrial planets are not split into plates but can be twisted, wrinkled up, or stretched out by the mantle. **Tectonics** is the processes of change in a crust due to the motion of hot material underneath. As a planet cools, the crust gets stiffer and the mantle may stop moving, so this process stops.

② **Volcanism** A second process, called **volcanism,** occurs when molten rock moves from a planet's hot interior onto its surface. The molten rock is called lava when it reaches the surface through an opening called a volcano. On Earth, lava often builds up into mountains. Volcanoes are found on Earth, Venus, and Mars. Lava can also flow onto large areas and cool into flat plains like the lunar maria. When the inside of a planet cools enough, no more molten rock reaches the surface.

③ **Weathering and Erosion** You have read about weathering on Earth and the Moon. Weather or small impacts break down rocks. The broken material is moved by a group of processes called erosion. The material may form dunes, new layers of rock, or other features. On Earth, water is important for weathering and erosion. However, similar things happen even without water. Wind can carry sand grains that batter at rocks and form new features. Even on a planet without air, rock breaks down from being heated in the daylight and cooled at night. The material is pulled downhill by gravity.

B

④ **Impact Cratering** A small object sometimes hits a planet's surface so fast that it causes an explosion. The resulting impact crater is often ten times larger than the object that produced it. On Earth, most craters have been erased by other processes. Impact craters are easier to find on other planets. If a planet or part of a planet is completely covered with impact craters, then the other processes have not changed the surface much in billions of years.

CHECK YOUR READING What processes affect the surfaces of terrestrial planets?

DIFFERENTIATE INSTRUCTION

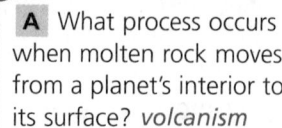

? More Reading Support

A What process occurs when molten rock moves from a planet's interior to its surface? *volcanism*

B What causes erosion on a planet with no air? *gravity*

English Learners Have students write definitions of *terrestrial planet, tectonics,* and *volcanism* in their Science Word Dictionaries. After reading about the four processes above, have English learners write a summary of each process.

Below Level Display topographic maps of Earth's surface and photographs of Earth from planes, space shuttles, or satellites to help students see what geological features look like from above.

Features of Rocky Planets

The processes that shape features on a planet's surface can be divided into four types. The features can tell you different things about the planet.

① Tectonics

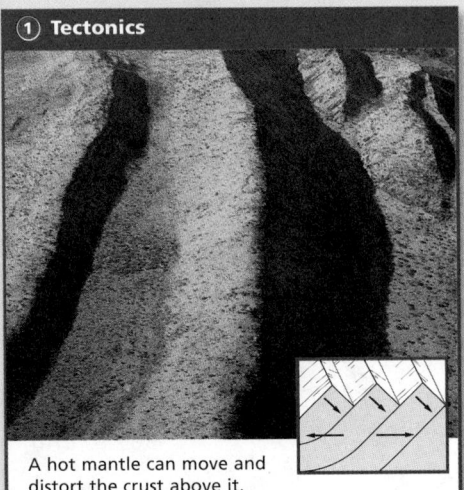

A hot mantle can move and distort the crust above it. This system of mountains and valleys on **Earth** formed as the crust was stretched.

② Volcanism

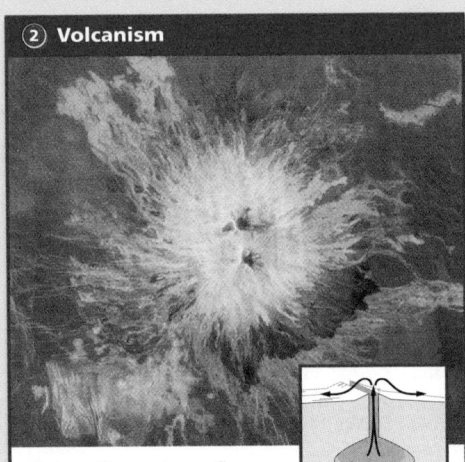

Hot, molten rock can flow or explode out onto the surface of a planet. At this volcano on **Venus**, lava flowed onto the surface several times.

③ Weathering and Erosion

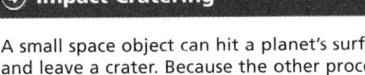

Rock can be broken down and moved. In this region of **Mars**, material broken from a cliff was moved by erosion into new slopes and dunes.

④ Impact Cratering

A small space object can hit a planet's surface and leave a crater. Because the other processes on **Mercury** are weak, newer craters can be seen on a background of older, more eroded craters.

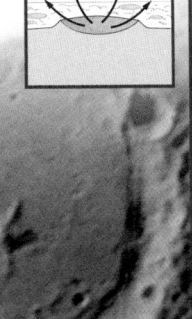

READING VISUALS Which two processes happen because of hot material beneath the surface?

Chapter 3: **Our Solar System** 87 **E**

Teach from Visuals

To help students interpret the visuals of four processes that can shape a planet's surface, ask:

- If the process of tectonics is occurring on a planet, what do you know about the planet's mantle? *It is hot.*
- What does the photograph of Mars show? *weathered material that has been moved by erosion*
- What causes craters? *small space objects hitting the surface of a planet* What do craters on Mercury look like? *circular, flat or bowl-shaped inside*

 This visual is also available as T22 in the Unit Transparency Book.

Teacher Demo

Help students gain experience in analyzing the formation of surface features on the basis of how the features overlap.

- Use a patch of dirt or pan of flour. Use three actions to represent processes in different sequences. You might draw lines, make footprints, and then smooth portions.
- Have volunteers determine the sequence of events from the final appearance only. *More recent actions overlie, cut, obliterate, or otherwise modify features from prior actions.*

Ongoing Assessment

Explain how four processes change the surfaces of solid planets.

Ask: What changes to a rock are evidence of weathering? *broken or worn pieces*

READING VISUALS *Answer: tectonics and volcanism*

INVESTIGATE Layers

PURPOSE To use a model to infer how a planet's layers formed

TIPS *40 min.* Use a potato peeler or a grater with large holes to get wax pieces.

WHAT DO YOU THINK? *The sand went to the bottom, and the wax floated. The materials were able to separate into layers of different densities because of melting.*

CHALLENGE *Sample answer: Use only materials that melt.*

 Datasheet, Layers, p. 165

Technology Resources

Customize this student lab as needed or look for an alternative. Print rubrics to assess student lab reports.

 Lab Generator CD-ROM

Integrate the Sciences

The gases in Earth's atmosphere are necessary for organisms to live. In turn, organisms affect the gases in the atmosphere. Plants give off oxygen during photosynthesis. Venus and Mars have no plant life and little or no oxygen in their atmospheres. Photosynthesis also removes carbon dioxide, a greenhouse gas, from the atmosphere. This gas affects Earth's average temperature, which in turn affects plant growth in the Earth system.

Ongoing Assessment

Identify how atmospheres form and then affect planets.

Ask: How can an atmosphere affect heat energy? *by moving it from warmer places to cooler places and slowing its loss from a planet's surface*

CHECK YOUR READING *Answer: Earth's gravity is strong enough to hold the gases from volcanoes and other sources.*

INVESTIGATE Layers

How do the layers inside of planets form?

In this model, the materials you use represent different rocks and metals that make up the solid planets.

SKILL FOCUS
Using models

MATERIALS
• container
• spoon
• firm gelatin
• sand
• wax pieces
• bowl of hot tap water

TIME
40 minutes

PROCEDURE

1. Put pieces of gelatin into the container until it is about one-quarter full.

2. Mix in a spoonful each of sand and wax. Use the spoon to break the gelatin into small pieces as you mix. Remove the spoon.

3. Place the container in a bowl of hot tap water (about 70°C) and observe what happens as the gelatin melts.

WHAT DO YOU THINK?

• What happened to each of the materials when the gelatin melted?

• How do the results resemble the core, mantle, and crust of Earth and other planets?

CHALLENGE How might you improve this model?

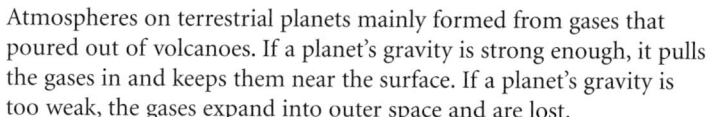

Atmospheres

 Atmospheres on terrestrial planets mainly formed from gases that poured out of volcanoes. If a planet's gravity is strong enough, it pulls the gases in and keeps them near the surface. If a planet's gravity is too weak, the gases expand into outer space and are lost.

Venus, Earth, and Mars each had gravity strong enough to hold heavy gases such as carbon dioxide. However, the lightest gases—hydrogen and helium—escaped into outer space. The atmospheres of Venus and Mars are mostly carbon dioxide.

An atmosphere can move energy from warmer places to cooler places. This movement of heat energy makes temperatures more uniform between a planet's day side and its night side and between its equator and its poles. An atmosphere can also make a planet's whole surface warmer by slowing the loss of energy from the surface.

 After Earth formed, its atmosphere of carbon dioxide kept the surface warm enough for water to be liquid. Oceans covered most of Earth's surface. The oceans changed the gases of the atmosphere, and living organisms caused even more changes. Earth's atmosphere is now mostly nitrogen with some oxygen.

CHECK YOUR READING Why is the solid Earth surrounded by gases?

DIFFERENTIATE INSTRUCTION

 More Reading Support

C What was the main source of gases in atmospheres? *volcanoes*

D After Earth formed, how did gases affect its surface? *kept it warm*

Inclusion To eliminate distractions, erase the board and have students remove all other materials from their desks before performing "Investigate Layers." Ask students to repeat the directions in their own words to make sure they understand what they are to do.

Craters cover the surface of Mercury.

Mercury, like the Moon, has smooth plains and many craters. The processes at work on Earth also affected Mercury.

Tectonics Long, high cliffs stretch across Mercury's surface. Scientists think that Mercury's huge core of iron shrank when it cooled long ago. The crust wrinkled up, forming cliffs, as the planet got a little smaller.

Volcanism Parts of the surface were covered with lava long ago. Large, smooth plains formed. The plains are similar to lunar maria.

Weathering and Erosion Small impacts and temperature changes have broken rock. Gravity has moved broken material downhill.

Impact Cratering Round features cover much of the surface. These craters show that the other processes have not changed Mercury's surface very much for a long time.

Mercury has the longest cycle of day and night of the terrestrial planets—three months of daylight and three months of darkness. There is no atmosphere to move energy from the hot areas to the cold areas. In the long daytime, it can get hotter than 420°C (about 800°F)—hot enough to melt lead. During the long, cold night, the temperature can drop lower than –170°C (about –280°F).

CHECK YOUR READING How is Mercury similar to the Moon?

—no data

Mercury

This map of Mercury was made from many images taken by one spacecraft. The blank patches show areas that were not mapped by the spacecraft.

Mass 6% of Earth's mass
Diameter 38% of Earth's diameter
Average distance from Sun 0.39 AU
Orbits in 88 Earth days
Rotates in 59 Earth days

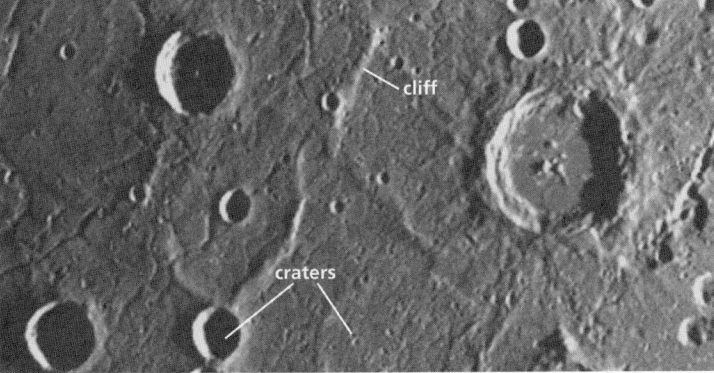

cliff

craters

Craters of all sizes cover Mercury's surface, but there are also flat lava plains and cliffs from long ago.

You may want to set up a slightly better model to demonstrate the formation of a planet's layers. Use either wax or petroleum jelly for the crust material. Put the sand, gelatin, and wax or petroleum jelly into a clear, heatproof container in simmering water (double boiler) to melt the crust material. Be careful, because the crust solidifies while the mantle is still fluid and hot.

Teach Difficult Concepts

Students may wonder how scientists can determine the masses of planets. Tell students that scientists calculate a planet's mass by measuring the gravitational effect it has on the motions of other space objects, such as moons and spacecraft. Ask: What object might have first been used to determine Earth's mass? *the Moon* How does a planet's mass affect its gravity? *The more mass a planet has, the greater its gravity.* How does a planet's gravity affect other space objects? *It pulls the objects toward the planet.*

Teach from Visuals

To help students interpret the images of Mercury, ask: What surface features does Mercury have? *craters, ridges, plains*

Ongoing Assessment

CHECK YOUR READING *Answer: Mercury has many craters and volcanic plains similar to lunar maria.*

DIFFERENTIATE INSTRUCTION

More Reading Support

E What features on Mercury were formed by tectonics? *cliffs*

F How much atmosphere does Mercury have? *none*

Inclusion Have students who may have trouble remembering start a set of information cards about the solar system. Starting with Mercury, have them include the planet's name, its distance from the Sun, its size, and a summary of what the planet is like. Encourage students to make a card for each planet or type of object in the solar system as they read. Students can later sort the cards by size, location, materials, or other characteristics.

Integrate the Sciences

Most types of living things on Earth need liquid water and an energy source that is either sunlight or can be traced through the food chain back to sunlight. For similar types of living things to survive and develop on another planet, the planet would need to be far enough away from the Sun that water would not boil away and close enough to the Sun that all the water would not freeze. Scientists are now studying life in extreme environments on Earth such as around hot vents on the ocean floor, inside volcanoes, deep inside rocks, and in the tundra and polar caps. Surprisingly, some living things live in these extreme environments. Determining the full range of environments possible for life on Earth can help determine the possibility of life on other planets.

Develop Critical Thinking

COMPARE AND CONTRAST Have students compare and contrast the atmospheres of Venus and Earth both when the planets' atmospheres first formed and today. *When the planets formed, both the atmospheres had a lot of carbon dioxide. Today, Venus still has an atmosphere that is mostly carbon dioxide. Earth's atmosphere is mostly nitrogen with some oxygen.*

Teach from Visuals

To help students interpret the images of Venus, ask:

- What makes Venus look white in visible light? *thick clouds*

- What did scientists use to make the map of Venus shown in the inset? *radio waves*

- What can you see on the surface of Venus in the photograph taken from a spacecraft? *weathered and eroded rock*

MAIN IDEA AND DETAILS When you see a new heading, remember to take notes about important ideas.

G

Thick clouds make it impossible to see Venus's surface in visible light. This inset shows a map of Venus that scientists made using radio waves.

Volcanoes shape the surface of Venus.

The planet Venus is only a little smaller than Earth and orbits a little closer to the Sun. As a result, Venus is sometimes called Earth's sister planet. However, Venus is different from Earth in important ways.

Venus takes about eight months to turn just once on its axis. Unlike most other planets, Venus rotates and orbits in opposite directions. The rotation and orbit together produce very long days and nights—two months of daylight followed by two months of darkness.

The atmosphere of Venus is very dense. Air pressure on Venus is 90 times that on Earth. Venus's atmosphere is mostly carbon dioxide. This gas slows the loss of energy and makes the surface very hot. The ground temperature on Venus is about 470°C (about 870°F). The atmosphere of Venus moves energy around so well that the long nights are as hot as the days and the poles are as hot as the equator. In addition, there are droplets of sulfuric acid, a corrosive chemical, in the atmosphere. These droplets form thick white clouds that completely cover the planet and hide the surface.

Like Mercury, Venus is affected by the same four types of processes that change Earth's surface. Scientists think that tectonics and volcanism may still be changing Venus's surface today.

Tectonics Patterns of cracks and cliffs have formed as movements of the hot mantle have stretched, wrinkled, and twisted the surface.

Volcanism Most of the surface of Venus has been covered with lava in the last billion years or so. Volcanoes and flat lava plains are found all over the surface.

Venus

Venus is nearly the size of Earth but has a thicker atmosphere and is much hotter than Earth. The surface is rocky, as you can see in the image below.

Mass 82% of Earth's mass
Diameter 95% of Earth's diameter
Average distance from Sun 0.72 AU

Orbits in 225 Earth days
Rotates in 243 Earth days

weathered and eroded rock

spacecraft

DIFFERENTIATE INSTRUCTION

? **More Reading Support**

G How does the air pressure on Venus compare with that on Earth? *It is 90 times the pressure on Earth.*

Weathering and Erosion Venus is too hot to have liquid water, and the winds do not seem to move much material. Erosion may be slower on Venus than on Earth.

Impact Cratering Round craters mark the surface here and there. Older craters have been erased by the other processes. Also, Venus's thick atmosphere protects the surface from small impacts.

 **CHECK YOUR READING** Why is Venus not covered with craters?

Erosion changes the appearance of Mars.

Mars is relatively small, with a diameter about half that of Earth. The orange color of some of the surface comes from molecules of iron and oxygen—rust. Mars has two tiny moons. They were probably once asteroids that were pulled into orbit around Mars.

Surface of Mars

The same processes that affect the other terrestrial planets affect Mars.

Tectonics Valleys and raised areas formed on Mars as the mantle moved. One huge system of valleys, called Valles Marineris, is long enough to stretch across the United States.

Volcanism Most of the northern hemisphere has smooth plains of cooled lava. Several volcanoes are higher than any mountain on Earth. The lava must have built up in the same spot for a long time, so scientists have inferred that the crust of Mars has cooled more than Earth's crust. On Earth, the tectonic plates move, so chains of smaller volcanoes form instead of single larger volcanoes.

Weathering and Erosion Fast winds carry sand that breaks down rocks. Wind and gravity move the broken material, forming new features such as sand dunes. There are also landforms that look like the results of gigantic flash floods that happened long ago.

Impact Cratering Round craters cover much of the southern hemisphere of Mars. Many craters are very old and eroded. A few impact craters on the volcanoes make scientists think that the volcanoes have not released lava for a long time.

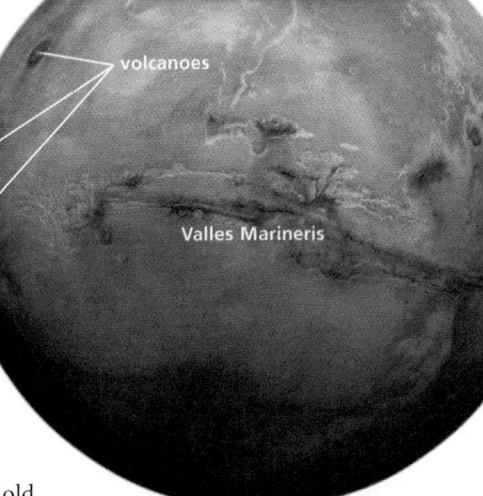

Mars

The atmosphere of Mars is thin but causes weathering and erosion.

Mass 11% of Earth's mass
Diameter 53% of Earth's diameter
Average distance from Sun 1.5 AU
Orbits in 1.9 Earth years
Rotates in 25 hours

volcanoes

Valles Marineris

Language Arts Connection

In 1877, the Italian astronomer Giovanni Schiaparelli used the term *canali* to describe streaks he thought he saw on the surface of Mars. This word was incorrectly interpreted as referring to artificial canals instead of natural channels. This led to a widespread myth that Schiaparelli believed that intelligent beings on Mars had built a system of canals to carry water. English dictionaries today have a definition of *canal* referring to these lines seen on the planet Mars.

Teach from Visuals

To help students interpret the table of information and the image of Mars, ask:

- What surface features are identified in the image? *volcanoes and Valles Marineris (valleys)*
- What processes might have produced these features? *volcanism and either tectonics or erosion*
- What is the atmosphere of Mars like? *thin but causing weathering and erosion*
- How does the mass of Mars compare with Earth's? *It is much less (11% of Earth's).*

Ongoing Assessment

CHECK YOUR READING *Answer: Other processes have erased older craters, and the thick atmosphere protects the surface from small impacts.*

DIFFERENTIATE INSTRUCTION

? More Reading Support

H What causes the orange color of Mars? *molecules of iron and oxygen*

I What covers much of the southern hemisphere? *impact craters*

English Learners The fifth question in this section's review (p. 92) may be confusing to English learners. While students may be familiar with the cause-and-effect structure of the sentence, they may not have seen it used as a question. Explain that the first part of the sentence states the effect, a surface with craters but no other features, while the second part of the sentence is asking for the cause of this effect.

Describe what the planets closest to the Sun are like.

Ask: What is one characteristic that the four planets closest to the Sun have in common? *Sample answer: All have rocky surfaces.*

 CHECK YOUR READING *Answer: Mars is smaller, has a thin atmosphere of carbon dioxide, and has no liquid water on the surface. Mars also is colder, and the temperature varies more from day to night.*

Reinforce (the **BIG** idea)

Have students relate the section to the Big Idea.

 Reinforcing Key Concepts, p. 166

3.2 ASSESS & RETEACH

Assess

A Section 3.2 Quiz, p. 43

Reteach

Have students make a four-column table of the four processes that shape features on a planet's surface. Have them list the processes in the first column, descriptions in the second column, examples of features caused by the processes in the third column, and inferences that can be made about planets in the fourth column.

Technology Resources

Have students visit **ClassZone.com** for reteaching of Key Concepts.

 CONTENT REVIEW

 CONTENT REVIEW CD-ROM

red dust carried by wind

distant hills

weathered and eroded rock

The sky of Mars is made red by dust that the wind picks up and carries to new places.

Gases and Water on Mars

The atmosphere of Mars is mostly carbon dioxide. The air pressure is only about 1 percent of the air pressure on Earth. The gas is not dense enough to keep the surface warm or to move much energy from cold areas to warmer areas. Therefore, temperatures may reach almost 20°C (about 60°F) in the daytime and −90°C (−130°F) at night. The large differences in temperature produce fast winds. The winds cause gigantic dust storms that sometimes cover most of the planet.

Like Earth, Mars has polar caps that grow in winter and shrink in summer. However, the changing polar caps of Mars are made mostly of frozen carbon dioxide—dry ice. The carbon dioxide of the atmosphere can also form clouds, fog, and frost on the ground.

There is no liquid water on the surface of Mars today. Any water would quickly evaporate or freeze. However, there were floods in the past, and there is still frozen water in the ground and in one polar cap. Water is important for life and will also be needed to make rocket fuel if humans are ever to make trips to Mars and back.

 **CHECK YOUR READING** In what ways is Mars different from Earth?

3.2 Review

KEY CONCEPTS

1. What are the four types of processes that shape planets' surfaces? For each, give one example of a feature that the process can produce.

2. How can an atmosphere affect the temperature of a planet's surface?

3. Which terrestrial planet has the oldest, least-changing surface?

CRITICAL THINKING

4. **Compare and Contrast** Make a chart with columns for the four types of processes and for an atmosphere. Fill out a row for each planet.

5. **Apply** If a planet had a surface with craters but no other features, what could you say about the inside of the planet?

♦ CHALLENGE

6. **Infer** Describe how a hot mantle can affect a planet's atmosphere. **Hint:** Which of the four processes is involved?

ANSWERS

1. tectonics: mountains or valleys; volcanism: volcanic mountains or flat plains; weathering and erosion: dunes, rock layers; impact cratering: craters

2. It can make a surface warmer and more uniform in temperature.

3. Mercury

4. Charts should include rows for Mercury, Venus, Earth, and Mars and columns for tectonics, volcanism, weathering and erosion, impact cratering, and atmosphere.

5. The mantle is not hot enough for tectonics and volcanism.

6. A hot mantle can produce volcanoes, which can give off gases that become an atmosphere.

SKILL: FORMING HYPOTHESES

What Shapes the Surface of Mars?

Many features on Mars, when seen close up, look a lot like features found on Earth. Astronomers use their knowledge of the four types of processes that affect the terrestrial planets to hypothesize about the features on Mars. Using what you know about the processes, make your own hypotheses to explain the features in the image to the left.

▶ Results of Research

- Small objects hit the surface, producing craters.
- Volcanoes erupt, creating mountains and flows of lava.
- The mantle moves the crust, producing mountains and valleys.
- Wind, water, and gravity move material on the surface, eroding some places and building up others.

▶ Observations

- Dark, raised triangles point roughly east.
- Patterns of light stripes run mostly north-south between the dark hills.
- The features are inside a huge impact crater.

dark hills

light stripes

This large image shows details of the area in the rectangle on the small black-and-white image below.

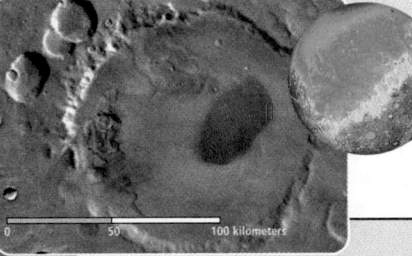

The red rectangle shows the area pictured in the large image at left. The red oval on the globe shows the location of the crater.

0   50   100 kilometers

0.5   1.0 kilometers

▶ Form a Hypothesis

On Your Own Consider one or more processes that might produce the hills and stripes seen in the image at left.

As a Group With a small group discuss possible hypotheses to explain the formation of these features. See if the group can agree on which one is most reasonable.

CHALLENGE Create a model that you can use to test your hypothesis. What will you use to represent the surface of Mars and the forces acting on it?

Chapter 3: **Our Solar System 93** **E**

THINK SCIENCE
Scientific Methods of Thinking

Set Learning Goal
To form a hypothesis to explain features on Mars, based on one of the four processes that affect terrestrial planets

Present the Science
The images were taken by spacecraft in orbit around Mars. Scientists use images taken in visible and in infrared light, as well as altitude measurements and other information, to make hypotheses about features on Mars.

Guide the Activity
- Remind students that a hypothesis is an explanation that can be tested.
- If some students see the hills as valleys, have them turn the book upside down and then look again.
- Display T22 in the Unit Transparency Book to review the results of research.
- Explain that students will use the results of research and their observations of the image of Mars to form a hypothesis to explain the features in the image.

COOPERATIVE LEARNING STRATEGY
Divide the class into groups of five. Have each group list all the possible hypotheses. A timekeeper can keep track of 10 minutes, while a recorder quickly writes all the hypotheses. Group members can suggest which hypotheses to keep and which ones to cross out or revise.

Close
Ask: What do astronomers know that helps them form hypotheses about the features of Mars? *They know the four processes that affect the surfaces of all terrestrial planets.*

ANSWERS

ON YOUR OWN *Students should consider details of the four processes. For erosion, they might consider water forming canyons or wind forming dunes.*
AS A GROUP *Sample answer: Mars has no surface water, but does have wind. Both types of features could be dunes.*
CHALLENGE *For a hypothesis that these are dunes, students might propose using two types of fine grains or powder and a fan to see if they can reproduce the features. They might, instead, create a model to disprove another hypothesis.*

3.3 FOCUS

▶ Set Learning Goals

Students will

- Recognize the four giant planets in the solar system.
- Describe what the atmospheres of the giant planets are like.
- Describe the rings of giant planets.
- Experiment with a model to determine why Saturn's rings seem to change.

◀ 3-Minute Warm-Up

Display Transparency 21 or copy this exercise on the board:

Draw a diagram comparing the inner solar system with the outer solar system. Use labels and captions to show additional information. *Diagrams should show four planets close together in the inner solar system, and five planets spread out in the outer solar system. See pp. 80–81.*

T 3-Minute Warm-Up, p. T21

3.3 MOTIVATE

THINK ABOUT

PURPOSE To imagine what Jupiter is like

DISCUSS Brainstorm with students what might be under Jupiter's clouds.

Accept any reasonable answers. Tell students that in this lesson they will find out what scientists have learned.

Ongoing Assessment

CHECK YOUR READING *Answer: Gravity pulls the material together and makes the gases very dense.*

3.3 The outer solar system has four giant planets.

◀ **BEFORE, you learned**

- Planets formed along with the Sun
- Vast distances separate planets
- The gravity of a terrestrial planet may be strong enough to hold the heavier gases

▶ **NOW, you will learn**

- About the four giant planets in the solar system
- What the atmospheres of giant planets are like
- About the rings of giant planets

VOCABULARY

gas giant p. 94
ring p. 97

THINK ABOUT

What is Jupiter like inside?

Most of Jupiter's huge mass is hidden below layers of clouds. Scientists learn about Jupiter by studying its gravity, its magnetic field, its motions, and its radiation. Scientists also use data from other space bodies to make models, from which they make predictions. Then they observe Jupiter to test their predictions. What might it be like under Jupiter's clouds?

VOCABULARY
Remember to draw a word triangle when you read a new term.

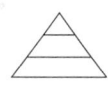

The gas giants have very deep atmospheres.

You have already read about the four rocky planets in the inner solar system, close to the Sun. Beyond Mars stretches the outer solar system, where the four largest planets slowly orbit the Sun. The **gas giants**—Jupiter, Saturn, Uranus (YUR-uh-nuhs), and Neptune—are made mainly of hydrogen, helium, and other gases.

When you think of gases, you probably think of Earth's air, which is not very dense. However, the giant planets are so large and have such large amounts of these gases that they have a lot of mass. The huge gravitational force from such a large mass is enough to pull the gas particles close together and make the atmosphere very dense. Inside the giant planets, the gases become more dense than water. The outermost parts are less dense and more like Earth's atmosphere.

 Why are the gas giants dense inside?

RESOURCES FOR DIFFERENTIATED INSTRUCTION

Below Level

UNIT RESOURCE BOOK
- Reading Study Guide A, pp. 169–170
- Decoding Support, p. 192

 **AUDIO CDS**

Advanced

UNIT RESOURCE BOOK
Challenge and Extension, p. 175

English Learners

UNIT RESOURCE BOOK
Spanish Reading Study Guide, pp. 173–174

 **AUDIO CDS**

- Audio Readings in Spanish
- Audio Readings (English)

The atmosphere of a giant planet is very deep. Imagine traveling into one. At first, the atmosphere is thin and very cold. There may be a haze of gases. A little lower is a layer of clouds that reflect sunlight, just like clouds on Earth. There are strong winds and other weather patterns. Lower down, it is warmer and there are layers of clouds of different materials. As you go farther, the atmosphere gradually becomes dense enough to call a liquid. It also gets thousands of degrees hotter as you get closer to the center of the planet. The materials around you become more and more dense until they are solid. Scientists think that each of the four gas giants has a solid core, larger than Earth, deep in its center.

Interior of a Giant Planet

Jupiter

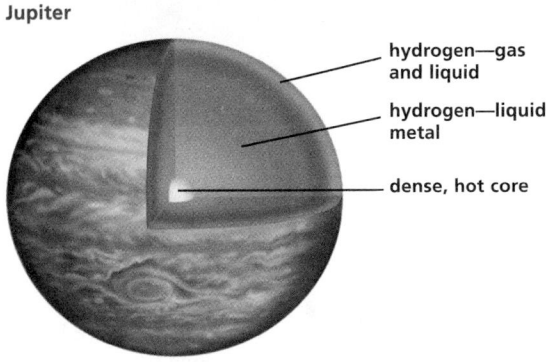

hydrogen—gas and liquid

hydrogen—liquid metal

dense, hot core

Jupiter is a world of storms and clouds.

A

Jupiter is the largest planet in the solar system. It is more than 10 times larger than Earth in diameter and more than 1200 times larger in volume. A jet plane that could circle Earth in about 2 days would take 23 days to circle Jupiter. If you could weigh the planets on a cosmic scale, all the other planets put together would weigh less than half as much as Jupiter.

Jupiter is more than five times farther from the Sun than Earth is. It moves more slowly through space than Earth and has a greater distance to travel in each orbit. Jupiter takes 12 years to go once around the Sun.

Even though it is big, Jupiter takes less than 10 hours to turn once on its axis. This fast rotation produces fast winds and stormy weather. Like Earth, Jupiter has bands of winds that blow eastward and westward, but Jupiter has many more bands than Earth does.

B

Jupiter

Jupiter's colorful stripes are produced by clouds at different levels in Jupiter's deep atmosphere.

Mass 318 Earth masses
Diameter 11 Earth diameters
Average distance from Sun 5.2 AU
Orbits in 12 Earth years
Rotates in 9.9 hours

DIFFERENTIATE INSTRUCTION

? More Reading Support

A How big is Jupiter compared with Earth? *much larger*

B What causes Jupiter's fast winds and stormy weather? *its fast rotation*

English Learners Write "the gravitational pull is weaker, so the gas particles can spread out more" (p. 96) on the board. Tell students that *so* in this context means "therefore" or "as a result" and indicates a cause-and-effect relationship between the clauses.

3.3 INSTRUCT

Teach from Visuals

To help students interpret the cross-section of Jupiter's interior, ask:

• Which giant planet is shown here? *Jupiter*

• How big is the core compared with the gas and liquid parts? *very small*

Address Misconceptions

IDENTIFY Ask: If you could throw a rock to hit Jupiter, what would happen to the rock? If students say that the rock would go right through, they may hold the misconception that that gases are not forms of matter and have no mass.

CORRECT Remind students that liquid water, ice, and water vapor (a gas) are different forms of the same substance. When liquid water changes to a gas, the matter is still present but spread through a larger volume. Ask students to think of other things that do not seem like much unless a lot is packed together. *Sample answer: feathers, paper*

REASSESS Ask: If you could take all the air in a large room and put it in a small container, how would it feel? *Answers should indicate a palpable sensation, such as heaviness or a liquid texture.*

Technology Resources

Visit **ClassZone.com** for background on common student misconceptions.

 MISCONCEPTION DATABASE

EXPLORE (the BIG idea)

Revisit "How Big Is Jupiter?" on p. 77. Have students explain their results.

Ongoing Assessment

Describe what the atmospheres of the giant planets are like.

Ask: How does the temperature of gases in a giant planet's atmosphere change from high above the planet to deep in its atmosphere? *goes from very cold to very hot*

Teach from Visuals

To help students interpret the images of Jupiter and Saturn, ask:

• What caused the shadow in the image of Jupiter? *one of Jupiter's moons; a solar eclipse*

• What do both the images on this page show? *Sample answer: stripes*

• What is Saturn's most noticeable feature? *ring system*

Teach Difficult Concepts

Help students understand how the mass of a gas giant affects its density. A planet with a greater mass has greater gravitational forces pulling its particles inward. As a result, the particles are more densely packed, and the density of the planet is greater. Remind students that Saturn is only a little smaller than Jupiter, but it has less than one-third the mass of Jupiter. Ask: How does Saturn's density compare with Jupiter's density? *Saturn has a much lower density.*

Teaching with Technology

If you have computer access to a remote telescope, see if Jupiter or Saturn is in a position to be viewed. Students can model the orientation of Saturn's rings or observe the motions of Jupiter's largest moons in images taken at least a few hours apart.

Ongoing Assessment

 **CHECK YOUR READING** *Answer: clouds of ice crystals*

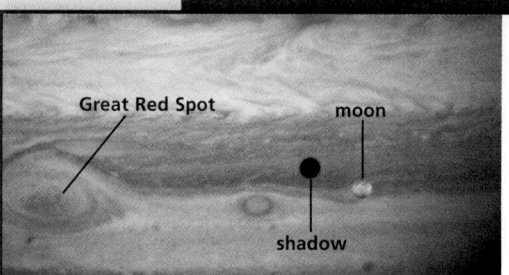

Great Red Spot   moon

shadow

This image shows one of Jupiter's moons casting a shadow on Jupiter. If you were in that shadow, you would experience a solar eclipse.

Stripes of cold clouds form along the bands. The clouds look white because they are made of crystals that reflect sunlight. The crystals in these high white clouds are frozen ammonia rather than frozen water, as on Earth. Between Jupiter's white bands of clouds, you can see down to the next layer. The lower clouds are brown or red and made of different chemicals. Sometimes there are clear patches in the brown clouds, where the next layer of bluish clouds shows through.

 **CHECK YOUR READING** What are Jupiter's white stripes?

 C

Storms can form between bands of winds that blow in opposite directions. Because Jupiter has no land to slow the storms, they can last for a long time. The largest of these storms is the Great Red Spot, which is twice as wide as Earth and at least 100 years old. Its clouds rise even higher than the white ammonia-ice clouds. Scientists are trying to find out which chemicals produce the spot's reddish color.

Saturn has large rings.

▼ **REMINDER**

Density is the amount of mass in a given volume. An object of low density can still have a great total mass if it has a large volume.

The sixth planet from the Sun is Saturn. Saturn is only a little smaller than Jupiter, but its mass is less than one-third that of Jupiter. Because there is less mass, the gravitational pull is weaker, so the gas particles can spread out more. As a result, Saturn has a much lower density than Jupiter. The storms and stripes of clouds form deeper in Saturn's atmosphere than in Jupiter's, so the details are harder to see.

? **D**

Saturn

Saturn has an average density less than that of liquid water on Earth. The diameter of Saturn's ring system is almost as great as the distance from Earth to the Moon.

Mass 95 Earth masses   **Orbits in** 29 Earth years
Diameter 9 Earth diameters   **Rotates in** 11 hours
Average distance from Sun 9.5 AU

DIFFERENTIATE INSTRUCTION

?  **More Reading Support**

C What can form between bands of winds on Jupiter? *storms*

D Why is Saturn less dense than Jupiter? *Its particles are more spread out.*

Advanced Challenge students to find out what spacecraft have taken images of Jupiter and Saturn and what NASA has planned for future explorations. Students can examine close-up images for evidence of storms and different cloud layers. Some spacecraft used other types of radiation to obtain images that show such things as auroras and lightning.

 Challenge and Extension, p. 175

Saturn was the first planet known to have rings. A planetary **ring** is a wide, flat zone of small particles that orbit a planet. All four gas giants have rings around their equators. Saturn's rings are made of chunks of water ice the size of a building or smaller. Larger chunks, considered to be tiny moons, orbit within the rings. Saturn's main rings are very bright. The outermost ring is three times as wide as the planet, but it is usually too faint to see. Saturn's rings have bright and dark stripes that change over time.

You can use Saturn's rings to see the planet's seasons. Like Earth's axis of rotation, Saturn's axis is tilted. The angle is 27 degrees. When the image on this page was taken, sunlight shone more on the northern hemisphere, so the north side of the rings was bright. The shadow of the rings fell on the southern hemisphere. Winter started in Saturn's northern hemisphere in May 2003 and will last more than seven Earth years. Saturn is almost ten times farther from the Sun than Earth is, so Saturn takes almost 30 Earth years to go around the Sun once.

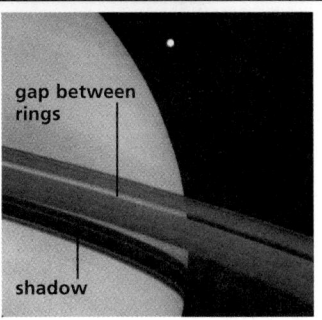

gap between rings

shadow

Sunlight shines from the upper right of this image. The rings cast shadows on Saturn's clouds.

INVESTIGATE Giant Planets

Why do Saturn's rings seem to change size?
PROCEDURE

(1) Poke the stick through the plate and cut off the plate's rim. Shape the clay onto both sides of the plate to make a model of a planet with rings.

(2) Model Saturn's orbit for your partner. Stand between your partner and the classroom clock. Point one end of the stick at the clock. Hold the model at the same height as your partner's eyes. Have your partner watch the model with just one eye open.

(3) Move one step counterclockwise around your partner and point the stick at the clock again. Make sure the model is as high as your partner's eyes. Your partner may need to turn to see the model.

(4) Continue taking steps around your partner and pointing the stick at the clock until you have moved the model all the way around your partner.

(5) Switch roles with your partner and repeat steps 2, 3, and 4.

WHAT DO YOU THINK?
- How did your view of the rings change as the model planet changed position?
- How many times per orbit do the rings seem to vanish?

CHALLENGE How do Saturn's axis and orbit compare with those of Earth?

SKILL FOCUS
Observing

MATERIALS
- ice-cream stick
- disposable plate
- scissors
- clay

TIME
20 minutes

97 **E**

Teach from Visuals

To help students interpret the image of Saturn's rings, have them compare this image with the one at the bottom of p. 96. Help them find the rings, the gap, and the shadow. Ask: How are the shadows different in the two images? *One is above, or north of, the rings; the other is below, or south of, the rings.*

INVESTIGATE Giant Planets

PURPOSE To observe a model of Saturn's rings to infer why the rings appear to change size

TIPS *20 min.* Help students check the model's height and axis direction at each step. Students should hold the model so that their hands do not block the seated students' views of the model.

WHAT DO YOU THINK? *The rings seemed to get bigger (more face on) and smaller (more edge on). Twice.*

CHALLENGE *Saturn's axis is tilted relative to its orbit, similar to Earth's.*

R Datasheet, Giant Planets, p. 176

Technology Resources

Customize this student lab as needed or look for an alternative. Print rubrics to assess student lab reports.

Lab Generator CD-ROM

Teaching with Technology

If a digital camera is available, have students use it to record the different views of the model rings as the model is moved to different positions. Students can use the photographs to explain why Saturn's rings seem to change size. Students can compare their photographs with images from space.

Ongoing Assessment

Describe the rings of giant planets.

Ask: Where are a planet's rings found? *around its equator*

Develop Critical Thinking

SYNTHESIZE Have students synthesize the information about Uranus to explain why it is more dense than Jupiter even though it has a diameter about one-third that of Jupiter. *Uranus is made up mostly of heavier gases than Jupiter is.*

Teach from Visuals

To help students interpret the two images of Uranus, ask:

- What color is Uranus in visible light? *blue-green*

- How is the pole different from the equator in the small image taken with infrared radiation? *The pole is more green; the equator is mostly blue.*

Ongoing Assessment

Recognize the four giant planets in the solar system.

Ask: How are Jupiter, Saturn, Uranus, and Neptune different from the terrestrial planets? *Sample answer: They are much larger and do not have solid surfaces.*

Uranus and Neptune are extremely cold.

F

The seventh and eighth planets from the Sun are Uranus and Neptune. These planets are similar in size—both have diameters roughly one-third that of Jupiter. Unlike Jupiter and Saturn, Uranus and Neptune are only about 15 percent hydrogen and helium. Most of the mass of each planet is made up of heavier gases, such as methane, ammonia, and water. As a result, Uranus and Neptune are more dense than Jupiter.

Uranus looks blue-green, and Neptune appears deep blue. The color comes from methane gas, which absorbs certain colors of light. Each planet has methane gas above a layer of white clouds. Sunlight passes through the gas, reflects off the clouds, then passes through the gas again on its way out. The gas absorbs the red, orange, and yellow parts of sunlight, so each planet's bluish color comes from the remaining green, blue, and violet light that passes back out of the atmosphere.

Uranus is a smooth blue-green in visible light. The small infrared image shows that the pole facing the Sun is warmer than the equator.

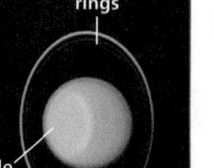

Uranus

Uranus is about twice Saturn's distance from the Sun. The farther a planet is from the Sun, the more slowly it moves along its orbit. The greater distance also results in a larger orbit, so it takes Uranus 84 Earth years to travel around the Sun.

Like the other gas giants, Uranus has a system of rings and moons around its equator. The ring particles and moons orbit Uranus in the same direction as the planet's spin. Unlike the other planets, Uranus has an axis of rotation that is almost in the plane of its orbit. As a result, Uranus seems to spin on its side. During a solstice, one pole of Uranus points almost straight toward the Sun.

Some scientists think that there was a large collision early in Uranus's history. The result left the planet and its system spinning at an unusual angle.

Uranus

Each pole of Uranus experiences more than 40 years of sunlight and then more than 40 years of darkness as the planet orbits the Sun.

Mass 15 Earth masses   **Orbits in** 84 Earth years
Diameter 4 Earth diameters   **Rotates in** 17 hours
Average distance from Sun 19 AU

E 98 Unit: **Space Science**

DIFFERENTIATE INSTRUCTION

? More Reading Support

F How big are Uranus and Neptune compared with Jupiter? *Their diameters are about one-third Jupiter's.*

Below Level Some students may have trouble understanding the meaning of "Uranus has an axis of rotation that is almost in the plane of its orbit." Have students use a plastic foam ball and a pencil or toothpicks to make a model of a planet and its axis. Help students use the model to demonstrate the meaning of the sentence.

Neptune

Neptune orbits about 10 AU farther from the Sun than Uranus, so you would expect it to be colder. However, Neptune has about the same outside temperature as Uranus because it is hotter inside.

Uranus is usually one smooth color, but light and dark areas often appear on Neptune. Clouds of methane ice crystals can form high enough in the atmosphere of Neptune to look white.

Storm systems can appear in darker shades of blue than the rest of the planet. One storm, seen during the flyby of the *Voyager 2* spacecraft in 1989, was named the Great Dark Spot. Unlike the huge storm on Jupiter, the Great Dark Spot did not stay at the same latitude. It moved toward Neptune's equator. The winds there may have broken up the storm. Images of Neptune obtained a few years later with the Hubble Space Telescope showed no sign of the Great Dark Spot.

 **CHECK YOUR READING** What are the white patches often seen on Neptune?

Neptune

Neptune has a large moon that orbits in a direction opposite to Neptune's rotation. Scientists think a giant collision might have occurred in Neptune's past.

Mass 17 Earth masses
Diameter 4 Earth diameters
Average distance from Sun 30 AU
Orbits in 164 Earth years
Rotates in 16 hours

High clouds cast shadows on the layer below.

cloud

shadow

3.3 Review

KEY CONCEPTS
1. Which planet has a greater mass than all the other planets put together?
2. What do you see instead of a solid surface when you look at an image of a giant planet?
3. Which planets have rings?

CRITICAL THINKING
4. **Compare and Contrast** Why do Jupiter and Saturn show a lot of white, while Uranus and Neptune are more blue in color?
5. **Analyze** Most of Saturn is much less dense than most of Earth. Yet Saturn's mass is much greater than Earth's mass. How can this be so?

⚠ CHALLENGE
6. **Apply** If Uranus had areas of ice crystals high in its atmosphere, how would its appearance change?

Chapter 3: Our Solar System **99** **E**

ANSWERS

1. Jupiter

2. the highest layer or layers of clouds

3. All four gas giants have rings: Jupiter, Saturn, Uranus, and Neptune.

4. Uranus and Neptune have methane gas, which absorbs reds and yellows.

5. Saturn is so much larger than Earth that its total mass is greater.

6. Uranus would develop white spots or stripes.

Ongoing Assessment

CHECK YOUR READING *Answer: clouds high in the atmosphere*

Teach from Visuals

To help students interpret the images of Neptune, ask:

- How can scientists tell that the clouds in the images are high in the atmosphere? *Their shadows fall on clouds below them.*

- What is unusual about Neptune's large moon? *It orbits in a direction opposite to Neptune's motion.*

Reinforce **the BIG idea**

Have students relate the section to the Big Idea.

 Reinforcing Key Concepts, p. 177

3.3 ASSESS & RETEACH

Assess

 Section 3.3 Quiz, p. 44

Reteach

Have students make cards for the four giant planets and then put them into groups according to one quality at a time. *Accept any logical sequences or groupings. Planets are given by initial letter.*

- size *J, S; U, N*
- color *J, S; U, N*
- rings *S; J, U, N*

Technology Resources

Have students visit **ClassZone.com** for reteaching of Key Concepts.

 CONTENT REVIEW

 CONTENT REVIEW CD-ROM

Chapter 3 **99** **E**

KEY CONCEPT

Small objects are made of ice and rock.

3.4 FOCUS

▶ Set Learning Goals

Students will

- Describe Pluto and the moons of the giant planets.
- Recognize how asteroids and comets are similar and different.
- Explain what happens when tiny objects hit Earth's atmosphere.

◀ 3-Minute Warm-Up

Display Transparency 21 or copy this exercise on the board:

Match each feature with the type of process that may have produced it.

Features

1. a round depression *d*
2. a mountain made of lava *b*
3. long mountains and valleys *a*
4. dunes *c*

Terms

a. tectonics
b. volcanism
c. weathering and erosion
d. impact cratering

T 3-Minute Warm-Up, p. T21

3.4 MOTIVATE

THINK ABOUT

PURPOSE To recognize that the four processes that affect terrestrial planets can also affect small space bodies

DISCUSS Ask students to recall what process has occurred if a space object has craters. *impact cratering*

Answer: Students should accept or reject tectonics and volcanism as possible.

Ongoing Assessment

CHECK YOUR READING *Answer: how close to the Sun the object formed*

◀ BEFORE, you learned

- Smaller bodies formed with the Sun and planets
- Planets in the inner solar system consist of rock and metal
- The outer solar system is cold

▶ NOW, you will learn

- About Pluto and the moons of the giant planets
- How asteroids and comets are similar and different
- What happens when tiny objects hit Earth's atmosphere

VOCABULARY

asteroid p. 103
comet p. 104
meteor p. 105
meteorite p. 105

THINK ABOUT

Do small space bodies experience erosion?

Very small bodies in space often have potato-like shapes. Some are covered with dust, boulders, and craters. Solar radiation can break down material directly or by heating and cooling a surface. Broken material can slide downhill, even on a small asteroid. What other processes do you think might act on small and medium-sized bodies in space?

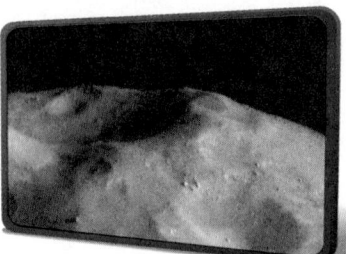

Pluto and most objects in the outer solar system are made of ice and rock.

READING TIP
The name of Earth's satellite is the Moon, but the word *moon* is also used to refer to other satellites.

The materials in a space body depend on where it formed. The disk of material that became the solar system was cold around the outside and hottest in the center, where the Sun was forming. Far from the center, chemicals such as carbon dioxide, ammonia, and water were frozen solid. These ices became part of the material that formed bodies in the outer solar system. Bodies that formed near the center of the solar system are made mostly of rock and metal. Bodies that formed far from the center are mostly ice with some rock and a little metal.

Some of the bodies had enough mass to become rounded. Some even melted and formed cores, mantles, and crusts. Many of these bodies have mountains and valleys, volcanoes, and even winds and clouds. The processes at work on Earth also affect other space bodies.

CHECK YOUR READING What do the proportions of ice, rock, and metal show about a space object?

E 100 Unit: Space Science

RESOURCES FOR DIFFERENTIATED INSTRUCTION

Below Level

UNIT RESOURCE BOOK
- Reading Study Guide A, pp. 180–181
- Decoding Support, p. 192

 **AUDIO CDS**

Advanced

UNIT RESOURCE BOOK
Challenge and Extension, p. 186

English Learners

UNIT RESOURCE BOOK
Spanish Reading Study Guide, pp. 184–185

AUDIO CDS

- Audio Readings in Spanish
- Audio Readings (English)

Pluto and Charon

Many space bodies of ice and rock orbit the Sun at the distance of Neptune and beyond. Since 1992, scientists have been using sophisticated equipment to find and study these bodies. However, one body has been known since 1930. Because Pluto was discovered decades before the other objects, it is considered one of the nine major planets.

Pluto is the smallest of the nine planets. It is smaller than the Moon. Pluto's mass is less than 0.3 percent of Earth's mass, so its gravitational pull is weak. However, Pluto is round and probably has a core, mantle, and crust. Pluto also has a thin atmosphere. No spacecraft has passed close to Pluto, so scientists do not have clear images of the planet's surface.

CHECK YOUR READING Why do scientists know less about Pluto than about other planets?

Pluto's moon, Charon, has a diameter half that of Pluto and a mass about 15 percent of Pluto's. Because Pluto and Charon orbit each other, they are sometimes called a double planet. Just as the Moon always has the same side facing Earth, Pluto and Charon always keep the same sides turned toward each other.

Pluto and Charon also move together around the Sun. Pluto's path around the Sun is not as round as the orbits of the rest of the planets, so its distance from the Sun changes a lot as it orbits. Pluto gets closer to the Sun than Neptune's distance of 30 AU. At the other side of its orbit, Pluto is about 50 AU from the Sun. Pluto's orbit is at an angle with respect to Neptune's, as you can see in the diagram below, so the two paths do not cross and the planets will not collide.

Pluto

This map of Pluto's surface shows only bright and dark areas because Pluto is very distant from Earth and no spacecraft has been close enough to see Pluto's surface in detail.

Mass 0.2% Earth's mass
Diameter 18% Earth's diameter
Average distance from Sun 40 AU
Orbits in 248 Earth years
Rotates in 6 Earth days

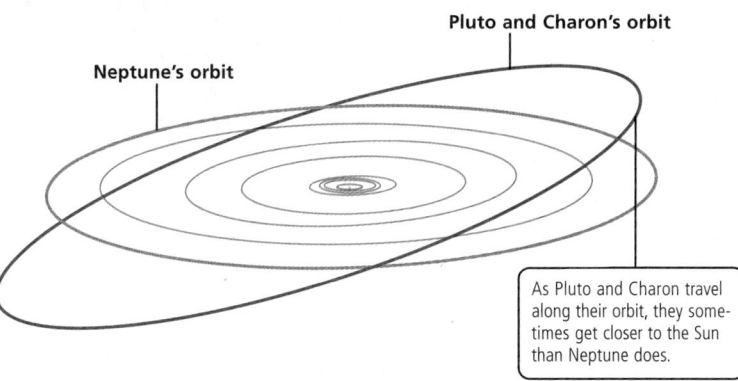

Neptune's orbit

Pluto and Charon's orbit

As Pluto and Charon travel along their orbit, they sometimes get closer to the Sun than Neptune does.

Chapter 3: **Our Solar System** 101 **E**

Teach from Visuals

To help students interpret the map of Pluto and the information box, ask:

• What does the map of Pluto show? *bright and dark areas*

• Why does this depiction of Pluto have less detail than those of other planets in the chapter? *because Pluto is so far away that no spacecraft has been able to see any more detail*

• On average, how much farther than Earth from the Sun is Pluto? *40 times*

Teacher Demo

To help students understand how a planet can be made partly of frozen carbon dioxide and similar materials that are gases on Earth, display a piece of dry ice (use safety precautions). Point out that the solid is frozen carbon dioxide, which usually exists as a gas in Earth's atmosphere. As the solid turns into a gas, students can see where the cold gas moves because it makes water vapor in the air condense into a cloud of droplets. Help students understand that different ices on cold worlds behave as rocks do on Earth.

Ongoing Assessment

CHECK YOUR READING *Answer: No spacecraft has been close enough to get clear images.*

DIFFERENTIATE INSTRUCTION

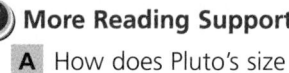
More Reading Support

A How does Pluto's size compare with the size of other planets? *smallest planet*

B What is Charon? *Pluto's moon*

English Learners Make sure English learners are not confused by phrasal verbs such as "died off" (p. 103) and "go by" (p. 105). Offer synonyms to make sure they comprehend the sense of the phrasal verbs. For example, substitute *became extinct* for *died off*, and *elapse* or *pass* for *go by*.

Teach Difficult Concepts

Students have learned that volcanoes are caused by molten rock that reaches the surface of a terrestrial planet. The ice volcanoes on Triton may confuse some students. A hot layer underneath the surface of the moon causes these volcanoes. The material that is heated and erupts is probably a combination of liquid nitrogen, dust, and methane compounds. The source of the heat energy might be sunlight.

Teach from Visuals

To help students interpret the images of moons of gas giants, ask them to identify any of the four types of processes shown in the images or described in the text.
Titan: no surface features visible; Triton: volcanism (also erosion); Europa: tectonics (also weathering); Io: volcanism (also weathering)

Ongoing Assessment

Describe Pluto and the moons of the giant planets.

Ask: Which planets are Pluto and the large moons most like? *the terrestrial planets*

 *Answer: the same processes that shape terrestrial planets (tectonics, volcanism, weathering and erosion, and impact cratering)*

READING VISUALS *Answer: Triton and Io*

Moons of Gas Giants

RESOURCE CENTER
CLASSZONE.COM

Learn more about the different moons of giant planets.

Each giant planet has a system of moons. Six of the moons are larger than Pluto. Their features are formed by the same processes that shape the terrestrial planets. Saturn's largest moon, Titan, has a dense atmosphere of nitrogen, as Earth does, although a haze hides Titan's surface. Neptune's largest moon, Triton, has a thin atmosphere and ice volcanoes. Jupiter has four large moons—Io, Europa, Ganymede, and Callisto. Io (EYE-oh) is dotted with volcanoes, which continue to erupt, so Io has few impact craters. Europa (yu-ROH-puh) has long ridges where the crust has been pushed and pulled by the material beneath it. The outer two moons have craters over most of their surfaces.

The other moons of the gas giants are all smaller than Pluto, with diameters ranging from about 1600 kilometers (1000 mi) down to just a few kilometers. The smallest moons have irregular shapes, and some may be bodies that were captured into orbit.

 What processes are at work on the largest moons?

Some Moons of Gas Giants

Moons in the outer solar system are shaped by the same processes that produce features on the terrestrial planets.

Saturn's moon **Titan** has a dense atmosphere of cold nitrogen gas. A thick haze hides this moon's surface.
haze

Jupiter's moon **Europa** has a crust of frozen water shaped by tectonics. Warm material below has broken the crust into many pieces.
ridges

Neptune's moon **Triton** has dark streaks that show where ice volcanoes have erupted. Winds in the thin atmosphere blow material to one side of an eruption.
ice volcano
streak

Jupiter's moon **Io** has a surface constantly being changed by volcanoes. New material covers the surface and then changes color over time.
volcano (color added)

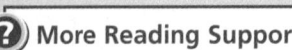 Which images show volcanoes?

E 102 Unit: **Space Science**

DIFFERENTIATE INSTRUCTION

? More Reading Support

C How many of the giant planets have systems of moons? *all of them*

Inclusion Enlarge the visual "Some Moons of Gas Giants" so that students with visual impairments are able to see details of features.

Asteroids and comets orbit the Sun.

Objects called asteroids and comets formed along with the Sun, planets, and moons. These objects still orbit the Sun at different distances. Most of the objects are much smaller than planets and had too little mass to become round. The objects that formed far from the Sun are made mostly of ice, with some rock and metal. The objects that formed closer to the Sun, where it was warmer, have little or no ice.

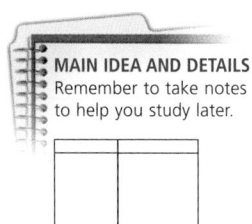

MAIN IDEA AND DETAILS
Remember to take notes to help you study later.

Asteroids

Small, solid, rocky bodies that orbit close to the Sun are called **asteroids.** They range from almost 1000 kilometers (600 mi) in diameter down to a kilometer or less. Except for the largest, their gravity is too weak to pull them into round spheres. Therefore, most asteroids have irregular shapes. Some asteroids are the broken pieces of larger, rounded asteroids.

Most asteroids have paths that keep them between the orbits of Mars and Jupiter. This huge region is called the asteroid belt, and contains more than 10,000 asteroids. However, the asteroids are so far apart that spacecraft from Earth have passed completely through the belt without danger of collision. The mass of all the asteroids put together is estimated to be less than the mass of our Moon.

large crater

This asteroid is small compared with a planet, but it is large compared with a person. The large crater at the bottom is about the size of a small city.

The surfaces of asteroids are covered with craters, broken rock, and dust. Even though asteroids are far apart, smaller objects do hit them from time to time. Impacts from very long ago are still visible because most asteroids are not massive enough to have formed cores, mantles, and crusts. Therefore, they do not have volcanism or tectonics to erase the craters. Most asteroids do not have atmospheres, so their surfaces change only when impacts happen or when gravity pulls material downhill.

 Why do asteroids have craters?

Some asteroids have collided with Earth in the past. The collisions left impact craters, some of which can still be seen today. Scientists have found evidence that an asteroid 10 kilometers (6 mi) in diameter hit Earth 65 million years ago. A cloud of dust from the collision spread around the world and probably affected surface temperatures. Many forms of life, including dinosaurs, died off at about that time, and the impact may have been part or all of the reason. Today astronomers are working to study all asteroids larger than 1 kilometer (0.6 mi) in diameter to determine whether any could hit Earth.

DIFFERENTIATE INSTRUCTION

More Reading Support

D What is a small, solid, rocky body that orbits close to the Sun? *an asteroid*

E Where is the asteroid belt? *between the orbits of Mars and Jupiter*

Advanced Have interested students find out more about asteroid Eros, shown above. Close-up images taken by the NEAR *Shoemaker* spacecraft can be used to discuss the asteroid's materials and structure, as well as different types of weathering and erosion at work on the asteroid.

R Challenge and Extension, p. 186

Teach from Visuals

To help students interpret the image of the asteroid,

- Have students read the caption and then study the image.
- Display T22 in the Unit Transparency Book and ask whether the asteroid shows evidence of any of the processes. *impact cratering and erosion*
- Ask: How big is the hollow crater at the bottom of the asteroid? *about the size of a small city*
- Brainstorm with students how much space where they live the whole asteroid might cover.

Integrating the Sciences

A huge asteroid or a group of asteroids hitting the Earth would have a drastic effect on many living organisms. The large amounts of dust and other matter thrown into the air could remain in the atmosphere and cover large portions of the planet. This could drastically reduce the amount of sunlight that reaches Earth's surface. At first, temperatures would be lower, and the climate might change. Perhaps more important would be the reduction in the amount of sunlight reaching plants, which need sunlight to make sugars for energy and growth. Almost all animals on Earth rely on plants, or on animals that eat plants, as their food source. As a result, many types of animals might not survive.

Ongoing Assessment

CHECK YOUR READING *Answer: Asteroids experience impacts that cause craters, and the craters are usually not erased by other processes.*

Teaching with Technology

If you have computer access to a remote telescope, see if there is a comet in a position to be viewed. Students can compare the comet's position relative to background stars in two images. If a tail is visible, students can try to determine the direction of the Sun.

Teach from Visuals

To help students interpret the diagram of a comet's orbit, ask:

- What is the shape of a comet's orbit? *ellipse*
- Where is the Sun in relation to the comet's orbit? *near the left side of ellipse*
- At what point in the comet's orbit do a coma and tails appear? *when the comet is near the Sun*

Ongoing Assessment

Recognize how asteroids and comets are similar and different.

Ask: What makes up asteroids and comets? *Asteroids are made of rocks and metal with little or no ice. Comets are made of different ices and some rocks and metal.*

READING VISUALS *Answer: A comet's tail is longest when the comet is closest to the Sun.*

Comets

Sometimes, a fuzzy spot appears in the night sky. It grows from night to night as it changes position against the background stars. The fuzzy spot is a cloud of material, called a coma (KOH-muh), around a small space object. An object that produces a coma is called a **comet.** A comet without its coma is a small, icy object that is difficult to see even with a powerful telescope. Scientists use the number of comets that have become visible to infer that vast numbers of comets exist.

Comets formed far from the Sun, so they are made of different ices as well as rock and some metal. Their orbits are usually more oval than the paths of planets. A comet's orbit may carry it from regions far beyond Pluto's orbit to the inner solar system.

When a comet gets close to the Sun, solar radiation warms the surface and turns some of the ice into gas. A coma forms as the gas moves outward, often carrying dust with it. High-speed particles and radiation from the Sun push this material into one or more tails that can stretch for millions of kilometers. A comet's tails point away from the Sun no matter which way the comet is moving. The coma and tails look bright because sunlight shines on them, even though they may be less dense than Earth's atmosphere.

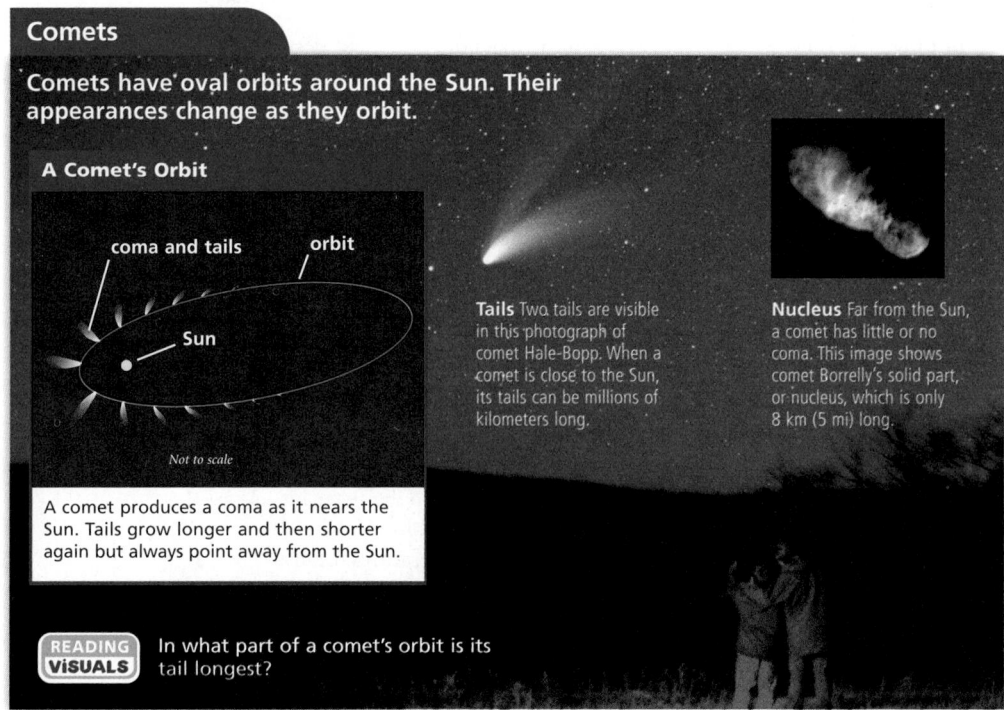

Comets

Comets have oval orbits around the Sun. Their appearances change as they orbit.

A Comet's Orbit

coma and tails   orbit

Sun

Not to scale

A comet produces a coma as it nears the Sun. Tails grow longer and then shorter again but always point away from the Sun.

Tails Two tails are visible in this photograph of comet Hale-Bopp. When a comet is close to the Sun, its tails can be millions of kilometers long.

Nucleus Far from the Sun, a comet has little or no coma. This image shows comet Borrelly's solid part, or nucleus, which is only 8 km (5 mi) long.

READING VISUALS In what part of a comet's orbit is its tail longest?

DIFFERENTIATE INSTRUCTION

 **More Reading Support**

F What is the fuzzy cloud of material around a comet? *coma*

G What turns some of a comet's ice into gas? *solar radiation*

Alternative Assessment Students can act out the changes as a comet orbits the Sun. They should walk in an elliptical path and use their arms to represent the direction and length of a tail. *The tail grows longer as the comet nears the Sun and shorter as the comet moves farther away. The tail always points away from the Sun, so sometimes it will be sideways to a student's motion and sometimes in the direction of the student's motion. Advanced students can move faster when near the Sun and slower when farther away.*

Most comets are too faint to be noticed easily from Earth. Many years can go by between appearances of bright comets, such as the one in the photograph on page 104.

 **CHECK YOUR READING** What makes a comet visible?

Meteors and Meteorites

Earth collides constantly with particles in space. Earth orbits the Sun at about 100,000 kilometers per hour (70,000 mi/h), so these particles enter Earth's thin upper atmosphere at very high speeds. The particles and the air around them become hot enough to glow, producing brief streaks of light called **meteors.** You may be able to see a few meteors per hour on a clear, dark night. Several times during the year, Earth passes through a stream of orbiting particles left by a comet. In the resulting meteor shower, you can see many meteors per hour.

A meteor produced by a particle from a comet may last less than a second. Bits of rock or metal from asteroids may produce brighter, longer-lasting meteors. Rarely, a very bright meteor, called a fireball, lights up the sky for several seconds.

An object with greater mass, perhaps 10 grams or more, may not be destroyed by Earth's atmosphere. A **meteorite** is a space object that reaches Earth's surface. The outside of a meteorite is usually smooth from melting, but the inside may still be frozen. Most meteorites come from the asteroid belt, but a few are rocky fragments that have been blasted into space from the Moon and Mars.

This piece of iron is part of a huge meteorite. The energy of the impact melted the metal and changed its shape.

 **CHECK YOUR READING** What is the difference between a meteor and a meteorite?

3.4 Review

KEY CONCEPTS

1. How are Pluto and most moons of the gas giant planets similar?
2. List two differences between asteroids and comets.
3. What causes meteors?

CRITICAL THINKING

4. **Apply** Of the four types of processes that shape terrestrial worlds, which also shape the surfaces of moons of giant planets?
5. **Compare and Contrast** How is a comet different from a meteor?

CHALLENGE

6. **Predict** What do you think Pluto would look like if its orbit brought it close to the Sun?

ANSWERS

1. They are made of ice as well as rock. Their features are formed by the same processes that shape terrestrial planets.

2. Asteroids are made more of rock, and comets are made more of ice. Comets are in the outer solar system and form a coma when they get close to the Sun. Comets have elongated orbits, while most asteroids have orbits between those of Mars and Jupiter.

3. a tiny particle hitting Earth's atmosphere

4. all four processes

5. A comet orbits the Sun; a meteor is a streak of light in Earth's atmosphere.

6. Pluto might look like a comet.

Ongoing Assessment

Explain what happens when tiny objects hit Earth's atmosphere.

Ask: What causes the brief streak of light known as a meteor? *When a small particle from space enters Earth's atmosphere at a high speed, the particle and the air around it become hot enough to glow.*

 CHECK YOUR READING *Answer: Solar radiation turns some of the comet's ice into gas, and sunlight reflects off the gases in the comet's coma and tail.*

 CHECK YOUR READING *Answer: A meteor is a brief streak of light that occurs when a particle from space enters Earth's atmosphere. A meteorite is a space object that is not destroyed in the atmosphere and reaches Earth's surface.*

Reinforce (the **BIG** idea)

Have students relate the section to the Big Idea.

R Reinforcing Key Concepts, p. 187

3.4 ASSESS & RETEACH

Assess

A Section 3.4 Quiz, p. 45

Reteach

Help students review material from this section by creating a table on the board with the following headings: "Pluto and Charon," "Moons of the Gas Giants," "Asteroids," "Comets," "Meteors," and "Meteorites." Students can decide what characteristics to put in each row.

Technology Resources

Have students visit **ClassZone.com** for reteaching of Key Concepts.

 CONTENT REVIEW

 CONTENT REVIEW CD-ROM

Focus

PURPOSE To design an experiment that tests effects of one variable on impact craters

OVERVIEW Students will use solid objects to make craters in a flour surface and then determine how changing one variable affects the resulting craters. Students should find one pattern, such as that the debris blanket gets larger with a longer drop or with larger masses.

Lab Preparation

• You will need to gather in advance colored powder (cocoa powder or salt with food coloring), a variety of objects of the same material but different sizes, and some materials of the same size but with different masses and densities. (Objects of known masses can be used instead of finding masses using a balance.)

• Prior to the investigation, have students read through the investigation. Or you may wish to copy and distribute datasheets and rubrics.

 UNIT RESOURCE BOOK, pp. 195–203

 SCIENCE TOOLKIT, F12

Lab Management

• Explain that surface coloring is necessary so that the ejecta blanket thrown out by the impact can be seen.

• Discourage use of the size of the crater bowl unless students see real variation in this size.

INCLUSION In steps 3–5, students with visual impairments might study effects such as sound or vibration of the container.

Teaching with Technology

A video camera can be used to record the impacts and resulting craters, or a digital camera can be used to record the craters.

CHAPTER INVESTIGATION

Exploring Impact Craters

DESIGN — YOUR OWN — EXPERIMENT

OVERVIEW AND PURPOSE Nearly 50,000 years ago, an asteroid plummeted through Earth's atmosphere and exploded near what is now Winslow, Arizona. The photograph at left shows the resulting impact crater, which is about 1.2 kilometers (0.7 mi) wide. Most of the other craters on Earth have been erased. However, some planets and most moons in the solar system have surfaces that are covered with craters. In this investigation you will

• use solid objects to make craters in a flour surface
• determine how one variable affects the resulting crater.

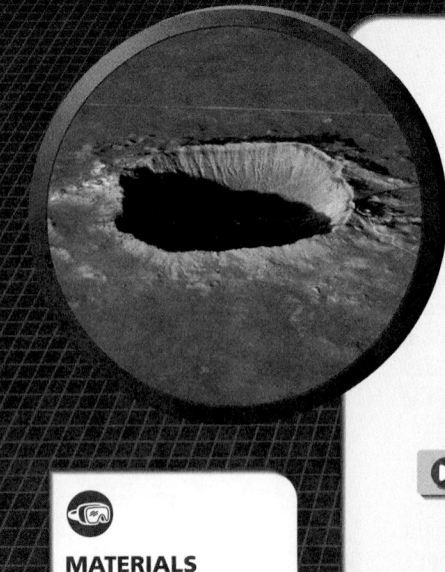

▶ Problem

Write It Up

How does one characteristic of an impact or a colliding object affect the resulting crater?

▶ Hypothesize

Write It Up

Complete steps 1–5 before writing your problem statement and hypothesis. Once you have identified a variable to test, write a hypothesis to explain how changing this variable will affect the crater. Your hypothesis should take the form of an "If . . . , then . . . , because . . ." statement.

MATERIALS
• newspapers
• container
• flour
• colored powder
• several objects
• meter stick
• ruler
• balance

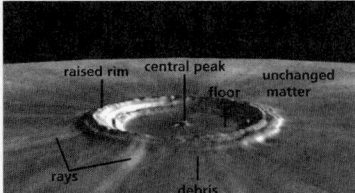

▶ Procedure

1 Place the container on newspapers and add flour to a depth of 2–4 cm. Stir the flour to break up any lumps, and then smooth the surface with a ruler. Sprinkle the top with colored powder.

2 Drop an object into the flour from waist height, then carefully remove it without disturbing the flour. Use the diagram to identify the various parts of the impact crater you made.

raised rim   central peak   unchanged matter   floor   rays   debris

3 To help you design your experiment, try several cratering methods. Make each new crater in a different location in the container. If your container becomes too full of craters, stir the flour, smooth it, and sprinkle on more colored powder.

INVESTIGATION RESOURCES

 CHAPTER INVESTIGATION, Exploring Impact Craters
• Level A, pp. 195–198
• Level B, pp. 199–202
• Level C, p. 203

Advanced students should complete Levels B & C.

 Writing a Lab Report, D12–13

Technology Resources

Customize this student lab as needed or look for an alternative. Print rubrics to assess student lab reports.

 Lab Generator CD-ROM

4. Design an experiment to test the effects of a variable. Choose just one variable to change—the height, the size or mass of the object, or perhaps the fluffiness of the flour. Determine how much you need to change your variable in order to get results different enough to see.

5. Experiment to find some part of the crater that is affected by changing your variable, such as the depth, the size of the blanket of debris, or the number of rays. Design your experiment so that you measure the part of the crater that changes the most.

6. Write a specific problem statement by completing the question, How does _____ affect _____? Write a hypothesis to answer your problem statement.

7. Perform your experiment. Do not change any factors except your chosen variable.

8. Make several trials for each value of your variable, because there are some factors you cannot control.

9. Record measurements and other observations and make drawings as you go along.

Observe and Analyze | Write It Up

1. **RECORD** Use a diagram to show how you measure the craters. Organize your data into a table. Include spaces for averages.

2. **IDENTIFY VARIABLES** List the variables and constants. The independent variable is the factor that you changed. The dependent variable is affected by this change. Use these definitions when you graph your results.

3. **CALCULATE** Determine averages by adding all of your measurements at each value of your independent variable, then dividing the sum by the number of measurements.

4. **GRAPH** Make a line graph of your average results. Place the independent variable on the horizontal axis and the dependent variable on the vertical axis. Why should you use a line graph instead of a bar graph for these data?

Conclude | Write It Up

1. **ANALYZE** Answer your problem statement. Do your data support your hypothesis?

2. **EVALUATE** Did you identify a trend in your results? Is your experiment a failure if you did not identify a trend? Why or why not?

3. **IDENTIFY LIMITS** How would you modify the design of your experiment now that you have seen the results?

4. **APPLY** What do you think would happen if a colliding object hit water instead of land?

INVESTIGATE Further

CHALLENGE How do the craters in this model differ from real impact craters? Design, but do not attempt, an experiment to simulate the cratering process more realistically.

Exploring Impact Craters
Problem How does _____ affect _____?
Hypothesize
Observe and Analyze
Table 1. Data and Averages

Conclude

Observe and Analyze | Write It Up

1. Students' crater diagrams should show what they measured, and their tables should include their data and spaces for averages.

2. Possible independent variables include height of drop; mass, size, density, or shape of object; and compactness or depth of flour. Possible dependent variables include diameter or width of debris blanket, depth of crater, and number of rays. For constants, see list of independent variables.

3. Students' averages will vary depending on their independent variables and their data.

4. Graphs might show that the dependent variable generally increases with increased energy (mass × height × a constant).

Conclude | Write It Up

1. The hypothesis is a possible answer to the problem statement. For the problem statement "How does the distance dropped affect the diameter of the debris blanket?" the hypothesis might be "If the distance increases, then the debris blanket will get larger, because the impact will have more energy." Students' data may or may not support their hypotheses.

2. There is likely to be a trend, but it may not persist through all values of the variable. Concluding that there is no trend can be a successful test of a hypothesis.

3. Students may determine that they need to keep something constant, such as the fluffiness of the flour.

4. The object would likely cause a splash that then filled in.

INVESTIGATE Further

CHALLENGE Real craters are produced when the impacting object explodes. Experiment designs might include objects that explode on impact.

Post-Lab Discussion

Write the different variables students tested on the board and ask what trends they saw in their results. Tell them that a student hypothesized that greater initial energy leads to a bigger impact. Ask students whether their results could be used to support this hypothesis. *It is likely that some, but not all, students will have results that can support the hypothesis.*

BACK TO

the BIG idea

Have students look at the image on pp. 76–77. Ask them to contrast the two objects in the image. *Sample answer: The planet is much larger and has much more mass than the moon. Jupiter is made mostly of hydrogen and helium, while the moon is made of ices and rock.*

◀ KEY CONCEPTS SUMMARY

SECTION 3.1
Ask students to contrast the inner solar system with the outer solar system. *Sample answer: The inner solar system has smaller planets, relatively close to the Sun, and asteroids; the outer solar system has large gas giants spread far apart, many moons, and comets.*

SECTION 3.2
Ask: What four processes produce surface features on terrestrial planets? *tectonics, volcanism, weathering and erosion, impact cratering*

Ask: Which of the four processes require a hot mantle? *tectonics and volcanism*

SECTION 3.3
Ask: What four planets have ring systems? *the four gas giants: Jupiter, Saturn, Uranus, Neptune*

Ask: Since the giant planets have no solid surfaces, what part of each planet reflects sunlight? *mostly clouds in the atmosphere*

SECTION 3.4
Ask: How do the compositions of asteroids and comets differ? *Asteroids are rocky, and comets are icy.*

Ask: Which can produce tiny fragments that may become meteors? *both asteroids and comets*

Review Concepts

- Big Idea Flow Chart, p. T17
- Chapter Outline, pp. T23–T24

---

3 Chapter Review

the BIG idea

Planets and other objects form a system around our Sun.

CONTENT REVIEW
CLASSZONE.COM

◀ KEY CONCEPTS SUMMARY

 Planets orbit the Sun at different distances.

The planets have different sizes and distances from the Sun. The solar system formed from a disk of dust and gas. Massive objects became round.

inner solar system
Mercury, Venus, Earth, Mars, asteroids

outer solar system
Jupiter, Saturn, Uranus, Neptune, Pluto, comets

VOCABULARY
astronomical unit (AU) p. 81
ellipse p. 81

 The inner solar system has rocky planets.

- The terrestrial planets are round and have layers.
- Atmospheres came from volcanoes and impacts.
- Four processes produce surface features.

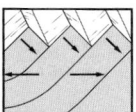 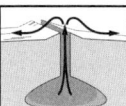 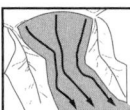 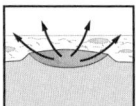

tectonics   volcanism   weathering and erosion   impact cratering

VOCABULARY
terrestrial planet p. 85
tectonics p. 86
volcanism p. 86

 The outer solar system has four giant planets.

- The gas giants have very dense, deep atmospheres with layers of clouds.
- All four giant planets have ring systems.

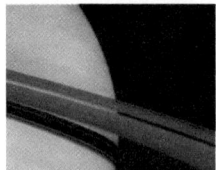

Close-up of Saturn's rings

VOCABULARY
gas giant p. 94
ring p. 97

 Small objects are made of ice and rock.

- Objects in the inner solar system are rocky.
- Pluto and most other objects in the outer solar system are made of ice and rock.
- Rocky asteroids and icy comets orbit the Sun and produce tiny fragments that may become meteors.

The asteroid Eros

VOCABULARY
asteroid p. 103
comet p. 104
meteor p. 105
meteorite p. 105

Technology Resources

Have students visit **ClassZone.com** or use the CD-ROM for a cumulative review of concepts.

 CONTENT REVIEW

CONTENT REVIEW CD-ROM

Engage students in a whole-class interactive review of Key Concepts. Edit content as you wish.

POWER PRESENTATIONS

Reviewing Vocabulary

Make a Venn diagram for each pair of terms. Put an important similarity in the overlapping part. Use the rest of the diagram to show an important difference.

Example:

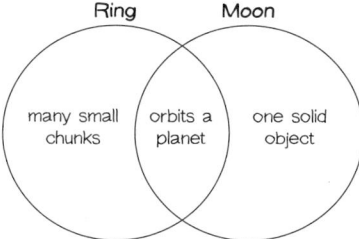

Ring   Moon

many small chunks | orbits a planet | one solid object

1. terrestrial planet, gas giant

2. volcanism, impact cratering

3. erosion, tectonics

4. asteroid, comet

5. meteor, meteorite

6. comet, meteor

Reviewing Key Concepts

Multiple Choice *Choose the letter of the best answer.*

7. Even though orbits are ellipses, what shape is a typical planet's orbit most like?
   a. a short rectangle
   b. an egg-shape with a pointy end
   c. a long, narrow oval
   d. a circle

8. How is a moon different from a planet?
   a. A moon is smaller than any planet.
   b. A moon is less massive than any planet.
   c. A moon is in orbit around a planet.
   d. A moon is unable to have an atmosphere.

9. Which of these appears in Earth's atmosphere?
   a. a moon   **c.** a meteor
   b. an asteroid   **d.** a comet

10. How did planets and other objects in the solar system form?
    a. After the Sun formed, it threw off hot pieces that spun and cooled.
    b. The Sun captured objects that formed in other places in the galaxy.
    c. Two stars collided, and the broken pieces went into orbit around the Sun.
    d. Material in a disk formed large clumps as the Sun formed in the center of the disk.

11. Which process occurs only when a small space object interacts with a larger space body?
    a. tectonics   **c.** erosion
    b. volcanism   **d.** impact cratering

12. Which processes occur because a planet or another space body is hot inside?
    a. tectonics and volcanism
    b. volcanism and erosion
    c. erosion and impact cratering
    d. impact cratering and tectonics

13. What do all four gas giants have that terrestrial planets do not have?
    a. atmospheres   **c.** moons
    b. solid surfaces   **d.** rings

14. What are the white stripes of Jupiter and the white spots of Neptune?
    a. clouds high in the atmosphere
    b. smoke from volcanoes
    c. continents and islands
    d. holes in the atmosphere

Short Answer *Write a short answer to each question.*

15. The solid part of a comet is small in comparison with a planet. However, sometimes a comet appears to be larger than the Sun. What makes it seem so large?

16. Why do all nine major planets orbit the Sun in the same direction?

Reviewing Vocabulary

1. *similarity: orbits the Sun; terrestrial planet: rocky; gas giant: gases*

2. *similarity: shape a space object's surface; volcanism: forms volcanoes; impact cratering: forms craters*

3. *similarity: shape a space object's surface; erosion: forms dunes and layers; tectonics: forms mountains and valleys*

4. *similarity: small space object that orbits the Sun; asteroid: made mostly of rock, may orbit between Mars and Jupiter; comet: made mostly of ice, elongated orbit*

5. *similarity: produced by small objects from space; meteor: streak of light in atmosphere; meteorite: solid object that hits Earth's surface*

6. *similarity: bright light in sky; comet: reflects sunlight; meteor: glows because material is hot*

Reviewing Key Concepts

7. *d*

8. *c*

9. *c*

10. *d*

11. *d*

12. *a*

13. *d*

14. *a*

15. *Solar radiation turns some of a comet's ice into gas, forming a coma around the comet and a tail extending from the comet. Sunlight reflecting from the gases in the coma and tail make the comet look much larger than it is.*

16. *The planets formed out of material that was already traveling in that direction within a swirling disk.*

Thinking Critically

17. Crater A is flatter and less distinct, so it is more eroded.

18. upper half: darker, full of craters; lower area: smoother, lighter in color, few craters

19. The heavily cratered area is older, because it took time to form all those craters. The smooth area formed later.

20. The inside of the moon was hot.

21. The crater formed first. The impact cratering would have erased the crack if the crack had formed first.

22. The Moon's surface might have mountains and valleys or volcanoes.

23. Venus's atmosphere makes its surface hotter and more uniform in temperature.

24. Mercury would be easier to land on because it is not as hot and has no atmosphere to destroy a lander.

25. The material that formed the solar system was moving in one direction, so something that moves in the opposite direction may not have formed out of that material.

26. comets, asteroids, or spacecraft

27. The white is swirling clouds, but the darker parts on Earth are solid and bodies of liquid. Jupiter's clouds appear mostly in bands around the planet.

28. Earth and the Sun are so very different in size, an approximation is often enough to compare them.

the **BIG** idea

29. Sample answer: Jupiter is much larger than Earth.

30. The least dense would be a moon of Uranus, because the object farthest from the Sun should have the most ice and so be least dense.

UNIT PROJECTS

Collect schedules, materials lists, and questions. Be sure dates and materials are obtainable.

 Unit Projects, pp. 5–10

Thinking Critically

Use the image of Jupiter's moon Ganymede to answer the next five questions.

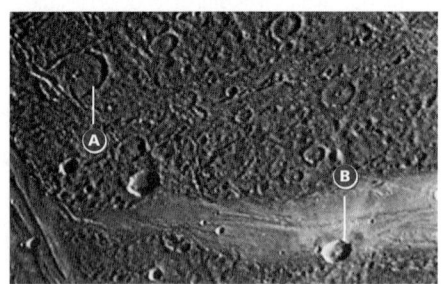

17. **OBSERVE** Which crater, A or B, is more eroded? Explain why you think so.

18. **COMPARE AND CONTRAST** Describe the differences between the surface in the upper half of the image and the long, triangular area near the bottom of the image.

19. **INFER** Explain which area of the surface, the smooth part or the heavily cratered part, is probably older.

20. **APPLY** The lighter area was produced by tectonic processes and may have been covered with molten material. What can you infer about the inside of this moon?

21. **SEQUENCE** A crack runs through part of crater A. Explain how you can tell whether the crack or the crater formed first. **Hint:** Think about what would have happened if the other feature had formed first.

22. **PREDICT** Suppose the Moon were hotter inside. How might its surface be different?

23. **IDENTIFY CAUSE** Mercury's surface is not as hot as Venus's, even though Mercury is closer to the Sun. In addition, the night side of Mercury gets very cold, while the night side of Venus is about as hot as the day side. Why are the temperature patterns on these two planets so different?

24. **EVALUATE** Would it be easier to design a lander mission for the surface of Venus or the surface of Mercury? Explain your reasoning.

---

25. **INFER** Some comets orbit in a direction opposite to that of the planets. Why might this make some scientists wonder if they formed with the rest of the solar system?

26. **HYPOTHESIZE** Scientists calculate the mass of a planet from the effects of its gravity on other objects, such as moons. However, Mercury and Venus have no moons. What other objects in space could have been used to determine the planets' masses?

27. **COMPARE AND CONTRAST** Images of Earth from space show white clouds above darker land and water. In what ways are they like and unlike images of Jupiter?

       Earth   **Jupiter**

28. **ANALYZE** Scientists sometimes use round numbers to compare quantities. For example, a scientist might say that the Sun's diameter is about 100 times Earth's diameter, even though she knows that the precise value is 109 times. Why might she use such an approximation?

the **BIG** idea

29. **APPLY** Look back at pages 76–77. Think about the answer you gave to the question about the large image of a planet and moon. How would you answer this question differently now?

30. **SYNTHESIZE** Ice is generally less dense than rock, which is generally less dense than metal. Use what you know about materials in the solar system to estimate whether a moon of Mars, a moon of Uranus, or the planet Mercury should be the least dense.

UNIT PROJECTS

Check your schedule for your unit project. How are you doing? Be sure that you have placed data or notes from your research in your project folder.

MONITOR AND RETEACH

If students have trouble applying the concept of the four processes that shape the surface of solid objects in the solar system in items 17–21, suggest that they review the images and diagrams on p. 87.

Students may benefit from summarizing one or more sections of the chapter.

 Summarizing the Chapter, pp. 213–214

Standardized Test Practice

For practice on your state test, go to . . . 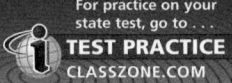 TEST PRACTICE CLASSZONE.COM

Interpreting a Passage

Read the following passage. Then answer the questions that follow.

Life in Extreme Environments

Could living organisms survive in the crushing, hot atmosphere of Venus? Could they thrive on a waterless asteroid or get their energy from tides in the dark ocean that might be beneath the surface of Europa? Scientists are looking for answers to these questions right here on Earth. They study extremophiles, which are life forms that can survive in extreme environments—very high or low temperatures or other difficult conditions. These environments have conditions similar to those on other planets, and those on moons, asteroids, and comets.

Scientists have found tiny organisms that grow in the scalding water of hot vents on the ocean floor, deep inside rock, and in miniature ponds within glaciers. Scientists have also found organisms that were dormant because they were frozen solid for thousands of years but that were still capable of living and growing after warming up. By studying extremophiles, scientists learn more about the conditions needed to support life.

Choose from the following four environments to answer each of the next three questions.

- the dark ocean that might be underneath Europa's surface
- the flood channels on Mars, which have been dry and frozen for a long time
- the very hot, high-pressure environment of Venus
- the dry rock of an asteroid that alternately heats and cools

1. Some organisms survive deep underwater, where photosynthesis does not occur because little or no sunlight reaches those depths. Which environment can these organisms teach about?
   a. under Europa's surface   **c.** Venus
   b. Martian flood channels   **d.** an asteroid

2. Some organisms survive in very deep cracks in rocks, where they are protected from changing temperatures. Where else might scientists look for these types of organisms?
   a. under Europa's surface   **c.** Venus
   b. Martian flood channels   **d.** an asteroid

3. Where might scientists look for tiny organisms that are dormant but that might revive if given warmth and water?
   a. under Europa's surface   **c.** Venus
   b. Martian flood channels   **d.** an asteroid

4. Where, outside Earth, should scientists look for tiny ponds of water within solid ice?
   a. the other terrestrial planets
   b. the gas giants
   c. small space objects in the inner solar system
   d. small space objects in the outer solar system

Extended Response

Answer the two questions in detail.

5. A class was given a sample of ordinary dormant, dry yeast that had been exposed to an extreme environment. Describe ways the students might test the yeast to see if it remained undamaged, or even survived, the conditions.

6. Imagine that scientists have found extremophiles in clouds of frozen water crystals high in Earth's atmosphere. How might this discovery affect a search for organisms on the gas giants?

Chapter 3: **Our Solar System** 111   **E**

Interpreting a Passage

1. *a*   2. *d*   3. *b*   4. *d*

Extended Response

5. RUBRIC
4 points for a clear description of two or more tests, with good reasoning about how each would give results.

Sample answer: The students might use a microscope to compare the yeast with ordinary yeast to look for damage. They might try to make the yeast grow to see if it survived.

3 points for a clear description of two or more tests with missing or faulty reasoning, or one test with good reasoning
2 points for a clear description of one test with missing or faulty reasoning, a list without descriptions, or good reasoning without a specific test
1 point for indications of a test or reasoning that might lead to a test

6. RUBRIC
4 points for an answer that correctly evaluates where and how scientists would search for organisms in terms of

- environment (clouds)
- form (frozen crystals)
- material (water)
- specific planet (Jupiter, Saturn, Neptune, Uranus)

Scientists could look for organisms in the white clouds of crystals high in the atmospheres of Jupiter and Neptune. However, these clouds are not frozen water but other materials, so they may not be able to support organisms.

3 points for an answer that accurately discusses three of the points or discusses all four points but has a minor inaccuracy
2 points for an answer that discusses two of the points with accuracy or discusses more than two of the points but has minor inaccuracies
1 point for an answer that discusses one point with accuracy or more than one, regardless of accuracy

---

METACOGNITIVE ACTIVITY

Have students answer the following questions in their **Science Notebook:**

1. What were you surprised to find out about the solar system?

2. What was one thing you did that helped you to better understand the similarities among objects in the solar system?

4 Stars, Galaxies, and the Universe

Earth Science
UNIFYING PRINCIPLES

PRINCIPLE 1

Heat energy inside Earth and radiation from the Sun provide energy for Earth's processes.

PRINCIPLE 2

Physical forces, such as gravity, affect the movement of all matter on Earth and throughout the universe.

PRINCIPLE 3

Matter and energy move among Earth's rocks and soil, atmosphere, waters, and living things.

PRINCIPLE 4

Earth has changed over time and continues to change.

Unit: Space Science
BIG IDEAS

CHAPTER 1
Exploring Space

People develop and use technology to explore and study space.

CHAPTER 2
Earth, Moon, and Sun

Earth and the Moon move in predictable ways as they orbit the Sun.

CHAPTER 3
Our Solar System

Planets and other objects form a system around our Sun.

CHAPTER 4
Stars, Galaxies, and the Universe
Our Sun is one of billions of stars in one of billions of galaxies in the universe.

CHAPTER 4
KEY CONCEPTS

SECTION 4.1

The Sun is our local star.

1. The Sun produces energy from hydrogen.

2. Energy flows through the Sun's layers.

SECTION 4.2

Stars change over their life cycles.

1. We classify stars by their characteristics.

2. Stars have life cycles.

SECTION 4.3

Galaxies have different sizes and shapes.

1. Our solar system lies within the Milky Way galaxy.

2. Galaxies vary in appearance.

SECTION 4.4

The universe is expanding.

1. Galaxies are moving farther apart in the universe.

2. Scientists are investigating the origin of the universe.

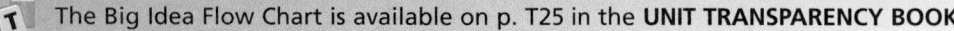

The Big Idea Flow Chart is available on p. T25 in the **UNIT TRANSPARENCY BOOK.**

Previewing Content

SECTION

4.1 The Sun is our local star. pp. 115–121

1. The Sun produces energy from hydrogen.

At the center of our solar system is a star called the Sun. It contains most of the mass in the solar system. The Sun is primarily made of hydrogen. Energy is produced when hydrogen in the Sun's core fuses into helium.

2. Energy flows through the Sun's layers.

The Sun's interior consists of the core, the radiative zone, and the convection zone.

- **Core** In the core, hydrogen particles collide and combine to form helium in a process called **fusion.** The energy travels outward through the layers of the Sun.
- **Radiative Zone** Energy moves through the radiative zone by radiation. This thick layer is hot and dense but not to the extent necessary for fusion to occur.
- **Convection Zone** Here energy moves mainly by **convection,** which is the transfer of energy from place to place by the motion of heated gas or liquid.

The Sun's atmosphere contains the photosphere, the chromosphere, and the **corona.** The photosphere is the visible layer of the Sun. The corona and the chromosphere are hotter than the photosphere but much less dense.

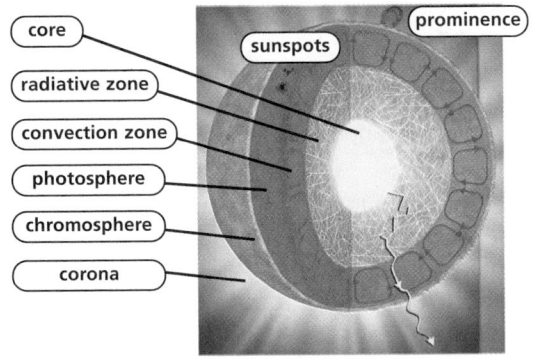

Features on the Sun, including **sunspots,** flares, and prominences, occur in areas of strong magnetic fields. **Solar wind,** which is a stream of electrically charged particles, flows outward in all directions from the corona to all parts of the solar system. The energy from solar-wind particles produces light displays, called auroras, in the skies over the polar regions.

SECTION

4.2 Stars change over their life cycles. pp. 122–129

1. We classify stars by their characteristics.

All stars are made of glowing gases that produce or have produced energy by fusion. However, stars differ in size, brightness, and temperature. Some stars are only the size of Earth, but giant and supergiant stars are ten to hundreds of times larger than the Sun.

Stars look small because they are so far away. The amount of light a star gives off and its distance determine how bright it appears from Earth (apparent magnitude). Distances to stars are measured in a unit called a **light-year,** which is the distance light travels in one year. Astronomers can determine distances to some stars by using **parallax**—the apparent shift in the position of an object when viewed from different locations.

Astronomers classify stars by color and surface temperature. The color of a star indicates its temperature. The hottest stars are blue-white. The coolest stars are red.

2. Stars have life cycles.

Stars form inside a cloud of gas and dust called a **nebula.** In some regions gravity pulls gas and dust together and forms a hot, dense sphere. The sphere becomes a star when its core is hot and dense enough for fusion to occur.

When stars are plotted according to their brightness and temperature in a Hertzsprung-Russell diagram, most fall within a band called the main sequence. The **main sequence** is the stage in a star's life cycle when the star fuses hydrogen into helium. Lower-mass stars remain in this stage for billions of years before they run out of hydrogen. Higher-mass stars remain in the main sequence for millions of years.

After the main-sequence stage, a lower-mass star becomes a giant star. Eventually, only its dead core, known as a white dwarf, remains. A higher-mass star becomes a supergiant and eventually undergoes an explosion called a supernova. The remnants of the collapsed supergiant may form a dense **neutron star** or an even denser **black hole,** which is invisible.

Most stars are found in pairs or groups held together by the gravity that exists between them. Scientists can learn about binary star systems when one star orbits in front of the other and blocks some of its light.

Common Misconceptions

LIGHT TRAVELS Some students may think that light does not travel from one place to another or that it cannot travel very far from its source. Yet light can travel enormous distances.

 This misconception is addressed on p. 116.

MISCONCEPTION DATABASE

CLASSZONE.COM Background on student misconceptions

MASS AND SIZE Students may think that mass is the same as size or volume. They may estimate the mass of an object from its appearance, without taking density into account. In fact, mass is simply the measure of how much matter an object contains. A small object can have greater mass than an object that is larger but less dense.

 This misconception is addressed on p. 126.

Previewing Content

1. Our solar system lies within the Milky Way galaxy.
The Milky Way is shaped like a disk with a bulge in the center. The galaxy is more than 100,000 light-years in diameter. Because Earth is located inside the disk, we have an edge-on view of part of the galaxy, which is why it appears as a hazy band of light in the sky.

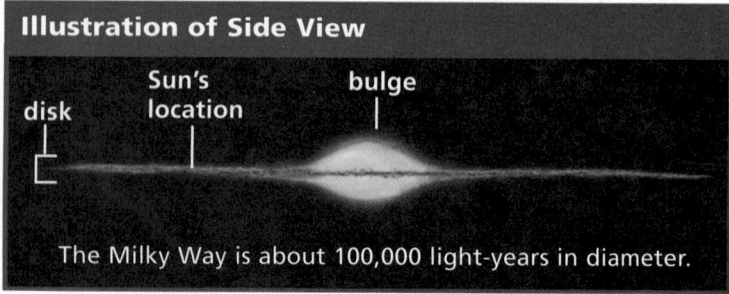

Illustration of Side View

disk   Sun's location   bulge

The Milky Way is about 100,000 light-years in diameter.

2. Galaxies vary in appearance.
Galaxies vary in size and shape. They are classified by their shape into three main types:

- **Spiral galaxies** have arms of stars, gas, and dust that curve away from the center of the galaxy in a spiral pattern. The Milky Way is a spiral galaxy.
- **Elliptical galaxies** are spherical or egg-shaped. They have almost no dust or gas between stars.
- **Irregular galaxies** have no definite shape. They are smaller than the other types of galaxies and have fewer stars.

Spiral Galaxy

Elliptical Galaxy

Irregular Galaxy

The centers of most large galaxies appear to be black holes. Though invisible, black holes can be detected by observing the behavior of matter surrounding them, such as a whirlpool of gas being drawn into a black hole. In some distant galaxies, the center is very bright, and is known as a **quasar.**

1. Galaxies are moving farther apart in the universe.
The universe contains about 100 billion galaxies. They occur in groups called superclusters, which are surrounded by nearly empty space. Though the universe is immense, studies indicate that the same elements and physical forces that exist on and near Earth exist throughout the universe.

The light we see from other galaxies left those galaxies millions or billions of years ago. Therefore, the images we see are the way the galaxies looked then. By viewing more and more distant galaxies, astronomers can look farther and farther back in time.

Astronomers use the Doppler effect to determine how galaxies are moving. The **Doppler effect** is the change in an observed wavelength or frequency of a wave that occurs when either the source of the wave or the observer is moving. This phenomenon occurs with both sound waves and light waves. Astronomers observe how the wavelengths of light from galaxies are either compressed or stretched, indicating that galaxies are either moving toward or away from us.

2. Scientists are investigating the origin of the universe.
Almost all astronomers accept the theory that the universe started to expand outward from an extremely hot, dense state in what is called the **big bang.** Evidence for the big bang includes the motions of galaxies, microwaves streaming through space in all directions, and the results of experiments and computer models.

Scientists are beginning to understand more about what the early universe was like and how it has developed. The earliest stages of the universe occurred in a fraction of a second. It took many thousands of years for the first elements to form. Stars, planets, and galaxies began to appear within a billion years of the big bang.

Previewing Labs

Lab Generator CD-ROM
Edit these Pupil Edition labs and generate alternative labs.

EXPLORE the BIG idea

How Can Stars Differ? p. 113
Students observe stars and compare their appearance.

TIME 10 minutes
MATERIALS star maps in Appendix

How Do Galaxies Move Apart? p. 113
Students inflate a balloon marked with dots to model the expanding universe.

TIME 10 minutes
MATERIALS balloon, felt-tip pen, mirror

Internet Activity: Galaxy Shapes, p. 113
Students use the Internet to explore galaxy shapes.

TIME 20 minutes
MATERIALS computer with Internet access

SECTION 4.1

EXPLORE Solar Atmosphere, p. 115
Students use a light bulb and an index card to model how the Sun's corona can become visible during an eclipse.

TIME 10 minutes
MATERIALS small paper clip, index card, lamp with 45-watt bulb

---

CHAPTER INVESTIGATION
Temperature, Brightness, and Color, pp. 120–121
Students construct a wax photometer to investigate the temperature, brightness, and color of different light sources.

 Photometer Instructions, p. 266

TIME 40 minutes
MATERIALS 2 paraffin blocks, aluminum foil, 2 rubber bands, 2 light-bulb holders, 2 miniature light bulbs, 3 AA batteries, 4 pieces of uninsulated copper wire 15 cm long, masking tape; for Challenge: incandescent lamp, dimmer switch, Photometer Instructions

---

SECTION 4.2

EXPLORE Characteristics of Stars, p. 122
Students use flashlights to observe how distance affects the apparent brightness of a light source.

TIME 10 minutes
MATERIALS 2 flashlights, meter stick, dark surface

INVESTIGATE Parallax, p. 123
Students use a meter stick and a pen to investigate how parallax can be used to determine the distance of objects.

TIME 10 minutes
MATERIALS meter stick, capped pen

SECTION 4.3

EXPLORE The Milky Way, p. 130
Students view tiny dots from varying distances to investigate why the Milky Way looks hazy from Earth.

TIME 10 minutes
MATERIALS white gel pen, black paper, tape

INVESTIGATE Galaxy Shapes, p. 131
Students view galaxy photos to classify galaxies by shape.

 Galaxy Photo Sheet, p. 245

TIME 15 minutes
MATERIALS Galaxy Photo Sheet, scissors

SECTION 4.4

EXPLORE Large Numbers, p. 135
Students estimate the thickness of a billion-page book to appreciate how large the number one billion is.

TIME 10 minutes
MATERIALS book, ruler, calculator

INVESTIGATE Galaxies, p. 138
Students mark, stretch, and measure a rubber band to model how the universe expands.

TIME 20 minutes
MATERIALS thick rubber band cut open, ballpoint pen, ruler

 Additional INVESTIGATION, Distance and Brightness, A, B, & C, pp. 276–284; Teacher Instructions, pp. 287–288

Previewing Chapter Resources

	INTEGRATED TECHNOLOGY	LABS AND ACTIVITIES

CHAPTER 4
Stars, Galaxies, and the Universe

CLASSZONE.COM
- eEdition Plus
- EasyPlanner Plus
- Misconception Database
- Content Review
- Test Practice
- Visualization
- Simulation
- Resource Centers
- Internet Activity: Galaxy Shapes
- Math Tutorial

 CD-ROMS
- eEdition
- EasyPlanner
- Power Presentations
- Content Review
- Lab Generator
- Test Generator

 AUDIO CDS
- Audio Readings
- Audio Readings in Spanish

 SCILINKS.ORG
SCI LINKS

 EXPLORE the Big Idea, p. 113
- How Can Stars Differ?
- How Do Galaxies Move Apart?
- Internet Activity: Galaxy Shapes

UNIT RESOURCE BOOK
Unit Projects, pp. 5–10

 Lab Generator CD-ROM
Generate customized labs.

SECTION
4.1 The Sun is our local star.
pp. 115–119

Time: 3 periods (1.5 blocks)
 Lesson Plan, pp. 215–216

 SIMULATION, Sun at Different Wavelengths

T UNIT TRANSPARENCY BOOK
- Big Idea Flow Chart, p. T25
- Daily Vocabulary Scaffolding, p. T26
- Note-Taking Model, p. T27
- 3-Minute Warm-Up, p. T28
- "Layers of the Sun" Visual, p. T30

 • EXPLORE Solar Atmosphere, p. 115
- CHAPTER INVESTIGATION, Temperature, Brightness, and Color, pp. 120-121

UNIT RESOURCE BOOK
- Photometer Instructions, p. 266
- CHAPTER INVESTIGATION Temperature, Brightness, and Color, A, B, & C, pp. 267–275

SECTION
4.2 Stars change over their life cycles.
pp. 122–128

Time: 2 periods (1 block)
 Lesson Plan, pp. 225–226

 • **RESOURCE CENTER,** Life Cycles Of Stars
- **MATH TUTORIAL**

T UNIT TRANSPARENCY BOOK
- Daily Vocabulary Scaffolding, p. T26
- 3-Minute Warm-Up, p. T28

 • EXPLORE Characteristics of Stars, p. 122
- INVESTIGATE Parallax, p. 123
- Math in Science, p. 129

UNIT RESOURCE BOOK
- Additional INVESTIGATION, Distance and Brightness, A, B, & C, pp. 276–284
- Datasheet, Parallax, p. 234
- Math Support & Practice, pp. 264, 265

SECTION
4.3 Galaxies have different sizes and shapes.
pp. 130–133

Time: 2 periods (1 block)
 Lesson Plan, pp. 236–237

 • **RESOURCE CENTERS,** Galaxies, Galaxy Collisions

T UNIT TRANSPARENCY BOOK
- Daily Vocabulary Scaffolding, p. T26
- 3-Minute Warm-Up, p. T29

 • EXPLORE The Milky Way, p. 130
- INVESTIGATE Galaxy Shapes, p. 131
- Extreme Science, p. 15

UNIT RESOURCE BOOK
- Galaxy Photo Sheet, p. 245
- Datasheet, Galaxy Shapes, p. 246

SECTION
4.4 The universe is expanding.
pp. 135–139

Time: 3 periods (1.5 blocks)
 Lesson Plan, pp. 248–249

T UNIT TRANSPARENCY BOOK
- Big Idea Flow Chart, p. T25
- Daily Vocabulary Scaffolding, p. T26
- 3-Minute Warm-Up, p. T29
- Chapter Outline, pp. T31–T32

 • EXPLORE Large Numbers, p. 135
- INVESTIGATE Galaxies, p. 138

UNIT RESOURCE BOOK
Datasheet, Galaxies, p. 257

KEY TO ICONS

 CD/CD-ROM
 INTERNET
 Pupil Edition
 TE Teacher Edition
 R UNIT RESOURCE BOOK
T UNIT TRANSPARENCY BOOK
A UNIT ASSESSMENT BOOK
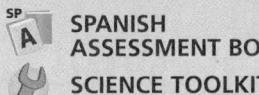 **SP A** SPANISH ASSESSMENT BOOK
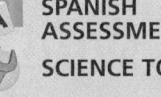 SCIENCE TOOLKIT

READING AND REINFORCEMENT

ASSESSMENT

STANDARDS

- Description Wheel, B20–21
- Choose Your Own Strategy, C35–44
- Daily Vocabulary Scaffolding, H1–8

 UNIT RESOURCE BOOK
- Vocabulary Practice, pp. 261–262
- Decoding Support, p. 263
- Summarizing the Chapter, pp. 285–286

 Audio Readings CD
Listen to Pupil Edition.

 Audio Readings in Spanish CD
Listen to Pupil Edition in Spanish.

- Chapter Review, pp. 141–142
- Standardized Test Practice, p. 143

A **UNIT ASSESSMENT BOOK**
- Diagnostic Test, pp. 60–61
- Chapter Test, A, B, & C, pp. 66–77
- Alternative Assessment, pp. 78–79
- Unit Test, pp. 80–91

SP A
- Spanish Chapter Test, pp. 205–208
- Spanish Unit Test, pp. 209–212

 Test Generator CD-ROM
Generate customized tests.

 **Lab Generator CD-ROM**
Rubrics for Labs

National Standards
A.2–8, A.9.a–f, B.3.a, G.1.a–b.
G.2.a–b

See p. 112 for the standards.

 UNIT RESOURCE BOOK
- Reading Study Guide, A & B, pp. 217–220
- Spanish Reading Study Guide, pp. 221–222
- Challenge and Extension, p. 223
- Reinforcing Key Concepts, p. 224

TE Ongoing Assessment, pp. 116, 118–119

PE Section 4.1 Review, p. 119

A **UNIT ASSESSMENT BOOK**
Section 4.1 Quiz, p. 62

National Standards
A.2–7, A.9.a–b, A.9.e–f, B.3.a,
G.1.a–b

 UNIT RESOURCE BOOK
- Reading Study Guide, A & B, pp. 227–230
- Spanish Reading Study Guide, pp. 231–232
- Challenge and Extension, p. 233
- Reinforcing Key Concepts, p. 235
- Challenge Reading, pp. 259–260

TE Ongoing Assessment, pp. 123–128

PE Section 4.2 Review, p. 128

A **UNIT ASSESSMENT BOOK**
Section 4.2 Quiz, p. 63

National Standards
A.2–8, A.9.a–c, A.9.e–f, B.3.a,
G.1.a–b

 UNIT RESOURCE BOOK
- Reading Study Guide, A & B, pp. 238–241
- Spanish Reading Study Guide, pp. 242–243
- Challenge and Extension, p. 244
- Reinforcing Key Concepts, p. 247

TE Ongoing Assessment, pp. 130–133

PE Section 4.3 Review, p. 133

A **UNIT ASSESSMENT BOOK**
Section 4.3 Quiz, p. 64

National Standards
A.2–7, A.9.a–b, A.9.e–f, B.3.a,
G.1.a–b

 UNIT RESOURCE BOOK
- Reading Study Guide, A & B, pp. 250–253
- Spanish Reading Study Guide, pp. 254–255
- Challenge and Extension, p. 256
- Reinforcing Key Concepts, p. 258

TE Ongoing Assessment, pp. 136–137, 139

PE Section 4.4 Review, p. 139

A **UNIT ASSESSMENT BOOK**
Section 4.4 Quiz, p. 65

National Standards
A.2–8, A.9.a–f, B.3.a, G.1.a–b

Previewing Resources for Differentiated Instruction

CHAPTER INVESTIGATION

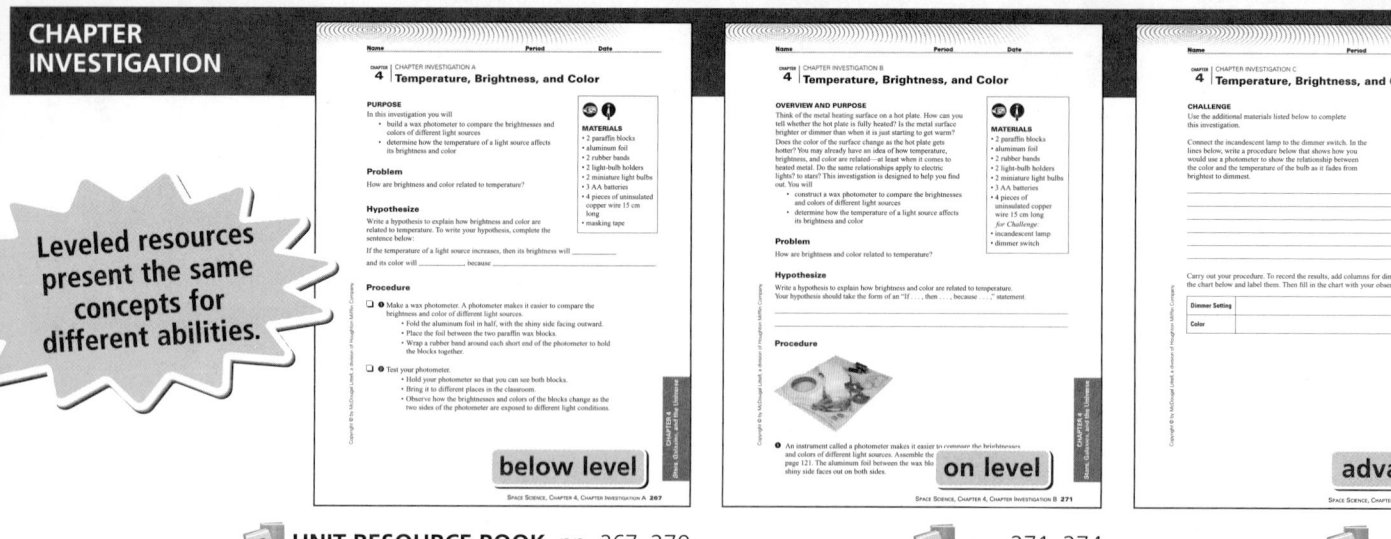

Leveled resources present the same concepts for different abilities.

below level

on level

advanced

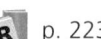 **UNIT RESOURCE BOOK,** pp. 267–270   pp. 271–274   pp. 271–275

READING STUDY GUIDE

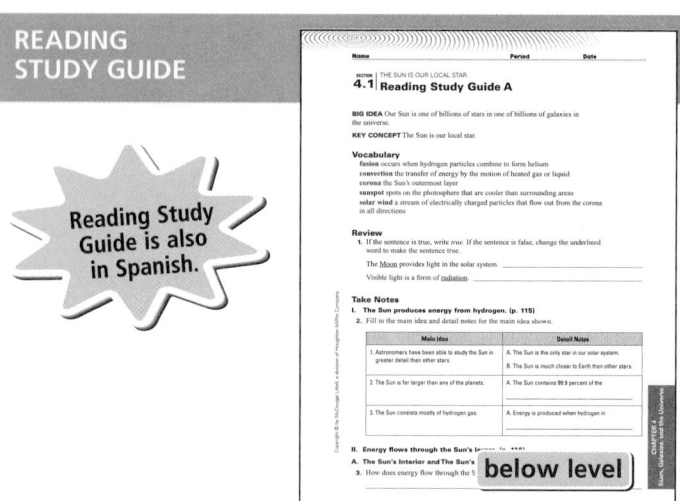

Reading Study Guide is also in Spanish.

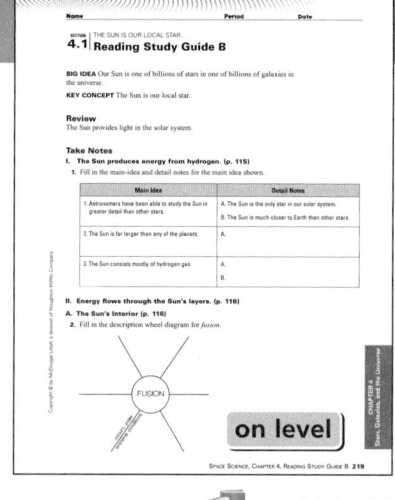

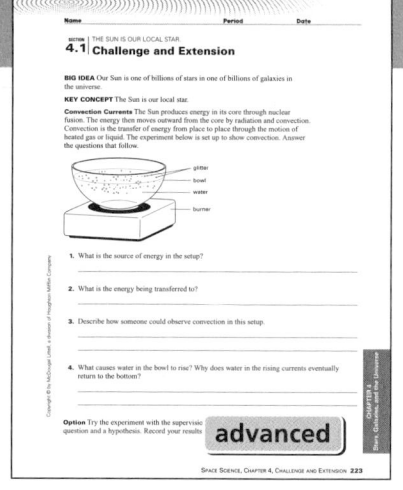

below level

on level

advanced

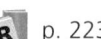 **UNIT RESOURCE BOOK,** pp. 217–218   pp. 219–220   p. 223

CHAPTER TEST

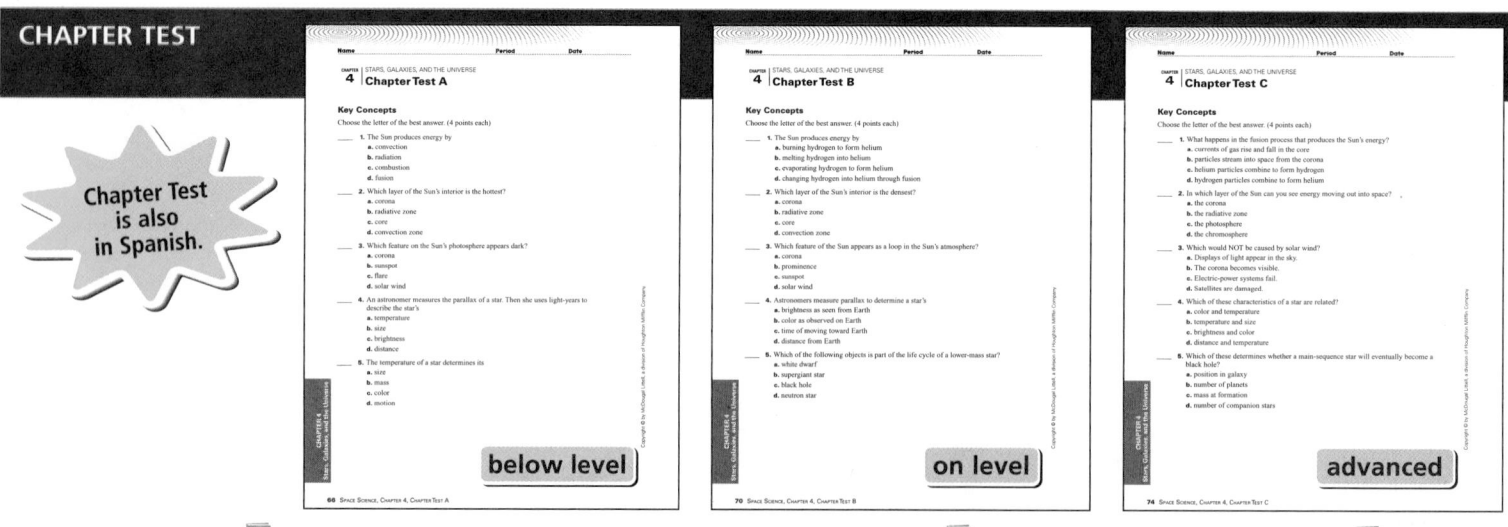

Chapter Test is also in Spanish.

below level

on level

advanced

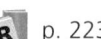 **UNIT ASSESSMENT BOOK,** pp. 66–69   pp. 70–73   pp. 74–77

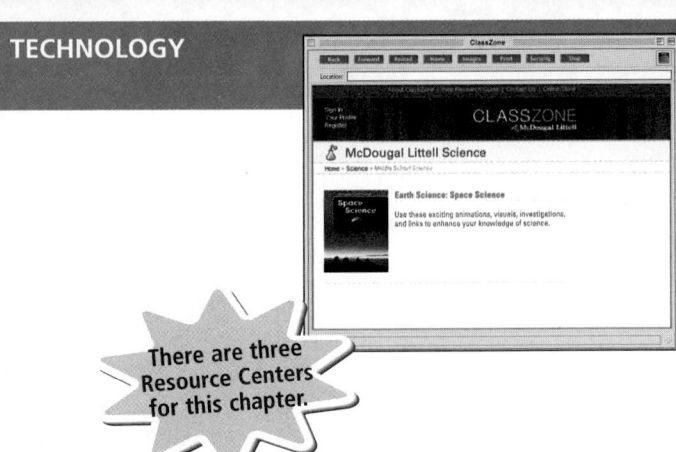

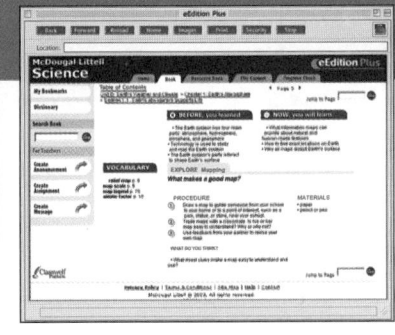

There are three Resource Centers for this chapter.

CLASSZONE.COM

CD/CD-ROMS

CLASSZONE.COM

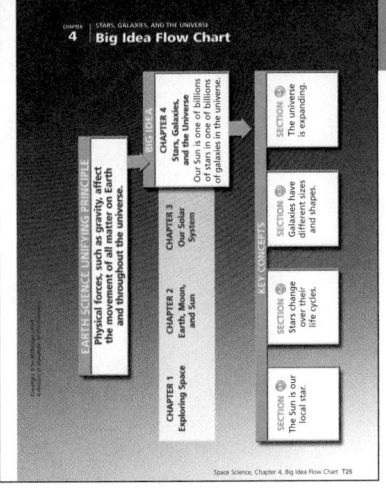

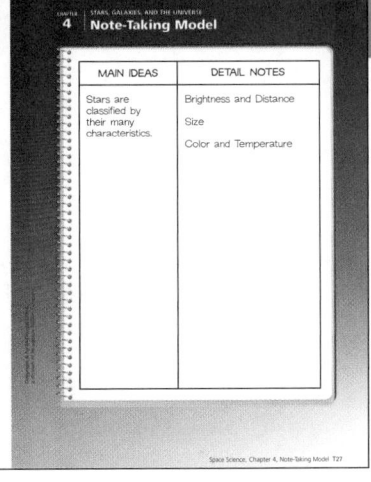

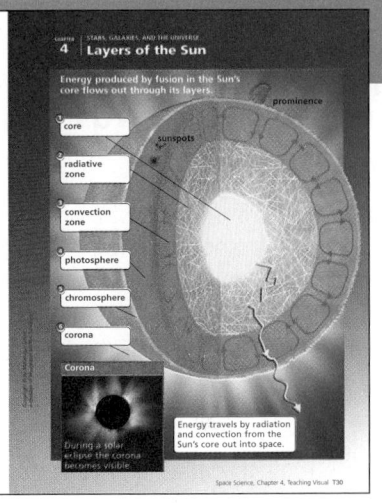

 UNIT TRANSPARENCY BOOK, p. T25

 p. T27

 p. T30

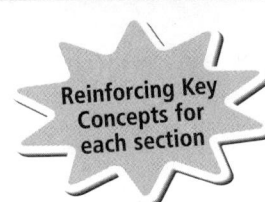

Reinforcing Key Concepts for each section

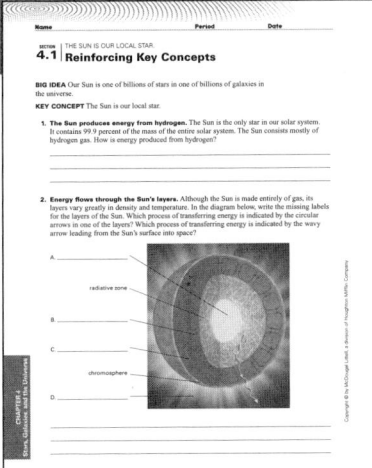

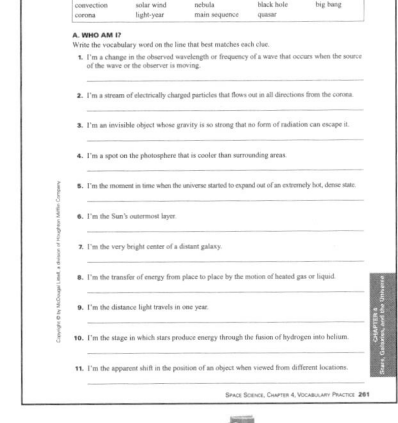

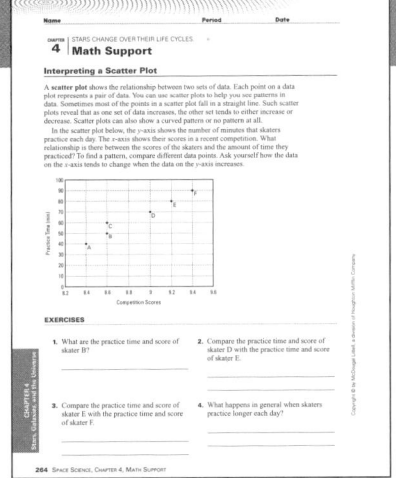

 **UNIT RESOURCE BOOK,** p. 224

 pp. 261–262

p. 264

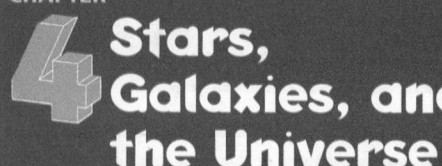

INTRODUCE

the **BIG** idea

Have students look at the photograph of a galaxy and discuss how the question in the box links to the Big Idea. For further discussion:

- What makes up the galaxy?
- What is the relationship of our Sun to a galaxy?
- What is the source of the light energy in this galaxy?

National Science Education Standards

Content

B.3.a Energy is a property of many substances and is associated with heat, light, electricity, mechanical motion, sound, nuclei, and the nature of a chemical. Energy is transferred in many ways.

Process

A.2–8 Design and conduct an investigation; use tools to gather and interpret data; use evidence to describe, predict, explain, model; think critically to make relationships between evidence and explanation; recognize different explanations and predictions; communicate scientific procedures and explanations; use mathematics.

A.9.a–f Understand scientific inquiry by using different investigations, methods, mathematics, technology, and explanations based on logic, evidence, and skepticism.

G.1.a–b Science as a human endeavor

G.2.a–b Nature of Science

CHAPTER

4 Stars, Galaxies, and the Universe

the **BIG** idea

Our Sun is one of billions of stars in one of billions of galaxies in the universe.

Key Concepts

SECTION 4.1 The Sun is our local star. Learn how the Sun produces energy and about the Sun's layers and features.

SECTION 4.2 Stars change over their life cycles. Learn how stars form and change.

SECTION 4.3 Galaxies have different sizes and shapes. Learn how galaxies are classified.

SECTION 4.4 The universe is expanding. Learn about the formation and expansion of the universe.

Internet Preview

CLASSZONE.COM
Chapter 4 online resources: Visualization, Simulation, three Resource Centers, Math Tutorial, Test Practice

What could be present in the light and dark areas in this galaxy?

INTERNET PREVIEW

CLASSZONE.COM For student use with the following pages:

Review and Practice
- Content Review, pp. 114, 140
- Math Tutorial: Scatter Plots, p. 129
- Test Practice, p. 143

Activities and Resources
- Internet Activity: Galaxy Shapes, p. 113
- Resource Centers: Life Cycles of Stars, p. 126; Galaxies, p. 132; Galaxy Collisions, p. 134
- Simulation: Sun at Different Wavelengths, p. 116

NSTA *SCLINKS*
scilinks.org

The Sun **Code: MDL060**

EXPLORE (the BIG idea)

How Can Stars Differ?

Look at the sky at night and find three stars that differ in appearance. Try to identify the locations of these stars, using the star maps in the Appendix at the back of this book.

Observe and Think
How did the characteristics of the stars differ?

How Do Galaxies Move Apart?

Blow air into a balloon until it is partially inflated. Use a felt-tip pen to make 12 dots on the round end. Then stand in front of a mirror and observe the dots as you completely inflate the balloon.

Observe and Think What caused the dots to move apart? What might cause galaxies to move apart in the universe?

Internet Activity: Galaxy Shapes

Go to **ClassZone.com** to explore the different shapes of galaxies in the universe.

Observe and Think
How do the types of galaxies differ from one another?

NSTA scilinks.org
SCI LINKS
The Sun **Code: MDL060**

Chapter 4: **Stars, Galaxies, and the Universe 113** **E**

TEACHING WITH TECHNOLOGY

Digital Cameras Students can take pictures of a stationary object from two different positions with a digital camera and explain how the photographs illustrate parallax as discussed on p. 123.

EXPLORE (the BIG idea)

These inquiry-based activities are appropriate for use at home or as a supplement to classroom instruction.

How Can Stars Differ?

PURPOSE To demonstrate to students that stars vary in brightness and color.

TIP *10 min.* Best viewing will be in an area away from bright lights. If students have binoculars, you might suggest that they use them.

Answer: Students should observe differences in brightness and color.

REVISIT after p. 124.

How Do Galaxies Move Apart?

PURPOSE To introduce students to the concept that galaxies move apart as the universe expands.

TIP *10 min.* Instead of using mirrors, students can work in pairs to observe each other's balloon.

Answer: The dots moved apart because the rubber between them expanded. The expansion of space between galaxies causes them to move apart.

REVISIT after p. 137.

Internet Activity: Galaxy Shapes

PURPOSE To introduce students to the types of galaxies in the universe.

TIP *20 min.* The classification system introduced in this activity includes some types of galaxies that are not discussed in the chapter.

Answer: They differ from one another in shape.

REVISIT after p. 132.

PREPARE

◑ CONCEPT REVIEW

Activate Prior Knowledge

Draw four concentric circles on the board. Tell students that the inner circle represents the solar system and the other circles represent larger structures in space. Ask students to label the three other circles.

◑ TAKING NOTES

Choose Your Own Strategy

Encourage students to discuss the strengths of each of the strategies to help them decide which ones to use.

Vocabulary Strategy

Description wheels can include as much information as students want to add. They become convenient study devices when students review their notes.

Vocabulary and Note-Taking Resources

- Vocabulary Practice, pp. 261–262
- Decoding Support, p. 263

- Daily Vocabulary Scaffolding, p. T26
- Note-Taking Model, p. T27

- Description Wheel, B20–21
- Choose Your Own Strategy, C35–44
- Daily Vocabulary Scaffolding, H1–8

CHAPTER 4
Getting Ready to Learn

◀ CONCEPT REVIEW

- Electromagnetic radiation carries information about space.
- Our solar system is in the Milky Way galaxy.
- A galaxy is a group of millions or billions of stars.

◀ VOCABULARY REVIEW

solar system p. 10
galaxy p. 10
universe p. 10
electromagnetic radiation p. 15
wavelength p. 16

 CONTENT REVIEW
CLASSZONE.COM
Review concepts and vocabulary.

▶ TAKING NOTES

CHOOSE YOUR OWN STRATEGY

Take notes using one or more of the strategies from earlier chapters—**main idea web, combination notes,** or **main idea and details.** Feel free to mix and match the strategies, or use an entirely different note-taking strategy.

VOCABULARY STRATEGY

Place each vocabulary term at the center of a **description wheel** diagram. Write some words describing it on the spokes.

See the Note-Taking Handbook on pages R45–R51.

SCIENCE NOTEBOOK

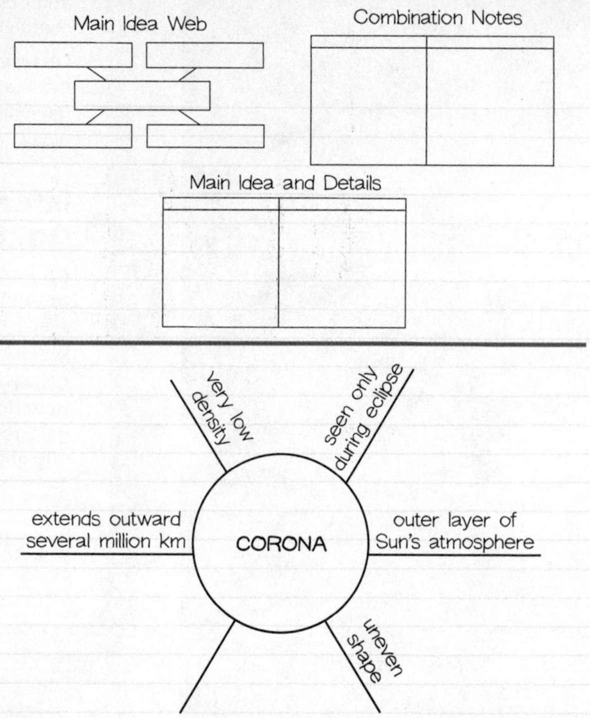

Main Idea Web

Combination Notes

Main Idea and Details

very low density

seen only during eclipse

extends outward several million km

CORONA

outer layer of Sun's atmosphere

uneven shape

E 114 Unit: Space Science

CHECK READINESS

Administer the Diagnostic Test to determine students' readiness for new science content and their mastery of requisite math skills.

 Diagnostic Test, pp. 60–61

Technology Resources

Students needing content and math skills should visit **ClassZone.com**.

- **CONTENT REVIEW**
- **MATH TUTORIAL**

 CONTENT REVIEW CD-ROM

KEY CONCEPT

The Sun is our local star.

◀ **BEFORE, you learned**
- There are different wavelengths of electromagnetic radiation
- The Sun provides light in the solar system

▶ **NOW, you will learn**
- How the Sun produces energy
- How energy flows through the Sun's layers
- About solar features and solar wind

VOCABULARY
fusion p. 116
convection p. 116
corona p. 116
sunspot p. 118
solar wind p. 119

EXPLORE Solar Atmosphere

How can blocking light reveal dim features?

PROCEDURE

① Unbend the paper clip and use it to make a tiny hole in the center of the card.

② Turn on the lamp, and briefly try to read the writing on the bulb.

③ Close one eye, and hold the card in front of your other eye. Through the hole, try to read the writing on the bulb.

MATERIALS
- small paper clip
- index card
- lamp with 45-watt bulb

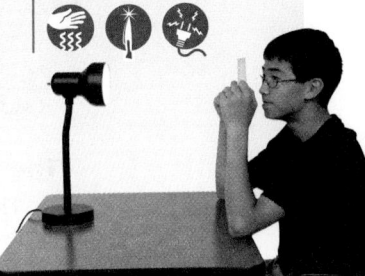

WHAT DO YOU THINK?
- How did looking through the hole affect your view of the writing?
- How might a solar eclipse affect your view of the Sun's dim outermost layer?

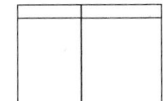

MAIN IDEA AND DETAILS
You could record information about the Sun by using a main idea and details table.

The Sun produces energy from hydrogen.

The Sun is the only star in our solar system. Astronomers have been able to study the Sun in more detail than other stars because it is much closer to Earth. As a result, they have learned a great deal about its size and composition and the way it produces energy.

The Sun is far larger than any of the planets. It contains 99.9 percent of the mass of the entire solar system. For comparison, imagine that Earth had the mass of a sparrow; then the Sun would have the mass of an elephant.

The Sun consists mostly of hydrogen gas. Energy is produced when hydrogen in the Sun's interior turns into helium. This energy is the source of light and warmth that make life possible on Earth.

Chapter 4: **Stars, Galaxies, and the Universe** 115 **E**

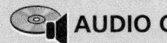

Chapter 4 **115** **E**

Address Misconceptions

IDENTIFY Ask: What happens to light that is given off by an object? Students' answers may reflect the misconception that light does not travel from place to place or that it cannot travel very far from its source.

CORRECT Ask students to list some distant bright objects that they have seen. They might mention stars, the Sun, the Moon, airplanes, or buildings. Explain that they see these objects because light travels from the objects to their eyes.

REASSESS Ask: Why are we able to see distant objects? *because our eyes gather light that has traveled from the objects*

Technology Resources

Visit **ClassZone.com** for background on common student misconceptions.

 MISCONCEPTION DATABASE

Teach Difficult Concepts

Some students may have difficulty understanding that the Sun is not on fire, although it appears to be "burning." Ask:

- What produces fire? *the release of energy by combustion, a rapid chemical reaction involving oxygen and fuel*

- How does the Sun produce energy? *Hydrogen particles in the core combine to form helium in a process called fusion, which releases energy.*

Ongoing Assessment

Explain how the Sun produces energy.

Ask: What happens in the Sun's core? *Hydrogen particles combine to form helium. This process, called fusion, releases energy that travels outward.*

CHECK YOUR READING *Answer: Its energy comes from fusion in the core.*

Energy flows through the Sun's layers.

Although the Sun is made entirely of gas, it does have a structure. Energy produced in the center of the Sun flows out through the Sun's layers in different forms, including visible light.

The Sun's Interior

The Sun's interior generally becomes cooler and less dense as you move away from the center.

REMINDER
Remember that radiation is energy that travels across distances as electromagnetic waves.

❶ **Core** The center of the Sun, called the core, is made of very dense gas. Temperatures reach about 15 million degrees Celsius. Under these extreme conditions, some hydrogen particles collide and combine to form helium in a process called **fusion.** The process releases energy that travels through the core by radiation.

❷ **Radiative Zone** Energy from the core moves by radiation through a thick layer called the radiative zone. Although this layer is very hot and dense, conditions in the radiative zone are not extreme enough for fusion to occur.

❸ **Convection Zone** In the convection zone, energy moves mainly by convection. **Convection** is the transfer of energy from place to place by the motion of heated gas or liquid. Rising currents of hot gas in the convection zone carry energy toward the Sun's surface.

A

CHECK YOUR READING Where does the Sun's energy come from?

 **SIMULATION**
CLASSZONE.COM
View the Sun at different wavelengths.

The Sun's Atmosphere

The Sun's outer layers are called its atmosphere. These layers are much less dense than the interior. The atmosphere generally becomes hotter and less dense as you move outward.

❹ **Photosphere** Visible light moves by radiation out into space from the photosphere. It takes about eight minutes for the light to reach Earth. Since the photosphere is the layer you see in photographs of the Sun, it is often called the Sun's surface. Convection currents beneath the photosphere cause it to have a bumpy texture.

❺ **Chromosphere** The chromosphere is the thin middle layer of the Sun's atmosphere. It gives off a pinkish light.

❻ **Corona** The Sun's outermost layer is called the **corona.** The corona, which varies in shape, extends outward several million kilometers. Both the chromosphere and the corona are much hotter than the photosphere. However, they have such low densities that you can see their light only during a total eclipse of the Sun, when the Moon blocks the much brighter light from the photosphere.

B

DIFFERENTIATE INSTRUCTION

❓ More Reading Support

A What layers are in the Sun's interior? *core, radiative zone, convection zone*

B What layers are in the Sun's atmosphere? *photosphere, chromosphere, corona*

English Learners Complex sentence structures may confuse English learners. Help students by rearranging sentences into simpler constructions. Write this example on the board for students and have them try to explain how the sentence changes:
Complex sentence—"Since the photosphere is the layer you see in photographs of the Sun, it is often called the Sun's surface."
Simpler sentence—"The Sun's surface is often called the photosphere because it is the layer you see in photographs of the Sun."

Layers of the Sun

Energy produced by fusion in the Sun's core flows out through its layers.

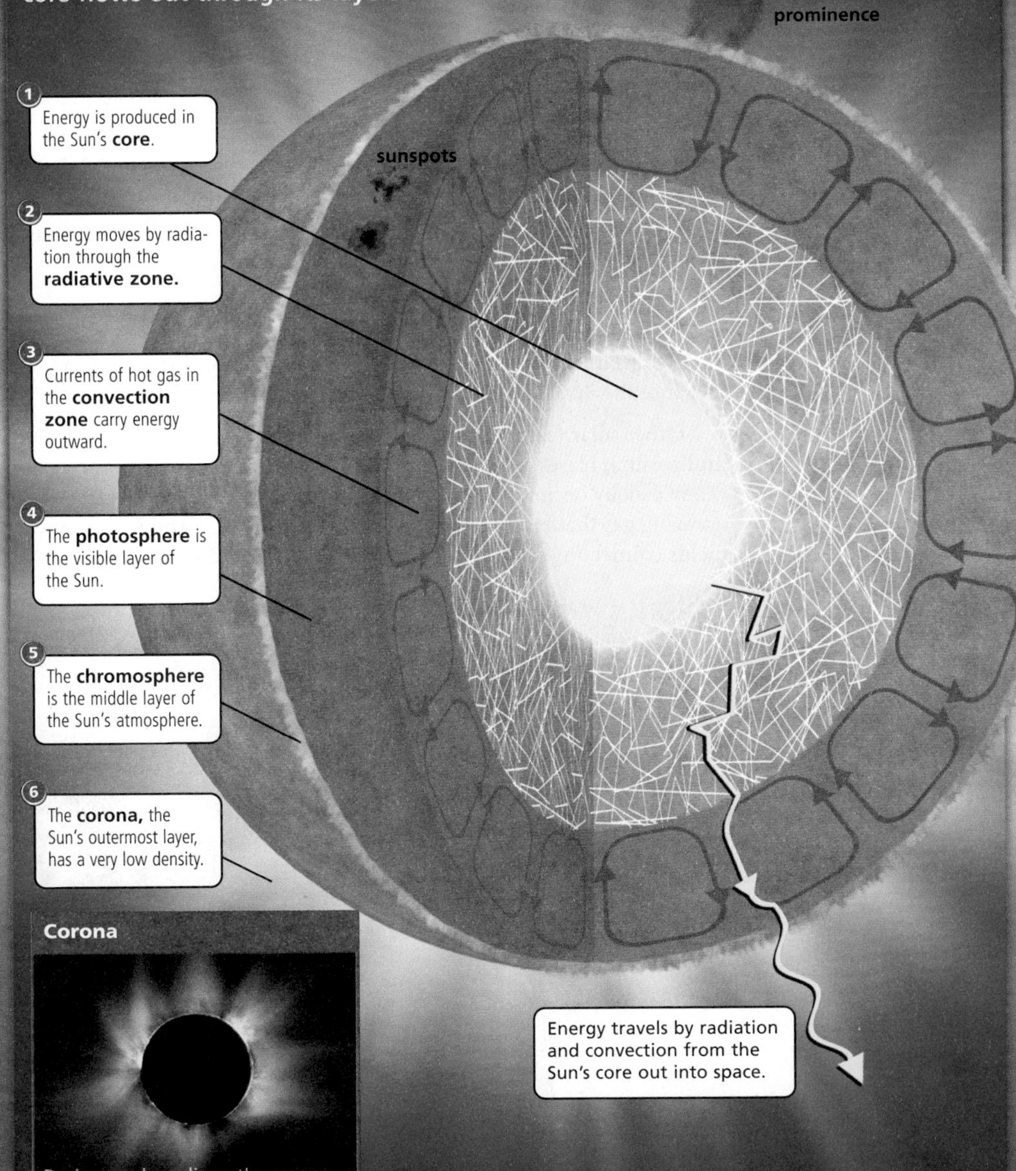

prominence

sunspots

(1) Energy is produced in the Sun's **core.**

(2) Energy moves by radiation through the **radiative zone.**

(3) Currents of hot gas in the **convection zone** carry energy outward.

(4) The **photosphere** is the visible layer of the Sun.

(5) The **chromosphere** is the middle layer of the Sun's atmosphere.

(6) The **corona,** the Sun's outermost layer, has a very low density.

Corona

During a solar eclipse, the corona becomes visible because the much brighter photosphere is hidden. The corona varies in shape.

Energy travels by radiation and convection from the Sun's core out into space.

Chapter 4: Stars, Galaxies, and the Universe **117** **E**

DIFFERENTIATE INSTRUCTION

Below Level Encourage students to retain new vocabulary by separating terms into their component word parts. For example, *corona* means "wreath," "garland," or "crown" in Latin; *photo* is from the Greek word *phōs,* meaning "light;" and *chromo* comes from *khrōma,* the Greek word for color. Have students provide explanations for why these words and word parts were used in naming parts of the Sun. *The corona is the outermost layer of the Sun, much like a wreath or crown. The photosphere is the layer from which light moves into space. The chromosphere gives off a pinkish light.*

Teach from Visuals

To help students interpret the diagram and photograph of the Sun, ask:

- Where is the energy produced in the Sun? *core*
- How does energy travel from the core to the photosphere? *by radiation through the radiative zone and by convection through the convection zone*
- What is the visible layer of the Sun? *photosphere.*
- What do the dark orange circular arrows represent in the convection zone? *currents of hot gas*
- What is the outermost layer? *corona*
- Why does the corona show up clearly in the photo of a solar eclipse? *because the much brighter photosphere is blocked out, allowing the less bright corona to become visible*

T This visual is also available as T30 in the Unit Transparency Book.

Real World Connection

You should never look directly at the Sun. Its light can permanently damage the retinas of your eyes, even if the Sun is mostly hidden during an eclipse. When only 1 percent of the Sun's surface is visible, it is still about 10,000 times brighter than a full moon. There are glasses with special filters that allow you to view the Sun safely. You can also use a mirror or pinhole to project the image of the Sun onto a surface, where it can be viewed without risk.

Develop Critical Thinking

COMPARE AND CONTRAST Have students prepare a table or paragraphs that explain how the structure of the Sun is similar to and different from that of Earth. For example, both objects have a layered structure, and the layers vary in density, temperature, and activity. Earth, however, consists of solids, liquids, and gases. The Sun is entirely made of gas.

Develop Critical Thinking

COMPARE AND CONTRAST Make a chart on the board with the headings *Sunspots, Flares,* and *Prominences.* Have students list similarities and differences among these solar features. *Similarities: All occur where a magnetic field is strong. Differences: Sunspots are cooler, dim areas on the photosphere; prominences are loops of hot gas that extend into the corona; flares are eruptions of hot gas.*

History of Science

Galileo discovered sunspots in the 1600s by using some of the first optical telescopes. By tracking the sunspots' movement, he also discovered that the Sun rotates. However, Galileo's direct observation of the Sun, especially through the lens of a telescope, probably lead to his blindness later in life.

Teach from Visuals

To help students interpret the images showing sunspots and prominences, point out where these features are shown in the illustration on p. 117. Then ask:

- In which layers of the Sun do these features appear? *Sunspots appear on the photosphere; prominences extend from the photosphere into the corona.*

- How are the two features related? *A prominence connects two sunspots.*

Ongoing Assessment

Understand how energy flows through the Sun's layers.

How does energy flow in the Sun's interior layers? *by radiation in the core and radiative zone, and by convection in the convective zone*

 *Answer: They are cooler and dimmer.*

Features on the Sun

Astronomers have observed features on the Sun that vary over time. Near the Sun's surface there are regions of magnetic force called magnetic fields. These magnetic fields get twisted into different positions as the Sun rotates. Features appear on the surface in areas where strong magnetic fields are located.

Sunspots are spots on the photosphere that are cooler than surrounding areas. Although they appear dark, sunspots are actually bright. They only seem dim because the rest of the photosphere is so much brighter.

Sunspot activity follows a pattern that lasts about 11 years. At the peak of the cycle, dozens of sunspots may appear. During periods of low activity, there may not be any sunspots.

 Sunspots move across the Sun's surface as it rotates. Astronomers first realized that the Sun rotates when they noticed this movement. Because the Sun is not solid, some parts rotate faster than others.

 Other solar features include flares and prominences (PRAHM-uh-nuhn-sihz). Flares are eruptions of hot gas from the Sun's surface. They usually occur near sunspots. Prominences are huge loops of glowing gas that extend into the corona. They occur where magnetic fields connecting sunspots soar into the outer atmosphere.

 How are sunspots different from other areas of the photosphere?

Solar Features

Features on the Sun appear in areas where a magnetic field is strong.

Sunspots

Sunspots on the photosphere can be larger than Earth.

Prominences

Prominences can soar more than 100,000 kilometers above the photosphere.

DIFFERENTIATE INSTRUCTION

 **More Reading Support**

C What do sunspots do as the Sun rotates? *move across its surface*

D What are eruptions of hot gas near sunspots? *flares*

Advanced Have students make a graph of the sunspot cycle over the last 50 years or so. The graph should include the current year and the next several years. Have students explain the pattern, where we currently fall within the pattern, and when the next peak period of activity can be expected.

R Challenge and Extension, p. 223

Solar Wind

Material in the Sun's corona is continually streaming out into space. The electrically charged particles that flow out in all directions from the corona are called the **solar wind.** The solar wind extends throughout our solar system.

Most of the solar wind flowing toward Earth is safely guided around the planet by Earth's magnetic field. When solar-wind particles do enter the upper atmosphere, they release energy, which can produce beautiful patterns of glowing light in the sky. Such displays of light are called auroras (uh-RAWR-uhz), or the northern and southern lights. Auroras often occur near the poles.

This circular green aurora occurred over Alaska when particles from the solar wind entered the atmosphere.

Earth's atmosphere usually prevents charged particles from reaching the surface. However, during the peak of the sunspot cycle, flares and other kinds of solar activity release strong bursts of charged particles into the solar wind. These bursts, called magnetic storms, can disrupt electric-power delivery across large regions by causing surges in power lines. They can also interfere with radio communication.

Magnetic storms are much more harmful above the protective layers of Earth's atmosphere. Bursts of particles in the solar wind can damage or destroy orbiting satellites. The solar wind also poses a danger to astronauts during space flights.

 **CHECK YOUR READING** What causes auroras to form?

4.1 Review

KEY CONCEPTS
1. How does the Sun produce energy?
2. How does energy move from the Sun's core to the photosphere?
3. How does the solar wind normally affect Earth?

CRITICAL THINKING
4. **Analyze** Why is the core the only layer of the Sun where energy is produced?
5. **Compare and Contrast** Make a diagram comparing sunspots, flares, and prominences.

CHALLENGE
6. **Infer** A communications satellite stops working while in orbit, and a surge in an electric power line causes blackouts in cities across a large region. What probably happened in the Sun's atmosphere shortly before these events?

ANSWERS

1. Energy is released from the fusion of hydrogen particles in the core.

2. The energy moves by radiation through the radiative zone and by convection through the convection zone.

3. Earth's magnetic field guides most of the solar wind around Earth, but some particles enter the upper atmosphere and produce auroras.

4. The core is the only layer hot and dense enough for fusion to occur.

5. Diagrams should accurately show the characteristics of these features.

6. A solar flare probably released a strong burst of particles into the solar wind.

Ongoing Assessment
Describe solar features and solar winds.

What is the relationship between sunspots and flares? *Flares occur near sunspots.* What is the relationship between sunspots and prominences? *Prominences occur where magnetic fields connect sunspots.*

CHECK YOUR READING *Answer: the release of energy from particles of solar wind entering the upper atmosphere*

Reinforce (the **BIG** idea)

Have students relate the section to the Big Idea.

 Reinforcing Key Concepts, p. 224

4.1 ASSESS & RETEACH

Assess
Section 4.1 Quiz, p. 62

Reteach
Write the following terms on the board: *Sun, solar wind, sunspot, prominence, core, Sun's interior, Sun's atmosphere, corona, aurora, solar eclipse*

- Have volunteers explain the meaning of each term.
- Help students put the terms together in a concept map.

Technology Resources

Have students visit **ClassZone.com** for reaching of Key Concepts.

 CONTENT REVIEW

 CONTENT REVIEW CD-ROM

CHAPTER INVESTIGATION

Focus

PURPOSE To compare the brightness and color of different light sources.

OVERVIEW Students will construct a wax photometer and observe how the photometer works. They will then connect a miniature light bulb to one battery and a second bulb to two batteries, and use the photometer to compare the light from these sources. To keep the instruction appropriate for middle-school students, this investigation is qualitative rather than quantitative. Students will determine the following:

- A cooler bulb will be dimmer and make the wax glow orange.
- A warmer bulb will be brighter and make the wax glow yellow.

Lab Preparation

- Wax blocks used for canning can be found in many hardware stores.
- If the blocks are stuck together, you can tap the short edge against a firm surface to separate them.
- To lower the expense of materials, cut blocks in half and have students construct a photometer from two halves instead of whole blocks.
- Prepare a photometer and light-bulb setup ahead of time so students can use them as models for making their own.
- Prior to the investigation, have students read through the investigation and prepare their data tables. Or you may wish to copy and distribute datasheets and rubrics.

 UNIT RESOURCE BOOK, pp. 266–275

 SCIENCE TOOLKIT, F14

Lab Management

Students may use a ruler if they have trouble finding an approximate midpoint between the lights for the photometer.

SAFETY The wires can get hot, especially those in the two-battery setup. Caution students not to touch them and to remove the bulb after step 7. Also caution students that the wire ends are sharp.

E **120** Unit: **Space Science**

CHAPTER INVESTIGATION

Temperature, Brightness, and Color

OVERVIEW AND PURPOSE Think of the metal heating surface on a hot plate. How can you tell whether the hot plate is fully heated? Is the metal surface brighter or dimmer than when it is just starting to get warm? Does the color of the surface change as the hot plate gets hotter? You may already have an idea of how temperature, brightness, and color are related—at least when it comes to heated metal. Do the same relationships apply to electric lights? to stars? This investigation is designed to help you find out. You will

- construct a wax photometer to compare the brightnesses and colors of different light sources
- determine how the temperature of a light source affects its brightness and color

MATERIALS

- 2 paraffin blocks
- aluminum foil
- 2 rubber bands
- 2 light-bulb holders
- 2 miniature light bulbs
- 3 AA batteries
- 4 pieces of uninsulated copper wire 15 cm long
- masking tape
for Challenge:
- incandescent lamp
- dimmer switch

▶ Problem

How are brightness and color related to temperature?

▶ Hypothesize

Write a hypothesis to explain how brightness and color are related to temperature. Your hypothesis should take the form of an "If . . . , then . . . , because . . ." statement.

▶ Procedure

1. An instrument called a photometer makes it easier to compare the brightnesses and colors of different light sources. Assemble the wax photometer as shown on page 121. The aluminum foil between the wax blocks should be folded so that the shiny side faces out on both sides.

2. Hold the photometer so that you can see both blocks. Bring it to different locations in the classroom, and observe how the brightnesses and colors of the blocks change as the two sides of the photometer are exposed to different light conditions.

3. Tape a piece of copper wire to each end of a battery, and connect the wires to a light-bulb holder. The battery will provide electricity to heat up the wire inside a light bulb.

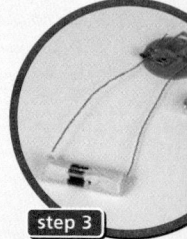

step 3

E 120 Unit: Space Science

INVESTIGATION RESOURCES

 CHAPTER INVESTIGATION, Temperature, Brightness, and Color
- Photometer Instructions, p. 266
- Level A, pp. 267–270
- Level B, pp. 271–274
- Level C, p. 275

Advanced students should complete Levels B & C.

 Writing a Lab Report, D12–13

Technology Resources

Customize this student lab as needed or look for an alternative. Print rubrics to assess student lab reports.

 Lab Generator CD-ROM

4. Tape the negative terminal, or flat end, of one battery to the positive terminal of another battery. Tape a piece of copper wire to each end, and connect the wires to a light-bulb holder. Because two batteries will provide electricity to the bulb in this holder, the wire in the bulb will be hotter than the wire in the bulb powered by one battery.

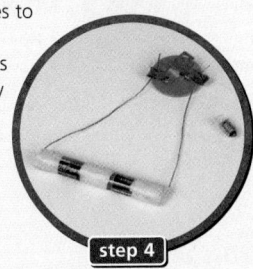
step 4

5. With the room darkened, insert a bulb into each light-bulb holder. If the bulb connected to two batteries does not light up, you may need to press the two batteries together with your fingers.

6. Place the photometer halfway between the two light bulbs. Compare the brightnesses of the two light sources. Record your observations in your **Science Notebook**.

7. Move the photometer closer to the cooler bulb until both sides of the photometer are equally bright. Compare the colors of the two light sources. Record your observations in your **Science Notebook**. To avoid draining the batteries, remove the bulbs from the holders when you have completed this step.

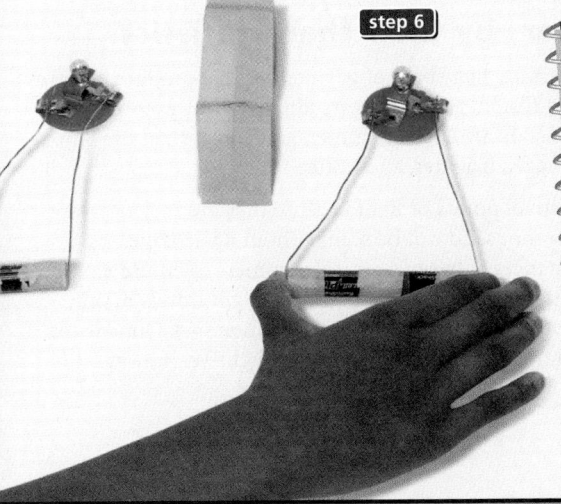
step 6

Observe and Analyze Write It Up

1. **RECORD OBSERVATIONS** Draw the setup of your photometer and light sources. Be sure your data table is complete with descriptions of brightness and color.

2. **IDENTIFY** Identify the variables in this experiment. List them in your **Science Notebook**.

Conclude Write It Up

1. **INTERPRET** Answer the question in the problem. Compare your results with your hypothesis.

2. **ANALYZE** How does distance affect your perception of the brightness of an object?

3. **APPLY** Judging by the results of the investigation, would you expect a red star or a yellow star to be hotter? Explain why.

INVESTIGATE Further

CHALLENGE Connect an incandescent lamp to a dimmer switch. Write a procedure to show how you would use a photometer to show the relationship between the color and the temperature of the bulb as it fades from brightest to dimmest. Then carry out your procedure.

Temperature, Brightness, and Color
Observe and Analyze
Table 1. Properties of Light from Two Sources

	Cooler Bulb (one battery)	Warmer Bulb (two batteries)
Brightness		
Color		

Chapter 4: **Stars, Galaxies, and the Universe** 121 **E**

Observe and Analyze Write It Up

1. See students' tables.

2. The independent variable is the temperature of the bulbs. The dependent variables are the brightness and the color of the bulbs.

Conclude Write It Up

1. The light becomes brighter and changes color as the temperature increases.

2. Objects appear brighter the closer they are.

3. A yellow star would be hotter. Objects that are heated give off yellow light at a higher temperature than when they give off red light.

INVESTIGATE Further

CHALLENGE The wire in the bulb would undergo the following changes in color as the bulb dims: white, yellow, orange, red.

Post-Lab Discussion

• Discuss the importance of having only one independent variable in the investigation. *If there were more independent variables, it would be unclear which one was causing the changes.*

• Discuss how you could modify the lab to measure the effect that distance has on brightness. *Use light bulbs of different wattages powered by the same number of batteries; use a ruler to measure distances.*

Students will

- Explain how stars are classified.
- Describe how stars form and change.
- Experiment with parallax to learn how it can be used to determine distance.

◀ 3-Minute Warm-Up

Display Transparency 28 or copy this exercise on the board:

Decide if these statements are true. If not, correct them.

1. The Sun is one of several stars in our solar system. *The Sun is the only star in our solar system.*

2. The planets revolve around the Sun. *true*

3. Most stars are too far away to see with your bare eyes. *true*

 3-Minute Warm-Up, p. T28

4.2 MOTIVATE

EXPLORE Characteristics of Stars

PURPOSE To demonstrate to students that an object's apparent brightness depends on its distance from the observer

TIP *10 min.* The darker the room, the more effective the results will be.

WHAT DO YOU THINK? *The light became dimmer as distance increased. The star appears dimmer the farther away it is from Earth.*

KEY CONCEPT

4.2 Stars change over their life cycles.

◀ **BEFORE, you learned**

- The Sun is our local star
- The other stars are outside our solar system
- There are huge distances between objects in the universe

▶ **NOW, you will learn**

- How stars are classified
- How stars form and change

VOCABULARY

light-year p. 122
parallax p. 123
nebula p. 125
main sequence p. 126
neutron star p. 126
black hole p. 126

EXPLORE Characteristics of Stars

How does distance affect brightness?

PROCEDURE

① In a darkened room, shine a flashlight onto a dark surface from 30 cm away while your partner shines a flashlight onto the surface from the same distance. Observe the two spots of light.

② Move one of the flashlights back 15 cm and then another 15 cm. Compare the two spots of light each time you move the flashlight.

MATERIALS
- 2 flashlights
- meter stick
- dark surface

WHAT DO YOU THINK?
- How did distance affect the brightness of the light on the dark surface?
- How does the distance of a star from Earth affect our view of it?

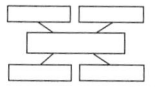

MAIN IDEA WEB
A main idea web would be a good choice for taking notes about the characteristics of stars.

We classify stars by their characteristics.

Like our Sun, all stars are huge balls of glowing gas that produce or have produced energy by fusion. However, stars differ in size, brightness, and temperature. Some stars are smaller, fainter, and cooler than the Sun. Others are much bigger, brighter, and hotter.

Stars look like small points of light because they are very far away. At most, only a few thousand can be seen without a telescope. To describe the distances between stars, astronomers often use a unit called the light-year. A **light-year** is the distance light travels in one year, which is about 9.5 trillion kilometers (6 trillion mi). Outside the solar system, the star closest to Earth is about 4 light-years away.

E 122 Unit: Space Science

RESOURCES FOR DIFFERENTIATED INSTRUCTION

Below Level
UNIT RESOURCE BOOK
- Reading Study Guide A, pp. 227–228
- Decoding Support, p. 263

 **AUDIO CDS**

R **Additional INVESTIGATION,**
Distance and Brightness, A, B, & C, pp. 276–284; Teacher Instructions, pp. 287–288

Advanced
UNIT RESOURCE BOOK
- Challenge and Extension, p. 233
- Challenge Reading, pp. 259–260

English Learners
UNIT RESOURCE BOOK
Spanish Reading Study Guide, pp. 231–232

AUDIO CDS

- Audio Readings in Spanish
- Audio Readings (English)

Brightness and Distance

If you look at stars, you will probably notice that some appear to be brighter than others. The amount of light a star gives off and its distance from Earth determine how bright it appears to an observer. A star that gives off a huge amount of light can appear faint if it is far away. On the other hand, a star that gives off much less light can appear bright if it is closer to Earth. Therefore, to determine the true brightness of a star, astronomers must measure its distance from Earth.

One way astronomers measure distance is by using **parallax,** which is the apparent shift in the position of an object when viewed from different locations. Look at an object with your right eye closed. Now quickly open it and close your left eye. The object will seem to move slightly because you are viewing it from a different angle. The same kind of shift occurs when astronomers view stars from different locations.

To measure the parallax of a star, astronomers plot the star's position in the sky from opposite sides of Earth's orbit around the Sun. They then use the apparent shift in position and the diameter of Earth's orbit to calculate the star's distance.

CHECK YOUR READING What factors affect how bright a star appears from Earth?

INVESTIGATE Parallax

How does the distance of an object affect parallax?

PROCEDURE

1. Stand 1 m away from a classmate. Have the classmate hold up a meter stick at eye level.

2. With your left eye closed, hold a capped pen up close to your face. Look at the pen with your right eye, and line it up with the zero mark on the meter stick. Then open your left eye and quickly close your right eye. Observe how many centimeters the pen seems to move. Record your observation.

3. Repeat step 2 with the pen held at arm's length and then with the pen held at half your arm's length. Record your observation each time.

WHAT DO YOU THINK?
• How many centimeters did the pen appear to move each time you observed it?
• How is parallax affected when you change the distance of the pen from you?

CHALLENGE How could you use this method to estimate distances that you cannot measure directly?

SKILL FOCUS
Measuring

MATERIALS
• meter stick
• capped pen

TIME
10 minutes

DIFFERENTIATE INSTRUCTION

More Reading Support

A What is one way astronomers measure distance? *parallax*

Additional Investigation To reinforce Section 4.2 learning goals, use the following full-period investigation:

 **Additional INVESTIGATION,** Distance and Brightness, A, B, & C, pp. 276–284, 287–288
(Advanced students should complete Levels B and C.)

Alternative Assessment Have students draw pictures to show what they observed in the investigation. Have them explain their pictures orally.

4.2 INSTRUCT

INVESTIGATE Parallax

PURPOSE To introduce students to a scientific method for measuring the distance of stars

TIPS *10 min.*

• Tell students to look at the same side of the pen throughout the investigation.

• Results may vary due to factors such as the actual distances between the pen and students' eyes. However, all students should see the same pattern.

DIFFERENTIATION If students only have vision in one eye, they can observe the parallax shift by moving their heads from side to side.

WHAT DO YOU THINK? *Sample results: pen near face: 20 cm; half arm's length: 10 cm; arm's length: 5 cm. The closer the pen is to the face, the greater is the parallax, or apparent shift in position.*

CHALLENGE *You could measure the apparent shift in position of an object against the background stars when that object is viewed from different angles. Objects with a greater shift are farther away.*

 Datasheet, Parallax, p. 234

Technology Resources

Customize this student lab as needed or look for an alternative. Print rubrics to assess student lab reports.

Lab Generator CD-ROM

Teaching with Technology

Have students use a digital camera to take pictures of a stationary object from two different positions. Have them explain how the photographs illustrate parallax.

Ongoing Assessment

CHECK YOUR READING *Answer: the amount of light a star gives off and the star's distance from Earth*

Teach from Visuals

To help students interpret the visual showing the relative sizes of various stars, ask:

- Rank the stars from smallest to largest. *white dwarf, the Sun, giant star, supergiant star*

- About how big would the giant star be if the circle for it was completed? *Answers will vary, but it would be at least the size of a large beach ball.*

- What is the diameter of a white dwarf? *14,000 km*

- What is the diameter of a giant star? *14 to 140 million km*

- If the colors in the drawing represent the colors of these stars, rank the stars from coolest to hottest. *supergiant, the Sun, white dwarf, giant star*

Mathematics Connection

Ask students how they could make a scale drawing that compares the sizes of Earth and the Sun. Discuss their suggested procedure and encourage them to make their drawings. *Given that the diameter of the Sun is about 100 times greater than that of Earth, measure the diameter of a circle representing Earth, then draw a circle with 100 times that diameter to represent the Sun. Students will have to make sure the diameter for Earth is small enough so that they could realistically draw a circle with 100 times that diameter.*

EXPLORE (the **BIG** idea)

Revisit "How Can Stars Differ?" on p. 113. Have students relate their observations to what they have read in the text.

Ongoing Assessment

Explain how stars are classified.

Ask: What are five characteristics of stars that are used to classify them? *brightness, distance, size, temperature, and color*

CHECK YOUR **READING** *Answer: The color of a star depends on its temperature.*

Size

It is hard to get a sense of how large stars are from viewing them in the sky. Even the Sun, which is much closer than any other star, is far larger than its appearance suggests. The diameter of the Sun is about 100 times greater than that of Earth. A jet plane flying 800 kilometers per hour (500 mi/h) would travel around Earth's equator in about two days. If you could travel around the Sun's equator at the same speed, the trip would take more than seven months.

Some stars are much larger than the Sun. Giant and supergiant stars range from ten to hundreds of times larger. A supergiant called Betelgeuse (BEET-uhl-JOOZ) is more than 600 times greater in diameter than the Sun. If Betelgeuse replaced the Sun, it would fill space in our solar system well beyond Earth's orbit. Because giant and supergiant stars have such huge surface areas to give off light, they are very bright. Betelgeuse is one of the brightest stars in the sky, even though it is 522 light-years away.

There are also stars much smaller than the Sun. Stars called white dwarfs are about 100 times smaller in diameter than the Sun, or roughly the size of Earth. White dwarfs cannot be seen without a telescope.

A star the size of the Sun
Diameter = 1.4 million kilometers (900,000 mi)

? B

White dwarf
1/100 the Sun's diameter

Giant star
10–100 times the Sun's diameter

Supergiant star
100–1000 times the Sun's diameter

Color and Temperature

If you observe stars closely, you may notice that they vary slightly in color. Most stars look white. However, a few appear slightly blue or red. The differences in color are due to differences in temperature.

You can see how temperature affects color by heating up metal. For example, if you turn on a toaster, the metal coils inside will start to glow a dull red. As they get hotter, the coils will turn a brighter orange. The illustration on page 125 shows changes in the color of a metal bar as it heats up.

Like the color of heated metal, the color of a star indicates its temperature. Astronomers group stars into classes by color and surface temperature. The chart on page 125 lists the color and temperature range of each class of star. The coolest stars are red. The hottest stars are blue-white. Our Sun—a yellow, G-class star—has a surface temperature of about 6000°C.

Stars of every class give off light that is made up of a range of colors. Astronomers can spread a star's light into a spectrum to learn about the star's composition. The colors and lines in a spectrum reveal which gases are present in the star's outer layers.

CHECK YOUR **READING** How does a star's temperature affect its appearance?

DIFFERENTIATE INSTRUCTION

? **More Reading Support**

B How do other stars compare in size with the Sun? *Some are larger and some are smaller.*

English Learners Help English learners break down the meaning of phrasal verbs such as "give off" (pp. 123, 124), "made up of" (p. 124), "end up" (p. 126), and "figure out" (p. 128). Make sure they do not take the prepositions literally. Offer synonyms for the terms.

Below Level To show the effect of size on brightness, darken the room and light two candles, one with a very small wick and one with a very large wick. Have students compare the size and the brightness of the flames.

Color and Temperature

Objects that radiate light change color as they heat up.

Classification of Stars

Class	Color	Surface Temperature (°C)
O	blue-white	above 25,000
B	blue-white	10,000–25,000
A	white	7500–10,000
F	yellow-white	6000–7500
G	yellow	5000–6000
K	orange	3500–5000
M	red	below 3500

Stars are classified according to their colors and temperatures. The Sun is a G-class star.

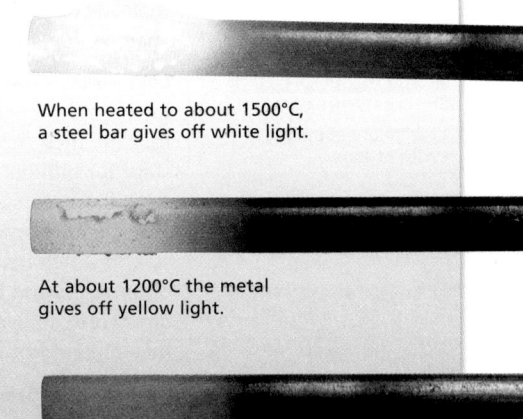

When heated to about 1500°C, a steel bar gives off white light.

At about 1200°C the metal gives off yellow light.

A steel bar glows red when heated to about 600°C.

Stars have life cycles.

Although stars last for very long periods, they are not permanent. Like living organisms, stars go through cycles of birth, maturity, and death. The life cycle of a star varies, depending on the mass of the star. Higher-mass stars develop more quickly than lower-mass stars. Toward the end of their life cycles, higher-mass stars also behave differently from lower-mass stars.

Stars form inside a cloud of gas and dust called a **nebula** (NEHB-yuh-luh). Gravity pulls gas and dust closer together in some regions of a nebula. As the matter contracts, it forms a hot, dense sphere. The sphere becomes a star if its center grows hot and dense enough for fusion to occur.

When a star dies, its matter does not disappear. Some of it may form a nebula or move into an existing one. There, the matter may eventually become part of new stars.

CHECK YOUR READING How is gravity involved in the formation of stars?

Colors have been added to this photograph of the Omega Nebula in order to bring out details.

Address Misconceptions

IDENTIFY Draw two circles on the board, one about the size of a bowling ball and the other about the size of a beach ball—about twice as big. Label the circles "bowling ball" and "beach ball." Ask: Which has more mass—a bowling ball or a beach ball? If students say "beach ball," they may hold the misconception that you can determine the mass of an object by its size or volume.

CORRECT Provide students with three objects of the same size but with different masses, such as cubes of wood, steel, and aluminum. Then give them three objects of different sizes but with about the same mass. Have students hold each object, or measure its mass on a balance. Then have them compare the sizes and masses of the objects.

REASSESS Ask: What does mass tell you about an object? *how much matter it has*

Integrate the Sciences

The explosion of stars makes life possible. Our planet and all living things are mostly made of elements that formed in the cores of stars toward the end of the stars' life cycles. Therefore, the human body contains matter that was once hurled into space in a supernova.

Ongoing Assessment

CHECK YOUR READING *Answer: Lower-mass stars expand into giant stars and end up as white dwarfs. Higher-mass stars expand into supergiants, which undergo supernova explosions and end up as neutron stars or black holes.*

RESOURCE CENTER
CLASSZONE.COM

Learn more about life cycles of stars.

A pulsar emits beams of radio waves as it spins rapidly. The pulsar seems to pulse as the beams rotate toward and away from Earth.

Stages in the Life Cycles of Stars

The diagram on page 127 shows the stages that stars go through in their life cycles. Notice that the length of a cycle and the way a star changes depend on the mass of the star at its formation.

Lower-Mass Stars The stage in which stars produce energy through the fusion of hydrogen into helium is called the **main sequence.** Because they use their fuel slowly, lower-mass stars remain in the main-sequence stage for billions of years. The Sun has been a main-sequence star for 4.6 billion years and will remain one for about another 5 billion years. When a lower-mass star runs out of hydrogen, it expands into a giant star, in which helium fuses into carbon. Over time a giant star sheds its outer layers and becomes a white dwarf. A white dwarf is simply the dead core of a giant star. Although no fusion occurs in white dwarfs, they remain hot for billions of years.

Higher-Mass Stars Stars more than eight times as massive as our Sun spend much less time in the main-sequence stage because they use their fuel rapidly. After millions of years, a higher-mass star expands to become a supergiant star. In the core of a supergiant, fusion produces heavier and heavier elements. When an iron core forms, fusion stops and gravity causes the core to collapse. Then part of the core bounces outward, and the star erupts in an explosion called a supernova.

For a brief period, a supernova can give off as much light as a galaxy. The outer layers of the exploded star shoot out into space, carrying with them heavy elements that formed inside the star. Eventually this matter may become part of new stars and planets.

? E

Neutron Stars and Black Holes

The collapsed core of a supergiant star may form an extremely dense body called a **neutron star.** Neutron stars measure only about 20 kilometers (12 mi) in diameter, but their masses are one to three times that of the Sun.

Neutron stars emit little visible light. However, they strongly emit other forms of radiation, such as x-rays. Some neutron stars emit beams of radio waves as they spin. These stars are called pulsars because they seem to pulse as the beams rotate.

Sometimes a supernova leaves behind a core with a mass more than three times that of the Sun. In such a case, the core does not end up as a neutron star. Instead, it collapses even further, forming an invisible object called a **black hole.** The gravity of a black hole is so strong that no form of radiation can escape from it.

? F

CHECK YOUR READING How do lower-mass stars differ from higher-mass stars after the main-sequence stage?

DIFFERENTIATE INSTRUCTION

? **More Reading Support**

E What kind of stars stay in the main sequence longer? *lower-mass stars*

F What may the collapsed core of a supergiant star form? *neutron star or black hole*

Advanced Have students search news stories for information about black holes, neutron stars, or any aspect of the life cycle of a star. Have them report their findings to the class. Encourage them to determine what questions are answered by the information and what questions remain unanswered.

Have students who are interested in the life cycles of stars read the following article:

 Challenge Reading, pp. 259–260

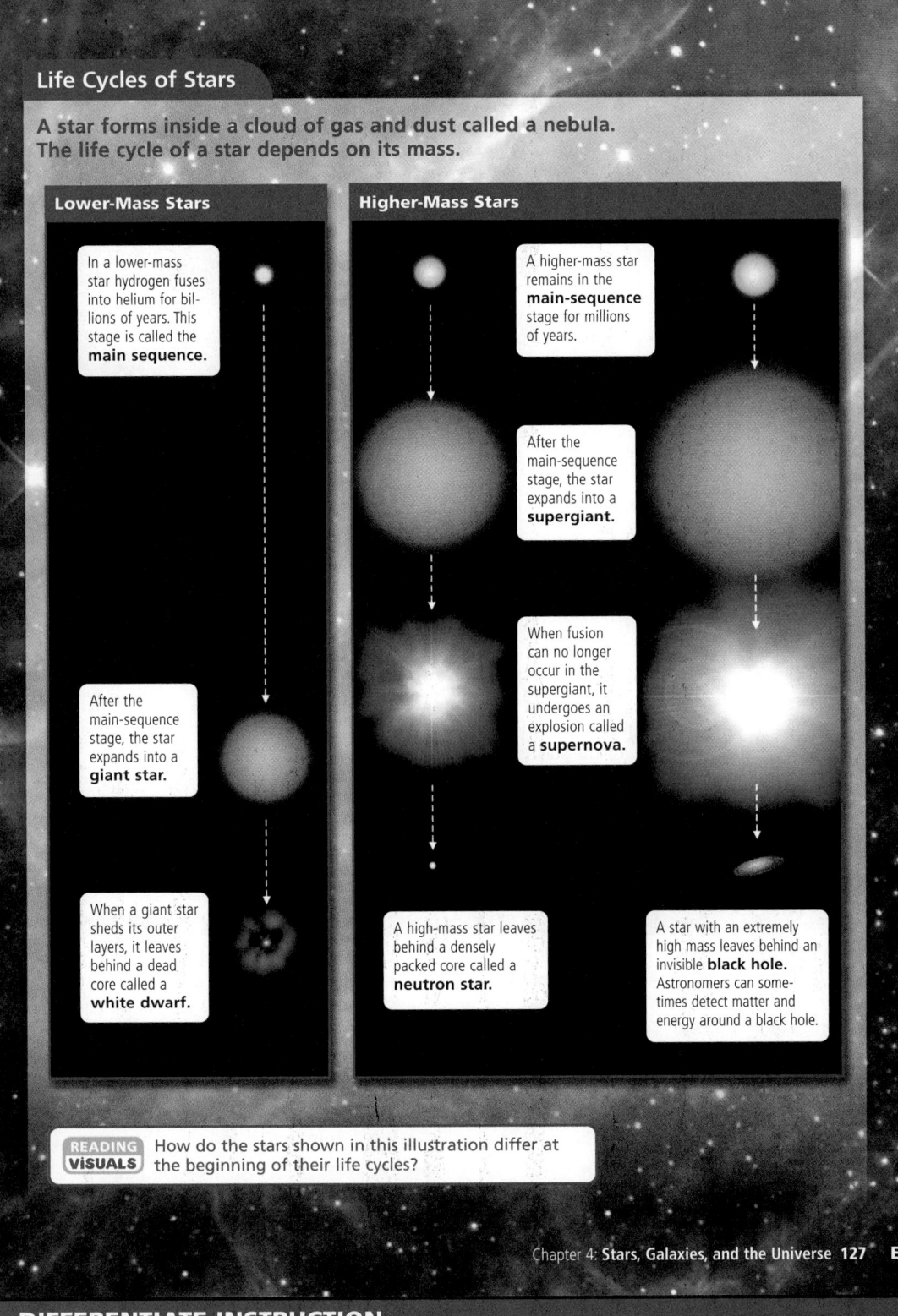

Life Cycles of Stars

A star forms inside a cloud of gas and dust called a nebula. The life cycle of a star depends on its mass.

Lower-Mass Stars

In a lower-mass star hydrogen fuses into helium for billions of years. This stage is called the **main sequence.**

After the main-sequence stage, the star expands into a **giant star.**

When a giant star sheds its outer layers, it leaves behind a dead core called a **white dwarf.**

Higher-Mass Stars

A higher-mass star remains in the **main-sequence** stage for millions of years.

After the main-sequence stage, the star expands into a **supergiant.**

When fusion can no longer occur in the supergiant, it undergoes an explosion called a **supernova.**

A high-mass star leaves behind a densely packed core called a **neutron star.**

A star with an extremely high mass leaves behind an invisible **black hole.** Astronomers can sometimes detect matter and energy around a black hole.

READING VISUALS How do the stars shown in this illustration differ at the beginning of their life cycles?

Chapter 4: **Stars, Galaxies, and the Universe** 127　**E**

Teach from Visuals

To help students interpret the visual showing the life cycles of stars, ask:

- What determines which life cycle a star will follow? *its mass*
- What is a main-sequence star? *a star that is fusing hydrogen into helium*
- Which kind of star stays in the main-sequence stage longer? *lower-mass star*
- What happens to stars after leaving the main sequence? *A lower-mass star expands into a giant star. A higher-mass star expands into a supergiant.*
- What happens to a giant star? *When it sheds its outer layers, it leaves behind a dead core called a white dwarf.*
- What happens to a supergiant? *When fusion can no longer occur, it undergoes an explosion called a supernova.*
- What determines whether a supergiant leaves behind a neutron star or a black hole after it explodes? *The mass of the star; only stars with an extremely high mass end up as black holes.*

Ongoing Assessment

Describe how stars form and change.

Ask: How do stars change during their life cycle? *In the beginning, fusion takes place, and then the star expands. When it dies, it leaves behind either a white dwarf, a neutron star, or a black hole.*

READING VISUALS *Answer: The lower-mass star remains in the main-sequence stage longer than the higher-mass stars.*

DIFFERENTIATE INSTRUCTION

Inclusion Point out to students with visual impairments the white dwarf and the difference in the sizes of objects at each stage in the diagram. Also, remind them that the picture at the bottom right only shows evidence of a black hole; the black hole itself is invisible.

Alternative Assessment Have teams of students make illustrated flipbooks to show the life cycles of stars. Flipbooks for lower-mass stars should have more illustrations for the main sequence, to indicate that the stars remain in this stage for longer periods.

Star Systems

Unlike our Sun, most stars do not exist alone. Instead, they are grouped with one or more companion stars. The stars are held together by the force of gravity between them. A binary star system consists of two stars that orbit each other. A multiple star system consists of more than two stars.

In many star systems, the stars are too close together to be seen individually. However, astronomers have developed ways of detecting such systems. For example, in a binary star system, one of the stars may orbit in front of the other when viewed from Earth. The star that orbits in front will briefly block some of the other star's light, providing a clue that more than one star is present. The illustration at right shows a binary star system that can be detected this way. Sometimes astronomers can also figure out whether a star is really a star system by studying its spectrum.

Star systems are an important source of information about star masses. Astronomers cannot measure the mass of a star directly. However, they can figure out a star's mass by observing the effect of the star's gravity on a companion star.

Binary Star System

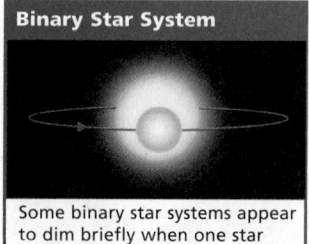

Some binary star systems appear to dim briefly when one star orbits in front of the other and blocks some of its light.

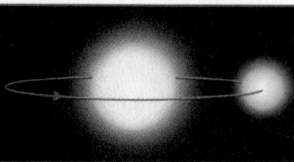

When neither star is in front of the other, the star system appears to give off more light.

 **CHECK YOUR READING** Why are star systems important to astronomers?

4.2 Review

KEY CONCEPTS

1. Why must astronomers figure out a star's distance to calculate its actual brightness?

2. How are color and temperature related in stars?

3. How does a star's mass affect its life cycle?

CRITICAL THINKING

4. **Analyze** Some of the brightest stars are red supergiants. How can stars with cooler red surfaces be so bright?

5. **Infer** Will the Sun eventually become a black hole? Why or why not?

❶ CHALLENGE

6. **Infer** At what stage in the life cycle of the Sun will it be impossible for life to exist on Earth? Explain.

ANSWERS

1. The star's distance from Earth affects its apparent brightness.

2. The temperature of a star determines its color.

3. Lower-mass stars develop more slowly than higher-mass stars and end up as white dwarfs rather than neutron stars or black holes.

4. Their surface areas are huge compared to with those of smaller stars.

5. It will not become a black hole because its mass is not great enough.

6. Life will be impossible when the Sun becomes a giant star, in about 5 billion years, because it will expand 10–100 times its size.

MATH in SCIENCE

SKILL: INTERPRETING A SCATTER PLOT

Brightness and Temperature of Stars

A star's brightness, or luminosity, depends on the star's surface temperature and size. If two stars have the same surface temperature, the larger star will be more luminous. The Hertzsprung-Russell (H-R) diagram below is a scatter plot that shows the relative temperatures and luminosities of various stars.

Example

Describe the surface temperature and luminosity of Spica.

(1) Surface temperature: Without drawing on the graph, imagine a line extending from Spica down to the temperature axis. Spica is one of the hottest stars.

(2) Luminosity: Imagine a line extending from Spica across to the luminosity axis. Spica has a high luminosity.

ANSWER Spica is one of the hottest and most luminous stars.

Hertzsprung-Russell (H-R) Diagram

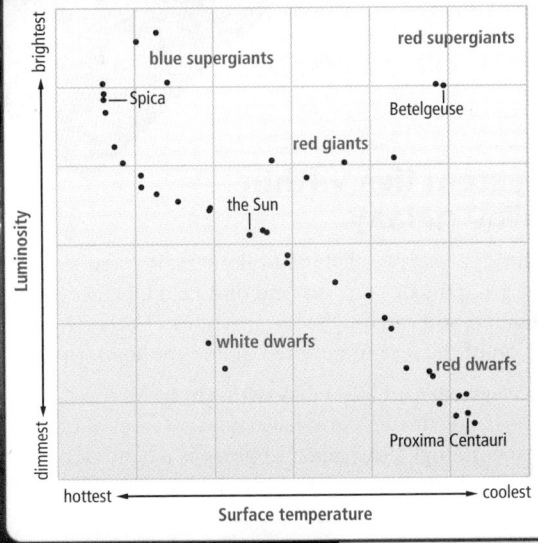

Use the diagram to answer the questions.

1. Describe the surface temperature and luminosity of Proxima Centauri.

2. Compare the surface temperature and luminosity of the Sun with the surface temperature and luminosity of Betelgeuse.

3. Compare the surface temperature and luminosity of the red dwarfs with the surface temperature and luminosity of the blue supergiants.

CHALLENGE When an old red giant star loses its outer atmosphere, all that remains is the very hot core of the star. Because the core is small, it does not give off much light. What kind of star does the red giant star become after it loses its outer atmosphere? How can you tell from the diagram?

MATH IN SCIENCE
Math Skills Practice for Science

Set Learning Goal

To determine the brightnesses and temperatures of stars by interpreting a scatter plot

Present the Science

The luminosity of a star depends on a combination of its size and temperature. If two stars are the same size, the hotter one is brighter.

Develop Graphing Skills

• Remind students that the key to understanding a scatter plot is to read and understand the labels on the axes. Review these items with students.

• Ask why the axes each have a double-headed arrow. *to indicate a range of values for surface temperature and luminosity*

• Ask why the graph is useful even though there are no values on the axes. Discuss examples. *The ranges indicate relative values, so you can determine, for example, whether a star is hotter than another star without knowing how hot either star is.*

DIFFERENTIATION TIP Provide visual learners with a ruler to place on the scatter plot.

Close

Ask students to use what they have learned from the scatter plot to describe the relationships among temperature, size, and luminosity. *Answer: Blue and white stars are hotter than red. Large stars are brighter than small ones.*

   • Math Support, p. 264
• Math Practice, p. 265

Technology Resources

Students can visit **ClassZone.com** to practice interpreting scatter plots.

   MATH TUTORIAL

ANSWERS

1. Proxima Centauri is a very cool star with low luminosity.

2. The Sun is hotter and less luminous than Betelgeuse.

3. The red dwarfs are much cooler and dimmer than the blue supergiants.

CHALLENGE It becomes a white dwarf. White dwarfs are the only hot stars on the diagram with low luminosity.

○ Set Learning Goals

Students will

- Describe the size and shape of the Milky Way.
- Analyze how galaxies are classified.
- Describe the centers of galaxies.
- Sort images in an experiment to learn about types of galaxies.

○ 3-Minute Warm-Up

Display Transparency 29 or copy this exercise on the board:

Draw a diagram to show the changes in a lower-mass star and a higher-mass star during their life cycles. *Diagrams should show that a lower-mass star becomes a giant, then a white dwarf. A higher-mass star becomes a supergiant, explodes in a supernova, and ends up as a neutron star or a black hole.*

 3-Minute Warm-Up, p. T29

4.3 MOTIVATE

EXPLORE The Milky Way

PURPOSE To demonstrate to students why the Milky Way appears hazy from Earth

TIP *10 min.* Students can use white correction fluid instead of the white gel pen.

WHAT DO YOU THINK? *Results will vary depending on size of dots and students' vision. Sample answer: about 5 m. The Milky Way only appears hazy because most of the stars we see are so far away.*

Ongoing Assessment

CHECK YOUR READING *Answer: Earth is inside the disk of the Milky Way, so we have only an edge-on view of part of the galaxy.*

KEY CONCEPT

4.3 Galaxies have different sizes and shapes.

◄ **BEFORE, you learned**

- Our solar system is part of a galaxy called the Milky Way
- Stars change over their life cycles

► **NOW, you will learn**

- About the size and shape of the Milky Way
- How galaxies are classified
- About the centers of galaxies

VOCABULARY

quasar p. 133

EXPLORE The Milky Way

Why does the Milky Way look hazy?

PROCEDURE

① Use a white gel pen to make 50 small dots close together on a piece of black paper.

② Tape the paper to a wall, and move slowly away from it until you have difficulty seeing the individual dots.

MATERIALS
- white gel pen
- black paper
- tape

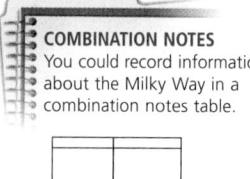

WHAT DO YOU THINK?
- At what distance did the dots become hazy?
- Why might some of the stars in the Milky Way appear hazy from Earth?

COMBINATION NOTES
You could record information about the Milky Way in a combination notes table.

Our solar system lies within the Milky Way galaxy.

The Sun lies within a galaxy called the Milky Way. Remember that a galaxy is a huge grouping of stars, gas, and dust held together by gravity. Without a telescope, you can only see nearby stars clearly. Those stars are a tiny fraction of the several hundred billion in the Milky Way.

The Milky Way is shaped like a disk with a bulge in the center. Because Earth is inside the disk, you have an edge-on view of part of the galaxy. On a dark night, the galaxy appears as a band of blended starlight. The Milky Way got its name from the hazy, or milky, appearance of this band of stars. You cannot see the center of the galaxy because it is hidden by dust.

 **CHECK YOUR READING** Why can't we see all of the Milky Way from Earth?

RESOURCES FOR DIFFERENTIATED INSTRUCTION

Below Level

UNIT RESOURCE BOOK
- Reading Study Guide A, pp. 238–239
- Decoding Support, p. 263

 AUDIO CDS

Advanced

UNIT RESOURCE BOOK
Challenge and Extension, p. 244

English Learners

UNIT RESOURCE BOOK
Spanish Reading Study Guide, pp. 242–243

 **AUDIO CDS**

- Audio Readings in Spanish
- Audio Readings (English)

The Milky Way

When you look at the Milky Way, it appears as a band of hazy light.

Illustration of Side View

disk
Sun's location
bulge

The Milky Way is about 100,000 light-years in diameter.

The disk of the Milky Way measures more than 100,000 light-years in diameter. The bulge of densely packed stars at the center is located about 26,000 light-years from the Sun. A large but very faint layer of stars surrounds the disk and bulge. In addition to stars, the Milky Way contains clouds of gas and dust called nebulae.

The stars and nebulae in the Milky Way orbit the galaxy's center at very high speeds. However, the galaxy is so large that the Sun takes about 250 million years to complete one orbit.

INVESTIGATE Galaxy Shapes

How can you classify galaxies according to shape?

PROCEDURE

① Cut out the photographs of galaxies on the Galaxy Photo Sheet.

② Sort the galaxies into different groups according to their shapes. You may need a group for galaxies that do not fit in other groups.

WHAT DO YOU THINK?

• How many groups did you sort the galaxies into?

• Describe each group briefly, and list which galaxies you put in each group.

CHALLENGE What is the connection between the apparent shape of a galaxy and the galaxy's relationship to the viewer? **Hint:** Think about how an edge-on view of a compact disc differs from a view of it lying flat on a table.

SKILL FOCUS
Classifying

MATERIALS
• Galaxy Photo Sheet
• scissors

TIME
15 minutes

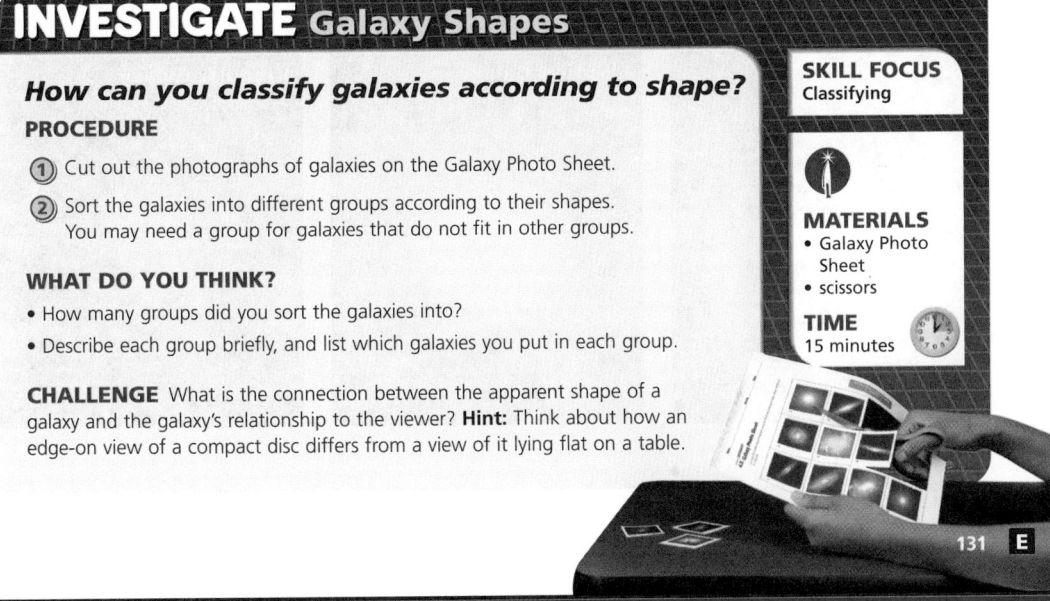

131 **E**

DIFFERENTIATE INSTRUCTION

English Learners Point out the phrases "seem to" and "seeming like a star" on p. 133. Have English learners read aloud the sentences in which these phrases appear. Tell students that in this context, words such as *seem* and *apparent* indicate the way objects may appear to us. The actual positioning and interaction of these objects may, in fact, be different than what we perceive from our point of view on Earth.

Alternative Assessment Have students explain orally the characteristics of the galaxies in each of the groups they made.

Teach from Visuals

To help students interpret the visuals showing the Milky Way, ask:

• Where is Earth located in the Milky Way galaxy? *the same place where the Sun is located—on the disk about halfway between the edge and the central bulge*

• Why does the Milky Way not cover the entire night sky with densely packed stars? *because our point of view shows only an edge-on view of the Milky Way*

INVESTIGATE Galaxy Shapes

PURPOSE To demonstrate that galaxies are classified according to their shape

TIPS *15 min.* Tell students that not all galaxies need be the exact same shape in order to be classified within a general shape category.

WHAT DO YOU THINK? *Accept reasonable responses. Students will likely have three or four groups. Students should provide accurate descriptions.*

CHALLENGE *Students may respond that any galaxy that isn't a sphere will look different when it is viewed from different angles.*

R • Galaxy Photo Sheet, p. 245
• Datasheet, Galaxy Shapes, p. 246

Technology Resources

Customize this student lab as needed or look for an alternative. Print rubrics to assess student lab reports.

Lab Generator CD-ROM

Ongoing Assessment

Describe the size and shape of the Milky Way.

Ask: What is the size and shape of the Milky Way? *100,000 light-years in diameter; shaped like a disk with a bulge in the center*

Teach Difficult Concepts

Students may have difficulty understanding that the Milky Way and similar galaxies are both disk-shaped and spiral-shaped. There are stars throughout the disk. However, the spiral arms within the disk are denser and brighter than the regions between the spiral arms.

EXPLORE (the BIG idea)

Revisit the Internet activity "Galaxy Shapes" on p. 113. Have students compare the results of their Internet research with what they read in the text.

Teach from Visuals

To help students interpret the photographs of galaxies, ask:

• What objects do spiral galaxies look like? *pinwheels, hurricanes*

• What do you think the two bright spots in the lower right of the elliptical-galaxy photo are? *probably other galaxies*

• Which of these three categories probably has the greatest variation? *irregular*

Ongoing Assessment

Analyze how galaxies are classified.

Ask: What is the main feature used to classify galaxies? *shape*

 *Answer: size and shape*

 **RESOURCE CENTER**
CLASSZONE.COM
Learn more about galaxies.

 **VOCABULARY**
Make a description wheel for each type of galaxy in your notebook.

Galaxies vary in appearance.

Galaxies differ greatly in size. Some contain as few as a hundred million stars, but the biggest have more than a trillion stars. Galaxies also vary in shape. Astronomers have classified galaxies into three main types based on their shape.

CHECK YOUR READING What are two ways in which galaxies can differ from one another?

Types of Galaxies

The three main types of galaxies are spiral, elliptical, and irregular. Most galaxies are either spiral or elliptical.

Spiral galaxies have arms of stars, gas, and dust that curve away from the center of the galaxy in a spiral pattern. The Milky Way is a spiral galaxy. Like the Milky Way, other spiral galaxies are disk-shaped and have a central bulge. Most of the stars in the disk and the bulge are old stars. However, the dense spiral arms within the disk contain many young, bright stars.

Elliptical galaxies are shaped like spheres or eggs. Unlike spiral galaxies, elliptical galaxies have almost no dust or gas between stars, and all of their stars are old.

Irregular galaxies are faint galaxies without a definite shape. They are smaller than the other types of galaxies and have many fewer stars.

Galaxies sometimes collide with other galaxies. These collisions can cause changes in their shapes. The Extreme Science feature on page 134 describes such collisions.

 **Spiral Galaxy**

 **Elliptical Galaxy**

 **Irregular Galaxy**

DIFFERENTIATE INSTRUCTION

? More Reading Support

B What type of galaxy is the Milky Way? *spiral*

C What type of galaxy has no definite shape? *irregular*

Below Level On the board, write headings for each of the three types of galaxies. Have students identify characteristics of each and write them under the correct heading.

Inclusion Help students comprehend and appreciate the difference between the number of stars in a small galaxy (a hundred million) and the number of stars in a large galaxy (a trillion). Write out both of these numbers on the board and point out that a trillion is 10,000 times a hundred million.

Centers of Galaxies

Most large galaxies seem to have supermassive black holes at their centers. The mass of a supermassive black hole can be millions or even billions of times greater than that of the Sun. At the center of the Milky Way, for example, is a black hole with a mass about three million times that of the Sun.

Like all black holes, a supermassive black hole is invisible. Astronomers can identify the presence of a black hole by the behavior of matter around it. The gravity of a supermassive black hole is so strong that it draws in a huge whirlpool of gas from nearby stars. As gases are pulled toward the black hole, they become compressed and extremely hot, so they give off very bright light. The motions of stars orbiting the black hole can also reveal its presence.

If the center of a galaxy is very bright, it may look like a star from a great distance. The very bright centers of some distant galaxies are called **quasars.** *Quasar* is a shortened form of *quasi-stellar,* which means "seeming like a star." The galaxy surrounding a quasar is often hard to see because the quasar is so much brighter than it.

Evidence of a Supermassive Black Hole

disk of gas swirling around the black hole

gas being drawn into the black hole

 **CHECK YOUR READING** How can astronomers detect the presence of a supermassive black hole at the center of a galaxy?

 **Review**

KEY CONCEPTS
1. What is the shape of the Milky Way?
2. Why does the Milky Way look like a hazy band of stars in the sky?
3. What keeps the stars in galaxies from moving apart?

CRITICAL THINKING
4. **Compare and Contrast** Make a diagram showing similarities and differences among the three main types of galaxies.
5. **Infer** How might our view of the Milky Way be different if the Sun were located inside the central bulge?

⬤ CHALLENGE
6. **Predict** If two spiral galaxies collide, what might eventually happen to the supermassive black holes at their centers?

Chapter 4: **Stars, Galaxies, and the Universe 133** **E**

ANSWERS

1. The Milky Way is a disk-shaped spiral galaxy with a bulge in the center.

2. The band results from our edge-on view of the Milky Way. Most of the stars that we see in the Milky Way are too distant to see clearly.

3. Gravity holds the stars together.

4. Students might make a Venn diagram with three overlapping circles. Students should include important characteristics such as general shape and what each type of galaxy contains.

5. The night sky would be brighter because it would contain many more visible stars, and the density of stars in the sky would be much greater.

6. The black holes might merge and become even larger.

Ongoing Assessment
Describe the centers of galaxies.

Ask: What is at the centers of most large galaxies? *a supermassive black hole that is invisible*

CHECK YOUR READING *Answer: Astronomers can detect a black hole by the behavior of matter around it.*

Metacognitive Strategy

Invite students to formulate questions about the centers of galaxies, then exchange their questions with a partner and try to answer the partner's questions. Students should support their answers by citing relevant information in the text.

Reinforce (the **BIG** idea)

Have students relate the section to the Big Idea.

R Reinforcing Key Concepts, p. 247

4.3 ASSESS & RETEACH

Assess
A Section 4.3 Quiz, p. 64

Reteach

Write the following pairs of terms on the board: *shape, Milky Way; elliptical, galaxy; spiral, irregular; center of galaxy, quasar; bulge, disk.* Instruct students to use each pair of terms in a sentence to show how they are related.

Technology Resources

Have students visit **ClassZone.com** for reteaching of Key Concepts.

 CONTENT REVIEW

 CONTENT REVIEW CD-ROM

Chapter 4 **133** **E**

Purpose

To understand how galaxies are affected by collisions

Present the Science

When galaxies collide, the individual stars that make them up rarely run into one another. Each star is tiny in comparison with the distances between stars. For example, the distance between the Sun and the next closest star is 4.3 light-years—more than 40 trillion kilometers.

Discussion Questions

To help students understand the material, ask the following questions:

- Why is the Milky Way not affected by the galaxies that move through it? *The other galaxies are smaller, and the stars rarely bump into each other.*

- What can happen when two galaxies collide? *The stars of the smaller one may become part of the larger one, or the galaxies may change in shape.*

- What can happen when two galaxies have a near miss? *The galaxies may change shape due to the effects of gravity.*

- How do computers help astronomers understand what happens when galaxies collide? *Astronomers make computer simulations to predict how stars and gas in galaxies are affected by a collision.*

Close

Invite students to summarize what they have learned about galaxies colliding. *Sample response: When galaxies collide, the stars rarely bump into each other. The stars of the smaller galaxy may become part of the larger galaxy, and the galaxies may change shape.*

Technology Resources

Students can visit **ClassZone.com** to find out more about galaxy collisions.

 RESOURCE CENTER

EXTREME SCIENCE

ASTRONOMY AND THE UNIVERSE

When Galaxies Collide

A small galaxy is moving through our galaxy, the Milky Way, right now!

- The small galaxy may be destroyed by the collision, but the Milky Way is not in danger.
- The same galaxy seems to have moved through the Milky Way ten times before.
- Other galaxies may also be moving through the Milky Way.

Not to Worry!

Galaxies containing many billions of stars are colliding all the time. What are the chances that their stars will crash into one another? The chances are very small, because there is so much empty space between stars.

Galactic Cannibals

When galaxies collide, a larger galaxy can "eat up" a smaller one.

- The stars of the smaller galaxy become part of the larger one.
- The collision of two spiral galaxies may form a new elliptical galaxy.

Bent Out of Shape

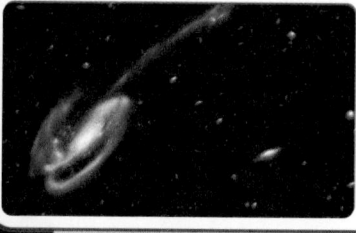

Sometimes galaxies pass very close to each other without actually colliding. In these near misses, gravity can produce some interesting new shapes. For example, the Tadpole Galaxy (left) has a long tail of dust and gas pulled out by the gravity of a passing galaxy.

Model Galaxies

Astronomers use computer simulations to predict how the stars and gas in galaxies are affected by a collision. To understand galaxy collisions better, they then compare the simulations with images of actual galaxies.

EXPLORE

1. **PREDICT** Draw the shape of the new galaxy that the two in the photograph on the left might form.

2. **CHALLENGE** Look at online images and simulations of galaxy collisions. Make a chart showing how these collisions can differ.

 **RESOURCE CENTER**
CLASSZONE.COM
Find out more about galaxy collisions.

Come back in a few billion years and you may see that these two spiral galaxies have become one elliptical galaxy.

E 134 Unit: Space Science

EXPLORE

1. **PREDICT** *Drawings should show an elliptical galaxy.*

2. **CHALLENGE** *Differences might include a galaxy's retaining its shape but increasing in size, and two galaxies forming a new shape.*

KEY CONCEPT

4.4 The universe is expanding.

◀ **BEFORE, you learned**
- Galaxies contain millions or billions of stars
- Electromagnetic radiation carries information about space

▶ **NOW, you will learn**
- How galaxies are moving apart in the universe
- What scientists are discovering about the development of the universe

VOCABULARY
Doppler effect p. 136
big bang p. 138

EXPLORE Large Numbers

How much is a billion?

PROCEDURE

1. Guess how thick a billion-page book would be. Write down your guess.

2. Count how many sheets of paper in a book add up to a millimeter in thickness. Multiply by 2 to calculate the number of pages.

3. Then divide 1 billion (1,000,000,000) by that number to determine how many millimeters thick the book would be. Divide your result by 1,000,000 to convert to kilometers.

WHAT DO YOU THINK?
- How thick would a billion-page book be?
- How close was your guess?

MATERIALS
- book
- ruler
- calculator

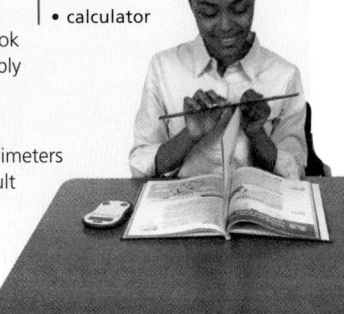

Galaxies are moving farther apart in the universe.

COMBINATION NOTES
You could record information about the expansion of the universe in a combination notes table.

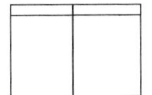

The universe is unbelievably huge. It consists of all space, energy, and matter. The Milky Way is just one of about 100 billion galaxies. These galaxies occur in groups that together form superclusters. Between the superclusters are huge areas of nearly empty space.

Because the universe is so huge, you might think that the most distant regions of the universe are very different from space near Earth. However, by looking at the spectra of light from stars and galaxies, astronomers have determined that the same elements are found throughout the universe. Scientific observations also indicate that the same physical forces and processes operate everywhere.

Chapter 4: Stars, Galaxies, and the Universe **135** **E**

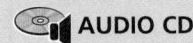

History of Science

Edwin Hubble (1889–1953) was the first scientist to provide evidence that the universe is expanding. He published his findings in 1929, basing them on analysis of the Doppler effect in light from distant galaxies. Hubble had earlier gained renown for proving that the Milky Way was only one of many galaxies in the universe. Hubble also devised a system for classifying galaxies that is still used today.

Teacher Demo

You may need to do this demonstration outside. Attach a device that makes a continuous noise to the end of a rope about 1 meter long. Standing away from the students, swing the rope around in a circle. Ask: What do you hear? *As the noisemaker approaches, the pitch rises. As it moves away, the pitch lowers.* Ask: How does this show the Doppler effect? *The pitch changes depending on whether the source is moving toward or away from you, shortening or lengthening the sound waves.*

Ongoing Assessment

Explain how galaxies are moving apart in the universe.

How does the Doppler effect indicate that the universe is expanding? *When the source of a wave moves, the wavelength or frequency of waves changes in relation to an observer. Since astronomers have observed that light from distant galaxies is stretching into longer wavelengths, they can conclude that those galaxies are moving apart.*

CHECK YOUR
READING *Answer: Because light takes time to travel to our eyes, the light we see now from distant objects left those objects long ago.*

Looking Back in Time

Light from the Andromeda Galaxy takes 2 million years to reach Earth.

When we look far out into space, we see galaxies by the light they gave off long ago. This light has traveled millions or even billions of years before reaching telescopes on Earth. The Andromeda Galaxy, for example, is the closest large galaxy. The light of its stars takes over 2 million years to reach Earth. When we view this galaxy through a telescope, we are seeing what happened in it 2 million years ago. To see what is happening there now, we would have to wait 2 million years for the light to arrive.

As astronomers look at galaxies farther and farther away, they see how the universe looked at different times in the past. These views are like photographs in an album that show someone at various stages of life. Astronomers can see how the universe has developed over billions of years.

 CHECK YOUR READING Why can astronomers learn about the past by looking at distant galaxies?

The Motion of Galaxies

Have you ever noticed that the sound of an ambulance siren changes as it travels toward and then away from you? The pitch of the siren seems to be higher as the ambulance approaches. As the ambulance passes you and starts moving away, the pitch of the siren seems to get lower. The shifting pitch of the siren is an example of the **Doppler effect,** which is a change in the observed wavelength or frequency of a wave that occurs when the source of the wave or the observer is moving.

The Doppler effect occurs with light as well as sound. If a galaxy is moving toward Earth, the light we receive will seem compressed to shorter wavelengths. This change is called a blue shift because the light shifts toward the blue end of the spectrum. If a galaxy is moving away from Earth, the light we receive will seem stretched to longer wavelengths. This change is called a red shift because the light shifts toward the red end of the spectrum.

In the early 1900s, astronomers discovered that light from distant galaxies is stretched to longer wavelengths. This fact indicates that the galaxies are moving apart. By analyzing the spectra of galaxies, astronomers also discovered that the galaxies are moving apart faster the farther away they are. These observations led astronomers to conclude that the universe has been expanding throughout its history.

DIFFERENTIATE INSTRUCTION

 More Reading Support

A When does the Doppler effect occur? *when source of a wave or observer is moving*

B In what way are galaxies moving? *They are moving apart.*

English Learners Have English learners who speak the same native language discuss the Doppler effect together in their native language. Then have them write out a description of the Doppler effect in English. They may also make an informative poster and present it to the class.

Tell students that "besides," on p. 139, does not literally mean "next to," but rather means "in addition to."

Evidence of an Expanding Universe

The Doppler effect can show how galaxies are moving in relation to Earth.

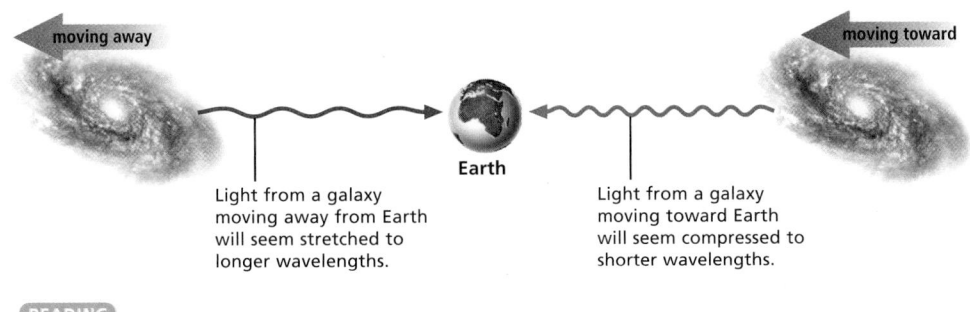

moving away

moving toward

Earth

Light from a galaxy moving away from Earth will seem stretched to longer wavelengths.

Light from a galaxy moving toward Earth will seem compressed to shorter wavelengths.

READING VISUALS What do the arrows on the light waves indicate?

The illustration of raisin-bread dough rising will help you imagine this expansion. Suppose you were a raisin. You would observe that all the other raisins are moving away from you as the dough expands. The raisins are being moved apart by the expanding dough. Furthermore, you would observe that distant raisins are moving away faster than nearby raisins. They move away faster because there is more dough expanding between you and those raisins.

As the dough rises, the raisins are pushed farther apart from each other. The more distance there is between raisins, the faster and farther they move apart.

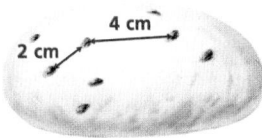

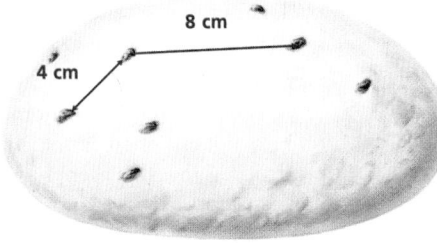

4 cm

2 cm

8 cm

4 cm

before dough rises

after dough rises

Like the dough that expands and moves raisins apart, space in the universe is expanding and moving galaxies apart. The universe does not expand into anything, since there is nothing outside the universe. Rather, the universe itself is expanding.

CHECK YOUR READING How are galaxies moving in relation to each other?

DIFFERENTIATE INSTRUCTION

 More Reading Support

C What does the rising-dough model represent? *the expanding universe*

Inclusion Have tactile learners and slower learners imagine that they are the raisins in the dough, or the galaxies in the universe. Have them stand close together and then slowly move apart. Point out that this is what is happening to the galaxies.

Teach from Visuals

To help students interpret the diagram of the Doppler effect, ask:

- What do the wavy arrows represent? *light from galaxies reaching Earth*
- How are the two wavy arrows different? *different colors, different wavelengths, moving from different directions*
- Which arrow shows a blue shift? *the blue arrow*
- Why is it called a blue shift? *because light from a galaxy moving toward Earth is shifted toward the blue end of the spectrum*

To help students interpret the diagram of expanding dough, ask:

- How far apart have the two raisins on the left moved after the dough has risen? *2 cm*
- How far apart have the two raisins at the top moved after the dough has risen? *4 cm*
- Why have the raisins on top moved farther than those on the left? *There is more dough between the raisins on top.*

Teach Difficult Concepts

Students may have difficulty understanding the concept that the expanding universe does not expand into anything because it includes all of space. Reassure them that imagining the nature of the universe is hard for everyone. Astronomers do not fully understand the geometry of the universe, so it is almost impossible to form a picture of it in one's mind.

EXPLORE (the **BIG** idea)

Revisit "How Do Galaxies Move Apart?" on p. 113. Have students compare their model with what they now know about the universe.

Ongoing Assessment

 *Answer: They indicate the direction in which the light waves are traveling.*

 *Answer: Galaxies are moving apart from one another.*

INVESTIGATE Galaxies

PURPOSE To model for students the expansion of the universe

TIPS *20 min.*

- Make sure that students subtract the original position of each mark from its current position to determine how far it has moved.

- Review with students how to estimate measurements that are between two lines on the ruler.

WHAT DO YOU THINK? *Results will vary depending on thickness of the rubber band. Sample data: 0 cm, 1 cm, 1.8 cm, 2.8 cm, 3.8 cm, 4.8 cm. The rate at which galaxies are moving away from our galaxy increases with distance.*

CHALLENGE *Divide the distance each mark moved by the time it took to stretch the rubber band. Sample: Mark 2 moved 1 mark per second.*

 Datasheet, Galaxies, p. 257

Technology Resources

Customize this student lab as needed or look for an alternative. Print rubrics to assess student lab reports.

 Lab Generator CD-ROM

Integrate the Sciences

Particle physics is the study of subatomic particles. To learn what the universe was like immediately after the big bang, scientists are studying how such particles behave at extremely high energy levels. Many physicists believe that in the earliest stage of the universe, particles had such high energy that there was only one unified force. As the universe expanded and cooled, this force separated into the four fundamental physical forces: gravity, electromagnetism, the strong force, and the weak force.

INVESTIGATE Galaxies

How does the universe expand?

PROCEDURE

1. Spread the cut rubber band against the ruler without stretching it. Mark off every centimeter for 6 centimeters.

2. Align the first mark on the rubber band with the 1-centimeter mark on the ruler and hold it in place tightly. Stretch the rubber band so that the second mark is next to the 3-centimeter mark on the ruler.

3. Observe how many centimeters each mark has moved from its original location against the ruler.

WHAT DO YOU THINK?

- How far did each mark on the rubber band move from its original location?

- What does this activity demonstrate about the expansion of the universe?

CHALLENGE How could you calculate the rates at which the marks moved when you stretched the rubber band?

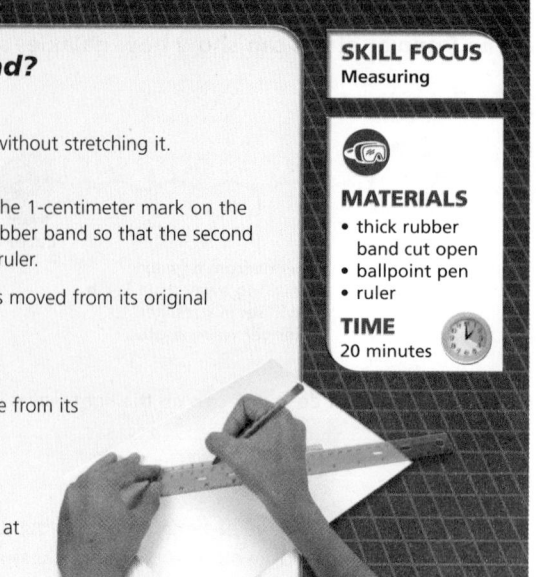

SKILL FOCUS
Measuring

MATERIALS
- thick rubber band cut open
- ballpoint pen
- ruler

TIME
20 minutes

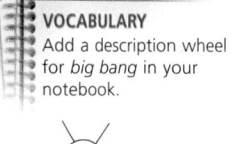

VOCABULARY
Add a description wheel for *big bang* in your notebook.

D

Scientists are investigating the origin of the universe.

After astronomers learned that galaxies are moving apart, they developed new ideas about the origin of the universe. They concluded that all matter was once merged together and then the universe suddenly began to expand. The evidence for this scientific theory is so strong that almost all astronomers now accept it.

The **big bang** is the moment in time when the universe started to expand out of an extremely hot, dense state. Astronomers have calculated that this event happened about 14 billion years ago. The expansion was very rapid. In a tiny fraction of a second, the universe may have expanded from a size much smaller than a speck of dust to the size of our solar system.

Evidence of the Big Bang

Evidence for the big bang comes from various sources. One important source of evidence is microwave radiation. Astronomers predicted in 1948 that the universe would still be filled with microwaves emitted shortly after the big bang. In 1965 researchers detected this kind of radiation streaming through space in all directions.

DIFFERENTIATE INSTRUCTION

 More Reading Support

D What is the big bang? *the moment in time when the universe began expanding*

Advanced Emphasize that the big bang theory, like all theories, is based on evidence. A theory explains observations and can be used to predict other observations and events. Ask: How would the big bang theory be affected if evidence showed that galaxies are not moving apart? *The theory would have to be revised or completely rejected.*

 Challenge and Extension, p. 256

Besides the presence of microwave radiation and the motions of galaxies, scientists have found other evidence of the big bang by observing space. For example, images of very distant galaxies provide information about the universe's development. Additional evidence of the big bang has come from experiments and computer models.

Development of the Universe

Immediately after the big bang, the universe was incredibly dense and hot—much hotter than the core of the Sun. Matter and energy behaved very differently than they do under present conditions. As the universe rapidly expanded, it went through a series of changes.

Scientists do not fully understand what conditions were like in the early universe. However, they are gaining a clearer picture of how the universe developed. One way that scientists are learning about this development is by performing experiments in particle accelerators. These huge machines expose matter to extreme conditions.

Scientists have found that the earliest stages in the universe's development occurred in a tiny fraction of a second. However, it took about 300,000 years for the first elements to form. Stars, planets, and galaxies began to appear within the next billion years. Some evidence suggests that the first stars formed only a few hundred million years after the big bang.

This Hubble telescope image of very distant galaxies has helped scientists learn what the universe was like about 13 billion years ago.

 **CHECK YOUR READING** What happened to the universe shortly after the big bang?

4.4 Review

KEY CONCEPTS

1. How are distant regions of the universe similar to space near Earth?

2. What does the Doppler effect indicate about the motion of galaxies?

3. How do scientists explain the origin of the universe?

CRITICAL THINKING

4. **Apply** If a star 100 light-years from Earth is beginning to expand into a giant star, how long will it take for astronomers to observe this development? Explain.

5. **Analyze** Why do scientists need to perform experiments to learn about the earliest stages of the universe?

● CHALLENGE

6. **Infer** Galaxy A and galaxy B both give off light that appears stretched to longer wavelengths. The light from galaxy B is stretched to even longer wavelengths than the light from galaxy A. What can you infer from these data?

Chapter 4: **Stars, Galaxies, and the Universe** 139 E

ANSWERS

1. They have the same elements, and the same physical forces and processes operate everywhere.

2. that the galaxies are moving apart and that they are moving faster the farther away they are

3. The universe expanded suddenly from a state in which all matter was merged together.

4. Since a light-year is the distance light travels in one year, it will take 100 years for astronomers to observe the change.

5. The earliest stages occurred too quickly for astronomers to observe even in the most distant galaxies, so the conditions of those stages must be re-created in experiments.

6. Galaxy B is moving away faster than galaxy A.

Ongoing Assessment

Understand what scientists are discovering about the development of the universe.

Ask: What do scientists think the universe was like in its earliest stage? *It was extremely hot and dense; matter and energy behaved differently than they do now.*

CHECK YOUR READING *Answer: The universe rapidly expanded and went through a series of changes.*

Reinforce (the **BIG** idea)

Have students relate the section to the Big Idea.

R Reinforcing Key Concepts, p. 258

4.4 ASSESS & RETEACH

Assess

A Section 4.4 Quiz, p. 65

Reteach

Provide students with the following information: NGC 5055 is a galaxy that is about 36 million light-years away. It is moving away at 550 km/sec. NGC 4486 is about 72 million light-years away. It is moving away at 1136 km/sec.

- Ask: Which galaxy is moving away faster? *The one that is farther away—NGC 4486.*

- Ask: What do these data provide evidence of? *the expansion of the universe*

Technology Resources

Have students visit **ClassZone.com** for reteaching of Key Concepts.

CONTENT REVIEW

CONTENT REVIEW CD-ROM

Chapter 4 **139** **E**

BACK TO

the BIG idea

Have students look back at the photograph on pp. 112–113. Ask them to use it to summarize what they have learned about the universe. *The photograph shows a spiral galaxy that contains millions or billions of stars. There are billions of other galaxies that are moving apart from one another as the universe expands.*

◑ KEY CONCEPTS SUMMARY

SECTION 4.1

Ask: What is the source of energy in the Sun? *fusion of hydrogen into helium in the core*

SECTION 4.2

Have students describe what happens during each stage in the life cycle of a lower-mass star. *main sequence: hydrogen fuses into helium; giant star: star expands; white dwarf: giant star sheds outer layers, leaving a dead core*

Have students describe what happens during each stage in the life cycle of a higher-mass star. *main sequence: hydrogen fuses into helium; supergiant: star expands; supernova: star explodes; neutron star or black hole: small, extremely dense bodies left behind after supernovas*

SECTION 4.3

Have students describe the three types of galaxies. *spiral: disk-shaped with central bulge; elliptical: spherical or egg-shaped; irregular: no definite shape*

SECTION 4.4

Ask: What is happening to the galaxies in the universe? *They are moving farther apart.*

Ask: What are scientists learning about the universe? *how it originated and developed*

Review Concepts

- Big Idea Flow Chart, p. T25
- Chapter Outline, pp. T31–T32

 # Chapter Review

the BIG idea

Our Sun is one of billions of stars in one of billions of galaxies in the universe.

 **CONTENT REVIEW** CLASSZONE.COM

◑ KEY CONCEPTS SUMMARY

4.1 The Sun is our local star.

The Sun produces energy from hydrogen. Energy flows through the Sun's layers. Features appear on the Sun's surface.

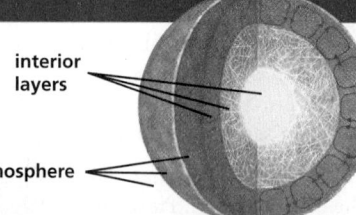
interior layers

atmosphere

VOCABULARY
fusion p. 116
convection p. 116
corona p. 116
sunspot p. 118
solar wind p. 119

4.2 Stars change over their life cycles.

Stars vary in brightness, size, color, and temperature. The development of a star depends on the mass of the star. Most stars are grouped with one or more companion stars.

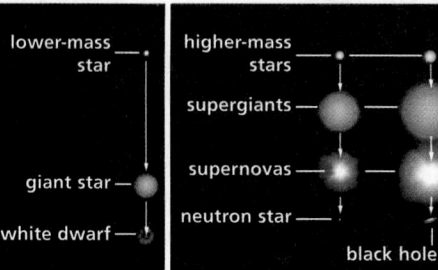
lower-mass star
higher-mass stars
supergiants
giant star
supernovas
white dwarf
neutron star
black hole

VOCABULARY
light-year p. 122
parallax p. 123
nebula p. 125
main sequence p. 126
neutron star p. 126
black hole p. 126

4.3 Galaxies have different sizes and shapes.

Our galaxy, the Milky Way, is a spiral galaxy. Galaxies can also be elliptical or irregular. Irregular galaxies have no definite shape.

  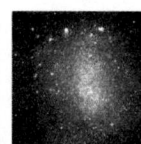
Spiral Galaxy   Elliptical Galaxy   Irregular Galaxy

VOCABULARY
quasar p. 133

4.4 The universe is expanding.

Galaxies are moving farther apart in the universe. Scientists are investigating the origin and development of the universe.

VOCABULARY
Doppler effect p. 136
big bang p. 138

Technology Resources

Have students visit **ClassZone.com** or use the CD-ROM for a cumulative review of concepts.

Engage students in a whole-class interactive review of Key Concepts. Edit content as you wish.

 CONTENT REVIEW

 CONTENT REVIEW CD-ROM

 POWER PRESENTATIONS

Reviewing Vocabulary

Make a frame for each of the vocabulary words listed below. Write the word in the center. Decide what information to frame it with. Use definitions, examples, descriptions, parts, or pictures. An example is shown below.

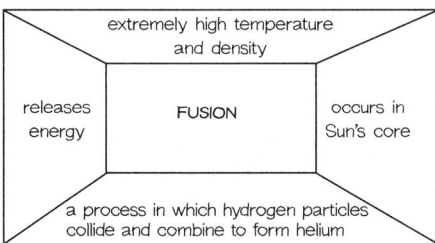

extremely high temperature and density

releases energy

FUSION

occurs in Sun's core

a process in which hydrogen particles collide and combine to form helium

1. convection
2. corona
3. sunspot
4. solar wind
5. nebula
6. black hole
7. Doppler effect
8. big bang

Reviewing Key Concepts

Multiple Choice *Choose the letter of the best answer.*

9. Which layer do you usually see in photographs of the Sun?
   a. convection zone
   b. photosphere
   c. chromosphere
   d. corona

10. Which statement is true of sunspots?
    a. They are permanent features on the Sun's surface.
    b. They are caused by solar wind.
    c. They are where fusion occurs.
    d. They are cooler than surrounding areas.

11. Which unit is usually used to describe the distances of stars?
    a. astronomical units
    b. light-years
    c. kilometers
    d. miles

12. Which example best shows the relationship between color and temperature?
    a. A rainbow forms when sunlight strikes raindrops.
    b. A flashlight beam looks red when passed through a red plastic filter.
    c. A chemical light-stick glows a yellow-green color.
    d. A metal rod in a fireplace changes in color from red to orange.

13. How do lower-mass stars differ from higher-mass stars?
    a. They develop more quickly.
    b. They develop more slowly.
    c. They end up as black holes.
    d. They have too little mass to produce energy.

14. Which term describes the Milky Way?
    a. spiral galaxy
    b. elliptical galaxy
    c. irregular galaxy
    d. quasar

15. The Doppler effect is used to determine
    a. the number of stars in a galaxy
    b. the number of galaxies in the universe
    c. the size of the universe
    d. whether a galaxy is moving toward or away from Earth

16. What is the big bang?
    a. the collision of galaxies
    b. the formation of the solar system
    c. the beginning of the universe's expansion
    d. the time when stars began to form

Short Answer *Write a short answer to each question.*

17. Why can't we see the Sun's corona under normal conditions?

18. How do astronomers use parallax to calculate a star's distance?

19. Where do heavy elements, such as iron, come from?

20. How can astronomers tell whether a black hole exists in the center of a galaxy?

ASSESSMENT RESOURCES

UNIT ASSESSMENT BOOK
- Chapter Test A, pp. 66–69
- Chapter Test B, 70–73
- Chapter Test C, pp. 74–77
- Alternative Assessment, pp. 78–79
- Unit Test, pp. 80–91

SPANISH ASSESSMENT BOOK
- Spanish Chapter Test, pp. 205–208
- Spanish Unit Test, pp. 209–212

Technology Resources

Edit test items and answer choices.

 Test Generator CD-ROM

Visit **ClassZone.com** to extend test practice.

 Test Practice

Reviewing Vocabulary

1. transfer of energy by the motion of heated gas or liquid; occurs in Sun's convection zone; rising and falling currents of gas; carries energy to photosphere

2. Sun's outermost layer; very low density; much hotter than photosphere; only seen during solar eclipse

3. spot on photosphere; cooler than surrounding areas; appears dim in contrast to brighter surroundings; moves across Sun as it rotates

4. stream of electrically charged particles; extends from Sun's corona throughout the solar system; can cause magnetic storms on Earth; produces auroras

5. cloud of gas and dust; stars form in regions that contract; gains matter from dead stars; part of a galaxy

6. invisible object left behind after supernova; extremely dense; no radiation can escape; most galaxies have a supermassive black hole in the center

7. change in the observed wavelength of a wave due to movement; indicates the movement of galaxies; light stretched to longer wavelengths if object is moving away; light compressed to shorter wavelengths if object is moving toward us

8. moment when universe started to expand; all matter originally merged together; happened about 14 billion years ago; theory supported by many types of evidence

Reviewing Key Concepts

9. b   10. d   11. b   12. d

13. b   14. a   15. d   16. c

17. The much brighter light of the photosphere blocks it out.

18. They calculate the distance using the apparent shift in the star's position when plotted from opposite sides of Earth's orbit.

19. They come from the fusion of elements in the cores of stars after the stars leave the main sequence.

20. They can observe how the gravity of the black hole affects matter pulled into it.

Thinking Critically

21. The speed and distance of NGC 2903 are about double those of NGC 7793.

22. A galaxy's speed is roughly proportional to its distance.

23. about 940 km/sec.

24. The solar wind would be dispersed more by the time it reaches the outer planets.

25. The star will soon leave the main sequence and begin fusing helium.

26. The planets are much closer to us.

27. The star could be part of a binary star system in which one of the stars orbits in front of the other every three days.

28. Both types spend most of their lives in the main sequence, expand, and then die. Higher-mass stars develop more quickly and leave behind neutron stars or black holes instead of white dwarfs.

29. An x-ray telescope would be much more useful because neutron stars give off large amounts of x-rays but little visible light.

30. Higher-mass stars in the galaxy produced the heavy elements after becoming supergiants.

31. Scientists inferred from this motion that matter must have originally existed in a hot, dense state.

32. As the universe expands, it will become colder and less dense.

33. Both types of galaxies have spherical regions of densely packed stars. Spiral galaxies have a disk-shaped region extending outward.

the BIG idea

34. Sample answer: stars, gas, dust

35. Answers might refer to obtaining information from a local university, observatory, or planetarium.

Thinking Critically

The table below shows the distances of some galaxies and the speeds at which they are moving away from the Milky Way. Use the table to answer the next three questions.

Galaxy	Distance (million light-years)	Speed (kilometers per second)
NGC 7793	14	241
NGC 6946	22	336
NGC 2903	31	472
NGC 6744	42	663

21. **COMPARE AND CONTRAST** How do the speed and distance of NGC 7793 compare with the speed and distance of NGC 2903?

22. **ANALYZE** What general pattern do you see in this data?

23. **APPLY** What would you estimate to be the speed of a galaxy located 60 million light-years away? **Hint:** Notice the pattern between the first and third rows and the second and fourth rows in the chart.

24. **INFER** Why might the solar wind have a stronger effect on inner planets than on outer planets in the solar system?

25. **PREDICT** The core of a particular star consists almost entirely of helium. What will soon happen to this star?

26. **ANALYZE** Planets shine by reflected light. Why do some planets in our solar system appear brighter than stars, even though the stars give off their own light?

27. **IDENTIFY CAUSE** A star dims for a brief period every three days. What could be causing it to dim?

28. **COMPARE AND CONTRAST** Describe the similarities and differences between the life cycles of lower-mass stars and higher-mass stars.

29. **EVALUATE** If you wanted to study a neutron star, would you use a visible-light telescope or an x-ray telescope? Explain why.

30. **INFER** Suppose that astronomers find evidence of iron and other heavy elements in a galaxy. On the basis of this evidence, what can you assume has already occurred in that galaxy?

31. **ANALYZE** Why did the discovery that galaxies are moving farther apart help scientists conclude that all matter was once merged together?

32. **PREDICT** What changes do you predict will happen in the universe over the next 10 billion years?

33. **COMPARE AND CONTRAST** The photographs above show a spiral galaxy and an elliptical galaxy. What similarities and differences do you see in these two types of galaxies?

the BIG idea

34. **INFER** Look again at the photograph on pages 112–113. Now that you have finished the chapter, how would you change your response to the question on the photograph? What else might be present?

35. **SYNTHESIZE** Think of a question that you still have about the universe. What information would you need to answer the question? How might you obtain this information?

UNIT PROJECTS

Evaluate all the data, results, and information in your project folder. Prepare to present your project.

Standardized Test Practice

For practice on your state test, go to . . .
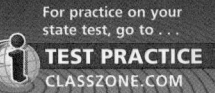 **TEST PRACTICE** CLASSZONE.COM

Analyzing a Chart

Use the chart and diagram to answer the next six questions.

Classification of Stars

Class	Color	Surface Temperature (°C)
O	blue-white	above 25,000
B	blue-white	10,000–25,000
A	white	7500–10,000
F	yellow-white	6000–7500
G	yellow	5000–6000
K	orange	3500–5000
M	red	below 3500

Hertzsprung-Russell (H-R) Diagram

highest — ①   ③

Luminosity   ②

lowest — ④

Surface temperature (°C): 40,000 20,000 10,000 5000 2500

1. Which class of star has the lowest surface temperature?

a. O   **c.** G

b. B   **d.** M

2. Which class of star has the highest surface temperature?

a. O   **c.** G

b. B   **d.** M

3. What would be the color of a star with a surface temperature of 8000°C?

a. blue-white   **c.** orange

b. white   **d.** red

4. Toward the end of their life cycles, very massive stars expand in size, and their surface temperature becomes lower. Which of the following is an example of this change?

a. A white star becomes a blue-white star.

b. A blue-white star becomes a red star.

c. A red star becomes a blue-white star.

d. A yellow star becomes a yellow-white star.

5. The H-R diagram above shows the surface temperatures and luminosities, or true brightnesses, of four stars. Which of the stars is a type O?

a. 1   **c.** 3

b. 2   **d.** 4

6. Which two stars on the H-R diagram have the most similar surface temperatures?

a. 1 and 2   **c.** 2 and 3

b. 1 and 3   **d.** 3 and 4

Extended Response

Answer the two questions below in detail.

7. Why is looking at a star in the night sky like seeing back into time?

8. How could you use two flashlights to demonstrate the concept that the apparent brightness of a star is affected by its distance from Earth? You can include a diagram as part of your answer.

Analyzing a Chart

1. d

2. a

3. b

4. b

5. a

6. d

Extended Response

7. RUBRIC

4 points for a response that correctly answers the question and uses the following facts accurately:

• Stars are very far away.
• Stars give off light.
• Light takes time to travel.
• Our eyes gather light.

Sample: Stars are so far away from Earth that the light they give off takes years to travel to Earth. When you look at a star, your eyes are gathering light that the star gave off years ago.

3 points for a response that correctly answers the question and uses three of the facts

2 points for a response that partially answers the question and uses two of the facts

1 point for a response that partially answers the question and uses one of the facts

8. RUBRIC

4 points for a response that indicates that the flashlights should be placed at different distances from an observer and that the farther one will appear dimmer to the observer.

Sample: Turn on the flashlights and point them in the same direction. Place one flashlight farther from an observer than the other. The flashlight that is farther will appear dimmer to the observer than the closer flashlight.

3 points for a response that indicates that the flashlights should be placed at different distances and that the farther one will appear dimmer

2 points for a response that indicates that the flashlights should be placed at different distances

---

METACOGNITIVE ACTIVITY

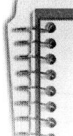

Have students answer the following questions in their **Science Notebook:**

1. What is one physical activity that helped you understand the content of this chapter?

2. What did you change your mind about after reading this chapter?

3. What helped you successfully complete your Unit Project?

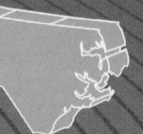

North Carolina Handbook

NORTH CAROLINA
HANDBOOK

Doing a Problem-Based Investigation

WHAT IS IT? A problem-based investigation puts you in the middle of an imaginary situation, or scenario, that is modeled on a real problem. You investigate the circumstances, review the data, form conclusions, and determine the best course of action. Although the scenario is made up, you will use real information to solve the problem.

HOW DO YOU DO IT? At the start of each investigation, you build your background knowledge. Then you complete several activities that provide you with the additional clues you need to work through the problem and develop a solution. There may be several good solutions to a problem. As long as the conclusions you reach are logical and are based on the data, you will succeed.

◯ Set Learning Goals

Students will

- Learn about the four principles of natural selection.
- Understand how populations of organisms can adapt to their environment over time.
- Analyze data to infer the processes that led to changes in an animal population.

 **INSTRUCT**

Introduce

PROBLEM-BASED INVESTIGATION

In this lesson, students play the role of a nature preserve manager. They will analyze data on an existent salamander population in North Carolina and propose an explanation for changes that have occurred in the population during the past 30 years.

Although this scenario is fictional, it is based on actual data. All of the material presented in the background information is scientifically accurate.

Present the Lesson

Have students conduct the investigation in the following order:

- Read this page as an introduction to the problem.
- Read the background information on pages NC4–NC6. (Make sure students understand that they must read those pages first, because they will be unable to answer the questions posed in the activities without this background.)
- Use the activities on page NC3 to work through the problem.

Ongoing Assessment

Build Your Background

◯ CHECK YOUR READING *Answers: Natural selection occurs when individuals with adaptations survive and produce more offspring than other individuals, causing the advantageous trait to be more common in the next generation; populations grow over time if many individuals have traits that increase their survival in their habitat.*

NC2 North Carolina Handbook

 **PROBLEM-BASED INVESTIGATION**
Natural Selection

BRIEFING

Is the Ecosystem Changing?

Natural selection is a process through which a species can adapt to a changing environment. In some cases, studying how the traits of certain species change over time can help scientists determine whether an ecosystem is healthy. For example, the characteristics of certain salamander populations can be used to determine how healthy moist woodland ecosystems are in North Carolina. Species used in this way are called indicator species.

Eurycea wilderae

The Blue Ridge two-lined salamander can be used as an indicator species for moist woodlands in North Carolina.

IDENTIFY THE PROBLEM

YOUR ROLE: Nature Preserve Manager

THE SCENARIO

Suppose that you are the manager of the Big River Nature Preserve. The population of an important indicator species in the Big River ecosystem, the two-lined salamander, has changed dramatically during the past 30 years.

YOUR ASSIGNMENT

Examine the data for the salamander population and the environmental conditions within the preserve. What is causing the changes in the salamander population?

BUILD YOUR BACKGROUND

Read the background information on natural selection on pages NC4–NC6 to learn about how species can change in response to changes in their environment. You may also want to review information on populations and ecosystems on pages D45–D51 and information on changing ecosystems on pages D63–D68.

 **CHECK YOUR READING** How does the process of natural selection work? What factors cause populations to grow or to decline?

NC2 North Carolina Handbook

NORTH CAROLINA STANDARDS

7.06 Investigate processes which, operating over long periods of time, have resulted in the diversity of plant and animal life present today:

- Natural selection.
- Adaptation.

WORK THROUGH THE PROBLEM

ANALYZE POPULATION DATA The table shows the population of two-lined salamanders in 1973 and 2003. Use the data to answer the questions below.

▶ How did the total salamander population change between 1973 and 2003?

▶ How did the number of salamanders without spots change?

Two-lined Salamander Population		
Type	1973	2003
Total two-lined salamanders	891	540
Two-lined salamanders with spots	636	189
Two-lined salamanders without spots	255	351

ANALYZE HABITAT DATA The two maps below show how the Big River Nature Preserve changed between 1973 and 2003. Study the maps and then answer the questions below.

Big River Nature Preserve, 1973

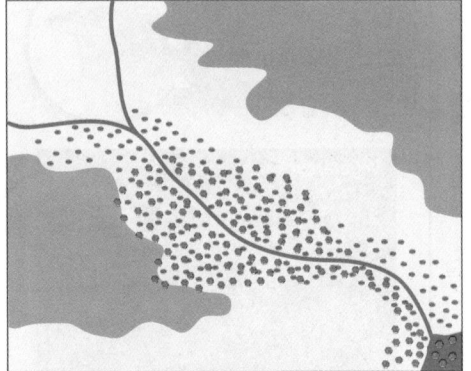

Big River Nature Preserve, 2003

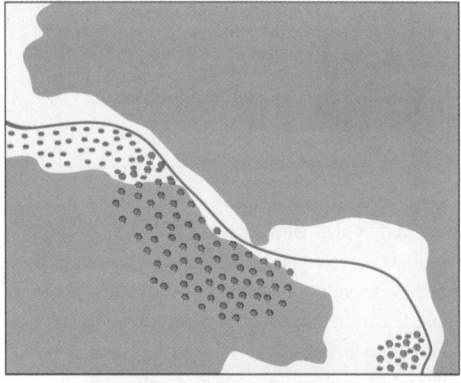

▶ How has the amount of wetland changed?

▶ How has the amount of forest changed?

▶ How did the salamander habitat and distribution change?

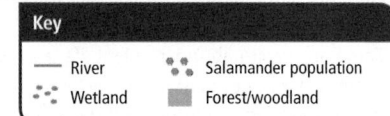

Key
— River   ⋰⋱ Salamander population
⋰⋱ Wetland   ▨ Forest/woodland

DEVELOP YOUR SOLUTION

SYNTHESIZE Review the salamander population data, the environmental conditions during each population measurement, and your knowledge of natural selection. Use this information to determine a possible explanation for the observations you have made.

▶ Describe how changes in the traits of the salamander population might have made the salamander species better suited to the new environment.

▶ How might the process of natural selection explain the changes in the numbers of spotted and unspotted salamanders?

PREDICT Suppose the Big River Nature Preserve contains many species that need a wetland environment in order to survive. On the basis of the conclusions you drew from the salamander data, what do you think might happen to the populations of other wetland species in the preserve?

North Carolina Handbook NC3

DIFFERENTIATE INSTRUCTION

Below Level To help students visualize the changes in the salamander populations, have them graph the population data as bar graphs (one graph for 1973, another for 2003). Encourage the students to think about why data might be graphed in different ways.

Advanced Have interested students quantify the changes in the preserve. Students can use tracing paper and graph paper to determine the relative area (as represented by the number of squares) of the salamander population, the wetland habitat, and the forested habitat in 1973 and in 2003.

Teach from Visuals

To help students interpret the table on this page, ask:

• What two groups make up the total population of two-lined salamanders? *those with spots and those without spots*

• What percentage of salamanders were without spots in 1973? *29%*

• What percentage of salamanders were without spots in 2003? *65%*

Ongoing Assessment
Work Through the Problem

Answers

Analyze Population Data: ▶ *The total population decreased.* ▶ *The number of salamanders without spots increased.*

Analyze Habitat Data: ▶ *The wetland habitat decreased in size.* ▶ *The forest/woodland habitat increased in size.* ▶ *The salamanders' habitat changed from mostly wetland to mostly forest and the population decreased and moved to one side of the river.*

Develop Your Solution

Answers: Answers will vary. ▶ *Sample answers: Unspotted individuals may have an advantage in the wooded habitat. Spotted individuals could be more noticeable against the colors and patterns of woodland vegetation and therefore are more visible to predators. Selection by the wooded habitat for unspotted individuals would account for the shift in the population.*

Predict

Answer: The populations of other species might decrease in size, or develop adaptations to the new environment.

CLOSE

As a class, consider traits in animals that students are familiar with. For each trait, discuss what factors may have been involved in selecting the trait. These factors may be natural pressures in the environment or artificial factors. For example, a certain breed of dog's keen sense of smell may have been selected over time by people who used the dog's ancestors for hunting.

North Carolina Handbook NC3

History Connection

You may wish to provide students with a historical context for Darwin's travels and work aboard the *Beagle.* When Darwin traveled aboard the *Beagle* in the 1800s, many countries were sending ships around the world to explore and chart new territories. A naturalist was typically hired for these voyages to make careful observations of the plant and animal life in each location visited. The specimens and various samples collected were then usually housed in the country's natural history museums and used for further scientific study.

The *Beagle* was first launched in 1820 under the British navy's new surveying program. In 1831, when Darwin joined the crew, the *Beagle's* primary mission was to chart lesser-known areas of the South American coast.

Background Information Natural Selection

Darwin's Observations

CHARLES DARWIN

In 1859 the British naturalist Charles Darwin published what would become the basis of the modern theory of evolution. As a young adult, Darwin spent five years as a naturalist aboard the *Beagle,* a ship in the British navy. He compared the new animals he was seeing with ones from his own country.

Darwin was only 22 when he embarked on the HMS *Beagle* in 1831. Darwin traveled with a crew of 68 people on the 90-foot-long vessel.

GALÁPAGOS ISLANDS

The differences Darwin saw in animals became more obvious when he visited the Galápagos Islands, a chain of volcanic islands off the South American coast. On the Galápagos Islands not only did plants and animals differ from those he saw on the main-

? A land, but some differed from island to island. For example, tortoises with short necks were living in damp areas with abundant plant life that grew close to the ground. Longer-necked tortoises were living in dry areas with cacti. He considered whether the different lengths of their necks made it possible for the tortoises to live in different environments.

DARWIN'S FINCHES

Darwin also found many different types of birds called finches living on the islands. On the different

? B islands he noticed a variety of beak shapes and sizes. Some finches had heavy, short beaks useful for crushing fruit, while others had long, thin beaks useful for capturing insects. These observations caused Darwin to question whether the species had evolved differently because they were on different islands.

Darwin's Finches

On the Galápagos Islands, Darwin observed similar-looking birds with very different beaks. These birds are closely related finch species that are suited to different habitats on the islands.

Woodpecker Finch

Vegetarian Finch

Large Ground Finch

Cactus Finch

DIFFERENTIATE INSTRUCTION

? Reading Support

A Describe the two different kinds of tortoises that Darwin observed. *short-necked and long-necked*

B What features of the finches varied from location to location? *beak size and shape*

Inclusion Tactile learners may benefit from the following activity. Provide each group of students with several different types and sizes of seeds and nuts. Pass, from group to group, a variety of tools, such as wire cutters, tweezers, blunt-end pliers, needle-nose pliers, and clothespins. These tools are the "beaks" with which they pick up the food. Have students determine the best tool for each type of food. Ask: How might the ability to collect food be related to a species' ability to survive?

DARWIN'S THEORY

After Darwin returned home, he struggled to develop an explanation for the amazing diversity of species he saw and for the relationships among them. Darwin knew from personal experience that breeders could produce new varieties of animals over time. For example, breeders produce a new breed of dog by selecting dogs that have certain desired traits and then allowing only those individuals to mate. Darwin's insight was that a similar process might be going on in nature. He proposed that, through a process he called natural selection, the members of a species that are best suited to their environment survive and reproduce at a higher rate than other members of the species.

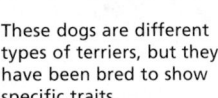

These dogs are different types of terriers, but they have been bred to show specific traits.

NORTH CAROLINA HANDBOOK

Principles of Natural Selection

OVERPRODUCTION

When most plants or animals reproduce, they usually produce more offspring than can possibly survive. For example, a female salmon may lay several thousand fertile eggs, but not all of them will hatch. Only a small percentage of the salmon that do hatch from the eggs will survive disease and avoid fish-eating predators. Only a small percentage of these survivors will live to adulthood. An even smaller number of these will successfully reproduce.

VARIATION

Within a species there are natural differences, or variations, in traits. For example, if you looked very closely at thousands of salmon, you might see slight differences among them. Some might have larger fins. Others might have distinctive patterns of spots on their scales. Such differences result from differences in the genetic material of the fish. Variations are passed on from one generation to the next.

ADAPTATION

A change in an individual's genetic material is referred to as a mutation. Sometimes a mutation occurs that makes an individual better able to survive than other members of a population. An adaptation is any inherited trait that gives an organism an advantage in its environment. For example, a slight change in the shape of the tail fin may increase a fish's chance of survival by helping it swim faster and avoid predators.

SELECTION

Because individual organisms with a particular adaptation are more likely to survive and reproduce, the adaptation becomes more common in the next generation. As this process repeats, more and more members of a species show the adaptation. If a change in the tail fin makes salmon better able to swim upstream and lay eggs, for example, scientists say the environment is selecting this trait.

---

natural selection the process through which members of a species that are best suited to their environment survive and reproduce at a higher rate than other members of the species

adaptation a characteristic, behavior, or inherited trait that makes an organism better able to survive and reproduce

---

DIFFERENTIATE INSTRUCTION

? Reading Support

C What is overproduction? *the production of more offspring than can survive*

D What causes the variation of traits within a species? *differences in genetic material*

English Learners Some students may find it helpful to break down the words associated with natural selection into their parts. Have students use the verbs *produce, vary, adapt,* and *select* to describe the four principles of natural selection.

Teach from Visuals

Have students examine the three terrier breeds shown on this page and hypothesize about which traits the ancestors of these individuals might have had. To help students think critically about the terriers, ask:

• What traits are different among the dogs shown? *Sample answers: size, ear shape, coloration*

• How might selective breeding have led to the different varieties shown? *by breeding only the dogs that had the traits people were looking for*

• What traits remain similar among the varieties shown? *Sample answers: shaggy fur, overall body shape*

Develop Critical Thinking

Ask students to consider how natural selection is similar to, and different from, artificial breeding. Students may write their answer in the form of a short paragraph.

Teach from Visuals

To help students interpret the visual, ask:

- What does the silver fish in the second box represent? *a fish with a mutation that causes a curve in its tail*

- What advantage is associated with a curved tail? *faster swimming*

- Why is this trait important in the presence of predators? *It helps the fish escape predators.*

- What other traits might give a fish an advantage? *Sample answers: good vision, fast reflexes, the ability to lay many eggs, a coloration that helps it blend in with its surroundings*

Natural Selection

Certain traits become more common in a group of organisms through the process of natural selection.

Overproduction

adult salmon

eggs

A fish may lay thousands of eggs, but only a small number of offspring will survive to reach adulthood.

Variation

curve

A mutation may cause a slight curve to develop in a fish's tail.

Adaptation

The fish with the curved tail is able to swim more quickly and so escapes predators. The fish is more likely to reproduce.

Selection

With each generation, more fish with curved tails survive to reproduce. Over time, they make up a larger part of the group.

NORTH CAROLINA HANDBOOK

DIFFERENTIATE INSTRUCTION

Below Level Some students may have trouble interpreting the drawings used in this illustration. For each box, ask students to write what the beige fish represent. *overproduction: fish that do not survive; variation: fish that do not have the trait; adaptation: fish that do not have the trait; selection: fish that do not have the trait*

Soil Science

○ Set Learning Goals

Students will

- Learn about the properties of soil that affect plant growth.
- Determine the quality of a soil sample.
- Form conclusions based on the quality of a soil.

BRIEFING

What's in the Dirt?

Soil is a valuable resource. The quality of soil in an area depends on many factors, including the climate and geologic history of the area, as well as agriculture and urban development. To best use soil, people must actively maintain its "health." In many parts of North Carolina, soils contain a lot of sand. Water and certain nutrients can move easily through these soils—and out of them. Gardeners, farmers, and scientists monitor such soils to ensure the ability of soil to support plant growth.

The quality of the soil is one factor that will determine how well these plants grow.

NORTH CAROLINA HANDBOOK

Introduce

PROBLEM-BASED INVESTIGATION

In this lesson, students play the role of a soil scientist. They will analyze the soil quality in the fictional Plant Avenue community vegetable garden and make recommendations to its gardeners based on their analysis.

Although this scenario is fictional, it is based on real issues facing growers in North Carolina. All of the information presented in the background pages is scientifically accurate.

IDENTIFY THE PROBLEM

YOUR ROLE: Soil Scientist

THE SCENARIO

Suppose the gardeners of the Plant Avenue community vegetable garden have contacted you for advice. The gardeners are concerned that recent heavy rains may have washed organic matter and nutrients out of the garden's soil.

YOUR ASSIGNMENT

Is the soil in the garden suitable for growing vegetables? Which vegetables do you recommend planting? How can the soil be made more fertile?

BUILD YOUR BACKGROUND

Read the background information on pages NC9–NC11 to learn about the properties of soil that affect plant growth. You may also want to review Section 4.2, "Weathering and organic processes form soil," on pages A122–A129.

 **CHECK YOUR READING** What can you tell about soil from its texture? Why do people test soil for acidity?

Present the Lesson

Have students conduct the investigation in the following order:

- Read this page as an introduction to the problem.
- Read the background information on pages NC9–NC11. (Make sure students understand that they must read those pages before proceeding. Students will not be able to answer the questions posed on page NC8 without having first read the background information.)
- Use the guide on the next page to work through the problem and formulate a solution.

Ongoing Assessment

Build Your Background

CHECK YOUR READING *Answers: how water moves through the soil; acidity determines the availability of nutrients to plants*

NORTH CAROLINA STANDARDS

3.05 Analyze soil properties that can be observed and measured to predict soil quality including: color, horizon profile, infiltration, soil temperature, structure, consistency, texture, particle size, pH, fertility, soil moisture.

3.08 Conclude that the good health of environments and organisms requires: monitoring of the pedosphere, taking steps to maintain soil quality, stewardship.

7.02 Investigate factors that determine the growth and survival of organisms including: mineral availability, soil/rock type.

Soil Analysis Activity

PREPARATION Before the activity, shovel a large sample of soil into a wide container. Try to disturb the soil as little as possible to maintain its structure. Cover the container to prevent the soil from drying out until use. On the day of the activity, divide the soil into smaller samples for each team.

PURPOSE To model the testing of soil properties in the Plant Avenue community vegetable garden.

Ongoing Assessment

Work Through the Problem

Answers

Analyze a Soil Sample: Answers will vary. Students' explanations should indicate that they understand what types of soil are best for growing plants.

Interpret the Report: ▶ *nitrogen and phosphorus* ▶ *Field peas would grow without the addition of any fertilizer or lime because the levels of nutrients and the acidity found in the test were within the range of requirements for this type of vegetable.*

Develop Your Solution

Answers: ▶ *Students' choices of vegetables should include field peas and three other vegetables.* ▶ *Students' recommendations and explanations should be consistent with the information provided in the tables on page NC11 and the soil test report.*

 **CLOSE**

You may wish to have teams write their recommendations in the form of a letter to the gardeners of the Plant Avenue community vegetable garden. To wrap up the lesson, have one member of each team present their recommendations to the class and explain their choices. Help students understand that there are no "right" answers, only logical conclusions.

WORK THROUGH THE PROBLEM

ANALYZE A SOIL SAMPLE Now that you have read the background information, you are ready to analyze a sample of soil on the basis of several soil properties. When you are finished with the activity, answer the question below.

Procedure

1. Copy Table 1 on the right into your notebook. Write the date and time.

2. Record the colors that are visible in the soil. Specify which color is the main color.

3. Use the ruler and the table on page NC9 to identify and record the soil structure (granular, blocky, prismatic, columnar, platy, single-grained, or massive).

4. Pick up a small amount of the soil and break it between your fingers. Record the soil consistency (loose, breakable, firm, or extremely firm).

5. Feel the rock particles in the soil and record their texture (mostly sand, mostly silt, mostly clay, or equal mix). You may refer to page NC10 for help in identifying texture.

6. Place some of the soil on the paper and observe it with the hand lens. Use the tweezers to separate individual particles. Record any other observations that you can make about the soil, including the presence of dead leaves, roots, or insects.

7. Wash your hands.

▶ **Judging by the properties you have observed, would you characterize this soil sample as good for growing plants? Why or why not?**

INTERPRET THE REPORT Suppose the soil-test report has come back for a sample of the Plant Avenue community garden soil. Compare the results of the report, at right, with the tables on page NC11.

▶ **Which nutrients are at levels that are too low to grow medium-feeding crops?**

▶ **According to this report, are there any vegetables that would grow well without the addition of any fertilizer or lime to the soil? Explain.**

Materials
- undisturbed soil sample
- metric ruler
- white paper
- hand lens
- tweezers

Table 1. Soil Observations

Property	Observations
Color	
Structure	
Consistency	
Texture	
Other	

Plant Avenue Soil Test

Variable	Measurement
Nitrogen (N)	1.6 lb/1000 ft²
Phosphorus (P)	1.5 lb/1000 ft²
Potassium (K)	2.0 lb/1000 ft²
Acidity	pH 5.8

DEVELOP YOUR SOLUTION

SYNTHESIZE Review the scenario on page NC7. Based on the results of the soil test and the answers you have given to the questions above, choose four types of vegetables that would be well suited to the soil in the Plant Avenue garden.

▶ **Which vegetables do you recommend? Explain.**

▶ **What, if anything, would you recommend adding to the soil to meet the requirements of the vegetables chosen? Explain.**

DIFFERENTIATE INSTRUCTION

Inclusion Pair any visually impaired student with another student who can explain the look and color of the soil in the activity. Have the visually impaired student determine some of the other properties of the soil—such as texture, structure, consistency, and moisture content—by handling the soil.

Background Information Soil Science

Soil Properties

(?) A Soil is a mixture of rock particles, air, water, and organic matter. Organic matter is matter that has come from the waste and remains of living organisms. Soils vary greatly in the types and amounts of materials they contain and in their ability to support plant growth. Soil scientists study the physical and chemical properties of soil. These properties include soil profile, color, structure, consistency, texture, particle size, infiltration, fertility, acidity, temperature, and moisture.

HORIZON PROFILE

The layers that soil forms in the ground are called soil horizons. A cross-section view of the horizons in a specific location is a soil profile. Dark-colored soil typically makes up the uppermost layer of soil, or topsoil. This layer has the most organic matter, and its rock particles are most weathered. Topsoil is nutrient-rich. The layer beneath the topsoil is often reddish in color, due to the clay and minerals it contains. The lowest layer of soil is often yellowish brown in color and contains the largest and least-weathered rock particles.

◄ MORE READING To see an example of a soil profile, turn to page A124.

This topsoil is dark colored because of the organic matter it contains. Topsoils in North Carolina contain a great deal of sand and tend to be beige or red in color.

soil structure the shape of masses of soil in the ground

STRUCTURE

Soil structure refers to the shape of masses of soil in the ground. The structure of soil can be granular, blocky, prismatic, columnar, or platy, **(?) B** as described in the table below. Granular, blocky, and prismatic structures are the best for plant growth because these soils contain spaces that can hold air and water, similar to a sponge. Because these structures are not too firm, plant roots can spread easily through them. Soil can also be structured as a single large mass (massive) or as individual particles (single-grained). In general, massive and single-grained soils are the least helpful for plant growth.

Soil Structures	
Structure	**Description**
Granular	like cookie crumbs, with most pieces less than 0.5 cm across
Blocky	blocks of different shapes, each 1.5–5.0 cm across
Prismatic	thin columns, each several centimeters long
Columnar	vertical columns that have salt at the top
Platy	thin, flat plates
Single-grained	small individual particles that do not stick together
Massive	single large block that is difficult to break apart

 **BACKGROUND**

Integrate the Sciences

Plants depend on good-quality soil to grow. They also help form soil. As plant roots grow, they break down rock into smaller pieces, forming soil. When plants die, they decay and add nutrients to the soil.

Discussion Questions

Runoff is the process by which water from precipitation flows over land and into rivers and streams. In some areas, runoff has stripped away the layer of topsoil. Ask: What do you think happens when water flows over a layer of single-grained soil? of massive soil?

Water would sink into a single-grained soil and continue to flow over a massive soil.

Teach from Visuals

Make sure students study this table carefully. They will need to refer to it later when they are analyzing a sample of actual soil. To help students remember the names for different structures, have them find word parts in the names that remind them of the shapes of the soil masses. For example, the soil masses in platy soils are flat like a plate.

DIFFERENTIATE INSTRUCTION

(?) Reading Support

A What is organic matter? *matter that has come from the waste and remains of living organisms*

B Which soil structures are the best for plant growth? *granular, blocky, and prismatic*

Below Level If students are having trouble with soil structure, have them make a large, two-column table. Have students write the name of the structure in the left column and draw a simple sketch of the structure in the right column, using the descriptions provided in the table above.

Teacher Demo

To demonstrate consistency, bring in a small sample of soil. Pass the sample around the class and have students squeeze a small piece of the soil between their fingers. Explain that soil consistency is a measure of how well a piece of soil sticks together or how easily it breaks apart. Consistency can be described as loose, breakable, firm, or extremely firm. Ask: How would you describe this soil's consistency? *Answer depends on what type of soil is used.*

Develop Critical Thinking

Have students make predictions about the impact that infiltration rate might have on the spread of water pollution through the ground. Students can write a paragraph to present their ideas, or work cooperatively in teams to prepare a brief oral presentation.

CONSISTENCY

Single-grained soil, such as sand, always has a loose consistency—that is, the grains of soil do not stick together. On the other hand, massive soil has an extremely firm consistency—that is, it is very difficult to break the soil apart. Soil structure and consistency determine a soil's ability to hold air and nutrient-containing water, both of which plants need to grow. Water and air cannot easily move through soils that are too firm. On the other hand, water drains out of soils that are too loose. Water and nutrients must therefore be added frequently to loose soils.

? **C**

TEXTURE

The texture of soil is related to, but different from, its structure. Soil texture depends on the sizes of the small rock particles in a soil. It is determined by the relative amounts of sand, silt, and clay in the soil. Sand particles are the largest and can be seen without a microscope. Silt particles are smaller and can be seen only with a microscope. The pieces of silt that are visible in the photograph below contain many, many particles. Clay particles are the smallest and, like silt, can be seen only with a microscope. Clay particles stick together forming large chunks, as shown in the picture.

Like structure and consistency, soil texture affects how well water and nutrients move through a soil. Very sandy soils have a high infiltration rate—that is, water drains into the soil easily. However, water also drains out of sandy soils easily and can take certain nutrients with it, such as nitrogen (N), phosphorus (P), and potassium (K). The best soil texture for retaining water—and therefore the best soil for growing plants—contains equal amounts of sand, silt, clay, and organic matter.

? **D**

◄ MORE READING To see magnified images of sand, silt, and clay particles, see page A128.

Soil Texture		
Sand	**Silt**	**Clay**
gritty in texture	silky, smooth, or lumpy	sticky, or hard and lumpy

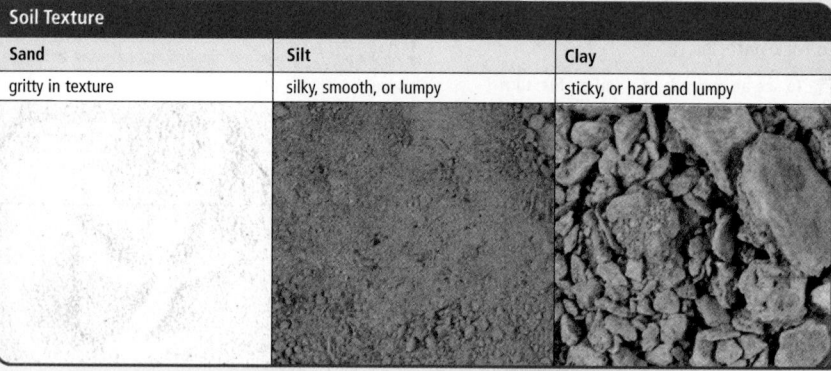

consistency the ability of soil to stick together
texture the sizes of rock particles in soil

infiltration the drainage of water into soil

DIFFERENTIATE INSTRUCTION

 Reading Support

C What must be added frequently to loose soils? *water and nutrients*

D Which nutrients can drain out of a soil? *nitrogen, phosphorus, potassium*

Alternative Assessment Students may create a photo essay of soil properties. Have students take photographs of as many different types of soils as they can find. Next to each photograph, students should describe the soil's color, structure, consistency, and texture. Encourage students to record the date and location in which the photograph was taken, as well as any other observations. Have students present their photo essays in the form of a booklet.

Soil Fertility

MINERALS AND ACIDITY

Soil fertility refers to the ability of soil to supply the nutrients that plants need for growth. There are several mineral nutrients dissolved in water that plants absorb through their roots. The three main nutrients that scientists test for are nitrogen, phosphorus, and potassium. Because these nutrients are dissolved in water, the properties that determine how well a soil holds water, such as structure and texture, affect the soil's fertility. The acidity, or pH, of a soil also affects its fertility. Some nutrients are most soluble within a range of optimum acidity levels. The acidity of a soil also influences its fertility by affecting bacteria in the soil. Soils that are too acidic hinder bacteria from breaking down nutrients into chemicals that plants can absorb.

SOIL TESTING

A soil test is an analysis of soil fertility in which the mineral nutrients in a soil are chemically removed and measured. Acidity and organic matter are also measured. The information provided by a soil test indicates what, if anything, should be added to the soil to promote plant growth. For example, lime can be added to the soil to make it less acidic (increase its pH). If the test shows a low level of nitrogen, phosphorus, or potassium, a fertilizer can be added that is highest in that nutrient. Results from a soil test can help growers add to the soil what is needed only. This practice improves the soil conditions for plants while saving money and reducing pollution. Excess fertilizer can pollute rivers, streams, and lakes.

NUTRIENT REQUIREMENTS

Nutrient and acidity requirements of different crops vary. Crops are described as light, medium, or heavy feeders, depending on how much of the three main nutrients they require for growth. The table below shows the nutrient requirements of each type of feeder. Even though soil is three-dimensional, nutrient requirements are often given in pounds per 1000 square feet of soil. It is always best to choose crops that are known to grow well in the soil and the temperatures in your area. The second table below shows vegetables that grow well in North Carolina and their requirements.

Nutrient Requirements (lb/1000 ft² of soil)			
Type of Feeder	N	P	K
Light	0.8	0.9	0.9
Medium	2.2	1.8	1.9
Heavy	3.0	2.8	2.8

North Carolina Vegetables and Their Requirements		
Vegetable	Nutrient Requirements	Optimum Acidity (pH)
Cabbage	heavy	6.0–6.4
Cucumbers	medium	5.0–6.0
Eggplant	medium	5.0–6.0
Field peas	light	5.5–6.5
Irish potatoes	heavy	5.8–6.5
Mustard greens	medium	6.0–6.5
Peppers	medium	6.0–8.1
Snap beans	medium	6.0–7.0
Sweet potatoes	medium	5.0–7.0
Tomatoes	heavy	5.0–7.0

soil fertility the ability of soil to supply nutrients to plants

---

Teach Difficult Concepts

Some students may have a difficult time understanding the pH scale. Explain that a lower pH indicates a higher acidity. Draw a vertical line on the board and label it with the numbers 0 to 14, with 0 on the bottom and 14 on the top. Next to the number 10, write *soap*. Next to the number 2, write *lemons*. Explain that soap has a pH of 10 and lemons have a pH of 2. Ask: Which is more acidic, soap or lemons? How do you know? *lemons, because they have a lower pH*

Teach from Visuals

To help students interpret the two tables on this page, ask:

- In the "Nutrient Requirements" table, what do *N, P,* and *K* stand for? *nitrogen, phosphorus, and potassium*
- According to the "North Carolina Vegetables and Their Requirements" table, which vegetables grow well in soils that have a pH lower than 6? *cucumbers, eggplant, field peas, Irish potatoes, sweet potatoes, tomatoes*
- How many pounds per square foot of nitrogen, phosphorus, and potassium do peppers need? *N: 2.2; P: 1.8, K: 1.9*

Teach with Technology

If students have probeware, they may want to use a soil pH probe to test the acidity of soil in their region. Soils in North Carolina tend to be acidic, which is one reason why soil tests are recommended there. Extensive information about North Carolina soils is available at the Web site of the Soil Science Society of North Carolina.

DIFFERENTIATE INSTRUCTION

Reading Support

E What does soil fertility measure? *the ability of a soil to supply the nutrients that plants need*

F What can be added to soil to make it less acidic? *lime*

SUPPORT

◉ Set Learning Goals

Students will

- Learn about the process of photosynthesis.
- Examine the significance of photosynthesis to other organisms.
- Understand that oxygen and carbon dioxide cycle into and out of the atmosphere.

Integrate the Sciences

Most of the carbohydrates that make up plant structures are cellulose molecules, whereas most of the carbohydrates that store energy within plant cells are starch molecules. Both cellulose and starch are polymers. Polymers are large, carbon-based molecules made of smaller, repeating units. The smaller, repeating units are called monomers. Monomers are linked together one after another like beads on a chain. For both cellulose and starch molecules, the monomer is glucose.

Additional Resources

Photosynthesis

THE PROCESS

Photosynthesis is the process by which plants and algae use energy from sunlight to convert carbon dioxide and water into sugar. Photosynthesis occurs in plant cells that have chloroplasts. Chloroplasts contain chlorophyll, a green, light-absorbing substance that traps the energy in sunlight. Chlorophyll is the substance that makes some parts of a plant appear green.

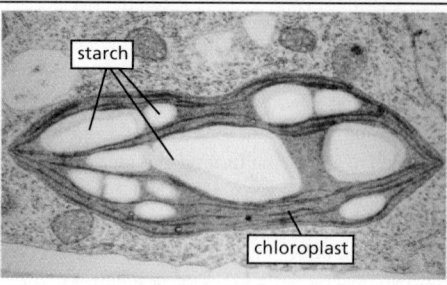

The starch in this chloroplast stores energy.

The process of photosynthesis involves a series of steps, as shown in the illustration on the next page.

1. **The starting materials** of photosynthesis are carbon dioxide and water.
2. **The process** takes place when carbon dioxide and water enter a plant's chloroplasts. Chlorophyll captures energy from sunlight, which is used to change carbon dioxide and water into new products.
3. **The products** of photosynthesis are simple sugar molecules and oxygen.

FOOD FOR PLANTS

Plants do not immediately use all of the sugar they make. Most of the sugar molecules are linked together to build large carbohydrates called starches. A plant can store starch and later break it down into glucose or other sugars when the plant needs energy. Chemical energy is stored in the bonds of sugars. When a sugar molecule is broken down, it is converted into different molecules that are used by the cell as an energy source.

FOOD FOR ANIMALS

Animals also use chemical energy to carry out life functions. In fact, the sugars and starches produced by plants supply the raw materials for energy to almost all organisms. Some animals obtain the stored chemical energy produced by photosynthesis by eating the plants. Animals that eat those animals also obtain chemical energy that results from photosynthesis, as do the animals that eat them.

THE OXYGEN-CARBON DIOXIDE CYCLE

Oxygen is another product of photosynthesis. In fact, most of the oxygen in Earth's atmosphere is a product of photosynthesis. Both plants and animals require oxygen to live. Plant cells and animal cells use oxygen to release the energy stored in sugars through a process called cellular respiration. In addition to releasing energy, cellular respiration produces carbon dioxide and water. Plants absorb carbon dioxide and water and use them in photosynthesis to store more energy and release more oxygen. In this way, oxygen and carbon dioxide are always cycling into and out of the atmosphere.

---

photosynthesis the process by which plants use sunlight to produce food

chlorophyll the substance in green plants that captures energy from sunlight

---

NORTH CAROLINA STANDARDS

4.01 Describe the flow of energy and matter in natural systems: water, nitrogen, carbon dioxide, and oxygen are substances cycled between the living and nonliving environments.

4.03 Examine evidence that green plants make food. Photosynthesis is a process carried on by green plants and other organisms containing chlorophyll. During photosynthesis, light energy is converted into stored energy which the plant, in turn, uses to carry out its life processes.

4.04 Evaluate the significance of photosynthesis to other organisms: the major source of atmospheric oxygen is photosynthesis; carbon dioxide is removed from the atmosphere and oxygen is released during photosynthesis; green plants are the producers of food that is used directly or indirectly by consumers.

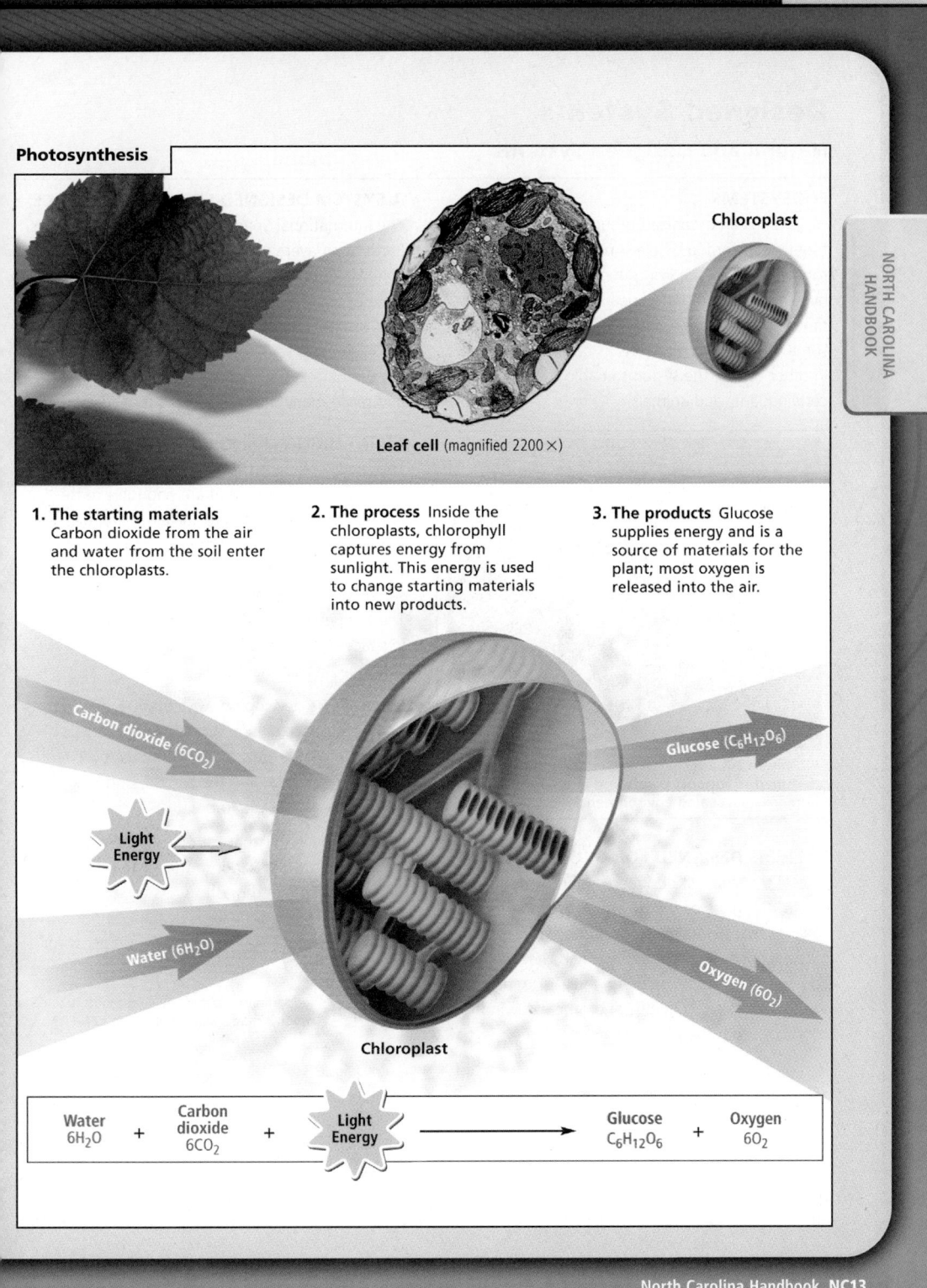

Photosynthesis

Leaf cell (magnified 2200×)

Chloroplast

1. **The starting materials** Carbon dioxide from the air and water from the soil enter the chloroplasts.

2. **The process** Inside the chloroplasts, chlorophyll captures energy from sunlight. This energy is used to change starting materials into new products.

3. **The products** Glucose supplies energy and is a source of materials for the plant; most oxygen is released into the air.

Carbon dioxide ($6CO_2$)

Light Energy

Water ($6H_2O$)

Glucose ($C_6H_{12}O_6$)

Oxygen ($6O_2$)

Chloroplast

| Water $6H_2O$ | + | Carbon dioxide $6CO_2$ | + | Light Energy | $\longrightarrow$ | Glucose $C_6H_{12}O_6$ | + | Oxygen $6O_2$ |

Teach from Visuals

To help students interpret the visual, ask:

• Where within plant cells does photosynthesis take place? *chloroplast*

• How does the chloroplast in the illustration look different from the chloroplasts in the photograph of the leaf cell? *The chloroplast in the illustration—which is shown cut in half—looks more rounded and rigid than the ones in the photograph. The chloroplasts in the image look striped.*

• What do the arrows in the illustration represent? *molecules and energy entering and exiting the chloroplast*

Ongoing Assessment

Photosynthesis

Ask: What is the significance of photosynthesis to animals? *Photosynthesis provides food and oxygen for animals.*

DIFFERENTIATE INSTRUCTION

Below Level If students are having trouble understanding photosynthesis and the cycling of matter, make a two-column, two-row table. Label the columns "Starting Materials" and "Products" and label the rows "Photosynthesis" and "Respiration." Have students volunteer terms to fill in the table. Ask: What products of photosynthesis are starting materials for respiration? What products of respiration are starting materials for photosynthesis? *glucose and oxygen; carbon dioxide and water*

◉ Set Learning Goals

Students will

- Examine systems designed to promote plant and animal growth.
- Construct a self-sufficient system for growing plants.

Teacher Demo

One of the main conditions to consider when designing systems for life in space is the apparent lack of gravity. Gravity exists in space, but its noticeable effects inside the space station are very small. *Microgravity* is the term used to describe conditions in which there is little net gravitational force.

To demonstrate microgravity, hold a clear plastic cup of colored water over a bucket. Ask students what they think will happen to the water as the cup is falling. Have students watch carefully as you drop the cup. The students will notice that the water stays suspended in the cup as it falls. Both the cup and the water fall at the same rate, just as the space station and the people inside of it "fall" around Earth at the same rate.

Develop Critical Thinking

Have students consider some characteristics of plants that would make them suitable for growing in space as a source of food. For example, plants that require little water, require a small amount of space, can grow in extreme conditions, or can provide a high level of nutrients might do well in space. Ask: Where on Earth might one look for plants that have some of these characteristics?

Sample answers: deserts (little water), urban gardens (small spaces), mountains (extreme conditions), farms (high levels of nutrients)

Designed Systems

Natural and Designed Systems

ECOSYSTEMS

A system is an organized group of parts that work together to form a whole. An ecosystem—an environment and all the living things that are supported by it—is a system that appears in nature. Sometimes humans design and build systems that have some of the same functions as natural ecosystems. In other words, the systems enable the growth of certain plants and animals.

Biosphere 2 is a research and education center designed to support plants and animals, including humans, in a sealed environment.

SYSTEMS DESIGNED FOR GROWING PLANTS

One of the simplest designed systems is a greenhouse. The glass of the greenhouse lets in the sunlight that plants need for photosynthesis, but it keeps out wind, rain, and animals that might damage the plants. The greenhouse also maintains the temperature, humidity, and other growing conditions that the plants need.

Hydroponics is the cultivation of plants in a limited space and without soil. A hydroponic system supplies warmth, sunlight, water, and nutrients to plants very efficiently. The nutrients are added directly to the water. The water can be reused as long as it still contains nutrients. This recycling reduces waste and pollution.

A SYSTEM DESIGNED FOR LIVING IN SPACE

The International Space Station (ISS), which orbits Earth at an average altitude of 220 miles, is a more complicated designed system. It must sustain a crew of astronauts between visits of the spacecraft that resupply it with food, water, and other necessities. The more self-sufficient the space station can be, the better. This means finding ways to recycle and reuse many of the resources that sustain life.

MAINTAINING LIVING CONDITIONS

The space station is designed to provide astronauts with living conditions that are enough like their natural living conditions to sustain them. Because the atmosphere at an altitude of 220 miles is very thin, the space station must provide a constant supply of oxygen for the astronauts to breathe. The temperature and air pressure are extremely low in space, so these conditions must be carefully controlled inside the station.

Scientists are developing ways to grow food on board the space station. Growing food plants on site will provide fresh, more nutritious food, reduce the cost of maintaining the station, and provide oxygen for astronauts to breathe.

Much of the water that astronauts use is condensed from water vapor in the air that they exhale. Water that the astronauts use to wash themselves is saved, filtered, cleaned, and then reused. The space station even has a process for reusing the water in astronauts' urine.

 MORE READING To learn more about the space station and conditions in space, read pages E24–E25.

NORTH CAROLINA STANDARDS

4.05 Evaluate designed systems for ability to enable the growth of certain plants and animals.

Designing Urban Environments

Here on Earth, people plan cities, parks, and other communities to support plants, animals, and humans living together. For example, land is developed to provide housing for a growing population. But some land is left undeveloped. In addition to the ecological benefits of preserving undeveloped land, environmental scientists have found that property values are higher near land that is preserved.

Many developers now consult environmental scientists to decide where to build. The scientists determine which areas to preserve on the basis of the land's ability to support certain plants and animals. They often recommend saving land that is an important part of a water system, that provides habitat to diverse species of plants and animals, or that contains especially fertile soil.

? A

◀ **MORE READING** For more on the role of ecology in urban planning, refer to page D88.

NORTH CAROLINA HANDBOOK

INVESTIGATE DESIGNED SYSTEMS

BUILD A TERRARIUM Follow the instructions below to build a closed, self-sufficient system for growing plants. You will determine the amount of water to add to the system during its construction so that no water will need to be added in the future.

Procedure

1. Add 2 cm of gravel to the bottom half of the bottle. Add 6 cm of potting soil on top of the gravel. Make a small hole about 2 cm deep in the soil with your finger. Place the plant cutting in the hole and lightly press the soil around the base of the plant.

2. Obtain a number from your teacher. This will be the number of sprays of water you will add to the soil. Write your number, as well as the date and your initials, on a piece of masking tape and apply it to the side of the bottle. Spray the soil the assigned number of times.

3. Tape the top half of the bottle to the bottom half with packing tape. Place the bottle in indirect sunlight with your classmates' bottles.

4. Observe the bottles for three days. Determine which systems had the ideal amount of water by looking for condensation on the inside walls of the bottle. There should be some condensation but not so much that you cannot see into the bottle.

▶ What is the ideal amount of water to add to the system? How is water recycled in this system?

▶ How does the plant get enough carbon dioxide for photosynthesis? How does it get enough oxygen for cellular respiration?

Materials

- 2 L bottle cut in half
- gravel
- metric ruler
- potting soil
- plant cutting
- spray bottle of water
- masking tape
- permanent marker
- clear packing tape

> **INVESTIGATE FURTHER** Design your own closed system for growing plants. You may wish to start with the system above and make a change to one variable, such as type or size of container, type of soil, amount of soil, pH of soil, amount of fertilizer, amount of gravel, type of plant, or location of the container. Choose another variable to measure, such as plant growth. Write a report of your findings.

Terrarium Activity

PREPARATION Soak the bottles in warm water to facilitate the removal of their labels. Cut each bottle in half before the activity. One Pothos plant should provide enough cuttings for the whole class.

PURPOSE To model a self-sufficient system designed to grow plants

TIPS Divide the class into four groups. Give each group one of the following numbers for the number of sprays to add: 15, 20, 25, 30.

- Make sure the bottles are clean and dry.
- If there is an adjustable nozzle on the spray bottle, set it to a fine mist rather than a direct spray.
- Make sure the lid is on tight and the tape is well-sealed around the bottle so that air cannot enter or exit the bottle.
- For bottles with too much condensation after three days, open the lid and let some of the water evaporate. For bottles with no condensation, add more water.

Ongoing Assessment
Investigate Designed Systems

Answers: ▶ *about 20 sprays, or 15 mL; water is absorbed by the roots of the plant and given off as water vapor by the leaves of the plant, then condenses on the sides of the container and drips down into the soil, where it is again absorbed by the roots of the plant* ▶ *the carbon dioxide in this system comes from cellular respiration by the plant, and the oxygen comes from photosynthesis*

 **CLOSE**

Ask: How could the terrarium described in the activity on this page be a useful model for growing plants in space? *The terrarium could be used to study plant growth in a closed, self-sustaining environment that requires little water.*

DIFFERENTIATE INSTRUCTION

? Reading Support

A What types of land do environmental scientists recommend be left undeveloped? *land that is an important part of a water system, provides habitat to diverse species, or contains very fertile soil*

Below Level If students are having trouble answering the second set of questions in the activity, remind them that animals are not the only organisms whose cells undergo respiration. Students may wish to review the information about respiration and photosynthesis on pages NC12–NC13. Ask: What are the products of respiration? What are the products of photosynthesis? *energy, carbon dioxide, and water; sugar and oxygen*

● Set Learning Goals

Students will

Learn about gems, minerals, precious metals, and rocks found in North Carolina.

Teach Difficult Concepts

Students may find it hard to understand that the Appalachian Mountains were once at the edge of the North American plate and that these mountains are much older than the Rockies in the western United States. Students tend to think that the tallest mountains must be the oldest. Explain that the eastern part of the continent has been built over 600 million years by a series of collisions with smaller plates and by the massive collision with Africa. In contrast, the Rockies are only 40 to 60 million years old. After each collision, more crust was added to the edge of the North American plate. As a result, the Appalachians lie far inland from the current coastline.

Also, scientists studying the composition of the folded rock in this area have discovered that the Appalachians once towered higher than the Himalayas. Over the past 600 million years, wind and water have slowly worn down the mountains to the rounded shapes that students see today. In time, the same process will happen to the younger, more jagged Rocky Mountains.

Ongoing Assessment

To wrap up the lesson, model the history of the Appalachians by using clay. The three-dimensional model should help students understand what happened to the original edge of the North American plate and why the Appalachians lie so far inland. Students may also use the model to understand how the mountains eroded over millions of years.

Rocks and Minerals of North Carolina

AN UNDERWATER PAST

The diversity of rocks, gems, minerals, and precious metals found in North Carolina provide evidence of its rich geologic past. The history of the Appalachian Mountains began about 600 million years ago when small tectonic plates collided with the original North American plate to form the eastern coast. Along the collision boundaries, ancient sea-floor sediments were pushed up into the Appalachians. Evidence of these sediments can be found in the rocks of the mountains today. The final mountain-building era occurred when North America and Africa collided to form part of the supercontinent, Pangaea.

> **MORE READING** Refer to page B96 to see an illustration of the formation of the Appalachians.

The Ocoee Basin, which lies in the interior of the southeastern United States, was once at the edge of the original North American plate. The basin, which now includes parts of the Carolinas, Tennessee, and Georgia, was underwater at that time. Over millions of years, the sea deposited materials, including clay, sand, and pebbles, into the basin. These materials gradually compressed to form layers of sedimentary rocks that contain deposits of copper, zinc, iron, and sulfur. Plate collisions gradually added more land to the eastern coast and pushed the basin and its minerals upward. Today, copper mining in the Ocoee Basin contributes to the country's economic growth.

HEAT AND COMPRESSION

Intense heat produced by the collision of continents melted the rocks in some areas, producing magma. Magma that cools slowly beneath the ground forms bodies of igneous rock called plutons. Some unusual rock formations in North Carolina, such as Looking Glass Rock near Asheville, are parts of plutons that have been exposed and weathered. Plutons are composed of valuable rocks, such as granite. Granite is often used in buildings, statues, monuments, and countertops.

Plutons also contain gemstones, such as emeralds, and valuable minerals such as feldspar, quartz, and mica. In fact, the largest emerald ever found in North America was discovered in North Carolina. Feldspar is useful as a component in glass, pottery, ceramics, and abrasive cleaners. See the table below for more information about the uses of minerals found in North Carolina.

The folding and faulting of continental plates have produced the metamorphic rocks found in North Carolina. Some of these rocks are shiny because they contain large amounts of mica. In other metamorphic rocks, minerals formed layers as the rocks were squeezed. Like igneous rocks, metamorphic rocks can become exposed at the surface over time. Faults in the southern Appalachians have acted as channels for melted metals such as gold. Gold was actively mined in North Carolina from the 1700s to the mid-1900s.

Common Rocks and Minerals of North Carolina	
Rock or Mineral	**Uses**
Clay	bricks for construction
Copper	electrical wires
Emeralds, garnets, rubies	gems
Feldspar	component of ceramic tiles and abrasive cleaners
Gold	jewelry, coins
Granite	construction of monuments, buildings, and roads
Limestone	all types of buildings
Mica	filler in paints, joint compound, plastics, and cosmetics
Phosphate	component of fertilizer, animal feed, pesticides, and ceramics
Quartz	gems, glass products, and computer components

NORTH CAROLINA STANDARDS

3.04 Describe the processes which form and the uses of earth materials: common gems, minerals, precious metals and rocks found in N.C.

Student Resource Handbooks

Making Observations

An **observation** is an act of noting and recording an event, characteristic, behavior, or anything else detected with an instrument or with the senses.

Observations allow you to make informed hypotheses and to gather data for experiments. Careful observations often lead to ideas for new experiments. There are two categories of observations:

- **Quantitative observations** can be expressed in numbers and include records of time, temperature, mass, distance, and volume.

- **Qualitative observations** include descriptions of sights, sounds, smells, and textures.

EXAMPLE

A student dissolved 30 grams of Epsom salts in water, poured the solution into a dish, and let the dish sit out uncovered overnight. The next day, she made the following observations of the Epsom salt crystals that grew in the dish.

> To determine the mass, the student found the mass of the dish before and after growing the crystals and then used subtraction to find the difference.

> The student measured several crystals and calculated the mean length. (To learn how to calculate the mean of a data set, see page R36.)

Table 1. Observations of Epsom Salt Crystals

Quantitative Observations	Qualitative Observations
• mass = 30 g • mean crystal length = 0.5 cm • longest crystal length = 2 cm	• Crystals are clear. • Crystals are long, thin, and rectangular. • White crust has formed around edge of dish.

> Photographs or sketches are useful for recording qualitative observations.

 Epsom salt crystals

MORE ABOUT OBSERVING

- Make quantitative observations whenever possible. That way, others will know exactly what you observed and be able to compare their results with yours.

- It is always a good idea to make qualitative observations too. You never know when you might observe something unexpected.

Predicting and Hypothesizing

A **prediction** is an expectation of what will be observed or what will happen. A **hypothesis** is a tentative explanation for an observation or scientific problem that can be tested by further investigation.

EXAMPLE

Suppose you have made two paper airplanes and you wonder why one of them tends to glide farther than the other one.

1. Start by asking a question.

2. Make an educated guess. After examination, you notice that the wings of the airplane that flies farther are slightly larger than the wings of the other airplane.

3. Write a prediction based upon your educated guess, in the form of an "If . . . , then . . ." statement. Write the independent variable after the word *if,* and the dependent variable after the word *then.*

4. To make a hypothesis, explain why you think what you predicted will occur. Write the explanation after the word *because.*

1. Why does one of the paper airplanes glide farther than the other?

2. The size of an airplane's wings may affect how far the airplane will glide.

3. Prediction: If I make a paper airplane with larger wings, then the airplane will glide farther.

> To read about independent and dependent variables, see page R30.

4. Hypothesis: If I make a paper airplane with larger wings, then the airplane will glide farther, because the additional surface area of the wing will produce more lift.

> Notice that the part of the hypothesis after *because* adds an explanation of why the airplane will glide farther.

MORE ABOUT HYPOTHESES

- The results of an experiment cannot prove that a hypothesis is correct. Rather, the results either support or do not support the hypothesis.

- Valuable information is gained even when your hypothesis is not supported by your results. For example, it would be an important discovery to find that wing size is not related to how far an airplane glides.

- In science, a hypothesis is supported only after many scientists have conducted many experiments and produced consistent results.

Inferring

An **inference** is a logical conclusion drawn from the available evidence and prior knowledge. Inferences are often made from observations.

SCIENTIFIC THINKING HANDBOOK

EXAMPLE

A student observing a set of acorns noticed something unexpected about one of them. He noticed a white, soft-bodied insect eating its way out of the acorn.

> The student recorded these observations.

▶ **Observations**
- There is a hole in the acorn, about 0.5 cm in diameter, where the insect crawled out.
- There is a second hole, which is about the size of a pinhole, on the other side of the acorn.
- The inside of the acorn is hollow.

> Here are some inferences that can be made on the basis of the observations.

▶ **Inferences**
- The insect formed from the material inside the acorn, grew to its present size, and ate its way out of the acorn.
- The insect crawled through the smaller hole, ate the inside of the acorn, grew to its present size, and ate its way out of the acorn.
- An egg was laid in the acorn through the smaller hole. The egg hatched into a larva that ate the inside of the acorn, grew to its present size, and ate its way out of the acorn.

> When you make inferences, be sure to look at all of the evidence available and combine it with what you already know.

MORE ABOUT INFERENCES

Inferences depend both on observations and on the knowledge of the people making the inferences. Ancient people who did not know that organisms are produced only by similar organisms might have made an inference like the first one. A student today might look at the same observations and make the second inference. A third student might have knowledge about this particular insect and know that it is never small enough to fit through the smaller hole, leading her to the third inference.

Identifying Cause and Effect

In a **cause-and-effect relationship,** one event or characteristic is the result of another. Usually an effect follows its cause in time.

There are many examples of cause-and-effect relationships in everyday life.

Cause	Effect
Turn off a light.	Room gets dark.
Drop a glass.	Glass breaks.
Blow a whistle.	Sound is heard.

Scientists must be careful not to infer a cause-and-effect relationship just because one event happens after another event. When one event occurs after another, you cannot infer a cause-and-effect relationship on the basis of that information alone. You also cannot conclude that one event caused another if there are alternative ways to explain the second event. A scientist must demonstrate through experimentation or continued observation that an event was truly caused by another event.

EXAMPLE

Make an Observation

Suppose you have a few plants growing outside. When the weather starts getting colder, you bring one of the plants indoors. You notice that the plant you brought indoors is growing faster than the others are growing. You cannot conclude from your observation that the change in temperature was the cause of the increased plant growth, because there are alternative explanations for the observation. Some possible explanations are given below.

- The humidity indoors caused the plant to grow faster.

- The level of sunlight indoors caused the plant to grow faster.

- The indoor plant's being noticed more often and watered more often than the outdoor plants caused it to grow faster.

- The plant that was brought indoors was healthier than the other plants to begin with.

To determine which of these factors, if any, caused the indoor plant to grow faster than the outdoor plants, you would need to design and conduct an experiment.

See pages R28–R35 for information about designing experiments.

Recognizing Bias

Television, newspapers, and the Internet are full of experts claiming to have scientific evidence to back up their claims. How do you know whether the claims are really backed up by good science?

SCIENTIFIC THINKING HANDBOOK

Bias is a slanted point of view, or personal prejudice. The goal of scientists is to be as objective as possible and to base their findings on facts instead of opinions. However, bias often affects the conclusions of researchers, and it is important to learn to recognize bias.

When scientific results are reported, you should consider the source of the information as well as the information itself. It is important to critically analyze the information that you see and read.

SOURCES OF BIAS

There are several ways in which a report of scientific information may be biased. Here are some questions that you can ask yourself:

1. **Who is sponsoring the research?**

   Sometimes, the results of an investigation are biased because an organization paying for the research is looking for a specific answer. This type of bias can affect how data are gathered and interpreted.

2. **Is the research sample large enough?**

   Sometimes research does not include enough data. The larger the sample size, the more likely that the results are accurate, assuming a truly random sample.

3. **In a survey, who is answering the questions?**

   The results of a survey or poll can be biased. The people taking part in the survey may have been specifically chosen because of how they would answer. They may have the same ideas or lifestyles. A survey or poll should make use of a random sample of people.

4. **Are the people who take part in a survey biased?**

   People who take part in surveys sometimes try to answer the questions the way they think the researcher wants them to answer. Also, in surveys or polls that ask for personal information, people may be unwilling to answer questions truthfully.

SCIENTIFIC BIAS

It is also important to realize that scientists have their own biases because of the types of research they do and because of their scientific viewpoints. Two scientists may look at the same set of data and come to completely different conclusions because of these biases. However, such disagreements are not necessarily bad. In fact, a critical analysis of disagreements is often responsible for moving science forward.

Identifying Faulty Reasoning

Faulty reasoning is wrong or incorrect thinking. It leads to mistakes and to wrong conclusions. Scientists are careful not to draw unreasonable conclusions from experimental data. Without such caution, the results of scientific investigations may be misleading.

EXAMPLE

Scientists try to make generalizations based on their data to explain as much about nature as possible. If only a small sample of data is looked at, however, a conclusion may be faulty. Suppose a scientist has studied the effects of the El Niño and La Niña weather patterns on flood damage in California from 1989 to 1995. The scientist organized the data in the bar graph below.

The scientist drew the following conclusions:

1. The La Niña weather pattern has no effect on flooding in California.
2. When neither weather pattern occurs, there is almost no flood damage.
3. A weak or moderate El Niño produces a small or moderate amount of flooding.
4. A strong El Niño produces a lot of flooding.

Flood and Storm Damage in California

Estimated damage (millions of dollars): 0, 500, 1000, 1500, 2000

Weak–moderate El Niño

Strong El Niño

Starting year of season
(July 1–June 30)

Starting year of season: 1989, 1992, 1995

SOURCE: *Governor's Office of Emergency Services, California*

For the six-year period of the scientist's investigation, these conclusions may seem to be reasonable. However, a six-year study of weather patterns may be too small of a sample for the conclusions to be supported. Consider the following graph, which shows information that was gathered from 1949 to 1997.

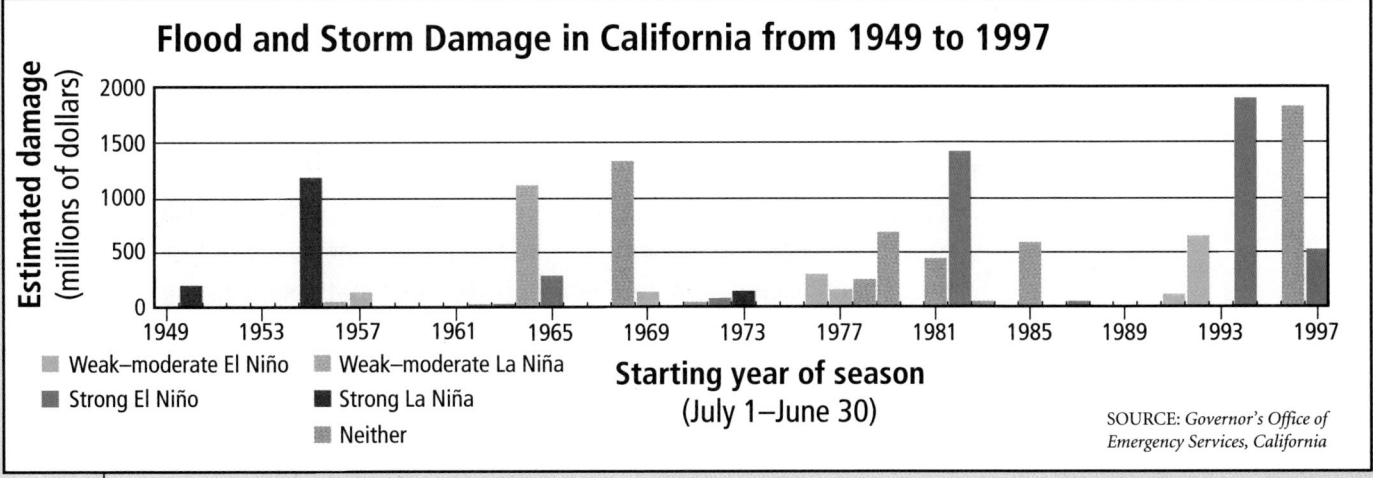

Flood and Storm Damage in California from 1949 to 1997

Estimated damage (millions of dollars): 0, 500, 1000, 1500, 2000

Starting year of season: 1949, 1953, 1957, 1961, 1965, 1969, 1973, 1977, 1981, 1985, 1989, 1993, 1997

■ Weak–moderate El Niño   ■ Weak–moderate La Niña
■ Strong El Niño   ■ Strong La Niña
■ Neither

Starting year of season
(July 1–June 30)

SOURCE: *Governor's Office of Emergency Services, California*

The only one of the conclusions that all of this information supports is number 3: a weak or moderate El Niño produces a small or moderate amount of flooding. By collecting more data, scientists can be more certain of their conclusions and can avoid faulty reasoning.

Analyzing Statements

To **analyze** a statement is to examine its parts carefully. Scientific findings are often reported through media such as television or the Internet. A report that is made public often focuses on only a small part of research. As a result, it is important to question the sources of information.

Evaluate Media Claims

To **evaluate** a statement is to judge it on the basis of criteria you've established. Sometimes evaluating means deciding whether a statement is true.

Reports of scientific research and findings in the media may be misleading or incomplete. When you are exposed to this information, you should ask yourself some questions so that you can make informed judgments about the information.

1. **Does the information come from a credible source?**

   Suppose you learn about a new product and it is stated that scientific evidence proves that the product works. A report from a respected news source may be more believable than an advertisement paid for by the product's manufacturer.

2. **How much evidence supports the claim?**

   Often, it may seem that there is new evidence every day of something in the world that either causes or cures an illness. However, information that is the result of several years of work by several different scientists is more credible than an advertisement that does not even cite the subjects of the experiment.

3. **How much information is being presented?**

   Science cannot solve all questions, and scientific experiments often have flaws. A report that discusses problems in a scientific study may be more believable than a report that addresses only positive experimental findings.

4. **Is scientific evidence being presented by a specific source?**

   Sometimes scientific findings are reported by people who are called experts or leaders in a scientific field. But if their names are not given or their scientific credentials are not reported, their statements may be less credible than those of recognized experts.

Differentiate Between Fact and Opinion

Sometimes information is presented as a fact when it may be an opinion. When scientific conclusions are reported, it is important to recognize whether they are based on solid evidence. Again, you may find it helpful to ask yourself some questions.

1. **What is the difference between a fact and an opinion?**

   A **fact** is a piece of information that can be strictly defined and proved true. An **opinion** is a statement that expresses a belief, value, or feeling. An opinion cannot be proved true or false. For example, a person's age is a fact, but if someone is asked how old they feel, it is impossible to prove the person's answer to be true or false.

2. **Can opinions be measured?**

   Yes, opinions can be measured. In fact, surveys often ask for people's opinions on a topic. But there is no way to know whether or not an opinion is the truth.

HOW TO DIFFERENTIATE FACT FROM OPINION

Human Activities and the Environment

Unfortunately, human use of fossil fuels is one of the most significant developments of the past few centuries. Humans rely on fossil fuels, a non-renewable energy resource, for more than 90 percent of their energy needs.

This careless misuse of our planet's resources has resulted in pollution, global warming, and the destruction of fragile ecosystems. For example, oil pipelines carry more than one million barrels of oil each day across tundra regions. Transporting oil across such areas can only result in oil spills that poison the land for decades.

Opinions
Notice words or phrases that express beliefs or feelings. The words *unfortunately* and *careless* show that opinions are being expressed.

Opinion
Look for statements that speculate about events. These statements are opinions, because they cannot be proved.

Facts
Statements that contain statistics tend to be facts. Writers often use facts to support their opinions.

Lab Handbook

Safety Rules

Before you work in the laboratory, read these safety rules twice. Ask your teacher to explain any rules that you do not completely understand. Refer to these rules later on if you have questions about safety in the science classroom.

Directions

- Read all directions and make sure that you understand them before starting an investigation or lab activity. If you do not understand how to do a procedure or how to use a piece of equipment, ask your teacher.
- Do not begin any investigation or touch any equipment until your teacher has told you to start.
- Never experiment on your own. If you want to try a procedure that the directions do not call for, ask your teacher for permission first.
- If you are hurt or injured in any way, tell your teacher immediately.

Dress Code

goggles

apron

gloves

- Wear goggles when
  — using glassware, sharp objects, or chemicals
  — heating an object
  — working with anything that can easily fly up into the air and hurt someone's eye
- Tie back long hair or hair that hangs in front of your eyes.
- Remove any article of clothing—such as a loose sweater or a scarf—that hangs down and may touch a flame, chemical, or piece of equipment.
- Observe all safety icons calling for the wearing of eye protection, gloves, and aprons.

Heating and Fire Safety

fire safety

heating safety

- Keep your work area neat, clean, and free of extra materials.
- Never reach over a flame or heat source.
- Point objects being heated away from you and others.
- Never heat a substance or an object in a closed container.
- Never touch an object that has been heated. If you are unsure whether something is hot, treat it as though it is. Use oven mitts, clamps, tongs, or a test-tube holder.
- Know where the fire extinguisher and fire blanket are kept in your classroom.
- Do not throw hot substances into the trash. Wait for them to cool or use the container your teacher puts out for disposal.

Electrical Safety

electrical safety

- Never use lamps or other electrical equipment with frayed cords.
- Make sure no cord is lying on the floor where someone can trip over it.
- Do not let a cord hang over the side of a counter or table so that the equipment can easily be pulled or knocked to the floor.
- Never let cords hang into sinks or other places where water can be found.
- Never try to fix electrical problems. Inform your teacher of any problems immediately.
- Unplug an electrical cord by pulling on the plug, not the cord.

Chemical Safety

chemical safety

poison

fumes

- If you spill a chemical or get one on your skin or in your eyes, tell your teacher right away.
- Never touch, taste, or sniff any chemicals in the lab. If you need to determine odor, waft. Wafting consists of holding the chemical in its container 15 centimeters (6 in.) away from your nose, and using your fingers to bring fumes from the container to your nose.
- Keep lids on all chemicals you are not using.
- Never put unused chemicals back into the original containers. Throw away extra chemicals where your teacher tells you to.
- Pour chemicals over a sink or your work area, not over the floor.
- If you get a chemical in your eye, use the eyewash right away.
- Always wash your hands after handling chemicals, plants, or soil.

LAB HANDBOOK

Wafting

Glassware and Sharp-Object Safety

sharp objects

- If you break glassware, tell your teacher right away.
- Do not use broken or chipped glassware. Give these to your teacher.
- Use knives and other cutting instruments carefully. Always wear eye protection and cut away from you.

Animal Safety

- Never hurt an animal.
- Touch animals only when necessary. Follow your teacher's instructions for handling animals.
- Always wash your hands after working with animals.

Cleanup

disposal

- Follow your teacher's instructions for throwing away or putting away supplies.
- Clean your work area and pick up anything that has dropped to the floor.
- Wash your hands.

Using Lab Equipment

Different experiments require different types of equipment. But even though experiments differ, the ways in which the equipment is used are the same.

LAB HANDBOOK

Beakers

- Use beakers for holding and pouring liquids.
- Do not use a beaker to measure the volume of a liquid. Use a graduated cylinder instead. (See page R16.)
- Use a beaker that holds about twice as much liquid as you need. For example, if you need 100 milliliters of water, you should use a 200- or 250-milliliter beaker.

Test Tubes

- Use test tubes to hold small amounts of substances.
- Do not use a test tube to measure the volume of a liquid.
- Use a test tube when heating a substance over a flame. Aim the mouth of the tube away from yourself and other people.
- Liquids easily spill or splash from test tubes, so it is important to use only small amounts of liquids.

Test-Tube Holder

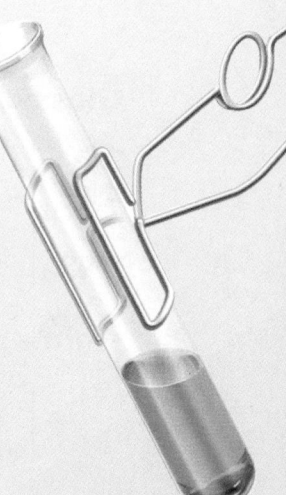

- Use a test-tube holder when heating a substance in a test tube.
- Use a test-tube holder if the substance in a test tube is dangerous to touch.
- Make sure the test-tube holder tightly grips the test tube so that the test tube will not slide out of the holder.
- Make sure that the test-tube holder is above the surface of the substance in the test tube so that you can observe the substance.

Test-Tube Rack

- Use a test-tube rack to organize test tubes before, during, and after an experiment.

- Use a test-tube rack to keep test tubes upright so that they do not fall over and spill their contents.

- Use a test-tube rack that is the correct size for the test tubes that you are using. If the rack is too small, a test tube may become stuck. If the rack is too large, a test tube may lean over, and some of its contents may spill or splash.

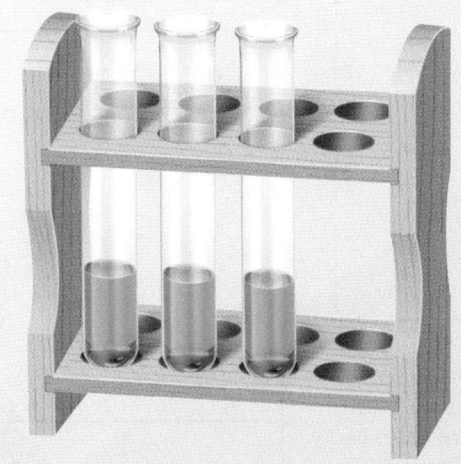

Forceps

- Use forceps when you need to pick up or hold a very small object that should not be touched with your hands.

- Do not use forceps to hold anything over a flame, because forceps are not long enough to keep your hand safely away from the flame. Plastic forceps will melt, and metal forceps will conduct heat and burn your hand.

Hot Plate

- Use a hot plate when a substance needs to be kept warmer than room temperature for a long period of time.

- Use a hot plate instead of a Bunsen burner or a candle when you need to carefully control temperature.

- Do not use a hot plate when a substance needs to be burned in an experiment.

- Always use "hot hands" safety mitts or oven mitts when handling anything that has been heated on a hot plate.

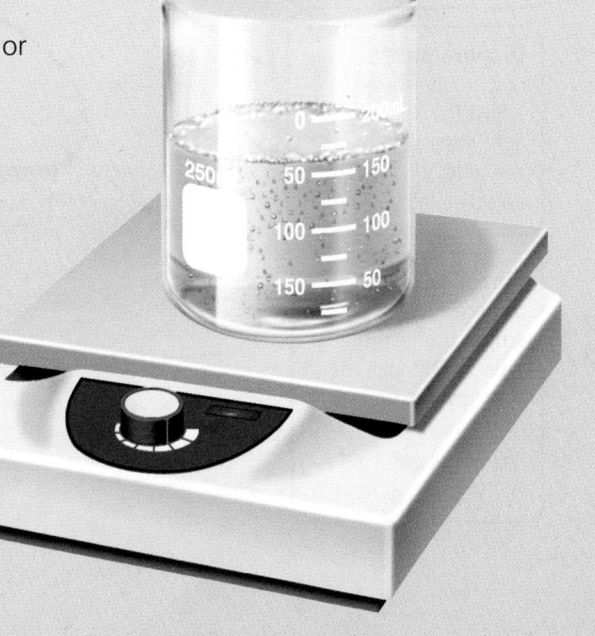

Microscope

Scientists use microscopes to see very small objects that cannot easily be seen with the eye alone. A microscope magnifies the image of an object so that small details may be observed. A microscope that you may use can magnify an object 400 times—the object will appear 400 times larger than its actual size.

LAB HANDBOOK

Eyepiece Objects are viewed through the eyepiece. The eyepiece contains a lens that commonly magnifies an image 10 times.

Coarse Adjustment This knob is used to focus the image of an object when it is viewed through the low-power lens.

Fine Adjustment This knob is used to focus the image of an object when it is viewed through the high-power lens.

Low-Power Objective Lens This is the smallest lens on the nosepiece. It magnifies an image approximately 10 times.

Arm The arm supports the body above the stage. Always carry a microscope by the arm and base.

Stage Clip The stage clip holds a slide in place on the stage.

Base The base supports the microscope.

Body The body separates the lens in the eyepiece from the objective lenses below.

Nosepiece The nosepiece holds the objective lenses above the stage and rotates so that all lenses may be used.

High-Power Objective Lens This is the largest lens on the nosepiece. It magnifies an image approximately 40 times.

Stage The stage supports the object being viewed.

Diaphragm The diaphragm is used to adjust the amount of light passing through the slide and into an objective lens.

Mirror or Light Source Some microscopes use light that is reflected through the stage by a mirror. Other microscopes have their own light sources.

VIEWING AN OBJECT

1. Use the coarse adjustment knob to raise the body tube.

2. Adjust the diaphragm so that you can see a bright circle of light through the eyepiece.

3. Place the object or slide on the stage. Be sure that it is centered over the hole in the stage.

4. Turn the nosepiece to click the low-power lens into place.

5. Using the coarse adjustment knob, slowly lower the lens and focus on the specimen being viewed. Be sure not to touch the slide or object with the lens.

6. When switching from the low-power lens to the high-power lens, first raise the body tube with the coarse adjustment knob so that the high-power lens will not hit the slide.

7. Turn the nosepiece to click the high-power lens into place.

8. Use the fine adjustment knob to focus on the specimen being viewed. Again, be sure not to touch the slide or object with the lens.

MAKING A SLIDE, OR WET MOUNT

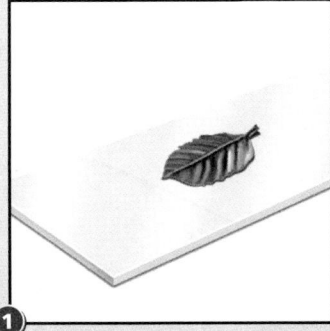

1 Place the specimen in the center of a clean slide.

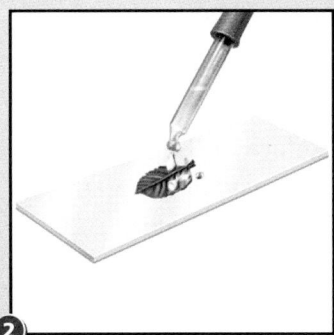

2 Place a drop of water on the specimen.

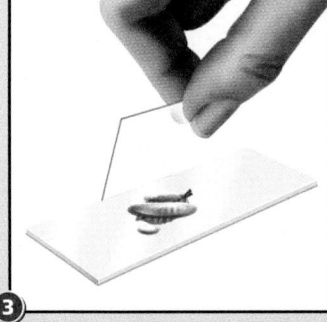

3 Place a cover slip on the slide. Put one edge of the cover slip into the drop of water and slowly lower it over the specimen.

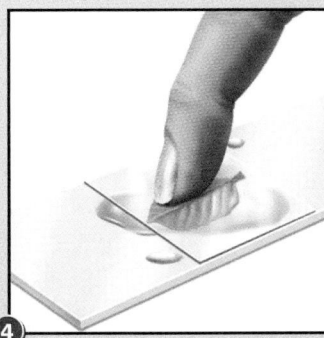

4 Remove any air bubbles from under the cover slip by gently tapping the cover slip.

5 Dry any excess water before placing the slide on the microscope stage for viewing.

Spring Scale (Force Meter)

- Use a spring scale to measure a force pulling on the scale.
- Use a spring scale to measure the force of gravity exerted on an object by Earth.
- To measure a force accurately, a spring scale must be zeroed before it is used. The scale is zeroed when no weight is attached and the indicator is positioned at zero.
- Do not attach a weight that is either too heavy or too light to a spring scale. A weight that is too heavy could break the scale or exert too great a force for the scale to measure. A weight that is too light may not exert enough force to be measured accurately.

Graduated Cylinder

- Use a graduated cylinder to measure the volume of a liquid.
- Be sure that the graduated cylinder is on a flat surface so that your measurement will be accurate.
- When reading the scale on a graduated cylinder, be sure to have your eyes at the level of the surface of the liquid.
- The surface of the liquid will be curved in the graduated cylinder. Read the volume of the liquid at the bottom of the curve, or meniscus (muh-NIHS-kuhs).
- You can use a graduated cylinder to find the volume of a solid object by measuring the increase in a liquid's level after you add the object to the cylinder.

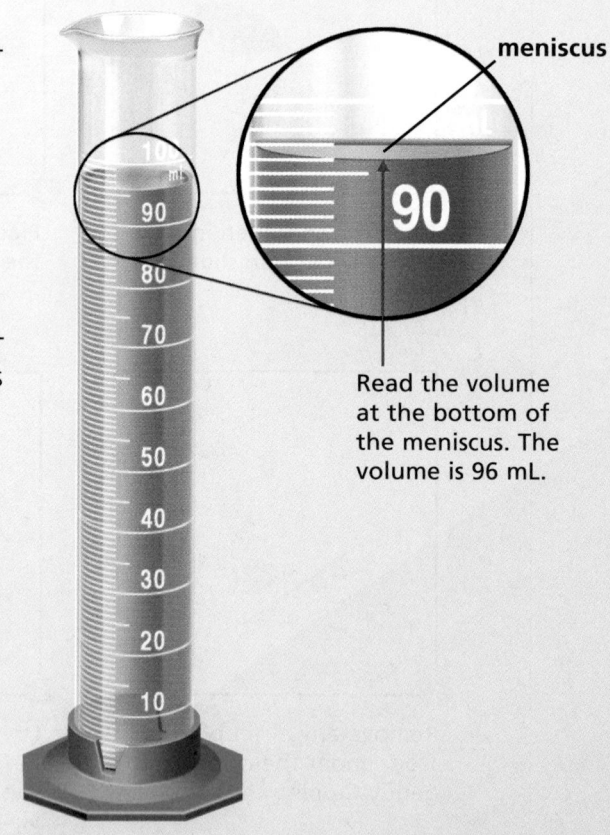

meniscus

Read the volume at the bottom of the meniscus. The volume is 96 mL.

Metric Rulers

- Use metric rulers or meter sticks to measure objects' lengths.

- Do not measure an object from the end of a metric ruler or meter stick, because the end is often imperfect. Instead, measure from the 1-centimeter mark, but remember to subtract a centimeter from the apparent measurement.

- Estimate any lengths that extend between marked units. For example, if a meter stick shows centimeters but not millimeters, you can estimate the length that an object extends between centimeter marks to measure it to the nearest millimeter.

- **Controlling Variables** If you are taking repeated measurements, always measure from the same point each time. For example, if you're measuring how high two different balls bounce when dropped from the same height, measure both bounces at the same point on the balls—either the top or the bottom. Do not measure at the top of one ball and the bottom of the other.

EXAMPLE

How to Measure a Leaf

1. Lay a ruler flat on top of the leaf so that the 1-centimeter mark lines up with one end. Make sure the ruler and the leaf do not move between the time you line them up and the time you take the measurement.

2. Look straight down on the ruler so that you can see exactly how the marks line up with the other end of the leaf.

3. Estimate the length by which the leaf extends beyond a marking. For example, the leaf below extends about halfway between the 4.2-centimeter and 4.3-centimeter marks, so the apparent measurement is about 4.25 centimeters.

4. Remember to subtract 1 centimeter from your apparent measurement, since you started at the 1-centimeter mark on the ruler and not at the end. The leaf is about 3.25 centimeters long (4.25 cm – 1 cm = 3.25 cm).

Triple-Beam Balance

This balance has a pan and three beams with sliding masses, called riders. At one end of the beams is a pointer that indicates whether the mass on the pan is equal to the masses shown on the beams.

1. Make sure the balance is zeroed before measuring the mass of an object. The balance is zeroed if the pointer is at zero when nothing is on the pan and the riders are at their zero points. Use the adjustment knob at the base of the balance to zero it.

2. Place the object to be measured on the pan.

3. Move the riders one notch at a time away from the pan. Begin with the largest rider. If moving the largest rider one notch brings the pointer below zero, begin measuring the mass of the object with the next smaller rider.

4. Change the positions of the riders until they balance the mass on the pan and the pointer is at zero. Then add the readings from the three beams to determine the mass of the object.

300 g	position of largest rider
90 g	position of middle rider
+ 3 g	position of smallest rider
393 g	mass of beaker

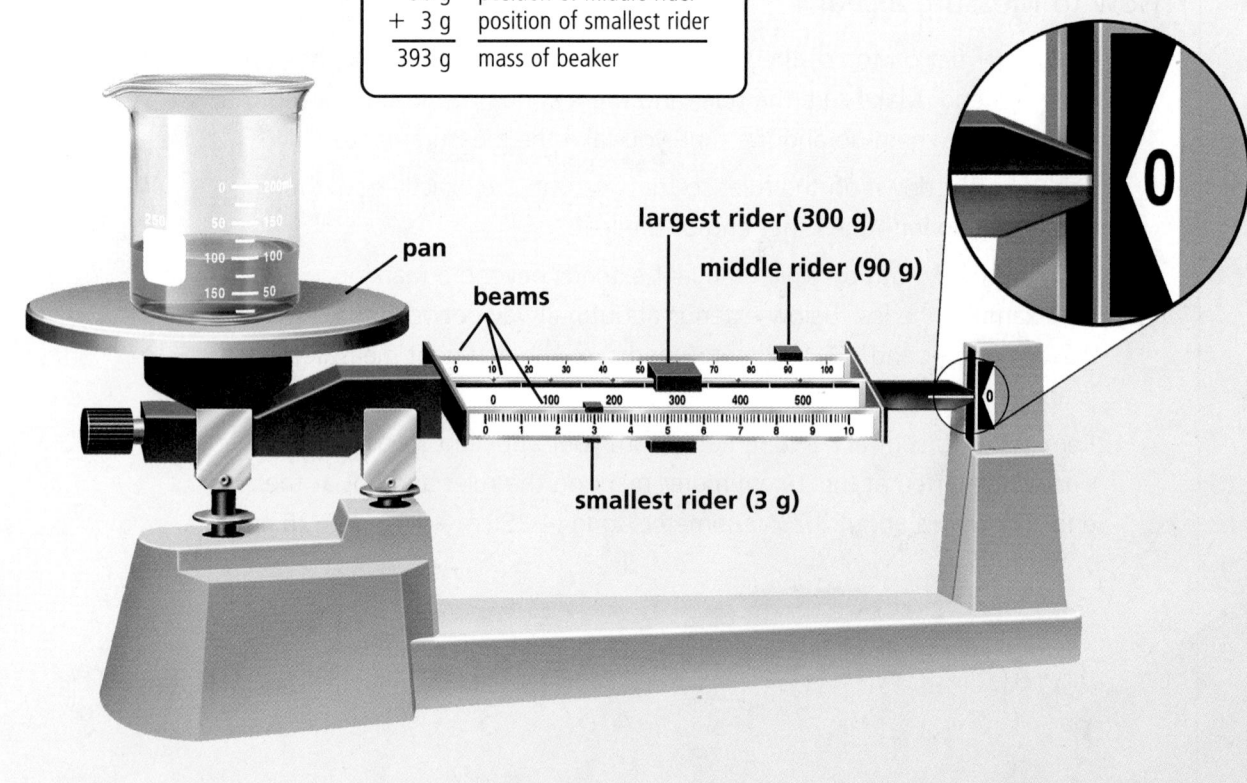

Double-Pan Balance

This type of balance has two pans. Between the pans is a pointer that indicates whether the masses on the pans are equal.

1. Make sure the balance is zeroed before measuring the mass of an object. The balance is zeroed if the pointer is at zero when there is nothing on either of the pans. Many double-pan balances have sliding knobs that can be used to zero them.

2. Place the object to be measured on one of the pans.

3. Begin adding standard masses to the other pan. Begin with the largest standard mass. If this adds too much mass to the balance, begin measuring the mass of the object with the next smaller standard mass.

4. Add standard masses until the masses on both pans are balanced and the pointer is at zero. Then add the standard masses together to determine the mass of the object being measured.

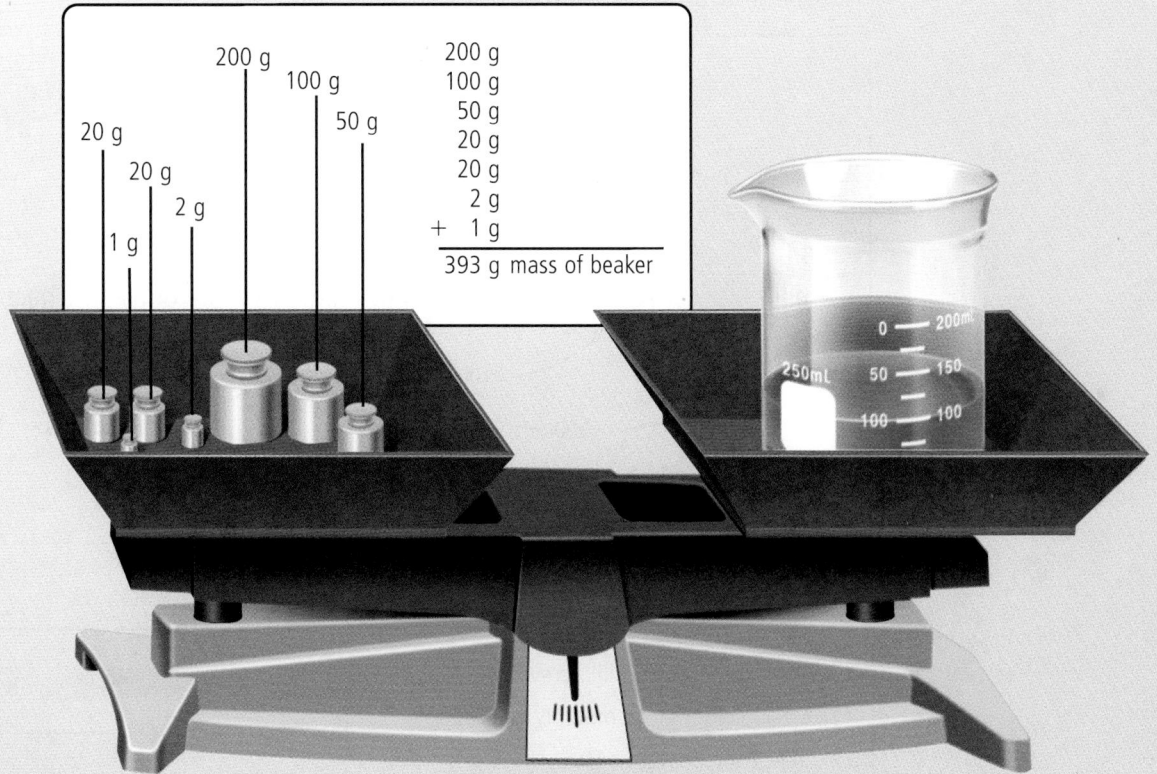

```
200 g
100 g
 50 g
 20 g
 20 g
  2 g
+ 1 g
─────
393 g  mass of beaker
```

Never place chemicals or liquids directly on a pan. Instead, use the following procedure:

1. Determine the mass of an empty container, such as a beaker.

2. Pour the substance into the container, and measure the total mass of the substance and the container.

3. Subtract the mass of the empty container from the total mass to find the mass of the substance.

The Metric System and SI Units

Scientists use International System (SI) units for measurements of distance, volume, mass, and temperature. The International System is based on multiples of ten and the metric system of measurement.

Basic SI Units		
Property	**Name**	**Symbol**
length	meter	m
volume	liter	L
mass	kilogram	kg
temperature	kelvin	K

SI Prefixes		
Prefix	**Symbol**	**Multiple of 10**
kilo-	k	1000
hecto-	h	100
deca-	da	10
deci-	d	$0.1 \left(\frac{1}{10}\right)$
centi-	c	$0.01 \left(\frac{1}{100}\right)$
milli-	m	$0.001 \left(\frac{1}{1000}\right)$

Changing Metric Units

You can change from one unit to another in the metric system by multiplying or dividing by a power of 10.

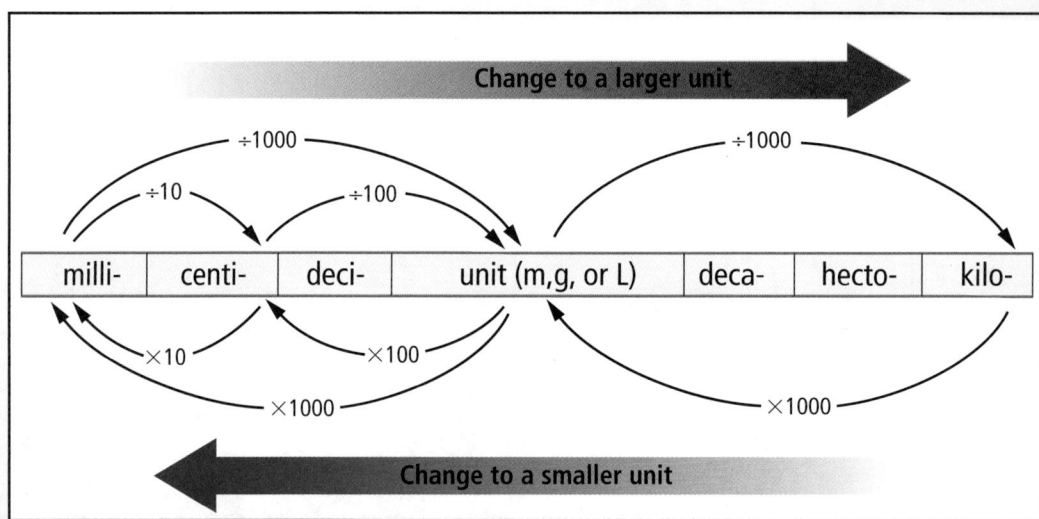

Example

Change 0.64 liters to milliliters.

(1) Decide whether to multiply or divide.

(2) Select the power of 10.

ANSWER 0.64 L = 640 mL

Change to a smaller unit by multiplying.

mL ⟵ × 1000 ⟶ L

0.64 × 1000 = **640.**

Example

Change 23.6 grams to kilograms.

(1) Decide whether to multiply or divide.

(2) Select the power of 10.

ANSWER 23.6 g = 0.0236 kg

Change to a larger unit by dividing.

g ⟶ ÷ 1000 ⟶ kg

23.6 ÷ 1000 = **0.0236**

Temperature Conversions

Even though the kelvin is the SI base unit of temperature, the degree Celsius will be the unit you use most often in your science studies. The formulas below show the relationships between temperatures in degrees Fahrenheit (°F), degrees Celsius (°C), and kelvins (K).

$$°C = \frac{5}{9}(°F - 32)$$

$$°F = \frac{9}{5}°C + 32$$

$$K = °C + 273$$

See page R42 for help with using formulas.

Examples of Temperature Conversions

Condition	Degrees Celsius	Degrees Fahrenheit
Freezing point of water	0	32
Cool day	10	50
Mild day	20	68
Warm day	30	86
Normal body temperature	37	98.6
Very hot day	40	104
Boiling point of water	100	212

Converting Between SI and U.S. Customary Units

Use the chart below when you need to convert between SI units and U.S. customary units.

SI Unit	From SI to U.S. Customary			From U.S. Customary to SI		
Length	**When you know**	**multiply by**	**to find**	**When you know**	**multiply by**	**to find**
kilometer (km) = 1000 m	kilometers	0.62	miles	miles	1.61	kilometers
meter (m) = 100 cm	meters	3.28	feet	feet	0.3048	meters
centimeter (cm) = 10 mm	centimeters	0.39	inches	inches	2.54	centimeters
millimeter (mm) = 0.1 cm	millimeters	0.04	inches	inches	25.4	millimeters
Area	**When you know**	**multiply by**	**to find**	**When you know**	**multiply by**	**to find**
square kilometer (km²)	square kilometers	0.39	square miles	square miles	2.59	square kilometers
square meter (m²)	square meters	1.2	square yards	square yards	0.84	square meters
square centimeter (cm²)	square centimeters	0.155	square inches	square inches	6.45	square centimeters
Volume	**When you know**	**multiply by**	**to find**	**When you know**	**multiply by**	**to find**
liter (L) = 1000 mL	liters	1.06	quarts	quarts	0.95	liters
	liters	0.26	gallons	gallons	3.79	liters
	liters	4.23	cups	cups	0.24	liters
	liters	2.12	pints	pints	0.47	liters
milliliter (mL) = 0.001 L	milliliters	0.20	teaspoons	teaspoons	4.93	milliliters
	milliliters	0.07	tablespoons	tablespoons	14.79	milliliters
	milliliters	0.03	fluid ounces	fluid ounces	29.57	milliliters
Mass	**When you know**	**multiply by**	**to find**	**When you know**	**multiply by**	**to find**
kilogram (kg) = 1000 g	kilograms	2.2	pounds	pounds	0.45	kilograms
gram (g) = 1000 mg	grams	0.035	ounces	ounces	28.35	grams

Precision and Accuracy

When you do an experiment, it is important that your methods, observations, and data be both precise and accurate.

low precision

precision, but not accuracy

precision and accuracy

Precision

In science, **precision** is the exactness and consistency of measurements. For example, measurements made with a ruler that has both centimeter and millimeter markings would be more precise than measurements made with a ruler that has only centimeter markings. Another indicator of precision is the care taken to make sure that methods and observations are as exact and consistent as possible. Every time a particular experiment is done, the same procedure should be used. Precision is necessary because experiments are repeated several times and if the procedure changes, the results will change.

EXAMPLE

Suppose you are measuring temperatures over a two-week period. Your precision will be greater if you measure each temperature at the same place, at the same time of day, and with the same thermometer than if you change any of these factors from one day to the next.

Accuracy

In science, it is possible to be precise but not accurate. **Accuracy** depends on the difference between a measurement and an actual value. The smaller the difference, the more accurate the measurement.

EXAMPLE

Suppose you look at a stream and estimate that it is about 1 meter wide at a particular place. You decide to check your estimate by measuring the stream with a meter stick, and you determine that the stream is 1.32 meters wide. However, because it is hard to measure the width of a stream with a meter stick, it turns out that you didn't do a very good job. The stream is actually 1.14 meters wide. Therefore, even though your estimate was less precise than your measurement, your estimate was actually more accurate.

Making Data Tables and Graphs

Data tables and graphs are useful tools for both recording and communicating scientific data.

Making Data Tables

You can use a **data table** to organize and record the measurements that you make. Some examples of information that might be recorded in data tables are frequencies, times, and amounts.

EXAMPLE

Suppose you are investigating photosynthesis in two elodea plants. One sits in direct sunlight, and the other sits in a dimly lit room. You measure the rate of photosynthesis by counting the number of bubbles in the jar every ten minutes.

1. Title and number your data table.
2. Decide how you will organize the table into columns and rows.
3. Any units, such as seconds or degrees, should be included in column headings, not in the individual cells.

Table 1. Number of Bubbles from Elodea

Time (min)	Sunlight	Dim Light
0	0	0
10	15	5
20	25	8
30	32	7
40	41	10
50	47	9
60	42	9

Always number and title data tables.

The data in the table above could also be organized in a different way.

Table 1. Number of Bubbles from Elodea

Light Condition	Time (min)						
	0	10	20	30	40	50	60
Sunlight	0	15	25	32	41	47	42
Dim light	0	5	8	7	10	9	9

Put units in column heading.

Making Line Graphs

You can use a **line graph** to show a relationship between variables. Line graphs are particularly useful for showing changes in variables over time.

EXAMPLE

Suppose you are interested in graphing temperature data that you collected over the course of a day.

Table 1. Outside Temperature During the Day on March 7

	Time of Day						
	7:00 A.M.	9:00 A.M.	11:00 A.M.	1:00 P.M.	3:00 P.M.	5:00 P.M.	7:00 P.M.
Temp (°C)	8	9	11	14	12	10	6

1. Use the vertical axis of your line graph for the variable that you are measuring—temperature.

2. Choose scales for both the horizontal axis and the vertical axis of the graph. You should have two points more than you need on the vertical axis, and the horizontal axis should be long enough for all of the data points to fit.

3. Draw and label each axis.

4. Graph each value. First find the appropriate point on the scale of the horizontal axis. Imagine a line that rises vertically from that place on the scale. Then find the corresponding value on the vertical axis, and imagine a line that moves horizontally from that value. The point where these two imaginary lines intersect is where the value should be plotted.

5. Connect the points with straight lines.

> Be sure to add a number and a title to your graph.

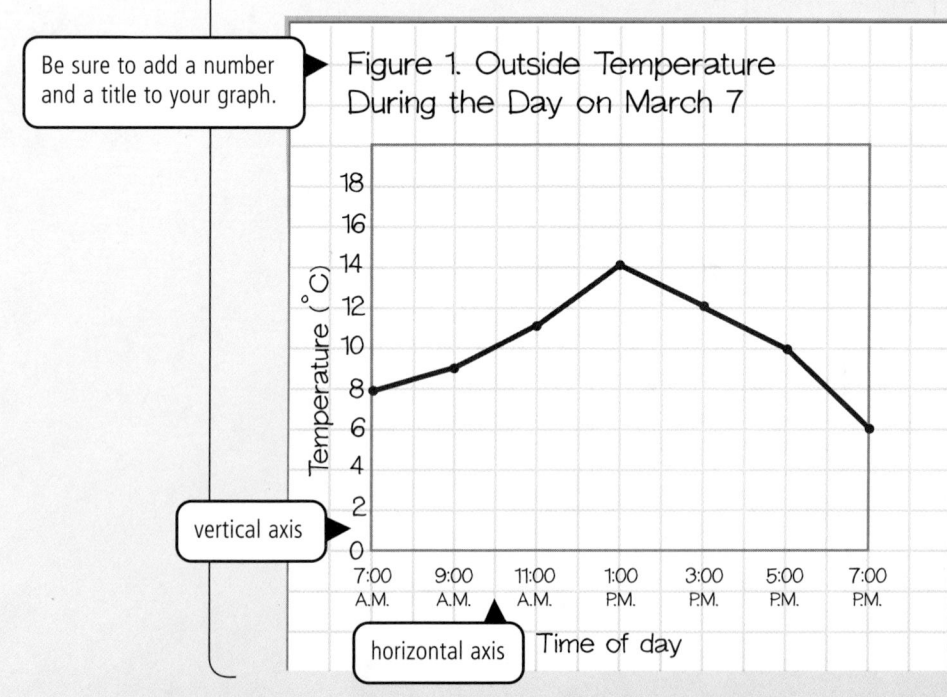

Figure 1. Outside Temperature During the Day on March 7

> vertical axis

> horizontal axis

Making Circle Graphs

You can use a **circle graph,** sometimes called a pie chart, to represent data as parts of a circle. Circle graphs are used only when the data can be expressed as percentages of a whole. The entire circle shown in a circle graph is equal to 100 percent of the data.

EXAMPLE

Suppose you identified the species of each mature tree growing in a small wooded area. You organized your data in a table, but you also want to show the data in a circle graph.

1. To begin, find the total number of mature trees.

    $56 + 34 + 22 + 10 + 28 = 150$

2. To find the degree measure for each sector of the circle, write a fraction comparing the number of each tree species with the total number of trees. Then multiply the fraction by 360°.

    Oak: $\dfrac{56}{150} \times 360° = 134.4°$

3. Draw a circle. Use a protractor to draw the angle for each sector of the graph.

4. Color and label each sector of the graph.

5. Give the graph a number and title.

Table 1. Tree Species in Wooded Area

Species	Number of Specimens
Oak	56
Maple	34
Birch	22
Willow	10
Pine	28

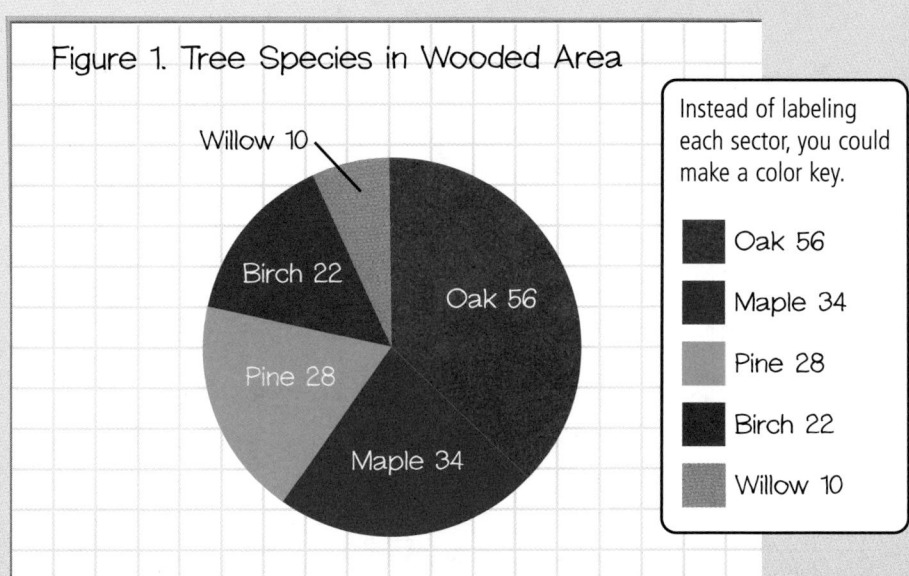

Figure 1. Tree Species in Wooded Area

Willow 10
Birch 22
Oak 56
Pine 28
Maple 34

Instead of labeling each sector, you could make a color key.

Oak 56
Maple 34
Pine 28
Birch 22
Willow 10

Bar Graph

A **bar graph** is a type of graph in which the lengths of the bars are used to represent and compare data. A numerical scale is used to determine the lengths of the bars.

EXAMPLE

To determine the effect of water on seed sprouting, three cups were filled with sand, and ten seeds were planted in each. Different amounts of water were added to each cup over a three-day period.

Table 1. Effect of Water on Seed Sprouting

Daily Amount of Water (mL)	Number of Seeds That Sprouted After 3 Days in Sand
0	1
10	4
20	8

1. Choose a numerical scale. The greatest value is 8, so the end of the scale should have a value greater than 8, such as 10. Use equal increments along the scale, such as increments of 2.

2. Draw and label the axes. Mark intervals on the vertical axis according to the scale you chose.

3. Draw a bar for each data value. Use the scale to decide how long to make each bar.

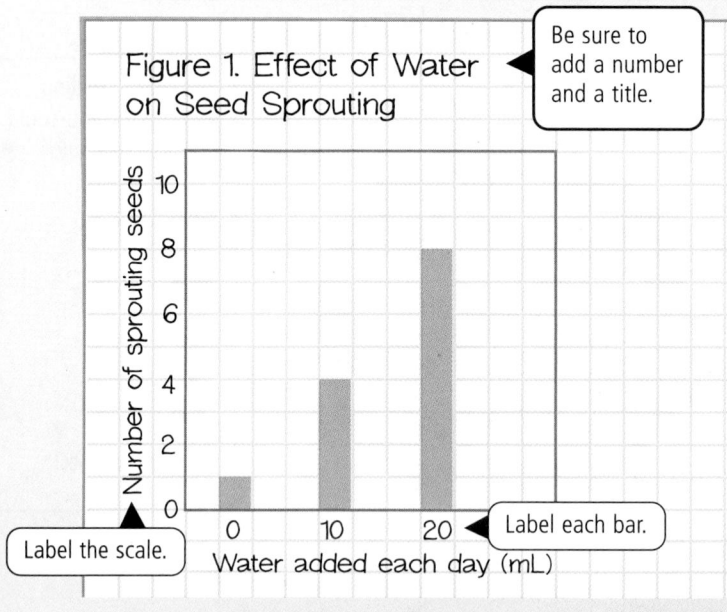

Figure 1. Effect of Water on Seed Sprouting

Be sure to add a number and a title.

Label the scale.

Label each bar.

Number of sprouting seeds

Water added each day (mL)

Double Bar Graph

A **double bar graph** is a bar graph that shows two sets of data. The two bars for each measurement are drawn next to each other.

EXAMPLE

The same seed-sprouting experiment was repeated with potting soil. The data for sand and potting soil can be plotted on one graph.

1. Draw one set of bars, using the data for sand, as shown below.

2. Draw bars for the potting-soil data next to the bars for the sand data. Shade them a different color. Add a key.

Table 2. Effect of Water and Soil on Seed Sprouting

Daily Amount of Water (mL)	Number of Seeds That Sprouted After 3 Days in Sand	Number of Seeds That Sprouted After 3 Days in Potting Soil
0	1	2
10	4	5
20	8	9

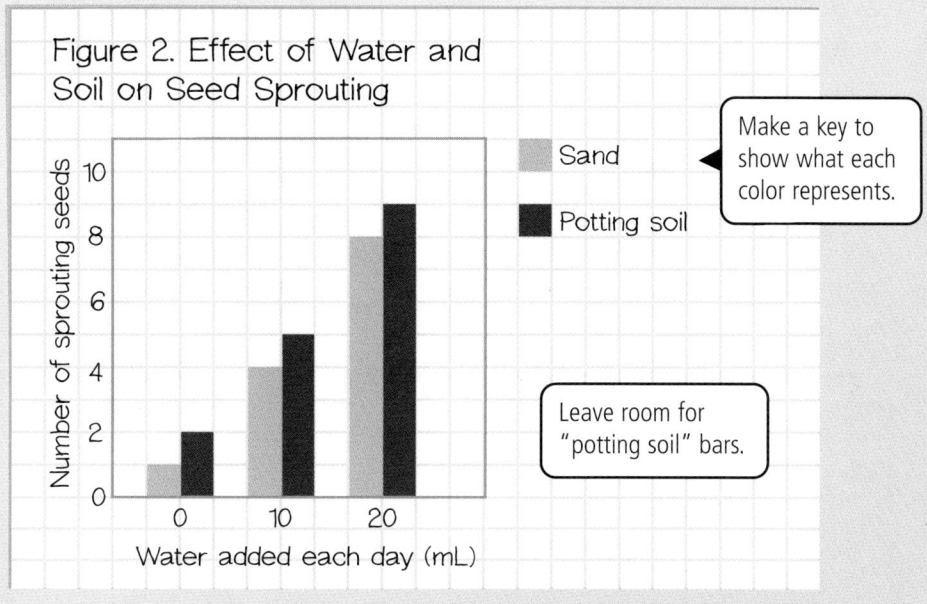

Figure 2. Effect of Water and Soil on Seed Sprouting

Make a key to show what each color represents.

Leave room for "potting soil" bars.

Designing an Experiment

Use this section when designing or conducting an experiment.

Determining a Purpose

Don't forget to learn as much as possible about your topic before you begin.

You can find a purpose for an experiment by doing research, by examining the results of a previous experiment, or by observing the world around you. An **experiment** is an organized procedure to study something under controlled conditions.

1. Write the purpose of your experiment as a question or problem that you want to investigate.

2. Write down research questions and begin searching for information that will help you design an experiment. Consult the library, the Internet, and other people as you conduct your research.

EXAMPLE

Middle school students observed an odor near the lake by their school. They also noticed that the water on the side of the lake near the school was greener than the water on the other side of the lake. The students did some research to learn more about their observations. They discovered that the odor and green color in the lake

came from algae. They also discovered that a new fertilizer was being used on a field nearby. The students inferred that the use of the fertilizer might be related to the presence of the algae and designed a controlled experiment to find out whether they were right.

Problem
How does fertilizer affect the presence of algae in a lake?

Research Questions
- Have other experiments been done on this problem? If so, what did those experiments show?
- What kind of fertilizer is used on the field? How much?
- How do algae grow?
- How do people measure algae?
- Can fertilizer and algae be used safely in a lab? How?

Research
As you research, you may find a topic that is more interesting to you than your original topic, or learn that a procedure you wanted to use is not practical or safe. It is OK to change your purpose as you research.

Writing a Hypothesis

A **hypothesis** is a tentative explanation for an observation or scientific problem that can be tested by further investigation. You can write your hypothesis in the form of an "If . . . , then . . . , because . . ." statement.

Hypothesis

If the amount of fertilizer in lake water is increased, then the amount of algae will also increase, because fertilizers provide nutrients that algae need to grow.

> **Hypotheses**
> For help with hypotheses, refer to page R3.

Determining Materials

Make a list of all the materials you will need to do your experiment. Be specific, especially if someone else is helping you obtain the materials. Try to think of everything you will need.

Materials

- 1 large jar or container
- 4 identical smaller containers
- rubber gloves that also cover the arms
- sample of fertilizer-and-water solution
- eyedropper
- clear plastic wrap
- scissors
- masking tape
- marker
- ruler

Determining Variables and Constants

EXPERIMENTAL GROUP AND CONTROL GROUP

An experiment to determine how two factors are related always has two groups—a control group and an experimental group.

1. Design an experimental group. Include as many trials as possible in the experimental group in order to obtain reliable results.

2. Design a control group that is the same as the experimental group in every way possible, except for the factor you wish to test.

Experimental Group: two containers of lake water with one drop of fertilizer solution added to each

Control Group: two containers of lake water with no fertilizer solution added

Go back to your materials list and make sure you have enough items listed to cover both your experimental group and your control group.

VARIABLES AND CONSTANTS

Identify the variables and constants in your experiment. In a controlled experiment, a **variable** is any factor that can change. **Constants** are all of the factors that are the same in both the experimental group and the control group.

1. Read your hypothesis. The **independent variable** is the factor that you wish to test and that is manipulated or changed so that it can be tested. The independent variable is expressed in your hypothesis after the word *if*. Identify the independent variable in your laboratory report.

2. The **dependent variable** is the factor that you measure to gather results. It is expressed in your hypothesis after the word *then*. Identify the dependent variable in your laboratory report.

Hypothesis
If the amount of fertilizer in lake water is increased, then the amount of algae will also increase, because fertilizers provide nutrients that algae need to grow.

Table 1. Variables and Constants in Algae Experiment

Independent Variable	Dependent Variable	Constants
Amount of fertilizer in lake water	Amount of algae that grow	• Where the lake water is obtained • Type of container used • Light and temperature conditions where water will be stored

Set up your experiment so that you will test only one variable.

MEASURING THE DEPENDENT VARIABLE

Before starting your experiment, you need to define how you will measure the dependent variable. An **operational definition** is a description of the one particular way in which you will measure the dependent variable.

Your operational definition is important for several reasons. First, in any experiment there are several ways in which a dependent variable can be measured. Second, the procedure of the experiment depends on how you decide to measure the dependent variable. Third, your operational definition makes it possible for other people to evaluate and build on your experiment.

EXAMPLE 1

An operational definition of a dependent variable can be qualitative. That is, your measurement of the dependent variable can simply be an observation of whether a change occurs as a result of a change in the independent variable. This type of operational definition can be thought of as a "yes or no" measurement.

Table 2. Qualitative Operational Definition of Algae Growth

Independent Variable	Dependent Variable	Operational Definition
Amount of fertilizer in lake water	Amount of algae that grow	Algae grow in lake water

A qualitative measurement of a dependent variable is often easy to make and record. However, this type of information does not provide a great deal of detail in your experimental results.

EXAMPLE 2

An operational definition of a dependent variable can be quantitative. That is, your measurement of the dependent variable can be a number that shows how much change occurs as a result of a change in the independent variable.

Table 3. Quantitative Operational Definition of Algae Growth

Independent Variable	Dependent Variable	Operational Definition
Amount of fertilizer in lake water	Amount of algae that grow	Diameter of largest algal growth (in mm)

A quantitative measurement of a dependent variable can be more difficult to make and analyze than a qualitative measurement. However, this type of data provides much more information about your experiment and is often more useful.

Writing a Procedure

Write each step of your procedure. Start each step with a verb, or action word, and keep the steps short. Your procedure should be clear enough for someone else to use as instructions for repeating your experiment.

> If necessary, go back to your materials list and add any materials that you left out.

Controlling Variables
The same amount of fertilizer solution must be added to two of the four containers.

Controlling Variables
All four containers must receive the same amount of light.

Procedure

1. Put on your gloves. Use the large container to obtain a sample of lake water.

2. Divide the sample of lake water equally among the four smaller containers.

3. Use the eyedropper to add one drop of fertilizer solution to two of the containers.

4. Use the masking tape and the marker to label the containers with your initials, the date, and the identifiers "Jar 1 with Fertilizer," "Jar 2 with Fertilizer," "Jar 1 without Fertilizer," and "Jar 2 without Fertilizer."

5. Cover the containers with clear plastic wrap. Use the scissors to punch ten holes in each of the covers.

6. Place all four containers on a window ledge. Make sure that they all receive the same amount of light.

7. Observe the containers every day for one week.

8. Use the ruler to measure the diameter of the largest clump of algae in each container, and record your measurements daily.

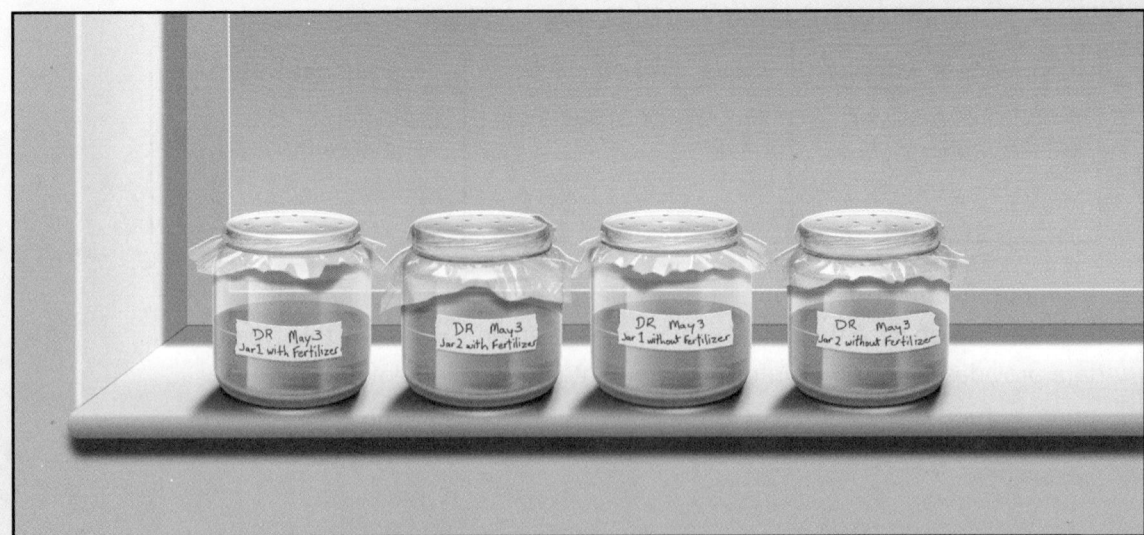

Recording Observations

Once you have obtained all of your materials and your procedure has been approved, you can begin making experimental observations. Gather both quantitative and qualitative data. If something goes wrong during your procedure, make sure you record that too.

Observations
For help with making qualitative and quantitative observations, refer to page R2.

For more examples of data tables, see page R23.

Table 4. Fertilizer and Algae Growth

Date and Time	Experimental Group		Control Group		Observations
	Jar 1 with Fertilizer (diameter of algae in mm)	Jar 2 with Fertilizer (diameter of algae in mm)	Jar 1 without Fertilizer (diameter of algae in mm)	Jar 2 without Fertilizer (diameter of algae in mm)	
5/3 4:00 P.M.	0	0	0	0	condensation in all containers
5/4 4:00 P.M.	0	3	0	0	tiny green blobs in jar 2 with fertilizer
5/5 4:15 P.M.	4	5	0	3	green blobs in jars 1 and 2 with fertilizer and jar 2 without fertilizer
5/6 4:00 P.M.	5	6	0	4	water light green in jar 2 with fertilizer
5/7 4:00 P.M.	8	10	0	6	water light green in jars 1 and 2 with fertilizer and in jar 2 without fertilizer
5/8 3:30 P.M.	10	18	0	6	cover off jar 2 with fertilizer
5/9 3:30 P.M.	14	23	0	8	drew sketches of each container

Notice that on the sixth day, the observer found that the cover was off one of the containers. It is important to record observations of unintended factors because they might affect the results of the experiment.

Use technology, such as a microscope, to help you make observations when possible.

Drawings of Samples Viewed Under Microscope on 5/9 at 100x

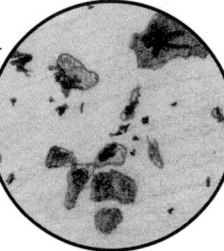
Jar 1 with Fertilizer

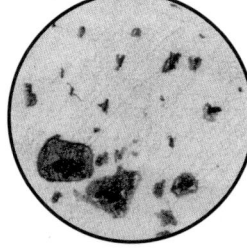
Jar 2 with Fertilizer

Jar 1 without Fertilizer

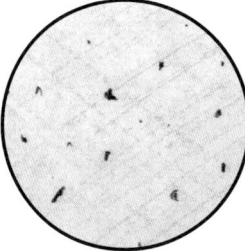
Jar 2 without Fertilizer

Summarizing Results

To summarize your data, look at all of your observations together. Look for meaningful ways to present your observations. For example, you might average your data or make a graph to look for patterns. When possible, use spreadsheet software to help you analyze and present your data. The two graphs below show the same data.

EXAMPLE 1

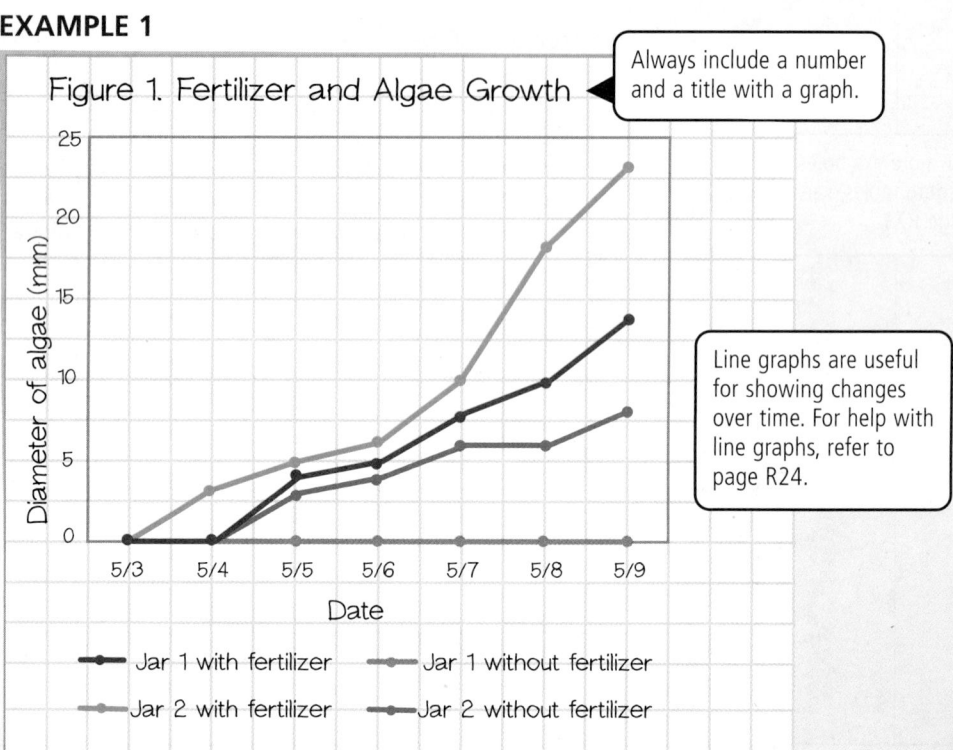

Always include a number and a title with a graph.

Line graphs are useful for showing changes over time. For help with line graphs, refer to page R24.

EXAMPLE 2

Bar graphs are useful for comparing different data sets. This bar graph has four bars for each day. Another way to present the data would be to calculate averages for the tests and the controls, and to show one test bar and one control bar for each day.

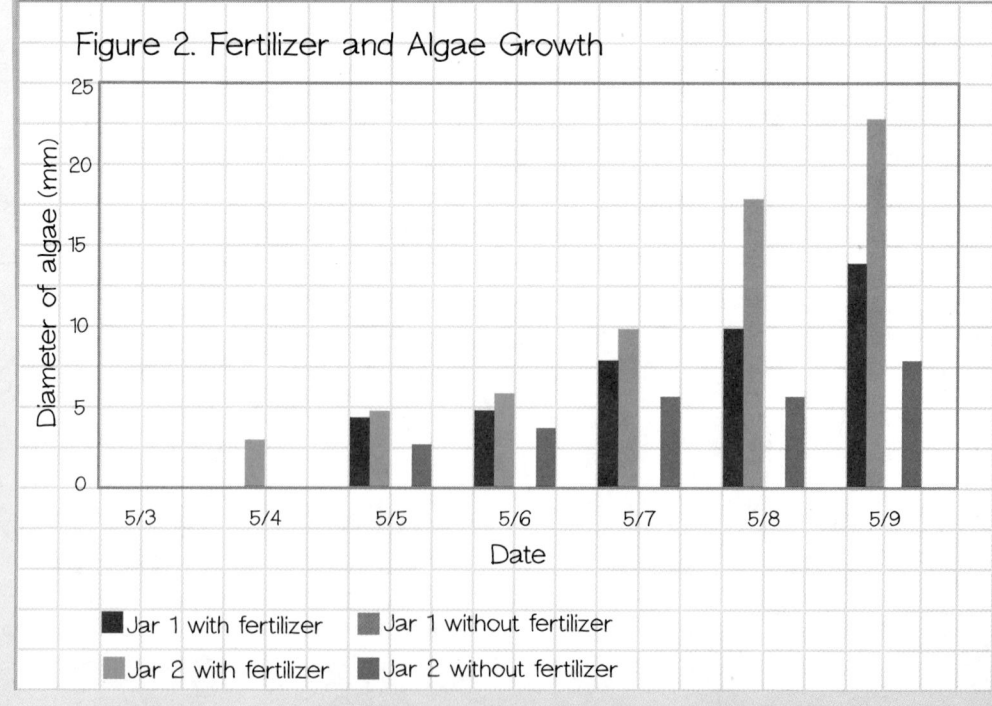

LAB HANDBOOK

Drawing Conclusions

RESULTS AND INFERENCES

To draw conclusions from your experiment, first write your results. Then compare your results with your hypothesis. Do your results support your hypothesis? Be careful not to make inferences about factors that you did not test.

> For help with making inferences, see page R4.

Results and Inferences

The results of my experiment show that more algae grew in lake water to which fertilizer had been added than in lake water to which no fertilizer had been added. My hypothesis was supported. I infer that it is possible that the growth of algae in the lake was caused by the fertilizer used on the field.

> Notice that you cannot conclude from this experiment that the presence of algae in the lake was due only to the fertilizer.

QUESTIONS FOR FURTHER RESEARCH

Write a list of questions for further research and investigation. Your ideas may lead you to new experiments and discoveries.

Questions for Further Research

- What is the connection between the amount of fertilizer and algae growth?
- How do different brands of fertilizer affect algae growth?
- How would algae growth in the lake be affected if no fertilizer were used on the field?
- How do algae affect the lake and the other life in and around it?
- How does fertilizer affect the lake and the life in and around it?
- If fertilizer is getting into the lake, how is it getting there?

Describing a Set of Data

Means, medians, modes, and ranges are important math tools for describing data sets such as the following widths of fossilized clamshells.

13 mm   25 mm   14 mm   21 mm   16 mm   23 mm   14 mm

Mean

The **mean** of a data set is the sum of the values divided by the number of values.

> **Example**
>
> To find the mean of the clamshell data, add the values and then divide the sum by the number of values.
>
> $$\frac{13 \text{ mm} + 25 \text{ mm} + 14 \text{ mm} + 21 \text{ mm} + 16 \text{ mm} + 23 \text{ mm} + 14 \text{ mm}}{7} = \frac{126 \text{ mm}}{7} = 18 \text{ mm}$$
>
> **ANSWER** The mean is 18 mm.

Median

The **median** of a data set is the middle value when the values are written in numerical order. If a data set has an even number of values, the median is the mean of the two middle values.

> **Example**
>
> To find the median of the clamshell data, arrange the values in order from least to greatest. The median is the middle value.
>
> 13 mm   14 mm   14 mm   16 mm   21 mm   23 mm   25 mm
>
> **ANSWER** The median is 16 mm.

Mode

The **mode** of a data set is the value that occurs most often.

> ### Example
>
> To find the mode of the clamshell data, arrange the values in order from least to greatest and determine the value that occurs most often.
>
> 13 mm   14 mm   14 mm   16 mm   21 mm   23 mm   25 mm
>
> **ANSWER** The mode is 14 mm.

A data set can have more than one mode or no mode. For example, the following data set has modes of 2 mm and 4 mm:

2 mm   2 mm   3 mm   4 mm   4 mm

The data set below has no mode, because no value occurs more often than any other.

2 mm   3 mm   4 mm   5 mm

Range

The **range** of a data set is the difference between the greatest value and the least value.

> ### Example
>
> To find the range of the clamshell data, arrange the values in order from least to greatest.
>
> 13 mm   14 mm   14 mm   16 mm   21 mm   23 mm   25 mm
>
> Subtract the least value from the greatest value.
>
> 13 mm is the least value.
> 25 mm is the greatest value.
>
> 25 mm − 13 mm = 12 mm
>
> **ANSWER** The range is 12 mm.

Using Ratios, Rates, and Proportions

You can use ratios and rates to compare values in data sets. You can use proportions to find unknown values.

Ratios

A **ratio** uses division to compare two values. The ratio of a value a to a nonzero value b can be written as $\frac{a}{b}$.

Example

The height of one plant is 8 centimeters. The height of another plant is 6 centimeters. To find the ratio of the height of the first plant to the height of the second plant, write a fraction and simplify it.

$$\frac{8 \text{ cm}}{6 \text{ cm}} = \frac{4 \times \overset{1}{\cancel{2}}}{3 \times \underset{1}{\cancel{2}}} = \frac{4}{3}$$

ANSWER The ratio of the plant heights is $\frac{4}{3}$.

You can also write the ratio $\frac{a}{b}$ as "a to b" or as $a:b$. For example, you can write the ratio of the plant heights as "4 to 3" or as $4:3$.

Rates

A **rate** is a ratio of two values expressed in different units. A unit rate is a rate with a denominator of 1 unit.

Example

A plant grew 6 centimeters in 2 days. The plant's rate of growth was $\frac{6 \text{ cm}}{2 \text{ days}}$. To describe the plant's growth in centimeters per day, write a unit rate.

$$\textbf{\textit{Divide numerator and}} \qquad \frac{6 \text{ cm}}{2 \text{ days}} = \frac{6 \text{ cm} \div 2}{2 \text{ days} \div 2}$$
$$\textbf{\textit{denominator by 2:}}$$

You divide 2 days by 2 to get 1 day, so divide 6 cm by 2 also.

$$\textbf{\textit{Simplify:}} \qquad\qquad = \frac{3 \text{ cm}}{1 \text{ day}}$$

ANSWER The plant's rate of growth is 3 centimeters per day.

Proportions

A **proportion** is an equation stating that two ratios are equivalent. To solve for an unknown value in a proportion, you can use cross products.

Example

If a plant grew 6 centimeters in 2 days, how many centimeters would it grow in 3 days (if its rate of growth is constant)?

$$\textit{Write a proportion:} \qquad \frac{6 \text{ cm}}{2 \text{ days}} = \frac{x \text{ cm}}{3 \text{ days}}$$

$$\textit{Set cross products:} \qquad 6 \cdot 3 = 2x$$

$$\textit{Multiply 6 and 3:} \qquad 18 = 2x$$

$$\textit{Divide each side by 2:} \qquad \frac{18}{2} = \frac{2x}{2}$$

$$\textit{Simplify:} \qquad 9 = x$$

ANSWER The plant would grow 9 centimeters in 3 days.

Using Decimals, Fractions, and Percents

Decimals, fractions, and percentages are all ways of recording and representing data.

Decimals

A **decimal** is a number that is written in the base-ten place value system, in which a decimal point separates the ones and tenths digits. The values of each place is ten times that of the place to its right.

Example

A caterpillar traveled from point *A* to point *C* along the path shown.

A   36.9 cm   B   52.4 cm   C

ADDING DECIMALS To find the total distance traveled by the caterpillar, add the distance from *A* to *B* and the distance from *B* to *C*. Begin by lining up the decimal points. Then add the figures as you would whole numbers and bring down the decimal point.

$$\begin{array}{r} 36.9 \text{ cm} \\ + \ 52.4 \text{ cm} \\ \hline 89.3 \text{ cm} \end{array}$$

ANSWER The caterpillar traveled a total distance of 89.3 centimeters.

Example continued

SUBTRACTING DECIMALS To find how much farther the caterpillar traveled on the second leg of the journey, subtract the distance from *A* to *B* from the distance from *B* to *C*.

$$\begin{array}{r} 52.4 \text{ cm} \\ -\ 36.9 \text{ cm} \\ \hline 15.5 \text{ cm} \end{array}$$

ANSWER The caterpillar traveled 15.5 centimeters farther on the second leg of the journey.

Example

A caterpillar is traveling from point *D* to point *F* along the path shown. The caterpillar travels at a speed of 9.6 centimeters per minute.

D   E   **33.6 cm**   F

MULTIPLYING DECIMALS You can multiply decimals as you would whole numbers. The number of decimal places in the product is equal to the sum of the number of decimal places in the factors.

For instance, suppose it takes the caterpillar 1.5 minutes to go from *D* to *E*. To find the distance from *D* to *E*, multiply the caterpillar's speed by the time it took.

$$\begin{array}{rl} 9.6 & \quad 1 \quad \text{decimal place} \\ \times\ 1.5 & \ +1 \quad \text{decimal place} \\ \hline 480 & \\ 96 & \\ \hline 14.40 & \quad 2 \quad \text{decimal places} \end{array}$$

Align as shown.

ANSWER The distance from *D* to *E* is 14.4 centimeters.

DIVIDING DECIMALS When you divide by a decimal, move the decimal points the same number of places in the divisor and the dividend to make the divisor a whole number.

For instance, to find the time it will take the caterpillar to travel from *E* to *F*, divide the distance from *E* to *F* by the caterpillar's speed.

9.6)33.6   ◀ Move each decimal point one place to the right.

$$\begin{array}{r} 3.5 \\ 96\ \overline{)336.} \\ \underline{288} \\ 480 \\ \underline{480} \\ 0 \end{array}$$

Line up decimal points.

ANSWER The caterpillar will travel from *E* to *F* in 3.5 minutes.

Fractions

A **fraction** is a number in the form $\frac{a}{b}$, where b is not equal to 0. A fraction is in **simplest form** if its numerator and denominator have a greatest common factor (GCF) of 1. To simplify a fraction, divide its numerator and denominator by their GCF.

Example

A caterpillar is 40 millimeters long. The head of the caterpillar is 6 millimeters long. To compare the length of the caterpillar's head with the caterpillar's total length, you can write and simplify a fraction that expresses the ratio of the two lengths.

Write the ratio of the two lengths: $\dfrac{\text{Length of head}}{\text{Total length}} = \dfrac{6 \text{ mm}}{40 \text{ mm}}$

Write numerator and denominator as products of numbers and the GCF: $= \dfrac{3 \times 2}{20 \times 2}$

Divide numerator and denominator by the GCF: $= \dfrac{3 \times \overset{1}{\cancel{2}}}{20 \times \underset{1}{\cancel{2}}}$

Simplify: $= \dfrac{3}{20}$

ANSWER In simplest form, the ratio of the lengths is $\dfrac{3}{20}$.

Percents

A **percent** is a ratio that compares a number to 100. The word *percent* means "per hundred" or "out of 100." The symbol for *percent* is %.

For instance, suppose 43 out of 100 caterpillars are female. You can represent this ratio as a percent, a decimal, or a fraction.

Percent	Decimal	Fraction
43%	0.43	$\frac{43}{100}$

Example

In the preceding example, the ratio of the length of the caterpillar's head to the caterpillar's total length is $\frac{3}{20}$. To write this ratio as a percent, write an equivalent fraction that has a denominator of 100.

Multiply numerator and denominator by 5: $\dfrac{3}{20} = \dfrac{3 \times 5}{20 \times 5}$

$= \dfrac{15}{100}$

Write as a percent: $= 15\%$

ANSWER The caterpillar's head represents 15 percent of its total length.

Using Formulas

A mathematical **formula** is a statement of a fact, rule, or principle. It is usually expressed as an equation.

The term *variable* is also used in science to refer to a factor that can change during an experiment.

In science, a formula often has a word form and a symbolic form. The formula below expresses Ohm's law.

Word Form

$$\text{Current} = \frac{\text{voltage}}{\text{resistance}}$$

Symbolic Form

$$I = \frac{V}{R}$$

In this formula, I, V, and R are variables. A mathematical **variable** is a symbol or letter that is used to represent one or more numbers.

Example

Suppose that you measure a voltage of 1.5 volts and a resistance of 15 ohms. You can use the formula for Ohm's law to find the current in amperes.

Write the formula for Ohm's law: $I = \dfrac{V}{R}$

Substitute 1.5 volts for V and 15 ohms for R: $I = \dfrac{1.5 \text{ volts}}{15 \text{ ohms}}$

Simplify: $I = 0.1$ amp

ANSWER The current is 0.1 ampere.

If you know the values of all variables but one in a formula, you can solve for the value of the unknown variable. For instance, Ohm's law can be used to find a voltage if you know the current and the resistance.

Example

Suppose that you know that a current is 0.2 amperes and the resistance is 18 ohms. Use the formula for Ohm's law to find the voltage in volts.

Write the formula for Ohm's law: $I = \dfrac{V}{R}$

Substitute 0.2 amp for I and 18 ohms for R: $0.2 \text{ amp} = \dfrac{V}{18 \text{ ohms}}$

Multiply both sides by 18 ohms: $0.2 \text{ amp} \cdot 18 \text{ ohms} = V$

Simplify: $3.6 \text{ volts} = V$

ANSWER The voltage is 3.6 volts.

Finding Areas

The area of a figure is the amount of surface the figure covers.

Area is measured in square units, such as square meters (m²) or square centimeters (cm²). Formulas for the areas of three common geometric figures are shown below.

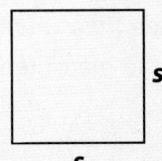

Area = (side length)²
A = s²

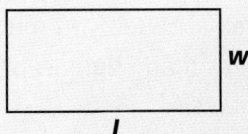

Area = length × width
A = lw

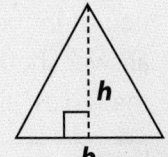

Area = $\frac{1}{2}$ × base × height

A = $\frac{1}{2}$ bh

Example

Each face of a halite crystal is a square like the one shown. You can find the area of the square by using the steps below.

3 mm

3 mm

Write the formula for the area of a square:	A = s²
Substitute 3 mm for s:	= (3 mm)²
Simplify:	= 9 mm²

ANSWER The area of the square is 9 square millimeters.

Finding Volumes

The volume of a solid is the amount of space contained by the solid.

Volume is measured in cubic units, such as cubic meters (m³) or cubic centimeters (cm³). The volume of a rectangular prism is given by the formula shown below.

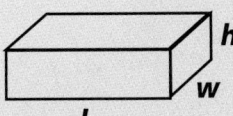

Volume = length × width × height
V = lwh

Example

A topaz crystal is a rectangular prism like the one shown. You can find the volume of the prism by using the steps below.

10 mm

12 mm

20 mm

Write the formula for the volume of a rectangular prism:	V = lwh
Substitute dimensions:	= 20 mm × 12 mm × 10 mm
Simplify:	= 2400 mm³

ANSWER The volume of the rectangular prism is 2400 cubic millimeters.

Using Significant Figures

The **significant figures** in a decimal are the digits that are warranted by the accuracy of a measuring device.

When you perform a calculation with measurements, the number of significant figures to include in the result depends in part on the number of significant figures in the measurements. When you multiply or divide measurements, your answer should have only as many significant figures as the measurement with the fewest significant figures.

Example

Using a balance and a graduated cylinder filled with water, you determined that a marble has a mass of 8.0 grams and a volume of 3.5 cubic centimeters. To calculate the density of the marble, divide the mass by the volume.

Write the formula for density: $\text{Density} = \dfrac{\text{mass}}{\text{Volume}}$

Substitute measurements: $= \dfrac{8.0 \text{ g}}{3.5 \text{ cm}^3}$

Use a calculator to divide: $\approx 2.285714286 \text{ g/cm}^3$

ANSWER Because the mass and the volume have two significant figures each, give the density to two significant figures. The marble has a density of 2.3 grams per cubic centimeter.

Using Scientific Notation

Scientific notation is a shorthand way to write very large or very small numbers. For example, 73,500,000,000,000,000,000,000 kg is the mass of the Moon. In scientific notation, it is 7.35×10^{22} kg.

Example

You can convert from standard form to scientific notation.

Standard Form	Scientific Notation
720,000	7.2×10^5
5 decimal places left	Exponent is 5.
0.000291	2.91×10^{-4}
4 decimal places right	Exponent is −4.

You can convert from scientific notation to standard form.

Scientific Notation	Standard Form
4.63×10^7	46,300,000
Exponent is 7.	7 decimal places right
1.08×10^{-6}	0.00000108
Exponent is −6.	6 decimal places left

Note-Taking Handbook

Note-Taking Strategies

Taking notes as you read helps you understand the information. The notes you take can also be used as a study guide for later review. This handbook presents several ways to organize your notes.

Content Frame

1. Make a chart in which each column represents a category.
2. Give each column a heading.
3. Write details under the headings.

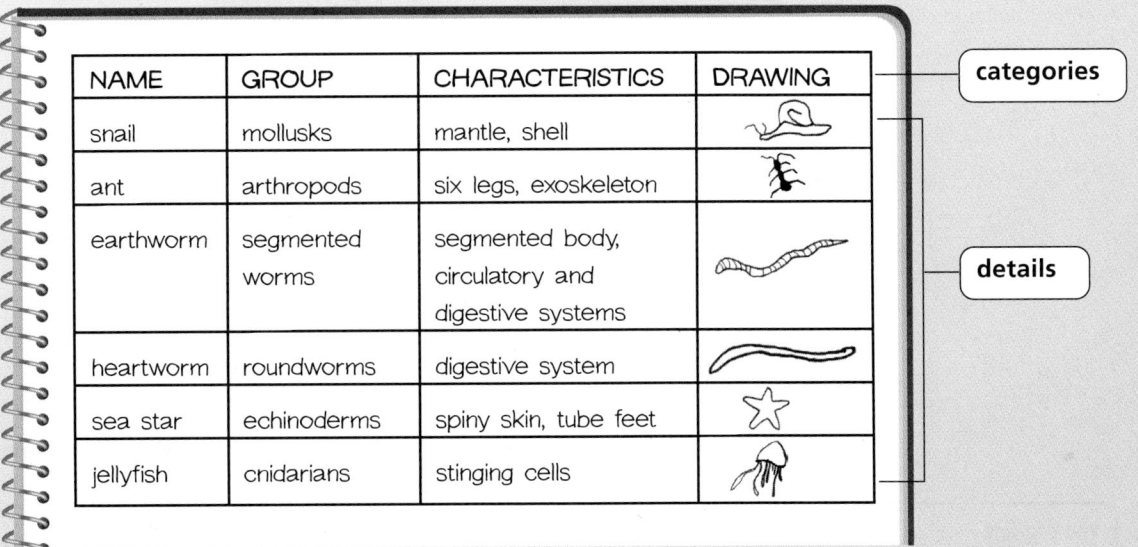

categories

details

Combination Notes

1. For each new idea or concept, write an informal outline of the information.
2. Make a sketch to illustrate the concept, and label it.

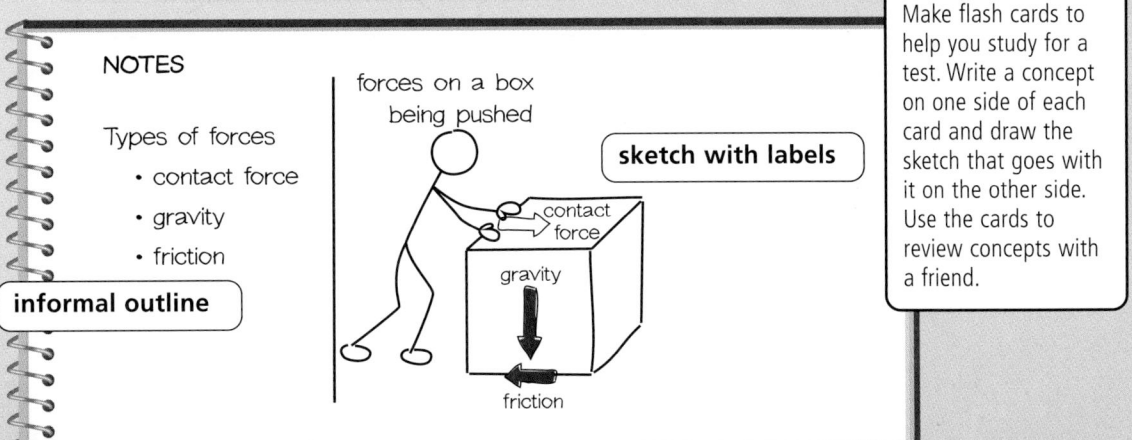

sketch with labels

informal outline

Make flash cards to help you study for a test. Write a concept on one side of each card and draw the sketch that goes with it on the other side. Use the cards to review concepts with a friend.

Main Idea and Detail Notes

1. In the left-hand column of a two-column chart, list main ideas. The blue headings express main ideas throughout this textbook.

2. In the right-hand column, write details that expand on each main idea.

You can shorten the headings in your chart. Be sure to use the most important words.

MAIN IDEAS	DETAIL NOTES
1. Latitude affects climate. *main idea 1*	1. Places close to the equator are usually warmer than places close to the poles. 1. Latitude has the same effect in both hemispheres. *details about main idea 1*
2. Altitude affects climate. *main idea 2*	2. Temperature decreases with altitude. 2. Altitude can overcome the effect of latitude on temperature. *details about main idea 2*

Main Idea Web

1. Write a main idea in a box.

2. Add boxes around it with related vocabulary terms and important details.

definition of *work*
Work is the use of force to move an object.

formula
Work = force · distance

main idea   Force is necessary to do work.

The joule is the unit used to measure work.
definition of *joule*

Work depends on the size of a force.
important detail

NOTE-TAKING HANDBOOK

Mind Map

1. Write a main idea in the center.

2. Add details that relate to one another and to the main idea.

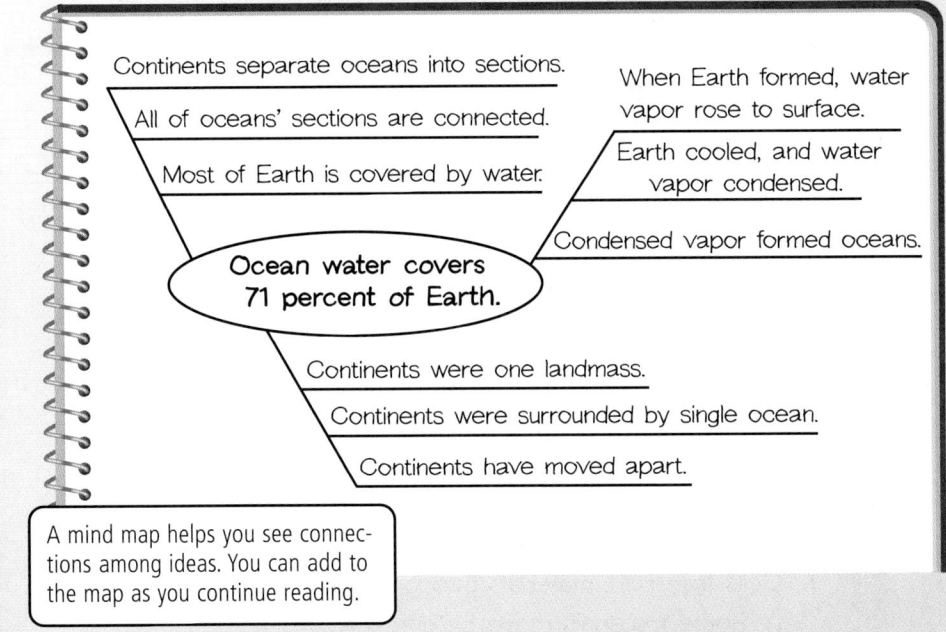

Continents separate oceans into sections.

All of oceans' sections are connected.

Most of Earth is covered by water.

When Earth formed, water vapor rose to surface.

Earth cooled, and water vapor condensed.

Condensed vapor formed oceans.

Ocean water covers 71 percent of Earth.

Continents were one landmass.

Continents were surrounded by single ocean.

Continents have moved apart.

A mind map helps you see connections among ideas. You can add to the map as you continue reading.

Supporting Main Ideas

1. Write a main idea in a box.

2. Add boxes underneath with information—such as reasons, explanations, and examples—that supports the main idea.

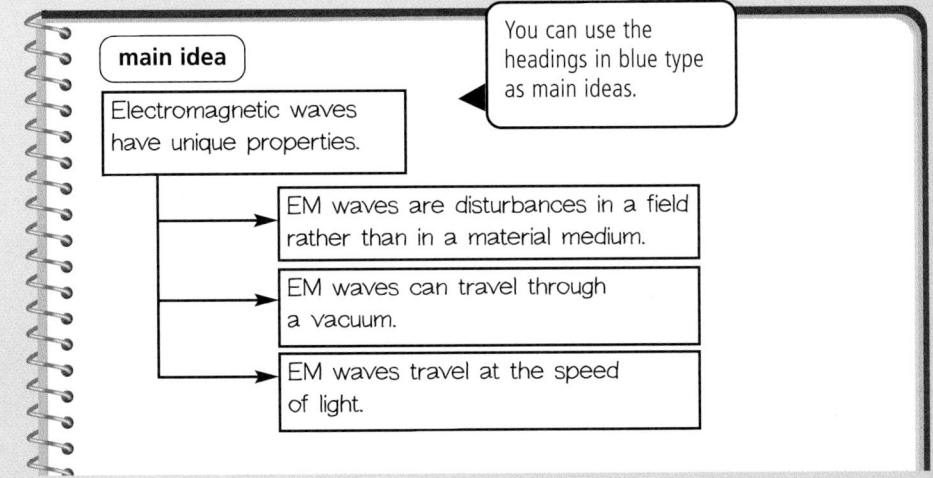

main idea

Electromagnetic waves have unique properties.

You can use the headings in blue type as main ideas.

EM waves are disturbances in a field rather than in a material medium.

EM waves can travel through a vacuum.

EM waves travel at the speed of light.

Outline

1. Copy the chapter title and headings from the book in the form of an outline.

2. Add notes that summarize in your own words what you read.

Cell Processes

1st key idea

I. Cells capture and release energy. — **1st subpoint of I**

  A. All cells need energy. —

  B. Some cells capture light energy. — **2nd subpoint of I**

1st detail about B —   1. Process of photosynthesis

2nd detail about B —   2. Chloroplasts (site of photosynthesis)

    3. Carbon dioxide and water as raw materials

    4. Glucose and oxygen as products

  C. All cells release energy.

    1. Process of cellular respiration

    2. Fermentation of sugar to carbon dioxide

    3. Bacteria that carry out fermentation

II. Cells transport materials through membranes.

  A. Some materials move by diffusion.

    1. Particle movement from higher to lower concentrations

    2. Movement of water through membrane (osmosis)

  B. Some transport requires energy.

    1. Active transport

    2. Examples of active transport

Correct Outline Form

Include a title.

Arrange key ideas, subpoints, and details as shown.

Indent the divisions of the outline as shown.

Use the same grammatical form for items of the same rank. For example, if A is a sentence, B must also be a sentence.

You must have at least two main ideas or subpoints. That is, every A must be followed by a B, and every 1 must be followed by a 2.

NOTE-TAKING HANDBOOK

Concept Map

1. Write an important concept in a large oval.

2. Add details related to the concept in smaller ovals.

3. Write linking words on arrows that connect the ovals.

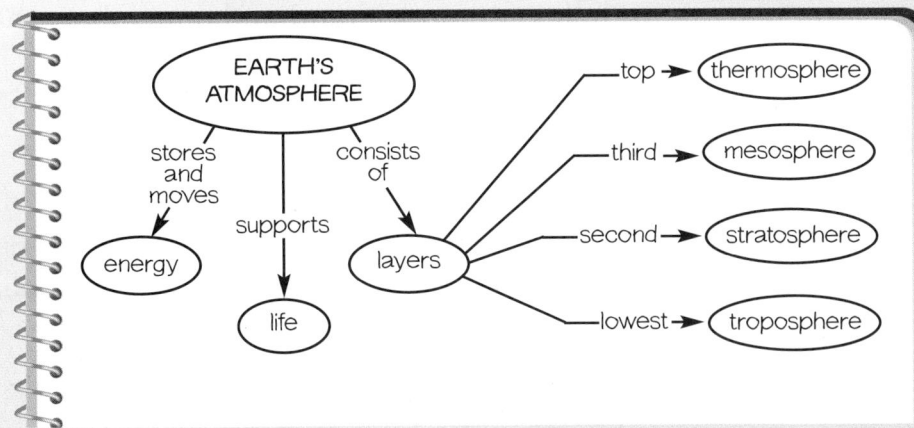

The main ideas or concepts can often be found in the blue headings. An example is "The atmosphere stores and moves energy." Use nouns from these concepts in the ovals, and use the verb or verbs on the lines.

Venn Diagram

1. Draw two overlapping circles, one for each item that you are comparing.

2. In the overlapping section, list the characteristics that are shared by both items.

3. In the outer sections, list the characteristics that are peculiar to each item.

4. Write a summary that describes the information in the Venn diagram.

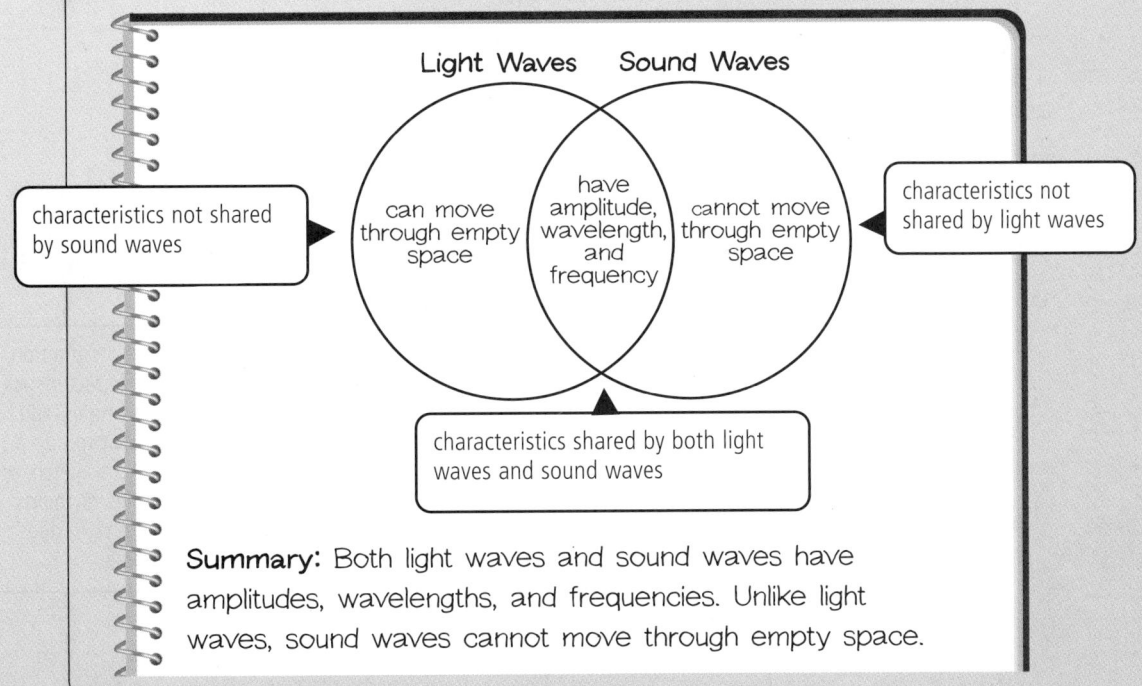

Summary: Both light waves and sound waves have amplitudes, wavelengths, and frequencies. Unlike light waves, sound waves cannot move through empty space.

Vocabulary Strategies

Important terms are highlighted in this book. A definition of each term can be found in the sentence or paragraph where the term appears. You can also find definitions in the Glossary. Taking notes about vocabulary terms helps you understand and remember what you read.

Description Wheel

1. Write a term inside a circle.
2. Write words that describe the term on "spokes" attached to the circle.

> When studying for a test with a friend, read the phrases on the spokes one at a time until your friend identifies the correct term.

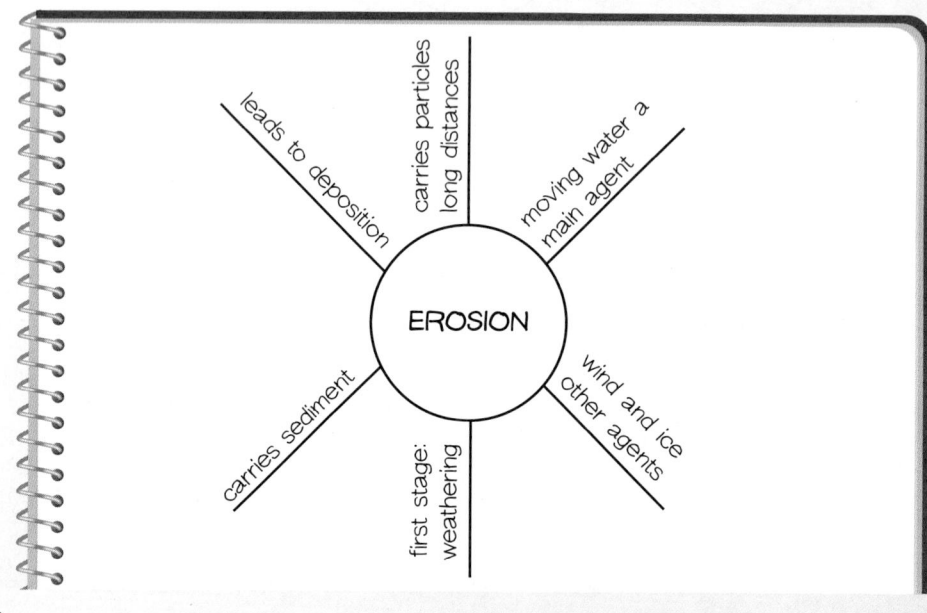

Four Square

1. Write a term in the center.
2. Write details in the four areas around the term.

Definition	Characteristics
any living thing	needs food, water, air; needs energy; grows, develops, reproduces
ORGANISM	
Examples	Nonexamples
dogs, cats, birds, insects, flowers, trees	rocks, water, dirt

> Include a definition, some characteristics, and examples. You may want to add a formula, a sketch, or examples of things that the term does *not* name.

Frame Game

1. Write a term in the center.
2. Frame the term with details.

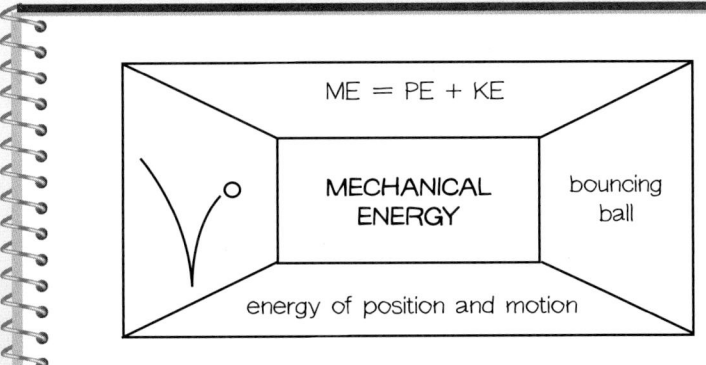

Include examples, descriptions, sketches, or sentences that use the term in context. Change the frame to fit each new term.

Magnet Word

1. Write a term on the magnet.
2. On the lines, add details related to the term.

You can also use phrases or sentences on the lines.

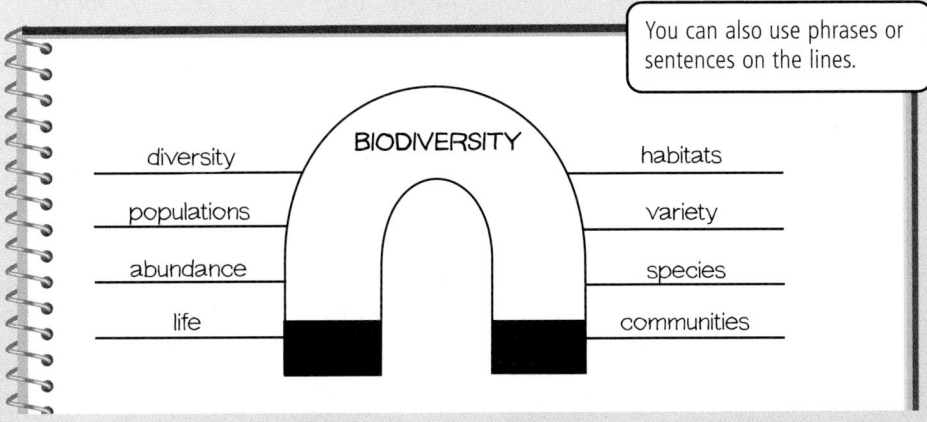

Word Triangle

1. Write a term and its definition in the bottom section.
2. In the middle section, write a sentence in which the term is used correctly.
3. In the top section, draw a small picture to illustrate the term.

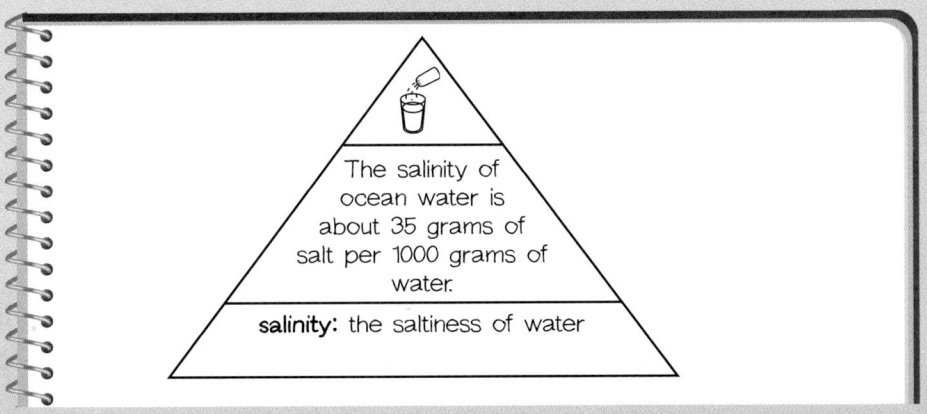

Appendix

Properties of Common Minerals

In this table, minerals are arranged alphabetically, and the most useful properties for identification are printed in *italic* type. Most minerals can be identified by means of two or three of the properties listed below. For some minerals, density is important; for others, cleavage is characteristic; and for others, the crystal shapes identify the minerals. The colors listed are the most common for each mineral.

Name	Hardness	Color	Streak	Cleavage	Remarks
Apatite	5	Green, brown	White	Poor in one direction	Nonmetallic (glassy) luster. Sp. gr. 3.1 to 3.2.
Augite	5–6	Dark green to black	Greenish	*Two directions, nearly at 90°*	Nonmetallic (glassy) luster. *Stubby four- or eight-sided crystals.* Common type of pyroxene. Sp. gr. 3.2 to 3.4.
Beryl	7.5–8	*Bluish-green, yellow, pink, colorless*	White	Imperfect in one direction	Nonmetallic (glassy) luster. *Hardness, greenish color, six-sided crystals.* Aquamarine and emerald are gem varieties. Sp. gr. 2.6 to 2.8.
Biotite mica	2.5–3	Black, brown, dark green	White	*Perfect in one direction*	Nonmetallic (glassy) luster. *Thin elastic films peel off easily.* Sp. gr. 2.8 to 3.2.
Calcite	3	White, colorless	White	*Perfect, three directions, not at 90° angles*	Nonmetallic (glassy to dull) luster. *Fizzes in dilute hydrochloric acid.* Sp. gr. 2.7.
Chalcopyrite	3.5–4	*Golden yellow*	Greenish black	Poor in one direction	Metallic luster. *Hardness distinguishes from pyrite.* Sp. gr. 4.1 to 4.3.
Chlorite	2–2.5	*Greenish*	Pale green to gray or brown	Perfect in one direction	Nonmetallic (glassy to pearly) luster. *Nonelastic flakes.* Sp. gr. 2.6 to 3.3.
Copper	2.5–3	*Copper red*	Copper	None	*Metallic luster on fresh surface. Dense.* Sp. gr. 8.9.
Corundum	9	Brown, pink, blue	White	None, parting resembles cleavage	Nonmetallic (glassy to brilliant) luster. *Barrel-shaped, six-sided crystals with flat ends.* Sp. gr. 4.0.
Diamond	10	Colorless to pale yellow	White	Perfect, four directions	Nonmetallic (brilliant to greasy) luster. *Hardest of all minerals.* Sp. gr. 3.5.

Sp. gr. = specific gravity

Name	Hardness	Color	Streak	Cleavage	Remarks
Dolomite	3.5–4	Pinkish, colorless, white	White	*Perfect, three directions, not at 90° angles*	Nonmetallic luster. *Scratched surface fizzes in dilute hydrochloric acid. Cleavage surfaces curved. Sp. gr. 2.8 to 2.9.*
Feldspar (Orthoclase)	*6*	*Salmon pink, red, white, light gray*	White	*Good, two directions, 90° intersection*	Nonmetallic (glassy) luster. *Hardness, color, and cleavage taken together are diagnostic.* Sp. gr. 2.6.
Feldspar (Plagioclase)	6	*White to light gray, can be salmon pink*	White	*Good, two directions, about 90°*	Nonmetallic (glassy to pearly) luster. *If striations are visible, they are diagnostic.* Sp. gr. 2.6 to 2.8.
Fluorite	4	Varies	White	*Perfect, four directions*	Nonmetallic (glassy) luster. In cubes or octahedrons as crystals. Sp. gr. 3.2.
Galena	2.5	*Lead gray*	Lead gray	*Perfect, three directions, at 90° angles*	*Metallic luster.* Occurs as crystals and masses. *Dense.* Sp. gr. 7.4 to 7.6.
Gold	2.5–3	*Gold*	Gold	None	Metallic luster. *Dense.* Sp. gr. 15.0 to 19.3.
Graphite	1–2	*Dark gray to black*	Grayish black	*Perfect in one direction*	Metallic or nonmetallic (earthy) luster. *Greasy feel, marks paper.* This is the "lead" in a pencil (mixed with clay). Sp. gr. 2.2.
Gypsum	*2*	Colorless, white, gray, yellowish, reddish	White	*Perfect in one direction*	Nonmetallic (glassy to silky) luster. *Can be scratched easily by a fingernail. Sp. gr. 2.3.*
Halite	2–2.5	Colorless, white	White	*Perfect, three directions, at 90° angles*	Nonmetallic (glassy) luster. *Salty taste.* Sp. gr. 2.2.
Hematite	5–6 (may appear softer)	*Reddish-brown, gray, black*	Reddish	None	Metallic or nonmetallic (earthy) luster. *Dense.* Sp. gr. 5.3.
Hornblende	5–6	*Dark green to black*	Brown to gray	*Perfect, two directions at angles of 56° and 124°*	Nonmetallic (glassy to silky) luster. Common type of amphibole. Long, slender, six-sided crystals. Sp. gr. 3.0 to 3.4.
Kaolinite	2	White, gray, yellowish	White	*Perfect in one direction*	Nonmetallic (dull, earthy) luster. Claylike masses. Sp. gr. 2.6.
Limonite group	4–5.5	*Yellow, brown*	Yellowish brown	None	Nonmetallic (earthy) luster. Rust stains. Sp. gr. 2.9 to 4.3.
Magnetite	5.5–6.5	*Black*	Black	None	Metallic luster. Occurs as eight-sided crystals and granular masses. *Magnetic. Dense.* Sp. gr. 5.2.

Sp. gr. = specific gravity

Properties of Common Minerals *continued*

Name	Hardness	Color	Streak	Cleavage	Remarks
Muscovite mica	2–2.5	Colorless in thin films; silvery, yellowish, and greenish in thicker pieces	*White*	Perfect in one direction	Nonmetallic (glassy to pearly) luster. *Thin elastic films peel off readily.* Sp. gr. 2.8 to 2.9.
Olivine	6.5–7	*Yellowish, greenish*	White	*None*	*Nonmetallic (glassy) luster. Granular.* Sp. gr. 3.3 to 4.4.
Opal	5–6.5	Varies	White	None	*Nonmetallic (glassy to pearly) luster. Conchoidal fracture.* Sp. gr. 2.0 to 2.2.
Pyrite	6–6.5	*Brass yellow*	Greenish black	None	Metallic luster. *Cubic crystals and granular masses. Dense.* Sp. gr. 5.0 to 5.1.
Quartz	7	*colorless, white; varies*	White	None	Nonmetallic (glassy) luster. *Conchoidal fracture. Six-sided crystals common.* Many varieties. Sp. gr. 2.6.
Serpentine	3–5	*Greenish (variegated)*	White	None or good in one direction, depending on variety	*Nonmetallic (greasy, waxy, or silky) luster. Conchoidal fracture.* Sp. gr. 2.5 to 2.6.
Sphalerite	3.5–4	*Yellow, brown, black*	Yellow to light brown	*Perfect, six directions*	*Nonmetallic (brilliant to resinous) luster.* Sp. gr. 3.9 to 4.1.
Sulfur	1.5–2.5	*Yellow*	Yellow	Poor, two directions	Nonmetallic (glassy to earthy) luster. Granular. Sp. gr. 2.0 to 2.1.
Talc	1	Apple-green, gray, white	White	Perfect in one direction	Nonmetallic (pearly to greasy) luster. Nonelastic flakes, *greasy feel.* Sp. gr. 2.7 to 2.8.
Topaz	8	Varies	White	Perfect in one direction	Nonmetallic (brilliant to glassy) luster. *Crystals commonly striated lengthwise.* Sp. gr. 3.4 to 3.6.
Tourmaline	7–7.5	*Black; varies*	White	None	Nonmetallic (glassy) luster. *Crystals often have triangular cross sections. Conchoidal fracture.* Sp. gr. 3.0 to 3.3.

Sp. gr. = specific gravity

Topographic Map Symbols

The U.S. Geological Survey uses the following symbols to mark human-made and natural features on all of the topographic maps the USGS produces.

Primary highway, hard surface
Secondary highway, hard surface
Light-duty road, hard or improved surface
Unimproved road
Trail
Railroad: single track
Railroad: multiple track
Bridge
Drawbridge
Tunnel
Footbridge
Overpass—Underpass
Power transmission line with located tower
Landmark line (labeled as to type) ... TELEPHONE

Dam with lock
Canal with lock
Large dam
Small dam: masonry—earth
Buildings (dwelling, place of employment, etc.)
School—Church—Cemeteries ... Cem
Buildings (barn, warehouse, etc.)
Tanks; oil, water, etc. (labeled only if water) ... Water Tank
Wells other than water (labeled as to type) ... Oil   Gas
U.S. mineral or location monument—Prospect
Quarry—Gravel pit
Mine shaft—Tunnel or cave entrance
Campsite—Picnic area
Located or landmark object—Windmill
Exposed wreck
Rock or coral reef
Foreshore flat
Rock: bare or awash

Benchmarks ... BM ×671   ×672
Road fork—Section corner with elevation ... 429   +58
Checked spot elevation ... × 5970
Unchecked spot elevation ... × 5970

Boundary: national
    State
    county, parish, municipio
    civil township, precinct, town, barrio
    incorporated city, village, town, hamlet
    reservation, national or state
    small park, cemetery, airport, etc.
    land grant
Township or range line, U.S. land survey
Section line, U.S. land survey
Township line, not U.S. land survey
Section line, not U.S. land survey
Fence line or field line
Section corner: found—indicated ... +   +
Boundary monument: land grant—other

Index contour   Intermediate contour
Supplementary cont   Depression contours
Cut—Fill   Levee
Mine dump   Large wash
Dune area   Distorted surface
Sand area   Gravel beach

Glacier   Intermittent streams
Seasonal streams   Aqueduct tunnel
Water well—Spring   Falls
Rapids   Intermittent lake
Channel   Small wash
Sounding—Depth curve ... 10   Marsh (swamp)
Dry lake bed   Land subject to controlled flooding

Woodland   Mangrove
Submerged marsh   Scrub
Orchard   Wooded marsh
Vineyard   Many buildings
Areas revised since previous edition

Source: U.S. Geological Survey

Properties of Rocks and Earth's Interior

Scheme for Sedimentary Rock Identification

TEXTURE	GRAIN SIZE	COMPOSITION	COMMENTS	ROCK NAME	MAP SYMBOL
Clastic (fragmental)	Pebbles, cobbles, and/or boulders embedded in sand, silt, and/or clay	Mostly quartz, feldspar, and clay minerals; may contain fragments of other rocks and minerals	Rounded fragments	Conglomerate	
			Angular fragments	Breccia	
	Sand (0.2 to 0.006 cm)		Fine to coarse	Sandstone	
	Silt (0.006 to 0.0004 cm)		Very fine grain	Siltstone	
	Clay (less than 0.0004 cm)		Compact; may split easily	Shale	

CHEMICALLY AND/OR ORGANICALLY FORMED SEDIMENTARY ROCKS

TEXTURE	GRAIN SIZE	COMPOSITION	COMMENTS	ROCK NAME	MAP SYMBOL
Crystalline	Varied	Halite	Crystals from chemical precipitates and evaporites	Rock Salt	
	Varied	Gypsum		Rock Gypsum	
	Varied	Dolomite		Dolostone	
Bioclastic	Microscopic to coarse	Calcite	Cemented shell fragments or precipitates of biologic origin	Limestone	
	Varied	Carbon	From plant remains	Coal	

Scheme for Metamorphic Rock Identification

TEXTURE		GRAIN SIZE	COMPOSITION	TYPE OF METAMORPHISM	COMMENTS	ROCK NAME	MAP SYMBOL
FOLIATED	MINERAL ALIGNMENT	Fine	MICA QUARTZ FELDSPAR AMPHIBOLE GARNET PYROXENE	Regional (Heat and pressure increase with depth)	Low-grade metamorphism of shale	Slate	
		Fine to medium			Foliation surfaces shiny from microscopic mica crystals	Phyllite	
					Platy mica crystals visible from metamorphism of clay or feldspars	Schist	
	BANDING	Medium to coarse			High-grade metamorphism; some mica changed to feldspar; segregated by mineral type into bands	Gneiss	
NONFOLIATED		Fine	Variable	Contact (Heat)	Various rocks changed by heat from nearby magma/lava	Hornfels	
		Fine to coarse	Quartz	Regional or Contact	Metamorphism of quartz sandstone	Quartzite	
			Calcite and/or dolomite		Metamorphism of limestone or dolostone	Marble	
		Coarse	Various minerals in particles and matrix		Pebbles may be distorted or stretched	Metaconglomerate	

Scheme for Igneous Rock Identification

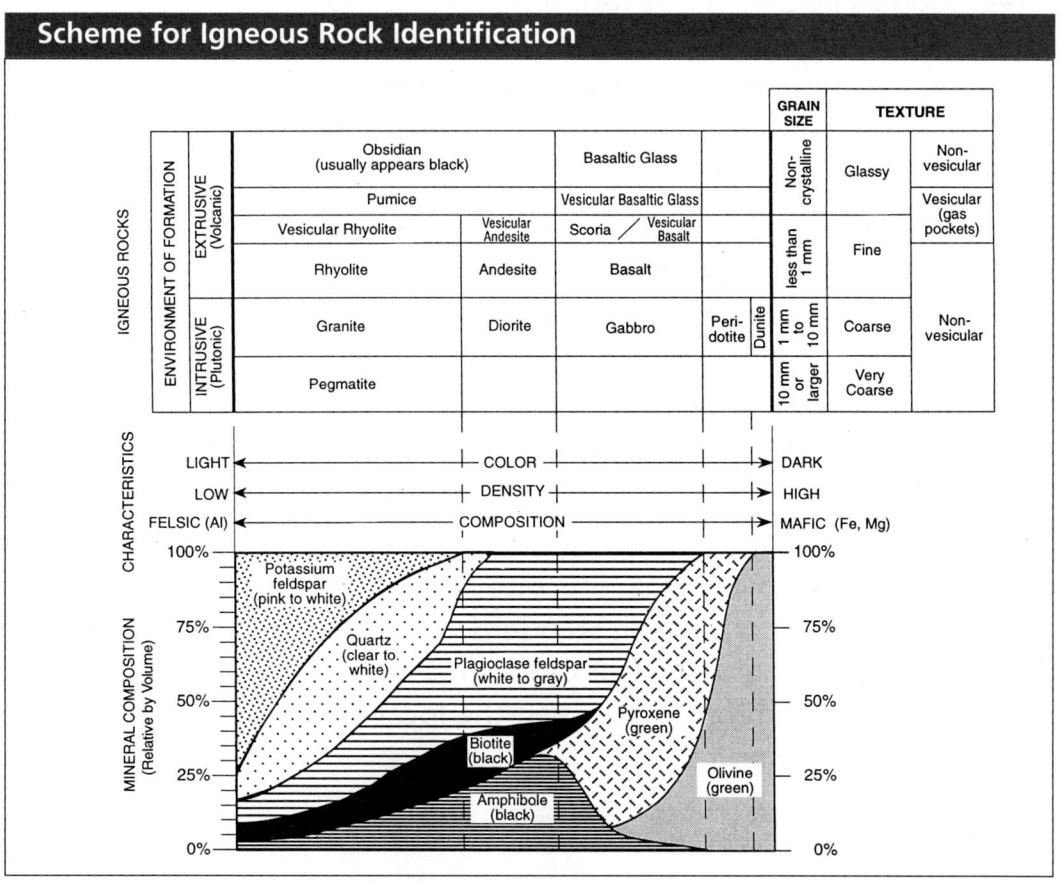

Inferred Properties of Earth's Interior

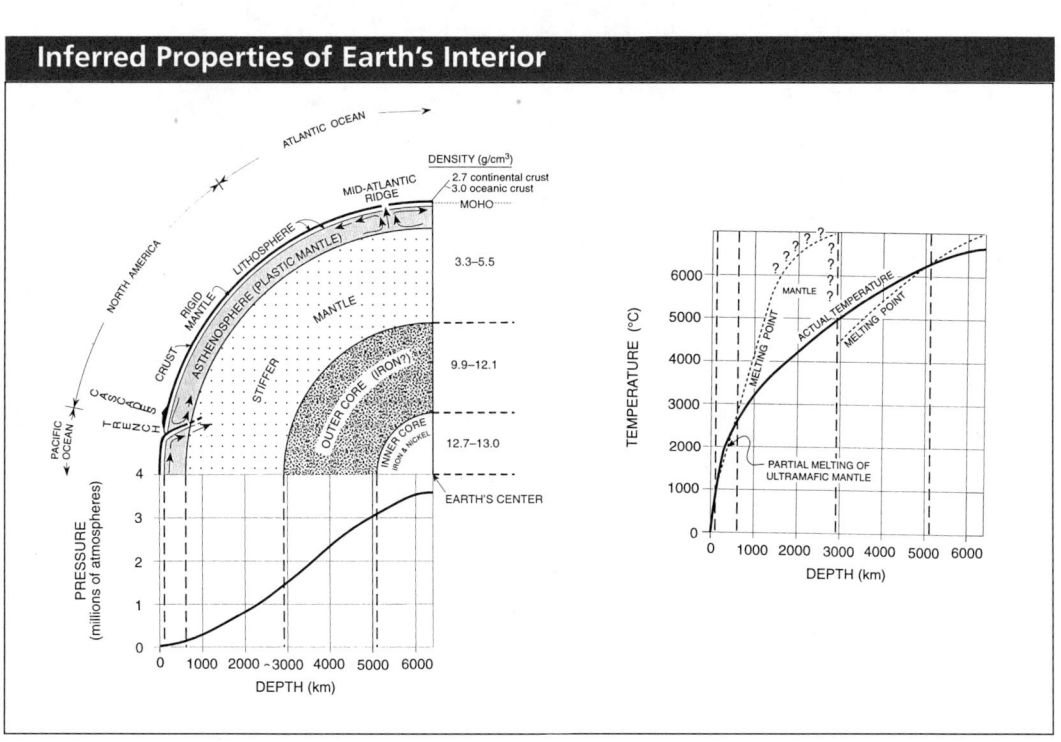

Time Zones

Because Earth rotates, noon can occur in one location at the same moment that the Sun is setting in another location. To avoid confusion in transportation and communication, officials have divided Earth into 24 time zones. Within a time zone, clocks are set to the same time of day.

Time zones are centered on lines of longitude, but instead of running straight, their boundaries often follow political boundaries. The starting point for the times zones is centered on the prime meridian (0°). The time in this zone is generally called Greenwich Mean Time (GMT), but it is also called Universal Time (UT) by astronomers and Zulu Time (Z) by meteorologists. The International Date Line is centered on 180° longitude. The calendar date to the east of this line is one day earlier than the date to the west.

In the map below, each column of color represents one time zone. The color beige shows areas that do not match standard zones. The labels at the top show the times at noon GMT. Positive and negative numbers at the bottom show the difference between the local time in the zone and Greenwich Mean Time.

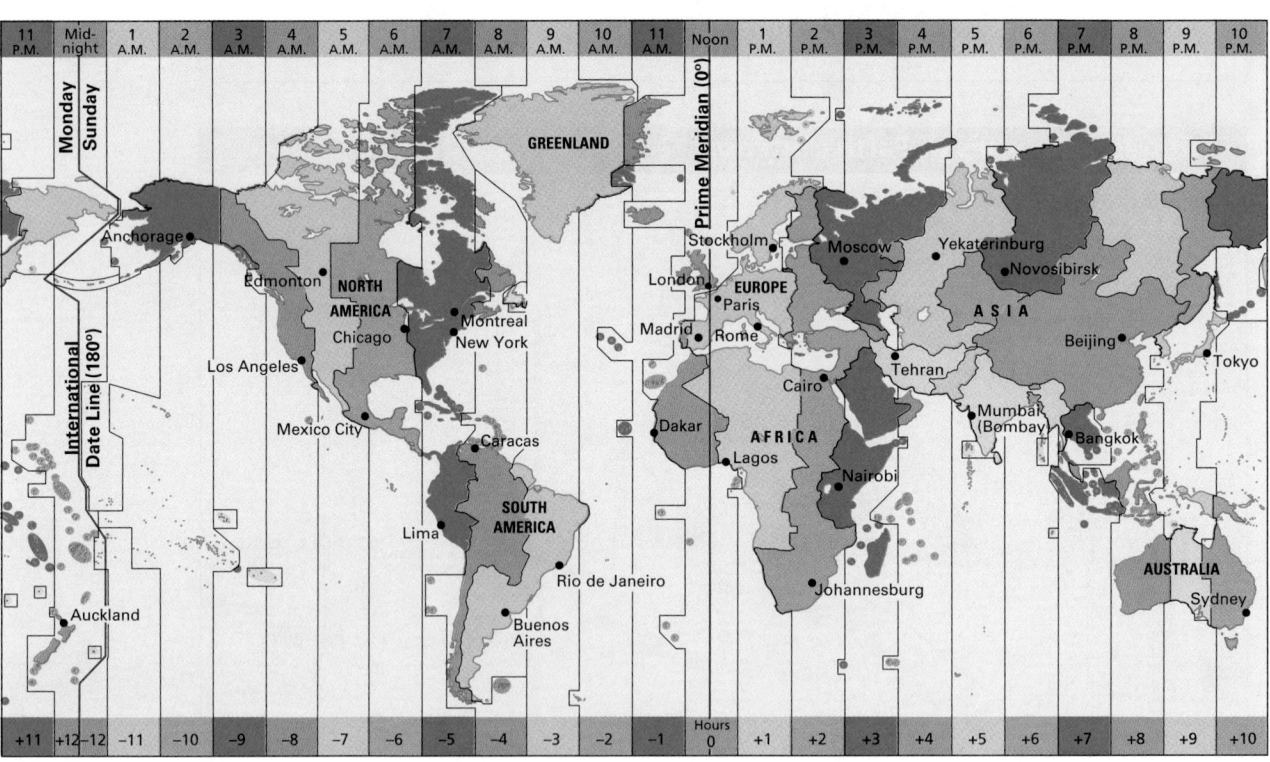

APPENDIX

Characteristics of Planets

Some data about the planets and Earth's satellite, the Moon, are listed below. Some data, such as the tilt of Mercury and the mass of Pluto, are not known as well as other data. One astronomical unit (AU) is Earth's average distance from the Sun, or 149,597,870 kilometers. For comparison, Earth's mass is 5.97×10^{24} kilograms, and Earth's diameter is 12,756 kilometers.

Eccentricity is a measure of how flattened an ellipse is. An ellipse with an eccentricity of 0 is a circle. An ellipse with an eccentricity of 1 is completely flat.

Venus, Uranus, and Pluto rotate backward compared to Earth. If you use your left thumb as one of these planets' north pole, your fingers curve in the direction the planet turns.

Characteristics of Planets

Characteristic	Mercury	Venus	Earth	Mars	Jupiter	Saturn	Uranus	Neptune	Pluto	Moon
Mean distance from Sun (AU)	0.387	0.723	1.00	1.52	5.20	9.55	19.2	30.1	39.5	
Period of revolution (Earth years)	0.241 (88 Earth days)	0.615 (225 Earth days)	1.00	1.88	11.9	29.4	83.7	164	248	0.075 (27.3 Earth days)
Eccentricity of orbit	0.206	0.007	0.017	0.093	0.048	0.056	0.046	0.009	0.249	0.055
Diameter (Earth = 1)	0.382	0.949	1.00	0.532	11.21	9.45	4.01	3.88	0.180	0.272
Volume (Earth = 1)	0.06	0.86	1.00	0.15	1320	760	63	58	0.006	0.02
Period of rotation	58.6 Earth days	243 Earth days	23.9 hours	24.6 hours	9.93 hours	10.7 hours	17.2 hours	16.1 hours	6.39 Earth days	27.3 Earth days
Tilt of axis (°) (from perpendicular to orbit)	0.1 (approximate)	2.6	23.45	25.19	3.12	26.73	82.14	29.56	60.4	6.67
Mass (Earth = 1)	0.0553	0.815	1.00	0.107	318	95.2	14.5	17.1	0.002	0.0123
Mean density (g/cm³)	5.4	5.2	5.5	3.9	1.3	0.7	1.3	1.6	2	3.3

Seasonal Star Maps

Your view of the night sky changes as Earth orbits the Sun. Some constellations appear throughout the year, but others can be seen only during certain seasons. And over the course of one night, the constellations appear to move across the sky as Earth rotates.

When you go outside to view stars, give your eyes time to adjust to the darkness. Avoid looking at bright lights. If you need to look toward a bright light, preserve your night vision in one eye by keeping it closed.

The star maps on pages R61–R64 show parts of the night sky in different seasons. If you are using a flashlight to view the maps, you should attach a piece of red balloon over the lens. The balloon will dim the light and also give it a red color, which affects night vision less than other colors. The following steps will help you use the maps:

1. Stand facing north. To find this direction, use a compass or turn clockwise 90° from the location where the Sun set.

2. The top map for each season shows some constellations that appear over the northern horizon at 10 P.M. During the night, the constellations rotate in a circle around Polaris, the North Star.

3. Now turn so that you stand facing south. The bottom map for the season shows some constellations that appear over the southern horizon at 10 P.M.

WINTER SKY to the NORTH, *January 15*

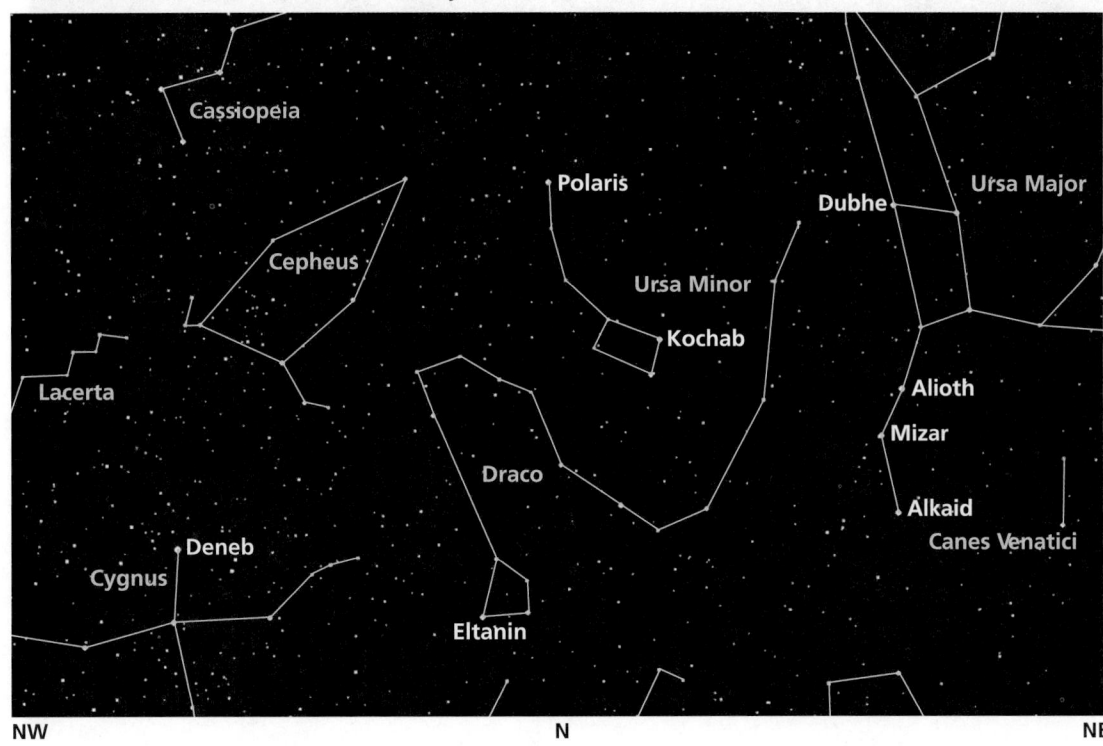

NW   N   NE

WINTER SKY to the SOUTH, *January 15*

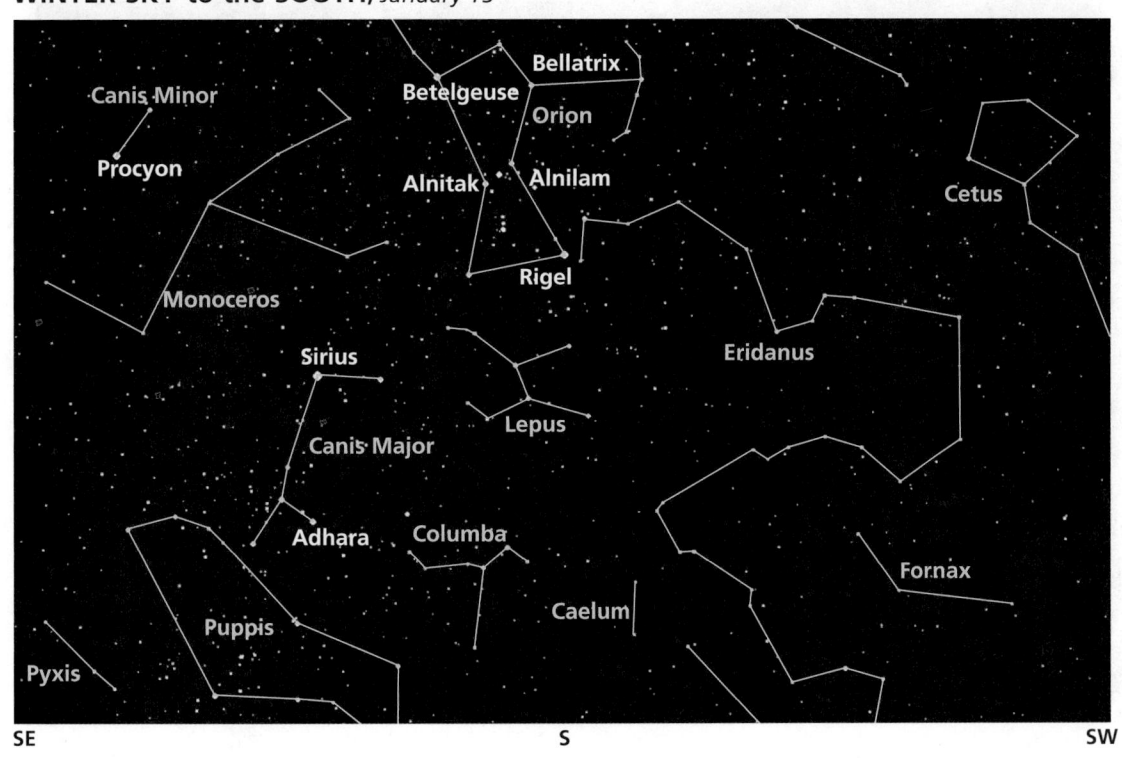

SE   S   SW

Seasonal Star Maps *continued*

SPRING SKY to the NORTH, *April 15*

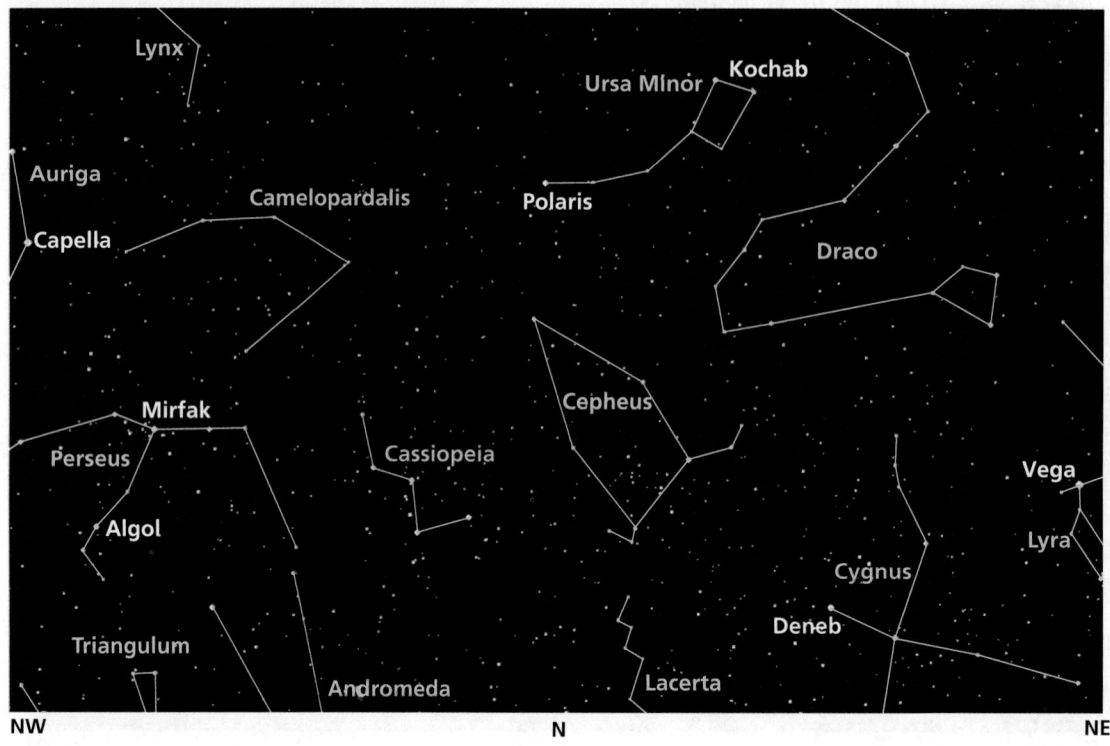

NW   N   NE

SPRING SKY to the SOUTH, *April 15*

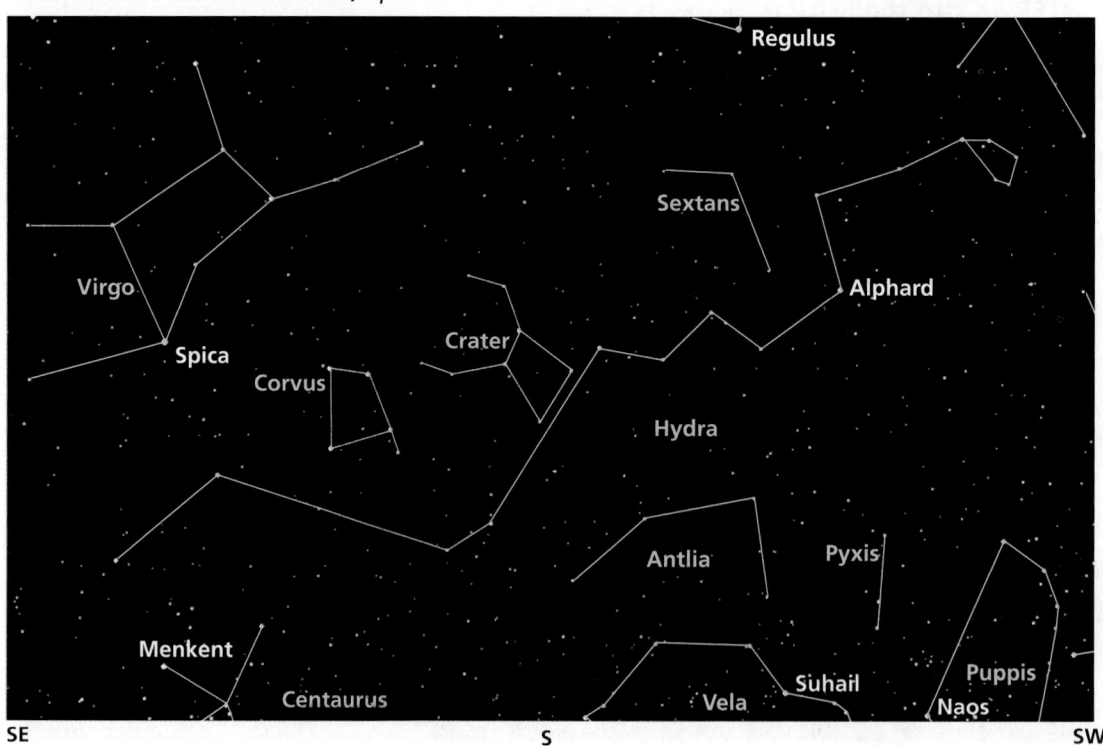

SE   S   SW

SUMMER SKY to the NORTH, *July 15*

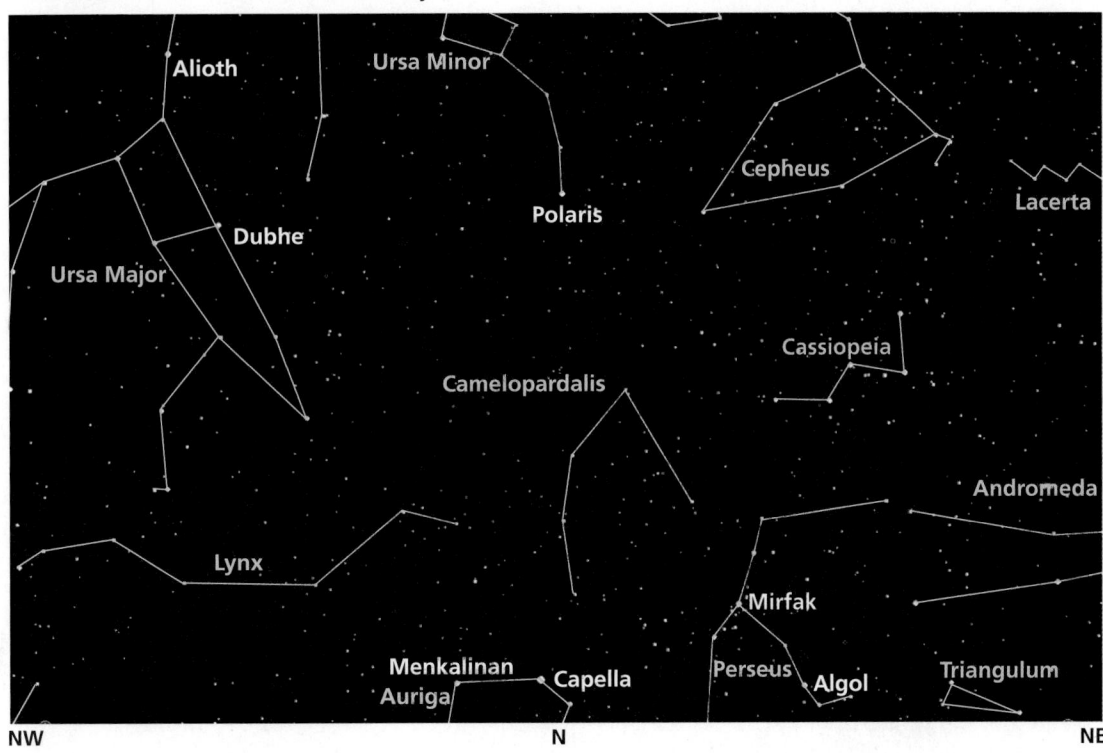

SUMMER SKY to the SOUTH, *July 15*

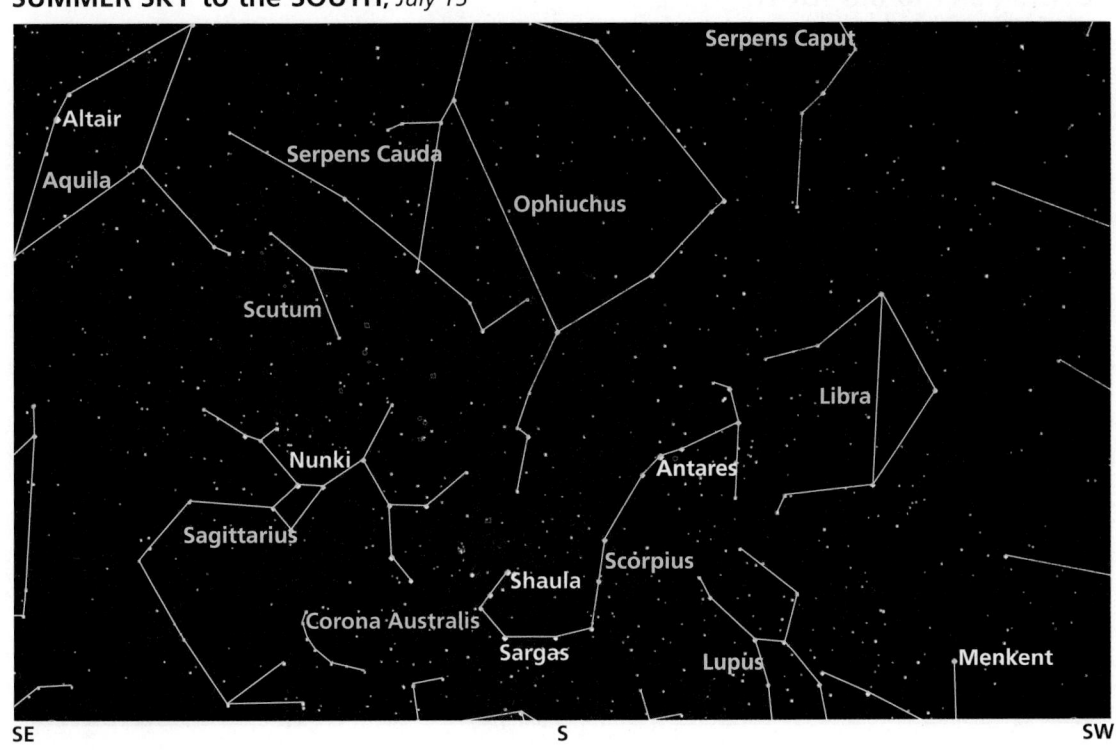

Seasonal Star Maps *continued*

AUTUMN SKY to the NORTH, *October 15*

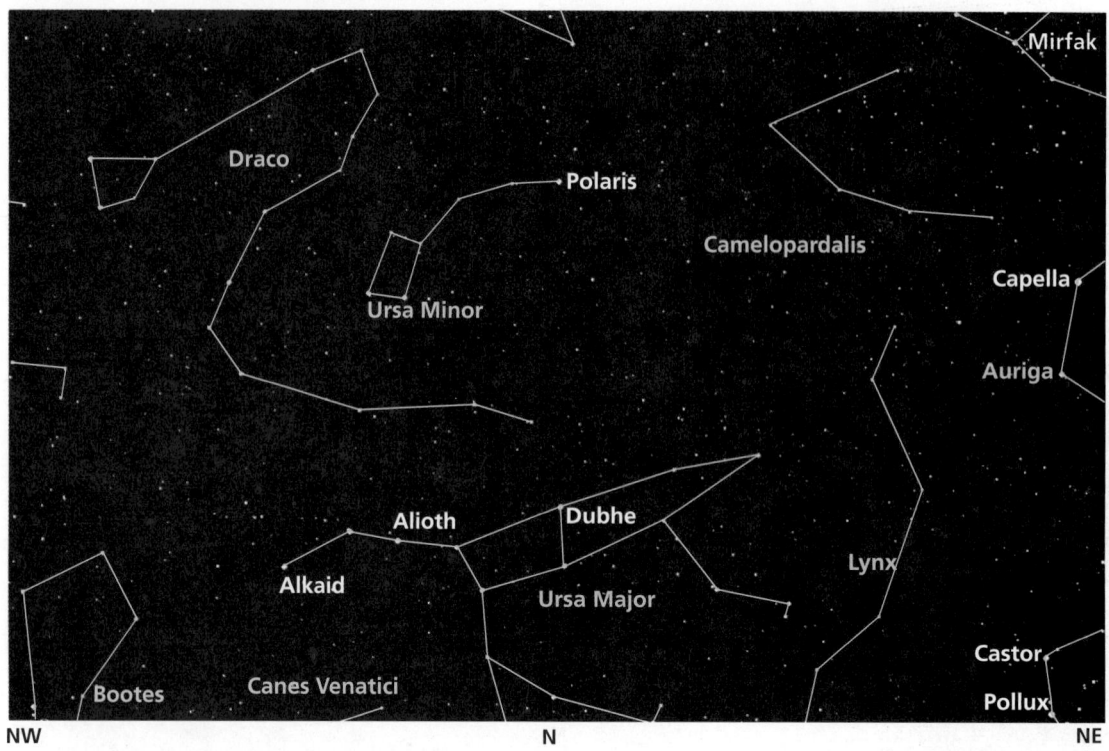

AUTUMN SKY to the SOUTH, *October 15*

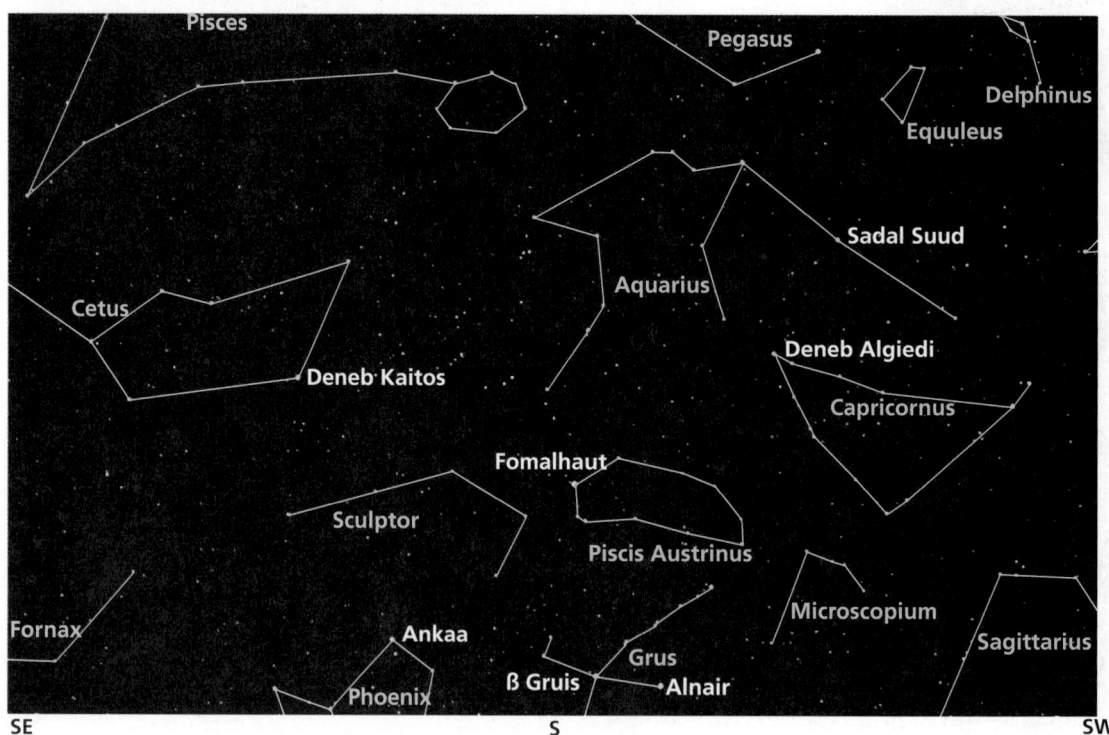

The Hertzsprung-Russell Diagram

The Hertzsprung-Russell (H-R) Diagram is a graph that shows stars plotted according to brightness and surface temperature. Most stars fall within a diagonal band called the main sequence. In the main-sequence stage of a star's life cycle, brightness is closely related to surface temperature. Red giant and red supergiant stars appear above the main sequence on the diagram. These stars are bright in relation to their surface temperatures because their huge surface areas give off a lot of light. Dim white dwarfs appear below the main sequence.

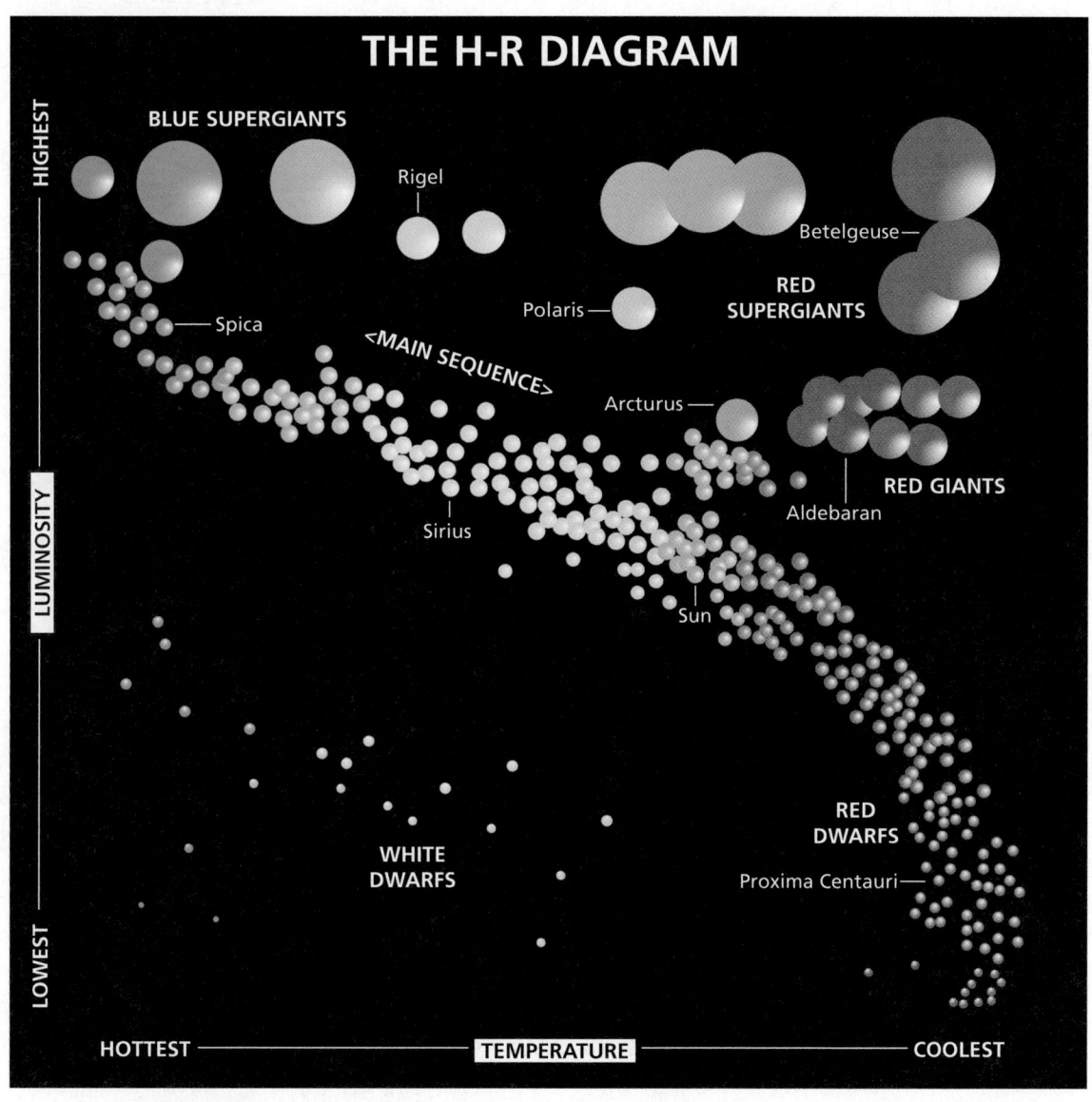

THE H-R DIAGRAM

HIGHEST

BLUE SUPERGIANTS

Rigel

Betelgeuse

RED SUPERGIANTS

Spica

Polaris

<MAIN SEQUENCE>

LUMINOSITY

Arcturus

RED GIANTS

Aldebaran

Sirius

Sun

RED DWARFS

WHITE DWARFS

Proxima Centauri

LOWEST

HOTTEST — TEMPERATURE — COOLEST

Tectonic Plates

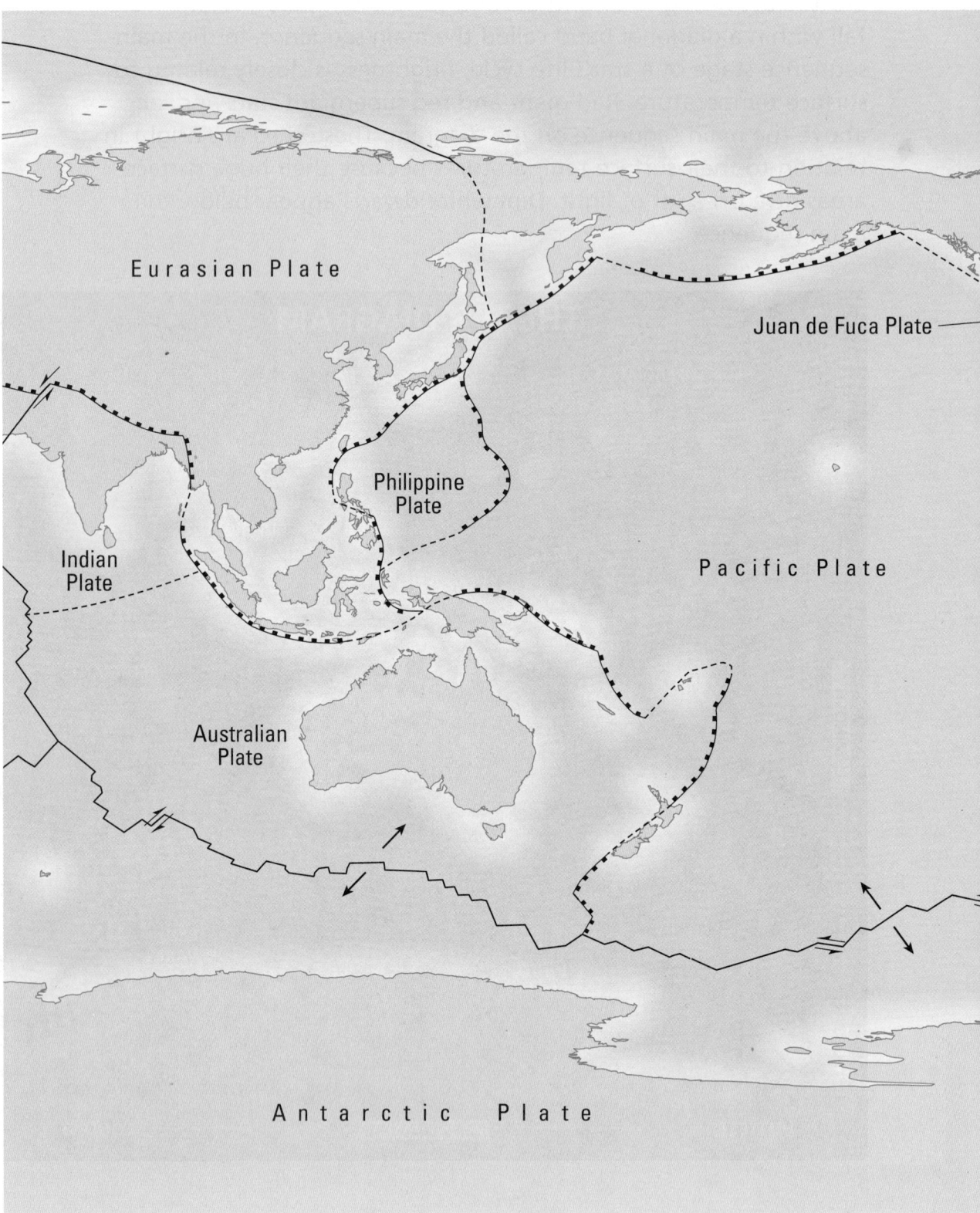

Eurasian Plate

Juan de Fuca Plate

Philippine Plate

Indian Plate

Pacific Plate

Australian Plate

Antarctic Plate

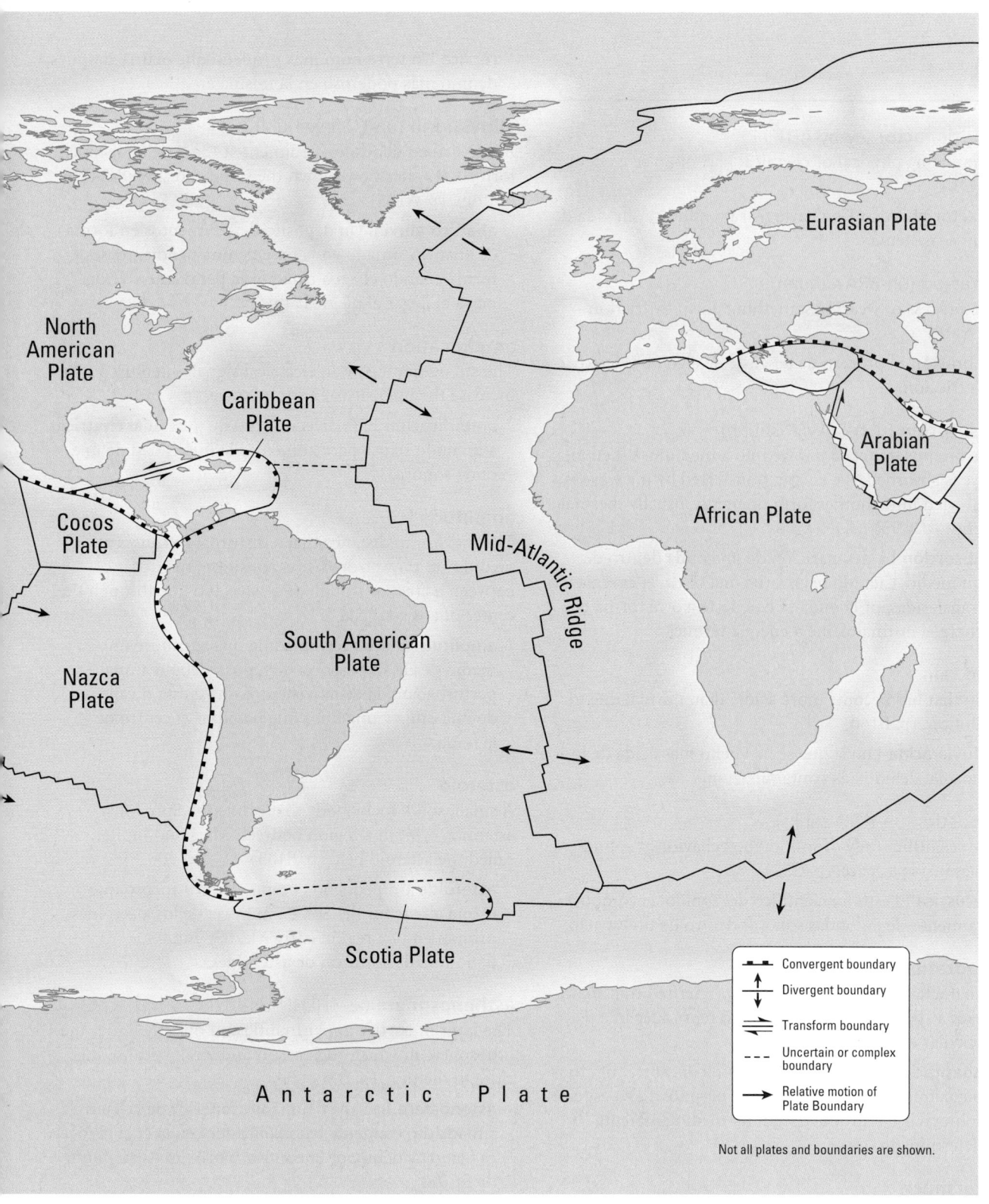

North American Plate

Eurasian Plate

Caribbean Plate

Cocos Plate

Arabian Plate

African Plate

Nazca Plate

Mid-Atlantic Ridge

South American Plate

Scotia Plate

Antarctic Plate

	Convergent boundary
	Divergent boundary
	Transform boundary
	Uncertain or complex boundary
	Relative motion of Plate Boundary

Not all plates and boundaries are shown.

Glossary

A

abiotic factor (ay-by-AHT-ihk)
A nonliving physical or chemical part of an ecosystem. (p. D10)

> **factor abiótico** Una parte física o química sin vida de un ecosistema.

abrasion (uh-BRAY-zhuhn)
The process of wearing something down by friction. (p. A116)

> **abrasión** El proceso de desgaste de algo por efecto de la fricción.

absorption (uhb-SAWRP-shuhn)
The disappearance of a wave into a medium. When a wave is absorbed, the energy transferred by the wave is converted into another form of energy, usually thermal energy. (p. C93)

> **absorción** La desaparición de una onda dentro de un medio. Cuando se absorbe una onda, la energía transferida por la onda se convierte a otra forma de energía, normalmente a energía térmica.

acid rain
Rain that has become more acidic than normal due to pollution. (p. B160)

> **lluvia ácida** Lluvia que se ha vuelto más ácida de lo normal debido a la contaminación.

acoustics (uh-KOO-stihks)
The scientific study of sound; the behavior of sound waves inside a space. (p. C55)

> **acústica** El estudio científico del sonido; el comportamiento de las ondas sonoras dentro de un espacio.

adaptation
A characteristic, a behavior, or any inherited trait that makes a species able to survive and reproduce in a particular environment. (p. xxxi)

> **adaptación** Una característica, un comportamiento o cualquier rasgo heredado que permite a una especie sobrevivir o reproducirse en un medio ambiente determinado.

aftershock
> A smaller earthquake that follows a more powerful earthquake in the same area. (p. B122)

> **réplica** Un terremoto más pequeño que ocurre después de uno más poderoso en la misma área.

alluvial fan (uh-LOO-vee-uhl)
A fan-shaped deposit of sediment at the base of a slope, formed as water flows down the slope and spreads at the bottom. (p. A153)

> **abanico aluvial** Un depósito de sedimentos en forma de abanico situado en la base de una pendiente; se forma cuando el agua baja por la pendiente y se dispersa al llegar al pie de la misma.

amplification
The strengthening of an electrical signal, often used to increase the intensity of a sound wave. (p. C55)

> **amplificación** El fortalecimiento de una señal eléctrica, a menudo se usa para aumentar la intensidad de una onda sonora.

amplitude
The maximum distance that a disturbance causes a medium to move from its rest position; the distance between a crest or trough of a wave and line through the center of a wave. (p. C17)

> **amplitud** La distancia máxima que se mueve un medio desde su posición de reposo debido a una perturbación; la distancia entre una cresta o valle de una onda y una línea que pasa por el centro de la onda.

asteroid
A small, solid, rocky body that orbits the Sun. Most asteroids orbit in a region between Mars and Jupiter called the asteroid belt. (p. E103)

> **asteroide** Un pequeño cuerpo sólido y rocoso que orbita alrededor del Sol. La mayoría de los asteroides orbitan en una región entre Marte y Júpiter denominada cinturón de asteroides.

asthenosphere (as-THEHN-uh-SFEER)
The layer in Earth's upper mantle and directly under the lithosphere in which rock is soft and weak because it is close to melting. (p. B71)

> **astenosfera** La capa del manto superior de la Tierra situada directamente bajo la litosfera en la cual la roca es blanda y débil por encontrarse próxima a su punto de fusión.

astronomical unit AU
Earth's average distance from the Sun, which is approximately 150 million kilometers (93 million mi). (p. E81)

unidad astronómica ua La distancia promedio de la Tierra al Sol, la cual es de aproximadamente 150 millones de kilómetros (93 millones de millas).

atmosphere (AT-muh-SFEER)
The outer layer of gases of a large body in space, such as a planet or star; the mixture of gases that surrounds the solid Earth; one of the four parts of the Earth system. (p. A10)

atmósfera La capa externa de gases de un gran cuerpo que se encuentra en el espacio, como un planeta o una estrella; la mezcla de gases que rodea la Tierra sólida; una de las cuatro partes del sistema terrestre.

atom
The smallest particle of an element that has the chemical properties of that element. (p. xxxv)

átomo La partícula más pequeña de un elemento que tiene las propiedades químicas de ese elemento.

axis of rotation
An imaginary line about which a turning body, such as Earth rotates. (p. E44)

eje de rotación Una línea imaginaria alrededor de la cual gira un cuerpo, como lo hace la Tierra.

B, C

barrier island
A long, narrow island that develops parallel to a coast as a sandbar builds up above the water's surface. (p. A160)

isla barrera Una isla larga y angosta que se desarrolla paralelamente a la costa al crecer una barra de arena hasta rebasar la superficie del agua.

big bang
The moment in time when the universe started to expand out of an extremely hot, dense state, according to scientific theory. (p. E138)

la gran explosión De acuerdo a la teoría científica, el momento en el tiempo en el cual el universo empezó a expandirse a partir de un estado extremadamente caliente y denso.

biodiversity
The number and variety of living things found on Earth or within an ecosystem. (p. D91)

biodiversidad La cantidad y variedad de organismos vivos que se encuentran en la Tierra o dentro de un ecosistema.

biology
The scientific study of life and all living things; ecology, zoology, and botany are examples of biological sciences.

biología El estudio científico de la vida y de todos los organismos vivos; la ecología, la zoología y la botántica son ejemplos de ciencias biológicas.

bioluminescence
The production of light by living organisms. (p. C89)

bioluminiscencia La producción de luz por parte de organismos vivos.

biome (BY-OHM)
A region of Earth that has a particular climate and certain types of plants. Examples are tundra, taiga, desert, grassland, temperate and tropical forests. (p. D30)

bioma Una región de la Tierra que tiene un clima particular y ciertos tipos de plantas. La tundra, la taiga, el desierto, la estepa, la selva tropical y el bosque templado son ejemplos de biomas.

biosphere (BY-uh-SFEER)
All living organisms on Earth in the air, on the land, and in the waters; one of the four parts of the Earth system. (p. A11)

biosfera Todos los organismos vivos de la Tierra, en el aire, en la tierra y en las aguas; una de las cuatro partes del sistema de la Tierra.

biotic factor (by-AHT-ihk)
A living thing in an ecosystem. (p. D10)

factor biótico Un organismo vivo en un ecosistema.

black hole
The final stage of an extremely massive star, which is invisible because its gravity prevents any form of radiation from escaping. (p. E126)

hoyo negro La etapa final de una estrella de enorme masa, la cual es invisible porque su gravedad evita que cualquier tipo de radiación escape.

calorie
The amount of energy needed to increase the temperature of one gram of water by one degree Celsius. (p. B46)

caloría La cantidad de energía que se necesita para aumentar la temperatura de un gramo de agua un grado centígrado.

carbon cycle
The continuous movement of carbon through Earth, its atmosphere, and the living things on Earth. (p. D18)

ciclo del carbono El movimiento continuo del carbono en la Tierra, su atmósfera y todos los seres vivos en ella.

carrying capacity
The maximum size that a population can reach in an ecosystem. (p. D65)

> **capacidad de carga** El tamaño máximo que una población puede alcanzar en un ecosistema.

cell
The smallest unit that is able to perform the basic functions of life. (p. xxxi)

> **célula** La unidad más pequeña capaz de realizar las funciones básicas de la vida.

chemical weathering
The breakdown or decomposition of rock that takes place when minerals change through chemical processes. (p. A118)

> **meteorización química** La descomposición de las rocas que ocurre cuando los minerales cambian mediante procesos químicos.

classification
The systematic grouping of different types of organisms by their shared characteristics.

> **clasificación** La agrupación sistemática de diferentes tipos de organismos en base a las características que comparten.

cleavage
The property of a mineral that describes its tendency to break along flat surfaces. (p. A53)

> **clivaje** La propiedad de un mineral que describe su tendencia a romperse a lo largo de una superficie plana.

climate
The characteristic weather conditions in an area over a long period of time.

> **clima** Las condiciones meteorológicas características de un lugar durante un largo período de tiempo.

comet
A body that produces a coma of gas and dust; a small, icy body that orbits the Sun. (p. E104)

> cometa Un cuerpo que produce una coma de gas y polvo; un cuerpo pequeño y helado que se mueve en órbita alrededor del Sol.

commensalism (kuh-MEHN-suh-LIHZ-uhm)
An interaction between two species in which one species benefits without harming the other; a type of symbiosis. (p. D59)

> **comensalismo** Una interacción entre dos especies en la cual una especie se beneficia sin causar daño a la otra; un tipo de simbiosis.

community
All the populations that live and interact with each other in a particular place. The community can live in a place as small as a pond or a park, or it can live in a place as large as a rain forest or the ocean. (p. D48)

> **comunidad** Todas las poblaciones que viven e interactúan entre sí en un lugar. La comunidad puede vivir en un lugar tan pequeño como una laguna o un parque o en un lugar tan grande como un bosque tropical o el océano.

competition
The struggle between two or more living things that depend on the same limited resource. (p. D55)

> **competencia** La lucha entre dos o más organismos vivos que dependen del mismo recurso limitado.

concave
Curved inward toward the center, like the inside of a spoon. (p. C116)

> **cóncavo** Dicho de una superficie con curvatura hacia dentro, como la parte interna de una cuchara.

conduction
The process by which energy is transferred from a warmer object to a cooler object by means of physical contact. (p. B51)

> **conducción** El proceso mediante el cual se transfiere energía de un objeto más caliente a un objeto más frío por medio de contacto físico.

conductor
1. A material that transfers energy easily. (p. B51)
2. A material that transfers electric charge easily.

> **conductor** 1. Un material que transfiere energía fácilmente. 2. Un material que transfiere cargas eléctricas fácilmente.

coniferous (koh-NIHF-uhr-uhs)
A term used to describe cone-bearing trees and shrubs that usually keep their leaves or needles during all the seasons of the year; examples are pine, fir, and spruce trees. (p. D32)

> **conífero** Un término usado para describir a los árboles y los arbustos que producen conos o piñas y que generalmente conservan sus hojas o agujas durante todas las estaciones del año; el pino, el abeto y la picea son ejemplos de coníferas.

conservation
The process of saving or protecting a natural resource. (p. D99)

> **conservación** El proceso de salvar o proteger un recurso natural.

constellation

A group of stars that form a pattern in the sky. (p. E12)

> **constelación** Un grupo de estrellas que forman un patrón en el cielo.

consumer

A living thing that gets its energy by eating other living things in a food chain; consumers are also called heterotrophs. (p. D24)

> **consumidor** Un organismo vivo que obtiene su energía alimentándose de oros organismos vivos en una cadena alimentaria; los consumidores también son llamados heterótrofos.

continental-continental collision

A boundary along which two plates carrying continental crust push together. (p. B91)

> **colisión continente-continente** Un límite a lo largo del cual dos placas de corteza continental empujan contra sí.

continental drift

The hypothesis that Earth's continents move on Earth's surface. (p. B74)

> **deriva continental** La hipótesis que postula que los continentes de la Tierra se mueven sobre la superficie del planeta.

contour interval

On a topographic map, the difference in elevation from one contour line to the next. (p. A26)

> **equidistancia entre curvas de nivel** En un mapa topográfico, la diferencia en elevación de una curva de nivel a la siguiente.

contour line

A line on a topographic map that joins points of equal elevation. (p. A25)

> **curva de nivel** Una línea en un mapa topográfico que une puntos de igual elevación.

convection

A process by which energy is transferred in gases and liquids, occurring when a warmer, less dense area of gas or liquid is pushed up by a cooler, more dense area of the gas or liquid. (pp. B52, E116)

> **convección** Un proceso mediante el cual se transfiere energía en los gases y los líquidos; ocurre cuando un área más fría y más densa del gas o del líquido empuja hacia arriba un área más caliente y menos densa de gas o de líquido.

convection current

A circulation pattern in which material is heated and rises in one area, then cools and sinks in another area, flowing in a continuous loop. (p. B77)

> **corriente de convección** Un patrón de circulación en el cual el material se calienta y asciende en un área, luego se enfría y se hunde en otra área, fluyendo en un circuito continuo.

convergent boundary (kun-VUR-juhnt)

A boundary along which two tectonic plates push together, characterized either by subduction or a continental collision. (p. B82)

> **límite convergente** Un límite a lo largo del cual dos placas tectónicas se empujan mutuamente; este límite se caracteriza por una zona de subducción o una colisión entre continentes.

convex

Curved outward, like the underside of a spoon. (p. C116)

> **convexo** Dicho de una superficie con curvatura hacia afuera, como la parte externa de una cuchara.

cooperation

A term used to describe an interaction between two or more living things in which they are said to work together. (p. D57)

> **cooperación** Un término que describe la interacción entre dos o más organismos vivos en la cual se dice que trabajan juntos.

cornea (KAWR-nee-uh)

A transparent membrane that covers the eye. (p. C127)

> **córnea** Una membrana transparente que cubre el ojo.

corona

The outer layer of the Sun's atmosphere. (p. E116)

> **corona** La capa exterior de la atmósfera del Sol.

crest

The highest point, or peak, of a wave. (p. C17)

> **cresta** El punto más alto, o el pico, de una onda.

crust

A thin outer layer of rock above a planet's mantle, including all dry land and ocean basins. Earth's continental crust is 40 kilometers thick on average and oceanic crust is 7 kilometers thick on average. (p. B71)

> **corteza** Una delgada capa exterior de roca situada sobre el manto de un planeta que incluye toda la tierra seca y todas las cuencas oceánicas. La corteza continental de la Tierra tiene un grosor promedio de 40 kilómetros y la corteza oceánica tiene un grosor promedio de 7 kilómetros.

crystal

A solid substance in which the atoms are arranged in an orderly, repeating, three-dimensional pattern. (p. A46)

cristal Una sustancia sólida en la cual los átomos están organizados en un patrón tridimensional y ordenado que se repite.

cycle

n. A series of events or actions that repeat themselves regularly; a physical and/or chemical process in which one material continually changes locations and/or forms. Examples include the water cycle, the carbon cycle, and the rock cycle.

v. To move through a repeating series of events or actions.

ciclo *s.* Una serie de eventos o acciones que se repiten regularmente; un proceso físico y/o químico en el cual un material cambia continuamente de lugar y/o forma. Ejemplos: el ciclo del agua, el ciclo del carbono y el ciclo de las rocas.

D

data

Information gathered by observation or experimentation that can be used in calculating or reasoning. *Data* is a plural word; the singular is *datum*.

datos Información reunida mediante observación o experimentación y que se puede usar para calcular o para razonar.

decibel dB

The unit used to measure the intensity of a sound wave. (p. C52)

decibel La unidad que se usa para medir la intensidad de una onda sonora.

deciduous (dih-SIHJ-oo-uhs)

A term used to describe trees and shrubs that drop their leaves when winter comes; examples are maple, oak, and birch trees. (p. D33)

caducifolio Un término usado para describir árboles y arbustos que dejan caer sus hojas cuando llega el invierno; el arce, el roble y el abedul son ejemplos de árboles caducifolios.

decomposer

An organism that feeds on and breaks down dead plant or animal matter. (p. D25)

organismo descomponedor Un organismo que se alimenta de y degrada materia vegetal o animal.

degree

Evenly divided units of a temperature scale. (p. B40)

grado Unidades de una escala de temperatura distribuidas uniformemente.

delta

An area of land at the end, or mouth, of a river that is formed by the buildup of sediment. (p. A153)

delta Un área de tierra al final, o en la desembocadura, de un río y que se forma por la acumulación de sedimentos.

density

A property of matter representing the mass per unit volume. (p. A54)

densidad Una propiedad de la materia que representa la masa por unidad de volumen.

deposition (DEHP-uh-ZISH-uhn)

The process in which transported sediment is laid down. (p. A145)

sedimentación El proceso mediante el cual se deposita sedimento que ha sido transportado.

desertification (dih-ZUR-tuh-fih-KAY-shuhn)

The expansion of desert conditions in areas where the natural plant cover has been destroyed. (p. A133)

desertificación La expansión de las condiciones desérticas en áreas donde la vegetación natural ha sido destruida.

diffraction

The spreading out of waves as they pass through an opening or around the edges of an obstacle. (p. C26)

difracción La dispersión de las ondas al pasar por una apertura o alrededor de los bordes de un obstáculo.

diffuse reflection

The reflection of parallel light rays in many different directions. (p. C114)

reflexión difusa La reflexión de rayos de luz paralelos en muchas direcciones diferentes.

divergent boundary (dih-VUR-juhnt)

A boundary along which two tectonic plates move apart, characterized by either a mid-ocean ridge or a continental rift valley. (p. B82)

límite divergente Un límite a lo largo del cual dos placas tectónicas se separan; este límite se caracteriza por una dorsal oceánica o un valle de rift continental.

diversity

A term used to describe the quality of having many differences. Biodiversity describes the great variety and many differences found among living things.

diversidad Un término usado para describir la cualidad de tener muchas diferencias. La biodiversidad describe la gran variedad y las muchas diferencias encontradas entre organismos vivos.

divide

A continuous high line of land—or ridge—from which water drains to one side or the other. (p. A151)

línea divisoria de aguas Una línea continua de tierra alta, o un cerro, desde donde el agua escurre hacia un lado o hacia el otro.

DNA

The genetic material found in all living cells that contains the information needed for an organism to grow, maintain itself, and reproduce. Deoxyribonucleic acid (dee-AHK-see-RY-boh-noo-KLEE-ihk).

ADN El material genético que se encuentra en todas las céulas vivas y que contiene la información necesaria para que un organismo crezca, se mantenga a sí mismo y se reproduzca. Ácido desoxiribunucleico.

Doppler effect

A change in the observed frequency of a wave, occurring when the source of the wave or the observer is moving. Changes in the frequency of light are often measured by observing changes in wavelength, whereas changes in the frequency of sound are often detected as changes in pitch. (pp. C50, E136)

efecto Doppler Un cambio en la frecuencia observada de una onda que ocurre cuando la fuente de la onda o el observador están en movimiento. Los cambios en la frecuencia de la luz a menudo se miden observando los cambios en la longitud de onda, mientras que los cambios en la frecuencia del sonido a menudo se detectan como cambios en el tono.

drainage basin

An area of land in which water drains into a stream system. The borders of a drainage basin are called divides. (p. A151)

cuenca tributaria Un área de tierra en la cual el agua **escurre a un sistema de corrientes**. Los límites de una cuenca tributaria se denominan líneas divisorias de aguas.

dune

A mound of sand built up by wind. (p. A161)

duna Un montículo de arena formado por el viento.

E

earthquake

A shaking of the ground caused by the sudden movement of large blocks of rocks along a fault. (p. B105)

terremoto Un temblor del suelo ocasionado por el movimiento repentino de grandes bloques de rocas a lo largo de una falla.

echolocation

The sending out of high-pitched sound waves and the interpretation of the returning echoes. (p. C59)

ecolocación El envío de ondas sonoras de tono alto y la interpretación de los ecos que regresan.

eclipse

An event during which one object in space casts a shadow onto another. On Earth, a lunar eclipse occurs when the Moon moves through Earth's shadow, and a solar eclipse occurs when the Moon's shadow crosses Earth. (p. E63)

eclipse Un evento durante el cual un objeto en el espacio proyecta una sombra sobre otro. En la Tierra, un eclipse lunar ocurre cuando la Luna se mueve a través de la sombra de la Tierra, y un eclipse solar ocurre cuando la sombra de la Luna cruza la Tierra.

ecology

The scientific study of how living things interact with each other and their environment. (p. D9)

ecología El estudio científico de cómo interactúan los organismos vivos entre sí y con su medio ambiente.

ecosystem

All the living and nonliving things that interact in a particular environment. An ecosystem can be as small as a meadow or a swamp or as large as a forest or a desert. (p. D9)

ecosistema Todos los organismos vivos y las cosas que interactúan en un medio ambiente específico. Un ecosistema puede ser tan pequeño como un prado o un pantano, o tan grande como un bosque o un desierto.

electromagnetic radiation
(ih-LEHK-troh-mag-NEHT-ihk)

Energy that travels across distances as certain types of waves. Types of electromagnetic radiation are radio waves, microwaves, infrared radiation, visible light, ultraviolet radiation, x-rays, and gamma rays. (p. E15)

radiación electromagnética Energía que viaja a través de las distancias en forma de ciertos tipos de ondas. Las ondas de radio, las microondas, la radiación infrarroja, la luz visible, la radiación ultravioleta, los rayos X y los rayos gama son tipos de radiación electromagnética.

electromagnetic spectrum EM spectrum

The range of all electromagnetic frequencies, including the following types (from lowest to highest frequency): radio waves, microwaves, infrared light, visible light, ultraviolet light, x-rays, and gamma rays. (p. C80)

espectro electromagnético La escala de todas las frecuencias electromagnéticas, incluyendo los siguientes tipos (de la frecuencia más baja a la más alta): ondas de radio, microondas, luz infrarroja, luz visible, luz ultravioleta, rayos X y rayos gamma.

electromagnetic wave EM wave
A type of wave, such as a light wave or radio wave, that does not require a medium to travel; a disturbance that transfers energy through a field. (p. C73)

onda electromagnética Un tipo de onda, como una onda luminosa o de radio, que no requiere un medio para propagarse; una perturbación que transfiere energía a través de un campo.

element
A substance that cannot be broken down into a simpler substance by ordinary chemical changes. An element consists of atoms of only one type. (p. A45)

elemento Una sustancia que no puede descomponerse en otra sustancia más simple por medio de cambios químicos normales. Un elemento consta de átomos de un solo tipo.

elevation
A measure of how high something is above a reference point, such as sea level. (p. A25)

elevación Una medida de lo elevado que está algo sobre un punto de referencia, como el nivel del mar.

ellipse
An oval or flattened circle. (p. E81)

elipse Un óvalo o círculo aplanado.

energy
The ability to do work or to cause a change. For example, the energy of a moving bowling ball knocks over pins; energy from food allows animals to move and to grow; and energy from the Sun heats Earth's surface and atmosphere, which causes air to move. (p. B10)

energía La capacidad para trabajar o causar un cambio. Por ejemplo, la energía de una bola de boliche en movimiento tumba los pinos; la energía proveniente de su alimento permite a los animales moverse y crecer; la energía del Sol calienta la superficie y la atmósfera de la Tierra, lo que ocasiona que el aire se mueva.

energy efficiency
A measurement of usable energy after an energy conversion; the ratio of usable energy to the total energy after an energy conversion. (p. B21)

eficiencia energética Una medida de la energía utilizable después de una conversión energética; la razón entre la energía utilizable y el total de energía después de una conversión energética.

energy pyramid
A model used to show the amount of energy available to living things in an ecosystem. (p. D28)

pirámide de energía Un modelo usado para mostrar la cantidad de energía disponible para organismos vivos en un ecosistema.

environment
Everything that surrounds a living thing. An environment is made up of both living and nonliving factors. (p. xxxi)

medio ambiente Todo lo que rodea a un organismo vivo. Un medio ambiente está compuesto de factores vivos y factores sin vida.

epicenter (EHP-ih-SEHN-tuhr)
The point on Earth's surface directly above the focus of an earthquake. (p. B112)

epicentro El punto en la superficie de la Tierra situado directamente sobre el foco sísmico.

equator
An imaginary east-west line around the center of Earth that divides the planet into the Northern Hemisphere and the Southern Hemisphere; a line set at 0° latitude. (p. A18)

ecuador Una línea imaginaria de este a oeste alrededor del centro de la Tierra y que divide al planeta en hemisferio norte y hemisferio sur; la línea está fijada a latitud 0°.

equinox (EE-kwuh-NAHKS)
In an orbit, a position and time in which sunlight shines equally on the Northern Hemisphere and the Southern Hemisphere; a time of year when daylight and darkness are nearly equal for most of Earth. (p. E46)

equinoccio En una órbita, la posición y el tiempo en los cuales la luz del Sol incide de la misma manera en el Hemisferio Norte y en el Hemisferio Sur; una época del año en la cual la luz del día y la oscuridad son casi iguales para la mayor parte de la Tierra.

erosion
The process in which sediment is picked up and moved from one place to another. (p. A145)

erosión El proceso en el cual el sedimento es recogido y transportado de un lugar a otro.

estuary
The lower end of a river where it meets the ocean and fresh and salt waters mix. (p. D36)

estuario La parte baja de un río donde desemboca en el océano y donde el agua dulce del río se mezcla con el agua salada del mar.

exfoliation (ex-FOH-lee-AY-shuhn)
In geology, the process in which layers or sheets of rock gradually break off. (p. A116)

exfoliación En geología, el proceso en el cual capas u hojas de roca se desprenden gradualmente.

experiment

An organized procedure to study something under controlled conditions. (p. xxxiii)

experimento Un procedimiento organizado para estudiar algo bajo condiciones controladas.

extinction

The permanent disappearance of a species. (p. xxxi)

extinción La desaparición permanente de una especie.

extrusive igneous rock (ihk-STROO-sihv)

Igneous rock that forms as lava cools on Earth's surface. (p. A83)

roca ígnea extrusiva Roca ígnea que se forma al enfriarse la lava sobre la superficie de la Tierra.

F

false-color image

A computer image in which the colors are not what the human eye would see. A false-color image can assign different colors to different types of radiation coming from an object to highlight its features. (p. A32)

imagen de color falso Una imagen computacional en la cual los colores no son los que el ojo humano observaría. Una imagen de color falso puede asignar diferentes colores a los diferentes tipos de radiación que provienen de un objeto para hacer destacar sus características.

fault

A fracture in Earth's lithosphere along which blocks of rock move past each other. (p. B105)

falla Una fractura en la litosfera de la Tierra a lo largo de la cual bloques de roca se mueven y pasan uno al lado de otro.

fault-block mountain

A mountain that forms as blocks of rock move up or down along normal faults in areas where the lithosphere is being pulled apart. (p. B142)

montaña de bloques de falla Una montaña que se forma cuando bloques de roca se mueven hacia arriba o hacia abajo a lo largo de fallas normales en las áreas donde la litosfera está siendo separada.

fiber optics

Technology based on the use of laser light to send signals through transparent wires called optical fibers. This technology is often used in communications. (p. C137)

fibra óptica Tecnología basada en el uso de luz de láser para mandar señales por alambres transparentes llamados fibras ópticas. Esta tecnología se usa a menudo en comunicaciones.

field

An area around an object where the object can apply a force—such as gravitational force, magnetic force, or electrical force—on another object without touching it.

campo Un área alrededor de un objeto donde el objeto puede aplicar una fuerza, como fuerza gravitacional, fuerza magnética o fuerza eléctrica, sobre otro objeto sin tocarlo.

floodplain

A flat area of land on either side of a stream that becomes flooded when a river overflows its banks. (p. A152)

planicie de inundación Un área plana de tierra en cualquier costado de un arroyo que se inunda cuando un río se desborda.

fluorescence (flu-REHS-uhns)

A phenomenon in which a material absorbs electromagnetic radiation of one wavelength and gives off electromagnetic radiation of a different wavelength. (p. C91)

fluorescencia Un fenómeno en el cual un material absorbe radiación electromagnética de una longitud de onda y emite radiación electromagnética de longitud de onda diferente.

focal length

The distance from the center of a convex lens to its focal point. (p. C123)

distancia focal La distancia del centro de un lente convexo a su punto focal.

focal point

The point at which parallel light rays reflected from a concave mirror come together; the point at which parallel light rays refracted by a convex lens come together. (p. C117)

punto focal El punto en el cual se unen los rayos paralelos de luz reflejados por un espejo cóncavo; el punto en el cual se unen los rayos paralelos de luz refractados por un lente convexo.

focus

In an earthquake, the point underground where the rocks first begin to move. (p. B112)

foco sísmico En un terremoto, el punto subterráneo donde comienza el movimiento de las rocas.

folded mountain

A mountain that forms as continental crust is compressed and rocks bend into large folds. (p. B140)

montaña plegada Una montaña que se forma cuando la corteza continental es comprimida y las rocas se doblan en grandes pliegues.

foliation

The arrangement of minerals within rocks into flat or wavy parallel bands; a characteristic of most metamorphic rocks. (p. A100)

foliación La organización de minerales en bandas paralelas planas u onduladas en las rocas; una característica de la mayoría de las rocas metamórficas.

food chain

A model used to show the feeding relationship between a single producer and a chain of consumers in an ecosystem. In a typical food chain, a plant is the producer that is eaten by a consumer, such as an insect; then the insect is eaten by a second consumer, such as a bird. (p. D26)

cadena alimentaria Un modelo usado para mostrar la relación de ingestión entre un solo productor y una cadena de consumidores en un ecosistema. En una cadena alimentaria típica, una planta es la productora que es ingerida por un consumidor como un insecto, y luego el insecto es ingerido por un segundo consumidor como un pájaro.

food web

A model used to show a feeding relationship in which many food chains overlap in an ecosystem. (p. D26)

red trófica Un modelo usado para mostrar una relación de consumo en la cual muchas cadenas alimentarias se empalman en un ecosistema.

force

A push or a pull; something that changes the motion of an object. (p. xxxiii)

fuerza Un empuje o un jalón; algo que cambia el movimiento de un objeto.

fossil

A trace or the remains of a once-living thing from long ago.

fósil Un rastro o los restos de un organismo que vivió hace mucho tiempo.

fracture

The tendency of a mineral to break into irregular pieces. (p. A53)

fractura La tendencia de un mineral a romperse en pedazos irregulares.

frequency

The number of waves that pass a fixed point in a given amount of time, usually one second; the number of cycles per unit time. (p. C17)

frecuencia El número de longitudes de onda (o crestas de onda) que pasan un punto fijo en un período de tiempo determinado, normalmente un segundo; el número de ciclos por unidad de tiempo.

friction

A force that resists the motion between two surfaces in contact. (p. xxxv)

fricción Una fuerza que resiste el movimiento entre dos superficies en contacto.

fusion

A process in which particles of an element collide and combine to form a heavier element, such as the fusion of hydrogen into helium that occurs in the Sun's core. (p. E116)

fusión Un proceso en el cual las partículas de un elemento chocan y se combinan para formar un elemento más pesado, como la fusión de hidrógeno en helio que ocurre en el núcleo del Sol.

G

galaxy

Millions or billions of stars held together in a group by their own gravity. (p. E10)

galaxia Millones o miles de millones de estrellas unidas en un grupo por su propia gravedad.

gamma rays

Part of the electromagnetic spectrum that consists of waves with the highest frequencies; electromagnetic waves with frequencies ranging from more than 10^{19} hertz to more than 10^{24} hertz. (p. C86)

rayos gamma Parte del espectro electromagnético que consiste de ondas con las frecuencias más altas; las ondas electromagnéticas con frecuencias de más de 10^{19} hertzios hasta más de 10^{24} hertzios.

gas giant

A large planet that consists mostly of gases in a dense form. The four large planets in the outer solar system—Jupiter, Saturn, Uranus, and Neptune—are gas giants. (p. E94)

gigante de gas Un planeta grande compuesto principalmente de gases en forma densa. Los cuatro planetas grandes en el sistema solar exterior—Júpiter, Saturno, Urano y Neptuno —son gigantes de gas.

genetic material

The nucleic acid DNA that is present in all living cells and contains the information needed for a cell's growth, maintenance, and reproduction.

material genético El ácido nucleico ADN, ue esta presente en todas las células vivas y que contiene la información necesaria para el crecimiento, el mantenimiento y la reproducción celular.

geographic information systems
Computer systems that can store, arrange, and display geographic data in different types of maps. (p. A33)

sistemas de información geográfica Sistemas computarizados que pueden almacenar, organizar y mostrar datos geográficos en diferentes tipos de mapas.

geosphere (JEE-uh-SFEER)
All the features on Earth's surface—continents, islands, and seafloor—and everything below the surface—the inner and outer core and the mantle; one of the four parts of the Earth system. (p. A12)

geosfera Todas las características de la superficie de la Tierra, es decir, continentes, islas y el fondo marino, y de todo bajo la superficie, es decir, el núcleo externo e interno y el manto; una de las cuatro partes del sistema de la Tierra.

geyser
A type of hot spring that shoots water into the air. (p. B160)

géiser Un tipo de fuente termal que dispara agua al aire.

glacier (GLAY-shuhr)
A large mass of ice that exists year-round and moves over land. (p. A165)

glaciar Una gran masa de hielo que existe durante todo el año y se mueve sobre la tierra.

gravity
The force that objects exert on each other because of their mass. (p. xxxv)

gravedad La fuerza que los objetos ejercen entre sí debido a su masa.

H

habitat
The natural environment in which a living thing gets all that it needs to live; examples include a desert, a coral reef, and a freshwater lake. (p. D46)

hábitat El medio ambiente natural en el cual un organismo vivo consigue todo lo que requiere para vivir; ejemplos incluyen un desierto, un arrecife coralino y un lago de agua dulce.

hardness
The resistance of a mineral or other material to being scratched. (p. A55)

dureza La resistencia de un mineral o de otro material a ser rayado.

heat
1. The flow of energy from an object at a higher temperature to an object at a lower temperature. (p. B44)
2. Energy that is transferred from a warmer object to a cooler object.

calor 1. El flujo de energía de un objeto a mayor temperatura a un objeto a menor temperatura. 2. Energía que se transfiere de un objeto más caliente a un objeto más frío.

hertz Hz
The unit used to measure frequency. One hertz is equal to one complete cycle per second. (p. C46)

hercio La unidad usada para medir frecuencia. Un hercio es igual a un ciclo completo por segundo.

hot spot
An area where a column of hot material rises from deep within a planet's mantle and heats the lithosphere above it, often causing volcanic activity at the surface. (p. B87)

punto caliente Un área donde una columna de material caliente surge del interior del manto de un planeta y calienta la litosfera situada sobre él, con frecuencia ocasionando actividad volcánica en la superficie.

humus (HYOO-muhs)
The decayed organic matter in soil. (p. A123)

humus La materia orgánica en descomposición del suelo.

hydrosphere (HY-druh-SFEER)
All water on Earth—in the atmosphere and in the oceans, lakes, glaciers, rivers, streams, and underground reservoirs; one of the four parts of the Earth system. (p. A10)

hidrosfera Toda el agua de la Tierra: en la atmósfera y en los océanos, lagos, glaciares, ríos, arroyos y depósitos subterráneos; una de las cuatro partes del sistema de la Tierra.

hypothesis
A tentative explanation for an observation or phenomenon. A hypothesis is used to make testable predictions. (p. xxxviii)

hipótesis Una explicación provisional de una observación o de un fenómeno. Una hipótesis se usa para hacer predicciones que se pueden probar.

I, J

igneous rock (IHG-nee-uhs)
Rock that forms as molten rock cools and becomes solid. (p. A78)

roca ígnea Roca que se forma al enfriarse la roca fundida y hacerse sólida.

image
A picture of an object formed by rays of light. (p. C115)

imagen Reproducción de la figura de un objeto formada por rayos de luz.

impact crater
A round pit left behind on the surface of a planet or other body in space after a smaller object strikes the surface. (p. E32)

cráter de impacto Un pozo circular en la superficie de un planeta u otro cuerpo en el espacio que se forma cuando un objeto más pequeño golpea la superficie.

incandescence (IHN-kuhn-DEHS-uhns)
1. The production of light by materials having high temperatures. (p. C89) 2. Light produced by an incandescent object.

incandescencia 1. La producción de luz por parte de materiales a altas temperaturas. 2. La luz producida por un objeto incandescente.

infrared light
Part of the electromagnetic spectrum that consists of waves with frequencies between those of microwaves and visible light. (p. C84)

luz infrarroja Parte del espectro electromagnético que consiste de ondas con frecuencias entre las de las microondas y las de la luz visible.

inner core
A solid sphere of metal, mainly nickel and iron, at Earth's center. (p. B70)

núcleo interno Una esfera sólida de metal, principalmente níquel y hierro, que se encuentra en el centro de la Tierra.

insulator
1. A material that does not transfer energy easily. (p. B51)
2. A material that does not transfer electric charge easily.

aislante 1. Un material que no transfiere energía fácilmente. 2. Un material que no transfiere cargas eléctricas fácilmente.

intensity
The amount of energy of a wave, per wavelength. Intensity is associated with the amplitude of a sound wave and with the quality of loudness produced by the sound wave. (p. C52)

intensidad La cantidad de energía de una onda sonora, por longitud de onda. La intensidad está asociada con la amplitud de una onda sonora y con la calidad del volumen producido por la onda sonora.

interaction
The condition of acting or having an influence upon something. Living things in an ecosystem interact with both the living and nonliving parts of their environment. (p. xxxi)

interacción La condición de actuar o influir sobre algo. Los organismos vivos en un ecosistema interactúan con las partes vivas y las partes sin vida de su medio ambiente.

interference
The meeting and combining of waves; the adding or subtracting of wave amplitudes that occurs as waves overlap. (p. C27)

interferencia El encuentro y la combinación de ondas; la suma o la resta de amplitudes de onda que ocurre cuando las ondas se traslapan.

intrusive igneous rock (ihn-TROO-sihv)
Igneous rock that forms as magma cools below Earth's surface. (p. A83)

roca ígnea intrusiva Roca ígnea que se forma al enfriarse el magma bajo la superficie de la Tierra.

joule J (jool)
A unit used to measure energy and work. One calorie is equal to 4.18 joules of energy; one joule of work is done when a force of one newton moves an object one meter. (p. B46)

julio Una unidad que se usa para medir la energía y el trabajo. Una caloría es igual a 4.18 julios de energía; se hace un joule de trabajo cuando una fuerza de un newton mueve un objeto un metro.

K

kettle lake
A bowl-shaped lake that was formed as sediment built up around a block of ice left behind by a glacier. (p. A169)

lago kettle Un lago en forma de tazón que se formó al acumularse sedimento alrededor de un bloque de hielo que quedó tras el paso de un glaciar.

kinetic energy
The energy of motion. A moving object has the most kinetic energy at the point where it moves the fastest. (p. B12)

energía cinética La energía del movimiento. Un objeto que se mueve tiene su mayor energía cinética en el punto en el cual se mueve con mayor rapidez.

kinetic theory of matter
A theory stating that all matter is made of particles in motion. (p. B38)

teoría cinética de la materia Una teoría que establece que toda materia está compuesta de partículas en movimiento.

L

lander
A craft designed to land on a planet's surface. (p. E28)

módulo de aterrizaje Una nave diseñada para aterrizar en la superficie de un planeta.

laser (LAY-zuhr)
A device that produces an intense, concentrated beam of light that can be brighter than sunlight. Lasers are often used in medicine and communications. (p. C135)

láser Un aparato que produce un intenso rayo de luz concentrado que es más brillante que la luz del Sol. Los láseres se usan a menudo en la medicina y las comunicaciones.

latitude
The distance in degrees north or south from the equator. (p. A18)

latitud La distancia en grados norte o sur a partir del ecuador.

lava
Molten rock that reaches a planet's surface through a volcano. (pp. A62, B147)

lava Roca fundida que llega a la superficie de un planeta a través de un volcán.

law
In science, a rule or principle describing a physical relationship that always works in the same way under the same conditions. The law of conservation of energy is an example.

ley En las ciencias, una regla o un principio que describe una relación física que siempre funciona de la misma manera bajo las mismas condiciones. La ley de la conservación de la energía es un ejemplo.

law of conservation of energy
A law stating that no matter how energy is transferred or transformed, it continues to exist in one form or another. (p. B20)

ley de la conservación de la energía Una ley que establece que no importa cómo se transfiere o transforma la energía, toda la energía sigue presente en alguna forma u otra.

law of reflection
A law of physics stating that the angle at which light strikes a surface (the angle of incidence) equals the angle at which it reflects off the surface (the angle of reflection). (p. C114)

ley de la reflexión Una ley de la física que establece que el ángulo al cual la luz incide sobre una superficie (el ángulo de incidencia) es igual al ángulo al cual se refleja (ángulo de reflexión) de la superficie.

lens
A transparent optical tool that refracts light. (p. C121)

lente Una herramienta óptica transparente que refracta la luz.

light-year
The distance light travels in one year, which is about 9.5 trillion kilometers (6 trillion mi). (p. E122)

año luz La distancia que viaja la luz en un año, la cual es de casi 9.5 billones de kilómetros (6 billones de millas).

limiting factor
A factor or condition that prevents the continuing growth of a population in an ecosystem. (p. D64)

factor limitante Un factor o una condición que impide el crecimiento continuo de una población en un ecosistema.

liquefaction
A process in which the shaking of ground causes loose, wet soil to act like a liquid. (p. B122)

licuación Un proceso en el cual el temblor del suelo ocasiona que la tierra húmeda y suelta actúe como un líquido.

lithosphere (LIHTH-uh-SFEER)
The layer of Earth made up of the crust and the rigid rock of the upper mantle, averaging about 40 kilometers thick and broken into tectonic plates. (p. B71)

litosfera La capa de la Tierra compuesta por la corteza y la roca rígida del manto superior, con un promedio de 40 kilómetros de grosor y fracturada en placas tectónicas.

loess (LOH-uhs)
Deposits of fine-grained, wind-blown sediment. (p. A162)

loes Depósitos de sedimento de grano fino transportado por el viento.

longitude
The distance in degrees east or west of the prime meridian. Longitude lines are numbered from 0° to 180°. (p. A19)

longitud La distancia en grados al este o al oeste del primer meridiano. Las líneas de longitud están numeradas de 0° a 180°.

longitudinal wave (LAHN-jih-TOOD-uhn-uhl)
A type of wave in which the disturbance moves in the same direction that the wave travels. (p. C14)

> **onda longitudinal** Un tipo de onda en la cual la perturbación se mueve en la misma dirección en la que viaja la onda.

longshore current
The overall direction and movement of water as waves strike the shore at an angle. (p. A159)

> **corriente litoral** La dirección y el movimiento general del agua conforme las olas golpean la costa en ángulo.

longshore drift
The zigzag movement of sand along a beach, caused by the action of waves. (p. A159)

> **deriva litoral** El movimiento en zigzag de la arena a lo largo de una playa, ocasionado por la acción de las olas.

luminescence
The production of light without the high temperatures needed for incandescence. (p. C89)

> **luminiscencia** La producción de luz sin las altas temperaturas necesarias para la incandescencia.

luster
The property of a mineral that describes the way in which light reflects from its surface. Major types of luster are metallic and nonmetallic. (p. A52)

> **brillo** La propiedad de un mineral que describe la manera en la cual la luz se refleja en su superficie. Los principales tipos de brillo son metálico y no metálico.

M

magma
Molten rock beneath Earth's surface. (p. A62)

> **magma** Roca fundida que se encuentra bajo la superficie de la Tierra.

magnetic reversal
A switch in the direction of Earth's magnetic field so that the magnetic north pole becomes the magnetic south pole and the magnetic south pole becomes the magnetic north pole. (p. B84)

> **inversión magnética** Un cambio en la dirección del campo magnético de la Tierra, de modo que el polo norte magnético se convierte en el polo sur magnético y el polo sur magnético se convierte en el polo norte magnético.

main sequence
The stage in which stars produce energy through the fusion of hydrogen into helium. (p. E126)

> **secuencia principal** La etapa en la cual las estrellas producen energía mediante la fusión de hidrógeno en helio.

mantle
The layer of rock between Earth's outer core and crust, in which most rock is hot enough to flow in convection currents; Earth's thickest layer. (p. B71)

> **manto** La capa de roca situada entre el núcleo externo y la corteza de la Tierra, en la cual la mayor parte de la roca es lo suficientemente caliente para fluir en corrientes de convección; la capa más gruesa de la Tierra.

map legend
A chart that explains the meaning of each symbol used on a map; also called a key. (p. A17)

> **clave del mapa** Una tabla que explica el significado de cada símbolo usado en un mapa.

map scale
The comparison of distance on a map with actual distance on what the map represents, such as Earth's surface. Map scale may be expressed as a ratio, a bar scale, or equivalent units. (p. A17)

> **escala del mapa** La comparación de la distancia en un mapa con la distancia real en lo que el mapa representa, como la superficie de la Tierra. La escala del mapa puede expresarse como una azón, una barra de escala o en unidades equivalentes.

mare (MAH-ray)
A large, dark plain of solidified lava on the Moon. The plural form of mare is maria (MAH-ree-uh). (p. E53)

> **mare** Una planicie grande y oscura de lava solidificada en la Luna. El plural de mare es maría.

mass wasting
The downhill movement of loose rock or soil. (p. A147)

> **movimiento de masa** El desplazamiento cuesta abajo de suelo o de roca suelta.

mechanical wave
A wave, such as a sound wave or a seismic wave, that transfers kinetic energy through matter. (p. C11)

> **onda mecánica** Una onda, como una onda sonora o una onda sísmica, que transfiere energía cinética a través de la materia.

mechanical weathering
The breakdown of rock into smaller pieces of the same material without any change in its composition. (p. A116)

meteorización mecánica El desmoronamiento de las rocas en pedazos más pequeños del mismo material, sin ningún cambio en su composición.

medium
A substance through which a wave moves. (p. C11)

medio Una sustancia a través de la cual se mueve una onda.

metamorphic rock (MEHT-uh-MAWR-fihk)
Rock formed as heat or pressure causes existing rock to change in structure, texture, or mineral composition. (p. A78)

roca metamórfica Roca formada cuando el calor o la presión ocasionan que la roca existente cambie de estructura, textura o composición mineral.

metamorphism (MEHT-uh-MAWR-FIHZ-uhm)
The process by which a rock's structure or mineral composition is changed by pressure or heat. (p. A96)

metamorfismo El proceso mediante el cual la estructura o la composición mineral de una roca cambia debido a la presión o al calor.

meteor
A brief streak of light produced by a small particle entering Earth's atmosphere at a high speed. (p. E105)

meteoro Un breve rayo luminoso producido por una partícula pequeña que entra a la atmósfera de la Tierra a una alta velocidad.

meteorite
A small object from outer space that passes through Earth's atmosphere and reaches the surface. (p. E105)

meteorito Un pequeño objeto del espacio exterior que pasa a través de la atmósfera de la Tierra y llega a la superficie.

microwaves
Part of the electromagnetic spectrum that consists of waves with higher frequencies than radio waves, but lower frequencies than infrared waves. (p. C83)

microondas Parte del espectro electromagnético que consiste de ondas con frecuencias mayores a las ondas de radio, pero menores a las de las ondas infrarrojas.

mid-ocean ridge
A long line of sea-floor mountains where new ocean crust is formed by volcanic activity along a divergent boundary. (p. B76)

dorsal oceánica Una larga línea de montañas en el fondo marino donde se forma nueva corteza oceánica debido a la actividad volcánica a lo largo de un límite divergente.

mineral
A substance that forms in nature, is a solid, has a definite chemical makeup, and has a crystal structure. (p. A43)

mineral Una sustancia sólida formada en la naturaleza, de composición química definida y estructura cristalina.

moraine (muh-RAYN)
A deposit of till left behind by a retreating glacier. Moraines can form along a glacier's sides and at its end. (p. A168)

morrena Un depósito de sedimentos glaciares dejado por un glaciar que retrocede. Las morrenas pueden formarse en los costados de un glaciar o en su extremo.

mutualism (MYOO-choo-uh-LIHZ-uhm)
An interaction between two species in which both benefit; a type of symbiosis. (p. D58)

mutualismo Una interacción entre dos especies en la cual ambas se benefician; un tipo de simbiosis.

N

natural resource
Any type of matter or energy from Earth's environment that humans use to meet their needs. (p. D84)

recurso natural Cualquier tipo de materia o energía del medio ambiente de la Tierra que usan los humanos para satisfacer sus necesidades.

nebula (NEHB-yuh-luh)
A cloud of gas and dust in space. Stars form in nebulae. (p. E125)

nebulosa Una nube de gas y polvo en el espacio. Las estrellas se forman en las nebulosas.

neutron star
A dense core that may be left behind after a higher-mass star explodes in a supernova. (p. E126)

estrella de neutrones Un núcleo denso que puede resultar después de que una estrella de mayor masa explota en una supernova.

niche (nihch)
The role a living thing plays in its habitat. A plant is a food producer, whereas an insect both consumes food as well as provides food for other consumers. (p. D47)

nicho El papel que juega un organismo vivo en su hábitat. Una planta es un productor de alimento mientras que un insecto consume alimento y a la vez sirve de alimento a otros consumidores.

nitrogen cycle
The continuous movement of nitrogen through Earth, its atmosphere, and the living things on Earth. (p. D19)

ciclo del nitrógeno El movimiento continuo de nitrógeno por la Tierra, su atmósfera y los organismos vivos de la Tierra.

nutrient (NOO-tree-uhnt)

A substance that an organism needs to live. Examples include water, minerals, and materials that come from the breakdown of food particles.

nutriente Una sustancia que un organismo necesita para vivir. Ejemplos incluyen agua, minerales y sustancias que provienen de la descomposición de partículas de alimento.

O

oceanic-continental subduction

A boundary along which a plate carrying oceanic crust sinks beneath a plate with continental crust. (p. B93)

subducción océano-continente Un límite a lo largo del cual una placa de corteza oceánica se hunde bajo una placa de corteza continental.

oceanic-oceanic subduction

A boundary along which a plate carrying oceanic crust sinks beneath another plate with oceanic crust. (p. B92)

subducción océano-océano Un límite a lo largo del cual una placa de corteza oceánica se hunde bajo otra placa de corteza oceánica.

optics (AHP-tihks)

The study of light, vision, and related technology. (p. C113)

óptica El estudio de la luz, la visión y la tecnología relacionada a ellas.

orbit

n. The path of an object in space as it moves around another object due to gravity; for example, the Moon moves in an orbit around Earth. (p. E10)

v. To revolve around, or move in an orbit; for example, the Moon orbits Earth.

órbita *s.* La trayectoria de un objeto en el espacio a medida que se mueve alrededor de otro objeto debido a la gravedad; por ejemplo, la Luna se mueve en una órbita alrededor de la Tierra.

orbitar *v.* Girar alrededor de algo, o moverse en una órbita; por ejemplo, la Luna orbita la Tierra.

ore

A rock that contains enough of a valuable mineral to be mined for a profit. (p. A64)

mena Una roca que contiene suficiente mineral valioso para ser extraído con fines lucrativos.

organism

An individual living thing, made up of one or many cells, that is capable of growing and reproducing. (p. xxxi)

organismo Un individuo vivo, compuesto de una o muchas células, que es capaz de crecer y reproducirse.

outer core

A layer of molten metal, mainly nickel and iron, that surrounds Earth's inner core. (p. B70)

núcleo externo Una capa de metal fundido, principalmente níquel y hierro, que rodea al núcleo interno de la Tierra.

P, Q

Pangaea (pan-JEE-uh)

A hypothetical supercontinent that included all of the landmasses on Earth. It began breaking apart about 200 million years ago. (p. B76)

Pangea Un supercontinente hipotético que incluía todas las masas continentales de la Tierra. Empezó a fracturarse aproximadamente hace 200 millones de años.

parallax

The apparent shift in the position of an object when viewed from different locations. (p. E123)

paralaje El cambio aparente en la posición de un objeto cuando se observa desde diferentes puntos.

parasitism (PAR-uh-suh-TIHZ-uhm)

A relationship between two species in which one species is harmed while the other benefits; a type of symbiosis. (p. D59)

parasitismo Una relación entre dos especies en la cual una especie es perjudicada mientras que la otra se beneficia; un tipo de simbiosis.

particle

A very small piece of matter, such as an atom, molecule, or ion.

partícula Una cantidad muy pequeña de materia, como un átomo, una molécula o un ión.

penumbra

A region of lighter shadow that may surround an umbra; for example, the spreading cone of lighter shadow cast by a space object. (p. E63)

penumbra Una región de sombra más tenue que puede rodear a una umbra; por ejemplo, la sombra más tenue cónica proyectada por un objeto espacial.

photosynthesis (FOH-toh-SIHN-thih-sihs)
The process by which green plants and other producers use simple compounds and energy from light to make sugar, an energy-rich compound. (p. D23)

fotosíntesis El proceso mediante el cual las plantas verdes y otros productores usan compuestos simples y energía de la luz para producir azúcares, compuestos ricos en energía.

pioneer species
The first species to move into a lifeless environment. Plants like mosses are typical pioneer species on land. (p. D66)

especie pionera La primera especie que ocupa un medio ambiente sin vida. Las plantas como los musgos son típicas especies pioneras terrestres.

pitch
The quality of highness or lowness of a sound. Pitch is associated with the frequency of a sound wave—the higher the frequency, the higher the pitch. (p. C45)

tono La cualidad de un sonido de ser alto o bajo. El tono está asociado con la frecuencia de una onda sonora: entre más alta sea la frecuencia, más alto es el tono.

planet
A spherical body, larger than a comet or asteroid, that orbits the Sun, or a similar body that orbits a different star.

planeta Un cuerpo esférico, más grande que un cometa o un asteroide, que orbita alrededor del Sol, o un cuerpo similar que orbita alrededor de una estrella distinta.

polarization (POH-luhr-ih-ZAY-shuhn)
A way of filtering light so that all of the waves vibrate in the same direction. (p. C96)

polarización Una manera de filtrar la luz para que todas las ondas vibren en la misma dirección.

pollution
The release of harmful substances into the air, water, or land. (p. D91)

contaminación La descarga de sustancias nocivas al aire, al agua o a la tierra.

population
A group of organisms of the same species that live in the same area. For example, a desert will have populations of different species of lizards and cactus plants. (p. D46)

población Un grupo de organismos de la misma especie que viven en la misma área. Por ejemplo, un desierto tendrá poblaciones de distintas especies de lagartijas y de cactus.

population density
A measure of the number of organisms that live in a given area. The population density of a city may be given as the number of people living in a square kilometer. (p. D86)

densidad de población Una medida de la cantidad de organismos que viven un área dada. La densidad de población de una ciudad puede expresarse como el número de personas que viven en un kilómetro cuadrado.

potential energy
Stored energy; the energy an object has due to its position, molecular arrangement, or chemical composition. (p. B13)

energía potencial Energía almacenada; o la energía que tiene un objeto debido a su posición, arreglo molecular o composición química.

predator
An animal that hunts other animals and eats them. (p. D55)

predador Un animal que caza otros animales y se los come.

prey
An animal that other animals hunt and eat. (p. D55)

presa Un animal que otros animales cazan y se comen.

primary colors
Three colors of light—red, green, and blue—that can be mixed to produce all possible colors. (p. C98)

colores primarios Tres colores de luz, rojo, verde y azul, que se pueden mezclar para producir todos los colores posibles.

primary pigments
Three colors of substances—cyan, yellow, and magenta—that can be mixed to produce all possible colors. (p. C99)

pigmentos primarios Tres colores de sustancias, cian, amarillo y magenta, que se pueden mezclar para producir todos los colores posibles.

prime meridian
An imaginary north-south line that divides the planet into the Eastern Hemisphere and the Western Hemisphere. The prime meridian passes through Greenwich, England. (p. A19)

primer meridiano Una línea imaginaria de norte a sur que divide al planeta en hemisferio oriental y hemisferio occidental. El primer meridiano pasa a través de Greenwich, Inglaterra.

prism
An optical tool that uses refraction to separate the different wavelengths that make up white light. (p. C97)

prisma Una herramienta óptica que usa la refracción para separar las diferentes longitudes de onda que componen la luz blanca.

probe
A spacecraft that is sent into a planet's atmosphere or onto a solid surface. (p. E29)

sonda espacial Una nave espacial enviada a la atmósfera de un planeta o a una superficie sólida.

producer
An organism that captures energy from sunlight and transforms it into chemical energy that is stored in energy-rich carbon compounds. Producers are a source of food for other organisms. (p. D23)

productor Un organismo que capta energía de la luz solar y la transforma a energía química que se almacena en compuestos de carbono ricos en energía. Los productores son una fuente de alimento para otros organismos.

projection
A representation of Earth's curved surface on a flat map. (p. A20)

proyección Una representación de la superficie curva de la Tierra en un mapa plano.

pupil
The circular opening in the iris of the eye that controls how much light enters the eye. (p. C127)

pupila La apertura circular en el iris del ojo que controla cuánta luz entra al ojo.

pyroclastic flow (PY-roh-KLAS-tihk)
A dense cloud of superheated gases and rock fragments that moves quickly downhill from an erupting volcano. (p. B148)

corriente piroclástica Una nube densa de gases sobrecalentados y fragmentos de rocas que desciende rápidamente de un volcán en erupción.

quasar
The very bright center of a distant galaxy. (p. E133)

quásar El centro muy brillante de una galaxia distante.

R

radiation (RAY-dee-AY-shuhn)
Energy that travels across distances in the form of electromagnetic waves. (p. B53)

radiación Energía que viaja a través de la distancia en forma de ondas electromagnéticas.

radio waves
The part of the electromagnetic spectrum that consists of waves with the lowest frequencies. (p. C82)

ondas de radio La parte del espectro electromagnético que consiste de las ondas con las frecuencias más bajas.

recrystallization
The process by which bonds between atoms in minerals break and re-form in new ways during metamorphism. (p. A97)

recristalización El proceso mediante el cual los enlaces entre los átomos de los minerales se rompen y se vuelven a formar de diferentes maneras durante el metamorfismo.

reflection
The bouncing back of a wave after it strikes a barrier. (p. C25)

reflexión El rebote de una onda después de que incide sobre una barrera.

refraction
The bending of a wave as it crosses the boundary between two mediums at an angle other than 90 degrees. (p. C25)

refracción El doblamiento de una onda a medida que cruza el límite entre dos medios a un ángulo distinto a 90 grados.

regular reflection
The reflection of parallel light rays in the same direction. (p. C114)

reflexión especular La reflexión de rayos de luz paralelos en la misma dirección.

relief
In geology, the difference in elevation between an area's high and low points. (p. A25)

relieve En geología, la diferencia en elevación entre los puntos altos y bajos de un área.

relief map
A map that shows the differences in elevation in an area. Relief maps can show elevations through the use of contour lines, shading, colors, and, in some cases, three-dimensional materials. (p. A16)

mapa de relieve Un mapa que muestra las diferencias en elevación de un área. Los mapas de relieve pueden mostrar elevaciones mediante del uso de curvas de nivel, sombreado, colores y, en algunos casos, materiales tridimensionales.

remote sensing
A method of using scientific equipment to gather information about something from a distance. Most remote-sensing methods make use of different types of electromagnetic radiation. (p. A30)

sensoramiento remoto Un método de reunir información sobre algo a distancia usando equipo científico. La mayoría de los métodos de sensoramiento remoto hacen uso de diferentes tipos de radiación electromagnética.

resonance
The strengthening of a sound wave when it combines with an object's natural vibration. (p. C48)

resonancia El fortalecimiento de una onda sonora cuando se combina con la vibración natural de un objeto.

retina (REHT-uhn-uh)
A light-sensitive membrane at the back of the inside of the eye. (p. C127)

retina Una membrana sensible a la luz en la parte trasera del interior del ojo.

revolution
The motion of one body around another, such as Earth in its orbit around the Sun; the time it takes an object to go around once. (p. E45)

revolución El movimiento de un cuerpo alrededor de otro, como la Tierra en su órbita alrededor del Sol; el tiempo que le toma a un objeto dar la vuelta una vez.

rift valley
A deep valley formed as tectonic plates move apart, such as along a mid-ocean ridge. (p. B83)

valle de rift Un valle profundo formado cuando las placas tectónicas se separan, como a lo largo de una dorsal oceánica.

ring
In astronomy, a wide, flat zone of small particles that orbit around a planet's equator. (p. E97)

anillo En astronomía, una zona ancha y plana de pequeñas partículas que orbitan alrededor del ecuador de un planeta.

rock
A naturally formed solid that is usually made up of one or more types of minerals. (p. A75)

roca Un sólido formado de manera natural y generalmente compuesto de uno o más tipos de minerales.

rock cycle
The set of natural, repeating processes that form, change, break down, and re-form rocks. (p. A78)

ciclo de las rocas La serie de procesos naturales y repetitivos que forman, cambian, descomponen y vuelven a formar rocas.

S

sandbar
A ridge of sand built up by the action of waves and currents. (p. A160)

barra de arena Una colina de arena que se forma por la acción de las olas y las corrientes.

satellite
An object that orbits a more massive object. (p. E23)

satélite Un objeto que orbita un objeto de mayor masa.

scattering
The spreading out of light rays in all directions as particles reflect and absorb the light. (p. C95)

dispersión La disipación de los rayos de luz en todas las direcciones a medida que las partículas reflejan y absorben la luz.

season
One part of a pattern of temperature changes and other weather trends over the course of a year. Astronomical seasons are defined and caused by the position of Earth's axis relative to the direction of sunlight. (p. E46)

estación Una parte de un patrón de cambios de temperatura y otras tendencias meteorológicas en el curso de un año. Las estaciones astronómicas se definen y son causadas por la posición del eje de la Tierra en relación a la dirección de la luz del Sol.

sediment
Solid materials such as rock fragments, plant and animal remains, or minerals that are carried by water or by air and that settle on the bottom of a body of water or on the ground. (p. A89)

sedimento Materiales sólidos como fragmentos de rocas, restos de plantas y animales o minerales que son transportados por el agua o el aire y que se depositan en el fondo de un cuerpo de agua o en el suelo.

sedimentary rock (SEHD-uh-MEHN-tuh-ree)
Rock formed as pieces of older rocks and other loose materials get pressed or cemented together or as dissolved minerals re-form and build up in layers. (p. A78)

roca sedimentaria Roca que se forma cuando los pedazos de rocas más viejas y otros materiales sueltos son presionados o cementados o cuando los minerales disueltos vuelven a formarse y se acumulan en capas.

seismic wave (SYZ-mihk)
The vibrations caused by an earthquake. (p. B111)

> **onda sísmica** Las vibraciones ocasionadas por un terremoto.

seismograph (SYZ-muh-GRAF)
An instrument that constantly records ground movements. (p. B116)

> **sismógrafo** Un instrumento que registra constantemente los movimientos del suelo.

sensor
A mechanical or electronic device that receives and responds to a signal, such as light. (p. A31)

> **sensor** Un dispositivo mecánico o electrónico que recibe y responde a una señal, como la luz.

sinkhole
An open basin that forms when the roof of a cavern becomes so thin that it falls in. (p. A155)

> **sumidero** Una cuenca abierta que se forma cuando el techo de una caverna se vuelve tan delgado que se desploma.

slope
A measure of how steep a landform is. Slope is calculated as the change in elevation divided by the distance covered. (p. A25)

> **pendiente** Una medida de lo inclinada de una formación terrestre. La pendiente se calcula dividiendo el cambio en la elevación por la distancia recorrida.

soil horizon
A soil layer with physical and chemical properties that differ from those of soil layers above or below it. (p. A124)

> **horizonte del suelo** Una capa del suelo con propiedades físicas y químicas que difieren de las de las capas del suelo superior e inferior a la misma.

soil profile
The soil horizons in a specific location; a cross section of soil layers that displays all soil horizons. (p. A124)

> **perfil del suelo** Los horizontes del suelo en un lugar específico; una sección transversal de las capas del suelo que muestra todos los horizontes del suelo.

solar cell
A type of technology in which light-sensitive materials convert sunlight into electrical energy. (p. B26)

> **celda solar** Un tipo de tecnología en el cual materiales sensibles a la luz convierten luz solar a energía eléctrica.

solar system
The Sun and its family of orbiting planets, moons, and other objects. (p. E10)

> **sistema solar** El Sol y su familia de planetas, lunas y otros objetos en órbita.

solar wind
A stream of electrically charged particles that flows out in all directions from the Sun's corona. (p. E119)

> **viento solar** Una corriente de partículas eléctricamente cargadas que fluye hacia fuera de la corona del Sol en todas las direcciones.

solstice (SAHL-stihs)
In an orbit, a position and time during which one hemisphere gets its maximum area of sunlight, while the other hemisphere gets its minimum amount; the time of year when days are either longest or shortest, and the angle of sunlight reaches its maximum or minimum. (p. E46)

> **solsticio** En una órbita, la posición y el tiempo durante los cuales un hemisferio obtiene su área máxima de luz del Sol, mientras que el otro hemisferio obtiene su cantidad mínima; la época del año en la cual los días son los más largos o los más cortos y el ángulo de la luz del Sol alcanza su máximo o su mínimo.

sonar
Instruments that use echolocation to locate objects underwater; acronym for "sound navigation and ranging." (p. C59)

> **sonar** Instrumentos que usan la ecolocación para localizar objetos bajo agua; acrónimo en inglés para "navegación y determinación de distancias por sonido".

sound
A type of wave that is produced by a vibrating object and that travels through matter. (p. C37)

> **sonido** Un tipo de onda que es producida por un objeto que vibra y que viaja a través de la materia.

space station
A satellite in which people can live and work for long periods. (p. E24)

> **estación espacial** Un satélite en el cual la gente puede vivir y trabajar durante períodos largos.

species
A group of living things that are so closely related that they can breed with one another and produce offspring that can breed as well. (p. xxxi)

> **especie** Un grupo de organismos que están tan estrechamente relacionados que pueden aparearse entre sí y producir crías que también pueden aparearse.

specific heat
The amount of energy required to raise the temperature of one gram of a substance by one degree Celsius. (p. B47)

calor específico La cantidad de energía que se necesita para aumentar la temperatura de un gramo de una sustancia un grado centígrado.

spectrum (SPEHK-truhm)
1. Radiation from a source separated into a range of wavelengths. 2. The range of colors that appears in a beam of visible light when it passes through a prism. See also electromagnetic radiation. (p. E16)

espectro 1. Radiación de una fuente separada en una gama de longitudes de onda. 2. La gama de colores que aparece en un haz de luz visible cuando éste pasa a través de un prisma. Ver también radiación electromagnética.

streak
The color of a mineral powder left behind when a mineral is scraped across a surface; a method for classifying minerals. (p. A51)

raya El color del polvo que queda de un mineral cuando éste se raspa a lo largo de una superficie; un método para clasificar minerales.

stress
The force applied by an object pressing on, pulling on, or pushing against another object. (p. B105)

tensión La fuerza aplicada por un objeto que presiona, jala o empuja contra otro objeto.

subduction
The process by which an oceanic tectonic plate sinks under another plate into Earth's mantle. (p. B90)

subducción El proceso mediante el cual una placa tectónica oceánica se hunde bajo otra placa y entra al manto de la Tierra.

substance
Matter of a particular type. Elements, compounds, and mixtures are all substances.

sustancia La materia de cierto tipo. Los elementos, los compuestos y las mezclas son sustancias.

succession (suhk-SEHSH-uhn)
A natural process that involves a gradual change in the plant and animal communities that live in an area. (p. D66)

sucesión Un proceso natural que involucra un cambio gradual en las comunidades de plantas y animales que viven en un área.

sunspot
A darker spot on the photosphere of the Sun. A sunspot appears dark because it is cooler than the surrounding area. (p. E118)

mancha solar Una mancha oscura en la fotosfera del Sol. Una mancha solar se ve oscura porque es más fría que el área que la rodea.

sustainable
A term that describes the managing of certain natural resources so that they are not harmed or used up. Examples include maintaining clean groundwater and protecting top soil from erosion. (p. D102)

sostenible Un término que describe el manejo de ciertos recursos naturales para que no se deterioren o se terminen. Ejemplos incluyen mantener limpia el agua subterránea y proteger de la erosión a la capa superficial del suelo.

symbiosis (SIHM-bee-OH-sihs)
The interaction between individuals from two different species that live closely together. (p. D58)

simbiosis La interacción entre individuos de dos especies distintas que viven en proximidad.

system
A group of objects or phenomena that interact. A system can be as simple as a rope, a pulley, and a mass. It also can be as complex as the interaction of energy and matter in the four parts of the Earth system.

sistema Un grupo de objetos o fenómenos que inter-actúan. Un sistema puede ser algo tan sencillo como una cuerda, una polea y una masa. También puede ser algo tan complejo como la interacción de la energía y la materia en las cuatro partes del sistema de la Tierra.

T

technology
The use of scientific knowledge to solve problems or engineer new products, tools, or processes.

tecnología El uso de conocimientos científicos para resolver problemas o para diseñar nuevos productos, herramientas o procesos.

tectonic plate (tehk-TAHN-ihk)
One of the large, moving pieces into which Earth's litho-sphere is broken and which commonly carries both oceanic and continental crust. (p. B73)

placa tectónica Una de las grandes piezas en movimiento en las que la litosfera de la Tierra se rompe y que comúnmente lleva corteza oceánica y continental.

tectonics

The processes in which the motion of hot material under a crust changes the crust of a space body. Earth has a specific type of tectonics called plate tectonics. (p. E86)

tectónica Los procesos en los cuales el movimiento del material caliente bajo una corteza cambia la corteza de un cuerpo espacial. La Tierra tiene un tipo específico de tectónica denominado tectónica de placas.

telescope

A device that gather visible light or another form of electromagnetic radiation. (p. E17)

telescopio Un aparato que reúne luz visible u otra forma de radiación electromagnética.

temperature

A measure of the average amount of kinetic energy of the particles in an object. (p. B39)

temperatura Una medida de la cantidad promedio de energía cinética de las partículas en un objeto.

terrestrial planet

Earth or a planet similar to Earth that has a rocky surface. The four planets in the inner solar system—Mercury, Venus, Earth, and Mars—are terrestrial planets. (p. E85)

planeta terrestre La Tierra o un planeta parecido a la Tierra que tiene una superficie rocosa. Los cuatro planetas en el sistema solar interior—Mercurio, Venus, la Tierra y Marte—son planetas terrestres.

theory

In science, a set of widely accepted explanations of observations and phenomena. A theory is a well-tested explanation that is consistent with all available evidence.

teoría En las ciencias, un conjunto de explicaciones de observaciones y fenómenos que es ampliamente aceptado. Una teoría es una explicación bien probada que es consecuente con la evidencia disponible.

thermal energy

The energy an object has due to the motion of its particles; the total amount of kinetic energy of particles in an object. (p. B45)

energía térmica La energía que tiene un objeto debido al movimiento de sus partículas; la cantidad total de energía cinética de las partículas en un objeto.

thermometer

A device for measuring temperature. (p. B41)

termómetro Un aparato para medir la temperatura.

till

Sediment of different sizes left directly on the ground by a melting, or retreating, glacier. (p. A168)

sedimentos glaciares Sedimentos de diferentes

tamaños depositados directamente en el suelo por un glaciar que se derrite o retrocede.

topography

All natural and human-made surface features of a particular area. (p. A24)

topografía Todas las características de superficie de origen natural y humano en un área particular.

transform boundary

A boundary along which two tectonic plates scrape past each other, and crust is neither formed nor destroyed. (p. B82)

límite transcurrente Un límite a lo largo del cual dos placas tectónicas se rozan y no se forma corteza ni se destruye.

transmission (trans-MIHSH-uhn)

The passage of a wave through a medium. (p. C93)

transmisión El paso de una onda a través de un medio.

transverse wave

A type of wave in which the disturbance moves at right angles, or perpendicular, to the direction in which the wave travels. (p. C13)

onda transversal Un tipo de onda en el cual la perturbación se mueve en ángulo recto, o perpendicularmente, a la dirección en la cual viaja la onda.

trough (trawf)

The lowest point, or valley, of a wave (p. C17)

valle El punto más bajo de una onda.

tsunami (tsu-NAH-mee)

A water wave caused by an earthquake, volcanic eruption, or landslide. (p. B122)

tsunami Una ola de agua ocasionada por un terremoto, erupción volcánica o derrumbe.

U

ultrasound

Sound waves with frequencies above 20,000 hertz, the upper limit of typical hearing levels in humans, used for medical purposes, among other things. (p. C46)

ultrasonido Ondas sonoras con frecuencias superiores a 20,000 hertzios, el límite superior de los niveles auditivos típicos de los humanos. Estas ondas tienen usos médicos, entre otros.

ultraviolet light

The part of the electromagnetic spectrum that consists of waves with frequencies higher than those of visible light and lower than those of x-rays. (p. C85)

luz ultravioleta La parte del espectro electromagnético que consiste de ondas con frecuencias superiores a las de luz visible y menores a las de los rayos X.

umbra
The dark, central region of a shadow, such as the cone of complete shadow cast by an object. (p. E63)

umbra La región central y oscura de una sombra, como la sombra completa cónica proyectada por un objeto.

universe
Space and all the matter and energy in it. (p. E10)

universo El espacio y toda la materia y energía que hay dentro de él.

urban
A term that describes a city environment.

urbano Un término que describe el medio ambiente de una ciudad.

V

vacuum
A space containing few or no particles of matter. (p. C41)

vacío Un espacio que no contiene partículas de materia o bien contiene muy pocas.

variable
Any factor that can change in a controlled experiment, observation, or model. (p. R30)

variable Cualquier factor que puede cambiar en un experimento controlado, en una observación o en un modelo.

vibration
A rapid, back-and-forth motion. (p. C37)

vibración Un movimiento rápido hacia delante y hacia atrás.

visible light
The part of the electromagnetic spectrum that consists of waves detectable by the human eye. (p. C84)

luz visible La parte del espectro electromagnético que consiste de ondas detectables por el ojo humano.

volcanism
The process of molten material moving from a space body's hot interior onto its surface. (p. E86)

vulcanismo El proceso del movimiento de material fundido del interior caliente de un cuerpo espacial a su superficie.

volcano
An opening in the crust through which molten rock, rock fragments, and hot gases erupt; a mountain built up from erupted materials. (p. B146)

volcán Una abertura en la corteza a través de la cual la roca fundida, fragmentos de roca y gases calientes hacen erupción; una montaña formada a partir de los materiales que surgen de una erupción.

W

water cycle
The continuous movement of water through Earth, its atmosphere, and the living things on Earth. (p. D17)

ciclo del agua El movimiento continuo de agua por la Tierra, su atmósfera y los organismos vivos de la Tierra.

wave
A disturbance that transfers energy from one place to another without requiring matter to move the entire distance. (p. C9)

onda Una perturbación que transfiere energía de un lugar a otro sin que sea necesario que la materia se mueva toda la distancia.

wavelength
The distance from one wave peak or crest to the next peak or crest. Wavelength can be measured as the distance from any part of one wave to the identical part of the next wave. (pp. C17, E16)

longitud de onda La distancia entre el pico o la cresta de una onda y el siguiente pico o cresta. La longitud de onda se puede medir como la distancia entre cualquier parte de una onda y la parte idéntica de la siguiente onda.

weathering
The process by which natural forces break down rocks. (p. A115)

meteorización El proceso por el cual las fuerzas naturales fragmentan las rocas.

X, Y, Z

x-rays
The part of the electromagnetic spectrum that consists of waves with high frequencies and high energies; electromagnetic waves with frequencies ranging from more than 1016 hertz to more than 1021 hertz. (p. C86)

rayos X La parte del espectro electromagnético que consiste de las ondas con altas frecuencias y altas energías; las ondas electromagnéticas con frecuencias de más de 1016 hertzios hasta más de 1021 hertzios.

Index

Page numbers for definitions are printed in **boldface** type.
Page numbers for illustrations, maps, and charts are printed in *italics*.

F

G

organic matter, A123, A126, A*127*, A138
organisms, xxxi. *See also* living things.
    groupings of, within ecosystems, D45–48, D*49*
    interaction of, D54–61, D70
oscilloscope, C49, C*49*
outer core, A**12**, B**70**, B*70*, B98
outer ear, C39, C*39*
outer solar system, E81, E94–99, E108. *See also* gas
    giant planets.
overproduction, NC5
overtone, C49
oxygen, xxxi, A11, A109, D17
oxygen–carbon dioxide cycle, NC12
ozone, A109

P, Q

Pacific Plate, B106
Pacific Tsunami Warning Center, B123
Pangaea, B76, B*76*, B**76**
pan balance, R19, R*19*
parallax, E**123**
parasitism, D**59**, D*60*, D*61*, D70
parent rocks, A96
particles
    kinetic theory, B*38*, B**38**, B58
    moving, B37
    speed of, B38, B39
    thermal expansion and, B42
penumbra, E**63**, E*63–64*
percents, **R41**
permafrost, D31
pesticides, D29, D76
petroleum, D91
phases of the Moon, E59–62, E*61*, E68
Philippine Islands, B92
phonograph, C63
photography, C139
photosynthesis, D12, D13, D22, NC12–13. *See also*
    producers.
    by algae, D*18*
    carbon cycle and, D*18*
    by plants, D*18*
phyllite, A*97*, A*100*
physical science, xxxiv. *See also* science.
phytoplankton, D35, D36
    as producers, D*23*, D35, D36
Pinchot, Gifford, D75
pioneer species, D**66**, D*66*, D66–68, D70
pitch, C**45**, C*46*, C47, C49, C*49*
    Doppler effect and, C50–51
plains, A**16**, A*16*
planar projections, A22
planetary rings, E**97**, E*97*, E108
planets, E14, E*14*, E26, E79–82, E*80*. *See also* Solar
    System; specific planets, e.g., Mars.
    characteristics of, *R59*
    cores, E85
    distances, E*80*, E81
    doubles, E101
    exploration, E27, E29
    gas giants, E**94**, E94–99, E102, E*102*
    landers, E**28**, E*28*, E28–29
    mantles, E85
    moons, E98, E101–102, E*102*

orbits of Sun, E81–82, E108
    processes and surface features, E86, E*87*
    rocky crusts, E85–92
    sizes, E79–81, E*80*
    terrestrial, E85–92
plants
    as abiotic factors, D*10*, D*38*
    coexistence among, D56
    competition among, D*55*
    growth, E35
    nitrogen sources, D19, D*20*
    as producers, D12, D13, D18, D*23*
    and soil formation, A116, A*117*, A126, A*127*
plateaus, A**16**, A*16*
plate tectonics, B66–101, B97, E86, E**86**, E*87*, E89–90,
    E108
    asthenosphere, B**71**, B*71*, B98
    boundaries, B82–97, B106, B*106*, B112, B149
    causes of movement, B77–78
    Chapter Investigation, B80–81
    coastal mountains, B92, B93, 98
    continental-continental collision, B**91**, B*91*, B98,
        B140
    continental drift, B**74**, B74–79, B*76*, B98
    convection currents, B**77**, B77–78, B*78*, B80–81
    convergent boundaries, B90–93, B*91*, B92, B95, B98,
        B140
    core, B70, B*70*
    crust, B*70*, B71, B98
    deep-ocean trenches, B**92**, B*92*, B93, B98
    density of materials, B69
    divergent boundaries, B**82**, B82–88, B*83*, B95, B98
    hot spots, B87–88, B*88*, B149
    inner core, B**70**, B*70*, B98
    Internet activity, B67
    island arcs, B**92**, B*92*, B98
    layers of Earth, B**70**, B70–72, B98
    lithosphere, B**71**, B*71*, B71–72, B98
    magnetic reversals, B**84**, B*84*, B84–85, B98
    mantle, B*70*, B**71**, B98
    mountain formation, B137
    oceanic-continental subduction, B*92*, B**93**, B98,
        B140, B*140*, B*141*
    oceanic-oceanic subduction, B92, B*92*, B98, B140,
        B*140*, B*141*, B149
    outer core, B**70**, B*70*, B98
    Pangaea, B76, B*76*, B**76**
    ridge push, B78, B*78*
    rift valleys, B86–87, B*86*, B87, B98, B149
    slab pull, B78, B*78*
    spreading centers, B77, B83
    subduction, B**90**, B90–93, B98
    tectonic plates, B**72**, B77–79, B*79*
    theory of, B76–79, B*78*, B96
    transform boundaries, B94, B*95*, B98
    Unit Project, B97
Pluto, E79, E*80–81*, E81, E100–101, E*101*, E108
polar bears, B*54*, B55
polar icecaps, fresh water in, D85
Polaris, E13
polarization, C*96*, C**96**
pollination, D*58*
pollution, A119, D**91**, D91–94, D*92*, D*93*, D*94*, D*108*
    reducing, D*103*, D*104*, D104–105
pond ecosystems, D10. *See also* freshwater biomes.
population mapping, A33

INDEX

INDEX

INDEX

INDEX

Acknowledgments

Photography

Cover © David Nunuk/Photo Researchers; **i** © David Nunuk/Photo Researchers; **iii** *left (top to bottom)* Photograph of James Trefil by Evan Cantwell; Photograph of Rita Ann Calvo by Joseph Calvo; Photograph of Linda Carnine by Amilcar Cifuentes; Photograph of Sam Miller by Samuel Miller; *right (top to bottom)* Photograph of Kenneth Cutler by Kenneth A. Cutler; Photograph of Donald Steely by Marni Stamm; Photograph of Vicky Vachon by Redfern Photographics; **vi** © Steve Starr, Boston Inc./PictureQuest; **vii** Stephen Alvarez/National Geographic Image Collection; **viii** © Steve Bloom/stevebloom.com; **x** © Chip Simons/Getty Images; **xi** © Alan Kearney/Getty Images; **xii** © Jeff Schultz/Alaska Stock.com; **xiii** © Wolcott Henry/National Geographic Image Collection; **xiv** © Roger Ressmeyer/Corbis; **xv** Courtesy of NASA/JPL/Caltech; **xx–xxi** Photographs by Sharon Hoogstraten; **xii** © Jeff Schultz/Alaska Stock.com; **xiii** © Wolcott Henry/National Geographic Image Collection; **xxx–xxxi** © Georgette Duowma/Taxi/Getty Images; **xxxii–xxxiii** © Aflo Foto Agency; **xxxiv–xxxv** © Larry Hamill/age fotostock america, inc.; **xxxvi** © Vince Streano/Corbis; **xxxvii** © Roger Ressmeyer/Corbis; **xxxviii** *left* University of Florida Lightning Research Laboratory; *center* © Roger Ressmeyer/Corbis; **xxxix** *center* © Mauro Fermariello/ Science Researchers; *bottom* © Alfred Pasieka/Photo Researchers; **xl–xli** © Stocktrek/ Corbis; *center* NOAA; **xli** *top* © Alan Schein Photography/Corbis; *right* Vaisala Oyj, Finland; **xlvii** © The Chedd-Angier Production Company.

Earth's Surface

Divider © Per Breiehagen/Getty Images; **A2–A3** Courtesy of NASA/JPL/Caltech; **A3** *top* Carla Thomas/NASA; *bottom* Diamonds North Resources, Ltd.; **A4** *top* Carla Thomas/NASA; *bottom* © The Chedd-Angier Production Company; **A5** © William Whitehurst/Corbis; **A6–A7** NASA; **A7** *top left* © NASA; *center left* SeaWiFS Project/NASA Goddard Space Flight Center; *bottom left* National Air & Space Museum/Smithsonian Institution; *top right* Courtesy of L. Sue Baugh; *center right* Bike Map courtesy of Chicagoland Bicycle Federation. Photograph by Sharon Hoogstraten; *bottom right* NASA Goddard Space Flight Center; **A9** Photograph by Sharon Hoogstraten; **A10–A11** NASA; **A10** *bottom left* © David Parker/Photo Researchers; *bottom center* © R. Wickllund/ OAR/National Undersea Research Program; **A11** *bottom center* University of Victoria, Victoria, British Columbia, Canada; *bottom right* © Peter and Georgina Bowater/Stock Connection/PictureQuest; **A12** © Photodisc/Getty Images; **A13** Photograph by Sharon Hoogstraten; **A14** © A. Ramey/PhotoEdit/PictureQuest; **A15** Photograph by Sharon Hoogstraten; **A16** U.S. Geological Survey; **A19** © David Parker/Photo Researchers; **A20** Photograph by Sharon Hoogstraten; **A23** © Jerry Driendl/Getty Images; **A24** Photograph by Sharon Hoogstraten; **A25** *top* © Stan Osolinski/Getty Images; *bottom* U.S. Geological Survey; **A26, A28** *top left* U.S. Geological Survey; *bottom left, center right, bottom right* Photographs by Sharon Hoogstraten; **A30, A31** *top right* © Space Imaging; *bottom background* © Paul Morrell/Getty Images; *bottom left* National Oceanic and Atmospheric Administration/Department of Commerce; **A32** *top left, top center* Eros Data Center/U.S. Geological Survey; *bottom right* Photograph by Sharon Hoogstraten; **A34** Photo courtesy of John D. Rogie, 1997; **A35** © Lynn Radeka/SuperStock Images; **A36** *top* NASA; *lower center* U.S. Geological Survey; *bottom left, background* © Paul Morrell/Getty Images; *bottom right* National Oceanic and Atmospheric Administration/ Department of Commerce; **A38** U.S. Geological Survey; **A40–A41** © Steve Starr, Boston Inc./ PictureQuest; **A41** *top right, center right* Photographs by Sharon Hoogstraten; *bottom right* © Dan Suzio/Photo Researchers; **A43** Photograph by Sharon Hoogstraten; **A44** © Andrew J. Martinez/Photo Researchers; **A45** *left* © Astrid & Hanns-Freider/Photo Researchers; *center* © Charles D. Winters/Photo Researchers; **A46** Photograph by Sharon Hoogstraten; **A47** *top left, center* © Charles D. Winters/Photo Researchers; *top right* Photograph by Malcolm Hjerstedt. Courtesy of F. John Barlow/SANCO Publishing; *bottom left* © Biophoto Associates/Photo Researchers; *bottom center* © Dorling Kindersley; *bottom right* © Phil Degginger/Color Pic, Inc.; *top* © David Young Wolff/PhotoEdit; *bottom* © Doug Martin/Photo Researchers; **A49** *background* © Joyce Photographics/Photo Researchers; *top* © Dorling Kindersley; **A50, A51** Photographs by Sharon Hoogstraten; **A52** *top left* © Charles D. Winters/Photo Researchers; *top right* © Mark A. Schneider/Photo Researchers; *bottom* Photograph by Sharon Hoogstraten; **A53, A54** Photographs by Sharon Hoogstraten; **A55** *top, center right* Photographs by Sharon Hoogstraten; *bottom right* © Thomas Hunn/Visuals Unlimited; **A56** Photograph by Sharon Hoogstraten; **A57** *top left, center* © Mark A. Schneider/Visuals Unlimited; *top right* Photograph by Sharon Hoogstraten; **A58** *top left* © Martin Miller/Visuals Unlimited; *bottom left, right* Photographs by Sharon Hoogstraten; **A59, A60** Photographs by Sharon Hoogstraten; **A61** *top left* © Geoff Tompkinson/PhotoResearchers; *center left* © A.J. Copely/Visuals Unlimited; *bottom left* © Charles D. Winters/Photo Researchers; *top right* © Charles Falco/Photo Researchers; *center right, bottom right* © Dorling Kindersley; **A63** *top right, center left* © Mark A. Schneider/Photo Researchers; *center right* © Andrew J. Martinez/Photo Researchers; *bottom right* © M. Claye/Photo Researchers; **A65** *top* © Mervyn P. Lawes/Corbis; *bottom* Photograph by Sharon Hoogstraten; **A66** Newmont Mining Corp.; **A67** *top left* © Dorling Kindersley; *top right* © Louis Goldman/Photo Researchers; *center left, bottom left* © Dorling Kindersley; **A68** *center* © Charles D. Winters/Photo Researchers; *bottom left* © Astrid & Hanns-Freider/ Photo Researchers; *bottom right top* © Photodisc/Getty Images; *bottom right middle* © Dorling Kindersley; *bottom right* © Photodisc/Getty Images; **A70** *left* NASA/Science Photo Library; *right* NASA; **A72–A73** Stephen Alvarez/NGS Image Collection; **A73** *top, center* Photographs by Sharon Hoogstraten; *bottom* Courtesy of L. Sue Baugh; **A75** Photograph by Sharon Hoogstraten; **A76** *top left* © Dorling Kindersley; *top right* © Doug Martin/Photo Researchers; *bottom* © The Image Bank/Getty Images; **A77** *top* © James Lyon/Lonely Planet Images; *bottom* Photograph by Sharon Hoogstraten; **A79** *center left, bottom* © Andrew J. Martinez/Photo Researchers; *center right* © Arthur R. Hill/Visuals Unlimited; **A81** *background* Arne Danielsen, Norway; *left* © Charles O'Rear/ Corbis; *right* © Detlev Van Ravenswaay/ Photo Researchers; **A82** Photograph by Sharon Hoogstraten; **A83** *top left* © Arthur R. Hill/Visuals Unlimited; *top center, top right* © Joyce Photographics/Photo Researchers; *bottom center* © Mark Schneider/Visuals Unlimited; *bottom right* © Dorling Kindersley; **A84** *top* © Andrew J. Martinez/Photo Researchers; *bottom* © Breck P. Kent; **A85** Photograph by Sharon Hoogstraten; **A86, A87** © Francois Gohier/Photo Researchers; **A88** *background* © Dr. Juero Aleon/Photo Researchers; **A89** Photograph by Sharon Hoogstraten; **A91** *left* © Carolyn Iverson/Photo Researchers; *right* © Ted Clutter/Pennsylvania State Museum Collection/Photo Researchers; **A92** *top left* Photograph by Sharon Hoogstraten; *center* Courtesy of L. Sue Baugh; *bottom right* © Norbert Wu/Norbert Wu Productions/ PictureQuest; *bottom left;* National Oceanic and Atmospheric Administration **A93** *top* © Look GMBH/eStockPhotography/PictureQuest; *bottom* © Corbis; **A94** Photograph by Sharon Hoogstraten; **A95** *left* © 1991 Ned Haines/ Photo Researchers; *center* © Wayne Lawler/Photo Researchers; *right* © Jim Steinberg/Photo Researchers; **A96** Photograph by Sharon Hoogstraten; **A97** *right (top to bottom)* © Andrew J. Martinez 1995/Photo Researchers; © Andrew J. Martinez 1995/Photo Researchers; The Boltin Picture Library; © Breck P. Kent; © 1996 Andrew J. Martinez/Photo Researchers; **A98** Photograph by Sharon Hoogstraten; **A100** *top left* The Boltin Picture Library; *top right* Photograph courtesy of John Longshore; *bottom left* © E.R. Degginger/Color-Pic, Inc.; *bottom right* © Patricia Tye/Photo Researchers; **A102** *top* Will Hart/PhotoEdit; *center, bottom* Photographs by Sharon Hoogstraten; **A103** © Corbis; **A104** *top left, top center* © Andrew J. Martinez/Photo Researchers; *upper center section left* Arthur R. Hill/Visuals Unlimited; *lower center section, left* © Andrew J. Martinez/Photo Researchers; *right* Photograph by Sharon Hoogstraten; *bottom left, center* © Andrew J. Martinez/Photo Researchers; *bottom right* © Breck P. Kent; **A106** © G.R. Roberts Photo Library; **A108** *top* © Chris Butler/Photo Researchers; *bottom* © Detlev van Ravenswaay/Photo Researchers; **A109** *top* © Jim Brandenburg/Minden Pictures; *center* J.W. Schopf/University of California, Los Angeles; *bottom* Japan Meteorological Agency; **A110** *top left* © Simon Fraser/Photo Researchers; *top right* © Chase Studios/Photo Researchers; *bottom* Courtesy of the Ocean Drilling Program; **A111** *top* NASA Goddard Space Flight Center; *bottom* STS-113 Shuttle Crew/NASA; **A112–A113** © Wendy Conway/Alamy Images; **A113** *top right, center* Photographs by Sharon Hoogstraten; **A115** Photograph by Sharon Hoogstraten; **A117** *background* © Photodisc/Getty Images; *inset top* © Susan Rayfield/Photo Researchers; *inset center, bottom left* Photographs courtesy of Sara Christopherson; *inset bottom right* © Kirkendall-Spring Photographer; **A118** Photograph by Sharon Hoogstraten; **A119** *top left* © Bettmann/Corbis; *top right* © Runk/Schoenberger/ Grant Heilman Photography; *bottom* © Cheyenne Rouse/Visuals Unlimited; **A121** *background* © Ecoscene/Corbis; *inset* © Michael Nicholson/Corbis; **A122**

Photograph by Sharon Hoogstraten; **A123** *left* © Joel W. Rogers/Corbis; *right* © Barry Runk/Grant Heilman Photography; **A124** © Barry Runk/Grant Heilman Photography; **A125** *top left* © Sally A. Morgan/Corbis; *top right* © Peter Falkner/Photo Researchers; *bottom left* © Tony Craddock/ Photo Researchers; *bottom left* © Tui de Roy/Bruce Coleman, Inc.; **A128** © Barry Runk/Grant Heilman Photography; **A129** © Jim Strawser/Grant Heilman Photography; **A130** *top left* © Larry Lefever/Grant Heilman Photography; *center right, bottom left* Photograph by Sharon Hoogstraten; **A132** © Cameron Davidson/Stock Connection, Inc./Alamy Images; **A133** AP/Wide World Photos; **A134** *top* © Steve Strickland/ Visuals Unlimited; *bottom* Betty Wald/Aurora; **A135** Photograph by Sharon Hoogstraten; **A136** *left* © Charles O'Rear/Corbis; *right* © Larry Lefever/Grant Heilman Photography; **A137** *center inset* Courtesy of Teska Associates, Evanston. Illinois; **A138** *top right* © Runk/Schoenberger/Grant Heilman Photography; *bottom* © Larry Lefever/Grant Heilman Photography; **A140** © Barry Runk/Grant Heilman Photography; **A142–A143** © A.C. Waltham/Robert Harding Picture Library/Alamy Images; **A143** *center right* Photograph by Sharon Hoogstraten; **A145** © Bernhard Edmaier/Photo Researchers; **A146** Photograph by Sharon Hoogstraten; **A147** AP/Wide World Photos; **A148** *top* Photograph by L.M. Smith, Waterways Experiment Station, U.S. Army Corps of Engineers. Courtesy, USGS; *bottom* © Thomas Rampton/Grant Heilman Photography; **A149** © Troy and Mary Parlee/Alamy Images; **A150** Photograph by Sharon Hoogstraten; **A151** © Bill Ross/Corbis; **A152** *top* © Kevin Horan/Stock Boston /PictureQuest; *bottom* © Yann Arthus-Bertrand/Corbis; **A153** © 1992 Tom Bean; **A154** © Charles Kennard/Stock Boston/PictureQuest; **A155** © Reuters NewMedia, Inc./Corbis; **A156** © Peter Bowater/Alamy Images; **A158** © John and Lisa Merrill/Getty Images; **A159** © Robert Perron; **A160** Photograph by Sharon Hoogstraten; **A161** © Tim Barnwell/Picturesque/ PictureQuest; **A162** © John Shaw/Bruce Coleman, Inc.; **A163** *top* © 1994 Tom Bean; *right* © Goodshoot/Alamy Images; **A164** *background* © Gustav Verderber/Visuals Unlimited; *inset left* © Gary Meszaros/Bruce Coleman, Inc.; *inset right* © Lee Rentz/Bruce Coleman, Inc.; **A165** Photograph by Sharon Hoogstraten; **A167** *left* © Bernard Edmaier/Photo Researchers; *right* © ImageState-Pictor/PictureQuest ; **A168** *top* © Norman Barett/Bruce Coleman, Inc.; *bottom* © Jim Wark/Airphoto; **A169** *top* © 1990 Tom Bean; *bottom* Photograph by Sharon Hoogstraten; **A171** © Charles W. Campbell/ Corbis; **A172** *top* © Bernhard Edmaier/Photo Researchers; *center* © John and Lisa Merrill/Getty Images; **A174** © Tom Bean.

Energy and the Changing Earth

Divider © Roger Ressmeyer/Corbis; **B2–B3** © Stephen and Donna O'Meara/Photo Researchers; **B3** *top* NASA/GSFC/METI/ERSDAC/JAROS, and U.S./Japan ASTER Science Team; **B4** *top left* U.S. Geological Survey; *inset* Photograph by T. Miller/U.S. Geological Survey; *bottom* The Chedd-Angier Production Company; **B5** NASA/GSFC/METI/ ERSDAJAROS, and U.S./Japan ASTER Science Team; **B6–B7** AP/Wide World Photos; **B7, B9** Photographs by Sharon Hoogstraten; **B10** © Alan Schein Photography/Corbis; **B11** *top* © Patrick Ward/Corbis; *bottom* © NASA/Photo Researchers; **B12** AP/Wide World Photos; **B13** *top* © George H. H. Huey/Corbis; *bottom* Photograph by Sharon Hoogstraten; **B14** *top* © Vladimir Pcholkin/Getty Images; *bottom* © Thomas Beach; **B15** © Adam Gault/Digital Vision; **B16** © Bill Aron/PhotoEdit; **B17** © TempSport/Corbis; **B18** © Robert Cameron/Getty Images; **B19** *left* © Gunter Marx Photography/Corbis; *right* © Lester Lefkowitz/Corbis; **B20** © Left Lane Productions/Corbis; **B21** © Dorling Kindersley; **B22** *top* © Grant Klotz/Alaska Stock Images/PictureQuest; *bottom* Photograph by Sharon Hoogstraten; **B23, B24** Photographs by Sharon Hoogstraten; **B25** *top left* © Royalty-Free/Corbis; *top right* Thinkstock, LLC; *bottom* AP/Wide World Photos; **B26** © AFP/Corbis; *inset* © John Farmar; Cordaiy Photo Library Ltd./Corbis; **B27** *top* © Sally A. Morgan; Ecoscene/Corbis; *bottom* Photograph by Sharon Hoogstraten; **B28** © Joe Sohm/Visions of America, LLC/PictureQuest; **B29** © Michael S. Lewis/Corbis; **B30** *top* © Vladimir Pcholkin/Getty Images; *bottom* © AFP/Corbis; **B34–B35** © Steve Bloom/stevebloom.com; **B35, B37** Photographs by Sharon Hoogstraten; **B38** © Tracy Frankel/Getty Images; **B39** Photographs by Sharon Hoogstraten; **B40** © Daryl Benson/Masterfile; *inset* © Spencer Grant/PhotoEdit; **B41** Photograph by Sharon Hoogstraten; **B42** *top* © Steve Vidler/SuperStock; *bottom* © Chase Jarvis/Getty Images; **B43** © FogStock/Alamy; *inset* © Gordon Wiltsie/Getty Images; **B44** © David Bishop/Getty Images; **B45** Thinkstock, LLC; **B46** Photograph by Sharon Hoogstraten; **B47** © Richard Bickel/Corbis; **B49** *top left* © Jeremy Samuelson/FoodPix; *bottom left* © William Reavell-StockFood Munich/StockFood; *right* © Martin Jacobs/FoodPix; **B50** Photograph by Sharon Hoogstraten; **B51** © Brand X Pictures/Alamy; **B53** © ImageState Royalty Free/Alamy; **B54** *top left* E.C. Humphrey; *top right* Creatas®; *bottom* © Uwe Walz Gdt/age fotostock america, inc.; **B56** *top* © Nancy Ney/Corbis; *bottom* Photograph by Sharon Hoogstraten; **B57** Photograph by Sharon Hoogstraten; **B58** © Photographs by Sharon Hoogstraten; *bottom* Thinkstock, LLC; **B62** © Don Farrall/Getty Images; **B63** *top left* © Sheila Terry/Photo Researchers; *top center, top right* © Dorling Kindersley; *bottom* © SEF/Art Resource, New York; **B64** *top left* Mary Evans Picture Library; *top right, bottom* © Dorling Kindersley; **B65** © Mark Wiens/Masterfile; **B66–B67** Tony Waltham/Geophotos; **B67, B69, B72, B74** Photographs by Sharon Hoogstraten; **B75** © 1995–2002 Geoclassics. All rights reserved.; **B80** Worldsat International/Photo Researchers; **B82, B85** Photographs by Sharon Hoogstraten; **B87** *top* © Christophe Ratier/NHPA/Photo Researchers; *bottom* © NASA/Photo Researchers; **B89** *left* © Dr. John Brackenbury/Photo Researchers; *right* NASA; **B90** Photograph by Sharon Hoogstraten; **B91** © John Coletti/Stock Boston/ PictureQuest; **B33** Photograph by Sharon Hoogstraten; **B94** © Lloyd Cluff/Corbis; **B95** © Paul Chesley/Getty Images; **B97** *left* © Albrecht G. Schaefer/Corbis; *right* © Mitch Diamond/Index Stock/PictureQuest; **B102–B103** © Robert Patrick/Corbis Sygma; **B103, B105, B107** Photographs by Sharon Hoogstraten; **B108** © Martin Miller/University of Oregon, Eugene, Oregon; **B109** NOAA/National Geophysical Data Center; **B110** *left* U.S. Geological Survey; *inset* © Bettmann/Corbis; **B111, B113** Photograph by Sharon Hoogstraten; **B119** AP/Wide World Photos; **B120** Photograph by Sharon Hoogstraten; **B121** © Mark Downey; **B122** U.S. Geological Survey; **B123** Commander Dennis J. Sigrist acting Director of the International Tsunami Information Center/NOAA; **B126** © Roger Ressmeyer/Corbis; **B128** *top* © Michael S. Yamashita/Corbis; *bottom left, bottom right* Photograph by Sharon Hoogstraten; **B129** Photograph by Sharon Hoogstraten; **B134–B135** © Douglas Peebles; **B135, B137** Photographs by Sharon Hoogstraten; **B138** U.S. Department of the Interior; **B139, B140** © Martin Miller/University of Oregon, Eugene, Oregon; **B141** © Tim Hauf Photography/Visuals Unlimited; **B142** Photograph by Sharon Hoogstraten; **B143** © Martin Miller/ University of Oregon, Eugene, Oregon; **B144** © Phil Schermeister/Corbis; **B145** © William Ervin/Photo Researchers; **B146, B148** Photograph by Sharon Hoogstraten; **B150** © G.R. Roberts Photo Library; **B151** *left* © Tom Bean/Corbis; *right* © Krafft-Explorer/Photo Researchers; **B152** © F. Gohier/Photo Researchers; **B153** NASA/Carnegie Mellon University; **B154** *top* © Krafft-Explorer/Photo Researchers; *bottom left, right* Photographs by Sharon Hoogstraten; **B156** *top* © James A. Sugar/Corbis; *bottom* © Mark E. Gibson/Corbis; **B157** *top* © Stephen and Donna O'Meara/Volcano Watch International/Photo Researchers; *bottom* © Sid Balatan/Black Star Publishing/PictureQuest; **B158** U.S. Department of the Interior, U.S. Geological Survey, Reston, Virginia; **B159** Photograph by Sharon Hoogstraten; **B160** © The Image Bank/Getty Images; **B161** © Simon Fraser/Photo Researchers; **B162** © Peter Ryan/Photo Researchers; **B163** *top right* © James Leynse/Corbis; *top left* © Raymond Gehman/Corbis; *center* Courtesy of the General Libraries, The University of Texas at Austin; *bottom* © Jeff Foott/Panoramic Images/National Geographic Image Collection; **B164** *bottom left* © Sid Balatan/Black Star Publishing/PictureQuest; *bottom center* © The Image Bank/Getty Images; *bottom right* © Simon Fraser/Photo Researchers; **B166** © Roger Ressmeyer/Corbis.

Waves, Sound, and Light

Divider © David Pu'u/Corbis; **C2–C3** © Paul Kuroda/SuperStock; **C3** *left* © B. Benoit/Photo Researchers; *right* © Powerstock/SuperStock; **C4** *top* © Stephen Frink/Corbis; *bottom* © The Chedd-Angier Production Company; **C5** © George Stetten, M.D., Ph.D; **C6–C7** © Peter Sterling/Getty Images; **C7, C9** Photographs by Sharon Hoogstraten; **C11** Photograph courtesy of Earthquake Engineering Research Institute Reconnaissance Team; **C12** © Michael Krasowitz/Getty Images; **C13** Photograph by Sharon Hoogstraten; **C15** © John Lund/Getty Images; **C16** © Greg Huglin/Superstock; **C17** © Arnulf Husmo/Getty Images; **C19** Richard Olsenius/National Geographic Image Collection; **C20** Photograph by Sharon Hoogstraten; **C22** *top* © 1990 Robert Mathena/ Fundamental Photographs, NYC; *bottom* Photographs by Sharon Hoogstraten; **C23, C24** Photographs by Sharon Hoogstraten; **C25** © 2001 Richard Megna/Fundamental Photographs, NYC; **C26** *top* © 1972 FP/Fundamental Photographs, NYC; *bottom* Photograph by Sharon Hoogstraten; **C27** © 1998 Richard Megna/Fundamental Photographs, NYC; **C28** © Hiroshi Hara/Photonica; **C29** Takaaki Uda, Public Works Research Institute, Japan/NOAA; **C30** *bottom center* © 2001 Richard Megna/Fundamental Photographs, NYC; *bottom right* © 1972 FP/Fundamental Photographs, NYC; **C34–C35** © Chip Simons/Getty Images; **C35, C37** Photographs by Sharon Hoogstraten; **C39** © Susumu Nishinaga/Photo Researchers; **C41** Photographs by Sharon Hoogstraten; **C42** © Jeff Rotman/Getty Images; **C43** © John Terence Turner/Getty Images; **C44** *left* © Reuters NewMedia Inc./Corbis; *background* © Jason Hindley/Getty Images; **C45** Photograph by Sharon Hoogstraten; **C47** *left (top to bottom)* © Will Crocker/Getty Images; © Dorling Kindersley; © Photodisc/Getty Images; © Dorling Kindersley; © Photodisc/Getty Images; © Stephen Dalton/Animals Animals; © Steve Bloom/Getty Images; *top right* © Don Smetzer/Getty Images; *bottom right* Brian Gordon Green/National

Geographic Image Collection; **C48** Photograph by Sharon Hoogstraten; **C49** © Dorling Kindersley; **C50** © Michael Melford/Getty Images; **C52** © Tom Main/Getty Images; **C53** Photograph by Sharon Hoogstraten; **C55** *left* © Roger Ressmeyer/Corbis; *right* Symphony Center, Home of the Chicago Symphony Orchestra; **C56** © Yehoash Raphael, Kresge Hearing Research Institute, The University of Michigan; **C57** © Chris Shinn/Getty Images; **C58** Photograph by Sharon Hoogstraten; **C59** *top left* © Stephen Dalton/OSF/Animals Animals; *top right* © Paulo de Oliveira/Getty Images; *bottom left* © AFP/Corbis; *bottom right* U.S. Navy photo by Photographer's Mate 3rd Class Lawrence Braxton/Department of Defense; **C60** © Fetal Fotos; **C63** © Andrew Syred/Photo Researchers; **C64** *top left* © Reuters NewMedia Inc./Corbis; *bottom* Photographs by Sharon Hoogstraten; **C65** Photograph by Sharon Hoogstraten; **C66** *bottom left* © Stephen Dalton/OSF/Animals Animals; *bottom right* © Paulo de Oliveira/Getty Images; **C68** © Photodisc/Getty Images; **C70–C71** © Alan Kearney/Getty Images; **C71** *top, center* Photographs by Sharon Hoogstraten; *bottom* The EIT Consortium/NASA; **C73** Photograph by Sharon Hoogstraten; **C75** NASA, The Hubble Heritage Team, STScl, AURA; **C76** Photograph by Sharon Hoogstraten; **C78** *top* Palomar Observatory/Caltech; *center* NASA/MSFC/SAO; *bottom* NASA/CXC/ASU/J. Hester et al; *background* NASA/JHU/AUI/R. Giacconi et al.; **C79** Photograph by Sharon Hoogstraten; **C80** *left* © China Tourism Press/Getty Images; *center* © David Nunuk/Photo Researchers; *right* © Dr. Arthur Tucker/Photo Researchers; **C81** *left to right* © Jeremy Woodhouse/Getty Images; © Sinclair Stammers/Photo Researchers; © Hugh Turvey/Photo Researchers; © Alfred Pasieka/Photo Researchers; **C84** Photograph by Sharon Hoogstraten; **C85** *top* © Dr. Arthur Tucker/Photo Researchers; *bottom* © Thomas Eisner, Cornell University; **C86** © Martin Spinks; **C87** © Photodisc/Getty Images; *inset* © David Young-Wolff/Getty Images; **C88** Robert F. Sisson/National Geographic Image Collection; **C89** © George D. Lepp/Corbis; **C90** *top* © Raymond Blythe/OSF/Animals Animals; *bottom* Photograph by Sharon Hoogstraten; **C92** © Traffic Technologies; **C93** Photograph by Sharon Hoogstraten; **C94** © Jeff Greenberg/Visuals Unlimited; **C95** © Raymond Gehman/Corbis; **C96** © Charles Swedlund; **C97** *top* © Ace Photo Agency/Phototake; *bottom* © Dorling Kindersley; **C98** Photograph by Sharon Hoogstraten; **C100** *top* © Michael Newman/PhotoEdit; *bottom* Photographs by Sharon Hoogstraten; **C101** Photographs by Sharon Hoogstraten; **C102** *center right* Robert F. Sisson/National Geographic Image Collection; *bottom* © Ace Photo Agency/Phototake; **C106** *top* The Granger Collection, New York; *bottom* © Jack and Beverly Wilgus; **C107** *top* The Granger Collection, New York; *center left* Diagram of the eye from the *Opticae thesaurus. Alhazeni Arabis libri septem, nunc primum editi* by Ibn al-Haytham (Alhazen). Edited by Federico Risnero (Basleae, 1572), p. 6. Private collection, London; *center right* Courtesy of NASA/JPL/Caltech; *bottom* © Royal Greenwich Observatory/Photo Researchers; **C108** *top* © Stock Connection/Alamy; *center* © Florian Marquardt; *bottom* © Museum of Holography, Chicago; **C109** *top* © Bettmann/Corbis; *bottom* © Bob Masini/Phototake; **C110–C111** © Tom Raymond/Getty Images; **C111** *top, center* Photographs by Sharon Hoogstraten; *bottom* © Philippe Plailly/Photo Researchers; **C112** Photograph by Sharon Hoogstraten; **C114** © Laura Dwight/Corbis; **C115** Photograph by Sharon Hoogstraten; **C116** © Michael Newman/PhotoEdit; **C117** Photographs by Sharon Hoogstraten; **C118** Peter McBride/Aurora; **C119** Photograph by Sharon Hoogstraten; **C120** © Richard H. Johnston/Getty Images; **C122** © Kim Heacox/Getty Images; *background* © Photodisc/Getty Images; **C123** © T. R. Tharp/Corbis; **C124** *top* © Ruddy Gold/age photostock america, inc.; *bottom* Photograph by Sharon Hoogstraten; **C125** Photographs by Sharon Hoogstraten; **C126** © CMCD, 1994; **C128** Photograph by Sharon Hoogstraten; **C130** © Argentum/Photo Researchers; **C131** Photograph by Sharon Hoogstraten; **C133** *top* © Andrew Syred/Photo Researchers; *center* Lunar and Planetary Institute, CIRS/Library; *bottom* NASA; **C134** Photograph by Sharon Hoogstraten; **C135** Use of Canon Powershot S45 courtesy of Canon USA; **C136** © Philippe Psaila/Photo Researchers; **C137** *top* © Photodisc/Getty Images; *bottom* © Tom Stewart/corbisstockmarket.com; **C138** Bradley C. Edwards, Ph.D.; **C139** *top* © Photodisc/Getty Images; *center* © PhotoFlex.com; *bottom* © Michael Goldman/Photis/PictureQuest; **C140** © Michael Newman/PhotoEdit.

Ecology

Divider © Richard du Toit/Nature Picture Library; **D2, D3** *background* © Mark Thiessen/National Geographic Image Collection; **D3** *top* © Frank Oberle/Getty Images; *bottom* © Hal Horwitz/Corbis; **D4** *top (both)* © Lawrence J. Godson; *bottom* Chedd-Angier Production Company; **D6, D7** © Jeff Schultz/Alaska Stock.com; **D7** *top* Photograph by Ken O'Donoghue; *center* Photograph by Frank Siteman; **D9** Photograph by Frank Siteman; **D10** © Mark Allen Stack/Tom Stack & Associates; **D11** *left* © Jim Brandenburg/Minden Pictures; *right* © Ted Kerasote/Photo Researchers, Inc.; **D12** *bottom left* © Grant Heilman Photography; **D13** © Frans Lemmens/Getty Images; **D14** *top* © Michael J. Doolittle/The Image Works, Inc.; *bottom* Photograph by Ken O'Donoghue; **D16** Photograph by Ken O'Donoghue; **D19** Photograph by Frank Siteman; **D21** © Randy Wells/Corbis; **D22** Photograph by Frank Siteman; **D23** *left* © Eric Crichton/Corbis; *top right* © E.R. Degginger/Color-Pic, Inc.; *bottom right* © T.E. Adams/Visuals Unlimited, Inc.; **D24** © Anthony Mercieca Photo/Photo Researchers, Inc.; **D25** *top* © Fred Bruemmer/DRK Photo; *bottom* Photograph by Ken O'Donoghue; **D27** *background* © Raymond Gehman/Corbis; **D29** © Arthur Gurmankin & Mary Morina/Visuals Unlimited, Inc.; *top right* © Carmela Leszczynski/Animals Animals; **D30** © Charles Melton/Visuals Unlimited, Inc.; **D31** © Michio Hoshino/Minden Pictures; **D32** *top left* © Tom Bean; *top right* © E.R. Degginger/Color-Pic, Inc.; *bottom* © Joe McDonald/Visuals Unlimited, Inc.; **D33** *left* © David Wrobel/Visuals Unlimited, Inc.; *right* © Tom Bean; **D34** *left* © Owaki-Kulla/Corbis; *right* © Frans Lanting/Minden Pictures; **D35** *top* Photograph by Ken O'Donoghue; *bottom* © Stephen Dalton/Photo Researchers, Inc.; **D36** *left* © Aaron Horowitz/Corbis; *center* © Hans Pfletschinger/Peter Arnold, Inc.; *right* © Arthur Gurmankin & Mary Morina/Visuals Unlimited, Inc.; **D37** *left* © Paul Rezendes; *center* © Richard Herrmann/Visuals Unlimited, Inc.; *right* © Norbert Wu; **D42, D43** © Wolcott Henry/National Geographic Image Collection; **D43** *top* Photograph by Frank Siteman; *center* Photograph by Ken O'Donoghue; **D45** Photograph by Frank Siteman; **D46** *left and center* © Frans Lanting/Minden Pictures; *right* © Robin Karpan/Visuals Unlimited, Inc.; **D50** © Walt Anderson/Visuals Unlimited, Inc.; **D51** ©Alan & Linda Detrick/Photo Researchers, Inc.; **D52** *top* © Patrick J. Endres/Visuals Unlimited, Inc.; *bottom left* Photograph by Frank Siteman; *bottom right* Photograph by Ken O'Donoghue; **D53** Photograph by Ken O'Donoghue; **D54** © Spencer Grant/PhotoEdit, Inc.; **D55** © Gary Braasch; **D56** *top* © Joe McDonald/Visuals Unlimited, Inc.; *bottom* © Stephen J. Krasemann/Photo Researchers, Inc.; **D57** *top* Photograph by Ken O'Donoghue; *bottom* © Michael Fogden/Bruce Coleman Inc.; **D58** © Michael & Patricia Fogden/Minden Pictures; **D59** © Bradley Sheard; **D60** *clockwise from top* © S.J. Krasemann/Peter Arnold, Inc.; © Ray Coleman/Visuals Unlimited, Inc.; © Astrid & Hanns-Frieder Michler/Science Photo Library; © E.R. Degginger/Color-Pic, Inc.; © Dwight R. Kuhn; © Phil Degginger/Color-Pic, Inc.; **D61** © Arthur Morris/Visuals Unlimited, Inc.; **D62** *left* © Kevin Fleming/Corbis; *inset* © David M. Dennis/Animals Animals; **D63** Photograph by Ken O'Donoghue; **D64** *top* © Shin Yoshino/Minden Pictures; *bottom* © Tim Fitzharris/Minden Pictures; **D65** Photograph by Frank Siteman; **D66** *bottom (background)* © Leo Collier/Getty Images; **D67** *bottom (background)* © David R. Frazier/Getty Images; **D69** © A. & J. Visage/Peter Arnold, Inc.; **D70** *top left* © Frans Lanting/Minden Pictures; **D74** *bottom left* Denver Public Library, Western History Collection, call#F-4659; *top center* © James Randklev/Getty Images; *bottom right* Library of Congress, Prints and Photographs Division (LC-USZ62-16709 DLC) cph 3a18915; **D75** *top left* © H.H. French/Corbis; *top right* © Bill Ross/Corbis; *center left* The Bancroft Library, University of California, Berkeley; *center right* © Corbis; *bottom* © Michael Sewell/Peter Arnold, Inc.; **D76** *top left* © Alfred Eisenstaedt/Getty Images; *top right* © Tom Bean/DRK Photo; *center right* © David Muench/Corbis; *bottom left* © Kevin Schafer/Corbis; *bottom right* Habitat Quality for San Joaquin Kit Fox on Managed and Private Lands reprinted from ESRI Map Book, Vol. 16 and used herein with permission. Copyright © 2001 ESRI. All rights reserved.; **D77** *top* © Tom Soucek/Alaska Stock Images; *bottom* © Richard Galosy/Bruce Coleman, Inc.; **D78, D79** ©Alex Maclean/Photonica; **D79** *top and center* Photographs by Ken O'Donoghue; **D81** Photograph by Frank Siteman; **D83** © Ray Pfortner/Peter Arnold, Inc.; **D84** Photograph by Ken O'Donoghue; **D85** *top* © John Elk III; *bottom* © Ted Spiegel/Corbis; **D86** *background* © ChromoSohm/Sohm/Photo Researchers, Inc.; *insets* Courtesy, USGS: EROS Data Center; **D87** © Mark E. Gibson/Visuals Unlimited, Inc.; **D88** © David Zimmerman/Corbis; **D89** © David Young-Wolff/PhotoEdit, Inc.; **D90** *left* © Richard Stockton/Iguazu Falls/Index Stock Imagery, Inc.; *right* © Bill Ross/Corbis; **D91** Photograph by Ken O'Donoghue; **D92** *bottom* © Tom Bean/DRK Photo; *inset* © Jenny Hager/The Image Works, Inc.; **D93** *bottom* © Natalie Fobes/Corbis; *inset* © Natalie Fobes/Getty Images; **D95** © Kent Foster Photgraphs/Visuals Unlimited, Inc.; **D96** *top* © Andrew J. Martinez/Photo Researchers, Inc.; *inset* © D. Cavagnaro/Visuals Unlimited, Inc.; **D97** © Tom Edwards/Visuals Unlimited, Inc.; **D98** Photographs by Ken O'Donoghue and Frank Siteman; **D99** © Frank Pedrick/The Image Works, Inc.; **D100** © Joe McDonald/Visuals Unlimited, Inc.; **D101** *top (background)* © Jim Wark/Airphoto; *top (inset)* Photograph by Scott Williams/U.S. Fish and Wildlife Service; *bottom (background)* © Tom Bean/Corbis; *bottom (insets)* Courtesy, San Diego State University, Soil Ecology and Restoration Group; **D102** © Melissa Farlow/National Geographic Image Collection; **D103** © Klein/Hubert/Peter Arnold, Inc.; **D104** *top* © Janis Miglavs; *bottom* © David Young-Wolff/PhotoEdit, Inc.; **D105** © Kevin Schafer/Corbis; **D106** *top* Tom Myers/Photo Researchers, Inc.; *bottom* Photograph by Frank Siteman; **D108** *center left* © Natalie Fobes/Corbis;

center right © Kent Foster Photographs/Visuals Unlimited, Inc.; *bottom left* © Joe McDonald/Visuals Unlimited, Inc.; *bottom right* © Klein/Hubert/Peter Arnold, Inc.

Space Science
Divider © David Nunuk/Photo Researchers; **E2–E3** © Charles O'Rear/Corbis; **E3** *top right* © D. Nunuk/Photo Researchers; **E4** © The Chedd-Angier Production Company; **E4–E5** © David Parker/Photo Researchers; **E5** *top center* NASA/JPL; **E6–E7** NASA; **E7, E9** Photographs by Sharon Hoogstraten; **E11** Johnson Space Center/NASA; **E12** Photograph by Sharon Hoogstraten; **E13** *top* © Roger Ressmeyer/Corbis; *bottom* Photograph by Sharon Hoogstraten; **E15** Photograph by Sharon Hoogstraten; **E16** *center left* Kapteyn Laboratorium/Photo Researchers; *center* National Optical Astronomy Observatories/Photo Researchers; *center right* A. Wilson (UMD) et al., CXC/NASA; **E18** © Roger Ressmeyer/Corbis; **E19** *top left* NASA Johnson Space Center; *top right* © STScI/NASA/ Photo Researchers; **E20** *top left* © ImageState-Pictor/PictureQuest; **E20–E21, E22** Photographs by Sharon Hoogstraten; **E23** *bottom, inset* NASA; **E24** Courtesy of NASA/JSC; **E25** *top* NASA; *bottom* Photograph by Sharon Hoogstraten; **E27** Photograph by Bill Ingalls/NASA; **E30** *left, inset* Chris Butler/Photo Researchers; **E31** NASA; **E32** Courtesy of V.R. Sharpton University of Alaska-Fairbanks and the Lunar and Planetary Institute; **E33** Photograph by Sharon Hoogstraten; **E34** NASA; **E35** *background* © Jan Tove Johansson/Image State-Pictor/ PictureQuest; *left inset* Andy Fyon, Ontariowildflower.com (Division of Professor Beaker's Learning Labs); *right inset* NASA; **E36** *top* Photograph by Sharon Hoogstraten; *center* © Roger Ressmeyer/Corbis; *bottom* NASA; **E40–E41** © Roger Ressmeyer/Corbis; **E41** *top right, center right* Photographs by Sharon Hoogstraten; *bottom right* NASA Goddard Space Flight Center; **E43** *left* NASA; *right* Photograph by Sharon Hoogstraten; **E44** *top* © 2003 The Living Earth Inc.; *bottom* Photograph by Sharon Hoogstraten; **E45** Photograph by Sharon Hoogstraten; **E47** NASA/JSC; **E49** © Arnulf Husmo/Getty Images; **E50** *top* © Christian Perret/jump; *bottom left, bottom right* Photograph by Sharon Hoogstraten; **E51, E52** Photographs by Sharon Hoogstraten; **E53** Courtesy of NASA and the Lunar and Planetary Institute; **E54** USGS Flagstaff, Arizona; **E55** *top right* Photograph by Sharon Hoogstraten; *bottom right* NASA; *right inset* NASA and the Lunar and Planetary Institute; **E58** Photograph by Steve Irvine; **E59** © DiMaggio/Kalish/Corbis; **E61** *background* Lunar Horizon View/NASA; **E62** Photograph by Sharon Hoogstraten; **E63** *top* © Roger Ressmeyer/Corbis; *bottom* Photograph by Jean-Francois Guay; **E64** *center* NASA/Getty Images; *bottom left* © Fred Espenak; **E65** *top* © Jeff Greenberg/MRP/Photo Researchers; *bottom* © 1999 Ray Coleman/Photo Researchers; **E67** *top left* © Peter Duke; *right inset* © David Parker/Photo Researchers; *bottom left* Public Domain; *bottom center* Barlow Aerial Photography, Ignacio, CO; **E68** *top left* © 2003 The Living Earth, Inc.; *center left* Photograph courtesy of NASA and the Lunar and Planetary Institute; **E70** *left* USGS Flagstaff, Arizona; *right* NASA Goddard Space Flight Center; **E72** Courtesy of Adler Planetarium & Astronomy Museum, Chicago, Illinois; **E73** *top left* © Stapleton/Corbis; *center* © Science Museum/Science & Society Picture Library; *right* provided by Roger Bell, University of Maryland, and Michael Briley, University of Wisconsin, Oshkosh; *bottom* Courtesy of Adler Planetarium & Astronomy Museum, Chicago, Illinois; **E74** *top left* © Harvard College Observatory/Photo Researchers; *top right* Robert Williams and the Hubble Deep Field Team (STScI) and NASA; *bottom* © Fermi National Accelerator Laboratory/Photo Researchers; **E75** *top* Ann Feild (STScI); *bottom* © NASA/Photo Researchers; **E76–E77** Courtesy of NASA/JPL/University of Arizona; **E77** *top right, center right* Photographs by Sharon Hoogstraten; **E79, E82** Photographs by Sharon Hoogstraten; **E83** *left* Photo © Calvin J. Hamilton; *right* Courtesy of NASA/JPL/Caltech; **E84** NASA; **E85** *top* Photograph by Sharon Hoogstraten; *bottom* Johnson Space Center NASA; **E87** *background* Mark Robinson/Mariner 10/NASA; *top right* NASA; *top left* © Walt Anderson/Visuals Unlimited; *bottom left* NASA/ JPL/Malin Space Science Systems; **E88** Photograph by Sharon Hoogstraten; **E89** *top* USGS; *bottom* Courtesy of NASA/JPL/ Northwestern University; **E90** *top, center, bottom* NASA; **E91** NASA/JSC; **E92** Courtesy of NASA/JPL/Caltech; **E93** *left* Courtesy of NASA/JPL/Malin Space Science Systems; *right* MAP-A-Planet/NASA; *right inset* NASA/Goddard Space Flight Center Scientific Visualization Studio; **E94, E95** Courtesy of NASA/JPL/Caltech; **E96** *top* Courtesy of NASA/JPL/Caltech; *bottom* Photograph by Sharon Hoogstraten; **E97** *top* NASA; *bottom* NASA and the Hubble Heritage Team (STScI/AURA); **E98** *top* E. Karkoschka(LPL) and NASA; *bottom* © Calvin J. Hamilton; **E99** *top* Courtesy of NASA/JPL/Caltech; *center* NASA; **E100** near.jhuapl.edu; **E101** Hubble Space Telescope, STScI-PR96-09a/NASA; **E102** *top left, inset* NASA; *bottom left* Courtesy of NASA/JPL/Caltech; *bottom left inset* NASA; *top right* © NASA/ JPL/Photo Researchers; *top right inset, bottom right, bottom right inset* NASA; **E103** Courtesy of NASA/JPL/Caltech; **E104** *background* © 1997 Jerry Lodriguss; *right* Courtesy of NASA/JPL/ Caltech; **E105** Fred R. Conrad/The New York Times; **E106** *top left* © James L. Amos/Corbis; *bottom left* Photograph by Sharon Hoogstraten; **E107** Photograph by Sharon Hoogstraten; **E108** *top* NASA; *bottom* Courtesy of NASA/JPL/Caltech; **E112–E113** David Malin Images/Anglo- Australian Observatory; **E113** *top left* © Jerry Schad/Photo Researchers; *center left* Photograph by Sharon Hoogstraten; **E115** Photograph by Sharon Hoogstraten; **E117** Photograph by Jay M. Paschoff, Bryce A. Babcock, Stephan Martin, Wendy Carlos, and Daniel B. Seaton © Williams College; **E118** *left* © John Chumack/Photo Researchers; *right* © NASA/Photo Researchers; **E119** © Patrick J. Endres/Alaskaphotographics.com; **E120** *top* © Dave Robertson/Masterfile; *left bottom, right bottom* Photograph by Sharon Hoogstraten; **E121, E122, E123** Photographs by Sharon Hoogstraten; **E125** *top* © Dorling Kindersley; *bottom* ESA and J. Hester (ASU),NASA; **E126** J. Hester et al./NASA/CXC/ASU; **E127** Hubble Heritage Team/AURA/STScI/NASA; **E129** © MPIA-HD, Birkle, Slawik/Photo Researchers; **E130** Photograph by Sharon Hoogstraten; **E131** *top* Allan Morton/Dennis Milon/Photo Researchers; *bottom* Photograph by Sharon Hoogstraten; **E132** David Malin Images /Anglo-Australian Observatory; **E133** Walter Jaffe/Leiden Observatory, Holland Ford/JHU/STScI, and NASA; **E134** *left* NASA and Hubble Heritage Team (STScI); *center* NASA, H. Ford (JHU), G. Illingworth (UCSC/LO), M. Clampin (STScI), G. Hartig (STScI), the ACS Science Team, and ESA; **E135** Photograph by Sharon Hoogstraten; **E136** © Jason Ware; **E138** Photograph by Sharon Hoogstraten; **E139** N. Benitez (JHU), T. Broadhurst (The Hebrew University), H. Ford (JHU), M. Clampin (STScI), G. Hartig (STScI), G. Illingworth (UCO/Lick Observatory), the AGS Science Team and ESA/NASA; **E140** *top* David Malin Images/Anglo-Australian Observatory; *bottom* N. Benitez (JHU), T. Broadhurst (The Hebrew University), H. Ford (JHU), M. Clampin (STScI), G. Hartig (STScI), G. Illingworth (UCO/Lick Observatory), the AGS Science Team and ESA/NASA; **E142** *left* Hubble Heritage Team (AURA/STScI/NASA); *right* Anglo-Australian Observatory/David Malin Images.

Handbooks
NC2 © David M. Dennis; **NC4** *left* © Volker Steger/Photo Researchers; *right, top to bottom* © Tui de Roy/Bruce Coleman, Inc.; © Tui De Roy/Minden Pictures; © Richard I'Anson/Lonely Planet Images; © Tui de Roy/Bruce Coleman, Inc.; **NC5** *left top, bottom* © Larry Allan/Bruce Coleman, Inc.; *right* © Hans Reinhard/Bruce Coleman, Inc.; **NC6** *left inset* © Bruce Coleman, Inc.; *right inset* © Paul Souders/Accent Alaska; **NC7** © Michael J. Doolittle/Image Works, Inc.; **NC9** © Royalty-Free/Corbis; **NC10** © Barry Runk/Grant Heilman Photography, Inc.; **NC12** © Kent Foster Photographs/Bruce Coleman Ltd.; **NC13** *top left, top middle* © Biophoto Associates/Science Source/Photo Researchers, Inc.; *top right, bottom*; **NC14** © Roger Ressmeyer/Corbis; **R28** © Photodisc/Getty Images.

Illustrations and Maps
Accurate Art Inc. **A39, A107, A175, B61, C33, E106**; Ampersand Design Group **B49, C139**; Argosy **C10, C13, C14, C18, C19, C25, C30, C55, C61**; Julian Baum **E57, E117, E127, E128, E131, E140**; Richard Bonson/Wildlife Art Ltd. **A83, B70–B71, B98, B100, B132, B139, B141, B143, B147, B161, B164, D28, D47, D49, D60** (background), **D70** (top right); Peter Bull/Wildlife Art Ltd. **A160, A162, A167, A169, B77, B100, B112, B118, B130, E26, E27, E47, E48, E68**; Eric Chadwick **C98, C99**; Bill Cigliano **E67, E137**; Steve Cowden **C12, C51, C54, C82, E48**; Sandra Doyle/Wildlife Art Ltd. **D27** (all), **D38** (bottom); Stephen Durke **A45, A53, B19, B84, B125, B127, B130, E12, E14, E18**; Chris Forsey **A99, B155**; Luigi Galante **A127, A138, D66–D67** (all insets), **D70** (bottom); Dan Gonzalez **D88, D94**; David A. Hardy **A12, A84, A86, A104, E11, E32, E80, E83, E95, E108**; Gary Hincks **A63, A79, A80, A149, A153, B83, B84, B86, B88, B91, B94, B95, B98, B150–B151, B164, D12** (bottom right), **D17, D18, D20, D36–D37** (background), **D38** (center), **D83**; Keith Kasnot **NC14**; Dan Maas/Maas Digital **E28, E36**; Mapquest.com, Inc. **A17, A18, A23, A32, A33, A34, A36, A64, A88, A110, A125, A166, A170, B48, B73, B76, B79, B83, B87, B88, B91, B92, B94, B95, B96, B98, B106, B117, B123, B124, B125, B130, B138, B141, B149, D31, D47** (top right), **D49** (top), **D85, E64, R58, R66–R67**; Morgan, Cain & Assoc. **A128**; Laurie O'Keefe **D29**; Mick Posen **NC6**; Precision Graphics **B108, B109, B130, B152**; Mike Saunders **A117, A120, A138**; Peter Scott **NC4**; SlimFilms **B127, B130**; Space.comCanada.Inc. **R61–R64**; Dan Stuckenschneider **C62, C77, C91, C102, C133, C135, C136, C140, E17, E36, R11–R19, R22, R32**; Raymond Turvey **A159**; Bart Vallecoccia **C38, C39, C126, C127, C129, C135, C140**; Rob Wood **A117, A154**; Ron Wood/Wood Ronsaville Harlin **E56, E68**.

Content Standards: 5–8

√ A. Science as Inquiry

As a result of activities in grades 5–8, all students should develop

Abilities Necessary to do Scientific Inquiry

A.1 Identify questions that can be answered through scientific investigations. Students should develop the ability to refine and refocus broad and ill-defined questions. An important aspect of this ability consists of students' ability to clarify questions and inquiries and direct them toward objects and phenomena that can be described, explained, or predicted by scientific investigations. Students should develop the ability to identify their questions with scientific ideas, concepts, and quantitative relationships that guide investigation.

A.2 Design and conduct a scientific investigation. Students should develop general abilities, such as systematic observation, making accurate measurements, and identifying and controlling variables. They should also develop the ability to clarify their ideas that are influencing and guiding the inquiry, and to understand how those ideas compare with current scientific knowledge. Students can learn to formulate questions, design investigations, execute investigations, interpret data, use evidence to generate explanations, propose alternative explanations, and critique explanations and procedures.

A.3 Use appropriate tools and techniques to gather, analyze, and interpret data. The use of tools and techniques, including mathematics, will be guided by the question asked and the investigations students design. The use of computers for the collection, summary, and display of evidence is part of this standard. Students should be able to access, gather, store, retrieve, and organize data, using hardware and software designed for these purposes.

A.4 Develop descriptions, explanations, predictions, and models using evidence. Students should base their explanation on what they observed, and as they develop cognitive skills, they should be able to differentiate explanation from description—providing causes for effects and establishing relationships based on evidence and logical argument. This standard requires a subject matter knowledge base so the students can effectively conduct investigations, because developing explanations establishes connections between the content of science and the contexts within which students develop new knowledge.

A.5 Think critically and logically to make the relationships between evidence and explanations. Thinking critically about evidence includes deciding what evidence should be used and accounting for anomalous data. Specifically, students should be able to review data from a simple experiment, summarize the data, and form a logical argument about the cause-and-effect relationships in the experiment. Students should begin to state some explanations in terms of the relationship between two or more variables.

A.6 Recognize and analyze alternative explanations and predictions. Students should develop the ability to listen to and respect the explanations proposed by other students. They should remain open to and acknowledge different ideas and explanations, be able to accept the skepticism of others, and consider alternative explanations.

A.7   Communicate scientific procedures and explanations. With practice, students should become competent at communicating experimental methods, following instructions, describing observations, summarizing the results of other groups, and telling other students about investigations and explanations.

✓ A.8   Use mathematics in all aspects of scientific inquiry. Mathematics is essential to asking and answering questions about the natural world. Mathematics can be used to ask questions; to gather, organize, and present data; and to structure convincing explanations.

Understandings about Scientific Inquiry

A.9.a   Different kinds of questions suggest different kinds of scientific investigations. Some investigations involve observing and describing objects, organisms, or events; some involve collecting specimens; some involve experiments; some involve seeking more information; some involve discovery of new objects and phenomena; and some involve making models.

A.9.b   Current scientific knowledge and understanding guide scientific investigations. Different scientific domains employ different methods, core theories, and standards to advance scientific knowledge and understanding.

✓ A.9.c   Mathematics is important in all aspects of scientific inquiry.

A.9.d   Technology used to gather data enhances accuracy and allows scientists to analyze and quantify results of investigations.

A.9.e   Scientific explanations emphasize evidence, have logically consistent arguments, and use scientific principles, models, and theories. The scientific community accepts and uses such explanations until displaced by better scientific ones. When such displacement occurs, science advances.

A.9.f   Science advances through legitimate skepticism. Asking questions and querying other scientists' explanations is part of scientific inquiry. Scientists evaluate the explanations proposed by other scientists by examining evidence, comparing evidence, identifying faulty reasoning, pointing out statements that go beyond the evidence, and suggesting alternative explanations for the same observations.

A.9.g   Scientific investigations sometimes result in new ideas and phenomena for study, generate new methods or procedures for an investigation, or develop new technologies to improve the collection of data. All of these results can lead to new investigations.

B. Physical Science

As a result of their activities in grades 5–8, all students should develop an understanding of

Properties and Changes of Properties in Matter

B.1.a   A substance has characteristic properties, such as density, a boiling point, and solubility, all of which are independent of the amount of the sample. A mixture of substances often can be separated into the original substances using one or more of the characteristic properties.

B.1.b   Substances react chemically in characteristic ways with other substances to form new substances (compounds) with different characteristic properties. In chemical reactions, the total mass is conserved. Substances often are placed in categories or groups if they react in similar ways; metals is an example of such a group.

B.1.c   Chemical elements do not break down during normal laboratory reactions involving such treatments as heating, exposure to electric current, or reaction with acids. There are more than 100 known elements that combine in a multitude of ways to produce compounds, which account for the living and nonliving substances that we encounter.

Motions and Forces

B.2.a   The motion of an object can be described by its position, direction of motion, and speed. That motion can be measured and represented on a graph.

B.2.b   An object that is not being subjected to a force will continue to move at a constant speed and in a straight line.

B.2.c   If more than one force acts on an object along a straight line, then the forces will reinforce or cancel one another, depending on their direction and magnitude. Unbalanced forces will cause changes in the speed or direction of an object's motion.

Transfer of Energy

B.3.a   Energy is a property of many substances and is associated with heat, light, electricity, mechanical motion, sound, nuclei, and the nature of a chemical. Energy is transferred in many ways.

B.3.b   Heat moves in predictable ways, flowing from warmer objects to cooler ones, until both reach the same temperature.

B.3.c   Light interacts with matter by transmission (including refraction), absorption, or scattering (including reflection). To see an object, light from that object—emitted by or scattered from it—must enter the eye.

B.3.d   Electrical circuits provide a means of transferring electrical energy when heat, light, sound, and chemical changes are produced.

B.3.e   In most chemical and nuclear reactions, energy is transferred into or out of a system. Heat, light, mechanical motion, or electricity might all be involved in such transfers.

B.3.f   The sun is a major source of energy for changes on the earth's surface. The sun loses energy by emitting light. A tiny fraction of that light reaches the earth, transferring energy from the sun to the earth. The sun's energy arrives as light with a range of wavelengths, consisting of visible light, infrared, and ultraviolet radiation.

C. Life Science

As a result of their activities in grades 5–8, all students should develop understanding of

Structure and Function in Living Systems

C.1.a Living systems at all levels of organization demonstrate the complementary nature of structure and function. Important levels of organization for structure and function include cells, organs, tissues, organ systems, whole organisms, and ecosystems.

C.1.b All organisms are composed of cells—the fundamental unit of life. Most organisms are single cells; other organisms, including humans, are multicellular.

C.1.c Cells carry on the many functions needed to sustain life. They grow and divide, thereby producing more cells. This requires that they take in nutrients, which they use to provide energy for the work that cells do and to make the materials that a cell or an organism needs.

C.1.d Specialized cells perform specialized functions in multicellular organisms. Groups of specialized cells cooperate to form a tissue, such as a muscle. Different tissues are in turn grouped together to form larger functional units, called organs. Each type of cell, tissue, and organ has a distinct structure and set of functions that serve the organism as a whole.

C.1.e The human organism has systems for digestion, respiration, reproduction, circulation, excretion, movement, control, and coordination, and for protection from disease. These systems interact with one another.

C.1.f Disease is a breakdown in structures or functions of an organism. Some diseases are the result of intrinsic failures of the system. Others are the result of damage by infection by other organisms.

Reproduction and Heredity

C.2.a Reproduction is a characteristic of all living systems; because no individual organism lives forever, reproduction is essential to the continuation of every species. Some organisms reproduce asexually. Other organisms reproduce sexually.

C.2.b In many species, including humans, females produce eggs and males produce sperm. Plants also reproduce sexually—the egg and sperm are produced in the flowers of flowering plants. An egg and sperm unite to begin development of a new individual. That new individual receives genetic information from its mother (via the egg) and its father (via the sperm). Sexually produced offspring never are identical to either of their parents.

C.2.c Every organism requires a set of instructions for specifying its traits. Heredity is the passage of these instructions from one generation to another.

C.2.d Hereditary information is contained in genes, located in the chromosomes of each cell. Each gene carries a single unit of information. An inherited trait of an individual can be determined by one or by many genes, and a single gene can influence more than one trait. A human cell contains many thousands of different genes.

C.2.e The characteristics of an organism can be described in terms of a combination of traits. Some traits are inherited and others result from interactions with the environment.

Regulation and Behavior

C.3.a All organisms must be able to obtain and use resources, grow, reproduce, and maintain stable internal conditions while living in a constantly changing external environment.

C.3.b Regulation of an organism's internal environment involves sensing the internal environment and changing physiological activities to keep conditions within the range required to survive.

C.3.c Behavior is one kind of response an organism can make to an internal or environmental stimulus. A behavioral response requires coordination and communication at many levels, including cells, organ systems, and whole organisms. Behavioral response is a set of actions determined in part by heredity and in part from experience.

C.3.d An organism's behavior evolves through adaptation to its environment. How a species moves, obtains food, reproduces, and responds to danger are based in the species' evolutionary history.

Populations and Ecosystems

C.4.a A population consists of all individuals of a species that occur together at a given place and time. All populations living together and the physical factors with which they interact compose an ecosystem.

C.4.b Populations of organisms can be categorized by the function they serve in an ecosystem. Plants and some microorganisms are producers—they make their own food. All animals, including humans, are consumers, which obtain food by eating other organisms. Decomposers, primarily bacteria and fungi, are consumers that use waste materials and dead organisms for food. Food webs identify the relationships among producers, consumers, and decomposers in an ecosystem.

C.4.c For ecosystems, the major source of energy is sunlight. Energy entering ecosystems as sunlight is transferred by producers into chemical energy through photosynthesis. That energy then passes from organism to organism in food webs.

C.4.d The number of organisms an ecosystem can support depends on the resources available and abiotic factors, such as quantity of light and water, range of temperatures, and soil composition. Given adequate biotic and abiotic resources and no disease or predators, populations (including humans) increase at rapid rates. Lack of resources and other factors, such as predation and climate, limit the growth of populations in specific niches in the ecosystem.

Diversity and Adaptations of Organisms

C.5.a Millions of species of animals, plants, and microorganisms are alive today. Although different species might look dissimilar, the unity among organisms becomes apparent from an analysis of internal structures, the similarity of their chemical processes, and the evidence of common ancestry.

C.5.b Biological evolution accounts for the diversity of species developed through gradual processes over many generations. Species acquire many of their unique characteristics through biological adaptation, which involves the selection of naturally occurring variations in populations. Biological adaptations include changes in structures, behaviors, or physiology that enhance survival and reproductive success in a particular environment.

C.5.c Extinction of a species occurs when the environment changes and the adaptive characteristics of a species are insufficient to allow its survival. Fossils indicate that many organisms that lived long ago are extinct. Extinction of species is common; most of the species that have lived on the earth no longer exist.

D. Earth and Space Science

As a result of their activities in grades 5–8, all students should develop an understanding of

Structure of the Earth System

D.1.a   The solid earth is layered with a lithosphere; hot, convecting mantle; and dense, metallic core.

D.1.b   Lithospheric plates on the scales of continents and oceans constantly move at rates of centimeters per year in response to movements in the mantle. Major geological events, such as earthquakes, volcanic eruptions, and mountain building, result from these plate motions.

D.1.c   Land forms are the result of a combination of constructive and destructive forces. Constructive forces include crustal deformation, volcanic eruption, and deposition of sediment, while destructive forces include weathering and erosion.

D.1.d   Some changes in the solid earth can be described as the "rock cycle." Old rocks at the earth's surface weather, forming sediments that are buried, then compacted, heated, and often recrystallized into new rock. Eventually, those new rocks may be brought to the surface by the forces that drive plate motions, and the rock cycle continues.

D.1.e   Soil consists of weathered rocks and decomposed organic material from dead plants, animals, and bacteria. Soils are often found in layers, with each having a different chemical composition and texture.

D.1.f   Water, which covers the majority of the earth's surface, circulates through the crust, oceans, and atmosphere in what is known as the "water cycle." Water evaporates from the earth's surface, rises and cools as it moves to higher elevations, condenses as rain or snow, and falls to the surface where it collects in lakes, oceans, soil, and in rocks underground.

D.1.g   Water is a solvent. As it passes through the water cycle it dissolves minerals and gases and carries them to the oceans.

D.1.h   The atmosphere is a mixture of nitrogen, oxygen, and trace gases that include water vapor. The atmosphere has different properties at different elevations.

D.1.i   Clouds, formed by the condensation of water vapor, affect weather and climate.

D.1.j   Global patterns of atmospheric movement influence local weather. Oceans have a major effect on climate, because water in the oceans holds a large amount of heat.

D.1.k   Living organisms have played many roles in the earth system, including affecting the composition of the atmosphere, producing some types of rocks, and contributing to the weathering of rocks.

Earth's History

D.2.a   The earth processes we see today, including erosion, movement of lithospheric plates, and changes in atmospheric composition, are similar to those that occurred in the past. Earth history is also influenced by occasional catastrophes, such as the impact of an asteroid or comet.

D.2.b   Fossils provide important evidence of how life and environmental conditions have changed.

Earth in the Solar System

D.3.a   The earth is the third planet from the sun in a system that includes the moon, the sun, eight other planets and their moons, and smaller objects, such as asteroids and comets. The sun, an average star, is the central and largest body in the solar system.

D.3.b   Most objects in the solar system are in regular and predictable motion. Those motions explain such phenomena as the day, the year, phases of the moon, and eclipses.

D.3.c   Gravity is the force that keeps planets in orbit around the sun and governs the rest of the motion in the solar system. Gravity alone holds us to the earth's surface and explains the phenomena of the tides.

D.3.d   The sun is the major source of energy for phenomena on the earth's surface, such as growth of plants, winds, ocean currents, and the water cycle. Seasons result from variations in the amount of the sun's energy hitting the surface, due to the tilt of the earth's rotation on its axis and the length of the day.

E. Science and Technology

As a result of activities in grades 5–8, all students should develop

Abilities of Technological Design

E.1   Identify appropriate problems for technological design. Students should develop their abilities by identifying a specified need, considering its various aspects, and talking to different potential users or beneficiaries. They should appreciate that for some needs, the cultural backgrounds and beliefs of different groups can affect the criteria for a suitable product.

E.2   Design a solution or product. Students should make and compare different proposals in the light of the criteria they have selected. They must consider constraints—such as cost, time, trade-offs, and materials needed—and communicate ideas with drawings and simple models.

E.3   Implement a proposed design. Students should organize materials and other resources, plan their work, make good use of group collaboration where appropriate, choose suitable tools and techniques, and work with appropriate measurement methods to ensure adequate accuracy.

E.4   Evaluate completed technological designs or products. Students should use criteria relevant to the original purpose or need, consider a variety of factors that might affect acceptability and suitability for intended users or beneficiaries, and develop measures of quality with respect to such criteria and factors; they should also suggest improvements and, for their own products, try proposed modifications.

E.5   Communicate the process of technological design. Students should review and describe any completed piece of work and identify the stages of problem identification, solution design, implementation, and evaluation.

Understandings about Science and Technology

E.6.a   Scientific inquiry and technological design have similarities and differences. Scientists propose explanations for questions about the natural world, and engineers propose solutions relating to human problems, needs, and aspirations. Technological solutions are temporary; technologies exist within nature and so they cannot contravene physical or biological principles; technological solutions have side effects; and technologies cost, carry risks, and provide benefits.

E.6.b   Many different people in different cultures have made and continue to make contributions to science and technology.

E.6.c   Science and technology are reciprocal. Science helps drive technology, as it addresses questions that demand more sophisticated instruments and provides principles for better instrumentation and technique. Technology is essential to science, because it provides instruments and techniques that enable observations of objects and phenomena that are otherwise unobservable due to factors such as quantity, distance, location, size, and speed. Technology also provides tools for investigations, inquiry, and analysis.

E.6.d   Perfectly designed solutions do not exist. All technological solutions have trade-offs, such as safety, cost, efficiency, and appearance. Engineers often build in back-up systems to provide safety. Risk is part of living in a highly technological world. Reducing risk often results in new technology.

E.6.e   Technological designs have constraints. Some constraints are unavoidable, for example, properties of materials, or effects of weather and friction; other constraints limit choices in the design, for example, environmental protection, human safety, and aesthetics.

E.6.f   Technological solutions have intended benefits and unintended consequences. Some consequences can be predicted, others cannot.

F. Science in Personal and Social Perspectives

As a result of activities in grades 5–8, all students should develop understanding of

Personal Health

F.1.a   Regular exercise is important to the maintenance and improvement of health. The benefits of physical fitness include maintaining healthy weight, having energy and strength for routine activities, good muscle tone, bone strength, strong heart/lung systems, and improved mental health. Personal exercise, especially developing cardiovascular endurance, is the foundation of physical fitness.

F.1.b   The potential for accidents and the existence of hazards imposes the need for injury prevention. Safe living involves the development and use of safety precautions and the recognition of risk in personal decisions. Injury prevention has personal and social dimensions.

F.1.c   The use of tobacco increases the risk of illness. Students should understand the influence of short-term social and psychological factors that lead to tobacco use, and the possible long-term detrimental effects of smoking and chewing tobacco.

F.1.d   Alcohol and other drugs are often abused substances. Such drugs change how the body functions and can lead to addiction.

F.1.e   Food provides energy and nutrients for growth and development. Nutrition requirements vary with body weight, age, sex, activity, and body functioning.

F.1.f   Sex drive is a natural human function that requires understanding. Sex is also a prominent means of transmitting diseases. The diseases can be prevented through a variety of precautions.

F.1.g   Natural environments may contain substances (for example, radon and lead) that are harmful to human beings. Maintaining environmental health involves establishing or monitoring quality standards related to use of soil, water, and air.

Populations, Resources, and Environments

F.2.a   When an area becomes overpopulated, the environment will become degraded due to the increased use of resources.

F.2.b   Causes of environmental degradation and resource depletion vary from region to region and from country to country.

Natural Hazards

F.3.a   Internal and external processes of the earth system cause natural hazards, events that change or destroy human and wildlife habitats, damage property, and harm or kill humans. Natural hazards include earthquakes, landslides, wildfires, volcanic eruptions, floods, storms, and even possible impacts of asteroids.

F.3.b   Human activities also can induce hazards through resource acquisition, urban growth, land-use decisions, and waste disposal. Such activities can accelerate many natural changes.

F.3.c   Natural hazards can present personal and societal challenges because misidentifying the change or incorrectly estimating the rate and scale of change may result in either too little attention and significant human costs or too much cost for unneeded preventive measures.

Risks and Benefits

F.4.a   Risk analysis considers the type of hazard and estimates the number of people that might be exposed and the number likely to suffer consequences. The results are used to determine the options for reducing or eliminating risks.

F.4.b   Students should understand the risks associated with natural hazards (fires, floods, tornadoes, hurricanes, earthquakes, and volcanic eruptions), with chemical hazards (pollutants in air, water, soil, and food), with biological hazards (pollen, viruses, bacterial, and parasites), social hazards (occupational safety and transportation), and with personal hazards (smoking, dieting, and drinking).

F.4.c   Individuals can use a systematic approach to thinking critically about risks and benefits. Examples include applying probability estimates to risks and comparing them to estimated personal and social benefits.

F.4.d   Important personal and social decisions are made based on perceptions of benefits and risks.

Science and Technology in Society

F.5.a   Science influences society through its knowledge and world view. Scientific knowledge and the procedures used by scientists influence the way many individuals in society think about themselves, others, and the environment. The effect of science on society is neither entirely beneficial nor entirely detrimental.

F.5.b   Societal challenges often inspire questions for scientific research, and social priorities often influence research priorities through the availability of funding for research.

F.5.c   Technology influences society through its products and processes. Technology influences the quality of life and the ways people act and interact. Technological changes are often accompanied by social, political, and economic changes that can be beneficial or detrimental to individuals and to society. Social needs, attitudes, and values influence the direction of technological development.

F.5.d   Science and technology have advanced through contributions of many different people, in different cultures, at different times in history. Science and technology have contributed enormously to economic growth and productivity among societies and groups within societies.

F.5.e   Scientists and engineers work in many different settings, including colleges and universities, businesses and industries, specific research institutes, and government agencies.

F.5.f   Scientists and engineers have ethical codes requiring that human subjects involved with research be fully informed about risks and benefits associated with the research before the individuals choose to participate. This ethic extends to potential risks to communities and property. In short, prior knowledge and consent are required for research involving human subjects or potential damage to property.

F.5.g   Science cannot answer all questions and technology cannot solve all human problems or meet all human needs. Students should understand the difference between scientific and other questions. They should appreciate what science and technology can reasonably contribute to society and what they cannot do. For example, new technologies often will decrease some risks and increase others.

G. History and Nature of Science

As a result of activities in grades 5–8, all students should develop understanding of

Science as a Human Endeavor

G.1.a   Women and men of various social and ethnic backgrounds—and with diverse interests, talents, qualities, and motivations—engage in the activities of science, engineering, and related fields such as the health professions. Some scientists work in teams, and some work alone, but all communicate extensively with others.

G.1.b   Science requires different abilities, depending on such factors as the field of study and type of inquiry. Science is very much a human endeavor, and the work of science relies on basic human qualities, such as reasoning, insight, energy, skill, and creativity—as well as on scientific habits of mind, such as intellectual honesty, tolerance of ambiguity, skepticism, and openness to new ideas.

Nature of Science

G.2.a Scientists formulate and test their explanations of nature using observation, experiments, and theoretical and mathematical models. Although all scientific ideas are tentative and subject to change and improvement in principle, for most major ideas in science, there is much experimental and observational confirmation. Those ideas are not likely to change greatly in the future. Scientists do and have changed their ideas about nature when they encounter new experimental evidence that does not match their existing explanations.

G.2.b In areas where active research is being pursued and in which there is not a great deal of experimental or observational evidence and understanding, it is normal for scientists to differ with one another about the interpretation of the evidence or theory being considered. Different scientists might publish conflicting experimental results or might draw different conclusions from the same data. Ideally, scientists acknowledge such conflict and work towards finding evidence that will resolve their disagreement.

G.2.c It is part of scientific inquiry to evaluate the results of scientific investigations, experiments, observations, theoretical models, and the explanations proposed by other scientists. Evaluation includes reviewing the experimental procedures, examining the evidence, identifying faulty reasoning, pointing out statements that go beyond the evidence, and suggesting alternative explanations for the same observations. Although scientists may disagree about explanations of phenomena, about interpretations of data, or about the value of rival theories, they do agree that questioning, response to criticism, and open communication are integral to the process of science. As scientific knowledge evolves, major disagreements are eventually resolved through such interactions between scientists.

History of Science

G.3.a Many individuals have contributed to the traditions of science. Studying some of these individuals provides further understanding of scientific inquiry, science as a human endeavor, the nature of science, and the relationships between science and society.

G.3.b In historical perspective, science has been practiced by different individuals in different cultures. In looking at the history of many peoples, one finds that scientists and engineers of high achievement are considered to be among the most valued contributors to their culture.

G.3.c Tracing the history of science can show how difficult it was for scientific innovators to break through the accepted ideas of their time to reach the conclusions that we currently take for granted.

1. The Nature of Science

By the end of the 8th grade, students should know that

1.A The Scientific World View

1.A.1   When similar investigations give different results, the scientific challenge is to judge whether the differences are trivial or significant, and it often takes further studies to decide. Even with similar results, scientists may wait until an investigation has been repeated many times before accepting the results as correct.

1.A.2   Scientific knowledge is subject to modification as new information challenges prevailing theories and as a new theory leads to looking at old observations in a new way.

1.A.3   Some scientific knowledge is very old and yet is still applicable today.

1.A.4   Some matters cannot be examined usefully in a scientific way. Among them are matters that by their nature cannot be tested objectively and those that are essentially matters of morality. Science can sometimes be used to inform ethical decisions by identifying the likely consequences of particular actions but cannot be used to establish that some action is either moral or immoral.

1.B Scientific Inquiry

1.B.1   Scientists differ greatly in what phenomena they study and how they go about their work. Although there is no fixed set of steps that all scientists follow, scientific investigations usually involve the collection of relevant evidence, the use of logical reasoning, and the application of imagination in devising hypotheses and explanations to make sense of the collected evidence.

1.B.2   If more than one variable changes at the same time in an experiment, the outcome of the experiment may not be clearly attributable to any one of the variables. It may not always be possible to prevent outside variables from influencing the outcome of an investigation (or even to identify all of the variables), but collaboration among investigators can often lead to research designs that are able to deal with such situations.

1.B.3   What people expect to observe often affects what they actually do observe. Strong beliefs about what should happen in particular circumstances can prevent them from detecting other results. Scientists know about this danger to objectivity and take steps to try and avoid it when designing investigations and examining data. One safeguard is to have different investigators conduct independent studies of the same questions.

1.C The Scientific Enterprise

1.C.1 Important contributions to the advancement of science, mathematics, and technology have been made by different kinds of people, in different cultures, at different times.

1.C.2 Until recently, women and racial minorities, because of restrictions on their education and employment opportunities, were essentially left out of much of the formal work of the science establishment; the remarkable few who overcame those obstacles were even then likely to have their work disregarded by the science establishment.

1.C.3 No matter who does science and mathematics or invents things, or when or where they do it, the knowledge and technology that result can eventually become available to everyone in the world.

1.C.4 Scientists are employed by colleges and universities, business and industry, hospitals, and many government agencies. Their places of work include offices, classrooms, laboratories, farms, factories, and natural field settings ranging from space to the ocean floor.

1.C.5 In research involving human subjects, the ethics of science require that potential subjects be fully informed about the risks and benefits associated with the research and of their right to refuse to participate. Science ethics also demand that scientists must not knowingly subject coworkers, students, the neighborhood, or the community to health or property risks without their prior knowledge and consent. Because animals cannot make informed choices, special care must be taken in using them in scientific research.

1.C.6 Computers have become invaluable in science because they speed up and extend people's ability to collect, store, compile, and analyze data, prepare research reports, and share data and ideas with investigators all over the world.

1.C.7 Accurate record-keeping, openness, and replication are essential for maintaining an investigator's credibility with other scientists and society.

3. The Nature of Technology

By the end of the 8th grade, students should know that

3.A Technology and Science

3.A.1 In earlier times, the accumulated information and techniques of each generation of workers were taught on the job directly to the next generation of workers. Today, the knowledge base for technology can be found as well in libraries of print and electronic resources and is often taught in the classroom.

3.A.2 Technology is essential to science for such purposes as access to outer space and other remote locations, sample collection and treatment, measurement, data collection and storage, computation, and communication of information.

3.A.3 Engineers, architects, and others who engage in design and technology use scientific knowledge to solve practical problems. But they usually have to take human values and limitations into account as well.

3.B Design and Systems

3.B.1 Design usually requires taking constraints into account. Some constraints, such as gravity or the properties of the materials to be used, are unavoidable. Other constraints, including economic, political, social, ethical, and aesthetic ones, limit choices.

3.B.2 All technologies have effects other than those intended by the design, some of which may have been predictable and some not. In either case, these side effects may turn out to be unacceptable to some of the population and therefore lead to conflict between groups.

3.B.3 Almost all control systems have inputs, outputs, and feedback. The essence of control is comparing information about what is happening to what people want to happen and then making appropriate adjustments. This procedure requires sensing information, processing it, and making changes. In almost all modern machines, microprocessors serve as centers of performance control.

3.B.4 Systems fail because they have faulty or poorly matched parts, are used in ways that exceed what was intended by the design, or were poorly designed to begin with. The most common ways to prevent failure are pretesting parts and procedures, overdesign, and redundancy.

3.C Issues in Technology

3.C.1 The human ability to shape the future comes from a capacity for generating knowledge and developing new technologies—and for communicating ideas to others.

3.C.2 Technology cannot always provide successful solutions for problems or fulfill every human need.

3.C.3 Throughout history, people have carried out impressive technological feats, some of which would be hard to duplicate today even with modern tools. The purposes served by these achievements have sometimes been practical, sometimes ceremonial.

3.C.4 Technology has strongly influenced the course of history and continues to do so. It is largely responsible for the great revolutions in agriculture, manufacturing, sanitation and medicine, warfare, transportation, information processing, and communications that have radically changed how people live.

3.C.5 New technologies increase some risks and decrease others. Some of the same technologies that have improved the length and quality of life for many people have also brought new risks.

3.C.6 Rarely are technology issues simple and one-sided. Relevant facts alone, even when known and available, usually do not settle matters entirely in favor of one side or another. That is because the contending groups may have different values and priorities. They may stand to gain or lose in different degrees, or may make very different predictions about what the future consequences of the proposed action will be.

3.C.7 Societies influence what aspects of technology are developed and how these are used. People control technology (as well as science) and are responsible for its effects.

4. The Physical Setting

By the end of the 8th grade, students should know that

4.A The Universe

4.A.1   The sun is a medium-sized star located near the edge of a disk-shaped galaxy of stars, part of which can be seen as a glowing band of light that spans the sky on a very clear night. The universe contains many billions of galaxies, and each galaxy contains many billions of stars. To the naked eye, even the closest of these galaxies is no more than a dim, fuzzy spot.

4.A.2   The sun is many thousands of times closer to the earth than any other star. Light from the sun takes a few minutes to reach the earth, but light from the next nearest star takes a few years to arrive. The trip to that star would take the fastest rocket thousands of years. Some distant galaxies are so far away that their light takes several billion years to reach the earth. People on earth, therefore, see them as they were that long ago in the past.

4.A.3   Nine planets of very different size, composition, and surface features move around the sun in nearly circular orbits. Some planets have a great variety of moons and even flat rings of rock and ice particles orbiting around them. Some of these planets and moons show evidence of geologic activity. The earth is orbited by one moon, many artificial satellites, and debris.

4.A.4   Large numbers of chunks of rock orbit the sun. Some of those that the earth meets in its yearly orbit around the sun glow and disintegrate from friction as they plunge through the atmosphere—and sometimes impact the ground. Other chunks of rocks mixed with ice have long, off-center orbits that carry them close to the sun, where the sun's radiation (of light and particles) boils off frozen material from their surfaces and pushes it into a long, illuminated tail.

4.B The Earth

4.B.1   We live on a relatively small planet, the third from the sun in the only system of planets definitely known to exist (although other, similar systems may be discovered in the universe).

4.B.2   The earth is mostly rock. Three-fourths of its surface is covered by a relatively thin layer of water (some of it frozen), and the entire planet is surrounded by a relatively thin blanket of air. It is the only body in the solar system that appears able to support life. The other planets have compositions and conditions very different from the earth's.

4.B.3   Everything on or anywhere near the earth is pulled toward the earth's center by gravitational force.

4.B.4   Because the earth turns daily on an axis that is tilted relative to the plane of the earth's yearly orbit around the sun, sunlight falls more intensely on different parts of the earth during the year. The difference in heating of the earth's surface produces the planet's seasons and weather patterns.

4.B.5   The moon's orbit around the earth once in about 28 days changes what part of the moon is lighted by the sun and how much of that part can be seen from the earth—the phases of the moon.

4.B.6   Climates have sometimes changed abruptly in the past as a result of changes in the earth's crust, such as volcanic eruptions or impacts of huge rocks from space. Even relatively small changes in atmospheric or ocean content can have widespread effects on climate if the change lasts long enough.

4.B.7   The cycling of water in and out of the atmosphere plays an important role in determining climatic patterns. Water evaporates from the surface of the earth, rises and cools, condenses into rain or snow, and falls again to the surface. The water falling on land collects in rivers and lakes, soil, and porous layers of rock, and much of it flows back into the ocean.

4.B.8   Fresh water, limited in supply, is essential for life and also for most industrial processes. Rivers, lakes, and groundwater can be depleted or polluted, becoming unavailable or unsuitable for life.

4.B.9   Heat energy carried by ocean currents has a strong influence on climate around the world.

4.B.10 Some minerals are very rare and some exist in great quantities, but—for practical purposes— the ability to recover them is just as important as their abundance. As minerals are depleted, obtaining them becomes more difficult. Recycling and the development of substitutes can reduce the rate of depletion but may also be costly.

4.B.11 The benefits of the earth's resources—such as fresh water, air, soil, and trees—can be reduced by using them wastefully or by deliberately or inadvertently destroying them. The atmosphere and the oceans have a limited capacity to absorb wastes and recycle materials naturally. Cleaning up polluted air, water, or soil or restoring depleted soil, forests, or fishing grounds can be very difficult and costly.

4.C Processes that Shape the Earth

4.C.1   The interior of the earth is hot. Heat flow and movement of material within the earth cause earthquakes and volcanic eruptions and create mountains and ocean basins. Gas and dust from large volcanoes can change the atmosphere.

4.C.2   Some changes in the earth's surface are abrupt (such as earthquakes and volcanic eruptions) while other changes happen very slowly (such as uplift and wearing down of mountains). The earth's surface is shaped in part by the motion of water and wind over very long times, which act to level mountain ranges.

4.C.3   Sediments of sand and smaller particles (sometimes containing the remains of organisms) are gradually buried and are cemented together by dissolved minerals to form solid rock again.

4.C.4   Sedimentary rock buried deep enough may be reformed by pressure and heat, perhaps melting and recrystallizing into different kinds of rock. These re-formed rock layers may be forced up again to become land surface and even mountains. Subsequently, this new rock too will erode. Rock bears evidence of the minerals, temperatures, and forces that created it.

4.C.5   Thousands of layers of sedimentary rock confirm the long history of the changing surface of the earth and the changing life forms whose remains are found in successive layers. The youngest layers are not always found on top, because of folding, breaking, and uplift of layers.

4.C.6   Although weathered rock is the basic component of soil, the composition and texture of soil and its fertility and resistance to erosion are greatly influenced by plant roots and debris, bacteria, fungi, worms, insects, rodents, and other organisms.

4.C.7   Human activities, such as reducing the amount of forest cover, increasing the amount and variety of chemicals released into the atmosphere, and intensive farming, have changed the earth's land, oceans, and atmosphere. Some of these changes have decreased the capacity of the environment to support some life forms.

4.D Structure of Matter

4.D.1 All matter is made up of atoms, which are far too small to see directly through a microscope. The atoms of any element are alike but are different from atoms of other elements. Atoms may stick together in well-defined molecules or may be packed together in large arrays. Different arrangements of atoms into groups compose all substances.

4.D.2 Equal volumes of different substances usually have different weights.

4.D.3 Atoms and molecules are perpetually in motion. Increased temperature means greater average energy, so most substances expand when heated. In solids, the atoms are closely locked in position and can only vibrate. In liquids, the atoms or molecules have higher energy, are more loosely connected, and can slide past one another; some molecules may get enough energy to escape into a gas. In gases, the atoms or molecules have still more energy and are free of one another except during occasional collisions.

4.D.4 The temperature and acidity of a solution influence reaction rates. Many substances dissolve in water, which may greatly facilitate reactions between them.

4.D.5 Scientific ideas about elements were borrowed from some Greek philosophers of 2,000 years earlier, who believed that everything was made from four basic substances: air, earth, fire, and water. It was the combinations of these "elements" in different proportions that gave other substances their observable properties. The Greeks were wrong about those four, but now over 100 different elements have been identified, some rare and some plentiful, out of which everything is made. Because most elements tend to combine with others, few elements are found in their pure form.

4.D.6 There are groups of elements that have similar properties, including highly reactive metals, less-reactive metals, highly reactive nonmetals (such as chlorine, fluorine, and oxygen), and some almost completely nonreactive gases (such as helium and neon). An especially important kind of reaction between substances involves combination of oxygen with something else—as in burning or rusting. Some elements don't fit into any of the categories; among them are carbon and hydrogen, essential elements of living matter.

4.D.7 No matter how substances within a closed system interact with one another, or how they combine or break apart, the total weight of the system remains the same. The idea of atoms explains the conservation of matter: If the number of atoms stays the same no matter how they are rearranged, then their total mass stays the same.

4.E Energy Transformations

4.E.1 Energy cannot be created or destroyed, but only changed from one form into another.

4.E.2 Most of what goes on in the universe—from exploding stars and biological growth to the operation of machines and the motion of people—involves some form of energy being transformed into another. Energy in the form of heat is almost always one of the products of an energy transformation.

4.E.3 Heat can be transferred through materials by the collisions of atoms or across space by radiation. If the material is fluid, currents will be set up in it that aid the transfer of heat.

4.E.4 Energy appears in different forms. Heat energy is in the disorderly motion of molecules; chemical energy is in the arrangement of atoms; mechanical energy is in moving bodies or in elastically distorted shapes; gravitational energy is in the separation of mutually attracting masses.

4.F Motion

4.F.1   Light from the sun is made up of a mixture of many different colors of light, even though to the eye the light looks almost white. Other things that give off or reflect light have a different mix of colors.

4.F.2   Something can be "seen" when light waves emitted or reflected by it enter the eye—just as something can be "heard" when sound waves from it enter the ear.

4.F.3   An unbalanced force acting on an object changes its speed or direction of motion, or both. If the force acts toward a single center, the object's path may curve into an orbit around the center.

4.F.4   Vibrations in materials set up wavelike disturbances that spread away from the source. Sound and earthquake waves are examples. These and other waves move at different speeds in different materials.

4.F.5   Human eyes respond to only a narrow range of wavelengths of electromagnetic radiation—visible light. Differences of wavelength within that range are perceived as differences in color.

4.G Forces of Nature

4.G.1   Every object exerts gravitational force on every other object. The force depends on how much mass the objects have and on how far apart they are. The force is hard to detect unless at least one of the objects has a lot of mass.

4.G.2   The sun's gravitational pull holds the earth and other planets in their orbits, just as the planets' gravitational pull keeps their moons in orbit around them.

4.G.3   Electric currents and magnets can exert a force on each other.

5. The Living Environment

By the end of the 8th grade, students should know that

5.A Diversity of Life

5.A.1 One of the most general distinctions among organisms is between plants, which use sunlight to make their own food, and animals, which consume energy-rich foods. Some kinds of organisms, many of them microscopic, cannot be neatly classified as either plants or animals.

5.A.2 Animals and plants have a great variety of body plans and internal structures that contribute to their being able to make or find food and reproduce.

5.A.3 Similarities among organisms are found in internal anatomical features, which can be used to infer the degree of relatedness among organisms. In classifying organisms, biologists consider details of internal and external structures to be more important than behavior or general appearance.

5.A.4 For sexually reproducing organisms, a species comprises all organisms that can mate with one another to produce fertile offspring.

5.A.5 All organisms, including the human species, are part of and depend on two main interconnected global food webs. One includes microscopic ocean plants, the animals that feed on them, and finally the animals that feed on those animals. The other web includes land plants, the animals that feed on them, and so forth. The cycles continue indefinitely because organisms decompose after death to return food material to the environment.

5.B Heredity

5.B.1 In some kinds of organisms, all the genes come from a single parent, whereas in organisms that have sexes, typically half of the genes come from each parent.

5.B.2 In sexual reproduction, a single specialized cell from a female merges with a specialized cell from a male. As the fertilized egg, carrying genetic information from each parent, multiplies to form the complete organism with about a trillion cells, the same genetic information is copied in each cell.

5.B.3 New varieties of cultivated plants and domestic animals have resulted from selective breeding for particular traits.

5.C Cells

5.C.1 All living things are composed of cells, from just one to many millions, whose details usually are visible only through a microscope. Different body tissues and organs are made up of different kinds of cells. The cells in similar tissues and organs in other animals are similar to those in human beings but differ somewhat from cells found in plants.

5.C.2 Cells repeatedly divide to make more cells for growth and repair. Various organs and tissues function to serve the needs of cells for food, air, and waste removal.

5.C.3 Within cells, many of the basic functions of organisms—such as extracting energy from food and getting rid of waste—are carried out. The way in which cells function is similar in all living organisms.

5.C.4 About two-thirds of the weight of cells is accounted for by water, which gives cells many of their properties.

5.D Interdependence of Life

5.D.1 In all environments—freshwater, marine, forest, desert, grassland, mountain, and others—organisms with similar needs may compete with one another for resources, including food, space, water, air, and shelter. In any particular environment, the growth and survival of organisms depend on the physical conditions.

5.D.2 Two types of organisms may interact with one another in several ways: They may be in a producer/consumer, predator/prey, or parasite/host relationship. Or one organism may scavenge or decompose another. Relationships may be competitive or mutually beneficial. Some species have become so adapted to each other that neither could survive without the other.

5.E Flow of Matter and Energy

5.E.1 Food provides molecules that serve as fuel and building material for all organisms. Plants use the energy in light to make sugars out of carbon dioxide and water. This food can be used immediately for fuel or materials or it may be stored for later use. Organisms that eat plants break down the plant structures to produce the materials and energy they need to survive. Then they are consumed by other organisms.

5.E.2 Over a long time, matter is transferred from one organism to another repeatedly and between organisms and their physical environment. As in all material systems, the total amount of matter remains constant, even though its form and location change.

5.E.3 Energy can change from one form to another in living things. Animals get energy from oxidizing their food, releasing some of its energy as heat. Almost all food energy comes originally from sunlight.

5.F Evolution of Life

5.F.1 Small differences between parents and offspring can accumulate (through selective breeding) in successive generations so that descendants are very different from their ancestors.

5.F.2 Individual organisms with certain traits are more likely than others to survive and have offspring. Changes in environmental conditions can affect the survival of individual organisms and entire species.

5.F.3 Many thousands of layers of sedimentary rock provide evidence for the long history of the earth and for the long history of changing life forms whose remains are found in the rocks. More recently deposited rock layers are more likely to contain fossils resembling existing species.

6. The Human Organism

By the end of the 8th grade, students should know that

6.A Human Identity

6.A.1 Like other animals, human beings have body systems for obtaining and providing energy, defense, reproduction, and the coordination of body functions.

6.A.2 Human beings have many similarities and differences. The similarities make it possible for human beings to reproduce and to donate blood and organs to one another throughout the world. Their differences enable them to create diverse social and cultural arrangements and to solve problems in a variety of ways.

6.A.3 Fossil evidence is consistent with the idea that human beings evolved from earlier species.

6.A.4 Specialized roles of individuals within other species are genetically programmed, whereas human beings are able to invent and modify a wider range of social behavior.

6.A.5 Human beings use technology to match or excel many of the abilities of other species. Technology has helped people with disabilities survive and live more conventional lives.

6.A.6 Technologies having to do with food production, sanitation, and disease prevention have dramatically changed how people live and work and have resulted in rapid increases in the human population.

6.B Human Development

6.B.1 Fertilization occurs when sperm cells from a male's testes are deposited near an egg cell from the female ovary, and one of the sperm cells enters the egg cell. Most of the time, by chance or design, a sperm never arrives or an egg isn't available.

6.B.2 Contraception measures may incapacitate sperm, block their way to the egg, prevent the release of eggs, or prevent the fertilized egg from implanting successfully.

6.B.3 Following fertilization, cell division produces a small cluster of cells that then differentiate by appearance and function to form the basic tissues of an embryo. During the first three months of pregnancy, organs begin to form. During the second three months, all organs and body features develop. During the last three months, the organs and features mature enough to function well after birth. Patterns of human development are similar to those of other vertebrates.

6.B.4 The developing embryo—and later the newborn infant—encounters many risks from faults in its genes, its mother's inadequate diet, her cigarette smoking or use of alcohol or other drugs, or from infection. Inadequate child care may lead to lower physical and mental ability.

6.B.5 Various body changes occur as adults age. Muscles and joints become less flexible, bones and muscles lose mass, energy levels diminish, and the senses become less acute. Women stop releasing eggs and hence can no longer reproduce. The length and quality of human life are influenced by many factors, including sanitation, diet, medical care, sex, genes, environmental conditions, and personal health behaviors.

6.C Basic Functions

6.C.1   Organs and organ systems are composed of cells and help to provide all cells with basic needs.

6.C.2   For the body to use food for energy and building materials, the food must first be digested into molecules that are absorbed and transported to cells.

6.C.3   To burn food for the release of energy stored in it, oxygen must be supplied to cells, and carbon dioxide removed. Lungs take in oxygen for the combustion of food and they eliminate the carbon dioxide produced. The urinary system disposes of dissolved waste molecules, the intestinal tract removes solid wastes, and the skin and lungs rid the body of heat energy. The circulatory system moves all these substances to or from cells where they are needed or produced, responding to changing demands.

6.C.4   Specialized cells and the molecules they produce identify and destroy microbes that get inside the body.

6.C.5   Hormones are chemicals from glands that affect other body parts. They are involved in helping the body respond to danger and in regulating human growth, development, and reproduction.

6.C.6   Interactions among the senses, nerves, and brain make possible the learning that enables human beings to cope with changes in their environment.

6.D Learning

6.D.1   Some animal species are limited to a repertoire of genetically determined behaviors; others have more complex brains and can learn a wide variety of behaviors. All behavior is affected by both inheritance and experience.

6.D.2   The level of skill a person can reach in any particular activity depends on innate abilities, the amount of practice, and the use of appropriate learning technologies.

6.D.3   Human beings can detect a tremendous range of visual and olfactory stimuli. The strongest stimulus they can tolerate may be more than a trillion times as intense as the weakest they can detect. Still, there are many kinds of signals in the world that people cannot detect directly.

6.D.4   Attending closely to any one input of information usually reduces the ability to attend to others at the same time.

6.D.5   Learning often results from two perceptions or actions occurring at about the same time. The more often the same combination occurs, the stronger the mental connection between them is likely to be. Occasionally a single vivid experience will connect two things permanently in people's minds.

6.D.6   Language and tools enable human beings to learn complicated and varied things from others.

6.E Physical Health

6.E.1   The amount of food energy (calories) a person requires varies with body weight, age, sex, activity level, and natural body efficiency. Regular exercise is important to maintain a healthy heart/lung system, good muscle tone, and bone strength.

6.E.2   Toxic substances, some dietary habits, and personal behavior may be bad for one's health. Some effects show up right away, others may not show up for many years. Avoiding toxic substances, such as tobacco, and changing dietary habits to reduce the intake of such things as animal fat increases the chances of living longer.

6.E.3   Viruses, bacteria, fungi, and parasites may infect the human body and interfere with normal body functions. A person can catch a cold many times because there are many varieties of cold viruses that cause similar symptoms.

6.E.4   White blood cells engulf invaders or produce antibodies that attack them or mark them for killing by other white cells. The antibodies produced will remain and can fight off subsequent invaders of the same kind.

6.E.5   The environment may contain dangerous levels of substances that are harmful to human beings. Therefore, the good health of individuals requires monitoring the soil, air, and water and taking steps to keep them safe.

6.F Mental Health

6.F.1   Individuals differ greatly in their ability to cope with stressful situations. Both external and internal conditions (chemistry, personal history, values) influence how people behave.

6.F.2   Often people react to mental distress by denying that they have any problem. Sometimes they don't know why they feel the way they do, but with help they can sometimes uncover the reasons.

8. The Designed World

By the end of the 8th grade, students should know that

8.A Agriculture

8.A.1   Early in human history, there was an agricultural revolution in which people changed from hunting and gathering to farming. This allowed changes in the division of labor between men and women and between children and adults, and the development of new patterns of government.

8.A.2   People control the characteristics of plants and animals they raise by selective breeding and by preserving varieties of seeds (old and new) to use if growing conditions change.

8.A.3   In agriculture, as in all technologies, there are always trade-offs to be made. Getting food from many different places makes people less dependent on weather in any one place, yet more dependent on transportation and communication among far-flung markets. Specializing in one crop may risk disaster if changes in weather or increases in pest populations wipe out that crop. Also, the soil may be exhausted of some nutrients, which can be replenished by rotating the right crops.

8.A.4   Many people work to bring food, fiber, and fuel to U.S. markets. With improved technology, only a small fraction of workers in the United States actually plant and harvest the products that people use. Most workers are engaged in processing, packaging, transporting, and selling what is produced.

8.B Materials and Manufacturing

8.B.1 The choice of materials for a job depends on their properties and on how they interact with other materials. Similarly, the usefulness of some manufactured parts of an object depends on how well they fit together with the other parts.

8.B.2 Manufacturing usually involves a series of steps, such as designing a product, obtaining and preparing raw materials, processing the materials mechanically or chemically, and assembling, testing, inspecting, and packaging. The sequence of these steps is also often important.

8.B.3 Modern technology reduces manufacturing costs, produces more uniform products, and creates new synthetic materials that can help reduce the depletion of some natural resources.

8.B.4 Automation, including the use of robots, has changed the nature of work in most fields, including manufacturing. As a result, high-skill, high-knowledge jobs in engineering, computer programming, quality control, supervision, and maintenance are replacing many routine, manual-labor jobs. Workers therefore need better learning skills and flexibility to take on new and rapidly changing jobs.

8.C Energy Sources and Use

8.C.1 Energy can change from one form to another, although in the process some energy is always converted to heat. Some systems transform energy with less loss of heat than others.

8.C.2 Different ways of obtaining, transforming, and distributing energy have different environmental consequences.

8.C.3 In many instances, manufacturing and other technological activities are performed at a site close to an energy source. Some forms of energy are transported easily, others are not.

8.C.4 Electrical energy can be produced from a variety of energy sources and can be transformed into almost any other form of energy. Moreover, electricity is used to distribute energy quickly and conveniently to distant locations.

8.C.5 Energy from the sun (and the wind and water energy derived from it) is available indefinitely. Because the flow of energy is weak and variable, very large collection systems are needed. Other sources don't renew or renew only slowly.

8.C.6 Different parts of the world have different amounts and kinds of energy resources to use and use them for different purposes.

8.D Communication

8.D.1 Errors can occur in coding, transmitting, or decoding information, and some means of checking for accuracy is needed. Repeating the message is a frequently used method.

8.D.2 Information can be carried by many media, including sound, light, and objects. In this century, the ability to code information as electric currents in wires, electromagnetic waves in space, and light in glass fibers has made communication millions of times faster than is possible by mail or sound.

8.E Information Processing

8.E.1   Most computers use digital codes containing only two symbols, 0 and 1, to perform all operations. Continuous signals (analog) must be transformed into digital codes before they can be processed by a computer.

8.E.2   What use can be made of a large collection of information depends upon how it is organized. One of the values of computers is that they are able, on command, to reorganize information in a variety of ways, thereby enabling people to make more and better uses of the collection.

8.E.3   Computer control of mechanical systems can be much quicker than human control. In situations where events happen faster than people can react, there is little choice but to rely on computers. Most complex systems still require human oversight, however, to make certain kinds of judgments about the readiness of the parts of the system (including the computers) and the system as a whole to operate properly, to react to unexpected failures, and to evaluate how well the system is serving its intended purposes.

8.E.4   An increasing number of people work at jobs that involve processing or distributing information. Because computers can do these tasks faster and more reliably, they have become standard tools both in the workplace and at home.

8.F Health Technology

8.F.1   Sanitation measures such as the use of sewers, landfills, quarantines, and safe food handling are important in controlling the spread of organisms that cause disease. Improving sanitation to prevent disease has contributed more to saving human life than any advance in medical treatment.

8.F.2   The ability to measure the level of substances in body fluids has made it possible for physicians to make comparisons with normal levels, make very sophisticated diagnoses, and monitor the effects of the treatments they prescribe.

8.F.3   It is becoming increasingly possible to manufacture chemical substances such as insulin and hormones that are normally found in the body. They can be used by individuals whose own bodies cannot produce the amounts required for good health.

9. The Mathematical World

By the end of the 8th grade, students should know that

9.A Numbers

9.A.1 There have been systems for writing numbers other than the Arabic system of place values based on tens. The very old Roman numerals are now used only for dates, clock faces, or ordering chapters in a book. Numbers based on 60 are still used for describing time and angles.

9.A.2 A number line can be extended on the other side of zero to represent negative numbers. Negative numbers allow subtraction of a bigger number from a smaller number to make sense, and are often used when something can be measured on either side of some reference point (time, ground level, temperature, budget).

9.A.3 Numbers can be written in different forms, depending on how they are being used. How fractions or decimals based on measured quantities should be written depends on how precise the measurements are and how precise an answer is needed.

9.A.4 The operations + and − are inverses of each other—one undoes what the other does; likewise x and ÷ .

9.A.5 The expression *a/b* can mean different things: *a* parts of size *1/b* each, *a* divided by *b*, or *a* compared to *b*.

9.A.6 Numbers can be represented by using sequences of only two symbols (such as 1 and 0, on and off); computers work this way.

9.A.7 Computations (as on calculators) can give more digits than make sense or are useful.

9.B Symbolic Relationships

9.B.1 An equation containing a variable may be true for just one value of the variable.

9.B.2 Mathematical statements can be used to describe how one quantity changes when another changes. Rates of change can be computed from differences in magnitudes and vice versa.

9.B.3 Graphs can show a variety of possible relationships between two variables. As one variable increases uniformly, the other may do one of the following: increase or decrease steadily, increase or decrease faster and faster, get closer and closer to some limiting value, reach some intermediate maximum or minimum, alternately increase and decrease indefinitely, increase or decrease in steps, or do something different from any of these.

9.C Shapes

9.C.1 Some shapes have special properties: triangular shapes tend to make structures rigid, and round shapes give the least possible boundary for a given amount of interior area. Shapes can match exactly or have the same shape in different sizes.

9.C.2 Lines can be parallel, perpendicular, or oblique.

9.C.3 Shapes on a sphere like the earth cannot be depicted on a flat surface without some distortion.

9.C.4 The graphic display of numbers may help to show patterns such as trends, varying rates of change, gaps, or clusters. Such patterns sometimes can be used to make predictions about the phenomena being graphed.

9.C.5 It takes two numbers to locate a point on a map or any other flat surface. The numbers may be two perpendicular distances from a point, or an angle and a distance from a point.

9.C.6 The scale chosen for a graph or drawing makes a big difference in how useful it is.

9.D Uncertainty

9.D.1 How probability is estimated depends on what is known about the situation. Estimates can be based on data from similar conditions in the past or on the assumption that all the possibilities are known.

9.D.2 Probabilities are ratios and can be expressed as fractions, percentages, or odds.

9.D.3 The mean, median, and mode tell different things about the middle of a data set.

9.D.4 Comparison of data from two groups should involve comparing both their middles and the spreads around them.

9.D.5 The larger a well-chosen sample is, the more accurately it is likely to represent the whole. But there are many ways of choosing a sample that can make it unrepresentative of the whole.

9.D.6 Events can be described in terms of being more or less likely, impossible, or certain.

9.E Reasoning

9.E.1 Some aspects of reasoning have fairly rigid rules for what makes sense; other aspects don't. If people have rules that always hold, and good information about a particular situation, then logic can help them to figure out what is true about it. This kind of reasoning requires care in the use of key words such as if, and, not, or, all, and some. Reasoning by similarities can suggest ideas but can't prove them one way or the other.

9.E.2 Practical reasoning, such as diagnosing or troubleshooting almost anything, may require many-step, branching logic. Because computers can keep track of complicated logic, as well as a lot of information, they are useful in a lot of problem-solving situations.

9.E.3 Sometimes people invent a general rule to explain how something works by summarizing observations. But people tend to overgeneralize, imagining general rules on the basis of only a few observations.

9.E.4 People are using incorrect logic when they make a statement such as "If *A* is true, then *B* is true; but *A* isn't true, therefore *B* isn't true either."

9.E.5 A single example can never prove that something is always true, but sometimes a single example can prove that something is not always true.

9.E.6 An analogy has some likenesses to but also some differences from the real thing.

10. Historical Perspectives

By the end of the 8th grade, students should know that

10.A Displacing the Earth from the Center of the Universe

10.A.1 The motion of an object is always judged with respect to some other object or point and so the idea of absolute motion or rest is misleading.

10.A.2 Telescopes reveal that there are many more stars in the night sky than are evident to the unaided eye, the surface of the moon has many craters and mountains, the sun has dark spots, and Jupiter and some other planets have their own moons.

10.F Understanding Fire

10.F.1 From the earliest times until now, people have believed that even though millions of different kinds of material seem to exist in the world, most things must be made up of combinations of just a few basic kinds of things. There has not always been agreement, however, on what those basic kinds of things are. One theory long ago was that the basic substances were earth, water, air, and fire. Scientists now know that these are not the basic substances. But the old theory seemed to explain many observations about the world.

10.F.2 Today, scientists are still working out the details of what the basic kinds of matter are and of how they combine, or can be made to combine, to make other substances.

10.F.3 Experimental and theoretical work done by French scientist Antoine Lavoisier in the decade between the American and French revolutions led to the modern science of chemistry.

10.F.4 Lavoisier's work was based on the idea that when materials react with each other many changes can take place but that in every case the total amount of matter afterward is the same as before. He successfully tested the concept of conservation of matter by conducting a series of experiments in which he carefully measured all the substances involved in burning, including the gases used and those given off.

10.F.5 Alchemy was chiefly an effort to change base metals like lead into gold and to produce an elixir that would enable people to live forever. It failed to do that or to create much knowledge of how substances react with each other. The more scientific study of chemistry that began in Lavoisier's time has gone far beyond alchemy in understanding reactions and producing new materials.

10.G Splitting the Atom

10.G.1 The accidental discovery that minerals containing uranium darken photographic film, as light does, led to the idea of radioactivity.

10.G.2 In their laboratory in France, Marie Curie and her husband, Pierre Curie, isolated two new elements that caused most of the radioactivity of the uranium mineral. They named one radium because it gave off powerful, invisible rays, and the other polonium in honor of Madame Curie's country of birth. Marie Curie was the first scientist ever to win the Nobel prize in two different fields—in physics, shared with her husband, and later in chemistry.

10.I Discovering Germs

10.I.1 Throughout history, people have created explanations for disease. Some have held that disease has spiritual causes, but the most persistent biological theory over the centuries was that illness resulted from an imbalance in the body fluids. The introduction of germ theory by Louis Pasteur and others in the 19th century led to the modern belief that many diseases are caused by microorganisms—bacteria, viruses, yeasts, and parasites.

10.I.2 Pasteur wanted to find out what causes milk and wine to spoil. He demonstrated that spoilage and fermentation occur when microorganisms enter from the air, multiply rapidly, and produce waste products. After showing that spoilage could be avoided by keeping germs out or by destroying them with heat, he investigated animal diseases and showed that microorganisms were involved. Other investigators later showed that specific kinds of germs caused specific diseases.

10.I.3 Pasteur found that infection by disease organisms—germs—caused the body to build up an immunity against subsequent infection by the same organisms. He then demonstrated that it was possible to produce vaccines that would induce the body to build immunity to a disease without actually causing the disease itself.

10.I.4 Changes in health practices have resulted from the acceptance of the germ theory of disease. Before germ theory, illness was treated by appeals to supernatural powers or by trying to adjust body fluids through induced vomiting, bleeding, or purging. The modern approach emphasizes sanitation, the safe handling of food and water, the pasteurization of milk, quarantine, and aseptic surgical techniques to keep germs out of the body; vaccinations to strengthen the body's immune system against subsequent infection by the same kind of microorganisms; and antibiotics and other chemicals and processes to destroy microorganisms.

10.I.5 In medicine, as in other fields of science, discoveries are sometimes made unexpectedly, even by accident. But knowledge and creative insight are usually required to recognize the meaning of the unexpected.

10.J Harnessing Power

10.J.1 Until the 1800s, most manufacturing was done in homes, using small, handmade machines that were powered by muscle, wind, or running water. New machinery and steam engines to drive them made it possible to replace craftsmanship with factories, using fuels as a source of energy. In the factory system, workers, materials, and energy could be brought together efficiently.

10.J.2 The invention of the steam engine was at the center of the Industrial Revolution. It converted the chemical energy stored in wood and coal, which were plentiful, into mechanical work. The steam engine was invented to solve the urgent problem of pumping water out of coal mines. As improved by James Watt, it was soon used to move coal, drive manufacturing machinery, and power locomotives, ships, and even the first automobiles.

11. Common Themes

By the end of the 8th grade, students should know that

11.A Systems

11.A.1 A system can include processes as well as things.

11.A.2 Thinking about things as systems means looking for how every part relates to others. The output from one part of a system (which can include material, energy, or information) can become the input to other parts. Such feedback can serve to control what goes on in the system as a whole.

11.A.3 Any system is usually connected to other systems, both internally and externally. Thus a system may be thought of as containing subsystems and as being a subsystem of a larger system.

11.B Models

11.B.1 Models are often used to think about processes that happen too slowly, too quickly, or on too small a scale to observe directly, or that are too vast to be changed deliberately, or that are potentially dangerous.

11.B.2 Mathematical models can be displayed on a computer and then modified to see what happens.

11.B.3 Different models can be used to represent the same thing. What kind of a model to use and how complex it should be depends on its purpose. The usefulness of a model may be limited if it is too simple or if it is needlessly complicated. Choosing a useful model is one of the instances in which intuition and creativity come into play in science, mathematics, and engineering.

11.C Constancy and Change

11.C.1 Physical and biological systems tend to change until they become stable and then remain that way unless their surroundings change.

11.C.2 A system may stay the same because nothing is happening or because things are happening but exactly counterbalance one another.

11.C.3 Many systems contain feedback mechanisms that serve to keep changes within specified limits.

11.C.4 Symbolic equations can be used to summarize how the quantity of something changes over time or in response to other changes.

11.C.5 Symmetry (or the lack of it) may determine properties of many objects, from molecules and crystals to organisms and designed structures.

11.C.6 Cycles, such as the seasons or body temperature, can be described by their cycle length or frequency, what their highest and lowest values are, and when these values occur. Different cycles range from many thousands of years down to less than a billionth of a second.

11.D Scale

11.D.1 Properties of systems that depend on volume, such as capacity and weight, change out of proportion to properties that depend on area, such as strength or surface processes.

11.D.2 As the complexity of any system increases, gaining an understanding of it depends increasingly on summaries, such as averages and ranges, and on descriptions of typical examples of that system.

12. Habits of Mind

By the end of the 8th grade, students should know that

12.A Values and Attitudes

12.A.1 Know why it is important in science to keep honest, clear, and accurate records.

12.A.2 Know that hypotheses are valuable, even if they turn out not to be true, if they lead to fruitful investigations.

12.A.3 Know that often different explanations can be given for the same evidence, and it is not always possible to tell which one is correct.

12.B Computation and Estimation

12.B.1 Find what percentage one number is of another and figure any percentage of any number.

12.B.2 Use, interpret, and compare numbers in several equivalent forms such as integers, fractions, decimals, and percents.

12.B.3 Calculate the circumferences and areas of rectangles, triangles, and circles, and the volumes of rectangular solids.

12.B.4 Find the mean and median of a set of data.

12.B.5 Estimate distances and travel times from maps and the actual size of objects from scale drawings.

12.B.6 Insert instructions into computer spreadsheet cells to program arithmetic calculations.

12.B.7 Determine what unit (such as seconds, square inches, or dollars per tankful) an answer should be expressed in from the units of the inputs to the calculation, and be able to convert compound units (such as yen per dollar into dollar per yen, or miles per hour into feet per second).

12.B.8 Decide what degree of precision is adequate and round off the result of calculator operations to enough significant figures to reasonably reflect those of the inputs.

12.B.9 Express numbers like 100, 1,000, and 1,000,000 as powers of 10.

12.B.10 Estimate probabilities of outcomes in familiar situations, on the basis of history or the number of possible outcomes.

12.C Manipulation and Observation

12.C.1 Use calculators to compare amounts proportionally.

12.C.2 Use computers to store and retrieve information in topical, alphabetical, numerical, and key-word files, and create simple files of their own devising.

12.C.3 Read analog and digital meters on instruments used to make direct measurements of length, volume, weight, elapsed time, rates, and temperature, and choose appropriate units for reporting various magnitudes.

12.C.4 Use cameras and tape recorders for capturing information.

12.C.5 Inspect, disassemble, and reassemble simple mechanical devices and describe what the various parts are for; estimate what the effect that making a change in one part of a system is likely to have on the system as a whole.

12.D Communication Skills

12.D.1 Organize information in simple tables and graphs and identify relationships they reveal.

12.D.2 Read simple tables and graphs produced by others and describe in words what they show.

12.D.3 Locate information in reference books, back issues of newspapers and magazines, compact disks, and computer databases.

12.D.4 Understand writing that incorporates circle charts, bar and line graphs, two-way data tables, diagrams, and symbols.

12.D.5 Find and describe locations on maps with rectangular and polar coordinates.

12.E Critical-Response Skills

12.E.1 Question claims based on vague attributions (such as "Leading doctors say...") or on statements made by celebrities or others outside the area of their particular expertise.

12.E.2 Compare consumer products and consider reasonable personal trade-offs among them on the basis of features, performance, durability, and cost.

12.E.3 Be skeptical of arguments based on very small samples of data, biased samples, or samples for which there was no control sample.

12.E.4 Be aware that there may be more than one good way to interpret a given set of findings.

12.E.5 Notice and criticize the reasoning in arguments in which (1) fact and opinion are intermingled or the conclusions do not follow logically from the evidence given, (2) an analogy is not apt, (3) no mention is made of whether the control groups are very much like the experimental group, or (4) all members of a group (such as teenagers or chemists) are implied to have nearly identical characteristics that differ from those of other groups.